HOST INDEX OF THE FUNGI
OF NORTH AMERICA

LONDON : HUMPHREY MILFORD

OXFORD UNIVERSITY PRESS

HOST INDEX

OF THE

FUNGI OF NORTH AMERICA

COMPILED BY

ARTHUR BLISS SEYMOUR

CAMBRIDGE, MASSACHUSETTS

HARVARD UNIVERSITY PRESS

1929

PRINTED AT THE HARVARD UNIVERSITY PRESS
CAMBRIDGE, MASS., U.S.A.

TO

THE MEMORY OF

WILLIAM GILSON FARLOW

PREFACE

THE primary object of this work is to indicate so far as recorded in the literature, for each host plant, all the fungi known to grow upon it and for each fungus all the hosts upon which it grows. In compiling such an index, most of the work is not botanical. One who knows the alphabet can sort the names and throw out duplicates. Some botanical experience, however, is needed to detect two or more names when they denote the same fungus, since synonyms are grouped in a brace. It is not the function of this work to solve botanical problems. Solutions may be included if available, but otherwise it must simply present problems to be solved by others. Some problems will be partially solved by studying the parasites on related hosts and some by studying those on unrelated hosts. They will suggest life histories to be traced in herbaria, cultures, and field work.

Our geographical area includes the whole of North America and neighboring islands from Trinidad and Panama to the northern limits of plant life from Greenland to Alaska. From this area, we include all publications containing parasitic fungi which a diligent search of more than fifty years has brought to light. The early manuscripts by Doctor Farlow were incorporated in the edition of 1888–91, and the contents of that edition have been included in the present one. The effort has been continued along similar lines through 1923, and since that time only those were included that came to the compiler's notice up to July 1, 1927. Beyond that date part 12 of Arthur's work on the Uredinales was included since it contained so many additions and corrections to the earlier parts. This index includes about 80,000 names of hosts and fungi as compared with 23,000 in the earlier work.

The genera of host plants are arranged as nearly as may be in the sequence indicated by Engler & Prantl, *Die natürlichen Pflanzenfamilien*, the seed plants being interpreted by Dalla Torre & Harms, *Genera Siphonogamarum*. The arrangement of the algal hosts is contributed by N. L. Gardner. Species are alphabetically arranged in each genus. If several related hosts have the same parasites, the hosts are grouped together for convenience and the parasites are printed but once, *e. g.*, Eriogonum, pp. 286, 287. Sometimes a host may be thrown slightly out of alphabetic order as in Berberis, p. 315. Insect groups are arranged systematically as far as families, and as far as subfamilies in the Coccidae. Insect genera and species are arranged alphabetically under the family or subfamily. In many cases a fungus has been men-

tioned as growing on a certain genus or larger subdivision without mention
of the species, and hence in searching for fungi to be found on a given species
one should examine the list of fungi placed at the end of the genus or other
subdivision under the general heading "sp. indet."

The naming of host plants is much more difficult than for the first edition.
During the interval of forty years which has elapsed, usage has become very
diverse, literature has multiplied and the geographic area has been extended
to include regions whose floras are less familiar. Formerly names to be
found in standard floristic works were preferred, while in the present index
we have attempted to apply the International Rules of Nomenclature and
to profit by special monographs in so far as limited time and library facilities
permitted. The names selected are sometimes open to question. Also
specific names current in 1891 often had a different significance from the
same names at present, *e. g.*, species of Acer, Rubus, Spartina, Myrica, and
others. In choosing the correct host name, the value of the original state-
ment is often impaired. On the other hand combinations for some species
in genera recognized by Dalla Torre and Harms have apparently never been
published, and to avoid any question of making them in this work, they have
been treated as in the following example. In the sense of this index, *Seri-
cotheca franciscana*, p. 359, belongs in Spiraea, but we have been unable to
find that it has ever been formally designated as such. Therefore it is
written:

> **Spiraea**
> (Sericotheca franciscana Rydb.)

When the authority for a host name cannot be found, it is credited to the
geographical division from which it came, *e. g.*, "ex Kansas," or to the
author who used it, *e. g.*, "ex Duss." There has been great difficulty in
finding authorities for host names; but this is not strange, for they are com-
monly written without authorities.

The monograph of Quercus by Trelease arrived just in time to give needed
help with the host species of that genus. Bailey's *Manual of Cultivated
Plants* arrived also in the early stages of printing, and has served as a standard throughout. As a result, cultivated plants have been more carefully
treated from a botanical standpoint than in 1891. In a few cases, as Brassica,
Citrus, and Holcus, common names are given in addition to scientific names,
especially for varieties. Where available books or skill in using them failed,
the compiler has consulted specialists some of whom decline to be mentioned.
Professor Oakes Ames has revised the orchid names, and assistance on
special groups has been given by N. C. Fassett, the late J. N. Rose, P. A.
Rydberg, and C. A. Weatherby.

Since it is not the province of the host index to designate a preferred name, each name has been written with authorities in full as if it were the accepted name. Each fungus name stands on its own merits and the compiler has not changed it by substituting or adding a name more correct or better understood. An exception is made to conserve space in the case of Agaricus. When an Agaricus name becomes a synonym of some other generic name, only the latter is given. The same name or a different name may designate the same fungus on a related host. By studying the names under different hosts, a considerable review of the synonymy may be gained, but each host has only the fungus names actually published for that host. The arrangement of synonyms is entirely different from that of the earlier work. In that the arrangement was chronological, giving the history of the name. To have continued such an arrangement, however, would have consumed an amount of time far beyond its additional value.

The International Rules of Nomenclature adopted at Brussels have never before been carried into effect for fungi in general. They require, for example, that Fries should be written as authority for Polyporus cinnabarinus, but they give permission to those who wish to do so, to write *Polyporus cinnabarinus* (Jacq.) ex Fr. Some botanists have availed themselves of this permission, notably E. A. Burt in his work on Thelephoraceae. The compiler also has attempted to give these pre-Friesian authorities — consequently the authorities for names used by Fries and earlier authors were verified and their histories traced.[1] For example, if the genus is not changed we should write *Boletus cinnabarinus* Jacq. ex Fr. If the genus has been changed by Fries, the name becomes *Polyporus cinnabarinus* (Jacq.) ex Fr. and by later change *Trametes cinnabarina* (Jacq.) ex Fr. When other authors change the genus, we have *Polystictus cinnabarinus* (Jacq. ex Fr.) Cke. and *Pycnoporus cinnabarinus* (Jacq. ex Fr.) Karst. Under *Cenangium ferruginosum* Fr., S. M. **2**: 187, the earlier name *Peziza Abietis* P. occurs as a synonym. This is a valid name because its identity is here recognized by Fries, and on this basis it is chosen by Rehm and should be written *Cenangium Abietis* (P. ex Fr.) Rehm. A few names as *Rhizina inflata* (Schaeff.) ex Quél. have been validated in this way by later authors. Certain early names have been in continuous use to the present time, but are not valid according to the rules, e. g., *Hypoxylon coccineum* Bull. and some of the Erysiphaceae as *Erysiphe Cichoracearum* DC. Such must be referred to the next congress and therefore have been marked with a dagger(†).

---

[1] In this work, S. F. Gray's Natural Arrangement of British Plants, 1821, is considered to be later than Fries, Systema Mycologicum, also 1821. In practice Persoon's Mycologia Europaea 1822–1828 must be considered as the date of departure for some groups published in the later volumes of Fries, according to our interpretation of the rules.

Authorities for names originating since the established dates of departure are written as found, unless special reason for study appears. Since a name for a perfect form cannot be based on that of an imperfect form, the first use of such a name is treated as a new name and it can have only the author who used it. If it is then transferred to another genus, its parenthetical authority is the author who first used it for the perfect stage. The authority for *Glomerella cingulata* is not (Atk.) Spaulding & v. Schrenk because Atkinson described an imperfect stage. Stoneman first placed it as a perfect fungus, *Gnomoniopsis cingulata*, and the authority should be written (Stoneman) Spaulding & v. Schrenk. *Aecidium Sarcobati* Pk. is given as the aecidial form of *Puccinia subnitens*. When the specific name is used for the teleutosporic stage, the name becomes *Dicaeoma Sarcobati* Arth., not *Dicaeoma Sarcobati* (Pk.) Arth., and under Puccinia it is *Puccinia Sarcobati* (Arth.) Bethel, not (Pk.) Bethel. The compiler interprets the rule as above. Some, however, hold that while Sarcobati cannot displace subnitens for the name of the species, yet it may be written *Puccinia Sarcobati* (Pk.) Bethel.

Under *Thalictrum thyrsoideum*, p. 315, is given
{ Dicaeoma Clematidis (Lagerh.) Arth. I.
{ Puccinia montanensis I. Fung. Dak. *104*.

This is not *Puccinia montanensis* Ell. but was erroneously so indicated with reference to the aecidial stage only, therefore I. is placed before the authority. If this were the aecidial stage of *P. montanensis* Ell. the I. would be placed after the authority, and similar cases have had the same treatment. Under *Anemone cylindrica*, p. 308, are *Puccinia missouriensis* I. Arth. and *Puccinia missouriensis* III. Arth., each illustrating this same idea. There is no *Puccinia missouriensis*, but these two stages have been so referred. The plant called *Puccinia consimilis* in Barthol., N. Am. Uredinales *835* is not the true *P. consimilis* but it is *P. monoica*. Therefore it is entered as a synonym of *P. monoica* with N. Am. Uredinales *835* in place of the authority, for properly it has no other.

When the usual authority is replaced by reference to page or number, the reference applies only to that particular place or possibly to two plants treated at that place, both different from the original to which the name belongs. For example *Caeoma Roestelites* Lk. is said to be *Gymnosporangium Sabinae* and the original reference was not American. As used by Schweinitz the name is now known to represent two species both different from Link's. *C. Roestelites* S. Am. Bor. 2900 p.p.[1] is *Gymnosporangium Juniperi-virginianae*, p. 366; *C. Roestelites* S. Am. Bor. 2900 p.p.[2] is *G. globosum*, p. 363. On p. 627 it is necessary to divide a parenthetical authority in like manner. See *Pseudotthia* in two braces. *Aecidium Compositarum*, var. *Eupatorii* (S.)

B., p. 641, is not a variety of *A. Compositarum* Mart. and there is no authority for *A. Compositarum* as thus modified. The entire name must be
regarded as an entity with the authority (S.) B. whose real identity is expressed by the name *Puccinia Eleocharidis* Arth. I. When two or more
authors have used identical names they are marked by dates of publication,
e. g., Dicaeoma Grossulariae and *Aecidium Grossulariae*, p. 351. Forms entered in the previous edition as species of Erineum are omitted in this, but an
occasional name may have been overlooked. At least one named Erineum is
a true fungus, *Cercospora fuscovirens* Sacc., p. 518. Fungi parasitic on insects are omitted from the secondary host; but fungi parasitic on fungi are
given with both primary and secondary host, *e. g., Darluca Filum* on *Puccinia Asparagi* on *Asparagus officinalis*.

The position of a brace of synonyms is determined by the name thought
to be most important. If the name expresses only an imperfect stage, that
is dominant, *e. g., Dicaeoma poculiforme* I. is placed as Aecidium, *Cronartium
Comandrae* I. is Peridermium, *Gymnosporangium globosum* I. is Roestelia.
Under *Viola papilionacea*, p. 516, the alphabet is to be interpreted as Aecidium, Cercospora, Puccinia. When the number of parasites on a single host
is large, the names are arranged under the proper orders and where there are
many species of some orders and few of others, the latter are placed under
the general heading Miscellanea. Close adherence to a system of classification results in too many short lists in groups having comparatively few parasitic species. No botanical question is involved since the function of the host
index is not to classify but to arrange for convenience in finding. Under
Quercus coccinea, p. 249, and elsewhere, the Erysiphaceae require a separate
grouping and are removed from the Pyrenomycetineae where they belong
and for convenience placed before that group as if coördinate. Under *Sambucus canadensis*, p. 623, Uredinales and Basidiomycetes are used as if coordinate. A fungus whose perfect stage is known is often placed with synonyms under the imperfect stage if the latter is more evident, more abundant,
or more destructive.

Variant spellings are not rare. Host names are spelled as indicated by the
best authorities. Fungus names are spelled as originally indicated by their
authors. Many discrepancies result. On *Allionia* is *Albugo platensis* and
elsewhere is the host name *Chrysothamnus plattensis*. On *Rynchospora
cyperoides* are *Guignardia Rhynchosporae* and *Uromyces Rhyncosporae*. On
Plumiera is *Coleosporium Plumierae* and *Septoria Plumeriae*. On Wisteria
we find *Septoria Wistariae* and *Botryosphaeria Wisteriae*. Under Gleditsia
are specific names of fungi *Gleditschiae, gleditsiicola* and *gleditschiicola*.
DeToni names *Aecidium Kellermannii* on Baptisia while elsewhere the spelling is *Kellermani* (from W. A. Kellerman). The earliest form for Marssonia

has "ss" from Marsson (see Fung. Eur. *1857*). Nummularia is correctly copied and so is Numulariola. The adjective hainensis is correct for one species and hainaensis is correct for another, pp. 418, 440. As the earliest form Fries wrote *Polyporus pargamenus*, much later he wrote *P. pergamenus*. Gray's Manual, 7 ed., gives Osmorhiza; species of fungi growing on it are *Osmorrhizae*. Yuccogena is preferred and allowed since Yucca is not a classical word. Genipa is correct but the parasite is *Phyllachora Gnipae*. On Ludvigia are fungi whose specific names are Ludwigiae. *Septoria Lobeliae-syphiliticae* grows on *Lobelia siphilitica*. *Cercospora Asclepiadorae* grows on Asclepiodora. An interesting variety of spellings will be found under *Aplopappus venetus*, p. 651. The genus Sabatia is host to species named Sabbatiae. On Kalmia, *Sphaeria atriella* is *Zignoella atrella*. *Patellaria agyrioides* is made a synonym of *Lecanidion argyroides*, p. 78. *Valsa nigrofacta* becomes *Valsaria nigrificata*. *Helianthus tracheliifolius* is host to *Aecidium trachelifoliatum*. *Uredo Kyllingiae* grows on Kyllinga. *Ipomoea pandurata* is host to *Cystopus Ipomoeae-panduranae*. *Vernonia missurica* is a host name, p. 638, *Puccinia missouriensis* is a fungus, p. 308. At the time of going to press, a paper on Pestalotia by E. F. Guba is received in which the treatment of the species and hosts is greatly improved. Persons having occasion to look up any species of Pestalozzia in this host index should consult this paper (see Phytopath. **19**: 191. 1 April 1929).

Species names are decapitalized whenever possible, but the capital is retained for specific names which at some time have been generic names and for genitives of generic names and personal names. In case of insects, however, only those retain the capital which are genitives of personal names. Where possible *ae* becomes *i* in compound specific names, *e. g., striiformis; -cola* should never be written *-colus* or *-colum*, *e. g., acicola; caerulea*, Latin, should not be written *coerulea*, which implies Greek origin and a different meaning.

To express doubt, the question mark is used. Following a fungus name it questions the accuracy of the determination and placed before a name or brace it expresses doubt regarding the host plant. Before a name in a brace it questions whether the name is truly a synonym of the others in the brace. The hyphen is used in specific names which consist of two distinct words, as Juniperi-virginianae but otherwise only when necessary to separate vowels as in albo-atrum. The asterisk (*) marks items not American introduced by way of explanation. The dagger (†) marks names which are not valid according to the International Rules and should be considered by the next congress. Numbers which refer to specimens are in italics as *Puccinia monoica* N. Am. Uredinales *835*.

The following fungi are noted as needing to be properly described, renamed or the combinations formally made:

Puccinia graminis P., var. Tritici-tertii, p. 129.
Eutypella spinosa (P. ex Fr.) Coons, p. 257.
Glenospora ramosa (S.), p. 272.
Uncinula Petersii, p. 278.
Endothia Ravenelii, p. 354.
Marasmius musicola McDougall 1925, pp. 212, 217, presumably not
Murrill 1915, p. 183.

No pains have been spared to make the index as complete and accurate as possible. It is not to be expected, however, that it will prove to be free from errors and omissions.

The following have generously contributed their services in reading proofs and in many other ways: J. F. Brenckle, Edith K. Cash, Margaret B. Church, G. P. Clinton, J. J. Davis, J. Dearness, C. W. Dodge, H. M. Fitzpatrick, C. H. Kauffman, C. L. Shear, P. Spaulding, F. L. Stevens, R. Thaxter, and C. Thom. The Peridermia of Abies have been revised by J. H. Faull, fungi on Citrus by H. S. Fawcett and Anna E. Jenkins. The entomogenous fungi have been revised by R. Thaxter. Nathan Banks, Curator of Insects in the Museum of Comparative Zoölogy, has generously given expert information regarding insect hosts.

Miss Eleanor H. Nickerson has helped with acute discernment and untiring industry, and A. P. D. Piquet has helped with the preparation of manuscript and correction of the proof of this as well as for the first edition. Dr. Susan P. Seymour has given valuable help in preparing the manuscript; Mrs. Anna C. Seymour has read proof for nearly all of this, as also for the first edition; Miss Mary E. Seymour has supervised part of the preparation and given other constructive assistance.

In conclusion it should be mentioned that the publication of this index has been made possible only through the constant interest and material assistance of the late Mrs. Farlow.

The compiler is grateful to all who have helped to make the book more accurate and more useful.

FARLOW HERBARIUM OF CRYPTOGAMIC BOTANY
Harvard University, Cambridge, Massachusetts
April 15, 1929

HOST INDEX OF THE FUNGI
OF NORTH AMERICA

PLANTAE

ALGAE

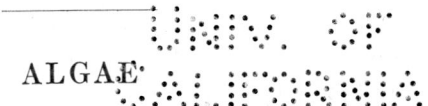

MYXOPHYCEAE

OSCILLATORIACEAE

Oscillatoria sp. indet.
  Chytridium subangulosum A. Br.
Lyngbya sp. indet.
  Humaria phycophila Clements.
  Lachnea pseudocrenulata (Clements) Sacc. &
    Lindau.
  Lachnea pygmaea (Clements) Sacc. & Lindau.

NOSTOCACEAE

Nostoc sp. indet.
  Skepperia spathularia (B. & C.) Pat.

BACILLARIACEAE

Cymbella lanceolatum (Ehrb.) Rabh.
  Lagenidium enecans Zopf.
Stauroneis Phoenicenteron (Nitzsch) Ehrenb.
  Lagenidium enecans Zopf.
Bacillariaceae gen. indet.
  Aphanomyces laevis D. By.
  Ectrogella Bacillariacearum Zopf.

CHLOROPHYCEAE

DESMIDIACEAE

Closterium sp. indet.
  Ancylistes Closterii Pfitzer.
  Olpidium intestinum A. Br.
Cosmarium De Baryi Arch.
  Olpidium ampullaceum (A. Br.) Auct. Amer.
Hyalotheca dissiliens (Smith) Breb.
  Harpochytrium Hyalothecae Lagerh.
Desmidiaceae gen. indet.
  Aphanomyces laevis DBy.

ZYGNEMACEAE

Spirogyra areolata Lagerh.
  Aphanomyces phycophilus DBy.
Spirogyra calospora Petit.
  Lagenidium americanum Atk.
Spirogyra crassa Ktz.
  Pythium gracile A. Schenk.

Spirogyra dubia Kützing.
  Aphanomyces phycophilus DBy.
Spirogyra insignis (Hass.) Kützing.
  Entophlyctis bulligera (Zopf) A. Fischer.
  Lagenidium americanum Atk.
  Phlyctochytrium aequale Atk.
Spirogyra porticalis (Müller) Cleve.
  Lagenidium entophytum (Pringsh.) Zopf.
  Pythium gracile A. Schenk.
  Vampyrella Spirogyrae (Cienk.) Sacc. & Scalia.
Spirogyra varians (Hass.) Kützing.
  Lagenidium americanum Atk.
  Phlyctochytrium planicorne Atk.
  Rhizophidium brevipes Atk.
  Rhizophidium minutum Atk.
Spirogyra sp. indet.
  Harpochytrium Hedenii Wille.
  Lagenidium Rabenhorstii Zopf.
  Olpidium sp. indet.
Zygnema sp. indet.
  Aphanomyces phycophilus D. By.
  Harpochytrium Hedenii Wille.
Mougeotia parvula Hass.
  Rhizophidium sphaerocarpum (Zopf)
    A. Fischer.

VOLVOCACEAE

Pandorina Morum (Müll.) Bory.
Eudorina elegans Ehrenb.
Platydorina caudata Kofoid.
  Dangeardia mamillata B. Schröder.

ULVACEAE

Ulva Californica Wille.
  Guignardia Ulvæ Reed.
Ulva crispa Lightf.
  Cephalosporium Saulcyanum Mont.
Prasiola borealis Reed.
  { Læstadia alaskana (Reed) Sacc. & D. Sacc.
  { Guignardia alaskana Reed.

ULOTHRICACEAE

Ulothrix scutata Jonsson.
  Rhizophidium Olla Henn.
Conferva utriculosa Kützing.
  Harpochytrium intermedium Atk.

OEDOGONIACEAE

Oedogonium sp. indet.
  Chytridium acuminatum A. Br.
  Olpidium entophytum A. Br.
  ⎰Olpidium ampullaceum (A. Br.) Auct. Amer.
  ⎱Rhizophidium ampullaceum (A. Br.)
  ⎭   A. Fischer.
  ⎱Rhizophidium ampullaceum (A. Br.) Schrt.
  ⎰Chytridium decipiens A. Br.
  ⎱Rhizophidium decipiens (A. Br.) A. Fischer.
  Rhizophidium Oedogonii Richt.

CLADOPHORACEAE

Cladophora caespitosa Crouan.
Cladophora fuliginosa Kützing.
  Blodgettia Borneti Wright.
Cladophora sp. indet.
  Achlya polyandra Hildbr.
  Achlyogeton entophytum A. Schenk.
  Myzocytium proliferum A. Schenk.
  Saprolegnia mixta D. By.
Acrosiphonia hystrix Strömfelt.
Acrosiphonia incurva Kjellman.
  Pleotrachelus Andreei Lagerh.

CODIACEAE

Codium fragile Suringar.
  Chytridium codicola Zeller.
  Rhizophidium codicola Zeller.
  Stemphylium Codii Zeller.

MELANOPHYCEAE

ECTOCARPACEAE

Ectocarpus littoralis Lyngb.
  Eurychasma Dicksonii (Wright) Magn.
  Pleotrachelus Rosenvingii Petersen.
  Rhizophidium Olla Petersen.

SPHACELARIACEAE

Sphacelaria sp. indet.
Cladostephus sp. indet.
  ⎰Chytridium Sphacellarum Kny.
  ⎱Olpidium Sphacellarum (Kny) A. Fischer.
Punctaria sp. indet.
  Eurychasma Dicksonii (Wright) Magn.

LAMINARIACEAE

Alaria fistulosa Post. & Rupr.
  Chytridium alarium Kibbe.
Laminaria longicruris De la Pyl.
  ⎰Dothidella Laminariae Rostr.
  ⎱Endodothella Laminariae (Rostr.) Theissen &
  ⎭ Syd.

FUCACEAE

Ascophyllum nodosum Stack.
  Sphaerella Ascophylli Cotton.
Cystoseira osmundacea (Menz.) Ag.
Halidrys dioica Gardner.
  Guignardia irritans Setch. & Estee.
Sargassum sp. indet.
  Phyllachorella oceanica Ferdinandsen &
    Winge.

RHODOPHYCEAE

GIGARTINACEAE

Chondrus crispus (L.) Stack.
  ⎰Leptosphaeria marina Rostr.
  ⎱Mycosphaerella marina (Rostr.) J. Lind.
  ⎭Sphaerella Chondri H. L. Jones.

RHODYMENIACEAE

Halosaccion ramentaceus Ag.
Rhodymenia palmata Grev.
  Eurychasma sacculus Petersen.

CERAMIACEAE

Callithamnion cruciatum Agardh.
Callithamnion Plumula Lyngb.
Callithamnion Pylaisaei Mont.
  Chytridium Plumulae Cohn.
Callithamnion sp. indet.
  Rhizophidium Polysiphoniae (Cohn) Petersen.

Algae fam. indet.
  Chytridium globosum A. Br.
  Chytridium minus Lacost & Suringar.
  Gliocladium penicillioides Cda.
  Microstelium hyalinum Pat.

FUNGI

MYXOMYCETES

Arcyria cinerea (Bull.) Schum.
  Stilbum echinatum Ell. & Ev.
  Stilbum tomentosum Schrad. ex Fr.
  Verticillium rexianum Sacc.
Chondrioderma spumarioides (Fr.) Rostf.
⎧ Hypomyces candicans Plow.
⎨ Lasionectria rexiana (Ell.) Cke.
⎩ Nectria rexiana Ell.
Fuligo septica (L.) Gmel.
⎧ Byssonectria violacea (Schm. ex Fr.) Seaver.
⎨ Hypomyces violaceus (Schm. ex Fr.) Tul.
⎩ Nectriopsis violaceus (Schm.) Maire.
Hemiarcyria clavata (P.) Rostf.
  Stilbum tomentosum Schrad. ex Fr.
Physarum sp. indet.
  Verticillium botryoides Sacc.
Spumaria alba DC.
⎧ Hypomyces candicans Plow.
⎨ Lasionectria rexiana (Ell.) Cke.
⎩ Nectria rexiana Ell.
Stemonitis sp. indet.
  Botrytis rhinotrichoides Sacc. & Ell.
  Hypomyces exiguus Pat.
Trichia varia P.
  Stilbum capillare Ell. & Ev.
Trichia sp. indet.
  Stilbum tomentosum Schrad. ex Fr.
Myxomycetes gen. indet.
  Rhinotrichum doliolum Pound & Clements.

PHYCOMYCETES

RHIZIDIACEAE

Harpochytrium Hedenii Wille.
  Harpochytrium Hedenii Wille

SAPROLEGNIACEAE

Saprolegnia ferax (Gruith) Nees.
  Olpidiopsis vexans Barrett.
  Olpidiopsis Saprolegniae, var. levis Coker.
Saprolegnia monoica Pringsh.
  Olpidiopsis Saprolegniae, var. levis Coker.
Saprolegnia Thuretii DBy.
  Olpidiopsis Saprolegniae (A. Br.) Cornu emend.
    A. Fischer.
Saprolegnia sp. indet.
  Harpochytrium Hedenii Wille.
Achlya acadiensis C. L. Moore.
  Olpidiopsis Saprolegniae (A. Br.) Cornu emend.
    A. Fischer.
Achlya apiculata DBy.
  Rhizophidium carpophilum (Zopf) A. Fischer.

Achlya conspicua Coker.
  Rhizidiomyces apophysatus Zopf.
  Rhizophidium carpophilum (Zopf) A. Fischer.
Achlya flagellata Coker.
  Aphanomyces parasiticus Coker.
  Olpidiopsis Saprolegniae (A. Br.) Cornu emend.
    A. Fischer.
  Rhizophidium carpophilum (Zopf) A. Fischer.
Achlya imperfecta Coker.
⎧ Olpidiopsis Saprolegniae (A. Br.) Cornu emend.
⎨   A. Fischer.
⎩ Olpidium Saprolegniae A. Br.
Achlya Orion Coker & Couch.
  Aphanomyces parasiticus Coker.
Aphanomyces laevis DBy.
  Olpidiopsis luxurians Barrett.

LEPTOMITACEAE

Blastocladia Pringsheimii Reinsch.
  Pleolpidium Blastocladiae Minden.

PYTHIACEAE

Pythium sp. indet.
  Aphanomyces exoparasiticus Coker & Couch.

ALBUGINACEAE

Cystopus Amaranti (S.) B.
  Rhizophidium pollinis (A. Br.) A. Fisher.

PERONOSPORACEAE

Peronospora effusa (Grev.) Rabh.
Sclerospora graminicola (Sacc.) Schrt.
  Rhizophidium pollinis (A. Br.) A. Fischer.
Peronospora obovata Bon.
  Macrosporium parasiticum Thm.

MUCORACEAE

Mucor Mucedo L. p. p. ex Bref.
⎧ Botrytis Jonesii B. & Br.
⎨ Chaetocladium Jonesii (B. & Br.) Fres.
⎩ Chaetocladium Brefeldii van Tiegh. & Le Mon.
Phycomyces nitens (Agardh) Kze.
  Chaetocladium Brefeldii van Tiegh. & Le Mon.
Pilobolus sp. indet.
  Syncephalis Cornu van Tiegh. & Le Mon.
Rhizopus sp. indet.
  Rhizophidium pollinis (A. Br.) A. Fischer.
Mucorineae gen. indet.
  Dispira americana Thax.
  Gonatobotrys flava Bon.
  Piptocephalis freseniana DBy.
  Syncephalis Cornu van Tiegh.
  Syncephalis nodosa van Tiegh.

5

ASCOMYCETES
EXOASCACEAE

Taphrina caerulescens (Mont. & Desm.) Tul.
  Pestalozzia taphrinicola Ell. & Ev.
  Phoma parasitica Ell. & Ev.
  ⎰Hendersonia taphrinicola Tracy & Earle
  ⎱Phyllohendersonia taphrinicola (Tracy & Earle)
    Tassi.
Taphrina Pruni Tul.
  Monilia fructigena (P.) ex Fr.

HELVELLACEAE

Geoglossum glabrum P.
  Hypomyces Geoglossi Ell. & Ev.
  Papulospora candida Sacc.
  Verticillium agaricinum (Lk.) Cda., var.
    clavisedum Sacc.
Geoglossum hirsutum Fr.
  ⎧Eleutheromyces Geoglossi (Ell. & Ev.) Seaver.
  ⎨Hypomyces Geoglossi Ell. & Ev.
  ⎩Peckiella Geoglossi (Ell. & Ev.) Sacc.
Spathularia sp. indet.
  Hypocrea alutacea (P.) Ces. & DeNot.
Helvella albipes Fckl.?
Helvella crispa (Scop.) ex Fr.
  Mycogone roseola Pound & Clements.
Helvella elastica Bull. ex Fr.
  ⎰Mycogone cervina Ditm. ex P.
  ⎱Sepedonium cervinum (Ditm. ex P.) Fr.
  Mycogone cinerea Morg.
Helvella infula Schaeff. ex Fr.
  Sphaeronaemella Helvellae Karst.

PEZIZACEAE

Barlaea hinnulea (B. & Br.) Sacc.
  ⎰Chromosporium fulvum (B. & C.) Sacc.
  ⎱Gymnosporium fulvum B. & C.
Lachnea hemisphaerica (Wigg.) Gill.
  ⎧Asterophora Pezizae Cda.
  ⎨Sepedonium tuberculiferum Ell. & Ev.
  ⎩Stephanoma strigosum Wallr.
  Verticillium discisedum Sacc. & Fairman.
Lachnea sepulta (Fr.) Sacc.
  Rhopalomyces nigripes Cost.
Lachnella citrina Pk.
  Dasyscypha turbinulata (S.) Sacc.
Macropodia fusicarpa (Gerard) Durand.
  Sepedonium tuberculiferum Ell. & Ev.
Macropodia Macropus (P. ex Fr.) Fckl.
  ⎰Mycogone cervina Ditm. ex P.
  ⎱Sepedonium cervinum (Ditm. ex P.) Fr.
Macropodia semitosta (B. & C.) Sacc.
  Synthetospora electa Morg.
Peziza sp. indet.
  Fusarium Berenice (B. & C.) Sacc.
  Mucor albovirens Fr.
Wynnea americana Thax.
  Syncephalis Wynneae Thax.

Coryne sarcoides (Jacq. ex P.) Tul.
  Aschersonia turbinata B.

CENANGIACEAE

Cenangium turgidum S.
  ⎰Patellaria cenangiicola Ell. & Ev.
  ⎱Patellea cenangicola (Ell. & Ev.) Sacc.
Dermatea olivacea Ell.
  Oospora hyalinula Sacc.
Tryblidiella nigrocinnabarina (S). Durand.
  ⎧Cenangium Ravenelii (B. & C.) Sacc.
  ⎨Peziza Ravenelii B. & C.
  ⎩Unguiculariopsis ilicincola (B. & Br.) Rehm.
Tryblidiella rufula (Spreng.) Sacc.
  Peziza Ravenelii B. & C.

TRYBLIDIACEAE

Hysterostomella Phoebes Syd.
  Uleomyces comedens Syd.

PHACIDIACEAE

Rhytisma acerinum (P.) ex Fr.
  Exosporium sociatum Ell. & Ev.
Rhytisma Nemopanthis Pk.
  Ramularia Nemopanthis Pk.
Rhytisma Prini (S.) Fr.
  Gloeosporium niveum J. J. Davis.
Rhytisma salicinum (P.) ex Fr.
  Gloeosporium niveum J. J. Davis.
  Tuberculina davisiana Sacc. & Trav.
Rhytisma Solidaginis S.
  Phyllosticta gallicola Ell. & Ev.

DICHAENACEAE

Dichaena quercina (P.) ex Fr.
  Titaea Clarkei Ell. & Ev.
Dichaena strumosa Fr.
  ⎧Helotium strumosum Ell. & Ev.
  ⎨Pseudohelotium strumosum (Ell. & Ev.) Sacc.
  ⎩Hypsotheca subcorticalis (C. & E.) Ell. & Ev.
  Titaea Clarkei Ell. & Ev.

HYSTERIACEAE

Cyclostomella disciformis Pat.
  Chaetocrea parasitica Syd.
Cyclostomella oncophora Syd.
  ⎰Metabotryon connatum Syd.
  ⎱Parabotryon connatum Syd.

EUTUBERACEAE

Genea hispidula B.
  Stephanoma strigosum Wallr.
Pseudohydnotria carnea Hark.
  ⎧Melanospora Setchellii (Hark.) Sacc.
  ⎨Nigrosphaeria Setchellii (Hark.) Gardner.
  ⎩Sphaeria Setchellii Hark.

BALSAMIACEAE

Geopora Harknessii E. Fisher.
Nigrospharia Setchellii (Hark.) Gardner.
Geopora magnata Hark.
Sphaeria Zobelli Tul.
Pseudobalsamia magnata (Hark.) Gilkey.
Sporophaga cyanea (Ces.) Hark.

ELAPHOMYCETACEAE

Elaphomyces cervinus (L. ex S. F. Gray) Schl.
{Cordyceps agariciformia (Bolt.) ex Seaver.
Cordyceps canadensis Ell. & Ev.
Cordyceps capitata (Holmsk. ex Fr.) Lk.
Torrubia capitata (Holmsk. ex Fr.) Tul.
Cordyceps ophioglossoides (Ehrb. ex Fr.) Lk.
Elaphomyces muricatus Fr.
{Cordyceps ophioglossoides (Ehrenb. ex Fr.) Lk.
Cordyceps parasitica (Willd.) ex Seaver.
Elaphomyces sp. indet.
Verticillium epimyces B. & Br.

ASPERGILLACEAE

Penicillium sp. indet.
Martensella pectinata Coemans

ERYSIPHACEAE

Erysiphe Cichoracearum DC.
Erysiphe Polygoni DC.
Microsphaera elevata Burrill.
Microsphaera extensa C. & P.
Microsphaera Grossulariae (Wallr.) Lév.
Phyllactinia corylea (P.) ex Karst.
Podosphaera Oxyacanthae (DC.) DBy.
Sphaerotheca Humuli (DC.) Burrill.
Uncinula necator (S.) Burrill.
Uncinula Salicis (DC.) Wint.
{Ampelomyces quisqualis Ces.
Cicinnobolus Cesatii DBy.
Erysiphaceae gen. indet.
Cicinnobolus major Dearness & Barthol.

PERISPORIACEAE

Appendiculella arecibensis (F. L. Stevens) Toro.
Coniothyrium glabroides F. L. Stevens.
Appendiculella Compositarum (Earle) Toro.
{Cicinnobella costaricensis Syd.
Dimerium costaricense Syd.
Paranectria meliolicola F. L. Stevens.
Trichothyrium dubiosum (Bomm. & Rouss.) Theissen.
Appendiculella Compositarum (Earle) Toro, var. **portoricensis** (F. L.. Stevens) Seaver & Chardon.
{Calonectria melioloides F. L. Stevens non Speg.
Subiculicola ambigua Speg.
Coniothyrium glabroides F. L. Stevens.
Dimerium piceum (B. & C.) Theissen.
Helminthosporium glabroides F. L. Stevens.

{Perisporina Meliolae (F. L. Stevens) Speg.
Perisporium Meliolae F. L. Stevens.
Dimerosporium Collinsii (S.) Thm.
Apiosporina Collinsii v. Höhnel.
{Fusisporium parasiticum Pk.
Fusarium Peckii Sacc.
Fusarium Sphaeriae Fckl., var. robustum J. J. Davis.
Dimerium Cayaponiae P. Garman.
Diplosporium album, var. fungicola F. L. Stevens.
Dimerium consimile Syd.
Calonectria inconspicua Wint.
Irene escharoides Syd.
Calloriopsis gelatinosa (Ell. & Martin) Syd.
Calonectria Adianti Rehm.
Calonectria inconspicua Wint.
{Cicinnobella consimilis Syd.
Dimerium consimile Syd.
Nectria pipericola Henn.
Paranectria meliolicola F. L. Stevens.
Irene hyptidicola (F. L. Stevens) Toro.
Calloriopsis gelatinosa (Ell. & Martin) Syd.
{Ectosticta costaricana Syd.
Stigme costaricana Syd.
Irene Melastomacearum (Speg.) Toro.
Arthrobotryum caudatum Syd.
Helminthosporium Melastomacearum F. L. Stevens.
Isthmospora glabra F. L. Stevens.
Trichothyrium dubiosum (Bomm. & Rouss.) Theissen.
Meliola ambigua Pat. & Gaill.
Arthrobotryum caudatum Syd.
Meliola amphitricha Fr.
Dimerosporium tropicale Speg.
Podosporium pallidum Pat.
Meliola Andirae Earle.
Calonectria graminicola F. L. Stevens
Meliola argentina Speg.
Phaeodimeriella guarapiensis (Speg.) Theissen.
Meliola asterinoides Wint.
Hyaloderma tricholomum Pat.
Podosporium Penicillium Speg.
Meliola bicornis Wint.
Arthrobotryum caudatum Syd.
Calonectria erubescens (Rob.) Sacc.
Dimerium piceum (B. & C.) Theissen.
Helminthosporium parathesicola F. L. Stevens.
Isthmospora glabra F. L. Stevens.
Meliola bidentata Cke.
Dimerosporium tropicale Speg.
Meliola brachycera Syd.
Trichothyrium dubiosum (Bomm. & Rouss.) Theissen.
Meliola Byrsonimae F. L. Stevens.
Isthmospora spinosa F. L. Stevens.

Meliola Chiococcae F. L. Stevens.
  Belonidium leucorrhodinum (Mont.) Sacc.
  Isthmospora spinosa F. L. Stevens.
Meliola clavulata Wint.
  Nectria perpusilla Sacc.
Meliola Comocladiae F. L. Stevens.
  Helminthosporium glabroides F. L. Stevens.
Meliola Cupaniae F. L. Stevens.
  Calonectria erubescens (Rob.) Sacc.
Meliola didymopanicis Henn.
  Arthrobotryum caudatum Syd.
  Helminthosporium glabroides F. L. Stevens.
Meliola Dieffenbachiae F. L. Stevens.
  Arthrobotryum Dieffenbachiae F. L. Stevens.
Meliola Dipholidis F. L. Stevens.
  Helminthosporium Helleri F. L. Stevens.
Meliola furcata Lév.
  Helminthosporium Helleri F. L. Stevens.
Meliola gaillardiana F. L. Stevens.
  Helminthosporium glabroides F. L. Stevens.
  Helminthosporium Helleri F. L. Stevens.
Meliola Gesneriae F. L. Stevens.
  Helminthosporium glabroides F. L. Stevens.
Meliola glabra B. & C.
  Belonidium leucorrhodinum (Mont.) Sacc.
  Isthmospora glabra F. L. Stevens.
  Podosporium? Penicillium Speg.
Meliola glabra B. & C., var. **Psychotriae** F. L.
    Stevens.
  Arthrobotryum caudatum Syd.
  Dimerium piceum (B. & C.) Theissen.
  Helminthosporium Melastomacearum F. L.
    Stevens.
Meliola glabroides F. L. Stevens.
  Arthrobotryum caudatum Syd.
  Arthrobotryum glabroides F. L. Stevens.
  Coniothyrium glabroides F. L. Stevens.
  Dimerium piceum (B. & C.) Theissen.
  Helminthosporium glabroides F. L. Stevens.
  Helminthosporium Helleri F. L. Stevens.
  Isthmospora glabra F. L. Stevens.
  Paranectria meliolicola F. L. Stevens.
Meliola Guareae Speg.
  Helminthosporium Helleri F. L. Stevens.
Meliola guareicola F. L. Stevens.
  Coniothyrium glabroides F. L. Stevens.
  Helminthosporium guareicola F. L. Stevens.
Meliola Guignardi Gaill.
  Helminthosporium Helleri F. L. Stevens.
Meliola gymnanthicola F. L. Stevens.
  Helminthosporium Helleri F. L. Stevens.
  Helminthosporium Philodendri F. L. Stevens.
Meliola Helleri Earle.
  Helminthosporium Helleri F. L. Stevens.
  Helminthosporium Philodendri F. L. Stevens.
  Isthmospora spinosa F. L. Stevens.
Meliola Hessii F. L. Stevens.
  Calonectria melioloides Speg.

Meliola Helminthosporium glabroides F. L. Stevens.
  Perisporium Paulliniae F. L. Stevens.
Meliola hyptidicola F. L. Stevens.
  Arthrobotryum caudatum Syd.
  Dimerina eutricha (Sacc. & Berl.) Theissen.
  Naemosphaera hyptidicola F. L. Stevens.
Meliola Ipomoeae Earle.
  Dimerium piceum (B. & C.) Theissen.
Meliola Lagunculariae Earle.
  Helminthosporium glabroides F. L. Stevens.
Meliola longipoda Gaill.
  Arthrobotryum caudatum Syd.
  Helminthosporium glabroides F. L. Stevens.
Meliola maricaensis F. L. Stevens.
  Helminthosporium glabroides F. L. Stevens.
Meliola monensis F. L Stevens.
  Calonectria melioloides Speg.
  Helminthosporium glabroides F. L. Stevens.
  Helminthosporium Helleri F. L. Stevens.
  Stevensula Monensis Speg.
Meliola Myrsinacearum F. L. Stevens.
  Helminthosporium Helleri F. L. Stevens.
Meliola nigra F. L. Stevens.
  Helminthosporium glabroides F. L. Stevens.
Meliola Ocoteae F. L. Stevens.
  Helminthosporium Ocoteae F. L. Stevens.
Meliola palmicola Wint.
  Helminthosporium Helleri F. L. Stevens.
Meliola Panici Earle.
  Arthrobotryum penicillium (Speg.) F. L.
    Stevens.
  Calonectria graminicola F. L. Stevens.
  Coniothyrium glabroides F. L. Stevens.
  Dimerium piceum (B. & C.) Theissen.
  Helminthosporium Panici F. L. Stevens.
  Porostigme microspora Toro.
  Podosporium? penicillium Speg.
Meliola parathesicola F. L. Stevens.
  Helminthosporium parathesicola F. L. Stevens.
Meliola Patouillardi Gaill.
  Helminthosporium Helleri F. L. Stevens.
Meliola Paulliniae F. L. Stevens.
  Acremonium Meliola F. L. Stevens.
  Arthrobotryum caudatum Syd.
  Calonectria melioloides Speg.
  Dimerium piceum (B. & C.) Theissen.
  Fusarium meliolicola F. L. Stevens.
  Helminthosporium Helleri F. L. Stevens.
  Helminthosporium Melastomacearum F. L.
    Stevens.
  Nectria meliolicola F. L. Stevens.
Meliola Philodendri F. L. Stevens.
  Helminthosporium Philodendri F. L. Stevens.
  Isthmospora spinosa F. L. Stevens.
Meliola polytricha Kalchbr. & Cke.
  Helminthosporium glabroides F. L. Stevens.
Meliola praetervisa Gaill.
Meliola Psidii Fr.
  Isthmospora spinosa F. L. Stevens.

Meliola Psychotriae Earle.
Arthrobotryum caudatum Syd.
Dimerina eutricha (Sacc. & Berl.) Theissen.
Helminthosporium glabroides F. L. Stevens.
Isthmospora glabra F. L. Stevens.
Meliola pteridicola F. L. Stevens.
Arthrobotryum caudatum Syd.
Coniothyrium glabroides F. L. Stevens.
Dimerium piceum (B. & C.) Theissen.
Helminthosporium glabroides F. L. Stevens.
Meliola Puiggarii Speg.
Helminthosporium glabroides F. L. Stevens.
Meliola rectangularis F. L. Stevens.
Helminthosporium Panici F. L. Stevens.
Helminthosporium parathesicola F. L. Stevens.
Nectria portoricensis F. L. Stevens.
Meliola Rudolphiae F. L. Stevens.
Belonidium leucorrhodinum (Mont.) Sacc.
Meliola Smilacis F. L. Stevens.
Isthmospora spinosa F. L. Stevens.
Meliola Tabernaemontanae Speg.
Jainesia meliolicola Fragoso & Ciferri.
Meliola Thouiniae Earle.
Helminthosporium Helleri F. L. Stevens.
Meliola tortuosa Wint.
Belonidium leucorrhodinum (Mont.) Sacc.
Calonectria erubescens (Rob.) Sacc.
Coniothyrium glabroides F. L. Stevens.
Dimerium piceum (B. & C.) Theissen.
Paranectria meliolicola F. L. Stevens.
{ Pseudomeliola (?) collapsa Earle.
{ Trichothyrium collapsum (Earle) Theissen.
Pseudonectria pipericola F. L. Stevens.
Stephanoma Meliolae Stevens & Dalbey.
Meliola toruloidea F. L. Stevens.
Helminthosporium glabroides F. L. Stevens.
Helminthosporium Helleri F. L. Stevens.
Meliola uncitricha Syd.
Bolosphaera cyanomela Syd.
Meliola sp. indet.
Arthrosporium parasiticum Wint.
Byssocallis Phoebes Syd.
Chaetosphaeria meliolicola Syd.
Dimerium nigrosporum Miles.
Grallomyces portoricensis F. L. Stevens.
Hyaloderma piliferum Pat.
Isariopsis penicillata Ell. & Ev.
Paranectria Miconiae F. L. Stevens.
Spegazzinia trichophila Atk.
Meliolaceae gen. indet.
Napicladium portoricense Speg., var.
Parodiella Cayaponiae P. Garman.
Diplosporium album Bon., var. fungicola F. L. Stevens.
Parodiopsis Stevensii Arnaud.
Eriomycopsis tenuis Syd.
Perisporium portoricense F. L. Stevens.
Helminthosporium glabroides F. L. Stevens.

Phaeoschiffnerula Compositarum Theissen.
{ Cicinnobella costaricensis Syd.
{ Dimerium costaricense Syd.
Henningsomyces escharoides Syd.
Calolepis congesta Syd.
Cicinnobella parodiellicola Henn.
Episoma parasiticum Syd.
Perisporiaceae gen. indet.
Belonidium leucorrhodinum (Mont.) Sacc.
Napicladium portoricense Speg., var.

ENGLERULACEAE

Hyalosphaeria Miconiae F. L. Stevens.
Paranectria Miconiae F. L. Stevens.
Englerulaceae gen. indet.
{ Cicinnobella costaricensis Syd.
{ Dimerium costaricense Syd.

MICROTHYRIACEAE

Trichothyrium sp. indet.
Calonectria inconspicua Wint.
Asterina Acalyphae Syd.
Ophiotexis perpusilla (Speg.) Theissen.
{ Cicinnobella asperula Syd.
{ Phaeodimeriella asperula Syd.
Asterina guaranitica Speg.
{ Cicinnobella exigua Syd.
{ Phaeodimeriella exiqua Syd.
Asterina Phenacis Syd.
{ Cicinnobella asperula Syd.
{ Phaeodimeriella asperula Syd.
Asterina Pittieri Bomm. & Rouss.
Dimerosporium imperspicuum Speg.
Asterina Sidae Earle.
Dimerosporium appendiculatum Earle.
Asterina sp. indet.
Helminthosporium glabroides F. L. Stevens.
Trichothyrium dubiosum (Bomm. & Rouss.) Theissen.
Trichothyrium Oleaceae Fragoso & Ciferri.
Microthyriaceae gen. indet.
Paranectria Miconiae F. L. Stevens.

POLYSTOMELLACEAE

Neostomella Tabernaemontanae Syd.
{ Cicinnobella consimilis Syd.
{ Dimerium consimile Syd.
Polystomellaceae gen. indet.
{ Cicinnobella asperula Syd.
{ Phaeodimeriella asperula Syd.

HYPOCREACEAE

Hypomyces sp. indet.
Gonatorrhodiella parasitica Thax.
Coniothyrium insuetum Syd.
Nectria sp. indet.
Zythia annularis (B. & Br.) Sacc.
Hypocrea sp. indet.
Gonatorrhodiella parasitica Thax.

Epichloe typhina (P.) Tul.
  Botrytis Epichloes Ell. & Dearness.
  ⎰Botrytis Sphaeriae-typhinae (Cda.) Sacc.
  ⎱Capillaria Sphaeriae-typhinae Cda.
  ⎰Leptosphaeria associata Rehm.
  ⎱Leptosphaeria consociata Rehm.

DOTHIDEACEAE

Plowrightia morbosa (S.) Sacc.
  Hendersonula morbosa Sacc.
  Nectria coccinea (P.) ex Fr.
  Sphaeronema Persicae (S.) Ell.
  ⎰Melanospora sphaerophila (Pk.) Sacc.
  ⎨Periconia sphaerophila Pk.
  ⎱Sporocybe sphaerophila (Pk.) Sacc.
  Sporotrichum parasiticum Pk.
  Trichothecium obovatum (B.) Sacc.
  Trichothecium roseum (P.) ex Fr.
Dothidea Kalmiae Pk.
  Peziza Kalmiae Pk.
Dothidina Fiebrigii (Henn.) Theissen & Syd.
  Araneomyces acariferus v. Höhnel.
  Paranectria juruana Henn.
Endodothella Picramniae Syd.
  Ascochytella cryptica Syd.
  Diaporthe bicincta (Bomm. & Rouss.) Syd.
  Phomopsis bicincta Syd.
Catacauma sp. indet.
  ⎰Dermatella mirabilis Syd.
  ⎱Pleurophomella mirabilis Syd.
Phyllachora flabella (S.) Sacc.
  ⎰Fusarium Pteridis Ell. & Ev.
  ⎱Septogloeum Pteridis (Ell. & Ev.) Wr.
Phyllachora graminis (P. ex Fr.) Fckl.
  Piricularia parasitica Ell. & Ev.
Phyllachora insueta Syd.
  Nectria prodigiosa Syd.
Phyllachora Maydis Maubl.
  Coniothyrium Phyllachorae Maubl.
Phyllachora microchita Syd.
  Perizomatium lachnoides (Rehm) Syd
Phyllachora peribebuyensis Speg.
  Trichothecium fusarioides F. L. Stevens.
Phyllachora rhopalina (Mont.) Sacc.
  Fusisporella vexans Syd.
Phyllachora veraguensis Syd.
  Metasphaeria occulta Syd.
Phyllachora sp. indet.
  Perizomella inquinans Syd.

SPHAERIALES
SORDARIACEAE

Sordaria sp. indet.
  Eoterfezia parasitica Atk.

SPHAERIACEAE

Bertia moriformis (Tode ex Fr.) De Not.
  Barya parasitica Fckl.

Sphaeria clypeata Nees.
  Sphaeria lagenaria P.
Sphaeria sp. indet.
  ⎰Calosphaeria scabriseta (S.) Sacc.
  ⎨Eutypa scabriseta (S.) B.
  ⎨Sphaeria scabriseta S.
  ⎱Valsa scabriseta (S.) Cke.
  ⎰Calonectria diminuta (B.) Berl. & Vogl.
  ⎨Dialonectria diminuta (B.) Cke.
  ⎨Dialonectria diploa, var. diminuta (B.) Ell. & Ev.
  ⎨Nectria diminuta (B.) Sacc.
  ⎱Nectria diploa B. & C. var. diminuta B.
  Cladosporium episphaeria S.
  ⎰Coniochaeta viridiatra (S.) Cke.
  ⎱Sphaeria viridiatra S.
  Dematium episphaericum S.
  Dematium virescens P.
  Diplosporium breve Pk.
  Helicoma ambiguum Morg.
  Hypocrea patella Pk.
  ⎰Hydrophora Fimbria Fr.
  ⎱Mucor Fimbria Nees ex Fr.
  Nectria flavella Pat.
  Nectria sanguinea (Sibth.) ex Fr.
  ⎰Dactylium sublutescens Pk.
  ⎱Trichothecium sublutescens (Pk.) Sacc.

MASSARIACEAE

Massaria sudans B. & C.
  Valsa parasitica C. & E.
Massaria vomitoria B. C.
  Calonectria Dearnessii Ell. & Ev.

VALSACEAE

Valsa congesta Pat.
  Nectria rhytidospora Pat.
Valsa didymospora Ell.
  Cenangium microspermum Sacc. & Ell.
Valsa sp. indet.
  Helotium parasiticum Ell. & Ev.
  Nectria episphaeria (Tode) ex Fr.
Eutypa limiformis (S.) B.
  Cenangium episphaeria S.
Eutypella lutescens (Ell.) Sacc.
  ⎰Lasionectria lasioderma (Ell.) Cke.
  ⎱Nectria lasioderma Ell.
Eutypella scoparia (S.) Ell. & Ev.
  Hypocrea contorta (S.) Pk.
Eutypella stellulata (Fr.) Sacc.
  ⎰Dialonectria episphaeria (Fr.) Cke.
  ⎱Nectria episphaeria (Tode) ex Fr.
Eutypella sp. indet.
  Nectria episphaeria var. minor Dearness & House.

MELANCONIDACEAE

Cryptosporella anomala (Pk.) Sacc.
  Fusarium episphaericum (C. & E.) Sacc.

DIATRYPEACEAE

Diatrype platystoma (S.) M. A. Curtis.
 Lasionectria poliosa Ell. & Ev.
 Nectria poliosa Ell. & Ev.
Diatrype Stigma (Hoffm.) ex Fr.
 Acanthostigma parasiticum Ell. & Ev.
 Calonectria cerea (B. & C.) Sacc.
 Dialonectria cerea (B. & C.) Cke.
 Dialonectria fulvida Ell. & Ev.
 Nectria fulvida Ell. & Ev.
 Ophionectria cerea (B. & C.) Ell. & Ev.
 Ophionectria Everhartii Ell. & Gall.
 Sphaeria cerea B. & C.
 Cenangium episphaeria S.
 Corticium episphaerium (Fr.) M. A. Curtis.
 Hymenochaete episphaeria (Fr.) Massee.
 Thelephora episphaeria Fr.
 Dialonectria episphaeria (Fr.) Cke.
 Nectria episphaeria (Tode) ex Fr.
 Sphaeria episphaeria Tode ex Fr.
 Hypsilophora fragiformis (S.) Cke.
 Tremella fragiformis S. Syn. Car.
 Lophiostoma floridanum Ell. & Ev.
 Melanomma parasiticum Ell. & Ev.
 Nectria poliosa Ell. & Ev.
 Dothidea episphaeria Pk.
 Phyllachora episphaeria (Pk.) Sacc.
 Septonema episphaericum Pk.
 Teichospora mycogena Ell. & Ev.
Diatrype tremellophora Ell.
 Byssosphaeria barbicincta Ell. & Ev.
 Trichosphaeria barbicincta (Ell. & Ev.) Sacc.
 Propolis parasitica (Ell. & Ev.) Sacc.
 Stictis parasitica Ell. & Ev.
Diatrype sp. indet.
 Cornularia Persicae (S.) Sacc.
 Berlesiella setosa (Ell. & Ev.) Sacc.
 Cucurbitaria echinata Ell. & Ev.
 Cucurbitaria setosa Ell. & Ev.
 Fusarium episphaericum (C. & E.) Sacc.
 Fusisporium episphaericum C. & E.
 Helminthosporium episphaericum C. & P.
 Sporotrichum anceps Sacc. & Ell.
Diatrypella favacea (Fr.) Ces. & De Not.
 Creonectria nipigonensis (Ell. & Ev.) Seaver.
 Nectria nipigonensis Ell. & Ev.
Diatrypella sp. indet.
 Nectria episphaeria (Tode) ex Fr.

MELOGRAMMATACEAE

Botryosphaeria Hibisci (S.) Sacc.
 Stigmatella aurantiaca B. & C.
Botryosphaeria sp. indet.
 Creonectria diploa (B. & C.) Seaver.
Melogramma campylosporum Fr.
 Helminthosporium episphaericum C. & P.

XYLARIACEAE

Nummularia Bulliardi Tul.
 Rhynchostoma sphaerincola (S.) Ell. & Ev.
 Sphaeria sphaerincola S.
Nummularia sp. indet.
 Nectria episphaeria (Tode) ex Fr.
Ustulina vulgaris Tul.
 Isaria congesta B. & C.
 Dialonectria episphaeria (Fr.) Cke.
 Nectria episphaeria (Tode) ex Fr.
 Stilbum Ustulinae Pat.
Hypoxylon coccineum Bull. †
 Botrytis geniculata Cda.
 Instilale acariforme Fr.
 Tubercularia fungicola Pk.
 Verticillium sphaerophilum Pk.
Hypoxylon effusum Nits.
 Isaria citrina P.
Hypoxylon Morsei B. & C.
 Helotium episphaericum Pk.
 Lophiostoma parasiticum (Pk.) Ell. & Ev.
 Lophiotrema parasiticum Pk.
Hypoxylon rubiginosum (P.) ex Fr.
 Isaria virginiensis Ell. & Ev.
 Trichopeziza episphaeria (Mart. ex Fr.) Lamb.
Hypoxylon Sassafras (S.) B.
 Melanomma Commonsii Ell. & Ev.
Hypoxylon Tinctor (B.) Cke.
 Graphium coryneoides (Ell. & Ev.) Sacc.
 Sphaerostilbe gracilipes Tul.
 Stilbum coryneoides Ell. & Ev.
Hypoxylon sp. indet.
 Amphisphaeria Hypoxylon Ell. & Ev.
 Melanomma Hypoxylon (Ell. & Ev.) Cke.
 Botrytis atroviridis C. & E.
 Botrytis geniculata Cda.
 Clasterosporium herculeum Ell.
 Cordierites coralloides B. & C.
 Hypocrella rubiginosa A. L. Sm.
 Lasiosphaeria actinodes (B. & C.) Sacc.
 Sphaeria actinodes B. & C.
 Lasiosphæria ovina (P. ex Fr.) Ces. & De Not.
 Nectria aglaeothele B. & C.
 Dialonectria episphaeria (Tode ex Fr.) Cke.
 Nectria episphaeria (Tode) ex Fr.
 Peziza episphaeria Mart.
 Coniothyrium parasitans (B. & Rav.) Tassi.
 Sphaeropsis parasitans B. & Rav.
 Venturia parasitica Ell. & Ev.
Daldinia concentrica Ces. & De Not.
 Cladosporium episphaerium S.
Kretzschmaria Clavus Fr.
 Hypoxylon coccineum (Bull.) ex Fr.
Xylaria allantoidea B.
 Hypoxylon allantoideum Mont.
 Hypocrea perpusilla Mont.
 Nectriella perpusilla (Mont.) Sacc.

Xylaria corniformis Fr.
Xylaria globosa Mont.
 Nectria episphaeria Fr.
Xylaria polymorpha (P.) ex Grev.
 Oospora heterospora Ell. & Ev.
 Kretzchmaria rugosa Earle.
Xylaria rhopaloides Mont.
 Nectria ostiolorum B. & Cke.
Xylaria sp. indet.
 Sphinctrina cubensis B. & C.
 Pseudodiplodia Xylariae Ferdinandsen &
 Winge.

BASIDIOMYCETES
USTILAGINACEAE

Ustilago Avenae (P.) Jensen.
 Fusarium Ustilaginis Kellerm. & Swingle.
 Macrosporium utile Kellerm. & Swingle.

MELAMPSORACEAE

Coleosporium Ipomoeae (S.) Burrill.
 Monosporium uredinicola F. L. Stevens.
 Ramularia Coleosporiae Sacc.
Coleosporium Solidaginis Thm.
 Darluca Filum (Biv.) Cast.
Melampsora Bigelowii Thm.
 Ramularia Uredinis (Voss) Sacc.
Melampsora sp. indet.
 Darluca Filum (Biv.) Cast.
Cronartium Comandrae Pk.
Cronartium Quercus Schrt.
 Tuberculina maxima Rostr.
Uredinopsis Pteridis Diet. & Holw.
 Tuberculina persicina (Ditm.) Sacc.

PUCCINIACEAE

Gymnoconia interstitialis (Schl.) Lagerh.
 Tuberculina persicina (Ditm.) Sacc.
Kuehneola Gossypii Arth.
 Darluca Filum (Biv.) Cast.
Kuehneola Potentillae Arth.
 Darluca bubakiana Kabát.
 Darluca Filum (Biv.) Cast.
Kuehneola Uredinis (Lk.) Arth.
 Darluca Filum (Biv.) Cast.
Desmella superficialis Syd.
 Ophionectria tropicalis Speg.
Gymnosporangium Juniperi-virginianae S.
 Discosia Podisomatis C. & E.
Uromyces Clignyi Pat. & Hariot.
Uromyces Dianthi Niessl.
Uromyces Junci-tenuis Syd.
Uromyces pyriformis Cke.
 Darluca Filum (Biv.) Cast.
Uromyces graminicola Burrill.
 Botrytis uredinicola Pk.
Uromyces Hedysari-paniculati (S.) Farl.
 Tuberculina flavogranulata Dearness & Bar·
 thol.

Uromyces Junci Auct.
Uromyces leptodermus Syd.
Uromyces Lespedezae-procumbentis (S.) M. A.
 Curtis.
Uromyces Polygoni Fckl.
Puccinia Asparagi DC.
 Darluca Filum (Biv.) Cast.
 Tubercularia persicina Ditm.
Puccinia Asteris Duby.
Puccinia Cannae Henn.
 Darluca Filum (Biv.) Cast.
Puccinia Conoclinii Seym.
 Eudarluca australis Speg.
Puccinia curtipes Howe.
Puccinia Eleocharidis Arth.
Puccinia Gouaniae Holw.
 Darluca Filum (Biv.) Cast.
 · Eudarluca australis Speg.
Puccinia graminis P.
 Darluca Filum (Biv.) Cast.
 Macrosporium Uredinis Ell. & Barthol.
Puccinia heterospora B. & C.
 Tuberculina Malvacearum Speg.
Puccinia hodgsoniana Kern.
 Tuberculina costaricana Syd.
Puccinia Huberi Holw.
 Darluca Filum (Biv.) Cast.
Puccinia Hyptidis Tracy & Earle.
 Tuberculina aecidiophila (Speg.) Pat.
Puccinia impedita Mains & Holw.
 Tuberculina costaricana Syd.
Puccinia Lantanae Farl.
 Darluca Filum (Biv.) Cast.
Puccinia levis (Sacc. & Bizz.) Magn.
 ⎰Olpidiella Uredinis Lagerh.
 ⎱Olpidium Uredinis (Lagerh.) A. Fischer.
Puccinia Malvacearum Mont.
 Septoria parasitica Fautrey.
Puccinia Menthae P.
 Darluca Filum (Biv.) Cast.
 Fusarium parasiticum Ell. & Kellerm.
Puccinia Panici Diet.
Puccinia Poarum Nielsen.
Puccinia Polygoni-amphibii P.
Puccinia punctata Lk.
Puccinia Rivinae (B. & C.) Speg.
 Darluca Filum (Biv.) Cast.
Puccinia Raunkiaerii Ferd. & Winge.
 Tuberculina persicina (Ditm.) Sacc.
Puccinia Ruelliae Lagerh.
 Darluca Filum (Biv.) Cast.
Puccinia Seymeriae Burrill.
 Fusarium parasiticum Ell. & Kellerm.
Puccinia substriata Ell. & Barthol.
 Darluca Filum (Biv.) Cast.
Puccinia Synedrellae Henn.
 Darluca Filum (Biv.) Sacc.
Uredo on Andropogon.
 Darluca arcuata Ell. & Ev.

Uredo Aeschynomenis Arth.
Uredo on Kyllinga.
Uredo Muelleri Schrt.
   Darluca Filum (Biv.) Cast.
Uredo on Panicum.
   Botrytis uredinicola Pk.
Uredo ramonensis Syd.
   Volutella urediniphila Syd.
Aecidium alliatum.
Aecidium of Berberis Fendleri.
Aecidium Euphorbiae S.
Aecidium Impatientis S.
Aecidium of Lupinus.
Aecidium Onobrychidis Burrill.
Aecidium Physalidis Burrill.
   Tuberculina persicina (Ditm.) Sacc.
Aecidium Podophylli S.
   Macrosporium Podophylli Ell. & Ev.
Aecidium porosum Pk.
Aecidium Psoraleae Pk.
Aecidium Ranunculi S.
Aecidium Solani Mont.
Aecidium of Zauschneria.
Roestelia Nelsoni Arth.
  { Synchytrium Jonesii Pk.
  | Tubercularia persicina Ditm.
  | Tuberculina Jonesii (Pk.) Sacc.
  { Tuberculina persicina (Ditm. Sacc.
Peridermium Peckii Thm.
   Darluca Filum (Biv.) Cast.

AURICULARIACEAE

Auricularia Auricula (L.) ex Schrt.
   Hypomyces aurantius (P. ex Fr.) Tul.
Auricularia nigrescens (Sw.) ex Farl.
   Hypomyces rosellus (A. & S. ex Fr.) Tul.

PILACRACEAE

Pilacre Bubonis Rostr.
   Roesleria Bubonis (Rostr.) Sacc. & Trott.

TREMELLACEAE

Exidia albida (Huds. ex Fr.) Bref.
  { Hypocrea tremellicola Ell. & Ev.
  { Hypocreopsis tremellicola (Ell. & Ev.) Seaver.
Exidia glandulosa Fr.
   Hypocrea citrina (P.) ex Fr.
   Hypocrea sulphurea (S.) Sacc.
Tremella sp. indet.
   Sphaeronema epiglaeum B. & C.
Tremellodon gelatinosum Fr.
   Isaria brachiata (Batsch) ex Fr.

DACRYOMYCETACEAE

Calocera glossoides (P.) ex Fr.
   Microcera pluriseptata Cke. & Massee.

THELEPHORACEAE

Hypochnus isabellinus Fr.
   Corticium arachnoideum B.

Hypochnus sp. indet.
   Conidiobolus villosus G. W. Martin.
Corticium ochroleucum Fr., var. resupinatum
   Ell. & Ev.
   Michenera artocreas B. & C.
Corticium (scutellare B. & C.?)
   Hypocrea corticiicola Ell. & Ev.
Corticium sp. indet.
   Chlorosplenium epimyces Cke.
   Hypocrea subcarnea Ell. & Ev.
   Melanomma spiniferum Ell. & Ev.
   Nectria episphaeria (Tode) ex Fries.
   Zygodesmus bicolor C. & E.?
Aleurodiscus amorphus (P.) Rabh.
   Aspergillus subgriseus Pk.
Peniophora sp. indet.
   Dendryphium pachysporum Ell. & Ev.
Stereum bicolor (P.) ex Fr.
  { Heptameria stereicola (Ell.) Cke.
  { Leptosphaeria stereicola Ell.
   Melanomma Porothelia (B. & C.) Sacc.
Stereum candidum S.
   Aleurodiscus candidus (S.) Burt.
Stereum fasciatum (S.) Fr.
  { Hypocrea Stereorum (S.) B. & C.
  { Sphaeria Stereorum S.
Stereum frustulosum (P.) ex Fr.
   Hydnum macrescens Banker.
   Stictis stereicola B. & C.
Stereum rugosum P.
  { Dialonectria sulfurea Ell. & Calkins.
  { Nectria sulfurea (Ell. & Calkins) Sacc.
Stereum spadiceum Fr.
   Penicillium Hypomycetis Sacc.
   Stilbum sebaceum Ell. & Ev.
Stereum subpileatum B. & C.
   Diplocladium melleum (B. & Br.) Sacc.
   Nectria lactea Ell. & Morgan.
Stereum versicolor Fr.
   Merulius rubellus Pk.
   Stilbum arcticum B.?
Stereum sp. indet.
   Hypomyces arenaceus A. L. Smith.
   Hypomyces aurantius (P. ex Fr.) Tul.
   Hypomyces aureonitens Tul.
Thelephora terrestris Ehrh. ex Fr.
   Peniophora arachnoidea Burt.
Thelephora sp. indet.
   Hypocrea citrina (P.) ex Fr., var. fungicola
    Karst.
   ?Phyllopta biparasitica Fr.

CLAVARIACEAE

Clavaria gigantea S.
  { Phyllopta parasitica (S.) Fr.
  { Tremella parasitica S.
Clavaria cristata (Holmsk.) Fr.
   Chaetosphaeria Clavariarum (Desm.) Massee.

Clavaria pistillaris L. ex Fr.
? { Hypomyces apiosporus Cke.
  { Peckiella apiospora (Cke.) Sacc.
Clavaria spinulosa P. ex Fr.
  Helminthosphaeria Clavariarum (Desm.) Fckl.
Clavaria sp. indet.
  Dactylium dendroides (Bull.) ex Fr.
  Penicillium No. 31. Thom.
  Rosellinia Clavariae (Tul.) Wint.
  Sepedonium macrosporum Pk.
Lachnocladium semivestitum B. & C.
  Aspergillus flavus Lk.
  Aspergillus glaucus (L.) ex Lk., var. oblongi-
    sporus Ell. & Ev.

HYDNACEAE

Hydnum Erinaceus Bull. ex Fr.
  Hypocrea parasitans B. & C.
Hydnum membranaceum Bull. ex Fr.
  Fusarium hydnicola Ell. & Ev.
Hydnum sp. indet.
  Dematium parasiticum Pk.
  { Hypoxylon hydnicola (S.) Sacc.
  { Sphaeria hydnicola S.
  Penicillium glaucum Lk.
  { Lachnellula cyphelloides (Ell. & Ev.) Sacc.
  { Peziza cyphelloides Ell. & Ev.
  Virgaria hydnicola Pk.

POLYPORACEAE

Merulius lacrimans (Wulf.) ex Fr.
  Aspergillus griseus Lk.
Merulius tremellosus Schrad. ex Fr.
  { Sphaeronema oxysporum B.
  { Sphaeronemella oxyspora (B.) Sacc.
Merulius sp. indet.
  Arcyria nutans (Bull.) Grev.
  Hyalopus parasitans B. & C.
Poria Cocos (S.) Wolf.
Pachyma Cocos S.   Syn.
  Granularia eurotioides Sacc. & Ell.
  Hypocrea solenostoma B. & Rav.
Poria Medulla-panis (P. ex Fr.) Cke.
  Hypocrea lactea Fr.
Poria mucida P.
  { Aspergillus maximus Ehrb.
  { Mucor ramosus Bull.
  { Mucor Syzygites DBy.
  { Sporodinia Aspergillus (Scop.) ex Schrt.
Poria ochracea Murrill.
  Institale alba Lloyd.
Poria spissa (Fr.) Cke.
  Orbilia vinosa (A. & S. ex Fr.) Karst.
Poria sp. indet.
  Gonatobotrys lateritia Pk.
  Poria Amesii Murrill.
  Trichoderma lignorum Harz.

Fomes applanatus (P. ex Fr.) Gill.
  Apiospora Polypori Ell. & Ev.
  Ceratostoma parasiticum Ell. & Ev.
  Thelephora dendritica B.
Fomes conchatus Karst.
  Sporotrichum chryseum Pk.
Fomes fomentarius (Fr.) Gill.
  Helotium mycetophilum Pk.
  Orbilia epipora (Nyl.) Karst.
Fomes igniarius (Fr.) Gill.
  Hypomyces rosellus (A. & S.) Tul.
  Institale? maximum S.
  Peziza mycogena Ell.
Fomes Pini (Fr.) Lloyd.
  Solenia fasciculata P.
Fomes pinicola (Fr.) Cke.
  Hypocrea fungicola (Karst.) Sacc.
  Poria vulgaris (Fr.) Quél.
  Stysanus Berkeleyi (Mont.) Sacc.
Ganoderma Curtisii (B.) Murrill.
  { Hypocrea Stereorum (S.) B. & C.
  { Sphaeria Stereorum S.
Ganoderma lucidum (Fr.) Karst.
  Chromocrea ceramica (Ell. & Ev.) Seaver.
Polyporus acanthoides (Bull.) ex Fr.
  Sepedonium flavidum Sacc. & Ell.
Polyporus Berkeleyi Fr.
  Aspergillus repens (Cda.) Sacc.
  Sepedonium flavidum Sacc. & Ell.
Polyporus betulinus Fr.
  Licea minima Fr.
  Orbilia rubinella (Nyl.) Karst.
Polyporus caesius (Schrad.) ex Fr.
Polyporus chioneus Fr.
  Hypocrea aurantiaca Pk.
  Hypocrea pallida Ell. & Ev.
Polyporus elegans (Bull.) ex Fr.
  { Pterula setosa Pk.
  { Lachnocladium setosum (Pk.) Sacc. Syll.
Polyporus frondosus Fr.
  Zythia compressa S.
  Hypomyces aurantius (P. ex Fr.) Tul.
Polyporus gilvus Fr.
  Poria spissa (S.) Cke.
Polyporus hispidus Fr.
  Trichothecium candidum Wallr.
Polyporus parvulus Klotzsch.
  Coprinus ephemerus Fr.
Polyporus resinosus Fr.
  Badhamia utricularis B.
  Diplocladium minus Bon.
  Hypomyces aurantius (P. ex Fr.) Tul.
  Diplocladium penicilloides Sacc.
Polyporus rheades P.
  Gloeoporus conchoides Mont.
Polyporus Schweinitzii Fr.
  Rhinotrichum armeniacum B. & C.

Polyporus sulphureus Fr.
Hypocrea maculiformis B. & C.
? {Hypomyces boleticola (S.) Sacc.
{Sphaeria boleticola S.
{Coniochaeta cladosporiosa (S.) Cke.
{Lasiosphaeria cladosporiosa (S.) Cke.
{Sphaeria cladosporiosa S.
Polyporus varius Fr.
Cladosporium epimyces Cke.
Diplosporium Polypori Dearness & House.
Heterosporium fungicolum Ell. & Ev.
Penicillium glaucum Lk.
Polystictus abietinus (Dicks. ex Fr.) Cke.
Heydenia fungicola Pk.
Hypomyces aurantius (P. ex Fr.) Tul.
Sphinctrina tigillaris B. & Br.
Polystictus fulvocinereus (Murrill) Sacc. &
Trott.
Poria subcorticola Murrill.
Polystictus perennis (Fr.) Karst.
Claudopus subdepluens Fitzpatrick.
Polystictus pergamenus Fr.
Bertia moriformis (Tode ex Fr.) De Not
Cephalothecium roseum Cda.
{Calicium tigillare (B. & Br.) Sacc.
{Sphinctrina tigillaris B. & Br.
Coniosporium mycophilum Ell. & Langlois.
Polystictus versicolor (L.) ex Fr.
Dactylium dendroides (Bull.) ex Fr.
{Hypomyces aurantius (Fr.) Tul.
{Nectria aurantia Fr.
{Sphaeria aurantia P. ex Fr.
Hypomyces polyporinus Pk.
Scopaphoma Corioli Dearness & House.
Trametes hydnoides Fr.
Badhamia nitens B.
Poria polyporicola Murrill.
Trametes rigida B. & Mont.
Hypomyces rosellus (A. & S. ex Fr.) Tul.
Trametes serpens Fr.
Mollisia Trametis Ell. & Ev.
Daedalea unicolor Fr.
Bertia moriformis (Tode ex Fr.) De Not.
{Cilicipodium aurifilum (Gerard) Sacc.
{Stilbum aurifilum Gerard.
Daedalea sp. indet.
Calocera fasciculata S.
Boletus luteus L. ex Fr.
Boletus subtomentosus L. ex Fr.
{Hypomyces chrysospermus (Bull. ex Fr.) Tul.
{Sepedonium chrysospermum (Bull.) ex Fr.
Boletus pictus Pk.
Sepedonium brunneum Pk.
Boletus scaber Bull. ex Fr.
Cladosporium epimyces Cke.
Hypomyces chrysospermus Tul.
Boletus sp. indet.
Aspergillus virens Lk.
Botrytis ramosa S. Syn. Car.

Botrytis spicata Mich.
{Hypomyces aurantius (P. ex Fr.) Tul.
{Sphaeria aurantia P. ex Fr.
Hypomyces boletinus Pk.
Hypomyces chlorinus Tul.?
Hypomyces chrysospermus Tul.
Hypomyces luteovirens (Fr.) Tul.
Hypomyces viridis B. & Br.
Isaria? saccharina P.
Mucor capitatoramosus S.
{Mucor paradoxus B. & C.
{Thamnidium? paradoxum (B. & C.) Berl. &
{ DeToni.
Mycogone puccinioides (Preuss) Sacc.
Penicillium stoloniferum Thom.
Sepedonium macrosporum Sacc.
Sepedonium tulasneanum (Plowr.) Sacc.
{Aspergillus maximus Lk.
{Mucor Syzygites DBy.
{Sporodinia Aspergillus (Scop.) ex Schrt.
{Sporodinia dichotoma Cda.
{Syzygites megalocarpus Ehrb.
Boletinus porosus (B.) Pk.
Zythia boleticola Ell. & Ev.
Polyporaceae gen. indet.
{Badhamia magna Pk.
{Dictydium magnum Pk.
{Brachysporium leptotrichum (C. & E.) Sacc.
{Helminthosporium leptotrichum C. & E.
Caliciopsis Ellisii Sacc.
Ceracea vernicosa Cragin.
Chaetostylum Fresenii van Tiegh.
Chromosporium vitellinum Sacc. & Ell.
Cladosporium epiphyllum Nees.
Coniophora subochracea Pk.
Hydnum nudum B. & C.
Hypocrea citrina (P.) Fr.
Hypocrea pallida Ell. & Ev.
Hypocrea rufa (P.) Fr.
Hypomyces aureonitens Tul.
{Hypomyces flavescens Cke.
{Sphaeria flavescens Fr., var. epimyces S.
{Botrytis agaricina Lk.
{Botrytis ramosa S. Syn. Car.
{Hypomyces ochraceus (P.) Tul.
{Verticillium agaricinum (Lk.) Cda.
Hypsilophora fragiformis Cke.
Lycogala epidendrum (L.) Fr.
{Melanospora lagenaria (P. ex Fr.) Fckl.
{Sphaeria lagenaria P. ex Fr.
Monilia megalospora (B. & C.) Sacc.
Mucor capitato-ramosus S.
Mucor rufus S. Am. Bor. *2727*.
Mycogone rosea Lk.
Nectria coccinea (P.) ex Fr.
Nectria lactea Ell. & Morg.
Nectria subiculosa B. & C.
{Peziza incrustata Ell.
{Pseudohelotium incrustatum (Ell.) Sacc.

Polyporaceae gen. indet. (*cont.*)
   ⎧Peziza myceticola B. & C.
   ⎪Peziza vulgaris Fr., var. myceticola B.
   ⎨Pezizella vulgaris Sacc., var. myceticola (B.)
   ⎩ Sacc.
   ?Phyllopta biparasitica Fr.
   Pleurotus septicus Fr.
   Polyporus adustus (Willd.) ex Fr.
   ⎰Polyporus favillaceus B. & C.
   ⎱Poria favillacea (B. & C.) Cke.
   Poria cinereicolor Murrill.
   Poria hymeniicola Murrill.
   Poria rivulosa (B. & C.) Sacc.
   ⎧Amphisphaeria mycophila (Fr.) Cke.
   ⎨Rosellinia mycophila (Fr.) Sacc.
   ⎩Sphaeria mycophila Fr.
   Sepedonium chrysospermum (Bull.) Fr.
   ⎰Sphaeronema oxysporum B.
   ⎱Sphaeronemella oxyspora (B.) Sacc.
   Stemonitis maxima S.
   Stilbum pellucidum Schrad.
   ⎰Graphium Berkeleyi Mont.
   ⎱Stysanus Berkeleyi (Mont.) Sacc.
   Thelephora granosa B. & C.

AGARICACEAE

Cantharellus aurantiacus (Wulf.) ex Fr.
?⎧Sphaeria aurantia P. ex Fr.
 ⎪Hypomyces aurantius (P. ex Fr.) Tul.
 ⎨Hypomyces Lactifluorum (S.) Tul.
 ⎩Sphaeria aurantia Rav. F. Car **5:** *64.*
Cantharellus cibarius Fr.
   Hypomyces Lactifluorum (S.) Tul.
   Hypomyces transformans Pk.
   Peckiella transformans (Pk.) Sacc.
Cantharellus sp. indet.
   Hypomyces insignis B. & C.
   ⎧Agaricus lycoperdoides (Bull.) ex Schrt.
   ⎨Asterophora clavus (Schaeff.) ex Murrill.
   ⎪Asterophora agaricoides Fr.
   ⎩Nyctalis Asterophora Fr.
Paxillus involutus Fr.
   Dicranophora fulva Schrt.
Coprinus atramentarius Fr.
Coprinus comatus Fr.
   Panaeolus epimyces Pk.
   Stropharia epimyces (Pk.) Atk.
Coprinus micaceus Fr.
   Collybia tuberosa Bull. ex Fr.
Gomphidius sp. indet.
   Hypomyces Lactifluorum (S.) Tul.
Nyctalis asterophora Fr.
   Hypomyces asterophorus Tul.
Lactarius camphoratus Fr.
   ⎰Hypomyces Camphorati Pk.
   ⎱Peckiella Camphorati (Pk.) Seaver
Lactarius deceptivus Pk.
   Penicillium pallidofulvum Pk.

Lactarius deliciosus (L.) ex Fr.
Lactarius Indigo (S.) Fr.
   ⎰Hypocrea lateritia Fr.
   ⎱Hypomyces lateritius (Fr.) Tul.
Lactarius piperatus (Scop.) ex Fr.
   ⎰Asterophora physaroides Fr.
   ⎱Hypomyces asterophorus Tul.
   ⎧Hypocrea Lactifluorum (S.) M. A. Curtis.
   ⎨Hypomyces Lactifluorum, (S.) Tul.
   ⎩Sphaeria Lactifluorum S.
   ⎧Agaricus lycoperdoides (Bull) ex Schrt.
   ⎨Asterophora agaricoides Fr.
   ⎪Asterophora clavus (Schaeff.) Murrill.
   ⎩Nyctalis asterophora Fr.
Lactarius subdulcis (Bull.) ex Fr.
   Verticillium Lactarii Pk.
Lactarius torminosus (Schaeff.) ex Fr.
   Hypocrea floccosa Fr.
   Hypomyces lateritius (Fr.) Tul.
   Hypomyces torminosus (Mont.) Tul.
Lactarius trivialis Fr.
   Hypomyces lateritius Fr.
Lactarius turpis Fr.
   Collybia tuberosa Bull. ex Fr.
Lactarius uvidus Fr.
   Peckiella hymenioides Pk.
   ⎰Hypomyces lateritius (Fr.) Tul.
   ⎱Peckiella lateritia (Fr.) Maire.
Lactarius vellereus Fr.
   Peckiella hymenii Pk.
   Penicillium No. 30.   Thom.
Lactarius volemus Fr.
   Peckiella lateritia (Fr.) Maire.
   Hypomyces Volemi Pk.
Lactarius zonarius Fr.
   Hypomyces lateritius (Fr.) Tul.
Lactarius sp. indet.
   Corticium simile B. & C.
   Hypomyces Banningii Pk.
   Hypomyces purpureus Pk.
   ⎰Hypocrea tomentosa B.
   ⎱Hypomyces tomentosus B.
   ⎰Peckiella luteovirens (Fr.) Maire.
   ⎱Peckiella viridis (A. & S.) ex Sacc.
   Sporotrichum agaricinum Lk.
Russula adusta (P.) ex Fr.
   Hypomyces asterophorus Tul.
   ⎧Agaricus lycoperdoides (Bull.) ex Schrt.
   ⎨Asterophora agaricoides Fr.
   ⎪Asterophora clavus (Schaeff.) Murrill.
   ⎩Nyctalis asterophora Fr.
Russula alutacea Fr.
   ⎧Hypocrea luteovirens Fr.
   ⎪Hypomyces luteovirens (Fr.) Tul.
   ⎪Hypomyces viridis (A. & S.) ex B. & Br.
   ⎨Peckiella luteovirens (Fr.) Maire.
   ⎪Peckiella viridis (A. & S.) ex Sacc.
   ⎪Sphæria luteovirens Fr.
   ⎩Sphaeria viridis (A. & S.) ex S.

Russula brevipes Pk.
Russula delica Fr.
    Hypomyces Lactifluorum (S.) Tul.
Russula foetens P. ex Fr.
    ⎰Hypocrea hyalina (S.) Fr.
    ⎱Hypomyces hyalinus (S.) Tul.
    Nyctalis parasitica Fr.
Russula nigricans (Bull.) ex Fr.
    Nyctalis asterophora Fr.
Russula sp. indet.
    Agaricus tuberosus (Bull.) ex Fr.
    Peckiella lateritia (Fr.) Maire.
Lentinus lepideus Fr.
    Sporodinia grandis Lk.
Lentinus ursinus Fr.
    Coniosporium mycophilum Ell. & Langlois.
Marasmius sp. indet.
    Verticillium enecans Speg.
Hypholoma velutinum (P.) ex Fr.
    ⎰Aspergillus maximus (Ehrenb.) ex Fr.
    ⎪Mucor ramosus Bull. ex Fr.
    ⎪Mucor Syzygites DBy.
    ⎨Sporodinia Aspergillus (Scop.) ex Schrt.
    ⎪Sporodinia dichotoma Cda.
    ⎪Sporodinia grandis Lk.
    ⎩Syzygites megalocarpus Ehrb. ex Fr.
Agaricus campestris L. ex Fr.
    Mucor griseolilacinus Povah.
    Mycogone perniciosa Magn.
    Penicillium candidum Lk. ex P., var. subcandidum Pk.
Cortinarius sp. indet.
    Sporodinia dichotoma Cda.
Flammula squalida Pk.
    ⎰Hypomyces ochraceus (P.) Tul.
    ⎱Verticillium agaricinum (Lk.) Cda.
Clitopilus abortivus B. & C.
    ⎰Sporodinia Aspergillus (Scop.) ex Schrt.
    ⎱Sporodinia grandis Lk.
Pleurotus ostreatus (Jacq.) ex Fr.
    Arthrobotrys superba Cda., var. oligospora (Fres.) Coemans.
    Cladosporium epimyces Cke.
    Cladosporium fuligineum Bon.
Pleurotus salignus (P.) ex Fr.
    Sphaeria cladosporiosa S.
Pleurotus sapidus Kalchbr.
    Tilmadoche polycephala S.
Pleurotus serotinus (Schrad.) ex Fr.
    ⎰Isaria agaricina P. ex Fr.
    ⎱Isaria brachiata Batsch ex Fr.
Pleurotus sp. indet.
    Jacobaschella alba (Bon.) O. Kuntze.
Omphalia sphaerospora B.
    Stilbum arcticum B.
Mycena polygramma (Lk.) Fr.
    ⎰Mucor fusiger Lk.
    ⎱Spinellus fusiger (Lk.) van Tiegh.
    Spinellus macrocarpus (Cda.) Karst.

Collybia dryophila (Bull.) ex Fr.
    Mucor saturninus Hagem.
    Phycomyces nitens (Agardh) Kze.
Collybia fusipes (Bull. ex Fr.) B.
    Spinellus fusiger (Lk.) van Tiegh.
Collybia velutipes (W. Curtis) ex Fr.
    Cladosporium fuligineum Bon.
    Diplocladium minus Bon.
Clitocybe sp. indet.
    ⎰Agaricus lycoperdoides (Bull.) ex Schrt.
    ⎪Asterophora agaricoides Fr.
    ⎨Asterophora clavus (Schaeff.) Murrill.
    ⎪Nyctalis asterophora Fr.
    ⎩Volvaria loveiana B.
Tricholoma Russula (Schaeff.) ex Fr.
    Verticillium agaricinum (Lk.) Cda.
Amanita rubescens P. ex Fr.
    Hypomyces hyalinus (S.) Tul.
    Hypomyces inaequalis Pk.
Armillaria mellea (Vahl) ex Fr.
    Aspergillus repens (Cda.) Sacc.
    ⎰Agaricus lycoperdoides (Bull.) ex Schrt.
    ⎪Asterophora agaricoides Fr.
    ⎨Asterophora clavus (Schaeff.) Murrill.
    ⎩Nyctalis Asterophora Fr.
    Cladosporium epimyces Cke.
    Exobasidium mycetophilum (Pk.) Burt.
    Sterigmatocystis butyracea Bain.
"Agaricus" sp. indet.
    Acrostalagmus fungicola Preuss.
    Acrostalagmus tetraclados A. L. Sm.
    Aspergillus candidus Lk. ex Fr.
    Aspergillus virens Lk. ex Fr.
    Botrytis ramosa S. Syn. Car.
    Dactylium dendroides (Bull.) ex Fr.
    ⎰Dialonectria perforata Ell. & Holw.
    ⎱Nectria perforata Ell. & Holw.
    ⎰Eleutheromyces subulatus (Tode ex Fr.) Fckl.
    ⎪Sphaeria subulata (Tode) ex Fr.
    ⎨Sphaeronema subulatum Fr.
    ⎩Zythia subulata (Fr.) S.
    Heterosporium fungicola Ell. & Ev.
    Hypocrea Petersii B. & C.
    ⎰Hypocrea tomentosa B.
    ⎱Hypomyces tomentosus B.
    Hypomyces vanbruntianus Gerard.
    ⎰Monilia candida Pk.
    ⎱Monilia mycophila Sacc.
    Mucor flavidus P. ex Fr.
    Mycogone incarnata P.
    Myrothecium fungicola Pk.
    Myrothecium inundatum Tode ex Fr.
    Nectria sulphurea (Ell. & Calkins) Sacc.
    Phoma agaricicola Rostr.
    Sclerotium fungorum P. ex Fr.
    Sepedonium chrysospermum (Bull.) Fr.
    Sporotrichum agaricinum Lk.
    Stilbum byssinum P. ex Fr.

LYCOPERDACEAE

Lycoperdon giganteum (Batsch) ex P.
⎰Monilia fungicola Ell. & Barthol.
⎱Oospora fungicola (Ell. & Barthol.) Sumstine.
Lycoperdon sp. indet.
  Cladosporium lycoperdinum Cke.
  Pleospora herbarum (P. ex Fr.) Rabh.
Calvatia sp. indet.
  Mucor varians Povah.

SCLERODERMATACEAE

Scleroderma verrucosum (Bull.) ex P.
⎰Boletus parasiticus Bull. ex Fr.
⎱Ceriomyces parasiticus (Bull. ex Fr.) Murrill.
Scleroderma vulgare Fr..
  Boletus parasiticus Bull. ex Fr.
  Cephalothecium roseum Cda.
  Cladosporium epimyces Cke.
⎰Fusarium Peckii Sacc.
⎱Fusarium Sclerodermatis Pk.
Scleroderma sp. indet.
  Cordyceps agariciformia (Bolt.) ex Seaver.

NIDULARIACEAE

Cyathus striatus Willd. ex P.
  Hypocrea latizonata Pk.
Cyathus vernicosus (Bull.) ex DC.
  Fusarium miniatum (B. & C.) Sacc.

FUNGI IMPERFECTI

SPHAERIOIDACEAE

Phyllosticta caryigena Ell. & Ev.
  Discosia rugulosa B. & C.
Cytospora sp. indet.
  Fusarium Volutella Ell. & Ev.
  Nectria episphaeria (Tode) ex Fr.
Sphaeropsis Asiminae Ell. & Ev.
  Macrosporium olivaceum Ell. & Ev.
Sphaeropsis sp. indet.
  Cheiromyces stellatus B. & C.
Diplodia Zeae (S.) Lév.
  Triposporium bicorne Morg.
Kellermannia sp. indet.
  Allantonectria Yuccae Earle.
Phleospora Mori Lev.
  Phyllosticta consors Sacc.
Micropera sp. indet.
⎰Sphaerographium Microperae (Cke.) Sacc.
⎱Sphaeronema Microperae Cke.
Aschersonia sp. indet.
  Aschersonia brunnea Petch.

MELANCONIACEAE

Thyrsidium botryosporum (Fr.) Mont.
  Periconia parasitica Pk.
Pestalozzia Guepini Desm.
⎰Dermatea lobata Ell.
⎱Lachnella rufo-olivacea (A. & S. ex Fr.) Phil.

MUCEDINACEAE

Oidium Caricae Nowak.
  Cicinnobolus Cesatii DBy.
Rhinotrichum sp. indet.
  Helicosporium griseum B. & C.
Ramularia Armoraciae Fckl.
  Macrosporium parasiticum Thm.

DEMATIACEAE

Fusicladium dendriticum (Wallr.) Fckl.
  Cephalothecium roseum Cda.
Helminthosporium Ravenelii M. A. Curtis.
⎰Dactylium Helminthosporii Thm.
⎱Trichothecium Helminthosporii (Thm.) Sacc.
  Trichothecium roseum P. ex Fr.
Helminthosporium sp. indet.
  Helicosporium brunneolum B. & C.
Heterosporium Colocasiae Massee.
  Cephalosporium acremonium Cda., var.
Sarcinella Milleriae Syd.
⎰Cicinnobella asperula Syd.
⎱Phaeodimeriella asperula Syd.
Cercospora Polygonorum Cke.
  Botrytis hypophylla Ell. & Kellerm.

STILBACEAE

Isaria farinosa (Dicks.) Fr.
  Ceratostoma biparasiticum Ell. & Ev.
  Melanospora parasitica Tul.

TUBERCULARIACEAE

Trichodochium disseminatum Syd.
  Dimerina epidochica Syd.
Tubercularia sp. indet.
  Tetracolium Tuberculariae (Nees) Lk.
Fusarium roseum Lk.
  Epicoccum purpurascens Ehrenb.
  Cercospora Caricae Speg.
  Zygosporium oscheoides Mont.
Fungi fam. indet.
  Badhamia foliicola Lister.
  Baryeidamia parasitica Karst.
  Cladosporium herbarum (P.) ex Lk.
  Collybia cirrhata Schum. ex Fr.
  Cordyceps flavella B. & C.
  Hypocrea patella Pk.
  Hypomyces macrosporus Seaver.
⎰Hypomyces tubericola (S.) Sacc.
⎱Sphaeria tubericola S.
  Isaria citrina P.
  Isaria intricata Fr.
  Isaria monilioides, var. b. S. Syn. Car.
  Mortierella polycephala Coemans.
  Mucor rammanianus Moll.
⎰Dialonectria mycetophila (Pk.) Cke.
⎱Nectria mycetophila (Pk.) Sacc.
⎱Nectriella mycetophila Pk.
  Nectria Peziza (Tode) ex Fr.

Fungi fam. indet. (*cont.*)
  Penicillium bicolor Fr.
  Penicillium No. 28 Thom.
  Periconia tenuissima Pk.
  Piptocephalis repens van Tiegh.
  Sepedonium roseum (Lk.) Fr.

ASCOLICHENES
PYRENOCARPEAE
VERRUCARIACEAE

Verrucaria sp. indet.
  Arthonia varians (Dav.) Nyl.

TRYPETHELIACEAE

Trypethelium carolinianum Tuckerm.
  Buellia Trypethelii Tuckerm.

GYMNOCARPEAE
LECIDEACEAE

Lecidea confluens Fr.
  Tichothecium gemmiferum Tayl.
Lecidea sp. indet.
  Capillaria rhizomorphina S.
Lopadium fuscoluteum (Dicks.) Mudd.
  Pharcidia epistigmella Nyl., var. meizospora Vouaux.
Lopadium fuscoluteum (Dicks.) Mudd., var. **bisporum** B. de Lesdain.
  Muellerella Lopadii Vouaux.
Rhizocarpon geographicum (L.) DC.
  { Leptosphæria polaris Sacc.
  { Sphæria no. 8 Th. Fr.
Rhizocarpon polycarpum (Hepp) Th. Fr.
  Phaeospora peregrina Flot.

CLADONIACEAE

Baeomyces rufus (Huds.) DC.
  Buellia saxatilis (Schär.) Körb.
Baeomyces placophyllus Wallenb.
  Buellia scabrosa (Ach.) Körb.
Cladonia amaurocraea (Fl.) Schär.
Cladonia coccifera (L.) Willd.
Cladonia extensa Schär.
Cladonia fimbriata (L.) Fr.
  Nesolechia oxysporella (Nyl.) Rehm.
Cladonia cariosa (Ach.) Spreng.
  { Coniothyrium Cladoniae (Ell. & Ev.) Sacc.
  { Sphaeropsis Cladoniae Ell. & Ev.
Cladonia cornuta (L.) Schaer.
  Lichenosticta podetiicola Zopf.
Cladonia digitata Hoffm.
  Nesolechia oxysporella (Nyl.) Rehm.
  Nesolechia punctum Massal.
Cladonia gracilis (L.) Willd.
  Lichenosticta podetiicola Zopf.
Cladonia Papillaria (Ehrh.) Hoffm.
  Biatora cladoniscum Willey.
  Biatora Papillariae Willey.

Stereocaulon alpinum Laur.
  Biatorina Stereocaulorum Th. Fr.
Stereocaulon sp. indet.
  Merulius lichenicola Burt.

STICTACEAE

Sticta pulmonaria (L.) Ach.
  Celidium Stictarum (De Not.) Tul.
Sticta sp. indet.
  Dothidea hymenicola B. & Br.
Lobaria sp. indet.
  Karschia Ricasoliae Vouaux.

PELTIGERACEAE

Peltigera aphthosa (L.) Hoffm.
  Hypochnus coriarius (Pk.) Burt.
  Illosporium carneum Fr.
Peltigera canina (L.) Hoffm.
  Illosporium carneum Fr.
  { Niptera Muelleri (Willey) Vouaux.
  { Phacopsis Muelleri Willey.
Peltigera sp. indet.
  { Biatora epiphylla Merrill.
  { Scutula epiphylla (Merrill) Vouaux.
  Clitocybe peltigerina Pk.
  { Leptosphaeria peltigerea (Merrill) Vouaux.
  { Trypethelium peltigereum Merrill.

PERTUSARIACEAE

Pertusaria communis DC.
  Buellia pertusaricola Willey.
  Calicium turbinatum P.
  Illosporium coccineum Fr.
Pertusaria multipuncta (Turn.) Nyl.
  { Gyalecta radiatilis Tuckerm.
  { Nesolechia radiatilis (Tuckerm.) Vouaux.
Pertusaria pustulata (Ach.) Nyl.
  Calicium tubiforme (Massal.)
Pertusaria subobducens Nyl.
  { Calicium turbinatum P.
  { Spinctrina turbinata (P.) ex Fr.
Pertusaria velata (Turn.) Nyl.
  Calicium pallidellum Willey.
  { Opegrapha quaternella Nyl.
  { Mycobilimbia quaternella (Nyl.) Vouaux.
Pertusaria sp. indet.
  { Buellia inquilina Tuckerm.
  { Calicium Stigonellum Muhl. Cat.
  Buellia minimula Tuckerm.
  Buellia parasitica (Fl.) Th. Fr.
  Discothecium gemmiferum (Tayl.) Vouaux.
  Karschia Pertusariae Vouaux.
  { Dactylospora parvula Arnold.
  { Leciographa parvula (Arnold) Sacc. & D. Sacc.

LECANORACEAE

Lecanora glaucoma Ach.
  { Buellia glaucomaria (Nyl.) Tuckerm.
  { Lecidea glaucomaria Nyl.

Lecanora pallescens (L.) Schaer.
  Buellia parasitica (Fl.) Th. Fr.
Lecanora pallescens (L.) Schaer., var. rosella
  Tuckerm.
  {Arthonia varians (Dav.) Nyl.
  {Celidium varians (Dav.) Arnold.
Lecanora rubina (Vill.) Ach.
  Arthonia clemens (Tul.) Nyl.
Lecanora saxicola Schaer.
  Pharcidia epicymatia (Wallr.) Wint.
Lecanora tartarea (L.) Ach.
  Buellia glaucomarioides Willey.
  Celidium varians (Dav.) Arnold.
Placodium ferrugineum Hepp., var. festivum A.
  L. Sm.
  Pharcidia epistigmella Nyl.
Placodium sp. indet.
  Pharcidia epistigmella Nyl., var. meizospora
  Vouaux.

PARMELIACEAE

Parmelia Borreri Turn.
  {Biatora oxyspora (Tul.) Tuckerm.
  {Nesolechia oxyspora (Tul.) Rehm.
  Buellia Parmeliarum (Sommf.) Tuckerm.
Parmelia olivacea (L.) Ach.
  Buellia Parmeliarum (Sommf.) Tuckerm.
Parmelia saxatilis (L.) Fr.
  {Abrothallus Parmeliarum (Sommf.) Nyl.
  {Buellia Parmeliarum (Sommf.) Tuckerm.
  {Dothidea Piggotii B. & Br.
  {Homostegia Piggotii (B. & Br.) Karst.
  Karschia egedeana (Linds.) Vouaux.
Parmelia tiliacea (Hoffm.) Flörk.
  Nectria rubefaciens Ell. & Ev.
Parmelia sp. indet.
  {Diplodia Parmeliae B. & C.
  {Diplodina Parmeliae (B. & C.) Sacc.
  Illosporium roseum (Schreb.) Mart. ex Sacc.
  {Nectria diplocarpa Ell. & Ev.
  {Nectria lecanodes Wint.
  {Sphaeria Peltigerae Mont.
  {Rhaphidospora Peltigerae Mont.
Cetraria fahlunensis (L.) Schaer.
  Buellia Parmeliarum (Sommf.) Tuckerm.

USNEACEAE

Usnea barbata (L.) Fr.
  Fusarium barbatum Ell. & Ev.
Thamnolia vermicularis (Sw.) Schär.
  {Epicymatia frigida Sacc.
  {Pharcidia frigida (Sacc.) Vouaux.

PHYSCIACEAE

Physcia aipolia Nyl., f. anthelina Cromb.
  Trichothecium pygmaeum Körber.
Physcia obscura (Ehrh.) Nyl.
  Illosporium roseum (Schreb.) Mart.
Physcia picta (Sw.) Nyl., var. sorediata (Fr.) Nyl.
  Nesolechia cerasina Müller Arg.
Physcia stellaris (L.) Nyl.
  Illosporium roseum (Schreb.) Mart. sec. Sacc.
Physcia sp. indet.
  Pleoscutula Arsenii Vouaux.

HYMENOLICHENES

Cora Pavonia Fr..
  Leptosphæria Coræ Pat.
Cephaleuros virescens Kunze.
  Zignoella algaphila F. L. Stevens.

Lichenes fam. indet.
  Badhamia foliicola Lister.
  {Buellia urceolata Th. Fr.
  {Leciographa urceolata (Th. Fr.) Rehm.
  {Chondrococcus coralloides (Thax.) Jahn.
  {Myxococcus coralloides Thax.
  {Chondromyces lichenicola Thax.
  {Podangium lichenicola (Thax.) Jahn.
  {Archangium serpens (Thax.) Jahn.
  {Chondromyces serpens Thax.
  Dematium rupicola Lk.
  Dendrodochium subeffusum Ell. & Ev.
  Dichosporidium glomeratum Pat.
  {Didymella sphinctrinoides (Zwackh) Sacc.,
  { var. borealis Vouaux.
  {Epicymatia borealis (Cke.) Sacc.
  {Pharcidia borealis (Cke.) Ell. & Ev.
  {Sphaerella borealis Cke.
  {Sphaeria no. 9. Th. Fr.
  Illosporium roseum (Schreb.) Mart. sec. Sacc.
  Myxococcus rubescens Thax.
  Nectria rubefaciens Ell. & Ev.
  Stigmatella aurantiaca B. & C.
  Torula opaca Cke.

BRYOPHYTA

HEPATICAE

Jungermannia sp. indet.
  Calonectria muscivora (B. & Br.) Sacc.
  Nectria muscivora (B. & Br.) Cke.
  Sphaeria muscivora B. & Br.
Marchantia polymorpha L.
  Cyathicula Marchantiae (Sommf. ex Fr.) Sacc.
  Humaria Ithacaensis Rehm.
Hepaticae sp. indet.
  Chondromyces Muscorum Thax.
  Nectria laeticolor B. & C.
  Peziza subcarnea C. & P.
  Phialea subcarnea (C. & P.) Sacc.
  Psathyra flavogrisea B.

MUSCI

SPHAGNACEAE

Sphagnum sp. indet.
  Boletinus grisellus Pk.
  Boletinus paluster Pk.
  Botrytis rhinotrichoides Sacc. & Ell.
  Botrytis Sphagnorum Cke.
  Cortinarius chrysolithus Murrill.
  Cortinarius uliginosus B.
  Cribraria microcarpa Rostf.
  Endogone Ludwigii Bucholtz.
  Endogone pisiformis Lk.
  Endogone sphagnophila Atk.
  Endogone xylogena Schrt.
  Entoloma variabile Pk.
  Flammula sphagnicola Pk.
  Galera Sphagnorum (P.) ex Fr.
  Lactarius helvus, var. aquifluus Pk.
  Lizonia Sphagni Cke.
  Mucor plumbeus Bon.
  Mycena palustris Pk.
  Mycena praelonga Pk.
  Omphalia sphagnophila Pk.
  Omphalia umbellifera (L.) ex Fr.
  Psilocybe uda (P.) ex Fr.
  Syncephalis tenuis Thax.
  Tilletia? Sphagni B. M. Davis.

DICRANACEAE

Dicranum fulvum Hook.
  Leocarpus fragilis (Dicks.) Rostf.
Dicranum scoparium (L.) ex Hedw.
  Vermicularia thecicola S.

POTTIACEAE

Weissia viridula (L.) ex Hedw.
  Epicoccum torquens Massee.

ORTHOTRICHACEAE

Ulota phyllantha Brid.
  Cladosporium epibryum Cke. & Massee.

BRYACEAE

Bryum pendulum (Hornsch) Schmp.
  Pleospora muscicola Cke. & Massee.
Leptobryum pyriforme (L. ex Hedw.) Schmp.
  Sarcoscypha Dawsoniensis Pk.

MEESEACEAE

Paludella squarrosa (L.) ex Brid.
  Mitrula gracilis Karst.

BARTRAMIACEAE

Bartramia pomiformis (L.) ex Hedw.
  Cladosporium epibryum Cke. & Massee.
Bartramia sp. indet.
  Dematium Muscorum Schleich.

WEBERACEAE

Webera nutans (Schreb.) ex Hedw.
  Mitrula muscicola Henn.

POLYTRICHACEAE

Catharinea sp. indet.
  Cyphella muscigena (P.) ex Fr.
Pogonatum alpinum (L. ex Hedw.) Rohl.
  Craterellus Pogonati Pk.
Polytrichum formosum Hedw.
  Hendersonia Rauii Ell.
  Stagonospora Rauii (Ell.) Sacc.
Polytrichum juniperinum Willd. ex Hedw.
  Coniosporium Polytrichi Pk.
  Macrosporium Polytrichi Pk.
  Septoria thecicola B. & Br.
Polytrichum sp. indet.
  Coniothyrium muscicolum Ell.
  Cyphella muscigena (P.) ex Fr.
  Galera cyanipes Kauffm.
  Neottiella Polytrichi (Schum.) emend. Massee.

CLIMACIACEAE

Climacium americanum Brid.
Climacium dendroides (L.) Wb. & Mohr.
Climacium Kindbergii (R. et C.) Grout.
  Eocronartium muscicola (P. ex Fr.) Fitzpatrick.
  Eocronartium typhuloides Atk.
  Pistillaria muscicola (P.) ex Fr.
  Typhula muscicola (P.) ex Fr.

ENTODONTACEAE

Entodon seductrix (Hedw.) C. Mull.
Pylaisia intricata (Hedw.) R. & C.
  Eocronartium muscicola (P. ex Fr.) Fitz-
    patrick.

LESKEACEAE

Anomodon rostratus (Hedw.) Schimp.
Leskea obscura Hedw.
Leskea polyantha Hedw.
  Eocronartium muscicola (P. ex Fr.) Fitz-
  patrick.
Thuidium delicatulum (L. ex Hedw.) Mitt.
  Helotium bryogenum Pk.
  { Eocronartium muscicola (P. ex Fr.) Fitzpat-
  rick.
  Pistillaria muscicola (P.) ex Fr.
Thuidium minutulum (Hedw.) Br. et Sch.
  Eocronartium muscicola (P. ex Fr.) Fitzpat-
  rick.
Thuidium paludosum (Sulliv.) Rau & Herv.
  Cyphella muscigena (P.) ex Fr.

HYPNACEAE

Amblystegium riparium Br. et Sch.
Amblystegium serpens (L.) Br. & Sch.
Amblystegium varium (Hedw.) Lindb.
  Eocronartium muscicola (P. ex Fr.) Fitzpat-
  rick.
Hypnum chrysophyllum (Brid.) Bryhn.
  Eocronartium muscicola (P. ex Fr.) Fitzpat-
  rick.
Hypnum Nuttallii (Wils.) Bryol. Eur.
  Leptosphaeria bryophila Sacc.
Hypnum sp. indet.
  Cantharellus lobatus (P.) ex Fr.
  Mitrula gracilis Karst.
Plagiothecium muellerianum Schimp.
  { Cantharellus muscigenus (Bull.) ex Fr.
  Dictyolus muscigenus (Bull. ex Fr.) Quél.
  Eocronartium muscicola (P. ex Fr.) Fitz-
  patrick.

BRACHYTHECIACEAE

Camptothecium megaptilum Sulliv.
  Cladosporium epibryum Cke. & Massee.
  Eocronartium muscicola (P. ex Fr.). Fitz-
  patrick.
Brachythecium oxycladon (Brid.) Jaeg. &
  Sauerb.
  Eocronartium muscicola (P. ex Fr.) Fitz-
  patrick.
Musci fam. indet.
  Arcyria denudata (L.) Macbr.
  Arcyria incarnata P.
  Cantharellus Muscorum (Roth.) ex Fr.
  { Chondrioderma gasterodes (Phil.) Cke.
  Diderma gasterodes Phil.
  Clavaria rugosa Fr.
  Clavaria tenuis S.
  Corticium laetum (Karst.) Bres.
  Cortinarius cylindripes Kauffman.
  Cyphella arachnoidea Pk.

Cyphella galeata (Schum.) ex Fr.
Cyphella muscicola Fr.
Dictyonema membranaceum Ag., var. guade-
  lupense Rabh.
Endogone sphagnophila Atk.
Entoloma nidorosum Fr.
Galera Hypnorum Fr.
Geoglossum americanum (Cke.) Sacc.
Geoglossum glutinosum P.
Helvella lacunosa Afz.
Hygrophorus coccineus Fr.
Hypocrea tenerrima Ell. & Ev.
Lamproderma violaceum (Fr.) Rostf.
Lindbladia effusa (Ehrh.) Rostf.
Lycogala epidendrum (L.) Fr.
Merulius spadiceus B. & C.
Microstelium hyalinum Pat.
Mitrula muscicola Henn.
{ Mycena flavo-alba Fr.
Mycena pumila (Bull. ex Fr.) Rostr.
Nolanea delicatula Pk.
Oligonema brevifilum Pk.
{ Perichaena flavidum Pk.
Oligonema flavidum Pk.
Omphalia Fibula Fr.
Omphalia Schwartzii Fr.
Omphalia sphaerospora B.
Pestalozzia sp. indet.
Peziza axillaris Nees.
Peziza cerea Sow. ex P.
Peziza Herminiera Rabh.
Peziza subcarnea C. & P.
Physarum virescens Ditmar.
Pleurotus tremulus (Schaeff.) ex Fr.
{ Polyporus Macouni Pk.
Polyporus dichrous Fr., var. Macouni Pk.
  Sacc. Syll.
Psathyra flavogrisea B.
{ Reticularia affinis B. & C.
Trichosporium Curtisii Massee.
Rhizoctonia Muscorum Fr.
{ Corticium sebaceum (P.) Massee.
Sebacina incrustans (P. ex Fr.) Tul.
Thelephora cristata (P.) ex Fr.
Spathularia "linguatus" A. E. Johnson.
Thelephora scoparia Pk.
Tubaria furfuracea (P. ex Fr.) W. Sm.
Tubaria Muscorum (Hoffm.) ex Fr.
Tubifera ferruginosa (Batsch) Macbr.
Tulasnella calospora (Boud.) Juel.

MISCELLANEA

Encalypta rhabdocarpa Schwaegr.
Grimmia doniana Sm.
Grimmia ovata Web. & Mohr.
Ptychomitrium Gardneri Lesq.
  Cladosporium epibryum Cke. & Massee.

PTERIDOPHYTA

FILICALES
HYMENOPHYLLACEAE
Trichomanes pinnatum Hedw.
- Arthonia candida, var. hypocreoides (Ferdinandsen & Winge) Wainio.
- Ascomycetella filicina Ell. & Ev.
- Myxotheca hypocreoides Ferdinandsen & Winge.

CYATHEACEAE
Cyathea arborea (L.) Sm.
- Griggsia cyathea Stevens & Dalby.
- Poria obducens (P.) Cke., var. carnea Pat.
- Xylobotryum portentosum (Mont.) Pat.

Cyathea Serra Willd.
- Xylobotryum portentosum (Mont.) Pat.

Cyathea werckleana C. Chr.
- Leptodothiorella cyathea Syd.

Cyathea sp. indet.
- Bioscypha Cyatheae Syd.

Alsophila aspera R. Br.
- Epithele Dussii Pat.
- Hypochnus Dussii Pat.
- Favolaschia cinnabarina (B. & C.) Pat.
- Laschia cinnabarina B. & C.
- Physarum citrinum Schum.
- Physarum leucophaeum Fr.

Alsophila quadripinnata (Gmel.). C. Chr.
- Acrospermum candidum Setch.

POLYPODIACEAE
Woodsia glabella R. Br.
Woodsia oregana D. C. Eaton.
Woodsia scopulina D. C. Eaton.
- Hyalopsora Polypodii (Diet.) Magn.
- Uredo Polypodii (P.) DC.

Woodsia ilvensis (L.) R. Br.
- Pleospora herbarum (P.) ex Rabh.

Cystopteris bulbifera (L.) Bernh.
- Uredinopsis Atkinsonii Magn.
- Uredinopsis Copelandi Syd.

Cystopteris fragilis (L.) Bernh.
- Cladosporium herbarum (P.) ex Lk.
- Fumago vagans Fr.
- Hyalopsora Polypodii (Diet.) Magn.
- Pucciniastrum Polypodii Diet.
- Uredo Polypodii (P.) DC.
- Pleospora vulgaris Niessl.
- Pyrenophora chrysospora (Niessl) Sacc.
- Pyrenophora filicina J. Lind.

Pteretis nodulosa (Michx.) Nieuwl.
- Aulographum Onoclea Dearness & House.
- Cryptosporium filicinum B. & C.
- Leptostromella filicina (B. & C.) Sacc.

- Sclerotium deciduum J. J. Davis.
- Taphrina Struthiopteridis Nishida.
- Uredinopsis Struthiopteridis Störmer.

Onoclea sensibilis L.
- Mycena pterigena Fr.
- Phoma Onocleae Tassi.
- Phyllactinia corylea (P.) Karst.
- Physarum sinuosum (Bull.) Weinm.
- Taphrina filicina Rostr.
- Taphrina lutescens Rostr.
- Gloeosporium mirabile Pk.
- Gloeosporium Phegopteridis Auct. Amer. p. p.
- Melampsora Scolopendrii Auct. Amer. p. p.
- Milesia mirabilis Arth.
- Rhabdospora mirabilis O. Kuntze.
- Septoria mirabilis Pk.
- Uredinopsis americana Syd.
- Uredinopsis mirabilis Magn.
- Uredinopsis Scolopendrii Auct. Amer.
- Uredo Filicum Fung. Car. **4:** 97.
- Uredo macrosperma Cke. p. p.
- Vermicularia filicina S.

Goniopteris guadalupensis Fée.
- Uredo Gymnogrammes Henn.

Meniscium sp. indet.
- Hyaloderma filicicola Pat.

Cyclopeltis semicordata (Sw.) J. Sm.
- Desmella Gymnogrammes Syd.

Dryopteris Carrii (Baker) C. Chr.
Dryopteris longicaudata (Liebm.) C. Chr.
Dryopteris rotundata (Willd.) C. Chr.
- Parmularia Stigmatopteridis Ferdinandsen & Winge.
- Parmulina Stigmatopteridis (Ferd. & Winge) Theissen & Syd.

Dryopteris dentata (Forsk.) C. Chr.
- Desmella supeficialis Syd.
- Uredo Gymnogrammes Henn.

Dryopteris Filix-mas (L.) Schott.
- Sphaerella Filicum (Desm.) Awd.
- Uredinopsis Struthiopteridis Störm.

Dryopteris fragrans (L.) Schott.
- Sphaerella minutissima Wint.

Dryopteris l'Herminieri (Kze.) C. Chr.
- Desmella superficialis (Speg.) Syd.

Dryopteris linnaeana C. Chr.
- Caeoma Aspidiotus Pk.
- Caeoma Filicum S. Am. Bor. 2836 non Lk.
- Hyalopsora Aspidiotus (Karst.) Magn.
- Hyalopsora Polypodii-dryopteridis Magn.
- Melampsora Aspidiotus (Karst.) Diet.
- Melampsorella Aspidiotus (Karst.) Magn.
- Pucciniastrum Aspidiotus Karst.
- Uredo Aspidiotus Pk.
- Uredo Polypodii Auct. Amer. p. p.

Dryopteris linnaeana C. Chr. (*cont.*)
  {Uredinopsis Phegopteridis Arth.
  {?Uredinopsis Scolopendrii Auct. Amer. p. p.
Dryopteris marginale (L.) Gray.
  Fusidium Pteridis Kalchbr.
  Milesia kriegeriana (Magn.) Arth.
Dryopteris normalis C. Chr.
  Cylindrocladium Pteridis Auct.
Dryopteris noveboracense (L.) Gray.
  Uredinopsis Atkinsonii Magn.
Dryopteris palustris (Mett.) O. Kuntze.
  Mycosphaerella indistincta (Pk.) Lindau.
  Taphrina lutescens Rostr.
  {Gloeosporium Phegopteridis Auct. Amer. p. p.
  {Melampsora Scolopendrii Auct. Amer. p. p.
  {Milesia Atkinsonii Arth.
  {Uredinopsis Atkinsonii Magn.
  {Uredinopsis Copelandi Syd.
  {Uredinopsis mirabilis Auct. Amer. p. p.
  {Uredo Polypodii Auct. Amer. p. p.
Dryopteris patens (Sw.) O. Kuntze.
  Desmella superficialis (Speg.) Syd.
  {Milesia consimilis Arth.
  {Milesina consimilis (Arth.) Trott.
  Uredo Gymnogrammes Henn.
Dryopteris poiteana (Pory.) Urban.
  Acrospermum Maxoni Farl.
  {Desmella superfialis Syd.
  {Uredo Gymnogrammes Henn.
Dryopteris spinulosa (Müll.) O. Kuntze.
  Leocarpus fragilis (Dicks.) Rostf.
  Leptostromella filicina (B. & C.) Sacc.
  Taphrina filicina Rostr.
Dryopteris subtetragonia (Lk.) Maxon.
  Desmella superficialis Syd.
Dryopteris sp. indet.
  Milesia columbiensis (Diet.) Arth.
Aspidium? sp. indet.
  Leptostroma Aspidiorum S.
Cyrtomium falcatum (L. f.) Presl.
  Completoria complens Lohde.
Polystichum acrostichoides (Michx.) Schott.
  Exoascus filicinus (Rostr.) Sacc.
  Uredinopsis Copelandi Syd.
  Uredo Polypodii Auct. Amer. p. p.
Polystichum adiantiforme (Forst.) J. Sm.
  Cylindrocladium Pteridis.
Polystichum Lonchitis (L.) Roth.
  {Phyllachora filicina Sacc. & Scalia.
  {Trabutiella filicina (Sacc. & Scalia) Theissen &
   Syd.
Polystichum munitum (Kaulf.) Presl.
  Hyalopsora laeviuscula (Diet. & Holw.) Arth.
  Milesia Polystichii Wineland.
Tectaria martinicensis (Spreng.) Copel.
  {Desmella superficialis Syd.
  {Uredo Gymnogrammes Henn.

Leptochilus alienus (Sw.) C. Chr., var. **flagelli**
  (Jenm.).
  Botryosphaeria simplex Syd.
Nephrolepis exaltata L.
  Cylindrocladium Pteridis Auct.
  Glomerella Nephrolepis Faris.
Nephrolepis rivularis (Vahl) Mett.
  Milesia columbiensis (Diet.) Arth.
Nephrolepis sp. indet.
  Colletotrichum Nephrolepis Faris.
Dennstaedtia rubiginosa (Kaulf.) T. Moore.
  Desmella superficialis Syd.
Athyrium angustifolium (Michx.) Milde.
  Septoria Asplenii Fll. & Ev.
Athyrium angustum (Willd.) Presl.
  Leptostroma filicinum Fr.
  {Melampsora Scolopendrii Auct. Amer. p. p.
  {Uredinopsis Atkinsonii Magn.
Athyrium Filix-femina (L.) Roth.
  {Melampsora Scolopendrii Auct. Amer. p. p.
  {Milesia Copelandi (Syd.) Arth.
  {Uredinopsis Atkinsonii Magn.
  {Uredinopsis Copelandi Syd.
Camptosorus rhizophyllus (L.) Lk.
  Cercospora Camptosori J. J. Davis.
Blechnum occidentale L.
  {Milesia australis Arth.
  {Uredo Blechni Diet. & Neger.
  Milesina Blechni Syd.
Blechnum volubile Kaulf.
  {Aspidothea Blechni Syd.
  {Phragmopeltis Blechni Syd.
  Desmella superficialis Syd.
  Ophionectria tropicalis Speg.
Woodwardia areolata (L.) Moore.
  {Melampsora Scolopendri Auct. Amer. p. p.
  {Uredinopsis americana Syd.
  {Uredinopsis mirabilis Magn.
Woodwardia virginica (L.) Sm.
  ?Uredinopsis mirabilis (Pk.) Magn.
  Uredinopsis Struthiopteridis Störmer.
Pityogramma calomelaena (L.) Lk.
  {Desmella superficialis Syd.
  {Uredo Gymnogrammes Henn.
  Mycosphærella tyrolensis (Awd.) Lindau.
  Septoria Pityrogrammae P. Garman.
Pityogramma sulphurea Desv.
  Mycosphaerella tyrolensis (Awd.) Lindau.
Pityogramma triangularis (Maxon) Kaulf.
  {Caeoma Cheilanthis Pk.
  {Hyalopsora Cheilanthis Arth.
  {Hyalopsora Pasadenae Syd.
  {?Uredo Filicum Auct. Amer. p. p.
  {?Uredo Polypodii Auct. Amer. p. p.
Cheilanthes Pringlei Davenport.
Cryptogramma Stelleri (Gmel.) Prantl.
Notholaena sinuata Sw. Kaulf.

Pellaea andromedaefolia Kaulf.
Pellaea atropurpurea (L.) Lk.
Pellaea flexuosa (Kaulf.) Lk.
Pellaea glabella Mett.
    Caeoma Cheilanthis Pk.
    Hyalopsora Cheilanthis Arth.
    Hyalopsora pellaeicola Arth.
    Uredo Pasadenae Syd.
    Uredo Pellaeae Diet. & Neger.
Hypolepis repens (L.) Pr.
    Desmella Gymnogrammes Syd.
Adiantum farleyense Moore sec. Bailey.
    Phyllosticta Pteridis Halsted.
Adiantum latifolium Lam.
    Desmella Gymnogrammes Syd.
    Desmella superficialis Syd.
    Uredo Gymnogrammes Henn.
    Helminthosporium glabroides F. L. Stevens.
    Meliola pteridicola F. L. Stevens.
    Micropeltis Marattae Henn.
Adiantum pedatum L.
    Rhizopogon diplophloeus Zeller & Dodge.
    Sclerotium deciduum J. J. Davis.
Adiantum petiolatum Desv.
Adiantum pulverulentum L.
    Hypocrella turbinata (B.) Seaver.
Adiantum tenerum Sw.
    Phyllosticta adianticola Young.
Pteris aculeata Sw.
    Taphrina tonduziana Henn.
Pteris argyraea Moore.
    Completoria complens Lohde.
Pteris cretica L.
    Completoria complens Lohde.
    Phyllosticta Pteridis Halsted.
Pteris sp. indet.
    Aschersonia cubensis B. & C.
    Phyllachora leptostromoidea Cke.
Pteridium caudatum (L.) Maxon.
    Uleodothis Pteridis F. L. Stevens.
    Uredinopsis macrosperma Magn.
    Uredinopsis Pteridis Diet. & Holw.
Pteridium latiusculum (Desv.) Maxon.
    Agyrium herbarum Fr.
    Cladosporium grumosum (P.) ex Lk.
    Cryptodiscus Andersoni Ell. & Ev.
    Cryptomyces Pteridis (Reb. ex Fr.) Rehm.
    Dothidea Pteridis (Reb.) ex Fr.
    Phyllachora Pteridis (Reb. ex Fr.) Fckl.
    Didymella pteridicola (B. & C.) Sacc.
    Sphaeria pteridicola B. & C.
    Hypoderma striiformis DC.
    Fusidium Pteridis Kalchbr.
    Gloeosporium necans Ell. & Ev.
    Gloeosporium Pteridis Hark.
    Marssonia necans (Ell. & Ev.) Sacc.
    Marssonina necans (Ell. & Ev.) Magn.
    Gloeosporium leptospermum Pk.
    Gloeosporium obtegens Syd.

Leptostroma aquilinum Massee.
Leptostroma filicinum Fr.
Leptostroma Pteridis Ehrenb.
    Hypoderma Pteridis (S.) Sacc.
    Hysterium Pteridis S.
    Leptostromella filicina (B. & C.) Sacc.
    Melasmia imitans Pk.
    Metasphaeria epipteridea (Cke. & Hark.) Sacc.
    Metasphæria papulosa, forma epipteridea
      Berl.
    Sphaeria epipteridis Cke. & Hark.
    Catacauma flabellum (S.) Theissen & Syd.
    Dothidea flabella (S.) B. & C.
    Phyllachora flabella (S.) Sacc.
    Sphaeria flabella S.
    Dothidea leptostromoidea Cke.
    Phyllachora leptostromoidea Cke.
    Sphaeria filicina Fr.
    Dothidea filicina Fr.
    Rhopographus filicinus (Fr.) Nits.
    Dothidea Filicum S.
    Leptostroma litigiosum Desm.
    Phyllachora Filicum (S.) Sacc.
    Rhopographus Pteridis (Sow.) Wint.
    Scleroderma Pteridis Shear.
    Sclerotium deciduum J. J. Davis.
    Fusarium Pteridis Ell. & Ev.
    Septogloeum Pteridis (Ell. & Ev.) Wr.
    Septoria aquilina Pass.
    Septoria Pteridis Pk.
    Solenia filicina Pk.
    Sphaerella aquilina (Fr.) Awd.
    Sphaeria aquilina Fr.
    Mycosphaerella indistincta (Pk.) Lindau.
    Sphaerella indistincta Pk.
    Peziza Pteridis A. & S.
    Trichopeziza Pteridis Rehm.
    Trichopeziza pulverulenta Thm. Myc. Univ.
      919.
    Typhula filicina Pk.
    Uleodothis Pteridis F. L. Stevens.

UREDINALES

Uredinopsis mirabilis Magn.
    Milesina Pteridis Syd.
    Uredinopsis macrosperma Magn.
    Uredinopsis Pteridis Diet. & Holw.
    Uredo Pteridis Diet. & Holw.
    Uredo Filicum (Lk.) Chev.
Pteridium latiusculum (Desv.) Maxon, var.
    pubescens Underw.
    Phyllachora Pteridis (Reb. ex Fr.) Fckl.
    Uredinopsis macrosperma Magn.
    Uredinopsis Pteridis Diet. & Holw.
Antrophyum lanceolatum (L.) Kaulf.
    Milesia australis Arth.
Polypodium californicum Kaulf.
Polypodium Glycyrrhiza Eaton.

Polypodium occidentale (Hook.) Maxon.
   { Hyalopsora laeviuscula (Diet. & Holw.) Arth.
     Thekopsora laeviuscula Diet. & Holw.
   { Uredo laeviuscula Diet. & Holw.
Polypodium induens Maxon.
    Acrospermum Maxoni Farl.
Polypodium Phyllitidis L.
    Cercospora Phyllitidis Hume.
   { Capnodiella maxima (B. & C.) Sacc.
     Capnodium maximum B. & C.
   { Corynelia pteridicola F. L. Stevens.
    Sorica maxima (B. & C.) Giesenhagen.
Polypodium virginianum L.
    (P. vulgare Auct. Amer.)
    Milesia pycnograndis Arth.
    Uredinopsis polypodophila Bell.
    Uredo Filicum (Lk.) Chev.
Polypodium sp. indet.
    Alternaria Polypodii Major.

GLEICHENIACEAE

Gleichenia sp. indet.
    Dothidella portoricensis F. L. Stevens.
Dicranopteris pectinata (Willd.) Underw.
    Dasyscypha Dicranopteridis Seaver & Whetzel.

SCHIZAEACEAE

Lygodium polymorphum (Cav.) H. B .K.
    Milesia australis Arth.
    Milesia Blechni (Syd.) Arth.
Aneimia adiantifolia (L.) Sw.
    Arthrobotryum caudatum Syd.
    Coniothyrium glabroides F. L. Stevens.
    Dimerium piceum (B. & C.) Theissen.
    Helminthosporium glabroides F. L. Stevens.
    Meliola pteridicola F. L. Stevens.
    Mycosphaerella subastoma Stevens & Dalbey.
Aneimia hirsuta (L.) Sw.
   { Desmella superficialis Syd.
   { Uredo superficialis (Speg.) Lagerh.

OSMUNDACEAE

Osmunda cinnamomea L.
    Agyrium rufum (P.) Fr.
   { Cyphella candida Pk.
   { Cyphella Peckii Sacc.
   { Cryptosporium filicinum B. & C.
   { Leptostromella filicina (B. & C.) Sacc.
    Gloeosporium Osmundae Ell. & Ev.
    Leptothyrium litigiosum (Desm.) Sacc.
    Monographos microsporus Niessl.
    Mycosyrinx Osmundæ Pk.
    Mycosyrinx Osmundæ Pk., var. cinnamomea
    Pk.
    Solenia filicina Pk.
    Stictis filicina Pk.
    Typhula filicina Pk.
   { Uredinopsis mirabilis Magn.
   { Uredinopsis Osmundae Magn.
   { Uredo Polypodii (P.) DC.

Osmunda claytoniana L.
   { Uredinopsis mirabilis Magn.
   { Melampsora Scolopendrii Auct. Amer. p. p.
   { Uredinopsis Osmundae Magn.
Osmunda regalis L., var. **spectabilis** (Willd.)
    Gray.
    Caeoma (Aecidium) osmundatum S.
   { Hypoderma Osmundae (S.) Sacc.
   { Hysterium Osmundae S.
   { Dothidea Osmundae G. W. Clinton.
   { Dothidella Osmundae (G. W. Clinton) Sacc.
   { Phyllachora Osmundae (G. W. Clinton) Cke.
    Uredinopsis Osmundae Magn.
   { Mycosyrinx Osmundæ Pk.
   { Ustilago Osmundæ Pk.
Osmunda sp. indet.
    Leptostroma filicinum Fr.
   { Peziza frondicola Ell. & Ev.
   { Pirottaea frondicola (Ell. & Ev.) Sacc.
   { Peziza Osmundae C. & E.
   { Trichopeziza Osmundae (C. & E.) Sacc.
    Peziza Pteridis A. & S. ex P.
   { ?Peziza tenella C. & E.
   { ?Mollisia tenella (C. & E.) Sacc.
    Peziza virginea Batsch.
    Vermicularia filicina S.
Filices fam. indet.
    Artotrogus intermedius (DBy) Atk.
    Cymatella marasmioides (B. & C.) Pat.
    Cyphella filicicola B. & C.
    ?Dasyscypha flavidula Rehm.
    Dothidella basirufa (B. & C.) Sacc.
    Fuligo septica Fr.
    Hypocrella cretacea v. Höhnel.
    Leptostromella filicina (B. & C.) Sacc.
   { Dialonectria filicina Cke. & Hark.
   { Nectria filicina (Cke. & Hark.) Berl. & Vogl.
    Phoma aquilina Sacc. & Penz.
   { Dothidea anomala B. & C.
   { Phyllachora anomala (B. & C.) Sacc.
    Pistillaria subpellucida B. & C.
    Pythium intermedium DBy.
    Stilbella flavida Henn.

EQUISETALES
EQUISETACEAE

Equisetum arvense L.
    Gloeosporium Equiseti Ell. & Ev.
    Leptosphaeria arvensis Speg.
    Septosporium Equiseti Pk.
   { Peziza Persoonii Moug. ex P. sec. Fr.
   { Stamnaria Equiseti (Hoffm.) ex Sacc.
   { Stamnaria Persoonii (P.) Fckl.
Equisetum limosum L.
    Stagonospora Equiseti Fautr.
Equisetum laevigatum A. Br.
    Gloeosporium Equiseti Fll. & Ev.
    Leptosphaeria Equiseti Karst.
    Titaeospora detospora Bubak.

Equisetum hyemale L.
   Amerosporium Equiseti (Pk.) Sacc.
   Excipula Equiseti Pk.
   Epicoccum vulgare Cda.
   Fusarium laxum Pk.
   Hypoderma Equiseti Ell. & Ev.
   Lachnum inquilinum (Karst.) Schrt.
   Septoria Equiseti Desm.
   Mycosphaerella altera (Pass.) House.
   Sphaerella altera Pass.
   Gloeosporium Equiseti Ell. & Ev.
   Stamnaria americana Massee & Morg.
   Peziza Persoonii Moug. ex P. sec. Fr.
   Stamnaria Equiseti (Hoffm.) ex Sacc.
   Stictis Saccardoi Rehm.

Equisetum sp. indet.
   Epicoccum Equiseti B.
   Helotium cyathoideum (Bull. ex P.) Karst.
   Rhizoctonia Solani Kühn.

LYCOPODIALES

LYCOPODIACEAE

Lycopodium annotinum L.
   Heptameria Crepini (Westd.) Cke.
   Heptameria lycopodina (Mont.) Cke.
   Heptameria marciensis (Pk.) Cke.
   Leptosphaeria Crepini (Westd.) DeNot.
   Leptosphaeria lycopodina (Mont.) Sacc.
   Leptosphaeria marciensis (Pk.) Sacc.
   Sphaeria Crepini Westd.
   Sphaeria lycopodina Mont.
   Sphaeria marciensis Pk.

Cladosporium herbarum (P.) ex Lk.
Lamproderma cribrarioides (L.) Raunk.
Sphaerella lycopodina Karst.

Lycopodium alpinum L.
   Leptosphaeria Crepini (Westd.) DeNot.

Lycopodium clavatum L.
   Leptosphaeria Crepini (Westd.) DeNot.
   Heptameria lycopodiicola (Pk.) Cke.
   Leptosphaeria lycopodiicola Pk.
   Pyrenophora chrysospora (Niessl) Sacc.
   Septoria cercosperma Rostr.
   Mycosphaerella Lycopodii (Pk.) House.
   Sphaerella Lycopodii Pk.

Lycopodium complanatum L.
   Pestalozzia lycopodina Ell. & Ev.

Lycopodium complanatum L., var. **flabelliforme** Fern.
   Didymella Chamaecyparissi Rehm.

Lycopodium obscurum L., var. **dendroideum** (Michx.) D. C. Eaton.
   Leptosphaeria Crepini (Westd.) DeNot.

Lycopodium Selago L.
   Leptosphaeria marciensis (Pk.) Sacc.
   Sphaeria marciensis Pk.
   Pleospora vulgaris Niessl.

Lycopodium sp. indet.
   Metasphaeria Lycopodii (B. & C.) Sacc.
   Sphaeria Lycopodii B. & C.

SELAGINELLACEAE

Selaginella rupestris (L.) Spring.
   Acrospermum urceolatum Olson.
   Pleospora farlowiana Rehm.

SPERMATOPHYTA

GYMNOSPERMAE
CYCADACEAE

Cycas revoluta Thunb.
Ascochyta cycadina Scalia.
Leptosphaeria irrepta Niessl.
Pestalozzia Cycadis Allesch.
Rhabdospora Cycadis Kauffman.
Cycas sp. indet.
Chaetophoma Cycadis Cke.
Macrosporium commune Rabh.
Zamia floridana A. DC.
Pestalozzia Cycadis Allesch.
Zamia integrifolia Ait.
Aschersonia cubensis B. & C.
Triposporium stelligerum Speg.
Zamia latifolia Pren.
Triposporium stelligerum Speg.
Zamia sp. indet.
Aschersonia turbinata B.

GINKGOACEAE

Ginkgo biloba L.
Fomes Meliae (Underw.) Murrill.
Glomerella cingulata (Stoneman) Spaulding & Schrenk.
Irpex Tulipiferae S.
Polyporus hirsutus (Wulf. ex Fr.) Fr.
Polyporus versicolor (L. ex Fr.) Fr.

TAXACEAE

Podocarpus coriaceus L. C. Rich.
Corynelia oreophila (Speg.) Starb.
Corynelia portoricensis Fitzpatrick.
Phaeospora cacticola F. L. Stevens.
Podocarpus macrostachya Parl.
Corynelia oreophila (Speg.) Starb.
Podocarpus purdieana Hook.
Corynelia clavata (L.) Sacc.
Corynelia jamaicensis Fitzpatrick.
Podocarpus salicifolius Kl. & Karst.
Corticium calceum Fr.
Panus Wrightii B. & C.
Cephalotaxus drupacea Sieb. & Zucc.
Taxus baccata L., var. fastigiata Loud.
Phomopsis juniperovora Hahn.
Phomopsis juniperovora Hahn, var. A.
Taxus baccata L.
Sphaerulina Taxi (Cke.) Massee.
Taxus brevifolia Nutt.
Armillaria mellea (Vahl) ex Fr.
Diplodia Taxi (Sow. ex Fr.) DeNot.
Fomes Hartigii Allescher.
{ Mycosphaerella Taxi (Cke.) G. H. Martin, Jr.
{ Sphaerella Taxi Cke.

Herpotrichia nigra Hartig.
Neopeckia Coulteri (Pk.) Sacc.
Polyporus Schweinitzii Fr.
Xenodomus Taxi Petrak.
Taxus canadensis Marsh.
Craterellus taxophilus Thom.
{ Diplodia Taxi (Sow. ex Fr.) DeNot.
{ Sphaeria Taxi Sow. ex Fr.
{ Heptameria taxicola (Pk.) Cke.
{ Leptosphaeria taxicola (Pk.) Sacc.
{ Sphaeria taxicola Pk.
{ Sphaerulina taxicola (Pk.) Berl.
Meliola pitya Sacc.
Merulius subaurantiacus Pk.
Mycena leaiana B.
Phacidium Taxi Fr.
Phacidium taxicola Dearness & House.
Rhizoctonia Solani Kühn.
Tricholoma terraeolens Pk.
Taxus cuspidata Sieb. & Zucc.
Phomopsis juniperovora Hahn, var. A.
Rhizoctonia Solani Kühn.

PINACEAE

Araucaria imbricata Pav.
Metasphaeria californica (Cke. & Hark.) Berl.
Araucaria sp. indet.
Hormodendron cladosporioides Sacc.
Pinus albicaulis Engelm.
Comatricha Suksdorfii Ell. & Ev.
Creosphaeria pinea Petrak.
{ Cronartium ribicola Fisch.
Fomes annosus (Fr.) Cke.
{ Fomes Pini (Brot. ex Fr.) Lloyd.
{ Trametes Pini (Brot. ex Fr.)
Fomes pinicola (Sw. ex Fr.) Cke.
Herpotrichia nigra Hartig.
Hysterium formosum Cke.
{ Lasiosphæria Coulteri (Pk.) Ell. & Ev.
{ Neopeckia Coulteri (Pk.) Sacc.
Lenzites sepiaria (Wulf.) ex Fr.
Patinella atroviridis Rehm.
Peniophora odorata (Karst.) Burt.
Polyporus Schweinitzii Fr.
Polystictus abietinus (Fr.) Cke.
Polystictus versicolor (L.) ex Fr.
Tympanis Pinastri Tul.
Pinus arizonica Engelm.
Ceratostomella minor Hedgc.
Fomes pinicola (Fr.) Cke.
Fomes roseus (A. & S. ex Fr.) Cke.
Graphium ambrosiigerum Hedgc.
Peridermium pyriforme Pk.
Polyporus Schweinitzii Fr.

Pinus attenuata Lemmon.
  Dasyscypha Agassizii (B. & C.) Sacc., var. rufipes Phil.
  Fomes pinicola (Fr.) Cke.
  Lecanosticta Pini Syd.
  { Cronartium Quercus Schrt. I.
  { Peridermium Cerebrum Pk.
  { Peridermium Harknessii Blasdale non Moore.
  { Cronartium Harknessii Meinicke. I.
  { Peridermium Harknessii J. P. Moore.
  Polyporus Schweinitzii Fr.
Pinus australis Michx. See Pinus palustris Mill.
Pinus austriaca Hoss. See Pinus laricio Poir.
Pinus balfouriana Jeffrey.
  Neopeckia Coulteri (Pk.) Sacc.
Pinus balfouriana Jeffrey, var. **aristata** Engelm.
  Fomes pinicola (Fr.) Cke.
Pinus banksiana Lamb.
  Boletus chromapes Frost.
  Botrytis cinerea P. †
  Ceratostomella pilifera (Fr.) Wint.
  Coniophora olivacea Karst.
  Corticium byssinum (Karst.) Burt.
  Corticium galactinum (Fr.) Burt.
  Corticium sulphureum Fr.
  { Corticium vagum B. & C.
  { Rhizoctonia Solani Kühn.
  { Fomes Pini (Brot. ex Fr.) Lloyd.
  { Trametes Pini (Brot.) ex Fr.
  Fomes pinicola (Fr.) Cke.
  Fomes roseus (A. & S. ex Fr.) Cke.
  Fusarium arthrosporioides Sherb.
  Fusarium Martii App. & Wr.
  Fusarium moniliforme Sheldon.
  Fusarium sporotrichioides Sherb.
  Gibberella Saubinetii (Mont.) Sacc.
  { Hypodermella ampla (J. J. Davis) Dearness.
  { Lophodermium amplum J. J. Davis.
  Lentinus lepideus Fr.
  Lenzites sepiaria (Wulf.) ex Fr.
  Lophodermium Pinastri (Schrad ex Fr.) Chev.
  Peniophora globifera Ell. & Ev.
  Pestalozzia funerea Desm.
  Phoma Betae Rostr.
  Phytophthora omnivora Auct. Amer.
  Polyporus anceps Pk.
  Polyporus ellisianus (Murrill) Sacc. & Trott.
  Polyporus Schweinitzii Fr.
  Polystictus abietinus (Fr.) Cke.
  Polystictus pergamenus Fr.
  Pythium artotrogus (Mont.) DBy.
  Pythium debaryanum Hesse.
  { Nematysporangium aphanidermatum (Edson) Fitzpatrick.
  { Rheosporangium aphanidermatum Edson.
  Rhizina inflata (Schaeff.) ex Quel.
  Rhizoctonia potomacensis Wr.
  Sclerophoma pithyophila (Cda.) v. Höhnel.

  Thelephora terrestris Ehrh. ex Fr.
  Tuberculina maxima Rostr.

UREDINALES

  { Caeoma strobilinum Arth.
  { Cronartium strobilinum Hedgc. & Hunt. I.
  { Coleosporium Helianthi Arth. I.
  { Peridermium Helianthi Hedgc. & Hunt.
  Coleosporium Ipomoeae Burrill. I.
  Coleosporium terebinthinaceae Arth. I.
  { Coleosporium Solidaginis Thm. I.
  { Peridermium acicola Underw. & Earle.
  { Cronartium Cerebrum Hedgc. & Long. I.
  { Cronartium Quercus Schrt. I.
  { Peridermium Cerebrum Pk.
  { Peridermium globosum Arth. & Kern.
  { Cronartium Comptoniae Arth. I.
  { Peridermium Comptoniae (Arth.) Orton & Adams.
  { Coleosporium Sonchi-arvensis I. Auct. Amer.
  { Peridermium Fischeri Klebahn.
  { Cronartium Comandrae Pk. I.
  { Cronartium pyriforme Hedgc. & Long. I.
  { Peridermium pyriforme Pk.
  Coleosporium ribicola Arth. I.
Pinus canariensis C. Sm.
  Peridermium Elephantopodis (Thm.) Hedgc. & Hahn.
Pinus caribaea Morelet.
  Hypoderma Hedgcockii Dearness.
  Cronartium strobilinum Hedgc. & Hahn I.
  Peridermium acicola Underw. & Earle.
  { Coleosporium apocynaceum Cke. I.
  { Peridermium apocynaceum (Cke.) Hedgc. & Hunt.
  { Coleosporium carneum H. S. Jackson. I.
  { Coleosporium Vernoniae B. & C. I.
  { Coleosporium delicatulum (Arth. & Kern) Hedgc. & Long. I.
  { Peridermium delicatulum Hedgc. & Long.
  { Coleosporium Elephantopodis Thm. I.
  { Peridermium Elephantopodis (Thm.) Hedgc. & Hahn.
  { Coleosporium Ipomoeae Burrill. I.
  { Peridermium Ipomoeae (Burrill) Hedgc. & Hunt.
Pinus Cembra L.
  { Cronartium ribicola Fisch. I.
  { Peridermium Strobi Klebahn.
Pinus cembroides Zucc.
  Fomes pinicola (Sw. ex Fr.) Cke.
  Polyporus Schweinitzii Fr.
Pinus chihuahuana Engelm.
  { Caeoma conigenum Pat.
  { Cronartium conigenum Hedgc. & Hunt. I.
  { Cronartium coleosporioides Arth. I.
  { Cronartium Harknessii Meinicke. I.
  { Peridermium Harknessii J. P. Moore.

Pinus chihuahuana (*cont.*)
Coleosporium Ipomoeae Burrill. I.
Fomes pinicola (Sw. ex Fr.) Cke.
Peridermium Cerebrum Pk.
Polyporus Schweinitzii Fr.
Pinus clausa Vasey.
Hypoderma Hedgcockii Dearness.
{ Cronartium Cerebrum (Pk.) Hedgc. & Long. I.
{ Peridermium Cerebrum Pk.
Coleosporium Vernoniae B. & C. I.
Pinus contorta Dougl.

PEZIZINEAE

Cenangium Abietis (P.) Duby.
Cenangium farinaceum (P.) ex Rehm.
Cenangium piniphilum Weir.
Dasyscypha Agassizii (B. & C.) Sacc.
{ Dasyscypha Agassizii (B. & C.) Sacc., var.
{ rufipes (Phil.) Sacc.
{ Peziza Agassizii B. & C., var. rufipes Phil.
Dasyscypha pulverulentum (Lib.) Sacc., var.
fructicola Kauffm.
Gorgoniceps aridula Karst.
Patinella atroviridis Rehm.
{ Peziza hyalina P.
{ Pseudohelotium hyalinum (P.) Fckl.

PHACIDIINEAE

Propolis faginea (Schrad. ex Fr.) Karst.

HYSTERIINEAE

Hypoderma deformans Weir.
Hypoderma deformans Weir, var. contorta
Dearness.
Hypoderma lineare (Pk.) Thm.
{ Hypodermella ampla (J. J. Davis) Dearness.
{ Lophodermium amplum J. J. Davis.
{ Hysterium formosum Cke.
{ Hysterographium formosum (Cke.) Sacc.
{ Hypodermella montivaga (Petrak) Dearness.
{ Lophodermella montivaga Petrak.
Hypodermella montivaga (Patrak) Dearness,
var. concolor Dearness.
Lophodermium arundinaceum (Schrad.
ex Fr.) Chev., var. apiculatum (Fr.)
Duby.
Lophodermium nervisequum (DC. ex Fr.)
Rehm.
{ Hysterium Pinastri Schrad. ex Fr.
{ Lophodermium Pinastri (Schrad. ex Fr.) Chev.

SPHAERIALES

{ Amphisphaeria tumulata (Cke.) Sacc.
{ Sphaeria tumulata Cke.
{ Xylosphaeria tumulata Cke.
Didymosphaeria euryasca Ell. & Gall.
Herpotrichia nigra Hartig.
{ Melanomma Pulvis-pyrius (P.) Fckl.
{ Sphaeria Pulvis-pyrius P.

{ Lasiosphaeria Coulteri .(Pk.) Ell. & Ev.
{ Neopeckia Coulteri (Pk.) Sacc.
{ Psilosphaeria myriocarpa (Fr.) Hark.
{ Rosellinia myriocarpa (Fr.) Cke.
{ Sphaeria myriocarpa Fr.

UREDINALES

{ Coleosporium Solidaginis Thm. I.
{ Peridermium acicola Underw. & Earle.
{ Peridermium montanum Arth. & Kern.
{ Cronartium Cerebrum Hedgc. & Long. I.
{ Peridermium Cerebrum Pk.
{ Cronartium Comptoniae Arth. I.
{ Peridermium Comptoniae (Arth.) Orton &
{ Adams.
{ Coleosporium delicatulum Hedgc. & Long. I.
{ Peridermium delicatulum Arth. & Kern.
{ Cronartium coleosporioides Arth. I.
{ Cronartium filamentosum Hedgc. & Long. I.
{ Cronartium Harknessii Meinecke. I.
{ Cronartium stalactiforme Arth. & Kern. I.
{ Peridermium filamentosum Pk.
{ Peridermium Harknessii J. P. Moore.
{ Peridermium stalactiforme Arth. & Kern.
Cronartium Harknessii I. Auct. Amer. p. p.
Coleosporium occidentale Arth. I.
{ Cronartium Comandrae Pk. I.
{ Cronartium pyriforme Hedgc. & Long. I.
{ Peridermium Betheli Hedgc. & Long.
{ Peridermium pyriforme Pk.
Peridermium Weirii Arth.
Rhizina inflata (Schaeff.) ex Quél.

THELEPHORACEAE

Corticium furfuraceum Bres.
{ Corticium carneum B. & Cke.
{ Peniophora carnea B. & Cke.
Peniophora odorata (Karst.) Burt.
Hymenochaete fimbriata Ell. & Ev.
Thelephora terrestris Ehrh. ex Fr.

POLYPORACEAE

{ Cryptoporus volvatus (Pk.) Hubbard.
{ Fomes volvatus (Pk.) Cke., var. obvolutus (B.
{ & Cke.) Sacc. Syll.
{ Polyporus obvolutus B. & Cke.
{ Polyporus volvatus Pk., var. obvolutus (B. &
{ Cke.) Pk.
{ Polyporus volvatus Pk.
Cryptoporus volvatus (Pk.) Hubbard, var.
Torreyi (Gerard) Sacc. Syll.
Fomes albogriseus Pk.
{ Fomes annosus (Fr.) Cke.
{ Polyporus annosus Fr.
{ Fomes Laricis Jacq. ex Murrill.
{ Fomes officinalis Fr.
{ Fomes Pini (Brot. ex Fr.) Lloyd.
{ Trametes Pini (Brot.) ex Fr.

Pinus contorta (*cont.*)
Fomes pinicola (Sw. ex Fr.) Cke.
Fomes roseus (A. & S. ex Fr.) Cke.
Irpex deformis Fr.
Irpex fuscoviolaceus Fr., var. resupinatus
  Kauffman.
Lenzites sepiaria (Wulf.) ex Fr.
Lenzites trabea Fr.
Merulius aureus Fr.
Merulius lacrimans (Wulf.) ex Fr.
Merulius molluscus Fr.
⎰Polyporus alutaceus Fr.
⎱Polyporus guttulatus Pk.
  Tyromyces guttulatus (Pk.) Murrill.
⎰Polyporus amorphus Fr.
⎱Tyromyces amorphus (Fr.) Murrill.
Polyporus cryptopus Ell.
Polyporus ellisianus (Murrill) Sacc. & Trott.
Polyporus hirtus Fr.
Polyporus labyrinthicus Fr.
⎰Polyporus leucospongia Cke. & Hark.
⎱Spongiporus leucospongia (Cke. & Hark.) Mur-
  rill.
Polyporus mollis P.
Polyporus Schweinitzii Fr.
⎰Laetiporus speciosus (Batt.) ex Murrill.
⎱Polyporus sulphureus (Bull.) ex Fr.
Poria attenuata Pk.
Poria callosa Fr.
Poria carbonaria B. & C.
Poria dichora Bres.
Poria fulvella Bres.
Poria marginella Pk.
Poria rufa Schrad.
Poria undata P.
⎰Trametes carnea Auct. Amer.
⎱Trametes subrosea Weir.
Trametes protracta Fr.
⎰Coriolellus serialis (Fr.) Murrill.
⎱Trametes serialis Fr.
Trametes setosus Weir.

MISCELLANEA

Amaurochaete fuliginosa (Sow.) Macbr.
Armillaria mellea (Vahl) ex Fr.
Coryneum cinereum Dearness.
⎰Dacryomyces deliquescens (Bull.) Duby.
⎱Dacryomyces tortus Fr.
Lentinus lepideus Fr.
Leptostroma Pinastri Desm.
Phlebia cinnabarina S.
Sclerophoma pithyophila (Cda.) v. Höhnel.
Secotium nubigenum Hark.
Stilbospora pinicola B. & C.

Pinus Coulteri Don.
~ Peridermium carneum Auct. Amer. p. p.
⎰Cronartium Cerebrum (Pk.) Hedgc. & Long. I.
⎱Peridermium Cerebrum Pk.

—Coleosporium delicatulum (Arth. & Kern)
  Hedgc. & Long. I.
⎰Cronartium coleosporioides Arth.
⎨Cronartium Harknessii Meinecke. I.
⎱Peridermium Harknessii J. P. Moore.
~ Coleosporium Solidaginis Thm. I.
Pinus densiflora Sieb. & Zucc.
⎰Cronartium Comptoniae Arth. I.
⎨Peridermium Comptoniae (Arth.) Orton &
⎱ Adams.
Pinus divaricata see Pinus banksiana Lamb.
Pinus echinata Mill.

UREDINALES

⎰Coleosporium Solidaginis Thm. I.
⎱Peridermium acicolum Underw. & Earle.
⎰Coleosporium carneum H. S. Jackson. I.
⎱Coleosporium Vernoniae B. & C. I.
⎰Peridermium carneum (Bosc) Seymour &
⎱ Earle.
  Peridermium intermedium Arth. & Kern.
⎧Aecidium deformans Mayr.
⎪Cronartium Cerebrum (Pk.) Hedgc. & Long. I.
⎨Cronartium Quercus Schrt. I.
⎪Peridermium Cerebrum Pk.
⎩Peridermium deformans (Mayr) Tubeuf.
⎰Cronartium ribicola Fisch. I.
⎱Peridermium Strobi Klebahn.
⎰Cronartium Comptoniae Arth. I.
⎨Peridermium Comptoniæ (Arth.) Orton &
⎱ Adams.
⎰Coleosporium delicatulum Hedgc. & Long. I.
⎱Peridermium delicatulum Arth. & Kern.
⎰Coleosporium Elephantopodis Thm. I.
⎨Peridermium Elephantopodis (Thm.) Hedgc.
⎱ & Hahn.
  Peridermium orientale Fung. Eur. *3315a.*
⎰Coleosporium Helianthi Arth. I.
⎱Peridermium Helianthi (Arth.) Hedgc. & Hunt.
⎰Coleosporium inconspicuum Hedgc. & Long.
⎱Peridermium inconspicuum Long.
⎰Coleosporium Ipomoeae Burrill. I.
⎨Peridermium Ipomoeae (Burrill) Hedgc. &
⎱ Hunt.
⎰Coleosporium Senecionis (P.) Fr. I.
⎱Peridermium oblongisporium Fckl.
  Peridermium Pini Lév.?
⎰?Coleosporium Terebinthinaceae Arth. I.
⎨Peridermium Terebinthinaceae (Arth.) Hedgc.
⎱ & Hunt.
  Cronartium strobilinum Hedgc. & Hunt. I.

POLYPORACEAE

⎰Fomes annosus (Fr.) Cke.
⎱Trametes radiciperda Hartig.
⎰Fomes Pini (Brot. ex Fr.) Lloyd.
⎱Trametes Pini (Brot.) ex Fr.

Pinus echinata (*cont.*)
  Fomes pinicola (Sw. ex Fr.) Cke.
  Lenzites sepiaria (Wulf.) ex Fr.
  Merulius ambiguus B.
  Polyporus amorphus Fr.
  Polyporus palustris B. & C.
  Polyporus Schweinitzii Fr.
  { Polyporus abietinus Dicks. ex Fr.
  { Polystictus abietinus (Dicks. ex Fr.) Cke.
  { Coriolus versicolor (L. ex Fr.) Murrill.
  { Polystictus versicolor (L.) ex Fr.
  Poria subacida (Pk.) Sacc. Syll.
  Poria subavellanea Murrill.
  { Polyporus vaporarius Fr.
  { Poria vaporaria (Fr.) Cke.

MISCELLANEA
  Armillaria mellea (Vahl) ex Fr.
  Ceratostomella Schrenkiana Hedgc.
  { Agaricus conigenus P. ex Fr.
  { Collybia conigena Fr.
  Corticium galactinum (Fr.) Moffatt.
  Corticium laeve (P.) ex Fr.
  { Cryptosporium acicola Thm.
  { Septoria acicola (Thm.) Sacc.
  Hormodendron griseum Hedgcock.
  Hypoderma Desmazieri Duby.
  Hypoderma Hedgcockii Dearness.
  Hypoderma lethale Dearness.
  Hysterographium flexuosum (S.) Sacc.
  Lentinus lepideus Fr.
  Lophodermium australe Dearness.
  Lophodermium pinastri (Schrad. ex Fr.) Chev.
  Meliola pinicola Dearness.
  Pezizella minuta Dearness.
  Rhizopogon parasiticus Coker & Totten.
Pinus edulis Engelm.
  { Fomes Pini (Brot. ex Fr.) Lloyd.
  { Trametes Pini (Brot.) ex Fr.
  Fomes pinicola (Sw. ex Fr.) Gill.
  Fomes roseus (A. & S. ex Fr.) Cke.
  { Cronartium Cerebrum Hedgc. & Long. I.
  { Peridermium Cerebrum Pk.
  { Cronartium occidentale Hedgc. et al.
  { Cronartium ribicola Auct. Amer. p. p.
  { Peridermium occidentale Hedgc. et al.
  { Coleosporium ribicola Arth. I.
  { Peridermium ribicola (Arth.) Long.
  { Hydnum cinnabarinum (S.) Fr.
  { Polyporus cinnabarinus Jacq. ex Fr.
  Polyporus Schweinitzii Fr.
  Sclerophoma pithyophila (Cda.) v. Höhnel.
Pinus Elliottii Engelm.
  Peridermium acicola Underw. & Earle.
  { Coleosporium Vernoniæ B. & C. I.
  { Peridermium carneum (Bosc) Seymour & Earle.
  Peridermium delicatulum Hedgc. & Long.

Pinus excelsa Wall.
  Botrytis cinerea P. †
  Cenangium Abietis (P. ex Fr.) Rehm.
  Chrysomyxa Abietis (Wallr.) Ung.
  { Cronartium ribicola Fisch. I.
  { Peridermium Strobi Klebahn.
  { Hypoderma brachysporum (Rostr.) Tubeuf.
  { Lophodermium brachysporum Rostr.
Pinus filifolia Lindl.
  Peridermium gracile Arth. & Kern.
  { Peridermium gracile Kern. p. p.
  { Peridermium guatemalense Arth. & Kern.
Pinus flexilis James.
  Armillaria mellea (Vahl) ex Fr.
  Cucurbidothis pityophila (Fr.) Petrak.
  Fomes annosus (Fr.) Cke.
  { Fomes Pini (Brot. ex Fr.) Lloyd.
  { Trametes Pini (Brot.) ex Fr.
  Fomes pinicola (Sw. ex Fr.) Gill.
  Fomes roseus (A. & S. ex Fr.) Cke.
  Hypodermella sulcigena (Lk.) Tubeuf.
  Leptostroma Pinastri Desm.
  Melogramma Spraguei B. & C.
  Neopeckia Coulteri (Pk.) Sacc.
  Peniophora odorata (Karst.) Burt.
  { Cronartium ribicola Fisch. I.
  { Peridermium Strobi Klebahn.
  Phacidium planum J. J. Davis.
  { Polyporus fragilis Fr.
  { Spongipellis fragilis (Fr.) Murrill.
  { Spongipellis sensibilis Murrill.
  Polyporus Schweinitzii Fr.
  Sclerophoma pithyophila (Cda.) v. Höhnel.
Pinus glabra Walt.
  Fomes pinicola (Sw. ex Fr.) Gill.
  Lenzites sepiaria (Wulf.) ex Fr.
  Lophodermium australe Dearness.
  { Coleosporium carneum H. S. Jackson. I.
  { Coleosporium Vernoniae B. & C. I.
  { Peridermium carneum (Bosc) Seymour &
  {   Earle.
  { Cronartium Cerebrum Hedgc. & Long. I.
  { Peridermium Cerebrum Pk.
  { Coleosporium delicatulum Hedgc. & Long. I.
  { Peridermium delicatulum Arth. & Kern.
  Peridermium minutum Hedgc. & Hunt.
  Polyporus Schweinitzii Fr.
Pinus halepensis Mill.
  Peridermium Cerebrum Pk.
  Peridermium fusiforme Pk.
Pinus heterophylla (Ell.) Sudw.
  { Cæoma strobilinum Arth.
  { Cronartium strobilinum Hedgc. & Hunt. I.
  Peridermium acicola Underw. & Earle.
  { Coleosporium Vernoniae B. & C. I.
  { Peridermium carneum (Bosc) Seymour &
  {   Earle.

Pinus heterophylla (*cont.*)
Peridermium Cerebrum Pk.
Peridermium delicatulum Arth. & Kern.
{ Peridermium fusiforme Pk.
{ Cronartium Quercus Schrt. I.
{ (Peridermium Harknessii Blasdale non Moore.
Pinus insignis Dougl.
See Pinus radiata Don.
Pinus Jeffreyi Murr.
{ Fomes Laricis (Fr.) Murrill ex Jacq.
{ Fomes officinalis (Fr.) Lloyd.
Fomes pinicola (Sw. ex Fr.) Cke.
Hypodermella Medusa Dearness.
Lentinus lepideus Fr.
Neopeckia Coulteri (Pk.) Sacc.
- Cronartium Cerebrum Hedgc. & Long. I.
- { Cronartium Comptoniae Arth. I.
- { Peridermium Comptoniae (Arth.) Orton &
Adams.
- { Cronartium coleosporioides Arth. I.
- { Cronartium filamentosum Hedgc. & Long. I.
- { Cronartium Harknessii Meinecke. I.
- { Cronartium stalactiforme Arth. & Kern. I.
- { Peridermium filamentosum Pk.
- { Peridermium Harknessii J. P. Moore.
- { Peridermium stalactiforme Arth. & Kern.
- Cronartium Harknessii Meinecke. I.
- Coleosporium filamentosum Hedgc. & Long. I.
- Coleosporium Madiae Cke. I.
Polyporus Schweinitzii Fr.
Polyporus sulphureus Fr.
Pinus koraiensis Sieb. & Zucc.
{ Cronartium ribicola Fisch. I.
{ Peridermium Strobi Klebahn.
Pinus lambertiana Dougl.
Armillaria mellea (Vahl) ex Fr.
{ Fomes Laricis (Jacq.) ex Murrill.
{ Fomes officinalis (Fr.) Lloyd.
{ Fomes Pini (Brot. ex Fr.) Lloyd.
{ Trametes Pini (Brot.) ex Fr.
Fomes pinicola (Sw. ex Fr.) Gill.
Lenzites sepiaria (Wulf.) ex Fr.
Lophodermium Pinastri (Schrad. ex Fr.) Chev.
Merulius brassicifolius S.
Neopeckia Coulteri (Pk.) Sacc.
- Peridermium Cerebrum Pk.
- Peridermium Harknessii Auct. p. p.
- { Cronartium ribicola Fisch. I.
- { Peridermium Strobi Klebahn.
Polyporus Schweinitzii Fr.
Polyporus sulphureus (Bull.) ex Fr.
{ Polyporus argillaceus Cke.
{ Poria argillacea (Cke.) Sacc.
Pythium debaryanum Hesse.
Pinus massoniana D. Don.
Poria roseitingens Murrill.
Pinus mayriana Sudworth.
Fomes pinicola (Sw. ex Fr.) Cke.
Peridermium acicola Underw. & Earle.

—Peridermium carneum Auct. Amer. p. p.
— Coleosporium delicatulum Hedgc. & Long. I.
— Peridermium Elephantopodis Hedgc. & Hahn.
Polyporus Schweinitzii Fr.
Pinus monophylla Torr. & Frem.
Fomes pinicola (Sw. ex Fr.) Cke.
Hypoderma robustum Tubeuf, var. Pini
Dearness.
— { Cronartium occidentale Hedgc., Bethel &
{ Hunt. I.
— { Peridermium occidentale Hedgc.
Polyporus Schweinitzii Fr.
Pinus montana Auct.
Peridermium pyriforme Pk.
Phoma acicola (Lév.) Sacc.
Pinus monticola Dougl. ex Lamb.
Ceratostomella pilifera (Fr.) Wint.
Corticium calceum Fr., emend. Romell & Burt.
Corticium furfuraceum Bres.
Dasyscypha Agassizii (B. & C.) Sacc., var.
rufipes Phil.
Dasyscypha fuscosanguinea Rehm.
Helotium citrinum Fr.
Herpotrichia nigra Hartig.
Hypoderma lineare Pk.
Hypodermella sulcigena (Lk.) Tubeuf.
Lophodermium Pinastri (Schrad. ex Fr.) Chev.
Neopeckia Coulteri (Pk.) Sacc.
— { Cronartium ribicola Fisch. I.
— { Peridermium Strobi Klebahn.
{ Rhizina inflata (Schaeff.) ex Quél.
{ Rhizina undulata Fr.
Scleroderris bacillifera (Karst.) Sacc.
Sclerophoma pithyophila (Cda.) v. Höhnel.
Trichosporium pinicola Dearness & Barthol.
Tympanis Buchsii (Henn.) Rehm.
Tympanis Pinastri Tul.

HYMENOMYCETINEAE

Fomes annosus (Fr.) Cke.
{ Fomes Laricis (Jacq.) ex Murrill.
{ Fomes officinalis (Fr.) Lloyd.
{ Fomes Pini (Brot. ex Fr.) Lloyd.
{ Trametes Pini (Brot.) ex Fr.
Fomes pinicola (Sw. ex Fr.) Cke.
{ Lenzites heteromorpha (Fr.)
{ Trametes heteromorpha (Fr.) Bres.
Lenzites sepiaria (Wulf.) ex Fr.
Merulius aureus Fr.
Merulius molluscus Fr.
Merulius montanus Burt.
Merulius squalidus Fr.
Peniophora Weiri Bres.
Pholiota adiposa Fr.
Polyporus amorphus Fr.
Polyporus chioneus Fr.
Polyporus dichrous Fr.
Polyporus fragilis Fr.

Pinus monticola (*cont.*)
Polyporus griseus Pk.
Polyporus leporinus Fr.
Polyporus Schweinitzii Fr.
Polyporus stipticus P.
Polyporus sulphureus (Bull.) ex Fr.
Polystictus versicolor (L.) ex Fr.
Poria attenuata Pk.
Poria aurantiaca Rost.
Poria Medulla-panis (P.) ex Fr.
Poria monticola Murrill.
Poria rufa (Schrad. ex Fr.) Cke.
Poria sanguinolenta S.
Poria subacida Pk.
Poria xantha Fr.
Septobasidium pinicola Snell.
Sparassis radicata Weir.
Thelephora terrestris (Ehrh.) Fr.
{ Trametes arctica B. ex Cke. nom. nud.
{ Trametes subrosea Weir.
Trametes protracta Fr.
Trametes serialis Fr.
Trametes setosus Weir.
Trametes tenuis Karst.

Pinus Mugho Poir.
{ Cronartium Comptoniae Arth. I.
{ Peridermium Comptoniae (Arth.) Orton &
    Adams.

Pinus muricata D. Don.
Peridermium Cerebrum Pk.
Peridermium Harknessii Auct. Amer. p. p.

Pinus nigra Arnold (Pinus Laricio Poir.)
Corticium vagum B. & C.
Diplodia acicola Sacc.
Hypoderma brachysporum (Rostr.) Tubeuf.
Lophodermium gilvum Rostr.
Merulius ambiguus B.
Mollisia fallax (Desm.) Massee.
Mycosphaerella Tulasnei Johans.
{ Chilonectria Cucurbitula Fung. Columb. *1433*.
{ Scoleconectria scolecospora (Bref.) Seaver.
Nectria Cucurbitula Cke.
Patellina caesia Elliott & Stansfield.
Peniophora duplex Burt.
{ Coleosporium Solidaginis Thm. I.
{ Peridermium acicola Underw. & Earle.
{ Coleosporium carneum H. S. Jackson. I.
{ Coleosporium Vernoniae B. & C. I.
{ Peridermium carneum (Bosc) Seymour &
    Earle.
{ Peridermium carneum Auct. Amer. p. p.
{ Peridermium intermedium Arth. & Kern.
Peridermium Cerebrum Pk.
{ Cronartium Comptoniae Arth. I.
{ Peridermium Comptoniae (Arth.) Orton &
    Adams.
{ Peridermium pyriforme Arth. & Kern non Pk.

{ Coleosporium delicatulum Hedgc. & Long. I.
{ Peridermium delicatulum (Arth. & Kern)
    Hedgc. & Long.
{ Cronartium pyriforme Hedgc. & Long. I.
{ Peridermium pyriforme Pk.
Pestalozzia peregrina Ell. & Martin.
Peziza lachnoderma B.
Sclerophoma pithyophila (Cda.) v. Höhnel.
Physalospora Cydoniae Arnaud.
Sphaeropsis Malorum B.
Pythium debaryanum Hesse.
Septocylindrium strobilinum (Sacc.) Fairman.
Sphaeropsis Ellisii (C. & E.) Sacc.
Sphæropsis Pinastri (Lév.) Sacc.
Thelephora laciniata (P.) ex Fr.

Pinus occidentalis Sw.
Lophodermium Pinastri (Schrad. ex Fr.) Chev.

Pinus oocarpa Schiede.
{ Peridermium cerebrum Pk.
{ Cronartium Quercus Schrt. I.
{ Peridermium mexicanum Arth. & Kern.
{ Peridermium Harknessii Blasdale non Moore.

Pinus palustris Mill.

ASCOMYCETES

Cenangium Abietis (P.) Rehm.
Cenangium ferruginosum Fr.
{ Ceratostoma piliferum (Fr.) Fckl.
{ Sphaeria pilifera Fr.
Hypoderma Hedgcockii Dearness.
Hysterium compressum Ell.& Ev.
Lophodermium australe Dearness.
{ Hysterium Pinastri Schrad. ex Fr.
{ Lophodermium Pinastri (Schrad. ex Fr.) Chev.
Oligostroma acicola Dearness.
Propolis rhodoleuca (Sommf.) Fr.
{ Propolis strobilina (Cke.) Sacc.
{ Stictis strobilina Cke.

UREDINALES

—{ Caeoma strobilinum Arth.
{ Cronartium strobilinum Hedgc. & Hahn. I.
Peridermium acicola Underw. & Earle.
{ Coleosporium apocynaceum Cke. I.
{ Peridermium apocynaceum (Cke.) Hedgc. &
    Hunt.
{ Coleosporium carneum H. S. Jackson. I.
{ Coleosporium Vernoniae B. & C. I.
{ Peridermium carneum (Bosc) Seymour &
    Earle.
Peridermium orientale N. A. F. *1026b*, Fung.
    Eur. *3315b*.
Tubercularia carnea Bosc.
Peridermium Cerebrum Pk.
{ Coleosporium delicatulum Hedgc. & Long. I.
{ Peridermium delicatulum Arth. & Kern.
{ Coleosporium Elephantopodis Thm. I.
{ Peridermium Elephantopodis Hedgc. & Hahn.

Pinus palustris (*cont.*)

  Peridermium filamentosum Pk.

  Peridermium floridanum Hedgc. & Hahn.

  Peridermium fragile Hedgc. & Hunt.

  { Cronartium fusiforme Hedgc. & Hunt.

  { Cronartium Quercus Schrt.

  Peridermium fusiforme Arth. & Kern.

  Peridermium Harknessii Blasdale non Moore.

  Peridermium guatemalense Arth. & Kern.

  { Coleosporium inconspicuum Hedgc. & Long. I.

  { Peridermium inconspicuum Long.

  { Coleosporium Ipomoeae Burrill. I.

  { Peridermium Ipomoeae Hedgc. & Hunt.

  Coleosporium Laciniariae Arth. I.

  Peridermium oblongisporium Fckl.

  Peridermium orientale Cke.

  { Coleosporium Terebinthinaceae Arth. I.

  { Peridermium Terebinthinaceae Hedgc. &

    Hunt.

POLYPORACEAE

{ Boletus hemichrysus B. & C.

{ Ceriomyces hemichrysus (B. & C.) Murrill.

{ Fomes annosus (Fr.) Cke.

{ Trametes radiciperda Hartig.

{ Fomes Laricis (Jacq.) ex Murrill.

{ Fomes officinalis (Fr.) Karst.

{ Fomes Pini (Brot. ex Fr.) Karst.

{ Trametes Pini (Brot.) ex Fr.

Fomes pinicola (Sw. ex Fr.) Cke.

Lentodium tigrinum (Bull. ex Fr.) Earle.

Lenzites sepiaria (Wulf.) ex Fr.

Lenzites trabea P. ex Fr.

{ Merulius ambiguus B.

{ Merulius fugax Rav. Fung. Car.

Merulius lacrimans (Wulf.) ex Fr.

Polyporus abietinus (Dicks.) ex Fr., var. resu-

  pinatus Thm.

{ Polyporus albidus Trog.

{ Tyromyces palustris Murrill.

Polyporus Schweinitzii Fr.

{ Laetiporus speciosus (Batt.) Murrill.

{ Polyporus sulphureus (Bull.) ex Fr.

Polystictus barbatulus Fr.

{ Fomes roseus Auct. Amer. p. p.

{ Polyporus carneus Auct. Amer.

{ Trametes carnea Lloyd.

{ Trametes subroseus Weir.

AGARICACEAE

Flammula sapinea Fr.

Lentinus lepideus Fr.

{ Claudopus nidulans (P. ex Fr.) Pk.

{ Panus dorsalis (Bosc) ex Fr.

MISCELLANEA

Corticium arachnoideum B.

Helminthosporium pinicola Ell. & Ev.

Hydnum pityophilum B. & C.

Lecanosticta Pini Syd.

{ Corticium giganteum Fr.

{ Peniophora gigantea (Fr.) Massee.

{ Thelephora gigantea Fr.

{ Cryptosporium acicola Thm.

{ Septoria acicola (Thm.) Sacc.

Pinus parviflora Sieb. & Zucc.

  { Cronartium ribicola Fisch. I.

  { Peridermium Strobi Klebahn.

Pinus patula Schiede & Deppe.

  { Cronartium Quercus Schrt. I.

  { Peridermium Cerebrum Pk.

  { Peridermium mexicanum Arth. & Kern.

Pinus pinea L.

  Peridermium ribicola Long.

Pinus ponderosa Dougl.

  Actinothyrium marginatum Sacc.

  Amaurochaete tubulina (A. & S.) Macbr.

  Atichia glomerulosa (Achar.) Flot.

  Botrytis cinerea Auct.

  { Cenangium Abietis (P.) ex Duby.

  { Cenangium ferruginosum Fr.

  { Cenangium farinaceum (P.) Rehm.

  { Cenangium piniphilum Weir.

  Ceratostomella pilifera (Fr.) Wint.

  Cladosporium herbarum P. ex Lk.

  Cryptocoryneum Simmonsii Sacc.

  Discosia Pini Heald.

  Fusarium acuminatum Ell. & Ev.

  Fusarium Solani Auct.

  Humaria tofacea Clements.

  Hypoderma deformans Weir.

  Hypodermella medusa Dearness.

  Lecanosticta acicola (Thm.) Syd.

  Leptostroma decipiens Petrak.

  Lophodermium Pinastri (Schrad. ex Fr.) Chev.

  Neopeckia Coulteri (Pk.) Sacc.

  Pestalozzia funerea Dcsm.

  Phacidium Pini (Fr.) Rehm.

  Pythium debaryanum Hesse.

  Rheosporangium aphanidermatus Edson.

  { Rhizina inflata (Schaeff.) ex Quél.

  { Rhizina undulata Fr.

  Rosellinia obliquata (Sommf.) Sacc., var.

    americana Ell. & Ev.

  Scoriomyces Andersoni Ell. & Gall.

  { Hymenula aciculosa Ell. & Hark.

  { Volutella aciculosa (Ell. & Hark.) Sacc.

UREDINALES

{ Coleosporium Solidaginis Thm.

{ Peridermium acicola Underw. & Earle.

{ Peridermium montanum Arth. & Kern.

{ Coleosporium carneum H. S. Jackson. I.

{ Coleosporium Vernoniae B. & C. I.

{ Peridermium carneum (Bosc) Seymour & Earle.

{ Cronartium Cerebrum Hedgc. & Long. I.

{ Peridermium Cerebrum Pk.

{ Peridermium Pini, var. corticola Auct.

Pinus ponderosa (*cont.*)

{Cronartium Comptoniae Arth. I.
Peridermium Comptoniae (Arth.) Orton &
  Adams.

{Coleosporium delicatulum Hedgc. & Long. I.
Peridermium delicatulum Arth. & Kern.

{Cronartium coleosporioides Auct. I.
Cronartium filamentosum Hedgc. I.
Peridermium filamentosum Pk.

{Cronartium coleosporioides Arth. I.
Cronartium Harknessii Meinecke. I.
Peridermium Harknessii J. P. Moore.

Peridermium Pini Auct.

{Cronartium Comandrae Pk. I.
Cronartium pyriforme Hedgc. & Long. I.
Peridermium pyriforme Pk.

Cronartium Quercus Schrt. I.

{Cronartium stalactiforme Arth. I.
Peridermium stalactiforme Arth.

THELEPHORACEAE

{Coniophora corrugis Burt.
Corticium corruge Burt nom. nud.

Corticium furfuraceum Bres.

{Corticium vagum B. & C.
Rhizoctonia Solani Kühn.

Hypochnus pannosus (B. & C.) Burt.
Zygodesmus pannosus B. & C.

Peniophora crassa Burt.
Peniophora gilvidula Bres.
Stereum sulcatum Burt.
Thelephora terrestris Ehrh. ex Fr.
Veluticeps fusca Humphrey & Long.

POLYPORACEAE

Fomes annosus (Fr.) Cke.

{Fomes Laricis (Jacq.) ex Murrill.
Fomes officinalis (Fr.) Lloyd.

{Fomes Pini (Brot. ex Fr.) Karst.
Trametes Pini (Brot.) ex Fr.

Fomes pinicola (Sw. ex Fr.) Cke.
Fomes putearius Weir.
Fomes roseus (Fr.) Cke.
Lentinus lepideus Fr.
Lentinus tigrinus Fr.
Lenzites sepiaria (Wulf.) ex Fr.
Lenzites trabea P. ex Fr.
Merulius ambiguus B.
Merulius tremellosus Schrad. ex Fr.
Polyporus albidus Trog.
Polyporus amorphus Fr.
Polyporus anceps Pk.
Polyporus ellisianus (Murrill) Sacc. & Trott.
Polyporus erubescens Fr.
Polyporus frondosus (Schrank) ex Fr.
Polyporus Pini-ponderosae Long.
Polyporus ponderosus v. Schrenk.
Polyporus Schweinitzii Fr.
Polyporus stipticus (P.) ex Fr.

Polyporus sulphureus (Bull.) ex Fr.
Polyporus volvatus Pk.
Poria callosa Fr.
Poria pulchella S.
Poria subspadicea Fr.
Poria violacea Fr.

{Poria vulgaris (Fr.) Cke. June 1886.
Poria vulgaris (Fr.) Quél. 1886.

{Trametes carnea Lloyd.
Trametes subrosea Weir.

Trametes serialis Fr.
Trametes setosus Weir.
Trametes tenuis Karst.

BASIDIOMYCETES MISCELLANEI

Armillaria mellea (Vahl) ex Fr.
Hydnum conigenum Pk.

Pinus ponderosa Dougl., var. **scopulorum**
  Engelm.

Peniophora gilvidula Bres.

{Coleosporium Solidaginis Thm. I.
Peridermium acicola Underw. & Earle.

{Coleosporium carneum H. S. Jackson. I.
Coleosporium Vernoniae B. & C. I.
Peridermium carneum (Bosc) Seymour &
  Earle.

Peridermium Cerebrum Pk.

Coleosporium delicatulum Hedgc. & Long. I.

{Cronartium coleosporioides Auct. Amer. p.p. I.
Cronartium filamentosum Hedgc. & Long. I.
Peridermium filamentosum Pk.

{Cronartium coleosporioides Arth. I.
Cronartium Harknessii Meinecke. I.
Peridermium Harknessii J. P. Moore.

Peridermium montanum Arth. & Kern.

{Cronartium Comandrae Pk. I.
Cronartium pyriforme Hedgc. & Long. I.
Peridermium pyriforme Pk.

Cronartium Quercus Schrt. I.

Pinus pumilio Haenk.

Cenangium Abietis (P.) ex Duby.
Herpotrichia nigra Hartig.
Peridermium acicola Underw. & Earle.

{Cronartium Comptoniae Arth. I.
Peridermium Comptoniae (Arth.) Orton &
  Adams.

Pinus pungens Lamb.

Crumenula pinicola (Reb.) ex Karst.

{Coleosporium Solidaginis Thm. I.
Peridermium acicola Underw. & Earle.

Peridermium Cerebrum Pk.
Peridermium Comptoniae (Arth.) Orton &
  Adams.

{Cronartium Comandrae Pk. I.
Cronartium pyriforme Hedgc. & Long. I.
Peridermium pyriforme Pk.

Polyporus amorphus Fr.

Pinus radiata D. Don.

{ Cenangium Abietis (P.) ex Duby.
{ Cenangium ferruginosum Fr.

{ Coniothyrium acuum (C. & E.) Hark.
{ Phoma acuum C. & E.

Dermatea Pini Phil. & Hark.

{ Hysterangium fuscum Hark.
{ Hysterangium Gardneri E. Fischer.

{ Eriosphaeria Vermicularia (Fr.) Sacc.
{ Lasiosphaeria Vermicularia (Fr.) Cke.
{ Sphaeria Vermicularia Nees ex Fr.

Lophium mytilinum (P.) ex Fr.

Lophodermium Pinastri (Schrad. ex Fr.) Chev.

−{ Coleosporium arnicale Arth. I.
−{ Coleosporium Madiae Cke. I.
− { Peridermium californicum Arth. & Kern.

≃ { Cronartium Cerebrum Hedgc. & Long. I.
⌐ { Cronartium Quercus Schrt. I.
− { Cronartium Quercuum Miyabe. I.
⌐ { Peridermium Cerebrum Pk.

⌐ { Cronartium Harknessii Meinecke. I.
⌐ { Peridermium Harknessii J. P. Moore.
⌐ { Peridermium Pini Hark. 1880.

−?Peridermium Pini, var. corticola Auct.

Polyporus carbonarius Murrill.

Polyporus dichrous Fr.

Polystictus versicolor (L.) ex Fr.

Poria spissa (S.) Cke.

Sphaerella acicola Cke. & Hark.

Stereum hirsutum (Willd.) ex Fr.

Tubercularia insignis Cke. & Hark.

Vermicularia Tiliae Lk.

Zygodesmus fuscus Cda.

Zygodesmus marginatus Cke. & Hark.

Pinus resinosa Ait.

{ Anthostoma pholidigena (Ell.) Cke.
{ Anthostomella pholidigena Ell.
{ Sphaeria pholidigena Ell.

Arcyria incarnata P.

Botrytis cinerea P. †

Cylindrium strobilinum Sacc.

Diplodia pinea Kickx.

Fusarium acuminatum Ell. & Ev. an Wr.

Fusarium arthrosporioides Sherb.

Fusarium discolor, var. sulphureum App. & Wr.

Fusarium elegans App. & Wr.

Fusarium hyperoxysporum Wr.

Fusarium moniliforme Sheldon.

Fusarium roseum Lk.

Fusarium sporotrichioides Sherb.

Fusarium vasinfectum Atk.

Fusoma parasiticum Tubeuf.

Gibberella Saubinetii (Mont.) Sacc.

Lophodermium australe Dearness.

Lophodermium Pinastri (Schrad. ex Fr.) Chev.

Pezizella ontariensis Rehm.

Phomopsis juniperovora Hahn.

Phytophthora Pini Leonian.

Pythium Artotrogus (Mont.) D By.

Pythium debaryanum Hesse.

{ Nematosporangium aphanidermatum (Edson)
{ Fitzpatrick.
{ Rheosporangium aphanidermatum Edson.

UREDINALES

{ Coleosporium Solidaginis Thm. I.
{ Peridermium acicola Underw. & Earle.

{ Colcosporium Vernoniae B. & C. I.
{ Peridermium carneum (Bosc) Seymour &
{ Earle.

{ Peridermium intermedium Auct. Amer. p. p.
{ Cronartium Cerebrum Hedgc. & Long. I.
{ Peridermium Cerebrum Pk.

{ Cronartium Comptoniae Arth. I.
? { Peridermium Comptoniae (Arth.) Orton &
{ Adams.

Coleosporium delicatulum Hedgc. & Long. I.

Cronartium pyriforme Hedgc. & Long. I.

{ Coleosporium Campanulae Lév. I.
{ Peridermium Rostrupi E. Fischer.

? { Coleosporium Senecionis Fr. I.
{ Peridermium sp. Bates 1907.

HYMENOMYCETINEAE

{ Corticium vagum B. & C.
{ Rhizoctonia Solani Kühn.

Flammula alnicola Fr.

{ Fomes Pini (Brot. ex Fr.) Karst.
{ Trametes Pini (Brot.) ex Fr.

Fomes pinicola (Fr.) Cke.

Fomes roseus (Fr.) Cke.

Lenzites sepiaria (Wulf.) ex Fr.

Merulius ambiguus B.

Polyporus anceps Pk.

Polyporus palustris B. & C.

{ Phaeolus sistotremoides (A. & S.) Murrill.
{ Polyporus Schweinitzii Fr.

Polyporus sulphureus (Bull.) ex Fr.

Polyporus volvatus Pk.

Polystictus abietinus (Dicks. ex Fr.) Cke.

Stereum Pini Fr.

Thelephora terrestris Ehrh. ex Fr.

Pinus rigida Mill.

PEZIZINEAE

Caliciopsis pinea Pk.

Cenangium Abietis (P.) ex Duby.

Crumenula pinicola (Reb.) ex Karst.

{ Dasyscypha calycina (Schum. ex Fr.) Fckl.
{ Dasyscypha Willkommii Hartig.

{ Dasyscypha ellisiana (Rehm) Sacc.
{ Helotium ellisianum Wettst.
{ Peziza ellisiana Rehm.

{ Dasyscypha lachnoderma (B.) Rehm.
{ Peziza lachnoderma B.

Pinus rigida (*cont.*)

Dasyscypha pulverulenta (Lib.) Sacc.
Dasyscypha solfatera (C. & E.) Sacc.
Peziza pulverulenta Lib.
Peziza solfatera C. & E.
Dermatea phyllophila Pk.
Peziza lethalis Ell.
Cenangium acuum C. & P.
Mollisia Pinastri (C. & P.) Sacc.
Peziza Pinastri C. & P.
Pezizella minuta Dearness.
Phialea pulchella (Fckl.) Sacc.
Tympanis Pinastri Tul.

PHACIDIINEAE

Phacidium convexum Dearness.
Propolis Leonis (Tul.) Rehm.
Propolis leucaspis Ell.
Stictis Leonis Tul.
Peziza conorum Ell.
Propolis rhodoleuca (Sommf. ex Fr.) Phil.
Stictis abietina Fr.

HYSTERIINEAE

Aulographum Pinorum Desm.
Hypoderma brachysporum (Rostr.) Tubeuf.
Hypoderma Desmazierii Duby.
Hypoderma Hedgcockii Dearness.
Hypoderma lethale Dearness.
Hypoderma strobicola Tubeuf.
Lophium mytilinum (P.) ex Fr.
Lophodermium brachysporum Rostr.
Hysterium Pinastri Schrad. ex Fr.
Lophodermium Pinastri (Schrad. ex Fr.) Chev.
Hysterium nova-caesariense Ell.
Hysterographium nova-caesariense (Ell.) Roum.
Mytilidion nova-caesariense (Ell.) Rehm.

PYRENOMYCETINEAE

Amphisphaeria pinicola Rehm.
Asterina Pinastri Sacc. & Ell.
Leptosphaeria squamata (C. & E.) Ell.
Metasphaeria squamata C. & E.
Sphaeria squamata C. & E.
Chilonectria Cucurbitula (Curr.) Sacc.
Creonectria Cucurbitula (Sacc.) Seaver
Nectria Cucurbitula Curr.
Parodiella rigida Ell. & Ev.
Pleosphaeria corticola Ell. & Ev.
Rosellinia abietina Fckl., var. trichota (C. & E.) Sacc.
Sphaeria abietina, var. trichota C. & E.
Valsa Abietis Fr.
Venturia barbula (B. & Br.) Cke., var. foliicola Ell.
Conisphaeria albocincta C. & E.
Sphaeria albocincta C. & E.
Zignoella albocincta (C. & E.) Sacc.

UREDINALES

Coleosporium Solidaginis Thm. I.
Peridermium acicola Underw. & Earle.
Coleosporium carneum H. S. Jackson. I.
Coleosporium Vernoniae B. & C. I.
Peridermium carneum (Bosc) Seymour & Earle.
?Peridermium orientale Cke. vel Auct.
Cronartium Cerebrum Hedgc. & Long. I.
Cronartium Quercus Schrt. I.
Peridermium Cerebrum Pk.
Cronartium Comptoniae Arth. I.
Peridermium Comptoniae (Arth.) Orton & Adams.
Peridermium pyriforme Herb. Ell. non Pk.
Coleosporium delicatulum Hedgc. & Long. I.
Peridermium delicatulum Arth. & Kern.
Peridermium inconspicuum N. Am. Uredinales 720.
Coleosporium Elephantopodis Thm. I.
Peridermium carneum Auct. Amer. p. p.
Peridermium Elephantopodis Hedgc. & Hahn.
Peridermium intermedium Arth. & Kern.
Coleosporium Laciniariae Arth. I.
Peridermium fragile Hedgc. & Hunt.
Peridermium fusiforme Pk.
Coleosporium Ipomoeae Burrill. I.
Peridermium Ipomoeae (Burrill) Hedgc. & Hunt.
Aecidium Pini Auct. p. p.
Peridermium Pini, var. acicola Auct. p. p.
Peridermium oblongisporium Fckl.
Cronartium pyriforme Hedgc. & Long. I.
Peridermium pyriforme Pk.
Coleosporium Campanulae Lév. I.
Peridermium Pini Ohio Fungi *104*.
Peridermium Rostrupi E. Fischer.
?Coleosporium Senecionis Fr. I.
Coleosporium Terebinthinaceae Arth. I.
Peridermium Terebinthinaceae (Arth.) Hedgc. & Hunt.

THELEPHORACEAE

Coniophora arida (Fr.) Cke.
Thelephora arida Fr.
Coniophora Cerebella P.
Corticium atrovirens Fr.
Corticium Overholtsii Burt.
Hypochnus granulosus (Pk.) Burt.
Peniophora carnosa Burt.
Peniophora crassa Burt.
Peniophora pubera (Fr.) Sacc.
Sebacina calcea (P.) Bres.
Stereum sanguinolentum Fr.
Thelephora sanguinolenta A. & S. ex Fr.

Pinus rigida (*cont.*)

POLYPORACEAE

Cryptoporus volvatus (Pk.) Hubbard.
Fomes volvatus Cke., var. obvolutus (B. & Cke.)
  Sacc.
Polyporus obvolutus B. & Cke.
Polyporus volvatus Pk.
Polyporus volvatus Pk., var. obvolutus (B. &
  Cke.) Pk.
Fomes Pini (Brot. ex Fr.) Karst.
Trametes Pini (Brot.) ex Fr.
Fomes pinicola (Sw. ex Fr.) Cke.
Ganoderma Tsugae Murrill.
Polyporus Tsugae (Murrill) Overholts.
Gloeophyllum hirsutum (Schaeff.) ex Murrill.
Lenzites sepiaria (Wulf.) ex Fr.
Merulius aureus Fr.
Polyporus amorphus Fr.
Polyporus circinatus Fr.
Polyporus Schweinitzii Fr.
Polyporus ursinus Lloyd.
Polyporus Weinmanni Fr.
Polystictus abietinus (Dicks. ex Fr.) Cke.
Coltriciella dependens (B. & C.) Murrill.
Polyporus dependens B. & C.
Polystictus dependens (B. & C.) Cke.
Poria Vaillantii (Fr.) Cke.
Poria vaporaria Fr.
Trametes protracta Fr.

MISCELLANEA

Armillaria mellea (Vahl) ex Fr.
Cylindrocolla acuum Ell. & Ev.
Dacryomyces corticioides Ell. & Ev., var. coni-
  genus Ell. & Ev.
Hendersonia rostrata Sacc. & Ell.
Hydnum Himantia S.
Hymenula fumosa C. & E.
Leptostroma Pinastri Desm.
Marasmius straminipes Pk.
Paxillus corrugatus Atk.
Pestalozzia funerea Desm.
Phoma acuum C. & E.
Pluteus umbrosus Fr.
Tubercularia insignis Cke. & Hark.

Pinus sabiniana Dougl.

Cenangium ferruginosum Fr.
Fomes pinicola (Sw. ex Fr.) Cke.
Aulographum acicola Hark.
Lembosia acicola (Hark.) Sacc.
Peridermium carneum Auct. Amer. p. p.
Cronartium Cerebrum Hedgc. & Long. I.
Peridermium Cerebrum Pk.
Cronartium coleosporioides Arth. I.
Peridermium fusiforme Pk.
Cronartium coleosporioides Arth. I.
Cronartium Harknessii Meinecke. I.
Peridermium Harknessii J. P. Moore.

Peridermium intermedium Auct. Amer. p. p.
Polyporus Schweinitzii Fr.
Polystictus hirsutus (Wulf.) ex Fr.
Trichosporium fuscescens Cke. & Hark.

Pinus serotina Michx.

Hypoderma lethale Dearness.
Coleosporium Solidaginis Thm. I.
Peridermium acicola Underw. & Earle.
Coleosporium carneum H. S. Jackson. I.
Coleosporium Vernoniae B. & C. I.
Peridermium carneum (Bosc) Seymour & Earle.
Cronartium Cerebrum Hedgc. & Long. I.
Peridermium Cerebrum Pk.
Coleosporium delicatulum Arth. & Kern. I.
Peridermium delicatulum Hedgc. & Long.
Coleosporium Elephantopodis Thm. I.
Peridermium Elephantopodis (Thm.) Hedgc.
  & Hahn.
Peridermium fusiforme Arth. & Kern.
Coleosporium Ipomoeae Burrill. I.
Peridermium Ipomoeae (Burrill) Hedgc. &
  Hunt.
Peridermium orientale Cke.
Coleosporium Terebinthinaceae Arth. I.
Peridermium Terebinthinaceae (Arth.) Hedgc.
  & Hunt.

Pinus sibirica Mayr.

Lenzites sepiaria (Wulf.) ex Fr.

Pinus strobiformis Engelm.

Trametes Pini (Brot.) ex Fr.
Fomes pinicola (Sw. ex Fr.) Cke.
Fomes roseus (A. & S. ex Fr.) Cke.
Polyporus Schweinitzii Fr.

Pinus Strobus L.

PEZIZINEAE

Biatorella resinae (Fr.) Mudd.
Peziza resinae Fr.
Caliciopsis pinea Pk.
Cenangella Pinastri (P.) Sacc.
Cenangium Pinastri (P.) Fr.
Tryblidiopsis Pinastri (P.) Karst.
Tympanis Pinastri (P.) Tul.
Cenangium Abietis (P.) ex Duby.
Cenangium ferruginosum Fr.
Cenangium acuum C. & P.
Dasyscypha Agassizii (B. & C.) Sacc.
Dasyscypha serinella (Quél.) Sacc.
Tympanis Buchsii (Henn.) Rehm.
Tympanis laricina (Fckl.) Sacc.

PHACIDIINEAE

Coccomyces Pini (Fr.) Karst.
Coccophacidium crustaceum (B. & C.) Durand.
Coccophacidium Pini (Fr.) Rehm.
Phacidium crustaceum B. & C. in Herb. Curtis.
Phacidium Pini (A. & S.) Schm. ex Fr.
Phacidium abietinum Schum. ex Fr.

Pinus Strobus (*cont.*)
  Phacidium planum J. J. Davis.
  Phacidium sparsum Pk.
  {Stictis hysterina Fr.
  {Xylogramma hysterinum (Fr.) Rehm.

HYSTERIINEAE
  {Hypoderma brachysporum (Rostr.) Tubeuf.
  {Hypoderma Desmazierii Duby.
  {Hypoderma strobicola Tubeuf.
  {Lophodermium brachysporum Rostr.
  {Bifusella linearis (Pk.) v. Höhnel.
  {Hypoderma lineare Pk.
  {Lophodermium lineare (Pk.) Ell. & Ev.
  {Rhytisma lineare Pk.
  {Hysterium Pinastri Schrad. ex Fr.
  {Lophodermium Pinastri (Schrad. ex Fr.) Chev.
  {Lophium fusisporum Cke.
  {Mytilidion fusisporum (Cke.) Sacc.

PYRENOMYCETINEAE
  {Asterina Pinastri (Fckl.) Sacc. & Ell.
  {Calothyrium Pinastri (Fckl.) Theissen.
  {Microthyrium Pinastri Fckl.
  {Parodiella rigida Ell. & Ev.
  Capnodium Pini B. & C.
  {Chilonectria Cucurbitula (Curr.) Sacc.
  {Nectria Cucurbitula (Curr.) Cke.
  {Lasiosphaeria hispida (Tode ex Fr.) Fckl.
  {Sphaeria hispida Tode ex Fr.
  {Ophionectria scolecospora Bref.
  {Scoleconectria scolecospora (Bref.) Seaver.
  Physalospora Cydoniae Arnaud.
  {Melogramma Spraguei B. & C.
  {Sphaeria Spraguei B. & C.
  {Thyridium Spraguei (B. & C.) Sacc.
  Valsa Abietis (A. & S.) ex Fr.
  {Sphaeria Colliculus Wormsk. ex Fr.
  {Valsa Colliculus (Wormsk. ex Fr.) B.
  Valsa Pini (A. & S.) ex Fr.

UREDINALES
  {Coleosporium Senecionis (Schum.) Fr.　I.
  {Peridermium oblongisporium Fckl.
  Cronartium Cerebrum Hedgc. & Long. I.
  {Cronartium ribicola Fisch.　I.
  {Peridermium Strobi Klebahn.

AURICULARIACEAE
  {Auricularia Auricula-judae (L. ex Fr.) Schrt.
  {Hirneola Auricula-judae (L. ex Fr.) B.
  Septobasidium pinicola Snell.

TREMELLACEAE
  Sebacina macrospora (Ell. & Ev.) Burt.
  Tremella foliacea P.
  {Tremella pinicola Pk.
  {Exidia pinicola (Pk.) Coker.

DACRYOMYCETACEAE
  {Dacryomyces corticioides Ell. & Ev.
  {Dacryomyces involutus S.
  Dacryomyces deliquescens (Bull.) ex Duby.
  Dacryomyces hyalina Quél.

THELEPHORACEAE
  Coniophora byssoidea (P.) ex Fr.
  Coniophora puteana B. & C.
  Corticium arachnoideum B.
  Corticium Berkeleyi Cke.
  Corticium bicolor Pk.
  {Corticium calceum Fr. emend. Romell & Burt.
  {Thelephora calcea Fr.
  Corticium canadense Burt.
  Corticium fuscostratum Burt.
  Corticium investiens (S.) Bres.
  Corticium ochraceum Fr.
  Corticium subcontinuum B. & C.
  {Corticium vagum B. & C.
  {Corticium vagum, var. Solani (Kühn) Burt.
  {Rhizoctonia Solani Kuhn.
  Hypochnus subvinosus Burt.
  Peniophora arachnoidea Burt.
  Peniophora gigantea (Fr.) Masses.
  Peniophora laminata Burt.
  Peniophora pinicola Burt.
  Peniophora Thujae Burt.
  Radulum pallidum B. & C.
  Stereum sanguinolentum Fr.
  Stereum spadiceum Fr.
  Thelephora laciniata (P.) ex Fr.

HYDNACEAE
  Grandinia cylindrica Burt.
  Hydnum Auriscalpium L. ex Fr.
  Hydnum caryophyllum B. & C.
  Hydnum coralloides Scop. ex Fr.
  Hydnum subfuscum Pk.

POLYPORACEAE
  Boletus hemichrysus B. & C.
  Boletus hemichrysus B. & C., var. mutabilis Pk.
  {Cryptoporus volvatus (Pk.) Hubbard.
  {Polyporus volvatus Pk.
  {Fomes annosus (Fr.) Cke.
  {Polyporus annosus Fr.
  {Trametes radiciperda Hartig.
  Fomes applanatus (P. ex Wallr.) Gill.
  {Fomes fuliginosus (Fr.) Cke.
  {Ischnoderma fuliginosum (Fr.) Murrill.
  Fomes igniarius (Fr.) Gill.
  {Fomes marginatus (Fr.) Gill.
  {Fomes ungulatus (Schaeff.) ex Sacc.
  {Fomes albogriseus Pk.
  {Fomes Laricis (Jacq.) ex Murrill.
  {Fomes officinalis (Fr.) Lloyd.
  {Polyporus officinalis Fr.

Pinus Strobus (*cont.*)

⎰Fomes Pini (Brot. ex Fr.) Karst.
⎱Porodaedalea Pini· (Brot. ex Fr.) Murrill.
Trametes Pini (Brot.) ex Fr.
Fomes pinicola (Sw. ex Fr.) Cke.
Fomes roseus (A. & S. ex Fr.) Cke.
Lenzites sepiaria (Wulf.) ex Fr.
Lenzites trabea (P.) ex Fr.
Lenzites vialis Pk.
Merulius aureus Fr.
Merulius bellus B. & C.
Merulius lacrimans (Wulf.) ex Fr.
Merulius tremellosus Schrad. ex Fr.
Polyporus amorphus Fr.
Polyporus Berkeleyi Fr.
⎰Polyporus ellisianus (Murrill) Sacc. & Trott.
⎱Tyromyces ellisianus Murrill.
Polyporus fragilis Fr.
⎰Polyporus maculatus Pk.
⎱Polyporus guttulatus Pk.
Polyporus osseus Kalchb.
Polyporus Schweinitzii Fr.
Polyporus Weinmannii Fr.
⎰Coriolus abietinus (Fr.) Quél.
⎱Polystictus abietinus (Fr.) Cke.
Poria calcea (Fr.) Cke., var. sulphurea Romell
ex Murrill.
⎰Poria lenis (Karst.) Sacc. 1888.
⎱Poria lenis (Karst.) Bres. 1897.
Poria mollusca (Fr.) Cke.
⎰Merulius incrassatus B. & C.
⎱Polyporus pineus Pk.
⎰Poria incrassata (B. & C.) Burt.
⎱Poria pinea Pk.
⎰Polyporus subacidus Pk.
⎱Poria subacida (Pk.) Sacc. Syll.
⎰Polyporus Vaillantii (DC.) Fr.
⎱Poria Vaillantii (Fr.) Cke.
⎰Poria vitellina (S.) Cke. 1886.
⎱Poria vitellina (S.) Sacc. 1888.
⎰Fomes carneus Auct. Amer. p. p.
⎱Trametes subrosea Weir.
Trametes variiformis Pk.

AGARICACEAE

Armillaria mellea (Vahl) ex Fr.
Clitocybe cyathiformis Fr.
Clitocybe pinophila Pk.
Collybia rubescentifolia Pk.
Lentinus lepideus Fr.
Marasmius androsaceus (L.) ex Fr.
Mycena rosella Fr.
Paxillus atrotomentosus Fr.
Paxillus panuoides Fr.
Pleurotus striatulus (P.) ex Fr.
Pluteus fuliginosus Murrill.
Russula atropurpurea Maire ex Krombh. non
Pk.

Schizophyllum commune Fr.
Tricholoma flavescens Pk.
Tricholoma rutilans (Schaeff.) ex Fr.

SPHAEROPSIDALES

⎰Aposphaeria hysterella Sacc.
⎱Sphaeronema subtile B. & C.
Diplodia conigena Desm.
Diplodia pinea (Desm.) Kickx.
Discosia Artocreas (Tode) ex Fr.
Discosia strobilina (Lib.) Fres.
Excipula Strobi Fr.
Glutinium exasperans Fr.
Haplosporella Pini Pk.
Hendersonia foliicola (B.) Fckl.
Leptostroma Pinastri C. & E.
Phoma acuum C. & E.
Phoma bacteriophila Pk.
Phoma Harknessii Sacc.
?Phoma Strobi B. & Br.
Phoma strobilinum Pk. & G. W. Clinton.
Phomopsis Strobi Syd.
⎰Rhabdospora mirabilissima (Pk.) Dearness.
⎱Septoria mirabilissima Pk.
Septoria parasitica Hartig.
Septoria spadicea Patterson & Charles.
Sphaeronema strobilinum Desm.
Sphaeropsis Ellisii Sacc.

MELANCONIALES

Cryptosporium Pini B. & C.
Hypodermium effusum S.
Pestalozzia funerea Desm.

HYPHOMYCETES

Coniosporium tumulosum Sacc.
⎰Coremium aureum (Hedgc.) Sacc.
⎱Graphium aureum Hedgc.
Fusarium roseum Lk.
Fusoma parasiticum Tubeuf.

MISCELLANEA

Amaurochaete cribrosa (Fr.) Sturgis.
Amaurochaete fuliginosa (Sow.) Macbr.
Pythium debaryanum Hesse.
Stemonitis fusca Roth.

Pinus sylvestris Linn.

Cenangium Abietis Pers.
Cenangium ferruginosum Fr.
Ceratostomella caerulea Münch.
⎰Corticium calceum Fr. emend. Romell & Burt.
⎱Thelephora calcea Fr.
⎰Cytospora Pinastri Fr.
⎱Phoma acuum C. & E.
⎰Dasyscypha calycina (Schum. ex Fr.) Fckl.
⎰Dasyscypha Willkommii Hartig.
⎱Peziza calycina Schum. ex Fr.
Dasyscypha pulverulenta (Lib.) Sacc.
Diplodia sapinea (Fr.) Fckl.
Dothiorella Pinastri (Fr.) Sacc.

Pinus sylvestris (*cont.*)
  {Fomes Pini (Brot. ex Fr.) Karst.
  {Trametes Pini (Brot.) ex Fr.
  Fusoma parasiticum Tubeuf.
  {Auriscalpium Auriscalpium (L.) S. F. Gray.
  {Hydnum Auriscalpium L. ex Fr.
  Hypodermella sulcigena (Lk.) Tubeuf.
  Lenzites sepiaria (Wulf.) ex Fr.
  Peniophora odorata (Karst.) Burt.
  Peniophora sordida (Karst.) Burt.
  Phoma geniculata (B. & Br.) Sacc.
  Phoma strobiligena Desm.
  Phytophthora Cactorum (Leb. & Cohn) Scht.
  Phytophthora omnivora D By.
  Pythium debaryanum Hesse.
  {Corticium vagum B. & C.
  {Rhizoctonia Solani Kühn.
  Sclerophoma pithyophila (Cda.) v. Höhnel.
  {Sphaeropsis Ellisii Sacc.
  {Sphaeropsis Pinastri C. & E.
  Tryblidiopsis Pinastri (P.) Karst.

UREDINALES

  {Cronartium Cerebrum Hedgc. & Long. I.
  {Cronartium Quercus Schrt. I.
  {Cronartium strobilinum Hedgc. & Hunt. I.
  {Cronartium Comptoniae Arth. I.
  {Peridermium Comptoniae (Arth.) Orton &
  { Adams.
  Coleosporium Sonchi Auct. p. p.
  {Coleosporium Sonchi-arvensis Lév. I.
  {Peridermium Fischeri Klebahn.
  Peridermium oblongisporium Fckl.
  Peridermium Pini Auct.
  Peridermium Pini, var. corticola Auct.
  {Cronartium pyriforme Hedgc. & Long. I.
  {Peridermium pyriforme Pk.

Pinus Taeda L.
  Ceratostomella pilifera (Fr.) Wint.
  Cryptoporus volvatus (Pk.) Hubbard, var.
    pleurostoma Pat.
  {Dacryomyces pedunculatus (B. & C.) Coker.
  {Exidia pedunculata B. & C.
  Diplodia megalospora B. & C.
  Fomes annosus (Fr.) Cke.
  Trametes Pini (Brot.) ex Fr.
  Fomes pinicola (Sw. ex Fr.) Cke.
  Hypoderma lethale Dearness.
  Lecanosticta Pini Syd.
  Lentinus lepideus Fr.
  Lenzites sepiaria (Wulf.) ex Fr.
  Lophodermium australe Dearness.
  Lophodermium Pinastri (Schrad. ex Fr.) Chev.
  Peniophora gigantea (Fr.) Massee.
  Pezizella minuta Dearness.
  {Dothiora elegans (B. & C.) Sacc.
  {Phacidium elegans B. & C.
  Polyporus Schweinitzii Fr.

Rhizopogon parasiticus Coker & Totten.
Schizophyllum commune Fr.
Scolecodothis pinicola Miles.
{Cryptosporium acicola Thm.
{Septoria acicola (Thm.) Sacc.
Trametes serialis Fr.
Tremella pinicola Britz.

UREDINALES

Caeoma strobilinum Arth.
Coleosporium Pini Gall.
{Coleosporium Solidaginis Thm. I.
{Peridermium acicola Underw. & Earle.
{Coleosporium apocynaceum Cke. I.
{Peridermium apocynaceum (Cke.) Hedgc. &
{ Hunt.
Coleosporium carneum H. S. Jackson. I.
Coleosporium Vernoniae B. & C. I.
Peridermium carneum (Bosc) Seymour &
  Earle.
Peridermium orientale N. A. F. *1026a*.
Peridermium Pini, var. acicola E. F. *224*.
{Cronartium Cerebrum Hedgc. & Long. I.
{Cronartium Quercus Schrt. I.
{Peridermium Cerebrum Pk.
{Peridermium corticola Rav. Fung. Am. an **Cke**.
{Cronartium Comptoniae Arth. I.
{Peridermium Comptoniae (Arth.) Orton &
{ Adams.
{Coleosporium delicatulum Hedgc. & Long. I.
{Peridermium delicatulum Arth. & Kern.
{Coleosporium Elephantopodis Thm. I.
{Peridermium Elephantopodis (Thm.) Hedgc.
{ & Hahn.
{Coleosporium Laciniariae Arth. I.
{Peridermium fragile Hedgc. & Hunt.
{Coleosporium Ipomoeae Burrill. I.
{Peridermium Ipomoeae (Burrill) Hedgc. &
{ Hunt.
{Coleosporium minutum Hedgc. & Hunt. I.
{Peridermium minutum Hedgc. & Hunt.
Peridermium Pini Auct. p. p.?
{Cronartium pyriforme Hedgc. & Long. I.
{Peridermium pyriforme Pk.
{Coleosporium Terebinthinaceae Arth. I.
{Peridermium Terebinthinaceae (Arth.) Hedgc.
{ & Hunt.

Pinus Thunbergii Parl.
{Coleosporium Solidaginis Thm. I.
{Peridermium acicola Underw. & Earle.

Pinus virginiana Mill.

ASCOMYCETES

Amphisphaeria pinicola Rehm.
Botryosphaeria Quercuum (S.) Sacc.
Ceratostomella exigua Hedgc.
{Ceratostoma piliferum (Fr.) Fckl.
{Ceratostomella pilifera (Fr.) Wint.

Pinus virginiana (*cont.*)
Hypoderma Hedgcockii Dearness.
Hypoderma lethale Dearness.
Hypodermella sulcigena (Lk.) Tubeuf.
Hypodermium sulcigenum Lk.
Hysterium nova-caesariense Ell.
Hysterographium nova-caesariense (Ell.)
Roum.
Mytilidion nova-caesariense Ell.
Lophodermium Pinastri (Schrad. ex Fr.) Chev.
Mollisia Pinastri (C. & P.) Sacc.
Peziza conorum Ell.
Pezizella minuta Dearness.
Phacidium lacerum Fr.
Propolis Leonis (Tul.) Rehm.
Propolis strobilina (Cke.) Sacc.
Rosellinia abietina Fckl., var. trichota (C. & E.)
Sacc.
Stictis fimbriata S.

UREDINALES
Coleosporium Pini Gall.
Gallowaya Pini (Gall.) Arth.
Gallowaya pinicola Arth.
Coleosporium Solidaginis Thm. I.
Peridermium acicola Underw. & Earle.
Caeoma pineum S. Am. Bor. *2903* p. p.
Cronartium Cerebrum Hedgc. & Long. I.
Cronartium Quercus Auct. Amer. I.
Peridermium Cerebrum Pk.
Cronartium Comptoniae Arth. I.
Peridermium Comptoniae (Arth.) Orton &
Adams.
Peridermium pyriforme, var. corticola N. A. F.
1021.
Coleosporium Helianthi Arth. I.
Peridermium Helianthi (Arth.) Hedgc. & Hunt.
Coleosporium inconspicuum Hedgc. & Long. I.
Peridermium inconspicuum Long.
Peridermium orientale Cke.
Peridermium pyriforme Pk.
Coleosporium Campanulae Lev. I.
Peridermium Rostrupi E. Fisch.
Peridermium Terebinthinaceae (Arth.) Hedgc.
& Hunt.

HYMENOMYCETINEAE
Corticium scutellare B. & C.
Cryptoporus volvatus (Pk.) Hubbard.
Fomes volvatus (Pk.) Cke.
Fomes Pini (Brot. ex Fr.) Karst.
Trametes Abietis Karst.
Trametes Pini (Brot.) ex Fr.
Fomes pinicola (Fr.) Cke.
Fomes roseus (A. & S.) Fr.
Lenzites sepiaria (Wulf.) ex Fr.
Odontia furfurella Bres.
Corticium giganteum Fr.
Peniophora gigantea (Fr.) Massee.

Polyporus dichrous Fr.
Polyporus pargamenus Fr.
Polystictus pergamenus Fr.
Polyporus Schweinitzii Fr.
Boletus abietinus Dicks.
Polyporus abietinus (Dicks.) ex Fr.
Polystictus abietinus (Fr.) Cke.
Polystictus pusio Sacc. & Cub.
Polyporus xanthus Fr.
Poria xantha (Fr.) Cke.
Schizophyllum commune Fr.
Stereum Pini Fr.
Fomes carneus Auct. Amer.
Polyporus Palliseri B. p. p.
Trametes subrosea Weir.
Tremella aurantia S.

MISCELLANEA
Bothrodiscus pinicola Shear.
Coniosporium strobilinum S.
Cytospora Curreyi Sacc.?
Illosporium conicola Ell. & Ev.
Periconia nana Ehrb.
Septoria conigena Sacc. & Roum.
Speira minor Sacc.
Pinus sp. indet.

MYXOMYCETES
Amaurochaeta fuliginosa (Sow.) Macbr.
Reticularia atra A. & S.
Arcyria nutans Grev.
Ceratiomyxa fruticulosa (Müll.) Macbr.
Comatricha elegans (Racib.) Lister.
Badhamia penetralis C. & E.
Comatricha ellisiana (Cke.) Ell. & Ev.
Comatricha Ellisii Morg.
Comatricha laxa Rostf.
Comatricha Stemonitis (Scop.) E. P. Sheldon.
Comatricha typhoides (Bull.) Rostf.
Comatricha subcaespitosa Pk.
Cribraria dictydioides Cke. & Balf.
Cribraria intricata Schrad.
Cribraria microcarpa (Schrad.) P.
Cribraria minima B. & C.
Cribraria minutissima S.
Cribraria purpurea Schrad.
Diachaea elegans N. A. F. *336.*
Diachaea leucopoda (Bull.) Rostf., var. cylin-
drica Massee.
Diderma asteroides Lister.
Chondrioderma albescens (Phil.) Cke.
Diderma albescens Phil.
Diderma niveum (Rostf.) E. P. Sheldon.
Didymium melanospermum (P.) Macbr.
Didymium nigripes Fr., var. eximium Lister.
Enerthenema berkeleyanum Rostf.
Enerthenema syncarpon Sturgis
Fuligo megaspora Sturgis.

Pinus sp. indet. (*cont.*)
Hemiarcyria clavata (P.) Rostf.
Hemitrichia clavata (P.) Rostf.
Hemitrichia stipitata Massee.
Lycogala epidendrum (Buxb.) Fr.
Physarum nutans P.
Tilmadoche alba (Bull.) E. P. Sheldon.
Physarum pulcherrimum B. & Rav.
Stemonitis axifera (Bull.) Macbr.
Stemonitis ferruginea Ehrenb. ex Lister p.p.
Stemonitis porphyra B. & C.

ASCOCORTICIACEAE
Ascocorticium anomalum (Ell. & Hark.) Schrt.
Ascomyces anomalus Ell. & Hark.
Exoascus anomalus (Ell. & Hark.) Sacc.

PEZIZINEAE
Agyrium brunneolum B. & C.
Agyrium rufum (P.) Fr.
Ascobolus carneus P. ex Fr.
Ascophanus carneus (P. ex Fr.) Boud.
Belonium pineti (Batsch ex Fr.) Rehm.
Peziza lurida P. ex Fr.
Peziza pineti Batsch.
Pseudohelotium pineti (Batsch ex Fr.) Fckl.
Coryne sarcoides (Jacq.) Tul.
Dasyscypha arida (Phil.) Sacc.
Peziza arida Phil.
Dasyscypha fuscosanguinea Rehm.
Dasyscypha calyciformis (Willd.) Rehm.
Dasyscypha chamaeleontina (Pk.) Sacc.
Peziza chamaeleontina Pk.
Dasyscypha latebrosa (Ell.) Sacc.
Peziza latebrosa Ell.
Dasyscypha leucoderma (B.) Rehm.
Dasyscypha ochracea (S.) Sacc.
Peziza ochracea S.
Dasyscypha subtilissima (Cke.) Sacc.
Peziza subtilissima Cke.
Dasyscypha uncinata (Phil.) Sacc.
Peziza uncinata Phil.
Cenangium populneum (P.) Rehm.
Dermatea fascicularis Fr.
Peziza fascicularis A. & S. ex Fr.
Erinella rhaphidospora (Ell.) Sacc.
Peziza rhaphidospora Ell.
Helotium conigenum (P.) ex Fr.
Peziza conigena P. ex Fr.
Helotium subtile Fr.
Humaria xanthomela (P.) Quél., var. americana Rehm.
Lachnea scutellata (L. ex Fr.) Rehm.
Peziza scutellata L. ex Fr.
Lachnea stercorea (P.) Gill.
Peziza scutellata Bolt.
Dasyscypha resinaria (Cke. & Phil.) Rehm.
Lachnellula resinaria (Cke. & Phil.) Rehm.

Lachnum bicolor (Bull. ex Fr.) Karst.
Peziza bicolor Bull. ex Fr.
Lecanidion fusco-atrum Rehm.
Orbilia vinosa (A. & S. ex Fr.) Karst.
Peziza vinosa A. & S. ex Fr.
Patellea hysterioides Ell. & Ev.
Patinella atroviridis Rehm.
Patinella flexella)Fr.) Sacc.
Peziza flexella (Ach.) ex Fr.
Peziza abdita Ell.
Peziza fumosella C. & E.
Peziza pulchella, var. b. A. & S.
Peziza strobilina Fr.
Pezizella hyalina (P.) Rehm.
Pseudohelotium hyalinum (P.) Fckl.
Pezizella vulgaris (Fr.) Sacc.
Phialea strobilina (Fr.) Sacc.
Placographa mexicana Rehm.
Cenangium pithyum Fr.
Tympanis pithya (Fr.) Karst.

PHACIDIINEAE
Naemacyclus niveus (P.) Fckl.
Propolis decidua (Ell. & Ev.) Sacc.
Stictis decidua Ell. & Ev.
Aporia obscura Duby.
Hysterium Pinastri M. A. Curtis in Herb. Duby.
Schizothyrium obscurum (Duby) Sacc.
Stictis hemisphaerica Fr.
Tryblidiopsis Novae-Fundlandiae Rehm.

HYSTERIINEAE
Aulographum pinorum Desm.
Glonium stellatum S.
Hypoderma conigenum DC. ex Duby.
Hysterium conigenum Fr.
Hysterium Gloniopsis Gerard.
Hysterium macrosporum Pk.
Hysterographium elatina (Ach.) Ell. & Ev., var. crispum (P.) Ell. & Ev.
Hysterium insidens S.
Hysterographium insidens (S.) Sacc.

PYRENOMYCETINEAE
Acanthostigma Scopula (C. & P.) Pk.
Lasiosphaeria Scopula C. & P.
Sphaeria Scopula C. & P.
Amphisphaeria applanata (Fr.) Ces. & DeNot.
Bombardia solaris (C. & E.) v. Höhnel.
Byssosphaeria solaris (C. & E.) Cke.
Lasiosphaeria solaris (C. & E.) Sacc.
Sphaeria solaris C. & E.
Trichosphaeria solaris (C. & E.) Ell. & Ev.
Capnodium australe Mont.
Ceratostoma conicum Ell. & Ev.
Ceratostoma fallax Cke. & Sacc.
Ceratostomella echinella Ell. & Ev.
Cucurbitaria elongata (Fr.) Grev.

Pinus sp. indet. (*cont.*)
{ Diaporthe tortuosa (Fr.) Sacc.
{ Sphaeria tortuosa Fr.
{ Valsa tortuosa (Fr.) Cke.
{ Endoxyla parallela (Fr.) Sacc.
{ Kalmusia parallela (Fr.) Ell. & Ev.
{ Sphaeria luteobasis N. A. F. *99* nec Ell. type.
{ Sphaeria parallela Fr.
  Herpotrichia nigra (Pk.) Sacc.
{ Byssosphaeria luteobasis (Sacc.) Cke.
{ Eutypa luteobasis Sacc.
  Hypocrea olivacea C. & E.
{ Hypomyces Tegillum B. & C.
{ Nectria Tegillum B. & C.
{ Lasiosphaeria canescens (Fr.) Karst.
{ Lasiosphaeria strigosa, var. canescens Berl.
{ Sphaeria canescens P. ex Fr.
{ Lasiosphaeria strigosa (Fr.) Sacc.
{ Sphaeria strigosa A. & S. ex Fr.
  Melanomma ramincola S. Herb.
  Melanomma sparsum Fckl.
  Melanopsamma alpina Ell. & Ev.
{ Melanopsamma graopsis (Ell.) Sacc.
{ Sphaeria graopsis Ell.
  Melanospora chionea (Fr.) Cda.
  Meliola fenestrata C. & E.
  Nectria dispersa C. & E.
{ Amphisphaeria? acicola (Cke.) Sacc.
{ Byssosphaeria acicola Cke.
{ Enchnosphaeria Coulteri (Pk.) Sacc.
{ Lasiosphaeria acicola Cke.
{ Neopeckia Coulteri (Pk.) Sacc.
{ Sphaeria Coulteri Pk.
  Pleurage amphicornis (Ell.) O. Kuntze.
{ Rosellinia hirtissima (Pk.) Sacc.
{ Sphaeria hirtissima Pk.
  Rosellinia pinicola Ell. & Ev.
  Scorias spongiosa (S.) Fr.
  Sphaerella acicola Cke. & Hark.
{ Peltosphaeria canadensis Berl.
{ Thyridella canadensis Sacc.
{ Thyridium canadense Ell. & Ev.
{ Lasiosphaeria fissurarum (B. & C.) Cke.
{ Sphaeria fissurarum B. & C.
{ Trichosphaeria fissurarum (B. & C.) Sacc.
{ Lasiosphaeria pilosa (Fr.) Cke.
{ Sphaeria pilosa P. ex Fr.
{ Trichosphaeria pilosa (Fr.) Fckl.
  Valsa Kunzei Fr.
  Valsa Pini (A. & S.) ex. Fr.
{ Hypoxylon nudicolle B. & C.
{ Sphaeria nudicollis B. & C.
{ Valsaria nudicollis (B. & C.) Sacc.
  Xylaria digitata (L.) ex Grev.
  Xylaria digitata, var. americana Pk.
{ Psilosphaeria diaphana (C. & E.) Cke.
{ Sphaeria diaphana C. & E.
{ Zignoella diaphana (C. & E.) Sacc.

{ Conisphaeria soluta (C. & E.) Cke.
{ Sphaeria soluta C. & E.
{ Zignoella soluta (C. & E.) Sacc.

UREDINALES
{ Caeoma pineum S. Am. Bor. 2903 p. p.
{ Peridermium intermedium Arth. & Kern.

TREMELLACEAE
Exidia pedunculata B. & C.
Exidia recisa Fr.
Exidia saccharina Fr.
{ Hydnum gelatinosum Scop.
{ Hydnogloeum gelatinosum Curr.
{ Tremellodon gelatinosum Fr.
Tulasnella Violae (Quél.) Bourdot & Galzin.

DACRYOMYCETACEAE
Arrhytidia flava B. & C.
{ Calocera albipes (Mont.) B.
{ Calocera stricta Fr.
Calocera cornea (Batsch) ex Fr.
Calocera cornea, var. minima Coker.
Calocera viscosa (P.) ex Fr.
{ Dacryomyces aurantia (S.) Farl.
{ Dacryomyces chrysospermus B. & C.
{ Guepiniopsis aurantia (S.) Pat.
{ Tremella aurantia S.
Dacryomyces chrysocomus (Bull.) ex Tul.
Dacryomyces deliquescens (Bull.) ex Duby.
Dacryomyces fragiformis (P.) Nees ex Fr.
Dacryomyces pallidus Coker.
{ Dacryomyces abietinus (P.) Schrt.
{ Dacryomyces stillatus Nees. ex Fr.
{ Tremella abietina P.
{ Dacryopsis nuda Massee.
{ Ditiola radicata (A. & S.) ex Fr.
Guepinia alpina Tracy & Earle.
Guepinia lutea Bres.
Guepinia occidentalis Lloyd.
Guepinia Peziza Tul.
Guepinia spathularia (S.) Fr.

THELEPHORACEAE
{ Asterostroma albidocarneum (S.) Massee.
{ Corticium albidocarneum (S.) Rav.
{ Corticium chrysocreas B. & C.
{ Thelephora albidocarnea S.
Asterostroma corticola Massee.
Coniophora arida (Fr.) Karst.
Coniophora atrocinerea Karst.
Coniophora byssoidea Fr.
Coniophora fusispora (C. & E.) Cke.
Coniophora inflata Burt.
{ Coniophora leucothrix Sacc. Syll.
{ Coniophora olivacea (Fr.) Karst.
{ Corticium Ellisii (B. & Cke.) Cke.
{ Corticium leucothrix B. & C.
{ Hymenochaete Ellisii B. & Cke.

Pinus sp. indet. (*cont.*)

{Coniophora sistotremoides (S.) Massee.
Corticium suffocata Pk.

Coniophora umbrina A. & S. ex Fr.
Corticium auberianum Mont.
Corticium Berkeleyi Cke.
Corticium bicolor Pk.
Corticium bombycinum (Sommerf.) Bres.
Corticium lividocaeruleum Karst.
Corticium Macounii Burt.
Corticium punctulatum Cke.
Corticium roseum P.
Corticium rubincundum Burt.
Corticium saccharinum B. & C.
Corticium subapiculatum Bres.
Corticium subceraeum Burt.
Corticium tessulatum Cke.
Corticium vescum Burt.
Hymenochaete asperata Ell. & Ev.
Hypochnus atroruber (Pk.) Burt.

{Corticium echinosporum Ell.
Hypochnus echinosporus (Ell.) Burt.

Hypochnus fuscus (P.) Fr.

{Hypochnus olivascens (B. & C.) Burt.
Zygodesmus olivascens B. & C.

Hypochnus pallescens (S.) Burt.

{Hypochnus pannosus (B. & C.) Burt.
Zygodesmus pannosus B. & C.

{Hypochnus zygodesmoides (Ell.) Burt.
Thelephora zygodesmoides Ell.

Peniophora candida (P.) Lyman.
Peniophora carnosa Burt.
Peniophora crassa Burt.
Peniophora gigantea (Fr.) Massee.
Peniophora glebulosa (Fr.) Sacc. Syll.

{Corticium incarnatum (P.) Fr.
Corticium incarnatum Fr., var. maculans Ell.
Peniophora incarnata (P.) Karst. Feb. 1889.
Peniophora incarnata (P.) Massee. July 1889.

Peniophora pilosa Burt.

{Corticium Sambuci P.
Corticium seriale Fr.
Peniophora Sambuci (P.) Burt.

Peniophora serialis (Bres.) v. Höhnel &
Litschauer.
Peniophora subalutacea (Karst.) v. Höhnel &
Litschauer.
Peniophora subapiculata (Bres.) Burt.
Peniophora subcremea v. Höhnel & Litschauer.
Peniophora subsulphurea (Karst.) v. Höhnel
& Litschauer.
Peniophora tenella Burt.

{Corticium velutinum Fr.
Peniophora velutina (DC. ex Fr.) Cke.

{Stereum hirsutum Willd. ex Fr.
Thelephora concentrica A. & S. ex Fr.
Thelephora ochracea P., var. crassior Fr.

Stereum imbricatum (S.) Lév.

Stereum radiatum Pk.
Stereum rufum Fr.
Stereum rugisporum (Ell. & Ev.) Burt.

{Corticium ochroleucum Fr., var. spumeum B.
& C.
Stereum spumeum Burt.

Thelephora puteana Schum.
Tulasnella violea (Quél.) Bourdot & Galzin.

CLAVARIACEAE

Clavaria pyxidata P.
Physalacria inflata (S.) Pk.
Sparassis Herbstii Pk.
Sparassis radicata Weir.

HYDNACEAE

Echinodontium tinctorium Ell. & Ev.
Grandinia alutacea B. & Rav.
Grandinia granulosa (P.) ex Fr.
Hydnochaete setigera Pk.
Hydnum alutaceum Fr.
Hydnum ciliolatum B. & C.
Hydnum ellisianum Thm.
Hydnum farinaceum P.
Hydnum nudum B. & C.
Hydnum pithyophilum B. & C.
Hydnum plumosum Duby.
Hydnum Stevensoni B. & Br.
Hydnum velatum B. & C.
Hydnum xanthum B. & C.
Irpex ambiguus Pk.
Irpex coriaceus B. & Rav.
Kneiffia setigera Fr.
Mucronella aggregata Fr.

{Hericium fasciculare (A. & S. ex Fr.) Banker.
Mucronella fascicularis (A. & S.) ex Fr.

Mucronella minutissima Pk.
Odontia fusca C. & E.
Odontia lateritia B. & C.

POLYPORACEAE

Boletellus Ananas (M. A. Curtis) Murrill.

{Daedalea Berkeleyi Sacc.
Daedalea rhabarbarina B. & Cke.
Gloeophyllum Berkeleyi (Sacc.) Murrill.
Lenzites rhabarbarina B. & C.

{Fomes annosus (Fr.) Cke.
Trametes radiciperda Hartig.

Fomes roseus (A. & S. ex Fr.) Cke.

{Lenzites sepiaria Fr., var. porosa Pk.
Sesia hirsuta (Schaeff.) ex Murrill, var. porosa
Murrill.

Lenzites striata (Fr.) ex Fr.
Merulius albus Burt.
Merulius Corium Fr.
Merulius Farlowii Burt.
Merulius himantioides Fr.
Merulius lacrimans (Wulf.) ex Fr., var. tenuis-
simus B.

Pinus sp. indet. (*cont.*)
Merulius porinoides Fr.
Merulius Ravenelii B.
Merulius rufus P.
Merulius sororius Burt.
{ Hapalopilus sublilacinus (Ell. & Ev.) Murrill.
{ Mucronoporus sublilacinus Ell. & Ev.
Polyporus aduncus Lloyd.
Polyporus adustus (Willd.) ex Fr.
Polyporus albiceps Pk.
Polyporus anceps Pk.
Polyporus borealis Fr.
Polyporus caesius (Schrad.) ex Fr.
Polyporus carbonarius Murrill.
{ Polyporus circinatus Fr., var. dualis Pk.
{ Polyporus dualis Pk.
Polyporus corticola Fr.
Polyporus crispellus Pk.
Polyporus cutifractus Murrill.
Polyporus distortus S.
Polyporus dryophilus B.
Polyporus epileucus Fr.
{ Polyporus fragilis Fr.
{ Polyporus sensibilis Murrill.
{ Spongipellis fragilis (Fr.) Murrill.
{ Spongipellis sensibilis Murrill.
Polyporus irregularis Underw.
{ Polyporus lacteus Fr.
{ Tyromyces lacteus (Fr.) Murrill.
Polyporus lucidus (Leyss.) ex Fr.
{ Coltricia obesa (Ell. & Ev.) Murrill.
{ Polyporus Montagnei Fr.
Polyporus ponderosus v. Schrenk.
Polyporus radicatus S.
Polyporus Schweinitzii Fr., var. hispidoides Pk.
{ Polyporus Smallii (Murrill) Sacc. & Trott.
{ Tyromyces Smallii Murrill.
{ Polyporus undosus Pk.
{ Tyromyces undosus (Pk.) Murrill.
Polystictus balsameus (Pk.) Cke.
{ Polyporus deglubens B. & C.
{ Polystictus deglubens (B. & C.) Cke.
{ Coriolus hexagoniformis Murrill.
{ Polystictus hexagoniformis (Murrill) Sacc. & Trott.
{ Polyporus parvulus S.
{ Polystictus parvulus (S.) Cke.
{ Polyporus sanguineus (L.) ex Fr.
{ Polystictus sanguineus (L.) ex Fr.
{ Polyporus triqueter Fr.
{ Polystictus triqueter (Fr.) Cke.
{ Polyporus velutinus (P.) ex Fr.
{ Polystictus velutinus (P. ex Fr.) Cke.
{ Polystictus versatilis (B.) Fr.
{ Trametes versatilis B.
{ Polyporus aneirinus Sommf. ex Fr.
{ Poria aneirina (Sommf. ex Fr.) Cke.
{ Trametes aneirina (Sommf. ex Fr.) Cke. & Quél.

{ Polyporus aurantiopallens B. & C.
{ Poria aurantiopallens (B. & C.) Cke.
Poria aurea Pk.
{ Polyporus chrysoloma Fr.
{ Poria chrysoloma (Fr.) Cke.
Poria cocos Wolf.
Poria contigua (P. ex Fr.) Cke.
{ Polyporus farinellus Fr.
{ Polyporus tenellus N. A. F.
{ Poria farinella (Fr.) Cke.
Poria favillacea (B. & C.) Cke.
Poria flavida Murrill.
{ Polyporus incarnatus P. ex Fr.
{ Poria incarnata (P. ex Fr.) Cke.
{ Polyporus Lindbladii B., var.
{ Poria Lindbladii (B.) Cke.
{ Boletus mucidus P.
{ Polyporus mucidus (P.) ex Fr.
{ Poria mucida P.
{ Polyporus Radula Fung. Am. *107*.
{ Poria omoema B. ex Cke.
Poria purpurea (Fr.) Cke.
{ Polyporus salmonicolor B. & C.
{ Poria salmonicolor (B. & C.) Cke.
Poria subacida (Pk.) Sacc. Syll.
{ Polyporus tenellus B. & Cke.
{ Poria tenella (B. & Cke.) Cke.
Poria subradiculosa Murrill.
Poria taxicola (P.) Bres.
{ Polyporus subacidus Pk., var. vesiculosus (B. & C.) Pk.
Polyporus vesiculosus B. & C.
Poria subacida (Pk.) Sacc. Syll., var. vesiculosa (B. & C.) Sacc. Syll.
{ Poria vesiculosa (B. & C.) Cke.
Poria violacea (Fr.) Cke.
Porothelium confusum B. & Br.
Porothelium fimbriatum (P.) Fr.
Porothelium Friesii Mont.
Trametes odorata (Wulf.) ex Fr.
Trametes sepium B.

AGARICACEAE

Cantharellus aurantiacus (Wulf.) ex Fr., var. pallidus Pk.
Cantharellus Ravenelii B. & C.
Clitocybe ectypoides Pk.
{ Collybia albipileata Pk.
{ Gymnopus albipileatus (Pk.) Murrill.
Collybia borealis Lloyd.
Collybia colorea Pk.
Collybia conigenoides Ell.
{ Collybia exsculpta Pk.
{ Gymnopus exsculptus (Pk.) Murrill.
Collybia maculata (A. & S.) ex Fr.
Collybia stipitaria Fr.
Cortinarius limonius Fr.
Cortinarius opimus Fr.

Pinus sp. indet. (*cont.*)

{Flammula carbonaria Fr.
Gymnopilus carbonarius (Fr.) Murrill.

{Flammula penetrans Fr.
Gymnopilus penetrans (Fr.) Murrill.

Flammula sapinea Fr.

{Flammula Underwoodii Pk.
Gymnopilus Underwoodii (Pk.) Murrill.

Hypholoma capnoides Fr.

Hypholoma epixanthum Fr.

Lentinus cochleatus Fr.

Lentinus cochleatus Fr., var. dentatus S.

Lentinus lepideus Fr.

Lentinus spretus Pk.

Marasmius androsaceus Fr.

Marasmius candidus (Bolt.) ex Fr.

Marasmius flammans Cke.

Marasmius perforans (Hoffm.) ex Fr.

Marasmius pityophilus B. & C.

Marasmius praeacutus Ell.

{Agaricus flavescens Pk. non Wallr.
Melanoleuca thompsoniana Murrill.

Melanoleuca unakensis Murrill.

{Mycena crystallina Pk.
Prunulus crystallinus (Pk.) Murrill.

{Mycena intertexta B. & C.
Prunulus intertextus (B. & C.) Murrill.

Mycena minutula Pk.

Mycena setosa (Sow.) ex Fr.

{Mycena splendidipes Pk.
Prunulus splendidipes (Pk.) Murrill.

{Mycena tenerrima B.
Prunulus tenerrimus (B.) Merrill.

{Mycena vulgaris (P.) ex Fr.
Prunulus vulgaris (P. ex Fr.) Murrill.

{Omphalia Bakeri Murrill.
Omphalopsis Bakeri Murrill.

Omphalia Campanella (Batsch) ex Fr.

{Omphalia chrysophylla (Fr.) Karst.
Omphalina chrysophylla (Fr.) Murrill.

Omphalia luteola Pk.

Panus foetens Fr.

Paxillus chrysophyllus Trog.

Paxillus corrugatus Atk.

Paxillus Curtisii B.

Paxillus rudis B. & C.

Pholiota flammans Fr.

Pleurotus mitis Fr.

{Geopetalum abietinum (Schrad. ex Fr.) Murrill.
Pleurotus niphetus Ell.
Pleurotus porrigens (P.) ex Fr.

Pluteus latifolius Murrill.

Psathyrella fragilis Earle.

Tapinia lamellosa (Sow.) ex Murrill.

{Cortinellus cinnamomeus Murrill.
Tricholoma cinnamomeum Murrill.

{Cortinellus hirtellus (Pk.) Murrill.
Tricholoma hirtellum Pk.

Tricholoma scalpturatum Fr.

NIDULARIINEAE

Crucibulum vulgare Tul.

Nidularia pisiformis Tul.

Nidularia rubella Ell. & Ev.

Sphaerobolus stellatus Tode ex Fr.

SPHAEROPSIDALES

Aposphaeria hemisphaerica (A. & S. ex Fr.) Sacc.

Aposphaeria hystrella Sacc.

Cytospora pinastri Fr.

Diplodia (?) subterranea Ell. & Barthol.

Hendersonia foliicola B.

Labrella infuscans Ell. & Barthol.

Leptostroma confluens Cke.

Leptostroma durissimum Cke.

{Leptothyrium Pini (Cda.) Sacc.
Sacidium Pini (Cda.) Fr.

{Macrophoma micromegala (B. & C.) Berl. & Vogl.
Phoma micromegala (B. & C.) Sacc.
Sphaeropsis micromegala B. & C.

Macrophoma pinea (Desm.) Petrak & Syd.

Microdiplodia conigena Allescher.

Phoma fibricola B.

Phoma Harknessii Sacc.

{Cryptosporium Pini B. & C.
Rhabdospora Pini (B. & C.) Sacc.

Septoria acicola (Thm.) Sacc.

Septoria parasitica Hartig.

Sphaeropsis Pinastri (Lév.) Sacc.?

Zythia resinae (Ehrenb.) Karst.

HYPHOMYCETES
MUCEDINACEAE

Botrytis cinerea P. †

Botrytis elegantula Cke.

?Botrytis epigaea Lk.

{Botrytis? Schweinitzii Sacc.
Circinotrichum candidum S.

Chromosporium atrobrunneum Pk.

Fusarium blasticola Rostr.

{Helicomyces aureus Cda.
Helicosporium aureum Auct.

Helicoon ellipticum (Pk.) Morg.

{Helicoon thysanophorum Ell. & Hark.
Helicosporium thysanophorum Ell. & Hark.

Menispora acicola Ell. & Ev.

Monilia antennata P.

Monilia penicillata Ell. & Ev.

{Oidium simile B.
Oospora similis (B.) Sacc.

Penicillium aureum Cda.

Penicillium pinophilum Thom.

Pinus sp. indet. (*cont.*)
  Rhinotrichum corticioides Cke.
  Rhinotrichum ramosissimum B. & C.
  Sporotrichum aeruginosum S.
  Trichoderma Koeningi Oud.
  Trichoderma lignorum (Tode) ex Harz.

DEMATIACEAE

Chalara acuaria C. & E.
Chalara fusidioides Cda.
Helicosporium fuscum B. & C.
Helicosporium olivaceum Pk.
Helicosporium vegetum Nees.
Hormiscium gelatinosum Hedgc.
Hormodendron cladosporioides (Fres.) Sacc.
Macrosporium leptotrichum C. & E.
Septocylindrium melleum Elliott & Stansfield.
Septocylindrium strobilinum (Sacc.) Fairman.
Septonema dendryphioides B. & C.
Septonema tabacinum Ell. & Hark.
Septonema toruloideum C. & E.
Sirodesmium Fumago (Cke.) Sacc.
{ Sirodesmium translucens (Cke.) Sacc.
{ Sporidesmium translucens Cke.
Sporidesmium antiquum Cda.
Stigmella pityophila Cke.
Torula ramosa Pk.
Torula sepulta Ell. & Barthol.
Torula sparsa B. & C.
Trichosporium fuscescens Cke. & Hark.
Virgaria indivisa Sacc.
Zygodesmus muricatus Ell. & Ev.
Zygodesmus ramosissimus B. & C.
Zygodesmus sublilacinus Ell. & Holw.
Zygodesmus trachychaetes Ell. & Ev.

STILBACEAE

Didymobotryum corticalis (C. & P.) Dearness
  & House.
{ Graphium smaragdinum (A. & S. ex Fr.) Sacc.
{ Stilbum smaragdinum A. & S. ex Fr.
Isaria radiata B. & C.
Riessia semiophora Fres.

TUBERCULARIACEAE

Cylindrocolla cylindrophora Ell. & Ev.
Dendrodochium compressum Ell. & Ev.
Epicoccum scabrum Cda.
{ Fusarium miniatum (B. & C.) Sacc.
{ Fusisporium miniatum B. & C.
Fusarium Pini Pollock ined.
Fusarium ventricosum App. & Wr.
Illosporium coccinellum Cke.
Illosporium persicinum Fr.
Sphaeridium citrinum Sacc.
Tubercularia dubia Lk.
Tubercularia microsperma B. & C.
Volutella citrina Ell. & Ev.

MISCELLANEA

{ Ascomyces anomalus Ell. & Hark.
{ Exoascus anomalus (Ell. & Hark.) Sacc.
Mitrula cucullata Fr.
Mucor griseolilacinus Povah.
Ozonium auricomum Lk.
Pilacre Petersii B. & C.
Rhizoctonia bicolor Ell.
Spragueola americana Massee.
{ Rhacodium Xylostroma P.
{ Xylostroma giganteum Tode ex Sacc.
Cedrus Deodara Loud.
  Armilaria mellea (Vahl) ex Fr.
  Trametes Pini (Brot.) ex Fr.
Larix decidua Mill.   (L. europaea DC.)
{ Caeoma Bigelowii (Thm.) Kauffm.
{ Melampsora Bigelowii Thm. I.
{ Uredo Bigelowii (Thm.) Arth. I.
{ Caeoma Medusae (Thm.) Kauffm.
{ Melampsora Medusae Thm. I.
{ Caeoma occidentale Arth.
{ Melampsora albertensis Arth. I.
{ Melampsoridium betulinum Klebahn I.
{ Peridermium Laricis (Klebahn) Arth. & Kern.
Phomopsis juniperovora Hahn.
Phomopsis juniperovora Hahn, var. A.
Polyporus Schweinitzii Fr.
Larix Laricina (DuRoi) Koch.

ASCOMYCETES

Chilonectria Cucurbitula (Curr.) Sacc.
{ Dasyscypha Agassizii (B. & C.) Sacc.
{ Peziza Agassizii B. & C.
{ Dasyscypha Willkommii Hartig.
{ Peziza Willkommii Hartig.
Hypodermella Laricis Tubeuf.
Lophodermium laricinum Duby.
Tympanis laricina (Fckl.) Sacc.
{ Tympanis laricina Pass.
{ Tympanis Pinastri Tul.
Valsa ambiens (P.) ex Fr.
{ Sphaeria Pini A. & S. ex Fr.
{ Valsa Pini (A. & S.) Fr.

UREDINALES

{ Caeoma Bigelowii (Thm.) Kauffm.
{ Melampsora Bigelowii Thm. I.
{ Uredo Bigelowii (Thm.) Arth. I.
{ Caeoma Medusae (Thm.) Kauffm.
{ Melampsora Medusae Thm. I.
{ Uredo Medusae (Thm.) Arth. I.
{ Melampsoridium Betulae Arth. I.
{ Melampsoridium betulinum Klebahn. I.
{ Peridermium Laricis (Klebahn) Arth. & Kern.

HYMENOMYCETINEAE

{ Aleurodiscus amorphus (P. ex Fr.) Rabh.
{ Corticium amorphum (P.) ex Fr.
Collybia myriadophila Pk.

Larix Laricina (*cont.*)

Corticium galactinum (Fr.) Burt.
Corticium giganteum Fr.
{ Fomes albogriseus Pk.
{ Fomes Laricis (Jacq.) ex Murrill.
{ Fomes officinalis (Fr.) Lloyd.
{ Fomes Pini (Brot. ex Fr.) Karst.
{ Trametes piceina Pk.
Trametes Pini (Brot.) ex Fr.
{ Fomes Pini (Brot. ex Fr.) Karst., var. Abietis
{ (Karst.) Overholts.
Trametes Pini, var. Abietis (Karst.) v Schrenk.
{ Fomes pinicola (Sw. ex Fr.) Cke.
{ Polyporus pinicola Sw. ex Fr.
Fomes roseus (A. & S. ex Fr.) Cke.
Irpex tabacinus B. & C.
Lentinus lepideus Fr.
Lentinus maximus Johnson.
Lentinus tigrinus (Bull.) ex Fr.
Lenzites sepiaria (Wulf.) ex Fr.
Merulius pulverulentus Fr.
Mycena alcalina Fr.
Mycena strobilina (P.) ex Fr.
Polyporus Schweinitzii Fr.
{ Polyporus abietinus (Dicks.) ex Fr., var. re-
{ supinatus Thm.
{ Polystictus abietinus (Fr.) Cke.
{ Corticium subzonatum Fr.
{ Stereum hirsutum (Willd.) ex Fr.
{ Thelephora ochracea S. Syn. Car. 1017.
{ Thelephora subzonata Fr.

MISCELLANEA

Cytospora Abietis Sacc.
{ Macroplodia Ellisii (Sacc.) O. Kuntze.
{ Sphaeropsis Ellisii (C. & E.) Sacc., var. Laricis
{ Pk.
Sphaeropsis pinastri C. & E., var. Laricis Pk.
Tremella mesenterica Retz ex Fr.
Trichothecium roseum Lk.

Larix leptolepis Murr.

Phomopsis juniperovora Hahn.
Phomopsis juniperovora Hahn, var. A.
Phomopsis Pseudotsugae M. Wilson.

Larix Lyallii Parlat.

{ Caeoma Bigelowii (Thm.) Kauffm.
{ Melampsora Bigelowii Thm. I.
Caeoma Medusae Kauffm.
{ Caeoma occidentale Arth.
{ Melampsora albertensis Arth. I.
Fomes pinicola (Sw. ex Fr.) Cke.
Grandinia granulosa P. ex Fr.
Lophodermium Laricis Dearness.
Polyporus alboluteus Ell.
Polyporus leucospongia Cke.
Polyporus Schweinitzii Fr.

⟜ **Larix occidentalis** Nutt.

UREDINALES

{ Caeoma Bigelowii (Thm.) Arth.
{ Melampsora Bigelowii Thm. I.
{ Uredo Bigelowii (Thm.) Arth. I.
{ Caeoma Medusae (Thm.) Kauffm.
{ Melampsora Medusae Thm. I.
{ Caeoma occidentale Arth.
{ Melampsora Albertensis Arth. I.

HYMENOMYCETINEAE

Aleurodiscus Weirii Burt.
Armillaria mellea (Vahl) ex Fr.
Corticium consimile Bres.
Corticium furfuraceum Bres.
Corticium lacteum Fr.
Corticium lividocaeruleum Karst.
Corticium racemosum Burt.
Corticium vellereum Ell. & Cragin.
Dacryomyces deliquescens (Bull.) ex Duby.
Fomes annosus (Fr.) Cke.
{ Fomes Laricis (Jacq.) ex Murrill.
{ Fomes officinalis (Fr.) Lloyd.
{ Fomes Pini (Brot. ex Fr.) Karst.
{ Trametes Abietis (Karst.) Sacc.
{ Trametes Pini (Brot.) ex Fr.
{ Fomes pinicola (Sw. ex Fr.) Cke.
{ Polyporus pinicola Sw. ex Fr.
Fomes putearius Weir.
Fomes roseus (A. & S. ex Fr.) Cke.
Lentinus lepideus Fr.
Lenzites sepiaria (Wulf.) ex Fr.
Merulius aureus Fr.
Merulius Corium Fr.
Merulius subaurantiacus Pk.
Polyporus adustus (Willd.) ex Fr.
Polyporus alboluteus Ell.
Polyporus anceps Pk.
Polyporus benzoinus Fr.
{ Grifola Berkeleyi (Fr.) Murrill.
{ Polyporus Berkeleyi Fr.
Polyporus caesius Fr.
Polyporus dichrous Fr.
Polyporus floriformis Quél.
Polyporus mollis P. ex Fr.
Polyporus Schweinitzii Fr.
Polyporus sulphureus (Bull.) ex Fr.
{ Polystictus pargamenus Fr.
{ Polystictus pergamenus Fr.
{ Polyporus versicolor (L.) ex Fr.
{ Polystictus versicolor (L.) ex Fr.
Poria attenuata Pk.
Poria subacida (Pk.) Sacc. Syll.
Sparassis radicata Weir.
Stereum purpureum P. †
Stereum radiatum Pk.
Stereum sulcatum Burt.

PINACEAE

51

Larix occidentalis (*cont.*)
Thelephora terrestris Ehrh. ex Fr.
Polyporus setosus (Weir) Lloyd.
Trametes isabellinus Fr.
Trametes setosus Weir.
Trametes tenuis Karst.
Trametes variiformis Pk.

Miscellanea

Botrytis Douglasii Tubeuf.
Dasyscypha arida (Phil.) Sacc.
Dasyscypha Willkommii Hartig.
Hypodermella Laricis Tubeuf.
Hypodermella Laricis Tubeuf, var. octospora
Dearness.
Leptostroma laricinum Fckl.
Lophodermium laricinum Duby.
Phomopsis Pseudotsugae M. Wilson.
Propolis Leonis (Tul.) Rehm, var. weiriana
Sacc.
Rhizina inflata (Schaeff.) ex Quél.
Rhizina undulata Fr.

Larix sp. indet.
Caeoma Laricis Westd.

Ascomycetes

Calonectria Leightonii (B.) Sacc.
Dasyscypha calycina (Fr.) Fckl.
Dasyscypha resinaria Rehm.
Dichaena strobilina (Holl. & Schm.) ex Fr.
Sphaeria strobilina Holl. & Schm. ex Fr.
Herpotrichia nigra Hartig.
Hypoxylon coccineum Bull. †
Lophodermium pinastri (Schrad. ex Fr.) Chev.
Nectria coccinea (P.) ex Fr.
Pseudohelotium laricinum Ell. & Ev.
Valsa Abietis Fr.

Protobasidiomycetes

Dacryomyces Larix Johnson.
Naematelia encephala (Willd.) ex Fr.
Tremella frondosa Fr.

Thelephoraceae

Corticium auberianum Mont.
Thelephora pubera S. Am. bor. 702.
Peniophora alutaria Burt.
Peniophora carnosa Burt.
Peniophora odorata (Karst.) Burt.
Peniophora subapiculata (Bres.) Burt.
Stereum Chailletii (P.) ex Fr.
Stereum purpureum P.†
Stereum rugisporum (Ell. & Ev.) Burt.

Polyporaceae

Fomes lucidus (Leyss. ex Fr.) Cke.
Ganoderma lucidum (Leyss. ex Fr.) Karst.
Fomes ungulatus (Schaeff.) ex Sacc.
Lenzites abietina (Bull.) ex Fr.

Polyporus adiposus B. & Br., var. armeniacus
Cke.
Polyporus armeniacus B.
Polyporus destructor (Schrad.) Fr.
Polyporus frondosus Fr.
Polyporus intybaceus Fr.
Polyporus osseus Fr.
Polyporus Spraguei B. & C.
Tyromyces Spraguei (B. & C.) Murrill
Polyporus violaceus Fr.
Polyporus volvatus Pk.
Polyporus incarnatus (P.) ex Fr.
Poria incarnata (P. ex Fr.) Cke.
Poria marginella (Pk.) Sacc.

Agaricaceae

Clitocybe cerrusatus Fr.
Collybia familia Pk.
Marasmius umbilicatus Johnson.
Pleurotus serotinus (Schrad.) ex Fr.
Pluteus tomentulosus Pk.
Schizophyllum commune Fr.

Miscellanea

Botrytis cinerea P.†
Comatricha Suksdorfii Ell. & Ev.
Exosporium laricinum Massee.
Pestalozzia funerea Desm.
Phlyctaena phomatella Sacc.?

Picea Abies (L.) Karst.
Ascochyta piniperda Lindau.
Chaetomium abietinum Ell. & Ev.
Coniophora byssoidea (P.) ex Fr.
Discosia strobilina (Lib.) Fres.
Ganoderma Tsugae Murrill.
Herpotrichia nigra Hartig.
Hypochnus avellaneus Burt.
Lentinus lepideus Fr.
Lenzites sepiaria (Wulf.) ex Fr.
Nectria coccinea (P.) ex Fr.
Cenangium Abietis, var. strobilinum Sacc.
Ombrophila strobilina (Sacc.) Rehm.
Pestalozzia abietina Vogl.
Pestalozzia conorum-Piceae Tubeuf.
Pestalozzia Stevensonii Pk.
Pestalozzia strobilicola Speg.
Pestalozzia truncatula Farl. in N. A. F. an
Fckl.?
Phoma conophila Sacc.
Phoma lineolata Desm.
Phoma piceana Karst.
Phoma strobiligena Desm.
Sclerotinia fuckeliana DBy.
Sphaeropsis Pinastri (Lév.) Sacc., var. Abietis
Auct.

Uredinales

Chrysomyxa Abietis Auct. p. p.

Picea Abies (*cont.*)

Aecidium conorum-Piceae Reess.
Melampsoropsis Pyrolae (Rostr.) Arth. I.
Peridermium conorum Thm.
Peridermium conorum-Piceae (Reess) Arth. &
  Kern.
Peridermium abietinum Thm.
Aecidium coloradense Diet.
Peridermium boreale Arth. & Kern.
Peridermium coloradense (Diet.) Arth. &
  Kern.
Pucciniastrum sparsum (Wint.) E. Fischer. I.

Picea albertiana S. Brown.

Peridermium coloradense (Diet.) Arth. &
  Kern.

Picea canadensis (Mill.) BSP.

PHACIDIINEAE

Cenangium pithyum, B. & C.
Scleroderris pitya (B. & C.) Sacc.

UREDINALES

Melampsoropsis Cassandrae (Tranz.) Arth. I.
Peridermium consimile Arth. & Kern.
Peridermium boreale Arth. & Kern.
Peridermium coloradense (Diet.) Arth. & Kern
Melampsoropsis Pyrolae (Rostr.) Arth. I.
Peridermium conorum-Piceae (Reess) Arth. &
  Kern.
Melampsoropsis ledicola (Lagerh.) Arth. I.
Peridermium decolorans Pk.
Aecidium ingenuum Arth.
Peridermium ingenuum Arth.

HYMENOMYCETINEAE

Asterostroma corticola Massee.
Clitocybe sulfurea Pk.
Fomes applanatus (P. ex Wallr.) Gill.
Fomes Pini (Brot. ex Fr.) Karst.
Trametes Pini (Brot.) ex Fr.
Fomes pinicola (Sw. ex Fr.) Cke.
Polyporus pinicola Sw. ex Fr.
Fomes roseus (A. & S. ex Fr.) Cke.
Lenzites sepiaria (Wulf.) ex Fr.
Polyporus anceps Pk.
Polyporus borealis Fr.
Polyporus subacidus Pk.
Polyporus sulphureus (Bull.) ex Fr.
Polyporus tephroleucus Fr., var. scruposus
  Lloyd.
Coriolus abietinus (Dicks. ex Fr.) Quél.
Polystictus abietinus (Dicks. ex Fr.) Cke.
Poria incrassata (B. & C.) Burt.
Trametes carnea Auct. Amer.
Trametes subrosea Weir.

MISCELLANEA

Ascochyta piniperda Lindau.
Phragmotrichum Chailletii Kze.
Pythium debaryanum Hesse.

Picea concolor Gordon.
Aecidium elatinum A. & S.

Picea Engelmanni (Parry) Engelm.

PEZIZINEAE

Cenangium alpinum Ell. & Ev.
Dasyscypha arida (Phil.) Sacc.
Dasyscypha incarnata Clements.
Helotium sulphuratum (Schum.) Phil., var.
  Piceae Kauffman.
Ombrophila janthina (Karst.) Rehm.
Phialea subtilis (Hedw.) Rehm.
Lachnum Engelmanni Tracy & Earle.
Trichopeziza Engelmanni (Tracy & Earle)
  Sacc. & Syd.

HYSTERIINEAE

Lophodermium Abietis Rostr.
Lophodermium nervisequum (DC. ex Fr.)
  Rehm.

PYRENOMYCETINEAE

Gibberella Saubinetii (Mont.) Sacc.
Herpotrichia nigra Hartig.
Herpotrichia quinqueseptata Weir.
Nectria Cucurbitula (Tode) ex Fr.
Neopeckia Coulteri (Pk.) Sacc.
Rhopographus hysteriiformis (Karst.) Sacc.
Rosellinia parasitica Ell. & Ev.
Rosellinia thelena Rabh.
Rosellinia weiriana Sacc.

UREDINALES

Chrysomyxa Weirii H. S. Jackson. I.
Peridermium abietinum Thm.
Aecidium abietinum, var. Engelmanni Fung.
  Columb. *876.*
Aecidium coloradense Diet.
Peridermium abietinum, var. Engelmanni Ell.
  & Ev.
Peridermium boreale Arth. & Kern.
Peridermium coloradense (Diet.) Arth. &
  Kern.
Melampsoropsis Cassandrae Arth. I.
Aecidium Engelmanni (Thm.) Diet.
Melampsoropsis Pyrolae (Rostr.) Arth. I.
Peridermium conorum-Piceae (Reess) Arth. &
  Kern.
Peridermium Engelmanni Thm.
Melampsoropsis ledicola (Lagerh.) Arth. I.
Peridermium decolorans Pk.

TREMELLINEAE

Sebacina monticola Burt.

DACRYOMYCETINEAE

Guepinia alpina Tracy & Earle.
Guepinia monticola Tracy & Earle.

Picea Engelmanni (*cont.*)

THELEPHORACEAE

Coniophora arida Fr.
Coniophora corrugis Burt.
Corticium lividum P.
Corticium vagum B. & C.
Peniophora crassa Burt.
Peniophora globifera Ell. & Ev.
Stereum rugispora (Ell. & Ev.) Burt.
Stereum sanguinolentum Fr.
Stereum sulcatum Burt.
Thelephora terrestris Ehrh. ex Fr.

HYDNACEAE

Echinodontium tinctorium Ell. & Ev
Hydnum coralloides Scop. ex Fr.

POLYPORACEAE

Fomes annosus (Fr.) Cke.
Fomes applanatus (P. ex Wallr.) Gill.
{ Fomes Laricis (Jacq.) ex Murrill.
{ Fomes officinalis (Fr.) Lloyd.
{ Fomes Pini (Brot. ex Fr.) Karst.
{ Polyporus Pini (Thoré) ex P.
{ Trametes Pini (Brot.) ex Fr.
Fomes pinicola (Sw. ex Fr.) Cke.
Fomes putearius Weir.
Fomes roseus (A. & S. ex Fr.) Cke.
Lenzites sepiaria (Wulf.) ex Fr.
Merulius lacrimans (Wulf.) ex Fr.
Merulius squalidus Fr.
Polyporus alboluteus Ell.
Polyporus amorphus Fr.
Polyporus aurantiacus Pk.
Polyporus benzoinus Fr.
Polyporus borealis Fr.
Polyporus dryadeus (P.) ex Fr.
Polyporus osseus Fr.
Polyporus picipes Fr.
Polyporus Schweinitzii Fr.
Polyporus sulphureus (Bull.) ex Fr.
Polyporus umbellatus (P.) ex Fr.
Polyporus volvatus Pk.
Poria crustulina Bres.
Poria marginella Pk.
Poria monticola Murrill.
Poria obducens (Pk.) Cke.
Poria omaema B.
Poria pereffusa Murrill.
Poria subacida (Pk.) Sacc. Syll.
Poria violacea Fr.

FUNGI IMPERFECTI

Botrytis cinerea P. †
Cytosporella pinicola Ell. & Ev.
Fusarium elegans App. & Wr.
Fusarium Martii App. & Wr.
Fusarium moniliforme Sheldon.
Fusarium Solani App. & Wr.

Fusarium sporotrichioides Sherb.
Pestalozzia Hartigii Tubeuf.
Phomopsis juniperovora Hahn.
Tubercularia atomospora Sacc.

MISCELLANEA

Marasmius piceinus Kauffm.
Mitrula cucullata (Batsch) ex Fr.
Pythium debaryanum Hesse.
Rhizoctonia potomacensis Wollenw.
Sparassis radicata Weir.

Picea mariana (Mill.) B. S. P.

ASCOMYCETES

Chilonectria Cucurbitula Curr.
Dasyscypha calycina (Fr.) Fckl.
Lophodermium Abietis Rostr.
Lophodermium Pinastri (Schrad. ex Fr.) Chev.
Phacidium expansum J. J. Davis.
Stictis minuscula Karst.

UREDINALES

{ Melampsoropsis abietina Arth. I.
{ Peridermium abietinum (A. & S.) Thm.
Peridermium coloradense (Diet.) Arth. & Kern.
{ Peridermium coloradense (J. J. Davis non Diet.) Arth. & Kern.
{ Peridermium elatinum A. & S.
{ Chrysomyxa Pyrolae Rostr. I.
{ Melampsoropsis Pyrolae (Rostr.) Arth. I.
{ Peridermium conorum-Piceae (Reess) Arth. & Kern.
{ Chrysomyxa Cassandrae Tranz. I.
{ Melampsoropsis Cassandrae (Tranz.) Arth. I.
{ Peridermium consimile Arth. & Kern.
{ Aecidium abietinum Auct. Amer. p. p.
{ Chrysomyxa ledicola Lagerh. I.
{ Melampsoropsis ledicola (Lagerh.) Arth. I.
{ Peridermium abietinum Auct. Amer. p. p.
{ Peridermium abietinum, var. decolorans (Pk.) Thm.
{ Peridermium decolorans Pk.

TREMELLACEAE

{ Auricularia Auricula-judae Fr.
{ Hirneola Auricula-judae (L.) ex Fr.

THELEPHORACEAE

Corticium cremoricolor B. & C.
Corticium subaurantiacum Pk.
Corticium subincarnatum Pk.
Corticium sulphureum Fr.
Hymenochaete abnormis Pk.
Peniophora cinerea (Fr.) Cke.
Stereum abietinum (P.) ex Fr.
Stereum ambiguum Pk.
Stereum radiatum Pk.
Stereum rugosum Fr.
Thelephora terrestris Ehrh. ex Fr.

Picea mariana (*cont.*)

HYDNACEAE

Caldesiella ferruginosa Sacc.
Hydnum farinaceum Fr.
Hydnum serratum Pk.
Irpex fuscoviolaceus (Schrad.) ex Fr.
Mucronella calva (A. & S.) Fr.
Odontia fusca C. & E.

POLYPORACEAE

{ Cryptoporus volvatus (Pk.) Hubbard.
{ Fomes volvatus (Pk.) Cke.
{ Polyporus volvatus Pk.
Fomes annosus (Fr.) Cke.
Fomes officinalis Fr.
{ Fomes Pini (Brot. ex Fr.) Karst.
{ Polyporus piceinus Pk.
{ Porodaedalea Pini (Brot. ex Fr.) Murrill.
Trametes piceina Pk.
Trametes Pini (Brot.) ex Fr.
{ Fomes Pini (Fr.) Karst., var. Abietis (Karst.)
{   Overholts.
{ Mucronoporus Abietis (Karst.) Ell. & Ev.
{ Trametes Abietis (Karst.) Sacc.
{ Trametes Pini (Brot.) ex Fr., var. Abietis
{   (Karst.) v. Schrenk.
{ Fomes pinicola (Sw. ex Fr.) Cke.
{ Polyporus pinicola Sw. ex Fr.
Fomes roseus (A. & S. ex Fr.) Cke.
Lenzites heteromorpha Fr.
{ Gloeophyllum hirsutum (Schaeff.) ex Murrill.
{ Lenzites sepiaria (Wulf.) ex Fr.
Merulius molluscus Fr.
Merulius Ravenelii B.
Polyporus aurantiacus Pk.
Polyporus borealis Fr.
Polyporus cincinnatus Morg.
Polyporus dualis Pk.
Polyporus guttulatus Pk.
{ Polyporus fissus B.
{ Polyporus picipes Fr.
Polyporus Schweinitzii Fr.
Polystictus abietinus (Fr.) Cke.
{ Polyporus balsameus Pk.
{ Polystictus balsameus (Pk.) Cke.
{ Polyporus variiformis Pk.
{ Polystictus variiformis (Pk.) Sacc.
{ Trametes variiformis Pk.
Polystictus variiformis (Pk.) Sacc., var. inter-
  ruptus (Pk.) Sacc., var. nodulosus (Pk.)
  Sacc., var. resupinatus (Pk.) Sacc.
{ Coriolus versicolor (L. ex Fr.) Quél.
{ Polystictus versicolor (L.) ex Fr.
{ Polyporus marginellus Pk.
{ Poria marginella Pk.
Poria mutans Pk.
Poria mutans, var. tenuis Pk.
Poria odora Pk.

{ Polyporus subacidus Pk.
{ Poria subacida (Pk.) Sacc. Syll.
{ Polyporus vaporarius Fr.
{ Poria vaporaria (Fr.) Cke.
{ Polyporus violaceus Fr.
{ Poria violacea (Fr.) Cke.
Poria vulgaris Fr.
{ Fomes carneus Auct. Amer.
{ Polyporus carneus Auct. Amer.
{ Polyporus Palliseri B.
{ Trametes carnea Lloyd.
{ Trametes subrosea Weir.
Trametes serpens Fr.

AGARICACEAE

Armillaria mellea (Vahl) ex Fr.
Clitocybe sulphurea Pk.
Lentinus lepideus Fr.
Marasmius perforans (Hoffm.) ex Fr.
Mycena hiemalis (Osbeck) ex Fr.
Mycena purpureofusca Pk.
{ Omphalia Austini Pk.
{ Omphalopsis Austini (Pk.) Murrill.
Schizophyllum commune Fr.

FUNGI IMPERFECTI

Cladosporium entoxylinum Cda.
Epicoccum diversisporum Preuss.
Hypodermium sparsum Lk.
Pestalozzia lignicola Cke.
Phragmotrichum Chailletii Kze.
Scleroderma vulgare Hornem.
Stilbum glomerulisporum Ell. & Ev.

Picea parryana (Andre) Parry.

{ Dasyscypha fuscosanguinea Rehm.
{ Peziza arida Phil.
{ Peziza fuscosanguinea N. A. F. *2146*.
Fomes pinicola (Sw. ex Fr.) Cke.
Fomes roseus (A. & S. ex Fr.) Cke.
Melampsoropsis Cassandrae (Tranz.) Arth. I.
Melampsoropsis ledicola (Lagerh.) Arth. I.
Peridermium abietinum Thm.
{ Aecidium coloradense Diet.
{ Peridermium boreale Arth. & Kern.
{ Peridermium coloradense (Diet.) Arth. & Kern.
Peridermium conorum-Piceae (Reess) Arth. &
  Kern.
Pestalozzia scirrofaciens N. A. Brown.
Polyporus Schweinitzii Fr.
Pythium debaryanum Hesse.

Picea rubra (DuRoi) Dietr.

UREDINALES

{ Melampsoropsis abietina Arth. I.
{ Peridermium abietinum Thm.
{ Peridermium boreale Kern.
{ Peridermium coloradense (Diet.) Arth. & Kern.
Peridermium conorum-Piceae (Reess) Arth. &
  Kern.

Picea rubra (*cont.*)

{ Melampsoropsis Cassandrae (Tranz.) Arth. I.
Peridermium consimile Arth. & Kern.
{ Melampsoropsis ledicola (Lagerh.) Arth. I.
Peridermium decolorans Pk.
Melampsoropsis Pyrolae (Rostr.) Arth.

HYMENOMYCETINEAE

Corticium vinososcabens Burt.
Fomes applanatus (P. ex Wallr.) Gill.
{ Fomes Pini (Brot. ex Fr.) Karst.
Trametes Pini (Brot.) ex Fr.
{ Fomes pinicola (Sw. ex Fr.) Cke.
Polyporus pinicola Sw. ex Fr.
Fomes roseus (A. & S. ex Fr.) Cke.
Hymenochaete abnormis Pk.
Lentinus lepideus Fr.
Lentinus piceinus Pk.
Lenzites sepiaria (Wulf.) ex Fr.
Lophodermium Abietis Rostr.
{ Polyporus borealis Fr.
Spongipellis borealis (Fr.) Pat.
Polyporus dichrous Fr.
Polyporus Schweinitzii Fr.
Polyporus ursinus Lloyd.
Polyporus volvatus Pk.
{ Coriolus abietinus (Fr.) Quél.
Polyporus abietinus (Dicks.) ex Fr.
Polystictus abietinus (Fr.) Cke.
{ Polystictus cinnabarinus (Jacq. ex Fr.) Cke.
Pycnoporus cinnabarinus (Jacq. ex Fr.) Karst.
Poria incrassata (B. & C.) Burt.
Schizophyllum commune Fr.
Trametes Abietis (Karst.) Sacc.
Trametes variiformis Pk.

FUNGI IMPERFECTI

Ascochyta piniperda Lindau.
Illosporium coccinellum Cke.
Phoma piceina Pk.

= **Picea sitchensis** Carr.

Aleurodiscus subincrustatus (B. & C.) Burt.
Ascochyta piniperda Lindau.
Chrysomyxa ledicola Lagerh. I.
Fomes applanatus (P. ex Wallr.) Gill.
{ Fomes Laricis (Jacq.) ex Murrill.
Fomes officinalis (Fr.) Lloyd.
{ Fomes Pini (Brot. ex Fr.) Karst.
Trametes Pini (Brot.) ex Fr.
Fomes pinicola (Sw. ex Fr.) Cke.
Fomes roseus (A. & S. ex Fr.) Cke.
Ganoderma oregonense Murrill.
Lentinus lepideus Fr.
Lenzites sepiaria (Wulf.) ex Fr.
Lenzites trabea P. ex Fr.
Lophodermium Pinastri (Schrad. ex Fr.) Chev.
Peniophora globifera Ell. & Ev.
Melampsoropsis Cassandrae (Tranz.) Arth. I.
Peridermium coloradense (Diet.) Arth. & Kern.

{ Melampsoropsis ledicola (Lagerh.) Arth. I.
Peridermium decolorans Pk.
Peziza fuscosanguinea (Rehm) Ell. & Ev.
Polyporus anceps Pk.
Polyporus Berkeleyi Fr.
Polyporus caesius (Schrad.) ex Fr.
Polyporus Schweinitzii Fr.
{ Polyporus versicolor (L.) ex Fr.
Polystictus versicolor (L.) ex Fr.
Poria incrassata (B. & C.) Burt.
Poria crustulina Bres.
Pythium debaryanum Hesse.
Sporonema strobilinum Desm.

Picea sp. indet.

PEZIZINEAE

Dasyscypha bicolor (Bull. ex Fr.) Fckl.
Dasyscypha flavovirens Bres.
Lachnellula microspora Ell. & Ev.
Scutellinia chaetoloma Clements.
Scutellinia irregularis Clements.
Vibrissea truncorum (A. & S.) ex Fr.

PHACIDIINEAE

Colpoma morbidum Sacc.

HYSTERIINEAE

Hypodermella macrospora (Hartig) Lagerberg.
Hysterographium insidens (S.) Sacc.
Lophium mytilinum (P.) ex Fr.
Lophodermium Abietis Rostr.

PYRENOMYCETINEAE

Amphisphaeria oronoensis (Ell. & Ev.) Sacc.
Hypoxylon ohiense Ell. & Ev.
Melanopsamma alpina Ell. & Ev.
Melanopsamma borealis Ell. & Ev.
{ Thyridella canadensis (Ell. & Ev.) Sacc.
Thyridium canadense Ell. & Ev.

UREDINALES

Chrysomyxa Rhododendri (DC.) DBy.

THELEPHORACEAE

Aleurodiscus amorphus (P.) Rabh.
Aleurodiscus penicillatus Burt.
Asterostroma bicolor Ell. & Ev.
Asterostroma corticola Massee.
Coniophora puteana (Schum.) ex Fr.
Corticium albulum Atk. & Burt.
Corticium erimineum Burt.
Corticium portentosum B. & C.
Corticium rubicundum Burt.
Corticium tessulatum Cke.
Hydnochaete setigera Pk.
Hypochnus tristis Karst.
Peniophora alba Burt.
Peniophora carnosa Burt.
Peniophora subincarnata (Pk.) Burt.
Peniophora sulphurina (Karst.) v. Höhnel &
Litschauer.

Picea sp. indet. (*cont.*)
Porothelium subtile (Schrad.) ex Fr.
Sebacina calcea (P.) Bres.
Stereum radiatum Pk., var. reflexum Pk.
Stereum tuberculosum Fr.
Thelephora laciniata Fr.

CLAVARIACEAE
Sparassis radicata Weir.

POLYPORACEAE
Fomes carneus, var. granularis Pk. & var. sub-
  zonatus Pk.
{ Fomes fuliginosus (Scop. ex Fr.) Cke.
{ Ischnoderma fuliginosum (Scop. ex Fr.) Murrill.
Fomes ungulatus (Schaeff.) ex Sacc.
Ganoderma nevadense Murrill.
Merulius bellus B. & C.
Polyporus galactinus B.
{ Polyporus leucospongia Cke. & Hark.
{ Spongiporus leucospongia (Cke. & Hark.)
{   Murrill.
Polyporus Schweinitzii Fr., var. hispidioides Pk.
Polyporus Weinmanni Fr.
Poria cinerea S.
Poria ferruginosa Fr.
Poria Medulla-panis (P. ex Fr.) Cke.
Poria odora (Pk.) Sacc.
Poria rufa Schrt.
Poria subacida (Pk.) Sacc. Syll.
Poria taxicola (P.) Bres.
Poria undata (P.) Bres.
Poria vaporaria (P.) Fr.
{ Trametes odorata Auct. Amer.
{ Trametes protracta Fr.
Trametes sepium B.
Trametes serialis Fr.
Trametes serialis Fr., var. resupinata Romell.
{ Fomes carneus Auct. Amer.
{ Trametes subrosea Weir.

AGARICACEAE
Claudopus nidulans (Fr.) Pk.
Claudopus multiformis Murrill.
Clitocybe decora Fr.
Collybia stipitaria Fr.
{ Flammula piceina Murrill.
{ Gymnopilus piceinus Murrill.
Hypholoma capnoides Fr.
Inocybe flocculosa B.
Marasmius androsaceus Fr.
Marasmius perforans Fr.
Marasmius prasiosmus Fr.
Omphalia aurantiaca Pk.
Omphalopsis Campanella (Batsch ex Fr.) Earle.
Paxillus atrotomentosus Fr.
Paxillus corrugatus Atk.

MISCELLANEA
Badhamia decipiens (M. A. Curtis) B.
Botrytis cinerea P.†

Coryneum abietinum Ell. & Ev.
Didymium melanospermum (P.) Macbr.
Didymium squamulosum (A. & S.) Fr.
Helicobasidium Peckii Burt.
Leptostromella conigena Dearness.
Pestalozzia funerea Desm.
Phlebia centrifuga Karst.
Phoma piceina Pk.
Sebacina calcea (P.) Bres.
Sphaerobolus carpobolus (L.) Schrt.
Torula ligniperda (Willk.) Sacc.
Tsuga Canadensis (L.) Carr. Including "Hem-
  lock," also Tsuga sp. indet. in regions
  where no other Tsuga is known.

MYXOMYCETES
Ceratiomyxa porioides (A. & S.) Schrt.
Cribraria macrocarpa Schrad.
Cribraria tenella Schrad.
Cytidium globuliferum Bull.
Leocarpus fragilis (Dicks.) Rostf.
Lindbladia effusa (Ehrb.) Rostf.
Physarum globuliferum (Bull.) Rostf.
Tubifera ferruginea (Batsch) Macbr.

ASCOMYCETES
Agyrium rufum (P.) Fr.
Cenangium balsameum Pk.
{ Cenangium balsameum Pk., var. abietinum Pk.
{ Gelatinosporium abietinum Pk.
Cenangium leptospermum B. & C.
Cenangium Pinastri (P.) ex Fr.
Chlorosplenium aeruginosum (Oeder) DeNot.
{ Chlorosplenium elatinum (A. & S. ex Fr.) Sacc.
{ Peziza elatina A. & S. ex Fr.
{ Dasyscypha chamaeleontina (Pk.) Sacc.
{ Peziza chamaeleontina Pk.
{ Discina Warnei (Pk.) Sacc.
{ Peziza Warnei Pk.
{ Rhizina helvetica Fckl.
Helvella infula Schaeff. ex Fr.
{ Hypoderma brachysporum (Rostr.) v. Tubeuf.
{ Lophodermium brachysporum Rostr.
{ Keithia Tsugae (Farl.) Durand.
{ Propolidium Tsugae (Farl.) Sacc.
{ Stictis Tsugae Farl.
Otidea onotica (P. ex Fr.) Fckl., var. ochracea
  (Fr.) Sacc.
Pezizella Fairmani Rehm.
{ Peziza pitya P.
{ Pitya vulgaris (P.) Fckl.
{ Sarea pitya (P.) Fr.
{ Bulgaria deligata Pk.
{ Peziza leucobasis Pk.
{ Pyronema leucobasis (Pk.) Sacc.
Tapesia fusca (P.) Fckl.

SPHAERIALES
Acanthostigma parasiticum (Hartig) Sacc.
{ Acanthostigma Scopula (C. & P.) Pk.
{ Sphaeria Scopula C. & P.

Tsuga canadensis (*cont.*)
Amphisphaeria abietina Fairman.
Amphisphaeria vestigialis Fairman.
Asterina nuda Pk.
Melanomma pulvispyrius (P. ex Fr.) Fckl.
{ Leptostroma laricinum Fckl
{ Mycosphaerella laricina (Fckl.) Dearness.
{ Sphaerella conicola Ell. & Ev. non Sacc.
{ Sphaerella conigena Pk. 38 Rept.
{ Sphaerella Peckii Sacc.
{ Sphaerella Tsugae House.
{ Mycosphaerella Peckii (Sacc.) Lindau.
{ Mycosphaerella Tsugae House.
{ Sphaeria livida P. †
{ Thyridium lividum (P.) ex Sacc.
Ustulina vulgaris Tul.
Valsa Abietis Fr.
Xylaria corniformis Fr.

UREDINALES
Chrysomyxa Abietis (Wallr.) Ung.
{ Melampsora Farlowii (Arth.) J. J. Davis.
{ Necium Farlowii Arth.
{ Caeoma Abietis-canadensis Farl.
{ Caeoma Tsugae Spaulding nom. nud.
{ Melampsora Abietis-canadensis C. A.
    Ludwig. I.
Melampsora Medusae Fraser. I.
Melampsora Populi-Tsugae J. J. Davis. I.
Peridermium fructigenum Arth.
Uredo Abietis-canadensis Cke.
{ Peridermium Hydrangeae Adams.
{ Pucciniastrum Hydrangeae (Farl.) Arth. I.
{ Aecidium Peckii (Thm.) Diet.
{ Peridermium Peckii Thm.
{ Pucciniastrum minimum Arth. I.
{ Pucciniastrum Myrtilli Arth. I.
{ Thekopsora minima (Arth.) Syd. I.

PROTOBASIDIOMYCETES
Dacryomyces corticioides Ell. & Ev.
Dacryomyces deliquescens Duby.
Dacryomyces stillatus Nees ex Fr.
Ditiola radicata (A. & S.) ex Fr.
Eichleriella leveilliana (B. & C.) Burt.
Sebacina calcea (P.) Bres.
Tremella aurantia S.
Tremella lutescens (P.) ex Fr.
Tremella mesenterica Retz.
Tremellodon gelatinosum (Scop.) ex Fr.

THELEPHORACEAE
{ Aleurodiscus amorphus (P. ex Fr.) Rabh.
{ Corticium amorphum (P.) ex Fr.
Aleurodiscus Farlowii Burt.
{ Coniophora cerebella P.
{ Coniophora puteana Fr.
Coniophora puteana Fr., var. rimosa Pk.
{ Coniophora olivascens (B. & C.) Massee.
{ Corticium chlorinum B. & C.

Coniophora Kalmiae (Pk.) Burt.
Coniophora polyporoidea (B. & C.) Burt.
{ Coniophora suffocata (Pk.) Massee.
{ Corticium suffocatum Pk.
Corticium alboflavescens Ell. & Ev.
Corticium ochraceum Fr.
Corticium pilosum Burt.
Corticium Pseudotsugae Burt.
Corticium rubicundum Burt.
Corticium tessulatum Cke.
Corticium Tsugae Burt.
Corticium vagum B. & C.
Corticium vinososcabens Burt.
Hymenochaete agglutinans Ell.
Hymenochaete tabacina (Sow. ex Fr.) Lév.
Hymenochaete tenuis Pk.
Peniophora crassa Burt.
Peniophora gigantea (Fr.) Massee.
Peniophora glebulosa (Fr.) Bres.
{ Corticium Petersii B. & C. p.p.
{ Peniophora sanguinea (Fr.) Bres.
Peniophora serialis (Bres.) v. Höhnel &
    Litschauer.
Solenia candida P.
Solenia villosa P.
Solenia villosa Fr., var. polyporoidea Pk.
Stereum frustulosum Fr.
Stereum hirsutum (Willd.) ex Fr.
{ Stereum Murrayi (B. & C.) Burt.
{ Stereum tuberculosum Fr.
Stereum radiatum Pk.
Stereum rugosum Fr.
Stereum sanguinolentum (A. & S.) ex Fr.
Stereum sulcatum Burt.

CLAVARIACEAE
Clavaria abietina Fr.
Clavaria tsugina Pk.

HYDNACEAE
{ Echinodontium tinctorium Ell. & Ev.
{ Fomes tinctorius Ell. & Ev.
Grandinia virescens Pk.
Hydnum arachnoideum Pk.
Hydnum farinaceum P. ex Fr.
Hydnum scabripes Pk.
Irpex mollis B. & C.
Irpex sinuosus Fr.
Irpex tabacinus B. & C.
Mucronella aggregata Fr.
Mucronella calva (A. & S.) ex Fr.
Odontia farinacea Fr.
Radulum Pini-canadensis S.

POLYPORACEAE
{ Fomes annosus (Fr.) Cke.
{ Elfvingia megaloma (Lév.) Murrill.
{ Fomes applanatus (P. ex Wallr.) Gill.
{ Polyporus applanatus (P.) ex Wallr.

Tsuga canadensis (*cont.*)
  Fomes applanatus (P. ex Wallr.) Gill., var.
    abietinus Thm.
  Fomes fomentarius (L. ex Fr.) Gill.
  ⎰Fomes lucidus (Leyss. ex Fr.) Cke.
  ⎱Ganoderma lucidum (Leyss. ex Fr.) Karst.
  ⎰Polyporus lucidus (Leyss.) ex Fr.
  Fomes officinalis Fr.
  ⎰Fomes Pini (Brot. ex Fr.) Karst.
  ⎱Trametes Pini (Brot.) ex Fr.
  Trametes Pini, var. Abietis Karst.
  Fomes marginatus (Fr.) ex Gill.
  ⎰Fomes pinicola (Sw. ex Fr.) Cke.
  ⎱Polyporus pinicola Sw. ex Fr.
  ⎰Fomes ungulatus Schaeff. ex Sacc.
  ⎱Fomes ungulatus, var. pinicola (Fr.) Neuman.
  Fomes roseus (Fr.) Cke.
  Fomes salicinus (P. ex Fr.) Cke.
  ⎰Fomes Tsugae (Murrill) Sacc. & D. Sacc.
  ⎱Ganoderma Tsugae Murrill.
  ⎱Polyporus Tsugae (Murrill) Overholts.
  Lenzites abietina (Bull.) ex Fr.
  Lenzites betulina (L.) ex Fr.
  Lenzites sepiaria (Wulf.) ex Fr.
  Lenzites vialis Pk.
  Merulius bellus B. & C.
  Merulius himantioides Fr.
  ⎰Merulius lacrimans Fr.
  ⎱Merulius lacrymans Fr.
  Merulius molluscus Fr.
  Merulius subaurantiacus Pk.
  Merulius tremellosus Schrad. ex Fr.
  Polyporus amorphus Fr.
  ⎰Polyporus anceps Pk.
  ⎱Tyromyces anceps (Pk.) Murrill.
  Polyporus aurantiacus Pk.
  ⎰Polyporus benzoinus (Wahlenb.) ex Fr.
  ⎱Trametes benzoinus (Wahlenb.) ex Fr.
  ⎰Polyporus borealis Fr.
  ⎱Spongipellis borealis (Fr.) Pat.
  ⎰Polyporus caesius (Schrad.) ex Fr.
  ⎱Tyromyces caesius (Fr.) Murrill.
  ⎰Polyporus crispellus Pk.
  ⎱Tyromyces balsameus (Pk.) Murrill.
  ⎱Tyromyces crispellus (Pk.) Murrill.
  ⎰Aurantiporus Pilotae (S.) Murrill.
  ⎱Fomes Pini-canadensis (S.) Cke.
  Polyporus croceus (P.) ex Fr.
  Polyporus hypococcinus B.
  Polyporus Pilotae S.
  Polyporus Pini-canadensis S.
  Polyporus epileucus Fr.
  Polyporus epileucus Fr., var. candidus Pk.
  ⎰Polyporus fragilis Fr.
  ⎱Spongipellis fragilis (Fr.) Murrill.
  ⎰Ischnoderma fuliginosum (Scop. ex Fr.) Murrill.
  ⎱Polyporus fuliginosum (Scop.) ex Fr.

  ⎰Bjerkandera fumosa (P. ex Fr.) Karst.
  ⎱Polyporus fumosus (P.) ex Fr.
  Polyporus giganteus (P.) ex Fr.
  ⎰Hapalopilus gilvus (S.) Murrill.
  ⎱Polyporus gilvus S.
  ⎰Polyporus guttulatus Pk.
  ⎱Polyporus maculatus Pk.
  ⎱Tyromyces guttulatus (Pk.) Murrill.
  Polyporus lucidus Auct. p. p.
  ⎰Polyporus mollis (P.) ex Fr.
  ⎱Polyporus Weinmanni Fr.
  ⎰Polyporus nidulans Fr.
  ⎱Polyporus rutilans Fr.
  ⎰Polyporus brumalis P. ex Fr.
  ⎱Polyporus Polyporus Murrill.
  Polyporus resinosus Fr.
  ⎰Phaeolus sistotremoides (A. & S. ex Fr.)
    Murrill.
  Polyporus Schweinitzii Fr.
  Polyporus spumeus Fr.
  ⎰Polyporus subpendulus (Atk.) Sacc. & Trott.
  ⎱Tyromyces subpendulus Atk.
  Polyporus sulphureus (Bull.) ex Fr.
  ⎰Polyporus undosus Pk.
  ⎱Tyromyces undosus (Pk.) Murrill.
  ⎰Polyporus fibrillosus Karst.
  ⎱Polystictus fibrillosus (Karst.) B. O. Dodge.
  ⎱Pycnoporellus fibrillosus (Karst.) Murrill.
  ⎰Coriolus nigromarginatus S.
  ⎱Polystictus hirsutus (Wulf.) ex Fr.
  ⎰Coriolus prolificans (Fr.) Murrill.
  ⎱Coriolus Sartwellii (B. & C.) Murrill.
  ⎱Polyporus Sartwellii B. & C.
  Polystictus pargamenus Fr.
  Polystictus pergamenus Fr.
  ⎰Coriolus versicolor (L. ex Fr.) Quél.
  ⎱Polyporus versicolor (L.) ex Fr.
  Poria attenuata Pk.
    var. subincarnata (Pk.) Murrill.
  Poria ferruginosa Fr.
  Poria incrassata (B. & C.) Burt.
  Poria laevigata Fr.
  Poria Macounii (Pk.) Overholts.
  ⎰Polyporus Medulla-panis (P.) ex Fr.
  ⎱Poria Medulla-panis (P. ex Fr.) Cke.
  ⎰Polyporus rhodellus Fr.
  ⎱Poria rhodella Fr.
  Poria salmonicolor B. & C.
  Polyporus subacidus Pk.
  Poria subacida (Pk.) Sacc. Syll.
  Polyporus subacidus Pk., var. tenuis Pk.
  Poria subacida (Pk.) Sacc. Syll., var. tenuis
    (Pk.) Sacc. Syll.
  Poria tomentocincta B. & Rav. sec. Cke.
  ⎰Fomitiporia tsugina Murrill.
  ⎱Poria tsugina (Murrill) Sacc. & Trott.
  ⎰Polyporus Vaillantii (DC.) ex Fr.
  ⎱Poria Vaillantii (DC. ex Fr.) Cke.

Tsuga canadensis (*cont.*)
{ Polyporus vulgaris Fr.
{ Poria vulgaris (Fr.) Cke.
 Porothelium fimbriatum Fr.
{ Lenzites heteromorpha Fr.
{ Trametes heteromorpha (Fr.) Bres.
 Trametes odorata (Wulf.) ex Fr.
{ Coriolellus sepium (B.) Murrill.
{ Trametes favescens (S.) Lloyd.
{ Trametes sepium B.

AGARICACEAE

Armillaria mellea (Vahl) ex Fr.
Clitocybe ectypoides Pk.
Collybia abundans Pk.
{ Collybia exsculpta Fr.
{ Gymnopus exsculptus (Fr.) Murrill.
Collybia familia Pk.
Collybia hirticeps Pk.
Collybia myriadophylla Pk.
Collybia platyphylla Fr.
Collybia rugosodisca Pk.
Collybia succosa Pk.
Collybia zonata Pk.
{ Flammula aromatica Murrill.
{ Gymnopilus aromaticus Murrill.
{ Flammula pulchrifolius Pk.
{ Gymnopilus pulchrifolius (Pk.) Murrill.
Lentinus lepideus Fr.
Lepiota adnatifolia Pk.
Marasmius filipes Pk.
Marasmius perforans (Hoffm.) ex Fr.
{ Mycena atro-umbonata Pk.
{ Prunulus atro-umbonatus (Pk.) Murrill.
Mycena epipterygia (Scop.) ex Fr.
Mycena haematopa Fr.
Mycena leaiana B.
{ Mycena lepiotiformis Murrill.
{ Prunulus lepiotiformis Murrill.
Mycena purpureofusca Pk.
{ Galactopus rugosodiscus (Pk.) Murrill.
{ Mycena rugosodisca (Pk.) Sacc. Syll.
{ Omphalia rugosodisca Pk.
Mycena subincarnata Pk.
Naucoria bellula Pk.
Naucoria geminella Pk.
{ Omphalia Campanella (Batsch) ex Fr.
{ Omphalopsis Campanella (Batsch ex Fr.) Earle.
{ Agaricus lilacinus Pk.
{ Omphalia lilacifolia Pk.
{ Omphalina lilacifolia (Pk.) Murrill.
{ Gymnopus Oculus (Pk.) Murrill.
{ Omphalia Oculus Pk.
Panus dorsalis (Bosc) Fr.
Panus lacunosus Pk.
Panus stipticus (Bull.) ex Fr.
Paxillus atrotomentosus (Batsch) ex Fr.
Paxillus corrugatus Atk.
Paxillus panuoides Fr.

Pholiota curvipes Pk.
Pleurotus albolanatus Pk.
Pleurotus candidissimus B. & C.
Pleurotus fimbriatus Fr., var. regularis Kauffm.
{ Geopetalum abietinum (Schrad. ex Fr.) Murrill.
{ Pleurotus porrigens (P.) ex Fr.
Pleurotus serotinus (Schrad.) ex Fr.
Pleurotus striatulus (P.) ex Fr.
Pleurotus sulfureoides Pk.
Pluteus tomentosulus Pk.
Tricholoma decorosum Pk.
Tricholoma multipunctum Pk.
Tricholoma resplendens Fr.
Tricholoma rutilans (Schaeff.) ex Fr.

SPHAEROPSIDALES

Cytospora Curreyi Sacc.
Excipulina obscura Pk.
Phoma Libertiana Speg. & Roum.
Phomopsis juniperovora Hahn.
Phomopsis juniperovora Hahn, var. A.
Sphaeronema truncatum Fr.

MELANCONIALES

Coryneum cupulatum Ell. & Ev.
{ Cryptosporium noveboracense B. & C.
{ Isaria monilioides, var. b. S. Syn. Car.
Gelatinosporium abietinum Pk.
Pestalozzia funerea Desm.

HYPHOMYCETES

Botrytis ceratioides Pk.
Botrytis lilacina S.
Cephalotrichum monilioides Lk.
{ Helicosporium ellipticum Pk.
{ Helicoön ellipticum (Pk.) Morg.
Helicosporium olivaceum Pk.
Helminthosporium stromatoideum Dearness.
Microcera erumpens Ell. & Ev.
{ Fusarium capitatum S.
{ Pionnotes capitata (S.) Fr.
Sporidesmium caespitosum Ell. & Ev.
Sporidesmium toruloides Ell. & Ev.
Torula colliculosa B. & C.
Torula colliculosa B. & C., var. orbicularis Pk.
Torula ligniperda (Willk.) Sacc.

Tsuga caroliniana Engelm.
{ Peridermium Peckii Thm.
{ Pucciniastrum minimum Arth. I.
{ Pucciniastrum Myrtilli Arth. I.

Tsuga heterophylla (Raf.) Sarg.

ASCOMYCETES

Dimerosporium Tsugae Dearness.
Herpotrichia nigra Hartig.
Microthyrium Harrimani Sacc.
Rhizina inflata Schaeff. ex Quél.

Tsuga heterophylla (*cont.*)

UREDINALES

{ Caeoma Abietis-canadensis Farl.
Caeoma dubium C. A. Ludwig.
Peridermium Peckii Thm.
Uredo Holwayi Arth.

HYMENOMYCETINEAE

Aleurodiscus penicillatus Burt.
Armillaria mellea (Vahl) ex Fr.
Coniophora cerebella P.
Echinodontium tinctorium Ell. & Ev.
Peniophora globifera Ell. & Ev.
Pholiota adiposa Fr.
Schizophyllum commune Fr.
Stereum hirsutum (Willd.) ex Fr.
Stereum sanguinolentum (A. & S.) ex Fr.
Stereum sulcatum Burt.

POLYPORACEAE

{ Cryptoporus volvatus (Pk.) Hubbard.
Polyporus volvatus Pk.
Fomes annosus (Fr.) Cke.
{ Fomes Laricis (Jacq.) ex Murrill.
Fomes officinalis Fr.
{ Fomes Pini (Brot. ex Fr.) Karst.
Trametes Pini (Brot.) ex Fr.
Fomes pinicola (Sw. ex Fr.) Cke.
Fomes roseus (A. & S. ex Fr.) Cke.
{ Fomes applanatus (P. ex Wallr.) Gill.
Fomes leucophaeus Mont.
Ganoderma applanatum (P. ex Wallr.) Pat.
Ganoderma Tsugae Murrill.
Lenzites heteromorpha Fr.
Lenzites sepiaria (Wulf.) ex Fr.
Polyporus benzoinus Fr.
Polyporus borealis Fr.
Polyporus caesius (Schrad.) ex Fr.
Polyporus chioneus Fr.
Polyporus dichrous Fr.
{ Inonotus dryadeus (P. ex Fr.) Murrill.
Polyporus dryadeus (P.) ex Fr.
Polyporus elegans (Bull.) ex Fr.
{ Polyporus perdelicatus Murrill.
Tyromyces perdelicatus Murrill.
Polyporus Schweinitzii Fr.
Polyporus sulphureus (Bull.) ex Fr.
{ Coriolus abietinus (Dicks. ex Fr.) Quél.
Polyporus abietinus (Dicks.) ex Fr.
Polystictus abietinus Dicks. ex Fr.
Polystictus aurantiacus Pk.
Polystictus versicolor (L.) ex Fr.
Poria dichroa Bres.
Poria incrassata (B. & C.) Burt.
{ Trametes carnea Auct. Amer. p. p.
Trametes subrosea Weir.

FUNGI IMPERFECTI

Aschersonia Aleyrodis Webber.
Botrytis Douglasii v. Tubeuf.
Phomopsis Pseudotsugae M. Wilson.

Tsuga mertensiana (Bong.) Carr.
Anthostomella brachystoma Ell. & Ev.
Blitrydium signatum Sacc.
Dasyscypha arida (Phil.) Sacc.
Echinodontium tinctorium Ell. & Ev.
{ Fomes Laricis (Jacq.) ex Murrill.
Fomes officinalis Fr.
{ Fomes Pini (Brot. ex Fr.) Karst.
Trametes Pini (Brot.) ex Fr.
Fomes pinicola (Sw. ex Fr.) Cke.
Herpotrichia nigra Hartig.
Lachnellula chrysophthalma (P.) Karst.
Lasiosphaeria stuppea Ell. & Ev.
Microthyrium Harrimani Sacc.
Neopeckia Coulteri (Pk.) Sacc.
Polyporus benzoinus Fr.
Polyporus dryadeus (P.) ex Fr.
Polyporus lucidus (Leyss.) ex Fr.
Polyporus Schweinitzii Fr.
Poria attenuata Pk.
Poria incrassata (B. & C.) Burt.
Pythium debaryanum Hesse.
Sporonema strobilinum Desm.
Xyloschizon weirianum Syd.

Tsuga sp. indet.
Asterodon ferruginosum Pat.
Asterodon setigera Pk.
Corticium galactinum (Fr.) Burt.
Dacryomyces hyalinus Quél.
Hypochnus olivaceus (B. & C.) Burt
Lentinus ursinus Fr.
Mitrula cucullata (Batsch) ex Fr.
Panus angustatus B.
Paxillus corrugatus Atk.
Pholiota albocrenulata Pk.
Pleurotus albolanatus Pk.
Pleurotus fimbriatus Fr., var. regularis Kauff-
man.
{ Ganoderma oregonense Murrill.
Polyporus oregonensis Murrill.
{ Polystictus cinnabarinus (Jacq. ex Fr.) Cke.
Pycnoporus cinnabarinus (Jacq. ex Fr.) Karst.
Poria aurea Pk.
Poria candidissima (S.) Cke.
Poria eupora, var. subincarnata (Pk.) Murrill.
Poria laetifica (Pk.) Sacc.
Poria myceliosa Pk.
Poria undata Lloyd.
Reticularia Lycoperdon Bull.
Stereum Chailletii (P.) ex Fr.
Stereum sanguinolentum (A. & S.) ex Fr.
Tapinia corrugata (Atk.) Murrill.
Trametes malicola B. & C.

Tsuga sp. indet. (*cont.*)
  Trametes serialis Fr.
  Trametes variiformis Pk.
Pseudotsuga macrocarpa (Torr.) Mayr.
  { Caeoma occidentale Arth.
  { Melampsora Albertensis Arth. I.
  Melampsora Medusae Thm. I.
  Poria Johnstonii Murrill.
Pseudotsuga taxifolia (Lam.) Britton.

UREDINALES

  { Caeoma dubium C. A. Ludwig.
  { Uredo Tsugae Holw. ined.
  { Caeoma occidentale Arth.
  { Caeoma Pseudotsugae, var. Douglasii v.Tubeuf.
  { Melampsora Albertensis Arth. I.
  { Melampsora Medusae Auct. p.p. I.
  Calyptospora columnaris Kühn. I.

THELEPHORACEAE

Aleurodiscus penicillatus Burt.
Aleurodiscus subcruentatus (B. & C.) Burt.
Coniophora cerebella P.
Corticium Pseudotsugae Burt.
Corticium racemosum Burt.
Corticium vagum B. & C.
Hymenochaete rugispora Ell. & Ev.
Hymenochaete spreta Pk.
Peniophora carnosa Burt.
Peniophora crassa Burt.
Peniophora glabra (B. & C.) Burt.
Peniophora odorata (Karst.) Burt.
Stereum Chailletii (P.) ex Fr.
Stereum sanguinolentum (A. & S.) ex Fr.
Thelephora terrestris Ehrh. ex Fr.

CLAVARIACEAE

Sparassis radicata Weir.

HYDNACEAE

Echinodontium tinctorium Ell. & Ev.
Hydnum Auriscalpium L. ex Fr.
{ Hydnum coralloides (Scop.) ex Fr.
{ Manina coralloides (Scop. ex Fr.) Banker.
{ Hydnum Erinaceus Bull. ex Fr.
{ Manina cordiformis (Scop.) ex Fr.
Hydnum ochraceum P. ex Fr.

POLYPORACEAE

{ Cryptoporus volvatus (Pk.) Hubbard.
{ Polyporus volvatus Pk.
Fomes annosus (Fr.) Cke.
{ Fomes Laricis (Jacq.) ex Murrill.
{ Fomes officinalis Fr.
{ Daedalea vorax Hark.
{ Fomes Pini (Brot. ex Fr.) Karst.
{ Trametes Pini (Brot.) ex Fr.
Fomes pinicola (Fr.) Cke.
Fomes putearius Weir.
Fomes roseus (A. & S. ex Fr.) Cke.

Fomes ungulatus (Schaeff.) ex Sacc.
{ Fomes applanatus (P. ex Wallr.) Gill.
{ Fomes leucophaeus Mont.
{ Ganoderma applanatum (P. ex Wallr.) Pat.
{ Fomes lucidus (Leyss. ex Fr.) Cke.
? { Ganoderma lucidum (Leyss. ex Fr.) Karst.
{ Polyporus lucidus (Leyss.) ex Fr.
Ganoderma oregonense Murrill.
?Ganoderma Tsugae Murrill.
{ Lenzites heteromorpha Fr.
{ Trametes heteromorpha (Fr.) Bres.
Lenzites sepiaria (Wulf.) ex Fr.
Lenzites trabea P. ex Fr.
Merulius americanus Burt.
Merulius brassicaefolius S.
Merulius lacrimans (Wulf.) ex Fr.
Polyporus adustus (Willd.) ex Fr.
Polyporus amarus Hedgc.
{ Polyporus aurantiacus Pk.
{ Polyporus fibrillosus Karst.
{ Polystictus aurantiacus (Pk.) Cke.
{ Pycnoporellus fibrillosus (Karst.) Murrill.
Polyporus benzoinus Fr.
{ Polyporus cutifractus Murrill.
{ Tyromyces cutifractus Murrill.
Polyporus frondosus Fr.
Polyporus giganteus (P.) ex Fr.
Polyporus hispidus (Bull.) ex Fr.
Polyporus Peakensis Lloyd.
{ Polyporus Pseudotsugae Murrill.
{ Tyromyces Pseudotsugae Murrill.
Polyporus Schweinitzii Fr.
Polyporus stipticus (P.) ex Fr.
Polyporus sulphureus (Bull.) ex Fr.
Coriolus abietinus (Dicks. ex Fr.) Quél.
Polystictus hirsutus (Wulf.) ex Fr.
Polystictus pargamenus Fr.
{ Polystictus serialis (Fr.) Cke.
{ Trametes serialis Fr.
Polystictus versicolor (L.) ex Fr.
Poria carbonaria B. & C.
Poria dichroa Bres.
Poria incrassata (B. & C.) Burt.
Poria Medulla-panis (P. ex Fr.) Cke.
Poria subspadicea Fr.
Trametes hispida Bagl.
Trametes protracta Fr.
Trametes sepiaria Lloyd.
Trametes setosus Weir.
{ Fomes roseus Auct. Amer. p. p.
{ Trametes carnea Auct. Amer. p. p.
{ Trametes subrosea Weir.

AGARICACEAE

Armillaria mellea (Vahl) ex Fr., var. bulbosa
  Pk.
Lentinus lepideus Fr.
Lepiota xylophila Pk.
Pholiota ventricosa Earle.

Pseudotsuga taxifolia (*cont.*)

MISCELLANEA

Atrichia glomerulosa (Ach.) Flot.
{Botrytis cinerea P. †
{Botrytis Douglasii v. Tubeuf.
Dacryomyces aurantia S.
{Didymella Douglasii Ell. & Ev.
{Sphaerella Andersonii Sacc.
{Sphaerella conigena Ell. & Ev.
Fusarium acuminatum Ell. & Ev.
Gelatinosporium abietinum Pk.
Helvella infula Schaeff. ex Fr.
Herpotrichia nigra Hartig.
Naematelia encephala (Willd.) ex Fr.
Neopeckia Coulteri (Pk.) Sacc.
Pestalozzia Hartigii v. Tubeuf.
Phacidium infestans Karst.
Phomopsis juniperovora Hahn.
Phomopsis juniperovora Hahn, var. A.
Phomopsis Pseudotsugae M. Wilson.
Pythium debaryanum Hesse.
Rhabdocline Pseudotsugae Syd.
Rhabdogloeum Pseudotsugae Syd.
Sclerotinia fuckeliana DBy.
Valsa Abietis Fr.

Abies amabilis (Dougl.) Forb.

Dimerosporium Abietis Dearness.
Echinodontium tinctorium Ell. & Ev.
Fomes annosus (Fr.) Cke.
Fomes pinicola (Sw. ex Fr.) Cke.
Hypoderma robustum v. Tubeuf.
Hypoderma robustum v. Tubeuf, var. latispora
    Dearness.
Hypodermella Abietis-concoloris Dearness.
Lophodermium nervisequum (DC. ex Fr.)
    Rehm.
{Peridermium balsameum Auct. p.p..
{Uredinopsis mirabilis Magn. I.
{Peridermium pseudobalsameum (Diet. &
{   Holw.) Arth. & Kern.
{Uredinopsis macrosperma Magn. I.
{Uredinopsis Pteridis Diet. & Holw. I.
{Calyptospora columnaris Kühn. I.
{Peridermium columnare (A. & S.) Kze. &
    Schm.
{Peridermium balsameum Auct. p. p.
{Uredinopsis Copelandi Syd. I.
Melampsorella elaṭina Arth. I.
{Peridermium pustulatum (P.) Kauffm.
{Pucciniastrum pustulatum Diet. I.
Peridermium rugosum H. S. Jackson.
Polyporus Schweinitzii Fr.
Poria incrassata (B. & C.) Burt.

Abies arizonica Merriam.

Bifusella Abietis Dearness.
Echinodontium tinctorium Ell. & Ev.
{Fomes Pini (Brot. ex Fr.) Karst.
{Trametes Pini (Brot.) ex Fr.
Fomes pinicola (Sw. ex Fr.) Cke.

Pucciniastrum pustulatum (Schrt.) Diet. I.
Polyporus Schweinitzii Fr.

Abies balsamea (L.) Mill.

MYXOMYCETES

Didymium flavidum Pk.
Lamproderma arcyrionema Rostf.
Leocarpus fragilis (Dicks.) Rostf.
Physarum flavidum Pk.
Physarum galbeum Wingate.
Physarum globuliferum (Bull.) P.

PEZIZINEAE

Agyrium rufum (P.) Fr.
Barlaea lacunosa Ell. & Ev.
Cenangella abietina Ell. & Ev.
{Cenangella Pinastri (P. ex Fr.) Sacc.
{Cenangium Pinastri (P.) ex Fr.
{Peziza Pinastri P. ex Fr.
{Tympanis Pinastri (P. ex Fr.) Tul.
Cenangium balsameum Pk.
Cenangium ferruginosum Fr.
{Dasyscypha Agassizii (B. & C.) Sacc.
{Peziza Agassizii B. & C.
Dasyscypha calycina (Schum. ex Fr.) Fckl.
Dasyscypha resinaria (Cke. & Phil.) Rehm.
Dermatea phyllophila Pk.
Gloeocalyx rufa (S.) Sacc., var. magna Pk.
Lachnea irregularis (Clements) Sacc. & D.
    Sacc.
Patellaria patinelloides (Sacc. & Roum.) Sacc.
{Peziza balsamicola Pk.
{Tapesia balsamicola (Pk.) Sacc.
Tympanis laricina (Fckl.) Sacc.

PHACIDIINEAE

Clithris Graphis Rehm.
Phacidium abietinellum Dearness.
Phacidium abietinum Schm. ex Fr.
Phacidium balsameae J. J. Davis.
Scleroderris abietina Ell. & Ev.
{Cenangium pityum B. & C.
{Scleroderris pitya (B. & C.) Sacc.
{Stictis hysterina Fr.
{Xylogramma hysterinum (Fr.) Rehm.

HYSTERIINEAE

Lophium mytilinum (P.) ex Fr.
{Hypodermella nervisequa (DC. ex Fr.) Lager-
{   berg.
{Hypoderma nervisequum (DC.) ex Fr.
{Lophodermium nervisequum (DC. ex Fr.)
{   Rehm.

PYRENOMYCETINEAE

{Adelopus balsamicola (Pk.) Theissen.
{Asterella nuda (Pk.) Sacc.
{Asterina nuda Pk.
{Cryptopus nudus (Pk.) Theissen.
{Dimerosporium balsamicola (Pk.) Ell. & Ev.
{Meliola balsamicola Pk.
{Zukalia balsamicola (Pk.) Sacc.

Abies balsamea (*cont.*)

Bertia moriformis (Tode ex Fr.) DeNot.
{ Chilonectria Cucurbitula Sacc.
Creonectria Cucurbitula (Sacc.) Seaver.
Nectria Cucurbitula (Curr) Cke..
{ Chilonectria balsamea (Cke. & Pk.) Sacc.
Chilonectria Rosellinii (Carsest.) Sacc.
Nectria balsamea Cke. & Pk.
Scoleconectria balsamea (Cke. & Pk.) Seaver.
Melogramma boreale Ell. & Ev.
Micropeltis pitya Sacc.
Montagnella abietina Ell. & Ev.
Scoleconectria scolecospora (Bref.) Seaver.
Valsa brevis Pk.
Valsa colliculus (Wormsk. ex Fr.) B.
Valsa Friesii (Duby) Fckl.

UREDINALES

{ Caeoma arcticum Kauffm. 1916.
Caeoma arcticum Fraser 1918.
{ Melampsora americana Arth. I.
Melampsora americana Jørstad. I.
Melampsora arctica I.
Melampsora humboldtiana Speg. I.
Milesia kriegeriana (Magn.) Arth. I.
{ Milesina kriegeriana Magn. I.
Milesina marginalis Faull & Watson. I.
{ Milesia pycnograndis Arth. I.
Milesia polypodophila (Bell) Faull. I.
Peridermium pycnogrande Bell.
Uredinopsis polypodophila Bell. I.
{ Aecidium balsameum Diet. p. p.
Peridermium balsameum Auct. p. p.
Uredinopsis mirabilis Arth. I.
{ Peridermium balsameum Auct. p. p.
Uredinopsis Atkinsonii Magn. I.
Uredinopsis Copelandi Syd. I.
{ Peridermium balsameum Auct. p. p.
Uredinopsis Osmundae Magn. I.
{ Peridermium balsameum Auct. p. p.
Uredinopsis Phegopteridis Arth. I.
{ Peridermium balsameum Auct. p. p.
Uredinopsis Struthiopteridis Störmer. I.
{ Calyptospora columnaris Kühn. I.
Calyptospora goeppertiana Kühn. I.
Peridermium columnare (A. & S.) Kze. &
Schm.
{ Aecidium elatinum A. & S.
Melampsorella Caryophyllacearum Schrt. I.
Melampsorella Cerastii (Wint.) Schrt. I.
Melampsorella elatina Arth. I.
Peridermium elatinum (A. & S.) Kze. & Schm.
Pucciniastrum Abietis-Chamaenerii Klebahn. I.
{ Peridermium pustulatum (P.) Kauffm.
Pucciniastrum Epilobii Otth. I.
Pucciniastrum pustulatum Diet. I.
{ Hyalopsora Aspidiotus (Karst.) Magn. I.
Peridermium pycnoconspicuum Bell.

AURICULARIALES

Hirneola Auricula-judae (L. ex Fr.) B.
Naematelia encephala (Willd.) ex Fr.
Ulocolla foliacea (P.) Bref.

THELEPHORACEAE

{ Aleurodiscus amorphus (P.) Rabh.
Corticium amorphum (P.) Fr.
Nodularia balsamicola Pk.
Peziza amorpha P.
Peziza balsamicola Cke. nec Pk.
Thelephora amorpha (P.) Fr.
Aleurodiscus Farlowii Burt.
Corticium confluens Fr.
Corticium lacteum Fr.
Corticium sulfureum Fr.
Hypochnus avellaneus Burt.
{ Corticium thelephoroides Ell. & Ev.
Hypochnus pallescens (S.) Burt.
Hypochnus thelephoroides (Ell. & Ev.) Burt.
{ Corticium giganteum Fr.
Peniophora gigantea (Fr.) Massee.
Peniophora globifera Ell. & Ev.
Stereum balsameum Pk.
Stereum sanguinolentum (A. & S.) ex Fr.
Thelephora laciniata (P.) ex Fr.
Tulasnella fuscoviolacea Bres.

CLAVARIACEAE

Sparassis radicata Weir.

HYDNACEAE

Grandinia crustosa Fr.
Hydnum Auriscalpium L. ex Fr.
Hydnum balsameum Pk.
Hydnum farinaceum P. ex Fr.

POLYPORACEAE

{ Cryptoporus volvatus (Pk.) Hubbard.
Polyporus volvatus Pk.
Fomes annosus (Fr.) Cke.
{ Fomes fuliginosus (Scop. ex Fr.) Cke.
Ischnoderma fuliginosum (Scop. ex Fr.) Murrill.
{ Fomes Pini (Brot. ex Fr.) Karst.
Polystictus piceinus Pk.
Trametes Pini (Brot.) ex Fr.
{ Fomes Pini (Fr.) Lloyd, var. Abietis (Karst.)
Overholts.
Trametes Abietis Karst.
Trametes Pini, var. Abietis (Karst.) v. Schrenk.
{ Fomes pinicola (Sw. ex Fr.) Cke.
Polyporus pinicola Sw. ex Fr.
Fomes roseus (A. & S. ex Fr.) Cke.
{ Lenzites sepiaria (Wulf.) ex Fr.
Sesia hirsuta (Schaeff.) ex Murrill.
Merulius aureus Fr.
Merulius subaurantiacus Pk.
Polyporus amorphus Fr.
{ Polyporus anceps Pk.
Tyromyces anceps (Pk.) Murrill.

Abies balsamea (*cont.*)

{ Polyporus borealis Fr.
{ Spongipellis borealis (Fr.) Pat.
  Polyporus caesius (Schrad.) ex Fr.
{ Polyporus cutifractus Murrill.
{ Tyromyces cutifractus Murrill.
{ Polyporus guttulatus Pk.
{ Tyromyces guttulatus (Pk.) Murrill.
{ Polyporus benzoinus Wahlenb.
  Polyporus resinosus (Schrad.) ex Fr.
  Polyporus Schweinitzii Fr.
{ Polyporus fissus B.
{ Polyporus picipes Fr.
{ Polyporus varius Fr.
  Coriolus abietinus (Dicks. ex Fr.) Quél.
  Polyporus abietinus (Dicks.) ex Fr.
  Polyporus abietinus (Dicks.) ex Fr., var. irpici-
    formis Pk.
  Polystictus abietinus (Dicks. ex Fr.) Cke.
{ Coriolus balsameus (Pk.) Murrill.
  Polyporus balsameus Pk.
  Polystictus balsameus (Pk.) Cke.
{ Tyromyces balsameus (Pk.) Murrill.
{ Polyporus subacidus Pk.
{ Poria subacida (Pk.) Sacc. Syll.
{ Polyporus vaporarius (P.) ex Fr.
{ Poria vaporaria (P. ex Fr.) Cke.
{ Polyporus violaceus Fr.
{ Poria violacea (Fr.) Cke.
  Poria Weirii Murrill.
  Trametes heteromorpha (Fr.) Bres.
  Trametes serialis Fr.

AGARICACEAE

  Armillaria mellea (Vahl) ex Fr.
  Clitocybe sulphurea Pk.
  Entoloma adirondackense Murrill.
{ Flammula subviridis Murrill.
{ Gymnopilus subviridis Murrill.
  Hypholoma capnoides Fr.
  Lactarius subdulcis Fr., var. oculatus Pk.
  Lentinus strigosus (S.) Fr.
  Marasmius androsaceus Fr.
  Marasmius filopes Pk.
{ Mycena avellanea Murrill.
{ Prunulus avellaneus Murrill.
  Mycena flavifolia Pk.
{ Mycena fuliginosa Murrill.
{ Prunulus fuliginosus Murrill.
{ Omphalia aurantiaca Pk.
{ Omphalopsis aurantiaca (Pk.) Murrill.
  Paxillus Curtisii B.
{ Pholiota flammans Fr.
{ Hypodendrum flammans (Batsch ex Fr.) Mur-
    rill.
{ Geopetalum Blakei (B. & C.) Murrill.
{ Pleurotus Blakei B. & C.
  Pleurotus mitis (P.) ex Fr.

SPHAEROPSIDALES

  Ceuthospora abietina Ell. & Ev.
{ Diplodia lignicola Pk.
{ Diplodiella lignicola (Pk.) Sacc.
  Discosia Artocreas (Tode) ex Fr.
  Hendersonia falcata Ell. & Ev.
  Leptostromella conigena Dearness.
  Phomopsis Pseudotsugae M. Wilson.

MELANCONIALES

  Coryneum abietinum Ell. & Ev.
  Cryptosporium falcatum Dearness.
  Cryptosporium macrospermum Pk.
  Cryptosporium noveboracense B. & C.
  Gloeosporium balsameae J. J. Davis.
  Monochaetia camptosperma (Pk.) Sacc.
  Pestalozzia? campsosperma Pk.
  Sacidium Pini (Cda.) Fr.
{ Myxocyclus cenangioides (Ell. & Rothrock)
    Petrak.
{ Steganosporium cenangioides Ell. & Rothrock.

HYPHOMYCETES

  Epicoccum diversisporum Preuss.
{ Fusarium Berenice Herb. Curt.
{ Fusarium Berenice (B. & C.) Sacc.
{ Fusisporium Berenice B. & C.
  Stilbum glomerulisporum Ell. & Ev.
  Stilbum resinarum Pk.
  Trimmatostroma abietinum Doherty.

— **Abies concolor** Lindl. & Gord.

  Aleurodiscus amorphus (P.) Rabh.
  Badhamia nitens B.
{ Caeoma americanum Arth.
{ Caeoma arcticum Fraser.
{ Melampsora americana Arth. I.
{ Melampsora americana Jørstad. I.
{ Melampsora arctica Rostr. I.
{ Melampsora humboldtiana Speg. I.
— Cryptocline abietina Petrak.
  Echinodontium tinctorium Ell. & Ev.
  Fomes applanatus (P. ex Wallr.) Gill.
{ Fomes Laricis (Jacq.) ex Murrill.
{ Fomes officinalis Fr.
{ Fomes Pini (Brot. ex Fr.) Karst.
{ Trametes Pini (Brot.) ex Fr.
  Fomes pinicola (A. & S. ex Fr.) Cke.
  Herpotrichia nigra Hartig.
  Hydnum coralloides (Scop.) ex Fr.
  Hypoderma robustum v. Tubeuf.
  Hypodermella Abietis-concoloris (Mayr)
    Dearness.
  Lentinus lepideus Fr.
  Lophodermium nervisequum (DC. ex Fr.)
— Rehm.
{ Calyptospora columnaris Kühn I.
{ Peridermium columnare (A. & S.) Kze. & Schm.
{ Melampsorella elatina Arth. I.
{ Peridermium elatinum (A. & S.) Schm. & Kze.

Abies concolor (*cont.*)
  Peridermium ornamentale Arth.
  Pucciniastrum Abietis-Chamaenerii Klebahn. I.
  { Peridermium pustulatum (P.) Kauffm.
  { Pucciniastrum pustulatum Diet. I.
  Phacidium infestans Karst.
  Phacidium infestans Karst., var. Abietis Dearness.
  Pholiota flammans Fr.
  Polyporus dryadeus (P.) ex Fr.
  Polyporus Schweinitzii Fr.
  Polystictus versicolor (L.) ex Fr.
  Poria incrassata (B. & C.) Burt.
  Schizophyllum commune Fr.
  Stegopezizella balsameae Syd.
  Stereum hirsutum (Willd.) ex Fr.

Abies Fraseri (Pursh) Lindl.
  { Calyptospora columnaris Kühn. I.
  { Peridermium columnare (A. & S.) Kze. & Schm.
  { Peziza crocea S.
  { Phialea crocea (S.) Sacc.
  Sparassis radicata Weir.
  Trichosphaeria parasitica Hartig.

Abies grandis Lindl.

ASCOMYCETES

Clypeothecium Weirii Petrak.
Dimerosporium Abietis Dearness.
Dimerosporium Tsugae Dearness.
Herpotrichia nigra Hartig.
Lachnea hirta (Schum. ex Fr.) Gill.
Lophodermium Abietis Rostr.
{ Hypodermella nervisequa (DC. ex Fr.) Lagerberg.
{ Lophodermium nervisequum (DC. ex Fr.) Rehm.
Meliola Abietis (Cke). Sacc.
Neopeckia Coulteri (Pk.) Sacc.
Phacidium infestans Karst.
Phacidium infestans Karst., var. Abietis Dearness.
Phaeophacidium abietinum Sacc.
Pitya vulgaris Fckl.
Rhizina inflata (Schaeff.) ex Quél.
Valsa Abietis Fr.

UREDINALES

{ Caeoma arcticum Fraser.
{ Melampsora americana Arth. I.
{ Melampsora arctica Auct. Amer. I.
{ Melampsora humboldtiana Speg. I.
{ Peridermium balsameum Auct. p. p.
{ Uredinopsis mirabilis Magn. I.
{ Uredinopsis Atkinsonii Magn. I.
{ Uredinopsis Copelandi Syd. I.

{ Aecidium pseudobalsameum Diet. & Holw.
{ Peridermium pseudobalsameum (Diet. & Holw.) Arth. & Kern.
Uredinopsis macrosperma Magn. I.
Uredinopsis Pteridis Diet. & Holw. I.
{ Calyptospora columnaris Kühn. I.
{ Peridermium columnare (A. & S.) Kze. & Schm.
{ Melampsorella elatina Arth. I.
{ Peridermium elatinum (A. & S.) Schm. & Kze.
{ Aecidium ornamentale (Arth.) Farl.
{ Peridermium Holwayi Arth.
{ Peridermium ornamentale Arth.
Pucciniastrum Abietis-Chamaenerii Klebahn. I.
{ Peridermium pustulatum (P.) Kauffm.
{ Pucciniastrum pustulatum Diet. I.
Peridermium rugosum H. S. Jackson.

THELEPHORACEAE

Aleurodiscus subcruentatus (B. & C.) Burt.
Aleurodiscus Weirii Burt.
Corticium furfuraceum Bres.
Corticium racemosum Burt.
Peniophora carnosa Burt.
Peniophora odorata (Karst.) Burt.
Stereum hirsutum (Willd.) ex Fr.
Stereum sulcatum Burt.
Thelephora terrestris Ehrh. ex Fr.

CLAVARIACEAE

Clavaria Stillingeri Coker.
Sparassis radicata Weir.

HYDNACEAE

Echinodontium tinctorium Ell. & Ev.
Hydnum Abietis Hubert.
Hydnum coralloides Scop. ex Fr.

POLYPORACEAE

{ Daedalea confragosa (Bolt.) ex Fr.
{ Trametes rubescens (A. & S.) ex Fr.
Fomes annosus (Fr.) Cke.
{ Fomes Laricis (Jacq.) ex Murrill.
{ Fomes officinalis Fr.
{ Fomes applanatus (P. ex Wallr.) Gill.
{ Fomes leucophaeus (Mont.) Cke.
Fomes pinicola (Sw. ex Fr.) Cke.
Fomes roseus (A. & S. ex Fr.) Cke.
Merulius armeniacus Bres.
Merulius niveus Fr.
Polyporus albellus Pk.
{ Aurantiporellus alboluteus (Ell. & Ev.) Murrill.
{ Polyporus alboluteus Ell. & Ev.
Polyporus amorphus Fr.
Polyporus aurantiacus Pk.
Polyporus benzoinus Fr.
Polyporus borealis Fr.
{ Polyporus caesius (Schrad.) ex Fr.
{ Tyromyces caesius (Schrad. ex Fr.) Murrill.
Polyporus chioneus (Schrad.) ex Fr.
{ Inonotus dryadeus (P. ex Fr.) Murrill.
{ Polyporus dryadeus (P.) ex Fr.

Abies grandis (*cont.*)
Polyporus fragilis Fr.
Polyporus mollis (P.) ex Fr.
Polyporus picipes Fr.
Polyporus Schweinitzii Fr.
Polyporus sensibilis Murrill.
Polyporus sulphureus (Bull.) ex Fr.
Polyporus undosus Pk.
{ Cryptoporus volvatus (Pk.) Hubbard.
Fomes volvatus (Pk.) Cke., var. Helix Henn.
Fomes volvatus (Pk.) Cke., var. Hystrix Henn.
Polyporus volvatus Pk.
{ Coriolus abietinus (Dicks. ex Fr.) Quél.
Polystictus abietinus (Dicks. ex Fr.) Cke.
Poria dichroa Bres.
Poria subacida (Pk.) Sacc. Syll.
Poria undata P.
{ Polyporus vaporarius (P.) ex Fr.
Poria vaporaria (P. ex Fr.) Cke.
Poria vicina Bres.
Poria zonata Bres.
{ Lenzites heteromorpha Fr.
Trametes heteromorpha (Fr.) Bres.
Trametes suaveolens L. ex Fr.

AGARICACEAE

{ Armillaria mellea (Vahl) ex Fr.
Armillaria mellea (Vahl) ex Fr., var. bulbosa Pk.
Lenzites sepiaria (Wulf.) ex Fr.
Pholiota adiposa Fr.
Pleurotus serotinus Fr.

MISCELLANEA

Botrytis Douglasii v. Tubeuf.
Dacryomyces deliquescens (Bull.) ex Duby.
Macrophoma parca Ell. & Ev. nom. nud. an B. & Br.
Toxosporium camptospermum (Pk.) Lind.

Abies homolepis Sieb. & Zucc.
Phomopsis juniperovora Hahn.
Phomopsis juniperovora Hahn, var. A.

Abies lasiocarpa (Hook.) Nutt.

ASCOMYCETES

Bifusella Abietis Dearness.
Dasyscypha Agassizii (B. & C.) Sacc.
Dasyscypha arida (Phil.) Sacc.
Herpotrichia nigra Hartig.
Hypodermella macrospora (Hartig) Lagerberg.
Lophodermium Abietis Rostr.
Lophodermium Pinastri (Schrad. ex Fr.) Chev.
{ Lasiosphaeria Coulteri (Pk.) Ell. & Ev.
Neopeckia Coulteri (Pk.) Sacc.
{ Phacidium balsameae J. J. Davis.
Stegopezizella balsameae (J. J. Davis) Syd.
Phacidium infestans Karst.
Valsa Abietis Fr.

UREDINALES

{ Peridermium pseudobalsameum (Diet. & Holw.) Arth. & Kern.
Uredinopsis Pteridis Diet. & Holw. I.
Calyptospora columnaris Kühn. I.
{ Calyptospora goeppertiana Kühn. I.
Peridermium columnare (A. & S.) Kze. & Schm.
Peridermium Holwayi Syd.
Peridermium ornamentale Arth.
Melampsora americana Arth. I.
Melampsora americana Jørstad. I.
Melampsora arctica Auct. Amer. I.
Melampsora humboldtiana Speg. I.
Melampsorella elatina Arth. I.
{ Peridermium elatinum (A. & S.) Schm. & Kze.
Pucciniastrum Abietis-Chamaenerii Klebahn. I.
{ Peridermium pustulatum (P.) Kauffm.
Pucciniastrum pustulatum Diet. I.
Peridermium balsameum Auct. p. p.
{ Uredinopsis Atkinsonii Magn. I.
Uredinopsis Copelandi Syd. I.

HYMENOMYCETINEAE

Aleurodiscus amorphus (P.) Rabh.
Armillaria mellea (Vahl) ex Fr.
Coniophora byssoidea Fr.
{ Coniophora corrugis Burt.
Corticium corruge Burt.
Corticium galactinum (Fr.) Burt.
Echinodontium tinctorium Ell. & Ev.
{ Auricularia Auricula-judae (L ex Fr.) Schrt.
Hirneola Auricula-judae (L.) ex Fr.
Lentinus lepideus Fr.
Peniophora Allescheri Bres.
Peniophora carnosa Burt.
Pholiota adiposa Fr.
Stereum ambiguum Pk.

POLYPORACEAE

{ Aurantiporellus alboluteus (Ell. & Ev.) Murrill.
Fomes alboluteus Ell. & Ev.
Polyporus alboluteus Ell. & Ev.
Daedalea unicolor (Bull.) ex Fr.
Fomes annosus (Fr.) Cke.
Fomes applanatus (P. ex Wallr.) Gill.
{ Fomes Pini (Brot. ex Fr.) Karst.
Trametes Pini (Brot.) ex Fr.
Fomes pinicola (Sw. ex Fr.) Cke.
Lenzites sepiaria (Wulf.) ex Fr.
Polyporus leucospongia Cke.
Polyporus resinosus Fr.
Polyporus Schweinitzii Fr.
Polystictus versicolor (L.) ex Fr.
Trametes heteromorpha (Fr.) Bres.
Trametes mollis (Sommerf.) ex Fr.
Trametes tenuis Karst.

FUNGI IMPERFECTI

Cystothyrium Abietis Dearness.

—**Abies magnifica** A. Murr.
Echinodontium tinctorium Ell. & Ev.
Fomes Laricis (Jacq.) ex Murrill.
Fomes officinalis Fr.
Fomes Pini (Brot. ex Fr.) Karst.
Porodaedalea Pini (Brot. ex Fr.) Murrill.
Trametes Pini (Brot.) ex Fr.
Fomes pinicola (Sw. ex Fr.) Cke.
Polyporus pinicola Sw. ex Fr.
Herpotrichia nigra Hartig.
Lophodermium nervisequum (DC. ex Fr.)
Rehm.
Calyptospora columnaris Kühn. I.
Peridermium columnare (A. & S.) Kze. & Schm.
Melampsorella elatina Arth. I.
Peridermium elatinum (A. & S.) Kze. & Schm.
Polyporus Schweinitzii Fr.
Polyporus sulphureus (Bull.) ex Fr.
Red fir.
Appendix to *Abies magnifica.* See also *Abies nobilis* and *Pseudotsuga.*
Aurantiporellus alboluteus (Ell. & Ev.) Murrill.
Fomes annosus Fr.
Ischnoderma fuliginosum (Scop.) ex Murrill.
Lepiota xylophila Pk.
Peniophora versata Burt.
Scutiger oregonensis Murrill.
Spongipellis sensibilis Murrill.
Polyporus carbonarius Murrill.
Tyromyces carbonarius Murrill.
Abies nigra (perhaps Picea mariana).
Clithris morbida (Pk.) Ell. & Ev.
Tryblidium morbidum Pk.
Periconia abietina (Pk.) Sacc.
Sporocybe abietina Pk.
Polyporus piceinus Pk.
Polystictus piceinus (Pk.) Sacc.
Cryptoporus volvatus (Pk.) Hubbard.
Polyporus volvatus Pk.
Fuscoporia marginella (Pk.) Murrill.
Polyporus marginellus Pk.
Poria marginella (Pk.) Sacc.
Stereum radiatum Pk.
Tympanis laricina (Fckl.) Sacc.
Abies nobilis Lindl.
Echinodontium tinctorium Ell. & Ev.
Hypoderma robustum Tubeuf.
Hypodermella Abietis-concoloris Dearness.
Fomes Pini (Brot. ex Fr.) Karst.
Trametes Pini (Brot.) ex Fr.
Fomes pinicola (Sw. ex Fr.) Cke.
Peridermium pseudobalsameum (Diet. & Holw.) Arth. & Kern.
Uredinopsis macrosperma Magn.
Uredinopsis Pteridis Diet. & Holw. I.
Calyptospora columnaris Kühn. I.
Peridermium columnare (A. & S.) Kze. & Schm.

Melampsorella elatina Arth. I.
Peridermium elatinum (A. & S.) Schm. & Kze.
Peridermium ornamentale Arth.
Peridermium balsameum Auct. p. p.
Uredinopsis Atkinsonii Magn. I.
Uredinopsis Copelandi Syd. I.
Polyporus Schweinitzii Fr.
Pucciniastrum pustulatum Diet. I.
Abies pectinata DC.
Acanthostigma parasiticum Ell. & Ev.
Chrysomyxa Abietis (Wallr.) Ung.
Cucurbitaria pithyophila (Schm. & Kze. ex Fr.) De Not.
Aecidium elatinum A. & S.
Pestalozzia Hartigii v. Tubeuf.
Phoma pectinata Dearness & House.
Abies religiosa Lindl.
Melampsorella elatina Arth. I.
Peridermium elatinum (A. & S.) Schm. & Kze.
Abies shastensis Lemmon.
Echinodontium tinctorium Ell. & Ev.
Fomes applanatus (P. ex Wallr.) Gill.
Fomes pinicola (Sw. ex Fr.) Cke.
Fomes roseus (A. & S. ex Fr.) Cke.
Herpotrichia nigra Hartig.
Melomastia shastensis Earle.
Polyporus Schweinitzii Fr.
Abies Veitchii Lindl.
Fusicoccum abietinum (Hartig) Prill. & Del.
Abies sp. indet.
Including earlier records of Picea, Tsuga and "fir."

MYXOMYCETES

Comatricha Suksdorfii Ell. & Ev.
Fuligo megaspora Sturgis
Physarum nefroideum Rostf.
Physarum virescens Ditm.
Trichia erecta Rex.
Trichia subfusca Rex.

PEZIZINEAE

Biatorella resinae (Fr.) Mudd.
Peziza resinae Fr.
Tromera resinae (Fr.) Körb.
Cenangium alpinum Ell. & Ev.
Dasyscypha acuum (A. & S. ex Fr.) Sacc.
Peziza acuum A. & S. ex Fr.
Dasyscypha lachnoderma (B.) Rehm.
Peziza lachnoderma A. & S.
Dasyscypha subtilissima (Cke.) Sacc.
Peziza subtilissima Cke.
Helotium lutescens (Hedw.) ex Fr.
Helotium nigripes (P.) ex Fr.
Peziza nigripes P. ex Fr.
Helotium subtile Fr.
Dasyscypha resinaria Rehm.
Lachnellula resinaria (Cke. & Phil.) Rehm.
Peziza badia P.
Peziza calycina Schum. ex Fr.

Abies sp. indet. (*cont.*)
   Peziza hyalina P.
{ Peziza fumosella C. & E.
   Phialea fumosella (C. & E.) Sacc.
{ Peziza strobilina Fr.
   Phialea strobilina (Fr.) Sacc.
   Rhizina undulata Fr.

PHACIDIINEAE
Stictis fimbriata S.

HYSTERIINEAE
Hypoderma abietinum Ell. & Ev.
Hypoderma conigenum (P. ex Fr.) Rehm.

SPHAERIALES
Acanthostigma parasiticum (Hartig) Sacc.
Ceratostomella pilifera (Fr.) Wint.
{ Colpoma morbidum (Pk.) Sacc.
   Tryblidium morbidum Pk.
Hypocrea lenta Fr.
Hypoxylon ohiense Ell. & Ev.
Lophiostoma excipuliforme (Fr.) Ces. & De
   Not., var. Abietis Ell. & Ev.
Meliola fenestrata C. & E.
{ Metasphaeria acuum (Cke. & Hark.) Sacc.
{ Sphaeria acuum Cke. & Hark.
   Sphaerulina acuum (Cke. & Hark.) Cke.
{ Endophlaea squamata (C. & E.) Cke.
{ Metasphaeria squamata (C. & E.) Sacc.
   Sphaeria squamata C. & E.
Rosellinia pulcherrima Ell. & Ev.
{ Aporia obscura Duby.
{ Hysterium Pinastri Curt. in Herb. Duby.
   Schizothyrium obscurum (Duby) Sacc.
Teichospora obducens (Fr.) Fckl., var. pinea
   Sacc. Syll.
{ Cucurbitaria macilenta Cke.
{ Gibberidea macilenta (Cke.) C. & E.
   Wallrothiella macilenta (Cke.) Sacc.

PHRAGMOBASIDIOMYCETES
Calocera cornea (Batsch) ex Fr..
Dacryomyces aurantia (S.) Farl.
Dacryomyces chrysocomus (Bull. ex Duby)
   Tul.
Tremella lutescens P. ex Fr.

THELEPHORACEAE
Aleurodiscus Weirii Burt.
Asterostroma ochrostroma Burt.
Corticium chlorinum B. & C.
Corticium cremoricolor B. & C.
Corticium crustaceum (Karst.) v. Höhnel &
   Litschauer.
Corticium lividocaeruleum Karst.
Hymenochaete abnormis Pk.
Peniophora crassa Burt.
Peniophora serialis (Bres.) v. Höhnel. & Lit-
   schauer.
Peniophora subapiculata (Bres.) Burt.

Corticium subincarnatum Pk.
Peniophora subincarnata (Pk.) Burt.
Peniophora subsulphurea (Karst.) v. Höhnel &
   Litschauer.
Peniophora viticola (S.) v. Höhnel & Litsch-
   auer.
Stereum ambiguum Pk.
Stereum Chailletii (P.) ex Fr.
Stereum rugisporum (Ell. & Ev.) Burt.

POLYPORACEAE
Fomes annosus Fr.
Fomes ungulatus (Schaeff.) ex Sacc.
Lenzites abietina (Bull.) ex. Fr.
Lenzites heteromorpha Fr.
Lenzites sepiaria (Wulf.) ex Fr., var. porosa
   Pk.
Merulius bellus B. & C.
{ Merulius confluens S.
   Merulius Corium Fr.
Merulius hexagonoides Burt.
Odontia fusca C. & E.
Polyporus destructor (Schrad.) ex Fr.
{ Polyporus fibrillosus Karst.
   Pycnoporellus fibrillosus (Karst.) Murrill.
Polyporus fissus B.
Polyporus fragilis Fr.
Polyporus fulvus Fr.
Polyporus leucospongia Cke. & Hark.
Polyporus ursinus Lloyd.
{ Mucronoporus circinatus Ell. & Ev.
{ Mucronoporus dualis Ell. & Ev.
{ Polyporus circinatus Fr.
   Polyporus dualis Pk.
Polystictus circinatus (Fr.) Cke.
{ Polyporus odorus Pk.
   Poria odora (Pk.) Sacc. Syll.
{ Polyporus sinuosus Fr.
{ Poria sinuosa (Fr.) Cke.
   Trametes sinuosa (Fr.) Cke. & Quél.
Poria subincarnata (Pk.) Murrill.
Poria taxicola (P.) Bres.
Poria undata (P.) Bres.
Poria vaporaria (P. ex Fr.) Cke.
{ Polyporus vulgaris Fr.
   Poria vulgaris (Fr.) Cke.
Trametes odorata (Wulf.) ex Fr.
{ Polyporus Stephensii B. & Br.
   Trametes serpens Fr.
{ Polyporus carneus Auct. Amer. p. p.
{ Trametes carnea Auct. Amer. p. p.
   Trametes subrosea Weir.

AGARICACEAE
{ Flammula oregonensis Murrill.
   Gymnopilus oregonensis Murrill.
Flammula piceina (Murrill) Sacc. & Trott.
Flammula subviridis Murrill.
Marasmius perforans (Hoffm.) ex Fr.

Abies sp. indet. (*cont.*)
{ Agaricus purpureofuscus Pk.
{ Mycena purpureofusca Pk.
{ Agaricus Austini Pk.
{ Omphalia Austini Pk.
Omphalia luteola Pk.
Psathyra conica Pk.

FUNGI IMPERFECTI

Chalara acuaria C. & E.
Cryptosporium candidum Dearness.
Cytospora Pinastri Fr.
Diplodia megalospora B. & C.
Eustilbum rehmianum Rabh.
{ Phoma abietina Hartig.
{ Fusicoccum abietinum (Hartig) Prillieux &
   Delacroix.
Helicosporium ellipticum Pk.
Helminthosporium obclavatum Sacc.
Pestalozzia tumefaciens Henn.
Phragmotrichum Chailletii Kunze.
Sphaeridium citrinum Sacc.
?Sphaeropsis Pinastri C. & E.
Sporidesmium pallidum B. & C.
Torula ligniperda (Willk.) Sacc.
Tubercularia nigricans (Bull.) ex Lk.

MISCELLANEA

Clavaria abietina P. ex Fr.
{ Hericium fasciculare Banker.
{ Mucronella fascicularis Fr.
Hydnum Auriscalpium L. ex Fr.
Mitrula cucullata Fr.
Ozonium auricomum Lk.
"Fir" (presumably **Abies** sp. indet.).
Lenzites rhabarbarina B. & C.
Mycena tenerrima B.
Nectria cytisporina Ell. & Ev.
Stereum tabacinum Fr.
Tremellodon gelatinosum (Scop.) ex Fr.
Sciadopitys verticillata Sieb. & Zucc.
Rhizoctonia Solani Kühn.
Sequoia gigantea Decsne.
{ Acanthostigma Sequoiae (Plowr.) Sacc.
{ Venturia Sequoiae Plowr.
Botrytis Douglasii Tubeuf.
Cercospora Sequoiae Ell. & Ev.
Clavaria cristata P. ex Fr.
Dacryomyces stillatus Nees ex Fr.
Hydnum niveum P. ex Fr.
{ Lachnea Sequoiae (Phil.) Sacc.
{ Peziza Sequoiae Phil.
Mytilidion californicum Ell. & Hark.
Peziza bulgarioides Rabh.
Phomopsis juniperovora Hahn.
Phomopsis juniperovora Hahn, var. A.
{ Cenangium Sequoiae Phil. & Plowr.
{ Scleroderris Sequoiae (Phil. & Plowr.) Sacc.
Stigmatea Juniperi Wint.

Trametes Sequoiae Copeland.
{ Laestadia consociata (Ell. & Hark.) Cke.
{ Physalospora consociata (Ell. & Hark.) Sacc.
{ Sphaeria consociata Ell. & Hark.
{ Wallrothiella consociata (Ell. & Hark.) Ell. &
   Ev.
{ Conisphaeria Sequoiae (Plowr.) Cke.
{ Sphaeria Sequoiae Plowr.
{ Zignoella Sequoiae (Plowr.) Sacc.
Sequoia sempervirens Endl.
{ Amphisphaeria Wellingtoniae (Cke. & Hark.)
{   Berl. & Vogl.
{ Sphaeria Wellingtoniae Cke. & Hark.
{ Xylosphaeria Wellingtoniae Cke. & Hark.
{ Chlorosplenium chloromelum (Phil. & Hark.)
{   Sacc.
{ Peziza chloromela Phil. & Hark.
Corticium caeruleum (Schrad.) ex Fr.
Corticium lacteum Fr.
Corticium sanguineum Fr.
Corticium umbrinum (A. & S.) ex Fr.
Cytospora Pinastri Fr.
{ Dasyscypha acuum (A. & S. ex Fr.) Sacc.
{ Peziza acuum A. & S. ex Fr.
Ganoderma Sequoiae Murrill.
{ Helotium sphaerophoroides (Phil. & Hark.)
{   Sacc.
{ Peziza sphaerophoroides Phil. & Hark.
Hymenochaete tabacina (Sow. ex Fr.) Lév.
Hypocrea rufa (P.) ex Fr.
Hypodermopsis Sequoiae Earle.
Hysterium angustatum A. & S. ex Fr.
{ Barlaea gemmea (Phil.) Sacc.
{ Lamprospora gemmea (Phil.) Seaver.
{ Peziza gemmea Phil.
Lasiosphaeria canescens (P. ex Fr) Karst.
Lepiota xylophila Pk.
Leptostroma Sequoiae Cke. & Hark.
{ Melanopsamma confertissima (Plowr.) Sacc.
{ Sphaeria confertissima Plowr.
Merulius hexagonoides Burt.
Merulius molluscus Fr.
Morchella conica P. †
Mystrosporium turbinatum Cke. & Hark.
Myxotrichum ochraceum B. & Br.
Naematelia encephala (Willd.) ex Fr.
Peziza fusca P.
Peziza ustorum B. & Br.
Phomopsis juniperovora Hahn.
Phomopsis juniperovora Hahn, var. A.
{ Peziza Cupressi Batsch ex Fr.
{ Peziza cupressina P.
{ Pitya Cupressi (Batsch ex Fr.) Rehm.
{ Pitya cupressina (P.) Fckl.
{ Peziza pitya P. ex Fr.
{ Pitya vulgaris Fckl.
Polyporus amorphus Fr.
Polystictus versicolor (L.) ex Fr.

Sequoia sempervirens (*cont.*)
  Byssosphaeria mutans (C. & P.) Cke.
  Rosellinia mutans (C. & P.) Sacc.
  Schizophyllum commune Fr.
  Solenia fasciculata P.
  Stereum hirsutum (Willd.) ex Fr.
  Stictis versicolor Fr.
  Trametes isabellina Fr.
  Trametes odorata (Wulf) ex Fr.
  Coriolellus Sequoiae (Copeland) Murrill.
  Trametes cuneata (Murrill) Sacc. & Trott.
  Trametes Sequoiae Copeland.
  Tremella mesenterica Retz ex Fr.
  Tremellodon gelatinosum (Scop.) ex Fr.
Sequoia sp. indet.
  Botrytis vulgaris Fr.
  Polyactis vulgaris Lk. ex Fr.
  Collybia umbonata Pk.
  Peziza carbonaria A. & S. ex Fr.
  Sporidesmium induratum Cke.
Cryptomeria japonica D. Don.
  Coniothyrium oospermum (Fckl.) Sacc.
  Phomopsis juniperovora Hahn, var. A.
Taxodium distichum (L.) Richard.
  Cenangium chlorascens (S.) Cke.
  Cenangium fallax B. & Rav.
  Chlorosplenium repandum Fr.
  Peziza chlorascens S.
  Coniothecium effusum Cda.
  Sporidesmium Lepraria B.
  Cytospora pallida Ell. & Ev.
  Favolus Taxodii (Murrill) Sacc. & D. Sacc.
  Hexagona Taxodii Murrill.
  Fomes geotropus Cke.
  Hysterium lineare B. nec Fr.
  Hysterium lineariforme Sacc.
  Illosporium album Ell. & Ev.
  Aulographum caespitosum Ell. & Ev.
  Lembosia caespitosa (Ell. & Ev.) Sacc.
  Lentinus lepideus Fr.
  Lentinus tigrinus (S.) Fr.
  Lenzites sepiaria (Wulf.) ex Fr.
  Lenzites trabea P. ex Fr.
  Melanopsamma cupressina Ell. & Ev.
  Metasphaeria cavernosa (Ell. & Ev.) Berl. & Vogl.
  Sphaeria cavernosa Ell. & Ev.
  Peniophora Taxodii Burt.
  Pestalozzia funerea Desm.
  Phomopsis juniperovora Hahn.
  Phomopsis juniperovora Hahn, var. A.
  Polyporus dendriticus Fr.
  Coriolus Drummondii (Klotzsch) Pat.
  Polystictus Drummondii (Klotzsch) Cke.
  Hapalopilus licnoides (Mont.) Murrill.
  Polystictus licnoides (Mont.) Cke.
  Polystictus versicolor (L.) ex Fr.
  Poria incrassata (B. & C.) Burt.
  Poria polyporicola Murrill.

  Peziza pomicolor B. & Rav.
  Pseudohelotium pomicolor (B. & Rav.) Sacc.
  Trichopeziza pomicolor (B. & Rav.) Sacc.
  Sphaerella Taxodii Cke.
  Daedalea sepium B.
  Trametes sepium B.
  Polyporus Stephensii B. & Br.
  Trametes serpens Fr.
  Trametes subnivosa Murrill.
  Blitrydium Taxodii (B.) Sacc.
  Peziza Taxodii B.
  Tryblidium Taxodii (B.) O. Kuntze.
Thujopsis dolobrata Sieb. ex Zucc.
  Lophodermium Pinastri (Schrad.) ex. Chev.
  Phomopsis juniperovora Hahn.
  Phomopsis juniperovora Hahn var. A.
— **Libocedrus decurrens** Torr.
  Daedalea vorax Hark.
  Fomes Pini (Brot. ex Fr.) Karst.
  Fomes pinicola (Sw. ex Fr.) Cke.
  Herpotrichia nigra Hartig.
  Hydnocystis compacta Hark.
  Lophodermium juniperinum (Fr.) DeNot.
  Lophodermium juniperinum (Fr.) DeNot., var. Cupressi-thyoides Sacc.
  Peziza alutipes Phil.
  Phialea alutipes (Phil.) Sacc.
  Gymnosporangium aurantiacum Syd.
  Gymnosporangium biseptatum, var. foliicola N. A. F. *3248.*
  Gymnosporangium blasdaleanum Kern.
  Gymnosporangium Libocedri (Henn.) Kern.
  Gymnosporangium Libocedri Mayr.
  Phragmidium Libocedri Henn.
  Roestelia Libocedri O. Kuntze.
  Phomopsis juniperovora Hahn, var. A.
  Fomes amarus (Hedgc.) Murrill.
  Polyporus amarus Hedgc.
  Polyporus Libocedris v. Schrenk.
  Polyporus Schweinitzii Fr.
  Polyporus volvatus Pk.
  Polystictus abietinus (Dicks. ex Fr.) Cke.
  Polystictus versicolor (L.) ex Fr.
  Stigmatea Sequoiae (Cke. & Hark.) Sacc.
  Cucurbitaria macilenta Cke.
  Gibberidea macilenta (Cke.) C. & E.
  Wallrothiella macilenta (Cke.) Sacc.
Thuja occidentalis L.

ASCOMYCETES

  Cenangella deformata Pk.
  Cenangella thujina Ell. & Barthol.
  Gloniella parvulata Dearness & House.
  Glonium nitidum Ell.
  Helotium limonicolor Bres.
  Helvella capucinoides Pk.
  Hysterium cedrinum Ell. & Ev.
  Hysterium Thujae (Rob.) House.
  Hysterium Thujarum C. & P.

Thuja occidentalis (*cont.*)
Hysterium tortile S.
Keithia thujina Durand.
Lophiostoma Thujae Ell. & Ev.
Lophodermium Pinastri (Schrad ex Fr.) Chev.
Lophodermium Thuyae J. J. Davis.
{ Ombrophila enterochroma (Pk.) Sacc.
{ Peziza enterochroma Pk.
{ Dacryomyces conglobatus Pk.
{ Ombrophila rubella (P.) Quél.
{ Peziza rubella P.
Ombrophila thujina Pk.
{ Helotium thujinum Pk.
{ Peziza Cupressi Batsch.
{ Pitya Cupressi (Batsch) ex Sacc.
{ Pitya cupressina (P.) Fckl.
{ Pitya thujina (Pk.) Sacc.

SPHAERIALES

{ Amphisphaeria thujina (Pk.) Sacc.
{ Sphaeria thujina Pk.
{ Botryosphaeria fuliginosa Ell. & Ev. p. p.
{ Melanops Quercuum (S.) Rehm. 1876.
{ Physalospora thyoidea (C. & E.) Sacc.
{ Sphaeria thyoidea C. & E.
Sphaerella canadensis Ell. & Ev.
{ Mycosphaerella conigena (Pk.) House.
{ Sphaerella conicola Pk. 62 Rept.
{ Sphaerella conigena Pk.
{ Mycosphaerella pinsapo (Thm.) House.
{ Sphaerella pinsapo Thm.
Valsa Thujae Pk.

THELEPHORACEAE

Hymenochaete tenuis Pk.
Peniophora Greschickii Bres.

POLYPORACEAE

{ Fomes Demidoffii (Lév.) Sacc. Cub. & Manc.
{ Fomes juniperinus (v. Schrenk) Sacc. & Syd.
Fomes roseus (A. & S. ex Fr.) Cke.
{ Bjerkandera adusta (Willd. ex Fr.) Karst.
{ Polyporus adustus (Willd.) ex Fr.
Polyporus aurantiacus Pk.
Polyporus balsameus Pk.
Polyporus hirtus Quél.
Polyporus Schweinitzii Fr.
Poria ferruginosa (Schrad. ex Fr.) Cke.
Poria incrassata (B. & C.) Burt.
Poria papyracea (S.) Cke.
Poria subiculosa (Pk.) Cke.
Poria taxicola (P.) Bres.
Poria vaporaria (Fr.) Cke.
Poria Weirii Murrill.
Trametes serpens Fr.
{ Fomes carneus C. L. Sm.
{ Polyporus carneus Auct. Amer. p. p.
{ Trametes carneus Auct. Amer. p. p.
{ Trametes subrosea Weir.

AGARICACEAE

Collybia campanella Pk.
Marasmius campanellus (Pk.) Atk. & House.
Marasmius thujinus Pk.
{ Omphalia Austini Pk.
{ Omphalopsis Austini (Pk.) Murrill.
{ Omphalia clavata Pk.
{ Omphalopsis clavata (Pk.) Murrill.
Schizophyllum commune Fr.

FUNGI IMPERFECTI

Coniosporium punctoideum Karst.
Coniosporium tumulosum Sacc.
Cytospora Dubyi Sacc., var. thyophila Sacc.
Diplodia thujina Pk. & Clinton.
{ Harknessia foeda Sacc. & Dearness.
{ Harknessia thujina Ell. & Ev.
{ Dothiorella magnifructa (Pk.) Petrak & Syd.
{ Macrophoma magnifructua (Pk.) Sacc.
{ Phoma magnifructa Pk.
Pestalozzia conigena Lév.
Pestalozzia funerea Desm.
Phoma thujina Thm.
Phomopsis juniperovora Hahn.
{ Didymobotryum corticalis (C. & P.) Dearness
{   & House.
{ Periconia corticalis C. & P.
{ Sporocybe corticalis (C. & P.) Sacc.

MISCELLANEA

Recurvaria thujaella Kearf.

Thuja orientalis L.
Phomopsis juniperovora Hahn.

Thuja plicata D. Don.
Aleurodiscus amorphus (P.) Rabh.
Aleurodiscus Weirii Burt.
Armillaria mellea (Vahl) ex Fr.
Clypeothecium Weirii Petrak.
Coniophora cerebella P.
Corticium ermineum Burt.
Corticium furfuraceum Bres.
Corticium racemosum Burt.
Corticium sociatum Burt.
Cucurbidothis conjuncta Petrak.
Exarmidium hysteriiforme Karst.
Herpotrichia nigra Hartig.
Keithia thujina Durand.
Leciographa dispersa Syd.
Microthyrium Thujae Dearness.
Mycosphaerella Thujae Petrak.
Neopeckia Coulteri (Pk.) Sacc.
Peniophora carnosa Burt.
Phomopsis juniperovora Hahn.
Sphaerella canadensis Ell. & Ev.
Thelephora terrestris Ehrh. ex Fr.
Valsa Abietis Fr.
Valsa weiriana Petrak.

Thuja plicata (*cont.*)

POLYPORACEAE

Fomes annosus (Fr.) Cke.
{Fomes Pini (Brot. ex Fr.) Karst.
{Trametes Pini (Brot.) ex Fr.
Polyporus adustus (Willd.) ex Fr.
Polyporus anceps Pk.
Polyporus chioneus Fr.
Polyporus dichrous Fr.
Polyporus Schweinitzii Fr.
Polyporus sulphureus (Bull.) ex Fr.
Polystictus abietinus (Dicks. ex Fr.) Cke.
Polystictus cinnabarinus (Jacq. ex Fr.) Cke.
Polystictus hirsutus (Wulf.) ex Fr.
Poria contigua (P. ex Fr.) Cke.
Poria incrassata (B. & C.) Burt.
{Fomitiporia Weirii Murrill.
{Poria Weirii Murrill.
{Coriolellus euneatus Murrill.
{Coriolus washingtonensis Murrill.
{Polystictus washingtonensis Murrill.
{Polystictus Sequoiae Copeland.
{Polystictus Sequoiae Lloyd.
{Trametes Sequoiae Copeland.
Trametes setosa Weir.

FUNGI IMPERFECTI

Coryneum juniperinum Ell.
Coryneum thujinum Dearness.
Hendersonia thyoides C. & E.

Thuja sp. indet.
{Coniothyrium albistratum (Pk.) Sacc.
{Phoma albistrata Pk.
Corticium calceum Fr. emend. Romell & Burt.
Corticium lividocaeruleum Karst.
Cylindrium elongatum Bon.
Cytospora Thujae Sacc. & Ell.
{Hydnum ochraceum P. ex Fr.
{Steccherinum ochraceum (P.) S. F. Gray.
Micropera tenella Sacc. & Ell.
Peniophora humifaciens Burt.
Peniophora serialis (Bres.) v. Höhnel &
  Litschauer.
Peniophora Thujae Burt.
Pestalozzia foedans Sacc. & Ell.
Pestalozzia funerea Desm.
{Polyporus cutifractus Murrill.
{Tyromyces cutifractus Murrill.
Poria Weirii Lloyd.
Pseudographis intermedia Rehm.
Thyridium lividum (P.) ex Sacc.
Valsa Thujae Pk., var. foliicola Ell. & Ev.

Cupressus arizonica Greene.
Gymnosporangium Cupressi Long & Gooding.
Phomopsis juniperovora Hahn.

Cupressus funebris Endl.
Phomopsis juniperovora Hahn.

Cupressus glabra Sudworth.
Ozonium omnivorum Shear.
Phomopsis juniperovora Hahn.

Cupressus goveniana Gord.

Cupressus lusitanica Mill., var., **Benthami** Carr.
Phomopsis juniperovora Hahn.

Cupressus macrocarpa Hartw.
Diplodia cyparissa Cke. & Hark.
Hydnum ochraceum P. ex Fr.
{Macrophoma Cupressi (Cke. & Hark.) Berl. &
  Vogl.
{Sphaeropsis Cupressi Cke. & Hark.
{Endophlaea anisometra Cke. & Hark.
{Metasphaeria anisometra (Cke. & Hark.) Sacc.
{Sphaeria anisometra Cke. & Hark.
Pestalozzia funerea Desm.
Pestalozzia heterospora Desm.
Phomopsis juniperovora Hahn.
Polyporus carbonarius Murrill.
Polyporus cutifractus Murrill.
Polyscytalum sericeum Sacc.

Cupressus sempervirens L.
Phomopsis juniperovora Hahn.

Cupressus sp. indet.
Pleiopatella Harperi Rehm.
Polyporus spurcus Lév.
Pseudographis intermedia Rehm.
Septobasidium mexicanum Syd.

Chamaecyparis lawsoniana (Murr.) Parl.
Lentinus lepideus Fr.
Lentinus tigrinus (S.) Fr.
Lenzites sepiaria (Wulf.) ex Fr.
Lenzites trabea P. ex Fr.
Phomopsis juniperovora Hahn.

Chamaecyparis nootkatensis (Lamb.) Spach.
Asterina cupressina Cke.
{Gymnosporangium nootkatensis Arth.
{Gymnotelium nootkatense (Arth.) Syd.
{Uredo Chamaecyparidis, var. nutkaensis
  v. Tubeuf.
{Uredo nootkatensis Trel.
Venturia lanea Dearness.

Chamaecyparis obtusa Sieb. & Zucc.
Phomopsis juniperovora Hahn.

Chamaecyparis pisifera Sieb. & Zucc.
Phomopsis juniperovora Hahn.

Chamaecyparis pisifera Sieb. & Zucc., var.
  plumosa Beissn.
Sphaeropsis Juniperi Pk.
Phomopsis juniperovora Hahn.

Chamaecyparis thyoides (L.) B. S. P.

ASCOMYCETES

{Asterina cupressina (Rehm) Cke.
{Venturia cupressina Rehm.
{Caliciopsis thujina (Ell. & Ev.) H. M. Fitz-
  patrick.
{Hypsotheca thujina Ell. & Ev.

Chamaecyparis thyoides (*cont.*)
Clithris morbida (Pk.) Ell. & Ev.
Glonium nitidum Ell.
Lophodermium juniperinum (Fr.) DeNot., **var.**
  Cupressi-thyoidis Sacc.
{ Dialonectria thujana (Rehm) Cke.
{ Nectria thujana (Rehm) Sacc.
{ Dialonectria truncata (Ell.) Cke.
{ Nectria truncata Ell.
{ Botryosphaeria fuliginosa Ell. & Ev. p. p.
{ Melanops Quercuum (S.) Rehm. 1876.
{ Physalospora thyoidea (C. & E. Sacc.
{ Sphaeria thyoidea C. & E.
{ Peziza Cupressi Batsch ex Fr.
{ Pitya Cupressi (Batsch) ex Sacc.
{ Physalospora Cupressi (B. & C.) Sacc.
{ Sphaeria Cupressi B. & C.
{ Nemacyclus griseus C. & E.
{ Propolis griseus (C. & E.) Sacc.
Rosellinia trichota (C. & E.) Ell. & Ev.
Trichosphaeria cupressina Rehm.
Valsa Abietis Fr.

UREDINALES

Gymnosporangium biseptatum Ell.
Gymnosporangium Botryapites (S.) Kern.
{ Gymnosporangium Ellisii (B.) Farl.
{ Gymnosporangium myricatum Fromme.
{ Hamaspora Ellisii (B.) Körn.
{ Phragmidium Ellisii (B.) De Toni.
{ Podisoma Ellisii B.
{ Tremella Ellisii (B.) Arth.
Gymnosporangium transformans (Ell.) Kern.
{ Gymnosporangium biseptatum, var. foliicola
{   Farl.
{ Gymnosporangium fraternum Kern.

HYMENOMYCETINEAE

Aleurodiscus nivosus (B. & C.) v. Höhnel &
  Litschauer.
Armillaria mellea (Vahl) ex Fr.
{ Collybia Ellisii Murrill.
{ Gymnopus Ellisii Murrill.
Coniophora leucothrix (B. & C.) Sacc. Syll.
Coniophora puteana (Schum.) ex Fr.
Corticium calceum Fr.
Corticium scutellare B. & C.
{ Hydnum Ballouii (Banker) Sacc. & Trott.
{ Radulum Ballouii (Banker) Lloyd.
{ Steccherinum Ballouii Banker.
{ Hydnum ellisianum Thm.
{ Hydnum subtile S. Am. Bor.
Hydnum Stevensoni B. & Br.
Hymenochaete simulans Ell. & Ev.
{ Corticium vagum Fung. Columb. *706*.
{ Hypochnus pallescens (S.) Burt.
{ Hypochnus pannosus (B. & C.) Burt.
{ Zygodesmus pannosus B. & C.
Lenzites betulina (L.) ex Fr.

Omphalia Campanella (Batsch) ex Fr.
? Paxillus aurantiacus Ell.
Polyporus abietinus Fr.
Polystictus floridanus (B.) Fr.
Polystictus pinsitus (Fr.) Cke.
Poria papyracea (S.) Cke.
Poria polyporicola Murrill.
Poria subincarnata (Pk.) Murrill.
Poria taxicola (P.) Bres.
Poria violacea (Fr.) Cke.

FUNGI IMPERFECTI

Coniothyrium subtile Cda.
Cytospora pustulata Ell. & Ev.
Cytospora Thujae Sacc. & Ell.
Diplodia thyoidea C. & E.
Discosia elliptica Fres.
Harknessia thujina Ell. & Ev.
Hendersonia foliicola (B.) Fckl.
Hendersonia thyoidea C. & E.
Hysteromyxa effugiens Sacc. & Ell.
Pestalozzia foedans Sacc. & Ell.
Pestalozzia unicornis C. & E.
Torula ligniperda (Willk.) Sacc.

White Cedar.
  (Appendix to Chamaecyparis and Thuja.)
  Kneiffia candidissima B. & C.
  Polyporus hispidellus Pk.

Juniperus barbadensis L.
{ Gymnosporangium bermudianum Earle.
{ Roestelia bermudiana Farl.
  Gymnosporangium globosum Farl.
{ Gymnosporangium Juniperi-virginianae S.
{ Gymnosporangium macropus Lk.
  Marasmiellus juniperinus Murrill.

Juniperus bermudiana L.
{ Gymnosporangium bermudianum Earle.
{ Roestelia bermudiana Farl.
  Hypocrea patella C. & P.
  Pitya Cupressi (Batsch) ex Rehm.
{ Pleurotopsis niduliformis Murrill.
{ Pleurotus niduliformis Murrill.
  Sarcoscypha minuscula Boud. & Torrend.
{ Polyporus carneus Auct. Amer.
{ Polyporus Palliseri B.
{ Trametes subroseus Weir.

Juniperus californica Carr.
  Fomes roseus (A. & S. ex Fr.) Cke.

Juniperus chinensis L.
  Gymnosporangium chinensis Long.
  Gymnosporangium haraeanum Syd.
{ Gymnosporangium japonicum Syd.
{ Gymnosporangium koreaense (Henn.) H. S.
{   Jackson.
  Gymnosporangium Photiniae Kern.

Juniperus chinensis L., **var. pfitzeriana** Spaeth.
  Phomopsis juniperovora Hahn.

Juniperus chinensis L., var. **procumbens** Sieb.
  Phomopsis juniperova Hahn.
  Phomopsis juniperovora Hahn., var. A.
Juniperus communis L.
  { Cenangella deformata (Pk.) Sacc.
  { Cenangium deformatum Pk.
  { Coryneum juniperinum Ell.
  { Exosporium juniperinum Jacz.
  Dermatea juniperina Ell.
  { Fomes Demidoffii (Lév.) Sacc. Cub. & Manc.
  { Fomes juniperinus (v. Schrenk) Sacc. & Syd.
  Guepinia elegans B. & C.
  Herpotrichia nigra Hartig.
  { Laestadia juniperina (Ell.) Sacc.
  { Sphaerella juniperina Ell.
  Lophodermium juniperinum (Fr.) DeNot.
  Peniophora parasitica Burt.
  { Coryneum unicolor M. A. Curtis, nom. nud.
  { Pestalozzia unicolor B. & C.
  Phomopsis juniperovora Hahn.
  Sphaerella juniperina Ell.

  Gymnosporangium Betheli Kern.
  Gymnosporangium clavariiforme (Jacq. ex
    P.) DC.
  { Gymnosporangium clavipes C. & P.
  { Gymnosporangium germinale Kern.
  { Gymnosporangium cornutum Arth.
  { Roestelia cornuta (P.) Fr.
  Gymnosporangium Davisii Kern.
  Gymnosporangium fuscum DC.?
  Gymnosporangium juniperinum (L. ex P.)
    Mart.
  Gymnosporangium Juniperi-virginianae S.
  Gymnosporangium Nelsoni Arth.
Juniperus communis L., var. **alpina** Gaud.
  Cercospora Sequoiae Ell. & Ev.
  Coryneum paraphysatum Rostr.
  Henriquesia cinerascens (Duby) Sacc.
  Lophodermium juniperinum (Fr.) DeNot.
Juniperus communis L., var. **depressa** Pursh.
  Asterina cupressina Cke.
  Cercospora Sequoiae, var. Juniperi Ell. & Ev.
  Gymnosporangium clavariiforme (Jacq. ex
    P.) DC.
  Gymnosporangium clavipes C. & P.
  Gymnosporangium Davisii Kern.
  Lophodermium juniperinum (Fr.) DeNot.
Juniperus communis L., var. **hemisphaerica**
    (Presl) Parl.
  Pestalozzia funerea Desm.
Juniperus communis L., var. **hibernica** Gord.
  Gymnosporangium clavariiforme (Jacq. ex P.)
    DC.
Juniperus horizontalis Moench.
  Gymnosporangium corniculans Kern.
  Gymnosporangium globosum Farl.

  Gymnosporangium Juniperi-virginianae S.
  Gymnosporangium juvenescens Kern.
  Gymnosporangium Nelsoni Arth.
  Gymnosporangium tubulatum Kern.
  Hypodermella Laricis v. Tubeuf.
  Phomopsis juniperovora Hahn.
  Sphaerella juniperina Ell.
Juniperus lucayana Britt.
  Phomopsis juniperovora Hahn.
Juniperus mexicana Schiede.
  Gymnosporangium exiguum Kern.
Juniperus monosperma (Engelm.) Sarg.
  Amphisphaeria Juniperi Tracy & Earle.
  { Fomes Earlei (Murrill) Sacc. & D. Sacc.
  { Fomes juniperinus (v. Schrenk) Sacc. & Syd.
  Fomes roseus (A. & S. ex Fr.) Cke.
  Fomes texanus (Murrill) Hedgc. & Long.
  Lophiostoma occidentale Tracy & Earle.
  Poria rimosa Murrill.
  Trametes rubricosa Bres.
  Trametes serialis Fr.
  Trematosphaeria Juniperi Tracy & Earle.

  Gymnosporangium multiporum Kern.
  Gymnosporangium Nelsoni Arth.
  Gymnosporangium nidus-avis Thax.
  { Gymnosporangium gracilens Kern & Bethel.
  { Gymnosporangium speciosum Pk.
Juniperus occidentalis Hook.
  Aleurodiscus nivosus (B. & C.) v. Höhnel &
    Litschauer.
  { Antennaria pinophila Nees ex Fr.
  { Antennaria pityophila Sacc.
  { Antennularia pinophila (Nees ex Fr.) Farl.
  { Hormiscium pityophilum Sacc.
  { ? " Hormodendron pinophilum Nees " G. H.
  {   Martin.
  Dimerium Juniperi Dearness.
  { Fomes juniperinus (v. Schrenk) Sacc. & Syd.
  { Fulvifomes juniperinus (v. Schrenk) Murrill.
  Fomes roseus (A. & S. ex Fr.) Cke.
  Gymnosporangium Betheli Kern.
  Gymnosporangium harknessianum Kern.
  Gymnosporangium inconspicuum Kern.
  Gymnosporangium juvenescens Kern.
  Gymnosporangium kernianum Bethel.
  Gymnosporangium Nelsoni Arth.
Juniperus oxycedrus Hochst.
  Gymnosporangium clavariaeforme (Jacq. ex
    P.) DC.
Juniperus pachyphloea Torr.
  Daedalea juniperina Murrill.
  Fomes roseus (A. & S. ex Fr.) Cke.
  Gymnosporangium exiguum Kern.
  Gymnosporangium kernianum Bethel.
  { Gymnosporangium gracilens Kern & Bethel.
  { Gymnosporangium speciosum Pk.

Juniperus pachyphloea (*cont.*)
Lenzites sepiaria (Wulf.) ex Fr.
Phomopsis juniperovora Hahn.
Trametes serialis Fr.

Juniperus Sabina L.
Phomopsis juniperovora Hahn.

Juniperus sabinoides (HBk.) Sarg.
Fomes Earlei (Murrill) Sacc.
Fomes texanus (Murrill) Hedgc. & Long.
Fomes roseus (A. & S. ex Fr.) Ckc.
Gymnosporangium exiguum Kern.
Gymnosporangium globosum Farl.
Peniophora texana Burt.
⎰Cyanospora Albicedrae Heald & Wolf.
⎱Robergea Albicedrae (Heald & Wolf) Sacc. &
Trav.

Juniperus scopulorum Sargent.
Cenangella deformata Pk.
⎰Fomes texanus (Murrill) Hedgc. & Long.
⎱Pyropolyporus texanus Murrill.
Gymnosporangium Betheli Kern.
Gymnosporangium clavipes C. & P.
Gymnosporangium globosum Farl.
Gymnosporangium Juniperi-virginianae S.
⎰Gymnosporangium juvenescens Kern.
⎱Gymnosporangium Nelsoni Fung. Columb.
5227.
Gymnosporangium Nelsoni Arth.
Gymnosporangium tubulatum Kern.
Peziza elaeodes Clements.
Phomopsis juniperovora Hahn.
Trametes serialis Fr.

Juniperus sibirica Burgsd.
Gymnosporangium clavariiforme (Jacq. ex
P.) DC.
Gymnosporangium clavipes C. & P.
Gymnosporangium Davisii Kern.
Gymnosporangium germinale Kern.
Gymnosporangium juniperinum (L.) ex P.
Herpotrichia nigra Hartig.
Phomopsis juniperovora Hahn.

Juniperus stricta Hort.
Sphaeropsis Juniperi Pk.

Juniperus utahensis Engelm.
Daedalea juniperina Murrill.
⎰Fomes Earlei (Murrill) Sacc. & D. Sacc.
⎱Fomes juniperinus (v. Schrenk) Sacc. & Syd.
Fomes roseus (A. & S. ex Fr.) Cke.
⎰Fomes texanus (Murrill) Hedgc. & Long.
⎱Pyropolyporus texanus Murrill.
Gymnosporangium durum Kern.
Gymnosporangium inconspicuum Kern.
Gymnosporanium kernianum Bethel.
Gymnosporangium multiporum Kern.
Gymnosporangium Nelsoni Arth.
⎰Gymnosporangium gracilens Kern & Bethel.
⎱Gymnosporangium speciosum Pk.

Juniperus virginiana L.

PEZIZINEAE

Agyrium rufum (P.) Fr.
Caldesia Sabinae (DeNot.) Rehm.
Cenangium Sequoiae Plowr.
⎰Lachnella cedrina (Cke. & Gerard) Sacc.
⎱Peziza cedrina Cke. & Gerard.
Patellaria dispersa Gerard.
⎰Cenangella deformata (Pk.) Sacc.
⎪Cenangium deformatum Pk.
⎨Karschia deformata Pk.
⎩Phaeangella deformata (Pk.) Sacc. & D. Sacc.
⎰Peziza cupressina P.
⎱Pitya Cupressi (Batsch) ex Rehm.
⎰Peziza incrustata Ell.
⎱Pseudohelotium incrustatum (Ell.) Sacc.
Tapesia sanguinea (P.) Fckl.

PHACIDIINEAE

⎰Clithris Juniperi (Karst.) Rehm.
⎪Colpoma juniperinum C. & P.
⎨Coccomyces Juniperi Karst.
⎪Hysterium Petersii B. & C.
⎩Lophodermium Petersii (B. & C.) Sacc.
Melittosporium hysterinum (Fr.) Gill.
Xylographa parallella Fr.

HYSTERIINEAE

Blitrydium Cucurbitaria Cke.
Hysterium Thujarum C. & P.
Mytilidion aggregatum (DC ex Fr.) Duby.
Mytilidion Juniperi Ell. & Ev.
⎰Hysterium tortile S.
⎱Mytilidion tortile (S.) Sacc.

SPHAERIALES

Ceratostoma juniperinum Ell. & Ev.
Chaetomastia juniperina (Karst.) Rehm.
⎰Cucurbitaria stipata (S.) Cke. ?
⎱Sphaeria stipata S.
⎰Diaporthe griseotingens (B. & C.) Sacc.
⎱Sphaeria griseotingens B. & C.
Diaporthe disputata Bomm. & Rouss.
Diatrype fibritecta C. & E.
⎰Coccodothis sphaeroidea (Cke.) Theissen &
⎪ Syd.
⎨Dothidea sphaeroidea Cke.
⎪Dothidella sphaeroidea (Cke.) Ell. & Ev.
⎩Phyllachora sphaeroidea Cke.
⎰Gibberella acervalis, var. Juniperi virginianae
⎨ Sacc.
⎩Sphaeria acervalis, var. Juniperi Desm.
Laestadia juniperina (Ell.) Sacc.
⎰Melanconis thelebola (Fr.) Sacc.
⎨Sphaeria thelebola Fr.
⎩Valsa thelebola Fr.
Melanomma Juniperi Ell. & Ev.
Melanopsamma cupressina Ell. & Ev.

Juniperus virginiana (*cont.*)

Microthyrium Juniperi (Desm.) Sacc.
Stigmatea Juniperi (Desm.) Wint.
Botryosphaeria fuliginosa Ell. & Ev. p. p.
Melanops Quercuum (S.) Rehm. 1876.
Melanops Quercuum (S.) Syd. sec. Dearness.
Melanops Quercuum (S.) Weese. 1925?
Melogramma fuliginosum Ell. p. p.
Physalospora thyoidea (C. & E.) Sacc.
Sphaeria thyoidea C. & E.
Rosellinia abietina Fckl.
Amphisphaeria deerrata (C. & E.) Cke.
Rosellinia deerrata (C. & E.) Sacc.
Sphaeria deerrata C. & E.
Thyridium lividum (P.) ex Sacc.
Valsa Abietis Fr.
Cytospora cenisia Sacc.
Valsa cenisia DeNot.
Valsa coryneoides B. & C.
Valsa juniperina Cke.

UREDINALES

Aecidium bermudianum Farl.
Gymnosporangium bermudianum Earle.
Tremella bermudiana Arth.
Gymnosporangium blasdaleanum Kern.
Gymnosporangium clavipes C. & P.
Gymnosporangium germinale Kern.
Gymnosporangium corniculans Kern.
Gymnosporangium cornutum Arth.
Gymnosporangium effusum Kern.
Gymnosporangium exiguum Kern.
Gymnosporangium externum Arth. & Kern.
Gymnosporangium flaviforme Earle.
Gymnosporangium floriforme Thax.
Gymnosporangium globosum Farl.
Puccinia globosa (Farl.) O. Kuntze.
Gymnosporangium Juniperi-virginianae S.
Gymnosporangium macropus Lk.
Podisoma macropus S.
Gymnosporangium juniperinum (L. ex P.) Fr.
Gymnosporangium juvenescens Kern.
Gymnosporangium Nelsoni Arth.
Gymnosporangium Juniperi Fung. Car. **5** : *87*.
Gymnosporangium Nidus-avis Thax.
Gymnosporangium trachysorum Kern.

DACRYOMYCETACEAE

Dacryomyces deliquescens (Bull.) ex Duby.
Guepinia Spathularia (S.) Fr.

TREMELLACEAE

Tremella aurantia S.

THELEPHORACEAE

Aleurodiscus nivosus (B.) v. Hoehnel & Lit-
  schauer.
Corticium acerinum, var. nivosum Thm.
Stereum acerinum Auct. Amer. p. p.
Stereum acerinum, var. nivosum B.
Stereum nivosum Rav. ex Underw. & Earle.

Coniophora brunneola (B. & C.) Sacc. Syll.
Coniophora Ellisii (B. & Cke.) Calkins.
Coniophora leucothrix (B. & C.) Sacc. Syll.
Corticium brunneolum B. & C.
Corticium Ellisii (B. & Cke.) Cke.
Hymenochaete Ellisii B. & Cke.
Corticium calceum Fr.
Cyphella cupulaeformis B. & Rav.
Grandinia tabacina C. & E.
Kneiffia candidissima B. & C.
Kneiffiella candidissima (B. & C.) Underw.
Neokneiffiella candidissima (B. & C.) Henn.
Kneiffia setigera Fr.
Neokneiffia aspera Earle.
Kneiffiella aspera Underw.
Peniophora carnosa Burt.
Peniophora flavidoalba Cke.
Peniophora laevigata (Fr.) Massee.
Peniophora Thujae Burt.
Stereum candidum S.
Stereum radiatum Pk.

POLYPORACEAE

Agaricus juniperinus Murrill.
Daedalea juniperina Murrill.
Fomes annosus (Fr.) Cke.
Fomes Demidoffii (Lév.) Sacc. Cub. & Manc.
Fomes Earlei (Murrill) Sacc. & D. Sacc.
Fomes juniperinus (v. Schrenk) Sacc. & Syd.
Fulvifomes juniperinus (v. Schrenk) Murrill.
Pyropolyporus Earlei Murrill.
Pyropolyporus juniperinus (v. Schrenk) Murrill.
Fomes roseus (A. & S. ex Fr.) Cke.
Lenzites sepiaria (Wulf.) ex Fr.
Gloeophyllum trabeum (P. ex Fr.) Murrill.
Lenzites vialis Pk.
Bjerkandera adusta (Willd. ex Fr.) Karst.
Polyporus adustus (Willd.) ex Fr.
Polyporus caesius (Schrad.) ex Fr.
Tyromyces caesius (Fr.) Murrill.
Polyporus dichrous Fr.
Hapalopilus gilvus (S.) Murrill.
Polyporus gilvus S.
Coriolus sericeohirsutus (Klotzsch) Murrill.
Funalia versatilis (B.) Murrill.
Funalia villosa (Sw. ex Fr.) Murrill.
Hexagona sericea Fr.
Hexagona sericeohirsuta (Klotzsch) M. A.
  Curtis.
Polyporus barbatulus (Fr.) Rav.
Polyporus pinsitus Fr.
Polyporus sericeohirsutus Klotzsch.
Polystictus barbatulus Fr.
Polystictus pinsitus (Fr.) Cke.
Polystictus villosus (Sw. ex Fr.) Cke.
Inonotus juniperinus Murrill.
Polyporus juniperinus (Murrill) Sacc. & Trott.
Polyporus pendulus (Fr.) Ell.
Porodisculus pendulus (S.) Murrill.

Juniperus virginiana (*cont.*)

- Coriolus versicolor (L. ex Fr.) Murrill.
- Polystictus versicolor (L.) ex Fr.
- Fuscoporia juniperina Murrill.
- Poria juniperina (Murrill) Sacc. & Trott.
- Polyporus leucolomeus Lév.
- Poria leucolomea (Lév.) Cke.
- Polyporus purpureus Fr.
- Poria purpurea (Fr.) Cke.
- Poria reticulata (Fr.) Cke.
- Poria vulgaris Fr.
- Poria Weirii Murrill.
- Porothelium Friesii Mont.
- Coriolellus sepium (B.) Murrill.
- Poria favescens (S.) Cke.
- Trametes favescens (S.) Lloyd.
- Trametes sepium B.
- Fomes carneus Auct. Amer. p. p.
- Polyporus carneus Auct. Amer. p. p.
- Polyporus Palliseri B.
- Trametes subrosea Weir.

Fungi Imperfecti

- Cercospora Sequoiae Ell. & Ev., var. Juniperi Ell. & Ev.
- Clasterisporium larvatum (C. & E.) Sacc.
- Sporidesmium larvatum C. & E.
- Dendrodochium densipes Sacc. & Ell.
- Diplodia kansensis Ell. & Ev.
- Diplodia virginiana Cke. & Rav.
- Discosia alnea (Fr.) B.
- Discosia virginiana Thm.
- Helminthosporium obclavatum Sacc.
- Botryodiplodia juniperina (Pk.) Petrak & Syd.
- Macrophoma juniperina Pk.
- Periconia Palmeri Earle.
- Pestalozzia funerea Desm.
- ?Phoma longipes B. & C.
- Phomopsis juniperovora Hahn.
- Macroplodia sabina House.
- Sphaeropsis Juniperi Pk.
- Cucurbitaria junipericola (S.) Cke.
- Sphaeria junipericola S.
- Sphaeropsis junipericola (S.) Cke.?
- Sphaeropsis maculans Pk.?
- Sphaeropsis juniperina Pk.
- Sporidesmium naviculum Dearness & House
- Sporidesmium pilulare Sacc.
- Stilbum lichenoideum B. & C.
- Streptothrix abietina Pk.
- Streptothrix atra B. & C.
- Streptothrix fusca Cda.
- Trichosporium olivatrum Sacc.
- Zygodesmus rudis Ell.

Miscellanea

- Clathroptychium rugulosum (Wallr.) Rostf.
- Crucibulum vulgare Tul.

Juniperus sp. indet.

- Aposphaeria fibricola (B.) Sacc.
- Phoma fibricola B.
- Asterostroma cervicoior (B. & C.) Massee.
- Corticium cervicolor B. & C.
- Cantharellus Petersii B. & C.
- Coniophora corrugis Burt.
- Corticium deglubens B. & C.
- Dendryphium Ellisii Cke.
- Didymosporium propolidioides Fairman.
- Dinemasporium galbulicola Rostr.
- Epicoccum scabrum Cda.
- Godronia Juniperi Rostr.
- Grandinia papillata B. & C.
- Herpotrichia nigra Hartig.
- Hydnum Caput-medusae Fr.
- Chromocrea ceramica (Ell. & Ev.) Seaver.
- Hypocrea ceramica Ell. & Ev.
- Illosporium coccinellum Cke.
- Endoxyla inusta (Cke.) Ell. & Ev.
- Kalmusia inusta (Cke.) Sacc.
- Sphaeria inusta Cke.
- Xylosphaeria inusta Cke.
- Karschia occidentalis Earle.
- Diplodia cupressina Cke.
- Microdiplodia cupressina (Cke.) Tassi.
- Ombrophila aurea Ell.
- Patinella flexella (Fr.) Sacc.
- Peziza flexella Fr.
- Phoma galbulorum Sacc. & Therry.
- Polyporus abietinus (Dicks.) ex Fr.
- Polyporus vulgaris Fr., var. calceus Fr.
- Septonema rude Sacc.
- Sporidesmium rude Ell.
- Stereum hirsutum (Willd.) ex Fr.
- Endoxyla Fraxini Ell. & Ev.
- Thyridaria Fraxini Ell. & Ev.
- Trametes Pini (Brot.) ex Fr.
- Tryblidiopsis occidentalis Earle.
- Conisphaeria albocincta C. & E.
- Sphaeria albocincta C. & E.
- Zignoella albocincta (C. & E.) Sacc.
- Zygodesmus bicolor C. & E.

Juniperus?? sp. indet. and "Cedar" gen. indet.

- Amphisphaeria aquatica (Ell. & Ev.) Berl. & Vogl.
- Didymosphaeria aquatica Ell. & Ev.
- Sphaeria aquatica Ell. & Ev.
- Amphisphaeria deformis Ell. & Langlois.
- Dacryomyces abietinus (P.) ex Schrt.
- Dacryomyces stillatus Nees ex Fr.
- Daedalea quercina L. ex Fr.
- Dendrodochium densipes Sacc. & Ell.
- Dendryphium Harknessii Ell.
- Gymnosporangium koreaense (Henn.) Jackson.
- Gymnosporangium Photiniae (Henn.) Kern.
- Helicomyces aureus Cda.
- Hypocrea armeniaca B. & C.
- Hypocrea minima Sacc. & Ell.

Juniperus sp. indet. (*cont.*)
  Lycogala epidendrum [Buxb. ex L.] Fr.
  Marasmius candidus (Bolt.) ex Fr.
  Marasmius praeacutus Ell.
  Melanomma deciduum Ell. & Ev.
  Merulius bellus B. & C.
  Mycena haematopoda Fr.
  Odontia fusca C. & E.
  Ombrophila subaurea Cke.
  Pestalozzia Hartigii v. Tubeuf.
  Peziza ancilis P.?
  Peziza caucus Reb. ex P.
  Pleiopatella Harperi Rehm.
  ⎰Mucronoporus circinatus (Fr.) Ell. & Ev.
  ⎱Polyporus circinatus Fr.
  Polyporus osseus Fr.
  Polyporus Schweinitzii Fr.
  Poria candidissima (S.) Cke.
  ⎰Polyporus farinellus Fr.
  ⎱Polyporus tenellus N. A. F.
  ⎱Poria farinella (Fr.) Cke.
  Poria subacida (Pk.) Sacc. Syll.
  Pseudographis intermedia Rehm.
  Sebacina deglubens (B. & C.) Burt.
  Solenia villosa Fr.
  Stereum rameale (S.) Reddick.
  Trametes Pini (Brot.) ex Fr.
  Xylographa parallela (Ach.) ex Fr.

Coniferae gen. indet.

MYXOMYCETES

  Arcyria denudata (L.) Sheldon.
  Dianema corticatum Lister.
  Physarum fulvum Lister.
  Tilmadoche alba (Bull.) Macbr.
  Trichia fallax P.

ASCOMYCETES

  Ascobolus xylophilus Seaver.
  Calloria atrosanguinea Rehm.
  Ciboria fuscocinerea Rehm.
  Lahmia Waghornii Rehm.
  Mycobilimbia atrosanguinea Rehm.
  Nectria indigens Gifford?
  Ophionectria scolecospora Bref.
  Otidea leporina (Batsch ex Fr.) Fckl.
  ⎰Lecanidion argyrioides (Rehm) Sacc. & Syd.
  ⎱Patellaria agyrioides Rehm.
  Patellaria subvelata Ell. & Ev.
  Peziza connivens Fr.
  Scleroderris Treleasei Sacc.
  Trichosphaeria breviseta Dearness.
  Trichothecium roseum Lk.
  Urnula terrestris (Niessl) Sacc.
  ⎰Hypoxylon Beaumontii B. & C.
  ⎱Valsaria? Beaumontii (B. & C.) Sacc.
  Sphaeria caerulea Ell. & Ev.
  ⎰Winteria caerulea (Ell. & Ev.) Berl. & Vogl.
  ⎱Winterina caerulea (Ell. & Ev.) Sacc.

THELEPHORACEAE

  Aleurodiscus cerussatus (Bres.) v. Höhnel &
    Litschauer.
  Coniophora avellanea Burt.
  Coniophora corrugis Burt.
  Coniophora laeticolor Karst.
  Coniophora olivascens (B. & C.) Massee.
  Coniophora sistotremoides (S.) Massee.
  Corticium abeuns Burt.
  Corticium bicolor Pk.
  Corticium canum Burt.
  Corticium cultum Burt.
  Corticium investiens (S.) Bres.
  Corticium involucrum Burt.
  Corticium lividum P.
  Corticium radiosum Fr.
  Corticium roseum P.
  Corticium vinaceum Burt.
  Hypochnus canadensis Burt.
  Hypochnus fibrillosus Burt.
  Hypochnus fumosus Fr.
  Hypochnus isabellinus Fr.
  ⎰Hypochnus olivascens (B. & C.) Burt.
  ⎱Zygodesmus olivascens B. & C.
  Hypochnus subferruginosus Burt.
  Hypochnus subviolaceus Pk.
  Hypochnus umbrinus (Fr.) Burt.
  Peniophora alba Burt.
  Peniophora coccineo-fulva (S.) Burt.
  Peniophora globifera Ell. & Ev.
  Peniophora longispora (Pat.) v. Höhnel.
  Peniophora miniata (B.) Burt.
  Peniophora Peckii Burt.
  Peniophora pertenuis (Karst.) Burt.
  Peniophora pilosa Burt.
  Peniophora pubera (Fr.) Sacc.
  Peniophora Roumeguerii Bres.
  Peniophora sanguinea (Fr.) Bres.
  Peniophora separans Burt.
  Peniophora sulphurina (Karst.) v. Höhnel &
    Litschauer.
  Peniophora tabacina Burt.
  Peniophora tenella Burt.
  Peniophora velutina (DC. ex Fr.) Cke.
  Peniophora verticillata Burt.
  Peniophora zonata Burt.
  Stereum complicatum Fr.

POLYPORACEAE

  ⎰Daedalea cervina (P.) Lloyd.
  ⎱Polyporus stereoides Fr.
  ⎱Trametes stereoides (Fr.) Bres.
  ⎰Cerrena unicolor (Bull. ex Fr.) Murrill.
  ⎱Daedalea unicolor (Bull.) ex Fr.
  Fomes connatus (Weinm.) Gill.
  Fomes putearius Weir.
  Merulius americanus Burt.
  Merulius Pinastri (Fr.) Burt.
  Merulius terrestris (Pk.) Burt.

Coniferae gen. indet. (*cont.*)
  Tyromyces guttulatus (Pk.) Murrill.
  { Leptoporus mexicanus Pat.
  { Polyporus mexicanus (Pat.) Sacc. & Syd.
  Polyporus perdelicatus Murrill.
  Polyporus pilosus Morg.
  { Coriolus serialia (Fr.) Murrill.
  { Polystictus serialis (Fr.) Cke.
  { Coltricia tomentosa (Fr.) Murrill.
  { Polystictus tomentosus (Fr.) Cke.
  Poria Dodgei Murrill.
  Poria montana Murrill.
  Poria semitincta Pk.
  Poria sericeo-mollis Romell.

AGARICACEAE

{ Flammula astragalina Fr.
{ Flammula laeticolor Murrill.
  Galera Coniferarum (Murrill) Sacc. & Trott.
  Galera lignicola (Murrill) Sacc. & Trott.
  Heliomyces pruinosipes Pk.
{ Lentinus lepideus Fr.
{ Lentodium squamosum (Schaeff.) ex Murrill.
  Marasmius papillatus Pk.
{ Mycena albogrisea Pk.
{ Prunulus albogriseus (Pk.) Murrill.
{ Mycena alcaliniformis Murrill.
{ Prunulus alcaliniformis Murrill.
  Mycena haematopa B.
{ Mycena occidentalis Murrill.
{ Prunulus occidentalis Murrill.
{ Mycena purpureofuscus Pk.
{ Prunulus purpureofuscus (Pk.) Murrill.
{ Mycena rugosoides Murrill.
{ Prunulus rugosoides Murrill.

{ Mycena subtenuipes Murrill.
{ Prunulus subtenuipes Murrill.
{ Omphalia luteicolor Murrill.
{ Omphalina luteicolor Murrill.
  Omphalia umbellifera(L.) ex Fr.
  Omphalia umbellifera (L.) ex Fr., var. abiegnus
    Pk.
  Pholiota marginella Pk.
  Tricholoma fallax Pk.

MISCELLANEA

Coniothecium toruloides Cda.
Fusarium oxysporum Schl.
Fusoma parasiticum v. Tubeuf.
Heterochaete microspora Burt.
Odontia latitans (Karst.) Kauffman.
Phlebia merismoides Fr.
Phlebia vaga Fr.
Phoma Pini Cke. & Hark.

GNETACEAE

Ephedra antisyphilitica C. A. Mey.
Ephedra californica Watson.
Ephedra pedunculata Engelm.
Ephedra torreyana Watson.
Ephedra trifurca Torr.
Ephedra viridis Coville.
  { Aecidium Pini, var. Ephedrae B. & C.
  { Peridermium Ephedrae Cke.
  { Peridermium Pini, var. minor B. & C.
Ephedra nevadensis Watson.
  Peridermium Ephedrae Cke.
  Schizostoma nevadensis Ell. & Ev.
Ephedra viridis Coville
  Teichospora megastega Ell. & Ev.

ANGIOSPERMAE

MONOCOTYLEDONEAE

TYPHACEAE

Typha angustifolia L.
  Cladosporium Typharum Desm.
  Leptosphaeria hydrophila Sacc.
  Melanconium Typhae Pk.
Typha latifolia L.
  Cladosporium fasciculatum Cda.
  Cladosporium herbarum (P.) ex Lk.
  Cladosporium Typhae S.
  Cladosporium Typharum Desm.
  Dictyosporium opacum Cke. & Hark.
  {Didymosphaerella Typhae (Pk.) Cke.
  {Didymosphaeria Typhae Pk.
  Epicoccum scabrum Cda.
  Epicoccum sphaerospermum B.
  Fusella Typhae Lindau.
  Hymenopsis hydrophila Sacc.
  Leptosphaeria luctuosa Niessl.
  Leptosphaeria Michotii (Westd.) Sacc.
  Leptosphaeria praeclara, var. typhiseda
    (Sacc. & Berl.) Berl.
  Leptosphaeria punctillum Rehm.
  Leptosphaeria Typhae Karst.
  Leptosphaeria Typharum Karst.
  {Hysterium typhinum Fr.
  {Lophodermium typhinum (Fr.) Lamb.
  Peniophora typhicola Burt.
  Peziza Typhae Pk.
  Phoma orthosticta Ell. & Ev.
  {Leptosphaeria Typharum (Desm.) Karst.
  {Phoma Typharum (Desm.) Sacc.
  Phoma typhicola Oud.
  {Phyllactinia corylea (P.) ex Karst.
  {Phyllactinia suffulta (Reb.) ex Sacc.
  Phyllosticta Renouana Sacc.
  Phyllosticta typhina Sacc. & Malbr.
  Pleospora infectoria Fckl.
  Pleospora rubicunda Niessl.
  Pleospora Typhae Pass.
  Scirrhia groveana Sacc.
  Scolecotrichum Typhae Ell. & Ev.
  Sphaerella Tassiana DeNot.
  {Mycosphaerella Typhae (Lasch) Lindau.
  {Sphaerella Typhae (Lasch) Awd.
  Sphaeria Typhae S.
  Sphaeropsis typhina Pk.
  Stagonospora typhoidearum (Desm.) Sacc.
Typha sp. indet.
  Aulographum maculare B. & Br.
  Chaetomium Typhae S.

  {Darluca angusta Cke.
  {Septoria angusta (Cke.) Sacc.
  {Didymella intercellularis (B. & C.) Sacc.
  {Sphaerella intercellularis (B. & C.) Cke.
  {Sphaeria intercellularis B. & C.
  Hendersonia Typhae Oud.
  Leptosphaeria typhicola Karst.

PANDANACEAE

Pandanus utilis Bory.
  Colletotrichum omnivorum Halsted.
  Diderma effusum (S.) Morg.
  Melanconium Pandani Lév.
  Phyllosticta pandanicola E. Young.
  Volutella mellea Clark.
  Zygosporium oscheoides Mont.
Pandanus sp. indet.
  Cladosporium herbarum (P.) ex Lk.
  Physalospora Pandani Ell. & Ev.

SPARGANIACEAE

Sparganium eurycarpum Engelm.
  Cylindrosporium Sparganii (Pass.) Ell. & Ev.
  Stagonospora Sparganii (Fckl.) Sacc.
  {Nigredo Sparganii (C. & P.) Arth.
  {Uromyces Sparganii C. & P.

NAIADACEAE

Potamogeton americanus C. & S.
  Ramularia aquatilis Pk.
Potamogeton epihydrus Raf.
Potamogeton natans L.
  {Doassansia martianoffiana (Thm.) Schrt.
  {Doassansiopsis martianoffiana (Thm.) Diet.
  {Doassansia occulta (Hoffm.) Cornu.
  {Doassansiopsis occulta (Hoffm.) Diet.
  Doassansia occulta, var. Farlowii (Cornu)
    Setch.
Potamogeton lucens L.
  Ramularia aquatilis Pk.
Potamogeton perfoliatus L., var. **lanceolatus**
  Robbins.
Potamogeton pusillus L.
Potamogeton Vaseyi Robbins.
  {Doassansia Farlowii Cornu.
  {Doassansia occulta, var. Farlowii (Cornu)
  { Setch.
  {Doassansia occulta (Hoffm.) Cornu.
  {Sclerotium occultum Hoffm.
Diplanthera Wrightii Aschers.
  Ostenfeldiella Diplantherae Ferd. & Winge.

JUNCAGINACEAE

Triglochin concinna Davy.
- Aecidium Triglochinis Diet. & Holw.
- Puccinia subnitens Diet. I.

Triglochin maritima L.
- Aecidium Triglochinis Diet. & Holw.
- Dicaeoma Sarcobati Arth. I.
- Puccinia subnitens Diet. I.
- Pleospora herbarum (P.) ex Rabh.

Triglochin palustris L.
- Asteroma Juncaginearum Rabh.
- Leptosphaeria Triglochinis Schrt.
- Pleospora herbarum (Fr.) Rabh., var., Triglochinis Dearness & House.
- Pleospora Triglochinis Hariot & Briard.

Triglochin striata R. & P.
- Aecidium Triglochinis Diet. & Holw.
- Dicaeoma Sarcobati Arth. I.

ALISMACEAE

Alisma Plantago-aquatica L.
- Ascochyta Alismatis Ell. & Ev.
- Cercospora Alismatis Ell. & Ev.
- Cercospora pachyspora Ell. & Ev.
- Cladochytrium Alismatis Büsgen.
- Cladochytrium maculare (Wallr.) J. J. Davis.
- Physoderma maculare Wallr.
- Protomyces macrosporus J. J. Davis p. p. non Ung.
- Cylindrosporium baudysianum Sacc.
- Doassansia Alismatis (Nees) Cornu.
- Phyllosticta Alismatis Sacc. & Speg., var. minor Ell. & Ev.
- Physoderma maculare Wallr.
- Pleospora Alismatis Ell. & Ev.
- Ramularia Alismatis Fautr.
- Rhynchosporium Alismatis (Oud.) J. J. Davis.
- Septoria Alismatis Oud.

Echinodorus cordifolius (L.) Griseb.
- Burrillia Echinodori G. P. Clinton.
- Doassansia Alismatis (Nees) Cornu?
- Doassansia Alismatis Hark. nec Cornu.
- Entyloma sp.

Lophotocarpus calycinus (Engelm.) J. G. Sm.
- Doassansia Sagittariae (Westd.) Fisch.

Sagittaria arifolia Nutt.
- Doassansia Sagittariae (Westd.) Fisch.
- Gloeosporium confluens Ell. & Dearness.

Sagittaria graminea Michx.
- Doassansia Sagittariae (Westd.) Fisch.

Sagittaria heterophylla Pursh.
- Cercospora Sagittariae Ell. & Kellerm.
- Doassansia (Doassansiopsis) furva J. J. Davis.
- Doassansia Sagittariae (Westd.) Fisch.
- Doassansia Sagittariae (Westd.) Fisch., var. confluens J. J. Davis.
- Ramularia Alismatis Fautr.
- Ramularia Sagittariae Bres.
- Rhynchosporium Alismatis (Oud.) J. J. Davis.

Sagittaria heterophylla Pursh, var. **angustifolia** Engelm.
- Doassansia deformans Setch.

Sagittaria lancifolia L.
- Cercospora Sagittariae Ell. & Kellerm.

Sagittaria latifolia Willd.
- Burrillia pustulata Setch.
- Cercospora Sagittariae Ell. & Kellerm.
- Doassansia deformans Setch.
- Doassansiopsis deformans (Setch.) Diet.
- Doassansia affinis Ell. & Dearness.
- Doassansia intermedia Setch.
- Doassansia obscura Setch.
- Doassansia opaca Setch.
- Doassansia Alismatis Trel. p. p.
- Burrillia pustulata Setch. non Cornu.
- Doassansiopsis pustulata (Setch.) Diet.
- Doassansia Alismatis Auct. Amer. p. p.
- Doassansia Sagittariae (Westd.) Fisch.
- Protomyces Sagittariae Fckl.
- Uredo Sagittariae Westd.
- Epicoccum vulgare Cda.
- Gloeosporium confluens Ell. & Dearness.

Sagittaria sp. indet.
- Cylindrosporium baudysianum Sacc.

GRAMINEAE

Euchlaena mexicana Schrad.
- Helminthosporium turcicum Pass.
- Ophiobolus heterostrophus Drechsler.
- Physoderma Zeae-maydis Shaw.
- Dicaeoma Sorghi (S.) O. Kuntze.
- Puccinia Maydis Bereng.
- Puccinia Sorghi S.
- Septoriella Mexicana Sacc.
- Sclerospora graminocila (Sacc.) Schrt.
- Poria Corcos Wolf.
- Ustilago Euchlaenae Arcang.
- Cf. Ustilago Zeae-Mays Trel. p. p.
- Ustilago Kellermanii G. P. Clinton.
- Ustilago Zeae (S.) Curt. Cat.
- Ustilago Zeae-Mays (DC.) Wint.

Zea Mays L.

MYXOMYCETES
- Craterium Maydis Morg.
- Physarum cinereum (Batsch) P.
- Physarum gravidum Morg.

PHYCOMYCETES
- Mucor Mucedo L. pp. ex Bref.
- Mucor rhizopodiformis Cohn.
- Physoderma Zeae-maydis Shaw.
- Phytophthora Cactorum (Lebert & Cohn) Schrt.
- Pythium debaryanum Hesse.
- Rhizopus nigricans Ehrenb. †
- Sclerospora graminicola (Sacc.) Schrt.
- Sclerospora macrospora Sacc.
- Sclerospora Maydis (Rac.) Butl.

Zea Mays (*cont.*)

Ascomycetes

Monascus purpureus Went.
Papulospora pannosa Hotson.
Papulospora sporotrichoides Hotson.

Pezizineae

Helotiella pygmaea Ell. & Ev.
{ Karschia imperfecta (Ell.) Sacc.
{ Patellaria imperfecta Ell.
Lecanidion atratum (Hedw. ex Fr.) Rabh.

Hypocreales

{ Calonectria Curtisii (B.) Sacc.
{ Dialonectria Curtisii (B.) Cke.
{ Nectria Curtisii B.
{ Dialonectria gibberelloides Ell. & Ev.
{ Nectria gibberelloides (Ell. & Ev.) Sacc.
{ Gibbera pulicaris Fr.
{ Gibberella pulicaris (Fr.) Sacc.
{ Sphaeria pulicaris Fr.
Gibberella pulicaris (Fr.) Sacc., var. Saubinetii Rehm.
{ Dothidea Zeae S.
{ Gibbera Saubinetii Mont.
{ Gibberella Saubinetii (Mont.) Sacc.
{ Sphaeria Maydis B.
{ Sphaeria Saubinetii Mont.
{ Sphaeria Zeae S.
Nectria pulicaris N. A. F. *81* non Fr.
Ophionectria cylindrothecia Seaver.

Dothideales

Dictyochora Gambellii Fairman.
Phyllachora Cynodontis (Sacc.) Niessl.
Phyllachora graminis (P. ex Fr.) Fckl.
Phyllachora Maydis Maubl.
{ Dothidea nigrescens S.
{ Phyllachora nigrescens (S.) Sacc.
Phyllachora sphaerosperma Wint.
Rhopographus clavisporus (C. & P.) Ell. & Ev.

Sphaeriales

{ Anthostoma mortuosum (Ell.) Sacc.
{ Sphaeria mortuosa Ell.
Chaetomium funicola Cke.
Chaetomium melioloides C. & P.
{ Diaporthe Kellermanniana Ell. & Ev. nec Wint.
{ Diaporthe incongrua Ell. & Ev.
Diaporthe Kellermanniana Wint.
{ Sphaeria Maydis B.
{ Diaporthe Maydis Ell. & Ev.
Erysiphe graminis DC. †
{ Conisphaeria ceratispora (B. & C.) Cke.
{ Heptameria ceratispora (B. & C.) Cke.
{ Leptosphaeria ceratispora (B. & C.) Sacc.
{ Sphaeria ceratispora B. & C.
Leptosphaeria eustoma (Fr.) Sacc.

{ Heptameria interspersa Cke.
{ Leptosphaeria interspersa (Cke.) Sacc.
{ Sphaeria interspersa Cke.
{ Heptameria orthogramma (B. & C.) Cke.
{ Leptosphaeria orthogramma (B. & C.) Sacc.
{ Sphaeria orthogramma B. & C.
Lophiosphaera zeicola Ell. & Ev.
Lophiostoma Arundinis (Fr.) Ces. & De Not.
Melanospora pampeana Speg.
{ Metasphaeria ceratotheca (Cke.) Sacc.
{ Sphaeria ceratotheca Cke.
{ Leptosphaeria hyalospora Sacc.
{ Metasphaeria hyalospora Sacc.
{ Sphaeria hyalospora N. A. F.
Ophiobolus acuminatus (Sow. ex Fr.) Duby.
Ophiobolus heterostrophus Drechsler.
{ Ophiobolus porphyrogonus (Tode) ex Sacc.
{ Ophiobolus rubellus (P. ex Fr.) Rehm.
Perisporium vulgare Cda.
Perisporium Zeae B. & C.
Physalospora zeicola Ell. & Ev.
Pleospora rubicunda Niessl.
{ Podospora minor Ell. & Fr.
{ Sordaria minor (Ell. & Ev.) Sacc. & Syd.
Sphaerella paulula Cke.
Sphaeria fissa P.?
Sphaeria striiformis var. g., S.
Xylaria filiformis (A. & S.) ex Fr., var. caulicola Rehm.

Ustilaginales

{ Sorosporium reilianum (Kühn) McAlpine.
{ Sphacelotheca reiliana (Kühn) G. P. Clinton.
{ Ustilago reiliana Kühn.
{ Ustilago reiliana Kühn, var. foliicola Kellerm.
?Ustilago Sorghi Auct.
{ Caeoma Zeae S. Am. Bor.
{ Uredo Zeae S. Syn. Car.
{ Ustilago Carbo Auct. Amer. p. p.
{ Ustilago Maydis Cda.
{ Ustilago Schweinitzii Tul.
{ Ustilago Zeae (Beckm.) Ung. 1836.
{ Ustilago Zeae (S.) Curt. Cat. 1867.
{ Ustilago Zeae-Mays (DC.) Wint.

Uredinales

{ Dicaeoma pallescens (Arth.) Arth. & Fromme.
{ Puccinia pallescens Arth.
{ Uredo pallida Diet. & Holw.
Puccinia purpurea Cke.
{ Dicaeoma Sorghi (S.) O. Kuntze.
{ Puccinia Maydis Bereng.
{ Puccinia Sorghi S.

Hymenomycetineae

Clavaria trichomorpha S.
Coprinus Brassicae Pk.
{ Corticium vagum B. & C.
{ Rhizoctonia Solani Kühn.
Entoloma demetriacum B. & Mont.

Zea Mays (*cont.*)

{ Hypochnus granulosus Burt.
{ Zygodesmus chlorochaites N. A. F. *423*.
Marasmius capillaris Morg.
{ Himantia stellifera Johnston.
{ Odontia saccharicola Burt.
Poria Cocos Wolf.
{ Schizophyllum alneum (L. ex Fr.) Schrt.
{ Schizophyllum commune Fr.

SPHAEROPSIDALES

Ascochyta zeicola Ell. & Ev.
Darluca Filum (Biv.) Cast.
Dinemasporium bicristatum Cke.
{ Dinemasporium graminum (Lib.) Lév.
{ Vermicularia graminum Lib.
Diplodia frumenti Ell. & Ev.
Diplodia macrospora Earle.
Macrodiplodia Zeae (S.) Petrak & Syd
{ Diplodia Maydis (B.) Sacc.
{ Diplodia Zeae (S.) Lév.
Hendersonia Zeae (S.) Hazsl.
Macrophoma Zeae Tehon & Daniels.
Phoma Maydis Ell. & Ev.
Phoma zeicola Ell. & Ev.
Vermicularia atramentaria B. & Br.

MELANCONIALES

{ Colletotrichum cereale Manns.
{ Colletotrichum graminicola G. W. Wilson.
{ Colletotrichum lineola Auct. Amer. an Cda.
{ Psilonia apalospora B. & C. nom. nud.

HYPHOMYCETES

MUCEDINACEAE

Aspergillus alutaceus B. & C.
Aspergillus flavus Lk.
Eurotium Aspergillus-glaucus DBy.
{ Aspergillus fuliginosus Pk.
{ Aspergillus niger van Tiegh.
{ Sterigmatocystis nigra van Tiegh.
{ Ustilago Fischeri Pass.
Basisporium gallarum Molliard.
Botrytis vulgaris (Lk.) ex Fr.
Cephalosporium acremonium Cda.
Cephalosporium Sacchari Butler.
Cephalothecium roseum Cda.
?Dactylium dendroides (Bull.) ex Fr.
Helicomyces mirabilis Pk.
Monilia candida Bon.
{ Monilia Martinii Ell. & Sacc.
{ Oospora Martinii (Ell. & Sacc.) Sumstine.
Monilia sitophila (Mont.) Sacc.
Oospora verticilloides Sacc.
Penicillium armeniacum B.
Penicillium glaucum (L.) ex Fr.
Penicillium purpurogenum Stoll.
Rhinotrichum cucumerinum B. & C.
Sporotrichum atropurpureum Pk.

Sporotrichum flavissimum Lk.?
Sporotrichum fuliginosum P.
Sporotrichum Himantiae S.

DEMATIACEAE

{ Alternaria fasciculata (C. & E.) Jones & Grout.
{ Macrosporium Maydis C. & E.
Cercospora Sorghi Ell. & Ev.
Cercospora Zeae-maydis Tehon & Daniels.
Cladosporium graminum Cda.
Cladosporium herbarum (P.) ex Lk.
Cladosporium herbarum (P.) ex Lk., var. indutum Thm.
Cladosporium tenuissimum Cke.
Cladosporium Zeae Pk.
Clasterosporium olivaceum Ell. & Ev.
Coniosporium Maydis Ell. & Barthol.
Coniosporium Gecevi Bubák.
{ Helicomyces cinereus (Pk.) Morg.
{ Helicosporium cinereum Pk.
{ Helicosporium lumbricoides Sacc.
Helicosporium vegetum Nees ex Fr.
Helminthosporium folliculatum Cda.
Helminthosporium gramineum Rabh.
Helminthosporium teres Sacc.
{ Helminthosporium inconspicuum C. & E.
{ Helminthosporium turcicum Pass.
Heterosporium Phragmitis (Opiz?) Sacc.
Isariopsis subulata Ell. & Ev.
Macrosporium culmorum Cke. & Hark.
Monotospora nigra Morg.
Mystrosporium erectum Ell. & Ev.
{ Periconia digitata (Cke.) Sacc.
{ Sporocybe digitata Cke.
Scolecotrichum graminis Fckl.
Septosporium praelongum Sacc.
Sporidesmium millegrana B. & C.
Tetraploa Ellisii Cke.
Torula herbarum Lk.
Trichosporium sphaericum Sacc.
Triposporium bicorne Morg.

TUBERCULARIACEAE

Epicoccum neglectum Desm.
Epicoccum sphaerospermum B. & C.
{ Fusarium cerealis (Cke.) Sacc.
{ Fusisporium cerealis Cke.
Fusarium culmorum (W. G. Sm.) Sacc.
Fusarium discolor, var. majus C. E. Lewis.
Fusarium graminum Cda.
Fusarium Helianthi C. E. Lewis.
{ Fusarium herbarum (Cda.) Fr.
{ Fusisporium rimosum Pk.
Fusarium moniliforme Sheldon.
Fusarium Poae (Pk.) C. E. Lewis.
Fusarium roseum Lk.
Fusarium succisae (Schrt.) Sacc.
Fusarium Zeae (Westd.) Sacc.
Fusisporium aurantiacum Lk.

Zea Mays (*cont.*)
  Fusisporium graminum Ces.
  { Fusisporium roseum Lk.
  { Haplographium griseum Ell. & Langlois.
  { Hymenella haematococca B. & C.
  { Hymenula haematococca (B. & C.) Sacc.
  Illosporium pallidum Cke.
  { Spegazzinia tessarthra (B. & C.) Sacc.
  { Sporidesmium tessarthra B. & C.
  Tubercularia sarmentorum Fr.

MISCELLANEA

  Mycorrhiza of Legumes F. R. Jones.
  Rhizoctonia grisea (Stevenson) Matz.
  Rhizoctonia pallida Matz.
  Sclerotium griseum Stevenson (ined.).
  Sclerotium Rolfsii Sacc.
  Streptothrix cinerea Morg.
  Ustilaginoidea virens (Cke.) Tak.

Tripsacum dactyloides L.
  Claviceps purpurea (Fr.) Tul.
  { Claviceps Tripsaci Stevens & Hall.
  { Spermoedia Tripsaci (Stevens & Hall) Hall.
  { Cf. Spermoedia Tripsaci M. A. Curtis.
  { Colletotrichum graminicola (Ces.) G. W.
  {   Wilson.
  { Vermicularia culmigena Auct. Amer. an Desm.
  Epicoccum neglectum Desm.
  { Puccinia pallescens Arth.
  { Uredo pallida Diet. & Holw.
  { Dicaeoma Ceanothi (Arth.) Arth. & Fromme.
  { Puccinia Ceanothi Arth.
  { Puccinia Pattersoniae Syd.
  { Puccinia Sorghi Myc. Ex. 116[b].
  { Puccinia Tripsaci Diet. & Holw.
  { Dicaeoma polysorum (Underw.) Arth.
  { Puccinia polysora Underw.
  Ustilago dieteliana Henn.

Tripsacum lanceolatum Rupr.
  Dicaeoma Ceanothi (Arth.) Arth. & Fromme.
  { Dicaeoma pallescens (Arth.) Arth. & Fromme.
  { Puccinia pallescens Diet. & Holw.
  { Uredo pallida Diet. & Holw.
  Dicaeoma polysorum (Underw.) Arth.

Tripsacum latifolium Hitchc.
  { Dicaeoma pallescens (Arth.) Arth. & Fromme.
  { Uredo pallida Diet. & Holw.
  { Dicaeoma polysorum (Underw.) Arth.
  { Puccinia polysora Underw.

Tripsacum laxum Nash.
  Puccinia Ceanothi Arth.
  Puccinia polysora Underw.

Coix Lacryma-Jobi L.
  Ustilago Coicis Bref.

Imperata brasiliensis Trin.
  { Dicaeoma infuscans (Arth. & Holw.) Arth. &
  {   Fromme.
  { Puccinia infuscans Arth. & Holw.

Imperata contracta (H. B. K.) Hitchc.
  Phyllachora Andropogonis (S.) Karst. &
    Hariot.
Miscanthus sinensis Anders.
  { Coccularia graminis Cke. in exs.
  { Chaetostroma atrum Sacc.
Saccharum officinarum L.

MYXOMYCETES

  Arcyria cinerea (Bull.) Schum.
  Arcyria denudata Fr.
  Craterium aureum (Schum.) Rostf.
  Craterium leucocephalum (P.) Rostf.
  Dictydium cancellatum (Batsch) Macbr.
  Fuligo septica (L.) Gmel.
  Lycogala epidendrum [Buxb. ex L.] Fr.
  Physarum cinereum (Batsch) P.
  Physarum compressum A. & S.
  Physarum nodulosum (Cke. & Balf.) Massee.
  Plasmodiophora Brassicae Wor.
  Plasmodiophora vascularum Matz.
  Stemonitis fusca Roth.
  Stemonitis splendens Rostf.

PHYCOMYCETES

  Pythium Artotrogus (Mont.) DBy.
  { Pythium Butleri Subramanian. sec. Coons.
  { Rheosporangium aphanidermatum Edson sec.
  {   Carpenter.
  { Pythium spec. indet. Drechsler.
  Pythium debaryanum Hesse.

ASCOMYCETES

  ?Acanthorhynchus Vaccinii Shear.
  Amphitrichum Sacchari Spreng.
  Calonectria gigaspora Massee.
  Chaetomium globosum Kze. ex Fr.
  Chromocrea gelatinosa (Fr.) Seaver.
  Chromocreopsis striispora Stevenson.
  { Creonectria laurentiana Marchal, Seaver &
  {   Chardon.
  { Nectria laurentiana Marchal.
  Creonectria rubrosulphurea Seaver.
  Eriosphaeria Sacchari Went.
  Eurotium argentinum Speg.
  Gibberella pulicaris (Fr.) Sacc.
  Gnomonia Iliau Edgerton.
  Hypocrea rufa (P. ex Fr.) Fr.
  Hypocrea Sacchari Went.
  Lachnea cubensis (B. & C.) Sacc.
  Leptosphaeria Sacchari van Breda de Haan.
  Leptosphaeria saccharicola Henn.
  Melanconis Sacchari Massee.
  Melanconium Iliau Lyon.
  Monascus purpureus Went.
  Mycosphaerella striatiformans Cobb.
  Nectria flavociliata Seaver.
  Physalospora tucumanensis Speg.
  Rosellinia paraguayensis Stark.
  Rosellinia pulveracea (Ehrh.) Fckl.

Saccharum officinarum (*cont.*)

Scirrhia lophodermioides Ell. & Ev.
{ Mycosphaerella Sacchari (Speg.) Seaver & Chardon.
{ Sphaerella Sacchari Speg.
Sphaerella saccharoides Pk.
Sphaerulina Sacchari Henn.
Thielavia paradoxa (B. & Br.) Zopf.
Trichosphaeria Sacchari Massee.
Valsa sacchari Stevenson (ined.) non DeNot.
Valsaria subtropica Speg.
Xylaria apiculata Cke.

UREDINALES

Puccinia purpurea Cke.
Uredo Kuhnii Wakker & Went.

DACRYOMYCETINEAE

Guepinia palmiceps B.
Guepinia spathulata Jung.

HYMENOMYCETINEAE

Asterostroma cervicolor (B. & C.) Massee.
Cladoderris dendritica P.
Corticium arachnoideum B.
{ Corticium vagum B. & C.
{ Rhizoctonia Solani Kühn.
Hydnum Sacchari Spreng.
Hypochnus Sacchari Speg.
Lentinus crinitus (L.) ex Fr.
Marasmius bambusinus Fr.
Marasmius borinquensis Stevenson.
Marasmius hiorami Murrill.
Marasmius plicatilis Wakker.
Marasmius Sacchari Wakker.
Marasmius Sacchari, var. hawaiiensis Cobb.
{ Marasmius plicatus Auct. Amer. non Wakk.
{ Marasmius semiustus B. & C.
{ Marasmius stenophyllus Mont.
Marasmius synodicus (Kze.) Fr.
Merulius byssoideus Burt.
Naucoria Sacchari Murrill.
Odontia Sacchari Burt.
{ Himantia stellifera Johnston.
{ Odontia saccharicola Burt.
Peniophora cinerea (Fr.) Cke.
Peniophora flavido-alba Cke.
Peniophora rimosissima (B. & C.) Burt.
Peniophora Sacchari Burt.
Polyporus occidentalis Klotzsch.
Polystictus sanguineus (Sw.) ex Fr.
Polystictus sinuosus (Fr.) Sacc.
Psilocybe atomatoides Pk.
{ Schizophyllum alneum (L. ex Fr.) Schrt.
{ Schizophyllum commune Fr.
Schizophyllum lobatum Went.
Scytinotus distantifolius Murrill.
Sphaerobolus stellatus Tode ex Fr.
Trametes nivosa (B.) Murrill.
Tremellodendron simplex Burt.

GASTEROMYCETES

Cyathus Poeppigii Tul.
Ithyphallus coralloides Earle.
Laternea columnata (Bosc ex Fr.) Nees.
Lycoperdon albidum Cke.
Lycoperdon pusillum Fr.
Lycoperdon pyriforme Schaeff.
Phallus aurantiacus Mont.

SPHAEROPSIDALES

Ceratocystis fimbriata Ell. & Halsted.
Coniothyrium Sacchari (Massee) Prill. & Delacr.
Cytospora Sacchari Butler.
Diplodia tubericola (Ell. & Ev.) Taubenhaus.
{ Diplodia cacaoicola Henn.
{ Lasiodiplodia Theobromae (Pat.) Griffon & Maubl.
{ Thyridaria tarda Bancroft.
{ Sphaeropsis Sacchari Cke.
{ Phoma Sacchari (Cke.) Sacc.
{ Macrophoma Sacchari (Cke.) Berl. & Vogl.
Phyllosticta Sacchari Speg.
Septoria Sacchari Johnston & Stevenson.
Vermicularia graminicola Westd.

MELANCONIALES

{ Colletotrichum cereale Manns.
{ Colletotrichum lineola Auct. Amer. an Cda.
{ Colletotrichum falcatum Went.
{ Coniothyrium melasporum (B.) Sacc.
{ Darluca melaspora B.
{ Diplodia melaspora (B.) Delacr.
{ Melanconium Sacchari (Ell. & Ev.) Massee.
{ Microdiplodia melaspora (B.) Griffon & Maublanc.
Trichosphaeria Sacchari Massee.
Trullula Sacchari Ell. & Ev.
Melanconium saccharinum Penz. & Sacc.
Pestalozzia fuscescens, var. Sacchari Wakker.

HYPHOMYCETES

Acrostalagmus albus Preuss.
Arthrinium saccharicola Stevenson.
Arthrobotrys superba Cda.
Aspergillus argentius Speg.
Aspergillus flavus Lk.
Aspergillus fumigatus Fres.
Aspergillus nidulans (Eidam) Wint.
Aspergillus niger van Tiegh.
Aspergillus repens (Cda.) Sacc.
Aspergillus terreus Thom.
Basisporium gallarum Moll.
Cephalosporium Sacchari Butler.
Cercospora Kopkei Krüger.
Cercospora longipes Butler.
Cercospora Sacchari van Breda de Haan.
Cercospora vaginae Krüger.
Chaetostroma aterrimum (Cke.) Sacc.

Saccharum officinarum (*cont.*)
Chaetostroma Sacchari Massee.
Cladosporium herbarum (P.) ex Lk.
Coniosporium Arundinis (Cda.) Sacc.
Graphium Sacchari Speg.
Gymnosporium vinosum B. & C.
Helminthosporium Sacchari Butler.
Hormiactella Sacchari Johnston.
Metarrhizium Anisopliae (Metsch.) Sorok.
{ Monilia crassa Shear & Dodge.
{ Neurospora crassa Shear & Dodge.
Monilia nigra C. A. Browne.
Monilia sitophila (Mont.) Sacc.
Morthierella Sacchari Ashby.
Myrothecium Verrucaria (A. & S. ex Fr.) Ditm.
Penicillium divaricatum Thom.
Penicillium expansum Lk. ex Thom.
Penicillium luteum Zukal.
Penicillium roseum Lk. ex P.
Periconia atra Cda.
Periconia Sacchari Johnston.
Septocylindricum suspectum Massee.
Septonema Sacchari Johnston & Stevenson.
Spegazzinia ornata Sacc.
Spegazzinia tessarthra (B. & C.) Sacc.
Tetraploa aristata B. & Br.
{ Thielaviopsis ethaceticus Went.
{ Thielaviopsis paradoxa (De Seynes) v.
{   Höhnel.
{ Thielaviopsis paradoxa, var. ethacetica Auct.
Tubercularia saccharicola Speg.
Verticicladium graminicola Johnston &
   Stevenson.

MISCELLANEA
Rhizoctonia ferrugena Matz.
{ Rhizoctonia grisea (Stevenson) Matz.
{ Sclerotium griseum Stevenson.
Rhizoctonia pallida sec. Matz.
Sclerotium Rolfsii Sacc.
Tetracoccosporium Sacchari Stevenson.
Trichoderma lignorum (Tode) ex Harz.
Ustilago Sacchari Rabh.
Erianthus contortus Ell.
Cerebella Andropogonis Ces.
Erianthus divaricatus (L.) Hitchc.
{ Heptameria orthogramma (B. & C.) Cke.
{ Leptosphaeria orthogramma (B. & C.) Sacc.
{ Sphaeria orthogramma B. & C.
Metasphaeria sphenispora Ell. & Ev.
Dicaeoma polysorum (Underw.) Arth.
Erianthus saccharoides Michx.
Cladosporium Erianthi Thm.
Erianthus sp. indet.
Claviceps sp. indet.
Dothidea graminis (P.) ex Fr.
Hendersonia Donacis Underw. & Earle.
{ Hendersonia Erianthi Atk.
{ Hendersonulina Erianthi (Atk.) Tassi.

Hysterium erianthicola Atk.
Lophidium anomalum Atk.
Ischaemum latifolium (Spreng.) Kunth.
{ Phyllachora Ischaemi Tehon.
{ Phyllachora Tehonis Trotter.
Rytilix granularis (L.) Skeels.
{ Dicaeoma leve (Sacc. & Bizz.) Arth. & Fromme.
{ Diorchidium leve Sacc. & Bizz.
{ Puccinia levis (Sacc. & Bizz.) Magn.
Olpidiella Uredinis Lagerh.
Holcus halepensis L.
Cercospora Sorghi Ell. & Ev.
Colletotrichum lineola Auct. Amer. an Cda.
Colletotrichum lineola, var. halepense Heald &
   Wolf.
Darluca filum (Biv.) Cast.
Helminthosporium turcicum Pass.
{ Lophiostoma implexum Ell. & Ev.
{ Lophionema implexum Sacc.
{ Ophiobolus implexus Berl.
Phyllachora graminis (P. ex Fr.) Fckl.
Puccinia graminis P., var. Sorghi Cke.
{ Dicaeoma purpureum (Cke.) O. Kuntze.
{ Puccinia purpurea Cke.
Septorella Sorghi Ell. & Ev.
Septoria pertusa Heald & Wolf.
Sorosporium reilianum (Kühn) McAlpine.
Sphacelotheca Sorghi (Lk.) G. P. Clinton.
Vermicularia affinis Sacc. & Briard.
Holcus Sorghum L.
Aspergillus flavus Lk.
Cercospora Sorghi Ell. & Ev.
Chaetomella atra Fckl.
Cladosporium graminum Lk., var. Sorghi Rav.
   Fung. Am.
{ Colletotrichum graminicola (Ces.) G. W.
{   Wilson.
{ Colletotrichum lineola Auct. Amer. an Cda.
{ Vermicularia sanguinea Ell. & Halsted.
Helminthosporium turcicum Pass.
Macrosporium ornatissimum Ell. & Barthol.
{ Phoma Sacchari (Cke.) Sacc.
{ Sphaeropsis Sacchari Cke.
{ Dicaeoma purpureum (Cke.) O. Kuntze.
{ Puccinia purpurea Cke.
{ Puccinia sanguinea Diet.
Sclerotium Rolfsii Sacc.
Septorella Sorghi Ell. & Ev.
Sorosporium reilianum (Kühn) McAlpine.
Sphacelotheca cruenta (Kühn) McAlpine.
{ Sphacelotheca Sorghi (Lk.) G. P. Clinton.
{ Ustilago Sorghi (Lk.) Pass.
Uredo alabamensis Diet.
Holcus Sorghum L., var. **cernuus** (Willd.)
   (Guinea-corn.)
{ Cintractia reiliana (Kühn) G. P. Clinton.
{ Sphacelotheca reiliana (Kühn) G. P. Clinton.
{ Cintractia Sorghi-vulgaris (Tul.) G. P. Clinton.
{ Sphacelotheca Sorghi (Lk.) G. P. Clinton.

Holcus sorghum var. **cernuus** (*cont.*)
Colletotrichum graminicola (Ces.) G. W. Wilson.
Marasmius Sacchari Wakker.
Puccinia purpurea Cke.
Puccinia Sorghi S.

Holcus Sorghum L., var. **Durra** L. H. Bailey. (Durra.)
Cercospora Sorghi Ell. & Ev.
Cintractia reiliana (Kühn.) G. P. Clinton.
{ Cintractia Sorghi Auct. Amer. sec. Atk.
  Cintractia Sorghi-vulgaris (Tul.) G. P. Clinton.
  Sphacelotheca Sorghi (Lk.) G. P. Clinton.
  Ustilago Sorghi (Lk.) Pass.

Holcus Sorghum, var. **Roxburghii** (Hack.) L. H. Bailey. (Shallu.)
Sphacelotheca Sorghi (Lk.) G. P. Clinton.

Holcus Sorghum L., var. **saccharatus** (L.) L. H. Bailey. (Sorgho.)
Phoma insidiosa Tassi.
Rhizoctonia ferruginea Matz.
{ Cintractia reiliana (Kühn) G. P. Clinton.
  Sorosporium reilianum (Kühn) McAlpine.
  Sorosporium reilianum (Kühn) McAlpine, var. foliicola Auct.
  Sphacelotheca reiliana (Kühn) G. P. Clinton.
  Ustilago reiliana Kühn.
{ ?Cintractia Sorghi Auct. Amer.
  Cintractia Sorghi-vulgaris (Tul.) G. P. Clinton.
  Sphacelotheca Sorghi (Lk.) G. P. Clinton.
  Ustilago Sorghi (Lk.) Pass.
  Ustilago Tulasnei Kühn.
Marasmius Sacchari Wakker.
{ Sphacelotheca cruenta (Kühn) Potter.
  Sphacelotheca Sorghi N. A. F. *1496.*
  Ustilago cruenta Kühn.

Holcus Sorghum L., var. **technicus** (Körn. & Wern.) L. H. Bailey. (Broom-corn.)
Aspergillus flavus Lk.
Aspergillus niger van Tiegh.
Ceratostoma subulatum Ell.
Cercospora Sorghi Ell. & Ev.
{ Cintractia reiliana (Kühn) G. P. Clinton.
  Sorosporium reilianum (Kühn) McAlpine.
  Sphacelotheca reiliana (Kühn) G. P. Clinton.
  Ustilago reiliana Kühn.
{ Cintractia Sorghi Auct. Amer.
  Cintractia Sorghi-vulgaris (Tul.) G. P. Clinton.
  Sphacelotheca Sorghi G. P. Clinton.
  Ustilago Sorghi (Lk.) Pass.
  Ustilago Tulasnei Kühn.
Puccinia purpurea Cke.
Sphacelotheca cruenta (Kühn) Potter.
Stachybotrys lobulata B.
Ustilago Crameri Körn.

Holcus Sorghum L., var. (Jerusalem corn.)
Cintractia reiliana (Kühn) G. P. Clinton.
Cintractia Sorghi-vulgaris (Tul.) G. P. Clinton.

Holcus sudanensis (Piper) L. H. Bailey.
{ Colletotrichum cereale Manns.
  Colletotrichum lineola Auct. Amer. an Cda.
Helminthosporium teres Sacc.
Helminthosporium turcicum Pass.
Phoma insidiosa Tassi.
Piricularia grisea Cke.
{ Dicaeoma purpureum (Cke.) O. Kuntze.
  Puccinia purpurea Cke.
Sphacelotheca reiliana (Kühn) G. P. Clinton.
Sphacelotheca Sorghi (Lk.) G. P. Clinton.

Holcus sp. indet.
Compare also Notholcus
{ Amerosporium punctiforme (B.) Sacc.
  Excipula punctiformis B.
Cercospora longipes Butler.
Colletotrichum falcatum Went.
Epicoccum purpurascens Ehrenb.
Epicoccum sphaerospermum B. & C.
{ Helminthosporium Cookei Sacc.
  Helminthosporium Sorghi S. 1832.
  Helminthosporium Sorghi Cke. 1877.
{ Heptameria sorghophila (Pk.) Cke.
  Leptosphaeria sorghophila (Pk.) Sacc.
  Sphaeria sorghophila Pk.
Macrosporium culmorum Cke. & Hark.
{ Sirodesmium culmigenum (Cke.) Sacc.
  Sporidesmium culmigenum Cke.

Heteropogon contortus (L.) Roem. & Schultes.
{ Dicaeoma versicolor (Diet. & Holw.) Arth.
  Puccinia versicolor Diet. & Holw.
Sorosporium contortum Griffiths.
Sphacelotheca Ischaemi (Fckl.) G. P. Clinton.
{ Sphacelotheca monilifera (Ell. & Ev.) G. P. Clinton.
  Ustilago monilifera Ell. & Ev.

Heteropogon melanocarpus (Ell.) Benth.
{ Dicaeoma versicolor (Diet. & Holw.) Arth.
  Puccinia versicolor Diet. & Holw.
{ Sphacelotheca Nealii (Ell. & Anderson) G. P. Clinton.
  Ustilago Nealii Ell. & Anderson.

Sorghastrum incompletum (Presl) Nash.
Dicaeoma virgatum (Ell. & Ev.) O. Kuntze.

Sorghastrum nutans (L.) Nash.
Cerebella Andropogonis Ces.
Cerebella Sorghi Tracy & Earle.
Cladosporium graminum Cda.
Claviceps sp. indet.
{ Colletotrichum graminicola (Ces.) G. W. Wilson.
  Colletotrichum lineola Auct. Amer. an Cda.
  Colletotrichum lineola, var. pachyspora Ell. & Kellerm.
Coniosporium Arundinis (Cda.) Sacc.
Darluca Filum (Biv.) Cast.
Ellisiella caudata Sacc.
Everhartia hymenuloides Sacc. & Ell.

Sorghastrum nutans (*cont.*)

{ Fusarium Bartholomaei Pk.
{ Trichofusarium Bartholomaei (Pk.) Sacc.

Hendersonia arundinacea (Desm.) Sacc.

Massarina Chrysopogonis Atk.

Metasphaeria graminum Sacc.

{ Mollisia hydrophila Karst.
{ Niptera hydrophila (Karst.) Sacc.
{ Peziza hydrophila Karst.

Nectria epichloe Speg.

{ Dothidea culmicola S.
{ Phyllachora culmicola (S.) Sacc.

Phyllachora graminis (P.) Fckl.

{ Pleospora Andropogonis, var. hysterioides (Ell.
{ & Ev.) Berl.
{ Pleospora hysterioides Ell. & Ev.

?Puccinia Andropogonis S.

{ Caeoma Andropogi S.
{ Dicaeoma virgatum (Ell. & Ev.) O. Kuntze.
{ Puccinia clavispora Ell. & Barthol.
{ Puccinia virgata Ell. & Ev.
{ Uredo alabamensis Diet.

Puccinia graminis P.

Schizothyrella hysterioides Atk.

{ Patellaria leucochaete Ell. & Ev.
{ Scutularia leucochaete (Ell. & Ev.) Sacc.

Sphacelotheca Chrysopogonis G. P. Clinton.

Tolyposporella Chrysopogonis Atk.

Vermicularia punctans S.

Xylogramma graminis Atk.

Andropogon bicornis L.

Endodothella tetraspora C. R. Orton.

Himantia stellifera Johnston.

Marasmius Sacchari Wakker.

Meliola Panici Earle.

Myriogenospora bresadoleana Henn.

Tolyposporella Brunkii (Ell. & Gall.) G. P.
Clinton.

Andropogon brevifolius Sw.

Phyllachora assimilis Theissen & Syd.

Phyllachora graminis (P. ex Fr.) Fckl.

{ Dicaeoma Kaernbachii (Arth.) Arth. &
{ Fromme.
{ Dicaeoma venustulum (Arth.) Arth. &
{ Fromme.
{ Puccinia Kaernbachii Arth.
{ Puccinia venustula Arth.
{ Uredo venustula Arth.

Nigredo Clignyi (Pat. & Hariot) Arth.

Andropogon citratus DC.

Himantia stellifera Johnston.

Melanconium saccharinum (?) Penz. & Sacc.

Andropogon condensatus H. B. K.

{ Dicaeoma Andropogonis (S.) O. Kuntze.
{ Puccinia Andropogonis S.

Dicaeoma Kaernbachii (Arth.) Arth. &
Fromme.

Andropogon emersus Fourn.

{ Dicaeoma Mariae-Wilsoni Arth. & Fromme.
{ Puccinia ellisiana Thm.

Andropogon furcatus Muhl.

Asteroma graminis Westd.

Epichloe typhina (P.) Tul.

Graphyllium graminis (Ell. & Ev.) Rehm.

Hypocrella Hypoxylon (Pk.) Sacc.

Hysterographium graminis Ell. & Ev.

Leptosphaeria culmorum Awd.

{ Sphaeria graminis P.
{ Sphaeria Andropogi S.
{ Sphaeria andropogicola S.
{ Dothidea graminis P. ex Fr.
{ Phyllachora graminis (P. ex Fr.) Fckl.

{ Sphaeria luteomaculata S.
{ Phyllachora luteomaculata (S.) C. R. Orton.

Septoria Andropogonis J. J. Davis.

Stagonospora Ischaemi Sacc.

Stagonospora simplicior Sacc. & Briard.

Stagonospora simplicior Sacc. & Berl., var.
Andropogonis Sacc.

{ Peziza distincta Pk.
{ Trichopeziza distincta (Pk.) Sacc.

USTILAGINALES

Sorosporium Ellisii Wint.

Sorosporium Ellisii Wint., var. provincialis
Ell. & Gall.

{ Spacelotheca Ischaemi (Fckl.) G. P. Clinton.
{ Ustilago Ischaemi Fckl.

{ Sorosporium Ellisii Wint., var. occidentalis
{ Seym.
{ Sphacelotheca occidentalis G. P. Clinton.
{ Ustilago Andropogonis Kellerm. & Swingle.

UREDINALES

?Caeoma Andropogi S.

{ Dicaeoma Andropogonis (S.) O. Kuntze.
{ Dicaeoma pustulatum Arth.
{ Puccinia Andropogi S.
{ Puccinia Andropogonis S.
{ Puccinia pustulata Arth.

{ Dicaeoma Mariae-Wilsoni Arth. & Fromme.
{ Puccinia americana Lagerh.
{ Puccinia Andropogi Auct. Amer. p. p.
{ Puccinia ellisiana Thm.

?Puccinia Phragmitis (Schum.) Körn.

{ Dicaeoma Sorghi (S.) O. Kuntze.
{ Puccinia Sorghi S.

{ Dicaeoma Ceanothi (Arth.) Arth. & Fromme.
{ Puccinia Andropogonis Auct. Amer. p. p.
{ Puccinia Ceanothi Arth.
{ Puccinia Tripsaci Diet. & Holw.

Andropogon glomeratus (Walt.) BSP.

{ Gorgoniceps dinemasporioides (Ell. & Ev.)
{ Sacc.
{ Peziza dinemasporioides Ell. & Ev.

Dicaeoma Andropogonis (S.) O. Kuntze.

Andropogon glomeratus (*cont.*)
{ Dicaeoma Mariae-Wilsoni Arth. & Fromme.
{ Puccinia ellisiana Thm.
Sorosporium Ellisii Wint.
Sorosporium Everhartii Ell. & Gall.
Sphacelotheca occidentalis (Seym.) G. P.
  Clinton.
{ Nigredo pedatata (J. Sheldon) Arth.
{ Uromyces Andropogonis Tracy.
{ Uromyces pedatatus J. Sheldon.
Andropogon Hallii Hack.
Colletotrichum graminicola (Ces.) G. W.
  Wilson.
Ellisiella caudata (Pk.) Sacc.
{ Dicaeoma Andropogonis (S.) O. Kuntze.
{ Puccinia Andropogi, S.
{ Puccinia Andropogonis S.
{ Puccinia ellisiana Fung. Columb. *1376*.
{ Puccinia pustulata Arth.
{ Dicaeoma Ceanothi (Arth.) Arth. & Fromme.
{ ?Puccinia Cesatii Auct. Amer.
{ Puccinia Ceanothi Arth.
{ Puccinia Tripsaci Diet. & Holw.
{ Sphacelotheca occidentalis (Seym.) G. P.
  Clinton.
{ Ustilago Andropogonis Kellerm. & Swingle.
Vermicularia affinis Sacc. & Briard.
Andropogon hirtifolius J. Presl., var. **pubiflorus**
  (Fourn.) Hack.
{ Sphacelotheca Andropogonis-hirtifolii (Henn.)
  G. P. Clinton.
{ Ustilago Andropogonis-hirtifolii Henn.
Andropogon hirtiflorus Kunth.
Leptostromella Andropogonis Dearness &
  House.
{ Nigredo Clignyi (Pat. & Hariot) Arth.
{ Uromyces Clignyi Pat. & Hariot.
Ustilago Andropogonis-hirtifolii Henn.
Andropogon leucostachyus H. B. K.
Dothichloe atramentosa (B. & C.) Atk.
Phyllachora luteomaculata (S.) C. R. Orton.
Andropogon Liebmanni Hack.
Dicaeoma Mariae-Wilsoni Arth. & Fromme.
Uromyces Clignyi Pat. & Hariot.
Andropogon muricatus Retz.
Chaetostroma aterrimum (Cke.) Sacc.
Didymella Andropogonis Ell. & Ev.
Didymosphaeria Andropogonis Ell. & Lan-
  glois.
Haplosporella tingens Ell. & Langlois.
Langloisula spinosa Ell. & Ev.
{ Leptosphaeria culmicola (Fr.) Karst.
{ Sphaeria culmicola Fr.
Leptosphaeria muricata Ell. & Ev.
Melanospora chrysomalla B. & Br.
Ophiobolus Andropogonis Ell. & Ev.
Ophiobolus Medusae Ell. & Ev., var. minor
  Ell. & Ev.

Andropogon occidentalis Scribn.
Epichloe typhina (P. ex Fr.) Tul.
Tilletia Earlei Griffiths.
Ustilago hypodytes (Schl.) Fr.
Andropogon Pringlei Scribn. & Merr.
Dicaeoma Andropogonis (S.) O. Kuntze.
Andropogon saccharoides Sw.
Phyllachora graminis (P. ex Fr.) Fckl.
{ Sphacelotheca Andropogonis-hirtifolii (Henn.)
  G. P. Clinton.
{ Ustilago Andropogonis-saccharoidis Henn.
{ Sphacelotheca Nealii (Ell. & Anderson) G. P.
  Clinton.
{ Ustilago Nealii Ell. & Anderson.
{ Sphacelotheca Ischaemi (Fckl.) G. P. Clinton.
{ Ustilago cylindrica Pk.
{ Tolyposporella Brunkii (Ell. & Gall.) G. P.
  Clinton.
{ Ustilago Brunkii Ell. & Gall.
Andropogon Schottii Rupr.
{ Nigredo Clignyi (Pat. & Hariot) Arth.
{ Uromyces Clignyi Pat. & Hariot.
Andropogon scoparius Michx.
Didymosphaeria crastophila Niessl.
Ellisiella caudata (Pk.) Sacc.
Graphyllium dakotense Rehm.
{ Peziza planodisca Pk. & Clinton.
{ Pezizella planodisca (Pk. & Clinton) Sacc.
Phoma culmicola S.
Phyllachora graminis (P. ex Fr.) Fckl.
Puccinia Baryi (B. & Br.) Wint.?
Puccinia Phragmitis (Schum.) Körn.
{ Dicaeoma ellisianum (Thm.) O. Kuntze.
{ Dicaeoma Mariae-Wilsoni Arth. & Fromme.
{ Puccinia americana Lagerh.
{ Puccinia Andropogonis Fung Dak. *40*.
{ Puccinia ellisiana Thm.
{ Puccinia Mariae-Wilsoni (Arth. & Fromme)
    Barthol.
{ Dicaeoma Andropogi (S.) O. Kuntze.
{ Dicaeoma Andropogonis (S.) O. Kuntze.
{ Dicaeoma pustulatum Arth.
{ Puccinia Andropogi S.
{ Puccinia Andropogonis S.
{ Puccinia pustulata Arth.
{ Helotiella aureococcinea (B. & C.) Massee.
{ Patellaria aureococcinea B. & C.
{ Solenopeziza aureococcinea (B. & C.) Rehm.
Sorosporium Ellisii Wint.
Sorosporium Everhartii Ell. & Gall.
Sphacelotheca Ischaemi (Fckl.) G. P. Clinton.
Sphaeria nervisequia S.
Nigredo pedatata (J. L. Sheldon) Arth.
Andropogon semiberbis (Nees) Kunth.
{ Dicaeoma Mariae-Wilsoni Arth. & Fromme.
{ Puccinia ellisiana Thm.

Andropogon stolonifera (Nash) Hitchc.

{ Dicaeoma Kaernbachii (Arth.) Arth. &
   Fromme.
{ Puccinia Kaernbachii Arth.

Andropogon tener Kunth.

   Cerebella Andropogonis Ces.
   Claviceps purpurea (Fr.) Tul.

Andropogon ternarius Michx.

   Phyllachora graminis (P. ex Fr.) Fckl.
   ?Puccinia americana Lagerh.

{ Dicaeoma Andropogonis (S.) O. Kuntze.
{ Puccinia Andropogi S.
{ Puccinia Andropogonis S.

{ Tolyposporella Brunkii (Ell. & Gall.) G. P.
   Clinton.
{ Ustilago Brunkii Ell. & Gall.

   Nigredo pedatata (J. Sheldon) Arth.

Andropogon virginicus L.

{ Anthostoma mortuosum (Ell.) Sacc.
{ Sphaeria mortuosa Ell.
{ Xylosphaeria mortuosa (Ell.) Cke.

   Aulographum culmigenum Ell.

{ Belonium aberrans (Pk.) Sacc.
   Belonium Andropogonis (B. & C.) Sacc.
{ Mollisia Andropogonis (B. & C.) Rehm.
   Peziza aberrans Pk.
   Peziza Andropogonis B. & C.

{ Dothichloe atramentosa (B. & C.) Atk.
   Dothichloe Hypoxylon (Pk.) Atk. p. p.
{ Hypocrea atramentosa B. & C.
   Hypocrella atramentosa (B. & C.) Sacc.
{ Ophiodothis atramentosa (B. & C.) Earle.

{ Fusarium Andropogonis Cke.
{ Fusisporium Andropogonis Cke.

   Gnomonia Andropogonis Ell. & Ev.
   Lophodermium arundinaceum (Schrad. ex Fr.)
     Chev.
   Metasphaeria infuscans Ell. & Ev.

{ Phyllachora Andropogi (S.) Ell. & Ev.
   Phyllachora graminis (P. ex Fr.) Fckl.
{ Sphaeria Andropogi S.

   Pleospora findens Ell. & Ev.

{ Fusarium Andropogonis Cke.
{ Fusisporium Andropogonis Cke.
{ Ramularia Andropogonis (Cke.) Wr.

{ Schmitzomia arundinacea (P.) Karst.
{ Stictis arundinacea P.

   Stictis Sesleriae N. A. F. *452.*

{ Peziza albotestacea Desm.
{ Trichopeziza albotestacea (Desm.) Sacc.

USTILAGINALES

   Sorosporium Ellisii Wint.

{ Sorosporium Everhartii Ell. & Gall.
{ Tolyposporium Everhartii (Ell. & Gall.) Diet.
{ Uredo Syntherismae Fung. Car. **2:** *98.*

   Sphacelotheca seymouriana G. P. Clinton.

UREDINALES

{ Dicaeoma Andropogonis (S.) O. Kuntze.
   Puccinia Andropogi S.
   Puccinia Andropogonis S.
   Puccinia Zizaniae S.
   Dicaeoma Mariae-Wilsoni Arth. & Fromme.
   Puccinia americana Lagerh.
{ Puccinia ellisiana Thm.
   ?Puccinia graminis P.

{ Puccinia Clematidis (DC.) Lagerh.
{ Puccinia wyomensis Arth.

   Uromyces graminicola Burrill.

{ Nigredo pedatata (J. L. Sheldon) Arth.
   Uromyces Andropogonis Tracy.
{ Uromyces pedatatus J. L. Sheldon.

Andropogon sp. indet.

PEZIZINEAE

{ Belonioscypha vexata (De Not.) Rehm.
   Belonium subgibbosum (Ell.) Sacc.
   Peziza subgibbosa Ell.
{ Peziza vexata De Not.

{ Belonidium clavatum (Ell.) Rehm.
{ Lecanidion clavatum (Ell.) Sacc.
{ Patellaria clavata Ell.

{ Belonidium tuberculosum (Ell.) Rehm.
{ Lecanidion tuberculosum (Ell.) Sacc.
{ Patellaria tuberculosa Ell.

   Helotium rhizogenum Ell. & Ev.

{ Peziza atriella Cke.
{ Mollisia atriella (Cke.) Sacc.

{ Peziza stenostoma B. & C.
{ Mollisia stenostoma (B. & C.) Sacc.

   Scutularia leucochaetes Ell. & Ev.

{ Peziza Atropae S. Syn. Car.
   Peziza relicina Fr.
{ Trichopeziza relicina (Fr.) Fckl.

PYRENOMYCETINEAE

{ Anthostomella phaeosticta (B.) Sacc.
{ Sphaeria phaeosticta B.

   Balansia discoidea Henn.
   Chaetomium olivaceum C. & E.
   Chaetomium setosum Wint.
   Dothidea culmicola S.

{ Heptameria latebrosa (Ell.) Cke.
{ Leptosphaeria latebrosa (Ell.) Sacc.
   Sphaeria latebrosa Ell.

{ Lophionema implexum (Ell. & Ev.) Sacc.
   ?Lophiostoma implexum Ell. & Ev.
{ Ophiobolus implexus (Ell. & Ev.) Berl.

{ Phomatospora Berkeleyi Sacc.
{ Sphaeria phomatospora B. & Br.

   Phyllachora Cynodontis Niessl.

BASIDIOMYCETES

   Corticium graminicola Ell. & Ev.
   Puccinia versicolor Diet. & Holw.
   Uromyces rotundus Holw. Herb.

Andropogon sp. indet. (*cont.*)

FUNGI IMPERFECTI

Chaetomella Andropogonis C. & E.
{ Coniosporium Arundinis (Cda.) Sacc.
{ Gymnosporium Arundinis Cda.
Darluca arcuata Ell. & Ev.
Dinemasporium graminum (Lib.) Lév.
Dinemasporium minimum C. & E.
Gonytrichum fulvum Ell.
Periconia Langloisii Earle.
Vermicularia velutina B. & Rav.

Anthephora hermaphrodita (L.) O. Kuntze.
Phyllachora Anthephorae Syd.
{ Puccinia Anthephorae Arth. & Johnston.
{ Uredo Anthephorae Syd.
{ Dicaeoma chaseanum Arth. & Fromme.
{ Puccinia chaseana Arth. & Fromme.
{ Uredo Anthephorae Mayor.

Hilaria cenchroides H. B. K.
Claviceps cinerea Griffiths.
{ Ustilago Aegopogonis Henn.
{ Ustilago Hilariae Griffiths non Ell & Tracy.
Ustilago affinis Ell. & Ev.

Hilaria Jamesii (Torr.) Benth.
{ Dicaeoma Sarcobati Arth.
{ Puccinia Sarcobati (Arth.) Bethel.
{ Puccinia subnitens Diet.
{ Uredo Hilariae (Ell. & Tracy) Sacc.
{ Ustilago Hilariae Ell. & Tracy.
Ustilago hypodytes (Schl.) Fr.

Hilaria mutica (Buckl.) Benth.
{ Claviceps cinerea Griffiths.
{ Spermoedia cinerea (Griffiths) Seaver.
Dicaeoma Sarcobati Arth.
Ustilago Hilariae Ell. & Tracy.

Hilaria rigida (Thurb.) Scribn.
Dicaeoma Sarcobati Arth.

Aegopogon cenchroides Humb. & Bonpl.
{ Dicaeoma Aegopogonis (Arth. & Holw.) Arth.
{   & Fromme.
{ Puccinia Aegopogonis Arth. & Holw.
Uromyces Aegopogonis Diet. & Holw.
Ustilago Aegopogonis Henn.

Aegopogon geminiflorus Humb. & Bonpl.
Aegopogon gracilis Vasey.
{ Nigredo Aegopogonis (Diet. & Holw.) Arth.
{ Uromyces Aegopogonis Diet. & Holw.

Aegopogon tenellus (Cav.) Trin.
{ Dicaeoma Aegopogonis (Arth. & Holw.) Arth.
{   & Fromme.
{ Puccinia Aegopogonis Arth. & Holw.

Arundinella deppeana Nees.
{ Dicaeoma Arundinellae Arth. & Fromme.
{ Uredo Arundinellae Arth. & Holw.

Paspalum boscianum Flügge.
Helminthosporium micropus Drechsler.

Paspalum Bushii Nash.
Dicaeoma substriatum (Ell. & Barthol.) Arth.

Paspalum candidum (Humb. & Bonpl.) Kunth.
Phyllachora parilis Syd.
{ Dicaeoma macrum (Arth. & Holw.) Arth. &
{   Fromme.
{ Puccinia macra Arth. & Holw.

Paspalum ciliatifolium Michx.
Dicaeoma substriatum (Ell. & Barthol.) Arth.

Paspalum ciliatum H.B.K.
{ Sclerotium Paspali S. p. p.
{ Spermoedia Paspali Fr.
{ Sphacelia Paspali (Fr.) Bornet.

Paspalum conjugatum Berg.
Helminthosporium folliculatum Cda., var.
  brevipilum Cda.
Helminthosporium mayaguezense Miles.
Myriogenospora bresadoleana Henn.
Myriogenospora Paspali Atk.
Phyllachora Eriochloae Speg.
Phyllachora graminis (P. ex Fr.) Fckl.
Phyllachora quadraspora Tehon.
{ Dicaeoma tubulosum (Arth.) Arth. & Fromme.
{ Puccinia tubulosa Arth.
{ Uredo paspalicola Henn.

Paspalum crassum Chase.
Dicaeoma leve (Sacc. & Bizz.) Arth. & Fromme.

Paspalum curtisianum Steud.

Paspalum denticulatum Trin.
Dicaeoma substriatum (Ell. & Barthol.) Arth.

Paspalum digitatum Kunth.
Fusarium gramineum Cda.
Fusarium heterosporum Nees.

Paspalum dilatatum Poir.
Fusarium gramineum Cda.
Fusarium heterosporum Nees.
Marasmius Sacchari Wakker?

Paspalum distichum L.
{ Claviceps Paspali Stevens & Hall.
{ Fusarium heterosporum Auct. Amer. p. p.
{ Claviceps Rolfsii Stevens & Hall.
{ Spermoedia Rolfsii (Stevens & Hall) Seaver.
Fusarium heterosporum Nees.
Fusarium roseum Lk.
Ustilago Paspali-notati Henn.

Paspalum fimbriatum H. B. K.
{ Dicaeoma leve (Sacc. & Bizz.) Arth. & Fromme.
{ Puccinia levis (Sacc. & Bizz.) Magn.
Puccinia substriata Ell. & Barthol.

Paspalum floridanum Michx.
?Claviceps Paspali Stevens & Hall.
Fusarium roseum Lk.
{ Dicaeoma substriatum (Ell. & Barth.) Arth.
{ Puccinia substriata Ell. & Barthol.

Paspalum glabrum Poir.
Phaeosphaerella Paspali Tehon.
Phyllachora graminis (P. ex Fr.) Fckl.
Phyllachora quadraspora Tehon.

Paspalum glabrum (*cont.*)
{ Dicaeoma Chaetochloae (Arth.) Arth. &
    Fromme.
{ Puccinia Chaetochloae Arth.
  Puccinia substriata Ell. & Barthol.

Paspalum Helleri Nash.
  Puccinia substriata Ell. & Barthol.
  Uredo stevensiana Arth.

Paspalum humboldtianum Flügge.
{ Dicaeoma leve (Sacc. & Bizz.) Arth. & Fromme.
{ Puccinia levis (Sacc. & Bizz) Magn.
{ Dicaeoma tubulosum (Arth.) Arth. & Fromme.
{ Puccinia tubulosa Arth.
{ Uredo paspalicola Henn.
{ Uredo stevensiana Arth.

Paspalum laeve Michx.
{ Claviceps Paspali Stevens & Hall.
{ Sclerotium Paspali S. p. p.
{ Spermoedia Paspali Fr.
{ Claviceps Rolfsii Stevens & Hall.
{ Sclerotium Paspali S. p. p.
  Myriogenospora Paspali Atk.
  ?Phyllachora graminis (P. ex Fr.) Fckl.
  Stagonospora Paspali Atk.

Paspalum Larranagai Arech.
{ Dicaeoma leve (Sacc. & Bizz.) Arth. &
    Fromme.
{ Puccinia levis (Sacc. & Bizz.) Magn.

Paspalum lividum Trin.
  Phyllachora graminis (P. ex Fr.) Fckl.

Paspalum millegrana Schrad.
{ Himantia stellifera Johnston.
{ Odontia saccharicola Burt.
  Phyllachora Andropogonis (S.) Karst.
{ Dicaeoma leve (Sacc. & Bizz.) Arth. &
    Fromme.
{ Puccinia levis (Sacc. & Bizz.) Magn.

Paspalum notatum Flügge.
  Phyllachora Andropogonis (S.) Karst. &
    Hariot.
{ Sphacelotheca Paspali-notati (Henn.) G. P.
    Clinton.
{ Ustilago Paspali-notati Henn.

Paspalum orbiculatum Poir.
{ Dicaeoma Chaetochloae (Arth.) Arth. &
    Fromme.
{ Puccinia Chaetochloae Arth.
  Puccinia substriata Ell. & Barthol.

Paspalum paniculatum L.
  Himantia stellifera Johnston.
  Meliola Panici Earle
  Phyllachora aserriensis Syd.
{ Dicaeoma Huberi (Henn.) Arth. & Fromme.
{ Dicaeoma substriatum (Ell. & Barthol.) Arth.
{ Puccinia dolosa Arth. & Fromme.
{ Puccinia Huberi Henn.
{ Puccinia substriata Ell. & Barthol.

{ Dicaeoma tubulosum (Arth.) Arth. & Fromme.
{ Puccinia tubulosa Arth.
{ Uredo stevensiana Arth.

Paspalum platycaule Poir.
  Coryneum Paspali Ell. & Ev.
{ Cerebella Paspali Cke. & Massee.
{ Langloisia tremelloides Ell. & Ev.
  Physarella oblonga (B. & C.) Morg.

Paspalum plicatulum Michx.
  Claviceps Paspali Stevens & Hall.
  Himantia stellifera Johnston.
  Meliola Stenotaphri F. L. Stevens.
{ Dicaeoma leve (Sacc. & Bizz.) Arth. &
    Fromme.
{ Puccinia levis (Sacc. & Bizz.) Magn.
{ Dicaeoma tubulosum (Arth.) Arth. &
    Fromme.
{ Puccinia tubulosa Arth.
{ Uredo paspalicola Henn.
{ Uredo stevensiana Arth.
  Spermoedia Stevensii Seaver.

Paspalum portoricense Nash.

Paspalum pusillum Vent.
  Puccinia substriata Ell. & Barthol.

Paspalum schreberianum (Fl.) Nash.
  Himantia stellifera Johnston.
  Meliola Panici Earle.
  Puccinia substriata Ell. & Barthol.

Paspalum secans Hitchc. & Chase.
  Himantia stellifera Johnston.
  Meliola Panici Earle.
{ Dicaeoma Chaetochloae (Arth.) Arth. &
    Fromme.
{ Puccinia Chaetochloae Arth.
  Puccinia substriata Ell. & Barthol.

Paspalum setaceum Michx.
  Phyllachora graminis (P. ex Fr.) Fckl.
{ Dicaeoma substriatum (Ell. & Barthol.) Arth.
{ Puccinia substriata Ell. & Barthol.
  Trichothecium griseum Cke., var. leptosper-
    mum Ell. & Kellerm.

Paspalum stramineum Nash.
  Phyllachora graminis (P. ex Fr.) Fckl.
{ Dicaeoma emaculatum (S.) O. Kuntze.
{ Puccinia emaculata S.
{ Dicaeoma substriatum (Ell. & Barthol.) Arth.
{ Puccinia substriata Ell. & Barthol.

Paspalum tenellum Willd.
{ Dicaeoma Huberi (Henn.) Arth. & Fromme.
{ Puccinia dolosa Arth. & Fromme.
{ Puccinia Huberi Henn.
  Dicaeoma substriatum (Ell. & Barthol.) Arth.

Paspalum Underwoodii Nash.
  Himantia stellifera Johnston.
  Phyllachora Andropogonis (S.) Karst. &
    Hariot.

Paspalum undulatum Poir.
  Piricularia grisea (Cke.) Sacc.
  Puccinia levis (Sacc. & Bizz.) Magn.
  Tilletia rugispora Ell.
Paspalum vaseyanum Scribn.
  Puccinia Paspali Tracy & Earle.
Paspalum velutinum Kunth.
  Nigredo Aegopogonis (Diet. & Holw.) Arth.
  Ustilago holwayana Henn.
Paspalum virgatum L.
  Himantia stellifera Johnston.
  Phyllachora cornuospora Atk.
  Phyllachora graminis (P. ex Fr.) Fckl.
  ⎰Dicaeoma Huberi (Henn.) Arth. & Fromme.
  ⎱Puccinia Huberi Henn.
  Puccinia Paspali Tracy & Earle.
  ⎰Dicaeoma substriatum (Ell. & Barthol.) Arth.
  ⎱Puccinia sybstriata Ell. & Barthol.
Paspalum sp. indet.
  ?Leptostroma Spiraeae Fr.
  Odontia saccharicola Burt.
  Phyllachora acuminata Starb.
  Scytinotus distantifolius Murrill.
  Sphacelotheca Paspali-notati (Henn.) G. P.
    Clinton.
Axonopus compressus (Sw.) Beauv.
  Myriogenospora bresadoleana Henn.
  ⎰Dicaeoma tubulosum (Arth.) Arth. & Fromme.
  ⎪Puccinia tubulosa Arth.
  ⎨Uredo paspalicola Henn.
  ⎩Uredo stevensiana Arth.
  Trichostroma Axonopi Tehon.
  Ustilago schroeteriana Henn.
Anthaenantia rufa Benth.
  ⎰Cerebella Anthaenantiae Tracy & Earle.
  ⎪Cerebella Paspali Tracy & Earle p. p.
  ⎨Colletotrichum graminicola (Ces.) G. W.
  ⎪ Wilson.
  ⎩Vermicularia graminicola Auct. Amer.
Eriochloa Lemmoni Vasey & Scribn.
  Dicaeoma substriatum (Ell. & Barthol.) Arth.
Eriochloa punctata (L.) Hamil.
  Puccinia substriata Ell. & Barthol.
  Sorosporium Eriochloae Griffiths.
Eriochloa subglabra (Nash) Hitchc.
  Basisporum gallarum Moll.
  Darluca Filum (Biv.) Cast.
  Gibberella pulicaris (Fr.) Sacc.
  Phyllachora graminis (P. ex Fr.) Fckl.
  ⎰Dicaeoma substriatum (Ell. & Barthol.) Arth.
  ⎱Puccinia substriata Ell. & Barthol.
Digitaria filiformis (L.) Koeler.
Digitaria Ischaemum Schreb.
  ⎰Ustilago destruens Auct. Amer. p. p.
  ⎱Ustilago rabenhorstiana Kühn.
Digitaria sanguinalis (L.) Scop.
  ⎰Colletotrichum graminicola (Ces.) G. W.
  ⎨ Wilson.
  ⎩Psilonia apalospora B. & C. nom. nud.

Erysiphe graminis DC. †
  ⎰Piricularia grisea (Cke.) Sacc.
  ⎱Trichothecium griseum Cke.
  Piricularia Oryzae Cav.
  Puccinia substriata Ell. & Barthol.
  ⎰Dicaeoma tubulosum (Arth.) Arth. & Fromme.
  ⎱Puccinia tubulosa Arth.
  Septoria graminum Desm.
  ⎰Sphacelotheca diplospora (Ell. & Ev.) G. P.
  ⎨ Clinton.
  ⎩Ustilago diplospora Ell. & Ev.
  Mycosphaerella Maydis (Pass.) F. L. Stevens.
  ⎰Neovossia corona Auct. p. p.
  ⎪Tilletia corona Auct. p. p.
  ⎨Tilletia pulcherrima Ell. & Gall.
  ⎩Tilletia rotundata E. F. *543*.
  ⎰Caeoma Syntherismae S.
  ⎪Sorosporium Syntherismae Auct. Amer. p. p.
  ⎪Ustilago Cesatii Auct. Amer. p. p.
  ⎨Ustilago Panici-miliacei Auct. Amer. p. p.
  ⎪Ustilago rabenhorstiana Kühn.
  ⎩Ustilago Syntherismae Auct. Amer. p. p.
Digitaria setosa Desv.
  Himantia stellifera Johnston.
  Puccinia substriata Ell. & Barthol.
  ⎰Dicaeoma tubulosum (Pat. & Gaill.) Arth. &
  ⎨ Fromme.
  ⎩Puccinia tubulosa (Pat. & Gaill.) Arth.
Panicum adspersum Trin.
  Puccinia Huberi Henn.
  Dicaeoma leve (Sacc. & Bizz.) Arth. & Fromme.
Panicum agrostoides Spreng.
  ⎰Dothichloe atramentosa (B. & C.) Arth.
  ⎪Dothidea vorax B. & C. p. p.
  ⎪Epichloe Hypoxylon Auct. p. p.
  ⎨Euryachora vorax Cke. p. p.
  ⎪Hypocrea Hypoxylon N. A. F. *2373*.
  ⎩Ophiodothis vorax Sacc. p. p.
  Phyllachora cornuospora Atk.
  Phyllachora graminis (P. ex Fr.) Fckl.
  ⎰Sorosporium Syntherismae (Pk.) Farl.
  ⎪Ustilago destruens Auct. Amer. p.p.
  ⎨Ustilago Panici-Miliacei Auct. Amer. p.p.
  ⎩Ustilago Syntherismae Pk.
  Tetraploa divergens Tracy & Earle.
Panicum altissimum Mey.
  Uromyces costaricensis Syd.
Panicum altum Hitchc. & Chase.
  Nigredo graminicola (Burrill) Arth.
Panicum amarulum Hitchc. & Chase.
  Nigredo leptoderma (Syd.) Arth.
Panicum amarum Ell.
  Dicaeoma Pammelii Arth.
  ⎰Nigredo leptoderma (Syd.) Arth.
  ⎱Uromyces leptodermus Syd.
  Uredo Panici Arth.
Panicum amplexicaule Rudge.
  Epichloe nigricans Speg.
  Epichloe strangulans Mont.

Panicum anceps Michx.
Dimerosporium erysipheoides Ell. & Ev.
Helminthosporium giganteum Heald & Wolf.
Hypocrella Hypoxylon (Pk.) Sacc.
Puccinia emaculata S.
{ Nigredo graminicola (Burrill) Arth.
{ Uromyces Panici Tracy.
Panicum barbinode Trin.
Basisporium gallarum Moll.
Darluca Filum (Biv.) Cast.
Gibberella pulicaris (Fr.) Sacc.
Marasmius Sacchari Wakker.
{ Nigredo leptoderma (Syd.) Arth.
{ Puccinia panicicola Arth.
{ Uromyces leptodermus Syd.
Panicum brevifolium L.
Puccinia emaculata S.
Panicum brizanthum Hochst.
Phyllachora stenostoma Ell. & Tracy.
Panicum bulbosum H.B.K.
{ Dicaeoma eslavense (Diet. & Holw.) Arth.
{ Puccinia eslavensis Diet. & Holw.
Panicum caespitosum Spreng.
Sorosporium ovarium Griffiths.
Panicum capillare L.
Colletotrichum cereale Manns.
Coniosporium capitulatum Sacc. & Dearness.
Mycorrhiza of Legumes F. R. Jones.
Phyllachora graminis (P.) Fckl.
{ Dicaeoma emaculatum (S.) O. Kuntze.
{ Puccinia emaculata S.
{ Puccinia graminis, var. brevicarpa Pk.
{ Puccinia Panici Snyder an Diet.?
{ Uredo sphaerospora B. & C.
{ Sorosporium Syntherismae (Pk.) Farl.
{ Ustilago Cesatii Auct. Amer. p.p.
{ Ustilago destruens Auct. Amer. p. p.
{ Ustilago Panici-Miliacei Auct. Amer. p.p.
{ ?Ustilago rabenhorstiana Underw. non Kühn.
{ Ustilago Syntherismae Pk. non S.
Panicum clandestinum L.
Helminthosporium giganteum Heald & Wolf.
Phyllachora graminis (P. ex Fr.) Fckl.
Phyllachora graminis (P. ex Fr.) Fckl., var.
Panici (S.) Shear.
Phyllachora Panici (S.) Sacc.
Phyllachora puncta (S.) C. R. Orton.
Panicum compactum Sw.
Calonectria graminicola F. L. Stevens.
Meliola Panici Earle.
Panicum condensum Nash.
Dicaeoma emaculatum (S.) O. Kuntze.
Panicum Curtisii Chapm. See **Panicum hemitomum** Schultes.
Panicum depauperatum Muhl.
{ Septoria graminum J. J. Davis non Desm.
{ Septoria tandilensis Speg.
{ Nigredo graminicola (Burrill) Arth.
{ Uromyces graminicola Burrill.

Panicum dichotomiflorum Michx.
Entyloma speciosum Schrt.
Helminthosporium giganteum Heald & Wolf.
Naemacyclus culmigenus Ell. & Langlois.
{ Sorosporium Syntherismae (Pk.) Farl.
{ Ustilago rabenhorstiana Fung. Columb. 748.
{ Ustilago Syntherismae Pk.
Ustilago pustulata Tracy & Earle.
Vermicularia discoidea Ell. & Langlois.
Panicum dichotomum L.
Cercospora fusimaculans Atk.
Metasphaeria Panicorum (Cke.) Sacc.
{ Sphaeria Panici S.
{ Sphaeria punctum S.
{ Dothidea graminis (P.) ex Fr.
{ Phyllachora graminis (P. ex Fr.) Fckl.
Phyllachora Panici (S.) Sacc.
Phyllachora puncta (S.) Orton.
Piricularia grisea (Cke.) Sacc.
Panicum divaricatum L.
Arthrobotryum penicillium (Speg.) F. L.
Stevens.
Calonectria graminicola F. L. Stevens.
Coniothyrium glabroides F. L. Stevens.
Darluca Filum (Biv.) Cast.
Dimerium piceum (B. & C.) Theissen.
Meliola brasiliensis Speg.
Meliola Panici Earle.
Melioliphila graminicola (F. L. Stevens) Speg.
Phyllachora graminis (P. ex Fr.) Fckl.
Phyllachora Lasiacis Syd.
{ Nigredo leptoderma (Syd.) Arth.
{ Uromyces leptodermus Syd.
Panicum fasciculatum Sw.
{ Dicaeoma leve (Sacc. & Bizz.) Arth.& Fromme.
{ Puccinia Huberi Henn.
Nigredo leptoderma (Syd.) Arth.
Panicum flexile (Gatt.) Scribn.
Dicaeoma emaculatum (S.) O. Kuntze.
Panicum Gattingeri Nash.
Helminthosporium giganteum Heald & Wolf.
Puccinia emaculata S.
Panicum geminatum Forsk.
Phyllachora Chardoni C. R. Orton.
?Panicum geniculatum.
Tilletia magnusiana Fisch. Wald.
Panicum glutinosum Sw.
{ Arthrobotryum penicillium (Speg.) F. L.
{ Stevens.
{ Podosporium penicillium Speg.
Dimerium piceum (B. & C.) Theissen.
Meliola Panici Earle.
Porostigme microspora Toro.
Panicum hebotes Trin.
?Puccinia panicicola Arth.
Panicum hemitomum Schultes.
Colletotrichum graminicola (Ces.) G. W.
Wilson.

Panicum hemitomum (*cont.*)
  Griphosphaerella Stevensonii Petrak.
  {Leptosphaeria culmifraga (Fr.) Ces. & De Not.
  {Sphaeria culmifraga Fr.
  Metasphaeria punctulata Ell. & Ev.
  {Metasphaeria stenotheca Ell. & Ev.
  {Sphaeria stenotheca Ell. & Ev.
  Myriogenospora bresadoleana Henn.
  Physalospora oxystoma Sacc. & Ell.
  Venturia erysiphioides Ell. & Ev.

Panicum hians Elliott.
  Leptostromella Panici Dearness.

Panicum holciforme Steud.
  Puccinia emaculata S.

Panicum huachucae Ashe.
  Phyllachora graminis (P. ex Fr.) Fckl.

Panicum implicatum Scribn.
  Epichloe strangulans Mont.

Panicum lanatum Rottb.
  Phyllachora Eriochloae Speg.
  Phyllachora graminis (P. ex Fr.) Fckl.
  {Dicaeoma eslavense (Diet. & Holw.) Arth.
  {Puccinia eslavensis Diet. & Holw.
  ?Puccinia substriata Ell. & Barthol.
  {Dicaeoma tubulosum (Arth.) Arth. & Fromme.
  {Puccinia tubulosa Arth.
  {Sphacelotheca Panici-leucophaei (Bref.) G. P.
  { Clinton.
  {Ustilago Panici-leucophaei Bref.
  Uromyces leptodermus Syd.

Panicum latifolium L.
  {Asterella? fumaginea Dearness & Barthol. ex
  { Trott.
  {Asterina fumagina Dearness & Barthol.
  {Dimeriella fumagina (Dearness & Barthol.)
  { F. L. Stevens.
  Cercospora Panici J. J. Davis.
  Meliola Panici Earle.
  {Dothidea graminis (P.) ex Fr.
  {Phyllachora graminis (P. ex Fr.) Fckl.
  Phyllachora Panici (S.) Sacc.
  Phyllachora puncta (S.) C. R. Orton.
  {Nigredo leptoderma (Syd.) Arth.
  {Uromyces leptodermus Syd.

Panicum laxum Sw.
  Himantia stellifera Johnston.
  Ustilaginoidea usambarensis Henn.

Panicum leucophaeum H. B. K.   See Panicum
    lanatum Rottb.

Panicum liebmannianum Trin.

Panicum
    (Lasiacis ligulata Hitchc. & Chase.)
  {Nigredo leptoderma (Syd.) Arth.
  {Uromyces leptodermus Syd.

Panicum Lindheimeri Nash.
  Epichloe strangulans Mont.

Panicum maximum Jacq.
  Colletotrichum lineola Auct. Amer. an Cda.
  {Collybia stipitaria Fr.
  {Crinipellis stipitarius (Fr.) Pat.
  Darluca Filum (Biv.) Cast.
  Himantia stellifera Johnston.
  Otthia Panici Stevens.
  Phyllosticta Panici E. Young.
  Puccinia emaculata S.
  Dicaeoma leve (Sacc. & Bizz.) Arth. & Fromme.
  Puccinia Panici Diet.
  Uredo Panici-maximi Rangel.
  Nigredo leptoderma (Syd.) Arth.

Panicum microcarpon Muhl.
  Epichloe strangulans Mont.

Panicum miliaceum L.   See also Setaria italica
    (L.) Beauv.
  Cercospora Sorghi Ell. & Ev.
  Fusarium rhizochromatistes C. P. Sideris.
  ?Helminthosporium teres Sacc.
  Metasphaeria nuda Pk.
  {Dicaeoma emaculatum (S.) O. Kuntze.
  {Puccinia emaculata S.
  Sclerospora graminicola (Sacc.) Schrt.
  {Sorosporium Syntherismae (S.) Farl.
  {Ustilago destruens Auct. Amer. p.p.
  {Ustilago Panici-miliacei Auct. Amer. p.p.
  Ustilago Crus-galli Tracy & Earle.
  Ustilago Sorghi Lk.

Panicum obtusum H. B. K.
  Tilletia pulcherrima Ell. & Gall.

Panicum palmifolium Poir.
  {Balansia trinitensis Cke. & Massee.
  {Ephelis trinitensis Cke. & Massee.

Panicum parvifolium Lam.
  {Nigredo leptoderma (Syd.) Arth.
  {Uromyces leptodermus Syd.

Panicum paspaloides P.
  Ustilago Panici-proliferi Henn.
  Ustilago Rickeri G. P. Clinton.

Panicum philadelphicum Bernh.
  Phyllachora graminis (P. ex Fr.) Fckl.
  {Dicaeoma emaculatum (S.) O. Kuntze.
  {Puccinia emaculata S.

Panicum proliferum, var. acuminatum Holw.
    nom. nud.
  Ustilago Panici-proliferi Henn.

Panicum rottboellioides H. B. K.
  Sphacelotheca diplospora (Ell. & Ev.) G. P.
    Clinton, var. glabra Clinton & Ricker.

Panicum saccharatum Buckley.
  {Dicaeoma eslavense (Diet. & Holw.) Arth.
  {Puccinia eslavensis Diet. & Holw.
  Sphacelotheca Panici-leucophaei (Bref.) G. P.
    Clinton.

Panicum Schiffneri Hack.
  Dicaeoma leve (Sacc. & Bizz.) Arth. &
    Fromme.
Panicum scoparium Lam.
  Phyllachora graminis (P. ex Fr.) Fckl.
Panicum scribnerianum Nash.
  Phyllachora graminis (P. ex Fr.) Fckl.
  Phyllachora graminis (P. ex Fr.) Fckl., var.
    Panici (S.) Shear.
Panicum Sloanei Griseb. See Panicum latifolium
  L.
Panicum sorghoideum Ham.
  Phyllachora graminis (P. ex Fr.) Fckl.
  Physalospora Bambusae (Rahb.) Sacc.
  { Nigredo leptoderma (Syd.) Arth.
  { Uromyces leptodermus Syd.
Panicum stipitatum Nash.
  Phyllachora cornuospora Atk.
  Phyllachora graminis (P. ex Fr.) Fckl.
Panicum sulcatum Aubl.
  Phyllachora Panici-sulcati (Henn.) Theissen &
    Syd.
Panicum tennesseense Ashe.
  Phyllachora graminis (P. ex Fr.) Fckl., var.
    Panici (S.) Shear.
Panicum texanum Buckl.
  Phyllachora graminis (P. ex Fr.) Fckl.
  Piricularia grisea (Cke.) Sacc.
Panicum tricanthum Nees.
  Balansia Hypoxylon (Pk.) Atk.
Panicum trichoides Sw.
  Darluca Filum (Biv.) Cast.
  { Dicaeoma Huberi (Henn.) Arth. & Fromme.
  { Dicaeoma leve (Sacc. & Bizz.) Arth. & Fromme.
  { Puccinia Huberi Henn.
Panicum utowanaeum Scribn.
  { Dicaeoma Huberi (Henn.) Arth. & Fromme.
  { Dicaeoma leve (Sacc. & Bizz.) Arth. & Fromme.
  { Puccinia Huberi Henn.
Panicum virgatum L.
  Botrytis uredinicola Pk.
  { Cerebella Panici Tracy & Earle.
  { Cerebella Paspali Tracy & Earle p.p.
  { Colletotrichum cereale Manns.
  { Colletotrichum graminicola G. W. Wilson.
  { Colletotrichum lineola Auct. Amer. an Cda.
  Didymosphaeria graminicola Ell. & Ev.
  { Exarmidium fusariisporum (Ell. & Ev.) Theis-
  {   sen & Syd.
  { Rhopographus fusariisporus Ell. & Ev.
  Hendersonia panicicola Petrak.
  Hysterographium graminis Ell. & Ev.
  Leptosphaeria occidentalis Ell. & Ev.
  Macrosporium Panici Ell. & Ev.
  Metasphaeria subseriata Ell. & Ev.
  Phyllachora graminis (P. ex Fr.) Fckl., var.
    Panici (S.) Shear.

  Phyllachora Panici (S.) Sacc.
  ?Puccinia graminis P.
  ?Puccinia Huberi Henn.
  { Dicaeoma Pammelii Arth.
  { Puccinia emaculata Auct. p.p.
  { Puccinia Pammelii Arth.
  { Puccinia Panici Diet.
  Septoria Donacis Pass., var. Panici Ell. &
    Barthol.
  Septoria sigmoidea Ell. & Ev.
  { Neovossia corona (Scribn.) Massee.
  { Tilletia corona Scribn.
  { Tilletia Maclagani (B.) G. P. Clinton.
  { Tilletia rotundata (Arth.) Massee.
  { Ustilago Maclagani B.
  { Ustilago rotundata Arth.
  Tilletia pulcherrima Ell. & Gall.
  { Nigredo graminicola (Burrill) Arth.
  { Uromyces graminicola Burrill.
  Ustilago pustulata Tracy & Earle.
  Vermicularia affinis Sacc. & Briard.
Panicum virgatum L., var. **cubense** Griseb.
  Dicaeoma Pammelii Arth.
Panicum wrightianum Scribn.
  Phyllachora puncta (S.) C. R. Orton.
Panicum sp. indet.
  Balansia trinitensis Cke. & Massee.
  Cercospora fusimaculans Atk.
  Coniosporium Arundinellae Ell. & Tracy.
  Conoplea hispidula P. ex Fr.
  Dothidea vorax B. & C.
  Helminthosporium flagelloideum Atk.
  { Leptosphaeria culmifraga (Fr.) Ces. & De Not.
  { Sphaeria culmifraga Fr.
  Leptostromella septorioides Sacc. & Roum.
  { Metasphaeria Panicorum (Cke.) Sacc.
  { Sphaerella Panicum Cke.
  { Ophiobolus porphyrogonus (Tode) ex Sacc.
  { Sphaeria rubella P. ex Fr.
  Phoma campylospora B. & C.
  { Asteroma Panici (S.) M. A. Curtis.
  { Dothidea Panici S.
  { Phyllachora Panici (S.) Sacc.
  Sphacelotheca diplospora (Ell. & Ev.) G. P.
    Clinton, var. verruculosa G. P. Clinton.
  Stagonospora curvula Bomm. & Rouss.
  Vermicularia sanguinea Ell. & Halsted.
  Volutella Ellisii Langlois.
Leptoloma cognatum (Schultes) Chase.
  Dicaeoma atrum (Diet. & Holw.) Arth.
  { Dicaeoma impositum (Arth.) Arth. & Fromme.
  { Puccinia imposita Arth.
  { Uredo Muhlenbergiae Diet.
Echinochloa colona (L.) Link.
  Piricularia grisea (Cke.) Sacc.
  Ustilago sphaerogena Burrill.

Echinochloa Crus-galli (L.) Beauv.
  Cercospora Echinochloae J. J. Davis.
  ⎰Cintractia Crus-galli (Tracy & Earle) Magn.
  ⎮Cintractia seymouriana (Diet.) Magn.
  ⎱Ustilago Crus-galli Tracy & Earle.
  ⎰Ustilago seymouriana Diet.
  ⎰Cintractia sphaerogena (Burrill) Hume.
  ⎱Ustilago sphaerogena Burrill.
  ⎰Colletotrichum graminicola G. W. Wilson.
  ⎮Colletotrichum lineola Auct. Amer. an Cda.
  ⎨Colletotrichum sanguineum (Ell. & Halsted)
  ⎮ Ell. & Ev.
  ⎱Vermicularia sanguinea Ell. & Halsted.
  Dinemasporium graminum (Lib.) Lév.
  Helminthosporium monoceras Drechsler.
  Leptosphaeria occidentalis Ell. & Ev.
  Metasphaeria hyalospora Sacc.
  ⎰Dicaeoma flaccidum (B. & Br.) O. Kuntze.
  ⎮Diorchidium flaccidum (B. & Br.) Lagerh.
  ⎨Puccinia confusa Burrill.
  ⎮Puccinia emaculata Auct. Amer. p.p.
  ⎱Puccinia flaccida B. & Br.
  ⎰Dicaeoma poculiforme (Wettst.) O. Kuntze.
  ⎱Puccinia vilis Arth.
  ⎰Sorosporium bullatum Schrt.
  ⎱Tolyposporium bullatum Schrt.
  ⎰Sphacelotheca diplospora (Ell. & Ev.) G. P.
  ⎨ Clinton.
  ⎱Ustilago diplospora Ell. & Ev.
  Sphaerella Crus-galli Ell. & Kellerm.
  Vermicularia affinis Sacc. & Briard.
Echinochloa holciformis (H. B. K.) Chase.
  Dicaeoma flaccidum (B. & Br.) O. Kuntze.
Echinochloa subglabra (Nash) Hitchc.
  Dicaeoma substriatum (Ell. & Barthol.) Arth.
Echinochloa Walteri (Pursh) Nash.
  Tolyposporium bullatum Schrt.
  Ustilago Crus-galli Tracy & Earle.
  Ustilago sphaerogena Burrill.
Echinochloa zelayensis (H. B. K.) Schultes.
  ⎰Dicaeoma flaccidum (B. & Br.) O. Kuntze.
  ⎱Puccinia flaccida B. & Br.
  Ustilago Crus-galli Tracy & Earle.
Ichnanthus pallens (Sw.) Munro.
  Arthrobotryum penicillium (Speg.) F. L.
    Stevens.
  ?Dothichloe Aristidae F. L. Stevens non Atk.
  Dothichloe nigricans Seaver non Speg.
  Dothichloe subnodosa (Atk.) Chardon.
  Meliola Panici Earle.
  Myriogenospora bresadoleana P. Henn.
  ⎰Dicaeoma inclitum (Arth.) Arth. & Fromme.
  ⎱Puccinia inclita Arth.
  Puccinia substriata Ell. & Barthol.
  ⎰Puiggarina Ichnanthi Speg.
  ⎨Trabutiella Ichnanthi (Speg.) Seaver &
  ⎱ Chardon

Tricholaena rosea Nees.
  Dothiorella Tricholenae Ciferri & Fragoso.
  Uromyces Tricholenae Fragoso & Ciferri.
Oplismenus Burmanni Beauv.
  Phyllachora Oplismeni Syd.
  Ustilago vittata Nees.
Oplismenus hirtellus (L.) Beauv.
  Meliola Panici Earle.
  Phyllachora puncta (S.) C. R. Orton.
  ⎰Dicaeoma inclitum (Arth.) Arth. & Fromme.
  ⎱Puccinia inclita Arth.
  ⎰Puccinia tubulosa Arth.
  ⎱Uredo Olyrae Arth.
  Septoria Carricerae Fairman.
Oplismenus humboldtianus Nees.
  Phyllachora Oplismeni Syd.
Oplismenus setarius (Lam.) Roem. & Schult.
  Meliola Panici Earle.
  Phyllachora graminis (P. ex Fr.) Fckl.
Setaria brevispica K. Schum.
  Puccinia substriata Ell. & Barthol.
Setaria geniculata Beauv.
  Ophiobolus Cariceti (B. & Br.) Sacc.
  ⎰Dicaeoma Setariae (Diet. & Holw.) Arth.
  ⎱Puccinia Setariae Diet. & Holw.
  ⎰Dicaeoma substriatum (Ell. & Barthol.) Arth.
  ⎱Puccinia substriata Ell. & Barthol.
  Sphacelotheca pamparum (Speg.) G. P.
    Clinton.
Setaria germanica Beauv. See Setaria italica
    (L.) Beauv.
Setaria glauca (L.) Beauv.
  Cercospora Setariae Atk.
  Cercospora setariicola Tehon & Daniels.
  Melasmia Setariae Atk.
  Piricularia grisea (Cke.) Sacc.
  Rhizoctonia Solani Kühn.
  Sclerospora graminicola (Sacc.) Schrt.
  ⎰Ustilago destruens Auct. Amer. p.p.
  ⎨Ustilago neglecta Niessl.
  ⎱Ustilago Panici-glauci (Wallr.) Wint.
Setaria Grisebachii Fourn.
  ⎰Dicaeoma atrum (Diet. & Holw.) Arth.
  ⎱Puccinia atra Diet. & Holw.
Setaria imberbis Roem. & Schult.
  Ephelis mexicana Fr. ?
  Puccinia substriata Ell. & Barthol.
  Sphacelotheca pamparum (Speg.) G. P. Clin-
    ton.
Setaria italica (L.) Beauv. See also Panicum
    miliaceum L.
  Piricularia grisea (Cke.) Sacc.
  ⎰Peronospora graminicola Sacc.
  ⎱Sclerospora graminicola (Sacc.) Schrt.
  Sclerospora graminicola (Sacc.) Schrt., var.
    Setariae-italicae Trav.
  Ustilago Crameri Körn.

Setaria lutescens (Weigel) Stuntz.
Sclerospora graminicola (Sacc.) Schrt.
Ustilago Crameri Körn.
Ustilago neglecta Niessl.

Setaria macrosperma K. Schum.
{ Dicaeoma Chaetochloae (Arth.) Arth. &
  Fromme.
{ Puccinia Chaetochloae Arth.
{ Uredo Chaetochloae Arth.

Setaria macrostachya (H. B. K.) Scribn. & Merr.
Dicaeoma Cameliae (Mayor) Arth. & Fromme.

Setaria magna Griseb.
Sclerospora graminicola (Sacc.) Schrt.

Setaria Onurus Griseb.
Dicaeoma Chaetochloae (Arth.) Arth. &
  Fromme.
Puccinia substriata Ell. & Barthol.

Setaria polystachya Scheele.
Dicaeoma Cameliae (Arth.) Arth. & Fromme.

Setaria scandens Schrad.
{ Dicaeoma Cameliae (Arth.) Arth. & Fromme.
{ Puccinia Cameliae Arth.
{ Uredo Cameliae Mayor.

Setaria setosa Beauv.
{ Dicaeoma Cameliae (Arth.) Arth. & Fromme.
{ Puccinia Cameliae Arth.
{ Uredo Cameliae Mayor.
Dicaeoma Chaetochloae (Arth.) Arth. &
  Fromme.
Puccinia substriata Ell. & Barthol.

Setaria sulcata (Aubl.) Raddi.
{ Phyllachora graminis (P. ex Fr.) Fckl., var.
  Panici-sulcati Henn.
{ Phyllachora Panici-sulcati (Henn.) Theissen &
  Syd.
Dicaeoma substriatum (Ell. & Barthol.) Arth.

Setaria verticillata (L.) Beauv.
{ Dicaeoma substriatum (Ell. & Barthol.) Arth.
{ Puccinia substriata Ell. & Barthol.

Setaria viridis (L.) Beauv.
Piricularia grisea (Cke.) Sacc.
{ Peronospora graminicola Sacc.
{ Sclerospora graminicola (Sacc.) Schrt.
Septoria graminum Desm.

Setaria sp. indet.
Acrothecium flacatum Tehon.
Cladosporium spongiosum B. & C.
Coniothyrium Setariae Atk.
{ Ustilago Pamparum Speg.
{ Sphacelotheca Pamparum (Speg.) G. P.
  Clinton.
{ Ustilaginoidea Setariae Bref.
{ Ustilago viridis Ell. & Ev.

Cenchrus carolinianus Walt.
Puccinia Cenchri Diet. & Holw.
Septoria cenchrina J. J. Davis.
Sorosporium Syntherismae (Pk.) Farl.

Cenchrus echinatus L.
Ephelis mexicana Fr.
Phyllachora sphaerosperma Wint.
{ Dicaeoma Cenchri (Diet. & Holw.) Arth.
{ Puccinia Cenchri Diet. & Holw.
Sorosporium Syntherismae (Pk.) Farl.

Cenchrus multiflorus J. & C. Presl.
Puccinia Cenchri Diet. & Holw.
{ Sorosporium Syntherismae (Pk.) Farl.
{ Ustilago Syntherismae Pk.

Cenchrus myosuroides H. B. K.
Phyllachora sphaerosperma Wint.

Cenchrus pauciflorus Benth.
Dicaeoma Cenchri (Diet. & Holw.) Arth.
Sorosporium Syntherismae (Pk.) Farl.

Cenchrus tribuloides L.
{ Colletotrichum graminicola (Ces.) G. W.
  Wilson.
{ Colletotrichum lineola Auct. Amer. an Cda.
{ Vermicularia graminicola Auct. Amer. non
  Westd.
{ Sorosporium Cenchri Henn.
{ Cf. Sorosporium Syntherismae (Pk.) Farl.
{ Sorosporium Syntherismae (Pk.) Farl.
{ Ustilago Cesatii Fisch. Wald.
{ Ustilago Syntherismae Pk.
Ustilago Cenchri Lagerh.

Cenchrus viridis Spreng.
Ephelis mexicana Fr.
Phyllachora sphaerosperma Wint.
{ Dicaeoma Cenchri (Diet. & Holw.) Arth.
{ Puccinia Cenchri Diet. & Holw.

Cenchrus sp. indet.
Cladosporium spongiosum B. & C.
Spegazzinia ornata Sacc.

Pennisetum bambusiforme Hemsl.
{ Dicaeoma atrum (Diet. & Holw.) Arth.
{ Puccinia atra Diet. & Holw.

Pennisetum crinitum (H. B. K.) Spreng.
{ Dicaeoma Arthuri (Syd.) Arth. & Fromme.
{ Puccinia Arthuri Syd.

Pennisetum glaucum (L.) R. Br.
Helminthosporium gramineum Rabh.

Pennisetum japonicum Trin.
Helminthosporium giganteum Heald & Wolf.

Pennisetum mexicanum Hemsl.
{ Puccinia Arthuri Syd.
{ Puccinia substriata A. & H. Ured. Exs. *42 c. d.*

Pennisetum multiflorum (Presl.) Fourn.
{ Dicaeoma Cenchri (Diet. & Holw.) Arth.
{ Puccinia Cenchri Diet. & Holw.

Stenotaphrum secundatum (Walt.) Ktze.
Meliola Stenotaphri F. L. Stevens.
Physarum cinereum (Batsch) P.
{ Ustilago affinis Ell. & Ev.
{ Ustilago Stenotaphri Massee.

Stenotaphrum species variae.
Himantia stellifera Johnston.

Olyra latifolia L.
Dimeriella fumagina (Dearness & Barthol.) F.
L. Stevens.
Dimeriella Olyrae Stevens.
Helminthosporium Panici F. L. Stevens.
Meliola Panici Earle.
{ Dicaeoma deformatum (B. & C.) O. Kuntze.
Puccinia deformata B. & C.
{ Dicaeoma phakopsoroides (Arth. & Mains)
Arth. & Fromme.
Puccinia phakopsoroides Arth. & Mains.
Olyra pauciflora Sw.
Dothidella flava F. L. Stevens.
Zizania aquatica L.
Ustilago esculenta Henn.
Zizania aquatica L., var. **angustifolia** Hitchc.
Claviceps sp. indet.
Entyloma lineatum (Cke.) J. J. Davis.
Sclerotium Zizaniae J. J. Davis.
Zizania aquatica L., var. **interior** Fassett.
Claviceps purpurea (Fr.) Tul.
Doassansia Zizaniae J. J. Davis.
{ Entyloma crastophilum Auct. Amer. p.p.
Entyloma lineatum (Cke.) J. J. Davis.
Entyloma Pammelii Hume.
Ustilago lineata Cke.
Puccinia Zizaniae S.
{ Mycosphaerella Zizaniae (S.) Lindau.
Sphaerella Zizaniae (S.) Ell. & Ev.
Sphaeria Zizaniae S.
Zizania sp. indet.
{ Heptameria zizaniicola (B. & C.) Cke.
Leptosphaeria zizaniicola (B. & C.) Sacc.
Sphaeria rimosa S. Herb.
Sphaeria zizaniicola B. & C.
Leptostroma Zizaniae S.
{ Lophiostoma Arundinis (Fr.) Ces. & De Not.
Sphaeria Arundinis Fr.
Sphaeria sulcigena S.
{ Arthrinium Sporophleum Kze. ex Lk.
Sporophleum gramineum (Kze.) ex Lk.
Oryza sativa L.
Cercospora Oryzae Miyake.
Cladosporium herbarum (P.) ex Lk.
Claviceps purpurea (Fr.) Tul.
Corticium vagum B. & C.
Epicoccum neglectum Desm.
Fusarium minimum Fckl.
?Helminthosporium inconspicuum Ell. & Ev.
Helminthosporium Oryzae van Breda de Haan.
Helminthosporium Oryzae Miyabe & Hori.
Macrosporium sp. indet.
Metasphaeria Cattanei Sacc.
Ophiobolus sp. indet.
Phoma glumarum Ell. & Tracy.
Piricularia grisea (Cke.) Sacc.
Piricularia Oryzae Br. & Cav.
Podosporiella verticillata O'Gara.

Pythium debaryanum Hesse.
Sclerotium Oryzae Catt.
Sclerotium Rolfsii Sacc.
Sphaerella Tulasnei Jancz.
Tilletia horrida Tak.
Ustilaginoidea Oryzae (Pat.) Bref.
Ustilaginoidea virens (Cke.) Tak.
Leersia hexandra Sw.
Tolyposporium globuligerum (B. & Br.) Ricker.
Leersia lenticularis Michx.
Tilletia corona Scribn.
Leersia oryzoides (L.) Sw.
Cladotrichum Leersiae Atk.
{ Dactylaria graminum (S.) Sacc.
Dactylium graminum S.
Phyllachora graminis (P. ex Fr.) Fckl.
Sphaerella Leersiae Pass.
Sphaerella Zizaniae (S.) Ell. & Ev.
{ Neovossia corona (Scribn.) Massee.
Tilletia corona Scribn.
{ Nigredo Halstedii (De Toni) Atk.
Uromyces Halstedii De Toni.
Leersia virginica Willd.
Cladotrichum Leersiae Atk.
Helminthosporium giganteum Heald & Wolf.
Helminthosporium Leersiae Atk.
Phyllachora graminis (P. ex Fr.) Fckl.
Piricularia grisea (Cke.) Sacc.
{ Neovossia corona (Scribn.) Massee.
Tilletia corona Scribn.
{ Nigredo Halstedii (DeToni) Arth.
Uromyces digitatus Halsted.
Uromyces Halstedii De Toni.
Leersia sp. indet.
Tilletia rotundata (Arth.) Ell. & Ev.
Phalaris amethystina Trin.
Puccinia sessilis Schneid.
Phalaris angusta Nees.
Dicaeoma poculiforme (Wettst.) O. Kuntze.
Dicaeoma Majanthae Arth.
Phalaris arundinacea L.
Claviceps purpurea (Fr.) Tul.
Cylindrosporium Phalaridis Sacc. & Dearness.
Helminthosporium giganteum Heald & Wolf.
Leptosphaeria amphibola Sacc.
Puccinia coronata P.?
{ Dicaeoma poculiforme (Wettst.) O. Kuntze.
Puccinia graminis P.
{ Aecidium Iridis Gerard.
Dicaeoma Majanthae (Arth. & Holw.) Arth.
{ Puccinia Majanthae Arth. & Holw.
Puccinia sessilis Schneid.
Puccinia striatula Pk.
Sclerotium rhizodes Awd.
Spermoedia Clavus (DC.) Fr.
Stagonospora intermixta (Cke.) Sacc.
Ustilago echinata Schrt.

Phalaris californica H. & A.
⎰Dicaeoma Majanthae (Arth. & Holw.) Arth.
⎱Puccinia Majanthae Arth. & Holw.

Phalaris canariensis L.
Cladosporium velutinum Ell. & Tracy.
Puccinia graminis P.
⎰Dicaeoma Majanthae (Arth. & Holw.) Arth.
⎱Puccinia Majanthae Arth. & Holw.

Phalaris caroliniana Walt.
⎰Puccinia coronata Cda.
⎱Puccinia Rhamni Wettst.

Phalaris intermedia Bosc.
Puccinia graminis P.

Phalaris minor Retz.
⎰Dicaeoma Majanthae (Arth. & Holw.) Arth.
⎱Puccinia Majanthae Arth. & Holw.

Phalaris paradoxa L.
Puccinia glumarum Erikss. & Henn.

Anthoxanthum aristatum Boiss.
Dicaeoma poculiforme (Wettst.) O. Kuntze.

Anthoxanthum odoratum L.
Helminthosporium dematioideum Bubák & Wróblewski.
Leptosphaeria culmifraga (Fr.) Ces. & De Not.
Puccinia Anthoxanthi Fckl.
⎰Dicaeoma poculiforme (Wettst.) O. Kuntze.
⎱Puccinia graminis P.
Puccinia graminis P., var. Avenae Erikss. & Henn.
⎰Dicaeoma epiphyllum (Wettst.) O. Kuntze.
⎱Puccinia Poarum Nielsen.
Sphaerella ignobilis Awd.
Tilletia Anthoxanthi Blytt.

Anthoxanthum Puelii Lecoq. & Lamotte.
Puccinia Anthoxanthi Fckl.
Puccinia graminis P., var. Avenae Erikss. & Henn.

Hierochloe alpina (Sw.) Roem. & Schult.
Cladosporium graminum Cda.
Clathrospora pentamera (Karst.) Berl.
Diplodia Simmonsii Rostr.
Laestadia graminicola Rostr.
Leptosphaeria Hierochloae Oud.
Leptosphaeria microscopica Karst.
Lophodermium arundinaceum (Schrad. ex Fr.) Chev.
⎰Naevia diminuens (Karst.) Rehm.
⎱Phacidium diminuens Karst.
Pleospora macrospora Schrt.
Pleospora pentamera Karst.
Pyrenophora phaeocomes (Reb.) ex Fr.
Septoria Oudemansii Sacc.
Sphaerella tassiana De Not.

Hierochloe macrophylla Thurb.
⎰Dicaeoma poculiforme (Wettst.) O. Kuntze.
⎱Puccinia poculiformis Wettst.
⎱Uredo quinqueporula Arth. & Fromme.

Hierochloe odorata (L.) Wahlenb.
Ophiobolus cariceti (B. & Br.) Sacc.
Dicaeoma Rhamni (Wettst.) O. Kuntze.
Septoria graminum Desm.

Hierochloe pauciflora R. Br.
Pleospora macrospora Schrt.

Aristida adscensionis L.
Dicaeoma Sarcobati Arth.

Aristida arizonica Vasey.
Nigredo Aristidae (Ell. & Ev.) Arth.

Aristida basiramea Engelm.
Sorosporium consanguineum Ell. & Ev.
⎰Nigredo seditiosa (Kern) Arth.
⎨Uromyces Aristidae Auct. p.p.
⎱Uromyces seditiosus Kern.

Aristida bromoides H. B. K.
Puccinia Aristidae Tracy.

Aristida Curtisii (Gray) Nash.

Aristida desmantha Trin. & Rupr.
Nigredo seditiosa (Kern) Arth.

Aristida dichotoma Michx.
⎰Dothichloe Aristidae Atk.
⎱Ophiodothis atramentosa, var. Aristidae (Atk.) Earle.
⎰Dothidea Aristidae (S.) Ell.
⎜Dothidella Aristidae (S.) Ell. & Ev.
⎨Euryachora? Aristidae Theissen & Syd.
⎜Phyllachora Aristidae (S.) Sacc.
⎝Sphaeria Aristidae S.
⎰Sorosporium confusum H. S. Jackson.
⎱Sorosporium Ellisii Wint. p.p.
Nigredo seditiosa (Kern) Arth.
⎰Uromyces Aristidae Fung. Columb. *2892*.
⎱Uromyces seditiosus Kern.

Aristida dispersa Trin. & Rupr.
⎰Puccinia aristidicola Arth. & Holw. an Henn
⎱Puccinia subnitens Diet.

Aristida gracilis Ell.
Sorosporium confusum H. S. Jackson.

Aristida longespica Poir.
Nigredo seditiosa (Kern) Arth.

Aristida longiramea J. Presl.
⎰Dicaeoma unicum (Holw.) Arth. & Fromme.
⎱Puccinia unica Holw.

Aristida longiseta Steud.
Nigredo seditiosa (Kern) Arth.

Aristida longiseta Steud., var. **robusta** Merr.
⎰Sorosporium consanguineum Ell. & Ev.
⎱Ustilago Aristidae Pk.

Aristida micrantha (Vasey) Nash.

Aristida oligantha Michx.
⎰Nigredo seditiosa (Kern) Arth.
⎨Uromyces Aristidae Fung. Columb. *2390*.
⎱Uromyces seditiosus Kern.

Aristida portoricensis Pilger.
Balansia discoidea Henn.
Dothichloe Aristidae Atk.

Aristida purpurascens Poir.
 Dothidea Aristidae (S.) Ell.
 Dothidella Aristidae (S.) Ell. & Ev.
 Euryachora Aristidae (S.) Theissen & Syd.
 Hendersonula Aristidae (S.) Ell.
 Phyllachora Aristidae (S.) Sacc.
 Sphaeria Aristidae S.
 Hendersonia effusa B. & C.
 Hypocrella Hypoxylon (Pk.) Sacc.
 Dothichloe Aristidae Atk.
 Ophiodothis atramentosa, var. Aristidae (Atk.)
  Earle.
 Sorosporium confusum H. S. Jackson.
 Sorosporium consanguineum Ell. & Ev.
 Nigredo seditiosa (Kern) Arth.
 Uromyces Aristidae Auct. p.p.
 Uromyces seditiosus Kern.

Aristida purpurea Nutt.
 Graphyllium Chloes Clements.
 Sorosporium consanguineum Ell. & Ev.
 Ustilago Aristidae Pk.
 Nigredo seditiosa (Kern) Arth.
 Uromyces Aristidae Auct. non Ell. & Ev.
 Uromyces seditiosus Kern.

Aristida ramosissima Engelm.
 Nigredo seditiosa (Kern) Arth.
 Uromyces seditiosus Kern.

Aristida Rusbyi Scribn.

Aristida schiedeana Trin. & Rupt.
 Sorosporium consanguineum Ell. & Ev.
 Ustilago Aristidae Pk.

Aristida stricta Michx.
 Dothidea Aristidae (S.) Ell.
 Euryachora? Aristidae (S.) Theissen & Syd.
 Hendersonia effusa B. & C.
 Hypocrella Hypoxylon (Pk.) Sacc.

Aristida tuberculosa Nutt.
 Nigredo seditiosa (Kern) Arth.
 Uromyces seditiosus Kern.

Stipa arida M. E. Jones.
 Dicaeoma Stipae (Arth.) O. Kuntze.

Stipa californica Merr. & Davy.
 Dicaeoma Stipae (Arth.) O. Kuntze.
 Puccinia Stipae Arth.

Stipa canadensis Poir.
 Sorosporium Williamsii Griffiths.
 Ustilago hypodytes (Schl.) Fr.

Stipa comata Trin. & Rupr.
 Allodus interveniens Auct, p. p.
 Dicaeoma Eurotiae Arth. & Fromme.
 Dicaeoma interveniens Auct. p. p.
 Puccinia Burnettii Griffiths.
 Puccinia interveniens Auct. p. p.
 Dicaeoma Stipae (Arth.) O. Kuntze.
 Puccinia Stipae Arth.
 Puccinia substerilis Ell. & Ev.
 Urocystis granulosa G. P. Clinton.
 Ustilago bromivora (Tul.) Fisch. Wald.

 Ustilago hypodytes (Schl.) Fr.
 Ustilago minima Arth.

Stipa coronata Thurb.
 Dicaeoma poculiforme (Wettst.) O. Kuntze.
 Ustilago hypodytes (Schl.) Fr.

Stipa Elmeri Piper & Brodie.
 Dicaeoma monoicum (Arth.) Arth. & Fromme.
 Puccinia monoica Arth.

Stipa eminens Cav.
 Allodus graminella (Diet. & Holw.) Arth.
 Puccinia graminella Diet. & Holw.
 Dicaeoma Stipae (Arth.) O. Kuntze.
 Puccinia Stipae Arth.
 Ustilago hypodytes (Schl.) Fr.
 Ustilago minima Arth.

Stipa eminens Cav., var. **Andersoni** Vasey.
 Allodus graminella (Diet. & Holw.) Arth.
 Allodus interveniens Bethel.
 Dicaeoma interveniens (Bethel) Arth. &
  Fromme.
 Tilletia Wilcoxiana Griffiths.

Stipa lepida Hitchc.
 Allodus interveniens (Pk.) Arth. & Orton.

Stipa Lettermani Vasey.
 Allodus interveniens Bethel.
 Dicaeoma interveniens (Bethel) Arth. &
  Fromme.
 Dicaeoma scaber (Ell. & Ev.) Arth.
 Puccinia substerilis Ell. & Ev.

Stipa minor (Vasey) Scribn.
 Claviceps purpurea (Fr.) Tul.
 Allodus interveniens Bethel.
 Dicaeoma interveniens (Bethel) Arth. &
  Fromme.
 Dicaeoma scaber (Ell. & Ev.) Arth.
 Puccinia substerilis Ell. & Ev.
 Dicaeoma Stipae (Arth.) O. Kuntze.
 Puccinia Stipae Arth.

Stipa Nelsonii Scribn.
 Dicaeoma scaber (Ell. & Ev.) Arth.

Stipa neomexicana (Thunb.) Vasey.
 Dicaeoma Stipae (Arth.) O. Kuntze.

Stipa occidentalis Thurb.
 Allodus interveniens Bethel.
 Dicaeoma interveniens (Bethel) Arth. &
  Fromme.
 Dicaeoma monoicum (Arth.) Arth. & Fromme.
 Ustilago hypodytes (Schl.) Fr.

Stipa pulchra Hitchc.
 Balansia Hypoxylon (Pk.) Atk.
 Allodus interveniens Bethel.
 Dicaeoma interveniens (Bethel) Arth. &
  Fromme.
 Puccinia interveniens Bethel.
 Dicaeoma Stipae (Arth.) O. Kuntze.
 Puccinia Stipae Arth.
 Ustilago hypodytes (Schl.) Fr.

Stipa Scribneri Vasey.
  Dicaeoma scaber (Ell. & Ev.) Arth.
  Puccinia substerilis Ell. & Ev.

Stipa spartea Trin.
  Dicaeoma Stipae (Arth.) O. Kuntze.
  Puccinia Stipae Arth.
  Ustilago hypodytes (Schl.)Fr.
  Ustilago minima Arth.

Stipa speciosa Trin. & Rupr.
  Allodus interveniens Auct. p. p.
  Dicaeoma Eurotiae Arth. & Fromme.
  Dicaeoma interveniens Auct. p. p.
  Puccinia interveniens Auct. p. p.

Stipa splendens Trin.
  Helminthosporium giganteum Heald & Wolf.

Stipa Vaseyi Scribn.
  Dicaeoma scaber (Ell. & Ev.) Arth.
  Puccinia scaber (Ell. & Ev.) Barthol.
  Puccinia substerilis Ell. & Ev.
  Uromyces scaber Ell. & Ev.
  Ustilago hypodytes (Schl.) Fr.

Stipa viridula Trin.
  ?Claviceps purpurea (Fr.) Tul.
  Dicaeoma scaber (Ell. & Ev.) Arth.
  Puccinia scaber (Ell. & Ev.) Barthol.
  Puccinia Stipae West Am. Fung. *6* and Fung.
    Columb. *1652.*
  Puccinia substerilis Ell. & Ev.
  Uredo luxurians Ell. & Ev.
  Sorosporium granulosum Ell. & Tracy.
  Ustilago hypodytes (Schl.) Fr.

Stipa sp. indet.
  Typhodium typhinum (P.) Seaver.

Oryzopsis asperifolia Michx.
  Asterina graminicola Ell. & Ev.
  Mycosphaerella Oryzopsidis Ell. & Ev.
  Phyllachora Oryzopsidis Theissen & Syd.
  Phyllachora graminis (P. ex Fr.) Fckl.
  Dicaeoma pygmaeum (Erikss.) Arth. &
    Fromme.
  Puccinia Milii Erikss.

Oryzopsis hymenoides (R. & S.) Ricker.
  Dicaeoma Eurotiae Arth. & Fromme.
  Dicaeoma interveniens Auct. p. p.
  Puccinia Burnettii Griffiths.
  Puccinia interveniens Auct. p. p.
  Dicaeoma scaber (Ell. & Ev.) Arth.
  Puccinia scaber (Ell. & Ev.) Barthol.
  Puccinia substerilis Ell. & Ev.
  Uredo Eriocomae Ell.
  Dicaeoma Stipae (Arth.) O. Kuntze.
  Puccinia Stipae Arth.
  Ustilago funalis Ell. & Ev.
  Ustilago hypodytes (Schl.) Fr.
  Ustilago Sporoboli Ell. & Ev.
  Ustilago minima Arth.

Oryzopsis micrantha Thurb.
  Dicaeoma micranthum (D. Griffiths) Arth. &
    Fromme.
  Puccinia micrantha Griffiths.

Milium effusum L.
  Laestadia effusa Rehm.
  Dicaeoma poculiforme (Wettst.) O. Kuntze.
  Puccinia graminis P.
  Dicaeoma pygmaeum (Erikss.) Arth. &
    Fromme.
  Puccinia Milii Erikss.

Milium sp. indet.
  Ophiobolus porphyrogonus (Tode) ex Sacc.
  Sphaeria rubella P. ex Fr.

Muhlenbergia ciliata (H. B. K.) Kunth.
  Dicaeoma dochmium (B. & C.) O. Kuntze.
  Puccinia dochmia B. & C.
  Ustilago Muhlenbergiae G. P. Clinton.

Muhlenbergia comata Benth.
  Nigredo minima (J. J. Davis) Arth
  Uromyces minimus J. J. Davis.

Muhlenbergia cuspidata (Torr.) Ryd.
  Dicaeoma poculiforme (Wettst.) O. Kuntze.
  Dicaeoma hibisciatum (Kellerm.) Arth.
  Phyllachora vulgata Theissen & Syd.

Muhlenbergia distichophylla Kunth.
  Ustilago mexicana Ell. & Ev.

Muhlenbergia exilis? Fourn.
  Dicaeoma dochmium (B. & C.) O. Kuntze.
  Puccinia dochmia B. & C.
  Puccinia Windsoriae, var. australis F. W.
    Anderson.

Muhlenbergia filiformis (Thurb.) Rydb.
  Dicaeoma hibisciatum (Kellerm.) Arth.

Muhlenbergia foliosa (R. & S.) Trin.
  Cercospora Muhlenbergiae Atk.
  Phyllachora graminis (P. ex Fr.) Fckl.
  Phyllachora vulgata Theissen & Syd.
  Puccinia Muhlenbergiae Arth. & Holw.

Muhlenbergia gracilis Trin.

Muhlenbergia gracillima Torr.
  Dicaeoma hibisciatum (Kellerm.) Arth.
  Puccinia Muhlenbergiae Arth. & Holw.

Muhlenbergia implicata (H. B. K.) Kunth.
  Dicaeoma dochmium (B. & C.) O. Kuntze.

Muhlenbergia Lemmoni Scribn.
  Uromyces Jacksonii Arth. & Fromme.

Muhlenbergia mexicana (L.) Trin.
  Didymella culmigena Sacc.
  Entyloma crastophilum Sacc.
  Helminthosporium giganteum Heald & Wolf.
  Phyllachora graminis (P. ex Fr.) Fckl.
  Dicaeoma poculiforme (Wettst.) O. Kuntze.
  Puccinia graminis P.

Muhlenbergia mexicana (*cont.*)
  {Dicaeoma hibisciatum (Kellerm.) Arth.
  {Puccinia dochmia Syd. Uredineen *1068*.
  {Puccinia hibisciata Kellerm.
  {Puccinia Muhlenbergiae Arth. & Holw.
  {Puccinia Windsoriae S.
  Scolecotrichum graminis Fckl.
  ?Sphaerella Muhlenbergiae Ell.
Muhlenbergia neomexicana Vasey.
Muhlenbergia Parishii Vasey.
  Phyllachora graminis (P. ex Fr.) Fckl.
Muhlenbergia parviglumis Vasey.
Muhlenbergia plumbea (Trin.) Hitchc.
  Dicaeoma hibisciatum (Kellerm.) Arth.
Muhlenbergia Porteri Scribn.
  Dicaeoma hibisciatum (Kellerm.) Arth.
  Ustilago Muhlenbergiae Henn.
Muhlenbergia Pringlei Scribn.
  Ustilago Muhlenbergiae Henn.
Muhlenbergia quitensis (H. B. K.) Hitch.
  {Dicaeoma dochmium (B. & C.) O. Kuntze.
  {Puccinia dochmia B. & C.
Muhlenbergia racemosa (Michx.) B. S. P.
  Dothidea Muhlenbergiae Ell.
  Leptosphaeria Muhlenbergiae Rehm.
  Phyllachora graminis (P. ex Fr.) Fckl.
  Phyllachora vulgata Theissen & Syd.
  Pleospora Andropogonis Niessl.
  {Dicaeoma hibisciatum (Kellerm.) Arth.
  {Puccinia hibisciata Kellerm.
  {Puccinia Muhlenbergiae Arth. & Holw.
  {Puccinia Windsoriae Burrill.
  {Nigredo minima (J. J. Davis) Arth.
  {Uromyces minimus J. J. Davis.
  {Ustilago montaniensis Ell. & Holw.
  {Sphacelotheca montaniensis (Ell. & Holw.) G.
    P. Clinton.
Muhlenbergia repens (Presl.) Hitchc.
  {Dicaeoma hibisciatum (Kellerm.) Arth.
  {Puccinia Muhlenbergiae Arth. & Holw.
Muhlenbergia Reverchonii Vasey.
  {Nigredo ignobilis Arth.
  {Nigredo major Arth.
  {Uromyces ignobilis Arth.
Muhlenbergia Richardsonii Rydb.
  Phyllachora graminis (P. ex Fr.) Fckl.
  Puccinia tosta Arth.
Muhlenbergia Schaffneri, var. **elongata** Fourn.
  Tilletia Muhlenbergiae G. P. Clinton.
Muhlenbergia Schreberi J. F. Gmel., (including
    M. diffusa Schreb.
  Cercospora Muhlenbergiae Atk.
  Fusarium graminum Cda.
  Helminthosporium giganteum Heald & Wolf.
  Phyllachora graminis (P. ex Fr.) Fckl.
  Phyllachora vulgata Theissen & Syd.
  {Dicaeoma dochmia (B. & C.) O. Kuntze.
  {Puccinia dochmia B. & C.

  {Dicaeoma hibisciatum (Kellerm.) Arth.
  {Dicaeoma Muhlenbergiae (Arth. & Holw.)
  { Arth.
  {Dicaeoma Windsoriae Auct. p. p.
  {Puccinia hibisciata Kellerm.
  Puccinia Muhlenbergiae Arth. & Holw.
  ?Puccinia Rubigo-vera Wint.
Muhlenbergia sobolifera (Muhl.) Trin.
  Phyllachora vulgata Theissen & Syd.
  {Dicaeoma hibisciatum (Kellerm.) Arth.
  {Puccinia hibisciata Kellerm.
Muhlenbergia squarrosa (Trin.) Rydb.
  Dicaeoma hibisciatum (Kellerm.) Arth.
Muhlenbergia stipoides Kunth.
  {Dicaeoma (?) Triniochloae (Arth. & Holw.)
  { Arth. & Fromme.
  {Uredo Triniochloae Arth. & Holw.
Muhlenbergia sylvatica Torr.
  Cercospora Muhlenbergiae Atk.
  Phyllachora graminis (P. ex Fr.) Fckl.
  Phyllachora vulgata Theissen & Syd.
  Dicaeoma dochmia (B. & C.) O. Kuntze.
  {Dicaeoma hibisciatum (Kellerm.) Arth.
  {Dicaeoma Muhlenbergiae (Arth. & Holw.)
  { Arth.
  {Dicaeoma Windsoriae Auct. p. p.
  {Puccinia hibisciata (S.) Kellerm.
  {Puccinia Muhlenbergiae Arth. & Holw.
  {Puccinia Windsoriae Burrill.
  Scolecotrichum graminis Fckl.
  {Nigredo minima (J. J. Davis) Arth.
  {Uromyces minimus J. J. Davis.
Muhlenbergia tenella (H.B. K.) Trin.
  {Dicaeoma dochmium (B. & C.) O. Kuntze.
  {Puccinia dochmia B. & C.
  {Puccinia Windsoriae, var. australis F. W.
  { Anderson.
Muhlenbergia tenuiflora (Willd.) B. S. P.
  {Dicaeoma hibisciatum (Kellerm.) Arth.
  {Puccinia Muhlenbergiae Arth. & Holw.
Muhlenbergia texana Thurb.
  Ustilago Muhlenbergiae Henn.
Muhlenbergia trifida Hack.
  Phyllachora vulgata Theissen & Syd.
  {Dicaeoma hibisciatum (Kellerm.) Arth.
  {Puccinia Muhlenbergiae Arth. & Holw.
Muhlenbergia sp. indet.
  Didymella culmigena Sacc.
  Epichloe typhina (P. ex Fr.) Tul.
  {Dothidea Muhlenbergiae Ell.
  {Phyllachora Muhlenbergiae (Ell.) Sacc.
  {Uromyces ignobilis (Syd.) Arth.
  {Nigredo major Arth.
  {Uromyces major, Arth.
  {Uromyces Peckianus Holw.
  Ustilago mexicana Ell. & Ev.

Brachyelytrum erectum (Schreb.) Beauv.
  ⎰Dothidea typhina (P.) ex Fr.
  ⎱Epichloe typhina (P. ex Fr.) Tul.
  ⎱Sphaeria typhina P. ex Fr.
  ⎰Phyllachora graminis (P. ex Fr.) Fckl.
  ⎱Sphaeria graminis P. ex Fr.
  Phyllactinia corylea (P.) ex Karst.
  Pyrenopeziza Caricis Rehm.

Lycurus phleoides H. B. K.
  Clathrospora permunda (Cke.) Berl.
  Ustilago lycuroides Griffiths.

Pereilema crinitum Presl.
  ⎰Dicaeoma dochmium (B. & C.) O. Kuntze.
  ⎱Puccinia dochmia B. & C.

Phleum alpinum L.
  ⎰Dicaeoma epiphyllum (Wettst.) O. Kuntze.
  ⎱Puccinia Poarum Nielsen.
  Scolecotrichum graminis Fckl.
  Sphaerella pusilla Awd.
  Sphaerella tassiana De Not.

Phleum asperum Jacq.
  Puccinia graminis, var. Avenae Erikss. &
    Henn.

Phleum pratense L.
  Cercospora graminicola Tracy & Earle.
  Claviceps microcephala (Wallr.) Tul.
  ⎰Claviceps purpurea (Fr.) Tul.
  ⎱Spermoedia clavus (DC.) Fr.
  Claviceps rubra Whetzel & Reddick.
  ⎰Colletotrichum cereale Manns.
  ⎱Colletotrichum graminicola (Ces.) G. W.
  ⎱ Wilson.
  Darluca Filum (Biv.) Cast.
  Diaporthe radicina Ell. & Ev.
  Dilophospora Alopecuri Fr.
  Entyloma crastophilum Sacc.
  Epichloe typhina (P. ex Fr.) Tul.
  Erysiphe graminis DC. †
  ⎰Fusarium Poae (Pk.) C. E. Lewis.
  ⎱Sporotrichum Poae Pk.
  Fusarium reticulatum Mont.
  Gibberella Saubinetii (Mont.) Sacc.
  Helminthosporium giganteum Heald & Wolf.
  Heterosporium Phlei Gregory.
  Leptosphaeria culmifraga (Fr.) Ces. & De Not.
  ⎰Hysterium arundinaceum Schrad. ex Fr., var.
  ⎱ gramineum (Duby) C. & E.
  ⎱Lophodermium arundinaceum (Schrad. ex Fr.)
  ⎱ Chev., var. gramineum Duby.
  Metasphaeria culmifida (Karst.) Sacc., var.
  ⎰Ophiobolus cariceti (B. & Br.) Sacc.
  ⎱Ophiobolus graminis Sacc.
  Phyllachora graminis (P. ex Fr.) Fckl.
  ⎰Laestadia oxyspora (Sacc. & Ell.) Cke.
  ⎱Physalospora? oxystoma Sacc. & Ell.
  ⎱Sphaeria (Physalospora) oxyspora Ell. & Sacc.
  ⎱ in N. A. F.

Pleospora infectoria Fckl.
Puccinia coronata Cda.
Puccinia glumarum Erikss. & Henn.
⎰Dicaeoma Phlei-pratense (Erikss. & Henn.) O.
⎱ Kuntze.
Dicaeoma poculiforme (Wettst.) O. Kuntze.
Puccinia graminis P.
⎰Puccinia graminis P., var. Avenae Erikss. &
⎱ Henn.
Puccinia graminis P., var. Phlei-pratensis
    (Erikss & Henn.) Stackman & Piemeisel.
Puccinia Phlei-pratensis Erikss. & Henn.
⎱Puccinia poculiformis Wettst.
Pyrenophora canadensis Ell. & Ev.
Rostrosphaeria Phlei Tehon & Daniels.
Sclerotium rhizodes Awd.
Scolecotrichum graminis Fckl.
Scolecotrichum sticticum (B. & Br.) Sacc.
Sirococcus Phlei Tehon & Daniels.
Sphaeropsis Phlei Ell. & Ev.
Ustilago Salvei Auct. Amer.
⎰Tilletia debaryana Fisch. Wald.
⎱Tilletia striiformis (Westd.) Oud.
⎱Ustilago striiformis (Westd.) Niessl.
Vermicularia culmigena Desm.

Alopecurus alpinus L.
  Cladosporium graminis Cda.
  ⎰Clathrospora pentamera (Karst.) Berl.
  ⎱Pleospora pentamera Karst.
  Diplodina arctica Lind.
  Homostegia gangraena (Fr.) Wint.
  Leptosphaeria culmorum Awd.
  Leptosphaeria microscopica Karst.
  Mastigosporium album Riess.
  Pleospora arctagrostidis Oud.
  Pleospora deflectens Karst.
  Pleospora discors (Mont.) Ces. & De Not.
  ⎰Dicaeoma epiphyllum (Wettst.) O. Kuntze.
  ⎱Puccinia Poarum Nielsen.
  ⎰Mycosphaerella lineolata (Rob.) Dearness.
  ⎱Sphaerella lineolata (Rob.) De Not.
  Sphaerella pusilla Awd.
  ⎰Mycosphaerella tassiana (De Not.) Johans.
  ⎱Sphaerella tassiana De Not.
  Sphaerella wichuriana Schrt.
  Stagonospora Alopecuri Rostr.

Alopecurus californicus Vasey.
  ⎰Dicaeoma poculiforme (Wettst.) O. Kuntze.
  ⎱Puccinia poculiformis Wettst.

Alopecurus geniculatus L.
  Entyloma speciosum Schrt. & Henn.
  Fusicladium Alopecuri Ell. & Ev.
  Puccinia graminis P.
  Puccinia graminis P., var. Avenae Erikss. &
    Henn.
  ⎰Dicaeoma epiphyllum (Wettst.) O. Kuntze.
  ⎱Puccinia Poarum Nielsen.

Alopecurus geniculatus (*cont.*)
Sclerospora graminicola (Sacc.) Schrt.
Scolecotrichum graminis Fckl.

Alopecurus geniculatus L., var. **aristulatus** Torr.
Colletotrichum cereale Manns.
{ Dicaeoma Rhamni (Wettst.) O. Kuntze.
{ Puccinia coronata Cda.
{ Puccinia Rhamni Wettst.
{ Dicaeoma poculiforme (Wettst.) O. Kuntze.
{ Puccinia graminis P.
Puccinia poculiformis Wettst.
{ Dicaeoma epiphyllum (Wettst.) O. Kuntze.
{ Puccinia Poarum Nielsen.
{ Nigredo Alopecuri (Seymour) Arth.
{ Uromyces Alopecuri Seymour.

Alopecurus pratensis L.
Claviceps microcephala Tul.
{ Claviceps purpurea (Fr.) Tul.
{ Spermoedia Clavus (DC.) Fr.
Colletotrichum cereale Manns.
Dilophospora Alopecuri Fr.
{ Dicaeoma Clematidis (Lagerh.) Arth.
{ Puccinia Clematidis Lagerh.
{ Puccinia perplexans Plowr.
{ Dicaeoma poculiforme (Wettst.) O. Kuntze.
{ Puccinia graminis P.
Scolecotrichum graminis Fckl.

Phippsia algida R. Br.
Cladosporium graminum Cda.
Leptosphaeria algida Rostr.
Leptosphaeria vagans Karst.
{ Mollisia graminis Karst.
{ Pyrenopeziza Karstenii Sacc.
Pleospora herbarum (Fr.) Rabh.
Pleospora infectoria Fckl.
Pleospora vagans Niessl.
Pleospora vulgaris Niessl.
Sphaerella pusilla Awd.
{ Mycosphaerella tassiana (De Not.) Johans.
{ Sphaerella tassiana De Not.

Sporobolus airoides Torr.
{ Dicaeoma luxuriosum (Syd.) Arth. & Fromme.
{ Puccinia luxuriosa Syd.
{ Puccinia tosta Fung. Columb. *4374.*
{ Puccinia tosta Arth., var. luxurians Arth.
Puccinia Cryptandri Ell. & Barthol.
{ Dicaeoma hibisciatum (Kellerm.) Arth.
{ Puccinia hibisciata Kellerm.
{ Puccinia tosta Arth.

Sporobolus argutus (Nees) Kunth.
{ Dicaeoma (?) egenulum Arth. & Fromme.
{ Uredo egenula Arth.

Sporobolus asper (Michx.) Kunth.
Cercospora seriata Atk.
{ Pleospora hysterioides Ell. & Ev.
{ Pleospora Andropogonis, subsp. hysterioides
{ Berl.

{ Dicaeoma poculiforme (Wettst.) O. Kuntze.
{ Puccinia graminis P.
Dicaeoma Sporoboli (Arth.) O. Kuntze.
Aecidium verbenicola III Auct. Amer.
{ Dicaeoma verbenicola (Ell. & Kellerm.) Arth.
{ Dicaeoma Vilfae (Arth. & Holw.) Arth.
{ Puccinia poculiformis E. F. *B 19.*
{ Puccinia Sporoboli Auct. Amer. p.p.
{ Puccinia sydowiana Diet.
{ Puccinia verbenicola Arth.
{ Puccinia Vilfae Arth. & Holw.
Scirrhia Sporoboli Atk.
{ Puccinia substerilis Ell. & Ev.
{ Uromyces scaber Ell. & Ev.
{ Nigredo Sporoboli (Ell. & Ev.) Arth.
{ Uromyces Sporoboli Ell. & Ev.
Volutella Bartholomaei Ell. & Ev.

Sporobolus asperifolius Thurb.
Phyllachora graminis (P. ex Fr.) Fckl.
{ Dicaeoma hibisciatum (Kellerm.) Arth.
{ Puccinia hibisciata Kellerm.
{ Puccinia Muhlenbergiae Arth. & Holw.
{ Puccinia tosta Arth.
{ Puccinia sydowiana Diet.
{ Puccinia Vilfae Arth. & Holw.
{ Tilletia asperifolia Ell. & Ev.
{ Tilletia fusca Auct. p. p.

Sporobolus auriculatus Vasey.
Clathrospora permunda (Cke.) Berl.
Dicaeoma hibisciatum (Kellerm.) Arth.
Stagonospora graminella Sacc.

Sporobolus berteroanus (Trin.) Hitchc.
Helminthosporium Ravenelii M. A. Curtis.

Sporobolus brevifolius (Nutt.) Scribn.
Phyllachora graminis (P. ex Fr.) Fckl.
Puccinia tosta Arth.
?Puccinia vexans Farl.
Puccinia Vilfae Diet. & Holw.

Sporobolus Buckleyi Vasey.
Dicaeoma hibisciatum (Kellerm.) Arth.

Sporobolus confusus Vasey.
Tilletia asperifolia Ell. & Ev.

Sporobolus contractus Hitchc.
{ Dicaeoma poculiforme (Wettst.) O. Kuntze.
{ Puccinia graminis P.
{ Puccinia poculiformis Wettst.
{ Puccinia graminis P., var. Secalis Erikss. &
{ Henn.
{ Dicaeoma simulans (Pk.) Arth. & Fromme.
{ Puccinia Cryptandri Ell. & Barthol.
{ Puccinia simulans (Pk.) Barthol.
{ Uromyces simulans Pk.
Puccinia Sporoboli Arth.
{ Nigredo Sporoboli (Ell. & Ev.) Arth.
{ Uromyces Sporoboli Ell. & Barthol.
{ Ustilago funalis Ell. & Ev.
{ Ustilago hypodytes (Schl.) Fr.
{ Ustilago Sporoboli Ell. & Ev.

Sporobolus cryptandrus (Torr.) Gray.
  Darluca Filum (Biv.) Cast.
  Phyllachora graminis (P. ex Fr.) Fckl.
Sporobolus cuspidatus Scribn.
  Phyllachora graminis (P. ex Fr.) Fckl.
  { Puccinia Muhlenbergiae Arth. & Holw.
  { Puccinia Schedonnardi Kellerm. & Swingle.
  { Puccinia tosta Arth.
  { Puccinia vexans Farl.
Sporobolus Drummondii Vasey.
  { Dicaeoma verbenicola Arth.
  { Puccinia verbenicola Arth.
  Uromyces ignobilis Arth.
Sporobolus gracillimus Scribn.
  ?Tilletia asperifolia Ell. & Ev.
  { Tilletia fusca Auct. p. p.
  { Tilletia montana Ell. & Ev.
Sporobolus heterolepis Gray.
  { Dicaeoma Sporoboli (Arth.) O. Kuntze.
  { Puccinia Sporoboli Arth.
Sporobolus indicus (L.) R. Br.
  Helminthosporium Ravenelii M. A. Curtis.
  Himantia stellifera Johnston.
  Phyllachora Cynodontis (Sacc.) Niessl.
  Tolyposporella Sporoboli H. S. Jackson.
  { Dactylium Helminthosporii Thm.
  { Trichothecium Helminthosporii (Thm.) Sacc.
  { Uromyces ignobilis Arth.
  { Uromyces major Arth.
Sporobolus Jacquemontii Kunth.
  Helminthosporium Ravenelii M. A. Curtis.
  Himantia stellifera Johnston.
Sporobolus junceus (Michx.) Kunth.
  Ustilago Sporoboli Tracy & Earle.
Sporobolus neglectus Nash.
  { Dicaeoma verbenicola Arth.
  { Puccinia sydowiana Diet.
  { Puccinia Schedonnardi Kellerm. & Swingle.
  { Puccinia tosta Arth.
  Tilletia subfusca Hume.
  { Nigredo Sporoboli (Ell. & Ev.) Arth.
  { Uromyces Sporoboli Ell. & Ev.
  Ustilago Vilfae Wint.
Sporobolus simplex Scribn.
  { Tilletia asperifolia Ell. & Ev. West. Am. Fung.
  {   *226.*
  { Tilletia montana Ell. & Ev.
Sporobolus tricholepis Coult.
  Phyllachora Blepharoneuri Fairman.
Sporobolus uniflorus (Muhl.) Scribn. & Merr.
  Phyllachora graminis (P. ex Fr.) Fckl.
Sporobolus utilis Torr.
  Puccinia tosta Arth.
Sporobolus vaginiflorus (Torr.) Wood.
  Dinemasporium graminum Lév.
  { Nigredo alliicola Arth.
  { Nigredo Sporoboli (Ell. & Ev.) Arth.
  Ustilago Vilfae Wint.

Sporobolus virginicus (L.) Kunth.
  { Nigredo ignobilis Arth.
  { Nigredo major Arth.
  { Uromyces ignobilis Arth.
Sporobolus Wrightii Munro.
  { Dicaeoma simulans (Pk.) Arth. & Fromme.
  { Puccinia Cryptandri Ell. & Barthol.
Epicampes Bourgaei Fourn. ex Hemsl.
  Rosellinia subiculata (S.) Sacc.
Epicampes macroura Benth.
  { Nigredo Epicampis (Diet. & Holw.) Arth.
  { Uromyces Epicampis Diet. & Holw.
Epicampes rigens Benth.
  { Dicaeoma hibisciatum (Kellerm.) Arth.
  { Puccinia Epicampis Arth.
  { Puccinia Schedonnardi Kellerm. & Swingle.
  Nigredo Epicampis (Diet. & Holw.) Arth.
Polypogon monspeliensis (L.) Desf.
  { Dicaeoma Rhamni (Wettst.) O. Kuntze.
  { Puccinia coronata Cda.
  { Puccinia Rhamni Wettst.
  { Dicaeoma poculiforme (Wettst.) O. Kuntze.
  { Puccinia graminis P.
  Puccinia graminis P., var. Avenae Erikss.
    Henn.
Thurberia arkansana (Nutt.) Benth.
  Dicaeoma hibisciatum (Kellerm.) Arth.
Arctagrostis arundinacea (Trin.) Beal.
  { Dicaeoma pygmaeum (Erikss.) Arth. &
  {   Fromme.
  { Puccinia pygmaea Erikss.
Arctagrostis latifolia (R. Br.) Griseb.
  Hendersonia arundinacea (Desm.) Sacc.
  Hendersonia crastophila Sacc.
  Laestadia graminicola Rostr.
  Leptosphaeria rousseliana (Desm.) Ces. & De
    Not.
  { Mollisia graminis Karst.
  { Pyrenopeziza Karstenii Sacc.
  Pleospora Arctagrostidis Oud.
  { Mycosphaerella tassiana (De Not.) Johans.
  { Sphaerella tassiana De Not.
Cinna arundinacea L.
  Acrospermum compressum Tode ex Fr.
  Erysiphe graminis DC. †
  Harpocephalum dematioides Atk.
  Helminthosporium catenarium Drechsler.
  Helminthosporium turcicum Pass.
  Leptosphaeria culmicola (Fr.) Karst.
  Phyllachora Cinnae Tehon & Daniels.
  Phyllachora graminis (P. ex Fr.) Fckl.
  { Dicaeoma Rhamni (Wettst.) O. Kuntze.
  { Puccinia coronata Cda.
  { Dicaeoma poculiforme (Wettst.) O. Kuntze.
  { Puccinia graminis P.
  { Puccinia poculiformis Wettst.
  { Dicaeoma Impatientis Arth.
  { Puccinia perminuta Arth.
  { Puccinia procera Auct. Amer. p. p.

Cinna latifolia (Trev.) Griseb.
{ Dicaeoma Rhamni (Wettst.) O. Kuntze.
{ Puccinia coronata Cda.
Dicaeoma Impatientis Arth.
Puccinia Elymi-Impatientis J. J. Davis.
{ Puccinia graminis P.
{ Puccinia poculiformis Wettst.
Stagonospora intermixta (Cke.) Sacc.
Agrostis alpina Scop.
{ Phyllachora graminis (P. ex Fr.) Fckl.
{ Sphaeria Agrostidis S.
Agrostis borealis Hartm.
Laestadia graminicola Rostr.
Agrostis canina L.
Laestadia graminicola Rostr.
Lophodermium arundinaceum (Schrad. ex Fr.)
Chev.
Puccinia graminis P., var. Agrostidis Erikss.
Sphaerella tassiana De Not.
Agrostis diegoensis Vasey.
Dicaeoma Rhamni (P.) O. Kuntze.
{ Dicaeoma poculiforme (Wettst.) O. Kuntze.
{ Puccinia poculiformis Wettst.
{ Puccinia Agrostidis Plowr.
{ Puccinia Elymi Westd.
Agrostis exarata Trin.
Erysiphe graminis DC. †
{ Dicaeoma Rhamni (Wettst.) O. Kuntze.
{ Puccinia coronata Cda.
{ Puccinia Rhamni Wettst.
{ Dicaeoma poculiforme (Wettst.) O. Kuntze.
{ Puccinia graminis P.
Puccinia graminis P., var. Avenae Erikss. &
Henn.
{ Dicaeoma Liatridis (Bethel) Arth. & Fromme.
{ Puccinia Koeleriae-Liatridis J. J. Davis.
Septoria graminum Desm.
Septoria Grylli Sacc.
Puccinia graminis P.
Puccinia Rhamni Wettst.
Agrostis foliosa Vasey.
Puccinia Rhamni Wettst.
Agrostis geminata Trin.
Septoria Grylli Sacc.
Sphaerella ignobilis Awd.
Agrostis Hallii Vasey.
{ Nigredo Jacksonii (Arth. & Fromme) Arth.
{ Uromyces Jacksonii Arth. & Fromme.
Agrostis hyemalis (Walt.) B. S. P.
Claviceps sp. indet.
{ Dicaeoma poculiforme (Wettst.) O. Kuntze.
{ Puccinia graminis P.
{ Puccinia poculiformis Wettst.
Puccinia graminis P., var. Avenae Erikss. &
Henn.
{ Dicaeoma Impatientis Arth.
{ Puccinia Impatientis Arth.
{ Puccinia perminuta Arth.

Dicaeoma Liatridis (Ell. & Anderson) Arth. &
Fromme.
Sclerotium rhizodes Awd.
Agrostis laxiflora Poir.
Leptosphaeria culmifraga (Fr.) Ces. & De Not.
Agrostis longiligula Hitchc.
{ Dicaeoma Rhamni (Wettst.) O. Kuntze.
{ Puccinia Rhamni Wettst.
Agrostis maritima Lam.
Dicaeoma poculiforme (Wettst.) O. Kuntze.
{ Dicaeoma Rhamni (Wettst.) O. Kuntze.
{ Puccinia Rhamni Wettst.
Dicaeoma Impatientis Arth.
{ Nigredo Jacksonii (Arth. & Fromme) Arth.
{ Uromyces Jacksonii Arth. & Fromme.
Agrostis microphylla Steud.
Puccinia Rhamni Wettst.
Agrostis pallens Trin.
{ Nigredo Jacksonii (Arth. & Fromme (Arth.).
{ Uromyces Jacksonii Arth. & Fromme.
Agrostis palustris Huds.
(Including A. alba, A. vulgaris and all vari-
eties.)
{ Claviceps purpurea (Fr.) Tul.
{ Spermoedia clavus (DC.) Fr.
{ Colletotrichum cereale Manns.
{ Colletotrichum graminicola (Ces.) G. W.
{ Wilson.
Corticium vagum B. & C.
Dilophospora Alopecuri Fr.
Entyloma crastophilum Sacc.
Erysiphe graminis DC. †
Fusarium Poae (Pk.) Lewis.
Helminthosporium dematioideum Bubák &
Wróblewski.
{ Ophiobolus cariceti (B. & Br.) Sacc.
{ Ophiobolus graminis Sacc.
Phyllachora Agrostidis C. R. Orton.
{ Dicaeoma Rhamni (Wettst.) O. Kuntze.
{ Puccinia coronata Cda.
{ Puccinia Rhamni Wettst.
{ Dicaeoma poculiforme (Wettst.) O. Kuntze.
{ Puccinia graminis P.
{ Puccinia poculiformis Wettst.
Puccinia graminis P., var. Agrostidis Erikss.
Puccinia graminis P., var. Avenae Erikss. &
Henn.
Puccinia graminis P., var. Tritici Erikss. &
Henn.
{ Dicaeoma Impatientis Arth.
{ Puccinia Impatientis Arth.
{ Puccinia perminuta Arth.
Sclerotium rhizodes Awd.
Scolecotrichum graminis Fckl.
Septocylindrium acutum J. J. Davis.
Sphaerella tassiana De Not.
Urocystis Agropyri (Preuss) Schrt.
Uromyces Jacksonii Arth.

Agrostis palustris (*cont.*)
  { Tilletia striiformis Oud.
  { Ustilago striiformis (Westd.) Niessl.
  { Ustilago washingtoniana Ell. & Ev.

Agrostis perennans (Walt.) Tuckerm.
  Acrospermum compressum Tode ex Fr.
  Helminthosporium dematioideum Bubák & Wröblewski.
  { Dicaeoma Impatientis Arth.
  { Puccinia Impatientis Arth.
  { Puccinia perminuta Arth.
  { Dicaeoma poculiforme (Wettst.) O. Kuntze.
  { Puccinia graminis P.

Agrostis stolonifera L.
  Corticium vagum B. & C.
  Erysiphe graminis DC.†
  Helminthosporium giganteum Heald & Wolf.
  Helminthosporium stenacrum Drechsler.
  Puccinia graminis P.
  Puccinia graminis P., var. Agrostidis Erikss.

Agrostis thurberiana Hitchc.
  Dicaeoma Impatientis Arth.
  { Dicaeoma Rhamni (Wettst.) O. Kuntze.
  { Puccinia praegracilis Arth.
  { Puccinia Rhamni Wettst.

Agrostis sp. indet.
  Cercospora Agrostidis Atk.
  Leptosphaeria leersiana Sacc.
  Rhizoctonia Solani Kühn.
  Sphaerella californica Cke.

Calamagrostis aleutica Bong.
  Claviceps microcephala (Wallr.) Tul.
  Leptosphaeria culmifraga (Fr.) Ces. & De Not.
  { Dicaeoma Rhamni (Wettst.) O. Kuntze.
  { Puccinia Rhamni Wettst.
  { Dicaeoma pygmaeum (Erikss.) Arth. & Fromme.
  { Puccinia pygmaea Erikss.

Calamagrostis canadensis (Michx.) Beauv.
  Acrospermum graminum Lib.
  Ascochyta graminicola Sacc.
  Balansia Hypoxylon (Pk.) Atk.
  Belonidium intermedium Rehm.
  Belonidium mediellum (Karst.) Rehm.
  Claviceps purpurea (Fr.) Tul.
  Colletotrichum graminicola (Ces.) G. W. Wilson.
  Cylindrosporium Calamagrostidis Ell. & Ev.
  Dilophospora Alopecuri Fr.
  Dothichloe atramentosa (B. & C.) Atk.
  { Epichloe typhina (P. ex Fr.) Tul.
  { Typhodium typhinum (P. ex Fr.) Seaver.
  Hadrotrichum lineare Pk.
  Mastigosporium album Riess, var. calvum Ell. & Davis.
  Mollisia rufula Sacc.
  Phyllachora graminis (P. ex Fr.) Fckl.

Pilidium graminicola Pk.
Puccinia amphigena Diet.
{ Dicaeoma Rhamni (Wettst.) O. Kuntze.
{ Puccinia coronata Cda.
{ Puccinia Rhamni Wettst.
{ Puccinia striatula J. J. Davis p.p. non Pk.
{ Dicaeoma poculiforme (Wettst.) O. Kuntze.
{ Puccinia graminis P.
{ Dicaeoma pygmaeum (Erikss.) Arth. & Fromme.
{ Puccinia pygmaea Erikss.
{ Puccinia striatula J. J. Davis p.p. non Pk.
{ Puccinia linearis Pk.
{ Puccinia sessilis Schneid.
{ Puccinia striatula Pk.
{ Sclerotium rhizodes Awd.
{ Sclerotium sp. indet. Davis.
Scolecotrichum graminis Fckl.
Septoria Bromi Sacc.
Septoria Calamagrostidis Ell. & Ev.
Septoria Everhartii Sacc. & Syd.
{ Peziza agrostina Pk.
{ Trichopeziza agrostina (Pk.) Sacc.
Urocystis Agropyri (Preuss) Schrt.
Urocystis occulta Auct. Amer.
{ Tilletia striiformis Auct. Amer. p. p.
{ Ustilago Calamagrostidis (Fckl.) G. P. Clinton.

Calamagrostis elongata Rydb.
  { Dicaeoma Rhamni (Wettst.) O. Kuntze.
  { Puccinia coronata Cda.

Calamagrostis epigeios Rydb.
  Dilophospora Alopecuri Fr.

Calamagrostis groenlandica Kunth.
  Claviceps purpurea (Fr.) Tul.

Calamagrostis inexpansa Gray.
  Alternaria tenuis Nees.
  Claviceps purpurea (Fr.) Tul.
  Hypocrella Hypoxylon (Pk.) Sacc.
  Lophodermium arundinaceum (Schrad. ex Fr.) Chev.
  { Dicaeoma Rhamni (Wettst.) O. Kuntze.
  { Puccinia coronata Cda.

Calamagrostis koelerioides Vasey.
  Dicaeoma Rhamni (Wettst.) O. Kuntze.

Calamagrostis lanceolata Roth.
  Pleospora vagans Niessl.

Calamagrostis Langsdorfii (Lk.) Trin.
  Claviceps microcephala (Wallr.) Tul.
  Hadrotrichum lineare Pk.
  Phyllachora graminis (P.) Fckl.
  Puccinia Rhamni Wettst.

Calamagrostis lapponica Trin.
  { Mollisia graminis Karst.
  { Pyrenopeziza Karstenii Sacc.
  Dicaeoma poculiforme (Wettst.) O. Kuntze.
  Puccinia Rubigo-vera (DC.) Wint.?

Calamagrostis **neglecta** (Ehrh.) Gaertner, Meyer,
& Scherbius.
{ Claviceps microcephala (Wallr.) Tul.
{ Spermoedia microcephala (Wallr.) Seaver.
Claviceps purpurea (Fr.) Tul.
Leptosphaeria Fuckelii Niessl.
Lophoderminum arundinaceum (Schrad. ex
Fr.) Chev.
Pleospora herbarum (P.) Rabh.
Dicaeoma Rhamni (Wettst.) O. Kuntze.
Sclerotium rhizodes Awd.
Calamagrostis **phragmitoides** Hartm.
Hendersonia crastophila Sacc.
Lophodermium arundinaceum (Schrad. ex Fr.)
Chev.
Septoria nebulosa Rostr.
Sphaerella tassiana De Not.
Calamagrostis **Pickeringii** Gray.
{ Tilletia striiformis Auct. Amer. p. p.
{ Ustilago Calamagrostidis (Fckl.) G. P. Clinton.
{ Ustilago Salveii Auct. Amer.
Calamagrostis **purpurascens** R. Br.
Diplodia Calamagrostidis Dearness.
Lophodermium arundinaceum (Schrad. ex Fr.)
Chev.
Physalospora leptosperma Rostr.
{ Dicaeoma Rhamni (Wettst.) O. Kuntze.
{ Puccinia coronata Cda.
Calamagrostis **rubescens** Buckl.
Dicaeoma Rhamni (Wettst.) O. Kuntze.
Calamagrostis **scabra** Presl.
Fusoma rubricosa Dearness & Barthol.
Calamagrostis **stricta** Trin.
Lophodermium arundinaceum (Schrad. ex Fr.)
Chev.
Septoria nebulosa Rostr.
Calamagrostis **Suksdorfii** Scribn.
Herpotrichia purpurea Ell. & Ev.
Calamagrostis sp. indet.
Lophiotrema pusillum Fckl.
Septoria graminum Desm.
Ammophila **breviligulata** Fern.
{ Camarosporium metableticum Trail.
{ Camarosporium graminicola Ell. & Ev.
Claviceps purpurea (Fr.) Tul.
{ Hysterium culmigenum, var. gramineum Fr.
{ Hysterium gramineum Fr.
{ Lophodermium arundinaceum (Schrad. ex Fr.)
{ Chev.
{ Lophodermium arundinaceum (Schrad. ex Fr.)
{ Chev., var. gramineum Duby.
{ Pleospora infectoria Fckl.
{ Sphaeria infectoria (Fckl.) Pk.
Pleospora scabra Mont.
Puccinia graminis P., var. Avenae Erikss. &
Henn.
Pyrenopeziza Ellisii Massee.
Ustilago striiformis (Westd.) Niessl.

Calamovilfa **gigantea** (Nutt.) Scribn. & Mer.
Dicaeoma amphigenum (Diet.) O. Kuntze.
Calamovilfa **longifolia** (Hook.) Hack.
Colletotrichum graminicola (Ces.) G. W. Wilson.
Epichloe typhina (P. ex Fr.) Tul.
{ Mollisia clavigera (Ell. & Ev.) Sacc.
{ Peziza clavigera Ell. & Ev.
{ Dicaeoma amphigenum (Diet.) O. Kuntze.
{ Puccinia amphigena Diet.
?Puccinia graminis P.
Niptera Ellisii N. A. F. *2329.*
{ Niptera Ellisii Rehm. nom. nud.
{ Pyrenopeziza Ellisii Massee.
Notholcus **lanatus** (L.) Nash.
(See also Holcus Sorghum L.).
Dilophospora Alopecuri Fr.
Entyloma crastophilum Sacc.
Helminthosporium triseptatum Drechsler.
{ Dicaeoma Rhamni (Wettst.) O. Kuntze.
{ Puccinia coronata Cke.
{ Puccinia coronifera Klebahn.
{ Puccinia Lolii Nielsen.
{ Puccinia Rhamni Wettst.
Puccinia graminis Auct.
Puccinia graminis, var. Avenae Erikss. &
Henn.
{ Dicaeoma holcinum (Erikss.) Arth. & Fromme
{ Puccinia holcina Erikss.
{ Tilletia Holci (Westd.) Rostr.
{ Tilletia Rauenhoffii Fisch. Wald.
Deschampsia **alpina** (L.) Roem. & Schult.
{ Durella groenlandica (Rostr.) Sacc.
{ Leptopeziza groenlandica Rostr.
Mollisia cinerea (Fr.) Karst.
{ Mollisia graminis Karst.
{ Pyrenopeziza Karstenii Sacc.
Phoma graminis Westd.
Pleospora Elynae (Rabh.) Ces. & De Not.
Pleospora herbarum (P.) ex Rabh.
Sphaerella ignobilis Awd.
Sphaerella tassiana De Not.
Deschampsia **arctica** Merr.
Leptosphaeria arundinacea (Sow. ex Fr.) Sacc.
Deschampsia **atropurpurea** (Wahlenb.) Scheele.
Lophodermium arundinaceum (Schrad. ex Fr.)
Chev.
{ Mollisia graminis Karst.
{ Pyrenopeziza Karstenii Sacc.
Stagonospora graminum Sacc. & Scalia.
Deschampsia **caespitosa** (L.) Beauv.
{ Dicaeoma Rhamni (Wettst.) O. Kuntze.
{ Puccinia coronata Cda.
{ Puccinia Rhamni Wettst.
{ Dicaeoma epiphyllum (Wettst.) O. Kuntze.
{ Puccinia Deschampsiae Arth.
{ Puccinia epiphylla Wettst.
Pyrenopeziza Karstenii Sacc.

Deschampsia caespitosa (*cont.*)
  Tilletia Airae Blytt.
  Tilletia cerebrina Ell. & Ev.
  ⎰Nigredo Jacksonii (Arth. & Fromme) Arth.
  ⎱Uromyces Jacksonii Arth. & Fromme.
Aira caespitosa (L.) Beauv., var. **arctica** (Trin.)
  Simmons.
  Pleospora pentamera Karst.
  ⎰Mycosphaerella pusilla (Awd.) Dearness.
  ⎱Sphaerella pusilla Awd.
  Mycosphaerella tassiana (De Not) Johans.
Deschampsia caespitosa (L.) Beauv., var. **brevifolia** (Bixb.) Vasey.
  Didymosphaeria arenaria Mouton, var. macrospora Sacc. & Scalia.
Deschampsia danthonioides Munro.
  Dicaeoma poculiforme (Wettst.) O. Kuntze.
Deschampsia elongata (Hook.) Munro.
  ⎰Dicaeoma poculiforme (Wettst.) O. Kuntze.
  ⎱Puccinia poculiformis Wettst.
  Nigredo Jacksonii (Arth. & Fromme) Arth.
  ⎰Puccinia Deschampsiae Fung. Columb. *4460.*
    N. Am. Ured. *1237.*
  ⎱Uromyces Jacksonii Arth. & Fromme.
Deschampsia flexuosa (L.) Trin.
  Lophodermium arundinaceum (Schrad. ex Fr.)
    Chev.
  Sphaerella tassiana De Not.
Deschampsia holciformis Presl.
  Dicaeoma poculiforme (Wettst.) O. Kuntze.
Trisetum canescens Buckl.
  Dicaeoma poculiforme (Wettst.) O. Kuntze.
Trisetum cernuum (Kunth.) Trin.
  ⎰Dicaeoma Rhamni (Wettst.) O. Kuntze.
  ⎨Puccinia coronata Cda.
  ⎱Puccinia Rhamni Wettst.
Trisetum deyeuxioides (H. B. K.) Kunth.
  ⎰Dicaeoma Clematidis (Lagerh.) Arth.
  ⎨Puccinia Elymi Westd.
  ⎨Puccinia monoica Arth.
  ⎱Puccinia Triseti Auct. Amer. an Erikss.
Trisetum majus (Vasey) Rydb.
  ⎰Aecidium monoicum Pk. III.
  ⎱Puccinia monoica Arth.
Trisetum fournieranum Hitchc.
Trisetum montanum Vasey.
  ⎰Dicaeoma Clematidis (Lagerh.) Arth.
  ⎱Puccinia Elymi Westd.
Trisetum pratense P.
  Rhizoctonia Solani Kühn.
Trisetum spicatum (L.) Richter.
  Cladosporium graminum Cda.
  Leptosphaeria culmorum Awd.
  Lophodermium arundinaceum (Schrad. ex Fr.)
    Chev.
  Pleospora discors (Dur. & Mont.) Ces. & De
    Not.
  Pleospora herbarum (P.) ex Rabh.
  Pleospora Karstenii Sacc.

  Pleospora pentamera Karst.
  ⎰Dicaeoma Clematidis (Lagerh.) Arth.
  ⎱Puccinia Elymi Westd.
  Dicaeoma epiphyllum (Wettst.) O. Kuntze.
  Puccinia graminis P., var. Avenae Erikss. &
    Henn.
  ⎰Aecidium monoicum III. Garrett.
  ⎨Dicaeoma monoicum (Arth.) Arth. & Fromme.
  ⎨Puccinia monoica Arth.
  ⎱Puccinia Triseti Auct. Amer. an Erikss.
  ⎰Dicaeoma Rhamni (Wettst.) O. Kuntze.
  ⎱Puccinia Rhamni Wettst.
  Septoria graminum Desm.
  Septoria nebulosa Rostr.
  ⎰Mycosphaerella tassiana (De Not.) Johans.
  ⎱Sphaerella tassiana De Not.
Trisetum Virletii Fourn.
  ⎰Dicaeoma leptosporum (Ricker) Arth. &
  ⎨ Fromme.
  ⎱Puccinia leptospora Ricker.
Avena barbata Brot.
  ⎰Dicaeoma Clematidis (Lagerh.) Arth.
  ⎨Puccinia Elymi Westd.
  ⎨Dicaeoma Rhamni (Wettst.) O. Kuntze.
  ⎨Puccinia Rhamni Wettst.
  ⎱Puccinia Lolii Nielsen, var. Avenae McAlpine.
  ⎰Dicaeoma poculiforme (Wettst.) O. Kuntze.
  ⎱Puccinia poculiformis Wettst.
  Puccinia graminis P., var. Avenae Erikss. &
    Henn.
  Sphaerographium avenaceum Fairman.
  Ustilago Avenae (P.) Jensen.
  Ustilago levis (Kellerm. & Swingle) Magn.
Avena brevis Roth.
  ⎰Dicaeoma Rhamni (Wettst.) O. Kuntze.
  ⎨Puccinia coronata Cda.
  ⎱Puccinia Rhamni Wettst.
  ⎰Dicaeoma poculiforme (Wettst.) O. Kuntze.
  ⎨Puccinia graminis P.
  ⎱Puccinia poculiformis Wettst.
  Puccinia graminis P., var. Avenae Erikss. &
    Henn.
  Puccinia Lolii Nielsen, var. Avenae McAlpine.
  Ustilago Avenae (P.) Jensen.
  Ustilago levis (Kellerm. & Swingle) Magn.
Avena fatua L.
  Dicaeoma Clematidis (Lagerb.) Arth.
Avena fatua L., var. **glabrata** Peterm.
  ⎰Dicaeoma poculiforme (Wettst.) O. Kuntze.
  ⎱Puccinia graminis P.
  Ustilago levis (Kellerm. & Swingle) Magn.
Avena Hookeri Scribn.
  Ophiobolus cariceti (B. & Br.) Sacc.
  Puccinia graminis P., var. Avenae Erikss. &
    Henn.
Avena nuda L.
  Puccinia graminis P., var. Avenae Erikss. &
    Henn.

Avena nuda (*cont.*)
Puccinia Lolii Nielsen, var. Avenae McAlpine.
Septoria Avenae Frank.
Ustilago Avenae (P.) Jensen.

Avena orientalis Schreb.
Puccinia graminis P., var. Avenae Erikss. &
Henn.
Puccinia Lolii Nielsen, var. Avenae McAlpine.

Avena pratensis L.
Puccinia graminis P., var. Avenae Erikss. &
Henn.

Avena purpurea Gueldst.
Puccinia graminis P., var. Avenae Erikss. &
Henn.
Puccinia Lolii Nielsen, var. Avenae McAlpine.

Avena sativa L.
Alternaria fasciculata (C. & E.) Jones & Grout.
Arthrobotrys rosea Massee.
Cladosporium graminum Cda.
Cladosporium herbarum (P.) ex Lk.
Claviceps purpurea (Fr.) Tul.
{ Colletotrichum cereale Manns.
{ Colletotrichum graminicola (Ces.) G. W.
    Wilson.
Dinemasporium graminum (Lib.) Lév.
Epicoccum neglectum Desm.
Erysiphe graminis DC. †
Fusarium arcuosporum Sherb.
Fusarium culmorum (W. G. Sm.) Sacc.
Fusarium culmorum (W. G. Sm.) Sacc., var.
leteus Sherb.
Fusarium oxysporum Schl.
Fusarium roseum Lk.
Fusicladium destruens Pk.
Gibberella Saubinetii (Mont.) Sacc.
Helminthosporium Avenae Eidam.
Helminthosporium Avenae-sativae (Br. &
Cav.) Lindau.
Helminthosporium avenaceum M. A. Curtis.
{ Helminthosporium gramineum Rabh.
{ Helminthosporium inconspicuum C. & E.
Helminthosporium inconspicuum C. & E., var.
britanicum Grove.
Helminthosporium teres Sacc.
{ Leptosphaeria avenaria Weber.
{ Septoria Avenae Frank.
Oidium monilioides Lk.
?Ophiobolus graminis Sacc.
Papulospora aspergilliformis Eidam.
Periconia pycnospora Fres.
Phyllosticta avenophila Tehon & Daniels.
Phytophthora Colocasiae Rac.?
{ Dicaeoma Rhamni (Wettst.) O. Kuntze.
| Puccinia coronata Cda.
| Puccinia coronifera Klebahn.
| Puccinia Lolii Nielsen, var. Avenae McAlpine.
| Puccinia Rhamni Wettst.
{ Puccinia simplex Fung. Columb. *3968, 3969.*

{ Dicaeoma poculiforme (Wettst.) O. Kuntze.
{ Puccinia graminis P.
{ Puccinia poculiformis Wettst.
Puccinia graminis P., var. Avenae Erikss. &
Henn.
Puccinia graminis P., var. Hordei Auct.
{ Puccinia graminis P., var. Phlei-pratensis
{   (Erikss. & Henn.) Stakman & Piemeisel.
{ Puccinia Phlei-pratensis Erikss. & Henn.
Puccinia graminis P., var. Tritici Erikss. &
Henn.
{ Dicaeoma Asperifolii Auct. p.p.
| Puccinia Elymi Westd.
| Puccinia Rubigo-vera, var. Tritici Carl.
{ Puccinia triticina Erikss.
Rhizoctonia crocorum (P.) ex. Fr.
Sclerotinia libertiana Fckl.
Scolecotrichum graminis Fckl.
Septoria Avenae Frank.
{ Caeoma segetum Lk. p.p.
| Uredo segetum P. p.p.
{ Ustilago Avenae (P.) Jensen.
| Ustilago Carbo Auct. p.p.
{ Ustilago segetum Ditm. p.p.
{ Ustilago Avenae (P.) Jensen., var. levis (Jen-
{   sen) Kellerm. & Swingle.
{ Ustilago levis (Kellerm. & Swingle) Magn.

Avena sterilis L.
Puccinia coronata Cda.
Puccinia Lolii Nielsen, var. Avenae McAlpine.
Puccinia graminis P., var. Avenae Erikss. &
Henn.

Avena sp. indet.
Monilia Avenae Pk.
Rhizoctonia Solani Kühn.

Arrhenatherum elatius (L.) Beauv.
{ Claviceps purpurea (Fr.) Tul.
{ Spermoedia clavus (DC.) Fr.
{ Colletotrichum cereale Manns.
{ Colletotrichum graminicola (Ces.) G. W.
    Wilson.
Dilophospora Alopecuri Fr.
{ Puccinia coronata Cda.
{ Puccinia Rhamni Wettst.
{ Dicaeoma poculiforme (Wettst.) O. Kuntze.
{ Puccinia Phlei-pratensis Erikss. & Henn.
Scolecotrichum graminis Fckl.
{ Cintractia Avenae Ell. & Tracy.
{ Ustilago perennans Rostr.
{ Ustilago segetum Auct. p.p.

Danthonia compressa Auct.
Ustilago residua G. P. Clinton.

Danthonia intermedia Vasey.
Lophodermium arundinaceum (Schrad. ex Fr.)
Chev.
Lophodermium arundinaceum (Schrad. ex Fr.)
Chev., var. alpinum Rehm.
Pleospora infectoria Fckl.
Ustilago residua G. P. Clinton.

Danthonia spicata (L.) Beauv.
  Balansia Hypoxylon (Pk.) Atk.
  Dothidea piluliformis B. & C.
  Ephelis borealis Ell. & Ev.
  Epichloe Hypoxylon Pk.
  Hypocrea Hypoxylon (Pk.) Cke.
  Hypocrella Hypoxylon (Pk.) Sacc.
  Ophiodothis vorax, var. piluliformis Sacc.
  Helminthosporium Cyclops Drechsler.
  Helminthosporum sativum Pammel, King &
    Bakke.
  Phyllachora graminis (P. ex Fr.) Fckl.
  Ustilago residua G. P. Clinton.
  Ustilago segetum Auct. p.p.
  Ustilago segetum, var. Danthoniae N. A. F.
    1893.
Microchloa indica Hackel.
  Ustilago Griffithsii Syd.
  Ustilago Microchloae Griffiths.
Cynodon Dactylon (L.) P.
  Coniosporium rhizophilum (Preuss) Sacc.
  Dimerosporium erysipheoides Ell. & Ev.
  Helminthosporium Cynodontis Marignoni.
  Helminthosporium giganteum Heald & Wolf.
  Marasmius graminis Murrill.
  Dicaeoma Cynodontis (Delacroix) O. Kuntze.
  Puccinia Cynodontis Delacroix.
  Sclerotium portoricense F. L. Stevens.
  Ustilago Cynodontis Henn.
Spartina alternifolia Loisel., var. **glabra** (Muhl.)
  Fern.
  Claviceps purpurea (Fr.) Tul.
  Sclerotium clavus DC.
  Spermoedia clavus Fr.
  Fusarium Spartinae Ell. & Ev.
  Phyllachora serialis Ell. & Ev.
  Dicaeoma Cephalanthi H. S. Jackson.
  Puccinia seymouriana Arth.
  Dicaeoma Fraxini Arth.
  Puccinia fraxinata Arth.
  Puccinia sparganioides Ell. & Barthol.
  Uredo peridermiospora Ell. & Tracy.
  Nigredo arguta (Kern) Arth.
  Uromyces argutus Kern.
  Nigredo Polemonii Arth.
  Uromyces acuminatus Arth.
  Uromyces Junci, var. Spartinae, Farl.
  Uromyces Polemonii (Pk.) Barthol.
  Uromyces Spartinae Farl.
Spartina Bakeri Merr.
  Dicaeoma Fraxini Arth.
Spartina cynosuroides (L.) Roth.
  Note: It is not practicable at this date to sep-
arate all the fungi which belong to the above
host from those which belong to **Spartina cyno-
suroides** Auct. Amer. non Roth. The latter is
referred to **S. michauxiana** Hitchc.
  Belonidium heteromorphum (Ell. & Ev.) Sacc.
  Peziza heteromorpha Ell. & Ev.

Didymosphaerella pardalina (Ell. & Ev.) Cke.
Didymosphaeria pardalina Ell. & Ev.
Dimerosporium Spartinae Ell. & Ev.
Meliola Spartinae (Ell. & Ev.) Berl. & Vogl.
Periconia nigriceps (Pk.) Sacc.
Sporocybe nigriceps Pk.
Peziza atriella Cke.
Dicaeoma Fraxini Arth.
Puccinia arundinacea N. A. F. 1851.
Puccinia fraxinata Arth.
Puccinia peridermiospora Arth.
Dicaeoma Distichlidis (Ell. & Ev.) O. Kuntze.
Puccinia Distichlidis Ell. & Ev.
Dicaeoma Cephalanthi H. S. Jackson.
Puccinia seymouriana Arth.
Sphaerella Spartinae Ell. & Ev.
Spartina gracilis Trin.
  Cerebella Spartinae Ell. & Ev.
  Dicaeoma Distichlidis (Ell. & Ev.) O. Kuntze.
  Puccinia Distichlidis Ell. & Ev.
  Puccinia Kelseyi Syd.
  Puccinia Phragmitis Myc. Ex. 103.
  Dicaeoma Fraxini Arth.
  Puccinia fraxinata Arth.
  Puccinia sparganioides Ell. & Barthol.
  Nigredo Polemonii Arth.
  Uromyces acuminatus Arth.
  Uromyces Spartinae Farl.
Spartina junciformis Engelm. & Gray.
  Dicaeoma Cephalanthi H. S. Jackson.
  Puccinia seymouriana Arth.
Spartina michauxiana Hitchc.
Spartina cynosuroides Auct. Amer. p. p.
  Ascochyta Spartinae Trel.
  Balansia Hypoxylon (Pk.) Atk.
  Belonidium heteromorphum (Ell. & Ev.) Sacc.
  Claviceps purpurea (Fr.) Tul.
  Phyllachora graminis (P. ex Fr.) Fckl.
  Dicaeoma Cephalanthi H. S. Jackson.
  Dicaeoma seymouriana (Arth.) House.
  Puccinia arundinacea N. A. F. 1474.
  Puccinia Phragmitis E. F. 69, Fung. Eur. 4026.
  Puccinia Cephalanthi (H. S. Jackson) Arth. ex
    House. 1920.
  Puccinia Cephalanthi (H. S. Jackson) Barthol.
    1922.
  Puccinia seymouriana Arth.
  Dicaeoma Distichlidis (Ell. & Ev.) O. Kuntze.
  Puccinia Distichlidis Ell. & Ev.
  Puccinia Kelseyi Syd.
  Dicaeoma Fraxini Arth.
  Puccinia Arundinariae Syd. Ured. 262, 1167.
  Puccinia fraxinata Arth.
  Puccinia peridermiospora Arth.
  Puccinia sparganioides Ell. & Barthol.
  Caeomurus acuminatus (Arth.) O. Kuntze.
  Nigredo acuminata Arth.
  Nigredo Polemonii Arth.
  Uromyces acuminatus Arth.

Spartina cynosuroides (*cont.*)
| Uromyces acuminatus Arth., var. magnatus (Arth.) J. J. Davis.
| Uromyces acuminatus Arth., var. Polemonii (Arth.) J. J. Davis.
| Uromyces acuminatus Arth., var. Steirone-matis (Arth.) J. J. Davis.
| Uromyces magnatus Arth.
| Uromyces Polemonii Barthol.
| Uromyces Spartinae Farl.
| Uromyces Steironematis Arth.

Note: The above names have been given to rusts on Spartina of which *Uromyces Spartinae* Farl. is representative. Four species are designated by Arthur in Mycologia **9**: 311. These are regarded by J. J. Davis, Tr. Wis. Acad. **20**: 410 as subspecies or varieties. Each has its aecidial stage on host plants of a different family, but the teleutosporic forms are not easy to distinguish and can scarcely be segregated in a bibliographic sense. If the names here listed are not strictly synonymous they are approximately so.

Spartina patens (Ait.) Muhl.
| Dicaeoma Fraxini Arth.
| Puccinia fraxinata Arth.
| Nigredo Polemonii Arth.
| Uromyces acuminatus Arth.
| Uromyces Spartinae Farl.

Spartina patens, var. juncea (Michx.) Hitchc.
| Leptothyrium Spartinae Pk.
| Tracylla Spartinae (Pk.) Tassi.
| ?Microthyrium microscopicum Desm.
| Nigredo Polemonii Arth.
| Uromyces Spartinae Farl.

Spartina pectinata Bosc.
| Claviceps purpurea (Fr.) Tul.
| Dicaeoma Distichlidis (Ell. & Ev.) O. Kuntze.
| Puccinia Distichlidis Ell. & Ev.

Spartina sp. indet.
| Heptameria sticta (Ell. & Ev.) Cke.
| Leptosphaeria albopunctata (Westd.) Sacc.
| Leptosphaeria sticta Ell. & Ev.
| Heptameria Spartinae (Ell. & Ev.) Cke.
| Leptosphaeria Spartinae Ell. & Ev.
| Leptosphaeria californica (Cke. & Hark.) Berl. & Vogl.
| Metasphaeria californica (Cke. & Hark.) Berl.
| Sphaeria californica Cke. & Hark.
| Heptameria marina (Ell. & Ev.) Cke.
| Leptosphaeria marina Ell. & Ev.
| Metasphaeria marina (Ell. & Ev.) Berl.
| Ophiobolus Medusae Ell. & Ev.
| Rhaphidospora Medusae (Ell. & Ev.) Cke.
| Heptameria incarcerata (B. & C.) Cke.
| Leptosphaeria incarcerata (B. & C.) Sacc.
| Passeriniella incarcerata (B. & C.) Berl.
| Sphaeria incarcerata B. & C.

Ctenium aromaticum (Walt.) Hitchc.
Puccinia Campulosi Thm.
Chloris elegans H. B. K.
Puccinia Chloridis Diet.
Sclerospora Farlowii Griffiths.
| Nigredo archeriana (Arth. & Fromme) Arth.
| Uromyces archerianus Arth. & Fromme.
Ustilago elegans Griffiths.
Chloris petraea Sw.
Cercospora caespitosa Ell. & Ev.
Dothichloe atramentosa (B. & C.) Atk.
Meliola Panici Earle.
Chloris submutica H. B. K.
Ustilago Ulei Henn.
Chloris swartziana Doell.
Cercospora caespitosa Ell. & Ev.
Chloris verticillata Nutt.
| Dicaeoma Chloridis (Speg.) O. Kuntze.
| Puccinia Chloridis Diet.
| Puccinia Chloridis Speg.
Pyrenochaeta graminis Ell. & Ev.
Chloris virgata Sw.
Dicaeoma Chloridis (Speg.) O. Kuntze.
Chloris sp. indet.
Ustilago chloridicola Henn.
Schedonnardus paniculatus (Nutt.) Trel.
| Dicaeoma hibisciatum (S.) Arth.
| Dicaeoma Schedonnardi O. Kuntze.
| Puccinia Muhlenbergiae Arth. & Holw.
| Puccinia Schedonnardi Kellerm. & Swingle.
Bouteloua aristidoides (H. B. K.) Griseb.
Dicaeoma vexans (Farl.) O. Kuntze.
Ustilago Hieronymi Schrt.
Ustilago minor J. B. S. Norton.
Bouteloua barbata Lag.
Dicaeoma jamesianum Arth.
Ustilago Hieronymi Schrt.
Bouteloua briseta Vasey.
Ustilago Hieronymi Schrt.
Ustilago calcara Griffiths.
Bouteloua bromoides Lag.
Ustilago Hieronymi Schrt.
Ustilago minor J. B. S. Norton.
Bouteloua curtipendula (Michx.) Torr.
Balansia discoidea Henn.
Phyllachora graminis (P. ex Fr.) Fckl.
| Dicaeoma Boutelouae (Jennings) Arth. & Fromme.
| Diorchidium Boutelouae Jennings.
| Puccinia Boutelouae (Jennings) Holw.
| Dicaeoma jamesianum Arth.
| Puccinia Bartholomaei Diet.
| Puccinia jamesiana Arth.
| Dicaeoma vexans (Farl.) O. Kuntze.
| Puccinia vexans Farl.
| Uromyces Brandegei Pk.
?Uredo Boutelouae Arth.
| Ustilago filifera J. B. S. Norton.
| Ustilago Hieronymi Schrt.

Bouteloua eriopoda Torr.
  Ustilago Hieronymi Schrt.
  Ustilago minor J. B. S. Norton.
Bouteloua filiformis (Fourn.) Griffiths.
Bouteloua gracilis (H. B. K.) Lag.
  ⎰Dicaeoma jamesianum Arth.
  ⎱Puccinia jamesiana Arth.
Bouteloua Havardi Vasey.
  Ustilago Hieronymi Schrt.
Bouteloua hirsuta Lag.
  ⎰Dicaeoma jamesianum Arth.
  ⎱Puccinia Bartholomaei Diet.
  ⎱Puccinia jamesiana Arth.
  Puccinia vexans Farl.
  Scaphidium Boutelouae Clements.
  ?Uredo Boutelouae Arth.
  Ustilago Boutelouae Kellerm. & Swingle.
  Ustilago minor J. B. S. Norton.
Bouteloua oligostachya (Nutt.) Torr.
  Epichloe typhina (Fr.) Tul.
  Graphyllium chloes Clements.
  Phyllachora graminis (P. ex Fr.) Fckl.
  Pleospora Oligostachyae Ell. & Ev.
  ⎰Puccinia Bartholomaei Diet.
  ⎱Puccinia jamesiana Arth.
  Puccinia graminis P.
  Puccinia vexans Farl.
  Ustilago Boutelouae Kellerm. & Swingle.
  Ustilago filifera J. B. S. Norton.
  Ustilago Hieronymi Schrt.
Bouteloua polystachya Torr.
  Ustilago Hieronymi Schrt.
  Ustilago minor J. B. S. Norton.
Bouteloua Pringlei Scribn.
  ⎰Dicaeoma exasperans (Holw.) Arth. &
  ⎱   Fromme.
  ⎱Puccinia exasperans Holw.
Bouteloua prostrata Lag.
  Ustilago Boutelouae Kellerm. & Swingle.
Bouteloua ramosa Scribn.
  ⎰Dicaeoma vexans (Farl.) O. Kuntze.
  ⎱Puccinia vexans Farl.
Beckmannia Syzigachne (Steud.) Fern.
  Colletotrichum cereale Manns.
  Erysiphe graminis DC. †
  ⎰Puccinia Beckmanniae McAlpine.
  ⎱Puccinia coronata Cda.
  ⎱Puccinia Rhamni Wettst.
  ⎰Dicaeoma poculiforme (Wettst.) O. Kuntze.
  ⎱Puccinia graminis P.
  ⎰Nigredo Beckmanniae (H. S. Jackson) Arth.
  ⎱Uromyces Beckmanniae H. S. Jackson.
  Ustilago striiformis (Westd.) Niessl.
Eleusine indica Gaertn.
  Helminthosporium Cynodontis Marignoni.
  Helminthosporium giganteum Heald & Wolf.
  Helminthosporium leucostylum Drechsler.

⎰Helminthosporium nodosum B. & C.
⎱Helminthosporium nodulosum Sacc.
  Myrothecium roridum Tode ex Fr..
Dactyloctenium aegyptium (L.) Richter.
  Cercospora tesselata Atk.
  ⎰Ustilago sparsa Underw.
  ⎱Ustilago destruens Rav. F. Am. *790*.
Leptochloa domingensis (Jacq.) Trin.
  Nigredo ignobilis Arth.
  Uredo paspalicola Henn.
Leptochloa dubia (H. B. K.) Nees.
  ⎰Dicaeoma jamesianum Arth.
  ⎱Puccinia Bartholomaei Diet.
  ⎱Puccinia Diplachnis Arth.
  ⎱Puccinia jamesiana Arth.
Leptochloa filiformis (Lam.) Beauv.
  ⎰Dicaeoma Leptochloae Arth. & Fromme.
  ⎱Puccinia Leptochloae Arth. & Fromme.
  Puccinia Bartholomaei Diet.
  Ustilago heterogena Henn.
  Ustilago ornata Tracy & Earle.
Leptochloa viscida Auct.
  Ustilago heterogena Henn.
Buchloe dactyloides (Nutt.) Engelm.
  Cercospora seminalis Ell. & Ev.
  Fusarium gramineum Cda.
  Helminthosporium inconspicuum C. & E.,
     var. Buchloes Ell. & Ev.
  Phyllachora graminis (P. ex Fr.) Fckl.
  ⎰Puccinia Buchloes Schofield.
  ⎱Puccinia vexans, var. Buchloes De Toni.
  ⎰Dicaeoma kansense (Ell. & Barthol.) Arth.
  ⎱Puccinia kansensis Ell. & Barthol.
  Tilletia buchloeana Kellerm. & Swingle.
  Ustilago Buchloes Ell. & Tracy.
Pappophorum Wrightii Watson.
  Ustilago Hieronymi Schrt.
  Ustilago minor J. B. S. Norton.
Cathestecum prostratum Presl.
  ⎰Tilletia Cathesteci (Henn.) G. P. Clinton.
  ⎱Ustilago Cathesteci Henn.
Scleropogon brevifolius Phil.
  ⎰Dicaeoma Sarcobati Arth.
  ⎱Puccinia Sarcobati (Arth.) Bethel.
Monanthochloe littoralis Engelm.
  Dicaeoma hibisciatum Arth.
Gynerium argenteum Nees.
  ⎰Chaetostroma? aterrima (Cke.) Sacc.
  ⎱Psilonia aterrima Cke.
  Fusarium Gynerii Cke. & Hark.
  ⎰Gymnosporium Arundinis Cda.
  ⎱Ustilago Gynerii Vize.
  Helminthosporium parvulum Cke.
  Isaria repens Cke.
  Mystrosporium consors Thm.
  ⎰Coniothyrium lineare Thm.
  ⎱Phoma linearis (Thm.) Sacc.
  Sphaeria apiospora Dur. & Mont.
  Torula fusoidea Cke. & Hark.

Gynerium sagittatum (Aubl.) Beauv.
  Monilia sitophila (Mont.) Sacc.
Munroa squarrosa Torr.
  Septoria munroae Ell. & Barthol.
Arundo Donax L.
  Leptostroma Donacis S.
  Monilia sparsa Lk.
Phragmites communis Trin.
  Claviceps microcephala (Wallr.) Tul.
  {Coniosporium Arundinis (Cda.) Sacc.
  {Gymnosporium Arundinis Cda.
  Graphyllium dakotense Rehm.
  Hadrotrichum lineare Pk.
  Hendersonia arundinacea (Desm.) Sacc.
  Leptosphaeria arundinacea (Sow. ex Fr.) Sacc.
  Lophiostoma Arundinis (Fr.) Ces. & De Not.
  Lophodermium arundinaceum (Schrad. ex Fr.) Chev.
  Lophodermium arundinaceum (Schrad. ex Fr.) Chev., var. vulgare Fckl.
  {Coniosporium Arundinis N. A. F. *2794.*
  {Melanconium sphaerospermum Lk.
  Metasphaeria lacustris (Fckl.) Sacc.
  Mollisia arundinacea (DC. ex. Fr.) Phil.
  Napicladium arundinaceum (Cda.) Sacc.
  Neovossia iowensis Hume & Hodson.
  Peziza albotestacea Desm.
  Pirostoma circinans Fr.
  Pleospora vagans Niessl.
  Pseudographis Phragmitis Dearness & House.
  {Dicaeoma rubellum (Arth.) Arth. & Fromme.
  {Puccinia arundinacea Hedw.
  {Puccinia Phragmitis Körn.
  {Puccinia rubella Arth.
  Puccinia Arundinariae S.
  Puccinia graminis P.?
  {Dicaeoma magnusianum (Körn.) O. Kuntze.
  {Puccinia magnusiana Körn.
  {Puccinia simillima Arth.
  {Dothidea clavispora (C. & P.) Pk.
  {Heptameria clavicarpa (Ell. & Ev.) Cke.
  {Hysterium clavisporum C. & P.
  {Leptosphaeria clavicarpa Ell. & Ev.
  {Rhopographus clavisporus (C. & P.) Sacc.
  Scolecotrichum maculicola Ell. & Kellerm.
  Sphaerella Phragmitis Ell. & Ev.
  {Stagonospora graminea ex errore.
  {Stagonospora graminella Sacc.
  Tilletia Moliniae (Thm.) Wint.
  ?Ustilago mirabilis Sorokin.
Phragmites sp. indet.
  Hendersonia Grantii Dearness.
  Leptosphaeria culmicola (Fr.) Karst.
  Phragmopeltis Phragmitis Dearness.
Tridens flavus (L.) Hitchc.
  {Mycosphaerella cruris-galli (Ell. & Kellerm.) Lindau.
  {Sphaerella crus-galli Ell. & Kellerm.

{Puccinia graminis P.?
{Puccinia poculiformis Wettst.
{Dicaeoma Windsoriae (S.) O. Kuntze.
{Puccinia emaculata Auct. Amer. p. p.
{Puccinia omnivora Ell. & Ev.
{Puccinia Windsoriae S.
Stagonospora Paspali Atk.
Ustilago Tricuspidis Ell. & Gall.
Vermicularia affinis Sacc. & Briard.
Tridens muticus (Torr.) Nash.
  {Dicaeoma Windsoriae (S.) O. Kuntze.
  {Puccinia Windsoriae S.
Tridens strictus (Nutt.) Nash.
  Dicaeoma simulans (Pk.) Arth. & Fromme.
Triplasis americanus Beauv.
  {?Ustilago segetum Auct. Amer. p. p.
  {Ustilago Triplasidis Ell. & Ev.
Triplasis purpurea (Walt.) Chapm.
  {Dicaeoma hibisciatum Arth.
  {Puccinia Triodiae Ell. & Barthol.
  Ustilago Sieglingiae Ricker.
Redfieldia flexuosa Vasey.
  {Dicaeoma Redfieldiae (Tracy) O. Kuntze.
  {Puccinia Redfieldiae Tracy.
  {Tilletia montana Auct. Amer.
  {Tilletia Redfieldiae G. P. Clinton.
Eragrostis capillaris (L.) Nees.
  {Dothidea atramentaria B. & C.
  {Dothidea vorax B. & C. p. p.
  Puccinia graminis P.?
  Nigredo Eragrostidis (Tracy) Arth.
Eragrostis cilianensis (All.) Lk.
  Helminthosporium giganteum, Heald & Wolf.
  Helminthosporium hadrotrichoides Ell. & Ev.
  Helminthosporium leucostylum Drechsler.
  Helminthosporium rostratum Drechsler.
  Nigredo Eragrostidis (Tracy) Arth.
  Uromyces peckianus Farl.
  Ustilago spermophora B. & C.
Eragrostis ciliaris (L.) Lk.
  {Nigredo Eragrostidis (Tracy) Arth.
  {Uromyces Eragrostidis Tracy.
Eragrostis cynosuroides Beauv.
  Puccinia cynosuroides (Henn.) Syd.
Eragrostis glomerata (Walt.) Dewey.
  Tilletia Eragrostidis G. P. Clinton & Ricker.
Eragrostis hypnoides (Lam.) B. S. P.
  Ustilago spermophora B. & C.
Eragrostis limbata Fourn.
Eragrostis lugens Nees.
  {Nigredo Eragrostidis (Tracy) Arth.
  {Uromyces Eragrostidis Tracy.
Eragrostis neomexicana Vasey.
  {Nigredo Eragrostidis (Tracy) Arth.
  {Uromyces Eragrostidis Tracy.
  {Sphacelotheca strangulans (Issat.) G. P. Clinton.
  {Ustilago strangulans Issat.

Eragrostis pectinacea (Michx.) Steud.
Colletotrichum lineola Auct. Amer. an Cda.
Helminthosporium giganteum Heald & Wolf.
Puccinia emaculata S.?
{ Nigredo Eragrostidis (Tracy) Arth.
{ Uromyces Eragrostidis Tracy.
Eragrostis pilosa (L.) Beauv.
Helminthosporium Ravenelii M. A. Curtis.
{ Nigredo Eragrostidis (Tracy) Arth.
{ Uromyces Eragrostidis Tracy.
Uromyces peckianus Farl.
Eragrostis rachitricha Hochst.
Helminthosporium geniculatum Tracy &
  Earle.
Eragrostis refracta (Muhl.) Scribn.
{ Dothichloe atramentosa (B. & C.) Atk.
{ Dothichloe hypoxylon Atk. p. p.
{ Ophiodothis atramentosa (B. & C.) Earle.
Eragrostis tephrosanthos (Spreng.) Roem. &
  Schult.
{ Nigredo Eragrostidis (Tracy) Arth.
{ Uromyces Eragrostidis Tracy.
Eragrostis trichodes (Nutt.) Nash.
{ Dothichloe atramentosa (B. & C.) Atk.
{ Dothichloe hypoxylon Atk. p. p.
{ Ophiodothis atramentosa (B. & C.) Earle.
Phyllachora graminis (P. ex Fr.) Fckl.
Uromyces Eragrostidis Tracy.
Eragrostis sp. indet.
Venturia nebulosa Ell. & Ev.
Sphenopholis nitida (Spreng.) Scribn.
{ Dicaeoma Eatoniae Arth.
{ Puccinia Eatoniae Arth.
Puccinia graminis P., var. Avenae Erikss. &
  Henn.
Sphenopholis obtusata (Michx.) Scribn.
Epichloe typhina (P. ex Fr.) Tul.
Erysiphe graminis DC. †
{ Dicaeoma Eatoniae Arth.
{ Puccinia Eatoniae Arth.
{ Puccinia Rubigo-vera Auct. Amer. p. p.
{ Dicaeoma poculiforme (Wettst.) O. Kuntze.
{ Puccinia graminis P.
{ Puccinia poculiformis Wettst.
Puccinia graminis P., var. Avenae Erikss. &
  Henn.
Sphenopholis pallens (Spreng.) Scribn.
Epichloe typhina (P. ex Fr.) Tul.
{ Dicaeoma Eatoniae Arth.
{ Puccinia Eatoniae Arth.
Puccinia Rubigo-vera Auct. Amer. p. p.
Sclerotium rhizodes Awd.
Koeleria cristata (L.) P.
Cladosporium herbarum, var cerealinum Sacc.
Claviceps purpurea (Fr.) Tul.
{ Epichloe typhina (P. ex Fr.) Tul.
{ Typhodium typhinum (P. ex Fr.) Seaver.
Lophodermium arundinaceum (Schrad. ex Fr.)
  Chev.

Macrophoma arens J. J. Davis.
{ Puccinia Fendleri H. S. Jackson.
{ Puccinia montanensis Ell.
{ Dicaeoma poculiforme (Wettst.) O. Kuntze.
{ Puccinia graminis P.
{ Puccinia poculiformis Wettst.
Puccinia graminis P., var. Agrostidis Erikss.
Puccinia graminis P., var. Avenae Erikss. &
  Henn.
Puccinia graminis P., var. Tritici Erikss. &
  Henn.
{ Dicaeoma Koeleriae (Arth.) Arth. & Fromme.
{ Puccinia Koeleriae Arth.
{ Dicaeoma Liatridis (Bethel) Arth. &
{   Fromme.
{ Puccinia Koeleriae Auct. p. p.
{ Puccinia Liatridis Bethel.
{ Dicaeoma monoicum (Arth.) Arth. & Fromme.
{ Puccinia monoica Arth.
Puccinia Rubigo-vera Auct. Amer. p. p.
{ Dicaeoma Stipae (Arth.) O. Kuntze.
{ Puccinia Stipae Arth.
Koeleria sp. indet.
Urocystis Agropyri (Preuss.) Schrt.
Catabrosa algida Fr.
Leptosphaeria microscopica Karst.
Mycosphaerella tassiana (De Not.) Johans.
Catabrosa aquatica (L.) Beauv.
Entyloma crastophilum Sacc.
Pleospora infectoria Fckl.
{ Dicaeoma epiphyllum (Wettst.) O. Kuntze.
{ Puccinia epiphylla Wettst.
{ Puccinia Poarum Nielsen.
Melica bromoides Gray.
{ Dicaeoma Clematidis Arth.
{ Puccinia Elymi Westd.
Melica imperfecta Trin.
Urocystis Agropyri (Preuss) Schrt.
Melica mutica Walt.
Claviceps cinerea Griffiths.
{ Dicaeoma hibisciatum (Kellerm.) Arth.
{ Puccinia hibisciata Kellerm.
{ Puccinia Melicae Auct. p. p.
{ Puccinia Schedonnardi Kellerm. & Swingle.
Melica Porteri Scribn.
{ Dicaeoma hibisciatum (Kellerm.) Arth.
{ Dicaeoma Melicae Auct. p. p.
{ Puccinia hibisciata Kellerm.
{ Puccinia Melicae Auct. p. p.
Melica Smithii (Porter) Vasey.
{ Dicaeoma paradoxicum (Ricker) Arth. &
{   Fromme.
{ Puccinia paradoxica Ricker.
Melica striata (Michx.) Hitchc.
Colletotrichum graminicola (Ces.) G. W.
  Wilson.
Phyllachora Melicae Dearness & House.

Melica striata (*cont.*)
{ Dicaeoma Rhamni (Wettst.) O. Kuntze.
{ Puccinia coronata Cda.
{ Puccinia Erikssonii Bubák.
{ Puccinia Melicae (Erikss.) Syd.
Septoria Avenae Frank.
Urocystis Agropyri (Preuss) Schrt.

Melica subulata (Bong.) Scribn.
{ Dicaeoma pygmaeum (Erikss.) Arth. &
{   Fromme.
{ Puccinia pygmaea Erikss.

Diarrhena diandra (Michx.) Wood.
Phyllachora Caricis (Fr.) Sacc.?
Phyllachora graminis (P. ex Fr.) Fckl.
{ Dicaeoma (?) Zeugitis Arth. & Fromme.
{ Uredo Zeugitis Arth. & Holw.

Zeugites Hartwegii Fourn. ex Hemsl.
Uredo Zeugitis Arth. & Holw.

Triniochloa stipoides (H. B. K.) Hitchc.
Uredo Triniochloae Arth. & Holw.

Pleuropogon Sabinii R. Br.
Mycosphaerella tassiana (De Not.) Johans.
Sphaerulina Pleuropogonis Rostr.

Uniola laxa (L.) B. S. P.
{ Balansia Hypoxylon (Pk.) Atk.
{ Dothidea pilulaeformis B. & C.
{ Dothidea vorax B. & C. p. p.
{ Ephelis Mexicana B.
{ Hypocrella Hypoxylon, var. piluliformis B. & C.
{ Ophiodothis atramentosa, var. piluliformis
{   Earle.
Phoma glumarum Ell. & Tracy.
Ustilago Uniolae Ell. & Ev.

Uniola paniculata L.
Phoma glumarum Ell. & Tracy.

Distichlis spicata (L.) Greene.
Cerebella Spartinae Ell. & Ev.
{ Dothidella Aristidae (S.) Ell. & Ev.
{ Euryachora? Aristidae (S.) Theissen & Syd.
{ Phyllachora Aristidae (S.) Sacc.
{ Dothidella Tracyi (Ell. & Ev.) Sacc.
{ Endodothella Tracyi (Ell. & Ev.) Theissen &
{   Syd.
{ Phyllachora Tracyi Ell. & Ev.
Fusarium heterosporum Nees.
Helminthosporium halodes Drechsler.
{ Homostegia diplocarpa Ell. & Ev.
{ Phyllachora diplocarpa Ell. & Ev.
Phyllachora graminis (P. ex Fr.) Fckl.
Phyllachora nuttalliana Fairman.
Physalospora Cynodontis Delacr.
Puccinia Aristidae Tracy.
Puccinia graminis P.
{ Dicaeoma Sarcobati (Bethel) Arth.
{ Puccinia Distichlidis Myc. ex. *68.*
{ Puccinia Sarcobati Bethel.
{ Puccinia subnitens Diet.

{ Nigredo peckiana Arth.
{ Uromyces graminum Auct. p. p.
{ Uromyces peckianus Farl.
{ Puccinia [subnitens] p. p.
Ustilago hypodytes (Schl.) Fr.

Briza maxima L.
{ Dicaeoma poculiforme (Wettst.) O. Kuntze.
{ Puccinia graminis P.

Dactylis glomerata L.
Claviceps microcephala (Wallr.) Tul.
{ Claviceps purpurea (Fr.) Tul.
{ Spermoedia clavus (DC.) ex Fr.
Colletotrichum cereale Manns.
{ Colletotrichum graminicola (Ces.) G. W.
{   Wilson.
Dilophospora Alopecuri Fr.
{ Epichloe typhina (P. ex Fr.) Tul.
{ Typhodium typhinum (Fr.) Seaver.
Erysiphe graminis DC. †
Gibberella Saubinetii (Mont.) Sacc.
Leptosphaeria culmorum Awd.
Phyllachora graminis (P. ex Fr.) Fckl.
{ Puccinia coronata Cda.
{ Puccina Rhamni Wettst.
{ Dicaeoma poculiforme (Wettst) O. Kuntze.
{ Puccinia graminis P.
{ Puccinia poculiformis Wettst.
{ Puccinia graminis P., var. Phlei-pratensis
{   (Erikss. & Henn.) Stakm. & Piemeisel.
{ Puccinia Phlei-pratensis Erikss. & Henn.
{ Puccinia graminis P., var. Tritici Erikss. &
{   Henn.
Rhynchosporium Secalis (Oud.) J. J. Davis.
Sclerotium rhizodes Awd.
Scolecotrichum graminis Fckl.
Septoria graminum Desm.
{ Nigredo Dactylidis (Otth) Arth.
{ Uromyces Dactylidis Otth.
Ustilago striiformis (Westd.) Niessl.
Vermicularia affinis Sacc. & Briard.

Lamarckia aurea (L.) Moench.
Puccinia Achyrodis Diet. & Holw.
Puccinia coronata Cda.
{ Dicaeoma poculiforme (Wettst.) O. Kuntze.
{ Puccinia graminis P.
{ Puccinia poculiformis Wettst.
Puccinia graminis P., var. Avenae Erikss. &
  Henn.
Puccinia Phlei-pratensis Erikss. & Henn.
Puccinia montanensis Ell.
Puccinia Poarum Nielsen.
{ Dicaeoma Rhamni (Wettst.) O. Kuntze.
{ Puccinia coronata Cda.
{ Puccinia Rhamni Wettst.

Poa abbreviata R. Br.
Ascospora graminis J. Lind.
Cladosporium graminum Cda.
{ Clathrospora pentamera (Karst.) Berl.
{ Pleospora pentamera Karst.

Poa abbreviata (*cont.*)
Hendersonia arundinacea (Desm.) Sacc.
Hendersonia Rostrupii J. Lind.
Leptosphaeria microscopica Karst.
Pleospora deflectens Karst.
Pleospora discors (Dur. & Mont.) Ces. & De Not.
Pleospora Karstenii Berl. & Vogl.
Rhabdospora groenlandica Lind.
Stagonospora arenaria Sacc.

Poa alpina L.
Hendersonia Poae Rostr.
Lophodermium arundinaceum (Schrad. ex Fr.) Chev.
{ Dicaeoma epiphyllum (Wettst.) O. Kuntze.
{ Puccinia Poarum Nielsen.
{ Mollisia graminis Karst.
{ Pyrenopeziza Karstenii Sacc.
Sphaerella tassiana De Not.
Uromyces Dactylidis Otth.?

Poa ampla Merrill.
{ Dicaeoma Clematidis (Lagerh.) Arth.
{ Puccinia Clematidis Lagerh.
{ Puccinia Elymi Westd.
{ Dicaeoma epiphyllum (Wettst.) O. Kuntze.
{ Puccinia epiphylla Wettst.

Poa annua L.
Ascochyta graminicola Lib.
Dendrophoma Poarum Ell. & Dearness.
Puccinia graminis P.
{ Dicaeoma epiphyllum (Wettst.) O. Kuntze.
{ Puccinia epiphylla Wettst.
{ Puccinia Poarum Nielsen.
Septoria annua Ell. & Ev.
Septoria graminum Desm.
Ustilago striiformis (Westd.) Niessl.

Poa arachnifera Torr.
Epicoccum neglectum Desm.
Erysiphe graminis DC. †
Dicaeoma Rhamni (Wettst.) O. Kuntze.
{ Dicaeoma epiphyllum (Wettst.) O. Kuntze.
{ Puccinia Poarum Nielsen.
Stagonospora intermixta (Cke.) Sacc.

Poa arctica
Crumenula pusiola Karst.
Rhabdospora Drabae (Fckl.) Berl. & Vogl.

Poa arida Vasey.
{ Dicaeoma Clematidis (DC.) Arth.
{ Puccinia cinerea Arth.
{ Puccinia Clematidis (DC.) Lagerh.
{ Dicaeoma poculiforme (Wettst.) O. Kuntze.
{ Puccinia graminis P.
{ Dicaeoma epiphyllum (Wettst.) O. Kuntze.
{ Puccinia Poarum Nielsen.

Poa autumnalis Muhl.
Erysiphe graminis DC. †
Leptosphaeria culmorum Awd.

Lophodermium arundinaceum (Schrad. ex Fr.) Chev.
{ Mollisia graminis Karst.
{ Pyrenopeziza Karstenii Sacc.
Sphaerella tassiana De Not.

Poa Bigelowii Vasey & Scribn.
{ Dicaeoma epiphyllum (Wettst.) O. Kuntze.
{ Puccinia epiphylla Wettst.

Poa brevipaniculata Scribn. & Williams.
{ Dicaeoma abundans Arth. & Fromme.
{ Puccinia Elymi Westd.

Poa cenisia All.
Diplodina arctica Lind.
Erysiphe graminis DC. †
Pleospora deflectens Karst.
Pleospora discors (Mont.) Ces. & De Not.
{ Clathrospora pentamera (Karst.) Berl.
{ Pleospora pentamera Karst.
Rhabdospora groenlandica J. Lind.
{ Mycosphaerella tassiana (De Not.) Johans.
{ Sphaerella tassiana De Not.
Mycosphaerella wichuriana (Schrt.) Johans.

Poa compressa L.
Claviceps purpurea (Fr.) Tul.
Erysiphe graminis DC. †
Lophodermium arundinaceum (Schrad. ex Fr.) Chev.
{ Ophiobolus cariceti (B. & Br.) Sacc.
{ Ophiobolus graminis Sacc.
{ Dicaeoma Rhamni (Wettst.) O. Kuntze.
{ Puccinia coronata Cda.
{ Puccinia Rhamni Wettst.
{ Dicaeoma poculiforme (Wettst.) O. Kuntze.
{ Puccinia graminis P.
{ Puccinia Phlei-pratensis Erikss. & Henn.
Puccinia graminis P., var. Poae Erikss. & Henn.
{ Dicaeoma epiphyllum (Wettst.) O. Kuntze.
{ Puccinia epiphylla Wettst.
{ Puccinia Poarum Nielsen.
Scolecotrichum graminis Fckl.
Ustilago striiformis (Westd.) Niessl.

Poa crocata Michx.
Dicaeoma epiphyllum (Wettst.) O. Kuntze.

Poa debilis Torr.
{ Tilletia striiformis (Westd.) Oud.
{ Ustilago striiformis (Westd.) Niessl.

Poa evagans Simmons.
Sphaerella tassiana DeNot.

Poa fendleriana (Steud.) Vasey.
{ Dicaeoma Clematidis (Lagerh.) Arth.
{ Puccinia cinerea Arth.
{ Puccinia Clematidis Lagerh.

Poa filipes Lange.
{ Mycosphaerella lineolata (Rob.) Dearness.
{ Sphaerella lineolata (Rob.) De Not.

Poa flexuosa, var. **elongata** Blytt.
Laestadia graminicola Rostr.
Phoma Drygalskii Allesch.
Septoria Oudemansii Sacc.
Sphaerella tassiana De Not.

Poa glauca Vahl.
Ascospora graminis Lind.
Cladosporium graminum Cda.
Clathrospora pentamera (Karst.) Berl.
Coniothecium helicoideum Sacc. & Roum.
Leptosphaeria culmorum Awd.
Leptostromella septorioides Sacc. & Roum.
Lophodermium arundinaceum (Schrad. ex Fr.) Chev.
Lophodermium arundinaceum (Schrad. ex Fr.) Chev., var. alpinum Rehm.
Mollisia graminis Karst.
Naevia fuscella (Karst.) J. Lind.
Pleospora deflectens Karst.
Pleospora infectoria Fckl.
Pleospora pentamera Karst.
{ Mollisia graminis Karst.
{ Pyrenopeziza Karstenii Sacc.
Rhabdospora Drabae (Fckl.) Berl. & Vogl.
Rhabdospora groenlandica J. Lind.
Septoria nebulosa Rostr.
Septoria semilunaris Johans.
Sphaerella pusilla Awd.
Sphaerella tassiana De Not.
Sphaeria arctica Fckl.

Poa Howellii Vasey & Scribn.
Dicaeoma poculiforme (Wettst.) O. Kuntze.

Poa interior Rydb.
Claviceps purpurea (Fr.) Tul.
Dicaeoma Clematidis (Lagerh.) Arth.
{ Dicaeoma epiphyllum O. Kuntze.
{ Puccinia Poarum Nielsen.

Poa juncifolia Scribn.
Dicaeoma Clematidis (Lagerh.) Arth.

Poa laevigata Scribn.
Puccinia graminis P.

Poa longiligula Scribn. & Williams.
Claviceps purpurea (Fr.) Tul.
{ Dicaeoma abundans (H. S. Jackson) Arth. & Fromme.
{ Puccinia Crandallii Pammel & Hume.

Poa longipedunculata Scribn.
Dicaeoma Clematidis (Lagerh.) Arth.
{ Dicaeoma epiphyllum (Wettst.) O. Kuntze.
{ Puccinia Poarum Nielsen.

Poa lucida Vasey.
Dicaeoma Clematidis (Lagerh.) Arth.
Dicaeoma epiphyllum (Wettst.) O. Kuntze.

Poa macrantha Vasey.
{ Dicaeoma epiphyllum (Wettst.) O. Kuntze.
{ Puccinia epiphylla Wettst.

Poa nemoralis L.
Erysiphe graminis DC. †
Mollisia graminis Karst.

Puccinia graminis P.
{ Dicaeoma epiphyllum (Wettst.) O. Kuntze.
{ Puccinia Poarum Nielsen.
Scolecotrichum graminis Fckl.

Poa nervosa Vasey.
Puccinia Clematidis Lagerh.

Poa nevadensis Vasey.
Melanospora Poae Griffiths.
{ Dicaeoma Clematidis (Lagerh.) Arth.
{ Puccinia cinerea Arth.
{ Puccinia Elymi Westd.
{ Puccinia Rubigo-vera Auct. Amer. p. p.
Sordaria minuta Fckl.

Poa palustris L.
Claviceps purpurea (Fr.) Tul.
Erysiphe graminis DC. †
Fusarium Poae (Pk.) C. E. Lewis.
Pleospora vagans Niessl.
{ Dicaeoma epiphyllum (Wettst.) O. Kuntze.
{ Puccinia epiphylla Wettst.
{ Puccinia Poarum Nielsen.
Ramularia graminicola Pk.
Scolecotrichum graminis Fckl.

Poa pratensis L.
Alternaria tenuis Nees.
Cladosporium graminum Cda.
Claviceps microcephala (Wallr.) Tul.
Claviceps purpurea (Fr.) Tul.
{ Colletotrichum cereale Manns.
{ Colletotrichum graminicola (Ces.) G. W. Wilson.
Corticium vagum B. & C.
Entyloma irregulare Johans.
Epichloe typhina (P. ex Fr.) Tul.
Erysiphe graminis DC. †
{ Fusarium Poae (Pk.) C. E. Lewis.
{ Sporotrichum anthophilum Pk.
{ Sporotrichum Poae Pk.
Helminthosporium giganteum Heald & Wolf.
Helminthosporium sativum Pammel, King, & Bakke.
Helminthosporium vagans Drechsler.
Leptosphaeria culmorum Awd.
Lophodermium arundinacearum (Schrad. ex Fr.) Chev.
Marasmius siccus S.
{ Mollisia graminis Karst.
{ Pyrenopeziza Karstenii Sacc.
Oidium monilioides Lk.
Phyllachora graminis (P. ex Fr.) Fckl.
Physarum cinereum (Batsch) P.
?Piricularia grisea (Cke.) Sacc.
Puccinia glumarum Erikss. & Henn.
{ Dicaeoma poculiforme (Wettst.) O. Kuntze.
{ Puccinia graminis P.
{ ?Puccinia Rubigo-vera Auct. p. p.
Puccinia graminis, var. Poae Erikss., Henn., & Levine.

Poa pratensis (*cont.*)
- Caeoma lineare S. Am. Bor. 2818 p. p.
- Dicaeoma epiphyllum (Wettst.) O. Kuntze.
- Puccinia epiphylla Wettst.
- Puccinia Poarum Nielsen.
- Uredo Boutelouae Arth.
- Dicaeoma Clematidis (Lagerh.) Arth.
- Puccinia triticina Erikss.
- Sclerotium rhizodes Awd.
- Scolecotrichum graminis Fckl.
- Septoria glumarum Pass.
- Septoria graminum Desm.
- Septoria nodosum B.
- Septoria Tritici Desm.
- Mycosphaerella tassiana (De Not.) Johans.
- Sphaerella tassiana De Not.
- Uromyces Dactyloides Otth.
- Nigredo Poae (Rabh.) Arth.
- Uromyces Poae Rabh.
- Tilletia striiformis (Westd.) Oud.
- Ustilago striiformis (Westd.) Niessl.

Poa reflexa Vasey & Scribn.
- Dicaeoma epiphyllum (Wettst.) O. Kuntze.
- Puccinia Poarum Nielsen.

Poa Sandbergii Vasey.
- Dicaeoma poculiforme (Wettst.) O. Kuntze.

Poa scabrella (Thurb.) Benth.

Poa scabriuscula T. A. Williams.
- Dicaeoma Clematidis (Lagerh.) Arth.

Poa serotina Ehrh. = P. palustris.

Poa Sheldonii Vasey.
- Puccinia cinerea Arth.
- Puccinia Clematidis Lagerh.
- Puccinia Elymi Westd.

Poa stenantha Trin.
- Sphaerella graminum Sacc. & Scalia.

Poa tenuiflora Light.
- ?Dicaeoma verbenicola Arth.
- Puccinia Rubigo-vera Fung Columb. *191*.

Poa tenuifolia Nutt.
- Cladosporium graminum Cda.
- Erysiphe graminis DC. †

Poa trivialis L.
- Napicladium gramineum Pk.
- Dicaeoma epiphyllum (Wettst.) O. Kuntze.
- Puccinia epiphylla Wettst.
- Rhizoctonia Solani Kühn.
- Uromyces Poae Rabh.

Poa Vaseyochloa Scribn.
- Puccinia epiphylla Wettst.

Poa Wheeleri Vasey.
- Dicaeoma Clematidis (Lagerh.) Arth.
- Puccinia cinerea Arth.
- Puccinia Elymi Westd.
- Dicaeoma epiphyllum (Wettst.) O. Kuntze.
- Puccinia epiphylla Wettst.
- Puccinia Poarum Nielsen.

Poa Wolfii Scribn.
- Erysiphe graminis DC. †

Poa sp. indet.
- Actinothyrium graminis Kze. ex Fr.
- Catharinia Rostrupii Berl.
- Leptopeziza groenlandica Rostr.
- Physarum vernum Sommerf.
- Pleospora deflectens Karst.
- Puccinia Crandallii Pammel & Hume.
- Uromyces seditiosus Kern.
- Vermicularia graminicola Westd.

Colpodium latifolium R. Br.
- Sphaerella tassiana De Not.

Dupontia Fischeri R. Br.
- ?Entyloma ambiens (Karst.) Johans.
- Leptosphaeria Hierochloae Oud.
- Leptosphaeria insignis Karst.
- Mollisia graminea Karst.
- Pleospora pentamera Karst.
- Septoria arctica B. & C.
- Sphaerella tassiana DeNot.
- Mycosphaerella wichuriana (Schrt.) Johans.
- Sphaerella wichuriana Schrt.

Scolochloa festucacea (Willd.) Link.
- Claviceps purpurea (Fr.) Tul.
- Dasyscypha diminuta (Rob. & Desm.) Sacc.
- Leptosphaeria culmorum Awd.
- Naucoria siparia Fr.
- Pezizella epicalamia (Fckl.) Rehm.
- Dicaeoma Clematidis (Lagerh.) Arth.
- Puccinia Elymi Westd.
- Dicaeoma Rhamni (Wettst.) O. Kuntze.
- Puccinia coronata Cda.
- Puccinia Rhamni Wettst.
- Ustilago Arthuri Hume.
- Ustilago Scolochloae Griffiths.

Puccinellia airoides (Nutt.) Wats. & Coult.
- Dicaeoma Clematidis (Lagerh.) Arth.
- Puccinia cinerea Arth.
- Puccinia Clematidis Lagerh.
- Dicaeoma poculiforme (Wettst.) O. Kuntze.
- Puccinia graminis P.
- Ustilago hypodytes (Schl.) Fr.

Puccinellia angustata (R. Br.) Rand & Redfield
- Cladosporium graminum Cda.
- Clathrospora pentamera (Karst.) Berl.
- Leptosphaeria vagans Karst.
- Mycosphaerella tassiana (De Not.) Johans.
- Mycosphaerella wichuriana (Schrt. Johans).

Puccinellia arctica (Hook.) Fern. & Weath.
- Leptostroma marginatum S.

Puccinellia distans (L.) Parl.
- Lophodermium arundinaceum (Schrad. ex Fr.) Chev.
- Sphaerella tassiana De Not.

Puccinellia maritima (Huds.) Parl.
- Leptosphaeria microscopica Karst.
- Lophodermium arundinaceum (Schrad. ex Fr.) Chev.

Puccinellia maritima (*cont.*)
{ Dicaeoma Clematidis (Lagerh.) Arth.
{ Puccinia cinerea Arth.
  Mycosphaerella tassiana (De Not.) Johans.
Puccinellia paupercula Fern. & Weath., var.
  alaskana (Scribn. & Merrill) Fern. & Weath.
  Dicaeoma Clematidis (Lagerh.) Arth.
Puccinellia phryganodes (Trin.) Scribn. & Merr.
  Goniosporium puccinioides (Fr.) Lk.
  Lophodermium arundinaceum (Schrad. ex Fr.)
    Chev.
  Puccinia Clematidis Lagerh.
  Septoria Arundinis (Mont.) Sacc.
{ Mycosphaerella tassiana (De Not.) Johans.
{ Sphaerella tassiana De Not.
Puccinellia vaginata (Lange) Fern. & Weath.
  Cladosporium graminum Cda.
Puccinellia vahliana (Liebm.) Scribn. & Mer.
  Lophodermium arundinaceum (Schrad. ex Fr.)
    Chev.
{ Mycosphaerella tassiana (De Not.) Johans.
{ Sphaerella tassiana De Not.
Glyceria acutiflora Torr.
{ Nigredo amphidyma (Syd.) Arth.
{ Uromyces amphidymus Syd.
  Uromyces Glyceriae Arth.
Glyceria aquatica Wahlb.
  Erysiphe graminis DC.†
Glyceria arundinacea Kunth.
  Ustilago longissima (Sow.) Tul.
Glyceria canadensis (Michx.) Trin.
  Cylindrosporium Glyceriae Ell. & Ev.
{ Epichloe typhina (P. ex Fr.) Tul.
{ Typhodium typhinum (P. ex Fr.) Seaver.
Glyceria elata Hitchc.
  Dicaeoma Rhamni (Wettst.) O. Kuntze.
Glyceria grandis Watson.
  Ascochyta graminicola Sacc.
  Claviceps purpurea (Fr.) Tul.
  Dicaeoma Clematidis (Lagerh.) Arth.
  Dicaeoma Rhamni (Wettst.) O. Kuntze.
{ Dicaeoma poculiforme (Wettst.) O. Kuntze.
{ Puccinia graminis P.
  Puccinia Paniculariae Arth.
  Sclerotium (?) globuliferum J. J. Davis.
  Ustilago Arthurii Hume.
  Ustilago longissima (Sow.) Tul.
Glyceria laxa Scribn.
  Ustilago longissima (Sow.) Tul., var. macro-
    spora J. J. Davis..
Glyceria nervata (Willd.) Trin.
  Belonidium Glyceriae Pk.
  Botrytis sphaeriae-typhinae (Cda.) Sacc.
  Claviceps (Sclerotium).
  Cylindrosporium Glyceriae Ell. & Ev.
{ Epichloe typhina (P. ex Fr.) Tul.
{ Typhodium typhinum (P. ex Fr.) Seaver.
  Erysiphe graminis DC.†
  Leptosphaeria consociata Rehm.

Dicaeoma Rhamni (Wettst.) O. Kuntze.
Sclerotium rhizodes Awd.
Ustilago longissima (Sow.) Tul.
Glyceria pallida (Torr.) Trin.
  Entyloma crastophilum Sacc.
Glyceria pauciflora Presl.
{ Dicaeoma poculiforme (Wettst.) O. Kuntze.
{ Puccinia graminis P.
{ Puccinia poculiformis Wettst.
  Puccinia graminis P., var. Avenae Erikss. &
    Henn.
{ Dicaeoma Rhamni (Wettst.) O. Kuntze.
{ Puccinia Rhamni Wettst.
Glyceria septentrionalis Hitchc.
{ Burrillia globulifera J. J. Davis.
{ Doassansia globulifera (J. J. Davis) Diet.
{ Sclerotium globuliferum J. J. Davis.
  Claviceps purpurea (Fr.) Tul.
{ Epichloe typhina (P. ex Fr.) Tul.
{ Typhodium typhinum (P. ex Fr.) Seaver.
  Fusarium heterosporium Nees.
  Scolecotrichum graminis Fckl.
{ Nigredo amphidyma (Syd.) Arth.
{ Uromyces amphidymus Syd.
{ Uromyces Glyceriae Arth.
{ Uromyces graminicola Myc. Ex. *154a*.
{ Uromyces Dactylidis Auct. Amer.
{ Uromyces Poae Rabh.
  Ustilago longissima (Sow.) Tul.
  Ustilago longissima (Sow.) Tul., var. macro-
    spora J. J. Davis.
Glyceria tenella Lange.
  Sphaerella tassiana De Not.
Festuca amplissima
  Ustilago sphaerocarpa Syd.
Festuca arizonica Vasey.
Festuca californica Vasey.
  Dicaeoma poculiforme (Wettst.) O. Kuntze.
Festuca capillata Lam.
  Marasmius on Festuca.
Festuca confinis Vasey.
{ Dicaeoma abundans (H. S. Jackson) Arth. &
    Fromme.
{ Puccinia abundans H. S. Jackson.
{ Puccinia Crandallii Pammel & Hume.
Festuca duriuscula L.
  Septoria cercosperma Rostr.
Festuca Eastwoodae Piper.
  Dicaeoma poculiforme (Wettst.) O. Kuntze.
Festuca elatior L.
  Claviceps purpurea (Fr.) Tul.
{ Colletotrichum cereale Manns.
{ Colletotrichum graminicola (Ces.) Wils.
  Dilophospora Alopecuri Fr.
  Helminthosporium dictyoides Drechsler.
  Helminthosporium teres Sacc.
  Ophiobolus Cariceti (B. & Br.) Sacc.

Festuca elatior (*cont.*)
  Dicaeoma Rhamni (Wettst.) O. Kuntze.
  Puccinia coronata Cda.
  Puccinia Festucae Plowr.
  Puccinia Lolii Nielsen.
  Puccinia Rhamni Wettst.
  Dicaeoma poculiforme (Wettst.) O. Kuntze.
  Puccinia graminis P.
  Puccinia poculiformis Wettst.
  Puccinia graminis P., var. Phlei-pratensis
    (Erikss. & Henn.) Stakm. & Piemeisel.
  Puccinia Phlei-pratensis Erikss. & Henn.
  Dicaeoma Piperi (Ricker) Arth. & Fromme.
  Pleomeris Piperi (Ricker) Syd.
  Puccinia Piperi Ricker.
  Dicaeoma epiphyllum (Wettst.) O. Kuntze.
  Scolecotrichum graminis Fckl.
  Septoria festucina Tehon & Daniels.
Festuca Elmeri Scribn. & Merr.
  Dicaeoma abundans (H. S. Jackson) Arth. &
    Fromme.
  Dicaeoma poculiforme (Wettst.) O. Kuntze.
Festuca gigantea (L.) Vill.
  Puccinia graminis P., var. Tritici Erikss. &
    Henn.
Festuca idahoensis Elmer.
  Dicaeoma abundans (H. S. Jackson) Arth. &
    Fromme.
  Puccinia abundans H. S. Jackson.
  Puccinia Crandallii Pammel & Hume.
Festuca Kingii (Watson) Vasey.
  Leptosphaeria culmifraga Fr.
  Leptosphaeria eustomella Sacc.
  Puccinia Crandallii Pammel & Hume.
  Mycosphaerella tassiana (De Not.) Johans.
  Sphaerella tassiana De Not.
Festuca megalura Nutt.
  Dicaeoma poculiforme (Wettst.) O. Kuntze.
  Puccinia poculiformis Wettst.
  Dicaeoma Piperi (Ricker) Arth. & Fromme.
  Puccinia Piperi Ricker.
Festuca microstachya Nutt.
  Tilletia fusca Ell. & Ev.
  Tilletia mixta Massee.
  Ustilago mulfordiana Ell. & Ev.
Festuca Myuros L.
  Dicaeoma epiphyllum (Wettst.) O. Kuntze.
  Dicaeoma poculiforme (Wettst.) O. Kuntze.
Festuca nutans Spreng.
  Epichloe typhina (P. ex Fr.) Tul.
Festuca occidentalis Hook.
  Dicaeoma abundans (H. S. Jackson) Arth. &
    Fromme.
  Puccinia Crandallii Pammel & Hume.
Festuca octoflora Walt.
  Ophiobolus cariceti (B. & Br.) Sacc.
  Dicaeoma poculiforme (Wettst.) O. Kuntze.
  Puccinia graminis P.
  Puccinia poculiformis Wettst.

  Puccinia graminis P., var. Avenae Erikss. &
    Henn.
  Niptera Ellisii Rehm nom. nud.
  Peziza denigrata (J. Kunze) Ell.
  Peziza denigrata N. A. F. *565*.
  Pyrenopeziza denigrata Rehm. p. p.
  Pyrenopeziza Ellisii Massee.
  Septoria tenella C. & E.
  Spermoedia Clavus (DC.) ex Fr.
  Tilletia fusca Ell. & Ev.
  Nigredo Hordei (Tracy) Arth.
  Uromyces Dactylidis E. F. *538*.
  Uromyces Hordei Tracy.
  Ustilago Festucae-tenellae Henn.
  Ustilago mulfordiana Ell. & Ev.
Festuca ovina L.
  Cladosporium graminum Cda.
  Claviceps purpurea (Fr.) Tul.
  Colletotrichum cereale Manns.
  Dilophospora Alopecuri Fr.
  Lophodermium arundinaceum (Schrad. ex
    Fr.) Chev.
  Mollisia graminis Karst.
  Pleospora pentamera Karst.
  Dicaeoma abundans (H. S. Jackson) Arth. &
    Fromme.
  Puccinia Crandallii Pammel & Hume.
  Mycosphaerella tassiana (De Not.) Johans.
  Sphaerella tassiana De Not.
  Mycosphaerella Wichuriana (Schrt.) Johans.
  Uromyces Dactylidis Otth.
  Ustilago striiformis (Westd.) Niessl.
Festuca ovina L., var. **brevifolia** (R. Br.) Hack.
  Pleospora discors (Dur. & Mont.) Ces. & DeNot.
Festuca pacifica Piper.
  Dicaeoma Piperi (Ricker) Arth. & Fromme.
  Puccinia Piperi Ricker.
  Dicaeoma poculiforme (Wettst.) O. Kuntze.
  Puccinia graminis P.
Festuca rubra L.
  Colletotrichum cereale Manns.
  Dilophospora Alopecuri Fr.
  Leptosphaeria Ophiopogonis, var. graminum
    Sacc.
  Lophodermium arundinaceum (Schrad. ex Fr.)
    Chev.
  Dicaeoma abundans (H. S. Jackson) Arth. &
    Fromme.
  Puccinia abundans H. S. Jackson.
  Dicaeoma Clematidis (Lagerh.) Arth.
  Puccinia Elymi Westd.
  Puccinia coronata Cda.
  Puccinia graminis P., var. Avenae Erikss. &
    Henn.
  Rhizoctonia Solani Kühn.
  Sphaerella pusilla Awd.
Festuca rubra L., var. **arenaria** Fr.
  Myosphaerella recuticta (Fr.) Johans.

Festuca rubra L., var. heterophylla (Lam.)
Mutel.
Claviceps sp. indet.
Festuca subulata Trin.
Dicaeoma Rhamni (Wettst.) O. Kuntze.
Puccinia coronata Cda.
Puccinia Rhamni Wettst.
Dicaeoma abundans (H. S. Jackson) Arth. &
Fromme.
Puccinia abundans H. S. Jackson.
Puccinia Crandallii Pammel & Humc.
Puccinia Kreageri Ricker.
Festuca tenuiflora Schrad.
Puccinia graminis P.
Festuca Thurberi Vasey.
Puccinia Agropyri Ell. & Ev.
Dicaeoma cockerellianum (Bethel) Arth. &
Fromme.
Puccinia cockerelliana Bethel.
Festuca sp. indet.
Corticium vagum B. & C.
Hendersonia trimera Cke.
Ophiobolus Festucae Tracy & Earle.
Ophiobolus graminis Sacc.
Puccinia epiphylla Wettst.
Ustilago striiformis (Westd.) Niessl.
Bromus altissimus Pursh.
Colletotrichum graminicola (Ces.) G. W.
Wilson.
Septoria Bromi Sacc.
Bromus arvensis L.
Ustilago bromivora Fisch. Wald.
Bromus briziformis Fisch. & Mey.
Puccinia glumarum Erikss. & Henn.
Bromus carinatus Hook.
Puccinia Agropyri Ell. & Ev.
Puccinia alternans Arth.
Puccinia Clematidis Lagerh.
Puccinia Rubigo-vera Auct. Amer. p. p.
Puccinia glumarum Erikss. & Henn.
Puccinia Rubigo-vera Auct. Amer. p. p.
Bromus ciliatus L.
Leptosphaeria culmifraga (Fr.) Ces. & De Not.
Phyllachora graminis (P. ex Fr.) Fckl.
Pleospora infectoria Fckl.
Pleospora vulgaris Niessl.
Dicaeoma Clematidis (Lagerh.) Arth.
Puccinia Agropyri Ell. & Ev.
Puccinia Clematidis Lagerh.
Puccinia hydnoides Arth.
Puccinia Rubigo-vera Auct. Amer. p. p.
Puccinia tomipara Trel.
Rostrupia tomipara (Trel.) Lagerh.
? Puccinia coronata Cda.
Puccinia Rhamni Wettst.
Puccinia graminis P., var. Avenae Erikss. &
Henn.
Sclerotium rhizodes Awd.
Septoria brevispora Ell. & Davis.

Septoria graminum Desm.
Ustilago bromivora Fisch. Wald.
Ustilago bromivora Fisch. Wald., var. macro-
spora Farl.
Bromus ciliatus L., var. laeviglumis Scribn.
Colletotrichum Vermicularia Sacc. & Dear-
ness.
Dicaeoma Clematidis (Lagerh.) Arth.
Puccinia tomipara Trel.
Bromus commutatus Schrad.
Dicaeoma Clematidis (Lagerh.) Arth.
Sclerospora macrospora Sacc.
Bromus condensatus Hack.
Claviceps purpurea (Fr.) Tul.
Bromus exaltatus Bernh.
Dicaeoma Clematidis (Lagerh.) Arth.
Puccinia Clematidis Lagerh.
Bromus eximius (Shear) Piper.
Ustilago bromivora (Tul.) Fisch. Wald.
Bromus grandis (Shear) Hitchc.
Dicaeoma Clematidis (Lagerh.) Arth.
Puccinia Clematidis Lagerh.
Bromus Gussoni Parl.
Ustilago bromivora (Tul.) Fisch. Wald.
Ustilago lorentziana Auct. Amer. p.p.
Bromus hookerianus Thurb.
Dicaeoma Clematidis (Lagerh.) Arth.
Puccinia Agropyri Ell. & Ev.
Puccinia alternans Arth.
Puccinia Clematidis Lagerh.
Puccinia Elymi Westd.
Dicaeoma glumarum (Erikss. & Henn.) Arth.
& Fromme.
Puccinia glumarum Erikss. & Henn.
Puccinia Rubigo-vera Auct. Amer. p. p.
Puccinia glumarum Erikss. & Henn., var.
Tritici Erikss. & Henn.
Ustilago bromivora (Tul.) Fisch. Wald.
Bromus hordeaceus L.
Dicaeoma Clematidis (Lagerh.) Arth.
Puccinia Clematidis Lagerh.
Puccinia glumarum Erikss. & Henn., var.
Tritici Erikss. & Henn.
Puccinia Rubigo-vera Auct. Amer. p. p.
Tilletia guyotiana Hariot.
Ustilago bromivora (Tul.). Fisch. Wald.
Bromus hordeaceus L. var. glabrescens Shear.
Ustilago bromivora (Tul.) Fisch. Wald.
Bromus inermis Leyss.
Claviceps purpurea (Fr.) Tul.
Spermoedia clavus Fr.
Erysiphe graminis DC.†
Helminthosporium Bromi Diedicke.
Helminthosporium giganteum Heald & Wolf.
Ophiobolus cariceti (B. & Br.) Sacc.
Ophiobolus Medusa Ell. & Ev., var. Bromi
Brenckle Fung. Dak. 536.
Puccinia? bromina Erikss.
Puccinia Clematidis Lagerh.

Bromus inermis (*cont.*)
  Puccinia coronata Cda.
  Puccinia graminis P., var. Avenae Erikss. &
    Henn.
  Pyrenophora Bromi (Died.) Drechsler.
  Rhynchosporium Secalis (Oud.) J. J. Davis.
  Septoria Bromi Sacc.
  Septoria bromigena Sacc.
  Ustilago bromivora (Tul.) Fisch.
Bromus japonicus Thunb.
  Dicaeoma Clematidis (DC.) Arth.
  Dicaeoma poculiforme (Wettst.) O. Kuntze.
Bromus Kalmii Gray.
  Ustilago bromivora (Tul.) Fisch. Wald.
Bromus latiglumis (Shear) Hitchc.
  Dicaeoma Clematidis (Lagerh.) Arth.
  Puccinia Clematidis Lagerh.
  Puccinia tomipara Trel.
  Puccinia coronata Cda.
Bromus madritensis L.
  Dicaeoma Clematidis (Lagerh.) Arth.
  Puccinia Andropogonis S.?
  Vermicularia affinis Sacc. & Briard.
Bromus marginatus Nees.
  Claviceps purpurea (Fr.) Tul.
  Erysiphe graminis DC.†
  Dicaeoma Clematidis (Lagerh.) Arth.
  Puccinia Clematidis Lagerh.
  Dicaeoma glumarum (Erikss. & Henn.) Arth.
    & Fromme.
  Puccinia glumarum Erikss. & Henn.
  Scolecotrichum graminis Fckl.
  Urocystis Agropyri (Preuss) Schrt.
  Ustilago bromivora (Tul.) Fisch. Wald.
  Ustilago bromivora (Tul.) Fisch. Wald., var.
    macrospora Farl.
Bromus pacificus Shear.
  Dicaeoma glumarum (Erikss. & Henn.) Arth.
    & Fromme.
  Puccinia glumarum Erikss. & Henn.
Bromus pendulinus Sesse.
  Dicaeoma Clematidis (Lagerh.) Arth.
  Dicaeoma Rhamni (Wettst.) O. Kuntze.
Bromus polyanthus Scribn.
  Dicaeoma Clematidis (Lagerh.) Arth.
  Dicaeoma Rhamni (Wettst.) O. Kuntze.
  Puccinia Rhamni Wettst.
  Puccinia glumarum Erikss. & Henn.
  Dicaeoma poculiforme (Wettst.) O. Kuntze.
  Ustilago bromivora (Tul.) Fisch. Wald.
Bromus Porteri (Coulter) Nash.
  Ophiobolus cariceti (B. & Br.) Sacc.
  Dicaeoma Clematidis (Lagerh.) Arth.
  Puccinia alternans Arth.
  Puccinia Clematidis Lagerh.
  Puccinia Rubigo-vera Auct. Amer. p. p.
  Dicaeoma Rhamni (Wettst.) O. Kuntze.
  Puccinia coronata Cda.

Bromus pumpellianus Scribn.
  Dicaeoma Clematidis (Lagerh.) Arth.
  Puccinia alternans Arth.
  Puccinia Clematidis Lagerh.
  Dicaeoma Rhamni (Wettst.) O. Kuntze.
  Puccinia coronata Cda.
  Puccinia Rhamni Wettst.
  Septoria bromigena Sacc.
  Ustilago bromivora (Tul.) Fisch. Wald.
Bromus purgans L.
  Colletotrichum graminicola (Ces.) Wilson.
  Dicaeoma Clematidis (Lagerh.) Arth.
  Puccinia Clematidis Lagerh.
  Puccinia Elymi Westd.
  Puccinia tomipara Trel.
  Dicaeoma poculiforme (Wettst.) O. Kuntze.
  Puccinia graminis P.
  Puccinia poculiformis Wettst.
  Puccinia graminis P., var. Avenae Erikss. &
    Henn.
  Puccinia graminis P., var. Secalis Erikss. &
    Henn.
Bromus racemosus L.
  Dicaeoma Clematidis (Lagerh.) Arth.
  Ustilago bromivora (Tul.) Fisch. Wald.
Bromus Richardsoni Lk.
  Dicaeoma Clematidis (Lagerh.) Arth.
  Puccinia alternans Arth.
  Puccinia Clematidis Lagerh.
  Dicaeoma Rhamni (Wettst.) O. Kuntze.
  Ustilago bromivora (Tul.) Fisch. Wald.
Bromus rigidus Roth.
  Dicaeoma Clematidis (Lagerh.) Arth.
Bromus rubens L.
  Dicaeoma Clematidis (Lagerh.) Arth.
  Puccinia Elymi Westd.
  Puccinia glumarum Erikss. & Henn.
Bromus scoparius L.
  Dicaeoma Clematidis (Lagerh.) Arth.
Bromus secalinus L.
  Colletotrichum cereale Manns.
  Colletotrichum graminicola (Ces.) G. W.
    Wilson.
  Fusarium sp. indet.
  Ophiobolus cariceti (B. & Br.) Sacc.
  Ophiobolus graminis Sacc.
  Phoma graminella Sacc.?
  Dicaeoma Clematidis (Lagerh.) Arth.
  Puccinia Clematidis Lagerh.
  ?Puccinia Rubigo-vera Auct. Amer. p. p.
  Dicaeoma poculiforme (Wettst.) O. Kuntze.
  Puccinia graminis P.
  Puccinia poculiformis Wettst.
  Septoria Bromi Sacc.
  Ustilago bromivora (Tul.) Fisch. Wald.
Bromus sitchensis Bong.
  Dicaeoma Clematidis (Lagerh.) Arth.
  Puccinia alternans Arth.
  Puccinia Clematidis Lagerh.

Bromus sitchensis (*cont.*)
⎰Dicaeoma glumarum (Erikss. & Henn.) Arth.
⎱ & Fromme.
Puccinia glumarum Erikss. & Henn.
Puccinia glumarum Erikss. & Henn., var.
  Tritici Erikss. & Henn.
Scolecotrichum graminis Fckl.
Bromus sterilis L.
⎰Dicaeoma Clematidis (Lagerh.) Arth.
⎱Puccinia Elymi Westd.
Puccinia Rubigo-vera Auct. Amer. p. p.
Bromus subvelutinus Shear.
⎰Dicaeoma Clematidis (Lagerh.) Arth.
⎱Puccinia Elymi Westd.
Bromus tectorum L.
Puccinia Clematidis Lagerh.
⎰Dicaeoma poculiforme (Wettst.) O. Kuntze.
⎱Puccinia graminis P.
Puccinia graminis P., var. Avenae Erikss. &
  Henn.
Puccinia graminis P., var. Secalis Erikss. &
  Henn.
Ustilago bromivora (Tul.) Fisch. Wald.
Ustilago bromivora (Tul.) Fisch. Wald., var.
  macrospora Farl.
Bromus unioloides (Willd.) H. B. K.
⎰Colletotrichum Bromi Jennings.
⎱Colletotrichum graminicola (Ces.) G. W.
  Wilson.
Erysiphe graminis DC. †
Dicaeoma glumarum (Erikss. & Henn.) Arth.
  & Fromme.
Steirochaete graminicola (Ces.) Sacc.
Ustilago bromivora (Tul.) Fisch. Wald.
Bromus villosus Forsk.
Bromus virens Buckl.
⎰Dicaeoma Clematidis (Lagerh.) Arth.
│Puccinia Agropyri Ell. & Ev.
│Puccinia alternans Arth.
│Puccinia Clematidis Lagerh.
│Puccinia tomipara Trel.
⎱Rostrupia tomipara (Trel.) Lagerh.
Bromus vulgaris Shear.
⎰Puccinia Clematidis Lagerh.
⎱Puccinia Rubigo-vera Auct. Amer. p. p.
Ustilago bromivora (Tul.) Fisch. Wald.
Bromus sp. indet.
Colletotrichum Vermicularia Sacc. & Dearness.
Gibberella Saubinetii (Mont.) Sacc.
Helminthosporium Bromi Diedicke.
Septoria bromigena Sacc.
Brachypodium mexicanum (Roem. & Schult.) Lk.
Puccinia subdigitata Arth. & Holw.
Nardus stricta L.
Leptosphaeria Nardi (Fr.) Ces. & De Not.
Lophodermium arundinaceum (Schrad. ex Fr.)
  Chev.
Sphaerella pusilla Awd.
Trochila exigua Rostrup.

Lolium multiflorum Lam.
Claviceps purpurea (Fr.) Tul.
Helminthosporium siccans Drechsler.
⎰Dicaeoma poculiforme (Wettst.) O. Kuntze.
│Puccinia graminis P.
⎱Puccinia poculiformis Wettst.
Puccinia graminis P., var. Avenae Erikss. &
  Henn.
⎰Dicaeoma Rhamni (Wettst.) O. Kuntze.
⎱Puccinia Rhamni Wettst.
Lolium perenne L.
Claviceps purpurea (Fr.) Tul.
Colletotrichum graminicola (Ces.) G. W. Wil-
  son.
Helminthosporium siccans Drechsler.
Leptosphaeria culmorum Awd.
⎰Dicaeoma Rhamni (Wettst.) O. Kuntze.
│Puccinia coronata Cda.
│Puccinia Lolii Nielsen.
⎱Puccinia Rhamni Wettst.
Puccinia glumarum Erikss. & Henn.
Puccinia graminis P.
Puccinia graminis P., var. Avenae Erikss. &
  Henn.
Lolium subulatum Vis.
⎰Dicaeoma poculiforme (Wettst.) O. Kuntze.
│Puccinia graminis P.
⎱Puccinia poculiformis Wettst.
Lolium temulentum L.
Puccinia graminis P.
Scribnera Bolanderi (Thurb.) Hack.
Nigredo Jacksonii (Arth. & Fromme) Arth.
Agropyron albicans Scribn. & Sm.
⎰Dicaeoma Clematidis (Lagerh.) Arth.
│Puccinia Clematidis Lagerh.
│Dicaeoma montanense (Ell.) O. Kuntze.
⎱Puccinia montanensis Ell.
Agropyron Bakeri E. Nels.
Ascochytula agropyrina Fairman.
Hendersonia subcultriformis Fairman.
Agropyron biflorum (Brignoli) R. & S.
Claviceps purpurea (Fr.) Tul.
Hendersonia Agropyri Rostr.
Hendersonia crastophila Sacc.
Lophodermium arundinaceum (Schrad. ex Fr.)
  Chev.
Phoma graminis Westd.
Pleospora herbarum (P.) ex Rabh.
Pleospora pentamera Karst.
Dicaeoma apocryptum (Ell. & Tracy) O.
  Kuntze.
⎰Dicaeoma Clematidis (Lagerh.) Arth.
│Puccinia Elymi Westd.
⎱Puccinia obliterata Arth.
Puccinia glumarum Erikss. & Henn.
Puccinia graminis P.
Sphaerella recutita (Fr.) Cke.
Sphaerella tassiana De Not.

Agropyron caninum (L.) Beauv.
  Claviceps purpurea (Fr.) Tul.
  Spermoedia clavus Fr.
  Erysiphe graminis DC. †
  Dicaeoma Clematidis (Lagerh.) Arth.
  Puccinia Agropyri Ell. & Ev.
  Puccinia Clematidis Lagerh.
  Puccinia Elymi Westd.
  Puccinia obliterata Arth.
  Puccinia glumarum Erikss. & Henn.
  Puccinia glumarum Erikss. & Henn., var.
    Tritici Erikss. & Henn.
  Dicaeoma poculiforme (Wettst.) O. Kuntze.
  Puccinia graminis P.
  Puccinia poculiformis Wettst.
  Puccinia graminis P., var. Secalis Erikss. &
    Henn.
  Puccinia graminis P., var. Tritici Erikss. &
    Henn.
  Dicaeoma montanense (Ell.) O. Kuntze.
  Sclerotium rhizodes Awd.
  Septoria graminum Desm.
  ?Ustilago lorentziana Thm.

Agropyron cristatum J. Gaertn.
  Claviceps purpurea (Fr.) Tul.
  Dicaeoma glumarum (Erikss. & Henn.) Arth.
    & Fromme.
  Puccinia glumarum Erikss. & Henn.
  Puccinia graminis P., var. Secalis Erikss. &
    Henn.
  Puccinia graminis P., var. Tritici Erikss. &
    Henn.

Agropyron dasystachyum (Hook.) Scribn.
  Claviceps purpurea (Fr.) Tul.
  Ophiobolus cariceti (B. & Br.) Sacc.
  Dicaeoma Clematidis (Lagerh.) Arth.
  Puccinia Clematidis Lagerh.
  Puccinia glumarum Erikss. & Henn.
  Puccinia Rubigo-vera Auct. Amer. p. p.
  Puccinia glumarum Erikss. & Henn., var.
    Tritici Erikss. & Henn.
  Puccinia Rubigo-vera Auct. Amer. p. p.
  Dicaeoma poculiforme (Wettst.) O. Kuntze.
  Puccinia graminis P.
  Puccinia poculiformis Wettst.
  Dicaeoma montanense (Ell.) O. Kuntze.
  Ustilago bromivora Fisch. Wald.

Agropyron desertorum Schult.
  Colletotrichum cereale Manns.
  Puccinia glumarum Erikss. & Henn.

Agropyron elongatum Host.
  Helminthosporium giganteum Heald & Wolf.

Agropyron flexuosum Piper.
  Dicaeoma Clematidis (Lagerh.) Arth.

Agropyon glaucum Roem. & Schult.
  Claviceps purpurea (Fr.) Tul.
  Erysiphe graminis DC. †
  Phyllachora graminis (P. ex Fr.) Fckl.

  Puccinia Agropyri Ell. & Ev.
  Puccinia Clematidis Lagerh.
  Puccinia obliterata Arth.
  Puccinia coronata Cda.
  Puccinia graminis P.
  Puccinia poculiformis Wettst.

Agropyron imbricatum Roem & Schult.
  Puccinia graminis P., var. Secalis Erikss. &
    Henn.

Agropyron inerme (Scribn. & Sm.) Rydb.
  Claviceps purpurea (Fr.) Tul.
  ?Puccinia glumarum Erikss. & Henn., var.
    Tritici Erikss. & Henn.
  Ustilago macrospora Desm.

Agropyron intermedium (Host.) Beauv.
  Helminthosporium giganteum Heald & Wolf.
  Puccinia glumarum Erikss. & Henn.

Agropyron lanceolatum Scribn. & Sm.
  Dicaeoma Clematidis (Lagerh.) Arth.
  Puccinia Clematidis Lagerh.
  Puccinia glumarum Erikss. & Henn.

Agropyron molle Rydb.
  Claviceps purpurea (Fr.) Tul.
  Dicaeoma Clematidis (Lagerh.) Arth.

Agropyron occidentale Scribn. See **Agropyron
  Smithii** Rydb.

Agropyron repens (L.) Beauv.
  Claviceps purpurea (Fr.) Tul.
  Spermoedia clavus (D.C.) ex Fr.
  Colletotrichum cereale Manns.
  Colletotrichum graminicola (Ces.) G. W. Wilson.
  Coniosporium rhizophilum (Preuss) Sacc.
  Dothidea glumarum B. & C.
  Erysiphe graminis DC. †
  Fusarium culmorum (W. G. Sm.) Sacc.
  Fusarium Poae (Pk.) C. E. Lewis.
  Gibberella Saubinetii (Mont.) Sacc.
  Helminthosporium giganteum Heald & Wolf.
  Helminthosporium sativum Pammel, King, &
    Bakke.
  Marasmius Tritici P. A. Young.
  Oidium monilioides Lk.
  Ophiobolus cariceti (B. & Br.) Sacc.
  Ophiobolus graminis Sacc.
  Ovularia pulchella (Ces.) Sacc.
  Ovularia pulchella (Ces.) Sacc., var. Agropyri
    J. J. Davis.
  Phyllachora graminis (P. ex Fr.) Fckl.
  Dicaeoma Rhamni (Wettst.) O. Kuntze.
  Puccinia coronata Cda.
  Dicaeoma Clematidis (Lagerh.) Arth.
  Puccinia Agropyri Ell. & Ev.
  Puccinia agropyrina Erikss.
  Puccinia Clematidis Lagerh.
  Puccinia Rubigo-vera Myc. Ex. *110b*.
  Puccinia Rubigo-vera, var., agropyrina
    (Erikss.) Mains & Jackson.

Agropyron repens (*cont.*)
- Dicaeoma poculiforme (Wettst.) O. Kuntze.
- Puccinia graminis P.
- Puccinia poculiformis Wettst.
- Puccinia graminis P., var. Secalis Erikss. & Henn.
- Pyrenophora relicina Fckl.
- Pyrenophora Tritici-repentis (Died.) Drechsler.
- Rhynchosporium Secalis (Oud.) J. J. Davis.
- Septoria Agropyri Ell. & Ev.
- Tilletia Earlei Griffiths.
- Urocystis Agropyri (Preuss) Schrt.
- Urocystis occulta (Wallr.) Rabh., var. Tritici Farl.
- Ustilago hypodytes (Schl.) Fr.
- Ustilago macrospora Desm.
- Tilletia striiformis (Westd.) Wint.
- Ustilago striiformis (Westd.) Niessl.
- Wojnowicia graminis (McAlpine) Sacc. & D. Sacc.

Agropyron Richardsonii Schrad.
- Claviceps purpurea (Fr.) Tul.
- Leptosphaeria culmorum Awd.
- Dicaeoma Clematidis (Lagerh.) Arth.
- Puccinia Clematidis Lagerh.
- Dicaeoma poculiforme (Wettst.) O. Kuntze.
- Puccinia graminis P.
- Puccinia graminis P., var. Tritici Erikss. & Henn.
- Ustilago bromivora Fisch. Wald

Agropyron riparium Scribn. & J. G. Sm.
- Puccinia Clematidis Lagerh.

Agropyron Smithii Rydb.
- Ascochyta graminicola Sacc.
- Cladosporium herbarum (P.) ex Lk.
- Claviceps purpurea (Fr.) Tul.
- Spermoedia clavus (DC.) ex Fr.
- Epichloe typhina (P. ex Fr.) Tul.
- Oidium monilioides Lk.
- Phoma lophiostomoides Sacc.
- Dicaeoma apocryptum (Ell. & Tracy) O. Kuntze.
- Dicaeoma Rhamni (Wettst.) O. Kuntze.
- Puccinia coronata Cda.
- Dicaeoma Clematidis (Lagerh.) Arth.
- Puccinia Agropyri Ell. & Ev.
- Puccinia apocrypta N. Am. Uredinales *2032*.
- Puccinia Clematidis Lagerh.
- ?Puccinia graminis Auct. p. p.
- Dicaeoma glumarum (Erikss. & Henn.) Arth. & Fromme.
- Puccinia glumarum Erikss. & Henn.
- Dicaeoma poculiforme (Wettst.) O. Kuntze.
- Puccinia graminis P.
- Puccinia poculiformis Wettst.
- Puccinia graminis P., var. Secalis Erikss. & Henn.

Puccinia graminis P., var. Tritici Erikss. & Henn.
Puccinia graminis P., var. Tritici-compacti Stakman & Piemeisel.
- Dicaeoma montanense (Ell.) O. Kuntze.
- Puccinia montanensis Ell.
Tilletia Earlei Griffiths.
Typhodium typhinum (P.) Seaver.
Urocystis Agropyri (Preuss) Schrt.
Ustilago hypodytes (Schl.) Fr.
Wojnowicia graminis (McAlpine) Sacc. & D. Sacc.

Agropyron Smithii Rydb., var. **Palmeri** (Scribn. & Sm.) A. Heller.
- Dicaeoma Clematidis (Lagerh.) Arth.
- Puccinia Clematidis Lagerh.
- Dicaeoma montanense (Ell.) O. Kuntze.

Agropyron spicatum (Pursh) Scribn. & J. G. Sm.
- Claviceps purpurea (Fr.) Tul.
- Dicaeoma Clematidis (Lagerh.) Arth.
- Puccinia Agropyri Ell. & Ev.
- Puccinia Clematidis Lagerh.
- Puccinia Elymi Westd.
- Dicaeoma pattersonianum (Arth.) Arth. & Fromme.
- Puccinia Agropyri Auct. Amer. p. p.
- Puccinia Rubigo-vera Myc. Ex. *110ᵃ*.
- Puccinia pattersoniana Arth.
- Puccinia glumarum Erikss. & Henn.
- ?Puccinia graminis Auct.
- Typhodium typhinum (P. ex Fr.) Seaver.
- Urocystis Agropyri (Preuss) Schrt.

Agropyron tenerum Vasey.
- Claviceps purpurea (Fr.) Tul.
- Spermoedia clavus Fr.
- Dinemasporium gramineum (Lib.) Lev., var. strigosulum Karst.
- Erysiphe graminis DC. †
- Leptosphaeria culmifraga (Fr.) Ces. & De Not.
- Ovularia pulchella (Ces.) Sacc., var. Agropyri J. J. Davis.
- Physalospora Festucae (Lib.) Sacc.
- Dicaeoma apocryptum (Ell. & Tracy) O. Kuntze.
- Puccinia apocrypta Ell. & Tracy.
- Dicaeoma Clematidis (Lagerh.) Arth.
- Puccinia Agropyri Ell. & Ev.
- Puccinia Clematidis Lagerh.
- Puccinia Elymi Westd.
- Puccinia tomipara Trel.
- Dicaeoma Rhamni (Wettst.) O. Kuntze.
- Puccinia coronata Cda.
- Dicaeoma poculiforme (Wettst.) O. Kuntze.
- Puccinia graminis P.
- Puccinia poculiformis Wettst.
- Puccinia graminis P., var. Secalis Erikss. & Henn.

Agropyron tenerum (*cont.*)

Puccinia graminis P., var. Tritici Erikss. &
Henn.

Dicaeoma montanense (Ell.) O. Kuntze.
Puccinia montanensis Ell.
Puccinia Rubigo-vera Auct. Amer. p. p.
Urocystis Agropyri (Preuss) Schrt.
Ustilago Agropyri G. P. Clinton.
Ustilago bromivora Fisch. Wald.

Agropyron sp. indet.
Lophiostoma Arundinis (Fr.) Ces. & De Not.

Secale cereale L.

Ascomycetes

Ceuthospora phaeocomes (Reb. ex Fr.) S.
Pyrenophora phaeocomes (Reb. ex Fr.) Pk.
Sphaeria phaeocomes Reb. ex Fr.
Chaetomium olivaceum C. & E.
Claviceps purpurea (Fr.) Tul.
Cordyceps purpurea Fr.
Spermoedia clavus Fr.
Endomyces Mali C. E. Lewis.
Erysiphe graminis DC. †
Erysiphe graminis DC., var. Secalis Marchal.
Gibberella Saubinetii (Mont.) Sacc.
Nectria secalina Ell. & Ev.
Ophiobolus cariceti (B. & Br.) Sacc.
Ophiobolus graminis Sacc.
Pyrenophora relicina (Fckl.) Sacc
Mycosphaerella leptopleura (De Not.) Earle.
Sphaerella leptopleura De Not.
Mycosphaerella maxima Miles.

Ustilaginales

Tilletia Secalis (Cda.) Kühn.
Tilletia Tritici (Bjerk.) Wint.
Urocystis occulta (Wallr.) Rabh.
?Ustilago levis (Kellerm. & Swingle) Magn.
?Ustilago nuda (Jensen) Kellerm. & Swingle.
Ustilago Tritici (P.) Rostr.

Uredinales

Caeoma Rubigo Lk.
Dicaeoma asperifolii (Wettst.) O. Kuntze.
Pleomeris dispersa (Erikss.) Syd.
Puccinia asperifolii Wettst.
Puccinia dispersa Erikss.
Puccinia Rubigo-vera Wint.
Pucinia Rubigo-vera Auct. Amer. p. p., var.
Secalis Carl.
Puccinia secalina Grove.
Trichobasis Rubigo Lév.
Uredo Rubigo Auct.
Uredo Rubigo-vera DC.
Dicaeoma glumarum (Erikss. & Henn.) Arth. &
Fromme.
Puccinia glumarum Erikss. & Henn.
Puccinia glumarum Erikss. & Henn., var.
Secalis Erikss.

Dicaeoma poculiforme (Wettst.) O. Kuntze.
Puccinia graminis P.
Puccinia poculiformis Wettst.
Puccinia graminis P., var. Agrostidis Erikss.
Puccinia graminis P., var. Hordei Freeman &
Johnson.
Puccinia graminis P., var. Phlei-pratensis
(Erikss. & Henn.) Stakman & Piemeisel.
Puccinia Phlei-pratensis Erikss. & Henn.
Puccinia graminis P., var. Secalis Erikss. &
Henn.
Puccinia graminis P., var. Tritici Erikss. &
Henn.
Trichobasis Rubigo-vera Rav. Fung. Am. *273.*

Fungi Imperfecti

Cladosporium compactum B. & C.
Cladosporium herbarum (P.) ex Lk.
Colletotrichum cereale Manns.
Colletotrichum graminicola (Ces.) G. W. Wil-
son.
Vermicularia graminicola Auct. Amer. an
Westd.
Dilophospora Alopecuri Fr.
Epicoccum sphaerospermum B.& C.
Fusarium culmorum (W. G. Sm.) Sacc.
Fusarium culmorum (W. G. Sm.) Sacc., var.
leteius Sherb.
Fusarium heterosporum Nees.
Fusarium redolens Wr.
Fusarium roseum Lk.
Fusarium heterosporium Ell. in Wr. pl. 123
non Nees.
Fusarium tricinctum (Cda.) Sacc.
Helminthosporium graminum Rabh.
Helminthosporium inconspicuum C. & E.
Helminthosporium sativum Pammel, King &
Bakke.
Helminthosporium teres Sacc.
Helminthosporium tuberosum Atk.
Periconia pycnospora Fres.
Rhynchosporium graminicola Heinsen.
Rhynchosporium Secalis (Oud.) J. J. Davis.
Septoria glumarum Pass.
Septoria nodorum B.
Septoria Passerinii Sacc.
Septoria secalina (Jancz.) Sacc.
Septoria Secalis Prill. & Delacr.
Septoria Tritici Desm.

Miscellanea

Marasmius Tritici P. A. Young.
Peronospora Trifoliorum DBy.

Secale sp. indet.
Marasmius graminum (Lib.) B.
Pyrenophora sarcocystis (B. & C.) Rav. Fung.
Am.
Pyrenophora trichostoma (Fr.) Sacc.

Aegilops cylindrica Host.
{ Dicaeoma glumarum (Erikss. & Henn.) Arth. &
Fromme.
Puccinia glumarum Erikss. & Henn.
{ Puccinia Clematidis Lagerh.
Puccinia triticina Erikss.
Triticum aestivum L.
including
Triticum sativum Lam.
Triticum turgidulum L.
Triticum vulgare Vill.
Triticum sp. indet. (Wheat).

PYRENOMYCETINEAE

Chaetomium aterrimum Ell. & Ev.
{ Claviceps purpurea (Fr.) Tul.
Spermoedia clavus (DC.) ex Fr.
Erysiphe graminis DC. †
Gibbera pulicaris Fr.
{ Dothidea glumarum B. & C.
Gibberella Saubinetii (Mont.) Sacc.
{ Catharinia straminis (Cke. & Hark.) Berl.
Leptosphaeria straminis Cke. & Hark.
Pleospora Harknessii Berl. & Vogl.
Leptosphaeria Tritici (Garovaglio) Pass.
Lophodermium arundinaceum (Schrad. ex
Fr.) Chev., var. culmigenum (Fr.) Fckl.
Mycosphaerella Tulasnei Jancz.
{ Ophiobolus cariceti (B. & Br.) Sacc.
Ophiobolus graminis Sacc.
Phyllachora graminis (P. ex Fr.) Fckl.
{ Pleospora sarcocystis (B. & C.) Sacc.
Pyrenophora sarcocystis Rav. Fung. Am.
Pyrenophora trichostoma (Fr.) Sacc.
Sphaeria sarcocystis B. & C.
Sphaeria trichostoma Fr.

USTILAGINALES

{ Ustilago foetens B. & C.
Tilletia laevis Kühn.
Tilletia foetens (B. & C.) Trel.
Tilletia Tritici N. A. F. *3236*.
{ Tilletia Caries (DC.) Tul.
Tilletia Tritici (Bjerk.) Wint.
Uredo foetida Bauer.
Urocystis Tritici Körn.
?Ustilago Avenae (P.) Jensen.
?Ustilago Hordei (P.) Kellerm. & Swingle.
?Ustilago levis (Kellerm. & Swingle) Magn.
?Ustilago nuda (Jensen) Kellerm. & Swingle.
{ Uredo segetum P. p. p.
Ustilago Carbo Auct. p. p.
Ustilago segetum Ditm. p. p.
Ustilago Tritici (P.) Rostr.

UREDINALES

Puccinia coronata Cda.
Puccinia dispersa Erikss.

Caeoma Rubigo Lk.
Dicaeoma Clematidis (Lagerh.) Arth.
Dicaeoma triticinum (Erikss.) Kern.
Puccinia Elymi Westd.
Puccinia vera Auct. p. p.
Puccinia Rubigo-vera, var. Tritici Carl.
Uredo Rubigo-vera DC.
Dicaeoma glumarum (Erikss. & Henn.) Arth.
& Fromme.
Puccinia glumarum Erikss. & Henn.
Puccinia Rubigo-vera Auct. Amer. p. p.
Puccinia Rubigo-vera, var. triticina (Erikss.)
Mains & Jackson.
Puccinia triticina Erikss.
Trichobasis Rubigo-vera Auct.-Amer. p. p.
Caeoma lineare Schl.
Dicaeoma poculiforme (Wettst.) O. Kuntze.
{ Puccinia graminis P.
Puccinia poculiformis Wettst.
Uredo linearis P.
Puccinia graminis P., var. Avenae Erikss. &
Henn.
Puccinia graminis P., var. Hordei Freeman &
Johnson.
Puccinia graminis P., var. Tritici Erikss. &
Henn.
Puccinia graminis P., var. Tritici-compacti
Stakman & Piemeisel.
Puccinia graminis P., var. Tritici-inficiens
Melchers & Parker.
[Puccinia graminis P., var. Tritici-tertii pro
tem.]

HYMENOMYCETINEAE

Marasmius scorodonius Fr.
Marasmius Tritici P. A. Young.

SPHAEROPSIDALES

Dilophospora Alopecuri Fr.
Diplodia Zeae Lév.
Leptostromella hysterioides Sacc.
Macrophoma suspecta Pk.
Septoria Agropyri Ell. & Ev.
{ Septoria curtisiana Sacc.
Septoria Tritici B. & C.
Septoria glumarum Pass.
Septoria nodorum B.
Septoria graminum Desm.
Septoria Tritici Desm.
Wojnowicia graminis (McAlpine) Sacc. & D.
Sacc.

MELANCONIALES

{ Colletotrichum cereale Manns.
Colletotrichum graminicola (Ces.) G. W. Wilson.

HYPHOMYCETES

Aspergillus flavus Lk.
Cephalothecium roseum Cda.
Cladosporium graminum Cda.

Triticum aestivum (*cont.*)
Cladosporium herbarum (P.) ex Lk.
Coniothecium glumarum Sacc.
Fusarium arthrosporioides Sherb.
Fusarium avenaceum (Fr.) Sacc.
{Fusarium culmorum (W. G. Sm.) Sacc.
{Fusisporium culmorum W. G. Sm.
Fusarium culmorum (W. G. Sm.) Sacc., var. leteius Sherb.
Fusarium graminum Cda., var. Tritici Coons.
Fusarium herbarum (Cda.) Fr.
Fusarium metachroum App. & Wr.
Fusarium redolens Wr.
Fusarium reticulatum Mont.
Fusarium roseum Lk.
Fusarium Scirpi Auct.
Fusarium Solani Auct.
Helminthosporium gramineum Rabh.
Helminthosporium sativum Pammel, King, & Bakke.
Hormodendron cladosporioides (Fres.) Sacc.
Hymenula cerealis Ell. & Ev.
Hymenula glumarum Cke. & Hark.
Macrosporium Uredinis Ell. & Barthol.
Oidium monilioides Lk.
Papulospora aspergilliformis Eidam.
Penicillium glaucum Lk.
Periconia pycnospora Fres.
Podosporiella verticillata O'Gara.
Rhynchosporium graminicola Heinsen.
Stemphylium Tritici Patterson.

MISCELLANEA
Endomyces Mali C. E. Lewis.
Lycoperdon giganteum (Batsch) ex P.
Pythium debaryanum Hesse.
Sclerospora macrospora Sacc.
Sclerotium rhizodes Awd.
Sclerotium Rolfsii Sacc.

Triticum compactum Host.
Erysiphe graminis DC. †
{Dicaeoma glumarum (Erikss. & Henn.) Arth. & Fromme.
{Puccinia glumarum Erikss. & Henn.
{Dicaeoma Clematidis (Lagerh.) Arth.
{Puccinia triticina Erikss.
{Dicaeoma poculiforme (Wettst.) O. Kuntze.
{Puccinia graminis P.
{Puccinia poculiformis Wettst.
Puccinia graminis P., var. Tritici Erikss. & Henn.
Puccinia graminis P., var. Tritici-compacti Stakman & Piemeisel.

Triticum dicoccoides Körn.
Dicaeoma Clematidis (Lagerh.) Arth.
{Dicaeoma poculiforme (Wettst.) O. Kuntze.
{Puccinia graminis P.

Triticum dicoccum Schrank.
Ophiobolus graminis Sacc.

Periconia pycnospora Fres.
Dicaeoma Clematidis (Lagerh.) Arth.
{Dicaeoma glumarum (Erikss. & Henn.) Arth. & Fromme.
{Puccinia glumarum Erikss. & Henn.
{Dicaeoma poculiforme (Wettst.) O. Kuntze.
{Puccinia graminis P.
Puccinia graminis P., var. Tritici Erikss. & Henn.
Puccinia graminis P., var. Tritici-compacti Stakman & Piemeisel.
Septoria nodorum B.
Tilletia Tritici (Bjerk.) Wint.

Triticum durum Desf.
{Dicaeoma glumarum (Erikss. & Henn.) Arth. & Fromme.
{Puccinia glumarum Erikss. & Henn.
{Dicaeoma poculiforme (Wettst.) O. Kuntze.
{Puccinia graminis P.
{Puccinia poculiformis Wettst.
Puccinia graminis P., var. Avenae Erikss. & Henn.
Puccinia graminis P., var. Tritici Erikss. & Henn.
{Dicaeoma Clematidis (Lagerh.) Arth.
{Puccinia triticina Erikss.

Triticum Freycenetii Host.
{Dicaeoma poculiforme (Wettst.) O. Kuntze.
{Puccinia graminis P.

Triticum monococcum L.
Erysiphe graminis DC. †
{Dicaeoma Clematidis (Lagerh.) Arth.
{Puccinia Clematidis Lagerh.
Puccinia glumarum Erikss. & Henn.
{Dicaeoma poculiforme (Wettst.) O. Kuntze.
{Puccinia graminis P.
Puccinia graminis P., var. Tritici Erikss. & Henn.

Triticum ovatum Rasp.
{Dicaeoma Clematidis (Lagerh.) Arth.
{Puccinia triticina Erikss.

Triticum polonicum L.
Erysiphe graminis DC. †
Phyllachora graminis (P. ex Fr.) Fckl.
Dicaeoma Clematidis (Lagerh.) Arth.
Puccinia glumarum Erikss. & Henn.
Dicaeoma poculiforme (Wettst.) O. Kuntze.
Puccinia graminis P., var. Tritici Erikss. & Henn.

Triticum Spelta L.
Colletotrichum cereale Manns.
Dilophospora Alopecuri Fr.
Erysiphe graminis DC. †
Gibberella Saubinetii (Mont.) Sacc.
Ophiobolus graminis Sacc.
Periconia pycnospora Fres.
{Dicaeoma glumarum (Erikss. & Henn.) Arth. & Fromme.
{Puccinia glumarum Erikss. & Henn.

Triticum Spelta (*cont.*)
{ Dicaeoma Clematidis (Lagerh.) Arth.
{ Puccinia triticina Erikss.
{ Dicaeoma poculiforme (Wettst.) O. Kuntze.
{ Puccinia graminis P.
{ Puccinia poculiformis Wettst.
Puccinia graminis P., var. Tritici Erikss. & Henn.
Tilletia Tritici (Bjerk.) Wint.
Ustilago Tritici (P.) Rostr.
Triticum Tumonia Schrad.
Dicaeoma poculiforme (Wettst.) O. Kuntze.
Triticum sp. indet.
Chaetomella Tritici Tehon & Daniels.
{ Chaetomium comatum (Tode) ex Fr.
{ Chaetomium elatum Kze. ex Fr.
{ Heptameria culmifraga (Fr.) Cke.
{ Leptosphaeria culmifraga (Fr.) Ces. & De Not.
{ Sphaeria culmifraga Fr.
Sporotrichum Poae Pk.
Hordeum boreale Scribn. & J. G. Sm.
Claviceps purpurea (Fr.) Tul.
Hordeum caespitosum Scribn.
{ Puccinia glumarum Erikss. & Henn.
{ Puccinia Rubigo-vera Auct. Amer. p. p.
{ Dicaeoma poculiforme (Wettst.) O. Kuntze.
{ Puccinia graminis P.
Puccinia graminis P., var. Tritici Erikss. & Henn.
Ustilago lorentziana Thm.
Hordeum deficiens Steud.
Helminthosporium californicum Mackie & Paxton.
Hordeum depressum Scribn. & J. G. Sm.
{ Dicaeoma glumarum (Erikss. & Henn.) Arth.
{ & Fromme.
{ Puccinia glumarum Erikss. & Henn.
Hordeum distichon L.
Helminthosporium californicum Mackie & Paxton.
{ Dicaeoma poculiforme (Wettst.) O. Kuntze.
{ Puccinia graminis P.
{ Puccinia poculiformis Wettst.
Rhynchosporium Secalis (Oud.) J. J. Davis.
Hordeum gussoneanum Parl.
{ Dicaeoma glumarum (Erikss. & Henn.) Arth.
{ & Fromme.
{ Puccinia glumarum Erikss. & Henn.
{ Dicaeoma poculiforme (Wettst.) O. Kuntze.
{ Puccinia graminis P.
{ Puccinia poculiformis Wettst.
{ Dicaeoma Hordei (Fckl.) Arth. & Fromme.
{ Puccinia Hordei Fckl.
Hordeum jubatum L.
Claviceps purpurea (Fr.) Tul.
Erysiphe graminis DC. †
Oidium monilioides Lk.
{ Puccinia anomala Rostr.
{ Puccinia simplex Erikss. & Henn.

{ Dicaeoma Clematidis (Lagerh.) Arth.
{ Puccinia Agropyri Ell. & Ev.
{ Puccinia Clematidis Lagerh.
{ Puccinia Elymi Westd.
{ Puccinia Rubigo-vera Auct. Amer. p. p.
{ Dicaeoma glumarum (Erikss. & Henn.) Arth.
{ & Fromme.
{ Puccinia glumarum Erikss. & Henn.
{ Puccinia montanensis Auct. Amer. p. p.
{ Puccinia Rubigo-vera Auct. Amer. p. p.
{ Dicaeoma poculiforme (Wettst.) O. Kuntze.
{ Puccinia graminis P.
{ Puccinia jubata Ell. & Barthol.
{ Puccinia poculiformis Wettst.
Puccinia graminis P., var. Avenae Erikss. & Henn.
Puccinia graminis P., var. Secalis Erikss. & Henn.
Puccinia graminis P., var. Tritici Erikss. & Henn.
Puccinia graminis P., var. Tritici-compacti Stakman & Piemeisel.
{ Dicaeoma Impatientis Arth.
{ Puccinia Impatientis Arth.
{ Dicaeoma montanense (Ell.) O. Kuntze.
{ Puccinia montanensis Ell.
Sclerotium rhizodes Awd.
Scolecotrichum graminis Fckl.
Septoria gramineum Desm.
Septoria Passerinii Sacc.
Urocystis Agropyri (Preuss) Schrt.
{ Nigredo Jacksonii (Arth. & Fromme) Arth.
{ Uromyces Jacksonii Arth. & Fromme.
{ Nigredo mystica Arth.
{ Uromyces Hordei Tracy.
{ Uromyces mysticus Arth.
Ustilago lorentziana Thm.
Hordeum maritimum With.
Ustilago Hordei (P.) Kellerm. & Swingle.
Ustilago lorentziana Thm.
Hordeum montanense Scribn.
Puccinia anomala Rostr.
Dicaeoma Hordei (Fckl.) Arth. & Fromme.
Hordeum murinum L.
Helminthosporium sativum Pammel, King, & Bakke.
Ophiobolus cariceti (B. & Br.) Sacc.
Puccinia anomala Rostr.
{ Dicaeoma glumarum (Erikss. & Henn.) Arth.
{ & Fromme.
{ Puccinia glumarum Erikss. & Henn.
{ Puccinia Rubigo-vera Auct. Amer. p. p.
{ Dicaeoma Hordei (Fckl.) Arth. & Fromme.
{ Puccinia Agropyri N. Am. Ured. *1740*.
{ Puccinia Hordei Fckl.
Ustilago lorentziana Thm.
Hordeum nodosum L.
Erysiphe graminis DC. †
Puccinia anomala Rostr.

Hordeum nodosum (*cont.*)
  Puccinia Clematidis Lagerh.
  { Dicaeoma glumarum (Erikss. & Henn.) Arth.
  { & Fromme.
  { Puccinia glumarum Erikss. & Henn.
  { Dicaeoma poculiforme (Wettst.) O. Kuntze.
  { Puccinia graminis P.
  { Puccinia poculiformis Wettst.
  Puccinia graminis P., var. Avenae Erikss. &
    Henn.
  Puccinia graminis P., var. Tritici Erikss. &
    Henn.
  { Dicaeoma Hordei (Fckl.) Arth. & Fromme.
  { Puccinia Rubigo-vera Syd. Ured. *1780.*
  Puccinia montanensis Ell.?
  Scolecotrichum graminis Fckl.
  Tilletia texana Long.
  { Nigredo Jacksonii (Arth. & Fromme) Arth.
  { Uromyces Jacksonii Arth. & Fromme.
  Nigredo mystica Arth.
  Ustilago Holwayi Diet.
  Ustilago lorentziana Thm.
Hordeum pusillum Nutt.
  Erysiphe graminis DC. †
  Ophiobolus cariceti (B. & Br.) Sacc.
  { Dicaeoma glumarum (Erikss. & Henn.) Arth.
  { & Fromme.
  { Puccinia glumarum Erikss. & Henn.
  Puccinia Rubigo-vera Auct. Amer. p. p.
  Puccinia graminis P., var. Avenae Erikss. &
    Henn.
  Puccinia graminis P., var. Secalis Erikss. &
    Henn.
  Puccinia graminis P., var. Tritici Erikss. &
    Henn.
  Tilletia texana Long.
  Uromyces Hordei Tracy.
  Ustilago lorentziana Thm.
Hordeum secalinum Schreb.
  Erysiphe graminis DC. †
  Puccinia graminis P.
  Puccinia Rubigo-vera Auct. Amer. p. p.
  Uromyces Dactylidis Otth.
  Uromyces Hordei Tracy.
Hordeum tetrastichon L.
  { Dicaeoma poculiforme (Wettst.) O. Kuntze.
  { Puccinia graminis P.
Hordeum trifurcatum Jacq.
  Ustilago Hordei (P.) Kellerm. & Swingle.
Hordeum vulgare L.
  Chaetomium contortum Pk.
  Cladosporium graminum Cda.
  Claviceps purpurea (Fr.) Tul.
  { Colletotrichum cereale Manns.
  { Colletotrichum graminicola (Ces.) G. W. Wil-
  { son.
  Dilophospora graminis Desm.
  Erysiphe graminis DC. †

Fusarium arcuosporum Sherb.
Fusarium arthrosporioides Sherb.
Fusarium culmorum (W. G. Sm.) Sacc.
Fusarium culmorum (W. G. Sm.) Sacc., var.
  leteius Sherb.
Fusarium heterosporum Nees.
Fusarium roseum Lk.
Gibberella Saubinetii (Mont.) Sacc.
Helminthosporium avenaceum M. A. Curtis.
Helminthosporium californicum Mackie &
  & Paxton.
{ Helminthosporium gramineum Rabh.
{ ?Helminthosporium inconspicuum C. & E.
Helminthosporium sativum Pammel, King, &
  Bakke.
Helminthosporium teres Sacc.
Marasmius Tritici P. A. Young.
Oidium monilioides Lk.
{ Ophiobolus cariceti (B. & Br.) Sacc.
{ Ophiobolus graminis Sacc.
Papulospora polyspora Hotson.
Periconia pycnospora Fres.
Pleospora gramineum Auct.
Pyrenophora teres (Died.) Drechsler.
Rhynchosporium graminicola Heinsen.
Rhynchosporium Secalis (Oud.) J. J. Davis.
{ Sclerotinia libertiana Fckl.
{ Sclerotinia sclerotiorum (Lib.) Schrt.
Scolecotrichum graminis Fckl.
Septoria graminum Desm.
Septoria Passerinii Sacc.

USTILAGINALES

Tilletia texana Long.
{ Uredo segetum S. Syn. Car. 483 p. p.
{ Ustilago Carbo Auct. Amer. p. p.
{ Ustilago Hordei (P.) Kellerm. & Swingle.
{ Ustilago segetum Auct. p. p.
{ Ustilago segetum, var. Hordei N. A. F. *1091.*
?Ustilago levis Auct. p. p.
{ Ustilago nuda (Jensen) Kellerm. & Swingle.
{ Ustilago segetum Ditm. p. p.
Ustilago Holwayi Diet.
Ustilago lorentziana Thm.

UREDINALES

{ Dicaeoma anomalum (Rostr.) Arth. & Fromme.
{ Puccinia anomala Rostr.
{ ?Puccinia graminis, var. simplex Selby.
{ ?Puccinia Rubigo-vera, var. simplex Auct.
{ Puccinia simplex (Körn.) Erikss. & Henn.
{ Puccinia straminis, var. simplex Körn.
{ Puccinia Asperifolii Rabh.
{ Puccinia Rubigo-vera Wint. p. p.
Puccinia coronata Cda.
{ Dicaeoma Clematidis (Lagerh.) Arth.
{ Puccinia Clematidis Lagerh.
{ Puccinia Elymi Westd.

Hordeum vulgare (*cont.*)

Dicaeoma glumarum (Erikss. & Henn.) Arth.
& Fromme.
Puccinia glumarum Erikss. & Henn.
Puccinia Rubigo-vera Auct. Amer. p. p.

Puccinia glumarum, var. Hordei Erikss.

Dicaeoma poculiforme (Wettst.) O. Kuntze.
Puccinia graminis P.
Puccinia poculiformis Wettst.

Puccinia graminis P., var. Avenae Erikss. &
Henn.

Puccinia graminis P., var. Hordei Freeman &
Johnson.

Puccinia graminis P., var. Tritici-compacti
Stakman & Piemeisel.

Puccinia Rubigo-vera, var. Tritici Carl.

Elymus ambiguus Vasey & Scrib.

Dicaeoma Clematidis (Lagerh.) Arth.
Puccinia Clematidis Lagerh.
Puccinia Elymi Westd.
Puccinia montanensis N. Am. Uredinales *952*.

Elymus americanus Vasey & Scrib.
See Elymus glaucus Buckl.

Elymus arenarius L.

Dicaeoma Clematidis (Lagerh.) Arth.
Puccinia Clematidis Lagerh.

Elymus arenarius L., var. **villosus** E. Mey.

Cladosporium graminum Cda.
Leptosphaeria arundinacea (Sow. ex Fr.) Sacc.
Lophodermium arundinaceum (Schrad. ex Fr.)
Chev.
Mollisia graminis Karst.
Pyrenopeziza Karstenii Sacc.
Phyllachora graminis (P. ex Fr.) Fckl.
Pleospora macrospora Schrt.
Pleospora vagans Niessl.
Pleospora vagans Niessl., var. arenaria Niessl.
Puccinia glumarum, var. Elymi Hungerford
& Owens.
Sphaerella pusilla Awd.
Urocystis Agropyri (Preuss) Schrt.

Elymus arenicola Scribn. & Smith.

Dicaeoma procerum (Diet. & Holw.) O.
Kuntze.
Puccinia procera Diet. & Holw.

Elymus australis Scribn. & Ball.

Dicaeoma Clematidis (Lagerh.) Arth.
Dicaeoma poculiforme (Wettst.) O. Kuntze.
Puccinia graminis P.

Elymus brachystachys Scribn. & Ball.

Dicaeoma Clematidis (Lagerh.) Arth.
Phyllachora graminis (P. ex Fr.) Fckl.
Puccinia graminis, var. Tritici Erikss. & Henn.

Elymus canadensis L.

Elymus canadensis Auct. Amer. saltem p. p.

Acrospermum compressum Tode ex Fr.
Claviceps purpurea (Fr.) Tul.
Spermoedia clavus (DC.) ex Fr.

Epichloe typhina (Fr.) Tul.
Erysiphe graminis DC. †
Helminthosporium sativum Pammel, King, &
Bakke.
Leptosphaeria culmicola (Fr.) Karst.
Leptosphaeria culmifraga, var. minuscula
Rehm.
Leptosphaeria culmorum Awd.
Leptosphaeria Elymi Atk.
Lophiostoma clavisporum Ell. & Ev.
Phyllachora graminis (P. ex Fr.) Fckl.
Piricularia parasitica Ell. & Ev.

Dicaeoma apocryptum (Ell. & Tracy) O.
Kuntze.
Puccinia apocrypta Ell. & Tracy.
Puccinia montanensis Fung. Columb. *1859*.

Dicaeoma Clematidis (Lagerh.) Arth.
Puccinia Agropyri Ell. & Ev.
Puccinia Clematidis Lagerh.
Puccinia Elymi Westd.

Dicaeoma Rhamni (Wettst.) O. Kuntze.
Puccinia coronata Cda.

Dicaeoma glumarum (Erikss. & Henn.) Arth.
& Fromme.
Puccinia glumarum Erikss. & Henn.
Puccinia Rubigo-vera Auct. Amer. p. p.

Puccinia graminis P.

Dicaeoma montanense (Ell.) O. Kuntze.
Puccinia apocrypta Auct. Amer. p. p.
Puccinia montanensis Ell.

Dicaeoma Impatientis Arth.
Puccinia Rubigo-vera Auct. Amer. p. p.

Septoria Elymi Ell. & Ev.
Sphaerulina divergens Rehm.
Stagonospora arenaria Sacc.

Urocystis Agropyri (Preuss) Schrt.
Urocystis occulta Auct. Amer. p. p.

Ustilago hypodytes (Schl.) Fr.
Ustilago macrospora Desm.
Ustilago striiformis (Westd.) Niessl.

Elymus canadensis, var. **glaucifolius** ((Muhl.)
Gray.

Puccinia Impatientis Arth.
Puccinia poculiformis Wettst.

Tilletia striiformis (Westd.) Wint.
Ustilago striiformis (Westd.) Niessl.

Elymus condensatus Presl.

Claviceps purpurea (Fr). Tul.
Cyathicula alpina Ell. & Ev.
Cylindrosporium infuscans Ell. & Ev.
Erysiphe graminis DC.†

Dicaeoma Clematidis (Lagerh.) Arth.
Puccinia Agropyri Ell. & Ev.
Puccinia Clematidis Lagerh.

Puccinia glumarum Erikss. & Henn.
Puccinia Rubigo-vera Auct. Amer. p. p.

Dicaeoma poculiforme (Wettst.) O. Kuntze.
Puccinia graminis P.
Puccinia poculiformis Wettst.

Elymus condensatus (*cont.*)
  Puccinia graminis P., var. Avenae Erikss. &
    Henn.
  Puccinia graminis P., var. Tritici Erikss. &
    Henn.
  Puccinia graminis P., var. Tritici-compacti
    Stakman & Piemeisel.
  Puccinia Impatientis Arth.
  { Dicaeoma montanense (Ell.) O. Kuntze.
  { Puccinia montanensis Ell.
  { Dicaeoma pattersonianum (Arth.) Arth. &
  {   Fromme.
  { Puccinia pattersoniana Arth.
  { Dicaeoma procerum (Diet. & Holw.) O.
  {   Kuntze.
  { Puccinia procera Diet. & Holw.
  Urocystis Agropyri (Preuss) Schrt.
  Ustilago hypodytes (Schl.) Fr.

Elymus curvatus Piper.

Elymus diversiglumis Scribn. & Ball.
  Dicaeoma Clematidis (Lagerh.) Arth.

Elymus dahuricus Turcz.
  Puccinia procera Diet. & Holw.

Elymus flavescens Scribn. & Smith.

Elymus glabriflorus (Vasey) Scribn. & Ball.
  Dicaeoma poculiforme (Wettst.) O. Kuntze.

Elymus glaucus Buckl.
  { Dicaeoma apocryptum (Ell. & Tracy) O.
  {   Kuntze.
  { Puccinia apocrypta Ell. & Tracy.
  Puccinia montanensis Fung. Utah *234.*
  { Dicaeoma Clematidis (Lagerh.) Arth.
  { Puccinia Clematidis Lagerh.
  Puccinia Rubigo-vera West Am. Fung. *366,*
    367.
  { Dicaeoma glumarum (Erikss. & Henn.) Arth.
  {   & Fromme.
  { Puccinia glumarum Erikss. & Henn.
  Puccinia Rubigo-vera Auct. Amer. p. p.
  { Dicaeoma poculiforme (Wettst.) O. Kuntze.
  { Puccinia graminis P.
  Puccinia graminis P., var. Tritici-compacti
    Stakman & Piemeisel.
  { Dicaeoma montanense (Ell.) O. Kuntze.
  { Puccinia montanensis Ell.
  Puccinia Rubigo-vera Fung. Utah *139.*
  Puccinia procera Diet. & Holw.
  Scolecotrichum graminis Fckl.
  Tilletia Elymi Diet. & Holw.
  Ustilago hypodytes (Schl.) Fr.
  Ustilago striiformis (Westd.) Niessl.

Elymus hirsutiglumis Scribn.
  Leptosphaeria culmifraga (Fr.) Ces. & De Not.
  Puccinia poculiformis Wettst.
  Puccinia Rubigo-vera Auct. Amer. p. p.

Elymus Howellii Scribn. & Merr.
  Dicaeoma Clematidis (Lagerh.) Arth.

Elymus innovatus Beal.
  Claviceps purpurea (Fr.) Tul.
  Dicaeoma Rhamni (Wettst.) O. Kuntze.
  Ophiobolus cariceti (B. & Br.) Sacc.

Elymus Macounii Vasey.
  Claviceps purpurea (Fr.) Tul.
  Oidium monilioides Lk.
  Puccinia Clematidis Lagerh.
  Puccinia glumarum Erikss. & Henn.
  { Dicaeoma poculiforme (Wettst.) O. Kuntze.
  { Puccinia graminis P.
  Puccinia graminis P., var. Tritici Erikss. &
    Henn.
  Puccinia graminis P., var. Tritici-compacti
    Stakman & Piemeisel.
  { Dicaeoma montanense (Ell.) O. Kuntze.
  { Puccinia montanensis Ell.

Elymus mollis Trin.
  Claviceps purpurea (Fr.) Tul.
  Lophodermium arundinaceum (Schrad. ex Fr.)
    Chev.
  Pleospora discors (Mont.) Ces. & De Not.
  Pleospora herbarum (Fr.) Rabh.
  { Dicaeoma Clematidis (Lagerh.) Arth.
  { Puccinia triarticulata B. & C.
  { Rostrupia Elymi (Westd.) Lagerh.
  { Dicaeoma procerum (Diet. & Holw.) O.
  {   Kuntze.
  { Puccinia procera Diet. & Holw.

Elymus rigidus J. G. Sm.
  Dicaeoma Clematidis (Lagerh.) Arth.
  Puccinia montanensis Ell.

Elymus robustus Scribn. & Sm.
  Claviceps purpurea (Fr.) Tul.
  Epichloe typhina (P. ex Fr.) Tul.
  Erysiphe graminis DC. †
  Phyllachora graminis (P. ex Fr.) Fckl.
  Puccinia graminis P.
  Puccinia graminis P., var. Secalis Erikss. &
    Henn.
  Puccinia graminis P., var. Tritici Erikss. &
    Henn.
  Puccinia Impatientis Arth.
  Puccinia Rubigo-vera Fung. Columb. *2071.*
  Scolecotrichum graminis Fckl.
  Urocystis Agropyri (Preuss) Schrt.
  { Ustilago macrospora Desm.
  { Ustilago striiformis (Westd.) Niessl.

Elymus striatus Willd.
  Acrospermum graminum Lib.
  Claviceps purpurea (Fr.) Tul.
  Erysiphe graminis DC. †
  Phyllachora graminis (P. ex Fr.) Fckl.
  Dicaeoma Clematidis (Lagerh.) Arth.
  { Puccinia glumarum Erikss. & Henn.
  { Puccinia Rubigo-vera Auct. Amer. p. p.
  { Dicaeoma poculiforme (Wettst.) O. Kuntze.
  { Puccinia graminis P.

Elymus striatus (*cont.*)
{ Dicaeoma Impatientis Arth.
  Puccinia Impatientis Arth.
{ Dicaeoma montanense (Ell.) O. Kuntze.
  Puccinia montanensis Ell.
  Puccinia Rubigo-vera Auct. Amer. p. p.
  Urocystis Agropyri (Preuss) Schrt.
  Ustilago hypodytes (Schl.) Fr.
Elymus triticoides Buckl
  Claviceps purpurea (Fr.) Tul.
Elymus vancouverensis Vasey.
  Puccinia Elymi Westd.
Elymus virescens Piper.
  Claviceps purpurea (Fr.) Tul.
{ Dicaeoma Clematidis (Lagerh.) Arth.
  Puccinia Elymi Westd.
Elymus virginicus L.
  Ascochyta Elymi Tehon & Daniels.
  Claviceps purpurea (Fr.) Tul.
  Cytodiplospora elymina J. J. Davis.
{ Epichloe typhina (P. ex Fr.) Tul.
  Typhodium typhinum (P. ex Fr.) Seaver.
  Erysiphe graminis DC. †
  Fusarium heterosporum Nees ex Fr.
  Helminthosporium giganteum Heald & Wolf.
  Lophiostoma Elymi Dearness.
  Ophiobolus cariceti (B. & Br.) Sacc.
  Phyllachora Elymi C. R. Orton.
{ Phyllachora graminis (P. ex Fr.) Fckl.
  Sphaeria graminis P. ex Fr.
  Piricularia parasitica Ell. & Ev.
{ Dicaeoma apocryptum (Ell. & Tracy) O.
    Kuntze.
  Puccinia apocrypta Ell. & Tracy.
  ?Dicaeoma Asperifolii (P.) O. Kuntze.
{ Dicaeoma Clematidis (Lagerh.) Arth.
  Puccinia Agropyri Ell. & Ev.
  Puccinia Clematidis Lagerh.
  Puccinia Elymi Westd.
  Puccinia montanensis Fung. Columb. *1969*.
  Puccinia Rubigo-vera Syd. Ured. *1380*.
  Puccinia glumarum Erikss. & Henn.
{ Dicaeoma poculiforme (Wettst.) O. Kuntze.
  Puccinia graminis P.
  Puccinia poculiformis Wettst.
  Puccinia graminis P., var. Tritici Erikss. &
    Henn.
{ Dicaeoma Impatientis Arth.
  Puccinia Elymi-Impatientis J. J. Davis.
  Puccinia Impatientis Arth.
  Puccinia montanensis N. Am. Uredinales *556*.
  Puccinia Rubigo-vera J. J. Davis, p. p.
{ Dicaeoma montanense (Ell.) O. Kuntze.
  Puccinia apocrypta N. Am. Uredinales *22*.
  Puccinia montanensis Ell.
  Rhopographus nucleatus Dearness.
  Scolecotrichum graminis Fckl.
  Septoria Bromi Sacc.
  Septoria Bromi Sacc., var. elymina J. J. Davis

Telimena Elymi Orton ex House.
Urocystis Agropyri (Preuss) Schrt.
Uromyces graminicola Burrill.
Ustilago striiformis (Westd.) Niessl.
Vermicularia affinis Sacc. & Briard.
Elymus sp. indet.
{ Clathrospora planispora (Ell.) Berl.
  Pleospora planispora Ell.
  Cytodiplospora elymina J. J. Davis.
  Epicoccum vulgare Cda.
  Fusarium culmorum, var. leteius Sherb.
  Leptosphaeria Elymi Atk.
  Leptosphaeria Michotii (Westd.) Sacc.
  Lophiostoma clavisporum Ell. & Ev.
{ Mycosphaerella baptisiicola (Cke.) Earle.
  Sphaerella baptisiicola (Cke.) Sacc.
  Sphaeria baptisiicola Cke.
Sitanion californicum J. G. Sm.
{ Dicaeoma Clematidis (Lagerh.) Arth.
  Puccinia Clematidis Lagerh.
  Ustilago hypodytes (Schl.) Fr.
  Ustilago lorentziana Thm.
Sitanion Hystrix (Nutt.) J. G. Sm.
{ Dicaeoma apocryptum (Ell. & Tracy) O.
    Kuntze.
  Puccinia apocrypta Ell. & Tracy.
  Dicaeoma Clematidis (Lagerh.) Arth.
  Puccinia Agropyri Ell. & Ev.
  Puccinia Clematidis Lagerh.
  Puccinia Elymi Westd.
  Puccinia montanensis Fung. Columb. *2567*.
{ Dicaeoma glumarum (Erikss. & Henn.) Arth.
    & Fromme.
  Puccinia glumarum Erikss. & Henn.
  Puccinia glumarum Erikss. & Henn., var.
    Tritici Erikss. & Henn.
{ Dicaeoma poculiforme (Wettst.) O. Kuntze.
  Puccinia graminis P.
{ Dicaeoma montanense (Ell.) O. Kuntze.
  Puccinia montanensis Ell.
  Ustilago hypodytes (Schl.) Fr.
  Ustilago lorentziana Thm.
Sitanion jubatum J. G. Sm.
{ Dicaeoma Clematidis (Lagerh.) Arth.
  Puccinia Clematidis Lagerh.
{ Dicaeoma glumarum (Erikss. & Henn.) Arth.
    & Fromme.
  Puccinia glumarum Erikss. & Henn.
{ Dicaeoma pattersonianum (Arth.) Arth. &
    Fromme.
  Puccinia pattersoniana Arth.
Sitanion rigidum J. G. Sm.
{ Puccinia Clematidis Lagerh.
  Puccinia Elymi Westd.
Asperella Hystrix (L.) Humb.
  Claviceps purpurea (Fr.) Tul.
{ Epichloe typhina (P. ex Fr.) Tul.
  Typhodium typhinum (P. ex Fr.) Seaver.
  Leptosphaeria culmicola (Fr.) Karst.

Asperella Hystrix (*cont.*)
  Phyllachora graminis (P. ex Fr.) Fckl.
  Phyllachora graminis (P. ex Fr.) Fckl., var.
    Hystricis Rehm.
  Piricularia parasitica Ell. & Ev.
  { Dicaeoma Clematidis (Lagerh.) Arth.
  { Puccinia Clematidis Lagerh.
  Puccinia Elymi Westd.
  Puccinia glumarum Erikss. & Henn.
  { Dicaeoma poculiforme (Wettst.) O. Kuntze.
  { Puccinia graminis P.
  Puccinia graminis P., var. Avenae Erikss. &
    Henn.
  Puccinia graminis P., var. Secalis Erikss. &
    Henn.
  Puccinia graminis P., var. Tritici Erikss. &
    Henn.
  { Dicaeoma Impatientis Arth.
  { Puccinia apocrypta J. J. Davis non Ell. &
    Tracy.
  { Puccinia Impatientis Arth.
  Puccinia Rubigo-vera Auct. Amer. p. p.
  { Dicaeoma montanense (Ell.) O. Kuntze.
  { Puccinia apocrypta Barthol. Uredinales *327*.
  { Puccinia montanensis Ell.
  Scolecotrichum graminis Fckl.
  Septoria microspora Eli.

Arundinaria macrosperma Michx.
  (For A. macrosperma Auct. Amer., see
    Arundinaria sp. indet.)
  { Apiospora apiospora (Dur. & Mont.) Underw.
    & Earle.
  { Apiospora Montagnei Sacc.
  { Sphaeria apiospora Dur. & Mont.
  { Belonidium Arundinariae (B. & C.) Massee.
  { Belonium? eustegiiformis (B. & C.) Sacc.
  { Peziza Arundinariae B. & C.
  { Peziza eustegiiformis B. & C.
  { Pyrenopeziza Arundinariae (B. & C.) Sacc.
  Coniosporium Arundinis (Cda.) Sacc.
  { Didymella eumorpha (B. & C.) Sacc.
  { Didymosphaeria eumorpha (B. & C.) Atk.
  { Leptosphaeria eumorpha (B. & C.) Earle.
  { Sphaeria arundinacea Rav. non Sow.
  { Sphaeria eumorpha B. & C.
  Didymosphaeria Arundinariae Ell. & Ev.
  Dothidella minima Sacc. & Syd.
  { Echinodothis tuberiformis (B. & Rav.) Atk.
  { Hypocrea tuberiformis B. & Rav.
  { Hypocrella tuberiformis (B. & Rav.) Atk.
  Hypoderma scirpinum DC.
  { Dicaeoma Arundinariae (S.) O. Kuntze.
  { Puccinia Arundinariae S.
  Sclerotium sacidioides Speg.

Arundinaria tecta (Walt.) Muhl.
  Belonium eustegiiformis (B. & C.) Sacc.
  Cercospora scolecotrichoides Atk.
  Chaetosphaeria brevispinosa Atk.

Coniosporium Arundinellae Ell. & Tracy.
Dacryomyces epiphyllus S.
{ Dussiella tuberiformis (B. & Rav.) Pat.
{ Echinodothis tuberiformis (B. & Rav.) Atk.
{ Hypocrea tuberiformis B. & Rav.
Hypoxylon perforatum (S.) Fr.
Leptosphaeria eumorpha (B. & C.) Earle.
Leptothyrium cylindricum Atk.
Meliola tenuis B. & C.
{ Mycosphaerella Arundinariae (Atk.) Earle.
{ Sphaerella Arundinariae Atk.
{ Dicaeoma Arundinariae (S.) O Kuntze.
{ Puccinia Arundinariae S.
{ Puccinia Phragmitis Underw. & Earle.   •
Scleroderris Arundinariae Atk.
Scolecotrichum graminis Fckl.
Stictis helicotricha Ell. & Ev.
Tetraploa Ellisii Cke.
Volutella tecticola Atk.

Arundinaria sp. indet.
  (including A. macrosperma Auct. Amer. p. p.)
  Acrocystis mirabilis B. & Br.
  { Acrothecium crustaceum (S.) Sacc.
  { Dactylium crustaceum S.
  Anthostomella albocincta Ell. & Ev.
  Asteroma Robergei Desm., var. Arundinariae
    Sacc.
  Aulographum Arundinariae Cke.
  Botryosphaeria Arundinariae Earle.
  Botrytis pallida B. & C.
  Calonectria Curtisii (B.) Sacc.?
  Cladosporium compactum B. & C.
  Colletotrichum graminicola (Ces.) G. W.
    Wilson.
  Cyphella Langloisii Burt.
  Dothidea graminis (P.) ex Fr.
  { Epicoccum simplex B. & C.
  { Epicoccum sphaerospermum B. & C.
  { Diatrype consobrina N. A. F. *2125* nec Mont.
  { Eutypella Arundinariae Berl.
  Gymnosporium inquinans B.
  Helicoma Berkeleyi M. A. Curtis.
  { Heptameria arundinacea (Sow. ex Fr.) Cke.
  { Leptosphaeria arundinacea (Sow. ex Fr.) Sacc.
  { Sphaeria arundinacea Sow. ex Fr.
  { Sphaeria striiformis, var. Arundinis A. & S. ex
    Fr.
  Hypoxylon culmorum Cke.
  { Hysterium arundinaceum Schrad. ex Fr.
  { Lophodermium arundinaceum (Schrad. ex Fr.)
    Chev.
  Lophodermium culmigenum (Fr.) Karst.
  { Macrophoma erumpens (B. & C.) Berl. & Vogl.
  { Phoma erumpens B. & C.
  Melanconium arundinaceum Ell. & Ev.
  Melanconium circumscissum Grove.
  { Melanconium sphaerospermum (P. ex Fr.) Lk.
  { Stilbospora sphaerosperma P.

Arundinaria sp. indet. (*cont.*)
{ Metasphaeria? Arundinariae (Cke.) Sacc.
{ Stigmatea Arundinariae Cke.
{ Metasphaeria rimularum (Cke.) Sacc.
{ Sphaeria rimularum Cke.
Physalospora conica Ell. & Ev.
Rosellinia geasteroides Ell. & Ev.
Stigmatea sclerotidea Cke.
Trichosphaeria Arundinariae Ell. & Ev.
Trichosphaeria Underwoodii Earle.
Ustilago hypodytes (Schl.) Fr.
{ Diatrype pustulans Ell. & Ev.
{ Valsaria pustulans (Ell. & Ev.) Sacc.

Arthrostylidium brevifolium Auct.
Arthrostylidium sarmentosum Pilger.
Dimeriopsis arthrostylidicola F. L. Stevens.
Phyllachora graminis (P. ex Fr.) Fckl.

Arthrostylidium multispicatum Pilger.
Gloniella rubra F. L. Stevens.

Arthrostylidium sp. indet.
Eutypa linearis Rehm.
Hypoxylon culmorum Cke.
Rosellinia amblystoma Berl. & Sacc.

Phyllostachys aurea A. & C. Riviere.
Phyllostachys Newinii Hance var. **hupehensis.**
{ Dicaeoma melanocephalum (Syd.) Arth. &
{   Fromme.
{ Puccinia melanocephala Syd.

Phyllostachys bambusoides Sieb. & Zucc.
Coniosporium Shiraianum (Syd.) Bubák.
Puccinia Arundinariae S.
{ Dicaeoma melanocephalum (Syd.) Arth. &
{   Fromme.
{ Puccinia melanocephala Syd.
Ustilago shiraiana Henn.

Phyllostachys henonis Mitford.
Phyllostachys nigra Munro.
Phyllostachys puberula Munro.
Phyllostachys Quilioi A. & C. Riviere.
Ustilago shiraiana Henn.

Phyllostachys sp. indet.
Cylindrosporium Bambusae Miyake & Hara.
Melanconium Bambusae Turconi.
Scirrhia Bambusae Turconi.

Chusquea abietifolia Griseb.
{ Ustilaginoidea strumosa (Cke.) G. P. Clinton.
{ Ustilago strumosa Cke.

Chusquea sp. indet.
Balansia chusqueicola Henn.

Bambusa arundinacea Willd.
Gymnosporium Bambusae N. A. F. *1628.*

Bambusa aureostriata Regel.
{ Dicaeoma melanocephalum (Syd.) Arth. &
{   Fromme.
{ Puccinia melanocephala Syd.

Bambusa vulgaris Schrad.
{ Dicaeoma ignavum Arth. & Fromme.
{ Puccinia (?) ignava (Arth. & Fromme) Arth.
{ Uredo ignava Arth.
{ Uredo paspalicola Auct. Amer. p. p.
Melanconium saccharinum Penz. & Sacc.
Sclerotium Rolfsii Sacc.

Bambusaceae gen. indet.
Agaricus bambusigenus B. & C.
Anthostomella Puiggarii Speg.
Ascochyta bambusicola Ciferri & Fragoso.
Balansia claviceps Speg.
Cladosporium graminum Cda.
Coniosporium Bambusae (Thm.) Sacc.
Coniosporium shiraianum (Syd.) Bubák.
Corticium Bambusae Burt.
Cyathus Poeppigii Tul.
Diplodia Bambusae Ell. & Langlois.
Eutypella linearis Viziol.
Geopetalum copulatum (Ehrenb.) Murrill.
Graphium squarrosum Ell. & Langlois.
Gymnosporium Bambusae Thm.
Hypoxylon fuscopurpureum (S.) B.
Hypoxylon perforatum (S.) Fr.
Lycogala epidendrum [Buxb. ex L.] Fr.
Macrosporium graminum Cke.
Melanconium Bambusae Turconi.
Melanconium sphaerospermum (P. ex Fr.) Lk.
Omphalopsis distantifolia Murrill.
{ Coriolus pinsitus Auct. Amer.
{ Polystictus villosus (Fr.) Cke.
Puccinia melanocephala Syd.
Schizophyllum multifidum Fr.
Solenia candida P.
Spegazzinia ornata Sacc.
Sphaerobolus stellatus (Tode) ex Fr.
Torula graminis Desm.
Ustilago shiraiana Henn.

Dendrocalamus giganteus Munro.
Puccinia (?) ignava (Arth. & Fromme) Arth.

Gramineae gen. indet.

PEZIZINEAE

Humaria Peckii House.
Lachnea rubra Phil.
{ Helotium album Cke. in Herb. Ell.
{ Helotium citrinulum Karst.
{ Pezizella citrinula (Karst.) Sacc.
{ Peziza culmicola Desm.
{ Phialea culmicola (Desm.) Gill.
{ Peziza nigrocincta B. & C.
{ Trichopeziza nigrocincta (B. & C.) Sacc.

PHACIDIINEAE

Stictis graminum Desm.

PYRENOMYCETINEAE

Byssonectria rosella Cke. & Hark.
Calonectria graminicola (B. & Br.) Wr.
Chaetomium lanosum Pk.

Gramineae gen. indet. (*cont.*)
  Chaetomium setosum Ell. & Ev.
  Claviceps pallida Pat.
  Claviceps patouillardiana Henn.
  ⎧Didymella nebraskae (B. & C.) Sacc.
  ⎩Sphaeria nebraskae B. & C.
  Erysiphe communis (Wallr.) Schl.?
  Eurotium Aspergillus-glaucus DBy.
  Hypocrea subviridis B. & C.
  ⎧Heptameria Beaumontii (B. & C.) Cke.
  ⎨Leptosphaeria Beaumontii (B. & C.) Sacc.
  ⎩Sphaeria Beaumontii B. & C.
  Leptosphaeria culmicola (Fr.) Karst.
  Leptosphaeria herpotrichoides De Not.
  Leptosphaeria Tritici (Garavaglio) Pass.
  ⎧Hysterium culmigenum Fr.
  ⎨Lophodermium arundinaceum, var. culmige-
  ⎪ num (Fr.) Fckl.
  ⎩Lophodermium culmigenum (Fr.) Karst.
  Ophiobolus herpotrichus Fr.
  ⎧Ophiobolus stictisporus (C. & E.) Sacc.
  ⎨Raphidospora stictispora C. & E.
  ⎩Sphaeria stictispora C. & E.
  Ophiobolus trechisporus Ell. & Ev.
  ⎧Dothidea delicatula S.
  ⎩Phyllachora delicatula (S.) Sacc.
  ⎧Leptosphaeria straminis Cke. & Hark.
  ⎩Pleospora Harknessii Berl. & Vogl.
  Pleospora laxa Ell. & Gall.
  Pleospora trichostoma (Fr.) Wint.
  Pyrenophora relicina Fckl.
  Rhopographus Bakeri Earle.
  Sphaerella californica Cke.
  ⎧Sphaerella coccineomaculata (S.) Cke.
  ⎩Sphaeria coccineomaculata S.
  Sphaerella perpusilla (Desm.) Sacc.
  Sphaerella philochorta Cke.
  Sphaeria subgemina B. & C.
  Xylaria clavulus B. & C.
  Xylaria graminicola Gerard.

BASIDIOMYCETES

  Bolbitius radians Morg.
  Marasmius capillaris Morg.
  Marasmius Curreyi B. & Br.
  ⎧Agaricus graminum Lib.
  ⎩Marasmius graminum (Lib.) B. & Br.
  Marasmius pruinatus B. & C.
  Marasmius subtomentosus Pk.
  ⎧Polyporus incrustans B. & C.
  ⎩Poria incrustans (B. & C.) Cke.
  Psilocybe sabulosa Pk.
  Rhizoctonia Solani Kühn.
  Thecaphora piluliformis B. & C.
  Thecaphora pustulata G. P. Clinton.
  Thelephora caesia P. ex Fr.
  Thelephora cristata (P.) ex Fr.

  Thelephora sebacea P.
  Ustilago leucoderma B. ?

FUNGI IMPERFECTI

  ⎧Amerosporium leucotrichum (Pk.) Sacc.
  ⎩Excipula leucotricha Pk.
  Arthrobotryum penicillium (Lév.) Seaver &
    Chardon.
  Ascochyta graminicola Sacc.
  Botryosporium pulchrum Cda.
  Chaetostroma graminis Ell. & Barthol.
  Cladosporium graminum Cda.
  Cladosporium herbarum (P.) ex Lk.
  Coelosporium fruticulosum Lk.
  Colletotrichum lineola, var. pachyspora Ell. &
    Kellerm.
  Colletotrichum sanguineum Ell. & Halsted.
  Cryptosporium atrum Lk.
  Dictyosporium opacum Cke. & Hark.
  Dinemasporium cruciferum Ell.
  Dinemasporium strigosum (Fr.) Sacc.
  Excipula hispidula (Schrad. ex Fr.) C. & E.
  Fusarium avenaceum (Fr.) Sacc.
  Fusarium moniliforme Sheldon.
  Fusarium rubiginosum App. & Wr.
  Fusarium subulatum App. & Wr.
  Fusicladium Alopecuri Ell. & Ev.
  Fusisporium foeni B. & Br.
  Helminthosporium Avenae Eidam.
  Helminthosporium Cyclops Drechsler.
  Helminthosporium gramineum Rabh.
  ?Helminthosporium septemseptatum Pk.
  ⎧Helminthosporium teres Sacc.
  ⎩Pyrenophora teres (Diedicke) Drechsler.
  Hendersonia herpotricha Sacc.
  Hymenopsis trochiloides Sacc.
  Illosporium helicoideum Sacc. & Ell.
  Leptostroma cereale S.
  Macrosporium pinguedinis B.
  ⎧Gloeosporium graminicola Ell. & Ev.
  ⎨Marssonia graminicola (Ell. & Ev.) Sacc.
  ⎩Marssonina graminicola (Ell. & Ev.) Magn.
  Myrothecium Verrucaria (A. & S.) Ditm. ex Fr.
  Mystrosporium Rubigo B. & C.
  Penicillium sparsum Lk.
  Periconia lateralis Ell. & Ev.
  Vermicularia hispidula (Lk.) S.
  ⎧Sphaeria relicina Fr.
  ⎩Vermicularia relicina Fr.
  Vermicularia straminis Cke. & Hark.
  Verticillium pyramidale Bon.
  Volutella Ellisii Langlois.

MISCELLANEA

  Mucilago spongiosa (Leyss.) Morg.
  Physarum cinereum (Batsch) P.
  Sclerotium Semen Tode ex Fr.

CYPERACEAE

Dulichium arundinaceum (L.) Brit.
 Pestalozzia scirpina Ell. & Martin.
 ⎰Dicaeoma Asterum Arth. & Kern.
 │Dicaeoma Dulichii (Syd.) Arth.
 │Dicaeoma extensicola (Plowr.) O. Kuntze.
 │Dicaeoma Urticae Auct. Amer. p. p.
 ⎨Puccinia Asterum Kern.
 │Puccinia Caricis Auct. Amer. p. p.
 │Puccinia Dulichii Syd.
 │Puccinia extensicola Plowr.
 ⎱Puccinia striola Auct. Amer. p. p.
 Rhizoctonia dimorpha Matz.

Cyperus articulatus L.
 Puccinia canaliculata (S.) Lagerh.
 Scirrhia ostiolata Ell. & Gall.

Cyperus atropurpureus Liebm.

Cyperus Baldwinii Torr.
 ⎰Dothidea canaliculata (S.) B.
 │Phyllachora canaliculata (S.) Sacc.
 ⎨Puccinia canaliculata (S.) Lagerh.
 ⎱Sphaeria canaliculata S.

Cyperus brunneus Sw.
 Dicaeoma Cyperi-tagetiformis (Kern) Arth.

Cyperus Buckleyi Britton.
 ⎰Dicaeoma Cyperi (Arth.) O. Kuntze.
 ⎱Puccinia Cyperi Arth.

Cyperus cylindricus (Ell.) Britton.
 ⎰Dicaeoma canaliculatum (S.) O. Kuntze.
 ⎱Puccinia canaliculata (S.) Lagerh.
 ⎰Dicaeoma Cyperi (Arth.) O. Kuntze.
 │Puccinia caricina Auct. Amer. p. p.
 ⎨Puccinia Caricis Auct. Amer. p. p.
 │Puccinia Cyperi Arth.
 ⎱Puccinia Striola Auct. Amer. p. p.

Cyperus diffusus Vahl.
 ⎰Dicaeoma antioquiense (Mayor) Arth.
 ⎱Puccinia antioquiensis Mayor.

Cyperus dissitiflorus Nees.
 Dicaeoma Cyperi (Arth.) O. Kuntze.

Cyperus distans L.
 ⎰Dicaeoma Cyperi-tagetiformis (Kern) Arth.
 ⎨Puccinia canaliculata Auct. p. p.
 ⎱Puccinia Cyperi-tagetiformis Kern.

Cyperus esculentus L.
 Phyllachora Cyperi Rehm.
 ⎰Dicaeoma canaliculatum (S.) O. Kuntze.
 │Puccinia angustata Auct. p. p.
 │Puccinia canaliculata (S.) Lagerh.
 ⎨Puccinia cellulosa B. & C.
 │Puccinia Cyperi Fung. Columb. *2146*.
 ⎱Puccinia Parishii Diet. & Holw. nom. nud.

Cyperus fendlerianus Böckl.
 ⎰Dicaeoma canaliculatum (S.) O. Kuntze.
 ⎱Puccinia canaliculata (S.) Lagerh.

Cyperus ferax Rich.
 Phyllachora greciana Syd.
 ⎰Dicaeoma abreptum (Kern) Arth.
 │Puccinia abrepta Kern.
 ⎨Puccinia canaliculata Arth. Ured. Costa Rica.
 │Dicaeoma canaliculatum (S.) O. Kuntze.
 ⎨Puccinia canaliculata (S.) Lagerh.
 ⎱Puccinia Cyperi Fung. Columb. *2144*.

Cyperus filiculmis Vahl.
 Cercospora caricina Ell. & Dearness.
 Cintractia Cyperi G. P. Clinton.
 Cintractia limitata G. P. Clinton.
 ⎰Dicaeoma canaliculatum Auct. Amer. p. p.
 │Dicaeoma Cyperi (Arth.) O. Kuntze.
 │Puccinia canaliculata N. Am. Ured. *2233*.
 ⎱Puccinia Cyperi Arth.

Cyperus flavicomus Michx.
 ⎰Dicaeoma Cyperi (Arth.) O. Kuntze.
 ⎱Puccinia Cyperi Arth.
 ⎰Dicaeoma Cyperi-tagetiforme (Kern) Arth.
 ⎱Puccinia Cyperi-tagetiformis Kern.

Cyperus Gatesii Torr.
 Cintractia leucoderma (B.) Henn.

Cyperus giganteus Vahl.
 Phyllachora Cyperi Rehm.
 ⎰Dicaeoma canaliculatum (S.) O. Kuntze.
 ⎱Puccinia canaliculata (S.) Lagerh.

Cyperus globosus Aubl.
 ⎰Dicaeoma Cyperi (Arth.) O. Kuntze.
 │Puccinia Cyperi Arth.
 ⎱Puccinia nigrovelata Syd. Ured. *1177*.

Cyperus Grayii Torr.
 ⎰Cintractia axicola Cornu.
 │Cintractia axicola (B.) Cornu, var. minor G. P.
 ⎨ Clinton.
 ⎱Ustilago axicola B., var.
 ⎰Dicaeoma Cyperi (Arth.) O. Kuntze.
 ⎱Puccinia Cyperi Arth.

Cyperus Hallii Britton.
 ⎰Dicaeoma canaliculatum (S.) O. Kuntze.
 ⎱Puccinia canaliculata (S.) Lagerh.
 ?Puccinia Cyperi Arth.

Cyperus haspan L.
 Puccinia canaliculata (S.) Lagerh.
 ⎰Dicaeoma Cyperi (Arth.) O. Kuntze.
 ⎱Puccinia Cyperi Arth.

Cyperus hermaphroditus (Jacq.) Standley.
 ⎰Dicaeoma Cyperi (Arth.) O. Kuntze.
 ⎱Puccinia Cyperi Arth.

Cyperus Houghtonii Torr.
 Cercospora caricina Ell. & Dearness.
 ⎰Dicaeoma canaliculatum (S.) O. Kuntze.
 ⎨Puccinia Caricis Auct. Amer. p. p.
 ⎱Puccinia canaliculata (S.) Lagerh.
 ⎰Dicaeoma Cyperi (Arth.) O. Kuntze.
 ⎱Puccinia Cyperi Arth.

Cyperus laevigatus L.
  Puccinia canaliculata (S.) Lagerh.
  {Dicaeoma Cyperi-tagetiforme (Kern) Arth.
  {Puccinia Cyperi-tagetiformis Kern.
Cyperus lancastriensis Porter.
  {Dicaeoma Cyperi (Arth.) O. Kuntze.
  {?Puccinia canaliculata Auct. Amer. p. p.
  {Puccinia Cyperi Arth.
Cyperus ligularis L.
  Cintractia limitata G. P. Clinton
  Phyllachora viequesensis Orton & Toro.
Cyperus Mutisii (H. B. K.) Griseb.
  {Dicaeoma canaliculatum (S.) O. Kuntze.
  {Puccinia canaliculata (S.) Lagerh.
  {Dicaeoma Cyperi (Arth.) O. Kuntze.
  {Puccinia Cyperi Arth.
Cyperus odoratus L.
  {Dicaeoma Cyperi-tagetiformis (Kern) Arth.
  {?Puccinia canaliculata Auct. Amer. p. p.
  {Puccinia Cyperi-tagetiformis Kern.
Cyperus ovularis (Michx.) Torr.
  Ophiodothis atramentosa, var. Cyperi Earle.
  {Dicaeoma Cyperi (Arth.) O. Kuntze.
  {Puccinia canaliculata Auct. Amer. p. p.
  {Puccinia Cyperi Arth.
Cyperus polystachyus Rottb.
  Puccinia canaliculata (S.) Lagerh.
  {Dicaeoma Cyperi-tagetiformis (Kern) Arth.
  {Puccinia Cyperi-tagetiformis Kern.
Cyperus pseudovegetus Steud.
  {Dicaeoma Cyperi (Arth.) O. Kuntze.
  {Puccinia Cyperi Arth.
Cyperus radiatus Rottb.
  Puccinia canaliculata (S.) Lagerh.?
  {Dicaeoma Cyperi-tagetiformis (Henn.)
  { Arth.
  {Puccinia canaliculata N. Am. Ured. *1745.*
  {Puccinia Cyperi-tagetiformis (Henn.) Kern.
Cyperus refractus Engelm.
  Puccinia canaliculata (S.) Lagerh. ?
  {Dicaeoma Cyperi (Arth.) O. Kuntze.
  {Puccinia Cyperi Arth.
Cyperus reticulatus L.
  {Dicaeoma canaliculatum (S.) O. Kuntze.
  {Puccinia canaliculata (S.) Lagerh.
Cyperus retrofractus (L.) Torr.
  {Dicaeoma Cyperi (Arth.) O. Kuntze.
  {Puccinia canaliculata Auct. Amer. p. p.
  {Puccinia Cyperi Arth.
  {Puccinia nigrovelata Auct. p. p. ?
Cyperus rotundus L.
  {Corticium vagum B. & C.
  {Rhizoctonia Solani Kühn.
  Phyllachora Cyperi Rehm.
  {Dicaeoma canaliculatum (S.) O. Kuntze.
  {Puccinia canaliculata (S.) Lagerh.
  {Puccinia Cyperi N. Am. Ured. *839.*
  {Puccinia nigrovelata Ell. & Tracy.

Cyperus Schweinitzii Torr.
  Cercospora caricina Ell. & Dearness.
  Phyllachora Cyperi Rehm.
  {Dicaeoma canaliculatum (S.) O. Kuntze.
  {Phyllachora canaliculata (S.) Sacc.
  {Dicaeoma Cyperi (Arth.) O. Kuntze.
  {Puccinia caricina Auct. p. p.
  {Puccinia Caricis Auct. p. p.
  {Puccinia Cyperi Arth.
  {Puccinia striola Auct. p. p.
Cyperus seslerioides H. B. K.
  {Dicaeoma canaliculatum (S.) O. Kuntze.
  {Puccinia canaliculata (S.) Lagerh.
Cyperus spectabilis Schreb.
  {Dicaeoma Cyperi (Arth.) O. Kuntze.
  {Puccinia Cyperi Arth.
Cyperus sphacelatus Rottb.
  {Cintractia axicola, var. minor G. P. Clinton
  {Cintractia minor (G. P. Clinton) H. S. Jackson.
  Himantia stellifera Johnston.
  Puccinia canaliculata (S.) Lagerh.?
  {Dicaeoma Cyperi-tagetiformis (Kern) Arth.
  {Puccinia Cyperi-tagetiformis Kern.
Cyperus strigosus L.
  Darluca Filum (Biv.) Cast.
  {Dicaeoma Cyperi (Arth.) O. Kuntze.
  {Puccinia canaliculata N. Am. Ured. *1884.*
  {?Puccinia Caricis Auct. Amer. p. p.
  {Puccinia Cyperi Arth.
  {Uredo ustulata B. & C.
  {Dicaeoma canaliculatum (S.) O. Kuntze.
  {?Puccinia angustata Auct. p. p.
  {Puccinia canaliculata (S.) Lagerh.
  {?Puccinia cellulosa B. & C.
  {Puccinia conclusa Thm.
  {Puccinia Cyperi Fung. Columb. *2449.*
  {Puccinia indusiata Diet. & Holw.
  {Puccinia nigrovelata Ell. & Tracy.
  {Puccinia obtecta E. F. *393.*
Cyperus surinamensis Rottb.
  {Dicaeoma canaliculatum (S.) O. Kuntze.
  {Puccinia canaliculata (S.) Lagerh.
  Dicaeoma Cyperi (Arth.) O. Kuntze.
  {Dicaeoma Cyperi-tagetiformis (Kern) Arth.
  {Puccinia Cyperi-tagetiformis Kern.
Cyperus tegetiformis Roxb.
  {Kawakamia Cyperi (Miyabe & Ideta) Miyabe.
  {Peronospora Cyperi Miyabe & Ideta.
Cyperus thyrsiflorus Jungh. (?).
  {Dicaeoma canaliculatum (S.) O. Kuntze.
  {Puccinia canaliculata (S.) Lagerh.
Cyperus virens Michx.
  Balansia Cyperi Edgerton.
Cyperus sp. indet.
  Ascochyta teretiuscula Sacc. & Roum.
  {Cintractia leucoderma (B.) Henn.
  {Ustilago leucoderma B.
  Leptostroma caricinum Fr.

Cyperus sp. indet. (*cont.*)
  Meliola argentina Speg.
  Meliola circinans Earle.
  Meliola Cyperi Pat.
  Nemacyclus macularis (B. & C.) Sacc.
  Phaeodimeriella Cayaponiae (Garman) Chardon & Seaver.
  Phaeodimeriella guarapiensis (Speg.) Theissen.
  Septoria Cyperi Ell. & Ev.
  Stictis macularis B. & C.
  Testicularia Cyperi Klotzsch.
Kyllinga brevifolia Rottb.
Kyllinga odorata Vahl.
Kyllinga pumila Michx.
  ⎰Dicaeoma Cyperi (Arth.) O. Kuntze.
  ⎱Puccinia canaliculata Auct. p. p.
  ⎰Puccinia Cyperi Arth.
  Uredo Kyllingiae Henn.
Kyllinga sp. indet.
  Darluca Filum (Biv.) Cast.
Eriophorum angustifolium Roth.
  Mollisia cymbispora Rostr.
  Mollisia junciseda Karst.
  ⎰Dicaeoma angustatum (Pk.) O. Kuntze.
  ⎱Puccinia angustata Pk.
  ⎰Dicaeoma Eriophori (Thm.) O. Kuntze.
  ⎱Puccinia Eriophori Thm.
  Sphaerella perexigua Karst.
  Sphaerella wichuriana Schrt.
  Trochila ignobilis Karst.
Eriophorum callitrix Cham.
  ⎰Mycosphaerella wichuriana (Schrt.) Johans.
  ⎱Sphaerella wichuriana Schrt.
  Mollisia cymbispora Rostr.
Eriophorum chamissonis C. A. Mey.
  Septoria chamissonis Sacc. & Scalia.
  Septoria eriophorella Sacc. & Scalia.
Eriophorum polystachion L.
  Rhabdospora Drabae (Fckl.) Berl. & Vogl.
Eriophorum Scheuchzeri Hoppe.
  Leptosphaeria microscopica Karst.
  Mollisia advena Karst.
  Mollisia cymbispora Rostr.
  Niptera advena (Karst.) J. Lind.
  Rhabdospora Drabae (Fckl.) Berl. & Vogl.
  ⎰Mycosphaerella tassiana (De Not.) Johans.
  ⎱Sphaerella tassiana De Not.
  Pleospora discors (Mont.) Ces. & De Not.
  Sclerotinia vahliana Rostr.
Eriophorum tenellum Nutt.
  ⎰Dicaeoma Eriophori (Thm.) O. Kuntze.
  ⎱Puccinia Eriophori Thm.
Eriophorum virginicum L.
  Epichloe Hypoxylon Auct.
  ⎰Dicaeoma angustatum Auct. Amer. p. p.
  ⎱Dicaeoma Eriophori (Thm.) O. Kuntze.
  ⎰Puccinia angustata Auct. Amer. p. p.
  ⎱Puccinia Eriophori Thm.

Eriophorum viridi-carinatum (Engelm.) Fern.
  Leptosphaeria microscopica Karst.
  Mollisia advena Karst.
  ⎰Mollisia melatephra (Lasch) Karst.
  ⎨Niptera melatephra Rostr.
  ⎱Peziza melatephra Lasch.
  ⎰Dicaeoma angustatum Auct. Amer. p. p.
  ⎱Dicaeoma Eriophori (Thm.) O. Kuntze.
  ⎰Puccinia angustata Auct. Amer. p. p.
  ⎱Puccinia Eriophori Thm.
  Septoria Eriophori Oud.
  Sphaerella tassiana De Not.
  ⎰Mycosphaerella wichuriana Schrt.
  ⎱Sphaerella wichuriana Schrt.
  Stagonospora Eriophori Rostr.
  Stilbum Simmonsii Rostr.
Fuirena breviseta Coville.
Fuirena hispida Ell.
Fuirena simplex Vahl.
Fuirena squarrosa Michx.
  ⎰Dicaeoma Fuirenae (Cke.) O. Kuntze.
  ⎱Puccinia Fuirenae Cke.
Fuirena glomerata Auct.
Fuirena umbellata Rottb.
  ⎰Dicaeoma fuirenicola Arth.
  ⎨Puccinia fuirenicola Arth.
  ⎱Uredo Fuirenae Henn.
Scirpus affinis Roth.
  Thecaphora cornuana Fisch. & Wald.
Scirpus americanus P.
  Cladosporium herbarum (P.) ex Lk.
  Gibbera Saubinetii Mont.
  Dicaeoma angustatum (Pk.) O. Kuntze.
  ⎰Dicaeoma obtectum (Pk.) O. Kuntze.
  ⎪Puccinia canaliculata West. Am. Fung. *353*.
  ⎨Puccinia obtecta Pk.
  ⎪Puccinia Scirpi N. A. F. *1472*.
  ⎪Uredo rimosa Herb. Fr. non S.
  ⎱Uromyces wyomensis N. Am. Ured. *1999*.
  Dicaeoma Scirpi (DC.) S. F. Gray.
  ⎰Nigredo Scirpi (Burrill) Arth.
  ⎱Uromyces Scirpi Burrill.
Scirpus atrocinctus Fern.
  ⎰Dicaeoma angustatum (Pk.) O. Kuntze.
  ⎱Puccinia angustata Pk.
Scirpus atrovirens Muhl.
  Didymaria scirpina Sacc.
  Kriegeria Eriophori Bres.
  Leptostromella scirpina Pk.
  ⎰Dicaeoma angustatum (Pk.) O. Kuntze.
  ⎱Puccinia angustata Pk.
  Septogloeum dimorphum Sacc.
  Sphaeria scirpicola S. Am. Bor. *1724* an DC.
  Synchytrium Scirpi J. J. Davis.
  Uromyces Scirpi Burrill.
Scirpus caespitosus L.
  ⎰Cintractia Caricis (P.) Magn.
  ⎱Ustilago Caricis (P.) Ung.

Scirpus caespitosus (*cont.*)
  Leptosphaeria juncicola Rehm.
  {Mollisia scirpina (Pk.) Sacc.
  {Peziza scirpina Pk.
  Dicaeoma angustatum (Pk.) O. Kuntze.
  {Puccinia Scirpi DC.
  {Uredo scirpina Westd.
  Sphaerella Scirpi-lacustris Awd.
Scirpus californicus Brit.
  Dicaeoma angustatum (Pk.) O. Kuntze.
  {Dicaeoma obtectum (Pk.) O. Kuntze.
  {Puccinia obtecta Pk.
  {Nigredo Scirpi (Burrill) Arth.
  {Uromyces Scirpi Burrill.
Scirpus campestris Brit.
  {Nigredo Scirpi (Burrill) Arth.
  {Uromyces Scirpi Burrill.
Scirpus cyperinus (L.) Kunth.
  Cheiromyces stellatus B. & C.
  Leptostromella scirpina Pk.
  {Dicaeoma angustatum (Pk.) O. Kuntze.
  {Puccinia angustata Pk.
  {Puccinia Caricis Auct. Amer. p. p.
  {Puccinia Striola Auct. Amer. p. p.
  Septocylindrium scirpinum Pk.
  Nigredo Scirpi (Burrill) Arth.
Scirpus fluviatilis (Torr.) Gray.
  Leptostroma scirpinum Fr.
  Leptostromella scirpina Pk.
  {Barclayella primaria (Ell. & Ev.) Sacc.
  {Neobarclaya primaria (Ell. & Ev.) Sacc.
  {Pestalozzia primaria Ell. & Ev.
  {Dicaeoma angustatum (Pk.) O. Kuntze.
  {Puccinia angustata Pk.
  Puccinia obtecta Pk.
  {Cryptosporium Scirpi Pk.
  {Rhabdospora Peckii (Sacc.) Allescher.
  {Septoria Peckii Sacc.
  {Nigredo Scirpi (Burrill) Arth.
  {Uromyces Scirpi Burrill.
Scirpus georgianus R. M. Harper.
  {Dicaeoma angustatum (Pk.) O. Kuntze.
  {Puccinia angustata Pk.
Scirpus hudsonianus (Michx.) Fern.
  {Dicaeoma Eriophori (Thm.) O. Kuntze.
  {Puccinia Eriophori Thm.
Scirpus lineatus Michx.
  Puccinia angustata Pk.
Scirpus microcarpus Presl.
  Puccinia angustata Pk.
  Puccinia mcclatchieana Diet. & Holw.
Scirpus nanus Spreng.
  Leptosphaeria culmorum Awd.
Scirpus occidentalis (Watson) Chase.
  Clasterosporium caricinum (Fr.) S.
  Darluca Filum (Biv.) Cast.
  Hypoderma scirpinum DC.
  {Dicaeoma obtectum (Pk.) O. Kuntze.
  {Puccinia obtecta Pk.

Scirpus Olneyi Gray.
  Pestalozzia scirpina Ell. & Martin.
  {Dicaeoma obtectum (Pk.) O. Kuntze.
  {Puccinia obtecta Pk.
Scirpus pacificus Britt.
  {Nigredo Scirpi (Burrill) Arth.
  {Uromyces Scirpi Burrill.
Scirpus pallidus (Brit.) Fern.
  Leptostromella scirpina Pk.
  {Dicaeoma angustatum (Pk.) O. Kuntze.
  {Puccinia angustata Pk.
Scirpus paludosus Nels.
  Uromyces Scirpi Burrill.
Scirpus pauciflorus Lightf.
  Septoria punctoidea Karst.
Scirpus pedicellatus Fern.
  Cercosporella scirpina J. J. Davis.
  {Dicaeoma angustatum (Pk.) O. Kuntze.
  {Puccinia angustata Pk.
Scirpus polyphyllus Vahl.
  Dicaeoma angustatum (Pk.) O. Kuntze.
Scirpus robustus Pursh.
  Epicoccum sphaerospermum B. & C.
  Macrosporium Scirpi Lasch.
  Pestalozzia scirpina Ell. & Martin.
  Septoria narvisiana Sacc.
  {Nigredo Scirpi (Burrill) Arth.
  {Uromyces Scirpi Burrill.
Scirpus rubrotinctus Fern.
  {Dicaeoma angustatum (Pk.) O. Kuntze.
  {Puccinia angustata Pk.
  {Dicaeoma mcclatchieanum (Diet. & Holw.)
  { Arth.
  {Puccinia angustata Auct. Amer. p. p.
  {Puccinia mcclatchieana Diet. & Holw.
  {Puccinia Scirpi Fung. Columb. *347.*
Scirpus sylvaticus L.
  Puccinia angustata Pk.
Scirpus triqueter L.
  Sphaeria Scirporum S.
  Uromyces Junci, var. Scirpi Vize.
Scirpus validus Vahl.
  Camptoum curvatum (Kze.) ex Lk.
  Cladosporium herbarum (P.) ex Lk.
  {Dasyscypha luteodisca (Pk.) Sacc.
  {Peziza luteodisca Pk.
  Hymenopsis trochiloides Sacc.
  {Hypoderma scirpinum DC.
  {Hysterium scirpinum (DC.) ex Fr.
  Naucoria scirpicola Pk.
  {Pleospora herbarum (Fr.) Rabh.
  {Sphaeria herbarum Fr.
  {Dicaeoma obtectum (Pk.) O.Kuntze.
  {Puccinia obtecta Pk.
  {Dicaeoma Scirpi (DC.) S. F. Gray.
  {Puccinia Scirpi DC.
  Spilocaea Scirpi Lk.

Scirpus validus (*cont.*)
- Nigredo Scirpi (Cast.) Arth.
- Uromyces Scirpi Burrill.
- Uromyces sp. indet. Fraser 1912.

Scirpus sp. indet.
- Anthostoma mortuosum (Ell.) Sacc.
- Balansia Cyperi Edgerton.
- Camptoum cuspidatum Cke. & Hark.
- ?Dothidea graminis Auct. p. p.
- Hendersonia scirpicola Cke. & Hark.
- Peziza apala B. & Br.
- Phaeosphaerella scirpicola Earle.
- Puccinia punctum Auct. Amer.
- Sporocybe nigriceps Pk.
- Tetraploa scabra Hark.
- Ustilago axicola B.

Stenophyllus capillaris (L.) Britton.
- Dothidea gangraena Fr.
- Homostegia gangraena (Fr.) Wint.
- Phyllachora gangraena (Fr.) Fckl.
- Sphaeria gangraena Fr.

Eleocharis acicularis (L.) R. & S.
- Entyloma parvum J. J. Davis.

Eleocharis arenicola Torr.
- Dicaeoma Eleochardis (Arth.) O. Kuntze.

Eleocharis caribaea (Rottb.) Blake.
- Dicaeoma Eleochardis (Arth.) O. Kuntze.
- Puccinia Eleocharidis Arth.

Eleocharis cellulosa Torr.

Eleocharis flaccida (Reichenb.) Urb.
- Dicaeoma libertum (Kern) Arth.
- ?Puccinia Eleocharidis Arth.
- Puccinia liberta Kern.

Eleocharis geniculata (L.) R. Br.
- Dicaeoma libertum (Kern) Arth.
- ?Puccinia Eleocharidis Arth.
- Puccinia liberta Kern.

Eleocharis intermedia (Muhl.) Schultes.
- Dicaeoma Eleocharidis (Arth.) O. Kuntze.
- Puccinia Eleocharidis Arth.

Eleocharis interstincta (Vahl) R. & S.
- Dicaeoma incompositum Arth.
- Puccinia Eleocharidis Arth. p. p.
- Uredo incomposita Kern.

Eleocharis montana (H. B. K.) R. & S.

Eleocharis mutata (L.) R. & S.
- Dicaeoma libertum (Kern) Arth.
- ?Puccinia Eleocharidis Arth. p. p.
- Puccinia liberta Kern.

Eleocharis obtusa (Willd.) Schultes.
- Dicaeoma Eleocharidis (Arth.) O. Kuntze.
- Puccinia Eleocharidis Arth.

Eleocharis olivacea Torr.
- Nigredo Eleocharidis Arth.

Eleocharis palustris (L.) R. & S.
- Cladochytrium Heliocharidis (Fckl.) Busg.
- Claviceps nigricans Tul.
- Claviceps nigriceps Tul.
- Spermoedia nigricans (Tul.) Seaver.

- Epicoccum purpurascens Ehrenb. ex S.
- Fusarium roseum Lk.
- Physoderma Eleocharidis (Fckl.) Schrt.
- Pleospora aquatica Griffiths.
- Septoria Cyperi Ell. Ev.
- Nigredo Eleocharidis Arth.

Eleocharis tenuis (Willd.) Schultes.
- Dicaeoma Eleocharidis (Arth.) O. Kuntze.
- Puccinia Eleocharidis Arth.

Eleocharis sp. indet.
- Cladosporium herbarum (P.) ex Lk.
- Darluca Filum (Biv.) Cast.

Fimbristylis annua Roem. & Schultes.
- Cintractia axicola (B.) Cornu.

Fimbristylis autumnalis (L.) R. & S.
- Cintractia axicola (B.) Cornu.
- Ustilago axicola B.
- Ustilago Fimbristylis Thm.
- Hendersonia trimera Cke.
- Stagonospora trimera (Cke.) Sacc.

Fimbristylis diphylla (Retz.) Vahl.
- Cintractia axicola (B.) Cornu.
- Ustilago Fimbristylis Thm.
- Dicaeoma Fimbristylidis Arth.
- Puccinia Fimbristylidis Arth.

Fimbristylis ferruginea (L.) Vahl.
- Cintractia axicola (B.) Cornu.
- Puccinia Fimbristylidis Arth.
- Dicaeoma superius Arth.
- Puccinia Fimbristylidis Arth. p. p.
- Uredo superior Arth.

Fimbristylis holwayana Fern.
- Puccinia Fimbristylidis Arth.

Fimbristylis miliacea Vahl.

Fimbristylis polymorpha Bock.

Fimbristylis puberula (Michx.) Vahl.
- Dicaeoma Fimbristylidis Arth.
- Puccinia Fimbristylidis Arth.

Fimbristylis spadicea (L.) Vahl.
- Dicaeoma superius Arth.
- Uredo superior Arth.

Dichromena ciliata Vahl.
- Himantia stellifera Johnston.
- Dicaeoma (?) Dichromenae Arth.
- Uredo Dichromenae Arth.

Dichromena radicans Cham. & Schl.
- Dicaeoma (?) Dichromenae Arth.
- ?Puccinia canaliculata Arth. p. p.
- Uredo Dichromenae Arth.

Schoenus nigricans L.
- Dicaeoma Rosenii Arth.
- Puccinia Rosenii Arth.

Reedia dulcis Hort.
- Asterina tropicalis Speg.

Cladium jamaicense Crantz.
- Coniothyrium Marisci Tehon.
- Meliola amphitricha Fr.
- Meliola circinans Earle.

Cladium jamaicense *(cont.)*
  Meliola Cyperi Pat.
  {Dicaeoma Cladii (Ell. & Tracy) Arth.
  {Puccinia Cladii Ell. & Tracy.
Rynchospora alba (L.) Vahl.
  {Cintractia Montagnei (Tul.) Magn.
  {Ustilago Caricis Auct. p. p.
  {Ustilago Montagnei Tul.
  Cintractia taubertiana (Henn.) G. P. Clinton.
  {Caeomurus Rhyncosporae (Ell.) O. Kuntze.
  {Nigredo Rhyncosporae (Ell.) Arth.
  {Uromyces Rhyncosporae Ell.
Rynchospora axillaris (Lam.) Britton.
  {Cintractia taubertiana (Henn.) G. P. Clinton.
  {Ustilago taubertiana Henn.
  {Nigredo Rhyncosporae (Ell.) Arth.
  {Uromyces Rhyncosporae Ell.
Rynchospora corniculata (Lam.) Gray.
  Cintractia leucoderma (B.) Henn.
  Cintractia pachyderma Syd.
  {Dicaeoma angustatoides (R. E. Stone) Arth.
  {Puccinia angustatoides R. E. Stone.
  {Nigredo Rhyncosporae (Ell.) Arth.
  {Uromyces Rhyncosporae Ell.
Rynchospora corymbosa (L.) Britton.
  Cintractia leucoderma (B.) Henn.
  {Cintractia leucoderma (B.) Henn., var.
  { utriculicola Henn.
  {Cintractia utriculicola (Henn.) G. P. Clinton.
  Meliola circinans Earle.
  Dicaeoma angustatoides (R. E. Stone) Arth.
  {Nigredo Rhyncosporae Arth. p. p.
  {Puccinia angustatoides R. E. Stone.
  Uromyces Rhyncosporae Auct. p. p.
  {Dicaeoma consobrinum (Arth. & Holw.) Arth.
  {Puccinia consobrina Arth. & Holw.
Rynchospora cymosa Ell.
  Cintractia taubertiana (Henn.) G. P. Clinton.
Rynchospora cyperoides (Sw.) Mart.
  Cintractia leucoderma (B.) Henn.
  Guignardia Rhynchosporae F. L. Stevens.
  Himantia stellifera Johnston.
  {Dicaeoma angustatoides (R. E. Stone) Arth.
  {Nigredo Rhyncosporae Arth. p. p.
  {Puccinia angustatoides R. E. Stone.
  {Uromyces Rhyncosporae Arth. p. p. non Ell.
Rynchospora distans (Michx.) Vahl.
  {Nigredo Rhyncosporae (Ell.) Arth.
  {Uromyces Rhyncosporae Ell.
Rynchospora eximia Böck.
  Cintractia Montagnei (Tul.) Magn.
Rynchospora fascicularis (Michx.) Vahl.
  {Cintractia taubertiana (Henn.) G. P. Clinton.
  {Ustilago taubertiana Henn.
  {Nigredo Rhyncosporae (Ell.) Arth.
  {Uromyces Rhyncosporae Ell.
Rynchospora fusca (L.) Ait. f.
  Cintractia taubertiana (Henn.) G. P. Clinton.

Rynchospora gigantea Lk.
  {Cintractia krugiana Magn.
  {Cintractia leucoderma (B.) Henn.
  Meliola circinans Earle.
Rynchospora glomerata (L.) Vahl.
  Cercospora crinospora Atk.
  {Cintractia Montagnei (Tul.) Magn.
  {Ustilago Caricis Auct. p. p.
  {Ustilago Montagnei Tul., var. major Desm.
  Dicaeoma Cladii (Ell. & Tracy) Arth.
  {Nigredo Rhyncosporae (Ell.) Arth.
  {Uromyces Rhyncosporae Ell.
  Ustilago bipustulata Pk.
Rynchospora gracilenta Gray.
  Nigredo Rhyncosporae (Ell.) Arth.
Rynchospora inexpansa (Michx.) Vahl.
  Cintractia taubertiana (Henn.) G. P. Clinton.
Rynchospora macrostachya Torr.
  Amerosporium macrochaeta Ell. & Ev.
  Cintractia affinis Pk.
  {Milleria herbatica Pk.
  {Testicularia Cyperi Klotzsch.
  Uromyces Rhyncosporae Ell.
Rynchospora megalocarpa Gray.
  Meliola amphitricha Fr.
  Meliola circinans Earle.
Rynchospora miliacea Gray.
  Meliola amphitricha Fr.
Rynchospora micrantha Vahl.
Rynchospora microcarpa Baldw.
Rynchospora perplexa Britton.
  {Nigredo Rhyncosporae (Ell.) Arth.
  {Uromyces Rhyncosporae Ell.
Rynchospora polyphylla Vahl.
  {Dicaeoma consobrinum (Arth. & Holw.) Arth.
  {Puccinia consobrina Arth. & Holw.
  {Nigredo Rhyncosporae (Ell.) Arth.
  {Uromyces Rhyncosporae Ell.
Rynchospora semiplumosa Gray.
  Sorosporium Rhynchosporae Henn.
Rynchospora setacea (Berg.) Böckl.
  Cintractia leucoderma (B.) Henn.
  Cintractia Montagnei (Tul.) Magn.
  Puccinia angustatoides R. E. Stone.
  {Nigredo Rhyncosporae (Ell.) Arth.
  {Uromyces Rhyncosporae Ell.
Rynchospora tenuis Lk.
  Cintractia Montagnei (Tul.) Magn.
Rynchospora sp. indet.
  {Cintractia axicola (B.) Cornu, var. spicularum
  { Juel.
  {Testicularia Cyperi Klotzsch, var. minor Tul.
  {Uromyces Scirpi Burrill.?
Scleria Baldwinii Steud.
  {Dicaeoma scleriicola Arth.
  {Puccinia scleriicola Arth.
Scleria canescens Böckl.
  {Nigredo Scleriae (Henn.) Arth.
  {Uromyces Scleriae Henn.

Scleria cubensis Böckl.
{ Dicaeoma Scleriae (Pazschke) Arth.
{ Puccinia Scleriae (Pazschke) Arth.

Scleria hemitaphra Steud.

Scleria hirtella Sw.
{ Dicaeoma scleriicola Arth.
{ Puccinia scleriicola Arth.

Scleria lithosperma (L.) Sw.
{ Nigredo Scleriae (Henn.) Arth.
{ Uromyces Scleriae Henn.

Scleria melaleuca Schl. & Cham.
Dicaeoma Scleriae (Pazschke) Arth.
Uromyces Scleriae Henn.

Scleria microcarpa Nees.
Dicaeoma Scleriae (Pazschke) Arth.

Scleria pauciflora Muhl.
Puccinia scleriicola Arth.

Scleria pratensis Lindl.
Uromyces Scleriae Henn.

Scleria pterota Presl.
Phyllachora Scleriae Rehm.
{ Dicaeoma Scleriae (Pazschke) Arth.
{ Puccinia Scleriae (Pazschke) Arth.
{ Nigredo Scleriae (Henn.) Arth.
{ Uromyces Scleriae Henn.

Scleria setacea Poir.
Dicaeoma scleriicola Arth.
Nigredo Rhyncosporae (Ell.) Arth.

Scleria setulosa-ciliata Böckl.
{ Dicaeoma Scleriae (Pazschke) Arth.
{ Puccinia Scleriae (Pazschke) Arth.

Scleria triglomerata Michx.
Phyllachora scleriicola Miles.

Scleria verticillata Muhl.
{ Dicaeoma scleriicola Arth.
{ Puccinia scleriicola Arth.

Scleria sp. indet.
Dothiorella pseudodiblasta Ferdinandsen & Winge.
Grallomyces portoricensis F. L. Stevens.
Meliola Cyperi Pat.
Phyllachora Cyperi Rehm.
{ Ustilaginoidea sp. indet.
{ Ustilago flavonigrescens B. & C.

Kobresia caricina Willd.
{ Cintractia Caricis (P.) Magn.
{ Ustilago Caricis (P.) Ung.
Goniosporium puccinioides DC. ex Lk.
Septoria punctoidea Karst.
Sphaerella pusilla Awd.
Trochila ignobilis Karst.

Kobresia scirpina Willd.
{ Cintractia Caricis (P.) Magn.
{ Ustilago Caricis (P.) Ung.
Pleospora pentamera Karst.
Rhabdospora Drabae (Fckl.) Berl. & Vogl.
Rhabdospora groenlandica Lind.

Septoria punctoidea Karst.
Sphaerella tassiana De Not.
Trochila ignobilis Karst.

Carex abbreviata Prescott.
Nigredo perigynia (Halsted) Arth.

Carex abdita Bicknell.
{ Dicaeoma Asterum (Kern) Arth. & Kern.
{ Puccinia Asterum Kern.

Carex ablata L. H. Bailey.
Dicaeoma Grossulariae (Lagerh.) Kern.

Carex acutina L. H. Bailey.
Puccinia Grossulariae Lagerh.
Puccinia urticata Kern.

Carex adusta Boott.
{ Puccinia Caricis Auct. Amer. p. p.
{ Puccinia hieraciata H. S. Jackson.
{ Puccinia patruelis Arth.
{ Thecaphora aterrima Tul.
{ Tolyposporium aterrimum (Tul.) Diet.

Carex aenea Fern.
Dicaeoma Asterum (Kern) Arth. & Kern.
{ Dicaeoma hieraciatum (Arth.) Arth. & Kern.
{ Puccinia patruelis Arth.

Carex aestivalis M. A. Curtis.
Dicaeoma Grossulariae (Lagerh.) Kern.

Carex alata Torr.

Carex albolutescens S.

Carex alma L. H. Bailey.
{ Dicaeoma Asterum (Kern) Arth. & Kern.
{ Puccinia Asterum Kern.

Carex amplifolia Boott.
Dicaeoma Urticae (Lagerh.) O. Kuntze.

Carex angustior Mackenzie.
Dicaeoma Asterum (Kern) Arth. & Kern.

Carex aquatilis Wahlenb.
Cintractia Caricis (P.) Magn.
Pleospora pentamera Karst.
{ Dicaeoma Urticae (Lagerh.) O. Kuntze.
{ Puccinia Caricis Schrt.
{ Puccinia Garrettii Arth.
{ Puccinia Urticae Lagerh.
{ Puccinia urticata Arth.
{ Dicaeoma Grossulariae (Lagerh.) Kern.
{ Puccinia Grossulariae Lagerh.
Rhabdospora Drabae (Fckl.) Berl. & Vogl.
Puccinia minutissima Arth.
Sphaerella tassiana De Not.
Sphaerella wichuriana Schrt.
Trochila fuscella Karst.

Carex aquatilis Wahlenb., var. **stans** Drejer.
Leptosphaeria epicarecta Cke.
{ Naevia fuscella (Karst.) Lind.
{ Phacidium fuscellum Karst.
{ Trochila fuscella Karst.
{ Naevia ignobilis (Karst.) Rehm.
{ Phacidium ignobilis Karst.
{ Trochila ignobilis Karst.
Sphaerella tassiana De Not.

Carex arcta Boott.
  Dicaeoma Asterum (Kern) Arth. & Kern.
  ⎧Dicaeoma Lysimachiae O. Kuntze.
  ⎨Puccinia limosae Magn.
  ⎩Puccinia lysimachiata Kern.
Carex arctata Boott.
  Cercospora caricina Ell. & Dearness.
  Cercospora Caricis Dearness & House.
  Cercospora microstigma Sacc.
  Cladosporium caricicola Cda.
  ⎧Dicaeoma Grossulariae (Lagerh.) Kern.
  ⎪Puccinia albiperidia Arth.
  ⎨Puccinia Grossulariae Lagerh.
  ⎩Puccinia uniporula C. R. Orton.
  Nigredo perigynia (Halsted) Arth.
Carex asagrayana L. H. Bailey.
  Nigredo perigynia (Halsted) Arth.
Carex atherodes Spreng.
  Dicaeoma hieraciatum (Arth.) Arth. & Kern.
  ⎧Dicaeoma Urticae (Lagerh.) O. Kuntze.
  ⎨Puccinia Urticae Lagerh.
  ⎩Puccinia urticata Kern.
Carex athrostachya Olney.
  ⎧Dicaeoma Asterum (Kern.) Arth. & Kern.
  ⎩Puccinia Asterum Kern.
  Septoria lunelliana Sacc.
  ⎧Nigredo perigynia (Halsted) Arth.
  ⎩Uromyces perigynius Halsted.
Carex atrata L.
  Cintractia Caricis (P.) Magn.
  Schizonella melanogramma (DC.) Schrt.
  Trochila diminuens Karst.
Carex atrata L., var. **ovata** (Rudge) Boott.
  ⎧Dicaeoma Lysimachiae O. Kuntze.
  ⎨Puccinia limosae Magn.
  ⎩Puccinia lysimachiata Kern.
Carex aurea Nutt.
  Cintractia Caricis (P.) Magn.
Carex Backii Boott.
  ⎧Dicaeoma eminens (Kern) Arth. & Kern.
  ⎩Puccinia eminens Kern.
  Puccinia extensicola Plowr.
Carex Barbarae Dewey.
  Dicaeoma Grossulariae (Lagerh.) Kern.
  ⎧Puccinia Caricis Auct. Amer. p. p.
  ⎩Puccinia urticata Kern.
Carex Bebbii Olney.
  ⎧Dicaeoma Asterum (Kern) Arth. & Kern.
  ⎪Puccinia Asterum Kern.
  ⎨Puccinia Caricis Auct. p. p.
  ⎩Puccinia ludibunda Ell. & Ev.
Carex Bicknellii Brit.
  ⎧Dicaeoma Asterum (Kern) Arth. & Kern.
  ⎩Puccinia Asterum Kern.
Carex bicolor All.
  Sphaerella tassiana De Not.
Carex Bigelowii Torr. & S.
  Dicaeoma Grossulariae (Lagerh.) Kern.

Carex blanda Dewey.
  Cintractia Caricis (P.) Magn.
  ⎧Dicaeoma Caricis-Solidaginis Arth. p. p.
  ⎪Dicaeoma extensicola H. S. Jackson p. p.
  ⎪Dicaeoma Grossulariae (Lagerh.) Kern.
  ⎪Puccinia albiperidia Arth.
  ⎨?Puccinia caricina Auct. Amer. p. p.
  ⎪Puccinia Caricis Fung. Columb. 2447.
  ⎪Puccinia Grossulariae Lagerh.
  ⎪Puccinia ludibunda Fung. Columb. 1968.
  ⎩Puccinia pringsheimiana Klebahn.
  Schizonella melanogramma (DC) Schrt.
Carex Bolanderi Olney.
Carex brevior (Dewey) Mackenzie.
  ⎧Dicaeoma Asterum (Kern) Arth. & Kern.
  ⎩Puccinia Asterum Kern.
Carex bromoides Schkuhr.
  ⎧Dicaeoma Asterum (Kern) Arth. & Kern.
  ⎨Puccinia Asterum Kern.
  ⎩?Puccinia Caricis Auct. Amer. p. p.
Carex brunnescens Poir.
  ⎧Dicaeoma Grossulariae (Lagerh.) Kern.
  ⎨Puccinia Caricis Auct. Amer. p. p.
  ⎩Puccinia Grossulariae Lagerh.
  Puccinia karelica Tranz.
  ⎧Dicaeoma hieraciatum (Arth.) Arth. & Kern.
  ⎩Puccinia patruelis Arth.
  ⎧Dicaeoma Lysimachiae O. Kuntze.
  ⎩Puccinia lysimachiata Kern.
  Trochila diminuens Karst.
  Trochila ignobilis Karst.
Carex bullata Schkuhr.
  ⎧Dicaeoma Asterum (Kern) Arth. & Kern.
  ⎪?Dicaeoma Urticae Auct. Amer. p. p.
  ⎨?Puccinia Caricis Auct. Amer. p. p.
  ⎪Dicaeoma Sambuci Arth.
  ⎩Puccinia Sambuci Arth.
Carex caespitosa L.
  Cintractia Caricis (P.) Magn.
  Helotium Scutula (P.) Karst., var. suspectum
    (Nyl.) Karst.
  Trochila diminuens Karst.
Carex canescens L.
  ⎧Cintractia Caricis (P.) Magn.
  ⎪Ustilago urceolorum Tul.
  ⎨Phacidium diminuens Karst.
  ⎩Trochila diminuens Karst.
  Puccinia Asterum Kern.
  ⎧Dicaeoma Grossulariae (Lagerh.) Kern.
  ⎩Puccinia Grossulariae Lagerh.
  ⎧Dicaeoma Trientalis Arth. & Kern.
  ⎨Puccinia karelica Tranz.
  ⎩Puccinia Trientalis (Arth. & Kern) House.
Carex capillaris L.
  Hendersonia arundinacea (Desm.) Sacc.
  Septoria punctoidea Karst.
Carex capitata L.
  Trochila diminuens Karst.

Carex caryophyllea Lat.
  Cintractia Caricis (P.) Magn.
Carex castanea Wahlenb.
  Cercospora caricina Ell. & Dearness.
  {Aecidium Urticae III Auct. Amer.?
  {Puccinia Caricis Auct. Amer. p. p.?
  {Dicaeoma Grossulariae (Lagerh.) Kern.
  {Puccinia Grossulariae Lagerh.
Carex cephalantha (L. H. Bailey) Bickn.
  Dicaeoma Asterum (Kern) Arth. & Kern.
Carex cephaloidea Dewey.
  Cercospora caricina Ell. & Dearness.
  {Dicaeoma Asterum (Kern) Arth. & Kern.
  {Puccinia Asterum Kern.
  {Puccinia extensicola Plowr.
  {?Septoria caricinella Sacc. & Roum.
Carex cephalophora Muhl.
  {Dicaeoma Asterum (Kern) Arth. & Kern.
  {Dicaeoma Caricis-Asteris Arth.
  {Puccinia Asterum Kern.
  {Puccinia extensicola Plowr.
  {Dicaeoma Peckii (Kellerm.) Arth.
  {Puccinia ludibunda Ell. & Ev.
  {Puccinia Peckii Kellerm.
  Dicaeoma Grossulariae (Lagerh.) Kern.
  Septoria caricinella Sacc. & Roum.
Carex cherokeensis S.
  Volutella caricicola Miles.
Carex chordorrhiza L. f.
  {Dicaeoma Peckii (Kellerm.) Arth.
  {Puccinia Peckii Kellerm.
  Septoria caricinella Sacc. & Roum.
Carex colorata Mackenzie.
  Dicaeoma Grossulariae (Lagerh.) Kern.
Carex communis L. H. Bailey.
  {Dicaeoma Asterum (Kern) Arth. & Kern.
  {Puccinia Asterum Kern.
  {Nigredo perigynia (Halsted) Arth.
  {Uromyces perigynius Halsted.
Carex comosa Boott.
  {Dicaeoma Sambuci Arth.
  {Puccinia bolleyana Sacc.
  {Puccinia caricina Ohio Fungi *148*.
  {Puccinia Sambuci Arth.
  {Dicaeoma macrosporum (Arth.) Arth. & Kern.
  {Puccinia macrospora Arth.
  {Dicaeoma Urticae (Kern) O. Kuntze.
  {Puccinia Caricis Auct. Amer. p. p.
  {Puccinia urticata Kern.
Carex compacta R. Br.
  Phoma Caricis (Fr.) Sacc.
  Sphaerella pusilla Awd.
  Sphaerella tassiana De Not.
  {Mycosphaerella wichuriana (Schrt.) Johans.
  {Sphaerella wichuriana Schrt.
Carex complanata Torr.
Carex concolor R. Br.
  {Dicaeoma Grossulariae (Lagerh.) Kern.
  {Puccinia Grossulariae Lagerh.

Carex conjuncta Boott.
  Puccinia Opizii Arth. non Bubák.
  Sordaria caricicola Ell. & Ev.
Carex conoidea Schkuhr.
  {Dicaeoma Caricis-Solidaginis Auct. p. p.
  {Dicaeoma Grossulariae (Lagerh.) Kern.
  {Puccinia Grossulariae Lagerh.
  {Puccinia uniporula C. R. Orton.
Carex convoluta Mack.
  Schizonella melanogramma (DC.) Schrt.
Carex Crawfordii Fern.
  {Dicaeoma Asterum (Kern) Arth. & Kern.
  {Puccinia Asterum Kern.
Carex crinita Lam.
  {Cintractia Caricis (P.) Magn.
  {Ustilago urceolorum Tul.
  {Dasyscypha crinella (Ell. & Ev.) Sacc.
  {Lachnella crinella (Ell. & Ev.) Rehm.
  {Peziza crinella Ell. & Ev.
  Goniosporium puccinioides (DC.) ex Lk.
  {Phyllachora Caricis (Fr.) Sacc.
  {Sphaeria Caricis Fr.
  {Dicaeoma Grossulariae (Lagerh.) Kern.
  {Puccinia albiperidia Arth.
  {Puccinia Grossulariae Lagerh.
  {Dicaeoma Sambuci Arth.
  {Puccinia Sambuci Arth.
  {Dicaeoma Urticae (Lagerh.) O. Kuntze.
  {Puccinia Caricis Auct. Amer. p. p.
  {Puccinia caricina Auct. Amer. p. p.
  {?Puccinia striola Auct. Amer. p. p.
  {Puccinia Urticae Lagerh.
  {Puccinia urticata Kern.
Carex cristata S.
  {Dicaeoma Asterum (Kern) Arth. & Kern.
  {Puccinia Asterum Kern.
  {Nigredo perigynia (Halsted) Arth.
  {Uromyces caricinus Ell. & Ev.
  {Uromyces perigynius Halsted.
Carex Crus-corvi Shuttlw.
  {Dicaeoma Sambuci Arth.
  {Puccinia Sambuci Arth.
Carex cryptolepis Mackenzie.
  Dicaeoma Urticae (Lagerh.) O. Kuntze.
Carex debilis Michx.
  Puccinia Grossulariae Lagerh.
  Puccinia Urticae Lagerh.
Carex debilis Michx., var. **Rudgei** L. H. Bailey.
  {Dicaeoma Grossulariae (Lagerh.) Kern.
  {Puccinia albiperidia Arth.
  {Puccinia Grossulariae Lagerh.
  {Puccinia uniporula C. R. Orton.
  Dicaeoma Peckii (Kellerm.) Arth.
  Septoria tenuis Dearness & House.
  {Nigredo uniporula (Kern) Arth.
  {Uromyces uniporulus Kern.

Carex deflexa Hornem.
Dicaeoma Asterum (Kern) Arth. & Kern.
{ Nigredo perigynia (Halsted) Arth.
{ Uromyces perigynius Halsted.
{ Uromyces Solidagini-Caricis Arth.

Carex densa L. H. Bailey.
{ Dicaeoma Asterum (Kern) Arth. & Kern.
{ Puccinia Asterum Kern.

Carex deweyana S.
{ Dicaeoma Asterum (Kern) Arth. & Kern.
{ Puccinia Asterum Kern.
{ ?Puccinia caricina Auct. Amer p. p.

Carex diandra Schrank.
{ Dicaeoma Asterum (Kern) Arth. & Kern.
{ Puccinia Asterum Kern.
{ Dicaeoma Trientalis Arth. & Kern.
{ Puccinia karelica Tranz.
{ Puccinia Trientalis (Arth. & Kern) House.
{ Dicaeoma Dracunculi Arth. & Kern.
{ Puccinia universalis Arth.
{ Dicaeoma Urticae (Lagerh.) O. Kuntze.
{ Puccinia urticata Kern.
{ Uredo fatiscens Arth.

Carex digitalis Willd.
Puccinia Grossulariae Lagerh.

Carex dioica L.
Cintractia Caricis (P.) Magn.

Carex disperma Dewey.
{ Dicaeoma Asterum (Kern) Arth. & Kern.
{ Puccinia Asterum Kern.
{ Puccinia caricina Auct. Amer. p. p.
{ Puccinia Caricis-Asteris Arth.
{ Puccinia extensicola Plowr.
{ Dicaeoma Grossulariae (Lagerh.) Kern.
{ Puccinia Grossulariae Lagerh.
Puccinia silvatica Auct. Amer. p. p.

Carex Douglasii Boott.
{ Dicaeoma atrofuscum (Dudley & Thompson)
{   Arth.
{ Puccinia atrofusca (Dudley & Thompson)
{   Holw.
{ Puccinia Caricis Auct. Amer. p. p.
{ Uromyces atrofuscus Dudley & Thompson.
Dicaeoma hieraciatum (Arth.) Arth. & Kern.
{ Dicaeoma Dracunculi Arth. & Kern.
{ Puccinia universalis Arth.
{ Cintractia Caricis (P.) Magn.
{ Ustilago Caricis (P.) Ung.
Ustilago Caricis, var. Douglasii Shear.

Carex eburnea Boott.
Colletotrichum graminicola (Ces.) G. W.
  Wilson.
{ Dicaeoma Allenii (G. W. Clinton) Arth. &
{   Fromme.
{ Puccinia Caricis-Shepherdiae J. J. Davis.
{ Dicaeoma Grossulariae (Lagerh.) Kern.
{ Puccinia Grossulariae Lagerh.

Carex Eleocharis L. H. Bailey.
Puccinia universalis Arth.

Carex elynoides Holm.
{ Cintractia Caricis (P.) Magn.
{ Ustilago Caricis (P.) Ung.

Carex Emoryi Dewey.
{ Dicaeoma Urticae (Lagerh.) O. Kuntze.
{ Puccinia Urticae Lagerh.

Carex exilis Dewey.
{ Dicaeoma Grossulariae (Lagerh.) Kern.
{ Puccinia Grossulariae Lagerh.
{ Dicaeoma Urticae (Lagerh.) O. Kuntze.
{ Puccinia urticata Kern.

Carex exsiccata L. H. Bailey.
Dicaeoma Grossulariae (Lagerh.) Kern.
{ Dicaeoma microsorum (Körn.) O. Kuntze.
{ Puccinia microsora Körn.
{ Dicaeoma Urticae (Lagerh.) O. Kuntze.
{ Puccinia urticata Kern.

Carex festiva Dewey.
Cintractia Caricis (P.) Magn.
Goniosporium puccinioides (DC.) ex Lk.
{ Puccinia Asterum Kern.
{ Puccinia Caricis-Asteris Arth.
Puccinia Grossulariae Lagerh.
Sphaerella tassiana De Not.
Stagonopsora Heliocharidis Trail, var. cari-
  cina Sacc. & Scalia.
Trochila diminuens Karst.

Carex festivella Mackenzie.
{ Dicaeoma Asterum (Kern) Arth. & Kern.
{ Puccinia Asterum Kern.
Puccinia Grossulariae Lagerh.
Puccinia universalis Arth.

Carex festucacea Schkuhr.
Cladosporium graminum Cda.
Cladosporium graminum, var. caricicola Sacc.
{ Dicaeoma Caricis-Erigerontis Arth.
{ Dicaeoma erigeronatum Arth.
{ Puccinia Asterum Kern.
{ Puccinia caricina W. Am. Fung. 277.
{ Puccinia Caricis-Erigerontis Arth.
{ Puccinia Caricis-Solidaginis Arth.
{ Puccinia extensicola Plowr.

Carex feta L. H. Bailey.
{ Dicaeoma Asterum (Kern) Arth. & Kern.
{ Puccinia Asterum Kern.

Carex filifolia Nutt.
{ Cintractia Caricis (P.) Magn.
{ Ustilago Caricis (P.) Ung.
{ Cintractia externa (Griffiths) G. P. Clinton.
{ Tilletia externa Griffiths.
{ Dicaeoma Dracunculi (Thum.) Arth. & Kern.
{ Puccinia caricina W. Am. Fung. 360, 360a.
{ Puccinia Caricis Fung. Columb. 1641, Syd.
{   Ured. 1712.
{ Puccinia universalis Arth.

Carex fissuricola Mackenzie.
　Dicaeoma Grossulariae (Lagerh.) Kern.
Carex flava L.
　⎰Dicaeoma Grossulariae (Lagerh.) Kern.
　⎱Puccinia Grossulariae Lagerh.
　⎰Nigredo perigynia (Halsted) Arth.
　⎱Uromyces perigynius Halsted.
Carex flexuosa Muhl.
　⎰Dicaeoma Grossulariae (Lagerh.) Kern.
　⎱Puccinia Grossulariae Lagerh.
　Dicaeoma Peckii (Kellerm.) Arth.
Carex foenea Willd.
　⎰?Dicaeoma Urticae (Lagerh.) O. Kuntze.
　⎱?Puccinia Caricis Auct. Amer. p. p.
　⎰Dicaeoma Asterum (Kern) Arth. & Kern.
　⎱Dicaeoma Caricis-Asteris Arth.
　⎰Puccinia Asterum Kern.
　⎱Puccinia Caricis-Asteris Arth.
　Puccinia extensicola Plowr.
Carex folliculata L.
　Cercospora Caricis Dearness & House.
　⎰Cintractia Caricis (P.) Magn.
　⎱Ustilago Caricis (P.) Ung.
　Leptosphaeria folliculata Ell. & Ev.
　⎰Metasphaeria Carectorum (B. & C.) Sacc.
　⎱Sphaerella Carectorum (B. & C.) Cke.
　⎰Sphaeria Carectorum B. & C.
　⎱Sphaerella perigynicola (S.) Cke.
　Sphaeria perigynicola S.
　⎰Ustilago caricicola Tracy & Earle.
　⎱Ustilago olivacea (DC.) Tul.
Carex folliculata L., var. **australis** Bailey.
　Cintractia Caricis (P.) Magn.
Carex Frankii Kunth.
　⎰Dicaeoma Sambuci Arth.
　⎱Puccinia bolleyana Sacc.
　⎰Puccinia Sambuci Arth.
　⎱Puccinia schoeleriana Auct. Amer.
　Puccinia Thompsonii Hume.
　⎰Dicaeoma Urticae (Lagerh.) O. Kuntze.
　⎱Puccinia Caricis Auct. Amer. p. p.
　⎰Dicaeoma microsorum (Körn.) O. Kuntze.
　⎱Puccinia microsora Körn.
　⎰Dicaeoma hieraciatum (H. S. Jackson) Arth.
　⎱　& Kern.
　Puccinia patruelis Arth.
Carex Fraseri Andrews.
　Botrytis torta Ell. & Ev.
　Epidochium melanochlorum Desm.
　Stachylidium caricinum Ell. & Ev.
　Trichaegum nodulosum Ell. & Ev.
　Zygodesmus graminicola Ell. & Ev.
Carex Geyerii Boott.
　⎰Cintractia Caricis (P.) Magn.
　⎱Ustilago Caricis (P.) Ung.
　⎰Dicaeoma Dracunculi Arth. & Kern.
　⎱Puccinia universalis Arth.

Carex glareosa Wahlenb.
　⎰Arthrinium curvatum Kze. ex Fr.
　⎱Camptoum curvatum (Kze. ex Fr.) Lk.
　⎰Cintractia Caricis (P.) Magn.
　⎱Ustilago Caricis (P.) Ung.
　Cladosporium caricicola Cda.
　Pleospora pentamera Karst.
　Mycosphaerella caricicola (Fckl.) J. Lind.
　Trochila ignobilis Karst.
Carex glareosa Wahlenb., var. **caespitosa**
　Böckl.
　Sphaerella pusilla Awd.
Carex Gmelini Hook. & Arn.
　Cintractia Caricis (P.) Magn.
Carex Goodenowii J. Gay.
　⎰Cintractia Caricis (P.) Magn.
　⎱Ustilago Caricis (P.) Ung.
　Leptosphaeria caricinella Karst.
　Lophodermium caricinum (Rob.) Duby.
　Metasphaeria macrotheca Rostr.
　Mollisia cinerea (Batsch. ex Fr.) Karst.
　Phoma Caricis (Fr.) Sacc.
　Puccinia Asterum Kern.
　⎰Dicaeoma Grossulariae (Lagerh.) Kern.
　⎱Puccinia Grossulariae Lagerh.
　Puccinia quadriporula Arth.
　⎰Puccinia Caricis Fung. Columb. *1759.*
　⎱Puccinia Urticae Lagerh.
　Septoria punctoidea Karst.
　Sphaerella tassiana De Not.
　Sphaerella wichuriana Schrt.
　Trochila fuscella Karst.
　Trochila ignobilis Karst.
Carex gracillima S.
　Cercospora caricina Ell. & Dearness.
　Leptosphaeria folliculata Ell. & Ev., var.
　　oxyspora J. J. Davis.
　?Puccinia Caricis-strictae Diet.
　⎰Dicaeoma Grossulariae (Lagerh.) Kern.
　⎱Puccinia albiperidia Arth.
　Puccinia Grossulariae Lagerh.
　Puccinia uniporula C. R. Orton.
　⎰Nigredo minuta (Diet.) Arth.
　⎱Uromyces minutus Diet.
　⎰Uromyces perigynius Halsted.
　⎱Uromyces Solidagini-Caricis Arth.
　⎰Nigredo uniporula (Kern) Arth.
　⎱Uromyces uniporulus Kern.
Carex Grahami Boott.
　Leptosphaeria epicarecta (Cke.) Sacc.
Carex granularis Muhl.
　Cercospora microstigma Sacc.
　Dicaeoma Grossulariae (Lagerh.) Kern.
Carex gravida L. H. Bailey.
　⎰Dicaeoma Asterum (Kern) Arth. & Kern.
　⎱Puccinia Asterum Kern.
　Puccinia tecta Ell. & Barthol.

Carex Grayii Carey.
  Dicaeoma Peckii (Kellerm.) Arth.
  Puccinia Peckii Kellerm.
  Dicaeoma Sambuci Arth.
  Puccinia Sambuci Arth.
  Uromyces perigynius Halsted.
  Uromyces perigynius Halsted, var. altiporulus
    J. J. Davis.
Carex grisea Wahlenb.
  Cercospora caricina Ell. & Dearness.
  Dicaeoma hieraciatum (Arth.) Arth. & Kern.
  Septocylindrium caricinum Sacc.
Carex gymnoclada Holm.
  Dicaeoma Grossulariae (Lagerh.) Kern.
  Puccinia Grossulariae Lagerh.
Carex Halleri Gunn.
  Sphaerella pusilla Awd.
  Sphaerella tassiana De Not.
  Trochila diminuens Karst.
Carex heliophila Mackenzie.
  Dicaeoma Dracunculi Arth. & Kern.
  Puccinia universalis Arth.
Carex hirtifolia Mackenzie.
  Dicaeoma albiperidium Arth.
  Dicaeoma Grossulariae (Lagerh.) Kern.
  Puccinia albiperidia Arth.
  Puccinia Grossulariae Lagerh.
  Puccinia pringsheimiana Klebahn.
  Puccinia uniporula C. R. Orton.
  Caeomurus perigynius (Halsted) O. Kuntze.
  Uromyces perigynius Halsted.
  Uromyces Solidagini-Caricis Arth.
  Nigredo minuta (Diet.) Arth.
  Uromyces minutus Diet.
  Uromyces perigynius N. Am. Ured. 893.
Carex hitchcockiana Dewey.
  Dicaeoma Grossulariae (Lagerh.) Kern.
  Puccinia Grossulariae Lagerh.
Carex Hoodii Boott.
  Puccinia Garrettii Arth.
  Dicaeoma hieraciatum (H. S. Jackson) Arth.
    & Kern.
  Puccinia caricina Garrett. 1911.
  Puccinia hieraciata H. S. Jackson.
  Puccinia patruelis Arth.
  Schizonella melanogramma (DC.) Schrt.
Carex hookeriana Dewey.
  Puccinia Asterum Kern.
  Puccinia Peckii Kellerm.
Carex hormathodes Fernald.
  Puccinia extensicola Plowr.
Carex Houghtonii Torr.
  Cercospora caricina Ell. & Dearness.
  Dicaeoma Asterum (Kern) Arth. & Kern.
  Puccinia Asterum Kern.
Carex hyalina Boott.
  Dicaeoma Asterum (Kern) Arth. & Kern.
Carex hystericina Muhl.
  Puccinia caricina DC.

Carex illota L. H. Bailey.
  Dicaeoma hieraciatum (H. S. Jackson) Arth.
    & Kern.
  Puccinia patruelis Arth.
Carex incomperta Bicknell.
  Dicaeoma Asterum (Kern) Arth. & Kern.
Carex incurva Lightf.
  Cintractia Caricis (P.) Magn.
  Rhabdospora Drabae (Fckl.) Berl. & Vogl.
  Mycosphaerella tassiana (De Not.) Johans.
  Sphaerella tassiana De Not.
Carex inops L. H. Bailey.
  Dicaeoma Dracunculi Arth. & Kern.
Carex intumescens Rudge.
  Cercospora caricina Ell. & Dearness.
  Phyllosticta Caricis J. J. Davis an Sacc.
  Stagonospora caricinella Brun.
  ?Puccinia Caricis-Asteris Arth.
  Dicaeoma Grossulariae (Lagerh.) Kern.
  Puccinia albiperidia Arth.
  Puccinia caricina Fung. Columb. 2350.
  Puccinia Caricis Auct. Amer. p. p.
  Puccinia Grossulariae Lagerh.
  Puccinia intensicola Plowr.
  Dicaeoma Sambuci Arth.
  Puccinia Sambuci Arth.
  Uromyces minutus Diet.
  Nigredo perigynia (Halsted) Arth.
  Uromyces perigynius Halsted.
Carex invisa L. H. Bailey.
  Cintractia Caricis (P.) Magn.
Carex Jamesii S.
  Dicaeoma Asterum (Kern) Arth.
  Dicaeoma Caricis-Asteris Arth.
  Puccinia Asterum Kern.
  Puccinia Caricis-Solidaginis Arth.
Carex Kelloggii Boott.
  Dicaeomá Grossulariae (Lagerh.) Kern.
  Puccinia Grossulariae Lagerh.
  Puccinia Urticae Lagerh.
  Anthracoidea subinclusa (Körn.) Bref.
  Cintractia subinclusa (Körn.) Magn.
  Ustilago subinclusa Körn.
Carex lacustris Willd.
  Cercospora caricina Ell. & Dearness.
  Dicaeoma Grossulariae (Lagerh.) Kern.
  Puccinia minuta Diet.
  Dicaeoma Peckii (Kellerm.) Arth.
  Dicaeoma Urticae (Lagerh.) O. Kuntze.
  Puccinia urticata Kern.
Carex laeviconica Dewey.
  Dicaeoma Peckii (Kellerm.) Arth.
  Puccinia Peckii Kellerm.
Carex laeviculmis Meinsh.
  Dicaeoma Asterum (Kern) Arth. & Kern.
  Puccinia Asterum Kern.
  Puccinia Caricis-Asteris Arth.

Carex laevivaginata (Kukenth.) Mackenzie.
Dothidella caricina Dearness & House.
Puccinia urticata Kern.

Carex lagopina Wahlenb.?
Cintractia Caricis (P.) Magn.
Sphaerella Tassiana De Not.
Trochila diminuens Karst.

Carex lanuginosa Michx.
⎰Cintractia subinclusa (Körn.) Magn.
⎱Ustilago subinclusa Körn.
⎰Dicaeoma Grossulariae (Lagerh.) Kern.
⎱Puccinia Grossulariae Lagerh.
⎰Dicaeoma Peckii (Kellerm.) Arth.
⎢Puccinia Caricis Fung. Columb. *1954*.
⎢Puccinia ludibunda Ell. & Ev.
⎱Puccinia Peckii Kellerm.
⎰Dicaeoma Urticae (Lagerh.) O. Kuntze.
⎢Puccinia caricina Auct. Amer. p. p.
⎢Puccinia Caricis Auct. Amer. p. p.
⎱Puccinia urticata Kern.
Dicaeoma Urticae (Schum.) Kuntze.
⎰Caeomurus Solidagini-Caricis Arth. p. p.
⎨Nigredo minuta (Diet.) Arth.
⎱Uromyces Solidagini-Caricis Arth. p. p.
Nigredo perigynia (Halsted) Arth.

Carex lasiocarpa Ehrh.
Cintractia Caricis (P.) Magn.
⎰Dicaeoma minutissimum (Arth.) H. S. Jackson.
⎨?Puccinia caricina Auct. Amer. p. p.
⎱Puccinia minutissima Arth.

Carex laxiflora Lam.
Cercospora microstigma Sacc.
⎰?Puccinia caricina Auct. Amer. p. p.
⎢?Puccinia Caricis Auct. Amer. p. p.
⎢Puccinia Grossulariae Lagerh.
⎱Puccinia pringsheimiana Klebahn.
Schizonella melanogramma (DC.) Schrt.

Carex laxiflora Lam., var. **latifolia** Boott.
Cercospora microstigma Sacc.

Carex Leavenworthii Dewey.
Carex leptalea Wahlenb.
Carex leptopoda Mackenzie.
⎰Dicaeoma Asterum (Kern) Arth. & Kern.
⎱Puccinia Asterum Kern.

Carex limosa L.
⎰Cintractia Caricis (P.) Magn.
⎱Ustilago Caricis (P.) Ung.
Ombrophila limosa Rehm.
⎰Dicaeoma Lysimachiae O. Kuntze.
⎨Puccinia limosae Magn.
⎱Puccinia lysimachiata Kern.
Puccinia Trientalis (Arth. & Kern) House.

Carex livida (Wahlenb.) Willd.
Ustilago Caricis (P.) Ung.

Carex longirostris Torr.
⎰Dicaeoma microsorum (Körn.) O. Kuntze.
⎱Puccinia microsora Körn.

⎰Dicaeoma hieraciata (H. S. Jackson) Arth. &
⎨ Kern.
⎱Puccinia patruelis Arth.
Puccinia Peckii Kellerm.
⎰Dicaeoma Phrymae (Arth.) Arth. & Kern.
⎱Puccinia Phrymae Arth.
Schizonella melanogramma (DC.) Schrt.

Carex lupuliformis Sartwell.
⎰Dicaeoma bolleyanum (Sacc.) O. Kuntze.
⎨Dicaeoma Sambuci Arth.
⎱Puccinia Sambuci Arth.
⎰Dicaeoma Grossulariae (Lagerh.) Kern.
⎱Puccinia Grossulariae Lagerh.
⎰Dicaeoma Peckii (Kellerm.) Arth.
⎱Puccinia Peckii Kellerm.

Carex lupulina Muhl.
Cercospora caricina Ell. & Dearness.
Cintractia subinclusa (Körn.) Magn.
⎰Puccinia caricina Auct. Amer. p. p.
⎨Puccinia Caricis Auct. Amer. p. p.
⎢Dicaeoma Sambuci Arth.
⎢Puccinia Sambuci Arth.
⎰Dicaeoma hieraciatum (H. S. Jackson) Arth.
⎨ & Kern.
⎱Puccinia patruelis Arth.
Torula caricina Ell. & Dearness.
Nigredo valens (Kern) Arth.

Carex lurida Wahlenb.
Puccinia Asterum Kern.
⎰Dicaeoma Sambuci Arth.
⎢Puccinia atkinsoniana Diet.
⎢Puccinia bolleyana Sacc.
⎱Puccinia Sambuci Arth.
⎰Dicaeoma Urticae (Lagerh.) O. Kuntze.
⎱Puccinia Caricis Auct. Amer. p. p.
⎰Dicaeoma microsorum (Körn.) O. Kuntze.
⎱Puccinia microsora Körn.
Vermicularia caricina Ell & Ev.

Carex lurida Wahlenb., var. **gracilis** (Boott)
  L. H. Bailey.
⎰Dicaeoma Urticae (Lagerh.) O. Kuntze.
⎱Puccinia urticata Kern.

Carex luzulifolia Watson.
Cintractia Caricis (P.) Magn.

Carex Lyngbyei Hornem.
Dicaeoma Grossulariae (Lagerh.) Kern.
⎰Puccinia Grossulariae Lagerh.
⎱Dicaeoma Urticae (Lagerh.) O. Kuntze.

Carex macrochaeta C. Meyer.
⎰Dicaeoma Grossulariae (Lagerh.) Kern.
⎱Puccinia Grossulariae Lagerh.

Carex madrensis L. H. Bailey.
Dicaeoma Caricis-polystachyae (Diet.) Arth.
  & Kern.
Puccinia karelica Tranz.

Carex magnifica Dewey.
Puccinia Grossulariae Lagerh.
⎰Puccinia Garrettii Arth.
⎱Puccinia urticata Kern.

Carex marcida Dewey.
Cintractia Caricis (P.) Magn.
{ Puccinia caricina W. Am. Fung. *339a*.
{ ?Puccinia Caricis Auct. Amer. p. p.
{ Puccinia Opizii Arth. non Bubák.
{ Puccinia patruelis Arth.
Puccinia universalis Arth.

Carex maritima O. F. Müll.
{ Dicaeoma Grossulariae (Lagerh.) Kern.
{ Puccinia Grossulariae Lagerh.

Carex mertensiana Auct.
Puccinia Grossulariae Lagerh.
Sphaerella leptospora Sacc. & Scalia.

Carex Mertensii Prescott.
{ Dicaeoma Grossulariae (Lagerh.) Kern.
{ Puccinia Grossulariae Lagerh.
{ Dicaeoma Urticae (Lagerh.) O. Kuntze.
{ Puccinia Urticae Lagerh.

Carex michauxiana Böckl.
Cintractia subinclusa (Körn.) Magn.

Carex microglochin Wahlenb.
Leptosphaeria gigaspora Niessl.
Trochila ignobilis Karst.

Carex mirata Dewey.
Puccinia microsora Körn.

Carex misandra R. Br.
Leptosphaeria caricinella Karst.
Leptosphaeria epicarecta (Cke.) Sacc.
Lophodermium caricinum (Rob.) Duby.
Marasmius caricicola Kauffman.
Pleospora discors (Dur. & Mont.) Ces. & De Not.
Septoria punctoidea Karst.
{ Mycosphaerella tassiana (De Not.) Johans.
{ Sphaerella tassiana De Not.
{ Mycosphaerella wichuriana (Schrt.) Johans.
{ Sphaerella wichuriana Schrt.
Stagonospora Caricis (Oud.) Sacc.

Carex Muhlenbergii Schkuhr.
{ Dicaeoma Asterum (Kern) Arth. & Kern.
{ Puccinia Asterum Kern.
{ Puccinia extensicola Plowr.
{ Dicaeoma Peckii Arth.
{ ?Puccinia Caricis Auct. Amer. p. p.
{ Puccinia ludibunda Ell. & Ev.
{ Puccinia Peckii Kellerm.

Carex multicaulis L. H. Bailey.
{ Dicaeoma Dracunculi Arth. & Kern.
{ Puccinia universalis Arth.

Carex multimoda L. H. Bailey.
Puccinia Asterum Kern.

Carex muricata L.
{ Puccinia Opizii Arth. non Bubák.
{ Puccinia patruelis Arth.

Carex muskingumensis S.
{ Dicaeoma Asterum (Kern) Arth. & Kern.
{ Puccinia Asterum Kern.

{ Nigredo minuta (Diet.) Arth.
{ Uromyces minutus Diet.

Carex nardina Fr.
{ Cintractia Caricis (P.) Magn.
{ Ustilago Caricis (P.) Ung.
Clathrospora pentamera (Karst.) Berl.
Diplodia Simmonsii Rostr.
Leptosphaeria gigaspora Niessl.
Pleospora discors (Dur. & Mont.) Ces. & De Not.
Pleospora Elynae (Rabh.) Ces. & De Not.
Rhabdospora Drabae (Fckl.) Berl. & Vogl.
Rhabdospora groenlandica J. Lind.
Septoria punctoidea Karst.
{ Mycosphaerella wichuriana (Schrt.) Johans.
{ Sphaerella wichuriana Schrt.
Stagonospora Caricis (Oud.) Sacc.

Carex nebraskensis Dewey.
Claviceps? caricina Griffiths.
{ Dicaeoma Grossulariae (Lagerh.) Kern.
{ Puccinia Grossulariae Lagerh.
{ Dicaeoma Urticae (Lagerh.) O. Kuntze.
{ Puccinia caricina W. Am. Fung. *339*.
{ ?Puccinia Caricis Auct. Amer. p. p.
{ Puccinia Garrettii Arth.
{ Puccinia Urticae Lagerh.
{ Puccinia urticata Kern.
Schizonella melanogramma (DC.) Schrt.

Carex neurophora Mackenzie.
Dicaeoma Grossulariae (Lagerh.) Kern.

Carex nigricans Mey.
Cintractia Caricis (P.) Magn.
{ Dicaeoma atrofuscum (Dudley & Thompson) Arth.
{ Puccinia atrofusca (Dudley & Thompson) Holw.
{ Dicaeoma Urticae (Lagerh.) O. Kuntze.
{ Puccinia urticata Kern.

Carex nigromarginata S.
Nigredo perigynia (Halsted) Arth.

Carex normalis Mackenzie.
{ Dicaeoma Asterum (Kern) Arth. & Kern.
{ Puccinia Asterum Kern.
{ Nigredo perigynia (Halsted) Arth.
{ Uromyces perigynius Halsted.

Carex novae-angliae S.
{ Nigredo perigynia (Halsted) Arth.
{ Uromyces perigynius Halsted.

Carex nudata Boott.
{ Dicaeoma Urticae (Lagerh.) O. Kuntze.
{ Puccinia urticata Kern.

Carex obesa All., var. **minor** Boott.
Phoma Caricis (Fr.) Sacc.
Pleospora Elynae (Rabh.) Ces. & De Not.
Pleospora heterospora De Not.
Sphaerella pusilla Awd.

Carex obnupta L. H. Bailey.
  Cintractia Caricis (P.) Magn.
{ Dicaeoma Grossulariae (Lagerh.) Kern.
  Puccinia Grossulariae Lagerh.
{ Dicaeoma Urticae (Lagerh.) O. Kuntze.
  Puccinia Caricis Auct. Amer. p. p.

Carex obtusata Lilj.
{ Dicaeoma Grossulariae (Lagerh.) Kern.
  Puccinia Grossulariae Lagerh.
{ Dicaeoma Dracunculi Arth. & Kern.
  Puccinia universalis Arth.

Carex occidentalis L. H. Bailey.
  Cintractia Caricis (P.) Magn.
{ Dicaeoma Peckii (Kellerm.) Arth.
  Puccinia Peckii Kellerm.

Carex Oederi Retz.
  Dicaeoma Allenii Arth. & Fromme.

Carex Oederi Retz., var. pumila (Cosson & Germain) Fernald.
{ Dicaeoma Asterum (Kern) Arth. & Kern.
  Puccinia Asterum Kern.
  Puccinia extensicola Plowr.
{ Dicaeoma Urticae (Lagerh.) O. Kuntze.
  Puccinia urticata Kern.

Carex oligocarpa Schkuhr.
{ Dicaeoma Asterum (Kern) Arth. & Kern.
  Puccinia Asterum Kern.
  Dicaeoma Grossulariae (Lagerh.) Kern.
{ Dicaeoma Dracunculi Arth. & Kern.
  Puccinia universalis Arth.

Carex oligosperma Michx.
{ Cintractia Caricis (P.) Magn.
  Ustilago urceolorum Tul.
  Cintractia subinclusa (Körn.) Magn.

Carex olympica Mackenzie.
  Dicaeoma Asterum (Kern) Arth. & Kern.
{ Dicaeoma hieraciatum (Arth.) Arth. & Kern.
  Puccinia patruelis Arth.

Carex oxycarpa Holm.
  Dicaeoma Grossulariae (Lagerh.) Kern.

Carex pachystachya Cham.
  Dicaeoma Asterum (Kern) Arth. & Kern.

Carex pallescens L.
{ Dicaeoma Grossulariae (Lagerh.) Kern.
{ Puccinia Caricis Orton Vt.
  Puccinia Grossulariae Lagerh.

Carex panicea L.
  Puccinia extensicola Plowr.

Carex parallela Sommf.
  Physalospora alpestris Niessl.
  Sphaerella pusilla Awd.

Carex parryana Dewey.
  Dicaeoma Urticae (Lagerh.) O. Kuntze.

Carex paupercula Michx.
{ Cintractia Caricis (P.) Magn.
{ Ustilago Caricis (P.) Ung.
  Ustilago urceolorum (DC.) Tul.

Carex pedata L.
  Septoria punctoidea Karst.
  Sphaerella saxatilis Schrt.
  Sphaerella tassiana De Not.

Carex pedunculata Muhl.
{ Cintractia Caricis (P.) Magn.
{ Ustilago Caricis (P.) Ung.
  Phyllachora Caricis (Fr.) Sacc.
  Dicaeoma Grossulariae (Lagerh.) Kern.

Carex pennsylvanica Lam.
{ Caeoma Caricis (P.) Lk.
  Cintractia Caricis (P.) Magn.
{ Uredo Caricis P.
  Ustilago Caricis (P.) Ung.
  Ustilago urceolorum Tul.
{ Dothidea Caricis Fr.
  Phyllachora Caricis (Fr.) Sacc.
{ Sphaeria Caricis Fr.
  Phyllosticta Caricis (Fckl.) Sacc.
{ Dicaeoma Asterum (Kern) Arth. & Kern.
  Puccinia Asterum Kern.
  Puccinia Caricis-asteris Arth.
  Puccinia Caricis-solidaginis Arth.
  Puccinia patruelis Arth.
{ Puccinia caricina W. Am. Fung. 277a and F. Dak. 106.
  Puccinia universalis Arth.
{ Dicaeoma Urticae (Lagerh.) O. Kuntze.
  Puccinia Caricis Auct. Amer. p. p.
{ Geminella foliicola Schrt.
  Geminella melanogramma (DC.) Magn.
  Schizonella melanogramma (DC.) Schrt.
  Urocystis pusilla C. & P.
  Septoria Caricis Pass.
  Septoria nematospora J. J. Davis.
  Septoria riparia Pass.
  Sorosporium atrum Pk.
{ Phyllosticta Caricis J. J. Davis an Sacc.
  Stagonospora caricinella Brun.
  Stegia Caricis Pk.
  Thecaphora aterrima Tul.
  Nigredo perigynia (Halsted) Arth.

Carex petasata Dewey.
{ Dicaeoma Dracunculi Arth. & Kern.
  Puccinia universalis Arth.

Carex phyllomanica Boott.
  Puccinia Asterum Kern.
  Puccinia Grossulariae Lagerh.

Carex picta Steud.
  Schizonella melanogramma (DC.) Schrt.

Carex pilulifera L.
  Trochila ignobilis Karst.

Dicaeoma Trientalis Arth. & Kern.
  Puccinia caricina Auct. Amer. p. p.
  Puccinia karelica Tranz.
  ?Puccinia striola Auct. Amer. p. p.
  Puccinia Trientalis (Arth. & Kern) House.

Carex planostachys Kunze.
{ Dicaeoma Asterum (Kern) Arth. & Kern.
{ Puccinia Asterum Kern.

Carex plantaginea Lam.
  Cercospora microstigma Sacc.
  Dicaeoma Grossulariae (Lagerh.) Kern.

Carex podocarpa R. Br.
{ Dicaeoma Grossulariae (Lagerh.) Kern.
{ Puccinia Grossulariae Lagerh.
{ Puccinia quadriporula Arth.

Carex polygama Schkuhr.
  Cintractia Caricis (P.) Magn.

Carex polystachya Sw.
  Dicaeoma Grossulariae (Lagerh.) Kern.
{ Dicaeoma Caricis-polystachyae (Diet.) Arth.
{   & Kern.
{ Puccinia Caricis-polystachyae Diet.
{ Puccinia Kellermanii Kern.
{ Ustilago caricicola Tracy & Earle.
{ Ustilago olivacea (DC.) Tul.

Carex praegracilis Boott.
{ Dicaeoma Asterum (Kern) Arth. & Kern.
{ Puccinia Asterum Kern.
{ Dicaeoma atrofuscum (Dudley & Thompson)
{   Arth.
{ Puccinia atrofusca (Dudley & Thompson)
{   Holw.
  Dicaeoma Grossulariae (Lagerh.) Kern.
{ Dicaeoma hieraciatum (H. S. Jackson) Arth.
{   & Kern.
{ Puccinia hieraciata H. S. Jackson.
{ Puccinia patruelis Arth.
{ Dicaeoma Dracunculi Arth. & Kern.
{ Puccinia universalis Arth.

Carex prairea Dewey.
{ Dicaeoma Asterum (Kern) Arth. & Kern.
{ Puccinia Asterum Kern.

Carex prasina Wahlenb.
{ Dicaeoma Grossulariae (Lagerh.) Kern.
{ Puccinia Grossulariae Lagerh.

Carex pratensis Drejer.
  Coniosporium puccinioides (DC.) ex Lk.
{ Puccinia hieraciata H. S. Jackson.
{ Puccinia patruelis Arth.
  Sphaerella wichuriana Schrt.

Carex praticola Rydb.
{ Dicaeoma hieraciatum (H. S. Jackson) Arth.
{   & Kern.
{ Puccinia patruelis Arth.

Carex Pseudo-Cyperus L.
  Cintractia Caricis (P.) Magn.
{ Dicaeoma Urticae (Lagerh.) O. Kuntze.
{ Puccinia urticata Kern.
  Uredo fatiscens Arth.

Carex pseudoscirpoidea Rydb.
  Cintractia Caricis (P.) Magn.

Carex pubescens Muhl.
  Nigredo minuta (Diet.) Arth.

Carex pyrenaica Wahlenb.
  Synchytrium Caricis Tracy & Earle.

Carex radiata (Wahl.) Small.
{ Dicaeoma Asterum (Kern) Arth. & Kern.
{ Puccinia Asterum Kern.

Carex rariflora Smith.
  Cladosporium graminum Cda.
  Leptostroma caricinum Fr.
  Sphaerella tassiana De Not.
  Sphaerella wichuriana Schrt.
  Trochila ignobilis Karst.

Carex redowskiana C. A. Mey.
  Cintractia Caricis (P.) Magn.

Carex reniformis (L. H. Bailey) Small.
  Dicaeoma Asterum (Kern) Arth. & Kern.

Carex reticulata Auct.

Carex retroflexa Muhl.
  Puccinia Caricis Auct. Amer. p. p.

Carex retrorsa S.
  Cercospora caricina Ell. & Dearness.
{ Dicaeoma Asterum (Kern) Arth. & Kern.
{ Puccinia Asterum Kern.
{ Puccinia Caricis Auct. Amer. p. p.
{ Puccinia Caricis-Asteris Arth.
{ Puccinia extensicola Plowr.
{ Dicaeoma Grossulariae (Lagerh.) Kern.
{ Puccinia Grossulariae Lagerh.
{ Dicaeoma Peckii (Kellerm.) Arth.
{ Puccinia Peckii Kellerm.
{ Dicaeoma Urticae (Lagerh.) O. Kuntze.
{ Puccinia urticata Kern.
  Stagonospora paludosa (Sacc. & Speg.) Sacc.

Carex Reynoldsii Dewey.
{ Dicaeoma hieraciatum (H. S. Jackson) Arth.
{   & Kern.
{ Puccinia patruelis Arth.

Carex rigida Good.
{ Cintractia Caricis (P.) Magn.
{ Ustilago Caricis (P.) Ung.
  Entyloma caricinum Rostr.
  Leptostroma caricinum Fr.
  Metasphaeria macrotheca Rostr.
  Mollisia cinerea (Batsch) ex Karst.
  Pleospora discors (Mont.) Ces. & De Not.
{ Mycosphaerella tassiana (De Not.) Johans.
{ Sphaerella tassiana De Not.
  Sphaerella pusilla Awd.
  Sphaerella wichuriana Schrt.
  Trochila ignobilis Karst.

Carex rigida Good., var. **Bigelowii** (Torr.) Tuck-
  erm.
  Metasphaeria macrotheca Rostr.
{ ?Puccinia Caricis Auct. Amer. p. p.
{ Puccinia Grossulariae Lagerh.

Carex riparia W. Curtis.
Amerosporium Caricum (Lib.) Sacc.
Puccinia angustata Auct. Amer. p. p.?
Dicaeoma Urticae (Lagerh.) O. Kuntze.
Puccinia Caricis Ohio Fung. *192.*
Puccinia Urticae Lagerh.
Puccinia urticata Kern.
Puccinia pringsheimiana Klebahn.
Puccinia riparia Holw.
Clasterosporium caricinum S.
Sporidesmium Clasterisporium Cda.
Stagonospora tetramera J. J. Davis.

Carex rosaeoides E. C. Howe.
Dicaeoma Asterum (Kern) Arth. & Kern.
Puccinia Asterum Kern.

Carex rosea Schkuhr.
Cercospora caricina Ell. & Dearness.
Dicaeoma Asterum (Kern) Arth.
Puccinia Asterum Kern.
Puccinia Caricis-Asteris Arth.
Puccinia tenuistipes Fung. Columb. *2366.*

Carex Rossii Boott.
Dicaeoma Asterum (Kern) Arth. & Kern.
Puccinia Asterum Kern.
Dicaeoma Dracunculi Arth. & Kern.
Puccinia universalis Arth.

Carex rostrata Stokes.
Cintractia Caricis (P.) Magn.
Ustilago urceolorum Tul.
Cintractia subinclusa (Körn.) Magn.
Dicaeoma Peckii (Kellerm.) Arth.
Puccinia Peckii Kellerm.
Dicaeoma Urticae (Lagerh.) O. Kuntze.
Puccinia Caricis Auct. Amer. p. p.
Puccinia Urticae Lagerh.)
Puccinia urticata Kern.
Trochila ignobilis Karst.
Nigredo valens (Kern) Arth.
Uromyces valens Kern.
Ustilago olivacea (DC.) Tul.

Carex rostrata Stokes, var. **utriculata** (Boott)
L. H. Bailey.
Cintractia subinclusa (Körn.) Magn.
Ustilago subinclusa Körn.
Helotium caricinellum Pk.
Niptera caricinella (Pk.) Sacc.
Puccinia Caricis Auct. Amer. p. p.
Puccinia Urticae Lagerh.
Caeomurus perigynius Auct. Amer. p. p.
Nigredo valens (Kern) Arth.
Uromyces valens Kern.
Ustilago olivacea (DC.) Tul.

Carex rotundata Wahlenb.
Sphaerella wichuriana Schrt.
Trochila diminuens Karst.

Carex rufina Drejer.
Trochila ignobilis Karst.

Carex rupestris All.
Cintractia Caricis (P.) Magn.
Ustilago Caricis (P.) Ung.
Cladosporium graminum Cda.
Hendersonia Stefansonii Rostr.
Pleospora Elynae (Rabh.) Ces. & De Not.
Pleospora pentamera Karst.
Rhabdospora Drabae (Fckl.) Berl. & Vogl.
Rhabdospora groenlandica Lind.
Septoria punctoidea Karst.
Sphaerella pusilla Awd.
Sphaerella tassiana De Not.
Mycosphaerella wichuriana (Schrt.) Johans.
Sphaerella wichuriana Schrt.
Trochila diminuens Karst.

Carex salina Wahlenb.
Cintractia Caricis (P.) Magn.
Lophodermium caricinum (Rob.) Duby.
Metasphaeria macrotheca Rostr.
Trochila ignobilis Karst.

Carex salina Wahlenb., var. **subspathacea**
(Wormsk.)
Mycosphaerella tassiana (De Not.) Johans.
Mycosphaerella wichuriana (Schrt.) Johans.

Carex Sartwellii Dewey.
Dicaeoma hieraciatum (H. S. Jackson) Arth. &
Kern.
Puccinia patruelis Arth.
Puccinia Peckii Kellerm.
Dicaeoma Urticae (Lagerh.) O. Kuntze.
Puccinia urticata Kern.

Carex saxatilis L.
Hendersonia gigantea J. Lind.
Leptosphaeria caricinella Karst.
Leptosphaeria epicarecta (Cke.) Sacc.
Lophodermium caricinum (Rob.) Duby.
Mollisia cymbispora Rostr.
Mycosphaerella tassiana (De Not.) Johans.
Rhabdospora groenlandica J. Lind.

Carex saximontana Mackenzie.
Dicaeoma eminens (Kern) Arth. & Kern.
Puccinia eminens Kern.

Carex scabrata L.
Dicaeoma Grossulariae (Lagerh.) Kern.
Puccinia Grossulariae Lagerh.
Dicaeoma microsorum (Körn.) O. Kuntze.
Puccinia microsora Körn.
Dicaeoma Peckii (Kellerm.) Arth.

Carex scirpoidea Michx.
Cintractia Caricis (P.) Magn.
Ustilago Caricis (P.) Ung.
Cladosporium graminum Cda.
Pleospora Elynae (Rabh.) Ces. & De Not.
Sphaerella pusilla Awd.
Trochila fuscella Karst.

Carex scirpoides Schkuhr.
Dicaeoma Asterum (Kern) Arth. & Kern.
Puccinia Asterum Kern.

Carex scoparia Schkuhr.
Dicaeoma Asterum (Kern) Arth. & Kern.
Puccinia Asterum Kern.
?Puccinia caricina Auct. Amer. p. p.
Puccinia Caricis-Asteris Arth.
Puccinia Caricis-Erigerontis Arth.
Puccinia Caricis-Solidaginis Arth.
Puccinia extensicola Plowr.
Peziza cervinula Cke.
Peziza multipuncta Pk.
Pyrenopeziza cervinula (Cke.) Sacc.
Pyrenopeziza multipuncta (Pk.) Sacc.
Nigredo perigynia (Halsted) Arth.
Uromyces caricinus Ell. & Ev.
Uromyces perigynius Halsted.

Carex setacea Dewey, var., **ambigua** (Barratt)
Fern.
Puccinia Asterum Kern.

Carex siccata Dewey.
Cintractia Caricis (P.) Magn.
Ustilago Caricis (P.) Ung.
Ustilago urceolorum Tul.
Dicaeoma Asterum (Kern) Arth. & Kern.
Puccinia atrofusca (Dudley & Thompson)
Holw.
Puccinia microsora Körn.
Dicaeoma hieraciatum (H. S. Jackson) Kern.
Puccinia hieraciata H. S. Jackson.
Puccinia Opizii Arth.
Puccinia patruelis Arth.
Dicaeoma Peckii (Kellerm.) Arth.
Puccinia Peckii Kellerm.
Puccinia urticata Kern.
Pyrenopeziza caricina (Lib.) Rehm.

Carex sitchensis Prescott.
Cintractia Caricis (P.) Magn.
Leptosphaeria sp. indet.
Dicaeoma Grossulariae (Lagerh.) Kern.
Puccinia Grossulariae Lagerh.

Carex sparganioides Muhl.
Dicaeoma Asterum (Kern) Arth. & Kern.
Puccinia Asterum Kern.
?Puccinia Caricis Auct. Amer. p. p.
Puccinia Caricis-Asteris Arth.
Puccinia Caricis-Solidaginis Arth.
Puccinia extensicola Plowr.
Puccinia tecta Ell. & Barthol.
Puccinia vulpinoidis Diet. & Holw.
Dicaeoma ludibundum (Ell. & Ev.) O. Kuntze.
Dicaeoma Peckii (Kellerm.) Arth.
Puccinia Asterum N. Am. Ured 1933.
Puccinia ludibunda Ell. & Ev.
Puccinia Peckii Kellerm.
Dicaeoma Grossulariae (Lagerh.) Kern.
Puccinia Grossulariae Lagerh.
Dicaeoma hieraciatum (H. S. Jackson) Arth.
& Kern.
Uromyces perigynius Halsted.

Carex squarrosa L.
Dicaeoma Grossulariae (Lagerh.) Kern.
Puccinia albiperidia Arth.
Puccinia caricina Ohio Fung. *149.*
Puccinia Grossulariae Lagerh.

Carex stans Drejer.
Leptosphaeria epicarecta (Cke.) Sacc.
Schizonella melanogramma (DC.) Schrt.
Sphaerella tassiana De Not.

Carex stellulata Good.
Cintractia Caricis (P.) Magn.
Ustilago urceolorum Tul.
Dicaeoma Asterum (Kern) Arth. & Kern.
Puccinia Asterum Kern.
Puccinia caricina Auct. Amer. p. p.
Peziza multipuncta Pk.
Pyrenopeziza multipuncta (Pk.) Sacc.

Carex stenophylla Wahlenb.
Cintractia Caricis (P.) Magn.
Ustilago Caricis (P.) Ung.
Ustilago urceolorum Tul.
Dicaeoma Dracunculi Arth. & Kern.
Puccinia Caricis Fung. Columb. *2446.*
Puccinia universalis Arth.

Carex sterilis Willd.
Cintractia Caricis (P.) Magn.
Ustilago Caricis (P.) Ung.
Puccinia Asterum Kern.

Carex stipata Muhl.
Pleospora laxa Ell. & Gall.
Dicaeoma Asterum (Kern) Arth. & Kern.
Puccinia Asterum Kern.
Puccinia Caricis-Solidaginis Arth.
Puccinia extensicola Plowr.
Dicaeoma Grossulariae (Lagerh.) Kern.
Puccinia Grossulariae Lagerh.
Dicaeoma Peckii (Kellerm.) Arth.
Puccinia Peckii Kellerm.
Dicaeoma Urticae (Lagerh.) O. Kuntze.
Puccinia Caricis Auct. Amer. p. p.
Puccinia urticata Kern.
Nigredo perigynia (Halsted) Arth.

Carex straminea Willd.
Pleospora laxa Ell. & Gall.
Dicaeoma Asterum (Kern) Arth. & Kern.
Dicaeoma Caricis-Asteris Arth.
Dicaeoma Caricis-Erigerontis Arth.
Puccinia Asterum Kern.
Puccinia extensicola Plowr.
Dicaeoma Urticae (Lagerh.) O. Kuntze.
Puccinia Caricis Auct. Amer. p. p.

Carex straminiformis L. H. Bailey.
Cintractia Caricis (P.) Magn.

Carex stricta Lam.
Cintractia Caricis (P.) Magn.
Ustilago urceolorum Tul.
Laestadia Caricis Dearness & House.
Leptothyrella Caricis Dearness & Barthol.
Macrosporium transversum Pk.

Carex stricta (*cont.*)

Dicaeoma Caricis-strictae (Diet.) Arth. & Kern.
Puccinia Caricis-strictae Diet.
Uromyces Caricis Pk.
Dicaeoma Grossulariae (Lagerh.) Kern.
Puccinia Grossulariae Lagerh.
Puccinia minutissima Arth.
Dicaeoma Urticae (Lagerh.) O. Kuntze.
Puccinia Caricis Auct. Amer. p. p.
Puccinia Urticae Lagerh.
Puccinia urticata Kern.
Puccinia caricina Auct. Amer. p. p.
Puccinia Caricis Auct. Amer. p. p.
?{ Puccinia punctum Auct. Amer. p. p.
Puccinia Striola Auct. Amer. p. p.
Uredo caricina Auct. Amer.
Stagonospora strictae Ell. & Ev.

Carex stricta Lam., var. **angustata** (Boott) L. H. Bailey.

Ascochyta teretiuscula Sacc. & Roum.
Phleospora Caricis Ell. & Ev.
Septoria lineolata Sacc. & Speg.

Carex stricta Lam., var. **decora** L. H. Bailey.

Dicaeoma Grossulariae (Lagerh.) Kern.
Puccinia Grossulariae Lagerh.
Puccinia quadriporula Arth.

Carex strictior Dewey.

Badhamia utricularis (Bull.) B.
Cintractia Caricis (P.) Magn.
Guignardia Caricis Dearness & House.
Dicaeoma Trientalis Arth. & Kern.
Puccina karelica Tranz.
Dicaeoma Urticae (Lagerh.) O. Kuntze.

Carex stygia Fr.

Dicaeoma Grossulariae (Lagerh.) Kern.
Puccinia Grossulariae Lagerh.

Carex stylosa C. A. Mey.

Lophodermium caricinum (Rob.) Duby.
Trochila ignobilis Karst.

Carex subbracteata Mackenzie.

Carex suberecta (Olney) Britton.

Carex subfusca Boott.

Dicaeoma Asterum (Kern) Arth. & Kern.
Puccinia Asterum Kern.

Carex substricta (Kükenth.) Mackenzie.

Dicaeoma Asterum Arth. & Kern.
Dicaeoma Grossulariae (Lagerh.) Kern.
Puccinia uniporula C. R. Orton.
Dicaeoma minutissimum (Arth.) H. S. Jackson
Dicaeoma Urticae (Lagerh.) O. Kuntze.

Carex supina Willd.

Pleospora Elynae (Rabh.) Ces. & De Not.
Pleospora heterospora De Not.
Septoria punctoidea Karst.

Carex Swanii (Fern.) Mackenzie.

Dicaeoma Asterum (Kern) Arth. & Kern.
Puccinia Asterum Kern.
Dicaeoma Grossulariae (Lagerh.) Kern.

Carex tenella Schkuhr.

Puccinia Asterum Kern.
Puccinia Caricis-Asteris Arth.
Puccinia extensicola Plowr.
Puccinia silvatica Auct. Amer. p. p.

Carex tenuiflora Wahlenb.

Dicaeoma Grossulariae (Lagerh.) Kern.

Carex tonsa E. P. Bicknell.

Cintractia Caricis (P.) Magn.

Carex triangularis Boeck.

Dicaeoma Asterum (Kern) Arth. & Kern.
Puccinia Asterum Kern.

Carex tribuloides Wahlenb.

Dicaeoma Asterum (Kern) Arth. & Kern.
Puccinia Asterum Kern.
Puccinia Caricis-Asteris Arth.
Dicaeoma Sambuci Arth.
Puccinia Sambuci Arth.
Stagonospora albescens J. J. Davis.
Nigredo perigynia (Halsted) Arth.
Uromyces perigynius Halsted.

Carex trichocarpa Muhl.

Dicaeoma bolleyanum (Sacc.) O. Kuntze.
Dicaeoma Sambuci Arth.
Puccinia bolleyana Sacc.
Puccinia Sambuci Arth.
Dicaeoma Grossulariae (Lagerh.) Kern.
Dicaeoma hieraciatum (H. D. Jackson) Arth. & Kern.
Dicaeoma Peckii Arth.
Puccinia caricina Ohio Fungi *28* p. p.
Puccinia Caricis Syd. Ured. *1576* p. p.
Puccinia Caricis-Oenotherae J. J. Davis.
Puccinia ludibunda Ell. &Ev.
Puccinia Peckii Kellerm.
Puccinia minuta Diet.
Dicaeoma Urticae (Lagerh.) O. Kuntze.
?Puccinia caricina Auct. Amer. p. p.
Puccinia Caricis Fung. Dak. *12.*
Puccinia Caricis Syd. Ured. *1575.*
Puccinia sylvatica Fung. Columb. *1468.*
Puccinia Urticae Lagerh.
Puccinia urticata Kern.
Nigredo minuta (Diet.) Arth.
Uromyces minutus Diet.

Carex trichocarpa Muhl., var. **aristata** (R. Br.) L. H. Bailey.

Puccinia Caricis Auct. Amer. p. p.
Puccinia Urticae Lagerh.
Puccinia urticata Kern.

Carex trichocarpa Muhl., var. **Deweyi** L. H. Bailey.

Cintractia subinclusa (Körn.) Magn.
Ustilago subinclusa Körn.

Carex trichocarpa Muhl., var. **imberbis** Gray.

Carex triquetra Boott.

Dicaeoma Urticae (Lagerh.) O. Kuntze.
Puccinia Urticae Lagerh.
Puccinia urticata Kern.

Carex trisperma Dewey.
  Darluca Filum (Biv.) Cast.
  Phyllosticta Caricis (Fckl.) Sacc.
  { Dicaeoma Asterum (Kern) Arth. & Kern.
  { Puccinia Asteris-Caricis Fraser.
  { Puccinia Asterum Kern.
  { Dicaeoma Grossulariae (Lagerh.) Kern.
  { Puccinia Grossulariae Lagerh.
Carex Tuckermani Dewey.
  { Dicaeoma microsorum (Körn.) O. Kuntze.
  { Puccinia microsora Körn.
Carex tumulicola Mackenzie.
  Dicaeoma Peckii (Kellerm.) Arth.
Carex turfosa Fr.
  Cintractia Caricis (P.) Magn.
Carex typhina Michx.
  { Dicaeoma Grossulariae (Lagerh.) Kern.
  { Puccinia Grossulariae Lagerh.
Carex umbellata Schkuhr.
  { Cintractia Caricis (P.) Magn.
  { Ustilago urceolorum Tul.
  Puccinia Asterum Kern.
  Puccinia universalis Arth.
  Septoria lineolata Sacc. & Speg.
Carex usta L. H. Bailey.
  { Puccinia atrofusca (Dudley & Thompson)
  {   Holw.
  { Uromyces atrofuscus Dudley & Thompson.
Carex ustulata Wahlenb.
  Sphaerella tassiana De Not.
Carex vaginata Tausch.
  Cintractia Caricis (P.) Magn.
Carex varia Muhl.
  { Cintractia Caricis (P.) Magn.
  { Uredo Caricis P.
  { Ustilago Caricis (P.) Ung.
  { Dicaeoma Asterum (Kern) Arth. & Kern.
  { Puccinia Asterum Kern.
  { Puccinia tenuistipes Syd. Ured. *2132*.
  Septoria lineolata Sacc. & Speg.
  Mycosphaerella recutita (Fr.) Johans.
  { Sphaerella recutita (Fr.) Cke.
  { Sphaeria recutita Fr.
  Nigredo perigynia (Halsted) Arth.
Carex venusta Dewey, var. **minor** Böckl.
  Dicaeoma Grossulariae (Lagerh.) Kern.
Carex verrucosa Muhl.
  { Dicaeoma minutum (Diet.) Arth. & Kern.
  { Puccinia minuta Diet.
Carex vesicaria L.
  { Lophodermium arundinaceum (Schrad. ex Fr.)
  {   Chev., var. caricinum (Desm.) Rehm.
  { Lophodermium caricinum (Desm.) Duby.
  { Phacidium fuscellum Karst.
  { Trochila fuscella Karst.
  Phyllosticta Caricis (Fckl.) Sacc.
  Septoria Caricis Pass.
  Stagonospora albescens J. J. Davis.

Carex vesicaria L., var. **monile** (Tuckerm.) Fern.
  { Cintractia Caricis (P.) Magn.
  { Ustilago Caricis (P.) Ung.
  Cintractia subinclusa (Körn.) Magn.
  Puccinia Grossulariae Lagerh.
Carex vestita Willd.
  Dicaeoma macrosporum (Pk.) Arth. & Kern.
Carex virescens Muhl.
  { ?Dicaeoma Urticae (Lagerh.) O. Kuntze.
  { ?Puccinia Caricis Auct. Amer. p. p.
  { Puccinia Grossulariae Lagerh.
  { Puccinia uniporula C. R. Orton.
  { Nigredo minuta (Diet.) Arth.
  { Uromyces minutus Diet.
  { Caeomurus perigynius (Halsted) O. Kuntze.
  { Nigredo perigynia (Halsted) Arth.
  { Uromyces perigynius Halsted.
  Uromyces Solidagini-Caricis Arth.
  Uromyces uniporulus Kern.
Carex vulpinoidea Michx.
  { Dicaeoma Asterum (Kern) Arth. & Kern.
  { Dicaeoma vulpinoidis (Diet. & Holw.) O.
  {   Kuntze.
  { Puccinia Asterum Kern.
  { ?Puccinia Caricis Auct. Amer. p. p.
  { Puccinia extensicola Plowr.
  { Puccinia vulpinoides Diet. & Holw.
  Puccinia Urticae Lagerh.
Carex Willdenowii Schkuhr.
  Dicaeoma Asterum (Kern) Arth. & Kern.
  { Dicaeoma Peckii (Kellerm.) Arth.
  { Puccinia Peckii Kellerm.
Carex sp. indet.

Ascomycetes

  Actidium caricinum S.
  Chaetomium elatum Kze. ex Fr.
  { Epichloe typhina (P. ex Fr.) Tul.
  { Typhodium typhinum (P. ex Fr.) Seaver.
  Helotium citrinulum, var. Seaveri Rehm.
  Humaria wisconsinensis Rehm.
  ?Hypocrella Hypoxylon (Pk.) Sacc.
  ?Sphaeria Scirporum S.
  { Leptosphaeria Michotii (Westd.) Sacc.
  { Sphaeria Michotii Westd.
  Lophiosphaera perpusilla Sacc.
  Peziza melatephra Lasch.
  { Peziza yogoensis Ell. & Gall.
  { Pyrenopeziza yogoensis (Ell. & Gall.) Sacc.
  ?Pyrenophora phaeocomes (Reb.) Fr.
  Sphaerulina pallens J. J. Davis.

Basidiomycetes

  { Cintractia Caricis (P.) Magn.
  { Cintractia Junci Overholts. 1923.
  Cyphella caricina Pk.
  Marasmius caricicola Kauffman.
  Puccinia silvatica Fung. Columb. *1382*.

Carex sp. indet. (*cont.*)

- Dicaeoma spatiosum (Kern) Arth. & Kern.
- Puccinia spatiosa Kern.

Puccinia Urticae Fung. Columb. *2676.*

Tilletia arctica Rostr.

Uromyces uniporulus Kern.

Ustilago leucoderma B.

FUNGI IMPERFECTI

Actinothyrium graminis Kze. ex Fr.

Arthrinium caricicola Kze. ex Fr.

Botrytis Epichloes Ell. & Dearness.

Cladosporium herbarum P. ex Lk.

Cladosporium nodulosum Cda.

Clasterosporium caricinum S.

- Cryptomela Caricis (Cda.) Sacc.
- Cryptosporium Caricis Cda.

Cryptosporium nubilosum Ell. & Ev.

Dinemasporium graminum Lév.

Epicoccum caricicola S.

Epicoccum sphaerospermum B. & C.

Leptostroma caricinum Fr.

Leptostroma inundatorum S.

Lophiostoma collinum Speg.

- Cometella caricina Fr.
- Macrosporium caricinum Fr.
- Periconia nigriceps (Pk.) Sacc.
- Sporocybe nigriceps Pk.

Periconia opaca Cke.

Phaeoseptoria Caricis Tehon & Daniels.

Phleospora Caricis Ell. & Ev.

Phyllosticta caricicola Sacc. & Scalia.

Pseudostegia nubilosa Bubák.

Ramularia canadensis Ell. & Ev.

Scolecotrichum Clavariarum (Desm.) Sacc.

Septoria carnea Ell. & Ev.

Septoria polita J. J. Davis.

Septoria riparia Pass.

Cyperaceae gen. indet.

Sclerotium rhizodes Awd.

PALMAE

Phoenix canariensis Hort. ex Chabaud.

Exosporium palmivorum Sacc.

Graphiola Phoenicis (Moug.) Poit.

Peronospora Phoenixae Talpin nom. nud.

Phoenix dactylifera L.

Colletotrichum Gossypii Southw.

Exosporium palmivorum Sacc.

Fomes australis Fr.

Graphiola Phoenicis (Moug.) Poit.

Peronospora Phoenixae Talpin nom. nud.

- Sterigmatocystis niger van Tiegh.
- Ustilago Phoenicis Cda.

Phoenix reclinata Jacq.

- Exosporium palmivorum Sacc.
- Graphiola Phoenicis (Moug.) Poit.

Pestalozzia Palmarum Cke.

Chamaerops humilis L.

Graphiola? compressa E. Fischer.

Graphiola Phoenicis (Moug.) Poit.

Thrinax floridana Sargent.

Graphiola on Thrinax.

Thrinax microcarpa Sarg.

Catacauma palmicola F. L. Stevens.

Thrinax ponceana O. F. Cook.

Catacauma palmicola F. L. Stevens.

Helminthosporium Helleri F. L. Stevens.

Meliola furcata Lév.

Thrinax praeceps O. F. Cook.

Graphiola Phoenicis (Moug.) Poit.

Meliola furcata Lév.

Thrinax sp. indet.

Helminthosporium spiculiferum Ell. & Ev.

Coccothrinax alta (O. F. Cook) Becc.

Meliola furcata Lév.

Coccothrinax argentea (Lodd.) Sargent.

Catacauma palmicola F. L. Stevens.

Ciferria Coccothrinacis Fragoso.

Didymella phacidiomorpha (Ces.) Sacc.

Meliola furcata Lév.

Pestalozzia funerea Desm.

Livistona sp. indet.

Melanconium luteocinctum Ell. & Ev.

Pritchardia sp. indet.

Phoma Pritchardiae Cke. & Hark.

Neowashingtonia filamentosa Sudw.

- Phaeochora Neowashingtoniae (Shear)
  Theissen & Syd.
- Sphaerodothis Neowashingtoniae Shear.

Neowashingtonia filifera (Linden) Sudw.

Macrophoma Pritchardiae (Cke. & Hark.) Sacc.

Ozonium omnivorum Shear.

Phoma palmicola Wint.

Sphaerodothis Neowashingtoniae Shear.

Washingtonia gracilis Parish.

Clitocybe tabescens (Scop. ex Fr.) Bres.

Pestalozzia palmicola Sacc. & Syd.

Sabal Adansoni Guerns.

Anthostomella sphaerotheca Earle.

Asterina inquinans Ell. & Ev.

Gnomonia sabalicola Earle.

Graphiola congesta B. & Rav.

- Cf. Helminthosporium spiculiferum Ell. & Ev.
- Helminthosporium spiculiforme Ell. & Ev.

Hendersonia sabaleos Ces.

- Meliola amphitricha B. Grev. 4: 158 p. p.
  non Fr.
- Meliola palmicola Wint.

Phyllosticta palmetto Ell. & Ev.

Sphaeropsis Sabal Cke.

Sphaeropsis sabalicola Ell. & Crav.

Zignoella sabalina El l. & Ev.

Sabal blackburnianum Glazebrook.
  Anthostomella minor Ell. & Ev.
  Anthostomella palmicola (Awd.) Rabh.
  Chaetomium globosum Kze. ex Fr.
  Creonectria ochroleuca Seaver.
  Eutypella sabalina (Cke.) Ell. & Ev.
  Graphiola Phoenicis (Moug.) Poit.
  Helicoma larvula Morg.
  Nectria Peziza (Tode) ex Fr.
  Ophionectria cylindrotheca Seaver.
  Rosellinia Cocoes Henn.
Sabal causiarum (O. F. Cook) Beccari.
  Graphiola Phoenicis (Moug.) Poit.
  Phytophthora palmivora Butler.
Sabal Palmetto (Walt.) Roem. & Schult.
  Amerosporium sabalinum Ell. & Ev.
  Anthostomella melanosticta Ell. & Ev.
  { Asterina inquinans Ell. & Ev.
  { Asterula inquinans (Ell. & Ev.) Theissen.
  { Ellisiodothis inquinans (Ell. & Ev.) Theissen.
  Blitrydium Sabalidis Ell. & Ev.
  Chaetophoma Sabal Cke.
  Cladosporium Palmetto Gerard.
  { Cocconia sparsa (Pk. & Clinton) Sacc.
  { Rhytisma sparsum Pk. & Clinton.
  Cyphella subcyanea Ell. & Ev.
  Dermatea Sabalidis Ell. & Martin.
  { Diatrype deusta Cke.
  { Diatrypella deusta (Cke.) Ell. & Martin.
  Epithele sulphurea Burt.
  Fomes aratus Sacc. & D. Sacc.
  Fomes zonatus Sacc. & D. Sacc.
  Ganoderma sulcatum Murrill.
  Graphiola congesta B. & Rav.
  Helminthosporium Palmetto Gerard.
  Helminthosporium spiculiferum Ell. & Ev.
  Hysterostomella sabalicola Tracy & Earle.
  Leptostroma micropunctum Cke.
  Linospora Palmetto Ell. & Ev.
  Marasmius Sabali B.
  { Meliola amphitricha Rav. Fung. Am. *81.*
  { Meliola furcata Lév. sec. Speg.
  Meliola palmicola Wint.
  Metasphaeria hyalospora Sacc.
  { Metasphaeria Palmetta (Cke.) Sacc.
  { Sphaeria Palmetta Cke.
  Metasphaeria Palmetta (Cke.) Sacc., var. foliicola Ell. & Ev.
  { Mycena Sabali Murrill.
  { Prunulus Sabali Murrill.
  Myriangium sabaleos Weedon.
  Ophiobolus versisporus Ell. & Martin.
  Peniophora investiens Burt.
  Phyllosticta Palmetto Ell. & Ev.
  Poria heteromorpha Murrill.
  { Septobasidium pedicellatum Auct.
  { Septobasidium pseudopedicellatum Burt.
  Thelephora pedicellata S. sec. Massee.
  Sphaerella sabaligena Ell. & Ev.

  Sphaeria sabalicola Ell. & Martin.
  Venturia sabalicola Ell. & Ev.
Sabal sp. indet.
  Asterina sabalicola Earle.
  { Clypeosphaeria sabaligera (B. & C.) Sacc.
  { Leptosphaeria sabaligera (B. & C.) Cke.
  { Sphaeria sabaligera B. & C.
  Coniosporium Arundinis (Cda.) Sacc.
  Dilophia sabalensis (Cke.) Sacc.
  { Eutypella sabalina (Cke.) Ell. & Ev.
  { Valsa sabalina Cke.
  Hymenochaete tenuis Pk.
  Marasmius Sabali B.
  Melanconium Palmarum Cke.
  Melogramma fuliginosum Ell. p. p.
  Metasphaeria sabalensis Ell. & Ev.
  Peniophora flammea Burt.
  Peniophora pertenuis (Karst.) Burt.
  Pestalozzia palmicola Sacc. & Syd.
  Ravenelula gainesvillensis Speg.
  Rhabdospora sabalensis Cke.
  Sphaeria Palmarum Duby.
  Torula conglutinata Cda.
Serenoa serrulata (Roem. & Schult.) Hook. f.
  { Allescherina deusta (Ell. & Martin) Berl.
  { Diatrype deusta (Ell. & Martin) Cke.
  { Diatrypella deusta Ell. & Martin.
  { Anthostomella leucobasis (Ell. & Martin) Sacc.
  { Sphaeria leucobasis Ell. & Martin.
  Anthostomella minor Ell. & Ev.
  { Anthostomella sabalensioides (Ell. & Martin) Sacc.
  { Sphaeria sabalensioides Ell. & Martin.
  Aulographum vagum Desm.
  { Cenangium Sabalidis (Ell. & Martin) Sacc.
  { Dermatea Sabalidis Ell. & Martin.
  Coniosporium palmicola Tracy & Earle.
  { Didymosphaeria serrulata Ell. & Martin.
  { Didymosphaerella serrulata (Ell. & Martin) Cke.
  { Dilophia sabalensis (Cke.) Sacc.
  { Metasphaeria sabalensis Cke.
  { Sphaeria sabalensis Cke.
  Gloniella Curtisii (Duby) Sacc.
  Hypoxylon perforatum (S.) Fr.
  { Gloniopsis lineolata (Cke.) Sacc.
  { Hysterium lineolatum Cke.
  { Hysterographium lineolatum (Cke.) Ell. & Ev.
  Hysterographium praelongum (S.) Sacc.
  { Laestadia serrulata (Ell. & Ev.) Sacc.
  { Sphaerella serrulata Ell. & Ev.
  { Heptameria sabalicola (Ell. & Martin) Cke.
  { Leptosphaeria sabalicola (Ell. & Martin) Sacc.
  { Sphaeria sabalicola Ell. & Martin.
  Melanconium Sabal Cke.
  Meliola palmicola Wint.
  { Ophiobolus versisporus Ell. & Martin.
  { Raphidospora versispora (Ell. & Martin) Cke.
  Sphaerella incisa Ell. & Martin.

Borassus flabellifer L.
Phytophthora palmivora Butler.
Mauritia sp. indet.
Dictyothyriella guianensis Stevens & Manter.
Caryota rumphiana Mart.
Glomerella cingulata (Stoneman) Spaulding &
v. Schrenk.
Arenga saccharifera Labill.
Graphiola Phoenicis (Moug.) Poit.
Chamaedorea bifurcata Oerst.
Lombosia possensis Syd.
Phoenicostroma Chamaedoreae Syd.
Chamaedorea sp. indet.
{ Botryosphaeria palmigena (B. & C.) Bomm. &
  Rouss.
  Hypoxylon palmigenum B. & C.
Oreodoxa oleracea Mart.
Depazea Arecae Spreng.
Nummularia pachyloma Lév.
Oreodoxa regia H. B. K.
Botrytis vulgaris Fr.
Colletotrichum gloeosporioides Penz.
Epicoccum neglectum Desm.
{ Flammula palmicola Murrill.
  Gymnopilus palmicola Murrill.
{ Flammula pholiotoides Murrill.
  Gymnopilus pholiotoides Murrill.
{ Atylospora Roystoniae (Earle) Murrill.
  Hypholoma Roystoniae (Earle) Morg.
Phoma Roystoneae Pk.
Phyllachora Roystoneae Johnston & Bruner.
{ Polyporus nivosellus (Murrill) Sacc. & Trott.
  Polyporus Palmarum (Murrill) Sacc. & Trott.
  Tyromyces nivosellus Murrill.
  Tyromyces Palmarum Murrill.
Roystonea borinquena O. F. Cook.
Meliola denticulata Wint.
Acrista monticola O. F. Cook.
Auerswaldia palmicola Speg.
Meliola furcata Lév.
Pestalozzia funerea Desm.
Euterpe globosa Gaert.
Dothidina palmicola (Speg.) Theissen & Syd.
Meliola furcata Lév.
Xylaria bruneriana Seaver.
Kentia canterburyana F. Muell.
Colletotrichum Kentiae Halsted.
Kentia sp. indet.
Gloeosporium Allescheri Bres.
Glomerella cingulata (Stoneman) Spaulding &
v. Schrenk.
Nectria depauperata Cke.
Areca Catechu L.
Pestalozzia Palmarum Cke.
Cocos Alphonsei Hort.
Didymella Cocos Weedon.
Hysterographium Cocos Weedon.
Cocos butyracea L.
Pleurotus hygrophanus Sacc. & Trav.

Cocos nucifera L.
(Including "coconut" and Cocos sp. indet.)

PHYCOMYCETES

Metarrhizium Anisopliae (Metsch.) Sorok.
Peronospora parasitica (P.) Fr.
Peronospora trichotoma Massee.
Phytophthora Colocasiae Racib.
Phytophthora Faberi Delacr. & Maubl.
Phytophthora omnivora DBy.
Phytophthora palmivora Butler.
Phytophthora parasitica Dastur.
Phytophthora terrestris Sherb.
Pythium debaryanum Hesse.
Pythium palmivorum Butler.
Vasculomyces Xanthosomae Ashby.

ASCOMYCETES

Endoxyla melanoxantha (B. & Br.) Petch.
Eutypella Cocos Ferdinandsen & Winge.
Herpotrichia albidostoma (S.) Sacc.
Herpotrichia diffusa (S.) Ell. & Ev.
Patellaria atrata (Bull.) Fckl.
Rosellinia sancta-cruciana Ferdinandsen &
Winge.
Sphaerella zonata Ell. & Ev.
Valsa chlorina Pat.

BASIDIOMYCETES

Asterostroma muscicola (B. & C.) Massee.
{ Collybia subnivulosa Murrill.
  Gymnopus subnivulosus Murrill.
Crepidotus subcuneiformis Murrill.
{ Flammula chrysotrichoides Murrill.
  Gymnopilus chrysotrichoides Murrill.
{ Flammula Earlei Murrill.
  Gymnopilus Earlei Murrill.
{ Flammula tenuis Murrill.
  Gymnopilus tenuis Murrill.
Fomes lucidus Fr.
Polyporus nivosellus (Murrill) Stevenson.
{ Elfvingia fasciata (Sw.) Murrill.
  Fomes sclerodermus (Lév.) Cke.
  Polyporus marmoratus B. & C.
{ Elfvingia tornata (P.) Murrill.
  Ganoderma tornatum (P.) A. Ames.
{ Lepiota cepaestipes (Sow.) ex Fr.
  Leucocoprinus cepaestipes (Sow. ex Fr.) Pat.
Lepiota jamaicensis Murrill.
Marasmius Sacchari Wakker.
Marasmius Underwoodii Murrill.
{ Geopetalum copulatum (Ehrenb.) Murrill.
  Panus copulatus Ehrenb.
{ Coriolus hirsutus (Fr.) Quél.
  Polystictus hirsutus Fr.
Polystictus sanguineus Fr.
{ Coriolus pinsitus (Fr.) Pat.
  Polystictus villosus (Fr.) Cke.
Poria borbonica Pat.
Uredo coccivora J. R. Johnston.

Cocos nucifera (*cont.*)

Fungi Imperfecti
Cephalosporium Lecanii Zimm.
Cytospora Palmarum Cke.
Cytospora palmicola B. & C.
{ Diplodia cacaoicola Henn.
{ Lasiodiplodia Theobromae (Pat.) Griffon & Maublanc.
{ Diplodia epicocos Cke.
{ Sphaeropsis Palmarum Cke.
Gloeosporium coccophilum Wakefield.
Gloeosporium nanoti Prill. and Del.
Hyalopus Yvonis Dop.
Pestalozzia funerea Desm., var. typica Sacc.
Pestaloziza Palmarum Cke.
{ Thielaviopsis ethaceticus Went.
{ Thielaviopsis paradoxa (De Seyn.) Höhnel.

Cocos plumosa Hook.
Exosporium palmivorum Sacc.
Glomerella cincta (Stoneman) Spaulding & v. Schrenk.
Graphiola Phoenicis Poit.
?Phytophthora palmivora Butler.
Septoria cocoina Ell. & Ev.

Acrocomia aculeata (Jacq.) Lodd.
Cercospora Acrocomiae Stevenson.

Acrocomia media O. F. Cook.
Cercospora Acrocomiae Stevenson.

Palmae gen. indet.

Ascomycetes
{ Anthostomella palmacea (Cke.) Sacc.
{ Didymosphaerella palmacea Cke.
{ Sphaeria palmacea Cke.
Capnodium Citri B. & Desm.
Cookeina tetraspora Seaver.
{ Coccostroma palmigenum (B. & C.) Theissen & Syd.
{ Hypoxylon palmigena B. & C.
Dothidina palmicola (Speg.) Theissen & Syd.
Haplosporella Palmaceae Fragoso & Ciferri.
Lasiosphaeria jamaicensis Seaver.
Meliola amphitricha Fr.
Meliola glabra B. & C.
{ Micropeltis erumpens B. & C.
{ Microthelia erumpens (B. & C.) Speg.
{ Pemphidium erumpens (B. & C.) Sacc.
{ Seynesia erumpens (B. & C.) Petak.
Micropeltis marginata Mont.
Mycosphaerella Palmae Miles.
Nectria suffulta B. & C.
Peziza caulicola Fr.
Peziza melastoma Sow. ex P.
Peziza palmicola B. & C.
Peziza sclerogena B. & C.
Phaeonectria olivacea (Seaver) Sacc. & Trott.
Rosellinia Diderma (S.) Sacc.

Sphaeria sepulta B. & C.
Sphaerostilbe Wrightii B. & C.

Basidiomycetes
Coprinus jamaicensis Murrill.
Cyphella Palmarum B. & C.
Cyphella sessilis Burt.
{ Flammula areolata Murrill.
{ Gymnopilus areolatus Murrill.
{ Flammula aureobrunnea Murrill.
{ Gymnopilus aureobrunneus (B. & C.) Murrill.
{ Flammula subpenetrans Murrill.
{ Gymnopilus subpenetrans Murrill.
Laschia auriscalpium Mont.
Laschia intermedia B. & C.
Lentinus strigosus Fr.
Pilosace palmigena (B. & C.) Morg.
{ Polyporus surinamensis Miq.
{ Rigidoporus micromegas (Mont.) Murrill.
{ Fuscoporella palmicola (B. & C.) Murrill.
{ Polyporus palmicola B. & C.
{ Poria palmicola (B. & C.) Cke.
Poria umbrinescens Murrill.
Schizophyllum alneum (L.) ex Schrt.
Solenia candida P.

Fungi Imperfecti
Aschersonia rufa B. & Br.
Cercospora Acrocomiae Stevenson.
Depazea Palmarum Rabh.
Exosporium palmivorum Sacc.
Helminthosporium dorycarpum Mont.
Phoma palmicola Wint. (?).
Septoria Palmaceae Fragoso & Ciferri.
{ Septonema solidum B. & C.
{ Sirodesmium solidum (B. & C.) Sacc.
{ Phoma maculata (Cke. & Hark.) Sacc.
{ Sphaeropsis maculata Cke. & Hark.
Torula palmicola B. & C.
Zygosporium oscheoides Mont.

ARACEAE

Anthurium acaule Schott.
Mycosphaerella Anthurii Miles.

Anthurium dominicense Schott.
Phyllachora Engleri Speg.

Anthurium gracile Lindl.
Botryosphaeria anthuriicola Massee.

Anthurium scandens Engl.
{ Dothidea Anthurii Bomm. & Rouss.
{ Phyllachora Anthurii (Bomm. & Rouss.) Speg.
Phyllachora Engleri Speg.
Uredo Anthurii (Hariot) Sacc.

Anthurium sp. indet.
Glomerella cincta (Stoneman) Spaulding & v. Schrenk.

Acorus Calamus L.
Darluca Filum (Biv.)Cast.
Ramularia aromatica (Sacc.) v.Höhnel.
⌠Cylindrosporium Acori Pk.
⌡Septocylindrium aromaticum Sacc.
Sphaerulina Acori Dearness & House.
⌠Nigredo pyriformis (Cke.) Arth.
⌡Uromyces pyriformis Cke.

Monstera pertusa (L.) Schott.
Macrophoma Philodendri Pk.
Macrophoma Philodendri Pk., var. maculi-
cola Pk.

Symplocarpus foetidus (L.) Nutt.
Botrytis cinerea P.†
Cercospora Symplocarpi Pk.
⌠Creonectria seminicola Seaver.
⌡Nectria seminicola Seaver.
Gloeosporium foetidophilum Stoneman.
Septoria spiculosa Ell. & Holw.

Orontium aquaticum L.
⌠Botrytis streptothrix (C. & E.) Sacc.
⌡Polyactis streptothrix C. & E.
Epicoccum duriaeanum Mont.
⌠Laestadia Orontii (Ell. & Ev.) Berl. & Vogl.
⌡Physalospora Orontii Ell. & Ev.
Phyllosticta Orontii Ell. & Martin.
Ramularia Orontii Ell. & Martin.
Sphaerella Orontii Ell. & Ev.
Stilbum aciculosum Ell. & Ev.
Volutella diaphana Ell.

Calla palustris L.
Cercospora Callae Pk. & G. W. Clinton.

Homalomena Wallisii (Mast.) Regel.
Glomerella cincta (Stoneman) Spaulding &
v. Schrenk.

Philodendron Krebsii Schott.
Colletotrichum Philodendri Henn.
Helminthosporium Philodendri F. L. Stevens.
Isthmospora spinosa F. L. Stevens.
Meliola Philodendri F. L. Stevens.
Scolecopeltella microcarpa Speg.
Trichopeltis reptans (B. & C.) Speg.

Philodendron tripartitum (Jacq.) Schott.
Chaetothyrium permixtum Syd.
Lembosia Philodendri Henn.
Pezolepis denigrata Syd.
Uredo jucunda Syd.

Dieffenbachia seguine (Jacq.) Schott.
Arthrobotryum Dieffenbachiae F. L. Stevens.
Cryptoderis Dieffenbachiae Fragoso & Ciferri.
Guignardia Dieffenbachiae Fragoso & Ciferri.
Meliola Dieffenbachiae F. L. Stevens.
Phyllosticta Colocasiae v. Höhnel.

Dieffenbachia ulmifolia ex Duss.
Phleospora Dieffenbachiae Pat.

Dieffenbachia sp. indet.
Helicomyces mirabilis Pk.
⌠Hypocrea epiphylla Massee.
⌡Hypocrella epiphylla (Massee) Sacc.

Peltandra virginica (L.) Kunth.
Cercospora Callae Pk. & G. W. Clinton.
Cercospora pachyspora Ell. & Ev.
Gloeosporium paludosum Ell. & Gall.
Pestalozzia aquatica Ell. & Ev.
Ramularia sp. indet.
⌠Perisporium Caladii S.
⌡Sclerotium Caladii S.
Aecidium Ari Auct. Amer.
Aecidium Caladii S.
Caeoma (Uredo) Ari-Virginici S.
Caeoma (Aecidium) aroidatum Lk.
Caeoma Caladii (S.) Lk.
Caeoma (Aecidium) dracontinatum S.
Caeomurus Caladii (Farl.) O. Kuntze.
Nigredo Caladii (Farl.) Arth.
Puccinia Ari-triphylli S.
Uredo Caladii S.
Uredo Caladii (S.) Spreng.
Uromyces Ari Farl.
Uromyces Arisaemae Cke.
Uromyces Ari-Virginici (S.) Howe.
Uromyces Caladii Farl.
⌡Uromyces Peltandrae Howe.

Richardia africana Kunth.
Cercospora Callae Pk. & G. W. Clinton.
Cercospora richardiaecola Atk.
Pestalozzia Richardiae Halsted.
Phyllosticta Richardiae Halsted.
Sphaeropsis averyana Gerard.

Alocasia sp. indet.
Diplodia tubericola (Ell. & Ev.) Taubenhaus.

Colocasia esculenta Schott.
Diplodia tubericola (Ell. & Ev.) Taubenhaus.
Fusarium caudatum Wr.
Fusarium oxysporum Schl.
Fusarium redolens Wr.
Fusarium Solani (Mart.) Sacc.
Hormiscium Colocasiae Ashby.
Hormiscium Xanthosomae Ashby.
Macrophoma subconica Ell. & Ev.
Rosellinia bunodes B. & Br.
Rosellinia Pepo Pat.
Sclerotium Rolfsii Sacc.
Vasculomyces Xanthosomae Ashby.

PHYCOMYCETES

Peronospora trichotoma Massee.
Phytophthora Colocasiae Racib.
Phytophthora palmivora Butler.
Pythium debaryanum Hesse.
Pythium hydnosporum (Mont.) Schrt.
Rhizopus Artocarpi Racib.
Rhizopus arrhizus Fisch.

Colocasia esculenta (*cont.*)
Rhizopus chinensis Saito.
Rhizopus delemar (Boid.) Wehmer & Hanzawa.
Rhizopus Maydis Bruderl.
Rhizopus nigricans Ehrenb.
Rhizopus nodosus Namysl.
Rhizopus Oryzae Wint.
Rhizopus reflexus Bain.
Rhizopus Tritici Saito.

Colocasia sp. indet.
Heterosporium Colocasiae Massee.
Phyllosticta colocasicola v. Höhnel.

Colocasia? sp. indet. (Including Yautia, Xanthosoma, Minty Coco and others.)
Gloeosporium affine Sacc.
Periconia pycnospora Fres.
Peronospora trichotoma Massee.
Phyllosticta Colocasiae v. Höhnel.
Phyllosticta Xanthosomatis Sacc.
Pythium debaryanum Hesse.
Sclerotium Caladii S.
Sclerotium Rolfsii Sacc.
Stilbella flavida Henn.
Vasculomyces Xanthosomae Ashby.

Caladium bicolor Vent.
Helminthosporium Caladii F. L. Stevens.

Caladium Colocasia Schott.
Peronospora trichomata Massee.
⎰ Nigredo Caladii (Farl.) Arth.
⎱ Uromyces Caladii Farl.

Xanthosoma sagittifolium (L.) Schott.
Cercospora pachyspora Ell. & Ev.
Diplodia tubericola (Ell. & Ev.) Taubenhaus.
Fusarium oxysporum Schl.

Xanthosoma sp. indet.
Periconia pycnospora Fres.

Arum arifolium Auct.
Laestadia Ari Ell. & Ev.
Vermicularia trichella Fr.

Arisaema Dracontium (L.) Schott.
⎧ Aecidium Caladii S.
⎪ Aecidium Dracontii M. A. Curtis.
⎪ Aecidium dracontinatum S.
⎪ Caeoma (Uredo) dracontinatum S.
⎨ Caeomurus Caladii (Farl.) O. Kuntze.
⎪ Nigredo Caladii (Farl.) Arth.
⎪ Uromyces Arisaemae Cke.
⎪ Uromyces Caladii Farl.
⎩ Uromyces Caladii Farl. I.

Arisaema macrospathum Benth.
⎧ Nigredo Caladii (Farl.) Arth.
⎨ Uromyces Arisaemae Cke.
⎩ Uromyces Caladii Farl.

Arisaema Stewardsonii Brit.
⎰ Nigredo Caladii (Farl.) Arth.
⎱ Uromyces Arisaemae Cke.

Arisaema triphyllum (L.) Schott.
Polyactis Streptothrix C. & E.
Ramularia Arisaematis Ell. & Dearness.
⎧ Aecidium Ari Auct. Amer.
⎪ Aecidium Caladii S.
⎪ Caeoma (Uredo) Ari-Virginici S.
⎪ Caeoma (Aecidium) aroidatum Lk.
⎪ Caeoma (Aecidium) dracontinatum S.
⎪ Caeomurus Caladii (Farl.) O. Kuntze.
⎨ Nigredo Caladii (Farl.) Arth.
⎪ Puccinia Ari-triphylli S.
⎪ Uromyces Ari Farl.
⎪ Uromyces Arisaemae Cke.
⎪ Uromyces Caladii Farl.
⎩ Uromyces Peltandrae Howe.

Araceae gen. indet.
Cercospora aricola Sacc.

LEMNACEAE

Spirodela polyrhiza (L.) Schleid.
⎰ Cornuella Lemnae Setch.
⎱ Tracya Lemnae (Setch.) Syd.

XYRIDACEAE

Xyris elata Chapm.
Cercospora Xyridis Miles.
Xyris fimbriata Ell.
Cladosporium Xyridis Tracy & Earle.

ERIOCAULONACEAE

Eriocaulon septangulare With.
Tolyposporium Eriocauli G. P. Clinton.
Ustilago Eriocauli (Massee) G. P. Clinton.

BROMELIACEAE

Bromelia Pinguin L.
Desmotascus portoricensis F. L. Stevens.
Marasmius Sacchari Wakker.
Perisporium Bromeliae F. L. Stevens.
⎰ Chaetosphaeria Bromeliae Ciferri & Fragoso.
⎱ Toroa dimerosporioides (Speg.) Syd.
Bromelia sp. indet.
Echidnodes Bromeliae Ryan.
Ananas comosus Merr.
(A. sativus Schult. f.)
⎰ Asterella aliena (Ell. & Gall.) Sacc. & Trott.
⎱ Asterina aliena Ell. & Gall.
Capnodium Citri B. & Desm.
Phytophthora parasitica Dastur.
Phytophthora terrestris Sherb.
Spegazzinia ornata Sacc.
⎧ Chalara paradoxa (Seynes) Sacc.
⎨ Thielaviopsis ethaceticus Went.
⎩ Thielaviopsis paradoxa (De Seynes) v. Höhnel.
Trichosphaeria Sacchari Massee.
Pitcairnia angustifolia Ait.
Diachaea leucopoda (Bull.) Rostf., var.
globosa Lister.

Pitcairnia corallina Linden.
  Glomerella cingulata (Stoneman) Spaulding &
    v. Schrenk.
Pitcairnia Palmeri Watson.
  {Dicaeoma (?) Pitcairniae (Lagerh.) Arth.
  {Puccinia Pitcairniae Lagerh.
Guzmania sp. indet.
  Toroa dimerosporioides (Speg.) Syd.
Tillandsia leiboldiana Schl.
  Ustilago Tillandsiae Patterson.
Tillandsia recurvata L.
  Colletotrichum Bromeliacearum Birge.
Tillandsia usneoides L.
  {Psilonia cylindrospora B. & C.
  {Volutella cylindrospora (B. & C.) Sacc.
Tillandsia sp. indet.
  Colletotrichum setosum Patterson.
Bromeliaceae gen. indet.
  Aulographum maculare B. & Br.
  Echinodes Bromeliacearum (Rehm) Theissen
    & Syd.

COMMELINACEAE

Commelina angustifolia Michx.
  Colletotrichum Commelinae Ell. & Ev.
  {Nigredo Commelinae (Cke.) Arth.
  {Uromyces Spegazzinii Arth.
Commelina coelestis Willd.
  {Dicaeoma (?) Commelinae (Holw.) Arth.
  {Puccinia Commelinae Holw.
Commelina elegans H.B.K.
  Illosporium Commelinae F. L. Stevens.
  {Phakopsora tecta Jackson & Holw.
  {?Uredo Commelyneae Kalchbr.
  Mycosphaerella tetraspora Seaver.
  {Nigredo Commelinae (Cke.) Arth.
  {Uredo commelinacea Ell. & Kelsey.
  {Uromyces Commelinae Cke.
  {Uromyces Spegazzinii Arth.
Commelina erecta L.
  {Nigredo Commelinae (Cke.) Arth.
  {Uromyces Spegazzinii Arth.
Commelina graminifolia H. B. K.
  Dicaeoma (?) Commelinae (Holw.) Arth.
Commelina longicaulis Jacq.
  Didymium nigripes (L.) Fr.
  Illosporium Commelinae F. L. Stevens.
  Phyllosticta commelinicola Young.
  Uredo Commelyneae Kalchbr.
  {Nigredo Commelinae (Cke.) Arth.
  {Uromyces Commelinae Cke.
Commelina pallida Willd.
Commelina persicariifolia Delile.
Commelina tuberosa L.
  {Dicaeoma (?) Commelinae (Holw.) Arth.
  {Puccinia Commelinae Holw.
Commelina virginica L.
  Illosporium Commelinae F. L. Stevens.
  Phakopsora tecta Jackson & Holw.

Commelina sp. indet.
  Stilbella flavida Henn.
Tradescantia cumanensis Kunth.
Tradescantia multiflora Sw.
Tradescantia Pringlei Watson.
  {Nigredo Commelinae (Cke.) Arth.
  {Uromyces Commelinae Cke.
Tradescantia virginiana L.
  Cylindrosporium Tradescantiae Ell. & Kel-
    lerm.
  Oidium crysiphoides Fr.
Campelia zanonia H.B.K.
  Uredo Campeliae Kern & Whetzel. 1 Jan. 1926.
  Uredo Campeliae Syd. 8 Dec. 1926.

PONTEDERIACEAE

Eichhornia crassipes Solms.
  Cercospora Piaropi Tharp.
  Uredo Eichhorniae Fragoso & Ciferri.
Pontederia cordata L.
  Cercospora Pontederiae Ell. & Dearness.
  {Mycosphaerella Pontederiae (Pk.) House.
  {Sphaerella paludosa Ell. & Ev.
  {Sphaerella Pontederiae Pk.
  {Nigredo Pontederiae (Gerard) Arth.
  {Uromyces Caladii Auct. p. p.
  {Uromyces Pontederiae Gerard. 1875.
  {Uromyces Pontederiae Cke. in Fung. Am. *793*.
  { 1882.
  {Uromyces Pontederiae Speg. 1888.
Pontederia sagittata Presl.
  Uromyces Pontederiae Gerard.
Pontederia sp. indet.
  Saprolegnia hypogyna Pringsh.

JUNCACEAE

Juncus aceticus Willd.
  {Clathrospora Elynae Rabh.
  {Pleospora Elynae (Rabh.) Ces. & De Not.
  Mollisia junciseda Karst.
Juncus acuminatus Michx.
  Cintractia Junci (S.) Trel.
  Nigredo Silphii Arth.
Juncus alpinus Vill.
  Mollisia alpina Rostr.
Juncus ater Rydb.
  {Nigredo Junci (Desm.) Arth.
  {Uromyces Junci (Desm.) Tul.
Juncus balticus Willd.
  Cladosporium fasciculatum Cda.
  Coniothyrium Junci Ell. & Ev.
  Graphyllium Chloes Clements, var. Junci Pk.
  Pleospora juncicola Ell. & Ev.
  Urocystis Junci Lagerh.
  {Caeomurus Junci (Desm.) O. Kuntze.
  {Nigredo Junci (Desm.) Arth.
  {Uromyces Junci (Desm.) Tul.
Juncus balticus Willd., var. montanus Engelm.
  Camptoum cuspidatum Cke. & Hark.

Juncus balticus Willd., var. **vallicola** Rydb.
  Leptothyrium juncinum Cke. & Hark.
Juncus biglumis L.
  Belonidium juncisedum (Karst.) J. Lind.
  Hendersonia arundinacea (Desm.) Sacc.
  Leptosphaeria juncina (Awd.) Sacc.
  Naevia pusilla (Lib.) Rehm.
  Rhabdospora Drabae (Fckl.) Berl. & Vogl.
  Mycosphaerella wichuriana (Schrt.) Johans.
  Sphaerella tassiana De Not.
Juncus Bolanderi Engelm.
  { Nigredo Junci-effusi (Syd.) Arth.
  { Uromyces Junci-effusi Syd.
Juncus canadensis J. Gay.
  Cercospora juncina Sacc.
Juncus castaneus Smith.
  { Belonidium juncisedum (Karst.) J. Lind.
  { Mollisia junciseda Karst.
Juncus dichotomus Ell.
  Metasphaeria defodiens (Ell.) Sacc.
  { Nigredo Silphii Arth.
  { Uromyces Junci-tenuis Syd.
  { Uromyces Silphii Arth.
Juncus diffusissimus Buckley.
  Cintractia Junci (S.) Trel.
Juncus Drummondii Mey.
  { Duplicaria acuminata Ell. & Ev.
  { Cf. Crandallia juncicola Ell. & Ev.
Juncus Dudleyi Wiegand.
  { Nigredo Silphii Arth.
  { Uromyces Junci Auct. Amer. p. p.
  { Uromyces Junci-tenuis Syd.
  { Uromyces Silphii Arth.
Juncus effusus L.
  { Cintractia Junci (S.) Trel.
  { Ustilago Junci (S.) B.
  { Dothidella Junci (Fr.) Sacc.
  { Phyllachora Junci (Fr.) Fckl.
  { Leptosphaeria defodiens Ell.
  { Metasphaeria defodiens (Ell.) Sacc.
  { Sphaeria defodiens Ell.
  Peziza luteodisca Pk.
  ?Puccinia obtecta Pk.
  { Nigredo Junci-effusi (Syd.) Arth.
  { Puccinia Junci S.
  { Trichobasis Junci Auct. Amer.
  { Uromyces effusus Arth.
  { Uromyces Junci Auct. Amer. p. p.
  { Uromyces Junci-effusi Syd.
Juncus ensifolius Wikstr.
Juncus falcatus E. Mey.
  { Nigredo Junci-effusi (Syd.) Arth.
  { Uromyces Junci N. Am. Uredinales *689*.
  { Uromyces Junci-effusi Syd.
Juncus filiformis L.
  { Dothidea Junci Fr.
  { Phyllachora Junci (Fr.) Fckl.
  { Sphaeria Junci Fr.
  { Sphaeria striiformis, var. Junci A. & S.

Juncus Uromyces Junci (Desm.) Tul.
  { Nigredo Junci-effusi (Syd.) Arth.
  { Uromyces Junci-effusi Syd.
Juncus georgianus Coville.
  { Nigredo Silphii Arth.
  { Uromyces Silphii Arth.
Juncus Greenei Oakes & Tuckerm.
  { Leptosphaeria Michotii (Westd.) Sacc.
  { Sphaeria Michotii Westd.
  { Nigredo Silphii Arth.
  { Uromyces Junci Auct. Amer. p. p.
  { Uromyces Junci-tenuis Syd.
  { Uromyces Silphii Arth.
Juncus interior Wiegand.
  Phyllachora Junci (Fr.) Fckl.
  { Nigredo Silphii Arth.
  { Uromyces Silphii Arth.
Juncus Lescurii Boland.
  Hendersonia culmicola Sacc.
  Hendersonia scirpicola Cke. & Hark.
  Leptothyrium juncinum Cke. & Hark.
  Trullula Junci Cke. & Hark.
  { Caeomurus Junci (Desm.) O. Kuntze.
  { Nigredo Junci (Desm.) Arth.
  { Uromyces Junci (Desm.) Tul.
Juncus longistylus Torr.
  { Nigredo Silphii Arth.
  { Uromyces Junci Auct. Amer. p. p.
  { Uromyces Silphii Arth.
Juncus marginatus Rostk.
  Ramularia Junci Pk.
  { Nigredo Silphii Arth.
  { Uromyces Silphii Arth.
Juncus maritimus L.
  { Leptosphaeria albopunctata (Westd.) Sacc.
  { Leptosphaeria sticta Ell. & Ev.
  { Hendersonia trimera Cke.
  { Stagonospora trimera (Cke.) Sacc.
Juncus mertensianus Bong.
  Nigredo Junci (Desm.) Arth.
  { Nigredo Junci-effusi (Syd.) Arth.
  { Uromyces Junci Auct. Amer. p. p.
  { Uromyces Junci-effusi Syd.
Juncus mexicanus Willd.
  { Nigredo Junci (Desm.) Arth.
  { Uromyces Junci (Desm.) Tul.
Juncus nevadensis Watson.
  { Uromyces Junci Syd. Ured. *1760*.
  { Uromyces Junci-effusi Syd.
Juncus nodosus L.
  Claviceps Junci Adams.
Juncus occidentalis Wiegand.
  { Nigredo Silphii Arth.
  { Uromyces Silphii Arth.
Juncus orthophyllus Coville.
Juncus oxymeris Engelm.
  { Nigredo Junci-effusi (Syd.) Arth.
  { Uromyces Junci Auct. Amer. p. p.
  { Uromyces Junci-effusi Syd.

Juncus patens E. Mey.
  {Nigredo Junci (Desm.) Arth.
  {Uromyces Junci (Desm.) Tul.
Juncus phaeocephalus Engelm.
  {Nigredo Junci-effusi (Syd.) Arth.
  {Uromyces Junci-effusi Syd.
Juncus robustus Watson.
  Uromyces Junci (Desm.) Tul.
Juncus saximontanus A. Nels.
  {Nigredo Junci-effusi (Syd.) Arth.
  {Uromyces Junci Auct. Amer. p. p.
Juncus setosus (Coville) Small.
  Nigredo Silphii Arth.
Juncus Suksdorfii Piper.
  Nigredo Junci-effusi (Syd.) Arth.
  Uromyces Junci (Desm.) Tul.
Juncus tenuis Willd.
  {Caeoma (Uredo) Junci S.
  {Cintractia Junci (S.) Trel.
  {Ustilago Junci (S.) M. A. Curtis.
  Ustilago Liebmanni Henn.
  Darluca Filum (Biv.) Cast.
  {Dothidella Junci (Fr.) Sacc.
  {Phyllachora Junci (Fr.) Fckl.
  {Mollisia stictoides (C. & E.) Sacc.
  Peziza stictoidea C. & E.
  Caeomurus Junci Auct. Amer.
  Nigredo Silphii Arth.
  {Uromyces Junci Auct. Amer. p. p.
  Uromyces Junci-tenuis Syd.
  {Uromyces Silphii Arth.
Juncus textilis Buchenau.
Juncus Torreyi Coville.
  {Nigredo Junci (Desm.) Arth.
  {Uromyces Junci (Desm.) Tul.
Juncus trifidus L.
  Mollisia junciseda Karst.
  Septoria Junci Desm.
  Trochila juncicola Rostr.
Juncus triglumis L.
  Hendersonia Luzulae Westd.
  Pleospora herbarum (Fr.) Rabh.
  Trochila juncicola Rostr.
Juncus xiphioides E. Mey.
  Nigredo Junci (Desm.) Arth.
  {Nigredo Junci-effusi (Syd.) Arth.
  {Uromyces Junci Auct. Amer. p. p.
  {Uromyces Junci-effusi Syd.
Juncus sp. indet.
  Ciboria juncigena Ell. & Ev.
  Coniothyrium Junci Ell. & Ev.
  {Darluca Filum (Biv.) Cast.
  {Sphaeronema consors B. & C.
  {Didymella juncina (B. & Rav.) Sacc.
  {Sphaeria juncina B. & Rav.
  Diplonaevia sphaerelloides (Ell.) Sacc.
  Propolis sphaerelloides Ell.
  {Discella tenuispora Cke. & Hark.
  {Discula tenuispora (Cke. & Hark.) Sacc.

  {Fusarium Curtisii Cke.
  {Fusarium glumarum Sacc.
  {Fusarium pallens B. & C.
  Gloeosporium? Junci Ell. & Ev.
  Leptosphaeria Michotii (Westd.) Sacc.
  {Pleospora infectoria, var. juncigena (Cke.) Berl.
  {Pleospora juncigena Cke.
  ?Sphaeria graminis P.
  Tureenia juncoidea J. G. Hall.
Luzula arctica Bl.
  Pleospora Elynae (Rabh.) Ces. & De Not.
  Trochila juncicola Rostr.
Luzula arcuata Meyer.
  Diplodia Simmonsii Rostr.
  Leptosphaeria culmorum Awd.
  Naevia pusilla (Lib.) Rehm.
  Septoria minuta Karst.
  {Mycosphaerella Luzulae (Cke.) Dearness.
  {Sphaerella Luzulae Cke.
  Stagonospora aquatica Sacc., var. luzulicola Sacc. & Scalia.
  {Hendersonia Luzulae Westd.
  {Stagonospora Luzulae (Westd.) Sacc.
  Trochila juncicola Rostr.
Luzula campestris (L.) DC.
  {Cintractia Luzulae (Sacc.) G. P. Clinton.
  {Ustilago Luzulae Sacc.
  Leptosphaeria culmorum Awd.
  {Dicaeoma obscurum (Schrt.) O. Kuntze.
  {Puccinia obscura Schrt.
  Puccinia obscura Schrt., var. vernalis Pk.
  Sphaerella tassiana De Not.
  {Hendersonia Luzulae Westd.
  {Stagonospora Luzulae (Westd.) Sacc.
  Trochila juncicola Rostr.
Luzula Carolinae Watson.
Luzula comosa Meyer.
  {Dicaeoma obscurum (Schrt.) O. Kuntze.
  {Puccinia obscura Schrt.
Luzula confusa Lindeberg.
  Diplodia Simmonsii Rostr.
  Hendersonia arundinacea (Desm.) Sacc.
  Naevia pusilla (Lib.) Rehm.
  {Clathrospora Elynae Rabh.
  {Pleospora Elynae (Rabh.) Ces. & De Not.
  Pleospora pentamera Karst.
  Rhabdospora Drabae (Fckl.) Berl. & Vogl.
  Sphaerella Luzulae Cke.
  {Mycosphaerella tassiana (De Not.) Johans.
  {Sphaerella tassiana De Not.
  Mycosphaerella wichuriana (Schrt.) Johans.
  Trochila juncicola Rostr.
Luzula intermedia A. Nels.
  {Dicaeoma obscurum (Schrt.) O. Kuntze.
  {Puccinia obscura Schrt.
Luzula multiflora Lej.
  Pleospora pentamera Karst.

Luzula nivalis Laest.
　Hendersonia arundinacea (Desm.) Sacc.
　Hendersonia crastophila Sacc.
　Naevia pusilla (Lib.) Rehm.
　{ Clathrospora pentamera (Karst.) Berl.
　{ Pleospora pentamera Karst.
　Mycosphaerella tassiana (De Not.) Johans.
　Trochila juncicola Rostr.
Luzula parviflora (Ehrh.) Desv.
　Mollisia luzulina Karst.
　{ Dicaeoma obscurum (Schrt.) O. Kuntze.
　{ Puccinia obscura Schrt.
Luzula saltuensis Fern.
　Puccinia obscura Schrt.
　Uromyces Junci (Desm.) Tul.
Luzula spicata (L.) DC.
　Leptosphaeria culmorum Awd.
　Leptostroma Luzulae Lib.
　Phoma Luzulae Rostr.
　Pyrenophora comata (Niessl) Sacc.
　Septoria minuta Schrt.
　Sphaerella tassiana De Not.
　Stagonospora Luzulae (Westd.) Sacc.
　Trochila juncicola Rostr.
Luzula sp. indet.
　Puccinia oblongata (Fisch.) Wint. ?

LILIACEAE

Tofieldia borealis Wahl.
　Hendersonia Luzulae Westd.
　Laestadia Tofieldiae Tassi.
　Metasphaeria borealis Rostr.
　Pleospora herbarum (Fr.) Rabh.
　Septoria semilunaris Johans.
　Sphaerella tassiana De Not.
Tofieldia coccinea Richards.
　Cladosporium herbarum (P.) ex Lk.
　Pleospora oligomera Sacc. & Speg.
　Pyrenophora chrysospora (Niessl) Sacc.
Tofieldia palustris Huds.
　Metasphaeria borealis Rostr.
　Microsticta vagans Desm.
　Phoma Tofieldiae Rostr.
　Pleospora herbarum (Fr.) Rabh.
　Sphaerella tassiana De Not.
Xerophyllum asphodeloides (L.) Nutt.
　{ Asteridium Xerophylli (Ell.) Sacc.
　{ Asterina Xerophylli Ell.
　Hendersonia Xerophylli Ell.
　{ Heptameria hysterioides (Ell. & Ev.) Cke.
　{ Leptosphaeria hysterioides Ell. & Ev.
　{ Leptosphaeria Xerophylli Ell.
　{ Metasphaeria Xerophylli (Ell.) Sacc.
　{ Sphaerulina Xerophylli (Ell.) Cke.
　Pestalozzia capitata Ell.
　{ Dicaeoma atropunctum (Pk. & Clinton) O.
　{ 　Kuntze.
　{ Puccinia atropuncta Pk. & Clinton.

Xerophyllum tenax Nutt.
　{ Leptosphaeria hysterioides Ell. & Ev.
　{ Massarina hysterioides (Ell. & Ev.) Berl.
　Leptostroma Xerophylli Petrak.
　Mycosphaerella Xerophylli Syd.
　Pleospora Xerophylli Petrak.
Helonias bullata L.
　{ Hendersonia heloniifolia (C. & E.) Cke.
　{ Leptosphaeria heloniifolia (C. & E.) Sacc.
　{ Sphaerella heloniifolia C. & E.
　{ Sphaeria heloniifolia C. & E.
Amianthium muscitoxicum (Walt.) Gray.
　{ Dicaeoma atropunctum (Pk. & Clinton) O.
　{ 　Kuntze.
　{ Puccinia atropuncta [var. Chrospermae].
Schoenocaulon dubium (Michx.) Small.
Schoenocaulon gracile Gray.
Stenanthium angustifolium Kunth.
　{ Dicaeoma atropunctum (Pk. & Clinton) O.
　{ 　Kuntze.
　{ Puccinia atropuncta Pk. & Clinton.
　Puccinia Zygadeni Trel.
　Uredo Schoenocauli Ell. & Ev.
Stenanthium occidentale Gray.
　{ Dicaeoma grumosum (Syd. & Holw.) Arth.
　{ Puccinia grumosa Syd. & Holw.
Zygadenus chloranthus Richards.
　{ Puccinia atropuncta Pk. & Clinton.
　{ Puccinia Zygadeni Trel.
Zygadenus elegans Pursh.
　{ Puccinia atropuncta Pk. & Clinton.
　{ Puccinia Zygadeni Trel.
　{ Dicaeoma grumosum (Syd. & Holw.) Arth.
　{ Puccinia grumosa Syd. & Holw.
　Urocystis Flowersii Garrett.
　Nigredo Zygadeni (Pk.) Arth.
Zygadenus falcatus Rydb.
Zygadenus Fremontii Torr.
　{ Nigredo Zygadeni (Pk.) Arth.
　{ Uromyces Fraserae Arth. & Ricker.
　{ Uromyces Zygadeni Pk.
Zygadenus glaucus Nutt.
　{ Dicaeoma atropunctum (Pk. & Clinton) O.
　{ 　Kuntze.
　{ Puccinia Zygadeni Trel.
　Nigredo Zygadeni (Pk.) Arth.
Zygadenus gramineus Rydb.
　{ Nigredo Zygadeni (Pk.) Arth.
　{ Uromyces Zygadeni Pk.
Zygadenus intermedius Torr.
　Dicaeoma grumosum (Syd. & Holw.) Arth.
　Nigredo Zygadeni (Pk.) Arth.
Zygadenus muscitoxicus Regel.
　Puccinia atropuncta Pk. & Clinton.
Zygadenus Nuttallii Gray.
Zygadenus paniculatus Watson.
Zygadenus venenosus Watson.
　{ Nigredo Zygadeni (Pk.) Arth.
　{ Uromyces Zygadeni Pk.

Melanthium parviflorum (Michx.) Watson.
  { Dicaeoma atropunctum (Pk. & Clinton) O.
     Kuntze.
  { Puccinia atropuncta Pk. & Clinton.
  Puccinia Melanthii Bubák.
Veratrum californicum Durand.
  Ascochyta veratrina Ell. & Ev.
  { Marssonia Veratri Ell. & Ev.
  { Marssonina Veratri (Ell. & Ev.) Magn.
  Puccinia atropuncta Pk. & Clinton.
  { Dicaeoma Veratri (Duby) O. Kuntze.
  { Puccinia Veratri Duby. 1830.
  { Puccinia Veratri Niessl. 1859.
  { Puccinia Veratri G. W. Clinton. 1875.
Veratrum eschscholtzianum (R. & S.) Rydb.
  Dicaeoma Veratri (Duby) O. Kuntze.
  Phoma majanthemum Pk.
Veratrum speciosum Rydb.
  Phyllosticta melanoplaca Thm.
  Puccinia atropuncta Pk. & Clinton.
  { Dicaeoma Veratri (Duby) O. Kuntze.
  { Puccinia Veratri Duby.
  { Puccinia Veratri Niessl.
  { Puccinia Veratri G. W. Clinton.
Veratrum tenuipetalum A. Heller.
  Dicaeoma Veratri (Duby) O. Kuntze.
Veratrum viride Ait.
  Cercosporella terminalis Pk.
  Cercosporella Veratri Pk.
  Cylindrosporium veratrinum Sacc. & Wint.
  Ophiobolus filisporus (C. & E.) Sacc.
  { Dothidea melanoplaca Desm.
  { Phyllachora melanoplaca (Desm.) Sacc.
  { Dicaeoma atropunctum (Pk. & Clinton) O.
     Kuntze.
  { Puccinia atropuncta Pk. & Clinton.
  { Dicaeoma Veratri (Duby) O. Kuntze.
  { Puccinia Veratri Duby.
  { Puccinia Veratri Niessl.
  { Puccinia Veratri G. W. Clinton.
  Uredo confluens, var. b., S. Syn. Car.
  Vermicularia veratrina Ell. & Ev.
Veratrum Woodii Robbins.
  { Dicaeoma atropunctum (Pk. & Clinton) O.
     Kuntze.
  { Puccinia atropuncta Pk. & Clinton.
Veratrum sp. indet.
  Diplodia Veratri Earle.
  Hymenoscypha cyathoidea Phil.
  Lachnum setigerum Lindau.
  Leptosphaeria Veratri Earle.
  Patinella Aloysii-sabaudiae Sacc.
  Peziza setigera Phil.
  Sclerotium durum P. ex Fr.
Uvularia grandiflora Sm.
  { Aecidium Convallariae Schum.
  { Aecidium Uvulariae S.
  { Dicaeoma Majanthae Arth. I.
  Diplodia Uvulariae J. J. Davis.

Phyllosticta cruenta (Fr.) Kickx.
  { Phyllosticta cruenta (Fr.) Kickx., var. dis-
     cincta J. J. Davis.
  { Phyllosticta discincta J. J. Davis.
  Phyllosticta Uvulariae Gall.
Uvularia perfoliata L.
  Uromyces acuminatus, var. magnatus Arth. I.
  { Aecidium Convallariae Schum.
  { Aecidium Majanthae Schum.
  { Aecidium Uvulariae S.
  { Aecidium uvulariatum S.
  { Caeoma alliatum Lk. p. p. I.
  { Caeoma convallariatum S. I.
  { Caeoma uvulariatum S. I.
  { Dicaeoma Majanthae Arth. I.
  { Puccinia Majanthae Arth. I.
  { Puccinia sessilis I. Auct. Amer.
  { Uredo Uvulariae Spreng. I.
  Phyllosticta Oakesiae Dearness & House.
  Phyllosticta Uvulariae Gall.
  Vermicularia Liliacearum Westd.
Uvularia sp. indet.
  Erysiphe communis var. Liliacearum Fr.
  Sphaeria Aegopodii P. ex Fr.
Oakesia sessilifolia (L.) Watson.
  { Aecidium Uvulariae S.
  { Caeoma (Aecidium) uvulariatum S.
  { Diplodia Uvulariae J. J. Davis.
  { Phyllosticta Uvulariae N. A. F. 2153.
  Phyllosticta cruenta (Fr.) Kickx.
  Phyllosticta Oakesiae Dearness & House.
  { Dicaeoma Majanthae Arth.
  { Puccinia Majanthae Arth. I.
Anthericum nanum Baker.
  Aecidium anthericicola Arth.
Chlorogalum pomeridianum Kunth.
  Heterosporium gracile Sacc.
  Mycosphaerella Chlorogali Fairman.
  Pleospora Chlorogali Fairman.
  Pleospora herbarum (Fr.) Rabh.
  { Pleospora permunda (Cke.) Sacc.
  { Sphaeria permunda Cke.
  Rhabdospora Chlorogali Cke. & Hark.
  Sphaerella fuscata Ell.
  Uromyces Chlorogali Diet. & Holw.
Hosta plantaginea (Lam.) Aschers.
  Sclerotium Semen (Tode) ex Fr.
Hosta undulata L. H. Bailey.
  Sclerotium Rolfsii Sacc.
Hosta sp. cult.
  Colletotrichum omnivorum Halsted.
Hemerocallis fulva L.
  Cercospora hemerocallis Tehon.
  Cladosporium herbarum (P.) ex Lk.
  Cyphella Capula (Holmsk.) Fr.
  Didymellina Iridis (Desm.) v. Höhnel.
  Heterosporium gracile Sacc.
  Vermicularia Liliacearum Westd.

Hemerocallis sp. indet.
> Excipula Liliorum (S.) Fr.
> Xyloma Liliorum S.
> Leptostroma sphaeroides Fr., var. nitens Fr.
> Xyloma nitens S.
> Asteroma lineola (S.) M. A. Curtis.
> Dothidea lineola S.
> Phyllachora lineola (S.) Sacc.

Phormium tenax Forst.
> Gloeosporium phomiforme Sacc. & Ell.
> Gloeosporium punctiforme Sacc. & Ell.
> Glomerella cingulata (Stoneman) Spaulding & v. Schrenk.
> Hymenula phormicola Cke. & Hark.
> Leptosphaeria phormicola Cke. & Hark.
> Heptameria phormicola Cke.
> Stachybotrys scabra Cke. & Hark.

Leucocrinum montanum Nutt.
> Aecidium sp. indet.
> Dicaeoma amphigenum (Diet.) O. Kuntze. I.
> Puccinia amphigena Diet. I.

Nothoscordum bivalve (L.) Britton.
> ?Puccinia sessilis Schneid. I.
> Uromyces Erythronii Pass.
> Nigredo Hordei (Tracy) Arth. I.
> Nigredo hordeina Arth. I.
> Uromyces Hordei Tracy. I.
> Uromyces Nothoscordi Syd.

Allium acuminatum Hook.
> Dicaeoma Allii (DC.) O. Kuntze.
> Puccinia Allii (DC.) Rudolphi.
> Puccinia Alliorum Cda.
> Puccinia Blasdalei Diet. & Holw.
> Puccinia mutabilis Ell. & Gall.
> Nigredo aemula Arth.
> Uromyces aemulus Arth.

Allium ampeloprasum L.
> Urocystis Cepulae Frost.

Allium ascalonicum L.
> Colletotrichum circinans (B.) Vogl.
> Fusarium malli Taubenhaus.
> Peronospora Schleideni Ung.
> Sclerotium cepivorum B.

Allium attenuifolium Kellogg.
> Dicaeoma Allii (DC.) O. Kuntze.
> Puccinia Blasdalei Diet. & Holw.

Allium bisceptrum Watson.
> Allodus Calochorti (Pk.) Arth.
> Puccinia Calochorti Pk.
> Puccinia Holwayi Diet.

Allium Brandegei Watson.
> Dicaeoma Allii (DC.) O. Kuntze.

Allium brevistylum Watson.
> Pocosphaeria Allii Griffiths.
> Dicaeoma mutabile (Ell. & Gall.) O. Kuntze.
> Puccinia mutabilis Ell. & Gall.
> Nigredo aemula Arth.
> Uromyces aemulus Arth.

Allium campanulatum Watson.
> Puccinia granulispora Ell. & Gall.

Allium canadense L.
> Acrothecium melanopus (S.) Sacc.
> Aecidium alliicola Wint.
> Nigredo alliicola Arth. I.
> Nigredo Sporoboli (Ell. & Ev.) Arth. I.
> Heterosporium Allii Ell. & Martin.
> Phoma alliicola Sacc. & Roum.
> Puccinia granulispora Ell. & Gall. I.
> Caeomurus bicolor (Ell.) O. Kuntze.
> Nigredo bicolor (Ell.) Arth.
> Uromyces amphigenus Fung. Columb. *2491*.
> Uromyces aterrimus Diet. & Holw.
> Uromyces bicolor Ell.
> Uromyces bicolor Ell. & Ev.
> Uromyces Erythronii Auct. Amer.
> Uromyces Lilii G. W. Clinton.
> ?Vermicularia Liliaceorum S. 1832.
> Vermicularia Liliacearum Westd. 1866.

Allium Cepa L.
> Acrothecium melanopus (S.) Sacc.
> Dactylium melanopus S.
> Alternaria Allii Nolla.
> Alternaria fasciculata (C. & E.) Jones & Grout.
> Aspergillus flavus Lk.
> Aspergillus niger Van Tiegh.
> Sterigmatocystis niger Van Tiegh.
> Baryeidamia parasitica Karst.
> Botrytis Allii Munn.
> Botrytis byssoidea Walker.
> Botrytis cinerea P. †
> Botrytis vulgaris Fr.
> Botrytis parasitica Cav.?
> Botrytis squamosa Walker.
> Cercospora duddiae Welles.
> Cladosporium sparsum S.
> Cleistothecopsis circinans (B.) F. L. Stevens.
> Colletotrichum chardonianum Nolla.
> Colletotrichum circinans (B.) Vogl.
> Vermicularia circinans B.
> Corticium vagum B. & C.
> Fusarium angustum Sherbakoff.
> Fusarium bulbigenum Cke. & Massee.
> Fusarium Cepae Hanzawa.
> Fusarium Cepae Hanz. emend Link. & Bailey.
> Fusarium cromyophthoron Sideris.
> Fusarium culmorum (W. G. Sm.) Sacc.
> Fusarium discolor App. & Wr.
> Fusarium discolor, App. & Wr., var. sulphureum App. & Wr.
> Fusarium loncheceras Sideris.
> Fusarium loncheceras Sideris, var. microsporon Sideris.
> Fusarium lutulatum Sherbakoff.
> Fusarium malli Taubenhaus.
> Fusarium Martii App. & Wr.
> Fusarium Martii Appel & Wr., var. minus Sherb.

Allium Cepa (*cont.*)
Fusarium moniliforme Sheldon.
Fusarium orthoceras App. & Wr., var. triseptatum App. & Wr.
Fusarium oxysporum Schl.
Fusarium oxysporum Schl., var. longius Sherbakoff.
Fusarium oxysporum Schl., var. resupinatum Sherbakoff.
Fusarium radicicola Wollenweber.
Fusarium redolens Wr.
Fusarium rhizochromatistes Sideris.
Fusarium rhizochromatistes Sideris, var. microsclerotium Sideris.
Fusarium sclerostromaton Sideris.
Fusarium vasinfectum Atk.
Fusarium zonatum Sherbakoff, forma 1 Wr.
{ Fusariella atrovirens B.
{ Fusisporium atrovirens (B.) Sacc. Syll.
Macrosporium Porri Ell.
Mucor subtilissimus B.
Mycorrhiza of Legumes F. R. Jones.
Papulospora aspergilliformis Eidam.
Papulospora coprophila (Zukal) Hotson.
{ Peronospora Schleideni Ung.
{ Peronospora schleideniana DBy.
Phoma alliicola Sacc. & Roum.
{ Dothidea Cepae S.
{ Phyllachora Cepae (S.) Sacc.
Phyllosticta Allii Tehon & Daniels.
{ Macrosporium parasiticum Thm.
{ Macrosporium Sarcinula B.
{ Macrosporium Sarcinula B., var. parasiticum Thm.
Pleospora Allii (Klotzsch) Ces. & De Not.
Pleospora herbarum (Fr.) Rabh.
Pleospora herbarum (Fr.) Rabh., var. Allii Rabh.
Puccinia Allii (DC.) Rudolphi.
{ Dicaeoma Asparagi (DC.) O. Kuntze.
{ Puccinia Asparagi DC.
{ Dicaeoma Porri (Wint.) O. Kuntze.
{ Puccinia Porri Wint.
Pythium debaryanum Hesse.
Sclerotinia libertiana Fckl.
Sclerotinia perplexa Lawrence.
Sclerotium cepivorum B.
Sclerotium Rolfsii Sacc.
{ Urocystis Cepulae Frost.
{ Urocystis Colchici, var. Cepulae (Frost) Cke.
{ Sphaeria Dematium P. ex Fr.
{ Vermicularia Dematium Fr.
Volutella circinans (B.) Stevens & True.
Allium cernuum Roth.
{ Dicaeoma Allii (DC.) O. Kuntze.
{ Puccinia Allii (DC.) Rudolphi.
{ Dicaeoma granulisporum (Ell. & Gall.) O. Kuntze.
{ Puccinia granulispora Ell. & Gall.

Allium Diehlii M. E. Jones.
Puccinia mutabilis Ell. & Gall. I.
Allium falcifolium Hook. & Arn.
Puccinia Alliorum Cda.
Allium fistulosum L.
Sclerotium cepivorum B.
Allium Geyeri Watson.
{ Dicaeoma mutabile (Ell. & Gall.) O. Kuntze.
{ Puccinia mutabilis Ell. & Gall.
Allium Heckmani Eastw.
Dicaeoma Allii (DC.) O. Kuntze.
Allium mutabile Michx.
Puccinia mutabilis Ell. & Gall.
?Puccinia Porri Wint.
{ Nigredo alliicola Arth. I.
{ Nigredo Sporoboli (Ell. & Ev.) Arth. I.
Allium nevadense Watson.
Puccinia Allii (DC.) Rudolphi.
Urocystis Cepulae Frost.
Allium Nevii Watson.
{ Dicaeoma granulisporum (Ell. & Gall.) O. Kuntze.
{ Puccinia granulispora Ell. & Gall.
Allium Nuttallii Watson.
Uromyces aterrimus Diet. & Holw.
Volutella Allii F. W. Patterson.
Allium Porrum L.
Colletotrichum circinans (B.) Vogl.
Macrosporium Porri Ell.
Sclerotium cepivorum B.
Urocystis Cepulae Frost.
Allium praecox Brand.
{ Dicaeoma Allii (DC.) O. Kuntze.
{ Puccinia Allii (DC.) Rudolphi.
Puccinia granulispora Ell. & Gall.
Allium recurvatum Rydb.
Puccinia Allii (DC.) Rudolphi.
{ Dicaeoma granulisporum (Ell. & Gall.) O. Kuntze.
{ Puccinia granulispora Ell. & Gall.
Puccinia mutabilis Ell. & Gall.
Allium reticulatum Don.
{ Aecidium alliicola Wint.
{ Nigredo alliicola Arth. I.
{ Nigredo Sporoboli (Ell. & Ev.) Arth. I.
{ Uromyces Sporoboli Ell. & Ev. I.
Aecidium Convallariae Schum.
?Puccinia mutabilis Ell. & Gall.
{ Allodus pagana (Arth.) C. R. Orton.
{ Puccinia pagana Arth.
Allium rigidum Coville & Funston.
Uromyces bicolor Ell.
Allium sativum L.
Macrosporium Sarcinula B., var. parasiticum Thm.
Sclerotium cepivorum B.
Sclerotium Rolfsii Sacc.
Allium scaposum Benth.
Dicaeoma Allii (DC.) O. Kuntze.

Allium Schoenoprasum L.
{ Dicaeoma Porri (Wint.) O. Kuntze.
{ Puccinia Porri Wint.
{ Sphaerella allicina (Fr.) Awd.
{ Sphaeria allicina Fr.

Allium serratum Watson.
{ Dicaeoma Allii (DC.) O. Kuntze.
{ Puccinia Allii (DC.) Rudolphi.
{ Puccinia Alliorum Cda.
{ Puccinia Blasdalei Diet. & Holw.
Uromyces Soroboli Ell. & Ev. I.

Allium stellatum Ker.
{ Aecidium alliicola Wint.
{ Nigredo alliicola Arth. I.
{ Nigredo Soroboli (Ell. & Ev.) Arth. I.
Dicaeoma granulisporum (Ell. & Gall.) O.
Kuntze.

Allium textile Nelson & Macbr.
{ Dicaeoma mutabile (Ell. & Gall.) O. Kuntze.
{ Puccinia mutabilis Ell. & Gall.

Allium tricoccum Ait.
Leptostroma Allii Dearness & House.
{ Septoria Alliorum Westd.
{ Septoria viridetingens M. A. Curtis.
Vermicularia Liliacearum Westd.
Vermicularia Schoenoprasi Awd.

Allium unifolium Kellogg.
{ Dicaeoma Allii (DC.) O. Kuntze.
{ Puccinia Blasdalei Diet. & Holw.
{ Nigredo bicolor (Ell.) Arth.
{ Uromyces aterrimus Diet. & Holw.
{ Uromyces bicolor Ell.

Allium validum Watson.
{ Nigredo aemula Arth.
{ Uromyces aemulus Arth.
Uromyces aureus Diet. & Holw.
{ Uromyces aterrimus Diet. & Holw.
{ Uromyces bicolor Ell.

Allium vineale L.
Heterosporium Allii Ell. & Martin.
Heterosporium Ornithogali (Klotzsch) Cke.

Allium sp. indet.
Chaetocladium Brefeldii Van Tieghem & Le
Mon.
{ Cladosporium fasciculare Fr.
{ Dematium articulatum P. ex Fr.
Fusariella viridi-atra Sacc.
Macrosporium caespitulum Cke.
{ Dothidea penicillata S.
{ Phyllachora penicillata (S.) Sacc.
{ Pleospora herbarum (Fr.) Rabh., var. subsul-
{ cata (Ell. & Ev.) Sacc. & Trav.
{ Pleospora subsulcata Ell. & Ev.
{ Dicaeoma Soroboli (Arth.) O. Kuntze I.
{ Puccinia Soroboli Arth. I.
Rhinotrichum tenellum B. & C.
Rhizoctonia Solani Kühn.

{ Sphaeria exuberans Fr.
{ Sphaeria Porri, var. exuberans S.
Uromyces Nothoscordi Syd.

Brodiaea capitata Benth.
{ Allodus moreniana (Dudley & Thompson)
{ C. R. Orton.
{ Micropuccinia moreniana (Dudley & Thomp-
{ son) Arth. & Jackson.
{ Puccinia moreniana Dudley & Thompson.
{ Dicaeoma nodosum (Ell. & Hark.) O. Kuntze.
{ Puccinia nodosa Ell. & Hark.
Uromyces Brodieae Ell. & Hark.

Brodiaea capitata Benth., var. **pauciflora** Torr.
{ Allodus carnegiana (Arth.) C. R. Orton.
{ Puccinia carnegiana Arth.
{ Puccinia lojkaiana Thm.
{ Puccinia nodosa Ell. & Hark.
{ Micropuccinia tumamocensis (Arth.) Arth. &
{ Jackson.
{ Puccinia tumamocensis Arth.

Brodiaea congesta Smith.
Puccinia Dichelostemmae Diet. & Holw.
{ Allodus subangulata (Holw.) C. R. Orton.
{ Puccinia subangulata Holw.

Brodiaea Douglasii Watson.
{ Allodus Dichelostemmae (Diet. & Holw.) C.
{ R. Orton.
{ Puccinia Dichelostemmae Diet. & Holw.
{ Dicaeoma pattersonianum (Arth.) Arth. &
{ Fromme. I.
{ Puccinia pattersoniana Arth. I.
{ Pucciniola Brodiaeae (Ell. & Hark.) Arth.
{ Uromyces Brodieae Ell. & Hark. I.

Brodiaea Howellii Watson.
{ Hendersonia cylindrocarpa Ell. & Ev.
{ Stagonospora cylindrocarpa (Ell. & Ev.) Sacc.

Brodiaea lactea (Lindl.) Watson.
Pucciniola Brodiaeae (Ell. & Hark.) Arth.

Brodiaea laxa Watson.
Uromyces Brodieae Ell. & Hark.

Hookera hyacinthina (Lindl.) O. Kuntze.
Uromyces Brodiaeae Ell. & Hark.

Hookera multiflora (Benth.) Brit.
Allodus Dichelostemmae (Diet. & Holw.) C.
R. Orton.

Hookera pulchella Salisb.
{ Allodus Dichelostemmae (Diet. & Holw.) C.
{ R. Orton.
{ Puccinia Dichelostemmae Diet. & Holw.
{ Allodus subangulata (Holw.) C. R. Orton.
{ Puccinia subangulata Holw.

Lilium auratum Lindl.
Rhizopus necans Massee.

Lilium canadense L.
Aecidium Convallariae Schum.
Gloniopsis Lathami Fairman, var. asymetrica
Fairman.

Lilium canadense (*cont.*)

⎧Nigredo Lilii (G. W. Clinton) Arth.
⎪Uromyces Erythronii Auct. Amer.
⎨Uromyces Holwayi Lagerh.
⎪Uromyces Liliacearum Auct. Amer.
⎩Uromyces Lilii G. W. Clinton.
Vermicularia Liliaceorum S.

Lilium candidum L.

Aecidium Convallariae Schum., var. Lilii Farl.
Phytophthora Cactorum (Leb. & Cohn) Schrt.
Sclerotinia libertiana Fckl.
⎧Nigredo Lilii (G. W. Clinton) Arth.
⎩Uromyces Lilii G. W. Clinton.

Lilium columbianum Hanson.

⎧Nigredo Lilii (G. W. Clinton) Arth.
⎪Uromyces Erythronii Auct. Amer.
⎨Uromyces Holwayi Lagerh.
⎪Uromyces Liliacearum Auct. Amer.
⎩Uromyces Lilii G. W. Clinton.

Lilium longiflorum Thunb.

Botrytis cinerea Auct.
Cercospora unicolor Sacc. & Penz.
Chaetomium contortum Pk.
Phytophthora? cryptogea Pethybridge & Lafferty.
Sclerotinia sclerotiorum (Lib.) Massee.
Uromyces Lilii G. W. Clinton.

Lilium pardalinum Kellogg.

Peziza atrata P., var. Liliacearum Phil. & Hark.

Lilium parviflorum (Hook.) Holz.

Uromyces Holwayi Lagerh.

Lilium parvum Kellogg.

Lilium philadelphicum L.

Lilium rubescens Watson.

Lilium washingtonianum Kellogg.

⎧Nigredo Lilii (G. W. Clinton) Arth.
⎪Uromyces Erythronii Auct. Amer.
⎨Uromyces Holwayi Lagerh.
⎪Uromyces Liliacearum Auct. Amer.
⎩Uromyces Lilii G. W. Clinton.

Lilium philadelphicum L., var. **andinum** (Nutt.) Ker.

Aecidium Lilii G. W. Clinton.
⎧Dicaeoma Sporoboli (Arth.) O. Kuntze I.
⎩Puccinia Sporoboli Arth. I.

Lilium pyrenaicum Gouan.

Phytophthora Cactorum (Leb. & Cohn) Schrt.

Lilium speciosum Thunb.

Rhizopus necans Massee.

Lilium superbum L.

⎧Leptosphaeria Lilii Ell. & Dearness.
⎪Phyllosticta Lilii Ell. & Dearness.
⎨Nigredo Lilii (G. W. Clinton) Arth.
⎪Uromyces Erythronii Auct. Amer.
⎪Uromyces Holwayi Lagerh.
⎩Uromyces Lilii G. W. Clinton.

Lilium tigrinum Ker.

Vermicularia Dematium Fr.
⎧?Vermicularia Liliaceorum S. 1824.
⎩Vermicularia Liliacearum Westd. 1866.

Lilium sp. indet.

Corticium vagum B. & C.
Phoma herbarum Westd.
Polyactis cana B.

Fritillaria camschatcensis Ker-Gawl.

Fritillaria lanceolata Pursh.

⎧Uromyces Erythronii Auct. Amer. p. p.
⎨Uromyces Liliacearum N. A. F. *1863.*
⎩Uromyces Miurae Syd.

Tulipa gesneriana L.

Botrytis Tulipae (Lib.) Hopkins.
Phytophthora Cactorum (Leb. & Cohn) Schrt.
⎧Rhizoctonia Tuliparum (Klebahn) Whetzel & J. M. Arthur.
⎩Sclerotium Tuliparum Klebahn.

Tulipa suaveolens Roth.

Tulipa sylvestris L.

Botrytis Tulipae (Lib.) Hopkins.

Tulipa sp. indet.

Botrytis parasitica Cav.
Fusarium udum (B.) Wr.
Sclerotinia fuckeliana (DBy.) Fckl.
Sclerotinia parasitica Massee.
Sclerotium Tulipae Therry?

Erythronium albidum Nutt.

Ustilago Heufleri Fckl.

Erythronium americanum Ker-Gawl.

Protomyces Erythronii Pk.
Sclerotinia Erythroniae Whetzel.
⎧Ustilago Erythronii G. W. Clinton.
⎪Ustilago Heufleri Fckl.
⎨Ustilago Ornithogali, var. Erythronii De Toni.
⎩Ustilago Tulipae Wint.

Erythronium giganteum Lindl.

⎧Teleutospora heteroderma (Syd.) Arth. & Bisby.
⎩Uromyces heterodermus Syd.

Erythronium grandiflorum Pursh.

Erythronium montanum Watson.

Erythronium obtusatum Gooding.

⎧Teleutospora heteroderma (Syd.) Arth. & Bisby.
⎨Uromyces Erythronii I. Fung. Columb. *750.*
⎩Uromyces heterodermus Syd.

Erythronium parviflorum (Watson) Gooding.

Asteroma tenerrimum Grogn., var. Erythronii Sacc.
⎧Teleutospora heteroderma (Syd.) Arth. & Bisby.
⎩Uromyces heterodermus Syd.

Erythronium virginicum Sm.

⎧Ustilago Heufleri Fckl.
⎩Ustilago Ornithogali Auct. Amer.

Calochortus albus Dougl.
Calochortus apiculatus Baker.
Calochortus bisceptrum Watson.
Calochortus elegans Pursh.
Calochortus euumbellatus A. Nels.
Calochortus flava Schultes f.
Calochortus Gunnisoni Watson.
Calochortus longebarbatus Watson.
Calochortus macrocarpus Dougl.
Calochortus Mawcanus Leichtl.
Calochortus nitidus Dougl.
Calochortus nudus Watson.
Calochortus Nuttallii Torr. & Gray.
Calochortus Pringlei B. L. Robinson.
Calochortus venustus Benth.
  Aecidium Calochorti pro tem.
  Allodus Calochorti (Pk.) Arth.
  Dicaeoma anachoreticum (Hark.) O. Kuntze.
  Dicaeoma Holwayi O. Kuntze.
  Puccinia anachoreta Hark.
  Puccinia Calochorti Pk.
  Puccinia Calochorti Pk. I.
  Puccinia Holwayi Diet.
Scilla praecox Willd.
  Ustilago Vaillantii Tul.
Camassia esculenta (Ker.) B. L. Robinson.
  Urocystis Colchici Auct. Amer.
  Urocystis Ornithogali Körn.
Ornithogalum umbellatum L.
  Aecidium ornithogaleum Bubák.
  Heterosporium Ornithogali (Klotzsch) Cke.
  Dicaeoma anomalum (Rostr.) Arth. &
    Fromme. I.
  Pleomeris simplex (Körn.) Syd. I.
  Puccinia anomala Rostr. I.
  Puccinia simplex (Körn.) Erikss. & Henn. I.
Hyacinthus orientalis L.
  Fusarium bulbigenum Cke. and Massee.
Hyacinthus sp. indet.
  Dictyuchus monosporus Leitg.
  Rhizophidium pollinis (A. Br.) Zopf.
  Ustilago Vaillantii Tul.
Muscari comosa Mill.
  Ustilago Vaillantii Tul.
Yucca aloifolia L.
  Anthostomella nigroannulata (B. & C.) Sacc.
  Sphaeria nigroannulata B. & C.
  Cladosporium atriellum Cke.
  Coniothyrium concentricum (Desm.) Sacc.
  Dialonectria depauperata Cke.
  Fusarium Yuccae Cke.
  Nectria depauperata Cke.
  Diplodia circinans B. & Br.
  Diplodia circinans B. & Br., var. diffusa B.
  Dothidea Pringlei Pk.
  Discella anomala Cke.
  Discula anomala (Cke.) Sacc.
  Kellermania yuccigena Ell. & Ev.

  Pleospora thuemeniana Sacc.
  Sphaeria Yuccae Fr.
Yucca arborescens Trel.
  Kellermania yuccigena Ell. & Ev.
Yucca baccata Torr.
  Camarosporium yuccisedum Fairman.
  Dothidea Pringlei Pk.
  Kellermania mutica Ell. & Ev.
  Septoria megaspora Speg.
Yucca brevifolia Engelm.
  Kellermania yuccigena Ell. & Ev.
Yucca Colusplei ex Baker.
  Leptosphaeria pacifica Rehm.
Yucca elephantipes Regel.
  Epicoccum asterinum Pat.
Yucca filamentosa L.
  Cercospora concentrica C. & E.
  Cercospora Yuccae Cke.
  Coniothyrium concentricum (Desm.) Sacc.
  Coniothyrium herbarum C. & E.
  Phoma concentrica Desm.
  Coniothyrium inops Sacc.
  Phoma concentrica Rav. Fung. Am.
  Diaporthe acervata Ell. & Ev.
  Diatrype acervata Ell. & Ev.
  Gloeosporium yuccigenum Ell. & Ev.
  Kellermania yuccigena Ell. & Ev.
  Leptosphaeria filamentosa Ell. & Ev.
  Macrophoma filamentosa (Cke.) Berl. & Vogl.
  Phoma filamentosa (Cke.) Sacc.
  Sphaeropsis filamentosa Cke.
  Macrosporium abruptum C. & E.
  Macrosporium commune Rabh.
  Pestalozziella Yuccae Karst.
  Phomatospora argyrostigma (B.) Sacc.
  Sphaeria argyrostigma B.
  Sphaeria argyrostoma Curt. Cat.
  Dothidea scapincola S.
  Phyllachora scapincola (S.) Sacc.
  Sclerotium hysteriiforme S.
  Sphaerella Yuccae Ell. & Ev.
  Sphaeria scapincola S.
  Vermicularia subeffigurata S., var. scapincola S.
Yucca glauca Nutt.
  Aecidium Yuccae Arth.
  Allantonectria Yuccae Earle.
  Coniothyrium concentricum (Desm.) Sacc.
  Coniothyrium herbarum C. & E.
  Coniothyrium concentricum (Desm.) Sacc.,
    var. Yuccae-glaucae Sacc.
  Cylindrosporium angustifolium Ell. & Kellerm.
  Didymella sphaerelloides Sacc.
  Didymosphaeria Clementsii Sacc. & D. Sacc.
  Phorcys minutus Clements.
  Didymosphaerella yuccogena Cke.
  Didymosphaeria yuccogena (Cke.) Sacc.
  Sphaeria yuccogena Cke.
  Kellermania yuccigena Ell. & Ev.

Yucca glauca (*cont.*)
  Dothidea Yuccae Ell. & Ev.
  Phaeodothis Yuccae (Ell. & Ev.) Sacc.
  Phyllachora? Yuccae Ell. & Ev.
  Phaeosporella weiriana Petrak.
  Dothidea conspicua Griffiths.
  Phragmodothis conspicua (Griffiths) Theissen & Syd.
  Sphaerella Yuccae Ell.
  Stachybotrys dakotensis Sacc.
  Torula maculans Cke., var. biformis Sacc.

Yucca glóriosa L.
  Coniothyrium concentricum (Desm.) Sacc.
  ?Kellermania yuccigena Ell. & Ev.
  Leptosphaeria obtusispora Speg.
  Plowrightia circumscissa Tracy & Earle.
  Septoria Yuccae Sacc.
  Sphaeria Yuccae Fr.
  Sphaeria Yuccae-gloriosae S.

Yucca macrocarpa Engelm.
  Coniothyrium concentricum (Desm.) Sacc.
  Auerswaldia Pringlei Sacc.
  Dothidea Pringlei Pk.
  Phyllachora Pringlei (Pk.) Cke.
  Sphaerodothis Pringlei (Pk.) Theissen & Syd.

Yucca rupicola Scheele.
  Cercospora floricola Heald & Wolf.
  Pestalozziella Yuccae Karst. & Hariot.

Yucca Whipplei Torr.
  Coniothyrium Bartholomaei Dearness & Barthol.
  Kellermania major Dearness & Barthol.

Yucca sp. indet.
  Badhamia macrocarpa (Ces.) Rostf.
  Badhamia macrocarpa (Ces.) Rostf., var. gracilis Macbr.
  Cercospora Henningsii Allescher.
  Coprinus Bakeri Copeland.
  Creonectria ochroleuca (S.) Seaver.
  Didymium Trochus Lister.
  Gloeosporium Manihot Earle.
  Macrosporium caudatum C. & E.
  Metasphaeria Yuccae Earle.
  Nectria depauperata Cke.
  Neottiospora yuccifolia J. G. Hall.
  Periconia pycnospora Fres.
  Phoma Yuccae Cke.
  Phyllosticta consimilis Ell. & Ev.
  Phyllosticta yuccigena Ell. & Ev.
  Physalospora uvispora Cke.
  Sphaeria uvispora Cke.
  Sphaeropsis marginata B. & C.
  Torula maculans Cke.

Hesperaloë Davyi Baker.
  Botryosphaeria hysterioides Ell. & Ev.
  Diplodia hesperaloes Ell. & Ev.
  Phleospora minor Ell. & Ev.

Nolina microcarpa Watson.
  Tolyposporella? Nolinae G. P. Clinton.

Dasylirion Wheeleri Watson.
  Botryosphaeria Dasylirii (Pk.) Theissen & Syd.
  Dothidea Dasylirii Pk.
  Phyllachora Dasylirii (Pk.) Sacc.
  Torula quaternata B. & C.

Dasylirion sp. indet.
  Coniothyrium hysterioideum Karst.

Dracaena Cooperi Walt.
  Cladosporium dracaenatum Thm.

Dracaena fragrans (L.) Ker-Gawl.
  Pestalozzina Aletridis Pat.
  Phyllosticta Dracaenae Griffon & Maubl.
  Phyllosticta maculicola Halsted.
  Physalospora Dracaenae Sheldon.
  Vermicularia concentrica Lév.

Dracaena goldieana Bull.
Dracaena Lindeni Hort.
  Vermicularia concentrica Lév.

Dracaena terminalis L.
  Glomerella cincta (Stoneman) Spaulding & v. Schrenk.
  Phyllosticta maculicola Halsted.

Dracaena sp. indet.
  Colletotrichum Dracaenae Halsted.
  Macrophomopsis Dracaenae Stevens & Baechler.

Asparagus medeloides Thunb.
  Puccinia Asparagi DC.

Asparagus officinalis L.

Ascomycetes

  Gibberella pulicaris (Fr.) Sacc.
  Gibbera Saubinetii Mont.
  Gibberella Saubinetii (Mont.) Sacc.
  Leptosphaeria Asparagi Pk.
  Heptameria comatella (C. & E.) Cke.
  Leptosphaeria comatella (C. & E.) Sacc.
  Sphaeria comatella C. & E.
  Pleospora Asparagi Rabh.
  Pleospora herbarum (Fr.) Rabh.
  Sphaeria herbarum Fr.

Basidiomycetes

  Armillaria mellea (Vahl) ex Fr.
  Corticium vagum B. & C.
  Dicaeoma Asparagi (DC.) O. Kuntze.
  Puccinia Asparagi DC.

Fungi Imperfecti

  Alternaria fasciculata (C. & E.) Jones & Grout.
  Amerosporium oeconomicum Ell. & Tracy.
  Cercospora Asparagi Sacc.
  Cercospora caulicola Wint.
  Cercospora cruenta Sacc.
  Cladosporium fasciculare Fr.
  Darluca Filum (Biv.) Cast.
  Diplodia Asparagi Pk.
  Epicoccum purpurascens Ehrenb.

Asparagus officinalis (*cont.*)

Dothiorella lanceolata (C. & E.) Petrak.
Macrophoma lanceolata (C. & E.) Berl. & Vogl.
Phoma lanceolata (C. & E.) Sacc.
Sphaeropsis lanceolata C. & E.
Macrosporium caespitulosum Cke.
Macrosporium commune Rabh.
Mycorrhiza of Legumes F. R. Jones.
Phoma Asparagi Sacc.
Phoma media Ell. & Ev.
Phoma microspora B. & C.
Rhizoctonia Solani Kühn.
Septoria phlyctaenoides B. & C.
Torula herbarum Lk.
Vermicularia Liliacearum Westd.

Asparagus plumosus Baker.

Physarum cinereum (Batsch) P.

Asparagus plumosus Baker, var. **nanus** Nichols.

Puccinia Asparagi DC.

Asparagus Sprengeri Regel.

Rhizoctonia Solani Kühn.

Asparagus verticillatus L.

Puccinia Asparagi DC.

Clintonia borealis (Ait.) Raf.

Micropuccinia mesomajalis (B. & C.) Arth. & Jackson.
Puccinia mesomajalis B. & C. in Pk. 25th Rept.
Puccinia mesomegala B. & C. in Grev. III.
Synchytrium aureum Schrt.

Clintonia umbellulata (Michx.) Morong.

Vermicularia Liliacearum Westd.

Clintonia uniflora (Schult.) Kunth.

Micropuccinia mesomajalis (B. & C.) Arth. & Jackson.
Puccinia mesomegala B. & C.

Smilacina amplexicaulis Nutt.

Cylindrosporium Smilacinae Ell. & Ev.
Phyllosticta cruenta (Fr.) Kickx.
Ramularia Vagnerae Barthol.
Urocystis Colchici (Schl.) Rabh.

Smilacina racemosa (L.) Desf.

Aecidium Convallariae Schum.
Aecidium Majanthae Schum.
Aecidium Smilacinae J. J. Davis.
Caeoma (Aecidium) convallariatum S. I.
Dicaeoma Majanthae (Arth. & Holw.) Arth. I
Puccinia Majanthae Arth. & Holw. I.
Puccinia sessilis Schneid. I.
Aecidium Convallariae Auct. Amer. p. p.
Aecidium magnatum Arth.
Nigredo Polemonii Arth. I.
Puccinia sessilis I. Auct. Amer. p. p.
Uromyces magnatus Arth. I
Colletotrichum Smilacinae Tehon & Daniels.
Diaporthe inquilina (Fr.) Nits.
Phyllosticta Convallariae P.
Depazea cruenta Fr.
Phyllosticta cruenta (Fr.) Kickx.

Phyllosticta cruenta (Fr.) Kickx, var. pallidior Pk.
Phyllosticta pallidior Pk.
Phyllosticta vagans P.
Ramularia Smilacinae J. J. Davis.
Sclerotinia smilacina Durand.
Septoria brunneola (Fr.) Niessl.
Septoria Smilacinae Ell. & Martin.
Vermicularia Liliacearum Westd.

Smilacina sessilifolia Nutt.

Cercospora Smilacinae Ell. & Ev.
Cercosporella idahoensis Sacc.
Phleospora Vagnerae Petrak.
Dicaeoma Majanthae (Arth. & Holw.) Arth. I.
Puccinia Majanthae Arth. & Holw. I.

Smilacina stellata (L.) Desf.

Aecidium Convallariae Schum.
Aecidium Majanthae Schum.
Caeoma convallariatum S. I.
Dicaeoma Majanthae (Arth. & Holw.) Arth. I.
Puccinia Majanthae Arth. & Holw. I.
Aecidium magnatum Arth.
Nigredo Polemonii Arth. I.
Puccinia sessilis Auct. Amer. p. p. I.
Uromyces acuminatus Arth. p. p. I.
Uromyces magnatus Arth. I.
Anthostomella smilacinina (Pk.) Sacc.
Sphaeria smilacinina Pk.
Guignardia Smilacinae Dearness & House.
Laestadia Smilacinae Dearness & House.
Heterosporium asperatum Massee.
Phyllosticta Convallariae P. ex Seaver.
Phyllosticta cruenta (Fr.) Kickx.
Phyllosticta pallidior Pk.
Phyllostictina pallidior (Pk.) Petrak & Syd.
Pleospora herbarum (Fr.) Rabh.
Septoria Smilacinae Ell. & Martin.
Tuburcinia Clintoniae Komarov.
Urocystis Colchici (Schl.) Rabh.
Vermicularia Liliacearum Westd.

Smilacina trifolia (L.) Desf.

Peckia Clintonii Pk.
Puccinia Majanthae Arth. & Holw. I.

Smilacina sp. indet

Mycosphaerella Vagnerae Earle.
Sphaerella Vagnerae (Earle) Sacc. & Trott.
Tuburcinia Clintoniae Komarov.
Tuburcinia Trientalis B. & Br.

Maianthemum canadense Desf.

Aecidium Majanthae Schum.
Dicaeoma Majanthae (Arth. & Holw.) Arth.
Puccinia Majanthae Arth. & Holw. I.
Puccinia sessilis Schneid. I.
Cercospora Maianthemi Fckl.
Cercospora subsanguinea Ell. & Ev.
Didymium Fairmani Sacc.
Dothidea reticulata (DC.) ex Fr.
Heterosporium asperatum Massee.

Maianthemum canadense (*cont.*)
  Phoma Maianthemi Pk.
  Phyllactinia corylea (P.) ex Karst.
Disporum lanuginosum (Michx.) Nichols.
  Discosia maculicola Gerard.
Prosartes trachycarpa Watson.
  Septoria Streptopidis Pk.
Streptopus amplexifolius (L.) DC.
  Botrytis cinerea P. †
  Cercospora Streptopi Dearness & Barthol.
  Mollisia atrata (P.) Karst.
  Sclerotium baccarum Rostr.
Streptopus roseus Michx.
  {Dicaeoma Majanthae (Arth. & Holw.) Arth. I.
  {Puccinia sessilis Schneid. I.
  Septoria Streptopidis Pk.
  {Tuburcinia Clintoniae Komarov.
  {Tuburcinia Trientalis Suppl. List.
  Vermicularia Liliacearum Westd.
Polygonatum biflorum (Walt.) Elliott.
  {Aecidium Convallariae Schum.
  {Aecidium magnatum Arth.
  {Aecidium Majanthae Schum.
  {Aecidium Smilacinae J. J. Davis.
  {Dicaeoma Majanthae (Arth. & Holw.) Arth. I.
  {Puccinia Majanthae Arth. & Holw. I.
  {Uromyces acuminatus Arth. I.
  {Uromyces magnatus Arth. I.
  Cladosporium herbarum (P.) ex Lk.
  Phyllosticta cruenta (Fr.) Kickx.
  Phyllosticta cruenta (Fr.) Kickx, var. longis-
    pora Dearness.
  Vermicularia Polygonati S.
  Vermicularia trichella Fr.
Polygonatum commutatum (R. & S.) Dietr.
  {Aecidium Convallariae Schum.
  {Aecidium Smilacinae J. J. Davis.
  {Puccinia Majanthae Arth. & Holw. I.
  {Aecidium Convallariae Fung. Dak. *226.*
  {Aecidium magnatum Arth.
  {Puccinia sessilis I. Auct. Amer. p. p.
  {Nigredo Polemonii Arth. I.
  {Uromyces magnatus Arth. I.
  Guignardia Polygonati (R. & S.) Dietr.
  Heterosporium asperatum Massee.
  {Hypoderma Polygonati (S.) Cke.
  {Hysterium Polygonati S.
  Labrella nitida S.
  Leptostroma Polygonati Lasch.
  Leptostroma Polygonati, var. americanum
    Tassi.
  {Leptostromella tenuissima (S.) Starb.
  {Sphaeria tenuissima S.
  {Depazea cruenta (Fr.) Chev.
  {Phyllosticta Convallariae P. ex Seaver.
  {Phyllosticta cruenta (Fr.) Kickx.
  {Sphaeria cruenta Fr.
  Sacidium Polygonati Ell. & Martin.
  Septoria brunneola (Fr.) Niessl.

  Tuburcinia Clintoniae Komarov.
  Urocystis Colchici (Schl.) Rabh.
Polygonatum sp. indet.
  Dothidea Asteroma Fr.
  {Laestadia Polygonati (S.) Sacc.
  {Sphaerella Polygonati (S.) Cke.
  {Sphaeria Polygonati S.
  Periconia pycnospora Fres.
  {Dothidea Polygonati S.
  {Phyllachora Polygonati (S.) Sacc.
  Sphaeria subradians Fr.
Convallaria majalis L.
  Asteroma reticulatum (DC.) Chev.
  Heterosporium asperatum Massee.
  {Depazea cruenta (Fr.) Chev.
  {Phyllosticta cruenta (Fr.) Kickx.
  Vermicularia Liliacearum Westd.
Convallaria sp. indet.
  Puccinia Majanthae Arth. & Holw.
Aspidistra lurida Sieb.
  Ascochyta Aspidistrae Massee.
  Colletotrichum omnivorum Halsted.
Aspidistra sp. indet.
  Labrella Aspidistrae Tehon & Daniels.
Medeola virginiana L.
  Medeolaria Farlowii Thax.
  Phyllosticta Medeolae Dearness & House.
Aletris aurea Walt.
Aletris farinosa L.
Aletris lutea Small.
  {Dicaeoma (?) Aletridis (B. & C.) O. Kuntze.
  {Puccinia Aletridis B. & C.
Trillium cernuum L.
  Phyllosticta Trillii Ell. & Ev.
  Septoria Trillii Pk.
Trillium chloropetalum Howell.
  Urocystis Trillii H. S. Jackson.
Trillium declinatum (Gray) Gleason.
  Septoria Trillii Pk.
  Vermicularia Peckii Sacc.
Trillium discolor Auct.
  Septoria Trillii Pk.
Trillium erectum L.
  Aecidium Trillii Burrill.
  Dicaeoma Majanthae (Arth. & Holw.) Arth. I.
  Septoria recurvata Ell. & Halsted.
  Septoria Trillii Pk.
Trillium grandiflorum (Michx.) Salisb.
  Aecidium Trillii Burrill.
  Septoria Trillii Pk.
Trillium ovatum Pursh.
  Heterosporium Trillii Ell. & Ev.
Trillium petiolatum Pursh.
  Cladosporium Trillii Ell. & Ev.
  Phyllosticta Trillii Ell. & Ev.
Trillium recurvatum Beck.
  Aecidium Trillii Burrill.
  Colletotrichum Trillii Tehon.
  Septoria Trillii Pk.

Trillium sessile L.
Gloeosporium Trillii Ell. & Ev.
Septoria Trillii Pk.

Trillium undulatum Willd.
Dicaeoma Majanthae (Arth. & Holw.) Arth. I.
{ Vermicularia concentrica Pk. & Clinton.
{ Vermicularia Peckii Sacc.

Smilax aspera L.
Metasphaeria Dearnessii Bubák.
Septonema isthmium Pound & Clements.

Smilax Bona-nox L.
Ascochyta Smilacis Ell. & Martin.
Cercospora mississippiensis Tracy & Earle.
Cercospora smilacina Sacc.
Cercospora Smilacis Thm.
Coniothyrium Fuckelii Sacc.
Diplodia smilacina B.
{ Hypoderma Smilacis (S.) Rehm.
{ Hysterium Smilacis S.
Phyllosticta Smilacis Ell. & Martin.
{ Dicaeoma amphigenum (Diet.) O. Kuntze. I.
{ Puccinia amphigena Diet. I.
{ Dicaeoma Smilacis (S.) O. Kuntze.
{ Puccinia Smilacis S.

Smilax coriacea Spreng.
Isthmospora spinosa F. L. Stevens.
Meliola Smilacis F. L. Stevens.

Smilax cumanensis Humb. & Bonpl.

Smilax domingensis Willd.
{ Dicaeoma Smilacis (S.) O. Kuntze.
{ Puccinia Smilacis S.

Smilax domingensis Willd.
Phyllachora smilacicola Chardon.

Smilax ecirrhata (Engelm.) Watson.
Ramularia subrufa Ell. & Holw.
Stagonospora Smilacis (Ell. & Martin) Sacc.

Smilax glauca Walt.
{ Aecidium macrosporum Pk.
{ Dicaeoma macrosporum Arth. & Kern. I.
Cercospora mississippiensis Tracy & Earle.
{ Cercospora smilacina Sacc.
{ Cercospora Smilacis Auct. Amer.
Diplodia smilacina B.
{ Cercospora Petersii (B. & C.) Atk.
{ Helminthosporium Petersii B. & C.
Pestalozzia Guepini Desm.
{ Dothidea Dioscoreae S.
?{ Phoma Dioscoreae (S.) Cke.
{ Phyllachora Dioscoreae (S.) Sacc.
Phyllosticta Smilacis Ell. & Martin.
Physalospora disrupta (B. & C.) Sacc.
{ Dicaeoma Smilacis (S.) O. Kuntze.
{ Puccinia Smilacis S.
{ Uredo Smilacis S.

Smilax havanensis Jacq.
{ Dicaeoma Smilacis (S.) O. Kuntze.
{ Puccinia Smilacis S.

Smilax herbacea L.
{ Dicaeoma amphigenum (Diet.) O. Kuntze. I.
{ Puccinia amphigena Diet. I.
Ascochyta fuscopapillata Bubák & Dearness.
Ascochyta londonensis Bubák & Dearness.
Ascochyta smilacigena Bubák & Dearness.
Ceratium insociabile Gerard.
Cercospora Smilacis Thm.
{ Dothiorella smilacina (Pk.) Petrak & Syd.
{ Macrophoma Smilacis (Ell. & Ev.) Bubák.
{ Phyllosticta Smilacis Ell. & Ev.
Macrophoma smilacina (Pk.) Berl. & Vogl.
{ Macrophoma pellucida Bubák & Dearness
{ Neophoma pellucida (Bubák & Dearness)
  Petrak & Syd.
Pestalozzia clavata C. & E.
Phaeoseptoria canadensis Bubák & Dearness.
Phyllosticta londonensis Bubák & Dearness.
Phyllosticta pellucida Bubák & Dearness.
Phyllosticta smilacigena Bubák & Dearness.
Pleosphaerulina canadensis Bubák & Dearness.
{ Aecidium Smilacis S.
{ Dicaeoma Smilacis (S.) O. Kuntze.
{ Puccinia Smilacis S.
Ramularia subrufa Ell. & Holw.
Septogloeum subnudum J. J. Davis.
Septoria pellucida Bubák & Dearness.
Septoria smilacina Dur. & Mont.
Sphaerella pellucida Bubák & Dearness.
Stagonospora pellucida Bubák & Dearness.
Stagonospora smilacigena Bubák & Dearness.
Stagonospora Smilacis (Ell. & Martin) Sacc.
Vermicularia albomaculata S.
Vermicularia Liliacearum Westd.

Smilax hispida Muhl.
{ Dicaeoma amphigenum (Diet.) O. Kuntze. I.
{ Puccinia amphigena Diet. I.
{ Aecidium macrosporum Pk.
{ Dicaeoma macrosporum (Arth.) Arth. & Kern.
  I.
{ Puccinia macrospora Arth. I.
Ascochyta confusa Ell. & Ev.
Ascochyta Smilacis Ell. & Ev.
Cercospora mississippiensis Tracy & Earle.
Cercospora smilacina Sacc.
Dendryphium subsessile Ell. & Ev.
Fusarium granulosum Ell. & Ev.
{ Haplosporella Smilacis (Ell. & Ev.) Petrak &
  Syd.
{ Sphaeropsis Smilacis Ell. & Ev.
{ Sphaeropsis Smilacis, var. latispora Pk.
Helminthosporium Petersii B. & C.
Phyllactinia corylea (P.) ex Karst.
Phyllosticta hispida Ell. & Dearness.
{ Phyllosticta smilacina (Pk.) Dearness.
{ Sphaeropsis smilacina Pk.
Phyllosticta Smilacis Ell. & Martin.

Smilax hispida (*cont.*)
- Aecidium Smilacis S.
- Dicaeoma Smilacis (S.) O. Kuntze.
- Puccinia Smilacis S.
- Septonema isthmium Pound & Clements.
- Sphaeropsis brunneola B. & C.
- Stagonospora Smilacis (Ell. & Martin) Sacc.

Smilax laurifolia L.
- Anthostomella sepelibilis (B. & C.) Sacc.
- Sphaeria sepelibilis Sacc.
- Cercospora Petersii (B. & C.) Atk.
- Eutypa sepulta (B. & C.) Sacc.
- Sphaeria sepulta B. & C.
- Leptostroma Smilacis Cke.
- Dichaena smilacina S. Am. bor.
- Microthyrium Smilacis Cke. an DeNot.?
- Rhytisma Smilacis Fr.
- Xyloma Smilacis S. Syn. Car.
- Pestalozzia funerea Desm.
- Aecidium Smilacis S.
- Aecidium smilacinatum S.
- Aecidium verrucosum Bon.
- Caeoma smilacinatum Lk. I.
- Dicaeoma Smilacis (S.) O. Kuntze.
- Puccinia Smilacis S.
- Puccinia Smilacis I. Auct. Amer.
- Uredo Smilacis Spreng. I.
- Sphaerella smilacicola (S.) Cke.

Smilax medica Schl. & Cham.
- Gloeosporium rufomaculans Thm.
- Glomerella cingulata (Stoneman) Spaulding & v. Schrenk.

Smilax Pseudo-China L.
- Coniothyrium Fuckelii Sacc.
- Dicaeoma Smilacis (S.) O. Kuntze.
- Puccinia Smilacis S.

Smilax pulverulenta Michx.
- Ascochyta smilacina Sacc.
- Stagonospora Smilacis (Ell. & Martin) Sacc.

Smilax pumila Walt.
- Puccinia Smilacis S.

Smilax rotundifolia L.
- Aecidium macrosporum Pk.
- Dicaeoma macrosporum (Arth.) Arth. & Kern. I.
- Puccinia macrospora Arth. I.
- Anthostomella sepelibilis (B. & C.) Sacc.
- Ascochyta confusa Ell. & Ev.
- Botryosphaeria fuliginosa (M. & N.) Ell. & Ev.
- Cercospora mississippiensis Tracy & Earle.
- Cercospora Petersii (B. & C.) Atk.
- Cercospora smilacina Sacc.
- Cercospora Smilacis Thm.
- Cladosporium Smilacis (S.) Fr.
- Dematium Smilacis S.
- Colletosporium atrum Lk., var. purpurascens S.
- Corticium incarnatum Fr.
- Coryneum Smilacis S.

- Eutypella sepulta (B. & C.) Dearness.
- Hainesia Lythri (Desm.) v. Höhnel.
- Sclerotiopsis concava (Desm.) Shear & Dodge.
- Leptostroma Smilacis Cke.
- Leptothyrium Smilacis Dearness.
- Macrophoma smilacina (Pk.) Berl. & Vogl.
- Phoma smilacina (Pk.) Sacc.
- Sphaeropsis smilacina Pk.
- Dichaena smilacina S. Am. Bor?
- Microthyrium Smilacis DeNot.
- Myiocopron Smilacis (DeNot.) Sacc.
- Rhytisma Smilacis Fr.?
- Xyloma Smilacis S. Syn. Car.?
- Phlyctaena Smilacis Cke.
- Phoma brunneola (B. & C.) Sacc.
- Sphaeropsis smilacina Pk.
- Phoma Smilacis Boyer & Jaczewski.
- Phyllosticta cruenta (Fr.) Kickx.
- Phyllosticta smilacina (Pk.) Dearness.
- Phyllosticta Smilacis Ell. & Ev.
- Phyllosticta Smilacis Ell. & Martin.
- Phyllosticta Smilacis Ell. & Martin, var. subeffusa Ell. & Kellerm.
- Phyllostictina subeffusa (Ell. & Ev.) Petrak & Syd.
- Phomatospora disrupta (B. & C.) Cke.
- Physalospora disrupta (B. & C.) Sacc.
- Sphaeria disrupta B. & C.
- Aecidium Smilacis S.
- Aecidium smilacinatum S.
- Aecidium verrucosum Bon.
- Caeoma smilacinatum Lk. I.
- Caeoma Smilacis Lk.
- Dicaeoma Smilacis (S.) O. Kuntze.
- Puccinia Smilacis S.
- Uredo Smilacis S.
- Uredo Smilacis Spreng. I.
- Mycosphaerella smilacicola (Cke.) Overholts.
- Sphaerella smilacicola Cke.
- Sphaeria (Depazea) smilacicola S.
- Sphaeropsis Smilacis Ell. & Ev.
- Ascochyta Smilacis Ell. & Martin.
- Stagonospora Smilacis Sacc.
- Steganosporium Smilacis (Ell. & Martin) Sacc.

Smilax tamnifolia Michx.
- Aecidium Smilacis S.
- Dicaeoma Smilacis (S.) O. Kuntze.
- Cercospora mississippiensis Tracy & Earle.
- Discosia maculicola Gerard.

Smilax sp. indet.

ASCOMYCETES

Acrospermum foliicola B.
- Anthostomella eliminata (B. & C.) Sacc.
- Sphaeria eliminata B. & C.
Anthostomella ludoviciana Ell. & Langlois.
Botryosphaeria muriculata Ell. & Ev.
Capnodium Citri B. & Desm.
Capnodium elongatum B. & Desm.

Smilax sp. indet. (*cont.*)
- Clithris grisea (S.) Ell. & Ev.
- Hysterium griseum S.
- Sporomega griseum (S.) Cke.
- Clypeosphaeria? aliquanta (C. & E.) Sacc.
- Heptameria aliquanta (C. & E.) Cke.
- Sphaeria polysticta B. & C.
- Diatrype infuscans Ell. & Ev.
- Didymella Smilacis Ell. & Ev.
- Didymosphaerella polysticta (B. & C.) Cke.
- Didymosphaeria polysticta (B. & C.) Sacc.
- Sphaeria polysticta B. & C.
- Dimerosporium nimbosum Ell. & Martin.
- Dothidea smilacicola Cke. & Gerard.
- Eutypella stellulata (Fr.) Sacc.
- Valsa stellulata Fr.
- Hypoxylon perforatum (S.) Fr.
- Hysterium virgultorum (DC.) Rob. & Desm.
- Calosphaeria Smilacis Karst. & Hariot.
- Massalongella Smilacis (Karst. & Hariot) Berl.
- Meliola amphitricha Fr.
- Meliola Smilacis F. L. Stevens.
- Mollisia nipteroides Ell. & Ev.
- Ophiobolus filisporus (C. & E.) Sacc.
- Raphidospora filispora C. & E.
- Sphaeria filispora C. & E.
- Sphaeria sepulta B. & C.
- Wegelina sepulta (B. & C.) Berl.
- Valsa tetraploa B. & C.

BASIDIOMYCETES

- Cyphella subcyanea Ell. & Ev.
- Sphenospora pallida Auct. p. p.
- Sphenospora smilacina Syd.
- Sphenospora yurimaguasensis (Henn.) H. S. Jackson.

FUNGI IMPERFECTI

- Aspergillus pulvinatus B. & C.
- Cercospora Smilacis Thm.
- Clasterosporium obclavatum (Cke.) Sacc.
- Sporidesmium obclavatum Cke.
- Cylindrosporium Smilacis Ell. & Ev.
- Cytospora Smilacis Cke.
- Didymobotryum pubescens (C. & E.) Sacc.
- Graphium pubescens C. & E.
- Diplodina ramulorum Ell. & Ev.
- Diplodina Smilacis Ell. & Ev.
- Diplodinula Smilacis (Ell. & Ev.) Tassi.
- Sphaerella smilacina Ell. & Ev.
- Fusarium marginatum B. & C.
- Helicosporium diplosporum Ell. & Ev.
- Helminthosporium siliquosum B. & C.
- Heterosporium asperatum Massee.
- Mystrosporium aterrimum B. & C.
- Periconia epiphylla S.?
- Pestalozzia clavata C. & E.
- Pestalozzia funerea Desm.
- Pestalozzia Guepini Desm.

- Sphaeria erumpens S.
- Phoma erumpens Cke.
- Phoma detegens Starb.
- Ramularia Dioscoreae Ell. & Ev.
- Ramularia subrufa Ell. & Holw.
- Septoria Smilacis Ell. & Ev.

Nemexia lasioneuron (Hook.) Rydb.
- Puccinia amphigena Diet. I.

Liliaceae gen. indet.
- Sclerotium Liliorum S.

AMARYLLIDACEAE

Galanthus nivalis L.
- Urocystis Galanthi Pape.

Amaryllis purpurea Ait.
- Phyllosticta Hymenocallidis Seaver.

Amaryllis sp. indet.
- Cercospora Amaryllidis Ell. & Ev.

Zephyranthes sp. indet.
- Aecidium modestum Arth.
- Aecidium Zephyranthis Shear.

Cooperia Drummondii Herb.

Cooperia pedunculata Herb.
- Dicaeoma Cooperiae (Long) Arth.
- Puccinia Cooperiae Long.

Crinum americanum L.
- Cercospora Pancratii Ell. & Ev.

Crinum broussonetianum Herb. Amaryl.
- Stagonospora Crini Bubák & Kabát.

Hymenocallis declinata (Jacq.) M. Roem.
- Cercospora Amaryllidis Ell.
- Gloeosporium Hemerocallidis Ell. & Ev.

Hymenocallis expansa Herb. App.
- Cercospora Amaryllidis Ell. & Ev.
- Gloeosporium Hemerocallidis Ell. & Ev.

Hymenocallis littoralis Salisb.
- Cercospora Hymenocallidis Pat.

Hymenocallis sp. indet.
- Phyllosticta Hymenocallidis Seaver.
- Mycosphaerella aggregata Earle.

Eucharis sp. indet.
- Aecidium delicatum Arth.

Narcissus sp. indet.
- Aegerita candida P. ex Fr.
- Rhizopus nigricans Ehrenb.
- Hendersonia Curtisii B.
- Stagonospora Curtisii (B.) Sacc.

Pancratium coronarium Leconte.
- Cercospora Pancratii Ell. & Ev.

Hippeastrum puniceum Urb.
- Sclerotium Rolfsii Sacc.

Hippeastrum sp. indet.
- Asterinella Hippeastri Ryan.
- Phyllosticta sp. indet.

Agave americana L.
- Allantonectria miltina (Mont.) Weese.
- Asterina mexicana Ell. & Ev.
- Colletotrichum Agaves Cav.

Agave americana (*cont.*)
  Coniothyrium Agaves (Mont.) Sacc.
  Coniothyrium concentricum (Desm.) Sacc.
  Hypocrea Agaves Maublanc.
  Melanconium americanum Pk. & Clinton.
  Melogramma Egelingii Ell. & Ev.
  Nectria bonanseana Sacc.
  Phytophthora Agaves Villada ex Gandara.
  Plowrightia Agaves Maublanc.
  Plowrightia williamsoniana Kellerm.
{Stachybotrys simplex Hark.
{Stachybotrys subsimplex Cke.
  Stagonospora gigantea Heald & Wolf.
  Stagonospora macrospora (Dur. & Mont.)
    Sacc.
  Trichothecium roseum Hoffm.

Agave atrovirens Karw.
{Asterina Agaves Ell. & Ev.
{Dimerium Agaves (Ell. & Ev.) Rehm.
  Colletotrichum Agaves Cav.
  Dimerosporium agavectona Pat. & Hariot.

Agave horrida Lem.
  Colletotrichum Agaves Cav.

Agave Lechequilla Torr.
{Kellermania mutica Ell. & Ev.
{Septoria megaspora Speg.?

Agave marmorata Roezl.
  Colletotrichum Agaves Cav.

Agave mexicana Lam.

Agave neo-mexicana Wooton & Standley.
  Asterina mexicana Ell. & Ev.

Agave potatorum Zucc.

Agave rigida Mill.
  Colletotrichum Agaves Cav.

Agave rigida Mill., var. **elongata** Auct.
  Coniothyrium concentricum (Desm.) Sacc.

Agave sisalana (Engelm.) Perrine.
  Colletotrichum Agaves Cav.
{Dothidella Parryi (Cke.) Theissen & Syd.
{Endothia Parryi Cke.
  Lembosia Dendrochili Lév.

Agave Shawii Engelm.
{Dothidella Parryi (Cke.) Theissen & Syd.
{Endothia Parryi Cke.
{Homostegia Parryi (Cke.) Holw.
{Plowrightia Parryi (Ckel.) Rehm.

Agave utahensis Engelm.
  Colletotrichum Agaves Cav.

Agave vestita Watson.
  Leptostroma vestitae Seymour & Patterson.

Agave virginica L.
  Metasphaeria nigromaculans Earle.
  Vermicularia Liliacearum S.

Agave sp. indet.
  Didymosphaeria sphaerophora Ell. & Ev.
  Lembosia Agaves Earle.
  Lembosia Dendrochili Lév.

{Phragmodothis circumscissa (Tracy & Earle)
{ Theissen & Syd.
{Plowrightia circumscissa Tracy & Earle.
  Torula diversa Cke.
  Tubercularia Agaves Pat.
  Vermicularia trichella Fr.

Fourcroya cubuya-integra Trel.
  Glomerella cingulata (Stoneman) Spaulding &
    v. Schrenk.

Fourcroya gigantea Vent.
  Coniothyrium concentricum (Desm.) Sacc.
  Rabenhorstia Fourcroyae Pass.

Fourcroya hexapetala Urb.
  Endothia Parryi (Farl.) Cke.

Fourcroya macrophylla Baker.
  Phoma Fourcroyae Thm.

Fourcroya tuberosa Ait.
  Echidnodella Fourcroyae Ryan.
{Dothidella Parryi (Cke.) Theissen & Syd.
{Endothia Parryi (Farl.) Cke.
  Phoma Fourcroyae Thm.

Bomarea acutifolia Herb.
{Dicaeoma (?) Bomareae (Lagerh.) Arth.
{Puccinia Bomareae Henn.
  Puccinia pallor Arth. & Holw.

Bomarea ovata Mirb.
{Dicaeoma (?) Bomareae (Lagerh.) Arth.
{Puccinia Bomareae Henn.

Curculigo sp. indet.
  Glomerella cingulata (Stoneman) Spaulding &
    v. Schrenk.

Hypoxis decumbens L.
{?Uredo globulosa Arth.
{?Uredo Hypoxidis (Bres.) Henn.
{Nigredo affinis (Wint.) Arth.
{Uromyces affinis Wint.

Hypoxis hirsuta (L.) Coville.
  Cylindrosporium guttatum Wint.
  Urocystis Hypoxyis Thax.
{Nigredo affinis (Wint.) Arth.
{Uromyces affinis Wint.

Hypoxis juncea Sm.
  Nigredo affinis (Wint.) Arth.

Amaryllidaceae gen.indet.
  Trichothecium candidum Wallr.

DIOSCOREACEAE

Dioscorea alata L.
  Cercospora carbonacea Miles.
  Puccinia valida Arth.

Dioscorea convolvulacea Cham. & Schl.
  Phyllachora Ulei Wint.
  Puccinia valida Arth.

Dioscorea polygonoides Humb. & Bonpl.
  Uredo Dioscoreae Henn.

Dioscorea villosa L.
  Cercospora Dioscoreae Ell. & Martin.
  Cercospora nubilosa Ell. & Ev.

Dioscorea villosa (*cont.*)
  Didymaria fulva Ell. & Ev.
  Leptostroma herbarum (Fr.) Lk.
  Leptothyrium vulgare (Fr.) Sacc.
  Phyllosticta Dioscoreae Cke.
  Ramularia Dioscoreae Ell. & Ev.
Dioscorea sp. indet.
  Cercospora carbonacea Miles.
  Corticium vagum Boc., var. Solani Kühn.
  {Didymella Dioscoreae (B. & C.) Sacc.
  {Sphaeria Dioscoreae B. & C.
  Gloeosporium ampelophagum (Pass.) Sacc.
  Metarrhizium Anisopliae (Metsch.) Sorok.
  {Phyllosticta Dioscoreae Cke.
  {Septoria Dioscoreae Cke.
  Rhizopus nigricans Ehrb. ex Fr.
  Rhizopus Tritici Saito.
  Rosellinia bunodes B. & Br.
  Uredo Dioscoreae (B. & Br.) Petch.
Rajania cordata L.
  Uredo Dioscoreae Henn.
Rajania hastata L.
Rajania microphylla Kunth.
  Sphaerella Rajaniae Ell. & Ev.

IRIDACEAE

Crocus sp. indet.
  Rhizoctonia sp. indet.
Iris alata Poir.
  Puccinia Iridis (DC.) Wallr.
Iris benacensis Kerner.
  Heterosporium gracile (Wallr.) Sacc.
Iris cristata Ait.
  Vermicularia Liliacearum Westd.
Iris douglasiana Herbert.
Iris fulva Ker-Gawl.
  {Caeoma Iridis S.
  {Dicaeoma Iridis (Rabh.) O. Kuntze.
  {Puccinia Iridis Rabh.
Iris florentina L., var. **albicans** Auct.
  Didymellina Iridis (Desm.) v. Höhnel.
Iris germanica L.
  {Didymellina Iridis (Desm.) v. Höhnel.
  {Heterosporium gracile (Wallr.) Sacc.
  Macrosporium Iridis C. & E.
  Oedocephalum intermixtum Pk..
  Puccinia Iridis Rabh.
Iris longipetala Herbert.
  {Caeoma (Uredo) Iridis S.
  {Dicaeoma Iridis (Rabh.) O. Kuntze.
  {Puccinia Iridis Rabh.
Iris missouriensis Nutt.
  Macrosporium iridicola Ell. & Ev.
  Macrosporium Iridis C. & E.
  Phoma iridina Sacc.
  {Dicaeoma Iridis (Rabh.) O. Kuntze.
  {Puccinia Iridis Rabh.
  {Mycosphaerella Iridis (Awd.) Schrt.
  {Sphaerella Iridis Awd.

Iris orientalis Mill.
  Heterosporium gracile (Wallr.) Sacc.
Iris pabularia Hort.
  Scolecotrichum punctulatum Tracy & Earle.
Iris pumila L.
  Heterosporium gracile (Wallr.) Sacc.
  Puccinia Iridis Rabh.
Iris sambucina L.
  Macrosporium Iridis C. & E.
Iris Swertii Hort.
  Heterosporium gracile (Wallr.) Sacc.
Iris tenax Dougl.
Iris tuberosa L.
  {Dicaeoma Iridis (Rabh.) O. Kuntze.
  {Puccinia Iridis Rabh.
Iris variegata L., var. **horizontalis** Auct.
  Didymellina Iridis (Desm.) v. Höhnel.
Iris versicolor L.
  {Aecidium Iridis Gerard.
  {Dicaeoma Majanthae I. Auct. Amer.
  {Puccinia Majanthae. I. Auct. Amer.
  {Puccinia sessilis I. Auct. Amer.
  Asteroma venulosum (Wallr.) Fckl.
  Cylindrosporium Iridis Ell. & Halsted.
  {Didymella Iridis (Desm.) Tisdale.
  {Didymellina Iridis (Desm.) v. Höhnel.
  {?Helminthosporium gracile Wallr.
  {Heterosporium gracile (Wallr.) Sacc.
  Heterosporium Allii Ell. & Martin, var. Sisy-
    rinchii Speg.
  Mollisia Iridis (Rehm) Sacc.
  Phyllosticta Iridis Ell. & Martin.
  {Dicaeoma Iridis (Rabh.) O. Kuntze.
  {Puccinia Iridis Rabh.
  {Uredo Iridis DC.
  Septoria breviuscula Bubák & Dearness.
  Sphaeria Iridis S.
Iris virginica L.
  Caeoma (Uredo) Iridis S.
  Cladosporium iridicola S.
  Helminthosporium gracile Wallr.
  Sphaeria iridicola S.
  Vermicularia acuminata S.
Iris xiphium L.
  {Dicaeoma Iridis (Rabh.) O. Kuntze.
  {Puccinia Iridis Rabh.
Iris sp. indet.
  Cladochytrium tenue Nowak.
  Corticium vagum B. & C.
  Didymellina macrospora Klebahn.
  Guignardia pullulans Klebahn.
  Macrophomopsis Dracaenae Stevens & Bae-
    cher.
  Sclerotinia sclerotiorum (Lib.) Mass.
  Sclerotium Rolfsii Sacc.
  Scolecotrichum Iridis Fautr. & Roum.
Belamcanda chinensis (L.) DC.
  Epicoccum nigrum Lk.
  Heterosporium gracile (Wallr.) Sacc.

Belamcanda sp. indet.
  Vermicularia Liliacearum Westd.
Sisyrinchium angustifolium Mill.
  Kellermania Sisyrinchii Ell. & Ev.
  {Nigredo houstoniata J. L. Sheldon.
  {Uromyces houstoniatus J. L. Sheldon.
Sisyrinchium bellum Watson.
  Kellermania Sisyrinchii Ell. & Ev.
Sisyrinchium bermudianum L.
  Uredo nominata Arth.
Sisyrinchium demissum Greene.
  Kellermania Sisyrinchii Ell. & Ev.
Sisyrinchium gramineum Curtis.
  Aecidium residuum Arth.
  {Nigredo houstoniata J. Ll Sheldon.
  {Uromyces houstoniatus J. L. Sheldon.
Sisyrinchium grandiflorum Dougl.
  {Nigredo proba Arth.
  {Uromyces probus Arth. I.
  {Uromyces probus Arth.
  {Uromyces Sisyrinchii N. A. F. *3137*.
Sisyrinchium sp. indet.
  Puccinia Sisyrinchii Mont.
  Uromyces Bunsteri H. S. Jackson.
  Vermicularia affinis Sacc. & Briard.
Freesia sp. indet.
  Heterosporium gracile (Wallr.) Sacc.
Gladiolus sp. indet.
  {Alternaria fasciculata (C. & E.) Jones & Grout.
  {Macrosporium fasciculatum C. & E.
  Amerosporium cinctum Ell. & Ev.
  Corticium vagum B. & C.
  Cyphella fumosa Cke.
  Diaporthe Gladioli Ell. & Ev.
  Didymellina Iridis (Desm.) v. Höhnel.
  {Dothiorella lanceolata (C. & E.) Petrak.
  {Sphaeropsis lanceolata C. & E.
  Fusarium oxysporum Schl.
  Fusarium oxysporum, var. Gladioli Massey.
  Heterosporium gracile (Wallr.) Sacc.
  {Macrophoma elongata (B. & C.) Berl. & Vogl.
  {Phoma elongata (B. & C.) Sacc.
  {Sphaeropsis elongata B. & C.
  {Macrophoma Gladioli (Cke.) Berl. & Vogl.
  {Phoma Gladioli (Cke.) Sacc.
  {Sphaeropsis Gladioli Cke.
  Macrosporium caudatum C. & E.
  Mystrosporium polytrichum Cke.
  Phyllosticta Gladioli Ell. & Ev.
  Pleospora subriparia (Cke.) Sacc.
  Polyactis cinerea (P.) B.
  Septoria Gladioli Pass.
  {Sphaerella minimipuncta Cke.
  {Sphaeria minimipuncta Cke.
  Sterigmatocystis ochracea (Wilhelm) van
    Tiegh.
Antholyza sp. indet.
  Heterosporium gracile (Wallr.) Sacc.

SCITAMINEAE

Musa sapientum L.
  (Including M. paradisiaca and all reported
  as "Banana.")

Ascomycetes

  {Antennularia (?) tenuis Earle.
  {Limacinula tenuis (Earle) Sacc. & Trott.
  {Phaeosaccardinula tenuis (Earle) Seaver &
    Chandon.
  Coccomyces Musae (Lév.) Sacc.
  Hypomyces Ipomoeae (Halsted) Wr.
  {Ciliaria cubensis (B. & C.) Pat.
  {Lachnea cubensis (B. & C.) Sacc.
  Lachnea scutellata (P. ex Fr.) Gill.
  Leptospora Musae Drost.
  Nectria foliicola B. & C.
  Creonectria ochroleuca (S.) Seaver.
  Nectria setosa Ferdinandsen & Winge.
  Nectria suffulta B. & C.
  Rosellinia bunodes B. & Br.
  Rosellinia Pepo Pat.
  Sphaerostilbe Musarum Ashby.

Basidiomycetes

  {Collybia musicola Murrill.
  {Gymnopus musicola Murrill.
  {Collybia orizabensis Murrill.
  {Gymnopus orizabensis Murrill.
  {Crepidotus fumosifolius Murrill.
  {Melanotus fumosifolius Murrill.
  Crepidotus mollis Fr.
  {Crepidotus musicola B. & C.
  {Melanotus musicola (B. & C.) Murrill.
  Cyphella Bananae Cke.
  Cyphella musaecola B. & C.
  Hygrophorus subpratensis Murrill.
  {Atylospora Musae (Earle) Murrill
  {Gymnochilus Musae Earle.
  {Hypholoma Musae (Earle) Morg.
  Lentinus orizabensis Murrill.
  Marasmius musicola Murrill.   1915.
  Marasmius Rotula (Scop.) ex Fr.
  Marasmius semiustus B. & C.
  Marasmius Sacchari Wakker.
  {Marasmius semiustus B. & C.
  {Marasmius stenophyllus Mont.
  Pholiota Musae (Earle) Murrill.
  Poria subcollapsa Murrill.
  {Volvaria Bakeri Murrill.
  {Volvariopsis Bakeri Murrill.

Sphaeropsidales

  Aschersonia cubensis B. & C.
  Chaetophoma Musae Cke.
  Diplodia cacaoicola Henn.
  {Macrophoma Musae (Cke.) Berl. & Vogl.
  {Phoma Musae (Cke.) Sacc.

Musa sapientum (*cont.*)
  Phoma Musarum Cke.
  { Coniothyrium Gastonis (Roum.) Berl. & Vogl.
  Phyllosticta Gastonis Roum.
  Phyllostictella Gastonis (Roum.) Tassi.
  Sphaeropsis paradisiaca Mont., var. minor
      Fragoso & Ciferri.
  { Hendersonia Musae Cke.
  Stagonospora Musae (Cke.) Sacc.

MELANCONIALES

  { Gloeosporium fructigenum B.
  Gloeosporium phomoides Sacc.
  Gloeosporium piperatum Ell. & Ev.
  Colletotrichum Musarum Coons & Nelson.
  Gloeosporium lagenarium (Pass.) Sacc. &
      Roum., var. Musarum Ell. & Ev.
  Gloeosporium Musae Cke. & Massee.
  Gloeosporium Musarum Cke. & Massee.
  Myxosporium Musae B. & C.
  Pestalozzia funerea Desm.
  Pestalozzia fuscescens, var. Sacchari Wakker.

HYPHOMYCETES

  Acremoniella occulta Cav.
  Cercospora Musarum Ashby.
  Cladosporium pannosum Cke.
  Fusarium anthophilum (A. Br.) Wr.
  Fusarium bullatum Sherb., var. brevius Wr. &
      Reink.
  Fusarium camptoceras Wr. & Reink.
  Fusarium chlamydosporum Wr. & Reink.
  Fusarium cubense Erw. Sm.
  Fusarium cubense Erw. Sm., var. inodoratum
      Brandes.
  Fusarium longipes Wr. & Reink.
  Fusarium moniliforme Sheldon.
  Fusarium moniliforme Sheldon, var. erumpens
      Wr. & Reink.
  Fusarium moniliforme Sheldon, var. majus
      Wr. & Reink.
  Fusarium moniliforme Sheldon, var. subgluti-
      nans Wr. & Reink.
  Fusarium orthoceras App. & Wr.
  Fusarium orthoceras App. & Wr., var. trisep-
      tatum Wr.
  Fusarium oxysporum Schl. em. Wr., var. Nico-
      tianae J. Johnson.
  Fusarium radicicola Wr.
  Fusarium semitectum B. & Rav.
  Fusarium vasinfectum Atk.
  { Haplographium atrobrunneum (Cke.) Sacc.
  Penicillium atrobrunneum Cke.
  Hymenula Musae Pat.
  Sporidesmium Fumago Cke.
  Stachybotrys subsimplex Cke.
  Stilbella flavida Henn.
  Thielaviopsis ethaceticus Went.

MISCELLANEA

  Pythium debaryanum Hesse.
  { Rhizoctonia grisea (Stevenson) Matz.
  Sclerotium griseum Stevenson
  Sclerotium Rolfsii Sacc.
  Ustilaginoidella musiperda Essed.
Musa textilis Née.
  Fusarium cubense Erw. Sm.
Heliconia borinquena Griggs.
Heliconia latispatha Benth.
Heliconia pendula Wawra.
Heliconia psittacorum L.
  { Puccinia Heliconiae Arth.
  Uredo Heliconiae Diet.
Scitamineae gen. indet.
  { Acia sericea Pat.
  Hydnum sericeum (Pat.) Sacc. & D. Sacc.

ZINGIBERACEAE

Zingiber officinale Roscoe.
  Allantospora radiicola Wakker.
Alpinia antillarum R. & S.
  { Catacauma Renalmiae (Rehm) Theissen &
      Syd.
  Phyllachora Renalmiae Rehm.
Costus speciosus Sm.
  Glomerella cingulata (Stoneman) Spaulding &
      v. Schrenk.

CANNACEAE

Canna coccinea Ait.
  Cladosporium herbarum (P.) ex Lk.
  Haplographium portoricesae Stevens & Dalbey.
  Puccinia Cannae Henn.
Canna glauca L.
  Cladosporium herbarum (P.) ex Lk.
  { Dicaeoma (?) Cannae (Henn.) Arth.
  Puccinia Cannae Henn.
  Uredo Cannae Wint.
Canna indica L.
  Anthostomella achira Speg.
  Macrosporium bulbotrichum Cke.
  Myrmaecium Cannae Dearness & House.
  Ophiobolus linosporoides Speg.
  { Dicaeoma Cannae (Henn.) Arth.
  Puccinia Cannae Henn.
  Uredo Cannae Wint.
Canna sp. indet.
  Aulographum maculare B. & Br.
  Darluca Filum (Biv.) Cast.

MARANTACEAE

Calathea lutea (Aubl.) G. F. W. Meyer.
Calathea macrocephala K. Schum.
  { Dicaeoma (?) Cannae (Henn.) Arth.
  Puccinia Cannae Henn.

Calathea vittata Körn.
  Glomerella cincta (Stoneman) Spaulding &
    v. Schrenk.
Maranta arundinacea L.
  Glomerella cingulata (Stoneman) Spaulding &
    v. Schrenk.
  Puccinia Cannae Henn.
  Puccinia Thaliae Diet.
Thalia dealbata Roscoe.
  Cercospora Thaliae Ell. & Langlois.
Thalia geniculata L.
  ⎰Dicaeoma (?) Cannae (Henn.) Arth.
  ⎱Puccinia Cannae Henn.

ORCHIDACEAE

Cypripedium acaule Ait.
  Cercospora Cypripedii Ell. & Dearness.
Cypripedium parviflorum Salisb.
  Cercospora Cypripedii Ell. & Dearness.
  ⎧Dicaeoma (?) Cypripedii (Arth. & Holw.) O.
  ⎨ Kuntze.
  ⎩Puccinia Cypripedii Arth. & Holw.
Cypripedium reginae Walt.
  Cercospora Cypripedii Ell. & Dearness.
Cordula insignis (Wall.) Raf.
  ⎰Mycosphaerella Cypripedii (Pk.) House.
  ⎱Sphaerella Cypripedii Pk.
Orchis aristata Fisch.
Habenaria albida R. Br.
  Botrytis cinerea P. †
  Septoria cercosperma Rostr.
Habenaria bracteata (Willd.) R. Br.
Habenaria dilatata (Pursh) Gray.
Habenaria stricta Ridl.
Habenaria viridiflora R. Br.
  ⎰Aecidium alaskanum Trel.
  ⎱Aecidium graebnerianum Henn.
Habenaria hyperborea (L.) R. Br.
  ⎰Aecidium alaskanum Trel.
  ⎱Aecidium graebnerianum P. Henn.
  Cladosporium herbarum (P.) ex Lk.
  ⎰Dasyscypha groenlandica (Rostr.) Sacc.
  ⎱Lachnum groenlandicum Rostr.
  ?Puccinia sessilis Schneid. I.
  Uredo Gynandrearum Cda.
Habenaria maculosa Lindl.
Habenaria monorrhiza (Sw.) R. Br.
  Uredo Gynandrearum Cda.
Habenaria saccata Greene.
  ⎰Aecidium alaskanum Trel.
  ⎱Aecidium graebnerianum Henn.
  ?Aecidium Orchidearum Desm.
Habenaria viridis (L.) R. Br., var. **bracteata**
    (Muhl.) Gray.
  Aecidium graebnerianum Henn.
Vanilla aromatica Auct.
  Ocellaria Vanillae Henn.

Vanilla fragrans (Salisb.) Ames.
  Fusarium Solani (Mart.) Sacc.
  ⎧?Calospora Vanillae Massee.
  ⎪Colletotrichum Vanillae Stoneman.
  ⎪Gloeosporium rufomaculans Thm.
  ⎪Glomerella cingulata (Stoneman) Spaulding &
  ⎪ v. Schrenk.
  ⎨Glomerella rufomaculans Spaulding & v.
  ⎪ Schrenk.
  ⎪Glomerella (?) Vanillae (Stoneman) Spaulding
  ⎪ & v. Schrenk.
  ⎪Gnomoniopsis Vanillae Stoneman.
  ⎩Lembosia Rolfsii Horne.
Vanilla sp. indet.
  Gloeosporium Bussei Henn.
Stenorrhynchus lanceolatus (Aubl.) Griseb.
  Uredo pustulata Henn.
Erythrodes Killipii Ames.
  Asterina Killipii Dearness & House.
Prescottia oligantha (Sw.) Lindl.
  Uredo Gynandrearum Cda.
Epipactis decipiens (Hook.) Ames.
  ⎰Pucciniastrum Goodyerae Arth.
  ⎱Uredo Goodyerae Tranz.
Calopogon pulchellus (Sw.) R. Br.
  ⎧Dicaeoma (?) Cypripedii (Arth. & Holw.) O.
  ⎨ Kuntze.
  ⎩Puccinia Cypripedii Arth. & Holw.
Corallorhiza maculata Raf.
Corallorhiza multiflora Nutt.
  ⎧Heptameria Corallorhizae (Pk.) Cke.
  ⎪Leptosphaeria Corallorhizae Pk.
  ⎨Leptosphaeria eustoma (Fr.) Sacc., var. Coral-
  ⎪ lorhizae (Pk.) Berl.
  ⎩Phoma corallorhiza Ell. & Ev.
Pleurothallis longissima Lindl.
  Phyllosticta Pleurothallidis Keissler.
Pleurothallis ruscifolia Sw.
  Guignardia Pleurothallis Dearness & House
Epidendrum bifidum ex Stevenson.
  Hendersonia Epidendri Keissler.
Epidendrum corymbosum Lindl.
  Uredo Guacae Mayor.
Epidendrum difforme Jacq.
Epidendrum rigidum Jacq.
  Uredo Guacae Mayor.
Epidendrum vitellinum Lindl.
  Uredo behnickiana Henn.
Epidendrum sp. indet.
  Aspergillus fuliginosus Pk.?
  Gloeosporium affine Sacc.
  Macrophoma surinamensis (B. & C.) Berl. &
    Vogl.
  Morenoella Calami Racib.
  Uredo Epidendri Henn.
  Uredo wittmackiana Henn. & Klitzing.

Cattleya dowiana Batem.
{ Hemileia americana Massee.
{ Uredo americana (Massee) Arth.
  Uredo behnickiana Henn.
Cattleya sp. indet.
  Macrophoma Oncidii Henn.
Laelia albida Batem.
Laelia furfuracea Lindl.
  Phyllosticta Laeliae Keissler.
Sobralia macrantha Lindl.
  Gloeosporium cinctum B. & C.
Phajus Wallichii Lindl.
  Coleosporium Bletiae Diet.
Limodorum tuberosum L. non Auct.
Bletia patula Hook.
  Uredo nigropuncta Henn.
Bletia sp. indet.
  Colletotrichum Bletiae Halsted.
  Uredo Cyrtopodii Syd.
  Volutella concentrica Halsted.
Aplectrum hyemale (Muhl.) Torr.
  Fusicladium Aplectri Ell. & Ev.
  Phyllosticta Aplectri Ell. & Ev.
  Uredo Cyrtopodii Syd.
Dendrobium moschatum Wall.
  Gloeosporium cinctum B. & C.
Maxillaria picta Hook.
{ Gloeosporium cinctum B. & C.
{ Colletotrichum cinctum (B. & C.) Stoneman.
{ Glomerella cincta (Stoneman) Spaulding &
{   v. Schrenk.
{ Gnomoniopsis cincta Stoneman.
Camaridium grandiflorum Ames.
  Gloeosporium cingulatum Atk.

Ionopsis utricularioides (Sw.) Lindl.
  Scolecopeltis Ionopsidis Toro.
Odontoglossum grande Lindl.
  Dendrodochium affine Sacc.
  Nectriella jucundina Sacc. & Speg.
Oncidium cavendishianum Batem.
  Hemileia americana Massee.
  Uredo behnickiana Henn.
Oncidium luridum Lindl.
  Hendersonia microspora Massee.
Oncidium sphacelatum Lindl.
  Gloeosporium Oncidii Oud.
  Macrophoma Oncidii Henn.
  Phoma Oncidii-sphacelati Tassi.
Oncidium sp. indet.
{ Glomerella cincta (Stoneman) Spaulding &
{   v. Schrenk.
{ Gnomoniopsis cincta Stoneman.
Orchidaceae gen. indet.
  Botrytis vulgaris Fr.
  Fusarium Solani (Mart. p. p.) App. & Wr., var.
    minus Wr.
  Gloeosporium Orchidearum Karst. & Har.
{ Leptostroma Orchidearum Mont.
{ Myiocopron Orchidearum (Mont.) Sacc.
  Nectria bulbicola Henn.
  Puccinia cinnamomea Diet. & Holw.
  Sclerotinia fuckeliana (D By.) Fckl.
  Sphaeropsis Orchidearum Ciferri & Fragoso.
  Sphaerostilbe nitida B. & C.
  Thielavia basicola (B. & Br.) Zopf.
  Uredo Orchidis Wint.
Monocotyledoneae fam. indet.
  Periola sphaeriiformis Mont.
  Solenopeziza grisea A. L. Smith.
  Sphaeronema caninum B. & C.

DICOTYLEDONEAE

CASUARINACEAE
Casuarina equisetifolia L.
Clitocybe tabescens (Scop. ex Fr.) Bres.

SAURURACEAE
Saururus cernuus L.
{ Cercospora Saururi Ell. & Ev.
{ Ramularia Saururi (Ell. & Ev.) Tharp.
Gloeosporium Saururi Ell. & Dearness.
Helotium salicellum Fr., var. Saururi Rehm.
Houttuynia californica Benth. & Hook.
Cercospora Saururi Ell. & Ev.

PIPERACEAE
Piper aduncum L.
Arthrobotryum caudatum Syd.
Cercospora portoricensis Earle.
Coniothyrium glabroides F. L. Stevens.
Dimerium piceum (B. & C.) Theissen.
Helminthosporium glabroides F. L. Stevens.
Helminthosporium Helleri F. L. Stevens.
{ Irene glabra (B. & C.) Toro.
{ Meliola glabra B. & C.
Meliola glabroides F. L. Stevens.
{ Meliola gaillardiana F. L. Stevens.
{ Meliola Piperis Earle.
Paranectria meliolicola F. L. Stevens.
Piper Amalgo L.
Cercoseptoria Piperis (Stevens & Dalbey) Petrak.
Fumago vagans P.
Guignardia pipericola F. L. Stevens.
Meliola tortuosa Wint.
Ramularia cylindrosporioides F. L. Stevens.
Septoriopsis Piperis Stevens & Dalbey.
Stigmatea Piperis Rehm.
Piper blattarum Spreng.
Meliola paucipes F. L. Stevens.
Piper hispidum Sw.
{ Cercospora pipericola Sacc. & Syd.
{ Cercospora Piperis Ell. & Ev.
Cercospora portoricensis Earle.
Meliola contorta F. L. Stevens.
Piper macrophyllum Sw.
Glomerella cingulata (Stoneman) Spaulding & v. Schrenk.
Stilbella flavida Henn.
Piper marginatum Jacq.
Guignardia pipericola F. L. Stevens.
Meliola glabroides F. L. Stevens.
Meliola tortuosa Wint.
Pseudonectria pipericola F. L. Stevens.
Piper Molleri C. DC.
Amazonia asterinoides (Wint.) Theissen.

Piper peltatum L.
Amazonia asterinoides (Wint.) Theissen.
Calonectria erubescens (Rob.) Sacc.
Cercospora portoricensis Earle.
Colletotrichum Piperis F. L. Stevens.
Meliola asterinoides Wint.
Meliola tortuosa Wint.
Pseudomeliola (?) collapsa Earle.
Stephanoma Meliola Stevens & Dalbey.
Trichothyrium collapsum (Earle) Theissen.
Trichothyrium lomatophorum (Ell. & Ev.) Toro.
Piper reticulatum L.
Crepidotus mollis Fr.
Meliola asterinoides Wint.
Piper scabrum Sw.
Cercospora portoricensis Earle.
Piper umbellatum L.
Belonidium leucorrhodinum (Mont.) Sacc.
Calonectria erubescens (Rob.) Sacc.
Cercospora portoricensis Earle.
Colletotrichum Piperis F. L. Stevens.
Coniothyrium glabroides F. L. Stevens.
Dimerium piceum (B. & C.) Theissen.
Meliola Ipomoeae Earle.
Meliola tortuosa Wint.
Paranectria meliolicola F. L. Stevens.
Pseudonectria pipericola F. L. Stevens.
Stephanoma Meliolae Stevens & Dalbey.
Piper sp. indet.
Acrostalagmus albus Preuss.
Aschersonia brunnea Petch.
{ Asterina reptans B. & C.
{ Trichopeltis (?) reptans (B. & C.) Speg.
Asteroma pulchellum Sacc.
Cyclodothis pulchella Syd.
Micropeltella? maxima Speg.
Paranectria meliolicola F. L. Stevens.
Podosporium effusum Pat.
Rhizoctonia pallida Matz.
Rosellinia bunodes B. & Br.
Trichothyrium dubiosum (Bomm. & Rouss.) Theissen.
Triposporium stelligerum Speg.
Peperomia hernandifolia (Vahl) A. Dietr.
Uredo Peperomiae Henn.
Uredo Piperis Henn.
Peperomia sp. indet.
Asterina bullata B. & C.
Microthyrium? albigenum B. & C.
Piperaceae gen. indet.
Asterina dubiosa Bomm. & Rouss.
Meliola furcata Lév.

SALICACEAE

Populus acuminata Rydb.
  Cytospora chrysosperma (P.) ex Fr.
  Fomes applanatus (P. ex Wallr.) Gill.
  { Melampsora albertensis Arth.
  { Melampsora occidentalis N. Am. Ured. *610.*
  Melampsora occidentalis H. S. Jackson.
? { Melampsora Medusae Thm.
  { Uredo Medusae (Thm.) Arth.
Populus alba L.
  Cercospora populina Ell. & Ev.
  Cytospora chrysosperma (P.) ex Fr.
  Dothichiza populea Sacc. & Briard.
  Fusicladium radiosum (Lib.) Lindr.
  { Fomes applanatus (P. ex Wallr.) Gill.
  { Ganoderma applanatum (P. ex Wallr.) Pat.
  Gloeosporium cytisporeum Pass.
  Lenzites sepiaria Fr.
  Marssonia pyriformis (Riess) Sacc.
  { Gloeosporium Populi (Lib.) Desm. & Mont.
  { Marssonia Castagnei (Desm. & Mont.) Sacc.
  { Marssonia Populi (Lib.) Sacc.
  { Marssonina Castagnei (Desm. & Mont.) Magn.
  { Marssonina Populi (Lib.) Magn.
  Melampsora Abietis-canadensis C. A. Ludwig.
  { Phyllosticta alcides Ell. & Kellerm.
  { Phyllosticta alcides Sacc., var. americana Sacc.
     & D. Sacc.
  Taphrina Johansonii Sadeb.
  Taphrina rhizophora Johans.
  Trametes serialis Fr.
  Valsa ambiens (P.) ex Fr.
Populus angustifolia James.

PYRENOMYCETINEAE
  Amphisphaeria Populi Tracy & Earle.
  Melanopsamma pomiformis (P. ex Fr.) Sacc.
  Melanopsamma pomiformis (P. ex Fr.) Sacc.,
     var. minor Sacc.
  Rosellinia pulveracea (Ehrh. ex Fr.) Fckl.
  Teichospora aspera Ell. & Ev.
  Teichospora oblongispora Ell. & Ev.
  { Strickeria Populi Earle.
  { Teichospora Populi (Earle) Sacc. & D. Sacc.
  Teichospora pygmaea Ell. & Ev.
  Uncinula Salicis (DC.) Wint. †
  Valsa sordida Nits.
  Zignoella Populi Ell. & Ev.

UREDINALES
  Melampsora albertensis Arth.
  { Melampsora Medusae Thm.
  { Melampsora populina Auct.
  { Uredo Medusae (Thm.) Arth.
  Melampsora occidentalis H. S. Jackson.

HYMENOMYCETINEAE
  { Fomes applanatus (P. ex Wallr.) Gill.
  { Ganoderma applanatum (P. ex Wallr.) Pat.
  { Polyporus applanatus P. ex Wallr.

  Fomes igniarius (L. ex Fr.) Gill.
  Peniophora Allescheri Bres.
  Polyporus adustus (Willd.) ex Fr.
  Polyporus spumeus (Sow.) ex Fr.
  Trametes hispida Bagl.
  Trametes Peckii Kalchb.

FUNGI IMPERFECTI
  Astrodochium coloradense Ell. & Ev.
  Coniothecium epidermis Cda.
  Coniothyrium myriocarpum (Fr.) Sacc.
  Cytospora chrysosperma (P.) ex Fr.
  { Diplodina Populi Ell. & Ev.
  { Diplodinula Populi (Ell. & Ev.) Tassi.
  { Hendersonia diplodioides Ell. & Ev.
  { Hendersonulina angustifolia (Ell. & Ev.)
     Tassi.
  Marssonia piriformis (Riess) Sacc.
  Phyllosticta brunnea Dearness & Barthol.
  Septoria musiva Pk.
  Septoria Populi Fung. Columb. *1257.*
Populus aurea Tidestrom.
  Melampsora albertensis Arth.
Populus balsamifera L.

ASCOMYCETES
  Eutypella radula (P. ex Fr.) Ell. & Ev.
  Hypoxylon pruinatum (Klotzsch) Cke.
  Leptosphaeria borealis Ell. & Ev., var. Populi
     Dearness & House.
  Mycosphaerella Populi Schrt.
  { Mycosphaerella populifolia (Cke.) House.
  { Sphaerella populifolia Cke.
  { Mycosphaerella populnea (Sacc.) House.
  { Sphaerella populnea Sacc.
  Taphrina aurea (P.) ex Fr. †
  { Uncinula adunca Lév.
  { Uncinula heliciformis Howe.
  { Uncinula Salicis (DC.) Wint. †

UREDINALES
  Melampsora Abietis-canadensis C. A. Ludwig.
  { Melampsora albertensis Arth.
  { Melampsora Medusae Fung. Columb. *3915,*
     4034, 4434, 4435, N. Am. Ured. *806.*
  { Melampsora Medusae Thm.
  { Uredo Medusae (Thm.) Arth.
  { Melampsora albertensis Fung. Columb. *4548.*
  { Melampsora occidentalis H. S. Jackson.
  { Melampsora populina West Am. Fung. *369.*

POLYPORACEAE
  { Fomes applanatus (P. ex Wallr.) Gill.
  { Fomes leucophaeus (Mont.) Cke.
  { Fomes igniarius (L. ex Fr.) Gill.
  { Pyropolyporus igniarius (L. ex Fr.) Murrill.
  Fomes pinicola (Sw. ex Fr.) Cke.
  Fomes salicinus Fr.
  { Bjerkandera adusta (Willd. ex Fr.) Karst.
  { Polyporus adustus (Willd.) ex Fr.

Populus balsamifera (*cont.*)
Polyporus subcinereus B.
⎰ Polyporus biformis Fr.
⎱ Polystictus biformis Fr.

FUNGI IMPERFECTI

Cytospora chrysosperma (P.) ex Fr.
Dothichiza populea Sacc. & Briard.
⎰ Cladosporium ramulosum Rob.
| Fusicladium radiosum (Lib.) Lindr.
| Fusicladium Tremulae Frank.
| Oidium radiosum Lib.
⎱ Fusicladium radiosum (Lib.) Lindr., var. balsamifera J. J. Davis.
⎰ Marssonia nigricans Ell. & Ev.
| Marssonina nigricans (Ell. & Ev.) Magn.
| Marssonia Populi (Lib.) Sacc.
| Marssonina Castagnei (Desm. & Mont.) Magn.
⎱ Marssonina Populi (Lib.) Magn.
Phyllosticta brunnea Dearness & Barthol.
⎰ Cylindrosporium oculatum Ell. & Ev.
⎱ Septoria musiva Pk., var. J. J. Davis.
Septoria Populi Fung. Columb. *3486.*
Septoria Populi Desm.
Septoria populicola Pk.
Septoria salicina Pk.

Populus candicans Ait.
Eutypa subtecta (Fr.) Fckl.
⎰ Gloeosporium brunneum Ell. & Ev.
| Marssonia brunnea (Ell. & Ev.) Sacc.
| Marssonina brunnea (Ell. & Ev.) Magn.
⎱ Marssonina Populi (Lib.) Magn.
Septoria populicola Pk.
⎰ Uncinula adunca Lév.
⎱ Uncinula Salicis (DC.) Wint. †
Melampsora Abietis-canadensis C. A. Ludwig.
⎰ Melampsora Medusae Thm.
| Melampsora populina Auct. Amer. p. p.
⎱ Uredo Medusae (Thm.) Arth.
Melampsora occidentalis H. S. Jackson.

Populus deltoides Marsh.
Including **Populus** (cottonwood).

MYXOMYCETES

Badhamia orbiculata Rex.
Comatricha irregularis Rex.
Cribraria violacea Rex.
Didymium anellus Morg.

PEZIZINEAE

Cenangella violacea Ell. & Ev.

EXOASCACEAE

Taphrina aurea (P.) ex Fr. †
⎰ Taphrina aurea Auct. Amer. p. p.
⎱ Taphrina rhizophora Johans.

PYRENOMYCETINEAE

Amphisphaeria separans Ell. & Ev.
Anthostomella thyridioides Ell. & Ev.

⎰ Caliciopsis calicioides (Ell. & Ev.) H. M. Fitzpatrick.
⎱ Caliciopsis Ellisii Sacc.
Hypsotheca calicioides Ell. & Ev.
Periconia calicioides (Fr.) B.
Sporocybe calicioides Fr.
Capnodium avellanum B. & Desm.
Capnodium elongatum B. & Desm.
⎰ Coelosphaeria fusariospora Ell. & Ev.
⎱ Sphaeria fusariospora Ell. & Ev.
Cryptosphaeria populina (P. ex Fr.) Sacc.
Didymosphaeria populifolia Ell. & Ev.
Herpotrichia diffusa (S.) Ell. & Ev.
Herpotrichia rhodospiloides Pk.
Lophidium pachystomum Ell. & Ev.
Lophidium rude Ell. & Ev.
Lophiostoma dakotense Ell. & Ev.
Lophiostoma granulosum (Crouan) Sacc.
Lophiostoma triseptatum Pk., var. pluriseptatum Ell. & Ev.
Melanomma dealbatum Ell. & Ev.
Melanomma gregarium Ell. & Ev.
Melanomma subcongruum Ell. & Ev.
⎰ Creonectria verrucosa (S.) Seaver.
⎱ Nectria verrucosa (S.) Sacc.
Nectria verrucosa (S.) Sacc., var. Populi Rehm.
Rosellinia muriculata Ell. & Ev.
Rosellinia subcompressa Ell. & Ev.
⎰ **Mycosphaerella macularis** (Fr.) Schrt.
⎱ Sphaerella macularis (Fr.) Awd.
Sphaerella populifolia Cke.
Teichospora aspera Ell. & Ev.
Teichospora fulgurata Ell. & Ev.
Teichospora Helenae Ell. & Ev.
Teichospora infuscans Ell. & Ev.
Teichospora mammoides Ell. & Ev.
Teichospora populina Ell. & Ev.
Teichospora pygmaea Ell. & Ev.
Trematosphaeria pertusa (P. ex Fr.) Fckl.
Uncinula Salicis (DC.) Wint. †
Valsa ambiens (P.) ex Fr.

UREDINALES

Melampsora Abietis-canadensis C. A. Ludwig.
⎰ Melampsora Medusae Thm.
| Melampsora populina West Am. Fung. *29.*
⎱ Uredo Medusae Arth.
⎰ ?Caeoma cylindricum Auct. Amer.
| ?Lecythea cylindrica Auct. Amer.
| ?Lecythea ovata Auct. Amer.
| ?Lecythea populina Auct. Amer.
| ?Melampsora Medusae Auct. Amer. p. p. an Thm.
| ?Melampsora populina Auct. Amer.
| ?Sclerotium populinum Auct. Amer.
⎱ ?Uredo cylindrica Auct. Amer.
Melampsora populina E. F. *194.*
Melampsora populina Ohio Fung. *75.*

Populus deltoides (*cont.*)

POLYPORACEAE

Elfvingia megaloma (Lév.) Murrill.
Fomes applanatus (P. ex Wallr.) Gill.
Fomes leucophaeus (Mont.) Cke.
Ganoderma applanatum (P. ex Wallr.) Pat.
Irpex lacteus Fr.
Lenzites sepiaria Fr.
Polyporus adustus (Willd.) ex Fr.
Polystictus versicolor (L.) ex Fr.
Funalia stuppea (B.) Murrill.
?Trametes funalis Auct. Amer. p. p.
Trametes hispida Bagl.
Trametes Peckii Kalchb.
Trametes Trogii B.

HYMENOMYCETINEAE

Hebeloma Colvini Pk., var. velatum Pk.
Hydnum Kauffmani Pk.
Marasmius Rotula Fr.
Ozonium auricomum Lk.
Peniophora occidentalis Ell. & Ev.
Pleurotus ostreatus (Jacq.) ex Fr.
Pleurotus sapidus Kalchb.
Thelephora rosella Pk.
Tremella subochracea Pk.

SPHAERIOIDALES

Aposphaeria kansensis Ell. & Ev.
Aposphaeria striolata Sacc.
Cytospora chrysosperma (P.) ex Fr.
Cytosporella macrospora Pk.
Diplodiella striispora Ell. & Barthol.
Dothichiza populea Sacc. & Briard.
Dothiorella multicocca Ell. & Barthol.
Hendersonia stygia Ell. & Ev.
Hendersonulina stygia (Ell. & Ev.) Tassi.
Hysteromyxa corticola Ell. & Ev.
Phoma canescens Ell. & Barthol.
Phoma Populi Fr.
Phyllosticta maculans Ell. & Ev.
Phyllosticta intermixta Seaver.
Phyllosticta populina (Fckl.) Sacc.
Phyllosticta populina (Fckl.) Sacc., var. parva Pk.
Septoria musiva Pk.
Septoria Populi Desm.
Septoria populicola Pk.
Septoria rhabdocarpa Ell. & Barthol.
Sphaeronema Populi B. & C.
Sphaeropsis Populi Ell. & Barthol.
Stagonospora Bartholomaei Sacc. & Syd.
Stagonospora Populi Ell. & Barthol.

MELANCONIALES

Cryptosporium coronatum Fckl.
Cylindrosporium oculatum Ell. & Ev.
Cytospora chrysosperma (P.) ex Fr.
Naemaspora populina (P.) ex Fr.
Gloeosporium fructigenum Auct. p. p.

Marsonia Populi (Lib.) Sacc.
Marssonina Populi (Lib.) Magn.
Gloeosporium stenosporum Ell. & Kellerm.
Marssonina stenospora (Ell. & Kellerm.) Magn.

HYPHOMYCETES

Alternaria tenuis Nees.
Botrytis vulgaris Lk., var. interrupta Fres.
Cercospora populina Ell. & Ev.
Cercospora reducta Syd.
Cercospora sessilis Ell. & Ev.
Cladosporium ramulosum Desm.
Cladosporium brevipes Ell. & Barthol.
Cladosporium subsessile Ell. & Barthol.
Clasterisporium kansense Ell. & Barthol.
Coniothecium effusum Cda.
Fusarium radicicola Wr.
Macrosporium caudatum C. & E.
Ramularia Uredinis (Voss) Sacc.
Sporidesmium suffultum Pound & Clements.
Dactylium sublutescens Pk.
Trichothecium sublutescens (Pk.) Sacc.
Zygodesmus obtusus Ell. & Ev.

Populus dilatata Ait.

Agaricus ostreatus Jacq. ex Fr.
Aposphaeria fibricola (B.) Sacc.
Phoma fibricola B.
Cenangium populinum S.
Cercospora populina Ell. & Ev.
Cytospora chrysosperma (P.) ex Fr.
Naemaspora chrysosperma P. ex Fr.
Naemaspora populina P. ex Fr.
Diatrypella variolosa (S.) Ell. & Ev.
Sphaeria variolosa S.
Fenestrella fenestrata (B. & Br.) Schrt.
Hendersonia pauciseptata B. & C.
Hypoxylon Malleolus B. & Rav.
Caeoma (Uredo) cylindricum S. Am. Bor. 2855.
Melampsora Medusae Thm.
Melampsora populina Auct. Amer. p. p.
Uredo Medusae (Thm.) Arth.
Melampsora occidentalis H. S. Jackson.
Microdiplodia Populi Dearness & House.
Myxosporium hyalinum (Ell.) Wint.
Polyporus Farlowii Lloyd.
Rhytisma nervale (A. & S. ex Fr.) Rehm.
Xyloma nervale A. & S. ex Fr.
Sclerotiopsis concava (Desm.) Shear & Dodge.
Sphaeropsis Populi Ell. & Barthol.
Ascomyces aureus Auct. Amer.
Taphrina aurea Auct. Amer. p. p.
Taphrina rhizophora Johans.
Teichospora populina Ell. & Ev.
Valsa operta (Schm. ex Fr.) Cke.
Valsa nivea (Hoffm.) ex Fr.
Xylaria corniformis Fr.

Populus Eugenei Simon-Louis.

Cytospora chrysosperma (P.) ex Fr.
Dothichiza populea Sacc. & Briard.

Populus Fremontii Watson.
Fusicladium radiosum (Lib.) Lindr.
Melampsora occidentalis H. S. Jackson.
Septoria musiva Pk.
Septoria Populi J. J. Davis Pacific Fung. 1723.
Taphrina rhizophora Auct. Amer.
Populus grandidentata Michx.

MYXOMYCETES

Physarum connatum Lister.
Hemitrichia stipata (S.) Macbr.
Hemitrichia stipitata Massee.
Trichia varia (P.) Rostf.

ASCOMYCETES

Cenangium populneum (P. ex Fr.) Rehm.
Cenangium populneum, var. singularis Rehm.
Pezicula cinnamomea (Phil.) Sacc.
Phacidium Populi Lasch.
{Mycosphaerella orbicularis (Pk.) House.
{Sphaerella orbicularis Pk.
Taphrina aurea (P.) ex Fr.†
{Taphrina aurea Auct. Amer. p. p
{Taphrina rhizophora Auct. Amer.
{Taphrina Johansonii Sadebeck.
Uncinula Salicis (DC.) Wint.†
{Sphaeria nivea Hoffm. ex Fr.
{Valsa nivea (Hoffm.) ex Fr.

UREDINALES

{Melampsora Abietis-canadensis C. A. Ludwig.
{Melampsora Populi-Tsugae J. J. Davis.
{Lecythea ovata Auct. Amer.
{Melampsora Medusae Thm.
{Melampsora populina Arth.
{Uredo Medusae (Thm.) Arth.

BASIDIOMYCETES

Corticium scutellare B. & C.
Fomes applanatus (P. ex Wallr.) Gill.
Fomes igniarius (L. ex Fr.) Gill.
Fomes nigricans (Fr.) Cke.
Fomes pinicola (Sw. ex Fr.) Cke.
Hydnum combinans Pk.
Hydnum Kauffmani Pk.
{Irpex lacteus Fr.
{Irpiciporus lacteus (Fr.) Murrill.
Pleurotus ostreatus (Jacq.) ex Fr.
Polyporus cuticularis Fr.
{Inonotus dryophilus (B.) Murrill.
{Polyporus dryophilus B.
{Polyporus vulpinus Fr.
{Inonotus perplexus (Pk.) Murrill.
{Polyporus perplexus Pk.
Polyporus zonatus Fr., var. imperfectus Pk.
{Fomitiporia obliquiformis Murrill.
{Poria obliquiformis (Murrill) Sacc. & Trott.
Schizophyllum commune Fr.
{Hypocrea Richardsonii B. & Mont.
{Stereum rufum Fr.

Trametes Peckii Kalchb.
Trametes suaveolens Fr.

FUNGI IMPERFECTI

Acalyptospora Populi Pk.
Cladosporium subsessile Ell. & Barthol.
Clasterosporium Populi Ell. & Ev.
Cytospora chrysosperma (P.) ex Fr.
Dicoccum populinum Ell. & Ev.
Diplodia populi Fckl.
{Helicoma Muelleri Cda.
{Helicosporium Muelleri (Cda.) Sacc.
{Gloeosporium brunneum Ell. & Ev.
{Marssonia Castagnei (Desm. & Mont.) Sacc.
{Marssonina Castagnei (Desm. & Mont.) Magn.
{Marssonia Populi (Lib.) Sacc.
{Marssonina Populi (Lib.) Magn.
{Gloeosporium populinum Pk.
{Marssonia rhabdospora Ell. & Ev.
{Marssonina rhabdospora (Ell. & Ev.) Magn.
Napicladium Tremulae (Frank) Sacc.
Phoma Populi Pk.
Septoria musiva Pk., var. grandis J. J. Davis.
{Myxormia populina Pk.
{Torula populina Pk.
Zythia ovata Pk.
Populus hastata Dode.
Melampsora occidentalis H. S. Jackson.
Populus heterophylla L.
{Cenangium Schweinitzii Sacc.
{Dermea populnea S.
{Coelosphaeria exilis (A. & S. ex Fr.) Sacc.
{Lasiosphaeria exilis (A. & S. ex Fr.) Cke.
{Sphaeria exilis A. & S. ex Fr.
{Diatrype variolosa Herb. B. sec. Cke.
{Sphaeria variolosa S.
Didymosporium minutissimum S.
{Dothidea sphaeroides (P.) ex Fr.
{Sclerotium sphaeroides P.
Fomes applanatus (P. ex Wallr.) Gill.
Melampsora Abietis-canadensis C. A. Ludwig.
{Caeoma cylindricum Auct. Amer. p. p.
?{Melampsora populina Auct. Amer. p. p.
{Uredo cylindrica Auct. Amer. p. p.
Monilia globosa S.
{Melanconium hyalinum Ell.
{Myxosporium Ellisii Sacc.
{Myxosporium hyalinum (Ell.) Wint.
Poria xanthospora (Underw.) Sacc.
{Uncinula adunca Lév.
{Uncinula heliciformis Howe.
{Uncinula luculenta Howe.
{Uncinula Salicis (DC.) Wint.†
{Sphaeria operta Schm. ex Fr.
{Valsa operta (Schm. ex Fr.) Cke.
Populus laurifolia Ledeb.
Taphrina aurea (P.) ex Fr.†
Populus MacDougali Rose.
Cytospora chrysosperma (P.) ex Fr.

Populus mexicana Wesm.
Melampsora albertensis Arth.
Populus nigra L.
Dothichiza populea Sacc. & Briard.
Melampsora Medusae Thm.
{ Melanconium hyalinum Ell.
{ Myxosporium Ellisii (Ell.) Sacc.
Taphrina rhizophora Johans.
Populus nigra L., var. **italica** DuRoi.
Cytospora chrysosperma (P.) ex Fr.
Dothichiza populea Sacc. & Briard.
Fomes applanatus (P. ex Wallr.) Gill.
{ Hainesia Lythri (Desm.) v. Hoehnel.
{ Sclerotiopsis concava (Desm.) Shear & Dodge.
Taphrina aurea Fr.
Populus occidentalis (Rydb.) Britton.
Coryneum effusum Pk.
Cytospora chrysosperma (P.) ex Fr.
Herpotrichia diffusa (S.) Ell. & Ev.
Melampsora Abietis-canadensis C. A. Ludwig.
Melampsora albertensis Arth.
{ Melampsora Medusae Thm.
{ Uredo Medusae (Thm.) Arth.
{ Funalia stuppea (B.) Murrill.
{ Polystictus stuppeus Cke.
Populus Sargentii Dode.
Anthostomella longispora Dearness & Barthol.
Melampsora Abietis-canadensis C. A. Ludwig.
Myxosporium alboluteum Dearness & Barthol.
Populus tremuloides Michx.

MYXOMYCETES

Arcyria incarnata P.
Hemitrichia vesparium (Batsch) Macbr.
Leocarpus fragilis (Dicks.) Rex.

PEZIZINEAE

{ Blitrydium fenestratum (C. & P.) Sacc.
{ Patellaria fenestrata C. & P.
Cenangium populneum (P. ex Fr.) Rehm.
Chlorosplenium aeruginascens (Nyl.) Karst.
Dermatella populina Petrak.
Dermea populnea S.
Helotium citrinum (Hedw.) ex Fr.
Helotium populinum Fckl.
? { Lachnella Campanula (Ell.) Sacc.
{ Peziza Campanula Ell.
Lachnella corticalis (P.) Fr.
Lachnella flammea (A. & S.) ex Fr.
Pezicula cinnamomea (Phil.) Sacc.
Tympanis conspersa Fr.

PHACIDINEAE

Cryptodiscus atrocyaneus (Fr.) Sacc.
Phacidium lignicola Pk.
Phacidium Populi Lasch.
Solenopezia fimbriata Ell. & Barthol.

HYSTERIINEAE

{ Hysterium vulvatum S.
{ Hysterographium vulvatum (S.) Rehm.

EXOASCACEAE

{ Ascomyces aureus Auct. Amer.
{ Exoascus Johansonii Sadebeck.
{ Taphrina aurea Auct. Amer. p. p.
{ Taphrina rhizophora Auct. Amer.
{ Taphrina Johansonii Sadebeck.

PYRENOMYCETINEAE

Anthostoma flavoviride Ell. & Holw.
{ Capnodium salicinum Mont.
{ Dematium salicinum A. & S.
Cryptosphaeria millepunctata Grev.
Cryptosphaeria populina (P. ex Fr.) Sacc.
Diatrype tumida Ell. & Ev., var. Populi
　　Rehm.
Dimerosporium Populi Ell. & Ev.
Eutypa subtecta (Fr.) Fckl.
{ Eutypella grandis (Nits.) Sacc.
{ Eutypella Radula (P. ex Fr.) Ell. & Ev.
{ Valsa Radula (P. ex Fr.) Cke.
Hypomyces aurantius (P. ex Fr.) Fckl.
{ Hypoxylon Holwayi Ell.
{ Hypoxylon pruinatum (Klotzsch) Cke.
Lophiotrema vestitum Pk.
Lophodermium maculare (Fr.) DeNot.
Platystomum alpinum Tracy & Earle.
Rosellinia rimincola Rehm.
{ Diatrype ferruginea P. ex Fr.
{ Melogramma ferrugineum (P. ex Fr.) Ces. &
　　De Not.
{ Sillia ferruginea (P. ex Fr.) Karst.
Mycosphaerella macularis (Fr.) Schrt.
{ Sphaerella macularis (Fr.) Awd.
{ Sphaerella maculosa Sacc.
Sydowia dothideoides Dearness & Barthol.
Teichospora patellarioides Sacc.
{ Uncinula adunca (Wallr.) Lév.
{ Uncinula heliciformis Howe.
{ Uncinula Salicis (DC.) Wint. †
Valsa ambiens (P.) ex Fr.
Valsa nivea (Hoffm.) ex Fr.
Valsa sordida Nits.

UREDINALES

{ Melampsora Abietis-canadensis C. A. Ludwig.
{ Melampsora populina Ohio Fungi *145*.
{ Melampsora Populi-Tsugae J. J. Davis.
{ Melampsora albertensis Arth.
{ Melampsora Medusae Fung. Columb. *2737*;
　　N. Am. Ured. *1511*.
{ Uredo albertensis Arth.
{ Melampsora Medusae Thm.
{ Melampsora populina Auct. Amer. p. p.
{ Uredo Medusae (Thm.) Arth.

POLYPORACEAE

Daedalea confragosa (Bolt.) ex Fr.
{ Elfvingia fomentaria (Fr.) Murrill.
{ Fomes fomentarius (Fr.) Gill.
{ Polyporus fomentarius Fr.

Populus tremuloides (*cont.*)
Fomes igniarius (L. ex Fr.) Gill.
Fomes nigricans (Fr.) Cke.
Fomes pinicola (Sw. ex Fr.) Cke.
Fomes populinus Fr.
Fomes roseus (Fr.) Cke.
Elfvingia megaloma (Lév.) Murrill.
Fomes applanatus (P. ex Wallr.) Gill.
Fomes leucophaeus (Mont.) Cke.
Ganoderma applanatum (P. ex Wallr.) Pat.
Lenzites sepiaria Fr.
Polyporus adustus (Willd.) ex Fr.
Polyporus cinnabarinus (Jacq.) ex Fr.
Polyporus crispus (P.) ex Fr.
Polyporus dichrous Fr.
Polyporus dryophilus B.
Polyporus elegans (Bull.) ex Fr.
Polyporus fumosus (P.) ex Fr.
Polyporus leucospongia Cke. & Hark.
Polyporus leucoxanthus Bres.
Polyporus picipes Fr.
Polyporus rheades P.
Polyporus salicinus (P.) ex Fr.
Coriolus prolificans Murrill.
Polyporus elongatus B.
Polyporus pargamenus Fr.
Polystictus pargamenus Fr.
Polyporus zonatus Fr., var. imperfectus Pk.
Polystictus zonatus Fr., var. imperfectus (Pk.) Sacc. & Syd.
Poria corticola (Fr.) Cke.
Polyporus radiculosus Pk.
Poria radiculosa (Pk.) Sacc. Syll.
Poria subacida Pk.
Trametes hispida Bagl.
Trametes malicola B. & C.
Trametes Peckii Kalchbr.
Trametes protracta Fr.
Trametes serialis Fr.
Trametes suaveolens Fr.

Basidiomycetes
Armillaria mellea (Vahl) ex Fr.
Corticium bombycinum (Sommerf.) Bres.
Corticium confluens Fr.
Corticium mutatum Pk.
Corticium pezizoideum (S.) v. Schrenk.
Hypocrea Richardsoni B. & Mont.
Stereum rufum Fr.
Tubercularia pezizoidea S.
Corticium vellereum Ell. & Cragin.
Crepidotus fulvotomentosus (Pk.) Sacc. Syll.
Hydnum populinum Pk.
Hydnum velatum B. & C.
Hymenochaete rubiginosa (Schrad. ex Fr.) Lév.
Lentinus pholiotoides Ell. & F. W. Anderson.
Lentinus vulpinus Fr.

Peniophora populnea (Pk.) Burt.
Stereum populneum Pk.
Phlebia merismoides Fr.
Phlebia reflexa B. & C.
Phlebia pileata Pk.
Phlebia spilomea B. & C.
Phlebia strigosozonata (S.) Kauffman.
Phlebia zonata B. & C.
Stereum fasciatum (S.) Fr.
Stereum versiforme B. & C.

Sphaeropsidales
Asteroma Populi Rob. & Desm.
Cytospora chrysosperma (P.) ex Fr.
Cytospora nivea Sacc.
Dothiorella populnea Thm.
Gloeosporium tremuloides Ell. & Ev.
Phoma Populi Pk.
Phyllosticta maculans Ell. & Ev.
Pleurophomella spermatiospora v. Höhnel.
Septoria musiva Pk.
Septoria musiva Pk. var. 5 J. J. Davis.
Septoria musiva Pk., var. tremuloidis Auct.
Sirodothis Populi Clements.

Melanconiales
Marssonia brunnea Ell. & Ev.
Marssonia Castagnei (Desm. & Mont.) Sacc.
Marssonina Castagnei (Desm. & Mont.) Magn.
Marssonia Populi (Lib.) Sacc.
Marssonina Populi (Lib.) Magn.
Marssonia coloradensis Dearness & Barthol.
Marssonina rhabdospora (Ell. & Ev.) Magn.
Septoria musiva Fung. Columb. *1587.*
Melanconium hyalinum Ell.
Septogloeum rhopaloideum Dearness & Bisby.

Hyphomycetes
Cladosporium herbarum (P.) ex Lk.
Cladosporium subsessile Ell. & Barthol.
Cladosporium ramulosum Rob.
Clasterosporium Populi Ell. & Ev.
Fusicladium radiosum (Lib.) Lindr.
Fusicladium Tremulae Frank.
Napicladium Tremulae (Frank) Sacc.
Oidium radiosum Lib.
Fusicladium radiosum (Lib.) Lindr., var. microscopicum (Sacc.) Allescher.
Helicomyces roseus Lk.
Macrophoma Populi (Pk.) Tassi.
Myrioconium comitatum J. J. Davis.
Septonema griseo-fulvum Ell. & Ev.
Stigmina Populi (Ell. & Ev.) Pk.

Miscellanea
Sclerotium bifrons Ell. & Ev.
Populus trichocarpa T. & G.

Ascomycetes
Eutypella Populi Ell. & Ev.
Hypoxylon serpens (P.) ex Fr.

Populus trichocarpa (*cont.*)
  Lachnea hirta (Schum. ex Fr.) Gill.
  Mollisia cinerea (Batsch ex Fr.) Karst.
  Nummularia repandoides Fckl.
  Rosellinia ligniaria (Grev.) Fckl.
  Rosellinia rimincola Rehm.
  {Exoascus aureus (P. ex Fr.) Sadebeck.
  {Taphrina aurea (P.) ex Fr. †
  Uncinula Salicis (DC.) Wint. †
  Xylaria digitata (L. ex Fr.) Grev.

UREDINALES
  {Melampsora albertensis Arth.
  {Melampsora Pseudotsugae Tubeuf.
  {Melampsora Medusae Thm.
  {Melampsora populina Auct. Amer. p. p.
  {Uredo Medusae (Thm.) Arth.
  {Melampsora Medusae Fung. Columb. *3143*.
  {Melampsora occidentalis H. S. Jackson.

POLYPORACEAE
  Fomes annosus (Fr.) Cke.
  Fomes applanatus (P. ex Wallr.) Gill.
  Fomes conchatus (Fr.) Karst.
  {Fomes Everhartii (Ell. & Gall.) v. Schrenk.
  {Pyropolyporus Everhartii (Ell. & Gall.) Murrill.
  Fomes fomentarius (L. ex Fr.) Gill.
  Fomes igniarius (L. ex Fr.) Gill.
  Fomes pinicola (Sw. ex Fr.) Cke.
  Polyporus adustus (Willd.) ex Fr.
  Polyporus albellus Pk.
  Polyporus brumalis (P.) ex Fr.
  Polyporus caesius (Schrad.) ex Fr.
  Polyporus cerifluus B.
  Polyporus crispellus Pk.
  {Gloeoporus dichrous (Fr.) Kauffman.
  {Polyporus dichrous Fr.
  Polyporus fumosus P. ex Fr.
  Polyporus picipes Fr.
  Polyporus spumeus (Sow.) ex Fr.
  Polystictus abietinus (Fr.) Cke.
  {Polyporus cinnabarinus (Jacq.) ex Fr.
  {Polystictus cinnabarinus (Jacq. ex Fr.) Cke.
  {Trametes cinnabarina (Jacq.) ex Fr.
  {?Polystictus biformis Auct. p. p.
  {Polystictus pargamenus Fr.
  {Trametes pargamenus (Fr.) Lloyd.
  Poria corticola Fr.
  Poria similis Bres.
  Trametes mollis Fr.
  Trametes Peckii Kalchbr.
  Trametes suaveolens Fr.

BASIDIOMYCETES
  Coprinus atramentarius Fr.
  Corticium analogum (Bourdot & Galzin) Burt.
  Corticium granulatum Burt.
  Corticium ochrofarctum Burt.

  {Corticium polygonium P. ex Fr.
  {Gloeocystidium polygonium (P. ex Fr.) v. Höhnel, var. fulvescens Bres.
  Eichleriella spinulosa (B. & C.) Burt.
  Lenzites sepiaria Fr.
  Sebacina adusta Burt.
  {Sebacina Burti Trotter.
  {Sebacina plumbea Burt.
  Stereum purpureum P. †

FUNGI IMPERFECTI
  Cytospora chrysosperma (P.) ex Fr.
  Dothichiza populea Sacc. & Briard.
  Macrophoma tumefaciens Shear.
  Marssonia Castagnei (Dur. & Mont.) Sacc.
  Phyllosticta Alcides Sacc.
  Phyllosticta maculans Ell. & Ev.
  Septoria Populi Desm.
  Septoria populicola Pk.
Populus Wislizeni Sarg.
  Cytospora chrysosperma (P.) ex Fr.
  Fomes applanatus (P. ex Wallr.) Gill.
  Melampsora Medusae Thm.
  Pleurotus ostreatus (Jacq.) ex Fr.
  Trametes Peckii Kalchb.
Populus sp. indet.

MYXOMYCETES
  Arcyria nutans (Bull.) Grev.
  Arcyria occidentalis Lister.
  Badhamia panicea (Fr.) Rostf.
  Badhamia utricularis (Bull.) B.
  Ceratiomyxa fructiculosa (Müll.) Macbr.
  Clathroptychium rugulosum (Wallr.) Rostf.
  Comatricha Stemonitis (Scop.) Sheldon.
  Didymium anomalum Sturgis.
  Hemiarcyria rubiformis Rostf.
  Hemitrichia clavata (P.) Rostf.
  Hemitrichia Karstenii (Rostf.) Lister.
  Lachnobolus occidentalis Macbr.
  Lycogala epidendrum [Buxb. ex L.] Fr.
  Perichaena corticalis (Batsch) Rostf.
  Physarum brunneolum (Phil.) Massee.
  Physarum contextum P.
  Tilmadoche compacta Wing.
  Trichia contorta (Ditm.) Rostf.
  Trichia contorta (Ditm.) Rostf., var. genuina Lister.
  Trichia decipiens (P.) Macbr.
  Trichia favoginea (Batsch) P.
  Trichia inconspicua Rostf.
  Trichia iowensis Macbr.
  Trichia persimilis Karst.

PEZIZINEAE
  Belonidium album (Crouan) Sacc.
  Ciboria caucus (Reb. ex P.) Fckl.
  Dermatea cinnamomea C. & P.
  Diplonaevia melaleuca Ell. & Ev.
  Helotium epiphyllum (P.) ex Fr.
  Helotium Friesii (Weinm.) Sacc.

Populus sp. indet. (*cont.*)

⎧Cenangium populneum (P.) Rehm.
⎪Dermatea fascicularis (A. & S.) ex Fr.
⎨Peziza fascicularis A. & S. ex Fr.
⎪Peziza populnea P.
⎩Hysteropatella clavispora (Pk.) Seaver.
⎧Patellaria clavispora (Pk.) Sacc.
⎩Patellaria atrata (Hedw.) ex Fr.
?Pezicula eximia Rehm.
⎧Peziza repandoides (Rehm) Sacc. & Trott.
⎩Plicaria repandoides Rehm.
Pustularia stevensoniana Rehm.

PHACIDIINEAE
Phacidium coronatum (Schum.) ex Fr.
Rhytisma nervale (A. & S.) Rehm.
Schizoxylon occidentalis Ell. & Ev.
Trochila Populorum Desm.

HYSTERIINEAE
Hysterographium Mori Rehm.

HYPOCREALES
Hypocrea sulfurea (S.) Sacc.
Nectria coccinea (P.) ex Fr.
Creonectria Coryli (Fckl.) Seaver.
⎧Creonectria purpurea (L.) ex Seaver.
⎩Nectria cinnabarina (Tode) ex Fr.

SPHAERIALES
Amphisphaeria bisphaerica (C. & E.) Sacc.
Anthostomella endoxyloides Fairman.
Apiosporium salicinum Kze. ex Fr.
Bertia moriformis (Tode ex Fr.) De Not.
⎧Botryosphaeria mutila (S.) Cke.
⎩Sphaeria mutila S.
Chaetomium murorum Cda.
Cryptosphaeria populina (P. ex Fr.) Sacc.
⎧Cucurbitaria acervata Fr.
⎩Sphaeria acervata Fr.
⎧Cucurbitaria insecura Ell.
⎨Teichospora insecura Ell. & Ev.
⎩Teichospora nautica Ell. & Ev.
Daldinia concentrica (Bolt. ex Fr.) Ces. & De Not.
Daldinia vernicosa S.
Diatrype bullata (Hoffm.) ex Fr.
⎧Diatrype sordida (P. ex Fr.) Cke.
⎩Sphaeria sordida P. ex Fr.
⎧Diatrypella angulata (Fr.) Ces. & De Not.
⎩Diatrypella nigro-annulata (Grev. ex Fr.) Nits.
Diatrypella hysterioides Ell. & Ev.
Diatrypella Populi Ell. & Holw.
Didymosphaeria populina Vuill.
⎧Didymotrichia diffusa (S.) Berl.
⎩Sphaeria diffusa S.
Dimerosporium Populi Ell. & Ev.
⎧Cytospora Acharii (Tul.) Sacc.
⎨Eutypa Acharii Tul.
⎨Eutypa eutypa (Fr.) House.
⎩Sphaeria eutypa Fr.

Hypoxylon pruinatum Cke.
⎧Hypoxylon udum (P.) ex Fr.
⎪Sphaeria confluens Tode ex Fr.
⎨Kalmusia surrecta (Cke.) Sacc.
⎪Sphaeria surrecta Cke.
⎩Xylosphaeria surrecta Cke.
Lasiosphaeria ovina (P. ex Fr.) Ces. & De Not.
Lophiostoma macrostomoides (De Not.) Ces. & De Not.
Lophiostoma triseptatum Pk.
Lophiotrema hysterioides Ell. & Langlois.
Massariovalsa sudans (B. & C.) Sacc.
⎧Melanconiella apocrypta (Ell.) Sacc.
⎨Melanconis apocrypta Ell.
⎩Melanconis occulta (Fckl.) Sacc.
Melanomma pulvis-pyrius (P. ex Fr.) Fckl.
Melanomma rhypodes Ell. & Ev.
Melanopsamma Waghornei House
Nummularia lateritia Ell. & Ev.
Rosellinia subcompressa Ell. & Ev.
Sphaerella orbicularis Pk.
⎧Strickeria trimorpha (Atk.) House.
⎩Teichospora trimorpha Atk.
⎧Quaternaria Persoonii Tul.
⎩Valsa quaternata (P.) ex Fr.
Venturia tremulae Aderh.

UREDINALES
Caeoma Laricis Arth. & Kern.
⎧Melampsora magnusiana G. Wagner.
⎩Melampsora Tremulae Auct. p. p.
Melampsora larici-populina Kleb.
Melampsora tremulae.

TREMELLACEAE
Calopposis nodulosa Lloyd.
Exidia glandulosa (Bull.) ex Fr.
Naematelia nucleata (S.) Fr.
Tremella mesenterica Fr.

DACRYOMYCETACEAE
Dacryomyces subochraceus (Pk.) Burt.

THELEPHORACEAE
Corticium Atkinsonii Burt.
Corticium bicolor Pk.
Corticium bombycinum (Sommerf.) Bres.
Corticium crustaceum (Karst.) v. Höhnel & Litschauer.
Corticium effuscatum C. & F.
Corticium roseopallens Burt.
Corticium roseum P. ex Fr.
Corticium salicinum Fr.
Corticium subnullum Burt.
Corticium tuberculatum Karst.
Corticium vagum B. & C.
Cyphella fulva B. & Rav.
Cyphella minutissima Burt.
Hypochnus atroruber (Pk.) Burt.
Peniophora albula Atk. & Burt.

Populus sp. indet. (*cont.*)
Peniophora Allescheri Bres.
Peniophora amoena Burt.
Peniophora arachnoides Burt.
Peniophora candida (P. ex Fr.) Lyman.
Peniophora guttulifera (Karst.) Sacc.
Peniophora incarnata (P. ex Fr.) Massee.
Peniophora laevis Fr.
Peniophora longispora (Pat.) v. Höhnel.
Peniophora martiniana (B. & C.) Burt.
Peniophora nuda (Fr.) Bres.
Peniophora Peckii Burt.
Peniophora velutina (DC. ex Fr.) Cke.
Solenia endophila (Ces.) Fr.
Stereum cinerascens (Fr.) Massee.
{ Corticium rufomarginatum Fung. Columb.
　　1817.
{ Stereum rufum Fr.
Stereum sericeum Fr.
Stereum versicolor Fr.

HYDNACEAE

Grandinia sp. indet.
Hydnum caryophylleum B. & C.
Hydnum chrysocomum Underw.
Hydnum ochraceum Fr.
{ Hydnum omnivorum Shear.
{ Ozonium omnivorum Shear.
Irpex cinnamomeus Fr.
Irpex nodulosus Pk.
Irpex tabacinus B. & C.
Irpex tulipiferae (S.) Fr.
Phlebia radiata Fr.
Radulum casearium Morg.
Radulum orbiculare Lloyd.

POLYPORACEAE

Daedalea unicolor Fr.
Favolus europaeus Fr.
Favolus Salicis (DC.) Wint.
Fomes connatus Fr.
Fomes Everhartii (Ell. & Gall.) v. Schrenk.
Fomes fomentarius (L. ex Fr.) Gill.
Fomes nigricans, var. populinus Neuman.
Lenzites betulina (L.) ex Fr.
Merulius tremulosus Fr.
Myriadoporus rubra Pk.
Polyporus borealis Fr.
Polyporus chioneus Fr.
Polyporus destruens Brond.
Polyporus dryadeus (P.) ex Fr.
Polyporus dryophilus B.
Polyporus fissus B.
Polyporus gilvus Fr.
Polyporus Inzengae De Not.
Polyporus lacteus S.
Polyporus pargamenus Fr.
Polyporus resinosus Schrad. ex Fr.
Polyporus rutilans Fr.

{ Coriolus subchartaceus Murrill.
{ Polyporus subchartaceus (Murrill) Overholts.
{ Polystictus subchartaceus (Murrill) Sacc. &
　　Trott.
Polyporus rigidus L.
Polyporus sulfureus (Bull.) ex Fr.
Polyporus trabeus Rostk.
{ Grifola Tuckahoe Güssow.
? { Polyporus Tuckahoe (Güssow) Lloyd. 1920.
{ Polyporus Tuckahoe (Güssow) Sacc. & Trott.
　　1925.
Polyporus versicolor (L.) ex Fr.
{ ?Fomes hirsutus Hoxie.
{ Polyporus hirsutus (Wulf.) ex Fr.
{ Polystictus hirsutus (Wulf.) Fr.
Polystictus placentiformis B. sec. Cke.
Polystictus pubescens Fr.
{ Coriolopsis rigida (B. & Mont.) Murrill.
{ Funalia rigida (B. & Mont.) House.
{ Polystictus rigidus (B. & Mont.) Cke.
{ Trametes rigida B. & Mont.
Polystictus virgineus Cke.
Polystictus zonatus Fr.
{ Poria Andersoni Ell. & Ev.
{ Xanthoporia Andersoni (Ell. & Ev.) Murrill.
Poria attenuata Pk.
Poria ferruginosa (Schrad. ex Fr.) Cke.
Poria hymeniicola Murrill.
Poria macer Sommerf.
Poria Medulla-panis (P. ex Fr.) Cke.
Poria mollusca (Fr.) Cke.
Poria nitida Cke.
Poria pulchella S.
{ Polyporus sulphurellus Pk.
{ Poria sulphurella (Pk.) Sacc.
Poria vaporaria (P. ex Fr.) Cke.
Poria vitellina S.
Poria vulgaris Fr.

AGARICACEAE

Armillaria mellea (Vahl) ex Fr.
Claudopus nidulans (P. ex Fr.) Pk.
Crepidotus croceitinctus Pk.
Crepidotus haustellaris (Fr.) Sacc. Syll.
Crepidotus versutus Pk.
Lentinus Lecomtei Fr.
Marasmius subvenosus Pk.
Omphalia Fibula (Bull.) ex Fr., var. conicus Pk.
Panus conchatus Fr.
Pholiota adiposa Fr.
Pholiota destruens (Lasch) Bres.
Pholiota spectabilis Fr.
Pleurotus atrocaeruleus (Fr.) Sacc. Syll.
Pleurotus ostreatus Fr.
Pleurotus salignus (P.) ex Fr.
Pleurotus serotinus Fr.
Pleurotus ulmarius (Bull.) ex Fr.
Trogia crispa Fr.

Populus sp. indet. (*cont.*)

SPHAEROPSIDALES

Cytospora leucosperma (P.) ex Fr.
Cytospora rubescens Fr.
Discosia Artocreas (Tode) ex Fr.
Dothiorella canadensis Ell. & Ev.
Dothiorella decorticata Ell. & Ev.
Phoma urens Ell. & Ev.
Phyllosticta intermixta Seaver.
Phyllosticta maculans Ell. & Ev.
Septoria ochroleuca B. & C.

MELANCONIALES

Cylindrosporium oculatum Ell. & Ev.
Marssonia curvata Bubák & Kabát.
Marssonia piriformis (Riess) Sacc.
Marssonia rhabdospora Ell. & Ev.
Marssonia stenospora (Ell. & Kellerm.) Sacc.
Melanconium populinum Pk.
Titaeosporina tremulae (Lib.) Luyk.

HYPHOMYCETES

Cladosporium epiphyllum (P.) ex Fr.
⎰ Fumago vagans Fr.
⎱ Cladosporium Fumago Lk. ex Fr.
Helicoma Curtisii B.
Helicomyces elegans Morg.
Rhinotrichum Curtisii B.
Torula erumpens Ell. & Ev.
Zygodesmus atroruber Pk.
Zygodesmus granulosus Pk.

MISCELLANEA

Chondromyces catenulatus Thax.
Phallogaster saccatus Morg.
Sclerotium bifrons Ell. & Ev.

Salix alaxensis (Anders.) Cov.
⎰ Melampsora Bigelowii Thm.
⎱ Uredo Bigelowii (Thm.) Arth.

Salix alba L.
Botryosphaeria Delilei (D. & M.) Sacc.
Corticium Berkeleyi Cke.
⎧ Melampsora Bigelowii Thm.
? ⎨ Melampsora farinosa Auct. Amer.
⎩ Melampsora Salicis-capreae Auct. Amer.
⎰ Melampsora americana Arth.
⎱ Melampsora humboldtiana Speg.
Pholiota squarrosa (Müll.) ex Fr.
⎰ Polyporus suaveolens (L.) ex Fr.
⎱ Trametes suaveolens (L.) ex Fr.
Valsa ambiens (P.) ex Fr.

Salix alba L., var. **vitellina** Koch.
Daedalea quercina Fr.
Gloeosporium Salicis Westd.
⎰ Melampsora americana Arth.
⎱ Melampsora americana Jørstad.
Melampsora Bigelowii Thm.
Melampsora vitellinae Thm.
Uncinula Salicis (DC.) Wint. †

Salix amphibia Small.
Melampsora Salicis-capreae (P.) Wint.

Salix amygdaloides Anders.
Cytospora chrysosperma (P.) ex Fr.
Lophiostoma nucula (Fr.) De Not.
⎧ Melampsora Bigelowii Thm.
⎪ Melampsora farinosa Fung. Columb. *1544,*
⎨ *1938.*
⎪ ?Melampsora salicina Auct. Amer. p. p.
⎪ Melampsora Salicis-capreae (P.) Wint.
⎩ Uredo Bigelowii (Thm.) Arth.
Paracytospora Salicis Petrak.
Peniophora occidentalis Ell. & Ev.
Phialea vulgaris (Fr.) Rehm.
Poria laminata Murrill.
Ramularia Uredinis (Voss) Sacc.
Rhytisma salicinum (P.) ex Fr.
Teichospora amygdaloides Ell. & Ev.
Uncinula Salicis (DC.) Wint. †

Salix anglorum Cham.
Melampsora arctica Rostr.
Melampsora Bigelowii Thm.

Salix arbusculoides Fisch.
⎰ Melampsora Bigelowii Thm.
⎱ Uredo Bigelowii (Thm.) Arth.

Salix arctica Pall.
Ceratostoma foliicola Fckl.
Coniothecium coloratum (Pk.) Rostr.
Cytospora Salicis (Cda.) Rabh.
Cytospora capitata Fckl.
Dothiopsis Salicis (Karst.) Allescher.
Excipula sphaeroides (P.) ex Fr.
Gnomonia salicella (Fr.) Schrt.
?Melampsora arctica Rostr.
⎧ Melampsora Bigelowii Thm.
⎨ Melampsora farinosa (P.) Schrt.
⎪ ?Melampsora salicina Auct. Amer.
⎩ Uredo Bigelowii (Thm.) Arth.
⎰ Pleospora paucitricha Fckl.
⎱ Pyrenophora paucitricha (Fckl.) Berl. & Vogl.
Pyrenopeziza sphaeroides (Fr.) Fckl.
Rhytisma salicinum (P.) ex Fr.
⎰ Hypoxylon arcticum (Fckl.) Rostr.
⎱ Rhizomorpha arctica Fckl.
Rosellinia arctica (Fckl.) Sacc.
⎰ Mycosphaerella Capronii (Sacc.) J. Lind.
⎱ Sphaerella Capronii Sacc.
Mycosphaerella salicicola (Fckl.) J. Lind.
Venturia chlorospora (Ces.) Karst.
Xylographa arctica Fckl.

Salix arctica Pall., var. **Brownei** Anders.
⎧ Lophodermium versicolor (Wahlenb. ex Fr.)
⎪ Schrt.
⎨ Pseudopeziza versicolor (Wahlenb. ex Fr.)
⎩ Rostr.
Rhytisma salicinum (P.) ex Fr.
Sphaeronema foliicola (Fckl.) J. Lind.
Venturia chlorospora (Ces.) Karst.

Salix arctica Pall., var. **groenlandica** Anders.
Melampsora arctica Rostr.
Melanomma cinereum (Karst.) Sacc.
Patellaria bacilligera Karst.
Phoma salicina Westd.
Pseudopeziza versicolor (Wahlenb. ex Fr.)
Rostr.
Pyrenophora paucitricha (Fckl.) Berl. & Vogl.

Salix argophylla Nutt.
{ Melampsora Bigelowii (Arth.) Fung. Columb.
  4032, Uredinales *1312*.
{ Melampsora confluens H. S. Jackson.

Salix argyrocarpa Nutt.
{ Melampsora americana Arth.
{ Melampsora humboldtiana Speg.

Salix babylonica L.
{ Cenangium sticticum (B. & C.) Sacc.
{ Tympanis stictica B. & C.
Comatricha longa Pk.
Cytospora chrysosperma (P.) ex Fr.
{ Helicoma Curtisii B.
{ Helicosporium Curtisii (B.) Sacc.
Hymenochaete rubiginosa (Schrad. ex Fr.)
Lév.
Lenzites Klotzschii B.
{ Melampsora americana Arth.
{ Melampsora humboldtiana Speg.

Salix balsamifera Barr.
Marssonina kriegeriana (Bres.) Magn.
{ Melampsora americana Arth.
{ Melampsora humboldtiana Speg.

Salix Barclayi Anders.
Salix barrattiana Hook.
Salix bella Piper.
?Salix Bigelowii Auct.
{ Melampsora Bigelowii Thm.
{ Uredo Bigelowii (Thm.) Arth.

Salix bonplandiana Kunth.
?Melampsora Bigelowii Thm.
Melampsora humboldtiana Speg.

Salix brachycarpa Nutt.
{ Melampsora Bigelowii Thm.
{ Uredo Bigelowii (Thm.) Arth.
Rhytisma salicinum (P.) ex Fr.

Salix candida Fluegge.
Melampsora Bigelowii Thm.
Melampsora humboldtiana Speg.

Salix Caprea L.
{ Melampsora americana Arth.
{ ?Melampsora farinosa Auct. Amer. p. p.
{ Melampsora humboldtiana Speg.
Uncinula Salicis (DC.) Wint. †

Salix caudata Nutt.
{ Melampsora Bigelowii Thm.
{ Uredo Bigelowii (Thm.) Arth.
Salix Chamissonis Anders.
Melampsora arctica Rostr.

Salix chilensis ex Salvador.
Melampsora humboldtiana Speg.
Salix caerulea E. Wolf.
Melampsora Bigelowii Thm.
Salix commutata Bebb.
Melampsora humboldtiana Speg.
Salix concolor Schleich.
Melampsora americana Arth.
Salix cordata Muhl.
Corticium salicinum Fr.
Cucurbitaria salicina Fckl.
Discella carbonacea (Fr.) B. & Br.
{ Fuckelia Morsei (B. & C.) Cke.
{ Hypoxylon Blakei B. & C.
{ Hypoxylon Morsei B. & C.
Gloeosporium boreale Ell. & Ev.
Marssonina kriegeriana (Bres.) Magn.
Melampsora confluens H. S. Jackson.
{ Melampsora americana Arth.
{ Melampsora Bigelowii Auct. Amer. p. p.
{ Melampsora farinosa Syd. Ured. *1099*.
{ Melampsora humboldtiana Speg.
{ Melampsora Hartigii Thm.
?{ Melampsora salicina Auct. Amer.
{ Melampsora Salicis-capreae Wint.
Ocellaria aurea Tul.
Ramularia Uredinis (Voss) Sacc.
Rhytisma salicinum (P.) ex Fr.
{ Septoria albaniensis Thm.
{ Septoria salicina Pk.
Septoria Salicis Westd.
Sphaerella salicina Ell. & Ev.
Sphaeropsis Salicis Ell. & Barthol.
Trimmatostroma Salicis Cda.
Tubercularia vulgaris Tode ex Fr.
Tuberculina davisiana Sacc. & Trav.
{ Erysiphe adunca Lk.
{ Erysiphe obtusata Lk.
{ Uncinula adunca (Lk.) Lév.
{ Uncinula heliciformis Howe.
{ Uncinula luculenta Howe.
{ Uncinula Salicis (DC.) Wint. †
Valsa boreella Karst.
Valsa salicina (P.) ex Fr.
Valsa socialis Ell. & Ev.

Salix curtiflora Anders.
{ Melampsora Bigelowii Thm.
{ Uredo Bigelowii (Thm.) Arth.

Salix discolor Muhl.
Anthostoma ontariensis Ell. & Ev
Corticium salicinum Fr.
Cytidia salicina (Fr.) Burt.
Exidia glandulosa (Bull.) ex Fr.
Habrostictis ocellata (P.) Fckl.
Lentinus suavissimus Fr.
Lenzites sepiaria Fr.
Marssonina kriegeriana (Bres.) Magn.

Salix discolor (*cont.*)

{ Melampsora americana Arth.
{ Melampsora arctica Auct. Amer. p. p.
{ Melampsora humboldtiana Speg.

{ Melampsora arctica Rostr.
{ Uredo rostrupiana Arth.

{ Melampsora Bigelowii Thm.
{ ?Melampsora caprearum Thm. p. p.
{ ?Melampsora farinosa Auct. Amer.
{ ?Melampsora salicina Auct. Amer.
{ ?Melampsora Salicis-capreae Wint.
{ Uredo Bigelowii (Thm.) Arth.

Myrioconium comitatum J. J. Davis, var. salicarium J. J. Davis.
Panus salicinus Pk.
Polyporus admirabilis Pk.
Ramularia rosea Fckl.
Rhytisma salicinum (P.) ex Fr.
Septogloeum salicinum (Pk.) Sacc.

{ Coniothecium toruloideum M. A. Curtis nec Cda.
{ Septonema connatum B. & C.
{ Trimmatostroma americanum Thm.
{ Trimmatostroma Salicis Cda.

{ Uncinula adunca Lév.
{ Uncinula Salicis (DC.) Wint. †

{ Cytospora fugax (Bull.) ex Fr.
{ Sphaeria salicina P. ex Fr.
{ Valsa salicina (P.) Fr.

Salix exigua Nutt.

{ Discula brenckleana (Sacc. & Syd.) Petrak.
{ Macrophoma Salicis Dearness & Barthol.

{ Melampsora Bigelowii Thm.
{ Uredo Bigelowii (Thm.) Arth.

Salix fendleriana Anders.

?Melampsora arctica Rostr.
{ Melampsora Bigelowii Thm.
{ Uredo Bigelowii (Thm.) Arth.

Septogloeum Salicis-fendlerianae Dearness & Barthol.

{ Septoria salicina Pk.
{ Septoria Salicis Fung. Columb. *3779*.

Salix fragilis L.

{ Elfvingia megaloma (Lév.) Murrill.
{ Fomes applanatus (P. ex Wallr.) Gill.
{ Ganoderma applanatum (P. ex Wallr.) Pat.
{ Polyporus applanatus (P.) ex Wallr.

Gloeosporium Salicis Westd.
Melampsora humboldtiana Speg.
Ramularia Uredinis (Voss) Sacc.

Salix fuscescens Anderss.

Uredo alpina (Juel) Arth.

Salix geyeriana Anders.

Melampsora confluens H. S. Jackson.
{ Melampsora Bigelowii Thm.
{ Uredo Bigelowii (Thm.) Arth.

Salix glauca L.

PEZIZINEAE

Lachnea scutellata (L. ex Fr.) Gill.
Mollisia cinerea (Batsch ex Fr.) Karst.
Niptera saliceti (Rehm) Sacc.
Ombrophila umbonata Karst.
Phialea macrospora Rostr.
Phialea virgultorum (Vahl ex Fr.) Sacc.
Pseudopeziza versicolor (Wahlenb. ex Fr.) Rostr.
Pyrenopeziza sphaerioides (P. ex Fr.) Fckl.
Tympanis saligna Tode ex Fr.

PHACIDIINEAE

Rhytisma salicinum (P.) ex Fr.
{ Stictis mollis P.
{ Stictis Pupula Fr.
Xylographa parallela (Ach.) ex Fr.

PYRENOMYCETINEAE

Antennatula arctica Rostr.
Diatrypella verruciformis (Ehrh. ex Fr.) Nits.
Dothiorella pyrenophora (Karst.) Sacc.
{ Fenestella fenestrata (B. & Br.) Schrt.
{ Fenestella princeps Tul.
Hypospila groenlandica Rostr.
Hypoxylon macrosporum Karst.
Leptosphaeria Coniothyrium (Fckl.) Sacc.
Leptostroma punctiforme Wallr.
Lophium dolabriforme Wallr.
Lophodermium hysterioides (P. ex Fr.) Sacc.
Melanomma salicinum Rostr.
Metasphaeria cinerea (Fckl.) Sacc.
{ Creonectria Coryli (Fckl.) Seaver.
{ Nectria Coryli Fckl.
Nectria episphaeria (Tode) ex Fr.
Otthia Winteri Rehm.
Peroneutypa corniculata (Ehrh. ex Fr.) Berl.
Physalospora hyalospora (Ces.) Sacc.
Pleosphaeria mutabilis Sacc.
Pyrenophora chrysospora (Niessl) Sacc.
Rosellinia protuberans Karst.
Sphaerella salicicola (Fr.) Fckl.
Uncinula Salicis (DC.) Wint. †
Venturia chlorospora (Ces.) Karst.

UREDINALES

{ Melampsora arctica Rostr.
{ Uredo rostrupiana Arth.
{ Melampsora Bigelowii Thm.
{ Uredo Bigelowii (Thm.) Arth.
{ Melampsora confluens H. S. Jackson.
{ Melampsora Ribesii-Salicum Bubák.
{ Uredo confluens P.
{ Melampsora farinosa Auct. Amer. p. p.
{ Melampsora Salicis-capreae Auct. Amer. p. p.
{ Uredo Bigelowii Auct. Amer. p. p.

BASIDIOMYCETES

Corticium comedens (Nees) ex Fr.
Corticium lacteum Fr.

Salix glauca (*cont.*)
Marasmius epiphyllus Fr.
Solenia anomala (P. ex Fr.) Fckl.
Tremella intumescens J. E. Sm. ex Fr.
Typhula candida Fr.

FUNGI IMPERFECTI

Asteroma Salicis Rob. & Desm.
Coniothecium complanatum (Nees ex Fr.) Sacc.
Cytospora nivea Sacc.
Cytospora Salicis (Cda.) Rabh.
Fusicolla corticalis Karst.
Macrosporium concinnum B. & Br.
Septoria salicella B. & Br.
Septoria salicina Pk.

Salix glaucophylla Bebb.
Fumago vagans Fr.
⎰Ramularia rosea (Fckl.) Sacc.
⎱Ramularia Uredinis J. J. Davis.
Uncinula Salicis (DC.) Wint. †

Salix glaucops Anders.
Melampsora arctica Rostr.

Salix Gooddingii Ball.
⎰Melampsora americana Arth.
⎨Melampsora americana Jørstad.
⎱Melampsora humboldtiana Speg.

Salix groenlandica (Anders.) Lundst.
Antennatula arctica Rostr.
Cladosporium herbarum (P.) ex Lk.
Coniosporium phaeospermum (Cda.) Sacc.
Coniothecium complanatum (Nees) ex Sacc.
Corticium lacteum Fr.
Cytospora nivea Sacc.
Cytospora salicella Sacc.
Cytospora Salicis (Cda.) Rabh.
Cytosporium Heclae Rostr.
Dasyscypha bicolor (Bull. ex Fr.) Fckl.
⎰Diaporthe salicella (Fr.) Sacc.
⎨Endophlaea salicella (Fr.) Cke.
⎱Sphaeria salicella Fr.
Diatrypella melaleuca (Kze.) Nits.
Diatrypella verruciformis (Ehrh. ex Fr.) Nits.
Discula microsperma (B. & Br.) Sacc.
Fumago vagans Fr.
Helotium aciculare (Bull.) ex P.
Helotium uliginosum Fr.
Lachnella corticalis (P.) Fr.
Lachnella flammea (A. & S.) ex Fr.
Lophium dolabriforme Wallr.
Lophodermium hysterioides (P. ex Fr.) Sacc.
⎰Melampsora arctica Rostr.
⎱Uredo rostrupiana Arth.
Melanomma salicinum Rostr.
Mollisia cinerea (Batsch ex Fr.) Karst.
Myxosporium salicinum Sacc. & Roum.
Naemaspora microspora Desm.
Phialea virgultorum (Vahl ex Fr.) Sacc.
Pyrenophora chrysospora (Niessl) Sacc.

Pyrenophora paucitricha (Fckl.) Berl. & Vogl.
Rhytisma salicinum (P.) ex Fr.
Rosellinia protuberans Karst.
Rosellinia pulveracea (Ehrh. ex Fr.) Fckl.
Septoria salicella B. & Br.
Solenia anomala (P. ex Fr.) Fckl.
⎰Sphaeria Acrospermum Tode ex Fr.
⎱Sphaeronema Acrospermum (Tode) ex Fr.
Tapesia fusca (P.) Fckl.
Teichospora pruniformis (Nyl.) Karst.
Topospora proboscidea Fr.
Torula antiqua Cda.
Trichopeziza fusca (Schum. ex Fr.) Sacc.
Venturia chlorospora (Ces.) Karst.
Venturia macrospora Rostr.
Volutella pulchra B. & C.

Salix herbacea L.
⎰Melampsora arctica Rostr.
⎱Uredo rostrupiana Arth.
Rhytisma salicinum (P.) ex Fr.
Sphaerella salicicola (Fr.) Fckl.
Venturia chlorospora (Ces.) Karst.

Salix hookeriana Barr.
Melampsora Bigelowii Thm.

Salix humboldtiana Willd.
? ⎰Melampsora Bigelowii Thm.
  ⎱Uredo Bigelowii (Thm.) Arth.
Melampsora humboldtiana Speg.

Salix humilis Marsh.
⎰Melampsora americana Arth. 1920.
⎨Melampsora americana Jørstad. 1923.
⎱Melampsora humboldtiana Speg.
?Melampsora Caprearum Thm.
Rhytisma salicinum (P.) ex Fr.
⎰Hainesia Lythri (Desm.) v. Höhnel.
⎱Sclerotiopsis concava (Desm.) Shear & Dodge.
Septogloeum salicinum (Pk.) Sacc.
Septoria salicicola (Fr.) Sacc.
⎰Uncinula adunca Lév.
⎱Uncinula Salicis (DC.) Wint. †

Salix irrorata Anders.
⎰Melampsora Bigelowii Thm.
⎱Uredo Bigelowii (Thm.) Arth.
⎰Melampsora Bigelowii Fung. Columb. *3717*,
⎨ Uredinales *717*.
⎱Melampsora confluens (Arth.) H. S. Jackson.

Salix laevigata Bebb.
⎰Melampsora Bigelowii Thm.
⎱Uredo Bigelowii (Thm.) Arth.

Salix lasiandra Benth.
Aleurodiscus helveolus Bres.
Cytospora aurora Mont. & Fr.
Cytospora chrysosperma (P.) ex Fr.
⎰Fomes igniarius (L. ex Fr.) Gill.
⎨Polyporus igniarius (L.) ex Fr.
⎱Pyropolyporus igniarius (L. ex Fr.) Murrill.

Salix lasiandra (*cont.*)
Fomes pinicola (Sw. ex Fr.) Cke.
Lenzites sepiaria Fr.
{ Melampsora Bigelowii Thm.
{ Uredo Bigelowii (Thm.) Arth.
?Melampsora farinosa Auct. Amer.
{ Polyporus pargamenus Fr.
{ Polystictus pargamenus Fr.
Propolis faginea (Schrad.) ex Karst.
Rhytisma salicinum (P.) ex Fr.

Salix lasiolepis Benth.
Craterium leucocephalum (P.) Rostf.
Cytospora fugax (Bull.) ex Fr.
{ Gloeosporium maculans (Hark.) Ell. & Ev.
{ Septogloeum maculans Hark.
Guepinia Peziza Tul.
{ Hysterium prominens Phil. & Hark.
{ Hysterographium prominens (Phil. & Hark.)
{ Berl. & Vogl.
{ Marssonia nigricans Ell. & Ev.
{ Marssonina nigricans (Ell. & Ev.) Magn.
?Melampsora americana Arth.
?Melampsora Bigelowii Auct. Amer. p. p.
Melampsora confluens (Arth.) H. S. Jackson.
?Melampsora farinosa Auct. Amer. p. p.
?Melampsora salicina Auct. Amer. p. p.
?Melampsora Salicis-capreae Auct. Amer. p. p.
Polystictus versicolor (L.) ex Fr.
Septoria rhabdocarpa Ell. & Barthol.
Uncinula Salicis (DC.) Wint. †

Salix Lemmoni Bebb.
{ Melampsora Bigelowii Thm.
{ Uredo Bigelowii (Thm.) Arth.

Salix linearifolia Rydb.
Melampsora Bigelowii Thm.
Rhytisma salicinum (P.) ex Fr.

Salix longifolia Muhl.
Cercospora salicina Ell. & Ev.
Coryneum salicinum (Cda.) Sacc.
Diaporthe salicella (Fr.) Sacc.
Eutypa subtecta (Fr.) Fckl.
Fomes conchatus (P. ex Fr.) Karst.
Gloeosporium Salicis Westd.
Hymenula fruticola Pound & Clements.
Lophiostoma turritum C. & P.
{ Discula brenckleana (Sacc. & Syd.) Petrak.
{ Macrophoma brenckleana Sacc. & Syd.
{ Boletus salicinus P.
{ Fomes conchatus (P. ex Fr.) Karst.
{ Fomes salicinus (P. ex Fr.) Cke.
{ Mucronoporus salicinus (P. ex Fr.) Ell. & Ev.
{ Polyporus salicinus (P.) ex Fr.
{ Pyropolyporus conchatus (P. ex Fr.) Murrill.
Myrioconium comitatum, var. salicarium J. J.
Davis.
{ Fusarium Uredinum Ell. & Ev.
{ Ramularia Uredinis (Voss) Sacc.
Rhytisma salicinum (P.) ex Fr.

Rosellinia Aquila (Fr.) De Not., var. byssiseda
(Tode) ex Fr.
Rosellinia pulveracea (Ehrh. ex Fr.) Fckl.
Septoria didyma Fckl.
Sphaerulina salicina Syd.
Sphaerulina Salicis Syd.
{ Uncinula adunca Lév.
{ Uncinula Salicis (DC.) Wint. †
Valsa boreella Karst.
Valsa salicina (P.) ex Fr.
Valsa salicina (P.) ex Fr., var. tetraspora Fckl.
Valsa socialis Ell. & Ev.
Valsa sordida Nits.
Valsa translucens De Not.
Valsella nigro-annulata Fckl.

UREDINALES

Melampsora americana Arth.
{ Melampsora Bigelowii Fung. Columb. *3033*,
{ Uredinales *2211*, *2816*, Fung. Dak. *37*, Syd.
{ Ured. *2444*.
{ Melampsora farinosa Fung. Columb. *1937*.
{ Melampsora humboldtiana Speg.
{ Melampsora Bigelowii Thm.
{ Uredo Bigelowii (Thm.) Arth.
?Melampsora farinosa Auct. Amer. p. p.
?Melampsora mixta Thm.
?Melampsora salicina Auct. Amer. p. p.
?Melampsora Salicis-Capreae Auct. Amer. p. p.

Salix lucida Muhl.
{ Corticium cruentum (P. ex Fr.) Schrt.
{ Corticium salicinum Fr.
{ Thelephora cruenta S. Syn. Car.
Cylindrosporium salicinum, var. albaniensis
Dearness.
{ Cylindrosporium salicinum, var. circinatum
{ Dearness.
{ Septogloeum salicinum Fung. Columb. *3872*.
Gloeosporium egenum J. J. Davis.
Gloeosporium Salicis Westd.
Helicodesmus albus Linder.
{ Hymenochaete agglutinans Ell.
{ Rhytisma adglutinatum S.
{ Gloeosporium apicale Ell. & Ev.
{ Marssonia apicalis Ell. & Ev.
{ Marssonina apicalis (Ell. & Ev.) Magn.
Marssonina Populi (Lib.) Magn.
{ Melampsora americana Arth.
{ Melampsora humboldtiana Speg.
Melampsora Bigelowii Thm.
?Melampsora farinosa Auct. Amer. p. p.
?Melampsora vitellinae Thm.
Phyllosticta apicalis J. J. Davis.
Ramularia lucidae J. J. Davis.
Rhytisma salicinum (P.) ex Fr.
Septogloeum salicinum (Pk.) Sacc.
{ Septoria albaniensis Thm.
{ Septoria salicina Pk.

Salix lutea Nutt.
  { Daedalea confragosa Bolt. ex Fr.
  { Daedalea rubescens (A. & S.) ex Fr.
  { Trametes rubescens Fr.
  { Melampsora Bigelowii Fung. Columb. *3718,*
    4937; Uredinales *1009, 1211.*
  { Melampsora confluens (Arth.) H. S. Jackson.
  ?Melampsora arctica Rostr.
  ?Uredo Bigelowii (Thm.) Arth. p. p.
  Rhytisma salicinum (P.) ex Fr.
  Uncinula Salicis (DC.) Wint. †
  Valsa salicina (P.) ex Fr.
  Valsa translucens De Not.
Salix luteosericea Rydb.
  ?Uredo Bigelowii (Thm.) Arth.
Salix mackenziana (Hook.) Barratt.
  Melampsora confluens (Arth.) H. S. Jackson.
  { Melampsora americana Arth. 1920.
  { Melampsora americana Jørstad. 1923.
  { Melampsora humboldtiana Speg.
  ?Melampsora arctica Rostr.
  ?Uredo Bigelowii (Thm.) Arth.
Salix melanopsis Nutt.
  Melampsora humboldtiana Speg.
  ?Uredo Bigelowii Arth. p. p.
Salix missouriensis Bebb.
  Cytospora salicella Sacc.
  { Melampsora Bigelowii N. Am. Uredinales *1416.*
  { Melampsora humboldtiana Speg.
  ?Uredo Bigelowii Arth. p. p.
  Rhytisma salicinum (P.) ex Fr.
  Trimmatostroma americanum Thm.
  Uncinula Salicis (DC.) Wint. †
Salix monochroma Ball.
  Melampsora humboldtiana Speg.
Salix monticola Bebb.
  Lachnella flammea (A. & S.) ex Fr.
  { Melampsora americana Arth.
  { Melampsora americana Jørstad.
  { Melampsora humboldtiana Speg.
  Melampsora confluens (Arth.) H. S. Jackson.
  { Cucurbitaria insecura Ell.
  { Strickeria insecura (Ell.) Tracy & Earle.
  { Teichospora insecura (Ell.) Ell. & Ev.
  { Teichospora nautica Ell. & Ev.
  ?Melampsora Bigelowii Thm.
Salix Myrsinitis L.
  Asteroma Salicis Rob. & Desm.
  Rhytisma salicinum (P.) ex Fr.
Salix myrtilloides L.
  Melampsora Bigelowii Thm.
Salix Nelsonii Ball.
  { Melampsora americana Arth.
  { Melampsora humboldtiana Speg.
Salix nigra Marsh.

ASCOMYCETES

  { Lophiostoma Langloisii Ell. & Ev.
  { Melanomma Langloisii (Ell. & Ev.) Berl.

{ Hysteropatella clavispora (Pk.) Seaver.
  Patellaria clavispora (Pk.) Sacc.
{ Patellaria Peckii House.
  Triblidiella clavispora (Pk.) Berl. & Vogl.
  Triblidium clavisporum Pk.
  Physalospora Salicis (Fckl.) Sacc.
  Trimmatostroma americanum Thm.
{ Uncinula adunca Lév.
{ Uncinula Salicis (DC.) Wint. †
  Valsa nivea (Hoffm.) ex Fr.
  Valsa salicina (P.) ex Fr.

UREDINALES

{ Melampsora americana Arth.
{ Melampsora Bigelowii Auct. Amer. p. p.
{ Melampsora humboldtiana Speg.
{ Melampsora Bigelowii Thm.
{ Melampsora Salicis-capreae Ohio Fungi *166.*
{ Uredo Bigelowii (Thm.) Arth.
{ Caeoma epiteum Auct. Amer.
 Lecythea epitea Auct. Amer.
 Lecythea salicina Auct. Amer.
 Melampsora Capraearum Thm.
? { Melampsora farinosa　Auct. Amer. p. p.
 Melampsora Hartigii Thm.
 Melampsora salicina Auct. Amer.
 Uredo caprearum Auct. Amer.
 Uredo epitea Auct. Amer.
{ Uredo saliceti Auct. Amer.

HYMENOMYCETINEAE

Corticium confluens Fr.
Corticium effuscatum C. & E.
Cyphella mellea Burt.
{ Corticium salicinum Fr.
{ Cytidia salicina (Fr.) Burt.
Daedalea Aesculi Murrill.
Daedalea confragosa (Bolt.) ex Fr.
Exidia glandulosa (Bull.) ex Fr.
Fomes applanatus (P. ex Wallr.) Gill.
{ Fomes connatus (Weinm. ex Fr.) Gill.
{ Polyporus connatus Fr.
Fomes igniarius (L. ex Fr.) Gill.
Lenzites Klotzschii B.
Merulius corium Fr.
{ Geopetalum alliaceum (B. & C.) Murrill.
{ Panus alliaceus B. & C.
Peniophora Bartholomaei Pk.
Peniophora cinerea (P. ex Fr.) Cke.
Peniophora incarnata (P.) Cke.
Peniophora velutina (DC. ex Fr.) Cke.
Polyporus admirabilis Pk.
{ Bjerkandera adusta (Willd. ex Fr.) Karst.
{ Polyporus adustus (Willd.) ex Fr.
Polyporus squamosus (Huds.) ex Fr.
{ Funalia stuppea (B.) Murrill.
{ Trametes hispida Bagl.
{ Trametes Peckii Kalchb.
{ Trametes stuppea B.

Salix nigra (*cont.*)
Poria pulchella S.
Poria vaporaria Fr.
{ Poria xanthospora (Underw.) Sacc.
{ Xanthoporia Andersoni (Ell. & Ev.) Murrill.

FUNGI IMPERFECTI

Aposphaeria pezizoides Ell. & Ev.
Cercospora salicina Ell. & Ev.
Cytidia salicina (Fr.) Burt.
Cytospora Salicis (Cda.) Rabh.?
Darluca Filum (Biv.) Cast.
Diplodia salicina Lév.
Gloeosporium Salicis Westd.
Hendersonia Lirella Cke.
Melanconium salicinum Ell. & Ev.
Phleospora dearnessiana Sacc.
Phoma atomica Sacc.
Phoma platysperma Pk.
Propolidium fuscocinereum Ell. & Ev.
Prosthemiella hysterioides Ell. & Langlois.
{ Fusarium Uredinum Ell. & Ev.
{ Ramularia Uredinis (Voss) Sacc.
Septoria albaniensis Thm.
Septoria salicina Pk.

Salix nigra Marsh., var. **falcata** (Pursh) Torr.
Hendersonia Lirella Cke.
Lophidium compressum (P. ex Fr.) Sacc.

Salix Nuttallii Sarg.
Fomes igniarius (L. ex Fr.) Gill.
Uncinula Salicis (DC.) Wint. †

Salix ovalifolia Trautv.
Melampsora arctica Rostr.

Salix ovalifolia Trautv., var. **camdensis** C. K. Schneid.
{ Melampsora Bigelowii Thm.
{ Uredo Bigelowii (Thm.) Arth.

Salix padophylla Rydb.
Uredo Bigelowii (Thm.) Arth.

Salix pedicellaris Marsh.
Melampsora arctica Rostr.
{ Melampsora americana Arth.
{ Melampsora humboldtiana Speg.
?Melampsora farinosa Auct. Amer. p. p.
?Melampsora Salicis-capreae Auct. Amer. p. p.
?Uredo Bigelowii (Thm.) Arth. p. p.
Ramularia rosea (Fckl.) Sacc.
Septogloeum salicinum (Pk.) Sacc.
Uncinula Salicis (DC.) Wint. †

Salix pennata Ball.
Melampsora confluens (Arth.) H. S. Jackson.

Salix pentandra L.
{ Melampsora Bigelowii Thm.
{ Uredo Bigelowii (Thm.) Arth.

Salix perrostrata Rydb.
{ Melampsora Bigelowii Fung. Columb. *3714.*
{ Melampsora confluens (Arth.) H. S. Jackson.

{ Melampsora americana Arth.
{ Melampsora humboldtiana Speg.
Uncinula Salicis (DC.) Wint. †

Salix petiolaris J. E. Sm.
Gloeosporium niveum J. J. Davis.
Marssonina kriegeriana (Bres.) Magn.
{ Melampsora americana Arth.
{ Melampsora humboldtiana Speg.
?Uredo Bigelowii (Thm.) Arth.
{ Dermatea inclusa Pk.
{ Ocellaria ocellata (P.) Schrt.
Ramularia rosea (Fckl.) Sacc.
{ Rhytisma amphigenum (Wallr.) Magn.
{ Rhytisma salicinum (P.) ex Fr.
Trimmatostroma americanum Thm.
Uncinula Salicis (DC.) Wint. †
Valsa pallida Ell. & Ev.

Salix petrophila Rydb.
Melampsora arctica Rostr.
?{ Melampsora Bigelowii Thm.
{ Uredo Bigelowii (Thm.) Arth.

Salix phylicifolia L.
Diatrypella Demetrionis Ell. & Ev.
Melampsora confluens (Arth.) H. S. Jackson.
Psilothecium incurvum Clements.

Salix Piperi Bebb.
Melampsora Bigelowii Thm.

Salix polaris Wahlenb.
{ Melampsora alpina Juel.
{ Uredo alpina (Juel) Arth.

Salix pseudocordata Anders.
Melampsora Bigelowii Thm.

Salix pseudomonticola Ball.
Melampsora confluens (Arth.) H. S. Jackson.

Salix pseudomyrsinites Anders.
{ Melampsora Bigelowii Thm.
{ Uredo Bigelowii (Thm.) Arth.

Salix pulchra Anders.
Hormiscium stilbosporum (Cda.) Sacc.
Leptosphaeria prope L. borealem Ell. & Ev.
Leptothyrium pulchrum Dearness.
{ Melampsora Bigelowii Thm.
{ ?Melampsora farinosa Auct. Amer. p. p.
{ Uredo Bigelowii (Thm.) Arth.
Mycosphaerella Capronii (Sacc.) J. Lind.

Salix purpurea L.
Cryptomyces maximus (Fr.) Rehm.
{ Melampsora americana Arth.
{ Melampsora humboldtiana Speg.
Pestalozzia lignicola Cke.
Rosellinia mastoidea Sacc.
Tympanis saligna Tode ex Fr.

Salix reticulata L.
Linospora insularis Johans.
{ Melampsora Bigelowii Thm.
{ Melampsora farinosa Auct. Amer. p. p.
{ Uredo Bigelowii (Thm.) Arth.
Pyrenophora paucitricha (Fckl.) Berl. & Vogl.
Rhytisma salicinum (P.) ex Fr.

Salix reticulata (*cont.*)
Mycosphaerella minor (Karst.) Dearness, var.
   reticulata Dearness.
Venturia chlorospora (Ces.) Karst.
Venturia subcutanea Dearness.

Salix Richardsoni Hook.
Mycosphaerella Capronii (Sacc.) J. Lind.
Scleroderris fuliginosa (Fr.) Karst.

Salix rostrata Richards.
Fomes conchatus (P. ex Fr.) Karst.
Fomes igniarius (L. ex Fr.) Gill.
Hypoxylon Blakei B. & C.
⎰Melampsora americana Arth.
⎱Melampsora Bigelowii Fung. Columb. *4331*.
⎱Melampsora humboldtiana Speg.
?Melampsora arctica Rostr.
Melampsora Bigelowii Thm.
Melampsora confluens (Arth.) H. S. Jackson.
?Melampsora farinosa Auct. Amer. p. p.
?Melampsora Salicis-capreae Auct. Amer. p. p.
Ramularia rosea (Fckl.) Sacc.
Rhytisma salicinum (P.) ex Fr.
Septogloeum salicinum (Pk.) Sacc.
Uncinula Salicis (DC.) Wint. †
Valsa boreella Karst.

Salix russelliana Smith.
Melampsora farinosa Auct. Amer. p. p.
Septonema connatum B. & C.
Trimmatostroma Salicis Cda.

Salix scouleriana Barratt.
Diatrype bullata (Hoffm.) ex Fr.
⎰?Caeoma arcticum Drayton.
⎱Melampsora arctica Rostr.
⎰Melampsora Bigelowii Thm.
⎱Uredo Bigelowii (Thm.) Arth.
⎰Melampsora Bigelowii Fung. Columb. *3142*;
⎱ N. Am. Uredinales *1417, 1815*.
Melampsora confluens (Arth.) H. S. Jackson.
Uredo confluens Arth. III.
Uredo confluens P.
⎰Melampsora americana Arth.
⎱Melampsora Bigelowii Fung. Columb. *4237*;
⎱ N. Am. Uredinales *1119*.
Melampsora humboldtiana Speg.
?Melampsora farinosa   Auct. Amer.
?Melampsora Salicis-capreae Auct. Amer.
Myxofusicoccum Salicis Died.
Nectria cinnabarina (Tode) ex Fr.
Phlebia merismoides Fr.
Rhytisma salicinum (P.) ex Fr.
Stereum erumpens Burt.
Trimmatostroma americanum Thm.
Uncinula Salicis (DC.) Wint. †
Valsa americana B. & C.
Valsa minutella Pk.
Valsa salicina (P.) ex Fr.
Valsella Salicis Fckl.

Salix sericea Muhl.
⎰Cryptomyces maximus (Fr.) Rehm.
⎱Rhytisma maximum Fr.
⎰Melampsora americana Arth.
⎱Melampsora humboldtiana Speg.
⎰Gloeosporium salicinum Pk.
⎱Septogloeum salicinum (Pk.) Sacc.
Septomyxa grisea Dearness & House.
Uncinula Salicis (DC.) Wint. †

Salix sessilifolia Nutt.
Uredo (Melampsora) Bigelowii (Thm.) Arth.

Salix sitchensis Sanson.
?Cladosporium Salicis-sitchensis Dearness &
  Barthol.
Melampsora arctica Rostr.
⎰Melampsora arctica N. Am. Uredinales *1507*.
⎱Melampsora Bigelowii Thm.
Melampsora confluens (Arth.) H. S. Jackson.
⎰Melampsora americana Arth.
⎱Melampsora Bigelowii N. Am. Uredinales *2522*.
⎱Melampsora humboldtiana Speg.
Septogloeum salicinum (Pk.) Sacc.
Uncinula Salicis (DC.) Wint. †

Salix stolonifera Cov.
Melampsora arctica Rostr.
?Melampsora farinosa Auct. Amer. p. p.
?Uredo Bigelowii Arth. p. p.

Salix subcaerulea Piper.
⎰Melampsora Bigelowii Fung. Utah *206*.
⎱Melampsora confluens (Arth.) H. S. Jackson.

Salix syrticola Fern.
Marssonina kriegeriana (Bres.) Magn.

Salix taxifolia H. B. K.
⎰Melampsora americana Arth.
⎱?Melampsora arctica Arth. p. p.
⎱Melampsora humboldtiana Speg.

Salix tenerrima Henderson.
⎰Melampsora Bigelowii Thm.
⎱Uredo Bigelowii (Thm.) Arth.

Salix tristis Ait.
Melampsora Bigelowii N. Am. Uredinales *1010*.
Melampsora confluens (Arth.) H. S. Jackson.
?Melampsora caprearum Auct. Amer. p. p.
?Melampsora farinosa Auct. Amer. p. p.

Salix Uva-ursi Pursh.
?Melampsora farinosa Auct. Amer. p. p.
?Melampsora caprearum Auct. Amer. p. p.
Rhytisma salicinum (P.) ex Fr.

Salix vestita Pursh.
⎰Melampsora Bigelowii Thm.
⎱Uredo Bigelowii (Thm.) Arth.

Salix Wardii Bebb.
Melampsora Salicis-capreae (P.) Wint.
⎰?Melampsora Bigelowii Auct. Amer. p. p.
⎱Melampsora humboldtiana Speg.
⎱?Uredo Bigelowii (Thm.) Arth.

Salix Watsoni Bebb.
  Melampsora confluens (Arth.) H. S. Jackson.
? { Melampsora Bigelowii Thm.
  { Uredo Bigelowii (Thm.) Arth.
  Platystomum compressum (P. ex Fr.) Trevisan.
  Trimmatostroma Salicis Cda.

Salix Wrightii Anders.
  Cytospora chrysosperma (P.) ex Fr.
  { Melampsora americana Arth.
  { Melampsora humboldtiana Speg.
  ?Melampsora arctica Rostr.
  ?Melampsora Bigelowii Thm.

Salix sp. indet.

MYXOMYCETES

Comatricha flaccida Lister.
Leocarpus fulvus Macbr.
Trichia fallax P.

PEZIZINEAE

{ Cenangium fuliginosum (P.) ex Fr.
{ Scleroderris fuliginosa (P. ex Fr.) Karst.
{ Sphaeria fuliginosa P. ex Fr.
Cenangium tryblidioides Ell. & Ev.
Chlorosplenium aeruginascens (Nyl.) Karst.
{ Chlorosplenium versiforme (P.) De Not.
{ Peziza versiformis P.
Ciboria Caucus (Reb. ex P.) Fckl.
Dermatea macrospora Clements.
{ Godronia Betheli Seaver.
{ Godronia striata (Ell. & Ev.) Seaver.
{ Lasiosphaeria striata Ell. & Ev.
Helotium marginatum Clements.
Helotium salicellum Fr.
{ Helotium sublenticulare (Fl. Dan.) ex Fr., var.
{   conscriptum Karst.
{ Hymenoscypha sublenticulare (Fl. Dan. ex Fr.)
{   Kauffm., var. conscriptum (Karst.) Kauffm.
Lachnum bicolor (Bull. ex Fr.) Karst.
Lasiobelonium subflavidum Ell. & Ev.
Patellaria atrata (Hedw.) Fr.
{ Patellaria difformis (Fr.) S.
{ Peziza difformis Fr.
{ Patellaria olivacea (Batsch ex Fr.) B. & Br.
{ Patinella olivacea (Batsch ex Fr.) Sacc.
{ Peziza citrinella S.
{ Pezizella citrinella (S.) Sacc.
?Peziza nigrescens Cke.
Pezizella albella (With. ex Fr.) Sacc.
Phialea ampla Ell. & Ev.
{ Peziza salicina P. ex Fr.
{ Phialea salicina (P. ex Fr.) Sacc.
Pseudopeziza salicis (Tul.) Pat.
Tapesia fusca (P.) Fckl.

PHACIDIINEAE

{ Coccophacidium salicinum Ell. & Ev.
{ Coccomyces salicinus (Ell. & Ev.) Sacc.
Cryptodiscus angulosus Karst.

Odontotrema minus Nyl., var. salicella Kauff-
  man.
Phacidium carbonaceum Fr.
Phacidium salicinum Fckl.
Propolis angulosa Karst.?
{ Propolis cylindrocarpa (Pk.) Sacc.
{ Stictis cylindrocarpa Pk.
Schizoxylon bicolor Ell. & Ev.
Schizoxylon dermateoides Rehm.
Stictis schizoxyloides Ell. & Ev.
Stictis serpentaria Ell. & Ev.
Triblidium minor Cke.
Triblidium occidentale Earle.

HYSTERIINEAE

{ Hysterium fibritectum S.
{ Glonium fibritectum (S.) Massee.
Hysterium Prostii Duby.
Hysterium rugulosum S.
Hysterium Mori S.
{ Hysterographium Mori (S.) Rehm.
{ Hysterographium Mori, var. Gerardii (C. &
{   P.) Ell. & Ev.
{ Hysterographium Rousselii (De Not.) Sacc.
Lophodermium maculare (Fr.) De Not.

PYRENOMYCETINEAE
PERISPORIALES

Phyllactinia corylea (P.) ex Karst.

HYPOCREALES

Gibberella acervalis (Moug.) Sacc.
Hypocrea lenta (Tode ex Fr.) B.
Hypocrea sulphurea (S.) Sacc.
Nectria coccinea (P.) ex Fr.
Nectria galligena Bres.
{ Creonectria ochroleuca (S.) Seaver.
{ Nectria ochroleuca (S.) M. A. Curtis.
Nectria Peziza Fr.
Nectria tremelloides Ell. & Ev.
Nectria sanguinea Fr.
Sphaerostilbe flammea (B. & Rav.) Tul.

SPHAERIALES

Amphisphaeria decolorans Rehm.
{ Amphisphaeria papillata (Schum. ex Fr.) De
{   Not.
{ Sphaeria papillata Schum. ex Fr.
Botryosphaeria Ribis (Tode ex Fr.) Grossen-
  bacher & Duggar, var. chromogena Shear
  et al.
Capnodium salicinum Mont.
Chaetomium glabrescens Ell. & Ev.
{ Cryptospora suffusa (Fr.) Tul.
{ Sphaeria suffusa Fr.
{ Valsa suffusa Fr.
Cucurbitaria borealis Ell. & Ev.
Cucurbitaria Fraxini Ell. & Ev.
Daldinia concentrica (Bolt. ex Fr.) Ces. & De
  Not.

Salix sp. indet. (*cont.*)

{ Diaporthe glyptica (B. & Currey) Sacc.
{ Valsa glyptica B. & Currey.
Diaporthe salicella Fr.
{ Diaporthe spiculosa (A. & S.) ex Nits.
{ Sphaeria spiculosa A. & S. ex Nits.
Diaporthe spina Fckl.
{ Diaporthe mucronata Sacc.
{ Diaporthe Tessella (P. ex Fr.) Rehm.
{ Sphaeria Tessella P. ex Fr.
{ Valsa mucronata Pk.   •
{ Valsa Tessella (P.) Fr.
{ Diaporthe Tessera (Fr.) Fckl.
{ Valsa Tessera (Fr.) Cke.
Diatrype albopruinosa (S.) Cke.
Diatrype albopruinosa (S.) Cke., var. salicina Rehm.
Diatrype dakotensis Rehm.
Diatrype linearis Ell. & Ev., var. Salicis Rehm.
Diatrype stigma (Hoffm.) ex Fr.
Diatrypella pulcherrima Ell. & Ev.
Didymella canadensis Ell. & Ev.
Dimerosporium xylogenum Ell. & Ev.
Eutypa leioplaca (Fr.) Cke.
Eutypa nitida (Nits.) Sacc.
{ Eutypa oppansa (Fr.) Cke.
{ Sphaeria oppansa Fr.
Eutypa scabrosa (Bull. ex Fr.) Awd.
Eutypa subcutanea (Wallr.) Sacc.
Eutypa velutina (Wallr.) Sacc.
{ Eutypella canodisca (Ell. & Holw.) Sacc.
{ Valsa canodisca Ell. & Holw.
Eutypella sheariana Berl.
Gibbera Saubinetii Mont.
Hypospila groenlandica Rostr.
Hypoxylon Botrys Nits.
Hypoxylon coccineum Bull. †
Hypoxylon glomiforme B. & C.
Hypoxylon investiens (S.) B.
Hypoxylon rubiginosum (P.) ex Fr.
Hypoxylon tinctor (B.) Cke.
Lasiosphaeria hystrix Ell. & Ev.
Leptosphaeria borealis Ell. & Ev.
Leptosphaeria consimilis Ell. & Ev.
Lophiosphaera fluviatilis Ell. & Ev.
Lophiosphaera gloniospora Ell. & Ev.
Lophiostoma erosum Ell. & Ev.
Lophiostoma insidiosum (Desm.) Ces. & De Not., var. Salicis Rehm.
Lophiostoma macrostomoides De Not.
Lophiostoma triseptatum Pk., var. diagonale Fairman.
Lophiostoma triseptatum Pk., var. pluri-septatum Ell. & Ev.
Lophiotrema littorale Speg.
{ Melanconiella obruta (Ell. & Ev.) Sacc. & Syd.
{ Melanconis obruta Ell. & Ev.
Melanconis salicina Ell. & Ev.

Melanomma cupulata Ell. & Ev.
Melanomma minutum Berl.
Melanopsamma salicaria (Karst.) Sacc.
Melanopsamma salicaria (Karst.) Sacc., var. fallax Sacc.
Physalospora Malorum Shear et. al.
Platystomum salicum Earle.
Rosellinia albolanata Ell. & Ev.
Rosellinia aquila (Fr.) De Not.
Rosellinia megaloecia Ell. & Ev.
{ Rosellinia myriocarpa (Fr.) Cke.
{ Sphaeria myriocarpa Fr.
Schizoparme straminea Shear.
Sphaerella Grossulariae (Fr.) Awd., var. salicella Sacc. & Scalia.
Strickeria inclusa Petrak.
Teichospora aberrans Rehm.
Teichospora Helenae Ell. & Ev.
Teichospora megastega Ell. & Ev.
Teichospora papillosa Ell. & Ev.
Valsa dissepta Fr.
Valsa orbicula B. & C.
Valsa salicina (P.) ex Fr., var. octospora Rehm.
Valsaria salicina Ell. & Ev.
Valsella nigro-annulata Fckl.
Valsella pulcherrima (Ell. & Ev.) Berl.
Xylaria corniformis Fr.
Xylaria fulvella B. & C.

UREDINALES

{ Melampsora confluens (Arth.) H. S. Jackson.
{ Melampsora maculosa West. Am. Fung *341*.
? { Caeoma Laricis Auct. III.
{ Melampsora Larici-capraearum Klebahn.
?Melampsora paradoxa Diet. & Holw.
Melampsora Ribesii-purpurae Klebahn.
?Melampsora Salicis-albae Klebahn.

TREMELLACEAE

Exidia impressa (P.) Fr.
{ Exidia recisa (Dittm.) ex Fr.
{ Peziza gelatinosa Bull. ex Fr.
Exidia spiculata S.
Tremella indecorata Sommerf. ex Fr.
Tremella lutescens (P.) ex Fr.

DACRYOMYCETINEAE

Dacryomyces cinnabarinus S.

THELEPHORACEAE

Aleurodiscus macrodens Coker.
{ Aleurodiscus Oakesii (B. & C.) Cke.
{ Corticium Oakesii B. & C.
Corticium bombycinum (Sommerf.) Bres.
Corticium confluens Fr.
Corticium confluens Fr., var. calceum Karst.
Corticium crustaceum (Karst.) v. Höhnel & Litschauer.
Corticium evolvens Fr.

Salix sp. indet. (*cont.*)
  Corticium lactescens B.
  Corticium lilacinofuscum B. & C.
  Corticium vellerum Ell. & Cragin.
  Cyphella fasciculata B. & C.
  Cytidia flocculenta (Fr.) v. Höhnel & Litschauer.
  Hymenochaete tabacina (Sow. ex Fr.) Lév.
  Peniophora flavido-alba Cke.
  Peniophora glebulosa Bres.
  Peniophora lepida Bres.
  Peniophora trachytricha Ell. & Ev.
  Peniophora violaceolivida (Sommerf.) Bres.
  Solenia anomala (P. ex Fr.) Fckl.
  Solenia ochracea Hoffm. ex Fr.
  Stereum erumpens Burt.
  Stereum purpurellum Fr.
  Stereum purpureum P. †
  {Hypocrea Richardsoni B. & Mont.
  {Stereum rufum Fr.

POLYPORACEAE

Daedalea pallidofulva B.
Daedalea unicolor (Bull.) ex Fr.
{Fomes abramsianus (Murrill) Sacc. & Trott.
{Pyropolyporus abramsianus Murrill.
Fomes fomentarius (L. ex Fr.) Gill.
Fomes fraxinophilus Pk.
Fomes nigricans (Fr.) Cke.
Ganoderma polychromum (Copeland) Murrill.
Lenzites betulina (L.) ex Fr.
Lenzites Cookei B.
Lenzites corrugata (Klotzsch) B. & C.
{Lenzites vialis Pk.
{Sesia pallidofulva (B.) Murrill.
Polyporus adustus (Willd.) ex Fr.
Polyporus albellus Pk.
Polyporus benzoinus Fr.
Polyporus caesius (Schrad.) ex Fr.
Polyporus chioneus Fr.
Polyporus epileucus Fr.
{Polyporus fumidiceps (Atk.) Sacc. & Trott.
{Tyromyces fumidiceps Atk.
{Bjerkandera fumosa (P. ex Fr.) Karst.
{Polyporus fumosus (P.) ex Fr.
Polyporus gilvus S.
Polyporus lacteus Fr.
Polyporus picipes Fr.
Polyporus pubescens (Schum.) ex Fr.
Polyporus Rheades P. ex Fr.
Polyporus salignus Fr.
{Polyporus semisupinus B. & C.
{Tyromyces semipileatus (Pk.) Murrill.
Polyporus sessilis Lloyd.
Polyporus squamosus (Huds.) ex Fr.
Polyporus sulfureus (Bull.) ex Fr.
Polyporus Tulipiferus (S.) Fr.
Polyporus Underwoodii Murrill.
Polystictus cinnabarinus (Jacq.) ex Fr.

Polystictus hirsutus (Schrad.) ex Fr.
Polystictus zonatus (Nees) ex Fr.
Poria contigua (P.) Karst.
Poria eupora (P. Karst.) Cke.
Poria ferruginosa (Schrad. ex Fr.) Cke.
Poria inermis Ell. & Ev.
Poria Medullae-panis Fr.
{Fomitiporella melleopora Murrill.
{Poria melleopora (Murrill) Sacc. & Trott.
Poria mollusca Fr.
Poria punctata Fr.
Poria purpurea Fr.
Poria salicina Murrill.
Trametes mollis Fr.
Trametes odora Fr.
Trametes Peckii Kalchbr.
Trametes sepium B.
Trametes serialis Fr.

AGARICACEAE

{Collybia velutipes (Curt.) Fr.
{Gymnopus velutipes (Curt. ex Fr.) Murrill.
Coprinus fuscescens (Schaeff.) ex Fr.
Coprinus micaceus Fr.
Flammula alnicola Fr.
Lentinus haematopus B.
{Agaricus ringens Fr., var. tenuissimus (S.) Fr.
{Lentinus tenuissimus (S.) Fr.
Marasmius dichrous B. & C.
Marasmius salignus Pk.
Omphalia tubiformis Pk.
Panus foetens Fr.
Panus torulosus (P.) ex Fr.
Pholiota destruens (Fr.) Bres.
{Hypodendrum oregonense Murrill.
{Pholiota oregonense Murrill.
Pleurotus dryinus (P.) ex Fr.
Pleurotus ostreatus (Jacq.) ex Fr.
Pleurotus salignus (P.) ex Fr.
Pleurotus sapidus Kalchb.
Pleurotus ulmarius Fr.
Schizophyllum commune Fr.
Trogia crispa (P.) ex Fr.

SPHAEROPSIDALES

Catinula saligna Ell. & Ev.
Coniothyrium spokanense Sacc.
Cytospora boreella Earle.
Cytospora salicella Sacc.
{Cytospora translucens Sacc.
{Valsa translucens De Not.
Cytospora xanthosperma Fr.
Diplodina Salicis Westd.
{Discella macrosperma Pk.
{Discula macrosperma (Pk.) Sacc.
Discella microsperma B. & Br.
Dothichiza populea Sacc. & Briard.
Dothiorella decorticata Ell. & Ev.
{Hendersonia lineolans (S.) Starb.
{Sphaeria lineolans S.

Salix sp. indet. (*cont.*)
　Mastomyces proboscidea (Fr.) Sacc.
　Phyllosticta salicicola Thm.
　Septoria didyma Fckl.
　Septoria salicina Pk.
　Septoria Ulmi Fr.
　{ Sphaeria hemisphaerica A. & S. ex Fr.
　{ Sphaeronema hemisphaericum (A. & S.) ex Fr.

Melanconiales
　Coryneum pezizoides Ell. & Ev.
　Cylindrosporium salicinum (Pk.) Dearness.
　Gloeosporium amentorum (Delacr.) J. Lind.
　Gloeosporium boreale Ell. & Ev.
　Gloeosporium Salicis Westd.
　{ Calogloeum weirianum (Sacc.) Syd.
　{ Gloeosporium weirianum Sacc.
　Marssonia apicalis Ell. & Ev.
　Marssonia kriegeriana Bres.
　Marssonina obscura (Romell) Magn.
　{ Marssonia rubiginosa Ell. & Ev.
　{ Marssonina rubiginosa (Ell. & Ev.) Magn.
　Myxosporium cytosporeum Sacc.
　Pestalozzia bicolor Ell. & Ev.

Hyphomycetes
　Bactridium flavum Kze. ex Fr.
　Botrytis patula Sacc. & Berl.
　Cladosporium Fumago Lk.
　Cladosporium polysporum Lk.
　Coniothecium toruloides Cda.
　Dematium cornutum (P.) Lk.
　Dematium virescens P. ex Fr.
　Dendrodochium densipes Sacc. & Ell., var.
　　prolificum Ell. & Ev.
　Dendryphium fumosum (Cda.) Fr.
　Exosporium Tiliae Lk.
　{ Fusicladium saliciperdum (Allescher & Tubeuf)
　{ 　J. Lind.
　{ Septogloeum saliciperdum Allescher & Tubeuf.
　Helminthosporium simplex Nees ex Fr.
　Hymenula glandicola Cke.
　Monilia Martinii Sacc. & Ell., var. incendia-
　　rum Ell. & Ev.
　Ramularia rosea (Fckl.) Sacc.
　{ Aspergillus laneus S. Am. bor.
　{ Rhinotrichum Curtisii B.
　Sphaerosporium lignatile S.
　Sporidesmium aurantiacum B. & C.
　{ Sporidesmium concinnum B.
　{ Vermicularia clavuligera S. Am. bor.
　Torula crustacea S.
　Trimmatostroma Salicis Cda.
　Volutella occidentalis Ell. & Anderson, var.
　　minor Ell. & Anderson.

Miscellanea
　Endogone pisiformis Lk. ex Fr.
　Hydnum pallidum C. & E.
　Lycoperdon quercinum P.

　Octaviania rosea Hark.
　Ozonium auricomum Lk.
　Pilacre Petersii B. & C.
　Sparassis laminosa Fr.
　Sphaerobolus stellatus Tode ex Fr.

MYRICACEAE
Myrica asplenifolia L.
　Gymnosporangium myricatum Fromme. I.
　{ Calosphaeria rimicola (S.) Cke.
　{ Sphaeria asplenifolia S.
　{ Sphaeria rimicola S.
　{ Valsa rimicola (S.) Cke.
　{ Cronartium asclepiadeum Auct. Amer.
　{ Cronartium asclepiadeum, var. Thesii Fung.
　{ 　Columb. *1724.*
　{ Cronartium Comptoniae Arth.
　Cucurbitaria Comptoniae C. & E.
　{ Diaporthe Comptoniae (S.) Ell. & Ev.
　{ Sphaeria Comptoniae S.
　{ Valsa Comptoniae (S.) Cke.
　Diatrype Comptoniae Ell. & Ev.
　{ Erinella rhabdocarpa (Ell.) Sacc.
　{ Peziza rhabdocarpa Ell.
　Isariopsis Dearnessii Bubák.
　{ Ovularia destructiva (Phil. & Plowr.) Massee.
　{ Ovularia monilioides Ell. & Martin.
　{ Barklayella flagellifera (Ell. & Ev.) Sacc.
　{ Pestalozzia flagellifera Ell. & Ev.
　{ Pseudovalsa Comptoniae Ell. & Ev.
　{ Thyridaria Comptoniae (Ell. & Ev.) Berl. &
　{ 　Vogl.
　Sphaeropsis Comptoniae Ell. & Ev.
　Valsa ambiens (P.) ex Fr.
　Valsa conscripta C. & E.
Myrica californica Cham.
　Eutypa lata (P. ex Fr.) Tul.
　Lasiosphaeria biformis (P. ex Fr.) Sacc.
　{ Lophodermium hysterioides (P. ex Fr.) Sacc.
　{ Lophodermium xylomoides (DC.) ex Chev.
Myrica carolinensis Mill.
　Gymnosporangium myricatum Fromme. I.
　Asterella Myricae Miles.
　Haplosporella Lathami Dearness.
　Mycosphaerella Myricae Miles.
Myrica cerifera L.
　Gymnosporangium myricatum Fromme. I.
　{ Appendiculella calostroma (Desm.) v. Höhnel.
　{ Meliola manca Ell. & Martin.
Myrica carolinensis Mill.
Myrica cerifera L.
　Note. Plants reported under these names can-
　not be segregated with reference to the fungi re-
　ported upon them.
　{ Aecidium myricatum S.
　{ Caeoma myricatum S.
　{ Gymnosporangium Ellisii (B.) Farl. I.
　{ Gymnosporangium myricatum Fromme. I.

Myrica cerifera *(cont.)*
  Botryosphaeria graphidea (B. & Rav.) Sacc.
  {Calonectria erubescens (Rob.) Sacc.
  {Dialonectria erubescens (Rob.) Cke.
  {Calosphaeria Myricae (C. & E.) Ell. & Ev.
  {Eutypella Myricae (C. & E.) Sacc.
  {Valsa Myricae C. & E.
  Cercospora diffusa Ell. & Ev.
  Cercospora dispersa Ell. & Ev.
  Cercospora Myricae Tracy & Earle.
  Cercospora Penicillus Ell. & Ev.
  Coronophora angustata Fckl.
  Corticium calceum Fung. Am. *126* non Fr.
  {Cronartium asclepiadeum Auct. Amer.
  {Cronartium Comptoniae Arth.
  {Dasyscypha callochaetes (Ell. & Ev.) Sacc.
  {Peziza callochaetes Ell. & Ev.
  Diaporthe phomaspora (C. & E.) Ell. & Ev.
  {Diaporthe tecta (Cke.) Sacc.
  {Valsa tecta Cke.
  Diatrype disciformis (Hoffm) ex Fr.
  Diatrypella verruciformis (Ehrh. ex Fr.) Nits.
  Didymella Myricae Ell. & Ev.
  Eutypa lata (P. ex Fr.) Tul.
  {Fracchiaea moricarpa (Cke.) Sacc.
  {Gibbera moricarpa Cke.
  Frankia Brunchorstii Möller.
  Gloniopsis cookeana (Gerard) Sacc.
  Gnomonia Myricae C. & E.
  Helminthosporium inflatum B. & Rav.
  Hymenochaete badioferruginea (Mont.) Lév.
  Hymenochaete rubiginosa (Schrad. ex Fr.)
    Lév.
  Hymenochaete scabriseta Cke.
  Hymenochaete tabacina (Sow. ex Fr.) Lév.
  Hypocrea ochroleuca B. & Rav.
  Hypoxylon marginatum (S.) B., var. effusum
    B.
  Lasiosphaeria biformis (P. ex Fr.) Sacc.
  {Lophodermium hysterioides (P. ex Fr.) Sacc.
  {Lophodermium xylomoides (DC.) ex Chev.
  Meliola manca Ell. & Martin.
  Melogramma graphideum B. & Rav.
  Merulius Corium Fr.
  Merulius Ulmi Pk.
  {Corticium flavidoalbum Rav. Fung. Am.
  {Peniophora flavidoalba Cke.
  Pestalozzia Myricae Ell. & Martin.
  Phyllosticta Myricae Cke.
  {Polyporus alabamae B. & Cke.
  {Poria alabamae (B. & Cke.) Cke.
  Septoria Myricae Ell. & Ev.
  {Peziza pruinata S.
  {Solenia poriaeformis (P. ex Fr.) Fckl.
  {Tapesia pruinata (S.) Sacc.
  ?Sphaerella Myricae Ell. & Ev.
  Sphaerella pardalota C. & E.
  Stagonospora Myricae Ell. & Ev.
  Stereum sericeum S.

  {Byssosphaeria acanthostroma (Mont.) Cke.
  {Sphaeria acanthostroma Mont.
  {Trichosphaeria acanthostroma (Mont.) Sacc.
  Valsa quernea Curr.
  Xylaria corniformis Fr.
  Zygodesmus pannosus B. & C.
Myrica Gale L.
  {Cronartium asclepiadeum Auct. Amer.
  {Cronartium Comptoniae Arth.
  {Dasyscypha bicolor (Bull. ex Fr.) Fckl.
  {Peziza bicolor Bull. ex Fr.
  {Dasyscypha sulphurella (Pk.) Sacc.
  {Peziza sulphurella Pk.
  {Diaporthe phomospora (C. & E.) Sacc.
  {Diaporthe Wibbei Pk. non Nits.
  {Valsa phomaspora C. & E.
  {Hormiscium curvatum (Pk.) Sacc.
  {Torula curvata Pk.
  Leptosphaeria Myricae Dearness & House.
  {Massarina Myricae (Pk.) Berl.
  {Metasphaeria Myricae Pk.
  {Ovularia destructiva (Phil. & Plowr.) Massee.
  {Ovularia monilioides Ell. & Martin.
  {Ovularia Sommeri (Eichilbaum) Sacc.
  {Ramularia monilioides Ell. & Ev.
  Teichospora Chevalierii Karst.
  {Peziza myricacea Pk.
  {Trichopeziza myricacea (Pk.) Sacc.
Myrica microcarpa Benth.
  Leptoporus stereinus (B. & C.) Pat.
Myrica sp. indet.
  Aspergillus Curtisii B.
  ?Favolus flaccidus Fr.
  {Fracchiaea subconnata (B. & C.) Cke.
  {Sphaeria subcongregata B. & C.
  {Sphaeria subconnata B. & C.
  Glenospora Curtisii B. & Desm.
  Grandinia granulosa (P.) ex Fr.
  {Hypoxylon marginatum Rav. Fung. Am.
  {Hypoxylon polyspermum Mont.
  {Capnodium grandisporum Ell. & Martin.
  {Limacinia grandispora (Ell. & Martin) Sacc.
  Microthyrium microscopicum Desm.
  Peziza nigripes Ell. non P.
  Polyporus barbiformis B. & C.
  Polyporus contiguus (P.) ex Fr.
  {Polyporus crocatus Fr.
  {Polystictus crocatus Fr.
  Polyporus floridanus B.
  {Polyporus holoxanthus B. & Cke.
  {Poria holoxantha B. & Cke.
  Polyporus niphodes B. & Br.
  Polyporus tenuis S.
  {Septobasidium pseudopedicellatum Burt.   •
  {Thelephora pedicellata S.
  Stilbum glaucum Cke.
  Tremella Myricae B. & Cke.
  {Peziza alboviridis Cke.
  {Trichopeziza alboviridis (Cke.) Sacc.

JUGLANDACEAE

Juglans californica Watson.
{ Fomes Everhartii (Ell. & Gall.) v. Schrenk.
{ Pyropolyporus Everhartii (Ell. & Gall.) Murrill.
{ Marssonia californica Ell. & Ev.
{ Mårssonina californica (Ell. & Ev.) Magn.
Juglans cinerea L.

MYXOMYCETES
{ Didymium subroseum Pk.
{ Physarum albicans Pk.

PEZIZINEAE
{ Dasyscypha virginea (Batsch ex Fr.) Fckl.
{ Peziza virginea Batsch ex Fr.
Karschia taveliana Rehm.
Lecanidion tetrasporum (Massee & Morg.) Sacc. & D. Sacc.
Orbilia coccinella (Sommf.) ex Fr.
Pseudohelotium fibrisedum (B. & C.) Sacc.
Tapesia fusca (P.) Fckl.
Tapesia sanguinea (P.) Fckl.

PHACIDIINEAE
Propolis faginea (Schrad.) ex Karst.

HYSTERIINEAE
Glonium simulans Gerard.
Glonium stellatum S.
Hysterium cinerascens S.
Hysterographium Mori (S.) Rehm.
Ostropa rugulosa S.

PYRENOMYCETINEAE
{ Ceratostoma drupivorum (S.) Cke.
{ Sphaeria drupivora S.
Cryptosphaeria juglandina Ell. & Holw.
{ Diaporthe bicincta (C. & P.) Sacc.
{ Valsa bicincta C. & P.
{ Diaporthe lixivia (Fr.) Sacc.
{ Sphaeria lixivia Fr.
{ Valsa lixivia Fr.
Gnomonia veneta (Sacc. & Speg.) Klebahn.
{ Lasiosphaeria ovina (P. ex Fr.) Ces. & De Not.
{ Sphaeria ovina P. ex Fr.
Diaporthe Juglandis Ell. & Ev.
{ Melanconis Juglandis (Ell. & Ev.) Graves.
{ Melanconium oblongum B.
Melanconis modonia Tul.
Microsphaera Alni (DC.) Wint. †
{ Byssosphaeria diffusa (S.) Cke.
{ Didymotrichia diffusa (S.) Berl.
* { Herpotrichia diffusa (S.) Ell. & Ev.
{ Neopeckia diffusa (S.) Starb.
{ Sphaeria diffusa S.
Phyllactinia corylea (P.) ex Karst.
Rosellinia limoniispora Ell. & Ev.
Rosellinia medullaris (Wallr.) Ces. & De Not.

Sphaeria umbonata Fr.
Teichospora vialis (Fr.) Berl. & Vogl.
Valsaria exasperans (Gerard) Sacc.

BASIDIOMYCETES
Corticium puberum Fr.
Corticium Sambuci Fr.
Crepidotus haerens Pk.
Daedalea confragosa (Bolt.) ex Fr.
Daedalea quercina Fr.
Exidia glandulosa (Bull.) ex Fr.
Fomes Everhartii (Ell. & Gall.) v. Schrenk.
{ Fomes igniarius (L. ex Fr.) Gill.
{ Pyropolyporus igniarius (L. ex Fr.) Murrill.
Hydnum luteopallidum S.
{ Irpex lacteus Fr.
{ Irpiciporus lacteus (Fr.) Murrill.
{ Microstroma brachysporum (Sacc.) Vestergren.
{ Microstroma Juglandis Auct. Amer.
{ Microstroma Juglandis, var. brachysporum Sacc.
{ Microstroma leucosporum Auct. Amer.
Mucronoporus ferruginosus (Schrad. ex Fr.) Ell. & Ev.
Polyporus admirabilis Pk.
Polyporus delectans Pk.
{ Polyporus pendulus (Fr.) Ell.
{ Porodisculus pendulus (Fr.) Murrill.
Polyporus Radula (P.) ex Fr.
Polyporus sulphureus (Bull.) ex Fr.
Poria subacida (Pk.) Sacc.

FUNGI IMPERFECTI
Cercospora Juglandis Kellerm. & Swingle.
{ Chaetophoma amorphula (S.) Starb.
{ Sphaeria amorphula S.
Depazea juglandina Fr.
Dichomera Juglandis Ell. & Ev.
Diplodia Juglandis Fr.
Diplodina epicarya Fairman.
Macroplodia juglandicola Dearness & House.
{ Gloeosporium Juglandis (Lib.) Mont.
{ Gnomonia leptostyla (Fr.) Ces. & De Not.
{ Marssonia Juglandis (Lib.) Sacc.
{ Marssonina Juglandis (Lib.) Magn.
Monosporium avellaneum Fairman.
Sphaeronema infuscans Ell. & Ev.
Sphaeropsis Juglandis Ell. & Barthol.
Sporodesmium opacum Sacc.
Stachylidium sp. indet.
Streptothrix atra B. & C.
Juglans Hindsii Hort.
Cylindrosporium Juglandis Wolf.
Microstroma Juglandis Auct. Amer.
Juglans major (Torr.) Heller.
{ Microstroma brachysporum (Sacc.) Vestergren.
{ Microstroma Juglandis Auct. Amer.

Juglans nigra L.

Bertia fructicola Henn.
Cucurbitaria juglandina Ell. & Barthol.
⎰ Eutypa scoparia (S.) Wint.
⎱ Valsa scoparia (S.) M. A. Curtis.
⎰ Sphaeria scoparia S.
Eutypella juglandicola (S.) Ell. & Ev.
Gibbera pulicaris Fr.
Glonium stellatum S.
Gnomonia leptostyla (Fr.) Ces. & De Not.
Hypoxylon perforatum (S.) Fr.
Hysterographium Mori (S.) Rehm.
⎰ Lasiosphaeria hispida (Tode ex Fr.) Fckl.
⎱ Sphaeria hispida Tode ex Fr.
⎰ Melanconium oblongum B.
⎨ Diaporthe Juglandis Ell. & Ev.
⎩ Melanconis Juglandis (Ell. & Ev.) Graves.
Microsphaera Alni (DC.) Wint. †
Nectria cinnabarina (Tode) ex Fr.
Pleospora Juglandis Ell. & Ev.
Schizoxylon compositum Ell. & Ev.
Sporormia leptosphaerioides Speg.
Uncinula macrospora Pk.
⎰ Sphaeria sphinctrina Fr.
⎱ Valsa sphinctrina Fr.
Valsa tetraploa B. & C.

BASIDIOMYCETES

Armillaria mellea (Vahl) ex Fr.
Daedalea ambigua B.
⎰ Fomes Everhartii (Ell. & Gall.) v. Schrenk.
⎨ Pyropolyporus Everhartii (Ell. & Gall.) Mur-
⎩   rill.
Fomes igniarius (L. ex Fr.) Gill.
⎰ Exidia auriformis (S.) Fr.
⎨ Hirneola auriformis (S.) Fr.
⎨ Peziza auriformis S.
⎩ Tremella auriformis (S.) Spreng.
Lenzites vialis Pk.
⎰ Microstroma brachysporum (Sacc.) Vestergen.
⎨ Microstroma Juglandis Auct. Amer.
⎩ Microstroma leucosporum Auct. Amer.
Peniophora Burtii Romell.
Polyporus hirsutus (Wulf.) ex Fr.
Polyporus sulphureus (Bull.) ex Fr.
⎰ Coriolus versicolor (L. ex Fr.) Quél.
⎱ Polystictus versicolor (L.) ex Fr.
⎰ Boletus juglandinus S.
⎨ Polyporus juglandinus S.
⎨ Poria juglandina (S.) Cke.
⎩ Poria spissa Fr.
Stereum albobadium S.
⎰ Coriolellus Sepium (B.) Murrill.
⎱ Trametes Sepium B.

FUNGI IMPERFECTI

Acontium velatum Morg.
Camarosporium Juglandis Ell. & Barthol.

Cercospora Juglandis Kellerm. & Swingle.
Cladosporium pericarpinum Cke.
Cylindrocladium scoparium Morg.
Cylindrosporium caryogenum Ell. & Ev.
Cytospora albiceps Ell. & Kellerm.
Cytospora juglandicola Ell. & Barthol.
Diplodia Juglandis Fr.
Fumago salicina Tul.
Fusarium juglandinum Pk.
Fusarium nucicola Karst. & Har.
Fusarium roseum Lk.
⎰ Gloeosporium Juglandis (Lib.) Mont.
⎨ Gnomonia Juglandis Stevens & Hall.
⎨ Gnomonia leptostyla (Fr.) Ces. & De Not.
⎨ Leptothyrium Juglandis Lib.
⎨ Marssonia Juglandis (Lib.) Sacc.
⎩ Marssonina Juglandis (Lib.) Magn.
Phleospora multimaculans Heald & Wolf.
⎰ Ozonium omnivorum Shear.
⎱ Phymatotrichum omnivorum (Shear) Duggar.
⎰ Rhabdospora Juglandis (S.) Sacc.
Septoria Juglandis (S.) B. & C.
⎰ Sphaeria Juglandis S. nec Fr.
⎨ Valsa Juglandis (S.) Curr.
⎩ Valsa Juglandis S. Herb. sec. Cke.
⎰ Haplosporella druparum (S.) Starb.
⎨ Sphaeria druparum S.
⎩ Sphaeropsis druparum (S.) Cke.
⎰ Haplosporella Juglandis Ell. & Barthol.
⎱ Sphaeropsis Juglandis Ell. & Barthol.
Sphaeropsis pericarpii Pk.
Stagonospora nuciseda Fairman.
Triposporium Juglandis Thm.
Verticillium candidum Sacc.

MISCELLANEA

Trichia difformis S.

Juglans regia L.

Armillaria mellea (Vahl) ex Fr.
Bertia fructicola Henn.
Caryospora putaminum (S.) De Not.
Cylindrosporium Juglandis Wolf.
Cytospora albiceps Ell. & Kellerm.
Diplodia Juglandis Fr.
Dothiorella gregaria Sacc.
⎰ Eutypella juglandina (C. & E.) Sacc.
⎱ Valsa juglandina C. & E.
Glomerella cingulata (Stoneman) Spaulding &
  v. Schrenk.
Gnomonia leptostyla (Fr.) Ces. & De Not.
⎰ Helotium fructigenum (Bull. ex Fr.) Fckl.
⎱ Peziza fructigena Bull. ex Fr.
Marssonia Juglandis (Lib.) Sacc.
Melanconium magnum B.
⎰ Melanconium oblongum B.
⎨ Diaporthe Juglandis Ell. & Ev.
⎩ Melanconis Juglandis (Ell. & Ev.) Graves.
Microsphaera Alni (DC.) Wint. †

Juglans regia (*cont.*)
⎰ Microstroma brachysporum (Pk.) Vestergren.
⎱ Microstroma Juglandis Auct. Amer.
Microstroma leucosporum Auct. Amer.
⎰ Mollisia abdita (Ell.) Sacc.
⎱ Peziza abdita Ell.
Naematelia nucleata (S.) Fr.
Phleospora multimaculans Heald & Wolf.
Polyporus squamosus (Huds.) ex Fr.
⎰ Agaricus alneus (L.) ex Schrt.
⎱ Schizophyllum commune Fr.
Sphaerella petiolicola (Desm.) Awd.
Tubercularia Ailanthi Cke.
Juglans rupestris Engelm.
⎰ Fomes Everhartii Ell. & Gall.
⎱ Pyropolyporus Everhartii (Ell. & Gall.) Murrill.
Fomes rimosus (B.) Cke.
Juglans sieboldiana Maxim.
Marssonia Juglandis (Lib.) Sacc.
⎰ Diaporthe Juglandis Ell. & Ev.
⎱ Melanconis Juglandis (Ell. & Ev.) Graves.
Melanconium oblongum B.
⎰ Ozonium omnivorum Shear.
⎱ Phymatotrichum omnivorum (Shear) Duggar.
Juglans sp. indet.

MYXOMYCETES

Lamproderma arcyrionema Rostf.
Perichaena depressa Lib.
Physarum polyaedron S.

ASCOMYCETES

⎰ Anthostoma juglandinum Rehm.
⎱ Lopadostoma juglandinum (Rehm) Sacc. & Trott.
⎰ Bolinia Tubulina (A. & S. ex Fr.) Sacc.
⎰ Hypoxylon Tubulina (A. & S.) ex Fr.
⎱ Sphaeria Tubulina A. & S. ex Fr.
Botryosphaeria fuliginosa (M. & N.) Ell. & Ev.
Botryosphaeria Ribis (Fr.) Grossenbacher & Duggar.
Cenangium Juglandis B. & C.
Dothidea (Ectostroma) petiolaris S.
⎰ Endothia gyrosa (S.) Tul.
⎱ Melogramma gyrosum (S.) Tul.
Peziza gyrosa (S.) Spreng.
Sphaeria gyrosa S.
⎰ Eutypa spinosa (P. ex Fr.) Tul.
⎱ Sphaeria spinosa P. ex Fr.
Hypoxylon multiforme Fr.
⎰ Hysterium cinerascens S.
⎱ Hysterographium cinerascens (S.) Ell. & Ev.
⎰ Hysterium mytilinum P. ex Fr.
⎱ Lophium mytilinum (P.) ex Fr.
⎰ Lachnea Erinaceus (S.) Sacc.
⎱ Peziza Erinaceus S.
Melanomma caryophagum (S.) Sacc.
Nectria punicea Fr.

Nectria sanguinea (Sibth.) ex Fr.
Orbilia delicatula Karst.
Patellaria atrata (Hedw.) ex Fr.
⎰ Dothidea acervulata Fr.
⎱ Phyllachora acervulata (Fr.) Sacc.
⎱ ?Sphaeria conferta S. Am. bor.
Rosellinia aquila (Fr.) De Not.
Rosellinia glanduliformis Ell. & Ev.
Rosellinia mutans (C. & P.) Sacc.
Sphaeria putaminum S., var.

BASIDIOMYCETINEAE

⎰ Crucibulum juglandicola (S.) De Toni.
⎱ Nidularia juglandicola S.
Fomes conchatus (Fr.) Karst
Hydnum Himantia S.
Hydnum ischodes B.
Lycoperdon quercinum P.
Marasmius Juglandis B. & C.
Marasmius musicola McDougall. 1925.
Peniophora coccineofulva (S.) Burt.
Polyporus adustus (Willd.) ex Fr.
⎰ Polyporus adustus (Willd.) ex Fr., var. resupinatus Cke.
⎱ Polyporus fumosogriseus C. & E.
Polyporus aneirinus Sommerf.
Polyporus biformis " Klotzsch."
⎰ Cyphella pendula (S.) Fr.
⎱ Peziza digitalis S. Syn. Car.
⎱ Peziza pendula S. Syn. Car.
⎱ Polyporus cupuliformis B. & C.
Polyporus spongiosus S. Am. bor.
⎰ Polyporus cinereus S.
⎱ Poria cinerea (S.) Cke.
Poria inermis Ell. & Ev.

FUNGI IMPERFECTI

Aposphaeria nucicola Ell. & Ev.
Cladosporium Juglandis G. H. Martin, Jr. nom. nud.
Dematium strigosum (P. ex Fr.) Lk.
Dothiorella gregaria Sacc.
Gloeosporium Caryae Ell. & Dearness.
Helicomyces bellus Morg.
Marssonia californica Ell. & Ev.
Monilia aurea (Lk.) Gmel., var. aurantiaca S. Syn. Car.
Phoma pustula (P.) ex Fr.
Polyporus aneirinus (Sommerf.) ex Fr.
Sphaeropsis gallae (S.) B. & C.
Carya alba (L.) K. Koch.
Cercospora Halstedii Ell. & Ev.
Cryptospora Caryae Pk.
Cytospora albiceps Ell. & Kellerm.
⎰ Dacrina cinnabarina (P. ex Fr.) S.
⎱ Dematium cinnabarinum P. ex Fr.
Daldinia vernicosa (S.) Ces. & De Not.
Dothiorella Hicoriae Dearness & House.
Eutypella tumidula (C. & P.) Sacc.

Carya alba (*cont.*)
Gloeosporium Caryae Ell. & Dearness.
Hypoxylon exaratum (S.) M. A. Curtis.
Sphaeria exarata S.
Anthostoma juglandinum Rehm, var. Caryae
    Rehm.
Lopadostoma juglandinum (Rehm) Sacc. &
    Trott., var. Caryae Rehm.
Melanconium oblongum B.
Amphisphaeria caryophaga (S.) Cke.
Melanomma caryophagum (S.) Fairman.
Sphaeria caryophaga S.
Microstroma brachysporum (Sacc.) Vestergren.
Microstroma Juglandis Auct. Amer.
Microstroma leucosporum Auct. Amer.
Myxosporium luteum Ell. & Ev.
Oidium pulvinatum Cke.
Corticium cinereum Fr.
Peniophora cinerea (Fr.) Cke.
Corticium fumigatum Thm.
Peniophora cinerea (Fr.) Cke., var. fumigata
    (Thm.) Sacc. Syll.
Phlebia coccineofulva S.
Phyllactinia corylea (P.) ex Karst.
Phyllactinia suffulta (Reb.) ex Sacc.
Phyllosticta convexula Bubák.
Poria Caryae (S.) Cke.
Poria proxima Bres.
Rhytisma Juglandis S.
Mycosphaerella convexula (S.) F. V. Rand.
Sphaerella convexula (S.) Thm.
Sphaeria convexula S.
Mycosphaerella maculiforme (P. ex Fr.) Schrt.
Sphaerella maculiformis (P. ex Fr.) Awd.
Stereum purpureum P. †
Stereum sanguinolentum (A. & S.) ex Fr.
Dermosporium atrum S.
Strumella atra (S.) Sacc.
Sphaeria juglandicola S.
Valsa juglandicola (S.) Cke.

Carya aquatica (Michx. f.) Nutt.
Fomes fasciatus (Sw. ex Fr.) Cke.
Fusicladium effusum Wint.
Microstroma brachysporum (Sacc.) Vestergren
Microstroma leucosporum Auct. Amer.
Pestalozzia sphaerelloides Ell. & Langlois.
Phyllosticta Caryae Pk.

Carya cordiformis (Wang.) K. Koch.
Clasterosporium uncinatum G. W. Clinton.
Ceratophorum uncinatum (G. W. Clinton)
    Sacc.
Ceuthospora Caryae Bubák & Dearness.
Cylindrosporium caryigenum Ell. & Ev.
Diaporthe caryigena Ell. & Ev.
Diplodia caryogena Ell. & Ev.
Fusarium carpineum J. J. Davis.
Fusicladium effusum Wint.
Fusicoccum Juglandis Died.

Gloeosporium Caryae (Pk.) Ell. & Dearness.
Gnomonia Caryae Wolf.
Phyllosticta Caryae Pk.   Jan. 1888.
Phyllosticta Caryae Ell. & Ev.   Oct. 1888.
Hysterium nucicola S.
Hysterographium nucicola (S.) Ell. & Ev.
Melanconiella pallida Rehm.
Microsphaera Alni (DC.) Wint. †
Microstroma Juglandis Auct. Amer.
Septoria Hicoriae Tharp.
Sphaerella convexula (S.) Thm.
Sphaeropsis Caryae C. & E.
Sphaeropsis linearis Pk.
Sphaeropsis pericarpii (S.) Ell. & Ev.
Valsa caryigena B. & C.
Valsa ceratophora Tul.

Carya glabra (Mill.) Spach.
Aposphaeria nucicola Ell. & Ev.
Diaporthe Woolworthii (Pk.) Sacc.
Diatrype Woolworthii (Pk.) Sacc.
Valsa Woolworthii Pk.
Eutypa ludibunda Sacc.
Eutypella constellata (B. & C.) Ell. & Ev.
Valsa constellata B. & C. in Herb. B.
Gloeosporium Caryae Ell. & Dearness.
Gloeosporium Caryae Ell. & Dearness, var.
    curvisporum Dearness.
Gnomonia setacea (P.) Ces. & DeNot., var.
    Caryae Dearness & House.
Hydnum caryophylleum B. & C.
Microstroma brachysporum (Sacc.) Vestergren.
Microstroma Juglandis Auct. Amer.
Phoma exocarpina B.
Pleurotus sapidus Kalchbr.
Poria incrassata (B. & C.) Burt.
Rosellinia aquila (Fr.) De Not.
Hainesia Lythri (Desm.) v. Höhnel.
Pezizella Lythri Shear & Dodge.
Sclerotiopsis concava (Desm.) Shear & Dodge.
Sphaeropsis pericarpii Pk.
Dermosporium atrum S.
Strumella atra (S.) Sacc.
Trematosphaeria nuclearia (De Not.) Sacc.

Carya illinoensis (Wang.) K. Koch.
Botryosphaeria berengeriana DeNot.
Dothiorella berengeriana (De Not.) Sacc.
Botryosphaeria Ribis (Tode ex Fr.) Grossen-
    bacher & Duggar, var. chromogena Shear
    et al.
Cephalothecium roseum Cda.
Cercospora fusca F. V. Rand.
Clasterosporium diffusum Heald & Wolf.
Cercospora Halstedii Ell. & Ev.
Coniothyrium caryogenum Rand.
Corticium Stevensii Burt.
Dendrodochium simile Ell. & Ev.
Eutypa heteracantha Sacc.
Fomes fasciatus (Sw. ex Fr.) Cke.

Carya illinoensis (*cont.*)

{ Fusicladium caryigenum Ell. & Langlois.
{ Fusicladium effusum Wint.

Helminthosporium Arbuscula B. & C.
Microsphaera Alni (DC.) Wint.†
Microstroma Juglandis Auct. Amer.
Microstroma Juglandis, var. robustum B. B.
    Higgins.

{ Glomerella cingulata (Stoneman) Spaulding &
{   v. Schrenk.
{ Mycosphaerella convexula (S.) F. V. Rand.
{ Phyllosticta convexula Bubák.

Myriangium Duriaei Mont. & B.

{ Myriangium Curtisii B. & Mont.
{ Myriangium tuberculans L. E. Miles.

Pestalozzia uvicola Speg.
Phyllosticta Caryae Pk.

{ ?Hydnum omnivorum Shear.
{ Ozonium omnivorum Shear.
{ Phymatotrichum omnivorum (Shear) Duggar.

Poria incrassata (B. & C.) Burt.
Septobasidium pedicillatum Pat.
Septoria Caryae Ell. & Ev.
Stereum heterosporum Burt.
Strumella coryneoidea Sacc. & Wint.

Carya laciniosa (Michx. f.) Loud.

Microsphaera Alni (DC.) Wint.†

{ Dermosporium atrum S.
{ Strumella atra (S.) Sacc.

Carya microcarpa Nutt.

Ceratophorum uncinatum G. W. Clinton & Pk.
Phyllosticta caryigena Ell. & Ev.

Carya ovata (Mill.) K. Koch.

PEZIZINEAE

Peziza floccosa S.

PHACIDIINEAE

Rhytisma Juglandis S.

HYSTERIINEAE

{ Gloniopsis cookeanum (Gerard) Sacc.
{ Hysterium cookeanum Gerard.
{ Hysterographium cookeanum (Gerard) Ell.
{   & Ev.

Hysterium magnosporium Gerard.

PYRENOMYCETINEAE

{ Broomella chlorina (Cke.) Sacc.
{ Hypocrea chlorina Cke.

Cryptospora Caryae Pk.
Endothia parasitica (Murrill) P. J. & H. W.
    Anderson.
Eutypa ludibunda Sacc.

{ Diatrype collariata C. & E.
{ Eutypella collariata (C. & E.) Berl.
{ Valsa caryigena B. & C. ?

{ Eutypella constellata (B. & C.) Berl. & Vogl.
{ Eutypella monticulosa (B. & C.) Sacc., var.
{   constellata (B. & C.) Berl. & Vogl.

{ Botryodiplodia juglandicola (S.) Sacc.
{ Diplodia juglandicola (S.) Curr.

{ Eutypella juglandicola (S.) Ell. & Ev.
{ Sphaeria juglandicola S.

{ Sphaeria juglandina Curr.
{ Valsa juglandicola (S.) Cke.

{ Gnomoniella tubiformis (Tode) Sacc.
{ Sphaeria tubiformis Sacc.

Melanconis Hicoriae Atk.
Microsphaera Alni (DC.) Wint. †
Nectria pallida Ell. & Ev.

{ Nectria missouriensis Ell. & Ev.
{ Pleonectria missouriensis (Ell. & Ev.) Sacc.
{ Thyronectria missouriensis (Ell. & Ev.) Seaver.

{ Dothidea juglandicola S.
{ Phyllachora juglandicola (S.) Sacc.

Dothichiza Caryae Bonar.
Rosellinia Caryae Bonar.

{ Mycosphaerella convexula (S.) F. V. Rand.
{ Sphaerella convexula (S.) Thm.

Sphaeria pericarpii S.

{ Amphisphaeria caryophaga (S.) Cke.
{ Hypoxylon nucitena B. & C.
{ Melanomma caryophagum (S.) Fairman.
{ Melanomma? nucitena (B. & C.) Sacc.
{ Sphaeria caryophaga S.
{ Sphaeria Curtisii B.

{ Trematosphaeria nuclearia Auct. Amer.
{ Trematosphaeria caryophaga (S.) Sacc.

Triblidium minor Cke.
Xylaria Hypoxylon (L. ex Fr.) Grev.

HYMENOMYCETINEAE

Clavaria spathulata Pk.
Collybia zonata Pk.

{ Corticium cinereum P. ex Fr.
{ Corticium cinereum P. ex Fr., var. fumigatum
{   Pk.

Corticium subgiganteum B.
Daedalea ambigua B.

{ Cerrena unicolor (Bull. ex Fr.) Murrill.
{ Daedalea unicolor (Bull.) ex Fr.

Fomes applanatus (P. ex Wallr.) Gill.
Hydnum Caput-ursi Fr.
Lentinus Lecomtei Fr.
Lenzites betulina (L.) ex Fr.

{ Microstroma brachysporum (Sacc.) Vestergren.
{ Microstroma Juglandis Auct. Amer.
{ Microstroma leucosporum Auct. Amer.

Pleurotus atrocaeruleus Fr., var. griseus Pk.
Pleurotus niger (S.) Sacc. Syll.
Pluteus chrysophlebius (B. & Rav.) Sacc.
    Syll.

{ Bjerkandera adusta (Willd. ex Fr.) Karst.
{ Polyporus adustus (Willd.) ex Fr.

Polyporus hispidus (Bull.) ex Fr.
Polyporus conglobatus B.

{ Daedalea obtusa (B.) Neuman.
{ Polyporus obtusus B.?

Carya ovata (*cont.*)

Polyporus pargamenus Fr.
Polystictus pergamenus Fr.
Polyporus Caryae S.
Poria Caryae (S.) Cke.
Schizophyllum alneum (L.) ex Schrt.
Schizophyllum commune Fr.
Stereum purpureum P. †

Fungi Imperfecti

Botrytis cinerella Sacc. & Wint.
?Valsa caryigena B. & C.
Cytospora caryigena (B. & C.) Ell. & Ev.
Diplodia Caryae Cke. & Ell.
Diplodia caryigena Ell. & Ev.
Fusicladium effusum Wint.
Discosia rugulosa B. & C.
Gloeosporium Caryae (Pk.) Ell. & Dearness. Mar. 1891.
Gloeosporium Caryae Ell. & Ev. 1893.
Gnomonia Caryae Wolf.
Phyllosticta Caryae Pk. Jan. 1888.
Phyllosticta Caryae Ell. & Ev. Oct. 1888.
Phyllosticta caryigena Ell. & Ev.
Hendersonia Davisii Ell. & Ev.
Phyllohendersonia Davisii (Ell. & Ev.) Tassi.
Illosporium caesium S.
Leptothyrium dryinum Sacc.
Melanconium gracile Ell. & Ev.
Melanconium intermedium Pk.
Melanconium pallidum Pk.
Myxosporium luteum Ell. & Ev.
Pestalozzia minuta Tracy & Earle.
Phoma exocarpina Pk.
Ramularia albomaculata Pk.
Septoria Caryae Ell. & Ev.
Sphaeropsis Caryae C. & E.
Sphaeropsis pericarpii (C. & E.) Pk.
Sporoschisma mirabile B. & Br.
Trichoderma lignorum (Tode) ex Harz.

Miscellanea

Tilmadoche gyrocephala (Mont.) Rostf.

Carya sp. indet.

Myxomycetes

Arcyria denudata (L.) Sheldon.
Comatricha crypta (S.) Morg.
Fuligo ovata (Schaeff.) Macbr.
Hemitrichia serpula (Scop.) Rostf.
Hemitrichia Vesparium (Batsch) Macbr.
Lamproderma arcyrionema Rostf.
Lycogala epidendron (L.) Fr.

Pezizineae

Ciboria Juglandis (Preuss) Sacc.
Ciboria sulphurella (Ell. & Ev.) Rehm.
Dermatella caryigena Ell. & Ev.
Discina orbicularis Pk.
Helotium citrinum (Hedw.) ex Fr.

Helotium fructigenum (Bull. ex Fr.) Fckl.
Hymenoscypha fructigena (Bull. ex Fr.) Phil.
Phialea fructigena (Bull. ex Fr.) Gill.
Helotium herbarum (P.) Fr.
Hysteropatella minor (Cke.) Rehm.
Karschia elaeospora Fairman.
Patellaria atrata (Hedw.) ex Fr.
Peziza palmicola B. & C.

Phacidiineae

Lichenopsis sphaeroboloidea S.
Propolis faginea (Schrad.) ex Karst.

Hysteriineae

Glonium caryigenum Ell. & Ev.
Glonium parvulum (Gerard) Sacc.
Hysterium ellipticum Fr.
Hysterium Juglandis S.
Hysterium pulicare, var. Juglandis S.

Pyrenomycetineae

Acanthostigma pulchrisetum (Pk.) Sacc.
Sphaeria pulchriseta Pk.
Trichosphaeria pulchriseta (Pk.) Ell. & Ev.
Venturia pulchriseta (Pk.) Cke.
Acrospermum viridulum B. & C.
Amphisphaeria Langloisii Ell. & Ev.
Amphisphaeria nucidoma Fairman.
Anthostoma gastrinum (Fr.) Sacc.
Argynna polyaedron (S.) Morg.
Caryospora minor Pk.
Caryospora putaminum (S.) De Not.
Chaetomium globosum Kze. ex Fr.
Chaetomium pusillum Ell. & Ev.
Coniochaeta ligniaria (Grev.) Trav.
Creonectria ochroleuca (S.) Seaver.
Creonectria purpurea (L.) ex Seaver.
Cryptosporella anomala (Pk.) Sacc.
Daldinia concentrica (Bolt. ex Fr.) Ces. & De Not.
Hypoxylon concentricum (Bolt. ex Fr.) Grev.
Sphaeria concentrica Bolt. ex Fr.
Diaporthe apocrypta (C. & E.) Sacc.
Valsa apocrypta C. & E.
Diaporthe eusticha Ell. & Ev.
Didymella nucis-hicoriae Fairman.
Didymosphaeria nuciseda Fairman.
Didymosphaeria vagans Ell. & Ev.
Dothiorella quercina C. & E.
Eutypa Acharii Tul.
Eutypa maura (Fr.) Cke.
Eutypella deusta Ell. & Ev.
Valsa deusta Ell. & Ev.
Eutypella stellulata (Fr.) Sacc.
Valsa stellulata Fr.
Fenestella amorpha Ell. & Ev.
Gibbera moricarpa Cke.
Gibberella Saubinetii (Mont.) Sacc.
Gnomonia Caryae Wolf.

Carya sp. indet. (*cont.*)
Gnomonia clavulata Ell.
Gnomonia leptostyla (Fr.) Ces. & De Not.
Gnomonia setacea (P.) Ces. & De Not., var.
  macrospora Ell. & Ev.
Hypocrea gelatinosa (Tode) ex Fr.
Hypoxylon atropurpureum Fr.
Hypoxylon fuscopurpureum (S.) B.
Hypoxylon serpens (P.) ex Fr.
Lasiosphaeria multiseptata Earle.
Leptosphaeria cacuminispora Fairman.
Leptosphaeria exocarpogena Fairman.
Leptosphaeria lyndonvillae Fairman.
⎰Lophiosphaera hysterioides Ell. & Ev.
⎱Schizostoma hysterioides (Ell. & Ev.) Sacc.
Lophiosphaera pulveracea Sacc.
Martindalea spironema Sacc. & Ell.
Massaria (Massariella) seriata Cke.
Massariovalsa sudans (B. & C.) Sacc.
⎰Melanopsamma abscondita Ell. & Ev.
⎱Zignoella abscondita (Ell. & Ev.) Fairman.
Melanopsamma nucigena Ell. & Ev.
⎰Endophlaea leiostega (Ell.) Cke.
⎱Metasphaeria leiostega (Ell.) Sacc.
⎰Sphaeria leiostega Ell.
⎰Nectria bicolor Ell. & Ev.
⎱Nectria flavociliata Seaver.
Nectria coccinea (P.) ex Fr.
Nectria polythalama B.
Nummularia albosticta Ell. & Morg.
Nummularia repanda (Fr.) Nits.
Physalospora gossypina N. E. Stevens.
Physalospora Malorum Shear et al.
Pseudovalsa Fairmani Ell. & Ev.
Pyrenomyxa invocans Morg.
Rhynchosphaeria nucicola Fairman.
Rhynchostoma nucis Fairman.
Rosellinia Caryae L. Bonar.
Rosellinia Hystrix Ell. & Ev.
Rosellinia mutans (C. & P.) Sacc.
Rosellinia pulveracea (Ehrh. ex Fr.) Fckl.
Schizocapnodium sarcinellum Fairman.
Scoriomyces Cragini Ell. & Sacc.
⎰Sphaerella dendroides (S.) Cke.
⎱Sphaeria dendroides S.
⎰Sphaerella punctiformis (P. ex Fr.) Rabh.
⎱Sphaeria punctiformis P. ex Fr.
Sphaeria drupivora S.
Sphaerostilbe cinnabarina Tul.
Sphaerostilbe gracilipes Tul.
Sphaerulina myriadea (DC.) Sacc.
Sporormia leptosphaerioides Speg.
Teichospora nucis Ell. & Ev.
⎰Sphaeria ambleia C. & E.
⎱Thyridium ambleium (C. & E.) Sacc.
Tryblidium insculptum Cke.
⎰Valsa ambiens (P.) ex Fr.
⎱Valsa conscripta C. & E.

⎰Calospora apatela (Ell. & Holw.) Sacc. & Syd.
⎱Valsa apatela Ell. & Holw.
⎰Valsa caryigena B. & C., var. chlorodisca Ell.
⎱ & Ev.
⎱Valsa chlorodisca C. & E.
Valsa decorticans Fr.
Valsaria insitiva Ces. & De Not.
Xylaria carpophila (P.) ex Fr.
Xylaria polymorpha (P. ex Fr.) Grev.
Zignoella nucivora Fairman.

PHRAGMOBASIDIOMYCETES

⎰Auricularia Auricula-judae (L. ex Fr.) Schrt.
⎱Hirneola Auricula-judae (L. ex Fr.) B.
Exidia glandulosa (Bull.) ex Fr.
Tremella intumescens J. E. Sm. ex Fr.

THELEPHORACEAE

Aleurodiscus Oakesii (B. & C.) Cke.
⎰Artocreas Micheneri B. & C.
⎱Corticium subgiganteum B.
⎱Michenera Artocreas B. & C.
⎰Asterostroma albidocarneum (S.) Massee.
⎱Corticium albidocarneum (S.) Rav.
⎱Thelephora albidocarnea S.
Corticium auberianum Mont.
Corticium effuscatum C. & E.
⎰Corticium leveillianum B. & C.
⎱Stereum leveillianum B. & C.
Corticium lacteum Fr.
Corticium lilacinofuscum B. & C.
Corticium roseolum Massee.
Corticium roseum P. ex Fr.
Corticium Sambuci Fr.
Corticium stramineum Bres.
Corticium vellereum Ell. & Cragin.
Cyphella Ravenelii B.
Hymenochaete corrugata (Fr.) Lév.
Hymenochaete purpurea Cke. & Morg.
Hymenochaete tabacina (Sow. ex Fr.) Lév.
Peniophora flavido-alba Cke.
Peniophora medioburiensis Burt.
Septobasidium retiforme (B. & C.) Pat.
Solenia fasciculata P.
Solenia ochracea Hoffm. ex Fr.
Stereum acerinum (P.) ex Fr.
Stereum albobadium (S.) Fr.
Stereum complicatum Fr.
Stereum fasciatum S.
Stereum hirsutum (Willd.) ex Fr.
Stereum rameale S.
Stereum spadiceum Fr.
Stereum umbrinum B. & C.

HYDNACEAE

Grandinia tuberculata B. & C.
Hydnum casearium Morg.
⎰Hericium coralloides (Scop. ex Fr.) Banker.
⎱Hericium laciniatum (Leers ex P.) Banker.
⎱Hydnum coralloides Scop. ex Fr.

Carya sp. indet. (*cont.*)
Hydnum Erinaceus Bull. ex Fr.
Hydnum farinaceum P. ex Fr.
Hydnum fascicularia B. & C.
Hydnum glabrescens B. & Rav.
Hydnum membranaceum Bull.
Hydnum mucidum Gmel. ex Fr.
⎰Hydnum pulcherrimum B. & C.
⎱Steccherinum pulcherrimum (B. & C.) Banker.
Hydnum velatum B. & C.
Irpex cinnamomeus Fr.
⎰Irpex lacteus Fr.
⎱Irpex pallescens Fr.
Irpex Tulipiferae S.
Radulum molare Fr.
Radulum pallidum B. & C.

POLYPORACEAE

?Favolus alutaceus B. & Mont.
⎰Favolus alveolaris (DC.) ex Fr.
⎪Favolus canadensis Klotzsch.
⎪Favolus europaeus Fr.
⎱Hexagona alveolaris (DC. ex Fr.) Murrill.
Fomes applanatus (P. ex Wallr.) Gill.
Fomes connatus (Weinm. ex Fr.) Gill.
Fomes Everhartii (Ell. & Gall.) v. Schrenk.
⎰Fomes igniarius (L. ex Fr.) Gill.
⎱Polyporus igniarius (L.) ex Fr.
Fomes marmoratus (B. & C.) Cke.
Fomes ungulatus Sacc.
Gloeoporus conchoides Mont.
Hexagona striatula (Ell. & Ev.) Murrill.
Polyporus abortivus Pk., var. subglobosus Pk.
Polyporus cuticularis (Bull.) ex Fr.
Polyporus endocrocinus B.
Polyporus fissus B.
⎰Hapalopilus gilvus (S.) Murrill.
⎨Polyporus gilvus S.
⎱Polystictus purpureofuscus Cke.
Polyporus hemileucus B. & C.
⎰Inonotus hirsutus (Scop.) ex Murrill.
⎱Polyporus hispidus (Bull.) Fr.
⎰Hapalopilus rutilans (Fr.) Murrill.
⎨Polyporus nidulans Fr.
⎱Polyporus rutilans Fr.
Polyporus niphodes B. & Br.
⎰Polyporus pendulus (S.) Ell.
⎱Porodisculus pendulus (S.) Murrill.
Polyporus picipes Fr.
Polyporus plebeius B.
Polyporus salleanus B.?
Polyporus scutellatus S.
⎰Mucronoporus spissus (S. in Fr. El.) Ell. & Ev.
⎨Polyporus spissus S. in Fr. El.
⎱Poria spissa (S. in Fr. El.) Cke.
Polyporus spumeus (Sow.) ex Fr.
Polyporus sulphureus (Bull.) ex Fr.

Polyporus vaporarius (P.) ex Fr.
Polystictus cinnabarinus (Jacq.) ex Fr.
Polystictus Fibula Fr.
Polystictus hirsutus (Wulf) ex Fr.
Polystictus versicolor (L.) ex Fr.
⎰Polyporus alabamae (B. & Cke.) Cke.
⎱Poria alabamae B. & Cke.
Poria attenuata Pk.
Poria Cocos (S.) F. A. Wolf.
⎰Polyporus incarnatus (P.) ex Fr.
⎱Poria incarnata (P. ex Fr.) Cke.
Poria Medulla-panis (Jacq. ex Fr.) Cke.
Poria nigra (B.) Cke.
Poria sinuosa Fr.
Poria submollusca Murrill.
Trametes sepium B.

AGARICACEAE

Armillaria mellea (Vahl) ex Fr.
Collybia velutipes (Curt.) Fr.
Crepidotus fulvotomentosus Pk.
Flammula lubrica Fr.
⎰Flammula viscida Pk.
⎱Gomphidius viscidus (Pk.) Murrill.
Marasmius musicola McDougall.   1925.
Panus farinaceus (Schum.) ex Fr.
Pleurotus atrocaeruleus Fr.
Pleurotus dryinus (P.) ex Fr., var. corticatus Atk.
Pleurotus ostreatus Jacq., var. euosmus B.
Pleurotus ulmarius Fr.
Stropharia micropoda Morg.
Volvaria bombycina (Schaeff.) ex Fr.

BASIDIOMYCETES
MISCELLANEA

Crucibulum vulgare Tul.
Pilacre Petersii B. & C.

SPHAEROPSIDALES

⎰Amerosporium microsporum (C. & E.) Sacc.
⎱Excipula microspora C. & E.
Aposphaeria allantella Sacc. & Roum.
Aposphaeria nucicola Ell. & Ev.
Cylindrium gossypinum Fairman.
Dinemasporium hispidulum (Schrad. ex Fr.) Sacc.
Dinemasporium Robiniae Gerard.
Diplodina epicarya Fairman.
Discosia Artocreas (Tode) ex Fr.
Hendersonia eximia B. & C.
⎰Hendersonia navicula (B. & C.) Cke.
⎱Hendersonia nobilis B. & C.
⎰Hendersonia pustulata Ell. & Ev.
⎱Hendersonulina pustulata (Ell. & Ev.) Tassi.
Hendersonia sarmentorum Westd.
⎰Leptostroma seriale (S.) Cke.
⎱Rhytisma seriale S.

Carya sp. indet. (*cont.*)

Macrophoma fitzpatriciana Fairman.

Phoma confertum Ell. & Ev.

{ Phoma pericarpii Cke.

{ Sphaeria pericarpii S. p. p.

Phyllosticta convexula Bubák.

Phyllosticta subtilis Pk.

Pyrenochaeta nucinata Fairman.

Rhabdospora baculum Grove.

Rhabdospora baculum, var. nucimaculans Fairman.

Sphaeropsis pallidula Fairman.

Stagonospora linearis Pk

Stagonospora nuciseda Fairman.

Vermicularia Dematium (P.) ex Fr.

Vermicularia exocarpinella Fairman.

MELANCONIALES

Cylindrosporium caryigenum Ell. & Ev.

Melanconium angustum Ell. & Ev.

Melanconium magnum B.

Melanconium stenosporum Ell. & Ev.

Pestalozzia nucicola Ell. & Ev.

Pestalozzia nuciseda Fairman.

HYPHOMYCETES

Bispora monilioides Cda.

Coniosporium nucifoedum Fairman.

Dactylaria mucronulata Ell. & Langlois.

Epicoccum purpurascens Ehrenb. ex S.

Fusarium roseum Lk.

Graphium albonigrescens Lindau.

{ Graphium Curtisii Sacc.

{ Graphium leucocephalum (B. & C.) Tul.

{ Stilbum leucocephalum B. & C.

{ Graphium rigidum (P.) Sacc.

{ Stilbum rigidum P.

Haplographium chlorocephalum Fres.

Helicomyces scandens Morg.

Helicosporium cinereum Pk.

Helicosporium olivaceum Pk.

Helicotrichum obscurum (Cda.) Sacc.

Helminthosporium rhopaloides Fres.

Sarcinella heterospora Sacc.

Septocylindrium nuculinum Fairman.

Strumella corynoidea Sacc. & Wint.

Trichothecium roseum Lk.

Tubercularia Pircuniae Speg.

Tubercularia vulgaris Tode ex Fr.

Volutella caryogena Fairman.

BETULACEAE

Carpinus caroliniana Walt.

(Including "Carpinus.")

EXOASCACEAE

{ Exoascus australis Atk.

{ Taphrina australis (Atk.) Giesenhagen.

PEZIZINEAE

Actidium? diatrypoides Cke.

{ Cenangella Ravenelii (B. & C.) Sacc.

{ Tympanis Ravenelii B. & C.

Cenangium rubiginosum (Fr.) Sacc.

Dermatella scotina Morg.

{ Lachnella flammea (A. & S.) ex Fr.

{ Peziza flammea A. & S. ex Fr.

Patellaria atrata (Hedw.) ex Fr.

{ Dermatea carpinea (P.) Fr.

{ Patellaria carpinea (Fr.) B.

{ Pezicula carpinea (P.) Tul.

{ Peziza carpinea P.

Peziza nivea (Hedw.) ex Fr.

Propolis faginea (Schrad.) ex Karst.

Pseudohelotium ammoides Sacc.

PHACIDIINEAE

Stictis compressa Ell. & Ev.

PYRENOMYCETINEAE

Calosphaeria microsperma Ell. & Ev.

{ Cryptospora aurea Fckl.

{ Valsa aurea Fckl.

Daldinia vernicosa (S.) Ces. & De Not.

{ Diaporthe Carpini (P. ex Fr.) Fckl.

{ Sphaeria Betuli P. ex Fr., var. tentaculata S.

{ Sphaeria Carpini P. ex Fr.

{ Valsa Carpini (P.) ex Fr.

{ Diaporthe carpinigera (B. & C.) Sacc.

{ Diatrype carpinigera B. & C.

Diaporthe decipiens Sacc.

{ Diaporthe Ellisii (Ell. & Ev.) Rehm.

{ Valsa Ellisii Ell. & Ev.

Diaporthe sulfurea Fckl.

Diatrype haustellata Pk. 23 Rept. 63.

Diatrype platystoma Ell. & Ev.

Diatrypella verruciformis (Ehrh. ex Fr.) Nits.

{ Eutypella cerviculata (Fr.) Sacc.

{ Sphaeria cerviculata Fr.

{ Valsa cerviculata Fr.

Eutypella cerviculata (Fr.) Sacc., var. Carpini Rehm.

{ Eutypella leaiana (B.) Sacc.

{ Sphaeria leaiana B.

{ Valsa leaiana (B.) M. A. Curtis.

Fenestella canadensis Ell. & Ev.

{ Cucurbitaria callista B. & C.

{ Fracchiaea callista (B. & C.) Sacc.

{ Sphaeria callista B. & C.

{ Gnomonia fimbriata (P. ex Fr.) Awd.

{ Gnomoniella fimbriata (P. ex Fr.) Sacc.

{ Mamiania fimbriata (P. ex Fr.) Ces. & DeNot.

{ Sphaeria fimbriata P. ex Fr.

Hypoxylon commutatum Nits., var. holwayanum Sacc. & Ell.

Hypoxylon epiphaeum B. & C.

Hypoxylon fuscum (P.) ex Fr.

Hypoxylon howeanum Pk.

Carpinus caroliniana (*cont.*)

Hypoxylon luridum Nits.
Hypoxylon Morsei B. & C.
Hypoxylon subchlorinum Ell. & Calkins.
{ Laestadia carpinea (Fr.) Sacc.
{ Sphaerella carpinea (Fr.) Awd.
{ Sphaeria carpinea Fr.
{ Lasiosphaeria canescens (P. ex Fr.) Karst.
{ Lasiosphaeria strigosa (Fr.) Sacc., var. canescens Berl.
{ Sphaeria canescens P. ex Fr.
Lasiosphaeria hirsuta (Fr.) Ces. & De Not.
{ Eutypella carpinicola Ell. & Ev.
{ Massalongella carpinicola (Ell. & Ev.) Berl.
Melanconis bitorulosa (B. & Br.) Ell. & Ev.
{ Melanconiella chrysostroma (Fr.) Sacc.
{ Melanconis chrysostroma (Fr.) Tul.
{ Diatrype lateritia Ell.
{ Hypoxylon myriangioides B. & Rav.
{ Melogramma Bulliardi Tul.
{ Melogramma campylosporum Fr.
{ Melogramma lateritium (Ell.) Cke.
{ Melogramma myriangioides Cke.
{ Melogramma vagans De Not.
{ Thyridaria lateritia (Ell.) Sacc.
{ Thyridaria? myriangioides Sacc.
Melogramma patens Morg.
{ Microsphaera Alni (DC.) Wint. †
{ Microsphaera penicillata (Wallr.) Lév.
Nectria coccinea (P.) ex Fr.
Nectria ditissima Tul.
{ Creonectria ochroleuca (S.) Seaver.
{ Nectria ochroleuca (S.) M. A. Curtis.
{ Phyllactinia corylea (P.) ex Karst.
{ Phyllactinia guttata (Wallr. ex Fr.) Lév.
{ Phyllactinia suffulta (Reb.) ex Sacc.
Pleomassaria Carpini (Fckl.) Sacc.
{ Karstenula carpinicola (Ell. & Ev.) Berl.
{ Pleospora carpinicola Ell. & Ev.
{ Diatrype Titan B. & Rav.
{ Pseudovalsa Titan (B. & Rav.) Sacc.
Rosellinia pulveracea (Ehrh. ex Fr.) Fckl.
{ Sphaeria acanthostroma Mont.
{ Trichosphaeria acanthostroma (Mont.) Sacc.
{ Lasiosphaeria subcorticalis (Pk.) Cke.
{ Sphaeria subcorticalis Pk.
{ Trichosphaeria subcorticalis (Pk.) Sacc.
Valsa ambiens (P.) ex Fr.
Valsa stellulata Fr.
{ Diatrype actidia Cke.
{ Valsaria actidia (Cke.) B. & Rav. in Herb. B.
Valsaria exasperans (Gerard) Sacc.
Xylaria flabelliformis (S.) Tul.

TREMELLACEAE

Naematelia cerebriformis Ell.
Tremella carneoalba Coker.

THELEPHORACEAE

{ Aleurodiscus Oakesii (B. & C.). Cke.
{ Corticium Oakesii B. & C.
Coniophora puteana (Schum.) ex Fr.
Corticium lacteum Fr.
Corticium ochroleucum Fr.
Corticium scutellare B. & C.
{ Corticium chlorascens Auct. Amer.
{ Heterobasidium chlorascens Massee.
Peniophora albomarginata (S.) Massee.
Peniophora cinerea (P. ex Fr.) Cke.
Peniophora heterocystidia Burt.
Septobasidium Langloisii Pat.
Septobasidium pseudopedicellatum Burt.
{ Peziza anomala P. ex Fr.
{ Solenia anomala (P. ex Fr.) Fckl.
Solenia ochracea Hoffm. ex Fr.
Stereum cinerascens S.
Stereum complicatum Fr.
Stereum purpureum P. †
Stereum rameale S.
{ Stereum sericeum (S.) Morg.
{ Thelephora sericea S.
Stereum striatum Fr.
Stereum styracifluum S.
{ Stereum pruinatum Rav. Fung. Am.
{ Thelephora setiformis B. & C.

HYDNACEAE

{ Hydnum ochraceum P. ex Fr.
{ Steccherinum ochraceum (P. ex Fr.) S. F. Gray.
Irpex deformis Fr.
Irpex Tulipiferae (S.) Fr.
Phlebia radiata Fr.
{ Radulum laetum S. Am. Bor.
{ Radulum molare Fr.?
{ Thelephora hypnoides S. Syn. Car.
{ Thelephora hypnoides S. Am. Bor.
Radulum orbiculare Fr.

POLYPORACEAE

Daedalea ambigua B.
Daedalea unicolor (Bull.) ex Fr.
Fomes applanatus (P. ex Wallr.) Gill.
Fomes igniarius (L. ex Fr.) Gill.
Fomes salicinus (P. ex Fr.) Cke.
Polyporus adustus (Willd.) ex Fr.
Polyporus arcularius Fr.
Polyporus croceus (P.) ex Fr.
Polyporus cupuliformis B. & C.
Polyporus gilvus S.
Polyporus pargamenus Fr.
Polystictus hirsutus (Wulf.) ex Fr.
Polystictus sericeus Fr.
Polystictus versicolor (L.) ex Fr.
Poria attenuata (Pk.) Cke.
Poria eupora (Karst.) Cke.
Poria punctata Fr.

Carpinus caroliniana (*cont.*)
Trametes sepium B.
Trametes serpens Fr.

AGARICACEAE

Pleurotus salignus (P.) ex Fr.
Plicatura lateritia (B. & C.) Murrill.
Xerotus viticola B. & C.

SPHAEROPSIDALES

Aschersonia carpinicola Ell. & Dearness.
Discella discoidea C. & P.
Discula discoidea (C. & P.) House.
Discula peckiana Sacc.
Cytospora leucosperma (P.) ex Fr.
Phoma sordida Sacc.
Phyllosticta hesperidearum (Catt.) Penz.
Depazea carpinea (S.) Sacc.
Depazea carpinicola (Fr.) M. A. Curtis.
Sphaeria carpinicola Fr.
Septoria carpinea (S.?) J. J. Davis.
Xyloma carpineum S.
Sphaeropsis carpinea Sacc. & Briard.

MELANCONIALES

Coryneum umbonatum Nees.
Cylindrosporium Dearnessii Ell. & Ev.
Gloeosporium Carpini (Lib.) Desm.
Gloeosporium carpinicola Ell. & Dearness.
Gloeosporium Robergei Desm.
Libertella betulina Desm.
Naemaspora aurea Fr.
Melanconium triangulare Ell. & Ev.
Myxosporium Carpini Pk.
Myxosporium incarnatum Fr.?
Cheirospora botryospora Fr.
Rhabdosporium effusum Chev.
Septomyxa Carpini Pk.
Stilbospora brevis B. & Rav.
Thyrsidium hedericola (De Not.) Dur. &
   Mont., var. Carpini Sacc.
Cheirospora Micheneri B. & C.
Thyrsidium Micheneri (B. & C.) Sacc.

HYPHOMYCETES

Clasterosporium pulcherrimum Ell. & Ev.
Fusarium carpineum J. J. Davis.
Fusarium cinnabarinum (B. & C.) Sacc.
Fusisporium cinnabarinum B. & C.
Helicoma Berkeleyi M. A. Curtis.
Helicosporium Berkeleyi (M. A. Curtis) Sacc.
Helminthosporium macrocarpon Grev.
Helminthosporium Tiara B. & Rav.
Periconia parasitica Pk.
Sporocybe parasitica (Pk.) Sacc.
Septosporium velutinum C. & E.
Stemphylium magnusianum Sacc.
Streptothrix atra B. & C.
Strumella steganosporioides Ell. & Ev.

MISCELLANEA

Nothomyces nigricans Sacc.
Pilacre Petersii B. & C.

Ostrya virginica Willd.
Actidium? diatrypoides Cke.
Cenangium rubiginellum Sacc.
Cenangium rubiginosum Cke.
Hysterographium Mori (S.) Rehm.
Stictis compressa Ell. & Ev.
Taphrina virginica Seymour & Sadebeck.

PYRENOMYCETINEAE

Amphisphaeria pseudo-umbrina Sacc.
Anthostomella mammoides Ell. & Ev.
Broomella Ravenelii (B.) Sacc.
Hypocrea Ravenelii B.
Ceratostomella rostrata (Fr.) Sacc.
Sphaeria rostrata Fr.
Daldinia concentrica (Bolt. ex Fr.) Ces. & De
   Not.
Hypoxylon concentricum (Bolt. ex Fr.) Grev.
Diaporthe albocarnis Ell. & Ev.
Diaporthe claviceps Ell. & Ev.
Diaporthe Ostryae Dearness.
Chorostate ostryigena (Ell. & Dearness) Sacc.
   & Trott.
Diaporthe ostryigena Ell. & Ev.
Diatrype albopruinosa (S.) C. & E.
Diatrype americana Ell. & Ev., var. Ostryae
   Rehm.
Diatrype discostoma Cke.
Diatrype platystoma (S.) M. A. Curtis.
Hypoxylon platystomum (S.) Rav.
Sphaeria platystoma S.
Didymosphaeria vagans Ell. & Ev.
Eutypa eutypa (Ach. ex Fr.) House.
Gnomoniella fimbriata (P. ex Fr.) Sacc.
Sphaeria fimbriata P. ex Fr.
Gnomonia vulgaris Ces. & De Not.
Gnomoniella Gnomon (Tode ex Fr.) House.
Gnomoniella vulgaris (Ces. & De Not.) Sacc.
Sphaeria Gnomon Tode ex Fr.
Hypoxylon coccineum Bull. †
Hypoxylon fragiforme (P. ex Fr.) B.
Institale acariforme Fr.
?Ptychogaster albus Cda.
Hypoxylon fuscopurpureum (S.) B. & C.
Hypoxylon fuscum (P.) ex Fr.
Hypoxylon howeianum Pk.
Melanconis bitorulosa (B. & Br.) Ell. & Ev
Microsphaera Alni (DC.) Wint. †
Nectria ditissima Tul.
Otthia ostryigena Ell. & Ev.
Phyllactinia corylea (P.) ex Karst.
Phyllactinia guttata (Wallr. ex Fr.) Lév.
Phyllactinia suffulta (Reb.) ex Sacc.
Physalospora Cydoniae Arnaud.
Rosellinia aquila (Fr.) De Not.
Rosellinia ligniaria (Grev.) Nits.

Ostrya virginica (*cont.*)

Strickeria praeclara (Rehm) House.
Teichospora praeclara Rehm.
Sphaeria culcitella B. & Rav.
Trichosphaeria acanthostroma (Mont.) Sacc.
Byssosphaeria corynephora Cke.
Trichosphaeria corynephora (Cke.) Sacc.
Trichosphaeria subcalva Ell. & Ev.
Uncinula macrospora Pk.
Valsa haustellata (Fr.) M. A. Curtis.
Diatrype actidia Cke.
Valsaria actidia B. & Rav. in Herb. B.
Zignoella anceps Sacc.

UREDINALES

Melampsoridium Betulae Arth.
Melampsoridium Carpini (Fckl.) Diet.

TREMELLACEAE

Exidia glandulosa (Bull.) ex Fr.

THELEPHORACEAE

Aleurodiscus Oakesii (B. & C.) Cke.
Corticium Oakesii B. & C.
Corticium amorphum (P.) ex Fr.
Corticium comedens (Nees) ex Fr.
Corticium diminuens B. & C.
Corticium laeve Fr.
Hymenochaete arida Karst.
Hymenochaete agglutinans Ell.
Hymenochaete epichlora (B. & C.) Cke.
Hymenochaete simulans Pk., non. B. & Rav.
Hymenochaeta tabacina (Sow. ex Fr.) Lév.
Peniophora flavido-alba Cke.
Stereum candidum (S.) Fr.
Stereum rameale S.
Stereum versicolor (Sw.) ex Fr.

BASIDIOMYCETES
MISCELLANEA

Daedalea aurea Fr.
Daedalea confragosa (Bolt.) ex Fr.
Daedalea unicolor (Bull.) ex Fr.
Fomes igniarius (L. ex Fr.) Gill.
Pyropolyporus igniarius (L. ex Fr.) Murrill.
Hydnum earleanum Sumstine.
Odontia fimbriata (P.) ex Fr.
Pleurotus similis Pk.
Polyporus adustus (Willd.) ex Fr.
Polyporus obliquus (P.) ex Fr.
Polystictus versicolor (L.) ex Fr.
Poria eupora (Karst.) Cke.
Poria ferruginosa (Schrad. ex Fr.) Cke.
Poria Medulla-panis (Jacq. ex Fr.) Cke.
Poria vaporaria Fr.

FUNGI IMPERFECTI

Brachysporium obovatum (B.) Sacc.
Cylindrosporium Dearnessii Ell. & Ev.
Cytospora incarnata Fr.

Fusarium miniatum (B. & C.) Sacc.
Gloeosporium Robergei Desm.
Gloeosporium Robergei Desm., var. dendriticum Auct.
Hendersonia ostryigena Ell. & Dearness.
Hendersonulina ostryigena (Ell. & Dearness) Tassi.
Melanconium bicolor Nees ex Fr.
Melanconium zonatum Ell. & Ev.
Fusisporium udum B.
Pionnotes uda (B.) Sacc.
Haplosporella Mali (Westd.) Petrak & Syd.
Sphaeropsis Malorum Pk.
Septoria Ostryae Pk.
Stagonospora sclerotioides Ell. & Ev.

Corylus americana Walt.

EXOASCACEAE

Taphrina Coryli T. Nishida.

PEZIZINEAE

Cenangium furfuraceum (Roth ex Fr.) De Not
Dermatea furfuracea (Roth) ex Fr.
Peziza furfuracea Roth ex Fr.

PYRENOMYCETINEAE

Cryptospora anomala (Pk.) Ell. & Ev.
Cryptosporella anomala (Pk.) Sacc.
Diatrype anomala Pk.
Diaporthe decedens (Fr.) Fckl.
Diaporthe mucronata (Pk.) Sacc.
Diaporthe Tessera (Fr.) Fckl.
Sphaeria Tessera Fr.
Valsa mucronata Pk.
Valsa Tessera (Fr.) Cke.
Diaporthe tumulata (C. & E.) Sacc.
Sphaeria tumulata C. & E.
Diatrype Frostii (Pk.) Cke.
Diatrypella Frostii Pk.
Diatrypella missouriensis Ell. & Ev.
Gnomonia Coryli (Batsch ex Fr.) Awd.
Gnomoniella Coryli (Batsch ex Fr.) Sacc.
Mamiania Coryli (Batsch ex Fr.) Ces. & De Not.
Hypoxylon fuscum (P.) ex Fr.
Massaria plumigera Ell. & Ev.
Microsphaera Alni (DC.) Wint. †
Microsphaera Hedwigii Lév.
Microsphaera penicillata (Wallr.) Lév.
Erysiphe guttata Lk.
Phyllactinia corylea (P.) ex Karst.
Phyllactinia corylea (P.) ex Karst., var. angulata Salmon.
Phyllactinia guttata (Wallr. ex Fr.) Lév.
Phyllactinia suffulta (Reb.) ex Sacc.
Sclerotium Erysiphe P. †
Sphaeria Aquila Fr., var. minor C. & E.
Valsa ambiens (P.) ex Fr.

Corylus americana (*cont.*)
HYMENOMYCETINEAE
Corticium cremoricolor B. & C.
Hymenochaete cinnamomea (P.) Bres.
Peniophora cinerea (P. ex Fr.) Cke.
Stereum ochraceoflavum (S.) Rav.

FUNGI IMPERFECTI
Cylindrosporium vermiforme J. J. Davis.
Diplodia Coryli Fckl.
⎰ Gloeosporium Coryli (Desm.) Sacc.
⎱ Phyllosticta corylina Ell. & Martin.
Helicomyces olivaceus Pk.
Helminthosporium macrocarpon Grev.
Phyllosticta Coryli West.
Scolecosporium Coryli Dearness & House.
⎰ Gloeosporium profusum Ell. & Ev.
⎱ Septogloeum profusum (Ell. & Ev.) Sacc.
Septoria corylina Pk.
⎧ Catinula turgida (Fr.) Desm.
⎨ Cenangium turgidum Fr.
⎩ Sphaeronema Coryli Pk.
Sphaeropsis Coryli Ell. & Ev.
Corylus avellana L.
⎰ Cryptospora anomala (Pk.) Ell. & Ev.
⎱ Cryptosporella anomala (Pk.) Sacc.
Cytospora phlyctaenoides Ell. & Ev.
⎰ Fusarium episphaericum (C. & E.) Sacc.
⎱ Fusisporium episphaericum C. & E.
Nematospora Coryli Peglion.
Sphaeropsis Coryli Ell. & Ev.
Corylus californica (DC.) Rose.
Gloeosporium Coryli (Desm.) Sacc.
Gnomonia Coryli (Batsch ex Fr.) Awd.
Poria contigua (P. ex Fr.) Cke.
Septoria corylina Pk.
Valsa microspora Cke. & Plowr.
Corylus rostrata Ait.
Catinula turgida (Fr.) Desm.
Cylindrosporium vermiforme J. J. Davis.
Diaporthe sulfurea Fckl.
Diaporthe tessera (Fr.) Fckl.
Diatrype albopruinosa (S.) Cke.
Diatrypella minutispora Dearness.
Dothidea? corylina Cke. & Hark.
Gloeosporium Coryli (Desm.) Sacc.
Gloeosporium rostratum Ell. & Ev.
⎰ Gnomonia Coryli (Batsch ex Fr.) Awd.
⎱ Gnomoniella Coryli (Batsch ex Fr.) Sacc.
⎰ Mamiania Coryli (Batsch ex Fr.) Ces. & De Not.
⎱ Sphaeria Coryli Batsch ex Fr.
Gnomonia setacea (P.) Ces. & De Not.
⎰ Microsphaera Alni (DC.) Wint.†
⎱ Microsphaera penicillata (Wallr.) Lév.
⎰ Phyllactinia corylea (P.) ex Karst.
⎱ Phyllactinia suffulta (Reb.) ex Sacc.
Phyllosticta corylaria Sacc.
Phyllosticta Coryli Westd.
Sarcinella heterospora Sacc.

Septoria corylina Pk.
Septoria corylina Pk., var. permaculata Pk.
Troposporium album Hark.
Corylus sp. indet.
Cryptospora suffusa (Fr.) Tul., var. nuda Pk.
⎰ Cucurbitaria conglobata (Fr.) Ces. & De Not.?
⎱ Sphaeria conglobata S. Am. bor.
Diaporthe anisomera Sacc. & Scalia.
Diaporthe decedens (Fr.) Fckl.
⎰ Diatrype bullata (Hoffm.) ex Fr.
⎱ Sphaeria bullata Hoffm. ex Fr.
⎰ Diatrype tocciaeana (De Not.) Auct. Amer.
⎱ Diatrypella tocciaeana De Not.
Diatrypella verruciformis (Ehrh. ex Fr.) Nits.
Didymella corylina Ell. & Ev.
Diplodia glandicola C. & E.
Eutypella cerviculata (Fr.) Sacc.
Eutypella Coryli Ell. & Ev.
Exidia candida Lloyd.
Fomes scutellatus (S.) Cke.
Gnomoniella Gnomon (Tode ex Fr.) House.
Hydnum fragilissimum B. & C.
Hymenochaete arida Karst.
Hypoxylon perforatum (S.) Sacc.
Lophiostoma triseptatum Pk.
Massaria vomitoria B. & C.
Metasphaeria corylina Ell. & Holw.
⎰ Creonectria Coryli (Fckl.) Seaver.
⎱ Nectria Coryli Fckl.
Nectria ditissima Tul.
Nectria episphaeria (Tode) ex Fr.
Phoma corylina (Thm.) Sacc.
⎧ Botryosphaeria pustulata (Cke.) Sacc.
⎨ Physalospora pustulata (Cke.) Sacc.
⎩ Sphaeria pustulata Cke.
⎰ Inonotus radiatus (Sow. ex Fr.) Karst.
⎱ Polyporus radiatus Sow. ex Fr.
Psilosphaeria moriformis (Tode ex Fr.) Cke.
⎰ Sillia ferruginea (P. ex Fr.) Karst.
⎱ Sphaeria ferruginea P. ex Fr.
Thelephora rugosa P.
Valsa corylina Tul.
Betula alba L.
⎧ Daedalea confragosa (Bolt.) ex Fr.
⎨ Daedalea corrugata Klotzsch.
⎩ Lenzites corrugata B. & C.
Diplosporium flavidum Dearness & House
Eutypella halseyana (S.) Berl. & Vogl.
Exidia glandulosa (Bull.) ex Fr.
Flammula betulina Pk.
⎰ Fomes fomentarius (L. ex Fr.) Gill.
⎱ Polyporus fomentarius (L.) ex Fr.
Fomes igniarius (L. ex Fr.) Gill.
Fomes nigricans (Fr.) Cke.
Fomes pinicola (Sw. ex Fr.) Cke.
⎰ Melampsoridium Betulae Arth.
⎱ Melampsoridium betulinum (Tul.) Klebahn.
Melanconis decoraensis Ell.

Betula alba (*cont.*)
Melanconis stilbostoma (Fr.) Tul.
Melanconium betulinum Schm. & Kze. ex Fr.
Omphalia maura Fr.
⎰Phyllactinia corylea (P.) ex Karst.
⎱Phyllactinia guttata (Wallr. ex Fr.) Lév.
Phyllosticta betulina Auct.
Plowrightia virgultorum (Fr.) Sacc.
⎰Piptoporus suberosus (L.) ex Murrill.
⎱Polyporus betulinus (Bull.) ex Fr.
Polystictus connatus Auct. p. p.
Psathyrella betulina Pk.
Pseudovalsa lanciformis (Fr.) Ces. & De Not.
Septoria Betulae (Lib.) Westd.
Sphaeropsis alnicola Pk.
Trogia crispa (P.) ex Fr.

Betula alba L., var **papyrifera** (Marsh.) Spach.
Boletus scaber Fr., var. fuscus Pk.
Cylindrosporium Betulae J. J. Davis.
Daldinia concentrica (Bolt. ex Fr.) Ces. & De Not.
Diatrypella betulina (Pk.) Sacc.
Diplodia valsoides Pk.
Eutypella cerviculata (Fr.) Sacc.
Exoascus betulinus (Rostr.) Sadebeck.
Gloeosporium Betulae-papyriferae Dearness & Overholts.
Gloeosporium Betularum Ell. & Martin.
Gnomonia provancheriana Thm.
Hypoxylon multiforme Fr.
Hypoxylon transversum (S.) Sacc.
Melampsoridium Betulae Arth.
⎰Melanconium betulinum Schm. & Kze. ex Fr.
⎱Melanconium bicolor Nees ex Fr.
⎰Phyllactinia corylea (P.) ex Karst.
⎱Phyllactinia suffulta (Reb.) ex Sacc.
Pleurotus ostreatus (Jacq.) ex Fr.
Sacidium microspermum (Pk.) J. J. Davis.
Schizophyllum commune Fr.
Septoria Betulae (Lib.) Westd.
Septoria betulicola Pk.
Sphaeropsis Betulae Cke., var. foliicola J. J. Davis.
Stereum pulverulentum Pk.
⎰Magnusiella flava (Farl.) Sadebeck.
⎱Taphrina flava Farl.
Trogia crispa (P.) ex Fr.
Valsella polyspora Nits.

POLYPORACEAE

Daedalea unicolor (Bull.) ex Fr.
Fomes applanatus (P. ex Wallr.) Gill.
⎰Fomes Everhartii Ell. & Gall.
⎱Pyropolyporus Everhartii (Ell. & Gall.) Murrill.
⎰Elfvingia fomentaria (L. ex Fr.) Murrill.
⎱Elfvingiella fomentaria (L. ex Fr.) Murrill.
⎱Fomes fomentarius (L. ex Fr.) Gill.

⎰Fomes igniarius (L. ex Fr.) Gill.
⎪Mucronoporus igniarius (L. ex Fr.) Ell. & Ev.
⎪Polyporus igniarius (L.) ex Fr.
⎱Pyropolyporus igniarius (L. ex Fr.) Murrill.
Fomes nigricans (Fr.) Cke.
Fomes pinicola (Sw. ex Fr.) Cke.
Fomes roseus (Fr.) Cke.
Lenzites betulina (L.) ex Fr.
⎰Piptoporus suberosus (L.) ex Murrill.
⎱Polyporus betulinus (Bull.) ex Fr.
Polyporus fuscus (P. ex Fr.) Cke.
⎰Polyporus cinnabarinus (Jacq.) ex Fr.
⎱Pycnoporus cinnabarinus (Jacq. ex Fr.) Karst.
Poria prunicola (Murrill) Sacc. & Trott., var. betulicola Pk.

Betula allegheniensis Brit.
Pyropolyporus igniarius (L. ex Fr.) Murrill.

Betula carpinifolia Sieb. & Zucc.
Cenangium compressum S.
Cenangium laminare Fr.
Cenangium molliusculum S.
⎰Hypoxylon transversum (S.) Sacc.
⎱Sphaeria transversa S.

Betula fontinalis Sargent.
Euryachora betulina (Fr.) Schrt.
Fomes fomentarius (L. ex Fr.) Gill.
Fomes pinicola (Sw. ex Fr.) Cke.
Phyllactinia corylea (P.) ex Karst.
Septoria betulicola Pk.

Betula glandulosa Michx.
Antennatula arctica Rostr.
Apiospora Rosenvingei Rostr.
⎰Cenangium pulveraceum (A. & S.) ex Fr.
⎱Peziza pulveracea A. & S. ex Fr.
Coniothecium betulinum Cda.
Dasyscypha bicolor (Bull. ex Fr.) Fckl.
Didymosphaeria nana Rostr.
Dothidella betulina (Fr.) Sacc.
Gloeosporium Betularum Ell. & Martin.
Gnomonia campylostyla Awd.
Melampsoridium Betulae Arth.
Mollisia cinerea (Batsch. ex Fr.) Karst.
⎰Exoascus bacteriospermus (Johans.) Sadebeck.
⎱Taphrina bacteriosperma Johans.
Taphrina carnea Johans.

Betula intermedia Thomas.
⎰Dothidella betulina (Fr.) Sacc.
⎱Euryachora betulina (Fr.) Schrt.
Mollisia fusca (P.) Karst.

Betula keniaca W. H. Evans.
Melampsoridium Betulae Arth.

Betula lenta L.

ASCOMYCETES

Daldinia concentrica (Bolt. ex Fr.) Ces. & De Not.
Diaporthe transversalis Karst. ?
Diatrype sublinearis Rehm.

Betula lenta (*cont.*)

- Diatrype favacea Fr.
- Diatrypella favacea (Fr.) Ces. & De Not.
- Sphaeria favacea Fr.
- Eutypella angulosa (Nits.) Sacc.
- Hypoxylon coccineum Bull. †
- Hypoxylon howeanum Pk.
- Massariella scoriadea (Fr.) Cke.
- Sphaeria scoriadea Fr.
- Microsphaera Alni (DC.) Wint. †
- Microsphaera penicillata (Wallr.) Lév.
- Creonectria coccinea (P. ex Fr.) Seaver.
- Nectria coccinea (P.) ex Fr.
- Phyllactinia corylea (P.) ex Karst.
- Melanconiella acrocystis (Pk.) Berl. & Vogl.
- Melanconiella biansata (Ell. & Ev.) Berl. & Vogl.
- Melanconis acrocystis (Pk.) Ell. & Ev.
- Melanconis biansata Ell. & Ev.
- Valsa acrocystis Pk.

BASIDIOMYCETES

- Amanita muscaria (L.) ex Fr.
- Crepidotus Betulae Murrill.
- Daedalea ferruginea (Schum.) ex Fr.
- Exidia picea B. & C.
- Fomes applanatus (P. ex Wallr.) Gill.
- Fomes robustus Karst.
- Pyropolyporus Bakeri Murrill.
- Fomes igniarius (L. ex Fr.) Gill.
- Fomes pinicola (Sw. ex Fr.) Cke.
- Polyporus pinicola Sw. ex Fr.
- Hymenochaete corrugata (Fr.) Lév.
- Hymenochaete unicolor B. & C.?
- Marasmius Rotula (Scop.) ex Fr.
- Melampsoridium betulinum (Tul.) Klebahn.
- Piptoporus suberosus (L.) ex Murrill.
- Polyporus betulinus (Bull.) ex Fr.
- Coriolus nigromarginatus (S.) Murrill.
- Polystictus hirsutus (Schrad.) ex Fr.
- Poria incrassata (B. & C.) Burt.
- Poria tomentocincta B. & Rav. sec. Cke.
- Solenia ochracea Hoffm. ex Fr.
- Stereum complicatum Fr.
- Stereum sericeum (S.) Morg.
- Stereum versicolor (Sw.) ex Fr.
- Trogia crispa (P.) ex Fr.

FUNGI IMPERFECTI

- Gelatinosporium betulinum Pk.
- Sphaerographium seriatum (B. & C.) Sacc.
- Sphaeronema seriatum B. & C.
- Gloeosporium Betularum Ell. & Martin.
- Institale acariforme Fr.
- Phyllosticta Betulae Ell. & Ev.
- Septoria betulicola Pk.
- Septoria microsperma Pk.

MISCELLANEA

- Badhamia fasciculata (Jungh.) Rostf.

Betula lutea Michx. f.

ASCOMYCETES

- Ciboria firma (P.) Fckl.
- Coccomyces comitialis (Batsch ex Fr.) Dearness & House.
- Diatrype Asterostroma B. & Br. non Ell. & Ev., var. Betulae Sacc.
- Diatrype betulina Pk.
- Diatrypella betulina Pk.
- Diatrypella Frostii Pk., var. betulina (Pk.) Sacc.
- Diatrypella decorata Nits.
- Eutypa crustata (Fr.) Sacc.
- Hypoxylon multiforme Fr.
- Hypoxylon rubiginosum (P.) ex Fr.
- Hypoxylon transversum (S.) Sacc.
- Diatrype nigrospora Pk.
- Melanconiella nigrospora (Pk.) Dearness & House.
- Valsaria nigrospora (Pk.) Berl. & Vogl.
- Melanospora vervecina (Desm.) Fckl.
- Melogramma melogramma (Bull. ex Fr.) House.
- Microsphaera Alni (DC.) Wint. †
- Nectria coccinea (P.) ex Fr.
- Nectria ditissima Tul.
- Phyllactinia corylea (P.) ex Karst.
- Phyllactinia suffulta (Reb.) ex Sacc.
- Rosellinia Desmazierii (B. & Br.) Sacc.
- Sphaeria Desmazierii B. & Br.
- Diatrype ferruginea Fr.
- Sillia ferruginea (Fr.) Karst.
- Zignoella pulviscula (Curr.) Sacc.

UREDINALES

- Melampsora betulina Tul.
- Melampsoridium Betulae Arth.
- Melampsoridium betulinum (Tul.) Klebahn.

THELEPHORACEAE

- Hypochnus vagus (Fr.) Kauffman.
- Peniophora tenuissima Pk.
- Solenia anomala (P. ex Fr.) Fckl.
- Stereum Murrayi (B. & C.) Burt.
- Stereum tuberculosum Fr.

HYDNACEAE

- Hydnum Caput-ursi Fr.
- Irpex lacteus Fr.
- Irpex Tulipiferae (S.) Fr.
- Mucronella minutissima, var. conferta Pk.
- Odontia tenuis Pk.
- Phlebia radiata Fr.

POLYPORACEAE

- Daedalea confragosa (Bolt.) ex Fr.
- Daedalea unicolor (Bull.) ex Fr.
- Daedalea unicolor (Bull.) ex Fr., var. fumosa Pk.
- Favolus europaeus Fr.

Betula lutea (*cont.*)

Fomes applanatus (P. ex Wallr.) Gill.
Fomes Everhartii (Ell. & Gall.) v. Schrenk.
⎰Elfvingia fomentaria (L. ex Fr.) Murrill.
⎱Elfvingiella fomentaria (L. ex Fr.) Murrill.
⎰Fomes fomentarius (L. ex Fr.) Gill.
⎱Polyporus fomentarius (L.) ex Fr.
⎰Fomes igniarius (L. ex Fr.) Gill.
⎱Pyropolyporus igniarius (L. ex Fr.) Murrill.
⎰Fomes nigricans (Fr.) Cke.
⎰Mucronoporus nigricans (Fr.) Ell. & Ev.
⎱Polyporus nigricans Fr.
Fomes pinicola (Sw. ex Fr.) Cke.
Fomes salicinus (P. ex Fr.) Cke.
⎰Fomes applanatus (P. ex Wallr.) Gill.
⎰Ganoderma applanatum (P. ex Wallr.) Pat.
⎱Polyporus applanatus (P.) ex Wallr.
?Ganoderma Tsugae Murrill.
Gloeophyllum hirsutum (Schaef.) ex Murrill.
Gloeoporus dichrous (Fr.) Kauffman.
Lenzites betulina (L.) ex Fr.
Merulius ochraceus Lloyd.
Merulius tremulosus Schrad. ex Fr.
Polyporus arcularius Fr.
Polyporus aureonitens Pat. & Pk.
⎰Piptoporus suberosus (L.) ex Murrill.
⎱Polyporus betulinus (Bull.) ex Fr.
⎰Coriolus biformis (Klotzsch) Pat.
⎱Polyporus biformis Fr.
Polyporus Burtii Pk.
⎰Coriolus pubescens (Schum. ex Fr.) Murrill.
⎰Polyporus pubescens (Schum.) ex Fr.
⎰Polyporus pubescens (Schum.) ex Fr., var. Grayii Ell. & Ev.
⎱Polystictus pubescens (Schum. ex Fr.) Lloyd.
Polyporus rutilans (P.) ex Fr.
⎰Polystictus cinnabarinus (Jacq. ex Fr.) Cke.
⎰Pycnoporus cinnabarinus (Jacq. ex Fr.) Karst.
⎱Trametes cinnabarina (Jacq.) ex Fr.
⎰Coriolus nigromarginatus (S.) Murrill.
⎱Polystictus hirsutus (Wulf.) ex Fr.
⎰Coriolus prolificans (Fr.) Murrill.
Polyporus elongatus B.
Polyporus pargamenus Fr.
Polyporus pseudopargamenus Thm.
⎰Polystictus pargamenus Fr.
⎱Polystictus pseudopargamenus (Thm.) Sacc. Syll.
⎰Polyporus radiatus Sow. ex Fr.
⎱Polystictus radiatus (Sow. ex Fr.) Cke.
Polystictus versicolor (L.) ex Fr.
⎰Fomitiporella betulina Murrill.
⎱Poria betulina (Murrill) Sacc. & Trott.
Poria mucida P. †
Poria nigrescens Bres.
Poria subacida (Pk.) Sacc.
Trametes sepium B.

AGARICACEAE

Armillaria mellea (Vahl) ex Fr.
Lentinus strigosus (S.) Fr.
Lentinus ursinus Fr.
⎰Mycena cyaneobasis Pk.
⎱Prunulus cyaneobasis (Pk.) Murrill.
Omphalia subgrisea Pk.
Panus stipticus (Bull.) ex Fr.
Panus strigosus B. & C.
Pholiota albocrenulata Pk.
Pholiota discolor Pk.
Pholiota limonella Pk.
Pholiota luteofolia (Pk.) Sacc. Syll.
Pholiota spectabilis Fr.
Pleurotus ostreatus Fr.
⎰Crepidopus serotinus (Schrad.) ex Murrill.
⎱Pleurotus serotinus (Schrad.) ex Fr.
Trogia crispa (P.) ex Fr.

FUNGI IMPERFECTI

Asterosporium betulinum Pk.
⎰Discosia Artocreas (Tode) ex Fr.
⎱Sphaeria Artocreas Tode ex Fr.
Gelatinosporium betulinum Pk.
Gelatinosporium fulvum Pk.
Gloeosporium Betulae-luteae Sacc. & Dearness.
Libertella betulina Desm.
Melanconium bicolor Nees ex Fr.
Septoria betulicola Pk.
⎰Haplosporella lutea (Dearness & House) Petrak & Syd.
⎱Sphaeropsis Betulae Cke., var. lutea Dearness & House.

MISCELLANEA

Guepinia spathularia (S.) Fr.
Lamproderma violaceum Rostf.
Pilocratera abnormis Pk.
Saccharomyces Betulae Pk. & Pat.
Stilbum madidum Pk.
Trichothecium subgriseum Pk.

Betula nana L.

Cladosporium herbarum (P.) ex Lk.
Coniothecium betulinum Cda.
Corticium lacteum Fr.
Coryneum Kunzei Cda.
Cytospora salicella Sacc.
Cytospora Salicis (Cda.) Rabh.
Didymosphaeria nana Rostr.
Diplodia Betulae Westd.
Dothidella betulina (Fr.) Sacc.
Gnomonia campylostyla Awd.
Mollisia ramealis Karst.
Taphrina alpina Johans.
⎰Taphrina bacteriosperma Johans.
⎱Exoascus bacteriospermus (Johans.) Sadebeck.
Taphrina carnea Johans.
Venturia ditricha (Fr.) Karst.

Betula nigra L.
  Aposphaeria pezizoides Ell. & Ev.
  Armillaria mellea (Vahl) ex Fr.
  Botrytis minutula S.
  { Calosphaeria affinis Nits.
  { Eutypella? niphoclina (Cke.) Sacc.
  { Valsa niphoclina Cke.
  Cladosporium caducum J. J. Davis.
  Coryneum compactum B. & Br.
  Cytospora betulina Ehrb. ex Fr.
  { Daedalea albida S.
  { Daedalea confragosa (Bolt.) ex Fr.
  { Daedalea discolor Fr.
  { Daldinia concentrica (Bolt. ex Fr.) Ces. & De
  {   Not.
  { Hypoxylon concentricum (Bolt. ex Fr.) Grev.
  { Enchnoa lanata Fr.
  { Sphaeria lanata Fr.
  Eutypella angulosa (Nits.) Sacc.
  { Fomes applanatus (P. ex Wallr.) Gill.
  { Polyporus applanatus (P.) ex Wallr.
  { Fomes Bakeri (Murrill) Sacc. & Trott.
  { Pyropolyporus Bakeri Murrill.
  Fomes fomentarius (L. ex Fr.) Gill.
  Fomes fulvus Fr.
  Fomes igniarius (L. ex Fr.) Gill.
  { Gloeosporidium Betularum (Ell. & Martin)
  {   Petrak.
  { Gloeosporium Betularum Ell. & Martin.
  Hypoxylon fuscum (P.) ex Fr.
  Hysterium angustatum A. & S. ex Fr.
  { Hysterium flexuosum S.
  { Hysterographium flexuosum (S.) Sacc.
  Hysterium pulicare P. ex Fr.
  Lachnella fraxinicola (B. & Br.) Phil.
  Melanconium betulinum Schm. & Kze. ex Fr.
  Melanconium bicolor Nees ex Fr.
  Nectria ditissima Tul.
  { Phyllactinia corylea (P.) ex Karst.
  { Phyllactinia suffulta (Reb.) ex Sacc.
  Polyporus adustus (Willd.) ex Fr.
  Polyporus betulinus (Bull.) ex Fr.
  Polyporus gilvus S.
  { Polyporus pargamenus Fr.
  { Polystictus pergamenus Fr.
  Poria ferruginosa (Schrad. ex Fr.) Cke.
  Sclerotiopsis concava (Desm.) Shear & Dodge.
  Steganosporium muricatum Bon.
  Valsaria insitiva Ces. & De Not.
  { Melanconiella Meschuttii (Ell. & Ev.) Berl.
  {   & Vogl.
  { Melanconis Meschuttii Ell. & Ev.
  { Valsaria nigrospora (Pk.) Berl. & Vogl.
Betula occidentalis Hook.
  Auricularia mesenterica (Dicks.) P.
  Eutypella angulosa (Nits.) Sacc.
  Exoascus bacteriospermus Sadebeck.
  Exoascus nanus Johans.
  Gnomonia campylostyla Awd.

  Helotium citrinum (Hedw.) ex Fr.
  { Melampsora betulina Tul.
  { Melampsoridium Betulae Arth.
  Pezoloma griseum Clements.
  { Phyllactinia corylea (P.) ex Karst.
  { Phyllactinia suffulta (Reb.) ex Sacc.
  Septoria betulicola Pk.

POLYPORACEAE

  Daedalea unicolor (Bull.) ex Fr.
  Fomes applanatus (P. ex Wallr.) Gill.
  Fomes conchatus (P. ex Fr.) Karst.
  Fomes fomentarius (L. ex Fr.) Gill.
  Fomes igniarius (L. ex Fr.) Gill.
  Fomes leucophaeus (Mont.) Cke.
  { Fomes Pini (Brot. ex Fr.) Lloyd.
  { Trametes Pini (Brot.) ex Fr.
  Fomes pinicola (Sw. ex Fr.) Cke.
  Irpex lacteus Fr.
  Lenzites betulina (L.) ex Fr.
  Lenzites sepiaria (Wulf.) ex Fr.
  Merulius niveus Fr.
  Merulius tremellosus Schrad. ex Fr.
  { Bjerkandera adusta (Willd. ex Fr.) Karst.
  { Polyporus adustus (Willd.) ex Fr.
  Polyporus albellus Pk.
  Polyporus betulinus (Bull.) ex Fr.
  Polyporus glomeratus Pk.
  Polyporus osseus Kalchb.
  Polyporus pubescens (Schum.) ex Fr.
  Polyporus Sartwellii B.
  { Polyporus cinnabarinus (Jacq.) ex Fr.
  { Polystictus cinnabarinus (Jacq. ex Fr.) Cke.
  Polystictus hirsutus (Wulf.) ex Fr.
  Poria fulvida Ell.
  Poria punctata Fr.
  Trametes mollis (Sommf.) ex Fr.
  Trametes variiformis Pk.

Betula odorata Bechst.
  Antennatula arctica Rostr.
  Cenangella Hartzii Rostr.
  Ceratostomella cirrhosa (P.) Sacc.
  Coniosporium miserrimum Karst.
  Coniothecium betulinum Cda.
  Corticium incarnatum Fr.
  Cryptosporium Neesii Cda.
  Cucurbitaria Karstenii Sacc.
  Cyphella lateritia Rostr.
  Cytospora leucosperma (P.) Fr.
  Daedalea unicolor (Bull.) ex Fr.
  Dasyscypha bicolor (Bull. ex Fr.) Fckl.
  Dendrodochium betulinum Rostr.
  Diaporthe aristata (Fr.) Karst.
  Diatrypella favacea (Fr.) Ces. & De Not.
  Discosia Artocreas (Tode) ex Fr.
  Exidia saccharina Fr.
  Fenestella princeps Tul.
  Glonium betulinum Rostr.
  Gnomonia campylostyla Awd.

Betula odorata (*cont.*)
Grandinia granulosa (P.) ex Fr.
Helminthosporium arbusculoides Pk.
Melanconium betulinum Schm. & Kze. ex Fr.
Melanomma Pulvis-pyrius (P. ex Fr.) Fckl.
Nectria cinnabarina (Tode) ex Fr.
Polyporus contiguus (P.) ex Fr.
Polyporus elegans (Bull.) ex Fr.
Polyporus nidulans Fr.
Polyporus nigricans Fr.
Polyporus vulpinus Fr.
Propolis faginea (Schrad.) ex Karst.
Pseudovalsa lanciformis (Fr.) Ces. & De Not.
Rosellinia pulveracea (Ehrh. ex Fr.) Fckl.
Hendersonia betulina Rostr.
Stagonospora betulina (Rostr.) Sacc.
Steganosporium taphrinum Sacc.
Stereum crispum (P.) Schrt.
Taphrina betulina Rostr.
Tomentella ferruginea (P.) Streinz.
Tremella albida Huds. ex Fr.
Tympanis conspersa Fr.
Valsa betulina Nits.
Valsaria Niesslii (Wint.) Sacc.
Venturia ditricha (Fr.) Karst.
Wallrothiella minima (Fckl.) Sacc.

Betula pendula Roth.
Agyrium rufum (P.) Fr.

Betula populifolia Marsh.

EXOASCACEAE
Exoascus flavus Farl.
Magnusiella flava (Farl.) Sadebeck.
Taphrina flava Farl.

PEZIZINEAE
Bulgaria rufa S.
Cenangium seriatum Fr.

PHACIDIINEAE
Pseudophacidium Betulae Rehm.
Cenangium betulinum Pk.
Scleroderris betulina (Pk.) Sacc.

HYSTERIINEAE
Gloniopsis australis (Duby) Sacc.

SPHAERIALES
Calosphaeria ciliatula (Fr.) Karst.
Sphaeria ciliatula Fr.
Valsa ciliatula Fr.
Cryptospora Betulae Tul.
Cryptospora Betulae, var. tomentella (Pk.) Berl. & Vogl.
Valsa tomentella Pk.
Diatrype discoidea C. & P.
Diatrypella discoidea C. & P.
Diatrypella favacea (Fr.) Ces. & De Not.
Eutypella angulosa (Nits.) Sacc.
Melanconiella decoraensis (Ell.) Sacc.
Melanconis decoraensis Ell.

Melanconiella decoraensis (Ell.) Sacc., var. major (Ell. & Ev.) Sacc.
Melanconis decoraensis Ell., var. major Ell. & Ev.
Melanconiella subviridis (Pk.) Dearness & House.
Melanconis decoraensis Ell., var. subviridis Ell. & Ev.
Melanconis stilbostoma (Fr.) Tul.
Otthia ambiens Niessl.
Phyllactinia corylea (P.) ex Karst.
Diatrype elliptica Pk.
Melanconis elliptica Pk.
Melanconis lanciformis (Fr.) Tul.
Pseudovalsa lanciformis (Fr.) Ces. & De Not., var. elliptica (Pk.) Sacc.
Sphaeria flavovirens Fr.
Valsaria Niesslii (Wint.) Sacc.
Valsella adhaerens Fckl.
Valsella adhaerens Fckl., var. americana Pk.
Sphaeria ditricha Fr.
Venturia ditricha (Fr.) Karst.
Venturia maculans Pk.
Vermicularia ditricha (Fr.) S.

UREDINALES
Melampsora betulina Tul.
Melampsoridium Betulae Arth.
Melampsoridium betulinum (Tul.) Klebahn.

HYMENOMYCETINEAE
Corticium galactinum (Fr.) Burt.
Daedalea confragosa (Bolt.) ex Fr., var. rubescens (A. & S.) ex Burnham & Latham.
Fomes applanatus (P. ex Wallr.) Gill.
Fomes fomentarius (L. ex Fr.) Gill.
Fomes igniarius (L. ex Fr.) Gill.
Fomes pinicola (Sw. ex Fr.) Cke.
Lenzites Cookei B.
Peniophora cinerea (P. ex Fr.) Cke.
Peniophora heterocystidia Burt.
Polyporus betulinus (Bull.) ex Fr.
Piptoporus suberosus (L.) ex Murrill.
Polyporus salicinus (P.) ex Fr.
Polystictus aureonitens (Pat.) Sacc.
Poria omoema Cke.
Poria betulina Murrill.
Stereum ochraceoflavum S.
Trogia crispa (P.) ex Fr.

FUNGI IMPERFECTI
Botryodiplodia valsoides (Pk.) Sacc.
Diplodia valsoides Pk.
Coryneum Kunzei Cda.
Cytospora horrida Sacc.
Discosia Artocreas (Tode) ex Fr.
Dothidella betulina (Fr.) Sacc.
Gloeosporium betulicola Sacc. & Dearness.

Betula populifolia (*cont.*)
  Helminthosporium arbusculoides Pk.
  Libertella betulina Desm.
  Melanconium betulinum Schm. & Kze. ex Fr.
  Melanconium bicolor Nees ex Fr.
  Melanconium parvulum Dearness & Barthol.
  Melanconium stilbostoma Fr.
  Melanconium subviridis Dearness & House.
  Naemaspora crocea (Bon.) Sacc.
  Septoria Betulae (Lib.) Westd.
  Septoria betulicola Pk.
  Septoria betulina Sacc.
  Sphaeropsis Betulae Cke., var. lutea Dearness
    & House.

Betula pumila L.
  Cylindrosporium Betulae J. J. Davis.
  Diatrypella betulina (Pk.) Sacc.
  Dothidella betulina (Fr.) Sacc.
  {Melampsora betulina Tul.
  {Melampsoridium Betulae Arth.
  {Melampsoridium betulinum (Tul.) Klebahn.
  Melanconium betulinum Schm. & Kze. ex Fr.
  Melanconis stilbostoma (Fr.) Tul.
  Microsphaera Alni (DC.) Wint.†
  Septoria Betulae (Lib.) Westd.
Betula sp. indet.

MYXOMYCETES

  Hemitrichia vesparium (Batsch) Macbr.
  Tilmadoche compacta Wing.

PEZIZINEAE

  {Bulgaria bicolor Pk.
  {Discina orbicularis (Pk.) Sacc.
  {Peziza orbicularis Pk.
  ?Cenangium Cerasi (P.) Fr.
  {Cenangium populneum (P.) Rehm.
  {Peziza fascicularis A. & S. ex Fr.
  {Peziza populnea P.
  Cenangium seriatum Fr.
  {Peziza sarcoides Auct.
  {Bulgaria sarcoides (Jacq.) ex Fr.
  {Coryne sarcoides (Jacq. ex Fr.) Tul.
  Coryne urnalis (Nyl.) Sacc.
  Dasyscypha Agassizii (B. & C.) Sacc.
  {Dasyscypha patula (P.) Sacc.
  {Peziza patula P.
  Dermatea fusispora Ell. & Ev.
  Erinella cervina Ell. & Ev.
  Helotium aeruginosum (Oeder) ex Fr.
  Orbilia occulta Rehm.
  {Lemalis olivaceovirens S.
  {Patellaria olivaceovirens (S.) Fr.
  {Peziza olivaceovirens S.
  Tapesia secamenti Fairman.

PHACIDIINEAE

  Coccomyces dentatus (Schm. ex Fr.) Sacc.
  Phacidium coronatum Fr.

HYSTERIINEAE

  Glonium lineare (Fr.) De Not.
  {Hysterium betulignum S.
  {Hysterium pulicare P. ex Fr., var. laeve Fr.

PYRENOMYCETINEAE

  Anthostoma microsporum Karst.
  {Anthostoma tuberculosum (S.) Ell. & Ev.
  {Sphaeria tuberculosa S.
  Bombardia fasiculata Fr.
  Caryospora callicarpa (Curr.) Nits.
  {Chaetosphaeria pannicola (B. & C.) Sacc.
  {Sphaeria pannicola B. & C.
  Clypeosphaeria minor Ell. & Ev.
  Cucurbitaria conglobata (Fr.) Ces. & De Not.
  Daldinia concentrica De Not.
  {Delacourea lichenalis (Pk.) Sacc.
  {Pleospora lichenalis (Pk.) Sacc.
  {Sphaeria lichenalis Pk.
  {Delacourea monosperma (Pk.) Cke.
  {Julella monosperma (Pk.) Sacc.
  {Sphaeria monosperma Pk.
  Diaporthe oxyspora (Pk.) Sacc.
  {Diaporthe platasca (Pk.) Sacc.
  {Diatrype platasca Pk.
  Diatrype asterostoma B. & C.
  Diatrype disciformis Fr.
  {Diatrype sordida (P. ex Fr.) Cke.
  {Sphaeria sordida P. ex Fr.
  Diatrype Stigma (Hoffm.) ex Fr.
  Diatrype verrucoides Pk.
  Diatrypella ciliatula (Fr.) Farl.
  {Diatrypella melasperma (Fr.) Sacc.
  {Sphaeria melasperma Fr.
  Diatrypella verruciformis (Ehrh. ex Fr.) Nits.
  {Didymella uberiformis Cke.
  {Sphaeria uberiformis S. Am. Bor. nec Fr.
  {Eutypa spinosa (P. ex Fr.) Tul.
  {Sphaeria spinosa P. ex Fr.
  {Eutypella halseyana (S.) Cke.
  {Sphaeria halseyana S.
  {Valsa halseyana (S.) Cke.
  {Gnomonia emarginata Fckl.
  {Gnomonia mirabilis (Pk.) Cke.
  {Gnomoniella mirabilis (Pk.) Sacc.
  {Sphaeria mirabilis Pk.
  {Gnomonia setacea (P. ex Fr.) Ces. & De Not.
  {Sphaeria setacea P. ex Fr.
  Guignardia Aesculi (Pk.) V. B. Stewart.
  Homostegia coscinodisca Ell. & Ev.
  Hypoxylon argillaceum Auct. an B.
  Hypoxylon atroviride Ell. & Ev.
  Hypoxylon commutatum Nits.
  Hypoxylon granulosum Bull. ex Fr.
  Hypoxylon Morsei B. & C.
  Hypoxylon multiforme Fr., var. adultum Fr.
  Hypoxylon perforatum (S.) Fr.

Betula sp. indet. (*cont.*)
⎰Lasiosphaeria xestothele (B. & C.) Sacc.
⎱Sphaeria xestothele B. & C.
 Leptosphaeria waghorniana Rehm.
 Massaria Argus (B. & Br.) Fres.
⎰Massaria siparia (B. & Br.) Ces. & De Not.
⎱Pleomassaria siparia (B. & Br.) Sacc.
 Nemania maxima (Haller) House.
⎰Dothidea asteromorpha (S.) Fr.
⎨Phyllachora asteromorpha (S.) Sacc.
⎩Xyloma asteromorpha S.
 Physalospora betulina Ell. & Ev.
 Rosellinia aquila (Fr.) De Not.
 Schizothyrella borealis Ell. & Sacc.
⎰Quaternaria dissepta (Fr.) Tul.
⎨Sphaeria dissepta Fr.
⎩Valsa dissepta Fr.
 Sphaerella sparsa (Wallr.) Awd.
⎰Sphaeria melasperma Fr.
⎱Sphaeria? uberiformis Fr.
⎰Erostella transversa Sacc. & Fairman.
⎱Togninia transversa (Sacc. & Fairman) House.
 Uncinula macrospora Pk.
 Valsa angulosa Nits., var. elliptica Pk.
 Valsa Betulae (Tul.) Ell. & Ev.
 Valsa ceratophora Tul.
 Valsa deformis Fr.
 Valsa pulchella (P.) ex Fr.
 Valsa quaternata (P.) Fr.
 Wallrothiella parvula Ell. & Ev.
 Xylaria subterranea (S.) Sacc.
⎰Sphaeria tuberculosa S.
⎱Xylosphaeria tuberculosa (S.) Cke.

HYPOCREALES
Creonectria Coryli (Fckl.) Seaver.
Creonectria ochroleuca (S.) Seaver.
Nectria betulina Rehm.
Nectria Cucurbitula Fr.?
Nectria nipigonensis Ell. & Ev.

TREMELLINEAE
Exidia spiculata S.
Naematelia nucleata S.

DACRYOMYCETINEAE
Dacryomyces cenangioides Ell. & Ev.
Dacryomyces Ellisii Coker.
Ditiola radicata (A. & S.) ex Fr.

THELEPHORACEAE
Coniophora puteana (Schum.) Fr.
Corticium bombycinum (Sommerf.) Bres.
Corticium confluens Fr.
Corticium laetum (Karst.) Bres.
Corticum Petersii B. & C.
Corticium roseopallens Burt.
Corticium roseum P.
Corticium scutellare B. & C.
Corticium subcinereum Burt.

Corticium vagum B. & C.
Hymenochaete cinnamomea (P.) Bres.
Hymenochaete fuliginosa (P.) Bres.
Hymenochaete rubiginosa (Schrad. ex Fr.) Lév.
Hypochnus ferrugineus (P.) ex Fr.
Peniophora guttulifera (Karst.) Sacc.
⎰Corticium martianum B. & C.
⎱Peniophora martiana (B. & C.) Burt.
Peniophora Peckii Burt.
Solenia anomala (P.) Fckl.
Solenia poriiformis (P.) Fr.
Stereum hirsutum Willd. ex Fr.
Stereum purpureum P. †
⎰Stereum rugosum P. ex Fr.
⎱Thelephora rugosa P.
Stereum sulphuratum B. & Rav.
Stereum versiforme B. & C.

CLAVARIACEAE
Clavaria pyxidata P. ex Fr.
Clavaria stricta P. ex Fr.

HYDNACEAE
Grandinia mucida Fr.
Hydnum pulcherrimum B. & C.
Irpex pallescens Fr.
⎰Thelephora setigera Fr.
⎱Kneiffia setigera Fr.
Odontia lateritia B. & C.
Odontia vesiculosa Burt.
Radulum Bennettii B. & C.

POLYPORACEAE
⎰Favolus microporus (Murrill) Sacc. & D. Sacc.
⎨Hexagona micropora Murrill.
⎩Hexagona striatula (Ell. & Ev.) Murrill.
Fomes borealis Lloyd.
Fomes connatus Fr.
⎰Fomes marginatus (P. ex Fr.) Gill.
⎱Polyporus marginatus (P.) ex Fr.
Fomes pinicola (Sw. ex Fr.) Cke.
Fomes roseus (A. & S. ex Fr.) Cke.
Fomes ungulatus (Schaeff.) ex Sacc.
Fomes ungulatus (Schaeff.) ex Sacc., var. pinicola Neuman.
Gloeoporus conchoides Mont.
Merulius gyrosus Burt.
Merulius incarnatus S.
Polyporus annosus S. Am. Bor. 401.
Polyporus aurantiacus Pk.
⎰Polyporus brumalis (P.) ex Fr.
⎱Polyporus Polyporus Murrill.
⎰Polyporus chioneus Fr.
⎨Tyromyces chioneus (Fr.) Karst.
⎨Boletus alneus S. Syn. Car.
⎨Polyporus cuticularis S. Am. bor.
⎩Polyporus conchatus (P.) ex Fr.
Polyporus caesius Fr.
Polyporus dryophilus B.

Betula sp. indet. (*cont.*)
  Polyporus epileucus Fr.
  Polyporus immitis Pk.
  Polyporus pargamenus Fr.
  Polyporus spissus S.?
  Polyporus squamosus (Huds.) ex Fr.
  Polyporus sulphureus (Bull.) ex Fr.
  Polyporus ulmarius (Sow.) ex Fr.
  Polyporus Underwoodii Pk.
  ⎰Irpex spathulatus S. Am. bor.
  ⎱Polyporus vaporarius (P.) ex Fr.
  ⎱Sistotrema spathulatum S. Syn. Car.
  ⎰Polyporus biformis Fr.
  ⎰Polyporus carolinensis B. & C.
  ⎱Polystictus biformis Fr.
  Polystictus molliusculus B.
  Polystictus velutinus (P.) ex Fr., var. glabri-
    usculus Bres.
  Polystictus zonatus (Nees) ex Fr.
  Poria ferruginosa (Schrad ex Fr.) Cke.
  Poria laevigata Fr.
  Poria Medulla-panis (Jacq. ex Fr.) Cke.
  Poria nigrescens Bres.
  Poria subacida Pk.
  ⎰Polyporus subacidus Pk., var. stalactiticus Pk.
  ⎰Poria subacida (Pk.) Sacc. Syll., var. stalacti-
  ⎱ tica (Pk.) Sacc. Syll.
  ⎰Boletus vitreus S. Syn. Car.
  ⎱Polyporus vitreus S. Am. bor.
  Polyporus vulgaris Fr.
  ⎱Poria vulgaris (Fr.) Cke.
  Porothelium fimbriatum (P.) ex Fr.
  Trametes suaveolens (L.) ex Fr.

AGARICACEAE

Cantharellus candidus Pk.
Crepidotus Betulae Murrill.
Crepidotus croceitinctus Pk.
Flammula alnicola Fr.
Lentinus cochleatus Fr.
Lentinus haematopus B.
Lentinus Lecomtei Fr.
Lentinus lepideus Fr.
Marasmius caespitosus Pk.
Naucoria pruinatipes (Pk.) Sacc.
Panus angustatus B.
⎰Panus betulinus Pk.
⎱Geopetalum betulinum (Pk.) Murrill.
Panus conchatus Fr.
Panus dorsalis (Bosc) ex Fr.
Pholiota destruens (Fr.) Bres.
Pholiota squarrosoides Pk.
Geopetalum albescens Murrill.
Pleurotus albolanatus (Pk.) Kauffm.
Pleurotus atrocoeruleus Fr.
Pleurotus circinatus Fr.
Pleurotus minutus Pk.
Pleurotus sapidus Kalchbr.

⎰Geopetalum semicaptum (B. & C.) Murrill.
⎱Pleurotus semicaptus B. & C.
Pluteus cervinus (Schaeff.) ex Fr.
Stropharia depilata Fr.

SPHAEROPSIDALES

Botryodiplodia betulina Ell. & Dearness.
Cytospora betulina Ehrenb. ex Fr.
Cytospora chrysosperma (P.) ex Fr.
Cytospora melasperma Fr.
Gelatinosporium magnum Ell.
Hendersonia glabra Cke.
Prosthemium betulinum Kze. ex Fr.
Septoria betulina Pass.
⎰Sphaeria oppilata S. Am. bor.
⎱Stagonospora oppilata (Fr.) Sacc.?
Sphaeropsis conglobata Sacc.

MELANCONIALES

Coryneum disciforme Schm. & Kze., var. el-
  lipticum B. & Br.
Cryptosporium Neesii Cda., var. betulinum
  Sacc.
Cylindrosporella microsperma (Pk.) Petrak.
Cylindrosporium Betulae J. J. Davis.
Cylindrosporium vermiforme J. J. Davis.
Didymosporium acuminatum S.
Didymosporium elevatum Lk.
Gloeosporium Betularum Ell. & Martin.
⎰Melanomma Verrucaria (Fr.) Sacc.
⎱Sphaeria Verrucaria Fr.?
Melanconium sphaeroideum Lk.
Stilbospora microsperma S. Syn. Car. 510.
Myxocyclus confluens Riess.
⎰Myxosporium croceum (P. ex Fr.) Lk.
⎱Naemaspora crocea P. ex Fr.
Myxosporium subviride Ell. & Ev.
⎰Myxosporium viride (B. & C.) Sacc.
⎱Naemaspora viridis B. & C.
⎰Coryneum irregulare B. & C.
⎱Steganosporium irregulare (B. & C.) Sacc.
Steganosporium muricatum Bon.

HYPHOMYCETES

Botrytis coccotrichoidea Sacc.
Cladosporium lignicola Cda.
Clasterosporium herculeum Ell.
Exosporium caespitosum Ell. & Barthol.
Nematogonium aurantiacum Desm.
Sporotrichum cylindrosporum Lk.
Zygodesmus granulosus Pk.
Zygodesmus sublilacinus Ell. & Holw.

MISCELLANEA

Atractobolus lutescens S.
Exoascus turgidus Sadebeck.
?Taphrina aurea (P.) ex Fr.†
Xylographa parallela (Ach.) ex Fr.

Alnus acuminata H. B. K.
Fomes igniarius (L. ex Fr.) Gill.
Melampsoridium Alni (Thm.) Diet.

Alnus crispa (Ait.) Pursh.

MYXOMYCETES
Plasmodiophora Alni (Wor.) Möller.

ASCOMYCETES
Acanthostigma Alni Rostr.
Dasyscypha bicolor (Bull. ex Fr.) Fckl.
Diaporthe marginalis Pk.
Dothidella Alni Pk.
Erysiphe aggregata (Pk.) Farl.
{ Gnomonia tubiformis (Tode ex Fr.) Awd.
{ Gnomoniella tubiformis (Tode ex Fr.) Sacc.
{ Sphaeria tubiformis Tode ex Fr.
Microsphaera divaricata Lév.
Mollisia fusca (P.) Karst.
{ Mycosphaerella alnicola (Pk.) House.
{ Sphaerella alnicola Pk.
Neottiella vitellina Rostr.
Phyllactinia corylea (P.) ex Karst.
Tympanis alnea (P.) ex Fr.
Venturia ditricha (Fr.) Karst.

HYMENOMYCETINEAE
Corticium comedens (Nees) ex Fr.
Corticium laeve (P.) ex Fr.
Cyphella Capula (Holmsk.) Fr.
Polyporus contiguus (P.) ex Fr.
Polyporus radiatus (Sow. ex Fr.) Cke.
Solenia stipitata Fckl.

FUNGI IMPERFECTI
Coryneum macrosporum B. & Br. sec. Rostr.
Cylindrosporium vermiforme J. J. Davis.
Cytospora leucosperma (P.) ex Fr.
Leptothyrium alneum (Lév.) Sacc.
Melanconium dimorphum Pk.
Myxosporium bellulum (Preuss) Sacc.
Phoma phillipsiana Sacc. & Roum.
Septoria alnifolia Ell. & Ev.

Alnus glutinosa Medic.
Coniothyrium valsoideum Pk.
{ Fuckelia Morsei (B. & C.) Cke.
{ Hypoxylon Blakei B. & C.
{ Hypoxylon Morsei B. & C.
Monilia foliicola Woronichin.
Physalospora Cydoniae Arnaud.
Rosellinia aquila (Fr.) De Not.
{ Haplosporella alnicola (Pk.) Petrak & Syd.
{ Sphaeropsis alnicola Pk.
{ Haplosporella Mali (Westd.) Petrak & Syd.
{ Sphaeropsis Malorum B.
Tympanis alnea (P.) ex Fr.
Tympanis conspersa Fr.

Alnus incana Willd.

EXOASCACEAE
{ Ascomyces Tosquinetii Auct. Amer.
{ Exoascus Alni DBy., var. strobilina Thm.
{ Exoascus Alni-incanae (Kühn) W. A. Orton.
{ Exoascus alnitorquus Auct. Amer.
{ Exoascus alnitorquus, var. Alni-incanae Kühn.
{ Exoascus amentorum Sadebeck.
{ Exoascus robinsonianus (Giesenh.) Sacc. &
{   Trott.
{ Exoascus Tosquinetii Sacc.
{ Taphrina Alni-incanae (Kühn) Magn.
{ Taphrina alnitorqua Auct. Amer.
{ Taphrina amentorum (Sadebeck) Br. & Cav.
{ Taphrina robinsoniana Giesenhagen.

PEZIZINEAE
{ Cenangium furfuraceum (Roth ex Fr.) De Not.
{ Dermatea furfuracea (Roth) ex Fr.
{ Peziza furfuracea Roth ex Fr.
Tympanis alnea (P.) ex Fr.

SPHAERIALES
{ Anthostoma Ellisii Sacc.
{ Anthostoma microsporum Karst.
Anthostoma Ellisii Sacc., var. exudans Pk.
{ Cryptospora femoralis (Pk.) Sacc.
{ Valsa femoralis Pk.
Diatrypella tocciaeana De Not.
Eutypella alpina Ell. & Ev.
Eutypella cerviculata (Fr.) Sacc.
Fenestella macrospora Fckl.
Hypoxylon fuscum (P.) ex Fr.
Hypoxylon Sassafras (S.) B.
Melanconis Alni Tul.
Melanconis Thelebola (Fr.) Sacc.
{ Mycosphaerella perparva (Sacc.) House.
{ Sphaerella minutissima Pk.
Valsa ceratophora Tul.
{ Diatrype moroides C. & P.
{ Valsaria moroides (C. & P.) Sacc.

PERISPORIALES
{ Erysiphe aggregata (Pk.) Farl.
{ Erysiphella aggregata Pk.
{ Microsphaera Alni (DC.) Wint. †
{ Microsphaera penicillata (Wallr.) Lév.
{ Microsphaera penicillata (Wallr.) Lév., var.
{   Alni C. & P.
{ Phyllactinia corylea (P.) ex Karst.
{ Phyllactinia suffulta (Reb.) ex Sacc.
Scorias spongiosa (S.) Fr.

HYMENOMYCETINEAE
Cyphella fasciculata B. & C.
Cyphella fulva B. & Rav.
Exidia glandulosa (Bull.) ex Fr.
{ Flammula viscida Pk.
{ Gymnopilus viscidus (Pk.) Murrill.

Alnus incana (*cont.*)

{ Fomes scutellatus (S.) Cke.
{ Polyporus scutellatus S.
Fomes scutellatus (S.) Cke., var. noveboracensis Sacc. Syll.
Hydnum rimulosum Pk.
Hymenochaete agglutinans Ell.
Hymenochaete tabacina (Sow. ex Fr.) Lév.
Kneiffia setigera Fr.
Lenzites sepiaria (Wulf.) ex Fr.
Marasmius salignus Pk.
Odontia rimosissima Pk.
Peniophora affinis Burt.
Pistillaria alnicola Pk.
Solenia anomala (P. ex Fr.) Fckl., var. orbicularis Pk.
Thelephora rosella Pk.
{ Cantharellus crispus (P.) Fr.
{ Merulius crispus P. ex Fr.
{ Trogia crispa (P.) ex Fr.

Fungi Imperfecti

Cylindrosporium vermiforme J. J. Davis.
{ Cytospora truncata (C. & P.) Sacc.
{ Valsa truncata C. & P.
Gloeosporium cylindrospermum (Bon.) Sacc.
{ Leptothyrium alneum (Lév.) Sacc.
{ Melasmia alnea Lév.
Melanconium bicolor Nees ex Fr.
Phyllosticta maculiformis Sacc.
Pilacre orientalis B. & Br.
Scolecosporium Fagi Lib.
Septoria Alni Sacc.
Septoria alnicola Cke.
Septoria alnifolia Ell. & Ev.
Torula alnea Pk.

Miscellanea

Frankia Alni Wor.
Alnus jorullensis H. B. K.
Melampsoridium Alni (Thm.) Diet.
Alnus mollis Fern.
Septoria alnifolia Ell. & Ev.
Alnus oregana Nutt.　(A. rubra Bongard.)

Exoascaceae

{ Ascomyces Tosquinetii Auct. Amer.
{ Exoascus amentorum Sadebeck.
{ Taphrina alnitorqua Auct. Amer.
{ Taphrina Alni-incanae (Kühn) Magn.

Sphaeriaceae

Diatrype bullata (Hoffm.) Fr.
Gnomonia Alni Plowr.
Gnomoniella tubiformis (Tode ex Fr.) Sacc.
Hypospila californica Dearness & Barthol.
Hypoxylon Bartholomaei Pk.
Hypoxylon fuscum (P.) ex Fr.
Melanconis thelebola (Fr.) Sacc.
Melanomma Pulvis-pyrius (P. ex Fr.) Fckl.

Microsphaera Alni (DC.) Wint. †
{ Phyllactinia corylea (P.) ex Karst.
{ Phyllactinia suffulta (Reb.) ex Sacc.
Rosellinia pulveracea (Ehrh. ex Fr.) Fckl.
Sphaerostilbe coccophila Tul.
Valsa femoralis Pk.
Valsella furva (Karst.) Sacc.
Valsella Salicis-Alni Dearness & Barthol.

Basidiomycetes

Armillaria mellea (Vahl) ex Fr.
Cyphella fasciculata (S.) B. & C.
{ Cerrena unicolor (Bull. ex Fr.) Murrill.
{ Daedalea unicolor (Bull.) ex Fr.
Fomes igniarius (L. ex Fr.) Gill.
Fomes pinicola (Sw. ex Fr.) Cke.
{ Elfvingia megaloma (Lév.) Murrill.
{ Fomes applanatus (P. ex Wallr.) Gill.
{ Ganoderma applanatum (P. ex Wallr.) Pat.
Hydnoporia fuscescens (S.) Murrill.
Hydnum ciliolatum B. & C.
Hymenochaete tabacina (Sow. ex Fr.) Lév.
Melampsoridium Alni (Thm.) Diet.
Naematelia nucleata (S.) Fr.
{ Coriolus nigromarginatus (S.) Murrill.
{ Polystictus hirsutus (Wulf.) ex Fr.
{ Coriolus versicolor (L. ex Fr.) Quél.
{ Polystictus versicolor (L.) ex Fr.
{ Fuscoporia ferruginosa (Schrad ex Fr.) Murrill.
{ Poria ferruginosa (Schrad. ex Fr.) Cke.
Radulum orbiculare Fr.

Fungi Imperfecti

Cercosporella Alni Dearness & Barthol.
Cryptosporium Neesii Cda.
Diplodia Alni-rubrae Pk.
Gloeosporium cylindrospermum (Bon.) Sacc.
Helminthosporium macrocarpum Grev. ex Fr.
Melanconium bicolor Nees ex Fr., var. candidum Pk.
Melanconium sphaeroideum Lk. ex Fr.
Septoria Alni Sacc.
Septoria alnifolia Ell. & Ev.

Alnus rhombifolia Nutt.

Coprinus alnicola Copeland.
Fomes igniarius (L. ex Fr.) Gill.
Gnomonia Alni Plowr.
Hypospila californica Dearness & Barthol.
Hypoxylon multiforme Fr.
?Melampsora betulina Tul.
Melampsoridium Alni (Thm.) Diet.
{ Melanconium Alni (C. & E.) Ell. & Ev.
{ Sphaeropsis Alni C. & E.
Melanconium bicolor Nees ex Fr.
Poria spissa (S.) Cke.
Septoria alnicola Cke.
Septoria alnifolia Ell. & Ev.
Tubercularia confluens P. ex Fr.

Alnus rugosa (Du Roi) Spreng.
(A. serrulata Willd.)

EXOASCACEAE

Exoascus alnitorquus (Tul.) Kühn.
Exoascus amentorum Sadebeck.
Exoascus Tosquinetii Sacc.
Taphrina Alni-incanae (Kühn) Magn.
Taphrina amentorum Sadebeck.
Taphrina robinsoniana Giesenhagen.

PEZIZINEAE

Cenangium populneum (P.) Rehm.
Dermatea fascicularis (A. & S.) ex Fr.
Peziza fascicularis A. & S. ex Fr.

HYSTERIINEAE

Glonium parvulum (Gerard) Cke.
Hysterium parvulum Gerard.

PYRENOMYCETINEAE

Capnodium elongatum B. & Desm.
Ceratostoma capillare Ell.
Ceratostomella capillaris (Ell.) Sacc.
Cryptospora femoralis (Pk.) Sacc.
Valsa femoralis Pk.
Cryptospora suffusa (Fr.) Tul.
Sphaeria suffusa Fr.
Valsa suffusa Fr.
Diatrype aspera Fr.
Diatrypella aspera (Fr.) Nits.
Diatrypella discoidea C. & P., var. Alni Cke.
Diatrype verruciformis (Ehrh.) Fr.
Diatrypella verruciformis (Ehrh.) Nits.
Sphaeria verruciformis Ehrh. ex Fr.
Erysiphe aggregata (Pk.) Farl.
Erysiphella aggregata Pk.
Diatrype megastoma Ell. & Ev.
Eutypella cerviculata (Fr.) Sacc.
Sphaeria cerviculata Fr.
Valsa cerviculata Fr.
Eutypella similis (Karst.) Sacc.
Eutypella stellulata (Fr.) Sacc., var. cucurbitarioides Rehm.
Valsa stellulata Rav. Fung Am.
Gnomoniella tubiformis (Tode ex Fr.) Sacc.
Hypocrea citrina (P.) ex Fr.
Hypocrea rufa (P.) ex Fr.
Hypoxylon coccineum Bull.†
Hypoxylon fuscum (P.) ex Fr.
Hypoxylon subchlorinum Ell. & Calkins.
Hypoxylon peckianum (B. & C.) Sacc.
Hypoxylon xanthoceras B. & C.
Hypocrea viridirufa B. & Rav.
Hypoxylon viridirufum (B. & Rav.) Cke.
Microsphaera Alni (DC.) Wint.†
Mycosphaerella Hippocastani (Jaap) Klebahn.
Nectria episphaeria (Tode) ex Fr.
Nummularia clypeus (S.) Cke.

Nummularia punctulata (B. & Rav.) Sacc.
Phyllactinia corylea (P.) ex Karst.
Phyllactinia suffulta (Reb.) ex Sacc.
Scorias spongiosa (S.) Fr.
Sphaerostilbe coccophila Tul.
Sphaeria americana B. & C.
Valsa americana B. & C.
Diatrype haustellata Rav. Fung. Car.
Sphaeria haustellata Fr.
Valsa haustellata (Fr.) M. A. Curtis.
Quaternaria Persoonii Tul.
Valsa quaternata (P.) ex Fr.
Valsa tetraploa B. & C.

BASIDIOMYCETES

Corticium confluens Fr.
Corticium lactescens B.
Cyphella fulva B. & Rav.
Cyphella Ravenelii Sacc.
Cyphella subgelatinosa B. & Rav.
Hymenochaete cinnamomea (P.) Bres.
Hymenochaete corrugata (Fr.) Lév.
Merulius tremellosus Schrad. ex Fr.
Peniophora cinerea (P. ex Fr.) Cke.
Phlebia radiata Fr.
Pholiota aurivella (Batsch) ex Fr.
Plicatura Alni Pk.
Trogia Alni Pk.
Fomes obliquus (P. ex Fr.) Cke.
Mucronoporus obliquus (P. ex Fr.) Ell. & Ev.
Polyporus obliquus (P.) ex Fr.
Polyporus vaporarius (P.) ex Fr.
Tremella enata B. & C.

FUNGI IMPERFECTI

Discosia alnea (P. ex Fr.) B.
Dothidea alnea (P.) ex Fr.
Ophiodothis alneum (P. ex Fr.) Ell. & Ev.
Xyloma alneum P. ex Fr.
Gloeosporium Alni Ell. & Ev.
Gloeosporium alnicola Dearness & House.
Gloeosporium cylindrospermum (Bon.) Sacc.
Haplosporella alnicola (Pk.) Petrak & Syd.
Sphaeropsis alnicola Pk.
Helicosporium microscopicum Ell.
Leptothyrium alneum (Lév.) Sacc.
Melasmia alnea Lév.
Melanconium Alni (C. & E.) Ell. & Ev.
Sphaeropsis Alni C. & E.
Phyllosticta maculiformis Sacc.

Alnus sinuata Rydb.
Microsphaera Alni (DC.) Wint.†

Alnus sitchensis Sarg.
Cucurbitaria conglobata (Fr.) Ces.
Diaporthe marginalis Pk.
Eutypella cerviculata (Fr.) Sacc.
Helotium virgultorum (Vahl) ex Fr.
Hymenoscypha virgultorum (Vahl ex Fr.) Phil.
Hypoxylon majusculum Cke.

Alnus sitchensis (*cont.*)
  Leptothyrium alneum (Lév.) Sacc.
  Melanconium apiocarpon Lk.
  Microsphaera Alni (DC.) Wint. †
  Septoria alnifolia Ell. & Ev.
Alnus tenuifolia Nutt.

EXOASCACEAE

{ Exoascus Tosquinetii Sacc.
{ Taphrina Alni-incanae (Kühn) Magn.

PEZIZINEAE

  Dasyscypha dryina (Karst.) Sacc.
  Godronia Betheli Seaver.
  Helotium Boudieri Sacc. & Trott.
  Helotium citrinum (Hedw.) Fr.
  Helotium virgultorum (Vahl) ex Fr.
  Lachnea hirta (Fr.) Gill.
  Lachnella flammea (A. & S.) ex Fr.
  Mollisia benesuada (Tul.) Phil.
  Mollisia melaleuca (Fr.) Sacc.
  Patinella flavobrunnea Petrak.
  Tapesia evilescens Karst.
  Tympanis alnea (P.) ex Fr.

PYRENOMYCETINEAE

  Anthostoma microsporum Karst.
  Cryptosphaeria vicinula (Nyl.) Karst.
  Daldinia concentrica (Bolt. ex Fr.) Ces. & De
    Not.
  Diaporthe nivosa Ell. & Holw.
  Diatrype megastoma Ell. & Ev.
  Diatrypella discoidea C. & P., var. Alni Cke.
  Diatrypella Placenta Rehm.
  Eutypella alnifraga (Wahlenb. ex Fr.) Sacc.
  Eutypella cerviculata (Fr.) Sacc.
  Gnomoniella tubiformis (Tode ex Fr.) Sacc.
  Hypoxylon fuscum (P.) ex Fr.
  Hypoxylon Morsei B. & C.
  Hypoxylon multiforme Fr.
{ Diaporthe marginalis Pk.
{ Melanconis marginalis (Pk.) Wehmeyer.
  Nectria episphaeria (Tode) ex Fr.
{ Phyllactinia corylea (P.) ex Karst.
{ Phyllactinia suffulta (Reb.) ex Sacc.
  Trematosphaeria corticola Ell.
  Valsa truncata C. & P.
  Valsaria moroides (C. & P.) Sacc.

BASIDIOMYCETES

  Corticium apiculatum Bres.
  Corticium laetum Karst.
  Hymenochaete corrugata (Fr.) Lév.
  Hymenochaete tabacina Sow.
{ Irpex lacteus Fr.
{ Irpex Tulipiferae (S.) Fr.
  Peniophora albo-straminea Bres.
  Peniophora rhodochroa Bres.
  Phlebia cinnabarina S.
  Stereum fasciatum S.

POLYPORACEAE

  Daedalea unicolor (Bull.) ex Fr.
  Fomes igniarius (L. ex Fr.) Gill.
  Fomes pinicola (Sw. ex Fr.) Cke.
  Merulius niveus Fr.
  Polyporus arcularius (Batsch) ex Fr.
  Polyporus pubescens (Schum.) ex Fr.
{ Polyporus semisupinus B. & C.
{ Poria semisupina (B. & C.) Weir.
{ Tyromyces semipileatus (Pk.) Murrill.
{ Tyromyces semisupinus (B. & C.) Murrill.
  Polystictus biformis Klotzsch.
  Polystictus hirsutus (Wulf.) ex Fr.
{ Inonotus radiatus (Sow. ex Fr.) Karst.
{ Polyporus radiatus (Sow.) ex Fr.
{ Polystictus radiatus (Sow. ex Fr.) Cke.
{ Poria ferruginosa (Schrad. ex Fr.) Cke.
{ Fomitiporia laminata Murrill.
{ Poria laminata Murrill.
  Trametes lacerata Lloyd.

FUNGI IMPERFECTI

  Cylindrosporium Alni Dearness.
  Cytospora umbrina (Bon.) Sacc.
  Gloeosporidium alneum (Lév.) v. Höhnel.
  Gloeosporium cylindrospermum (Bon.) Sacc.
  Melanconium apiocarpon Lk.
  Septoria weiriana Sacc.
Alnus trifolia ex Weir.
  Polyporus gilvus S.
Alnus sp. indet.

HELVELLINEAE

{ Clavaria contorta S. non Fr..
{ Microglossum rufum (S.) Underw.

PEZIZINEAE

  Cenangium tuberculiforme Ell. & Ev.
  Chlorosplenium aeruginascens (Nyl.) Karst.
  Helotium fastidiosum Pk.
  Helotium foliicola Schrt.
  Helotium sublenticulare (Fl. Dan.) ex Karst.
  Orbilia vinosa (A. & S. ex Fr.) Karst.
  Patellaria rhabarbarina B.
  Phialea alniella (Nyl.) Sacc.

PHACIDIINEAE

  Phacidium alneum (Wormsk.) ex Fr.

HYPOCREALES

{ Calonectria diminuta (B.) Berl. & Vogl.
{ Dialonectria diminuta (B.) Cke.
{ Dialonectria diploa (B. & C.) Cke., var. dimi-
{   nuta (B.) Ell. & Ev.
{ Nectria diminuta (B.) Sacc.
{ Nectria diploa B. & C., var. diminuta B.
  Hypocrea contorta (S.) B. & C.
  Hypocrea gelatinosa (Tode) ex Fr.
  Hypocrea sulfurea (S.) Sacc.
  Nectria aglaeothele B. & C.

Alnus sp. indet. (*cont.*)

Nectria coccinea (P.) ex Fr.

⎰Creonectria diploa (B. & C.) Seaver.
⎱Nectria diploa B. & C.

⎰Creonectria pithoides (Ell. & Ev.) Seaver.
⎱Nectria pithoides Ell. & Ev.

<h3 style="text-align:center">PYRENOMYCETINEAE</h3>

?Anthostoma gastrinum (Fr.) Sacc.

Bertia moriformis (Tode ex Fr.) De Not.

Calosphaeria alnicola Ell. & Ev.

⎰Calospora inconspicua (C. & E.) Sacc.
⎱Cryptospora inconspicua (C. & E.) Ell. & Ev.
⎱Valsa inconspicua C. & E.

⎰Cryptospora paucispora (Pk.) Ell. & Ev.
⎱Cryptosporella paucispora (Pk.) Berl. & Vogl.
⎱Valsa paucispora Pk.

Cryptospora suffusa (Fr.) Tul.

Cryptospora suffusa (Fr.) Tul., var. nuda Pk.

Diatrype bullata Fr.

Diaporthe leiphaemia (Fr.) Sacc.

Diaporthe nivosa Ell. & Holw.

Diatrype nigro-annulata (Grev. ex Fr.) Cke.

Diatrype Stigma (Hoffm.) ex Fr.

Diatrypella rimosa Shear.

Diatrypella tocciaeana De Not., var. subeffusa Ell. & Ev.

Didymosphaeria nana Rostr.

Didymosphaeria nana Rostr., var. brachyspora Sacc.

Ditopella fusispora De Not.

Eutypella cerviculata (Fr.) Sacc., var. Carpini Rehm.

Fenestella leucostoma Ell. & Ev.

Homostegia? obscura Ell. & Ev.

Hypoxylon atropurpureum Fr.

⎰Hypoxylon coccineum Bull. †
⎱Instilale acariforme (Sow.) ex Fr.

Hypoxylon commutatum Nits.

Hypoxylon commutatum Nits., var. holwayanum Sacc. & Ell.

Hypoxylon granulosum Bull. ex Fr.

Hypoxylon multiforme Fr.

Hypoxylon rubiginosum (P.) ex Fr.

Lasiosphaeria mutabilis (P. ex Fr.) Fckl.

Lasiosphaeria strigosa (A. & S. ex Fr.) Ell. & Ev.

Limacinia? alaskensis Sacc. & Scalia.

Lophiostoma macrostomoides (De Not.) Ces. & De Not.

Massariella scoriadea (Fr.) Sacc.

Melanconis thelebola (Fr.) Sacc.

⎰Melanopsamma Papilla (S.) Sacc.
⎱Sphaeria Papilla S.

⎰Erysiphe divaricata S. Am. bor.
⎱Microsphaera divaricata Lév.

⎰Otthia alnea (Pk.) Sacc.
⎱Cucurbitaria alnea Pk.

Pseudovalsa lanciformis (Fr.) Ces. & De Not.

Physalospora Malorum Shear et al.

⎰Calospora tribulosa (B. & C.) Sacc.
⎱Pseudovalsa tubulosa (B. & C.) Sacc.
⎱Valsa tribulosa B. & C.
⎱Valsa tubulosa B. & C.

Saccardinula Alni Dearness & House.

Sphaerella conglomerata (Wallr.) Awd.

⎰Sphaeria obducens Fr.
⎱Teichospora obducens (Fr.) Fckl.

Valsa alni Pk.

⎰Sphaeria centripeta Fr.
⎱Valsa centripeta (Fr.) Pk. 26th Rept.

Valsa tenera Ell. & Ev.

Valsaria moroides (C. & P.) Sacc.

<h3 style="text-align:center">TREMELLINEAE</h3>

Tremella intumescens J. E. Sm. ex Fr

Tremella mesenterica Retz.

Tremella subanomala Coker.

⎰Tremella foliacea P.
⎱Ulocolla foliacea (P.) Brefeld?

<h3 style="text-align:center">DACRYOMYCETINEAE</h3>

⎰Dacryomyces Ellisii Coker.
⎱Dacryomyces Harperi Bres.

<h3 style="text-align:center">CLAVARIACEAE</h3>

Calocera cornea Fr.

Typhula phacorrhiza Fr.

<h3 style="text-align:center">THELEPHORACEAE</h3>

Aleurodiscus Zelleri Burt.

Corticium auberianum Mont.

Corticium bombycinum (Sommerf.) Bres.

Corticium laetum (Karst.) Bres.

Corticium Litschaueri Burt.

Corticium lividocaeruleum Karst.

Corticium pilosum Burt.

Corticium roseum P. ex Fr.

Corticium salicinum Fr.

Corticium scutellare B. & C.

Corticium stramineum Bres.

Corticium subalbum Burt.

Cyphella conglobata Burt.

Cyphella furcata B. & C.

Hymenochete spreta Pk.

Hypochnus cinerascens Karst.

Peniophora albula Atk.

Peniophora arachnoidea Burt.

Peniophora aurantiaca Bres.

Peniophora borealis (Pk.) Burt.

Peniophora candida (P. ex Fr.) Lyman.

Peniophora firma Burt.

⎰Corticium incarnatum Fr.
⎱Peniophora incarnata Fr.

Peniophora Peckii Burt.

⎰Corticium laeve Rav. Fung. Am. *720.*
⎱Peniophora Ravenelii Cke.

Peniophora Sheari Burt.

Alnus sp. indet. (*cont.*)
  { Corticium scariosum B. & C.
  { Corticium secedens Sacc.
  { Sebacina scariosa (B. & C.) Burt.
  { Septobasidium pseudopedicellatum Burt.
  { Thelephora pedicellata Auct. Amer.
Solenia anomala (P. ex Fr.) Fckl.
Solenia gracilis Copeland.
Solenia ochracea Hoffm. ex Fr.
Stereum complicatum Fr.
Stereum erumpens Burt.
Stereum fuscum (Schrad. ex Fr.) Quél.
Stereum hirsutum (Willd.) ex Fr.
Stereum purpureum P. †
Stereum rameale (S.) Reddick.
Thelephora episphaeria Fr.
Thelephora rugosa P.

HYDNACEAE
Grandinia corrugata Fr.
Grandinia granulosa (P.) ex Fr.
Hydnum farinaceum P. ex Fr.
Hydnum fusco-atrum Fr.
Hydnum ochraceum P. ex Fr.
Radulum molare Fr.
Radulum pallidum B. & C.

POLYPORACEAE
Daedalea confragosa (Bolt.) ex Fr.
Fomes conchatus (P. ex Fr.) Karst.
Irpex fuscescens S.
Irpex obliquus (Schrad.) ex Fr.
Irpex paradoxus (Schrad.) ex Fr.
Lenzites betulina (L.) ex Fr.
Lenzites abietinellus (Murrill) Sacc.
  { Cantharellus confluens S.
  { Merulius confluens S.
  { Merulius Corium Fr.
Merulius haedinus B. & C.
Merulius rimosus B.
  { Fuscoporia fulvida (Ell. & Ev.) Murrill.
  { Mucronoporus fulvidus Ell. & Ev.
Polyporus adustus (Willd.) ex Fr.
Polyporus dichrous Fr.
Polyporus elegans (Bull.) ex Fr.
Polyporus gilvus S.
Polyporus lacteus Fr.
Polyporus McMurphyi Murrill.
Polyporus picipes Fr.
Polyporus sulphureus (Bull.) ex Fr.
  { Polyporus aureonitens Pat.
  { Polystictus aureonitens (Pat.) Sacc.
Polystictus velutinus Fr.
Polystictus virgineus S.?
Polystictus zonatus Fr.
Poria ambigua Bres.
Poria attenuata (Pk.) Cke.
Poria eupora (Karst.) Cke.
Poria inermis Ell. & Ev.

Poria subincarnata (Pk.) Murrill.
Poria undata (P.) Bres.
Trametes heteromorpha (Fr.) Bres.

AGARICACEAE
Crepidotus submollis Murrill.
Flammula alnicola Fr.
Marasmius alnicola (Murrill) Sacc. & Trott.
Marasmius praeacutus Ell.
Naucoria badia Murrill.
Panus nigrifolius Pk.
Panus operculatus B. & C.
Pholiota marginata (Batsch) ex Fr.
  { Agaricus atrocaeruleus Fr.
  { Pleurotus atrocaeruleus Fr.
Pleurotus serotinus Fr.
Pluteus latifolius Murrill.
Schizophyllum commune Fr.

FUNGI IMPERFECTI
Fusarium roseum Lk.
Gloeosporium cylindrospermum (Bon.) Sacc.
Helminthosporium persistens Cke.
Institale see Hypoxylon.
  { Phoma Amenti (Cke. & Hark.) Sacc.
  { Sphaeropsis Amenti (Cke. & Hark.)
Polyactis pulvinata B. & C.
Rhinotrichum Curtisii B.
  { Rhabdospora maculans (B. & C.) Sacc.
  { Septoria maculans B. & C.
Septonema dichaenoides Pk. & Clinton.
Sphaeronema pruinosum Pk.
Sphaeropsis pennsylvanica B. & C.
Sporodesmium sicynum Thm.
  { Dactylium sublutescens Pk.
  { Trichothecium sublutescens (Pk.) Sacc.

MISCELLANEA
Caeoma aberrans Pk.
Dianema Andersoni Morg.

FAGACEAE

Fagus grandifolia Ehrh. (F. americana Sweet.)

MYXOMYCETES
Arcyria incarnata P.
Didymium melanospermum (P.) Macbr.
Hemitrichia stipitata (Massee) Macbr.
Stemonitis maxima S.
Tilmadoche viridis (Bull.) Sacc.
Trichia inconspicua Rostf.

PEZIZINEAE
Arachnopeziza Aurelia (P.) Fckl.
Coryne urnalis (Nyl.) Sacc.
  { Dasyscypha fuscescens (P.) Rehm.
  { Peziza fuscescens P.
Dichaena faginea (P.) Fr.
Durella compressa (P.) Tul.

Fagus grandifolia (*cont.*)
- Geopyxis pallidula (C. & P.) Sacc.
- Peziza pallidula C. & P.
- Helotium albopunctum Pk.
- Pezizella albopuncta (Pk.) Sacc.
- Helotium macrosporum Pk.
- Lachnea scutellata (P. ex Fr.) Gill.

PHACIDIINEAE
- Lecanidion pusillum (Pk.) Sacc.
- Patellaria pusilla Pk.

HYSTERIINEAE
Coccomyces comitialis (Batsch) Dearness & House.
- Coccomyces tumida (Fr.) De Not.
- Hysterium tumidum Fr.
- Lophodermium tumidum (Fr.) Rehm.

PYRENOMYCETINEAE
- Anthostoma atropunctatum (S.) Sacc.
- Hypoxylon atropunctatum (S.) Cke.
- Sphaeria atropunctata S.
- Anthostoma hiascens (Fr.) Nits.
- Anthostoma turgidum (P. ex Fr.) Nits.
- Bertia submoriformis (Plowr.) Sacc.
- Calosphaeria fagicola Ell. & Ev.
- Valsa fagicola Ell. & Ev.
- Ceratostomella echinella Ell. & Ev.
- Ceratostomella microspora Ell. & Ev.
- Cryptospora compta (Tul.) Ell. & Ev.
- Cryptosporella compta (Tul.) Sacc.
- Valsa compta Tul.
- Daldinia vernicosa (S.) Ces. & De Not.
- Diaporthe fagina (Curr.) Sacc.
- Diatrype albopruinosa (S.) C. & E.
- Diatrype euphorea (Fr.) Cke.
- Sphaeria euphorea Fr.
- Diatrype disciformis (Hoffm.) ex Fr.
- Sphaeria disciformis Hoffm. ex Fr.
- Diatrype Stigma (Hoffm.) ex Fr.
- Diatrype verrucoides Pk.
- Diatrype virescens (S.) Rav. Fung. Car. **4:** *48.*
- Diatrype virescens (S.) M. A. Curtis.
- Sphaeria virescens S.
- Endothia gyrosa Fr. p. p.
- Endothia radicalis Farl.
- Melogramma gyrosum Tul. min. p.
- Peziza gyrosa (S.) Spreng.
- Sphaeria gyrosa S.
- Melogramma gyrosum Tul. pl. p.
- Sphaeria radicalis S. ex Fr.
- Eutypa ludibunda Sacc.
- Eutypa spinosa (P.) Tul.
- Eutypella grandis (Nits.) Sacc.
- Sphaeria Radula P. ex Fr.
- Valsa Radula (P.) ex Fr. Cke.
- Fragosphaeria purpurea Shear.
- Gnomonia errabunda (Rob.) Awd.
- Sphaerella errabunda (Rob.) Awd.
- Sphaeria errabunda Rob.

- Hypocrea pallida Ell. & Ev.
- Hypocrea polyporoidea B. & C.
- Hypoxylon argillaceum (P.) ex Fr.
- Hypoxylon Bagnisii Sacc.
- Hypoxylon coccineum Bull. †
- Hypoxylon fragiforme (P. ex Fr.) B.
- Institale acariforme Fr.
- Isaria umbrina P.
- Sphaeria fragiformis P. ex Fr.
- Hypoxylon cohaerens (P.) ex Fr.
- Sphaeria cohaerens P. ex Fr.
- Hypoxylon commutatum Nits., var. holwayanum Sacc. & Ell.
- Hypoxylon effusum Nits.
- Hypoxylon enteromelum (S.) B.
- Hypoxylon fuscum (P.) ex Fr.
- Hypoxylon marginatum (S.) B.
- Hypoxylon rubiginosum (P.) ex Fr.
- Hypoxylon stigmateum Cke.
- Hypoxylon turbinulatum (S.) B.
- Sphaeria turbinulata S.
- Hypoxylon vernicosum (S.) M. A. Curtis.
- Sphaeria vernicosa S.
- Lasiosphaeria crinita (P. ex Fr.) Sacc.
- Sphaeria crinita P. ex Fr.
- Lasiosphaeria viridicoma (C. & P.) Sacc.
- Sphaeria viridicoma C. & P.
- Lophiostoma pulveraceum Sacc.
- Melanomma inspissum (S.) Cke.
- Melogramma horridum Ell. & Ev.
- Microsphaera Alni (DC.) Wint. †
- Microsphaera erineophila Pk.
- Microsphaera penicillata Lév.
- Mycosphaerella punctiformis (P. ex Fr.) Schrt.
- Creonectria coccinea (P. ex Fr.) Seaver.
- Nectria coccinea (P.) ex Fr.
- Sphaeria coccinea P. ex Fr.
- Nectria Peziza (Tode) ex Fr.
- Sphaeria Peziza Tode ex Fr.
- Nummularia Bulliardi Tul.
- Nummularia nummularia (Bull. ex Fr.) Schrt. 1897.
- Nummularia nummularia (Bull. ex Fr.) House. 1921.
- Numulariola nummularia (Bull. ex Fr.) House.
- Phyllactinia corylea (P.) ex Karst.
- Phyllactinia guttata (Wallr. ex Fr.) Lév.
- Phyllactinia suffulta (Reb.) ex Sacc.
- Phyllactinia corylea (P.) ex Karst., var. angulata Salmon.
- Quaternaria Persoonii Tul.
- Quaternaria quaternata (P. ex Fr.) Schrt.
- Sphaeria quaternata P. ex Fr.
- Valsa quaternata (P.) ex Fr.
- Rosellinia aquila (Fr.) De Not.
- Bombardia fasciculata Fr.
- Rosellinia fasciculata (Fr.) Cke.
- Sphaeria Bombarda Batsch ex Fr.

Fagus grandifolia (*cont.*)
Rosellinia ligniaria (Grev.) Fckl.
Rosellinia mammiformis (P. ex Fr.) Ces. &
 De Not.
Sphaeria mammiformis P. ex Fr.
Botrytis spongiosa S.
Dacryomyces giganteus Spreng.
Scorias spongiosa (S.) Fr.
Sphaerella macularis Awd.
Sphaerella maculiformis (P. ex Fr.) Awd.
Sphaeria maculiformis P. ex Fr.
Sphaerella sparsa (Wallr.) Awd.
Sphaeria melogramma S. Am. bor.
Sphaeria radicum S.
Valsa ambiens (P.) ex Fr.
Valsa Auerswaldii Nits.
Valsa decorticans Fr.
Valsa microspora Cke. & Plowr.
Valsa minutella Pk.
Diatrype exasperans Gerard.
Diatrype obesa B. & C.
Diatrype quadrata (S.) B.
Melogramma obesum (S.) Rav. Fung. Am.
Myrmaecium obesum (S.) Rehm.
Myrmaecium quadratum (S.) Rehm.
Sphaeria quadrata S.
Valsaria exasperans (Gerard) B.
Valsaria quadrata (S.) Sacc.
Sphaeria carpophila P. ex Fr.
Xylaria carpophila (P.) ex Fr.
Xylaria castorea B.
Xylaria corniformis Fr.
Xylaria digitata (L. ex Fr.) Grev.

AURICULARIINEAE

Exidia Auricula-judae (L.) ex Fr.
Exidia glandulosa (Bull.) ex Fr.
Onygena decorticata S. Syn. Car. 429.
Onygena faginea Fr.
Pilacre faginea (Fr.) B. & Br.

DACRYOMYCETACEAE

Guepinia Spathularia (S.) Fr.
Hormomyces fragiformis Cke.

THELEPHORACEAE

Corticium cinereum P. ex Fr.
Corticium subgiganteum B.
Corticium corrugatum Fr.
Hymenochaete corrugata (Fr.) Lév.
Thelephora corrugata Fr.
Hymenochaete rubiginosa (Schrad. ex Fr.)
 Lév.
Peniophora unicolor Pk.
Peniophora viticola (S.) v. Höhnel & Litsch-
 auer.
Solenia fasciculata P.
Stereum complicatum Fr.
Stereum fasciatum S.

Stereum lobatum (Kze.) ex Fr.
Thelephora lobata Kze. ex Fr.
Stereum rameale (S.) Reddick.
Stereum sericeum S.
Stereum spadiceum (S.) Fr.
Stereum versicolor (Sw.) ex Fr.

HYDNACEAE

Grandinia Burtii Pk.
Hydnum alutaceum Fr.
Hericium Caput-ursi (Fr.) Banker.
Hydnum Caput-ursi Fr.
Hericium coralloides (Scop. ex Fr.) P.
Hericium laciniatum (Leers ex Fr.) Banker.
Hydnum coralloides Scop. ex Fr.
Hydnum laciniatum Leers ex Fr.
Hericium Erinaceus (Bull. ex Fr.) P.
Hydnum Erinaceus Bull. ex Fr.
Hydnum farinaceum P. ex Fr.
Hydnum fuscoatrum Fr.
Hydnum septentrionale Fr.
Irpex ambiguus Pk.
Irpex cinnamomeus S.
Hydnochaete olivaceum (S.) Banker.
Irpex mollis B. & C.
Irpex Tulipiferae (S.) Fr.
Polyporus tulipiferus (S.) Overholts.
Phlebia pileata Pk.
Phlebia radiata Fr.
Phlebia strigoso-zonata (S.) Lloyd.
Sistotrema globularis Raf.

POLYPORACEAE

Daedalea confragosa (Bolt.) ex Fr.
Daedalea unicolor (Bull.) ex Fr.
Favolus Boucheanus Klotzsch.
Favolus canadensis Klotzsch.
Favolus europaeus Fr.
Fomes applanatus (P. ex Wallr.) Gill.
Ganoderma applanatum (P. ex Wallr.) Pat.
Fomes Everhartii (Ell. & Gall.) v. Schrenk.
Fulvifomes Everhartii (Ell. & Gall.) Murrill.
Pyropolyporus Everhartii (Ell. & Gall.) Mur-
 rill.
Xanthochrous Everhartii (Ell. & Gall.) Pat.
Elfvingia fomentaria (L. ex Fr.) Murrill.
Elfvingiella fomentaria (L. ex Fr.) Murrill.
Fomes fomentarius (L. ex Fr.) Gill.
Polyporus fomentarius (L.) ex Fr.
Boletus graveolens S.
Fomes conglobatus (B.) Cke.
Fomes graveolens (S.) Cke.
Globifomes graveolens (S.) Murrill.
Polyporus conglobatus B.
Polyporus graveolens (S.) Fr.
Trametes graveolens (S.) Ell.
Fomes igniarius (L. ex Fr.) Gill.
Polyporus igniarius (L.) ex Fr.
Pyropolyporus igniarius (L. ex Fr.) Murrill.

Fagus grandifolia (*cont.*)
> Fomes nigricans (Fr.) Cke.
> Polyporus nigricans Fr.

> Fomes pinicola (Sw. ex Fr.) Cke.
> Polyporus pinicola (Sw.) ex Fr.

Gloeoporus dichrous (Fr.) Kauffman.
Lenzites betulina (Bull.) ex Fr.
Lenzites betulina (Bull.) ex Fr., var. radiata Pk.
Merulius himantioides Fr.
Merulius rubellus Pk.
Merulius tremulosus Schrad. ex Fr.

> Mucronoporus isidioides (B.) Ell. & Ev.
> Polyporus isidioides B.

Polyporus arcularius (Batsch) ex Fr.
Polyporus benzoinus Fr.
Polyporus borealis Fr.
Polyporus cupuliformis B. & C.
Polyporus cuticularis (Bull.) ex Fr.
Polyporus sulphureus (Bull.) ex Fr.
Polyporus Underwoodii Murrill.

> Polyporus biformis Fr.
> Polystictus biformis Fr.

> Coriolus nigromarginatus (S.) Murrill.
> Polyporus hirsutus (Schrad.) ex Fr.
> Polystictus hirsutus (Schrad.) ex Fr.

> Coriolus prolificans (Fr.) Murrill.
> Polyporus pergamenus Fr.
> Polystictus pergamenus Fr.

> Coriolus pubescens (Schum. ex Fr.) Murrill.
> Polyporus pubescens (Schum.) ex Fr.
> Polystictus pubescens (Schum. ex Fr.) Lloyd.

Polyporus elegans (Bull.) ex Fr.

> Hapalopilus gilvus (S.) Murrill.
> Polyporus gilvus S.

Polyporus lacteus Fr.
Polyporus nodulosus Fr.
Polyporus obtusus B.
Polyporus resinosus (Schrad.) ex Fr.

> Hapalopilus rutilans (P. ex Fr.) Murrill.
> Polyporus rutilans (P.) ex Fr.

Polyporus semipileatus Pk.

> Coriolus subluteus (Ell. & Ev.) Murrill.
> Polyporus subluteus Ell. & Ev.

> Polyporus radiatus (Sow.) ex Fr.
> Polystictus radiatus (Sow. ex Fr.) Cke.

Polystictus versicolor (L.) ex Fr.
Poria ambigua Bres.
Poria fagicola Bres.

> Polyporus pulchellus S.
> Polyporus vitreus S. Am. Bor. 446.
> Poria vitrea Auct. Amer.

Trametes cinnabarina (Jacq.) ex Fr.
Trametes merisma Pk.
Trametes sepium Fr.

AGARICACEAE
Armillaria mucida (Schrad.) ex Fr.
Claudopus nidulans (Fr.) Pk.
Crepidotus croceitinctus Pk.

Hypholoma appendiculatum (Bull.) ex Fr.
Lentinus ursinus Fr.
Mycena leaiana (B.) Sacc.

> Mycena subcoerulea Pk.
> Prunulus cyaneobasis (Pk.) Murrill.

Mycena Tintinnabulum Fr.
Panus conchatus (Bull.) ex Fr.
Panus dorsalis (Bosc) ex Fr.
Pholiota adiposa Fr.
Pholiota heteroclita Fr.
Pholiota limonella Pk.
Pholiota squarrosoides Pk., var. faginea Pk.
Pleurotus atrocoeruleus Fr.
Pleurotus lignatilis Fr.
Pleurotus niger (S.) Sacc. Syll.
Pleurotus sapidus Kalchb.
Schizophyllum commune Fr.

> Cantharellus crispus (P.) ex Fr.
> Trogia crispa (P.) ex Fr.

FUNGI IMPERFECTI
Bispora monilioides Cda.
Cilicipodium Magnusii Oud.
?Clasterosporium herculeum Ell.
Dendrodochium compressum Ell. & Ev.

> Discosia faginea Lib.
> Discosia Artocreas (Tode) ex Fr.

Endobotrya elegans B. & C.
Fairmania singularis Sacc.
Fusarium lateritium Nees ex Fr.
Gloeosporium Fagi (Rob.) Westd.
Gloeosporium Fagi (Rob.) Westd., var. americanum Ell. & Ev.
Graphium album (Cda.) Sacc.
Libertella faginea Desm.
Melanconium? grandis C. & E.

> Myxosporium croceum (P. ex Fr.) Lk.
> Naemaspora crocea P. ex Fr.

> Phyllosticta fagicola Ell. & Morg.
> Phyllosticta faginea Pk.

Schizothyrella borealis Ell. & Sacc.
Septonema radians B. & Rav.
Sporotrichum sulfureum Grev.
Stilbum glomerulisporum Ell. & Ev.
Stilbum rubicundum Tode ex Fr.
Thyrsidium botryospermum Mont.
Zygodesmus violaceofuscus Sacc.

Fagus sylvatica L.
Diaporthe galericulata (Tul.) Sacc.
Diatrype virescens (S.) M. A. Curtis.
Endothia gyrosa Auct.

> Patellaria rhabarbarina B.
> Peziculata rhabarbarina (B.) Tul.

Polyporus squamosus Huds. ex Fr.
Septonema radicans B. & Rav.

Fagus sp. indet.

PEZIZINEAE
Helotium fagineum (P.) Fr.
Mollisia pseudohelotium Rehm.

Fagus sp. indet. (*cont.*)
Pezizella hyalinosulphurea Rehm.
Phialea fructigena (Bull. ex Fr.) Gill.
Sarcosoma rufum (S.) Rehm.

PHACIDIINEAE
Coccomyces coronatus (Schum. ex Fr.) De Not.

PYRENOMYCETINEAE
Caryospora cariosa Fairman.
Ceratostoma avocetta (C. & E.) Sacc.
Diaporthe syngenesia (Fr.) Fckl.
Diatrype asterostroma B. & C.
Hypoxylon atropurpureum Fr.
Hypoxylon howeanum Pk.
Hypoxylon multiforme Fr.
{ Herpotrichia Pezizula B. & C.
{ Lasiosphaeria Pezizula (B. & C.) Sacc.
Melanomma asterostomum Ell. & Ev.
Melanopsamma subrhombispora Fairman.
Melogramma spiniferum (Wallr.) De Not.
Nummularia tinctor (B.) Ell. & Ev.
Numulariola atropunctata (S.) House.
Ohleria modesta Fckl.
Rhynchosphaeria nucicola Fairman.
Sphaerella punctiformis (P. ex Fr.) Rabh.
Trematosphaeria faginea Morg.

HYPOCREALES
Nectria ditissima Tul.
Nectria episphaeria (Tode) ex Fr.
Nectria episphaeria (Tode) ex Fr., var. minor
  Dearness & House.
Nectria microspora C. & E.

TREMELLACEAE
Sebacina podlachia Bres.
Tremella intumescens J. E. Sm. ex Fr.
Tremella lutescens (P.) ex Fr.

THELEPHORACEAE
Corticium lilacinofuscum B. & C.
Corticium roseopallens Burt.
Corticium sulphureum Fr.
Peniophora cinerea (P. ex Fr.) Cke., var.
  fumigata (Thm.) Sacc. Syll.
Peniophora heterocystidia Burt.
Peniophora incarnata (Fr.) Massee.
Peniophora Kauffmanii Burt.
Peniophora mutata (Pk.) Bres.
Peniophora velutina (DC. ex Fr.) Cke.
Stereum rugosum P. ex Fr.
Stereum spumeum Burt.

CLAVARIACEAE
Clavaria stricta Fr.

HYDNACEAE
{ Hydnum ochraceum P. ex Fr.
{ Steccherinum ochraceum (P. ex Fr.) S. F. Gray.

{ Creolophus septentrionalis (Fr.) Banker.
{ Hydnum septentrionale Fr.
{ Steccherinum septentrionale (Fr.) Banker.
Irpex lacteus Fr.

POLYPORACEAE
Fomes badius (B.) Cke.
{ Fomes connatus (Weinm. ex Fr.) Gill.
{ Fomes populinus Auct. Amer.
Fomes fuliginosus (Scop. ex Fr.) Cke.
{ Ischnoderma fuliginosum (Scop. ex Fr.) Mur-
    rill.
Fomes ungulatus (Schaeff.) ex Sacc.
Gloeoporus conchoides Mont.
Hexagona striatula (Ell. & Ev.) Murrill.
Merulius dubius Burt.
Merulius incarnatus S.
{ Bjerkandera adusta (Willd. ex Fr.) Karst.
{ Polyporus adustus (Willd.) ex Fr.
{ Polyporus albellus Pk.
{ Tyromyces lacteus (Fr.) Murrill.
Polyporus brumalis (P.) ex Fr.
Polyporus fagicola Murrill.
Polyporus fuscus P. ex Fr.
Polyporus glomeratus Pk.
{ Polyporus occidentalis (Murrill) Kauffman.
    1911.
{ Polyporus occidentalis (Murrill) Sacc. &
    Trott. 1912.
{ Spongipellis occidentalis Murrill.
Polyporus pennsylvanicus Sumstine.
{ Inonotus perplexus (Pk.) Murrill.
{ Polyporus perplexus Pk.
Polyporus picipes Fr.
{ Polyporus Spraguei B. & C.
{ Tyromyces Spraguei (B. & C.) Murrill.
{ Fomitella supina (Sw. ex Fr.) Murrill.
{ Polyporus supinus (Sw.) ex Fr.
Polyporus umbellatus (P.) ex Fr.
Polystictus molliusculus B.
Polystictus velutinus (P. ex Fr.) Cke.
Poria Caryae (S.) Cke.
Poria corticola (Fr.) Cke.
Poria ferruginosa (Schrad. ex Fr.) Cke.
Poria incerta (P.) Murrill.
Poria Medulla-panis (P. ex Fr.) Cke.
Poria nigrescens Bres.
Poria omoema B. sec. Cke.
{ Fomitiporia pereffusa Murrill.
{ Poria pereffusa (Murrill) Sacc. & Trott.
Poria subrufa Ell. & Dearness.
Poria undata (P.) Bres.
{ Antrodia mollis (Sommf. ex Fr.) Karst.
{ Trametes mollis (Sommf.) ex Fr.

AGARICACEAE
Collybia radicata (Relh.) ex Fr.
Collybia zonata Pk.
Crepidotus crocophyllus B.

Fagus sp. indet. (*cont.*)
Crepidotus hygrophanus Murrill.
Flammula fagicola Murrill.
Lenzites betulina Fr.
Marasmius capillaris Morg.
Marasmius fagineus Morg.
Marasmius ramealis Fr.
Marasmius Rotula (Scop.) ex Fr.
Panus rudis Fr.
Panus stipticus (Bull.) ex Fr.
Panus strigosus B. & C.
Panus torulosus (P.) ex Fr., var. conchatus Fr.
Pholiota acericola Pk.
Pholiota lutea Pk.
Pholiota muricata Fr.
Pleurotus albolanatus Pk.
Pleurotus ostreatus (Jacq.) ex Fr.
{ Crepidopus serotinus (Schrad. ex Fr.) Murrill.
Pleurotus serotinus (Schrad.) ex Fr.
Pleurotus sulphureoides Pk.
Pleurotus ulmarius Fr.
Russula atropurpurea Maire ex Krombh. non Pk.
Stropharia depilata Fr.
Volvaria bombycina Fr.

FUNGI IMPERFECTI
Fusarium acuminatum Ell. & Ev. em. Wr.
Fusarium cavispermum Cda.
Fusella olivacea (Cda.) Sacc.
Menispora ciliata Cda.
Perichaena marginata S.
Phyllostica Fraxini Ell. & Martin.
Sporoschisma mirabile B. & Br.

Castanea crenata Sieb. & Zucc.
Cytospora ceratophora? Sacc.
Daedalea quercina (L.) ex Fr.
{ Diaporthe parasitica Murrill.
Endothia parasitica (Murrill) P. J. & H. W. Anderson.
{ Pestalozzia affinis Ell. & Ev.
Pestalozzia Everhartii Sacc.
Polyporus Pocula (S.) B. & C.
Septoria gilletiana Sacc.
Castanea dentata (Marsh.) Borkh.

MYXOMYCETES
{ Arcyria globosa S.
Craterium globosum (S.) Fr.
Lachnobolus globosus (S.) Rostf.
Nassula globosa (S.) Fr.

PEZIZINEAE
Cenangium alboatrum Ell. & Ew.
Ciboria americana Durand.
{ Ciboria echinophila (Bull. ex Fr.) Sacc.
Peziza echinophila Bull. ex Fr.
{ Dasyscypha turbinulata (S.) Sacc.
Lachnella citrina Pk.
Peziza turbinulata S.

{ Helotium papillare (Bull. ex Fr.) Karst.
Peziza granuliformis A. & S. ex Fr.
Patellaria congregata B. & C.
Peziza alboviolascens A. & S. ex Fr.
{ Helotium fructigenum (Bull. ex Fr.) Fckl.
Peziza fructigena Bull. ex Fr.
Phialea fructigena (Bull. ex Fr.) Gill.

HYSTERIINEAE
Gloniella ovata (Cke.) Sacc.
Glonium parvulum (Gerard) Sacc.
Hysterium Castaneae S.

PYRENOMYCETINEAE
Anthostoma dryophilum (Curr.) Sacc.
{ Cryptospora cinctula (C. & P.) Sacc.
Valsa cinctula C. & P.
{ Cryptosporella innata (B. & C.) Sacc.
Diaporthe innata (B. & C.) Sacc.
Diatrype innata B. & C.
Diatrype Stigma (Hoffm.) ex Fr.
{ Cytospora sp. F. W. Patterson.
Diaporthe parasitica Murrill.
Endothia gyrosa, var. parasitica (Murrill) G. P. Clinton.
Endothia parasitica (Murrill) P. J. & H. W. Anderson.
Valsonectria parasitica (Murrill) Rehm.
{ Endothia fluens Shear & Stevens.
Endothia radicalis (S.) De Not.
Endothia virginiana P. J. & H. W. Anderson.
Melanconis modonia Tul.
{ Microsphaera Alni (DC.) Wint. †
Microsphaera Friesii Lév., var. Castaneae C. & P.
Microsphaera Hedwigii Lév., var. Castaneae Ell.
{ Erysiphe orbicularis Ehrb.
Phyllactinia corylea (P.) ex Karst.
Phyllactinia guttata (Wallr. ex Fr.) Lév.
Phyllactinia suffulta (Reb.) ex Sacc.
Phyllactinia corylea (P.) ex Karst., var. angulata Salmon.
{ Endothia fluens, var. mississippiensis Shear & Stevens.
Endothia radicalis, var. mississippiensis Shear & Stevens.
{ Endothia gyrosa Fr. 1849 p. p.
Endothia radicalis Farl.
Guignardia echinophila (S.) Lindau.
Laestadia echinophila (S.) Sacc.
{ Phomatospora echinophila (S.) Cke.
Sphaerella echinophila (S.) Awd.
Sphaeria echinophila S.
Physalospora Cydoniae Arnaud.
Physalospora Malorum Shear et al.
{ Mycosphaerella maculiformis (P. ex Fr.) Schrt.
Sphaerella maculiformis (P. ex Fr.) Awd.
Sphaerella punctiformis (P. ex Fr.) Rabh.

Castanea dentata (*cont.*)
  Sphaerella sparsa (Wallr.) Awd.
  Valsa coronata (Hoffm.) ex Fr.

HYMENOMYCETINEAE
MISCELLANEA

Guepinia Spathularia Fr.
Hydnum xanthum B. & C.
Hymenochaete rubiginosa (Schrad. ex Fr.) Lév.
Odontia hydnoidea (S.) Morg.
Peniophora quercina (P. ex Fr.) Cke.
Stereum versiforme B. & C.?

POLYPORACEAE

Daedalea quercina (L.) ex Fr.
Fistulina hepatica Fr.
Fistulina pallida B. & Rav.
Lenzites corrugata (Klotzsch) B. & C.
Lenzites sepiaria (Wulf.) ex Fr.
Lenzites trabea (P.) ex Fr.
{ Mucronoporus gilvus (S.) Ell. & Ev.
{ Polyporus gilvus S.
{ Polyporus cupuliformis B. & C.
{ Polyporus pendulus (Fr.) Ell.
{ Polyporus Pocula (S.) ex B. & C.
{ Porodisculus pendulus (S.) Murrill.
{ Porodiscus pendulus (S.) Murrill.
{ Aurantiporus Pilotae (S.) Murrill.
{ Polyporus croceus P. ex Fr.
{ Polyporus Pilotae S.
Polyporus spumeus Fr.?
Polyporus frondosus Fr.
Polyporus Spraguei B.
{ Laetiporus speciosus (Batarr.) ex Murrill.
{ Polyporus sulphureus (Bull.) ex Fr.
{ Polyporus hirsutus (Wulf.) ex Fr.
{ Polystictus hirsutus (Wulf.) ex Fr.
{ Polyporus elongatus B.
{ Polyporus pargamenus Fr.
{ Polystictus elongatus (B.) Fr.
{ Polystictus pargamenus Fr.
{ Polyporus versicolor L. ex Fr.
{ Polystictus versicolor (L.) ex Fr.
Poria cremor (B. & C.) Cke.
Trametes ohiensis B.

AGARICACEAE

Armillaria mellea (Vahl) ex Fr.
{ Hypholoma perplexum Pk.
{ Hypholoma sublateritium Fr.
Lepiota americana Pk.
Schizophyllum commune Fr.

SPHAEROPSIDALES

Aposphaeria brunneotincta Farl.
Diplodia longispora C. & E.
{ Discosia Artocreas (Tode) ex Fr.
{ Sphaeria Artocreas Tode ex Fr.
{ Fusicoccum castaneum Sacc.
{ Phomopsis castanea (Sacc.) Diedicke.

Phoma castanea Pk.
Phyllosticta Castaneae Ell. & Ev.
Phyllosticta fusispora Ell. & Ev.
{ Hendersonia geographica Ell. & Ev.
{ Phyllohendersonia geographica (Ell. & Ev.)
{   Tassi.
Leptothyrium Castaneae (Spreng.) Sacc.
Leptothyrium? castanicola Ell. & Ev.
{ Haplosporella Mali (Westd.) Petrak & Syd.
{ Sphaeropsis Malorum Pk.
{ Coryneum Kunzei Cda., var. Castaneae-
{   vescae Thm.
{ Steganosporium Castaneae Lib. nom. nud.

MELANCONIALES

Coryneum pustulatum Pk.
Cytosporella carnea Ell. & Ev.
Gloeosporium castanicola Ell. & Ev.
Hainesia Lythri (Desm.) v. Höhnel.
Monochaetia Desmazierii Sacc.
Monochaetia pachyspora Bubák.
Myxosporium castaneum Pk.
{ Cryptosporium epiphyllum C. & E.
{ Gloeosporium ochroleucum (B. & C.) Ell. &
{   Ev.
{ Marssonia ochroleuca (B. & C.) J. E. Hum-
{   phrey.
{ Phyllosticta ochroleuca (B. & C.) Pk.
{ Septogloeum ochroleucum (B. & C.) Dearness.
{ Septoria ochroleuca B. & C.
Scolecosporium Fagi Lib.

HYPHOMYCETES

Helminthosporium macrocarpon Grev.
Helminthosporium persistens Cke.
Sporotrichum Quercuum Shear.
Stilbum piliforme P.
Strumella coryneoidea Sacc. & Wint.
{ Tubercularia Castaneae P. ex Fr.
{ Tubercularia minor Lk.
Volutella stellata Pk.
Castanea pumila (L.) Mill.
{ Diaporthe parasitica Murrill.
{ Endothia parasitica (Murrill) P. J. & H. W
{   Anderson.
{ Gnomoniella vulgaris (Ces. & De Not.) Sacc.
{ Sphaeria Gnomon Tode ex Fr.
{ Helminthosporium caudatum B. & C.
{ Helminthosporium macrocarpon Grev.
Leptothyrium dryinum Sacc.
Melanconium cinctum B. & C.
Microsphaera Alni (DC.) Wint. †
Monochaetia pachyspora Bubák.
Pestalozzia concentrica B. & Rav.
Phyllosticta Castaneae Ell. & Ev.
Polyporus croceus Fr.
Polyporus Pilotae (S.) B. & C.
Polyporus sulphureus (Bull.) ex Fr.
Thelephora albomarginata S.

Castanea sativa Mill.
(Spanish chestnuts in laboratory.)
Acrospeira mirabilis B. & Br.
Endothia parasitica (Murrill) P. J. & H. W. Anderson.
Marssonia ochroleuca (B. & C.) J. E. Humphrey.
Melanospora anomala Hotson.
Microsphaera Alni (DC.) Wint. †
{ Ozonium omnivorum Shear.
{ Phymatotrichum omnivorum (Shear) Duggar.
Phyllactinia corylea (P.) ex Karst.
Spirospora Castaneae Mangin & Vincens.
Castanea sp. indet.

PEZIZINEAE

Agyrium nigricans Fr.
Agyrium rufum (P.) Fr.
{ Arachnopeziza rhaphidospora (Ell.) Rehm.
{ Peziza rhaphidospora Ell.
Cenangium Castaneae S.
Cenangium fibrisedum S.
{ Chlorosplenium Schweinitzii Fr.
{ Peziza chlora S.
Coryne sarcoides (Jacq. ex Fr.) Tul.
{ Dasyscypha trabinelloides (Rehm) Massee.
{ Helotiella Nuttallii Ell. & Ev.
{ Dasyscypha translucida (B. & C.) Sacc.
{ Peziza translucida B. & C.
{ Dasyscypha vixvisibilis (S.) Sacc.
{ Peziza vixvisibilis S.
Dermatea purpurascens Ell. & Ev.
Haematomyces orbicularis Pk.
{ Helotiella cornuta (Ell.) Sacc.
{ Peziza cornuta Ell.
Peziza Aranea De Not.
Trichopeziza Aranea (De Not.) Sacc.
{ Cyphella punctiformis (Fr.) Cke.
{ Peziza punctiformis Fr.
{ Trichopeziza punctiformis (Fr.) Fckl.

PHACIDIINEAE

Phacidium coronatum Fr.

HYSTERIINEAE

Angelina rufescens (S.) Duby.
Hysterium insidens S.
{ Hysterium Gerardi C. & P.
{ Hysterographium Gerardi (C. & P.) Sacc.
{ Hysterium variabile C. & P.
{ Hysterographium variabile (C. & P.) Sacc.

PYRENOMYCETINEAE

Actinopelte japonica Sacc.
{ Botryosphaeria Castaneae (S.) Sacc.
{ Melogramma Castaneae (S.) M. A. Curtis.
{ Sphaeria Castaneae S.
{ Calosphaeria assecla (S.) Sacc.
{ Sphaeria assecla S.
{ Valsa assecla (S.) Cke.

{ Calosphaeria scabriseta (S.) Sacc.
{ Eutypa scabriseta (S.) B.
{ Sphaeria scabriseta S.
{ Valsa scabriseta (S.) Sacc.
Ceratostoma carpophilum Ell.
{ Coniochaeta monstrosa (S.) Cke.
{ Sphaeria monstrosa S.
{ Dialonectria fibriseda (S.) Cke.
{ Nectria fibriseda (S.) Sacc.
{ Sphaeria fibriseda S.
{ Didymella castanella (C. & E.) Sacc.
{ Endophlaea castanella C. & E.
{ Sphaeria castanella C. & E.
{ Eutypa spinosa (P.) Tul.
{ Sphaeria limiformis S.
{ Fenestella castanicola (B. & C.) Sacc.
{ Valsa castanicola B. & C.
{ Valsa castanophila B. & C.?
Gnomonia setacea (P. ex Fr.) Ces. & De Not.
{ Hypoxylon enteromelum (S.) B.
{ Sphaeria enteromela S.
Hypoxylon multiforme Fr.
Laestadia castanicola Ell. & Ev.
Laestadia rubescens Ell. & Ev.
{ Melanomma Pulvis-pyrius (P. ex Fr.) Fckl.
{ Sphaeria Pulvis-pyrius P. ex Fr.
{ Amphisphaeria Eckfeldtii (Ell.) Cke.
{ Melanomma Eckfeldtii (Ell.) Sacc.
{ Melanopsamma Eckfeldtii (Ell.) Ell. & Ev.
{ Sphaeria Eckfeldtii Ell.
{ Melanopsamma ferrugineum (P. ex Fr.) Ces. & De Not.
{ Sillia ferruginea (P. ex Fr.) Karst.
{ Sphaeria ferruginea P. ex Fr.
{ Dothidea Castaneae S.
{ Phyllachora Castaneae (S.) Sacc.
{ Rosellinia Corticium (S.) Sacc.
{ Sphaeria aquila Fr., var. Corticium (S.) Fr.
{ Sphaeria Corticium S.
Schizoparme straminea Shear.
Sphaeria enteroxantha S.
Sphaeria fuscescens S.
Sphaeria inversa Fr.
Valsa caryigena B. & C.
{ Sphaeria oligostoma S.
{ Valsa oligostoma (S.) Cke.
Valsa pullula B. & C. in Herb. B.
{ Sphaeria pusilla P. ex Fr.
{ Valsa pusilla (P.) ex Fr.
{ Psilosphaeria squalidula C. & P.
{ Sphaeria squalidula C. & P.
{ Wallrothiella squalidula (C. & P.) Sacc.

THELEPHORACEAE

Corticium illaqueatum Bourdot & Galzin.
Corticium incarnatum (P.) ex Fr.
Corticium quercinum P. ex Fr., var. scutellatum Ell.
Peniophora velutina (DC. ex Fr.) Cke.

Castanea sp. indet. (*cont.*)

Peniophora violaceo-livida (Sommerf.) Bres.
{ Stereum abietinum (P.) ex Fr.
{ Thelephora abietina P. ex Fr.
{ Stereum Chailletii (P.) Fr.
{ Thelephora Chailletii P.
Stereum erumpens Burt.
Stereum purpureum P. †
Thelephora nuda S. Am. bor.

POLYPORACEAE

Favolus abnormis S.
{ Boletus radicatus S.
{ Fistulina radicata (S.) Fr.
Fomes ungulatus (Schaeff.) ex Sacc.
Hydnum fuscoatrum Fr.
Irpex sinuosus Fr.
Merulius Corium (P.) Fr.
Odontia lateritia B. & C.
Polyporus adustus (Willd.) ex Fr.
Polyporus Berkeleyi Fr.
Polyporus castanophilus Atk.
{ Boletus crispus P. ex Fr.
{ Polyporus crispus (P.) ex Fr.
Polyporus fimbriporus S.
Polyporus frondosus Fr.
{ Polyporus dryadeus S. Am. bor.
{ Polyporus scruposus Fr.
{ Polyporus Spraguei B. & C.
{ Tyromyces Spraguei (B. & C.) Murrill.
Polyporus spumeus Fr., var. malicola Lloyd.
{ Fuscoporia ferruginosa (Schrad. ex Fr.) Mur-
{   rill.
{ Poria ferruginosa (Schrad. ex Fr.) Cke.
Poria mutans Pk.
{ Polyporus tenuis S.
{ Poria tenuis (S.) Sacc.

AGARICACEAE

Deconica pyrispora Murrill.
Flammula flavidella (Murrill) Sacc. & Trott.
Lentinus cochleatus Fr.
Mycena corticola (Schum.) ex Fr.
Pholiota adiposa Fr.

FUNGI IMPERFECTI
SPHAEROPSIDALES

Phoma brunneotincta B. & C.
{ Pseudographium capillare (Ell. & Hark.) Jacz.
{ Sphaerographium capillare (Ell. & Hark.) Sacc.
{ Sphaeronema capillare Ell. & Hark.
Sphaeronema parabolicum (Tode) ex Fr.
Sphaeronema ventricosum (Ach.) ex Fr.

MELANCONIALES

Cylindrium elongatum Bon.
Gloeosporium quercinum Westd.
{ Coryneum castanicola B. & C.
{ Steganosporium castanicola (B. & C.) Sacc.

{ Septoria nigricans Lk.
{ Stilbospora epiphylla S.

HYPHOMYCETES

{ Ceratophorum epiphyllum (S.) Sacc.
{ Coryneum epiphyllum S.
{ Sporidesmium epiphyllum (S.) B. & C.
Clasterosporium sigmoideum Ell. & Ev.
{ Ceratophorum subulatum C. & E.
{ Clasterosporium subulatum C. & E
Coremium glaucum Lk. ex Fr.
Fusarium coccineum S.
Fusidium caesium S.
{ Dematium Castaneae S.
{ Helminthosporium fasciculatum S.
Helminthosporium obovatum B. & Br.
Oidium croceum Lk. ex Fr.
Spicaria fumosa Ell. & Ev.
{ Coniothecium effusum Cda.
{ Sporidesmium Lepraria B.
Sporotrichum cohaerens S.
Sporotrichum lateritium Ehrenb.
Zygodesmus granulosus Pk.

MISCELLANEA

{ Dacryomyces fragiformis S. Am. Bor.
{ Hormomyces aurantiacus Sacc.
{ Hypsilophora fragiformis Cke.
{ Tremella fragiformis S. Syn. Car.
Hirneola Auricula-Judae (L.) Fr.
Mucor echinophilus S.
Sclerotium applanatum S.
{ Sphaerobolus minutissimus S.
{ Thelebolus? minutissimus (S.) De Toni.
Typhula ramealis S.

Castanopsis chrysophylla A. DC.
{ Cronartium Quercus Schrt.
{ Cronartium Quercuum Miyabe.
{ Peridermium Cerebrum Pk. III.
Dothidella Castanopsidis Dearness.
Fomes igniarius (L. ex Fr.) Gill.
Gloeosporium Castanopsidis Dearness & House.
Phyllosticta castanicola Ell. & Ev.
Sphaerella weiriana Sacc.
{ Ascomyces Quercus Cke.
{ Taphrina caerulescens (Mont. & Desm.) Tul.

Quercus agrifolia Née.

EXOASCACEAE

{ Ascomyces caerulescens Mont. & Desm.
{ Taphrina caerulescens (Mont. & Desm.) Tul.

PEZIZINEAE

Helotium furfuraceum Phil. & Hark.
{ Microphyma nigellum (Phil. & Hark.) Sacc.
{ Phillipsiella nigella Phil. & Hark.
Pocillum Cesatii (Mont.) DeNot.

PHACIDIINEAE

{ Phacidium coronatum (Schum.) ex Fr.
{ Xyloma pezizoides (P.) ex Fr.

Quercus agrifolia (*cont.*)

HYSTERIINEAE

Aulographum reticulatum Phil. & Hark.
Dichaena quercina (P.) ex Fr.
Hysterium pulicare P. ex Fr.

PYRENOMYCETINEAE

Amphisphaeria decorticata (Cke. & Hark.)
  Berl. & Vogl.
Melanomma decorticata (Cke. & Hark.) Cke.
Sphaeria decorticata Cke. & Hark.
Botryosphaeria Quercuum (S.) Sacc.
Melogramma fuliginosum Ell. p. p.
Melogramma Quercuum (S.) Fr.
Melanops Quercuum (S.) Rehm.
Sphaeria Quercuum S.
Endothia radicalis Farl.
Erysiphe trina Hark.
Melanospora papillata Hotson.
Physalospora agrifolia Ell. & Ev.
Laestadia bina (Hark.) Cke.
Physalospora bina Hark.
Albigo lanestris (Hark.) O. Kuntze.
Oidium ventricosum Hark.
Sphaerotheca lanestris Hark.
Rhytisma erythrosporum B. & C.
Trabutia erythrospora (B. & C.) Cke.
Trabutia quercina (Fr. & Rud.) Sacc. & Roum.

UREDINALES

Caeoma conigenum Pat.
Cronartium Cerebrum Hedgc. & Long.
Cronartium conigenum Hedgc. & Hunt.
Cronartium fusiforme Hedgc. & Hunt.
Cronartium Quercus Schrt.
Cronartium Quercuum Miyabe.
Cronartium strobilinum Hedgc. & Hahn.
Uredo Quercus Brond.

HYMENOMYCETINEAE

Armillaria mellea (Vahl) ex Fr.
Elfvingia megaloma (Lév.) Murrill.
Fomes applanatus (P. ex Wallr.) Gill.
Elfvingia tornata (P.) Murrill.
Ganoderma tornatum (P.) A. Ames.
Grandinia crustosa (P.) ex Fr.
Irpex obliquus (Schrad.) ex Fr.
Hapalopilus gilvus (S.) Murrill.
Polyporus gilvus S.
Inonotus Leei Murrill.
Polyporus Leei Murrill.
Poria Leei (Murrill) Sacc. & Trott.
Stereum ochraceoflavum (S.) Rav.
Stereum rugosum P. ex Fr.
Thelephora rugosa P.

FUNGI IMPERFECTI

Beltrania querna Hark.
Chaetophoma quercifolia Cke.

Chaetophoma setigera Pk.
Gloeosporium querneum Hark.
Helicosporium vegetum Nees ex Fr.
Helminthosporium persistens Cke.
Papulospora sporotrichoides Hotson.
Pestalozzia monochaeta Desm.
Pestalozzia Saccardoi Speg.
Phoma discosiiformis Cke. & Hark.
Phyllosticta agrifolia Ell. & Ev.
Phyllosticta phomiformis Sacc.
Polyscytalum sericeum Sacc.
Sphaeropsis quercina Cke. & Hark.
Zygodesmus pannosus B. & C.

Quercus alba L.

MYXOMYCETES

Clathroptychium rugulosum (Wallr.) Rostf.
Hemiarcyria clavata (P.) Rostf.
Hemiarcyria rubiformis (P.) Rostf.
Licea applanata B.

EXOASCACEAE

Taphrina caerulescens (Mont. & Desm.) Tul.
Taphrina Quercus (Cke.) Sacc.

HELVELLINEAE

Psilopezia flavida B. & C.

PEZIZINEAE

Cenangium confusum S.
Cenangium sphaeriimorphum S.
Coryne urnalis (Nyl.) Sacc.
Dermatea Cucurbitaria Cke.
Patellaria Cucurbitaria (Cke.) Rehm.
Dermatea lobata Ell.
Dermatea tabacina Cke.
Helotium lenticulare (Bull.) ex Fr.
Peziza lenticularis Bull. ex Fr.
Lachnea Erinaceus (S.) Sacc.
Lachnea scutellata (P. ex Fr.) Gill.
Lachnum viridulum Massee & Morg.
Lachnum ciliare (Schrad. ex Fr.) Rehm.
Peziza capitata Pk.
Peziza echinulata Awd.
Trichopeziza capitata (Pk.) Sacc.
Trichopeziza ciliaris (Schrad. ex Fr.) Rehm.

PHACIDIINEAE

Blitrydium Cucurbitaria (Cke.) Sacc.
Coccomyces comitialis (Batsch) Dearness &
  House.
Coccomyces coronatus (Schum. ex Fr.) DeNot.
Cenangium triangulare (S.) Fr.
Coccomyces triangularis (S.) Sacc.
Peziza triangularis S.
Cryptodiscus niveopurpureus (Ell. & Ev.)
  Sacc.
Stictis niveopurpurea Ell. & Ev.
Schizoxylon moniliferum Ell. & Ev.

Quercus alba (*cont.*)

HYSTERIINEAE

Blitrydium hiascens (B. & C.) Sacc.
Hysterium hiascens B. & C.
Tryblidium hiascens (B. & C.) Cke.
Dichaena quercina (P.) ex Fr.
Gloniopsis cookeana (Gerard) Sacc.
Hysterium cookeanum Gerard.
Hysterographium cookeanum Ell. & Ev.
Hysterium stygium Cke.
Hysterographium stygium (Cke.) Sacc.

ERYSIPHACEAE

Microsphaera Alni (DC.) Wint. †
Microsphaera Alni (DC.) Wint., † var. extensa
  (C. & P.) Salmon.
Microsphaera extensa C. & P.
Microsphaera quercina (S.) Burrill.
Sphaerotheca lanestris Hark.
?Uncinula circinata C. & P.

SPHAERIALES

Amphisphaeria fallax DeNot.
Amphisphaeria quercetis Cke. & Mass.
Anthostoma dryophilum (Curr.) Sacc.
Calosphaeria barbirostris (Dufour) Ell. & Ev.
Valsa lasiostoma Ell. & Ev.
Calosphaeria pulchelloidea (C. & E.) Ell. & Ev.
Valsa pulchelloidea C. & E.
Cryptospora farinosa (Ell.) Ell. & Ev.
Cryptosporella farinosa (Ell.) Sacc.
Valsa farinosa Ell.
Cryptospora leiphaemoides Dearness & House.
Daldinia vernicosa (S.) Ces. & De Not.
Diaporthe leiphaemia (Fr.) Sacc.
Diaporthe raveneliana Thm. & Rehm.
Sphaeria leiphaemia Fr.
Valsa leiphaemia Fr.
Aglaospora Taleola (Fr.) Tul.
Diaporthe Taleola (Fr.) Sacc.
Sphaeria Taleola Fr
Valsa Taleola Fr.
Diatrype albopruinosa (S.) C. & E.
?Diatrype Duriaei Thm. M. U.
Diatrype americana Ell. & Berl.
Diatrype Stigma (Hoffm.) ex Fr.
Endothia fluens Shear & Stevens.
Endothia fluens, var. mississippiensis Shear &
  Stevens.
Endothia gyrosa Fr. p. p.
Endothia parasitica (Murrill) P. J. & H. W.
  Anderson.
Eutypa velutina (Wallr.) Sacc.
Fenestella phaeospora Sacc.
Valsa phaeospora Sacc.
Gnomonia veneta (Sacc. & Speg.) Klebahn.
Hypoxylon annulatum (S.) Mont.
Hypoxylon marginatum (S.) B.
Sphaeria annulata S.
Sphaeria marginata S.

Hypoxylon durissimum (S.) Fr.
Sphaeria durissima S.
Hypoxylon perforatum (S.) Fr.
Hypoxylon Petersii B. & C.
Hypoxylon serpens (P.) ex Fr.
Lophiostoma macrosporum Speg.
Didymosphaeria atrogrisea C. & P.
Massaria bufonia (B. & Br.) Tul.
Massariella bufonia (B. & Br.) Speg.
Massaria sudans B. & C.
Massariella sudans (B. & C.) Sacc.
Massariovalsa sudans (B. & C.) Sacc.
Melanconis chrysostoma (Fr.) Tul.
Melanopsamma corticola Ell. & Ev.
Melanopsamma papilla (S.) Sacc.
Nummularia Bulliardi Tul.
Nummularia nummularia (Bull. ex Fr.) Schrt.
Numulariola nummularia (Bull. ex Fr.) House.
Diatrype punctulata B. & Rav.
Hypoxylon punctulatum B. & Rav.
Nummularia punctulata (B. & Rav.) Sacc.
Otthia quercicola Ell. & Ev.
Physalospora Cydoniae Arnaud.
Pseudovalsa sigmoidea (C. & E.) Sacc.
Sphaerella maculiformis (P. ex Fr.) Awd.
Mycosphaerella spleniata (C. & P.) House.
Sphaerella spleniata C. & P.
Sphaerella dendroides (S.) Cke.
Sphaerella myriadea (DC. ex Fr.) Awd.
Sphaeria dendroides S.
Sphaeria myriadea DC. ex Fr.
Sphaerulina myriadea (DC. ex Fr.) Sacc.
Valsa ceratophora Tul.
Valsa leiphaemioides B. & C.
Valsaria rubricosa (Fr.) Sacc.
Sphaeria Orbicula S.
Venturia Orbicula (S.) C. & P.
Xylaria Hypoxylon (L.) ex Fr.
Xylaria polymorpha (P. ex Fr.) Grev.

HYPOCREALES

Acrospermum viridulum B. & C.

UREDINALES

Cronartium Quercus Schrt.
Uredo Quercus Brond.

TREMELLINEAE

Exidia glandulosa (Bull.) ex Fr.
Exidia gelatinosa (Bull. ex Fr.) Duby.
Exidia recisa Fr.

DACRYOMYCETINEAE

Dacryomyces stillatus Nees ex Fr.

EXOBASIDIINEAE

Microstroma album (Desm.) Sacc.

THELEPHORACEAE

Aleurodiscus Oakesii (B. & C.) Cke.
Corticium Oakesii B. & C.

Quercus alba *(cont.)*
Coniophora Harperi Burt.
Corticium caeruleum (Schrad.) ex Fr.
Corticium citrinum B. & Rav.
⌠Corticium corticola B. & Rav.
⌡Hymenochaete corticolor B. & Rav.
⌠Hymenochaete Curtisii (B.) Morg.
⌡Stereum Curtisii B.
⌡Thelephora Curtisii B.
Hymenochaete rubiginosa (Schrad. ex Fr.) Lév.
Hypochnus pilosus Burt.
Peniophora flavido-alba Cke.
⌠Septobasidium pseudopedicellatum Burt.
⌡Thelephora pedicellata Auct. Amer. p. p.
Stereum candidum (S.) Fr.
Stereum complicatum Fr.
⌠Stereum fasciatum (S.) Fr.
⌡Stereum molle (Lév.) Fr.
⌠Stereum frustulosum Fr.
⌡Thelephora frustulata P.
Stereum gausapatum Fr.
Stereum hirsutum (Willd.) ex Fr.
Stereum lobatum (Kze.) ex Fr.
Stereum rameale (S.) Reddick.
⌠Stereum spadiceum Fr
⌡Thelephora spadicea S. Syn. Car.
Stereum spadiceum Fr., var. plicatum Pk.
Stereum subpileatum B. & C.
Stereum sulphuratum B. & Rav.
⌠Peniophora intermedia Massee.
⌡Stereum papyrinum Rav. Fung. Car. **2**: *36.*
⌡Stereum umbrinum B. & C.
Stereum versicolor (Sw.) ex Fr.
⌠Peniophora Ellisii Massee.
⌡Stereum versiforme B. & C.
Thelephora terrestris Ehrh. ex Fr.

HYDNACEAE

⌠Hydnum adustum S.
⌡Steccherinum adustum (S.) Banker.
Hydnum Caput-ursi Fr.
Hydnum chrysocomum Underw.
Hydnum coralloides Scop. ex Fr.
⌠Hydnum Erinaceus Bull. ex Fr.
⌡Manina cordiformis (Scop.) ex Fr.
Hydnum ochraceum P. ex Fr.
⌠Hydnum pulcherrimum B. & C.
⌡Steccherinum pulcherrimum (B. & C.) Banker.
⌠Hydnum Rhois S.
⌡Steccherinum Rhois (S.) Banker.
⌠Irpex cinnamomeus Fr.
⌡Irpex fuscescens S.
Irpex mollis B. & C.

POLYPORACEAE

Daedalea extensa Pk.
Daedalea quercina (L.) ex Fr.
Daedalea unicolor (Bull.) ex Fr.
Fistulina pallida B. & Rav.

⌠Fomes applanatus (P. ex Wallr.) Gill.
⌡Ganoderma applanatum (P. ex Wallr.) Pat.
⌡Polyporus applanatus (P.) ex Wallr.
⌠Fomes Everhartii (Ell. & Gall.) v. Schrenk.
⌡Pyropolyporus Everhartii (Ell. & Gall.) Murrill.
⌠Elfvingia lobata (S.) Murrill.
⌡Fomes lobatus (S.) Cke.
⌡Polyporus lobatus S.
Lenzites betulina (L.) ex Fr.
Lenzites trabea P. ex Fr.
⌠Lenzites vialis Pk.
⌡Sesia pallidofulva (B.) Murrill.
Merulius ceracellus B. & C.
Merulius Corium Fr.
⌠Cantharellus incarnatus S.
⌡Merulius incarnatus S.
Merulius rubellus Pk.
Merulius tremellosus Schrad. ex Fr.
⌠Polyporus benzoinus Fr.
⌡Polyporus resinosus (Schrad.) ex Fr.
⌠Grifola Berkeleyi (Fr.) Murrill.
⌡Polyporus Beatiei Banning.
⌡Polyporus Berkeleyi Fr.
Polyporus biformis Fr.
Polyporus compactus Overholts.
Polyporus dichrous Fr.
Polyporus dryadeus (P.) ex Fr.
⌠Inonotus dryophilus (B.) Murrill.
⌡Polyporus dryophilus B.
Polyporus frondosus (Schrank) ex Fr.
Polyporus gilvus S.
Polyporus obtusus B.
Polyporus Pilotae S.
Polyporus Schweinitzii Fr.
Polyporus sulphureus (Bull.) ex Fr.
⌠Boletus cinnabarinus Jacq. ex Fr.
⌡Hydnum cinnabarinum (Jacq.) ex Fr.
⌡Polyporus cinnabarinus (Jacq.) ex Fr.
⌡Polystictus cinnabarinus (Jacq. ex Fr.) Cke.
⌡Sistotrema cinnabarinum (Jacq. ex Fr.) S.
⌡Trametes cinnabarina (Jacq.) ex Fr.
⌠Coriolus pargamenus (Fr.) Pat.
⌡Coriolus prolificans (Fr.) Murrill.
⌡Polyporus elongatus B.
⌡Polyporus laceratus M. A. Curtis.
⌡Polyporus pargamenus Fr.
⌡Polystictus elongatus (B.) Fr.
⌡Polystictus pargamenus Fr.
⌡Polystictus pseudopargamenus (Thm.) Sacc. Syll.
⌠Coriolus versicolor (L. ex Fr.) Quél.
⌡Polyporus versicolor L. ex Fr.
⌡Polystictus versicolor (L.) ex Fr.
Poria lacerata Murrill.
Poria pulchella (S.) Cke.
Poria subviolacea Ell. & Ev.
Poria undata (P.) Bres.
Trametes pusilla Lloyd.

Quercus alba (*cont.*)

AGARICACEAE

Armillaria mellea (Vahl) ex Fr.
Flammula sapinea Fr.
Lentinus lepideus Fr.
Lenzites betulina (L.) ex Fr.
Omphalia corticola Pk.
Omphalopsis corticola (Pk.) Murrill.
Panus stipticus (Bull.) ex Fr.
Pholiota luteofolia Pk.
Schizophyllum alneum (L.) ex Schrt.
Schizophyllum commune Fr.

GASTEROMYCETES

Lycoperdon pyriforme Schaef.
Scleroderma vulgare Fr.

SPHAEROPSIDALES

Botryodiplodia osteolata Ell. & Ev.
Cytospora pustulata B. & C.
Cytosporella paucispora Pk.
Diplodia longispora C. & E.
Harknessia caudata Ell. & Ev.
Mastigonetron caudatum (Ell. & Ev.) v.
  Höhnel.
Leptothyrium dryinum Sacc.
Macrophoma nervicola Ell. & Ev
Dothiorella phomiformis (Sacc.) Petrak &
  Syd.
Macrophoma phomiformis (Sacc.) Tassi.
Phyllosticta phomiformis Sacc.
Phoma glandicola Lév.
Phoma vixvisibilis Thm.
Phyllosticta Quercus Sacc. & Speg.
Phyllosticta tumoricola Pk.
Haplosporella linearis (Pk.) Petrak & Syd.
Sphaeropsis linearis Pk.
Physalospora Malorum Shear et al.
Sphaeropsis Malorum B.
Dothiorella quercina (C. & E.) Sacc.
Sphaeropsis quercina C. & E.

MELANCONIALES

Bactridium flavum Kze.
Coryneum canadense Bubák & Dearness.
Coryneum Kunzei Cda.
Cylindrosporium microspilum Sacc. & Wint.
Gloeosporium canadense Ell. & Ev.
Gloeosporium nervisequum (Fckl.) Sacc.
Gnomonia veneta (Sacc. & Speg.) Klebahn.
Myxosporium valsoideum (Sacc.) Allescher.
Sporonema Platani Bäumler.
Gloeosporium divergens Pk.
Gloeosporium quercinum Westd.
Gloeosporium septorioides Sacc.
Gloeosporium umbrinellum B. & Br.
Hainesia Lythri (Desm.) v. Höhnel.
Sclerotiopsis concava (Desm.) Shear & Dodge.

Marssonia Martini Sacc. & Ell.
Marssonina Martini (Sacc. & Ell.) Magn.
Marssonia Quercus Pk.
Marssonina Quercus (Pk.) Magn.
Melanconium bicolor Nees ex Fr.
Pestalozzia monochaeta Desm.
Pestalozzia Peckii G. W. Clinton.
Pestalozzia nervalis Ell. & Ev.
Pestalozzia pallida Ell. & Martin.
Pestalozzia Saccardoi Speg.
Pestalozzia taphrinicola Ell. & Ev.

HYPHOMYCETES

Acrosporium compactum C. & E.
Cladosporium brevipes Pk.
Cylindrium elongatum Bon.
Epidochium nigricans Fr.
Fumago vagans Fr.
Helminthosporium Tiara B. & Rav.
Oidium obductum Ell. & Langlois.
Polyscytalum sericeum Sacc.
Sporidesmium fumosum Ell. & Ev.
Strumella coryneoidea Sacc. & Wint.

Quercus arizonica Sarg.
Fomes Everhartii (Ell. & Gall.) v. Schrenk.
Irpex lacteus Fr.
Irpex sinuosus Fr.
Irpiciporus lacteus (Fr.) Murrill.
Irpex Tulipiferae (S.) Fr.
Polyporus Tulipiferae (S.) Fr.
Polyporus dryophilus B.

Quercus bicolor Willd.
Cronartium conigenum Hedgc. & Hunt.
Cronartium Quercus Schrt.
Cronartium strobilinum Hedgc. & Hahn.
Daedalea quercina (L.) ex Fr.
Fomes Everhartii (Ell. & Gall.) v. Schrenk.
Fulvifomes Everhartii (Ell. & Gall.) Murrill.
Gloeosporium bicolor J. J. Davis.
Gloeosporium canadense Ell. & Ev.
Gnomonia veneta (Sacc. & Speg.) Klebahn.
Hysterium hiascens B. & C.
Hysterium pulicare N. A .F.
Hysterographium hiascens (B. & C.) Rehm.
Marssonia Martinii Sacc. & Ell.
Microsphaera abbreviata Pk.
Microsphaera Alni (DC.) Wint.†
Microsphaera quercina (S.) Burrill.
Phyllosticta phomiformis Sacc.
Phyllosticta quercea J. J. Davis.
Polyporus sulphureus (Bull.) ex Fr.
Septogloeum querceum J. J. Davis.
Mycosphaerella spleniata (C. & P.) House.
Sphaerella nigrita (C. & P.) Cke.
Sphaerella spleniata C. & P.

Quercus Castanea Née.
Cronartium Quercus Schrt.
Cystotheca Wrightii B. & C.

Quercus Catesbaei Michx.
{ Chaetophoma Catesbeyi (Thm.) Cke.
{ Phoma Catesbeyi Thm.
Coniothyrium epiphyllum Cke.
Graphium explicatum B. & C.
{ Microsphaera abbreviata Pk.
{ Microsphaera Alni (DC.) Wint. †
Microsphaera quercina (S.) Burrill.
{ Phoma nervisequa (Cke.) Sacc.
{ Sphaeropsis nervisequa Cke.
Phyllactinia corylea (P.) ex Karst.
Polyporus graveolens (S.) Fr.
Sphaerella Catesbeyi Cke.
Trichopeziza punctiformis (Fr.) Fckl., var. nivea Sacc.

Quercus Chapmani Sarg.
Leptothyrium dryinum Sacc.

Quercus chrysolepis Liebm.
Cercospora macrochaeta Ell. & Ev.
Dimerosporium echinatum Ell. & Ev.
Phyllosticta agrifolia Ell. & Ev.
Polyporus dryophilus B.
Polyporus sulphureus (Bull.) ex Fr.
Sphaerella operculata Sacc.

Quercus chrysolepis Liebm., var. **vacciniifolia** Engelm.
{ Hysterium foliicola Fr.
{ Lophodermium hysterioides (P.) Sacc.

Quercus cinerea Michx.
Microsphaera Alni (DC.) Wint., var. extensa (C. & P.) Salmon.
Microsphaera quercina (S.) Burrill.
{ Oospora insularis (Thm.) Sacc. & Vogl.
{ Torula insularis Thm.
Phyllosticta vesicatoria Thm.
Septoria quercicola (Desm.) Sacc.
{ Ascomyces Quercus Cke.
{ Taphrina caerulescens (Mont. & Desm.) Tul.
{ Taphrina Quercus (Cke.) Sacc.

Quercus coccinea Muench.

EXOASCACEAE
{ Ascomyces caerulescens Mont. & Desm.
{ Ascomyces Quercus Cke.
{ Exoascus caerulescens (Mont. & Desm.) Sadebeck.
{ Taphrina caerulescens (Mont. & Desm.) Tul.
{ Taphrina Quercus (Cke.) Sacc.

PEZIZINEAE
Bulgaria inquinans (P.) Fr.
Bulgaria polymorpha (Oeder ex Fr.) Wettst.
{ Cenangium tetrasporum (Ell.) Sacc.
{ Dermatea tetraspora Ell.
{ Cenangium turgidum Fr.
{ Peziza quernea S.
Dermatea tabacina Cke.

{ Patellaria cenangiicola Ell. & Ev.
{ Patellea cenangiicola (Ell. & Ev.) Sacc.

PHACIDIINEAE
{ Propolidium glaucum (Ell.) Sacc.
{ Propolis glauca Ell.
Schizoxylon compositum Ell. & Ev.
Schizoxylon moniliferum Ell. & Ev.
{ Hysterographium hiascens (B. & C.) Rehm.
{ Tryblidium hiascens (B. & C.) Cke.

ERYSIPHACEAE
Microsphaera Alni (DC.) Wint. †
Microsphaera Alni, var. extensa (C. & P.) Salmon.
Microsphaera quercina (S.) Burrill.
{ Phyllactinia corylea (P.) ex Karst.
{ Phyllactinia suffulta (Reb.) ex Sacc.

PYRENOMYCETINEAE
{ Anthostoma atropunctatum (S.) Sacc.
{ Hypoxylon atropunctatum (S.) Frost's Cat.
{ Sphaeria atropunctata S.
{ Anthostoma dryophilum (Curr.) Sacc., var. minor (Cke.) Rehm.
{ Diatrype dryophila Curr., var. minor Cke.
{ Anthostoma grandineum (B. & Rav.) Sacc.
{ Camarops grandinea (B. & Rav.) Cke.
{ Diatrype grandinea B. & Rav.
{ Fuckelia grandinea (B. & Rav.) Cke.
Byssosphaeria luteobasis (Ell.) Cke.
{ Calosphaeria Cookei Ell. & Ev.
{ Valsa parasitica C. & E.
{ Calosphaeria pulchelloidea (C. & E.) Ell. & Ev.
{ Valsa pulchelloidea C. & E.
Diaporthe densissima Ell.
{ Didymosphaeria circinans Hark.
{ Didymosphaeria Cupula (Ell.) Sacc.
{ Sphaeria Cupula Ell.
Endothia fluens Shear & Stevens.
{ Endothia gyrosa Fr. p. p.
{ Endothia radicalis Farl.
{ Eutypella lutescens (Ell.) Sacc.
{ Valsa lutescens Ell.
{ Hypsotheca subcorticalis (C. & E.) Ell. & Ev.
{ Sphaeronema subcorticale C. & E.
{ Laestadia polystigma Ell. & Ev.
{ Sphaerella polystigma Ell. & Ev.
{ Laestadia quercifolia Cke.
{ Physalospora quercifolia (Cke.) Ell. & Ev.
{ Lasionectria lasioderma (Ell.) Cke.
{ Nectria lasioderma Ell.
Metasphaeria fuscata Ell. & Ev.
Nectria galligena Bres.
Pseudovalsa longipes (Tul.) Sacc.
Valsa clausa C. & E.
Valsa multiplex C. & E.

Quercus coccinea (*cont.*)
  Diatrype quadrata (S.) B.
  Massaria obesa B. & C.
  Valsaria quadrata (S.) Sacc.
  Venturia Orbicula (S.) C. & P., var. sparsa Ell.
    & Ev.

UREDINALES

  Crinula paradoxa B. & C. nom. nud.
  Cronartium asclepiadeum (Willd.) Fr., var.
    Quercuum DeToni.
  Cronartium Cerebrum Hedgc. & Long.
  Cronartium conigenum Hedgc. & Hunt.
  Cronartium fusiforme Hedgc. & Hunt.
  Cronartium paradoxum (B. & C.) Farl.
  Cronartium Quercus Schrt.
  Cronartium strobilinum Hedgc. & Hahn.
  Pistillaria paradoxa (B. & C.) Cke.

HYMENOMYCETINEAE

  Aleurodiscus Artocreas (B. & C.) Massee.
  Michenera Artocreas B. & C.
  Armillaria mellea (Vahl) ex Fr.
  Corticium rubrocanum Thm.
  Irpex cinnamomeus Fr.
  Gausapia pedicellata (S.) Fr.
  Septobasidium pedicellatum (S.) G. H. Martin
    non Pat.
  Septobasidium Schweinitzii Burt.
  Thelephora pedicellata S.
  Stereum subpileatum B. & C.

POLYPORACEAE

  Fomes applanatus (P. ex Wallr.) Gill.
  Fomes Everhartii (Ell. & Gall.) v. Schrenk.
  Mucronoporus Everhartii Ell. & Gall.
  Pyropolyporus Everhartii (Ell. & Gall.) Mur-
    rill.
  Fomes graveolens (S.) Cke.
  Globifomes graveolens (S.) Murrill.
  Polyporus cupuliformis B. & C.
  Polyporus dryophilus B.
  Polyporus frondosus (Schrank) ex Fr.
  Mucronoporus gilvus (S.) Ell. & Ev.
  Polyporus gilvus S.
  Polyporus obtusus B.
  Polyporus Spraguei B.
  Polyporus sulphureus (Bull.) ex Fr.
  Polystictus hirsutus (Wulf.) ex Fr.
  Polystictus pargamenus Fr.

FUNGI IMPERFECTI

  Cytospora chrysosperma (P.) ex Fr.
  Diplodia longispora C. & E.
  Gloeosporium nervisequum (Fckl.) Sacc.
  Gnomonia veneta (Sacc. & Speg.) Klebahn.
  Myxosporium valsoideum (Sacc.) Allescher.
  Gloeosporium septorioides Sacc.

  Harknessia caudata Ell. & Ev.
  Mastigonetron caudatum (Ell. & Ev.) v. Höh-
    nel.
  Harknessia hyalina Ell. & Ev.
  Leptothyrium dryinum Sacc.
  Pestalozzia microspora Ell. & Ev.
  Pestalozzia minor Ell. & Ev.
  Pestalozzia taphrinicola Ell. & Ev.
  Phoma parasitica Ell. & Ev.
  Sporotrichum Quercuum Shear.
  Strumella coryneoidea Sacc. & Wint.

Quercus densiflora Hook. & Arn.
  Ceuthocarpon conflictum (Cke.) Berl.
  Linospora conflicta (Cke.) Sacc.
  Sphaeria conflicta Cke.
  Chalara setosa Hark.
  Cronartium Quercus Schrt.
  Laestadia caelata Hark.
  Marasmius Copelandi Pk.
  Peniophora stratosa Burt.

Quercus discolor Ait.
  Microsphaera Alni, var. extensa (C. & P.)
    Salmon.
  Phyllactinia corylea (P.) ex Karst., var. angu-
    lata Salmon.

Quercus Douglasii Hook. & Arn.
  Ascomyces Quercus Cke.
  Coryneum umbonatum Nees ex Fr.
  Cronartium conigenum Hedgc. & Hunt.
  Cronartium strobilinum Hedgc. & Hahn.
  Phyllosticta livida Ell. & Ev.
  Sporodesmium foliicola Desm.

Quercus dumosa Nutt.
  Cronartium asclepiadeum (Willd.) Fr., var.
    Quercuum De Toni.
  Cronartium Cerebrum Hedgc. & Long.
  Cronartium Quercus Schrt.
  Nummularia Clypeus (S.) Cke.
  Stereum hirsutum (Willd.) ex Fr.

Quercus durata Jepson.
  Cronartium Cerebrum Hedgc. & Long.
  Cronartium Quercus Schrt.

Quercus ellipsoidalis E. J. Hill.
  Cronartium Quercus Schrt.
  Leptothyrium dryinum Sacc.
  Microsphaera Alni (DC.) Wint. †
  Taphrina coerulescens (Desm. & Mont.) Tul.

Quercus Emoryi Torr.
  Cronartium conigenum Hedgc. & Hunt.
  Cronartium Quercus Schrt.
  Cronartium strobilinum Hedgc. & Hahn.
  Fomes applanatus (P. ex Wallr.) Gill.
  Polyporus dryophilus B.

Quercus Engelmanni Greene.
  Cronartium strobilinum (Arth.) Hedgc. &
    Hahn.

Quercus eugeniifolia Liebm.
  Orthoscypha concinna Syd.

Quercus falcata Michx.
⎧Anthostoma atropunctatum (S.) Sacc.
⎪Diatrype atropunctata (S.) M. A. Curtis.
⎪Hypoxylon atropunctatum (S.) Frost's Cat.
⎨Nummularia atropunctata (S.) v. Höhnel.
⎪Nummularia cinerea Rehm.
⎩Sphaeria atropunctata S.
⎧Cronartium Cerebrum Hedgc. & Long.
⎨Cronartium Quercus Schrt.
⎩Cronartium strobilinum Hedgc. & Hahn.
⎰Endothia gyrosa Fr. p. p.
⎱Endothia radicalis Farl.
Fomes applanatus (P. ex Wallr.) Gill.
⎰Fomes Everhartii (Ell. & Gall.) v. Schrenk.
⎱Mucronoporus Everhartii Ell. & Gall.
Fomes fomentarius (L. ex Fr.) Gill.
Massaria texana Rehm.
Merulius incarnatus S.
Microsphaera Alni (DC.) Wint. †
Microsphaera quercina (S.)
    Burrill, var. abbreviata Atk.
⎧Hypoxylon nummularium Bull. ex Fr.
⎪Nummularia Bulliardi Tul.
⎨Nummularia nummularia (Bull. ex Fr.) Atk.
⎩Sphaeria nummularia (Bull.) ex Fr.
?Phoma gloeosporioides Atk.
⎰Phyllactinia corylea (P.) ex Karst.
⎱Phyllactinia suffulta (Reb.) ex Sacc.
Polyporus dryophilus B.
Polyporus frondosus (Schrank) ex Fr.
Ramularia crypta Cke.
⎰Cenangium concinnum B. & C.
⎱Scleroderris concinna (B. & C.) Sacc.
Septoria dryina Cke.
Sphaerotheca lanestris Hark.
Taphrina caerulescens (Mont. & Desm.) Tul.
Tremella lutescens (P.) ex Fr.
⎰Melogramma obesa (B. & C.) Rav. Fung. Am.
⎱Valsaria quadrata (S.) Sacc.

Quercus Fendleri Liebm.
Diatrype albopruinosa (S.) C. & E.
Hysterium standleyanum Fairman.
⎰Rosellinia pulveracea (Ehrh. ex Fr.) Fckl.
⎱Sphaeria pulveracea Ehrh. ex Fr.
Teichospora obducens (Fr.) Fckl.

Quercus Gambelii Nutt.
Aleurodiscus cremeus Burt.
⎰Calopactis singularis Syd.
⎱Endothia singularis (Syd.) Shear & Stevens.
Cladoderris floridana Lloyd.
Corticium rubellum Burt.
Coryneum megaspermum Syd.
Exidia recisa (Ditm.) ex Fr.
Fomes Everhartii (Ell. & Gall.) v. Schrenk.
Fomes scutellatus S.
Polyporus cinnabarinus (Jacq.) ex Fr.
Polyporus dryophilus B.

Polyporus sulphureus (Bull.) ex Fr.
Polystictus hirsutus (Wulf.) ex Fr.
Polystictus versicolor (L.) ex Fr.

Quercus garryana Dougl.
Coniophora flavomarginata Burt.
Daldinia vernicosa (S.) Ell. & Ev.
Fomes igniarius (L. ex Fr.) Gill.
Hypoxylon atropunctatum (S.) Frost's Cat.
Microsphaera Alni (DC.) Wint. †
Microsphaera Alni (DC.) Wint.†, var. calo-
    cladophora Atk.
Nectria coccinea (P.) ex Fr.
Nectria galligena Bres.
Peniophora decorticans Burt.
Polyporus dryophilus B.
Polyporus Spraguei B. & C.
Polyporus sulphureus (Bull.) ex Fr.
Poria contigua (P. ex Fr.) Cke.
Poria cylindrospora Lloyd.
Radulum Owensii Lloyd.
Strumella coryneoidea Sacc. & Wint.

Quercus geminata Small.
⎰Cronartium Quercus Schrt.
⎱Cronartium strobilinum Hedgc. & Hahn

Quercus georgina M. A. Curtis.
Endothia gyrosa Fr. p. p.

Quercus glauca Oersted.
Macrophoma mexicana Sacc.

Quercus glaucoides Martens & Galeotti.
Macrophoma mexicana Sacc.

Quercus Gunnisonii (Torr.) Rydb.
Quercus heterophylla Michx.
⎰Cronartium Cerebrum Hedgc. & Long.
⎨Cronartium strobilinum Hedgc. & Hahn.
⎱Peridermium Cerebrum Pk. III.

Quercus hypoleuca Engelm.
Asteroma Pringlei Pk.
Cronartium conigenum Hedgc. & Hunt.
Cronartium Quercus Schrt.
Polyporus dryophilus B.

Quercus ilicifolia Wang.
Corticium corrugatum Fr.
⎰Cronartium Quercus Schrt.
⎱Peridermium Cerebrum Pk. III.
Diatrype albopruinosa (S.) Cke.
Endothia gyrosa Fr. p. p.
Helminthosporium macrocarpum Grev. ex Fr.
Hypoxylon Morsei B. & C.
⎧Cleistophoma dryina (B. & C.) Petrak & Syd.
⎨Macrophoma dryina (B. & C.) Berl. & Vogl.
⎩Macrophoma versabilis Pk.
⎧Marssonia Martini Sacc. & Ell.
⎪Marssonina Martini (Sacc. & Ell.) Magn.
⎨Gloeosporium Quercus Pk.
⎪Marssonia Quercus Pk.
⎩Marssonina Quercus (Pk.) Magn.

Quercus ilicifolia (*cont.*)

〔Erysiphe quercina S.
〔Microsphaera quercina (S.) Burrill.
Peniophora incarnata (P. ex Fr.) Massee.
Phoma glandicola Desm.
Phoma nervisequa (Cke.) Sacc.
〔Melanconis sigmoideum C. & E.
〔Pseudovalsa sigmoidea (C. & E.) Sacc.
Sphaeropsis linearis Pk.
Stereum ochraceoflavum S.
Titaea Clarkeae Ell. & Ev.

Quercus imbricaria Michx.

Cenangium confusum S.
Cenangium turgidum Fr.
Cronartium strobilinum Hedgc. & Hahn.
Endothia gyrosa Fr. p. p.
Fomes Everhartii (Ell. & Gall.) v. Schrenk.
Pyropolyporus Everhartii (Ell. & Gall.) Murrill.
〔Fomes igniarius (L. ex Fr.) Gill.
〔Pyropolyporus igniarius (L. ex Fr.) Murrill.
Hydnum Erinaceus Bull. ex Fr.
Irpex mollis B. & C.
〔Gloeosporium septorioides Sacc.
〔Marssonia quercina Wint.
Marssonia Martini Sacc. & Ell.
Microsphaera Alni (DC.) Wint. †
Microsphaera extensa C. & P.
Microsphaera quercina (S.) Burrill.
Microstroma album (Desm.) Sacc.
〔Acrosporium obductum (Ell. & Langlois) Sumstine.
〔Oidium obductum Ell. & Langlois.
Polyporus dryophilus B.
Polystictus pergamenus Fr.
Poria undata (P.) Bres.
Stagonospora septorioides Ell. & Ev.
Stereum fasciatum S.
Stictis radiata (L.) ex P.
Taphrina caerulescens (Mont. & Desm.) Tul.
Trematosphaeria mastoidea (Fr.) Wint.

Quercus Kelloggii Newberry.

〔Cronartium Cerebrum (Pk.) Hedgc. & Long.
〔Cronartium Quercus Schrt.
〔Cronartium strobilinum Hedgc. & Hahn.
〔Peridermium Cerebrum Pk. III.
Cylindrosporium Kelloggii Ell. & Ev.
Merulius confluens S.
Peniophora albostraminea Bres.
Phyllactinia corylea (P.) ex Karst.
Phyllactinia corylea (P.) ex Karst., var. angulata Salmon.
Polyporus dryophilus B.
〔Boletus croceus S. Syn. Car.
〔Laetiporus sulphureus (Bull. ex Fr.) Murrill.
〔Polyporus sulphureus (Bull.) ex Fr.
Septogloeum defolians Hark.

Quercus laurifolia Michx.

PEZIZINEAE

Ascomycetella floridana Ell. & Martin.
Helotium castaneum Sacc. & Ell.
〔Articulariella aurantiaca (Ell. & Martin) v. Höhnel.
〔Ascomycetella aurantiaca Ell. & Martin.
Leptophyma aurantiacum (Ell. & Martin) Sacc
〔Patellaria cyanea Ell. & Martin nec. Cke.
〔Patellea cyanea (Ell. & Martin) Sacc.

PERISPORIALES

〔Asterella discoidea (Ell. & Martin) Sacc.
〔Asterina discoidea Ell. & Martin.
〔Microthyriella discoidea (Ell. & Martin) Theissen.
〔Microthyrium discoideum (Ell. & Martin) Theissen.
〔Asterella patelloides (Ell. & Martin) Sacc.
〔Asterina erysiphoides Ell. & Martin.
〔Asterina patelloides Ell. & Martin.
〔Microthyriella patelloides (Ell. & Martin) Theissen.
〔Asterella pustulata (Ell. & Martin) Sacc.
〔Asterina pustulata Ell. & Martin.
〔Calothyrium pustulatum (Ell. & Martin) Theissen.
〔Asterella stomatophora (Ell. & Martin) Sacc.
〔Asterina stomatophora Ell. & Martin.
〔Calothyrium stomatophorum (Ell. & Martin) Theissen.
〔Asterella subcyanea (Ell. & Martin) Sacc.
〔Asterina subcyanea Ell. & Martin.
〔Dictyothyrium subcyaneum (Ell. & Martin) Theissen.
〔Microthyrium subcyaneum (Ell. & Martin) Theissen.
〔Microsphaera Alni (DC.) Wint. †, var. calocladophora (Atk.) Salmon.
〔Microsphaera calocladophora Atk.
Microsphaera densissima (S.) C. & P.
Microsphaera quercina (S.) Burrill.
Saccardia Martinii Ell. & Sacc.

HYPOCREALES

〔Calonectria erubescens (Rob.) Sacc.
〔Dialonectria erubescens (Rob.) Cke.

SPHAERIALES

〔Rhytisma tostum B. & C.
〔Trabutia tosta (B. & C.) Cke.
Trabutia quercina (Fr. & Rud.) Sacc. & Roum.
Venturia asterinoides Ell. & Martin.
Venturia cupulata Ell. & Martin.

MISCELLANEA

Helminthosporium folliculatum Cda., var. caroliniense Sacc.
Polyporus gilvus S.
Polyporus plebeius B.

Quercus laurifolia (*cont.*)
Septoria serpentaria Ell. & Martin.
Spongipellis fissilis (B. & C.) Murrill.
{ Ascomyces Quercus Cke.
{ Taphrina caerulescens (Mont. & Desm.) Tul.
Quercus leptophylla Rydb.
Endothia singularis (Syd.) Shear & Stevens.
Quercus lobata Nee.
Armillaria mellea (Vahl) ex Fr.
Cronartium strobilinum Hedgc. & Hahn.
Exoascus Quercus-lobatae Mayr.
{ Ganoderma polychromum (Copeland) Murrill.
{ Polyporus polychromus Copeland.
Polyporus dryophilus B.
Polyporus sulphureus (Bull.) ex Fr.
Quercus lyrata Walt.
{ Hypoxylon colliculosum (S.) M. A. Curtis.
{ Sphaeria colliculosa S.
Microsphaera Alni (DC.) Wint. †
Microsphaera quercina (S.) Burrill.
Polyporus dryophilus B.
Stereum subpileatum B. & C.
Quercus Macdonaldi Greene.
Dothiorella Gallae (S.) Starb.
Quercus macrocarpa Michx.

EXOASCACEAE
Taphrina caerulescens (Mont. & Desm.) Tul.
Taphrina Quercus (Cke.) Sacc.
{ Ascomyces extensus Pk.
{ Taphrina extensa (Pk.) Sacc.

HYSTERIINEAE
{ Hysterium pulicare N. A. F.
{ Hysterographium hiascens Rehm.
Hysterographium kansense Ell. & Ev.
{ Propolis faginea (Schrad.) ex Karst.
{ Stictis versicolor Schrad. ex Fr.

PYRENOMYCETINEAE
Daldinia vernicosa S.
{ Diatrype americana Ell. & Ev.
{ Phaeotrype Brencklei Sacc.
Diatrype americana Ell. & Ev., var. Quercus Rehm.
Endothia parasitica (Murrill) P. J. & H. W. Anderson.
Eutypa astera (Nits.) Fckl.
Eutypa lata (P. ex Fr.) Tul.
Microsphaera Alni (DC.) Wint. †
Microsphaera Alni (DC.) Wint. †, var. extensa (C. & P.) Salmon.
Microsphaera quercina (S.) Burrill.
Nummularia Bulliardi Tul.
Nummularia repanda (Fr.) Nits., var. querceti Rehm.
{ Phyllactinia corylea (P.) ex Karst.
{ Phyllactinia suffulta (Reb.) ex Sacc.
Phyllactinia corylea (P.) ex Karst., v. arangulata Salmon.

Rosellinia Gaudefroyi Fabre.
Sphaerella maculiformis (P. ex Fr.) Awd.
Sphaerella spleniata C. & P.
{ Albigo lanestris O. Kuntze.
{ Sphaerotheca lanestris Hark.
Teichospora obducens (Fr.) Fckl.
Valsa macrocarpa Ell. & Ev.
Venturia Orbicula (S.) C. & P.

UREDINALES
{ Cronartium conigenum Hedgc. & Hunt.
{ Cronartium Quercus Schrt.
{ Cronartium strobilinum Hedgc. & Hahn.
{ Uredo Quercus Brond.

THELEPHORACEAE
Aleurodiscus Oakesii (B. & C.) Cke.
Hymenochaete Curtisii B.
Stereum frustulatum Fr.
Stereum gausapatum Fr.

HYDNACEAE
Irpex flavus Klotzsch.

POLYPORACEAE
Daedalea quercina (L.) ex Fr.
Fomes applanatus (P. ex Wallr.) Gill.
{ Fomes Everhartii (Ell. & Gall.) v. Schrenk.
{ Pyropolyporus Everhartii (Ell. & Gall.) Murrill.
Fomes fraxinophilus Pk.
Fomes ohiensis B.
Polyporus dryadeus (P.) ex Fr.
Polyporus dryophilus B.
{ Hapalopilus gilvus (S.) Murrill.
{ Polyporus gilvus S.
Polyporus graveolens S.
Polyporus obtusus B.
Polyporus Radula (P.) ex Fr.
Polyporus sulphureus (Bull.) ex Fr.
Polyporus hirsutus (Schrad.) ex Fr.
Polystictus versicolor (L.) ex Fr.
{ Poria Andersoni (Ell. & Ev.) Neuman.
{ Xanthoporia Andersoni (Ell. & Ev.) Murrill.

FUNGI IMPERFECTI
Botrytis glauca Ell. & Ev.
{ Ceratophorum uncinatum (G. W. Clinton) Sacc.
{ Clasterosporium uncinatum G. W. Clinton.
{ Sporidesmium helicosporum Sacc.
Coryneum effiguratum S.
Fusarium nucicola Karst. & Har.
Gloeosporium canadense Ell. & Ev.
Gloeosporium nervisequum (Fckl.) Sacc.
Gloeosporium septorioides Sacc.
Helminthosporium macrocarpum Grev. ex Fr.
{ Gloeosporium Martini Sacc. & Ell.
{ Marssonia Martini Sacc. & Ell.
{ Marssonina Martini (Sacc. & Ell.) Magn.

Quercus macrocarpa (*cont.*)
Pestalozzia kansensis Ell. & Barthol.
Phleospora punctiformis Sacc.
Phyllosticta livida Ell. & Ev.
Phyllosticta Quercus Sacc. & Speg.
Volutella quercina S.

Quercus marilandica Muench.
⎧ Cronartium Cerebrum Hedgc. & Long.
⎪ Cronartium conigenum Hedgc. & Hunt.
⎨ Cronartium Quercus Schrt.
⎪ Peridermium Cerebrum Pk. III.
Endothia fluens Shear & Stevens.
Endothia gyrosa Fr. p. p.
⎧ Fomes Everhartii (Ell. & Gall.) v. Schrenk.
⎨ Pyropolyporus Everhartii (Ell. & Gall.) Mur-
⎩ rill.
Fomes igniarius (L. ex Fr.) Gill.
Hydnoporia fuscescens (S.) Murrill.
Microsphaera Alni (DC.) Wint. †
Microsphaera calocladophora Atk.
Microsphaera quercina (S.) Burrill.
Phyllactinia suffulta (Reb.) ex Sacc.
Polyporus dryophilus B.
Polyporus gilvus S.
Polyporus obtusus B.
Polyporus Spraguei B.
Polystictus pergamenus Fr.
⎧ Coriolus versicolor (L. ex Fr.) Quél.
⎨ Polystictus versicolor (L.) ex Fr.
Stereum subpileatum B. & C.
Taphrina caerulescens (Mont. & Desm.) Tul.

Quercus Michauxii Nutt.
Microsphaera Alni (DC.) Wint. †
Polyporus dryophilus B.
Stereum subpileatum B. & C.

Quercus montana Willd.
Coelosphaeria exilis (A. & S. ex Fr.) Sacc.
Fenestella condensata (B. & C.) Sacc.

Quercus Morehus Kellogg.
Leptothyrium californicum Bubák.
Phleospora Hanseni Bubák.

Quercus Muhlenbergii Engelm.
Fuligo ellipsoidea Lister.
Irpex mollis B. & C.
⎧ Marssonia Martini Sacc. & Ell.
⎨ Marssonina Martini (Sacc. & Ell.) Magn.
Microsphaera Alni (DC.) Wint. †
Microsphaera quercina (S.) Burrill.
Mycosphaerella maculiformis (P. ex Fr.)
Schrt.

Quercus nigra L.

EXOASCACEAE
⎧ Ascomyces caerulescens Mont. & Desm.
⎪ Ascomyces Quercus Cke.
⎨ Taphrina caerulescens (Mont. & Desm.) Tul.
⎩ Taphrina Quercus Sacc.

PEZIZINEAE
Bulgaria inquinans (P.) Fr.

PHACIDIINEAE
Phacidium dentatum Schm. ex Fr.

HYSTERIINEAE
⎧ Angelina conglomerata Fr.
⎪ Angelina rufescens (S.) Duby.
⎨ Ascobolus conglomeratus S.
⎩ Hysterium rufescens S.
Aulographum gracile Ell. & Martin.
Aulographum maculare B. & Br.
Dichaena strumosa Fr.
⎧ Glonium chlorinum (B. & C.) Sacc.
⎨ Glonium Cyrillae (B. & C.) Sacc.
⎩ Hysterium chlorinum B. & C.
Hypoderma ilicinum De Not.
⎧ Aulographum Liturae Cke.
⎨ Echidnodes Liturae (Cke.) Theissen & Syd.
⎩ Lembosia Liturae (Cke.) Sacc.

PERISPORIACEAE
Actinopelte japonica Sacc.?
⎧ Microsphaera Alni (DC.) Wint. †
⎪ Microsphaera Hedwigii Auct. Amer. p. p.
⎪ Microsphaera penicillata Auct. Amer. p. p.
⎪ Microsphaera quercina (S.) Burrill, var. ab-
⎪ breviata Atk.
⎨ Microsphaera Alni (DC.) Wint., var. calo-
⎪ cladophora (Atk.) Salmon.
⎪ Microsphaera calocladophora Atk.
⎩ Microsphaera quercina Auct. p. p.
⎧ Microsphaera Alni (DC.) Wint., var. extensa
⎪ (C. & P.) Salmon.
⎨ Microsphaera extensa C. & P.
⎪ Microsphaera quercina, var. extensa (C. & P.)
⎩ Atk.
Microsphaera quercina (S.) Burrill.
⎧ Phyllactinia corylea (P.) ex Karst.
⎪ Phyllactinia guttata (Wallr. ex Fr.) Lév.
⎨ Phyllactinia suffulta (Reb.) ex Sacc.
⎪ Phyllactinia suffulta (Reb.) ex Sacc., var.
⎩ macrospora Atk.

HYPOCREALES
Sphaerostilbe coccophila Tul.

SPHAERIALES
⎧ Byssosphaeria acanthostroma (Mont.) Cke.
⎨ Sphaeria acanthostroma Mont.
⎩ Trichosphaeria acanthostroma (Mont.) Sacc.
Diatrype bispora B. & C.
Diatrype dryophila Curr., var. minor Cke.
Diatrype subferruginea B. & Rav.
⎧ Endothia gyrosa Fr. p. p.
⎨ Endothia radicalis Farl.
Gnomonia clavulata Ell.
Hypoxylon glomiforme B. & C.
Hypoxylon marginatum (S.) B.
Laestadia polystigma Ell. & Ev.

Quercus nigra (*cont.*)

Diatrype Clypeus (S.) B.
Hypoxylon Clypeus (S.) M. A. Curtis.
Nummularia Bulliardi Auct. Amer. p. p.
Nummularia Clypeus (S.) Cke.
Sphaeria Clypeus S.
Sphaerella aquatica (S.) Cke.
Mycosphaerella punctiformis (P. ex Fr.) Schrt.
Sphaerella punctiformis (P. ex Fr.) Rabh.
Sphaeria punctiformis P. ex Fr.
Trabutia quercina (Fr. & Rud.) Sacc. & Roum.
Valsa ceratophora Tul.
Sphaeria Orbicula S.
Venturia Orbicula (S.) C. & P.

UREDINALES

Cronartium asclepiadeum Auct. Amer. p. p.
Cronartium asclepiadeum, var. Quercuum De Toni.
Cronartium Cerebrum Hedgc. & Long.
Cronartium Quercus Schrt.
Cronartium strobilinum Hedgc. & Hahn.
Uredo Quercus Brond.

AURICULARIACEAE

Septobasidium Langloisii Pat.
Septobasidium pseudopedicellatum Burt.

POLYPORACEAE

Cerrena unicolor (Bull. ex Fr.) Murrill.
Daedalea unicolor (Bull.) ex Fr.
Fomes Calkinsii (Murrill) Sacc. & D. Sacc.
Pyropolyporus Calkinsii Murrill.
Fomes Everhartii (Ell. & Gall.) v. Schrenk.
Mucronoporus Everhartii Ell. & Gall.
Fomes fomentarius (L. ex Fr.) Gill.
Boletus graveolens S.
Fomes graveolens (S.) Cke.
Globifomes graveolens (S.) Murrill.
Polyporus conglobatus B.
Polyporus graveolens (S.) Fr.
Fomes marmoratus B.
Ganoderma sessile Murrill.
Gloeoporus conchoides Mont.
Polyporus dryadeus (P.) ex Fr.
Inonotus dryophilus (B.) Murrill.
Polyporus dryophilus B.
Boletus hispidus Bull.
Polyporus hispidus (Bull.) ex Fr.
Polyporus sulphureus (Bull.) ex Fr.
Daedalea obtusa (B.) Neumann.
Polyporus obtusus B.
Polyporus unicolor S.
Spongipellis unicolor (S.) Murrill.
Polyporus cinnabarinus (Jacq.) ex Fr.
Polystictus cinnabarinus (Jacq. ex Fr.) Cke.
Poria incrassata (B. & C.) Burt.
Polyporus xantholoma S.
Poria xantholoma (S.) Cke.
Trametes subnivosa Murrill.

FUNGI IMPERFECTI

Chaetophoma quercifolia Cke.
Discella quercina Cke.
Discula quercina (Cke.) Sacc.
Gloeosporium septorioides Sacc.
?Gloeosporium septorioides Sacc., var. major Ell. & Ev.
Graphium explicatum B. & C.
Helminthosporium macrocarpum Grev. ex Fr.
Leptothyrium dryinum Sacc.
Microcera coccophila Desm.
Monochaetia Desmazierii Sacc.
Pestalozzia flagellata Earle.
Pestalozzia hysteriiformis B. & C.
Pestalozzia taphrinicola Ell. & Ev.
Phoma dendritica Thm.
Phyllosticta apiculata Sacc. & Syd.
Phyllosticta marginalis Ell. & Ev.
Phyllosticta livida Ell. & Ev.
Phyllosticta ludoviciana Ell. & Martin.
Polyscytalum cylindroides Sacc. & Ell.
Cylindrocolla miniata Sacc.
Sphaeridium miniatum Sacc.

Quercus nitescens Rydb.

Endothia singularis (Syd.) Shear & Stevens.

Quercus oblongifolia Torr.

Fomes Everhartii (Ell. & Gall.) v. Schrenk.
Polyporus dryophilus B.
Eutypa Mela (S.) Cke.
Eutypa quercina (Sacc.) Berl.
Eutypa velutina (Wallr.) Sacc., var. quercina Sacc.
Sphaeria Mela S.
Sphaeria velutina Wallr.

Quercus obtusiloba Michx.

Capnodium carolinense B. & Desm.
Cryptospora albofusca (C. & E.) Ell. & Ev.
Cryptosporella albofusca (C. & E.) Sacc.
Valsa albofusca C. & E.
Excipula subcalva Ell. & Ev.
Leptothyrium dryinum Sacc.
Ascochyta Quercus Trel.
Marssonia Martini Sacc. & Ell.
Marssonina Martini (Sacc. & Ell.) Magn.
Microsphaera Alni (DC.) Wint. †
Taphrina caerulescens (Mont. & Desm.) Tul.

Quercus palustris Muench.

Fomes applanatus (P. ex Wallr.) Gill.
Fomes Everhartii (Ell. & Gall.) v. Schrenk.
Mucronoporus Everhartii Ell. & Gall.
Pyropolyporus Everhartii (Ell. & Gall.) Murrill.
Microcera coccophila Desm.
Microsphaera Alni (DC.) Wint. †
Microsphaera Alni, var. extensa (Cke. & Pk.) Salmon.
Microsphaera extensa C. & P.
Microsphaera quercina Burrill p. p.

Quercus palustris (*cont.*)
Pestalozzia maura Ell. & Ev.
Phyllactinia corylea (P.) ex Karst.
Phyllactinia suffulta (Reb.) ex Sacc.
Phyllactinia corylea (P.) ex Karst, var. angulata Salmon.
Polyporus dryophilus B.
Septobasidium pseudopedicellatum Burt.
· Stereum subpileatum B. & C.
Taphria caerulescens (Mont. & Desm.) Schrt.
Taphrina caerulescens (Mont. & Desm.) Tul.
Trichopeziza capitata (Pk.) Sacc.
Quercus Phellos L.
Cronartium Quercuum Miyabe.
Cronartium strobilinum Hedgc. & Hahn.
Peridermium fusiforme Arth. & Kern. III.
Uredo Quercus Brond.
Endothia gyrosa Fr. p. p.
Hypospila Pustula (P. ex Fr.) Karst.
Phoma Pustula (P.) ex Fr.
Sphaeria Pustula P. ex Fr.
Melasmia Quercuum Atk.
Rhytisma tostum B. & C.
Microsphaera Alni (DC.) Wint. †
Microsphaera quercina (S.) Burrill.
Phyllactinia corylea (P.) ex Karst.
Phyllactinia suffulta (Reb.) ex Sacc.
Phyllactinia suffulta (Reb.) ex Sacc., var. macrospora Atk.
Polyporus dryophilus B.
Septobasidium pseudopedicellatum Burt.
Septoria neglecta Earle.
Sphaerella Phellos (S.) Cke.
Sphaeria Phellos S.
Stereum subpileatum B. & C.
Taphrina caerulescens (Desm. & Mont.) Tul.
Quercus Phellos L., var. **arenaria** Chapin,
Asterella intricata (Ell. & Martin) Sacc.
Asterina intricata Ell. & Martin.
Microthyriella? intricata (Ell. & Martin) Theissen.
Plochmopeltis intricata (Ell. & Martin) Theissen.
Quercus prinoides Willd.
Cronartium Quercus Schrt.
Cronartium strobilinum Hedgc. & Hahn.
Uredo Quercus Brond.
Diaporthe parasitica (Murrill) P. J. & H. W. Anderson.
Diatrype albopruinosa (S.) C. & E.
Marssonia Martini Sacc. & Ell.
Microsphaera Alni (DC.) Wint. †
Microsphaera Alni, var. extensa (C. & P.) Salmon.
Microsphaera quercina (S.) Burrill.
Phyllosticta Quercus-Prini Ell. & Ev.
Polyporus dryophilus B.
Polyscytalum sericeum Sacc.
Sphaerella spleniata C. & P.

Quercus Prinus L.

ASCOMYCETES

Ascomycetella Conidia.
Coelosphaeria exilis (A. & S. ex Fr.) Sacc.
Lasiosphaeria exilis (A. & S. ex Fr.) Cke.
Sphaeria exilis A. & S. ex Fr.
Cyathicula quisquiliaris Ell. & Ev.
Endothia fluens Shear & Stevens.
Endothia fluens, var. mississippiensis Shear & Stevens.
Endothia gyrosa Fr. p. p.
Endothia parasitica (Murrill) P. J. & H. W. Anderson.
Fenestella condensata (B. & C.) Sacc.
Fenestella tumida (P. ex Fr.) Sacc.
Valsa condensata B. & C.
Microsphaera Alni, var. extensa (C. & P.) Salmon.
Microsphaera quercina (S.) Burrill.
Mitrula phalloides (Bull.) ex Chev.
Mollisia prinicola (Ell. & Ev.) Sacc.
Peziza prinicola Ell. & Ev.
Physalospora Cydoniae Arnaud.
Pseudovalsa sigmoidea (C. & E.) Sacc.
Venturia Orbicula (S.) C. & P.

UREDINALES

Cronartium Quercus Schrt.
Cronartium strobilinum Hedgc. & Hahn.

HYMENOMYCETINEAE

Fomes Everhartii (Ell. & Gall.) v. Schrenk.
Fomes igniarius (L. ex Fr.) Gill.
Polyporus dryadeus (P.) Fr.
Polyporus rheades Fr.
Polyporus Spraguei B.
Polystictus hirsutus (Wulf.) ex Fr.
Stereum candidum (S.) Fr.
Stereum complicatum Fr.
Stereum subpileatum B. & C.

FUNGI IMPERFECTI

Actinopelte japonica Sacc.?
Cylindrium griseum Bon.
Diplodia longispora C. & E.
Diplodia suberina Dur. & Mont.
Dothiorella quercina (Pk.) Sacc.
Gloeosporium nervisequum (Fckl.) Sacc.
Gloeosporium septorioides Sacc.
Isaria verticillata Atk.
Marssonia Martini Sacc. & Ell.
Marssonia Quercus Pk.
Myxosporium castaneum, var. Quercus Pk.
Phyllosticta phomiformis Sacc.
Phyllosticta Quercus-Prini Ell. & Ev.
Polyscytalum sericeum Sacc.
Sphaeropsis abundans Pk.
Sphaeropsis Malorum B.
Sphaeropsis quercina Cke. & Ell.
Strumella coryneoidea Sacc. & Wint.

Quercus pungens Leibm.
  Endothia singularis (Syd.) Shear & Stevens.

Quercus robur L.
  Cronartium strobilinum Hedgc. & Hahn.
  Cytospora chrysosperma (P.) ex Fr.
  Daedalea quercina (L.) ex Fr.
  Marssonia Martini Sacc. & Ell.
  Microsphaera Alni (DC.) Wint. †
  Microsphaera quercina (S.) Burrill.
  Polyporus dryophilus B.
  Polyporus rubriporus Quél.
  Polystictus hirsutulus (S.) Cke.
  Taphrina caerulescens (Mont. & Desm.) Tul.

Quercus rubra L.

MYXOMYCETES

  Clastoderma debaryanum Blytt.
  Orcadella operculata Wingate.
  Orthotrichia microcephala Wingate.

EXOASCACEAE

{ Ascomyces caerulescens Mont. & Desm.
{ Taphrina caerulescens (Mont. & Desm.) Tul.
{ Ascomyces rubrobrunneus Pk.
{ Taphrina rubrobrunnea (Pk.) Sacc.

PEZIZINEAE

  Bulgaria inquinans (P.) Fr.
{ Cenangium populneum (P.) Rehm.
{ Dermatea fascicularis (A. & S.) ex Fr.
  Dasyscypha Rhytismatis (Phil.) Cke.
{ Durella similis (Gerard) Sacc.
{ Patellaria similis Gerard.
{ Peziza pollinaria Cke.
{ Trichopeziza pollinaria (Cke.) Sacc.

PHACIDIINEAE

  Coccomyces dentatus (Schm. ex Fr.) Sacc.
  Propolidium atrovirens (Fr.) Rehm.

HYSTERIINEAE

  Angelina rufescens (S.) Duby.
  Morenoella (?) quercina (Ell. & Martin)
    Theissen.

PERISPORIALES

  Microsphaera Alni (DC.) Wint. †
  Microsphaera calocladophora Atk.
{ Microsphaera Alni (DC.) Wint., var. extensa
    (C. & P.) Salmon.
{ Microsphaera extensa C. & P.
{ Erysiphe quercinum S.
{ Microsphaera abbreviata Pk.
{ Microsphaera quercina (S.) Burrill.
{ Phyllactinia corylea (P.) ex Karst.
{ Phyllactinia suffulta (Reb.) ex Sacc.
  Phyllactinia corylea (P.) ex Karst., var. angu-
    lata Salmon.
{ Albigo lanestris (Hark.) O. Kuntze.
{ Sphaerotheca lanestris Hark.

SPHAERIALES

  Actinopelte japonica Sacc.?
  Anthostoma atropunctatum (S.) Sacc.
  Botryosphaeria quercuum (S.) Sacc.
  Ceratostomella pluriannulata Hedgc.
{ Diatrype quercina (P.) ex Fr.
{ Diatrypella quercina (P. ex Fr.) Nits.
{ Sphaeria quercina P. ex Fr.
  Didymella lophospora Sacc.
  Endothia fluens Shear & Stevens.
{ Endothia gyrosa Fr. p. p.
{ Endothia radicalis Farl.
  Eutypa Eutypa (Achar. ex Fr.) House.
{ Eutypa limiformis (S.) B.
{ Eutypa spinosa (P. ex Fr.) Tul.
{ Eutypella spinosa (P. ex Fr.) Coons. Note.
{ Sphaeria limiformis S.
{ Sphaeria penicillosa S.
{ Sphaeria spinosa P. ex Fr.
{ Valsa spinosa (P. ex Fr.) Nits.
  Hypoxylon serpens (P.) ex Fr.
{ Byssosphaeria luteobasis (Ell.) Cke.
{ Eutypa luteobasis (Ell.) Sacc.
{ Lasiosphaeria luteobasis (Ell.) Ell. & Ev.
{ Sphaeria luteobasis Ell.
  Lasiosphaeria mutabilis (P. ex Fr.) Fckl.
  Nectria cinnabarina (Tode) ex Fr.
  Nummularia Clypeus Cke.
  Sphaerella maculiformis (P. ex Fr.) Awd.
  Sphaeria obscura S.
{ Coniosphaeria inflata (Ell.) Cke.
{ Sphaeria inflata Ell.
{ Teichospora inflata (Ell.) Ell. & Ev.
{ Teichosporella inflata (Ell.) Berl.
{ Zignoella inflata (Ell.) Sacc.
?Valsa leucostoma (P.) ex Fr., var. parvifructa
    Pk.
{ Valsaria exasperans (Gerard) Sacc.
{ Valsaria insitiva Fung. Columb. *3900.*

UREDINALES

{ Cronartium Cerebrum Hedgc. & Long.
{ Cronartium conigenum Hedgc. & Hunt.
{ Cronartium Quercus Schrt.

THELEPHORACEAE

{ Stereum fasciatum (S.) Fr.
{ Thelephora fasciata S.
{ Thelephora versicolor, var. fasciata (S.) **Fr.**
  Stereum frustulosum (P.) Fr.
  Stereum spadiceum (S.) Fr.
  Stereum subpileatum B. & C.

HYDNACEAE

  Hydnum Erinaceus Bull. ex Fr.
{ Hydnum flabel'iforme B.
{ Hydnum Rhois S.
{ Irpex crassus B. & C.
{ Irpex mollis B. & C.
{ Irpiciporus mollis (B. & C.) Murrill.

Quercus rubra (*cont.*)

POLYPORACEAE

Boletus hemichrysus B. & C.
Favolus canadensis Klotzsch.
Fomes applanatus (P. ex Wallr.) Gill.
{ Fomes Everhartii (Ell. & Gall.) v. Schrenk.
{ Pyropolyporus Everhartii (Ell. & Gall.) Murrill.
{ Fomes graveolens (S.) Cke.
{ Globifomes graveolens (S.) Murrill.
Fomes igniarius (L. ex Fr.) Gill.
Fomes lobatus (S.) Cke.
{ Polyporus cuticularis (Bull.) ex Fr.
{ Xanthochrous fuscovelutinus Pat.
Polyporus adustus (Willd.) ex Fr.
Polyporus croceus (P.) ex Fr.
Polyporus dryadeus (P.) ex Fr.
Polyporus dryophilus B.
Polyporus hirsutus (Wulf.) ex Fr.
Polyporus obtusus B.
Polyporus sanguineus (L.) ex Fr.
Polyporus Spraguei B.
{ Laetiporus speciosus (Batt.) ex Murrill.
{ Polyporus sulphureus (Bull.) ex Fr.
Polyporus versicolor (L.) ex Fr.
{ Coriolus biformis (Fr.) Pat.
{ Polyporus biformis Fr.
{ Polyporus carolinensis B. & C.
{ Polystictus biformis Fr.
{ Polyporus pargamenus Fr.
{ Polystictus pergamenus Fr.
Poria Medulla-panis (P. ex Fr.) Cke.

AGARICACEAE

Armillaria mellea (Vahl) ex Fr.
Cortinarius elegantior Fr., var.
Cortinarius rubipes Kauffman.
Marasmius Copelandi Pk.
{ Lentinus strigosus (B. & C.) Henn.
{ Panus strigosus B. & C.
Lenzites betulina (L.) ex Fr.
Pleurotus ostreatus (Jacq.) ex Fr.
Russula emetica Fr.

SPHAEROPSIDALES

{ ?Aposphaeria allantella Sacc. & Roum.
{ " Aposphaeria allantella Pk." sec. Sacc.
{ Phoma allantella Pk.
Cytospora intermedia Sacc.
Discosia Artocreas (Tode) ex Fr.
Leptothyrium dryinum Sacc.
Phoma glandicola Lév.
Phomopsis fraterna Fairman.
Phyllosticta Quercus-rubrae Gerard.
Septoria querceti Thm.
Septoria quercicola (Desm.) Sacc.
{ Botryodiplodia ostiolata Ell. & Ev.
{ Sphaeropsis gallae (S.) Archer.
Sphaeropsis quercina Cke. & Hark.

MELANCONIALES

Coryneum Kunzei Cda.
{ Gloeosporium canadense Ell. & Ev.
{ Gloeosporium nervisequum (Fckl.) Sacc.
Gloeosporium quercinum Westd.
Gloeosporium septorioides Sacc.
{ Hainesia Lythri (Desm.) v. Höhnel.
{ Sclerotiopsis concava (Desm.) Shear & Dodge.
{ Gloeosporium Martini Sacc. & Ell.
{ Marssonia Martini Sacc. & Ell.
{ Marssonina Martini (Sacc. & Ell.) Magn.
Melanconium bicolor Nees ex Fr.
Monochaetia Desmazierii Sacc.
Monochaetia taphrinicola (Ell. & Ev.) Sacc.
Pestalozzia clavispora Atk.
Pestalozzia flagellata Earle.

HYPHOMYCETES

Cephalothecium roseum Cda.
{ Botrytis macrospora Ditm. ex Fr.
{ Dactylium macrosporum (Ditm.) ex Fr.
Graphium rigidum (P.) Sacc.
Strumella coryneoidea Sacc. & Wint.
Tubercularia quercina Opiz.

Quercus stellata Wang.

ASCOMYCETES

Acrospermum viridulum B. & C.
Capnodium caroliniense B. & Desm.
{ Capnodium quercinum B. & Desm.
{ Fumago quercina P.
{ Coccomyces dentatus (Schm. ex Fr.) Sacc.
{ Phacidium dentatum Schm. ex Fr.
{ Cryptosporella albofusca (C. & E.) Sacc.
{ Valsa albofusca C. & E.
Diatrype Stigma (Hoffm.) ex Fr.
Eutypa velutina (Wallr.) Sacc.
Microsphaera Alni (DC.) Wint. †
{ Microsphaera penicillata Auct. Amer. p. p.
{ Microsphaera quercina (S.) Burrill.
Phyllactinia suffulta (Reb.) ex Sacc.
{ Sphaerella punctiformis (P. ex Fr.) Rabh.
{ Sphaeria punctiformis P. ex Fr.
{ Albigo lanestris (Hark.) O. Kuntze.
{ Sphaerotheca lanestris Hark.
Taphrina caerulescens (Mont. & Desm.) Tul.
Valsa leiphaemioides B. & C.

UREDINALES

{ Cronartium conigenum Hedgc. & Hunt.
{ Cronartium Quercus Schrt.
{ Cronartium strobilinum Hedgc. & Hahn.
{ Uredo Quercus Brond.

HYMENOMYCETINEAE

Fomes Everhartii (Ell. & Gall.) v. Schrenk.
{ Hymenochaete Curtisii (B.) Morg.
{ Stereum Curtisii B.

Quercus stellata (*cont.*)

⎰ Hymenochaete tabacina (Sow. ex Fr.) Lév.
⎱ Stereum tabacinum (Sow.) ex Fr.
Irpex mollis B. & C.
Lentinus Lecomtei Fr.
Lenzites betulina (L.) ex Fr.
⎰ Boletus cinnabarinus Jacq. ex Fr.
⎱ Polyporus cinnabarinus (Jacq.) ex Fr.
Polyporus cupuliformis B. & C.
Polyporus dryadeus (P.) ex Fr.
Polyporus dryophilus B.
Polyporus obtusus B.
Polyporus sulphureus (Bull.) ex Fr.
Schizophyllum commune Fr.
⎰ Stereum candidum (S.) Fr.
⎨ Thelephora candida S. Syn. Car.
⎱ Thelephora candidissima S. Am. bor.
Stereum ochraceoflavum (S.) Rav.
Stereum subpileatum B. & C.

FUNGI IMPERFECTI

⎰ Camarosporium variabile (B. & C.) Sacc.
⎱ Hendersonia variabilis B. & C.
Cladosporium microspermum B. & C.
⎰ Cylindrium pallidum Thm.
⎱ Fusidium pallidum (Thm.) Sacc.
Excipula subcalva Ell. & Ev.
Gloeosporium Lathami Dearness.
⎰ Gloeosporium Martini Ell. & Ev.
⎱ Marssonia Martini (Ell. & Ev.) Sacc. & Ell.
Helminthosporium macrocarpon Grev., var. caudatum B. & C.
Isaria verticillata Atk.
Phoma innumerabilis Thm.
Phoma vixvisibilis Thm.
Phyllosticta phomiformis Sacc.
Rhinotrichum breve B. & C.

MISCELLANEA

Geasteroides texensis Long.

Quercus texana Buckley.

Fomes Everhartii (Ell. & Gall.) v. Schrenk.
Fomes igniarius (L. ex Fr.) Gill.
Polyporus dryadeus (P.) ex Fr.
Polyporus dryophilus B.
Polyporus obtusus B.
Stereum subpileatum B. & C.

Quercus tomentella Engelm.

Comatricha nigra (P.) Schrt.
Hydnum ochraceum P. ex Fr.
Merulius pilosus Burt.
Naematelia nucleata (S.) Fr.
Odontia viridis (A. & S. ex Fr.) Bres.
Rosellinia aquila (Fr.) De Not.

Quercus tomentosa Willd.

⎰ Cronartium Quercus Schrt.
⎱ Cronartium Quercuum Miyabe.

Quercus Toumeyi Sargent.

Polyporus dryophilus B.

Quercus undulata Torr.

Amphisphaeria melantera Ell. & Ev.
Astrodochium Coloradense Ell. & Ev.
Cucurbitaria quercina Ell. & Ev.
Fomes Everhartii (Ell. & Gall.) v. Schrenk.
⎰ Fomes praerimosus (Murrill) Sacc. & D. Sacc.
⎱ Pyropolyporus praerimosus Murrill.
Haplosporella microspora Ell. & Ev.
Polyporus dryophilus B.
Taphrina caerulescens (Mont. & Desm.) Tul.

Quercus utahensis Rydb.

⎰ Calopactis singularis Syd.
⎱ Endothia singularis (Syd.) Shear & Stevens.
Diatrype paurospora Sacc.
Sphaerella spleniata C. & P.
Stemonitis pallida Wingate.
Tremella lutescens (P.) ex Fr.

Quercus velutina Lam.

EXOASCACEAE

⎰ Taphrina caerulescens (Mont. & Desm.) Tul.
⎱ Taphrina Quercus (Cke.) Sacc.

PEZIZINEAE

⎰ Articularia quercina (Pk.) v. Höhnel.
⎨ Ascomycetella quercina Pk.
⎱ Cookella quercina (Pk.) Sacc.
Bulgaria inquinans (P.) Fr.
⎰ Cenangium sticticum (B. & C.) Sacc.
⎱ ?Tympanis stictica B. & C.
⎰ Chlorosplenium chlora (S.) Massee.
⎱ Peziza crocitincta B. & C.
⎰ Pezizella crocitincta (B. & C.) Sacc.
⎰ Durella fusco-atra (Ell.) Rehm.
⎨ Lecanidion fusco-atrum (Ell.) Rehm.
⎱ Patellaria fusco-atra Ell.
Peziza occidentalis S.

PHACIDIINEAE

Urnula Craterium (S.) Fr.

HYSTERIINEAE

⎰ Dichaena quercina (P.) ex Fr.
⎱ Psilospora quercina (P. ex Fr.) Wint.
Dichaena strumosa Fr.
Hysterium pulicare P. ex Fr.
⎰ Gloniella hyalina (C. & P.) Sacc.
⎨ Gloniopsis gerardiana Sacc.
⎨ Gloniopsis gloniopsis (Gerard) House.
⎨ Glonium hyalosporum Gerard.
⎨ Hysterium gloniopsis Gerard.
⎨ Hysterium hyalinum C. & P.
⎨ Hysterium hyalosporum Gerard sec Ell. & Ev.
⎨ Hysterographium gloniopsis (Gerard) Ell. & Ev.
⎨ Hysterium flexuosum Rav. Fung. Car.
⎨ Hysterium flexuosum Myc. Univ. *181*.
⎨ Hysterium vulvatum S.
⎱ Hysterographium vulvatum (S.) Sacc.

Quercus velutina (*cont.*)

ERYSIPHACEAE

Microsphaera Alni (DC.) Wint.†
Microsphaera quercina, var. abbreviata Atk.
Microsphaera Alni, var. extensa (C. & P.) Salmon.
{ Erysiphe densissima S.
{ Microsphaera densissima (S.) C. & P.
Microsphaera quercina (S.) Burrill.
{ Phyllactinia corylea (P.) ex Karst.
{ Phyllactinia guttata (Wallr. ex Fr.) Lév.
{ Phyllactinia suffulta (Reb.) ex Sacc.
Phyllactinia corylea, var. tomentosa Macbr. & Pk.

SPHAERIALES

{ Anthostoma atropunctatum (S.) Sacc.
{ Sphaeria atropunctata S.
Anthostoma dryophilum (Curr.) Sacc., var. minor Rehm.
{ Ceratostomella cirrhosa (P. ex Fr.) Sacc.
{ Sphaeria cirrhosa P. ex Fr.
Chaetomium elatum Kze. ex Fr.
Diatrype albopruinosa (S.) Cke., var. macrospora Berl.
Diatrype platystoma (S.) M. A. Curtis.
Diatrype roseola Wint.
Diatrype Stigma (Hoffm.) ex Fr.
{ Didymella clavulata (Ell.) Sacc.
{ Gnomonia clavulata Ell.
Didymosphaeria cupula (Ell.) Sacc.
Endothia fluens, var. mississippiensis Shear & Stevens.
Endothia gyrosa Fr. p. p.
Endothia parasitica (Murrill) P. J. & H. W. Anderson.
{ Endothia fluens Shear & Stevens.
{ Endothia virginiana P. J. & H. W. Anderson.
Eutypa velutina (Wallr.) Sacc.
Hypoxylon annulatum (S.) Mont.
Hypoxylon multiforme Fr.
{ Laestadia polystigma (Ell. & Ev.) Sacc.
{ Sphaerella polystigma Ell. & Ev.
{ Herpotrichia Pezizula (B. & C.) Wint.
{ Lasiosphaeria Pezizula (B. & C.) Sacc.
{ Sphaeria Pezizula B. & C.
Metasphaeria quercina Ell. & Ev.
Nectria lecanodes Ces.
Nummularia Bulliardi Tul.
Nummularia punctulata (B. & Rav.) Sacc.
Ophiobolus hamasporus Ell. & Ev.
{ Melanconis sigmoideum C. & E.
{ Pseudovalsa sigmoidea (C. & E.) Sacc.
Rosellinia albolanata Ell. & Ev.
Valsa clausa C. & E.
Valsa lutescens Ell.
Valsa multiplex C. & E.

Diatrype obesa B. & C.
Diatrype quadrata (S.) B.
Melogramma obesum Rav. Fung. Am.
Valsaria quadrata (S.) Sacc.
{ Sphaeria Orbicula S.
{ Venturia Orbicula (S.) C. & P.
Xylaria corniformis Fr.
Xylaria Hypoxylon (L.) ex Grev.

UREDINALES

{ Cronartium asclepiadeum (Willd.) Fr., var. Quercuum De Toni.
Cronartium Cerebrum (Pk.) Hedgc. & Long.
Cronartium conigenum Hedgc. & Hunt.
Cronartium Quercus Schrt.
Cronartium Quercuum Miyabe.
Cronartium strobilinum Hedgc. & Hahn.
Peridermium Cerebrum Pk. III.

TREMELLACEAE

Exidia recisa Fr.
Naematelia nucleata (S.) Fr.
Ulocolla foliacea (P.) Bref.

THELEPHORACEAE

{ Aleurodiscus Micheneri (B. & C.) Massee.
{ Artocreas Micheneri B. & C.
{ Corticium subgiganteum B.
{ Michenera Artocreas B. & C.
{ Corticium galactinum (Fr.) Burt.
{ Thelephora galactina Fr.
Hymenochaete scabriseta Cke.
Stereum complicatum Fr.
Stereum fasciatum (S.) Fr.
Stereum subpileatum B. & C.
Stereum versicolor (Sw.) ex Fr.

HYDNACEAE

Hydnum Erinaceus Bull. ex Fr.
Irpex mollis B. & C.
Irpex tabacinus B. & C.
Radulum orbiculare Fr.
Radulum quercinum (P.) ex Fr

POLYPORACEAE

Boletus speciosus Frost.
{ Cerrenella Ravenelii (B.) Murrill.
{ Daedalea Ravenelii B.
Fomes applanatus (P. ex Wallr.) Gill.
{ Fomes Everhartii (Ell. & Gall.) v. Schrenk.
{ Pyropolyporus Everhartii (Ell. & Gall.) Murrill.
{ Fomes lucidus (Fr.) Cke.
{ Ganoderma lucidum (Fr.) Karst.
{ Ganoderma sessile Murrill.
{ Polyporus lucidus Fr.
Lenzites betulina (L.) ex Fr.
Merulius ambiguus B.
{ Boletus adustus Willd. ex Fr.
{ Myriadoporus adustus (Willd. ex Fr.) Pk.
{ Polyporus adustus (Willd.) ex Fr.

Quercus velutina (*cont.*)
Polyporus amygdalinus B. & Rav.
Polyporus Berkeleyi B.
Polyporus dryadeus (P.) ex Fr.
Polyporus dryophilus B.
Polyporus epileucus Fr.
{ Boletus frondosus S. Syn. Car.
{ Polyporus frondosus (Schrank) ex Fr.
Polyporus gilvus S.
{ Inonotus hirsutus (Scop. ex Fr.) Murrill.
{ Polyporus hispidus (Bull.) ex Fr.
Polyporus pargamenus Fr.
{ Polyporus cupuliformis B. & C.
{ Polyporus pocula (S.) B. & C.
{ Porodisculus pendulus (S.) Murrill.
{ Porodiscus pendulus (S.) Murrill.
Polyporus reniformis ? Morg.
Polyporus rutilans (P.) ex Fr.
Polyporus Spraguei B.
Polyporus stipticus (P.) ex Fr.
Polyporus sulphureus (Bull.) ex Fr.
Polyporus sulphureus (Bull.) Fr., var. Over-
    holtsii Rosen.
Polyporus trabeus Rostk.
{ Polyporus obtusus B.
{ Polyporus unicolor S.
{ Trametes unicolor (S.) Murrill.
{ Polyporus cinnabarinus (Jacq.) ex Fr.
{ Polystictus cinnabarinus (Jacq. ex Fr.) Cke.
{ Pycnoporus cinnabarinus (Jacq. ex Fr.) Karst.
{ Trametes cinnabarina (Jacq.) ex Fr.
Polystictus hirsutulus S.
{ Polyporus versicolor (L.) ex Fr.
{ Polystictus versicolor (L.) ex Fr.
{ Polyporus purpureus Fr.
{ Poria purpurea (Fr.) Cke.
Poria Radula P. ex Fr.

AGARICACEAE

Crepidotus applanatus (P.) ex Fr.
Lentinus tigrinus (Bull.) ex Fr.
Marasmius amadelphus (Bull.) ex Fr.
Marasmius foetidus (Sow.) ex Fr.
Panus stipticus (Bull.) ex Fr.
Pholiota adiposa Fr.
Tricholoma transmutans Pk.

SPHAEROPSIDALES

Asteroma tinctorium Cke.
Chaetophoma maculosa Ell. & Morg.
{ Cytospora pallida Ell. & Ev.
{ Neocytispora pallida Ell. & Ev. in herb.
{ Fusicoccum ellisianum Sacc. & Syd.
{ Fusicoccum quercinum Ell. & Ev.
Phoma nervisequia (Cke.) Sacc.
Septoria dryina Cke.
Septoria querceti Thm.
{ Dothiorella quercina (C. & E.) Sacc.
{ Sphaeropsis quercina C. & E.

MELANCONIALES

Gloeosporium septorioides Sacc.
{ ?Gloesporium septorioides Sacc., var. major
{   Ell. & Ev.
{ Marssonia quercina Wint.
{ Gloeosporium nervisequum (Fckl.) Sacc.
{ Gnomonia veneta (Sacc. & Speg.) Klebahn.
{ Myxosporium valsoideum (Sacc.) Allescher.
{ Hainesia Lythri (Desm.) v. Höhnel.
{ Sclerotiopsis concava (Desm.) Shear & Dodge.
Marssonia Martini Sacc. & Ell.
Myxosporium stellatum Dearness.
Pestalozzia hysteriiformis B. & C.
Pestalozzia monochaeta Desm.
Pestalozzia stellata B. & C.
Pestalozzia taphrinicola Ell. & Ev.
Pestalozzia uncinata Ell. & Kellerm.

HYPHOMYCETES

Polyscytalum sericeum Sacc.
Strumella coryneoidea Sacc. & Wint.
Trichoderma lignorum (Tode) ex Harz.

MISCELLANEA

Hemitrichia stipitata (Mass.) Macbr.
Lycoperdon leprosum B. & Rav.

Quercus virginiana Mill.

EXOASCACEAE

Taphrina caerulescens (Mont. & Desm.) Tul.

PEZIZINEAE

Patellaria cyanea Ell. & Martin nec Cke.
Pocillum americanum Cke.
Phillipsiella atra Cke.

PHACIDIINEAE

Stictis quercifolia C. & E.

HYSTERIINEAE

{ Blitrydium hiascens (B. & C.) Sacc.
{ Hysterium hiascens B. & C.
Hypoderma ilicinum De Not.
{ Aulographum quercinum Ell. & Martin.
{ Lembosia quercina (Ell. & Martin) Tracy &
{   Earle.
{ Morenoella (?) quercina (Ell. & Martin) Theis-
{   sen.

PYRENOMYCETINEAE

Endothia gyrosa Fr. p. p.
Hypoxylon bicolor Ell. & Ev.
{ Dothidella Janus (B. & C.) v. Höhnel.
{ Heptameria Janus (B. & C.) Cke.
{ Leptosphaeria Janus (B. & C.) Sacc.
{ Sphaeria Janus B. & C.
Saccardia quercina Cke.
Sphaerella caespitosa Ell. & Ev.
{ Criella erythrospora (B. & C.) Speg.
{ Rhytisma erythrosporum B. & C.
{ Trabutia erythrospora (B. & C.) Theissen &
{   Syd.

Quescus virginiana (*cont.*)
⎰ Rhytisma tostum B. & C.
⎱ Trabutia quercina (Fr. & Rud.) Sacc. & Roum.
⎰ Trabutia tosta (B. & C.) Cke.

UREDINALES

⎰ Cronartium asclepiadeum (Willd.) Fr., var.
⎰   Quercuum De Toni.
⎱ Cronartium Quercus Schrt.
⎰ Cronartium strobilinum Hedgc. & Hahn.
⎱ Uredo Quercus Brond.

THELEPHORACEAE

Hymenochaete rubiginosa (Schrad. ex Fr.) Lév.
Stereum fasciatum S.
Stereum subpileatum B. & C.

POLYPORACEAE

⎰ Fomes Calkinsii (Murrill) Sacc. & D. Sacc.
⎱ Pyropolyporus Calkinsii Murrill.
⎰ Fomes dependens (Murrill) Sacc. & Trott.
⎱ Pyropolyporus dependens Murrill.
Fomes igniarius (L. ex Fr.) Gill.
Fomes torulosus (P.) Lloyd.
⎰ Polyporus amygdalinus B. & Rav.
⎱ Trametes amygdalinus (B. & Rav.) Murrill.
Polyporus dryophilus B.
⎰ Elfvingiella marmorata (B. & C.) Murrill.
⎱ Polyporus marmoratus B. & C.
Polyporus pseudosulphureus Long.
Polyporus sulphureus (Bull.) ex Fr.
⎰ Fomitiporia dryophila Murrill.
⎱ Poria dryophila (Murrill) Sacc. & Trott.
Poria Medulla-panis (P. ex Fr.) Cke.

FUNGI IMPERFECTI

Cercospora polytricha Cke.
⎰ Ascochyta Quercuum (Cke.) Sacc.
⎰ Diplodina Quercuum (Cke.) Tracy & Earle.
⎱ Sphaerellopsis Quercuum Cke.
Hendersonia taphrinicola Tracy & Earle.
⎰ Hendersonia virens Ell. & Martin.
⎱ Stagonospora virens Ell. & Martin.
Passalora? melioloides Tracy & Earle.
Pestalozzia concentrica B. & Rav.
Pestalozzia maura Ell. & Ev.
Phoma glandicola Lév.
Phyllosticta Quercus-Ilicis Sacc.
Phyllosticta virens Ell. & Ev.
Polyscytalum cylindroides Sacc. & Ell.

Quercus Watsoni Trel.
Teichospora brachyasca Ell. & Ev.

Quercus Wislizeni A. DC.
Laestadia auripuncta Hark.
Phyllosticta Wislizeni Ell. & Ev.
Polyporus dryophilus B.
Polyporus sulphureus (Bull.) ex Fr.

Quercus sp. indet.

MYXOMYCETES

Arcyria cinerea (Bull.) P.
Arcyria denudata (E. P. Sheldon) Macbr.
Arcyria nutans (Bull.) Grev.
Badhamia decipiens (M. A. Curtis) B.
Cienkowskia reticulata (A. & S.) Rostf.
Comatricha flaccida (Lister) Morg.
Comatricha Stemonitis (Scop.) E. P. Sheldon.
Craterium leucocephalum (P.) Ditm.
Cribraria aurantiaca Schrad.
Diachaea leucopoda (Bull.) Rostf.
Diderma floriforme (Bull.) P.
Diderma hemisphaericum (Bull.) Hornem.
Diderma testaceum (Schrad.) P.
Didymium cinereum (Batsch) Fr.
Didymium furfuraceum (Schum.) Fr.
Didymium xanthopus (Ditm.) Fr.
Enteridium splendens Morg.
Fuligo ovata (Schaeff.) Macbr.
Hemiarcyria longifila Rex.
Lamproderma scintillans (B. & Br.) Lister.
Leocarpus fragilis (Dicks.) Rostf.
Lycogala epidendrum [Buxb. ex L.] Fr.
⎰ Ophiotheca chrysosperma Curr.
⎱ Perichaena depressa Lib.
Ophiotheca Wrightii B. & C.
⎰ Diderma brunneolum Phil.
⎱ Physarum brunneolum Phil.
Physarum nutans P.
Physarum nutans P., var. leucophaeum (Fr.)
    Lister.
Physarum sinuosum (Bull.) Weinm.
Stemonitis confluens C. & E.
Tubifera stipitata (B. & Rav.) Macbr.

PEZIZINEAE

Agyrium nigricans Fr.
⎰ Arachnopeziza Aurelia (P.) Fckl.
⎰ Belonidium Aurelia (P.) De Not.
⎱ Peziza Aurelia P.
Ascomycetella sulphurea Wint.
⎰ Cenangium Abietis (P.) ex Duby.
⎱ Cenangium ferruginosum Fr.
⎰ Cenangium chlorascens (S.) Cke.
⎰ Cenangium fallax B. & Rav.
⎱ Peziza chlorascens S.
Chlorosplenium aeruginascens (Nyl.) Karst.
⎰ Chlorosplenium aeruginosum (Oeder ex Fr.)
⎰   De Not.
⎰ Helotium aeruginosum (Oeder) ex Fr.
⎱ Peziza aeruginosa Oeder ex Fr.
⎰ Chlorosplenium versiforme (P.) De Not.
⎱ Helotium versiforme (P.) Fr.
Ciboria renispora (Ell.) Sacc.
⎰ Dasyscypha clandestina (Bull. ex Fr.) Fckl.
⎱ Peziza clandestina Bull. ex Fr.

Quercus sp. indet. (*cont.*)

Dasyscypha epixantha (Cke.) Sacc.
Peziza epixantha Cke.
Dasyscypha fuscescens (P.) Rehm.
Peziza fuscescens P.
Dasyscypha nivea (Hedw. f. ex Fr.) Sacc.
Peziza nivea (Hedw. f.) ex Fr.
Dasyscypha succina (Phil.) Sacc.
Peziza succina Phil.
Dasyscypha uncinata (Phil.) Sacc.
Peziza uncinata Phil.
Dasyscypha virginea (Batsch ex Fr.) Fckl.
Durella compressa (P.) Tul.
Durella macrospora Fckl.
Peziza compressa P.
Peziza macrospora Auct. Amer.
Peziza nigropunctula Gerard.
Durella connivens (Fr.) Rehm.
Patellaria connivens Fr.
Durella corrugata (C. & P.) Sacc.
Durella Lecideola (Fr.) Rehm.
Patellaria Lecideola Fr.
Peziza Lecideola Fr.
Durella radiocincta (Cke.) Sacc.
Peziza radiocincta Cke.
Haematomyxa ascoboloides Ell. & Ev.
Haematomyces vinosus C. & E.
Haematomyxa vinosa (C. & E.) Sacc.
Helotium citrinum (Hedw.) ex Fr.
Helotium claroflavum (Grev.) B.
Helotium crocinum B. & C.
Helotium fructigenum (Bull. ex Fr.) Fckl.
Phialea fructigena (Bull. ex Fr.) Gill.
Helotium herbarum (P.) Fr.
Holwaya gigantea (Pk.) Durand.
Hysterium Prostii Duby.
Hysteropatella Prostii (Duby) Rehm.
Karschia sphaerioides Ell. & Ev.
Melaspilea emergens Rehm?
Mollisia cinerea (Batsch ex Fr.) Karst.
Peziza cinerea Batsch ex Fr.
Mollisia introviridis (C. & E.) Sacc.
Peziza introviridis C. & E.
Mycolecidea triseptata Karst.
Bulgaria decolorans B. & C.
Ombrophila decolorans (B. & C.) Sacc.
Calloria coccinella (Sommf. ex Fr.) Sacc.
Orbilia coccinella (Sommf.) ex Fr.
Peziza coccinella Sommf. ex Fr.
Orbilia cruenta (S.) Morg.
Peziza rufula S.
Pezizella rufula (S.) Sacc.
Orbilia leucostigma Fr.
Peziza leucostigma Fr.
Orbilia rubella (P.) Karst.
Peziza rubella P.
Orbilia rubella (P.) Karst., var. rufula Sacc.

Lecanidion atratum (Hedw. ex Fr.) Rabh.
Patellaria atrata (Hedw.) ex Fr.
Patellaria congregata B. & C.
Patellaria nigrovirens Ell. & Sacc.
Patellea sanguinea (P.) Rehm.
Peziza sanguinea P.
Tapesia sanguinea (P.) Fckl.
Peziza vulgaris Fr.
Pezizella vulgaris (Fr.) Sacc.
Peziza myceticola B. & C.
Peziza vulgaris Fr., var. myceticola B.
Pezizella vulgaris Sacc., var. myceticola Sacc.
Peziza coccinea (Scop.) ex Fr.
Sarcoscypha coccinea (Scop. ex Fr.) Sacc.
Bulgaria globosa S. non Fr.
Bulgaria rufa S.
Sarcosoma rufa (S.) Rehm.
Ciboria pseudotuberosa (Ell.) Rehm.
Peziza pseudotuberosa Ell.
Sclerotinia pseudotuberosa (Ell.) Rehm.
Peziza culcitella C. & E.
Tapesia culcitella (C. & E.) Sacc.
Tapesia fusca (P.) Fckl.
Peziza prolifica Ell.
Tapesia prolifica (Ell.) Sacc.
Tryblidium occidentale Earle.
Peziza comata S.
Trichopeziza comata (S.) Sacc.
Peziza marginata Cke.
Trichopeziza marginata (Cke.) Sacc.
Peziza obscura Cke.
Trichopeziza obscura (Cke.) Sacc.
Peziza variecolor Fr.
Trichopeziza variecolor Fr.

PHACIDIINEAE

Cenangium quercinum (P.) ex Fr.
Clithris quercina (P. ex Fr.) Ell. & Ev.
Colpoma quercinum (P.) Wallr.
Hysterium quercinum P. ex Fr.
Lichenopsis sphaeroboloidea S.
Lichenopsis sphaeroboloidea B. in Herb. p. p. nec. S.
Platysticta simulans Cke. & Massee.
Coccomyces tumida (Fr.) De Not.
Hysterium tumidum Fr.
Lophodermium tumidum (Fr.) Rehm.
Phacidium glandicola S.
Phacidium minutissimum Awd.
Phacidium quercinum S.
Schizothyrium reticulatum (Phil. & Hark.) v. Höhnel.
Schizoxylon aeruginosum Fckl.
Stictis dryophila C. & E.
Mellitosporium hysterinum (Fr.) Gill.?
Stictis hysterina Fr.
Stictis linearis C. & E.
Xylogramma linearis (C. & E.) Sacc.
Stictis quercina Pk.

Quercus sp. indet. (*cont.*)

HYSTERIINEAE

{ Gloniella ovata (Cke.) Sacc.
{ Hysterium ovatum Cke.

Gloniopsis australis (Duby) Sacc.

{ Gloniopsis stictoidea (C. & E.) Sacc.
{ Hysterium stictoideum C. & E.

Glonium parvulum (Gerard) Cke.

Glonium simulans Gerard.

Glonium stellatum Muhl. ex Fr.

{ Glonium varium (Fr.) Sacc.
{ Hysterium varium Fr.

Hypoderma variegatum Duby.

Hysterium complanatum Duby.

Hysterium Gerardi C. & P.

{ Hysterium lineare B. nec. Fr.
{ Hysterium lineariforme Sacc.

Hysterium magnosporum Gerard.

Hysterium petiolare A. & S. ex Fr.

Hysterium proteiforme Duby.

Hysterium pulicare P. ex Fr., var. lenticulare
  Fr.

Hysterium punctiforme Fr.

Hysterium tumidum Fr., var. trigonum Fr.

Hysterium versisporum Gerard.

{ Hypoderma virgultorum DC., var. petiolare
{   Cke.
{ Hysterium virgultorum (DC.) Rob. & Desm.,
{   var. petiolare Cke.

{ Hysterium flexuosum S.
{ Hysterographium flexuosum (S.) Sacc.

{ Gloniopsis lineolata (Cke.) Sacc.
{ Hysterium lineolatum Cke.
{ Hysterographium lineolatum (Cke.) Ell. & Ev.

Hysterographium praelongum (S.) Ell. & Ev.

{ Hysterium Mori S.
{ Hysterographium Mori (S.) Rehm.

{ Hysterium subrugosum C. & E.
{ Hysterographium subrugosum (C. & E.) Sacc.

{ Hysterium maculare Fr.
{ Lophodermium maculare (Fr.) De Not.

Lophium leptothecium Earle.

Lophodermium petiolicola Fckl.

Lophodermium punctiforme (Fr.) Fckl.

Ostropa hysterioides S.

ASPERGILLACEAE

Eurotium herbariorum Lk., var. epixylon Ell.

PYRENOMYCETINEAE
PERISPORIALES

Meliola amphitricha Fr.

Meliola manca Ell. & Martin.

Saccardia quercina Cke.

HYPOCREALES

{ Calonectria chlorinella (Cke.) Sacc.
{ Nectria chlorinella Cke.

{ Hypocrea contorta (S.) B. & C.
{ Sphaeria contorta S.

Hypocrea corticiicola Ell. & Ev.

Hypocrea lactea Fr.

Hypocrea lenta (Tode ex Fr.) B.

Hypocrea olivacea C. & E.

Hypocrea Patella C. & P.

Hypocrea rufa (P.) ex Fr.

Hypomyces aurantius (P. ex Fr.) Tul.

{ Creonectria purpurea (L.) ex Seaver.
{ Nectria cinnabarina (Tode) ex Fr.

Nectria coccinea (P.) ex Fr.

{ Calonectria fulvida (Ell. & Ev.) Berl. & Vogl.
{ Dialonectria fulvida Ell. & Ev.
{ Nectria fulvida Ell. & Ev.

Ophionectria cerea (B. & C.) Ell. & Ev.

Ophionectria Everhartii Ell. & Gall.

Sphaerostilbe coccophila Tul.

DOTHIDEALES

{ Dothidea maculans S.
{ Phyllachora maculans (S.) Sacc.

SPHAERIALES
SPHAERIACEAE

{ Acanthostigma atrobarbum (C. & E.) Ell. &
{   Ev.
{ Chaetosphaeria atrobarba (C. & E.) Sacc.
{ Sphaeria atrobarba C. & E.

Acanthostigma decastylum (Cke.) Sacc.

Acanthostigma perpusillum De Not.

Lasiosphaeria subvelutina Ell. & Ev.

{ Psilosphaeria cariosa (C. & E.) Cke.
{ Sphaeria cariosa C. & E.

{ Sphaeria decastyla Cke.
{ Venturia decastyla Cke.
{ Zignoella cariosa (C. & E.) Sacc.

{ Byssosphaeria parietalis (B. & C.) Cke.
{ Enchnosphaeria parietalis (B. & C.) Sacc.
{ Herpotrichia parietalis (B. & C.) Ell. & Ev.
{ Sphaeria parietalis B. & C.

Chaetosphaeria innumera (B. & Br.) Tul.

{ Melanomma Pulvis-pyrius (P. ex Fr.) Fckl.
{ Sphaeria Pulvis-pyrius P. ex Fr.

{ Conisphaeria texensis Cke.
{ Melanopsamma texensis (Cke.) Sacc.
{ Sphaeria texensis Cke.

{ Rosellinia aquila (Fr.) DeNot.
{ Sphaeria aquila Fr.

{ Rosellinia Corticium (S.) Sacc.
{ Rosellinia aquila (Fr.) DeNot., var. Corticium
{   Ell. & Ev.
{ Sphaeria Corticium S.

{ Bombardia fasciculata Fr.
{ Rosellinia fasciculata (Fr.) Cke.
{ Sphaeria Bombarda Batsch ex Fr.

Rosellinia ligniaria Nits.

{ Rosellinia mammiformis (P. ex Fr.) Ces. &
{   De Not.
{ Sphaeria mammiformis P. ex Fr.

Quercus sp. indet. (*cont.*)

{ Rosellinia millegrana (S.) Sacc.
{ Sphaeria millegrana S.

Rosellinia pulveracea (Ehrh. ex Fr.) Fckl.

{ Byssosphaeria purpureofusca (S.) Cke.
{ Rosellinia purpureofusca (S.) Ell. & Ev.
{ Sphaeria purpureofusca S.

Rosellinia quercina Hartig.

{ Byssosphaeria subiculata (S.) Cke.
{ Hypoxylon subiculosum B.
{ Rosellinia subiculata (S.) Sacc.
{ Sphaeria subiculata S.

{ Psilosphaeria melanostigma (C. & E.) Cke.
{ Sphaeria melanostigma C. & E.
{ Wallrothiella melanostigma (C. & E.) Sacc.

{ Psilosphaeria diaphana (C. & E.) Ell. & Ev.
{ Sphaeria diaphana C. & E.
{ Zignoella diaphana (C. & E.) Sacc.

{ Conisphaeria querceti Cke. & Massee.
{ Zignoella querceti (Cke. & Massee) Sacc.

CERATOSTOMATACEAE

{ Ceratostoma piliferum (Fr.) Fckl.
{ Ceratostomella pilifera (Fr.) Wint.

Ceratostoma setigerum Ell. & Ev.

Ceratostoma subrufum Ell. & Ev.

CUCURBITARIACEAE

{ Cucurbitaria botryosa (Tode ex Fr.) Ces. & De
  Not.
{ Sphaeria botryosa Tode ex Fr.

Cucurbitaria confluens Plowr.

{ Coelosphaeria radicalis (Cke.) Sacc.
{ Cucurbitaria radicalis (Cke.) Sacc.
{ Nitschkea radicalis Cke.

CORYNELIACEAE

Caliciopsis subcorticalis (C. & E.) Fitzpatrick.

AMPHISPHAERIACEAE

{ Amphisphaeria botulispora (Cke.) Sacc.
{ Sphaeria botulispora Cke.
{ Xylosphaeria botulispora Cke.

Amphisphaeria granulosa Ell. & Ev.

Amphisphaeria umbrina (Fr.) De Not.

Ohleria rugulosa Fckl.

{ Ohleria modesta Fckl.
{ Ohleria rugulosa, var. nigerrima Ell.

{ Pleosphaeria chlorospora (Ell. & Ev.) Sacc.
{ Teichospora chlorospora Ell. & Ev.

{ Sphaeria disseminata B. & C.
{ Teichospora disseminata (B. & C.) Sacc.

Teichospora minima Ell. & Ev.

{ Sphaeria phellogena B. & C.
{ Teichospora phellogena (B. & C.) Sacc.

{ Winteria crustosa Ell. & Ev.
{ Winterina crustosa (Ell. & Ev.) Sacc.

LOPHIOSTOMATACEAE

{ Lophiosphaera heterostoma (Ell. & Ev.) Berl.
  & Vogl.
{ Lophiostoma heterostomum Ell. & Ev.

{ Lophiostoma abbreviatum (S.) Sacc.
{ Sphaeria abbreviata S.

Lophiostoma hysterioides Ell. & Langlois nec
Sacc.

Lophiostoma macrostomum (Tode ex Fr.)
Ces. & De Not.

Lophiostoma vagabundum Sacc., var. steno-
carpum Ell. & Ev.

Lophiotrema mollerianum (Wint.) Berl. &
Vogl.

Lophiotrema stenogramma (Dur. & Mont.)
Sacc.

MYCOSPHAERELLACEAE

{ Sphaerella dryophila (S.) Cke.
{ Sphaeria dryophila S.

Sphaerella pandurata Ell. & Ev.

Sphaerella Ravenelii Cke.

Sphaerella simulans Cke.

{ Sphaerella tigrinans (S.) Cke.
{ Sphaeria tigrinans S.

PLEOSPORACEAE

Didymosphaeria denudata Ell. & Gall.

{ Leptosphaeria dryophila (Cke. & Hark.) Sacc.
{ Sphaerella dryophila Cke. & Hark.
{ Sphaerulina dryophila Cke. & Hark.

Leptosphaeria puteana Ell. & Kellerm.

{ Diplodia gossypina Cke.
{ Physalospora gossypina (Cke.) N. E. Stevens.

Physalospora Malorum Shear et al.

{ Physalospora microtheca (C. & E.) Sacc.
{ Sphaeria microtheca C. & E.

Schizoparme straminea Shear.

{ Venturia ditricha (Fr.) Karst.
{ Vermicularia ditricha (Fr.) S.

MASSARIACEAE

Enchnoa infernalis (Kze. ex Fr.) Sacc.

Phorcys bufonia (B. & Br.) Schr.

GNOMONIACEAE

Cryptoderis gallae Trotter.

Gnomonia setacea (P. ex Fr.) Ces. & De Not.

Gnomonia veneta (Sacc. & Speg.) Klebahn.

CLYPEOSPHAERIACEAE

Clypeosphaeria pseudobufonia Rehm.

{ Hypospila bifrons (Schm. & Kze.) ex Fr.
{ Sphaeria bifrons Schm. & Kze. ex Fr.

Trabutia conzattiana Sacc.

VALSACEAE

{ ?Anthostoma amplisporum (Cke.) Berl. & Vogl.
{ ?Fuckelia amplispora Cke.

Quercus sp. indet. (*cont.*)

Anthostoma gastrinum (Fr.) Sacc.
Diatrype gastrina Rav. Fung. Car.
Fuckelia gastrina (Fr.) Cke.
Melogramma gastrinum (Fr.) Tul.
Sphaeria gastrina Fr.
Sphaeria irregularis Sow. ex Fr.
Valsa gastrina (Fr.) M. A. Curtis.
Anthostoma melanotes (B. & Br.) Sacc.
Sphaeria melanotes B. & Br.
Diaporthe crinigera Ell. & Ev.
Diaporthe oxyspora (Pk.) Sacc.
Diaporthe subpyramidata (B. & C.) Sacc.
Eutypa subpyramidata B. & C.
Diaporthe Woolworthii (Pk.) Sacc.
Valsa Woolworthii Pk.
Endoxyla macrostoma Fckl.
Camarops quercicola B. & Cke.
Endoxylina quercicola (B. & Cke.) Sacc.
Eutypa quercicola B. in Herb. see Cke.
Eutypa Acharii Tul.
Eutypa micropunctata Cke.
Eutypa rhypodes (B. & C.) Sacc.
Hypoxylon rhypodes B. & C.
Eutypella deusta Ell. & Ev.
Eutypella glandulosa (Cke.) Ell. & Ev.
Eutypella stellulata (Fr.) Sacc.
Fenestella vestita (Fr.) Sacc.
Kalmusia pachyascus (C. & E.) Sacc.
Sphaeria pachyascus C. & E.
Xylosphaeria pachyascus (C. & E.) Cke.
Peroneutypa corniculata (Ehrh. ex Fr.) Berl.
Valsa ambiens (P.) ex Fr.
Sphaeria conspurcata S.
Valsa conspurcata (S.) Cke.
Valsa coronata (Hoffm.) ex Fr.
Sphaeria deformis Fr.
Valsa deformis Fr.
Sphaeria haustellata Fr.
Valsa haustellata (Fr.) M. A. Curtis.
Valsa subclypeata C. & P.
Valsa trichospora C. & P.

MELANCONIDACEAE

Cryptospora trichospora (C. & P.) Sacc.?
Melanconis longipes Tul.
Diatrype cincta (Curr.) B. & Br.
Valsaria cincta (Curr.) Sacc.
Valsaria insitiva Ces. & De Not.

DIATRYPACEAE

Coronophora Ootheca (B. & C.) Sacc.
Neoarcangelia Ootheca (B. & C.) Berl.
Sphaeria mucida Fr., var. rostellata S.
Sphaeria Ootheca B. & C.
Valsa Ootheca (B. & C.) Cke.
Allescherina sparsa (Ell. & Ev.) Berl.
Cryptovalsa sparsa Ell. & Ev.
Diatrype bullata (Hoffm.) ex Fr.

Diatrype corniculata (Ehrh. ex Fr.) Rav. Fung. Car.
Diatrype disciformis (Hoffm.) ex Fr.
Diatrype quercina (P.) ex Fr., var. lignicola C. & E.
Diatrype virescens (S.) Cke.
Diatrype aspera Fr.
Diatrypella aspera (Fr.) Nits.
Diatrypella spissa (S.) Ell. & Ev.
Sphaeria spissa S.
Diatrype verruciformis (Ehrh.) ex Fr.
Diatrypella verruciformis (Ehrh. ex Fr.) Nits.

MELOGRAMMATACEAE

Botryosphaeria fuliginosa (M. & N.) Ell. & Ev.
Botryosphaeria Ribis (Tode ex Fr.) Grossenbacher & Duggar.
Nectria Ribis (Tode ex Fr.) Oud.
Botryosphaeria Ribis (Tode ex Fr.) Grossenbacher & Duggar, var. chromogena Shear et al.
Botryosphaeria dichaenoides (B. & C.) Cke.
Diaporthe dichaenoides (B. & C.) Sacc.
Melogramma dichaenoides B. & C.
Myrmaecium dichaenoides (B. & C.) Ell. & Ev.
Diatrype ferruginea (P.) ex Fr.
Melogramma ferrugineum (P. ex Fr.) Ces & De Not.
Sillia ferruginea (P. ex Fr.) Karst.
Sphaeria ferruginea P. ex Fr.
?Melogramma spiniferum (Wallr.) De Not.
Sphaeria podoides P. ex Fr.
Sphaeria scabrosa (Bull.) ex Fr., var. podoides P. ex Fr.

XYLARIACEAE

Daldinia concentrica (Bolt. ex Fr.) Ces. & De Not.
Daldinia tuberosa (Scop. ex Fr.) Schrt.
Hypoxylon concentricum (Bolt.) ex Grev.
Hypoxylon argillaceum Auct. an B.
Hypoxylon atropurpureum Fr.
Hypoxylon atrorufum Ell. & Ev.
Hypoxylon atroviride Ell. & Ev.
Hypoxylon Caries (S.) Sacc.
Hypoxylon coccineum Bull. †
Hypoxylon cohaerens (P.) ex Fr
Hypoxylon commutatum Nits.
Hypoxylon effusum Nits.
Hypoxylon fuscum (P.) ex Fr.
Hypoxylon gregale (S.) B.
Hypoxylon howeianum Pk.
Hypoxylon investiens (S.) B.
Sphaeria investiens S.
Hypoxylon leucocreas B. & Rav.
Hypoxylon malleolus B. & Rav.
Hypoxylon marginatum (S.) B.
Hypoxylon notatum B. & C.
Hypoxylon pallidum Ell. & Ev.
Hypoxylon Petersii B. & C.

Quercus sp. indet. (*cont.*)

Hypoxylon marginatum Rav. Fung. Am.
Hypoxylon confluens Rav. Fung. Am.
Hypoxylon polyspermum Mont.
Hypoxylon Ravenelii Rehm.
Hypoxylon rubiginosum (P.) ex Fr.
Sphaeria rubiginosa P. ex Fr.
Hypoxylon rutilum Tul.
Hypoxylon spondylinum Fr.
Hypoxylon stigmateum Cke.
Hypoxylon udum (P.) ex Fr.
Sphaeria uda P. ex Fr.
Nummularia repanda (Fr.) Nits.
Nummularia rumpens Cke.
Numulariola atropunctata (S.) House.
Nemania maxima (Haller ex Tul.) House.
Ustulina vulgaris Tul.
Xylaria apiculata Cke.
Xylaria arbuscula Sacc.
Xylaria longiana Rehm.

SPHAERIALES MISCELLANEA

Sphaeria inversa Fr.
Sphaeria micheliana Fr.
Sphaeria obscura S.
Sphaeria populina P. ex Fr.
Sphaeria putaminum S., var. b.
Sphaeria stilbosporans S.

AURICULARIALES

Auricularia Auricula-Judae (L. ex Fr.) Schrt.
Exidia Auricula-Judae (L.) ex Fr.
Hirneola Auricula-Judae (L. ex Fr.) B.
Tremella Auricula Mart. ex Streinz.
Tremella Auricula-Judae L. ex Fr.
Auricularia sambucina Mart. ex Fr.
Pilacre Petersii B. & C.
Saccoblastia ovispora Moeller, var. caroliniana Coker.

TREMELLACEAE

Eichleriella leveilliana (B. & C.) Burt.
Stereum leveillianum B. & C.
Exidia glandulosa (Bull.) ex Fr., var. levior Sacc.
Exidia truncata Fr.
Naematelia encephala (Wild.) ex Fr.
Tremella encephala Willld. ex Fr.
Naematelia nucleata (S.) Fr.
Naematelia quercina Coker.
Tremella albida Huds. ex Fr.
Tremella aspera Coker.
Tremella aurantia S.
Tremella enata B. & C.
Tremella fimbriata P.
Tremella foliacea P.
Ulocolla foliacea (P.) Bref.
Tremella frondosa Fr.
Tremella fuciformis B.
Tremella lutescens (P.) ex Fr.

Tremella marmorata B. & C.
Tremella mesenterica Retz. ex Fr.
Tremella torta (Willd.) ex Fr.
Tremella virens S.

DACRYOMYCETINEAE

Calocera cornea (Batsch) ex Fr., var.?
Calocera glossoides (P.) ex Fr.
Calocera palmata (Schum.) ex Fr.
Dacryomyces deliquescens (Bull.) ex Duby.
Dacryomyces Ellisii Coker.
Dacryomyces fuscominus Coker.
Dacryomyces minor Pk.
Guepinia fissa B.
Guepinia Spathularia (S.) Fr.

AURICULARIACEAE

Septobasidium canescens Burt.
Septobasidium tropicale Burt.

THELEPHORACEAE

Aleurodiscus acerinus (P. ex Fr.) Höhnel & Litschauer.
Aleurodiscus candidus (S.) Burt.
Aleurodiscus disciformis (DC. ex Fr.) Pat.
Asterostroma cervicolor (B. & C.) Massee.
Coniophora dryina (B. & C.) Massee.
Corticium dryinum B. & C.
Coniophora laxa (Fr.) Sacc. Syll.
Corticium laxum Fr.
Thelephora laxa Fr.
Coniophora polyporoidea (B. & C.) Burt.
Corticium polyporoideum B. & C.
Corticium alutaceum (Schrad. ex Fr.) Bres.
Corticium analogum (Bourdot & Galzin) Burt.
Corticium arachnoideum B.
Corticium caeruleum (Schrad.) ex Fr.
Corticium comedens (Nees) ex Fr.
Corticium cremoricolor B. & C.
Corticium effuscatum C. & E.
Corticium lactescens B.
Corticium laeve (P.) ex Fr.
Corticium ochroleucum Fr., var. erimosum B. & C.
Corticium spumeum B. & Rav.
Corticium ochroleucum Fr., var. spumeum Arth.
Corticium diminuens B. & C.
Corticium portentosum B. & C.
Corticium roseopallens Burt.
Corticium scutellare B. & C.
Corticium simillimum Pk.
Craterellus turbinatus Burt.
Cyphella pezizoides Zopf.
Cyphella texensis B. & C.
Cyphella trachychaeta Ell. & Ev.
Hymenochaete agglutinans Ell.
Hymenochaete cervina B. & C.
Hymenochaete corrugata (Fr.) Lév.
Hymenochaete corticolor B. & Rav.

Quercus sp. indet. (*cont.*)

Hymenochaete crocata (Fr.) Lév.
{ Hymenochaete asperata Ell. & Ev.
{ Hymenochaeta epichlora (B. & C.) Cke.
Hymenochaete setosa B. & C.
{ Hymenochaete umbrina B. & C.
{ Stereum umbrinum B. & C.
{ Hypochnus botryoides (S.) Burt.
{ Thelephora granosa B. & C.
Hypochnus subferrugineus Burt.
{ Corticium albulum Atk. & Burt. nom. nud.
{ Peniophora albula Atk. & Burt.
Peniophora caesia Bres.
Peniophora cinerea (P. ex Fr.) Cke.
Peniophora coccineofulva (S.) Burt.
Peniophora incarnata (Fr.) Cke.
Peniophora laevis Fr.
Peniophora nuda (Fr.) Bres.
Peniophora Peckii Burt.
{ Corticium puberum Fr.
{ Peniophora pubera (Fr.) Sacc. Syll.
{ Corticium quercinum P. ex Fr.
{ Peniophora quercina (P. ex Fr.) Cke.
Peniophora Ravenelii Cke.
Peniophora Roumeguerii Bres.
Peniophora trachytricha Ell. & Ev.
Peniophora velutina (DC.) Cke.
Peniophora violaceo-livida (Sommerf.) Bres.
Solenia anomala (P. ex Fr.) Fckl.
Solenia cinerea Burt.
Solenia ochracea Hoffm. ex Fr.
Solenia poriiformis (P. ex Fr.) Fckl.
Solenia villosa Fr.
{ Stereum albobadium (S.) Fr.
{ Thelephora albobadia S.
{ Corticium cinerascens (S.) B.
{ Stereum cinerascens (S.) Massee.
{ Thelephora cinerascens S.
Stereum fimbriatum Ell.
Stereum frustulosum Fr.
Stereum Galeottii B.
Stereum heterosporum Burt.
Stereum insigne Bres.
{ Peniophora papyrina (Mont.) Cke.
{ Stereum papyrinum Mont.
Stereum patelliforme Burt.
Stereum purpureum P. †
{ Corticium lilacinofuscum B. & C.
{ Stereum roseocarneum (S.) Fr.
Stereum sericeum S.
Stereum spumeum Burt.

CLAVARIACEAE

Clavaria mucida P. ex Fr.
Clavaria spinulosa P. ex Fr.
Clavaria subtilis P. ex Fr.
Pterula angustata Lév., var. fodinaria Sacc.
Sparassis laminosa Fr.

HYDNACEAE

{ Hydnochaete olivaceum (S.) Banker.
{ Hydnoporia fuscescens (S.) Murrill.
Hydnum Artocreas B.
Hydnum Caput-medusae Bull. ex Fr.
Hydnum cirrhatum P. ex Fr.
Hydnum fallax Fr.
Hydnum farinaceum P. ex Fr.
Hydnum flabelliforme B.
Hydnum Himantia S.
Hydnum laeticolor B. & C.
{ Hydnum mucidum Gmel. ex Fr.
{ Hydnum trichodontium B. & Rav.
Hydnum pallidum C. & E.
Hydnum Ramaria Fr.
Hydnum septentrionale Fr.
Hydnum Stevensoni B. & Br.
Hydnum udum Fr.
Irpex coriaceus B. & Rav.
Irpex deformis Fr.
{ Irpex niveus S.
{ Sistotrema niveum S.
{ Cerrenella tabacina (B. & C.) Murrill.
{ Irpex tabacinus B. & C.
Kneiffia ambigua Karst.
Kneiffia setigera Fr.
Kneiffia tessulata B. & C.
Mucronella minutissima Pk.
Odontia alutacea Fr.
Odontia fimbriata Fr.
Odontia fragilis Karst.
Odontia lateritia B. & C.
Phlebia albida Fr.
Phlebia anomala B. & Rav.
Phlebia hydnoides S.
Phlebia orbicularis B. & C.
Phlebia radiata Fr.
{ Phlebia rubiginosa B. & Rav.
{ Phlebia strigosozonata (S.) Lloyd.
{ Phlebia zonata B. & C.
Radulum Botrytis Fr.
Radulum molare Fr.
Radulum pallidum B. & C.
Sistotrema quercinum P. ex Fr.

POLYPORACEAE

Boletus chromapes Frost.
Boletus Frostii Russell.
Boletus gracilis Pk.
Boletus indecisus Pk.
Boletus purpureus Fr.
Ceriomyces Neumanii Bres.
Daedalea aurea Fr.
Daedalea confragosa (Bolt.) ex Fr.
Daedalea ochracea Lloyd.
{ Favolus alutaceus B. & Mont.
{ Favolus canadensis Klotzsch.
{ Favolus europaeus Auct. Amer.

Quercus sp. indet. (*cont.*)

Favolus Rhipidium (B.) Sacc. Syll.
Polyporus Rhipidium B.
Boletus hepaticus Huds. ex Fr.
Fistulina hepatica (Huds.) ex Fr.
Fistulina firma Pk.
Fistulina pallida B. & Rav.
Fistulina spathulata B. & C.
Fomes Bakeri Baker 5188.
Folyporus gilvus S.
Fomes Bakeri (Murrill) Sacc. & Trott.
Pyropolyporus Bakeri Murrill.
Fomes conchatus (P. ex Fr.) Karst.
Fomes Everhartii Ell. & Gall.
Fomes fasciatus (Sw. ex Fr.) Cke.
Fomes igniarius (L. ex Fr.) Gill.
Fomes lobatus (S.) Cke.
Polyporus lucidus (Leyss.) ex Fr.
Fomes rimosus (B.) Cke.
Fomes salicinus (P. ex Fr.) Cke.
Fomes Curtisii (B.) Cke.
Ganoderma Curtisii (B.) Murrill.
Polyporus Curtisii B.
Ganoderma pseudoboletus Auct. Amer.
Gloeoporus conchoides Mont.
Lenzites corrugata Klotzsch.
Lenzites tricolor (Bull.) ex Fr.
Merulius ambiguus B.
Merulius aurantiacus Klotzsch.
Merulius lacrimans (Wulf.) ex Fr., var. verru-
  cifer Quél.
Merulius porinoides Fr.
Merulius rufus (P.) Fr.
Merulius tremellosus Schrad. ex Fr.
Polyporus adustus Willd. ex Fr.
Agaricus Aesculi (Fr.) Murrill.
Daedalea ambigua B.
Polyporus Aesculi (S.) ex Fr.
Polyporus albellus Pk.
Polyporus anax B.
Polyporus arcularius (Batsch) ex Fr.
Polyporus Berkeleyi Fr.
Polyporus borealis Fr.
Polyporus brumalis (P.) ex Fr.
Polyporus caesius (Schrad.) ex Fr.
Polyporus chioneus Fr.
Tyromyces chioneus (Fr.) Karst.
Polyporus croceus P. ex Fr.
Abortiporus distortus (S.) Murrill.
Polyporus distortus (S.) Fr.
Polyporus rufescens (P.) ex Fr.
Polyporus endocrocinus B.
Polyporus fumosus (P.) ex Fr.
Polyporus galactinus B.
Polyporus giganteus (P.) ex Fr.
Polyporus graveolens S.
Polyporus intybaceus Fr.
Polyporus labyrinthicus Fr.
Polyporus laceratus B.

Polyporus lacteus Fr.
Polystictus lacteus Fr.
Polyporus leusculum B. & C.
Hapalopilus licnoides (Mont.) Murrill.
Polyporus licnoides Mont.
Polyporus nidulans Fr.
Polyporus occidentalis (Murrill) Kauffman.
Spongipellis occidentalis Murrill.
Inonotus perplexus (Pk.) Murrill.
Polyporus perplexus Pk.
Polyporus phaeoxanthus B. & Mont.
Polyporus picipes Fr.
Cerrenella coriacea (B. & Rav.) Murrill.
Cerrenella farinacea (Fr.) Murrill.
Polyporus planellus Murrill.
Polyporus portoricensis Fr.
Polyporus pubescens (Schum.) ex Fr.
Polyporus quercinus (Schrad.) ex Fr.
Polyporus radiatus Sow. ex Fr.
Polyporus radicatus S.
Polyporus rheades P.
Polyporus semipileatus Pk.
Polyporus semisupinus B. & C.
Polyporus squamosus (Huds.) ex Fr.
Polyporus supinus (Sw.) ex Fr.
Polyporus tomentoso-quercinus Johnson.
Grifola ramosissima (Scop. ex Fr.) Murrill.
Polyporus umbellatus Fr.
Polyporus unicolor S.
Spongipellis unicolor (S.) Murrill.
Polystictus abietinus (Dicks.) ex Fr.
Polyporus arcticus Fr.
Polystictus arcticus (Fr.) Cke.
Polystictus circinatus (Fr.) Cke.
Polystictus conchifer S.
Coltriciella dependens (B. & C.) Murrill.
Polystictus dependens (B. & C.) Cke.
Polyporus ectypus B. & C.
Polystictus ectypus (B. & C.) Cke.
Polystictus Fibula Fr.
Coriolus floridanus (B.) Pat.
Polyporus floridanus B.
Polystictus floridanus (B.) Fr.
Polystictus mutabilis B. & C.
Coriolus ochrotinctellus Murrill.
Polystictus ochrotinctellus (Murrill) Sacc. &
  Trott.
Polystictus planus Pk.
Boletus sanguineus L. ex Fr.
Odontia albominiata B. & C.
Polyporus sanguineus (L.) ex Fr.
Polystictus sanguineus (L.) ex Fr.
Polyporus dryadeus S. Am. bor. 402.
Polyporus scruposus Fr.
Mucronoporus tabacinus (Mont.) Ell. & Ev.
Polyporus tabacinus Mont.
Polystictus tabacinus (Mont.) Cke.
Polystictus zonatus Fr.
Poria ambigua Bres.

Quercus sp. indet. (*cont.*)

Poria arachnoidea Murrill.
Polyporus argillaceus Cke.
Poria argillacea (Cke.) Sacc.
Poria attenuata (Pk.) Cke.
Poria barbiformis B. & C.
Poria Caryae (S.) Cke.
Poria contigua (P. ex Fr.) Cke.
Poria floccosa Auct. Amer.
Poria corticola Fr.
Polyporus Cremor B. & C.
Poria Cremor (B. & C.) Sacc.
Polyporus croceus S. in litt.
Polyporus crociporus B. & C.
Polyporus nitidus Fr.
Poria crocipora (B. & C.) Cke.
Polyporus cruentatus Mont.
Poria cruentata (Mont.) Cke.
Polyporus dryinus B. & Cke.
Poria dryina (B. & Cke.) Cke.
Fomitiporia Earleae Murrill.
Poria Earleae (Murrill) Sacc. & Trott.
Poria eupora (Karst.) Cke.
Polyporus farinellus Fr.
Poria farinella (Fr.) Cke.
Poria ferruginosa (Schrad. ex Fr.) Cke.
Boletus pezizoides S.
Poria fimbriata (Fr.) Lloyd.
Porothelium lacerum Fr.
Porothelium pezizoides S.
Porothelium subtile (Schrad.) ex Fr.
Polyporus holoxanthus B. & Cke.
Poria holoxantha B. & Cke.
Poria inermis Ell. & Ev.
Poria interna S.
Polyporus Lindbladii B.
Polystictus Lindbladii (B.) Cke.
Poria Lindbladii (B.) Cke.
Fuscoporella ludoviciana Murrill.
Poria ludoviciana (Murrill) Sacc. & Trott.
Poria Medulla-panis (P. ex Fr.) Cke.
Melanoporia niger (B.) Murrill.
Polyporus niger B.
Poria nigra B.
Poria nitida P. ex Fr.
Boletus nigropurpureus S.
Polyporus nigropurpureus S.
Poria nigropurpurea (S.) Cke.
Polyporus obducens P.
Poria obducens (P.) Cke.
Fomitiporia obliquiformis Murrill.
Poria obliquiformis (Murrill) Sacc. & Trott.
Poria ochracea Murrill.
Poria purpurea (Fr.) Cke.
Poria rufa (Schrad. ex Fr.) Cke., var. lilacina Ell. & Ev.
Poria sanguinolenta (A. & S. ex Fr.) Cke.
Poria semitincta (Pk.) Cke.
Poria spissa Fr.

Poria subacida (Pk.) Sacc.
Poria subfuscoflavida Rostk.
Polyporus tomentocinctus B. & Rav. Herb.
Poria tomentocincta B. & Rav.
Poria Vaillantii Fr.
Poria vaporaria (P. ex Fr.) Cke.
Poria vincta B.
Fuscoporia viticola (S.) Murrill.
Poria viticola (S.) Cke.
Polyporus vulgaris Fr.
Poria vulgaris (Fr.) Cke.
Polyporus xanthus Fr.
Poria xantha (Fr.) Cke.
Poria xantholoma S.
Chromosporium isabellinum Ell. & Sacc.
Chromosporium pactolinum Cke.
Corticium pactolinum Cke. & Hark.
Poria xanthospora (Underw.) Sacc.
Coriolellus sepium (B.) Murrill.
Daedalea sepium B.
Trametes favescens (S.) Lloyd.
Trametes sepium B.
Trametes gilvoides Lloyd.
Trametes hispida Bagl.
Trametes kansensis Cragin.
Trametes Peckii Kalchbr.
Trametes quercina Lloyd.
Trametes robiniophila Murrill. ?
Trametes rubescens (A. & S.) ex Fr.
Trametes scutellata Morg.
Trametes Sepium B.

AGARICACEAE

Armillaria mellea (Vahl) ex Fr.
Armillaria putrida (Scop.) ex Murrill.
Cantharellus flabelliformis B. & Rav.
Claudopus nidulans (P. ex Fr.) Pk.
Clitocybe illudens S.
Clitocybe tabescens (Scop. ex Fr.) Bres.
Collybia exsculpta Fr.
Collybia griseifolius Murrill.
Gymnopus griseifolius Murrill.
Collybia platyphylla Fr.
Collybia velutipes (W. Curtis) ex Fr.
Collybia Volkertii Murrill.
Gymnopus Volkertii Murrill.
Collybia zonata Pk.
Coprinus fuscescens (Schaeff.) ex Fr.
Cortinarius radians Earle.
Crepidotus fulvifibrillosus Murrill.
Crepidotus sepiarius Pk.
Crepidotus versutus Pk.
Galera lirata B. & C.
Galerula lirata (B. & C.) Murrill.
Hypholoma californicum Earle.
Hypholoma fasciculare (Huds.) ex Fr.
Hypholoma lachrymabundum (Bull.) ex Fr.
Hypholoma perplexum Pk.
Hypholoma sublateritium (Schaeff.) ex Fr.

Quercus sp. indet. (*cont.*)
Lentinus Chama (Bosc) ex Fr.
Lentinus pelliculosus Fr.
Lentinus pectinatus S.
Lentinus umbilicatus Pk.
Lentinus Underwoodii Pk.
Lenzites betulina L. ex Fr.
Lenzites saepiaria Fr.
Lepiota dryophila Murrill.
Marasmius brevipes B. & Rav.
Marasmius capillaris Morg.
Marasmius epiphyllus Fr.
Marasmius insititius Fr.
Marasmius plicatulus Pk.
Marasmius prasiosmus Fr.
Marasmius ramealis Fr.
Marasmius rigidus Mont.
Marasmius rubrophyllus Pennington.
Marasmius saccharinus Fr.
Marasmius spodoleucus B. & Br.
Marasmius spongiosus B. & C.
Marasmius urens (Bull.) ex Fr.
Marasmius viticola B. & C.
Mycena californiensis B. & C.
{ Mycena collybiiformis Murrill.
{ Prunulus collybiiformis Murrill.
Mycena galericulata (Scop.) ex Fr.
Mycena strobilina (P.) ex Fr.
Mycena stylobates (P.) ex Fr.
Naucoria erinacea Fr.
Naucoria vernalis Pk.
Omphalia campanella (Batsch) ex Fr.
Omphalia gracillima (Weinm.) ex Fr.
Panus levis B.
Panus Robinsonii B. & Mont.
Panus rudis Fr.
Panus tomentosus Bundy
Panus torulosus (P.) ex Fr.
Paxillus reniformis B. & Rav.
Pholiota fulvosquamosa Pk.
Pholiota spectabilis Fr.
Pholiota squarrosa (Mull.) ex Fr.
Pleurotus applicatus (Batsch) ex Fr,
Pleurotus dryinus (P.) ex Fr.
Pleurotus petaloides (Bull.) ex Fr.
Pleurotus pubescens Pk.
Pleurotus sapidus Kalchb.
Pleurotus subpalmatus Fr.
Pleurotus tessellatus (Bull.) ex Fr.
Pluteus praerugosus Murrill.
Stropharia micropoda Morg.
Volvaria bombycina (Schaeff.) ex Fr.
{ Volvaria Earleae Murrill.
{ Volvariopsis Earleae Murrill.

SPHAEROPSIDALES

Aposphaeria conica Sacc.
{ Asteroma geographicum (DC.) Desm.
{ Dothidea geographica (DC.) Fr.

Botryodiplodia Ravenelii Sacc.
{ Cryptoderis gallae Trotter.
{ Sphaeropsis gallae Rav. Fung. Am. *148* p. p.
{ Cryptostictis glandicola Starb.
{ Sphaeria glandicola S. p. p.
Cytospora difformis S.
{ Cytospora Frustrum-Coni (S.) Starb.
{ Sphaeria Frustrum-Coni S.
{ Valsa Frustrum-Coni (S.) M. A. Curtis.
{ Dinemasporium hispidulum (Schrad. ex Fr.)
{   M. A. Curtis.
{ Peziza hispidula Schrad. ex Fr.
{ Diplodia tumorum (S.) Ell. & Ev.
{ Sphaeria tumorum S.
{ Diplodina gallae Ell. & Ev.
{ Diplodinula gallae (Ell. & Ev.) Tassi.
{ Diplodia periglandis Cke. & Hark.
{ Diplodina periglandis (Cke. & Hark.) Sacc.
{ Diplodina quercina Pk.
{ Diplodinula quercina (Pk.) Tassi.
{ Discosia Artocreas (Tode) ex Fr.
{ Sphaeria Artocreas Tode ex Fr.
Lemalis quercina S.
{ Macrophoma dryina (B. & C.) Berl. & Vogl.
{ Phoma dryina (B. & C.) Sacc.
{ Sphaeropsis dryina B. & C.
{ Phoma glandicola Cke.
{ Phoma glandicola (Desm.) Lév.
{ Phoma quercina (Pk.) Sacc.
{ Sphaeropsis quercina Pk.
Phyllosticta Quercus Sacc. & Speg.
Phyllosticta vesicatoria Thm.
Plenodomus destruens Harter.
Rhabdospora baculum Grove.
Septoria herbarum B. & C.
Septoria querceti Desm.
Septoria quercicola Sacc.
Sphaeronema glomeratum Mont.
{ Botryodiplodia gallae (S.) Petrak & Syd.
{ Botryodiplodia ostiolata Ell. & Ev.
{ Diplodia gallae (S.) Cke.
{ Diplodia longispora C. & E.
{ Dothiorella gallae (S.) Ell. & Ev. 1892.
{ Dothiorella gallae (S.) Starb. 1894.
{ Dothiorella glandicola (S.) Starb.
{ Dothiorella quercina (C. & E.) Sacc.
{ Sphaeria gallae S.
{ Sphaeria glandicola S.
{ Sphaeropsis gallae (S.) B. & C. 1867.
{ Sphaeropsis gallae Rav. Fung. Am. *148* p. p.
{   1878.
{ Sphaeropsis gallae (S.) Archer. 1926.
{ Sphaeropsis quercina C. & E.
Sphaeropsis insignis B. & C.
Staurochaeta membranacea Cke.

MELANCONIALES

Coryneum pustulatum Pk.
Coryneum umbonatum Nees ex Fr.

Quercus sp. indet. (*cont.*)

Cylindrosporium microspilum Sacc. & Wint.
Cylindrosporium Quercus Sorok.
{ Gloeosporium gallarum Ch. Rich.
{ Glomerella rufomaculans (Stonem.) Spaulding & v. Schrenk.
Melanconium hysterioideum C. & E.
{ Myxosporium croceum (P. ex Fr.) Lk.
{ Naemaspora crocea P. ex Fr.
Naemaspora croceola Sacc.
Pestalozzia Castagnei Desm.
Pestalozzia montellica Sacc.
{ Steganosporium pyriforme (Hoffm. ex Fr.) Cda.
{ Stilbospora pyriformis Hoffm. ex Fr.
Stilbospora angustata P. ex Fr.
Stilbospora multiseptata S.

Hyphomycetes
mucedinaceae

Aspergillus laneus S.
Asterophora effusa S.
{ Botrytis atrofumosa C. & E.
{ Virgaria atrofumosa (C. & E.) Sacc.
Botrytis atroviridis C. & E.
Botrytis geniculata Cda., var. quercina Sacc.
Botrytis griseolilacina Ell. & Ev.
Botrytis prasina B. & C.
Fusidium album Desm.
{ Fusidium griseum Lk.
{ Fusisporium griseum (Lk.) Fr.
Fusidium tenuissimum S.
Haplaria fusca Cke.
Menispora ciliata Cda.
Oidium candidum S.
Oospora cuboidea Sacc. & Ell.
{ Monilia aureofulva C. & E.
{ Oidium simile B.
{ Oospora similis (B.) Sacc.
Penicillium aureum Cda.
Physospora elegans Morg.
Dendryphium Ellisii Cke.
{ Dematium ramosum S.
{ Glenospora Curtisii B. & Desm.
{ Glenospora ramorum B. & C.
{ Glenospora ramosum (S.) Note.
{ Oedemium ramorum Fr.
{ Rhacodium ramosum S.
Gonytrichum caesium Nees.
{ Helicomyces aureus Cda.
{ Helicosporium aureum Auct.
Helicomyces cinereus Pk.
Helicomyces fuscus (B. & C.) Morg.
{ Helicomyces olivaceus Pk.
{ Helicosporium olivaceum Pk.
Helicomyces scandens Morg.
{ Ozonium omnivorum Shear.
{ Phymatotrichum omnivorum (Shear) Duggar.
Rhinotrichum Curtisii B.

Rhinotrichum ramosissimum B. & C.
Sporotrichum gratum S.
Sporotrichum intertextum S.
Sporotrichum sulfureum Grev.
Verticillium puniceum C. & E.

dematiaceae

{ Bispora aterrima B. & Rav.
{ Chaetopsis roseola Ell. & Ev.
{ Chloridium glaucum Ell. & Ev.
Cladosporium epiphyllum (P.) ex Fr.
Cladosporium fumagineum Sacc.
Cladosporium herbarum (P.) ex Lk.
Cladosporium lignicola Cda.
{ Clasterosporium adscendens (B.) Sacc.
{ Sporidesmium adscendens B.
{ Clasterosporium atrum (Lk.) Sacc.
{ Sporidesmium atrum Lk.
Clasterosporium Hirudo Sacc.
{ Clasterosporium strumorum Cke.
{ Sporidesmium strumorum Cke.
Helicoma ambiens Morg.
Helicoma Berkeleyi M. A. Curtis.
{ Helicoma monilipes Ell. & Johnson.
{ Helicosporium monilipes (Ell. & Johnson) Sacc.
Helminthosporium apiculatum Cda.
Helminthosporium corniculatum S.
{ Brachysporium leptotrichum (C. & E.) Sacc.
{ Helminthosporium leptotrichum C. & E.
Helminthosporium rectum B. & C.
Helminthosporium septemseptatum Pk.
Helminthosporium subulatum Nees ex Fr.
Hormodendron cladosporioides (Fres.) Sacc.
Macrosporium subglobosum Cke. & Rav.
Periconia calicioides (Fr.) B.
Septonema multiplex B. & C.
Septonema spilomeum B.
Sporidesmium acinosum B. & C.
{ Sirodesmium compositum (B. & Rav.) Sacc.
{ Sporidesmium compositum B. & Rav.
Sporidesmium exasperatum Ell. & Barthol.
Sporidesmium helicoides Ell. & Ev.
Sporidesmium inquinans Ell. & Ev.
Sporidesmium insulare Ell. & Ev.
{ Coniothecium effusum Cda.
{ Sporidesmium Lepraria B.
Sporidesmium mundulum Cke.
Sporidesmium nigrum B.
Sporidesmium Peziza C. & E.
Sporidesmium polymorphum Cda.
Sporidesmium translucens Cke.
Sporidesmium velutinum Cke.
{ Epochnium glaucum Cke. & Hark.
{ Stemphylium glaucum (Cke. & Hark.) Sacc.
Streptothrix atra B. & C.
Torula abbreviata Cda.
Torula binale C. & E.
Torula dissita B. & C.
Torula sphaeriiformis C. & E.

Quercus sp. indet. (*cont.*)
- Memnonium effusum Cda .
- Trichosporium effusum (Cda.) Sacc.
- Virgaria fuscopurpurea B. & C.
- Virgaria olivacea Ell. & Ev.
- Virgaria uniseptata B. & C.
- Zygodesmus effusus B. & C.
- Zygodesmus fuscus Cda.
- Zygodesmus rubiginosus Pk.

STILBACEAE
Arthrosporium compositum Ell.
Coremium glaucum Lk.
Graphium subulatum (Nees ex Fr.) Sacc.
Podosporium glandicola S.

TUBERCULARIACEAE
Cylindrocolla quercina C. & E.
Fusarium glandicola Cke. & Gerard.
Fusarium udum (B.) Wr.
Sphaerosporium lignatile S.

MISCELLANEA
Crucibulum vulgare Tul.
Lycoperdon gemmatum Batsch ex Fr.
Ozonium auricomum Lk.
Queletia mirabilis Fr.
Rhizomorpha subcorticalis P. ex Fr., var. diffusa Ell. & Ev.
Sclerotium erumpens S.
Sclerotium frustulatum S.
Sclerotium gallarum S.

URTICACEAE

Ulmus alata Michx.
- Aleurodiscus candidus (S.) Burt, var. sphaerosporus Coker.
- Cylindrosporium tenuisporum Heald & Wolf.
- Gloeosporium ulmeum L. E. Miles.
- Gnomonia ulmea (S.) Thm.
- Cylindrosporium ulmicola Ell. & Ev.
- Mycosphaerella Ulmi Klebahn.
- Phleospora Ulmi (Fr.) Wallr.
- Phyllactinia corylea (P.) ex Karst.
- Phyllactinia guttata (Wallr. ex Fr.) Lév.
- Phyllactinia suffulta (Reb.) ex Sacc.
- Phyllactinia corylea (P.) ex Karst., var. angulata Salmon.
- Phyllosticta ulmicola Sacc.
- Septogloeum profusum (Ell. & Ev.) Sacc.
- Uncinula intermedia B. & C.
- Uncinula clandestina Auct. Amer.
- Uncinula macrospora Pk.

Ulmus americana L.

EXOASCACEAE
Taphrina Ulmi (Fckl.) Johans.

PEZIZINEAE
Bulgaria inquinans (P.) Fr.
Karschia lignyota (Fr.) Sacc.
Mollisia lilacina Clements.
Orbilia rufula Massee.
Peziza cruenta S.
Peziza fibriseda B. & C.
Pseudohelotium fibrisedum (B. & C.) Sacc.

PHACIDIINEAE
Blitrydium Cucurbitaria (Cke.) Sacc.

HYSTERIINEAE
Acrospermum compressum, var. foliicola (B.) Riddle.
Acrospermum foliicola B.
Hysterium Prostii Duby.
Hysterium vixvisibile Gerard.
Hysterium proteiforme Duby.
Hysterographium gloniopsis (Gerard) Ell. & Ev.
Hysteropatella elliptica (Fr.) Rehm.

HYPOCREALES
Calonectria chlorinella Cke.
Dialonectria chlorinella Cke.
Nectria chlorinella Cke.
Hypocrea contorta (S.) Pk.
Nectria cinnabarina (Tode) ex Fr.
Thyronectria chrysogramma Ell. & Ev.
Thyronectroidea chrysogramma (Ell. & Ev.) Seaver.

ERYSIPHACEAE
Microsphaera Alni (DC.) Wint. †
Phyllactinia corylea (P.) ex Karst.
Phyllactinia guttata (Wallr. ex Fr.) Lév.
Phyllactinia suffulta (Reb.) ex Sacc.
Physalospora Cydoniae Arnaud.
Uncinula adunca B. Grev. 4: 159 p. p., non Lév.?
Uncinula intermedia B. & C.
Uncinula macrospora Pk.

SPHAERIALES
Botryosphaeria fuliginosa (M. & N.) Ell. & Ev.
Byssosphaeria phaeostroma (Dur. & Mont.) Cke.
Chaetosphaeria phaeostroma (Dur. & Mont.) Fckl.
Sphaeria phaeostroma Dur. & Mont.
Clypeosphaeria ulmicola Ell. & Ev.
Cryptovalsa Nitschkei Fckl.
Diatrype radiata Ell.
Dothidea tetraspora B. & Br.
Dothidea ulmea (S.) Thm.
Dothidella ulmea (S.) Ell. & Ev.
Eutypa lata (P. ex Fr.) Tul.

Ulmus americana (*cont.*)

Eutypa longirostris Pk.
Eutypa scoparia (S.) Wint.
Eutypella longirostris Pk.
Eutypella scoparia (S.) Ell. & Ev.
Peroneutypella scoparia (S.) Berl.
Valsa scoparia (S.) M. A. Curtis.
Eutypella stellulata (Fr.) Sacc., var. diatry-
    peoides Rehm.
Eutypella fraxinicola (C. & P.) Sacc.
Eutypella tumida (Ell. & Ev.) Wehmeyer.
Fenestella ulmicola Ell. & Ev.
Fenestella vestita Sacc.
Gnomonia ulmea (S.) Thm.
Hypoxylon Caries (S.) Sacc.
Hypoxylon Morsei B. & C.
Lophiostoma asperum Ell. & Ev.
Massaria Ulmi Fckl.
Melanopsamma kansensis Ell. & Ev.
Nummularia discreta (S.) Tul.
Nummularia repanda (Fr.) Nits.
Ohleria Ulmi J. H. Fabre.
Pleosphaeria fairmaniana Sacc.
Pleosphaeria zabriskieana (Ell. & Ev.) Berl.
Pyrenophora zabriskieana Ell. & Ev.
Rosellinia ostiolata Ell. & Ev.
Teichospora Helenae Ell. & Ev.
Valsa ambiens (P.) ex Fr.
Diatrype quadrata (S.) B.
Valsaria quadrata (S.) Sacc.

THELEPHORACEAE

Coniophora vaga Burt.
Peniophora cinerea (P. ex Fr.) Cke.
Corticium filamentosum B. & C.
Peniophora filamentosa (B. & C.) Burt.
Peniophora neglecta Pk.
Stereum neglectum Pk.

HYDNACEAE

Caldesiella ferruginosa (Fr.) Sacc.
Hydnum chrysocomum Underw.
Hydnum parasitans B. & C.
Hydnum sulphureum S.
Irpex farinaceus Fr.
Mucronella Ulmi Pk.
Radulum molare Fr.

POLYPORACEAE

Elfvingia megaloma (Lév.) Murrill.
Fomes applanatus (P. ex Wallr.) Gill.
Fomes igniarius (L. ex Fr.) Gill.
Pyropolyporus igniarius (L. ex Fr.) Murrill.
Ganoderma Curtisii (B.) Murrill.
Merulius Ulmi Pk.
Polyporus admirabilis Pk.
Polyporus fragrans Pk.
Polyporus galactinus B.
Spongipellis galactinus (B.) Pat.

Polyporus occidentalis (Murrill) Kauffman.
Spongipellis occidentalis Murrill.
Polyporus squamosus (Huds.) ex Fr.
Polyporus sulphureus (Bull.) ex Fr.
Boletus conchifer S.
Boletus virgineus S.
Polyporus conchifer (S.) Fr.
Polyporus virgineus (S.) Fr.
Polystictus conchifer (S.) Sacc.
Polystictus virgineus (S.) Cke.
Poronidulus conchifer (S.) Murrill.
Polystictus versicolor (L.) ex Fr.
Fuscoporia tenerrima (B. & Rav.) Murrill.
Polyporus tenerrimus B. & Rav.
Poria tenerrima (B. & Rav.) Cke.

AGARICACEAE

Collybia velutipes (Curt.) ex Fr.
Gymnopus velutipes (Curt. ex Fr.) Murrill.
Lentinus Lecomtei Fr.
Pholiota comosa Fr.
Pleurotus ostreatus (Jacq.) ex Fr.
Pleurotus salignus (P.) ex Fr.
Pleurotus serotinoides Pk.
Micromphale ulmarium (Bull. ex Fr.) Murrill.
Pleurotus ulmarius (Bull.) ex Fr.

SPHAEROPSIDALES

Camarosporium Ulmi Ell. & Dearness.
Camarosporulum Ulmi (Ell. & Dearness) Tassi.
Coniothyrium Fuckelii Sacc.
Cytospora carbonacea Fr.
Dinemasporium decipiens (De Not.) Sacc.
Dinemasporium Robiniae Gerard.
Diplodia melaena Lév.
Diplodia Ulmi Dearness.
Haplosporella diatrypoides Ell. & Barthol.
Melasmia ulmicola B. & C.
Mycosphaerella Ulmi Klebahn.
Phleospora Ulmi (Fr.) Wallr.
Septoria Ulmi Fr.
Phoma cincta B. & C.
Phyllosticta confertissima Ell. & Ev.
Phyllosticta erratica Ell. & Ev.
Phyllosticta melaleuca Ell. & Ev.
Phyllosticta ulmicola Sacc.
Piggotia astroidea B. & Br.
Sacidium Ulmi-gallae Kellerm. & Swingle.
Sphaeropsis Malorum B.
Haplosporella ulmea (Ell. & Barthol.) Petrak
   & Syd.
Sphaeropsis ulmea Ell. & Barthol.
Sphaeropsis Ulmi Sacc. & Roum.
Botryodiplodia hypodermia (Sacc.) Petrak.
Macrophoma ulmicola Ell. & Ev. 1903.
Macrophoma ulmicola Dearness. 1917.
Sphaeropsis ulmicola Ell. & Ev.

Ulmus americana (*cont.*)

MELANCONIALES

Coryneum tumoricola Pk.
Cylindrosporium ulmicola Ell. & Ev.
{ Gloeosporium profusum Ell. & Ev.
{ Septogloeum profusum (Ell. & Ev.) Sacc.
Gloeosporium ulmicola Miles.
{ Dothidella ulmea (S.) Ell. & Ev.
{ Dothidella Ulmi Auct. Amer.
{ Gloeosporium ulmeum (S.) Miles.
{ Gnomonia ulmea (S.) Thm.
{ Sphaeria ulmea (S.) Fr.
{ ?Systremma Ulmi Auct. Amer.
{ Xyloma ulmeum S.
Pestalozzia insidens Zabriskie.

HYPHOMYCETES

Botrytis cinereoglauca Ell. & Kellerm.
Ceratophorum ulmicola Ell. & Kellerm.
Dendrostilbe Ulmi Dearness.

MISCELLANEA

Ozonium auricomum Lk.

Ulmus campestris L.
Coniothyrium Ulmi Tharp.
Eutypella stellulata (Fr.) Sacc.
Gloeosporium inconspicuum Cav.
{ Mycosphaerella Ulmi Klebahn.
{ Phleospora Ulmi (Fr.) Wallr.
{ Septogloeum Ulmi (Fr.) Br. & Cav.
Phyllosticta ulmicola Sacc.
Sphaeropsis ulmicola Ell. & Ev.
Taphrina Ulmi (Fckl.) Johans.

Ulmus crassifolia Nutt.
Cylindrosporium tenuisporum Heald & Wolf.
{ Gloeosporium ulmeum Miles.
{ Gnomonia ulmea (S.) Thm.
Urnula Geaster Pk.

Ulmus fulva Michx.
Corticium incarnatum Fr.
Corticium maculiforme Fr.
{ Diatrype daldiniana N. A. F. *2525* nec De Not.
{ Diatrype tumida Ell. & Ev.
{ Eutypella tumida (Ell. & Ev.) Wehmeyer.
Didymosporium effusum S.
Euryachora ulmea (S.) J. J. Davis.
{ Eutypa scoparia (S.) Wint.
{ Eutypella scoparia (S.) Ell. & Ev.
Heterosporium variabile Cke.
Hypocrea bicolor Ell. & Ev.
Hysterium pulicare P. ex Fr., var. lenticulare
    Fr.
Irpex coriaceus B. & Rav.
Irpex farinaceus Fr.
Microsphaera Alni (DC.) Wint. †
Mucronoporus Everhartii Ell. & Gall.
{ Creonectria coccinea (P. ex Fr.) Seaver.
{ Nectria coccinea (P.) ex Fr.
Nectria Peziza (Tode) ex Fr.
Nectria vulpina Cke.

Nummularia repanda (Fr.) Nits.
Polyporus hirsutus (Wulf.) ex Fr.
Septogloeum profusum (Ell. & Ev.) Sacc.
{ Sphaerella apertiuscula (S.) Cke.
{ Sphaeria apertiuscula S.
Stereum subpileatum B. & C.
Uncinula macrospora Pk.
Valsa ambiens (P.) ex Fr.

FUNGI IMPERFECTI

{ Dothidella ulmea (S.) Ell. & Ev.
{ Euryachora ulmea (S.) J. J. Davis.
{ Gloeosporium ulmeum (S.) Miles.
{ Gnomonia ulmea (S.) Thm.
{ Sphaeria ulmea (S.) Fr.
Excipula ulmicola S.
Haplosporella commixta Barthol. 1905.
Haplosporella commixta Pk. 1906.
{ Haplosporella diatrypoides Ell. & Barthol.
{ Haplosporella rhizophila Shear.
{ Haplosporella ulmea (Ell. & Barthol.) Petrak
{   & Syd., var. rhizophila (Shear) Petrak & Syd.
{ Mycosphaerella Ulmi Klebahn.
{ Phleospora Ulmi (Fr.) Wallr.
{ Septoria Ulmi Fr.
Phyllosticta confertissima Ell. & Ev.
Phyllosticta erratica Ell. & Ev.
Phyllosticta Ulmi Westd.
Phyllosticta ulmicola Sacc.
Sacidium Ulmi-gallae Kellerm. & Sw.
{ Phleospora Ulmi Auct. p. p.
{ Septogloeum ulmeum J. J. Davis.
Septoria Ulmi Ell. & Ev.
Sphaeropsis crataegicola Cavara, forma Ulmi
    Ell. & Ev.

HYPHOMYCETES

Ceratophorum ulmicola Ell. & Hark.
Dendrodochium sepultum Ell. & Ev.
Tubercularia vulgaris Tode ex Fr.
Volutella gilva (P.) Sacc., var. albopilosa
    Pound & Clements.

Ulmus montana With.
Phleospora Ulmi (Fr.) Wallr.
Polyporus squamosus (Huds.) ex Fr.

Ulmus parvifolia Jacq.
Ozonium omnivorum Shear.

Ulmus pumila L.
Nectria cinnabarina (Tode) ex Fr.

Ulmus racemosa Thomas.
Fomes igniarius (L. ex Fr.) Gill.
{ Gloeosporium ulmeum Miles.
{ Gnomonia ulmea (S.) Thm.
Melasmia ulmicola B. & C.
Phyllactinia corylea (P.) ex Karst.
{ Phyllosticta melaleuca Ell. & Ev.
{ Phyllosticta ulmicola Sacc.
Uncinula macrospora Pk.

Ulmus rhombifolia Hort.
    Septoria Ulmi Ell. & Ev.

Ulmus serotina Sarg.
    Gnomonia ulmea (S.) Thm.

Ulmus sp. indet.

MYXOMYCETES

Ceratiomyxa plumosa Atk.
Comatricha longa Pk.
Hemiarcyria ablata Morg.
Leocarpus fragilis (Dicks.) Rostf.
Lycogala repletum Morg.
Ophiotheca Wrightii B. & C.
Perichaena corticalis (Batsch) Rostf.
Tilmadoche polycephala (S.) Macbr.

PEZIZINEAE

Helotium fibuliforme (Bolt.) ex Fr.
Mollisia discolor (Mont.) Phill.
⎰Orbilia rubella (P.) Karst.
⎱Peziza rubella P.
Patellaria atrata (Hedw.) ex Fr.
⎰Peziza leonina S.
⎱Trichopeziza leonina (S.) Sacc.
?Sphaeria Fraxini Fr.
?Tympanis Fraxini (S.) ex Fr.

PHACIDIINEAE

Rhytisma Ulmi Fr.

HYSTERIINEAE

Hysterium pulicare P. ex Fr.

HYPOCREALES

⎧Calonectria canadensis (Ell. & Ev.) Berl. &
⎪   Vogl.
⎨Scoleconectria canadensis (Ell. & Ev.) Seaver.
⎪Tubercularia canadensis (Ell. & Ev.) Berl. &
⎩   Vogl.
⎰Creonectria purpurea (L.) Seaver.
⎱Nectria cinnabarina (Tode) ex Fr.
Nectria rhizogena Cke.
Nectria Russellii B. & C.

SPHAERIALES

Amphisphaeria polymorpha Rehm.
Anthostomella suberumpens Ell. & Ev.
Bertiella botryosa Morg.
⎧Cryptospora ciliata (P. ex Fr.) Ell. & Ev.
⎨Sphaeria ciliata P. ex Fr.
⎩Valsa ciliata (P.) ex Fr.
Cryptovalsa Nitschkei Fckl.
Cucurbitaria naucosa (Fr.) Fckl.
Cucurbitaria ulmicola Fckl.
Daldinia concentrica (Bolt. ex Fr.) Ces. & De
    Not.
Diaporthe apiospora Ell. & Ev.
Diaporthe saccardiana Kze.
Diaporthe ulmicola Ell. & Ev.
Diaporthe Woolworthii (Pk.) Sacc.

Diatrype Hochelagae Ell. & Ev.
Diatrype Stigma (Hoffm.) ex Fr.
Didymosphaeria vagans Ell. & Ev.
Dothidea collecta (S.) Ell. & Ev.
Eutypa ludibunda Sacc.
Eutypella exigua Ell. & Ev.
⎰Eutypella innumerabilis Sacc.
⎱Valsa innumerabilis Pk.
⎰Gnomoniella tubiformis (Tode ex Fr.) Sacc.
⎱Sphaeria tubiformis Tode ex Fr.
Hypoxylon fuscum (P.) ex Fr.
Hypoxylon leucocreas B. & Rav.
Hypoxylon multiforme Fr.
Hypoxylon perforatum (S.) Fr.
Hypoxylon rubiginosum (P.) ex Fr.
Hypoxylon tinctor B.
Lasiosphaeria hirsuta (Fr.) Ces. & De Not.
⎰Leptosphaeria ramulicola (Pk.) Sacc.
⎱Sphaeria ramulicola Pk.
Lophiostoma caespitosum Fckl.
⎰Lophiostoma Jerdoni B. & Br.
⎱Lophiotrema praemorsum (Lasch) Sacc.
Massaria foedans Fr.
Massaria vomitoria B. & C.
Massariovalsa caudata Ell. & Ev.
Nummularia discreta (S.) Tul.
Ohleria modesta Fckl.
Pseudovalsa ulmicola Ell. & Ev.
Rosellinia compressa Ell. & Dearness.
Rosellinia limoniispora Ell. & Ev.
Rosellinia velutina Fckl.
Teichospora crossata Ell. & Ev.
Teichospora patellarioides Sacc.
⎰Sphaeria phellogena B. & C.
⎱Teichospora phellogena (B. & C.) Sacc.
Uncinula Bivonae Lév.
⎰Valsa ambiens (P.) ex Fr.
⎱Valsa coaperta Cke.
⎰Sphaeria fibrosa (P.) ex Fr.
⎱Valsa fibrosa (P.) ex Fr.
⎰Sphaeria modesta S.
⎱Valsa modesta (S.) Cke.
⎰Sphaeria stellulata Fr.
⎱Valsa stellulata Fr.
Valsaria exasperans (Gerard) Sacc.
⎰Sphaeria melastroma Fr.
⎨Valsa melastroma Fr.
⎩Valsaria melastroma (Fr.) Sacc.
Xylaria polymorpha (P. ex Fr.) Grev.

PHRAGMOBASIDIOMYCETES

Exidia glandulosa (Bull.) ex Fr.
Hirneola Auricula-Judae (L. ex Fr.) B.
Naematelia nucleata (S.) Fr.
Tremellodon gelatinosum Fr.

HOLOBASIDIOMYCETES

Guepinia elegans B. & C.

Ulmus sp. indet. (*cont.*)

THELEPHORACEAE

{Aleurodiscus Oakesii (B. & C.) Cke.
{Corticium Oakesii B. & C.
{Coniophora olivascens (B. & C.) Massee.
{Corticium olivascens B. & C.
Corticium crustaceum (Karst.) v. Höhnel & Litschauer.
Corticium lactescens S.
Corticium roseum (P.) ex Fr.
Corticium vellereum Ell. & Cragin.
Hymenochaete corticolor B. & Rav.
Peniophora admirabilis Burt.
Peniophora Allescheri Bres.
Peniophora candida (P. ex Fr.) Lyman.
{Hymenochaete cinerascens (S.) Lév.
{Peniophora cinerascens (S.) Sacc.
{Stereum cinerascens (S.) Massee.
Stereum disciforme (DC.) ex Fr.
Stereum rameale (S.) Reddick.

HYDNACEAE

Grandinia Burtii Pk.
Grandinia mucida Fr.
Hydnum Caput-ursi Fr.
Hydnum Caput-medusae Bull. ex Fr.
{Hydnum laeticolor B. & C.
{Irpex lacticolor (B. & C.) Morg.
{Hydnum omnivorum Shear.
{Ozonium omnivorum Shear.
{Hydnum septentrionale Fr.
{Steccherinum septentrionale (Fr.) Banker.
Phlebia merismoides Fr.
Radulum orbiculare Fr.

POLYPORACEAE

{Bjerkandera puberula (B. & C.) Murrill.
{Daedalea puberula B. & C.
Daedalea unicolor (Bull.) ex Fr.
{Favolus europaeus Fr.
{Hexagona alveolaris (DC. ex Fr.) Murrill.
Fistulina pallida B. & Rav.
Fomes conchatus (P. ex Fr.) Karst.
Fomes connatus (Weinm. ex Fr.) Gill.
Fomes geotropus Cke.
Fomes nigricans Fr.
{Fomes ulmarius (Sow. ex Fr.) Cke.
{Polyporus ulmarius (Sow.) ex Fr.
Fomes ungulatus (Schaeff.) ex Sacc.
Ganoderma applanatum (P. ex Wallr.) Pat.
{Ganoderma sessile Murrill.
{Polyporus sessilis (Murrill) Lloyd.
Gloeoporus dichrous (Fr.) Kauffman.
Lenzites betulina (L.) ex Fr.
{Bjerkandera adusta (Willd. ex Fr.) Karst.
{Polyporus adustus (Willd.) ex Fr.
Polyporus albellus Pk.
Polyporus arcularius (Batsch) ex Fr.
Polyporus benzoinus Fr.

Polyporus brumalis (P.) ex Fr.
Polyporus caudicinus (Scop. ex Fr.) Murrill.
{Polyporus delectans Pk.
{Spongipellis delectans (Pk.) Murrill.
Polyporus fissus B.
{Bjerkandera fragrans (Pk.) Murrill.
{Bjerkandera fumosa (P. ex Fr.) Karst.
{Polyporus fragrans Pk.
{Polyporus fumosus (P.) ex Fr.
{Polyporus holmiensis Fr.
Polyporus frondosus (Schrank) ex Fr.
Polyporus gilvus S.
Polyporus picipes Fr.
Polyporus radiatus Sow. ex Fr.
Polyporus resinosus (Schrad.) ex Fr.
{Polyporus scruposus Fr.
{Polyporus ulmarius S. Am. bor.
Polyporus Spraguei B. & C.
Polyporus spumeus (Sow.) ex Fr.
Polystictus hirsutus (Schrad.) ex Fr.
Polystictus molliusculus B.
{Coriolopsis occidentalis (Klotzsch ex Fr.) Murrill.
{Polystictus occidentalis (Klotzsch) Fr.
{Coriolus prolificans (Fr.) Murrill.
{Polystictus pergamenus Fr.
Polystictus zonatus Fr.
Poria ambigua Bres.
Poria attenuata Pk.
Poria ferruginosa (Schrad. ex Fr.) Cke.
Poria fimbripora S.
Poria Medulla-panis (P. ex Fr.) Cke.
Poria salmonicolor Pk.
Poria subacida (Pk.) Sacc. Syll.
Poria undata (P.) Bres.
Xanthoporia Andersoni (Ell. & Ev.) Murrill.
Trametes serpens Fr.

AGARICACEAE

{Annularia sphaerospora Pk.
{Chamaeota sphaerospora (Pk.) Kauffman.
Clitocybe illudens S.
Coprinus atratus B. & Br.
Coprinus fuscescens (Schaeff.) ex Fr.
Coprinus radians Desm.
Flammula lubrica Fr.
Flammula penetrans Fr.
Hypholoma sublateritium (Schaeff.) ex Fr.
Lentinus tigrinus Fr.
Lentinus ursinus Fr.
Lentinus vulpinus Fr.
Marasmius fagineus Morg.
Marasmius spodoleucus B. & Br.
Mycena corticola (P.) ex Fr.
Panus dealbatus B.
Panus meruliiceps Pk.
Pholiota adiposa Fr.
Pholiota curvipes Fr.
Pleurotus candidissimus B. & C.

Ulmus sp. indet. (*cont.*)

Pleurotus dryinus (P.) ex Fr.

{ Micromphale elongatipes (Pk.) Murrill.
Pleurotus elongatipes Pk.

Pleurotus fimbriatus F., var. regularis Kauffman.

Pleurotus lignatilis (P.) ex Fr.

Pleurotus mastrucatus Fr.

{ Pleurotus euosmus B.
Pleurotus ostreatus (Jacq.) ex Fr., var. euosmus (B.) McIlvaine & Macadam.

Pleurotus sapidus (Kalchb.) Sacc. Syll.

Pleurotus serotinus (Schrad.) ex Fr.

Pleurotus striatulus (P.) ex Fr.

Pleurotus subareolatus (Pk.) Sacc. Syll.

Pleurotus ulmarius Fr.

Volvaria bombycina (Schaeff.) ex Fr.

SPHAEROPSIDALES

Cornularia ulmicola Ell. & Ev.

Cytospora ambiens Sacc.

{ Diplodia clavispora Ell. & Barthol.
Microdiplodia clavispora (Ell. & Barthol.) Tassi.

Excipula canadensis Ell. & Ev.

Phyllosticta confertissima Ell. & Ev.

{ Hendersonia Lophiostoma C. & E.
Stagonospora Lophiostoma (C. & E.) Sacc.

MELANCONIACEAE

Myxosporium Ulmi (Cud.) Sacc.

{ Hainesia Lythri (Desm.) v. Höhnel.
Sclerotiopsis Lythri (Desm.) Shear & Dodge.

HYPHOMYCETES

Cephalothecium roseum Cda.

Cercospora sphaeriiformis Cke.

Fusarium udum (B.) Wr.

Helicoma Berkeleyi M. A. Curtis.

{ Helicoma limpidum Morg.
Helicosporium limpidum (Morg.) Sacc.

Helicoön sessile Morg.

Helminthosporium fusiforme Cda.

Hormiscium gelatinosum Hedge.

Hormodendron cladosporioides (Fres.) Sacc.

Martindalia spironema Sacc. & Ell.

Septonema atrum Sacc.

Sporidesmium cellulosum Fr.

Sporotrichum alutaceum S.

Torula occulta Ell. & Barthol.

MISCELLANEA

Cornuvia Wrightii B. & Cke.

Typhula subfasciculata Ell. & Ev.

Planera aquatica (Walt.) Gmel.

Sporidesmium punctans Ell. & Ev.

Celtis australis L.

Cytospora Celtidis Ell. & Ev.

Fusarium Celtidis Ell. & Tracy.

Celtis brevipes Watson.

Phyllosticta Celtidis Ell. & Kellerm.

Celtis mississippiensis Bosc.

Cylindrosporium Celtidis Earle.

Cylindrosporium defoliatum Heald & Wolf.

Polyporus sulphureus (Bull.) ex Fr.

Ramularia Celtidis Ell. & Kellerm.

{ Uncinula parvula C. & P.
Uncinula Torreyi Gerard.
Uncinula Petersii Note.
Uncinula polychaeta B. & C. in Rav. Fung. Car.
Uncinula polychaeta (B. & C.) Tracy & Gall. p. p.

Celtis occidentalis L.

PHYCOMYCETES

{ Peronospora Celtidis Waite.
Plasmopara Celtidis (Waite) Berl.
Pseudoperonospora Celtidis (Waite) G. W. Wilson.

HYSTERIINEAE

{ Blitrydium hiascens (B. & C.) Sacc.
Hysterium hiascens B. & C.
Hysterographium hiascens (B. & C.) Rehm.

ERYSIPHACEAE

{ Albigo phytoptophila (Kellerm. & Swingle) O. Kuntze.
Sphaerotheca phytoptophila Kellerm. & Swingle.
Uncinula parvula C. & P.
Uncinula Torreyi Gerard.
Pleochaeta Curtisii Sacc. & Speg. p. p.
Uncinula confusa Massee.
Uncinula polychaeta B. & C. in Grev.
Erysiphe polychaeta B. & C. in Grev.
Pleochaeta Curtisii Sacc. & Speg. p. p.
Uncinula Petersii Note.
Uncinula polychaeta B. & C. in Rav. Fung Car.

SPHAERIALES

Amphisphaeria nuda Ell. & Ev.

Anthostoma formosum Ell. & Ev.

Coelosphaeria fusariospora Ell. & Ev.

Cucurbitaria Celtidis Shear.

Diaporthe cercophora (Ell.) Sacc.

{ Didymella Celtidis (B. & C.) Sacc.
Endophlaea Celtidis (B. & C.) Cke.
Sphaeria Celtidis B. & C.

Didymosphaeria Celtidis Ell. & Ev.

Eutypella cerviculata (Fr.) Sacc.

Eutypella stellulata (Fr.) Sacc.

{ Massaria foedans Fr.
Sphaeria foedans Fr.

Rosellinia caespitosa Ell. & Ev.

Rosellinia pulveracea (Ehrh. ex Fr.) Fckl.

Sphaerella maculiformis (P. ex Fr.) Awd.

Teichospora nubilosa Ell. & Ev.

Teichospora piriospora Ell. & Ev.

Celtis occidentalis (*cont.*)
Valsa Celtidis Ell. & Ev. 1897.
{ Pseudovalsa Celtidis Cke.
{ Valsa Celtidis Cke. 1876.
{ Valsaria Celtidis (Cke.) Sacc.

HYMENOMYCETINEAE

Polyporus albellus Pk.
Polyporus robiniophilus Murrill ex Lloyd.
Polyporus spumeus (Sow.) ex Fr.
Poria incrassata (B. & C.) Burt.
{ Septobasidium retiforme (B. & C.) Pat.
{ Thelephora retiformis B. & C.

SPHAERIOIDACEAE

Camarosporium Celtidis Ell. & Ev.
Cytospora Celtidis Ell. & Ev.
Dinemasporium radiatum Ell. & Ev.
{ Diplodia celtidigena Ell. & Barthol.
{ Diplodia inquinans Ell. & Barthol.
{ Microdiplodia celtidigena (Ell. & Barthol.)
    Tassi.
Dothiorella Celtidis Pk.
Gloeosporium Celtidis Ell. & Ev.
Hendersonia Celtidis Ell. & Ev.
Hendersonia celtifolia Cke.
{ Botryodiplodia Celtidis (Ell. & Ev.) Petrak &
    Syd.
{ Macrophoma celtidicola Dearness & House.
{ Macrophoma Celtidis Ell. & Ev.
Phleospora Celtidis Ell. & Martin.
Phoma Celtidis Cke.
Phyllosticta Celtidis Ell. & Kellerm..
Placosphaeria Celtidis Dearness & House.
Septogloeum Celtidis Dearness.
Septoria carpogena Ell. & Ev.
Septoria Celti-gallae Gerard.
Septoria gigaspora Ell. & Ev.
{ Haplosporella Celtidis Ell. & Ev.
{ Sphaeropsis Celtidis Ell. & Ev.

MELANCONIALES

Didymosporium Celtidis S.

HYPHOMYCETES

Cercospora Spegazzinii Sacc.
{ Cercosporella Celtidis (Ell. & Kellerm.) J. J.
    Davis.
{ Ramularia Celtidis Ell. & Kellerm.
Coniothecium Celtidis Pk.
Fusarium Celtidis Ell. & Tracy.
Fusarium lateritium Nees ex Fr.
Gyroceras Celtidis (Biv.) ex Mont. & Ces.
Gyroceras divergens Pk.
Macrosporium antenniforme B. & C.
Tubercularia hamata Ell. & Ev.

Celtis reticulata Torr.
Cylindrosporium defoliatum Heald & Wolf.
Ramularia Celtidis Ell. & Kellerm.

{ Uncinula polychaeta (B. & C.) Ell. & Ev.
{ Uncinula Petersii Note.

Celtis sp. indet.
{ Acrospermum compressum, var. foliicola
    (B.) Riddle.
{ Acrospermum foliicola B.
Cylindrosporium Celtidis Earle.
Cylindrosporium defoliatum Heald & Wolf.
{ Dasyscypha succinea (Phil.) Sacc.
{ ?Peziza succinea Phil.
Hymenochaete purpurea Cke. & Morg.
Hypoxylon notatum B. & C.
Lichenopsis sphaeroboloidea S.
Melanconium Celtidis Ell. & Ev.
Nummularia fuscella Rehm.
Patellaria atrata (Hedw.) ex Fr.
Peniophora vernicosa Ell. & Ev. ex Burt.
{ Ozonium omnivorum Shear.
{ Phymatotrichum omnivorum (Shear) Duggar.
Rosellinia pulveracea (Ehrh. ex Fr.) Fckl.,
    var. tetraspora Auct.
Sphaeropsis gallae (S.) B. & C.
Trichothecium roseum Lk.
{ Diatrype obesa B. & C.
{ Valsaria quadrata (S.) Sacc.

Momisia iguanaea (Jacq.) Rose & Standley.
Phyllosticta momisiana E. Young.
Sphaerella dominicana Fragoso & Ciferri.

Maclura pomifera (Raf.) Schneider.
Camarosporium Maclurae Pk.
Cercospora Maclurae Ell. & Ev.
Coelosphaeria corticata Ell. & Ev.
Corticium Sambuci P.
{ Cytispora Maclurae Ell. & Barthol.
{ Eutypella Maclurae (C. & E.) Ell. & Ev.
{ Valsa Maclurae C. & E.
Dacryomyces minor Pk.
Diatrype Maclurae Ell. & Ev.
Diplodia Maclurae Speg.
Diplodia radicina C. & E.
{ Dothidea collecta (S.) Ell. & Ev.
{ Dothidea crystallophora B. & C.
{ Dothidea tetraspora B. & Br.
{ Parodiella tetraspora (B. & Br.) Kellerm. &
    Carleton.
{ Sphaeria collecta S.
Dothidea ribesia (P.) ex Fr.
{ Eutypella stellulata (Fr.) Sacc.
{ Eutypella tetraploa (B. & C.) Sacc.
{ Valsa tetraploa B. & C.
Glonium parvulum (Gerard) Cke.
{ Haplosporella Maclurae (Cke.) Ell. & Ev.
{ Sphaeropsis Maclurae Cke.
{ Coniothyrium minus (Ell. & Barthol.) Petrak
    & Syd.
{ Haplosporella minor Ell. & Barthol.
Hendersonia lophiostomoides Ell. & Barthol.
Heterosporium didymosporum Clements.

Maclura pomifera (*cont.*)

{ ?Hydnum omnivorum Shear.
{ Ozonium omnivorum Shear.
{ Phymatotrichum omnivorum (Shear) Duggar.

Lecanidion atratum (Hedw. ex Fr.) Rabh.

Lophiostoma triseptatum Pk., var. pluriseptatum Ell. & Ev.

{ Leptosphaeria Maclurae Ell. & Ev.
{ Metasphaeria Maclurae (Ell. & Ev.) Sacc.

{ Diplodia compressa Ell. & Barthol.
{ Macrodiplodia compressa (Ell. & Barthol.)
  Tassi.

Nectria episphaeria (Tode) ex Fr.

Ovularia Maclurae Ell. & Langlois.

Phyllosticta Maclurae Ell. & Ev.

Physalospora Cydoniae Arnaud.

{ Cerotelium Fici (Cast.) Arth.
{ Physopella Fici (Cast.) Arth.
{ Uredo Citri Cke.

{ Boletus ferruginosus Schrad. ex Fr.
{ Mucronoporus ferruginosus (Schrad. ex Fr.)
  Ell. & Ev.
{ Polyporus ferruginosus (Schrad.) ex Fr.
{ Poria ferruginosa (Schrad. ex Fr.) Cke.

Rhytidhysterium Scortechinii Sacc. & Berl.

Septoria angustissima Pk.

Sphaerella Maclurae Ell. & Ev.

Sporidesmium Maclurae Thm.

Tryblidiella rufula (Spreng. ex Fr.) Sacc.

Morus alba L.

PEZIZINEAE

Cenangium fatiscens S.

{ Peziza conchella S.
{ Pezizella conchella (S.) Sacc.

{ Peziza cruenta S.
{ Pezizella cruenta (S.) Sacc.

{ Sclerotinia carunculoides Siegler & Jenkins.
{ Spermatomyces Mori W. A. Orton.

PYRENOMYCETINEAE

Botryosphaeria moricola (Ces. & De Not.)
  Sacc.

{ Diatrype collecta (S.) Cke.
{ Sphaeria collecta S.

Dothidea moriformis (Ach.) ex Fr.

Fracchiaea americana Berl.

Massaria epileuca B. & C.

{ Massaria olivacea Cke.
{ Massaria olivaceohirta (S.) Ell. & Ev.
{ Sphaeria olivaceohirta S. p. p.

Nectria dematiosa (S.) M. A. Curtis.

{ Creonectria verrucosa (S.) Seaver.
{ Nectria verrucosa (S.) Sacc.
{ Sphaeria verrucosa S.

Physalospora Cydoniae Arnaud.

{ Sphaerella Mori-albae Cke.
{ Sphaeria Mori-albae S.

HYMENOMYCETINEAE

Fomes applanatus (P. ex Wallr.) Gill.

Coprinus micaceus (Bull.) ex Fr.

{ Corticium cinerascens (S.) B.
{ Hymenochaete cinerascens (S.) Lév.
{ Peniophora cinerascens (S.) Sacc.
{ Peniophora Schweinitzii Massee.
{ Stereum cinerascens (S.) Massee.
{ Thelephora cinerascens S.

Pholiota adiposa Fr.

FUNGI IMPERFECTI

Cercospora moricola Cke.

Cercosporella Mori Pk.

Dendrodochium sepultum Ell. & Ev.

{ Dendrophoma olivaceohirta Starb.
{ Sphaeria olivaceohirta S. p. p.

{ Didymosporium pezizoideum S.
{ Epiclinium pezizoideum (S.) Fr.

Gonytrichum caesium Nees ex Fr.

Melanconium conglomeratum Lk. ex Fr.

Myxosporium Diedickei Syd.

Periconia pycnospora Fres.

{ Phleospora Mori (Lév.) Sacc.
{ Septoria Mori Lév.

Phleospora moricola (Pass.) Sacc.

{ Phoma longipes B. & C.
{ Phoma moricola Sacc.

Phyllosticta consors Sacc.

{ Sphaeropsis Dearnessii Sacc. & Syd.
{ Sphaeropsis Mori Berl. 1885.
{ Sphaeropsis Mori Ell. & Ev. 1893.
{ Sphaeropsis sepulta Ell. & Ev.

{ Haplosporella longipes Ell. & Barthol.

{ Haplosporella Mori (Berl.) Petrak & Syd., var.
  valsoidea (C. & E.) Petrak & Syd.
{ Haplosporella valsoidea (C. & E.) Ell. & Ev.
{ Sphaeropsis valsoidea C. & E.

Tubercularia vulgaris Tode ex Fr.

MISCELLANEA

Ostracoderma spadiceum S.

Ozonium auricomum Lk.

Spermodermium rufum S.

Morus alba L., var. **latifolia** Bureau.

Diplodia Mori B.

Diplodia Mori Westd.

Dothidea Sambuci (P.) ex Fr.

Fusarium lateritium Nees ex Fr.

Nectria coccinea (P.) ex Fr.

{ Nectria ochroleuca (S.) M. A. Curtis.
{ Sphaeria ochroleuca S.

Sphinctrina microscopica B. & C.

Valsa morigena B. & C. in Herb. B.

Valsa pusio B. & C.

Morus alba L., var. **tatarica** Loudon.

Dermatea Mori Pk.

Haplosporella longipes Ell. & Barthol.

Morus alba var. **tatarica** (*cont.*)
{ Creonectria purpurea (L.) Seaver.
  Nectria cinnabarina (Tode) ex Fr.
  Creonectria verrucosa (S.) Seaver.
  Nectria verrucosa (S.) Sacc.
  Phleospora Mori (Lév.) Sacc.
{ Diatrype Aethiops C. & E.
  Melogramma Aethiops (C. & E.) Cke.
  Valsaria Aethiops (C. & E.) Sacc.
  Valsaria insitiva (Tode ex Fr.) Ces. & De Not.

Morus multicaulis Raf.
  Dothidea Sambuci (P.) ex Fr.
{ Nectria Russellii B. & C.
  Sphaeria radiella B. & C.
  Phleospora Mori (Lév.) Sacc.
  Valsa morigena B. & C.
  Valsa pusio B. & C.

Morus rubra L.
{ Cercospora missouriensis (Sacc. & Wint.) Wint.
  Cercospora pulvinulata Sacc. & Wint.
  Cercospora moricola Cke.
  Cylindrosporium ulmicola Ell. & Ev.
  Diplodia Mori B.
{ Eutypa Mori-rubrae (S.) Cke.
  Sphaeria Mori-rubrae S.
  Fomes applanatus (P. ex Wallr.) Gill.
  Hendersonia epileuca C. & E.
  Herpotrichia diffusa (S.) Ell. & Ev.
  Hymenochaete agglutinans Ell.
  Massaria epileuca B. & C.
  Massaria olivacea Cke.
{ Nectria dematiosa (S.) M. A. Curtis.
  Sphaeria dematiosa S.
{ Creonectria verrucosa (S.) Seaver.
  Nectria verrucosa (S.) Sacc.
{ Calloria vinosa (A. & S.) ex Fr.
  Orbilia vinosa (A. & S. ex Fr.) Karst.
  Peziza vinosa A. & S. ex Fr.
{ Phleospora Mori (Lév.) Sacc.
  Septoria Mori Lév.
  Phoma longipes B. & C.
  Phyllosticta moricola Ell. & Ev.
  Pleurotus campanulatus Pk.
  Sphaeropsis sepulta Ell. & Ev.
  Uncinula geniculata Gerard.

Morus sp. indet.

PEZIZINEAE
{ Blitrydium Cucurbitaria (Cke.) Sacc.
  Dermatea Cucurbitaria Cke.
  Dermatella Cucurbitaria (Cke.) Sacc.
  Patellaria Cucurbitaria (Cke.) Rehm.
  Tryblidium Cucurbitaria (Cke.) Rehm.
{ Blitrydium subsiduum (C. & E.) Sacc.
  Patellaria subsidua C. & E.
  Hysteropatella minor (Cke.) Rehm.
{ Lecanidion indigoticum (C. & P.) Sacc.
  Patellaria indigotica C. & P.

PHACIDIINEAE
{ Stictis mollis P.
  Stictis Pupula Fr.
{ Tryblidiella minor (Cke.) Sacc.
  Tryblidium minor Cke.
{ Hysterium rufulum Spreng. ex Fr.
  Tryblidiella rufula (Spreng. ex Fr.) Sacc.
  Tryblidium rufulum (Spreng. ex Fr.) Cke.

HYSTERIINEAE
{ Hysterium Mori S.
  Hysterographium Mori (S.) Rehm.
{ Gloniopsis lineolata (Cke.) Sacc.
  Gloniopsis praelongum (S.) Underw. & Earle.
  Hysterium lineolatum Cke.
{ Hysterium praelongum S.
  Hysterographium lineolatum (Cke.) Ell. & Ev.
  Hysterographium praelongum (S.) Ell. & Ev.

HYPOCREALES
{ Creonectria purpurea (L.) ex Seaver.
  Nectria cinnabarina (Tode) ex Fr.
  Nectria Russellii B. & C.
  Sphaerostilbe cinnabarina (Mont.) Tul.

PYRENOMYCETINEAE
{ Bagnisiella moricola (C. & E.) Sacc.
  Bagnisiopsis moricola (C. & E.) Theissen & Syd.
  Botryosphaeria berengeriana De Not.
  Botryosphaeria fuliginosa N. A. F. *862.*
  Dothidea moricola C. & E.
  Melogramma fuliginosum Ell. p. p.
  Diatrype asterostoma B. & C.
  Diatrype capnostoma B. & Rav.
{ Eutypa ludibunda Sacc.
  Eutypella stellulata (Fr.) Sacc., var. Ravenelii Rehm.
  Valsa stellulata Rav. Fung. Am.
{ Fracchiaea subcongregata (B. & C.) Ell. & Ev.
  Fracchiaea subconnata (B. & C.) Cke.
  Sphaeria botryosa C. & E. non Fr.
  Sphaeria subcongregata B. & C.
  Gibberella moricola Ces. & De Not.
{ Lophidium fenestrale (C. & E.) Sacc.
  Lophiostoma fenestralis C. & E.
  Melanomma moricola Ell. & Ev.
  Phyllactinia corylea (P.) ex Karst.
  Rosellinia aquila (Fr.) De Not.
  Mycosphaerella Mori (Pass.) Fckl.
  Mycosphaerella moricola Pass.
{ Mycosphaerella morifolia (Pass.) Auct.
  Sphaerella morifolia Pass.
  Valsa ambiens (P.) ex Fr.

HYMENOMYCETINEAE
  Armillaria mellea (Vahl) ex Fr.
  Collybia velutipes Curt.
  Ozonium omnivorum Shear.

Morus sp. indet. (*cont.*)
{ Peniophora moricola (B.) Massee.
{ Stereum moricola B.
  Pleurotus ulmarius Bull. ex Fr.
  Polyporus adustus (Willd.) ex Fr.
  Polyporus Medulla-panis (B.) Fr.
  Schizophyllum commune Fr.

SPHAEROPSIDALES
{ Dinemasporium hispidulum (Schrad. ex Fr.)
{   M. A. Curtis.
{ Excipula hispidula (Schrad. ex Fr.) C. & E.
  Diplodia atramentaria C. & E.
  Diplodia moricola C. & E.
  Dothiorella Mori Berl.
  Hendersonia epileuca C. & E.
  Phleospora maculans (Bereng.) Allescher.

MELANCONIALES
  Melanconium Dothidea S.

HYPHOMYCETES
  Alternaria tenuis (Nees) ex Fr.
  Fumago vagans Fr
  Helminthosporium virgultorum S.
  Microcera coccophila Desm.
  Periconia Commonsii Earle.
  Sporidesmium polymorphum Cda.
  Tubercularia mutabilis Nees.

MISCELLANEA
  Dematophora necatrix Hartig.
Broussonetia papyrifera (L.) Vent.
{ Creonectria purpurea (L.) Seaver.
{ Nectria cinnabarina (Tode) ex Fr.
  Ozonium auricomum Lk.
{ Sphaeria papyrifera S.
{ Valsa papyrifera (S.) Cke.
{ Valsella papyrifera (S.) Berl. & Vogl.
Dorstenia Contrajerva L.
{ Asterina Dorsteniae Syd.
{ Asterostomella Dorsteniae Syd.
  Uredo rubescens Arth.
Dorstenia Houstoni L.
  Uredo rubescens Arth.
Artocarpus Camansi Blanco.
  Uredo Artocarpi B. & Br.
Artocarpus communis Forst.
  Cladosporium Artocarpi Fragoso & Ciferri.
  Cladosporium herbarum (P.) ex Lk.
  Ganoderma australe (Fr.) Pat.
  Hypoxylon coccineum Bull. †
  Hypoxylon porosum Mont.
  Lentinus vellereus B. & C.
  Macrosporium commune Rabh.
  Pestalozzia funerea Desm., var. typica Sacc.
  Rosellinia bunodes (B. & Br.) Sacc.
{ Physopella (?) Artocarpi Arth.
  Uredo Artocarpi B. & Br.
  Sclerotium Rolfsii Sacc.
  Zignoella algaphila F. L. Stevens.

Artocarpus integrifolia L.
  Crepidotus alveolus (Lasch) Fr.
Artocarpus sp. indet.
  Ascophora fusca B. & C.
Castilloa elastica Cerv.
  Diplodia rapax Massee.
  Lasiodiplodia Theobromae Griff. & Maubl.
  Nectria Castilloae Turconi & Maffei.
  Uredo Artocarpi B. & Br.
Castilloa sp. indet.
  Diplodia cacaoicola Henn.
  Rosellinia bunodes (B. & Br.) Sacc.
  Thyridaria tarda Bancroft.
Ficus aurea Nutt.
  Colletotrichum elasticae Tassi.
{ Cerotelium Fici Arth.
{ Kuehneola Fici (Arth.) Butler.
{ Physopella ficina Arth.
{ Uredo ficina Juel.
  Ophiodothella Fici E. Bessey.
  Phyllosticta Roberti Boy. & Jacz.
Ficus brevifolia Nutt.
  Colletotrichum gloeosporioides Penz.
Ficus Carica L.
{ Aspergillus niger van Tiegh.
{ Sterigmatocystis niger van Tiegh.
{ Botryosphaeria Ficus (Cke.) Sacc.
{ Melogramma Ficus Cke.
  Botrytis cinerea P. †
{ Ceratostoma hystricinum Cke.
{ Ceratostomella hystricina (Cke.) Sacc.
  Cercospora bolleana (Thm.) Speg.
  Cercospora Fici Heald & Wolf.
  Cercospora ficina Tharp.
  Cladosporium herbarum (P.) ex Lk.
  Colletotrichum elasticae Tassi.
  Corticium laetum Karst.
  Corticium salmonicolor Karst.
  Dematophora necatrix Hartig.
  Diplodia sycina Mont., var. syconophila Sacc.
  Eurotium verruculosum Vuill.
  Fumago vagans Fr.
  Fusarium moniliforme J. L. Sheldon.
  Fusarium moniliforme J. L. Sheldon, var. Fici
    Caldis.
  Fusarium roseum Lk.
{ Colletotrichum Carica Stevens & Hall.
{ Glomerella cingulata (Stoneman) Spaulding &
{   v. Schrenk.
{ Glomerella fructigena (G. P. Clinton) Sacc.
{ Glomerella rufomaculans Spaulding & v.
{   Schrenk.
{ Gloniella sycnophila (Cke.) Berl. & Vogl.
{ Hysterium sycnophilum Cke.
{ Opegrapha varia P. (Lichen.)
{ Cerotelium Fici Arth.
{ Kuehneola Fici (Arth.) Butler.
{ Physopella Fici Arth.
{ Uredo Fici Cast.

Ficus Carica (*cont.*)
  Macrophoma Fici Alm. & Cam.
  Mycosphaerella bolleana Hig.
  Ozonium auricomum Lk.
  Ozonium omnivorum Shear.
  Physalospora Cydoniae Arnaud.
  Rhizoctonia microsclerotia Matz.
  Rhizopus nigricans Ehrenb.
  {Sterigmatocystis Ficuum (Reich.) Henn.
  {Ustilago Ficuum Reich.
  {Sclerotinia libertiana Fckl.
  {Sclerotinia sclerotiorum (Lib.) Massee.
  Sclerotium Rolfsii Sacc.
  Trichothecium roseum Lk.
  Tubercularia Ailanthi Cke.
  Tubercularia Fici Edgerton.

Ficus Combsii Warb.
  Cerotelium Fici Arth.

Ficus crassinerva Desf.
  {Cerotelium Fici Arth.
  {Kuehneola Fici (Arth.) Butler.

Ficus dubia Wall.
  Rosellinia echinata Massee.

Ficus elastica Roxb.
  Cerotelium Fici Arth.
  Colletotrichum Ficus Koorders.
  {Gloeosporium cingulatum Atk.
  {Gloeosporium elasticae Cke. & Massee.
  {Glomerella cingulata (Stonem.) Spaulding &
  { v. Schrenk.
  Glomerella cincta (Stonem.) Spaulding & v.
    Schrenk.
  Leptostromella elastica Ell. & Ev.
  Macrosporium caudatum C. & E.
  Macrosporium Fici Ell. & Kelsey.
  Phyllosticta Roberti Boy. & Jacz.
  Stemphylium elasticae Patterson.

Ficus indica L.
  Eutypa erumpens Massee.
  Rosellinia Hartii Massee.

Ficus Jimenezii Standl.
  Linochora galophila Syd.
  Ophiodothella galophila Syd.

Ficus laurifolia Lam.
  Zygosporium oscheoides Mont.

Ficus laevigata Vahl.

Ficus lentiginosa Vahl.
  {Cerotelium Fici Arth.
  {Kuehneola Fici (Arth.) Butler.
  {Physopella ficina Arth.

Ficus longifolia Schott.
  Glomerella cingulata (Stonem.) Spaulding &
    v. Schrenk.

Ficus nitida Blume.
  Eutypa erumpens Massee.
  {Hypoxylon anthracodes (Fr.) Mont.
  {Nummularia anthracodes (Fr.) Bruner?
  Nummularia Bulliardi Tul.

Ficus padifolia H. B. K.
  Cerotelium Fici Arth.

Ficus parcelli Veitch.
  Cladosporium Fici Patterson.

Ficus radula Willd.

Ficus religiosa L.
  Cerotelium Fici Arth.
  Cladosporium Fici Patterson,
  Libertella ulcerata Massee.
  Macrosporium Cheiranthi Fr.
  Melophia costaricenses Speg.
  Microcera Tonduzii Pat.
  Nectria Cucurbitula (Tode?) ex Fr.
  Peziza vinosa A. & S. ex Fr.
  Physalospora Hoyae v. Höhnel.
  Pilidium (?) Ficus Cke.
  ?Puccinia sepulta B. & C.
  Sporocybe byssoides (P.) ex Fr.
  Tubercularia granulata P. ex Fr.
  Tubercularia vulgaris Tode ex Fr.

Ficus Stahlii Warb.
  Catacauma repens (Cda.) Theissen & Syd.

Ficus sp. indet.
  {Botrytis vulgaris (I.k.) ex Fr.
  {Polyactis vulgaris Lk. ex Fr.
  Cytospora ficicola B. & C.
  Eutypella Fici Ell. & Ev.
  Fusarium ensiforme Wr. & Reink.
  Fusarium lateritium Nees ex Fr.
  Fusarium microspermum B. & C.
  {Gibbera ficina Cke. & Hark.
  {Gibberella ficina (Cke. & Hark.) Sacc.
  {Hendersonia findens Sacc.
  {Hendersonia fissurata Cke.
  {Hendersonula findens (Sacc.) Tassi.
  Peniophora Roumeguerii Bres.
  Phyllosticta Roberti Boy. & Jacz.
  Septobasidium pedicellatum Pat.
  Sphaerostilbe coccophila Tul.

Cecropia peltata L.
  Anthostomella Cecropiae (Rehm) v. Höhnel.
  Appendiculella tonkinensis (Karst. & Roum.)
    Toro.
  Auerswaldia Cecropiae Henn.
  Passalora Cecropiae F. L. Stevens.
  Midotis heteromera Mont.
  {Leptoporus duracinus Pat.
  {Polyporus duracinus (Pat.) Sacc. & D. Sacc.
  {Tyromyces duracinus (Pat.) Murrill.

Cecropia sp. indet.
  Phialea Cecropiae (Henn.) Seaver.

Humulus Lupulus L.
  Aecidium Humuli Hotson nom. nud.
  Ceriospora Dubyi Niessl.
  Cylindrosporium Humuli Ell. & Ev.
  Erysiphe Cichoracearum DC. †
  Fumago vagans Fr.
  Fusarium parasiticum Ell. & Kellerm.

Humulus Lupulus (*cont.*)
- Metasphaeria humulina (Pk.) Sacc.
- Sphaeria humulina Pk.
- Zignoella humulina Pk.
- Pestalozzia compacta B. & C.
- Phyllosticta decidua Ell. & Kellerm.
- Phyllosticta Humuli Sacc. & Speg.
- Phyllosticta Humuli Sacc. & Speg., var. major Ell. & Ev.
- Plasmopara Humuli Miyabe & Takahashi.
- Pseudoperonospora Humuli Miyabe.
- Pseudoperonospora Celtidis (Waite) Wilson, var. Humuli J. J. Davis.
- Pyrenophora Penicillus (Schm. ex Fr.) Sacc.
- Sphaeria Penicillus Schm. ex Fr.
- Septoria Humuli Westd.
- Septoria lupulina Ell. & Kellerm.
- Sphaerella erysiphina (B. & Br.) Cke.
- Sphaerotheca Castagnei Lév. p. p.
- Sphaerotheca Humuli (DC.) Burrill. †
- Oidium Fragariae Harz.
- Sphaerotheca Humuli (DC.) Burrill, var. fuliginea (Schl.) Salmon.
- Stagonospora Humuli-americani Fairman.

Humulus japonica Sieb. & Zucc.
- Sphaerotheca Humuli (DC.) Burrill. †

Cannabis sativa L.
- Botryosphaeria Marconii (Cav.) Charles & Jenkins.
- Botrytis cinerea Auct.
- Hypomyces Cancri (Rutg.) Wr.
- Nectria Cancri Rutgers.
- Ozonium omnivorum Shear.
- Phymatotrichum omnivorum (Shear) Duggar.
- Sclerotinia libertiana Fckl.
- Sclerotium Rolfsii Sacc.
- Septoria cannabina Westd. (1846.)
- Septoria cannabina Pk. 1885.
- Septoria Cannabis (Lasch) Sacc.
- Sphaeria Cannabis S.

Urtica Breweri Watson.
- Dicaeoma Urticae (Lagerh.) O. Kuntze. I.

Urtica cardiophylla Rydb.
- Dicaeoma Urticae (Lagerh.) O. Kuntze. I.
- Puccinia Urticae Lagerh. I.

Urtica chamaedryoides Pursh.
- Aecidium libertum Arth.
- Septoria urticaria Tharp.

Urtica dioica L.
- Aecidium Urticae Schum.
- Dicaeoma Urticae (Lagerh.) O. Kuntze. I.
- Puccinia Caricis Reb. I.
- Puccinia Urticae Lagerh. I.
- Puccinia urticata Kern. I.
- Heptameria doliolum (P. ex Fr.) Cke.
- Leptosphaeria doliolum (P. ex Fr.) De Not.
- Sphaeria doliolum P. ex Fr.
- Ramularia Urticae Ces.

Urtica gracilis Ait.
- Acrospermum compressum (Tode) ex Fr.
- Aecidium Urticae Schum.
- Caeoma (Aecidium) urticatum Lk.
- Dicaeoma Urticae (Lagerh.) O. Kuntze. I.
- Puccinia Caricis Reb. I.
- Puccinia Urticae Lagerh. I.
- Puccinia urticata Kern. I.
- Cornularia Urticae Ell. & Ev.
- Dasyscypha virginea (Batsch ex Fr.) Fckl.
- Dendryphium nodulosum Sacc.
- Didymella eupyrena Sacc.
- Helminthosporium Urticae Pk.
- Herpotrichia brenckleana Petrak.
- Leptosphaeria conoidea De Not.
- Metasphaeria chaetostoma Sacc., var. Urticae Rehm.
- Creonectria tuberculariformis (Rehm) Seaver.
- Nectria tuberculariformis (Rehm) Wint.
- Peronospora Urticae (Lib.) DBy.
- Phialea Urticae (P.) Sacc.
- Phoma nebulosa (P. ex Fr.) B.
- Pleospora permunda Cke.
- Ramularia Urticae Ces.
- Sclerotium rhizodes Awd.
- Septoria Urticae Desm. & Rob.
- Sphaerella superflua (Fckl.) Ell. & Ev.

Urtica holosericea Nutt.
- Aecidium Urticae Schum.
- Dicaeoma Urticae (Lagerh.) O. Kuntze. I.
- Didymella superflua (Awd.) Sacc.
- Phoma nebulosa (P. ex Fr.) B.
- Ramularia Urticae Ces.
- Sphaeropsis lanceolata C. & E.

Urtica Lyallii Watson.
- Aecidium Urticae Schum.
- Dicaeoma Urticae (Lagerh.) O. Kuntze. I.
- Puccinia Urticae Lagerh. I.
- Puccinia urticata Kern. I.
- Cylindrosporium Urticae Dearness.
- Didymella eupyrena Sacc.
- Macrosporium toruloides Ell. & Ev.
- Phoma acuta (Fckl.) Mich.

Urtica urens L.
- Sclerotinia libertiana Fckl.

Urtica sp. indet.
- Cylindrocolla Urticae (P. ex Fr.) Bon.
- Discella olivacea Cke. & Hark.
- Discula olivacea (Cke. & Hark.) Sacc.
- Fumago vagans Fr.
- Helminthosporium Urticae Pk.
- Heptameria doliolum (P. ex Fr.) Cke.
- Leptosphaeria doliolum (P. ex Fr.) De Not.
- Sphaeria doliolum P. ex Fr.
- Ophiobolus erythrosporus (Riess) Wint.
- Ophiobolus Urticae (Rabh.) Sacc.
- Rhaphidospora Urticae Rabh.
- Sphaeria Urticae Auct. Amer.?

Urtica sp. indet. (*cont.*)
Peziza fusarioides B.
⎰Phoma elevatum (S.) Cke.
⎱Rhytisma elevatum S.
Phoma nebulosa (P.) Mont.
Rhytisma Urticae Fr.
Septoria Urticae Rob.
Urera sp. indet.
Rosellinia Bakeri Ell.
Laportea canadensis (L.) Gaud.
⎧Aecidium Dicentrae Trel. III.
⎨Cerotelium Dicentrae Mains & And.
⎩Cerotelium Urticastri Mains.
Erysiphe Cichoracearum DC. †
Gloeosporium Laporteae Pk.
Ophiobolus porphyrogonus (Tode ex Fr.) Sacc.
Peronospora Urticae (Lib.) DBy.
Phyllactinia corylea (P.) ex Karst.
Ramularia Urticae Ces.
Septoria Pileae Thm.
Septoria Urticae Rob.
⎰Synchytrium cellulare J. J. Davis.
⎱Synchytrium pulvereum J. J. Davis.
⎰Peziza urticina Pk.
⎱Trichopeziza urticina (Pk.) Sacc.
Pilea nummularifolia (Sw.) Wedd.
Meliola Earlii F. L. Stevens.
Pilea parietaria (L.) Blume.
Meliola Earlii F. L. Stevens.
⎰Irene triloba (Wint.) Theissen & Syd.
⎱Meliola triloba Wint.
Pilea pumila Gray.
Erysiphe Cichoracearum DC. †
Septoria Pileae Thm.
Boehmeria cylindrica (L.) Sw.
Aecidium Boehmeriae Arth.
Aecidium Urticae Schum.
Cercospora Boehmeriae Pk.
Phyllosticta boehmeriicola J. J. Davis.
Septoria tenuissima Wint.
Synchytrium cellulare J. J. Davis.
Phenax hirta Wedd.
Asterina Phenacis Syd.
⎰Cicinnobella asperula Syd.
⎱Phaeodimeriella asperula Syd.
Parietaria canadensis.
Parietaria debilis Forst.
Erysiphe Cichoracearum DC. †
Parietaria pennsylvanica Muhl.
Erysiphe Cichoracearum DC. †
⎧Peronospora illinoensis Farl.
⎨Plasmopara illinoensis (Farl.) J. J. Davis.
⎩Rhysotheca illinoensis (Farl.) G. W. Wilson.
Ramularia Parietariae Pass.
Septoria Parietariae J. J. Davis.
Rousselia humilis (Sw.) Urban.
Uredo Rousseliae Kern. & Whetzel.

PROTEACEAE

Roupala veraguensis Kl.
Actinodochium concinnum Syd.
Atichia Millardeti Racib.
Chaetothyrium permixtum Syd.
⎰Cicinnobella exigua Syd.
⎱Phaeodimeriella exigua Syd.
Clasterosporium Roupalae Syd.
Fusisporella vexans Syd.
Helminthosporium glabroides F. L. Stevens.
Metathyriella Roupalae Syd.
Microcallis amadelpha Syd.
Microcallis consociata Syd.
Microthyriella Roupalae Syd.
Phyllachora rhopalina (Mont.) Sacc.
Protopeltis Roupalae Syd.
Ptychopeltis Roupalae Syd.
Stigmopeltella costaricana Syd.
Stigmopeltis Roupalae Syd.

LORANTHACEAE

Loranthus crassipes Oliver.
Patellaria Loranthi Henn.
⎰Nigredo socia (Arth. & Holw.) Arth.
⎱Uromyces socius Arth. & Holw.
Loranthus densiflorus Benth.
Pseudomeliola seleriana Henn.
⎰Nigredo socia (Arth. & Holw.) Arth.
⎱Uromyces socius Arth. & Holw.
Loranthus pyrifolia H. B. K.
⎰Pucciniola urbaniana (Henn.) Arth.
⎱Uromyces urbanianus Henn.
Loranthus Sonorae Watson.
⎰Nigredo ornatipes Arth.
⎱Uromyces ornatipes Arth.
Loranthus spicatus Jacq.
Uromyces urbanianus Henn.
Loranthus sp. indet.
Aecidium Loranthi Thm.
Meliola amphitricha Fr.
Psittacanthus calyculatus (DC.) Don.
Aecidium Loranthi Thm.
Arceuthobium pusillum Pk.
⎧Psilosphaeria Arceuthobii (Pk.) Cke.
⎨Sphaeria Arceuthobii Pk.
⎩Wallrothiella Arceuthobii (Pk.) Sacc.
Phoradendron flavescens (Pursh) Nutt.
⎰Botryosphaerostroma Visci (Sollm.) Petrak.
⎱Ceuthospora Visci Sollm.
Diplodia Phoradendri Cke.
Diplodia Visci (DC.) Fr.
Exosporium Phoradendri Tharp.
Macrophoma Phoradendri Wolf.
⎰Sphaeria atrovirens A. & S. ex Fr.
⎱Sphaeropsis atrovirens (A. & S. ex Fr.) Lév.
⎰Macroplodia Visci Westd.
⎱Sphaeropsis Visci (Westd.) Archer.

Phoradendron flavescens (*cont.*)
  Melogramma Phoradendri B. & C.
  Valsaria Phoradendri (B. & C.) Berl. & Vogl.
  Verticillium rosellum B. & C.
Phoradendron longispicum Trel..
  Uredo Phoradendri H. S. Jackson.
  Volutella? weiriana Syd.
Phoradendron macrophyllum (Engelm.) Cockerell.
  Chaconia (?) texensis Arth.
Phoradendron racemosum (Aubl.)Krug.& Urban.
  Asterinella Phoradendri Ryan.
Phoradendron villosum Nutt.
  Uredo Phoradendri H. S. Jackson.
Phoradendron sp. indet.
  Nigredo (?) euphlebia (Syd.) Arth.
  Uromyces euphlebius Syd.

SANTALACEAE

Comandra livida Richards.
  Cronartium Comandrae Pk.
  Cronartium pyriforme Hedgc. & Long.
Comandra pallida A. DC.
  Phoma exigua Desm.
Comandra pallida A. DC.
Comandra umbellata (L.) Nutt.
  Aecidium Hamiltoniae Thm.
  Aecidium pustulatum M. A. Curtis.
  Dicaeoma Andropogonis (S.) O. Kuntze. I.
  Dicaeoma pustulatum Arth. I.
  Puccinia Andropogi S. I.
  Puccinia Andropogonis S. I.
  Puccinia pustulata Arth. I.
  ?Puccinia Thesii Webber. I.
  Caeoma Comandrae Pk.
  Cronartium asclepiadeum Auct. Amer. p. p.
  Cronartium asclepiadeum, var. Thesii B.
  Cronartium Comandrae Pk.
  Cronartium pyriforme (Pk.) Hedgc. & Long.
  Cronartium Thesii (B.) Lagerh.
  Peridermium pyriforme Pk. III.
  Micropuccinia Comandrae (Pk.) Arth. & Jackson.
  Puccinia Comandrae Pk.
Comandra umbellata Nutt.
  Cercospora Comandrae Ell. & Dearness.
  Tuberculina persicina (Ditm. ex Fr.) Sacc.

OLACACEAE

Heisteria coccinea Jacq.
  Marasmius concolor B. & C.

ARISTOLOCHIACEAE

Asarum arifolium Michx.
  Laestadia Ari Ell. & Ev.
  Sphaerella asarifolia Cke.
Asarum canadense L.
  Synchytrium Asari Arth. & Holw.

Asarum canadense L., var. **reflexum** (Bicknell) Robinson.
Asarum caudatum Lindl.
Asarum Lemmoni Watson.
  Micropuccinia asarina (Kunze) Arth. & Jackson.
  Puccinia Asari Lk.
  Puccinia asarina Kze. III.
Asarum virginicum L.
  Depazea concentrica B. & C.
  Sphaerella concentrica (B. & C.) Cke.
  Sphaeria concentrica (B. & C.) Sacc.
Asarum sp. indet.
  Sclerotinia sclerotiorum (Lib.) Massee.
Aristolochia Clematitis L.
  Sphaeropsis Aristolochiae Dearness & House.
Aristolochia macrophylla Lam.
  Cercospora guttulata Ell. & Kellerm.
Aristolochia Serpentaria L.
  Cercospora Serpentaria Ell. & Ev.
  Diplodia radicicola Tassi.
Aristolochia sp. indet.
  Phyllosticta Aristolochiae Tassi.
  Sphaeropsis Squiereae G. W. Clinton.

POLYGONACEAE

Koenigia islandica L.
  Sphaerella Polygonorum (Crié) Sacc.
  Ustilago Koenigiae Rostr.
Chorizanthe cuspidata Auct..
Chorizanthe pungens Benth.
Chorizanthe staticoides Benth.
  Nigredo intricata (Cke.) Arth.
  Uromyces Chorizanthis Ell. & Hark.
  Uromyces intricatus Cke.
Oxytheca dendroidea Nutt.
  Nigredo intricata (Cke.) Arth.
Eriogonum alatum Torr.
  Hendersonia Eriogoni Fairman.
Eriogonum biumbellatum Rydb.
Eriogonum brevicaule Nutt.
Eriogonum cernuum Nutt.
Eriogonum compositum Dougl.
Eriogonum croceum Small.
Eriogonum dichotomum Dougl.
Eriogonum divergens Small.
Eriogonum dumosum Greene.
Eriogonum elongatum Benth.
Eriogonum fasciculatum Benth.
Eriogonum flavum Nutt.
Eriogonum gracile Benth.
Eriogonum heracleoides Nutt.
Eriogonum irrigatum Benth.
Eriogonum Jamesii Benth.
Eriogonum Kennedyi Porter.
Eriogonum lonchophyllum Torr. & Gray..
Eriogonum marifolium Torr. & Gray.
Eriogonum microthecium Nutt.
Eriogonum multiceps Nees.

Eriogonum niveum Dougl.
Eriogonum orendense Nelson.
Eriogonum ovale Auct.
Eriogonum ovalifolium Nutt.
Eriogonum parviflorum Nutt.
Eriogonum pauciflorum Pursh.
Eriogonum Piperi Greene.
Eriogonum polyanthum Benth.
Eriogonum proliferum Torr. & Gr.
Eriogonum racemosum Nutt.
Eriogonum ramosissimum Eastw.
Eriogonum saxatile Watson.
Eriogonum scoparium Small.
Eriogonum Simpsoni Benth.
Eriogonum stellatum Benth.
Eriogonum subalpinum Greene.
Eriogonum sulphureum Greene.
Eriogonum ursinum Watson.
Eriogonum vimineum Dougl.
Eriogonum Wrightii Torr.
  Nigredo intricata (Cke.) Arth.
  Uromyces arizonicus Tracy & Gall.
  Uromyces Chorizanthis Ell. & Hark.
  Uromyces Eriogoni Ell. & Hark.
  Uromyces Eriogoni Ell. & Hark., var. foliicola
    Ell. & Ev.
  Uromyces intricatus Cke.
Eriogonum elatum Dougl.
  Erysiphe Cichoracearum DC. †
Eriogonum latifolium Sm.
  Phoma herbarum Westd.
  Uromyces Eriogoni Ell. & Hark.
Eriogonum molle Greene.
  Cercospora Eriogoni Ell. & Ev.
Eriogonum nudum Dougl.
  Erysiphe Cichoracearum DC. †
  Nigredo intricata (Cke.) Arth.
  Uromyces Eriogoni Ell. & Hark.
  Uromyces intricatus Cke.
Eriogonum subreniforme Watson.
  Aecidium Sarcobati Pk.
  Puccinia subnitens Diet. I.
Eriogonum tomentosum Michx.
  ?Cercospora ferruginea Fckl.
  Cercospora rubella Cke.
  Pestalozzia? anomala Hark.
Eriogonum trichopes Torr.
  Aecidium Sarcobati Pk.
  Dicaeoma Sarcobati Arth. I.
  Puccinia subnitens Diet. I.
Eriogonum umbellatum Torr.
  Coniothyrium Eriogoni Earle.
  Gloeosporium Eriogoni Ell. & Ev.
  Uromyces arizonicus Tracy & Gall.
  Uromyces Chorizanthis Ell. & Hark.
  Uromyces Eriogoni Ell. & Hark.
  Uromyces Eriogoni Ell. & Hark., var. foliicola
    Ell. & Ev.
  Uromyces intricatus Cke.

Eriogonum virgatum Benth.
  Pestalozzia? anomala Hark.
  Uromyces Eriogoni Ell. & Hark.
Eriogonum sp. indet.
  Camarosporium Eriogoni Ell. & Ev.
  Heterosporium sphaeriiforme Ell. & Ev.
  Leptostromella Eriogoni Earle.
  Pyrenophora Eriogoni Earle.
Rumex Acetosa L.
  Coniosporium harknessioides (Ell. & Holw.)
    Sacc.
  Gloeosporium Rumicis Ell. & Ev.
  Sclerotium durum P. ex Fr.
  Septoria pleosporoides Sacc.
Rumex Acetosella L.
  Cercospora Acetosellae Ell.
  Coniosporium harknessioides (Ell. & Holw.)
    Sacc.
  Diaporthe discrepans Sacc.
  Didymella lophospora (Ell.) Sacc. & Speg.
  Lophiotrema lophosporum (Ell.) Rehm.
  Sphaeria lophospora Ell.
  Dicaeoma Acetosae (Körn.) O. Kuntze.
  Puccinia Acetosae Körn.
  Rhizoctonia Solani Kühn.
  Sphaerella tassiana De Not.
  Ustilago kuehneana G. P. Clinton.
  Ustilago Rumicis (B.) G. P. Clinton.
  Ustilago utriculosa (Nees) Tul., var. Rumicis B.
Rumex altissimus Wood.
  Aecidium rubellum Gmel. ex P.
  Dicaeoma rubellum (Arth.) Arth. & Fromme. I.
  Puccinia Phragmitis Körn. I.
  Puccinia rubella Arth. I.
  Erysiphe Cichoracearum DC. †
  Ovularia obliqua (Cke.) Oud.
  Phyllosticta circuligerens Tehon & Daniels.
  Dicaeoma punctiforme (Diet. & Holw.) Arth.
  Puccinia punctiformis Diet. & Holw.
  Ramularia occidentalis Ell. & Kellerm.
  Septoria Rumicis Ell.
  Ustilago Parlatorei Fisch. Wald.
Rumex britannica L.
  Aecidium rubellum Gmel. ex P.
  Dicaeoma rubellum (Arth.) Arth. & Fromme. I.
  Puccinia Phragmitis Körn. I.
  Puccinia rubella Arth. I.
  Cladochytrium majus (Schrt.) A. Fisch.
  Urophlyctis major Schrt.
  Micropuccinia ornata (Arth. & Holw.) Arth. &
    Jackson.
  Puccinia ornata Arth. & Holw.
  Ramularia decipiens Ell. & Ev.
  Ramularia macrospora Auct. Amer. p. p.
  Ramularia occidentalis Ell. & Kellerm.
  Ramularia pratensis Sacc.
  Septoria Rumicis Trail.
  Ustilago Parlatorei Fisch. Wald.

Rumex crispus L.
Cercospora Acetosellae Ell., var. maculosa Pk.
{ Aecidium rubellum Gmel. ex P.
{ Puccinia Phragmitis Körn. I.
{ Puccinia rubella Arth. I.
Colletotrichum erumpens Sacc.
{ Ovularia monosporia (Westd.) Pound & Clement.
{ Ovularia obliqua (Cke.) Oud.
{ Peronospora obliqua Cke.
{ Ramularia decipiens Ell. & Ev.
{ Ramularia macrospora Auct. Amer. p. p.
{ Ramularia obovata Fckl.
{ Dicaeoma punctiforme (Diet. & Holw.) Arth.
{ Puccinia punctiformis Diet. & Holw.
Ramularia occidentalis Ell. & Kellerm.
Sphaerella Rumicis (Desm.) Cke.
Sphaeropsis sphaerelloides Ell. & Ev.
Vermicularia rugulosa Ell. & Ev.

Rumex hastatulus Baldw.
{ Dicaeoma Acetosae (Körn.) O. Kuntze.
{ Puccinia Acetosae Körn.
{ Ustilago Rumicis (B.) G. P. Clinton.
{ Ustilago utriculosa (Nees) Tul., var. Rumicis B.

Rumex hymenosepalus Torr.
{ Aecidium Sarcobati Pk.
{ Dicaeoma Sarcobati Arth. I.
{ Puccinia Sarcobati (Arth.) Bethel. I.
{ Puccinia subnitens Diet. I.
{ Dicaeoma punctiforme (Diet. & Holw.) Arth.
{ Puccinia punctiformis Diet & Holw.

Rumex mexicanus Meisn.
{ Aecidium rubellum Gmel. ex P.
{ Dicaeoma rubellum (Arth.) Arth. & Fromme. I.
{ Puccinia Phragmitis Körn. I.
{ Puccinia rubella Arth. I.
{ Dicaeoma punctiforme (Diet. & Holw.) Arth.
{ Puccinia punctiformis Diet. & Holw.
{ Puccinia Rumicis Blasdale nom. nud.
Septoria Rumicis Trail.
Sphaerella Rumicis (Desm.) Cke.
Ustilago Parlatorei Fisch. Wald.

Rumex obtusifolius L.
Cercospora Rumicis Ell. & Langlois.
Cylindrosporium pulchrum Speg.
Gloeosporium Rumicis Ell. & Ev.
Macrosporium commune Rabh.
{ Ovularia obliqua (Cke.) Oud.
{ Ramularia decipiens Ell. & Ev.
{ Ramularia macrospora Auct. Amer. p. p.
{ Ramularia obovata Fckl.
Ramularia circumfusa Ell. & Ev.
Sphaerella Rumicis (Desm.) Cke.
Sphaeropsis sphaerelloides Ell. & Ev.

Rumex occidentalis Watson.
{ Aecidium rubellum Gmel. ex P.
{ Dicaeoma rubellum (Arth.) Arth. & Fromme. I.
{ Puccinia Phragmitis Körn. I.
{ Puccinia rubella Arth. I.
Heterosporium caulicola Ell. & Ev.
Puccinia Acetosae Körn.
{ Dicaeoma punctiforme (Diet. & Holw.) Arth.
{ Puccinia punctiformis Diet. & Holw.
{ Puccinia Rumicis Blasdale nom. nud.
Puccinia ornata Arth. & Holw.
Ramularia pratensis Sacc.
Sphaerella Rumicis (Desm.) Cke.
Mycosphaerella stromatoidea Dearness.

Rumex paucifolius Nutt.
Puccinia Polygoni-alpini Cruchet & Mayor.
Puccinia uniformis Pammel & Hume.
Uromyces fuscatus Arth.
Uromyces Polygoni (P.) Fckl.
{ Nigredo rickeriana Arth.
{ Uromyces rickerianus Arth.

Rumex persicarioides L.
Puccinia Acetosae Körn.
Ramularia pratensis Sacc.

Rumex venosus Pursh.
{ Aecidium rubellum Gmel. ex P.
{ Aecidium Rumicis Hoffm.
{ Dicaeoma rubellum (Arth.) Arth. & Fromme. I.
{ Puccinia Phragmitis Körn. I.
{ Puccinia rubella Arth. I.
Ramularia decipiens Ell. & Ev.
Septoria Rumicis Ell.

Rumex verticillatus L.
Excipula rumicicola S.
Ramularia decipiens Ell. & Ev.
Ramularia pratensis Sacc.
{ Septoria rumicicola Allescher.
{ Septoria Rumicis Ell.
Urophlyctis major Schrt.

Rumex sp. indet.
?Aecidium minutulum H. S. Jackson.
Didymella lophospora (Ell.) Sacc. & Speg., var. Acetosella Ell.
Phlyctaena arcuata B.
{ Haplosporella rumicicola (Sacc.) Petrak & Syd.
{ Sphaeropsis rumicicola Sacc.
Sporocybe byssoides (P.) Fr.
Uromyces Acetosae Schrt.
Uromyces Rumicis (Schum.) Wint.

Oxyria digyna (L.) Hill.
Cladosporium herbarum (P.) ex Lk.
Coleroa Oxyriae Rostr.
Leptosphaeria Oxyriae Rostr.
Mollisia cinerea (Batsch) Karst.
Ophiobolus brachystomus Sacc.
Pleospora herbarum (P.) ex Rabh.
{ Dicaeoma Oxyriae (Fckl.) O. Kuntze.
{ Puccinia Oxyriae Fckl.
Pyrenophora chrysospora (Niessl) Sacc.

Oxyria digyna (*cont.*)
  Pyrenophora comata (Awd. & Niessl) Sacc.
  { Heteropatella umbilicata (P.) Jaap.
  { Rhabdospora cercosperma (Rostr.) Sacc.
  { Septoria cercosperma Rostr.
  Sclerotium Oxyriae Rostr.
  Septoria pleosporoides Sacc.
  { Mycosphaerella pachyasca (Rostr.) Vestergren.
  { Sphaerella pachyasca Rostr.
  { Mycosphaerella Polygonum (Crié) J. Lind.
  { Sphaerella Polygonorum (Crié) Sacc.
  Ustilago vinosa (B.) Tul.

Rheum Rhaponticum L.
  { Aecidium rubellum Gmel. ex P.
  { Dicaeoma rubellum (Arth.) Arth. & Fromme. I.
  { Puccinia Phragmitis Körn. I.
  { Puccinia rubella Arth. I.
  Armillaria mellea (Vahl) ex Fr.
  { Ascochyta Rhei Ell. & Ev.
  { Phyllosticta halstediana (Ell. & Ev.) Alle-
  {   scher.
  { Phyllosticta Rhei Ell. & Ev.
  Cercospora Rhapontici Tehon & Daniels.
  Colletotrichum erumpens Sacc.
  { Corticium vagum B. & C.
  { Rhizoctonia Solani Kühn.
  Ozonium omnivorum Shear.
  Peronospora Rumicis Cda.
  Phoma herbarum Westd.
  Phyllosticta straminella Bres.
  { Phytophthora Cactorum (Lebert & Cohn)
  {   Schrt.
  { Phytophthora omnivora DBy.
  Phytophthora parasitica, var. Rhei Godfrey.
  Phytophthora terrestris Sherb.
  Sclerotium Rolfsii Sacc.
  Septoria Rhapontici Thm.
  Vermicularia Polygoni-virginici S.

Polygonum acre H. B. K.
  Cercospora avicularis Wint.
  { Cercospora Hydropiperis (Thm.) Speg.
  { Cercospora Polygonorum Cke.
  Cladosporium effusum B. & C.
  Cladosporium pelliculosum B. & C.
  Darluca Filum (Biv.) Cast.
  Diaporthe discrepans Sacc., var. Polygoni Ell.
    & Ev.
  { Dialonectria consors Ell. & Ev.
  { Nectriella consors (Ell. & Ev.) Sacc.
  { Dicaeoma Polygoni-amphibii (P.) Arth.
  { Puccinia Polygoni-amphibii P.
  { Uredo Polygonorum DC.
  { Trichobasis Polygonorum Rav. Fung. Am.
  Sphacelotheca Hydropiperis (Schum.) DBy.
  Uromyces Polygoni (P.) Fckl.
  { Melanopsichium austro-americanum (Speg.)
  {   Beck.
  { Ustilago austro-americana Speg.
  Ustilago utriculosa (Nees) Tul.

Polygonum acre H. B. K., var. **leptostachyum**
  Meisn.
  Uromyces Polygoni (P.) Fckl.

Polygonum alpinum All.
  Puccinia Bistortae DC.
  Puccinia Polygoni-alpini Cruchet & Mayor.
  Uromyces fuscatus Arth.

Polygonum amphibium L.
  Clathrospora permunda (Cke.) Berl.
  { Puccinia amphibii Fckl.
  { Puccinia concentrica S.
  { Puccinia Polygoni A. & S.
  { Puccinia Polygoni-amphibii P.
  { Puccinia Polygoni-pensilvanici S.
  { Puccinia Polygonorum Schl.
  { Trichobasis Polygonorum Rav. Fung. Am.
  { Uredo Polygonorum DC.
  Ramularia rufomaculans Pk.
  { Caeoma utriculosum Nees.
  { Ustilago utriculosa (Nees) Tul.

Polygonum amphibium L., var. **Hartwrightii**
  (Gray) Bissell.
  Darluca Filum (Biv.) Cast.
  { Dicaeoma Polygoni-amphibi (P.) Arth.
  { Dicaeoma Polygoni-convolvuli (Hedw. f.) Arth.
  { Puccinia Polygoni A. & S.
  { Puccinia Polygoni-amphibii P.
  Ramularia rufomaculans Pk.

Polygonum aviculare L.
  { Aecidium Polygoni Chev.
  { Dicaeoma Sarcobati Arth. I.
  { Puccinia Sarcobati (Arth.) Bethel. I.
  { Puccinia subnitens Diet. I.
  { Uromyces Polygoni I. Fung. Columb. *1897.*
  Cercospora avicularis Wint.
  { Erysiphe communis Auct. Amer.
  { Erysiphe Polygoni DC. †
  { Ovularia avicularis Pk.
  { Ovularia rigidula J. J. Davis non Delacr.
  { Peronospora Polygoni Thm.
  { Peronospora Rumicis Auct. Amer.
  Septocylindrium rufomaculans (Pk.) Pound &
    Clements.
  Tilmadoche polycephala (S.) Macbr.
  { Caeomurus Polygoni (P.) O. Kuntze.
  { Nigredo Polygoni (P.) Arth.
  { Uromyces Aviculariae (DC.) Schrt.
  { Uromyces Polygoni (P.) Fckl.
  Vermicularia dematium (P.) Fr.

Polygonum Bistorta L.
  Puccinia Bistortae DC.
  Sphacelotheca borealis (G. P. Clinton) Schel-
    lenberg.
  Sphacelotheca Hydropiperis (Schum.) DBy.

Polygonum bistortoides Pursh.
  { Dicaeoma Bistortae (DC.) O. Kuntze.
  { Puccinia Bistortae DC.

Polygonum bistortoides (*cont.*)
 Dicaeoma Polygoni-vivipari (H. Dietr.) Arth.
 Puccinia Bistortae Fung. Columb. *2349*, N.
   Am. Uredinales *126*.
 Puccinia Polygoni-vivipari H. Dietr.
 Sphacelotheca borealis (G. P. Clinton) Schel-
   lenberg..
 Sphacelotheca Hydropiperis (Schum.) DBy.,
   var. borealis G. P. Clinton.
 Ustilago Bistortarum (DC.) Körn.

Polygonum buxiforme Small.
 Erysiphe Polygoni DC. †
 Nigredo Polygoni (P.) Arth.
 Septoria Polygonorum Desm.

Polygonum Careyi Olney.
 Puccinia Polygoni A. & S.

Polygonum cilinode Michx.
 Ramularia cilinodis J. J. Davis.
 Septoria polygonina Thm.
 Septoria Polygonorum Desm. ?
 Ustilago anomala J. Kunze.
 Ustilago pallida Schrt.

Polygonum coccineum Muhl.
 Dicaeoma Polygoni-amphibii (P.) Arth.

Polygonum Convolvulus L.
 Ascochyta biguttulata Daniels.
 Cercospora polygonacea Ell. & Ev.
 Erysiphe Polygoni DC. †
 Peronospora Polygoni Thm.
 Phlyctaena complanata (B. & C.) Sacc.
 Puccinia Convolvuli P.
 Dicaeoma Polygoni-amphibii (P.) Arth.
 Dicaeoma Polygoni-Convolvuli (Hedw.f.) Arth.
 Puccinia Polygoni A. & S.
 Puccinia Polygoni-amphibii P.
 Puccinia Polygoni-Convolvuli Hedw. f.
 Ramularia anomala Pk.
 Septoria Polygonorum Desm.
 Ustilago anomala J. Kunze.

Polygonum cuspidatum Sieb. & Zucc.
 Leptosphaeria fusispora Niessl.

Polygonum Davisiae Brewer.
 Dicaeoma amphispilusum (Diet. & Holw.)
   Arth.
 Puccinia amphispilusa Diet. & Holw.
 Puccinia Bistortae DC.
 Ustilago Piperi G. P. Clinton.

Polygonum densiflorum Meisn.
 Dicaeoma Polygoni-amphibii (P.) Arth.
 Puccinia Polygoni-amphibii P.

Polygonum dumetorum L.
 Peronospora Polygoni Thm.
 Peronospora Rumicis Auct. Amer.
 Ustilago anomala J. Kunze.

Polygonum dumetorum L., var. **cristatum** (Engelm. & Gray) B. L. Robinson.
 Dicaeoma Polygoni-amphibii (P.) Arth.

Polygonum erectum L.
 Aecidium biforme Pk.
 Dicaeoma Sarcobati Arth. I.
 Puccinia Sarcobati (Arth.) Bethel. I.
 Puccinia subnitens Diet. I.
 Cercospora avicularis Wint.
 Colletotrichum erumpens Sacc.
 Erysiphe communis Auct. Am.
 Erysiphe Polygoni DC. †
 Ovularia Bistortae (Fckl.) Sacc
 Ovularia rigidula Delacr.
 ?Puccinia Polygoni-amphibii P.
 Caeomurus Polygoni (P.) O. Kuntze.
 Nigredo Polygoni (P.) Arth.
 Uromyces Polygoni (P.) Fckl.
 Ustilago utriculosa (Nees) Tul.

Polygonum exsertum Small.
 Erysiphe Polygoni DC. †

Polygonum Fowleri Robinson.
 Nigredo Polygoni (P.) Arth.
 Uromyces Polygoni (P.) Fckl.

Polygonum hirsutum Walt.
 Dicaeoma Polygoni-amphibii (P.) Arth.
 Puccinia Polygoni-amphibii P.

Polygonum Hydropiper L.
 Botrytis hypophylla Ell. & Kellerm.
 Cercospora Hydropiperis (Thm.) Speg.
 Cercospora Polygonorum Cke.
 Helminthosporium Hydropiperis Thm.
 Helminthosporium polygonicola Coons.
 Phoma herbarum Westd.
 Septoria polygonicola (Lasch) Sacc.
 Septoria Polygonorum Desm.
 Sphacelotheca Hydropiperis (Schum.) DBy.
 Ustilago Candollei Tul.
 Melanopsichium austro-americanum (Speg.)
   Beck.
 Ustilago austro-americana Speg.
 Ustilago utriculosa (Nees) Tul.

Polygonum hydropiperoides Michx.
 Cercospora Hydropiperis (Thm.) Speg.
 Septoria Polygonorum Desm.
 Dicaeoma Polygoni-amphibii (P.) Arth.
 Puccinia Polygoni A. & S.
 Puccinia Polygoni-amphibii P.
 Sphacelotheca Hydropiperis (Schum.) DBy.
 Ustilago austro-americana Speg.
 Ustilago utriculosa (Nees) Tul.

Polygonum imbricatum Nutt.
 Puccinia Bistortae DC.

Polygonum lapathifolium L.
 Cercospora polygonacea Ell. & Ev.
 Colletotrichum erumpens Sacc.
 Diplodia polygonicola Pk.
 Phoma demetriana Bubák.
 Dicaeoma Polygoni-amphibii (P.) Arth.
 Puccinia Polygoni-amphibii P.
 Ramularia rufomaculans Pk.
 Septoria Polygonorum Desm.

Polygonum lapathifolium (*cont.*)
{ Melanopsichium austro-americanum (Speg.)
    G. Beck.
  Ustilago austro-americana Speg.
  Ustilago Bistortarum Auct. Amer.
  Ustilago utriculosa (Nees) Tul.
Polygonum linearifolium Greene.
  Puccinia Bistortae DC.
Polygonum longistylum Small.
  Melanopsichium austro-americanum (Speg.)
    G. Beck.
Polygonum maritimum L.
{ Nigredo Polygoni (P.) Arth.
{ Uromyces Polygoni (P.) Fckl.
Polygonum Muhlenbergii (Meisn.) Watson.
{ Cercospora Hydropiperis (Thm.) Speg.
  Cercospora Polygonorum Cke.
{ Depazea Polygonorum Crié.
{ Mycosphaerella Polygonorum Dearness &
    House.
  Gloeosporium Polygoni Dearness & House.
  Pleospora compressa Hark.
{ Dicaeoma Polygoni-amphibii (P.) Arth.
  Puccinia amphibii Fckl.
  Puccinia concentrica S.
{ Puccinia Polygoni Reb.
  Puccinia Polygoni-amphibii P.
  Puccinia [Polygoni-emersi] ex Arth.
  Puccinia Polygonorum DC.
  Ramularia rufomaculans Pk.
  Septoria Polygonorum Desm.
  Vermicularia Polygoni-virginici S.
Polygonum neglectum Besser.
  Nigredo Polygoni (P.) Arth.
Polygonum Newberryi Small.
{ Dicaeoma amphispilusum (Diet. & Holw.)
    Arth.
  Puccinia amphispilusa Diet. & Holw.
{ Dicaeoma Bistortae (DC.) O. Kuntze.
{ Puccinia Bistortae DC.
  Ustilago punctata G. P. Clinton.
Polygonum orientale L.
  Septoria Polygonorum Desm.
Polygonum pennsylvanicum L.
  Cercospora Hydropiperis (Thm.) Speg.
{ Macrophoma pulchrispora (Pk. & Clinton)
    Sacc.
  Phoma callospora Pk. & Clinton.
  Sphaeropsis pulchrispora Pk. & Clinton.
{ Mollisia discolor (Mont. & Fr.) Phil.
{ Patellaria discolor Mont. & Fr.
  Physalospora Polygoni Ell. & Ev.
{ Dicaeoma Polygoni-amphibii (P.) Arth.
  Puccinia amphibii Fckl.
  Puccinia Polygoni Reb. 1804.
{ Puccinia Polygoni A. & S. 1805.
  Puccinia Polygoni-amphibii P.
  Puccinia Polygoni-pensilvanici S.
{ Puccinia Polygonorum Schl.

Septoria Polygonorum Desm.
Ustilago anomala J. Kunze.
{ Melanopsichium austro-americanum (Speg.)
    G. Beck.
{ Tilletia bullata Auct. Amer.
  Ustilago austro-americana Speg.
{ Ustilago Bistortarum Auct. Amer.
  Ustilago utriculosa (Nees) Tul.
Polygonum Persicaria L.
{ Mollisia Polygoni (Lasch) Gill.
{ Niptera Polygoni (Lasch) Rehm.
  Peziza lactuosa Cke.
  Peziza Polygoni Lasch.
{ Dicaeoma Polygoni-amphibii (P.) Arth.
  Puccinia Polygoni Reb.
{ Puccinia Polygoni-amphibii P.
  Septoria Polygonorum Desm.
{ Melanopsichium austro-americanum (Speg.)
    G. Beck.
  Ustilago austro-americanum Speg.
  Ustilago utriculosa (Nees) Tul.
Polygonum phytolaccifolium (Meisn.) Small.
{ Dicaeoma Polygoni-alpini (Cruchet & Mayor)
    Arth.
{ Puccinia Polygoni-alpini Cruchet & Mayor.
  Ustilago Piperi G. P. Clinton.
Polygonum polymorphum Ledeb.
{ Clathrospora permunda (Cke.) Berl.
{ Pleospora compressa Hark.
  Kellermania Polygoni Ell. & Ev.
  Trichopeziza setigera (Phil.) Sacc.
(Polygonum) psychrophila (Greene) Auct.
  Puccinia Polygoni-amphibii P.
Polygonum ramosissimum Michx.
  Puccinia subnitens Diet. I.
  Cercospora polygonacea Ell. & Ev.
{ Erysiphe communis Auct. Amer.
{ Erysiphe Polygoni DC. †
  Peronospora americana Gäumann.
  Peronospora Rumicis Cda.
{ Nigredo Polygoni (P.) Arth.
{ Uromyces Polygoni (P.) Fckl.
Polygonum sagittatum L.
  Cercospora avicularis Wint., var. sagittati Atk.
  Sphaeria Polygoni-sagittati S.
{ Sphacelotheca Hydropiperis (Schum.) DBy.
{ Ustilago Candollei Tul.
{ Ustilago Hydropiperis (Schum.) Schrt.
Polygonum sawatchense Small.
  Phoma exigua Desm.
  Nigredo Polygoni (P.) Arth.
Polygonum scandens L.
  Aecidium Sommerfeltii Johans.
  Cercospora polygonacea Ell. & Ev.
  Erysiphe Polygoni DC. †
{ Metasphaeria Polygoni-sagittati (S.) Ell. & Ev.
{ Sphaeria Polygoni-sagittati S.
{ Peronospora Polygoni Thm.
{ Peronospora Rumicis Cda.

Polygonum scandens (*cont.*)
Peronospora Potentillae DBy.
{ Dicaeoma parcum Arth.
{ Puccinia mammillata E. F. *367.*
{ Puccinia parca Arth.
{ Puccinia septentrionalis Auct. Amer. p. p.
{ Dicaeoma Polygoni-amphibii (P.) Arth.
{ Dicaeoma Polygoni-Convolvuli (Hedw.) Arth.
{ Puccinia Polygoni A. & S.
{ Puccinia Polygoni-amphibii P.
{ Puccinia Polygoni-Convolvuli Hedw.
Ramularia anomala Pk.
Ramularia rufomaculans Pk.
Septoria Polygonorum Desm.
Spegazzinia rubra Dearness & House.
Ustilago anomala J. Kunze.
Polygonum setaceum Baldw.
{ Dicaeoma Polygoni-amphibii (P.) Arth.
{ Puccinia Polygoni-amphibii P.
Uromyces Polygoni (P.) Fckl.
Polygonum spergulariiforme Meisn.
Dicaeoma Bistortae (DC.) O. Kuntze.
Nigredo Polygoni (P.) Arth.
Polygonum virginianum L.
Pestalozzia Polygoni Ell. & Ev.
{ Phlyctaena complanata (B. & C.) Sacc.
{ Septoria complanata B. & C.
Phyllactinia corylea (P.) ex Karst.
{ Dicaeoma Polygoni-amphibii (P.) Arth.
{ Puccinia Polygoni Reb. 1804.
{ Puccinia Polygoni A. & S. 1805.
{ Puccinia Polygoni-amphibii P.
{ Puccinia Polygonorum Schl.
{ Uromyces Polygoni N. Am. Uredinales *992.*
Rhabdospora Polygoni Dearness & House.
?Uromyces Polygoni (P.) Fckl.
{ Melanopsichium austro-americanum (Speg.) Beck.
{ Ustilago austro-americana Speg.
Vermicularia Polygoni-virginici S.
Polygonum viviparum L.
Bostrichonema alpestre Ces.
Kellermania cercosperma (Rostr.) Lind.
Phacidium Polygoni Rostr.
Pleospora comata Niessl.
Pleospora herbarum (P.) ex Rabh.
Pleospora platyspora Sacc.
Puccinia Bistortae DC.
Dicaeoma Polygoni-vivipari (H. Dietr.) Arth.
Pyrenophora chrysospora (Niessl) Sacc.
Stigmatea Polygonorum Fr.
Ustilago punctata G. P. Clinton.
Verticillium distans B. & Br.
{ Dicaeoma Sommerfeltii Arth.
{ Puccinia Sommerfeltii (Arth.) Stevenson.
{ Puccinia septentrionalis Juel.
Ramularia Bistortae Fckl.
{ Pseudopeziza Bistortae (DC. ex Fr.) Fckl.
{ Rhytisma Bistortae (DC. ex Fr.) Rostr.

Septoria Polygonorum Desm.
Sphacelotheca Hydropiperis (Schum.) DBy.
Sphacelotheca Polygoni-vivipari Schellenberg.
Polygonum Watsonii Small.
{ Dicaeoma Bistortae (DC.) O. Kuntze.
{ Puccinia Bistortae DC.
{ Puccinia uniformis Pammel & Hume.
Polygonum sp. indet.
{ Anthostoma mortuosum (Ell.) Sacc.
{ Sphaeria mortuosa Ell.
{ Botrytis fascicularis (Cda.) Sacc.
{ Polyactis fascicularis Cda.
{ Gnomonia eccentrica (C. & P.) Cke.
{ Gnomoniella eccentrica (C. & P.) Sacc.
{ Sphaeria eccentrica C. & P.
Nitschkia Polygoni Tehon & Daniels.
Ophiobolus acuminatus (Sow.) ex Duby.
Phialea Scutula (P.) Gill.
Phialea Scutula (P.) Gill., var. fucata (Phil.) Sacc.
Sphaerella eucarpa Karst.
{ Mycosphaerella Polygonorum (Crié) Dearness.
{ Sphaerella Polygonorum (Crié) Sacc.
Sphaerella Vivipari Wint.
Ustilago Bistortarum (DC.) Körn.
Ustilago Bistortatum (DC.) Körn., var. inflorescentiae Trel.
Fagopyrum esculentum Moench.
Alternaria fasciculata (C. & E.) Jones & Grout.
Ascochyta Bresadolae Sacc. & Syd.
Ascochyta Fagopyri Bres.
Ascochyta Fagopyri Thm., var. italica Trav.
Erysiphe Polygoni DC. †
Galerula sulcatipes (Pk.) Murrill.
Phyllosticta Polygonorum Sacc.
Ramularia anomala Pk.
Ramularia rufomaculans Pk.
Rhizoctonia Solani Kühn.
Polygonella articulata (L.) Meisn.
Dicaeoma Polygoni-amphibii (P.) Arth.
{ Gnomonia curvicolla (Pk.) Cke.
{ Gnomoniella curvicolla (Pk.) Sacc.
{ Sphaeria curvicolla Pk.
Brunnichia cirrhoe Gaertn.
Leptothyrium Brunnichiae Tehon.
Muehlenbeckia platyclada (F. v. M.) Lindau.
Erysiphe Polygoni DC. †
Coccoloba diversifolia Jacq.
Microclava Coccolobae F. L. Stevens.
Tremella rufolutea B. & C.
Coccoloba grandifolia Jacq.
Meliola praetervisa Gaill.
Coccoloba laurifolia Jacq.
Helminthosporium Panici F. L. Stevens.
Lembosia portoricensis Ryan.
Meliola rectangularis F. L. Stevens.
Phyllachora simplex Starb.
Scolecopeltis pachyasca Speg
Seynesia Coccolobae Ryan.

Coccoloba nivea Jacq.
{ Podoscypha affinis (B. & C.) Pat.
{ Thelephora affinis B. & C.
{ Clypeotrabutia portoricensis (F. L. Stevens)
{   Seaver & Chardon
{ Trabutia portoricensis F. L. Stevens.

Coccoloba pyrifolia Desf.
Lembosidium portoricense Speg
Meliola praetervisa Gaill.

Coccoloba sintenisii Urb.
Isthmospora spinosa F. L. Stevens.
Meliola praetervisa Gaill.

Coccoloba uvifera (L.) Jacq.
Asterina Coccolobae Ferdinandsen & Winge.
Crepidotus pyrrhus B. & C.
Endothia Coccolobii Vizioli.
{ Gloeoporus conchoides Mont.
{ Leptoporus conchoides (Mont.) Pat.
Hendersonia coccolobina Fairman.
Lembosia Coccolobae Earle.
Lembosia Philodendri Henn.
Lembosia tenella Lév.
Pestalozzia Coccolobae Ell. & Ev.
Phyllosticta Coccolobae Ell. & Ev.
Phyllosticta Coccolobae Ell. & Ev., var.
  dominicana Ciferri & Fragoso.
{ Botryodiplodia Coccolobae (Fairman) Petrak
{   & Syd.
{ Sphaeropsis Coccolobae Fairman.
Uredo Coccolobae Henn.
Uredo uviferae Syd.
Verticicladium effusum Earle.

Coccoloba sp. indet.
Melasmia Coccolobiae F. L. Stevens.
Meliola Coccolobis Stevens & Tehon.
Micropeltella constricta Stevens & Manter.

Nitrophila occidentalis (Nutt.) Watson.
{ Aecidium Sarcobati Pk.
{ Dicaeoma Sarcobati Arth. I.

CHENOPODIACEAE

Beta vulgaris L.

PHYCOMYCETES

{ Albugo Bliti (Biv.) O. Kuntze.
{ Cystopus Bliti (Biv.) Lév.
Albugo? occidentalis G. W. Wilson.
Mucor Mucedo L.
Oedomyces leproides Trab.
Peronospora Schachtii Fckl.
Pythium debaryanum Hesse.
{ Aphanomyces levis Edson non DBy.
{ Pythium aphanidermatum (Edson) Fitzpat-
{   rick.
{ Nematosporangium aphanidermatum (Edson)
{   Fitzpatrick.
{ Rheosporangium aphanidermatum Edson.

Urophlyctis leproides (P. Maz.) Trab.
  (Rhizopus species inoculated.)
Rhizopus arrhizus Fischer.
Rhizopus delemar (Boid.) Wehmer & Hanzawa.
Rhizopus Maydis Bruderl.
Rhizopus nigricans Ehrenb. ex Fr.
Rhizopus nodosus Namysl.
Rhizopus Oryzae Went & Pr. Geerling.
Rhizopus Tritici Saito.

UREDINALES

{ Dicaeoma Sarcobati Arth. I.
{ Puccinia Sarcobati (Arth.) Bethel. I.
{ Puccinia subnitens Diet. I.
{ Nigredo Betae (Lév.) Arth.
{ Trichobasis Betae Lév.
{ Uredo Betae P.
{ Uromyces Betae Lév.

HYMENOMYCETINEAE

{ Corticium vagum B. & C.
{ Corticium vagum B. & C., var. Solani Burt.
{ Rhizoctonia Betae Eidam non Kühn.
{ Rhizoctonia Solani Kühn.
Ozonium omnivorum Shear.
Rhizoctonia Crocorum (P.) ex Fr.

FUNGI IMPERFECTI

Actinomyces chromogenus Gasperini.
{ Actinomyces scabies (Thax.) Güssow.
{ Oospora scabies Thax.
Cephalothecium roseum Cda.
{ Cercospora Betae Coons.
{ ?Cercospora beticola Sacc.
{ Cercospora longissima C. & E.
Clasterosporium putrefaciens (Fckl.) Sacc.
Fusarium Betae (Desm.) Sacc.
Fusarium culmorum, var. leteius Sherb.
Fusarium ventricosum Appel & Wr.
Gloeosporium Betae Dearness & Barthol.
Papulospora parasitica (Karst.) Hotson.
Phoma Betae Frank. 1892.
Phoma Betae Rostr. 1894.
Phyllosticta Betae Oud.
Phyllosticta tabifica Auct.
Rhopalomyces elegans Cda.
Septoria Betae Westd.
Sporidesmium putrefaciens Fckl.
Volutella oxyspora Atk.

MISCELLANEA

Plasmodiophora Brassicae Wor.
{ Sclerotinia libertiana Fckl.
{ Sclerotinia sclerotiorum (Lib.) Schrt.
Sclerotinia perplexa Lawrence.
Sclerotium Rolfsii Sacc.
Sorolpidium Betae Nemec.
Thielavia basicola (B. & Br.) Zopf.

Chenopodium album L.
⎰Aecidium Chenopodii-fruticosi Fung. Columb.
⎱ *1501.*
Aecidium Ellisii Tracy & Gall.
⎧Dicaeoma Sarcobati Arth. I.
⎨Puccinia Sarcobati (Arth.) Bethel. I.
⎩Puccinia subnitens Diet. I.
Uromyces peckianus Farl. I.
⎰Cercospora Chenopodii Fres.
⎱Cercospora dubia (Riess) Wint.
⎰Diaporthe picea (P. ex Fr.) Sacc.
⎱Sphaeria picea P. ex Fr.
⎰Diplodia hyalospora C. & E.
⎱Diplodina Ellisii Sacc.
⎧Dothidella longissima (P. ex Fr.) Ell. & Ev.
⎨Phoma longissima (P. ex Fr.) Westd.
⎩Sphaeria longissima P. ex Fr.
Gloeosporium melleum Dearness & Overh.
⎰Heptameria eutypoides (Pk.) Cke.
⎱Leptosphaeria eutypoides Pk.
Leptosphaeria doliolum (P.) DeNot.
Leptostromella Chenopodii Dearness & House.
Leptothyrium Chenopodii Dearness & Barthol.
Macrosporium Amaranthi Pk.
Metasphaeria anthelmintica (Cke.) Dearness.
Metasphaeria complanata (Tode ex Fr.) Sacc.
⎰Ophiobolus acuminatus (Sow. ex Fr.) Duby.
⎱Sphaeria acuminata Sow. ex Fr.
Ophiobolus collapsus Ell. & Ev.
⎰Peronospora effusa (Grev.) Rabh.
⎱Peronospora farinosa (Fr.) Keissler.
Peronospora effusa (Grev.) Rabh., var. minor
DBy.
⎰Pleospora calvescens (Fr.) Tul.
⎱Pyrenophora calvescens (Fr.) Sacc.
⎧Ascochyta Atriplicis Lasch nom. nud.
⎪Phleospora Chenopodii (Westd.) Ell. & Kellerm.
⎪Phyllosticta Atriplicis Desm.
⎪Phyllosticta Chenopodii Auct. Amer.
⎨Septogloeum Atriplicis Fung. Columb. *1062.*
⎪Septoria Atriplicis (Westd.) Fckl.
⎪Septoria Chenopodii Westd.
⎪Septoria Westendorpii Wint.
⎩Stagonospora Chenopodii (Westd.) Pk.
Phyllosticta chenopodiicola Tehon & Daniels.
Ramularia dubia Riess.

Chenopodium ambrosioides L.
⎰Diaporthe euspina (C. & E.) Sacc.
⎱Sphaeria euspina C. & E.
Phyllosticta ambrosioides Thm.
Pyrenophora calvescens (Fr.) Sacc.

Chenopodium ambrosioides L., var. **anthelminti-
cum** Gray.
Cercospora anthelmintica Atk.
Cercospora Chenopodii Fres.
Chaetophoma anthelmintica Cke.
⎰Fusarium pallidoroseum (Cke.) Sacc.
⎱Fusisporium pallidoroseum Cke.

⎧Heptameria anthelmintica Cke.
⎨Leptosphaeria anthelmintica (Cke.) Sacc.
⎩Sphaeria anthelmintica Cke.
Sporocybe byssoides (P.) ex Fr.
Chenopodium boscianum Moq.
Cercospora dubia (Riess) Wint.
Chenopodium capitatum (L.) Watson.
⎰Aecidium biforme Pk.
⎱Dicaeoma Sarcobati Arth. I.
Ascochyta Chenopodii (Karst.) Rostr.
Cercospora dubia (Riess) Wint.
⎰Albugo occidentalis G. W. Wilson.
⎱Cystopus occidentalis (G. W. Wilson) Sacc. &
Trott.
⎧?Septogloeum Atriplicis (Desm.) Ell. & Ev.
⎨Septoria Atriplicis (Westd.) Fckl.
⎩Septoria Chenopodii Westd.
Chenopodium Fremontii Watson.
⎰Dicaeoma Sarcobati Arth. I.
⎱Puccinia subnitens Diet. I.
Chenopodium glaucum L.
Puccinia subnitens Diet. I.
Leptosphaeria anthelmintica (Cke.) Sacc.
Urophlyctis pulposa (Wallr.) Schrt.
Chenopodium hybridum L.
⎧[Aecidium biforme Pk.]
⎪Dicaeoma Sarcobati Arth. I.
⎨Puccinia Sarcobati (Arth.) Bethel. I.
⎩Puccinia subnitens Diet. I.
⎰Cercospora Chenopodii Fres.
⎱Cercospora dubia (Riess) Wint.
Peronospora Chenopodii Schl.
⎰Peronospora effusa (Grev.) Rabh.
⎱Peronospora farinosa (Fr.) Keissler.
Septoria Atriplicis (Lasch) Fckl.
Chenopodium incanum (Watson) Heller.
Chenopodium lanceolatum Muhl.
⎧Aecidium Sarcobati Pk.
⎪Dicaeoma Sarcobati Arth. I.
⎨Puccinia Sarcobati (Arth.) Bethel. I.
⎩Puccinia subnitens Diet. I.
Chenopodium leptophyllum Nutt.
⎧Aecidium Chenopodii-fruticosi Auct. Amer.
⎪Aecidium Ellisii Tracy & Gall.
⎨Dicaeoma Sarcobati Arth. I.
⎩Puccinia subnitens Diet. I.
Cercospora dubia (Reiss) Wint.
Mycosphaerella Chenopodii Dearness & Bar-
thol.
Peronospora effusa (Grev.) Rabh.
Rhizoctonia Solani Kühn.
Chenopodium leptospermum ex Wilson.
Peronospora farinosa (Fr.) Keissler.
Chenopodium murale L.
⎧[Aecidium biforme Pk.]
⎪Dicaeoma Sarcobati Arth. I.
⎨Puccinia Sarcobati (Arth.) Bethel. I.
⎩Puccinia subnitens Diet. I.
Uromyces Peckianus Farl. I.

Chenopodium pratericola Rydb.
Chenopodium pugonum Reich.
  Aecidium biforme Pk.
  Dicaeoma Sarcobati Arth. I.
  Puccinia subnitens Diet. I.
Chenopodium rubrum L.
  Aecidium biforme Pk.
  Dicaeoma Sarcobati Arth. I.
  Puccinia subnitens Diet. I.
  Albugo occidentalis G. W. Wilson.
  Cercospora Chenopodii Fres.
  Stagonospora Chenopodii Pk.
Chenopodium salinum Standley.
  Dicaeoma Sarcobati Arth. I.
  Puccinia subnitens Diet. I.
Chenopodium sp. indet.
  ?Albugo Bliti Lév.
  Camarosporium Chenopodii Ell. & Ev.
  Diplodina Ellisii Sacc.
  Heptameria eriophora Cke.
  Leptosphaeria eriophora (Cke.) Sacc.
  Pocosphaeria eriophora (Cke.) Berl.
  Sphaeria eriophora Cke.
  Macrosporium commune Rabh.
  Perisporium galba Fr.
  Sphaeria galbana Fr.
  Dothidea Chenopodii S.
  Phyllachora Chenopodii (S.) Sacc.
  Dothidea ramosa S.
  Phyllachora ramosa (S.) Sacc.
  Sphaeria fumosa S.
  Sphaeria rubicunda S.
  Torula herbarum Lk.
Monolepis nuttalliana (R. & S.) Watson.
  Aecidium Ellisii Pk.
  Dicaeoma Sarcobati Arth.
  Puccinia Sarcobati (Arth.) Bethel. I.
  Puccinia subnitens Diet. I.
  Peronospora effusa (Grev.) Rabh.
Spinacia oleracea Mill.
  Aecidium Ellisii Pk.
  Dicaeoma Sarcobati Arth.
  Puccinia Sarcobati (Arth.) Bethel. I.
  Puccinia subnitens Diet. I.
  Cercospora beticola Sacc.
  Cercospora dubia (Riess) Wint.
  Cercospora flagelliformis Ell. & Halsted.
  Cladosporium macrocarpum Preuss.
  Cladosporium nodulosum Cke.
  Cladosporium subnodosum Cke.
  Colletotrichum Spinaciae Ell. & Halsted.
  Corticium vagum B. & C.
  Rhizoctonia Solani Kühn.
  Entyloma Ellisii Halsted.
  Fusarium Solani Auct. p. p.
  Fusarium Spinaciae Hungerford.
  Heterosporium variabile Cke.
  Macrosporium Cheiranthi (Lib.) Fr.

Peronospora effusa (Grev.) Rabh.
Phyllosticta Chenopodii Sacc.
Phytophthora Cactorum (Cohn & Leb.) Schrt.
Pythium debaryanum Hesse.
Sclerotinia libertiana Fckl.
Sclerotium Rolfsii Sacc.
Stagonospora Spinaciae Ell. & Ev.
Atriplex californica Moq.
  Pucciniola Atriplicis Arth.
Atriplex canescens James.
  Camarosporium patagonicum Speg.
  Eutypella herbicola Ell. & Ev.
  Uromyces Atriplicis Arth.
Atriplex confertifolia Watson.
  Aecidium Salicorniae DC.?
  Aecidium Atriplicis Shear.
  Uromyces Atriplicis Arth.
  Uromyces shearianus Arth. I.
  Melanopsammina utahensis Petrak.
  Teichospora solitaria Ell.
Atriplex leucophylla Dietr.
  Uromyces shearianus Arth. I.
Atriplex littoralis L.
  Uromyces peckianus Farl.
Atriplex magdalenae Brandegee.
  Camarosporium patagonicum Speg.
Atriplex Nuttallii Watson.
  Aecidium Atriplicis Shear.
  Uromyces Atriplicis Arth.
Atriplex patula L.
  Cercospora dubia (Riess) Wint.
  Uromyces peckianus Farl. I.
  Urophlyctis pulposa (Wallr.) Schrt.
Atriplex patula L., var. **hastata** (L.) Gray.
  Aecidium Atriplicis Shear.
  Aecidium biforme Pk.
  Dicaeoma Sarcobati Arth. I.
  Puccinia Aristidae Tracy. I.
  Uromyces peckianus Farl. I.
  Cercospora Chenopodii Fres.
  Cercospora dubia (Riess) Wint.
  Ramularia dubia Riess.
  Diplodina Atriplicis Vestergren.
  Peronospora effusa (Grev.) Rabh.
  Ascochyta Atriplicis Lasch. nom. nud.
  Septoria Atriplicis (Westd.) Fckl.
  Stagonospora Atriplicis (Westd.) J. Lind.
  Stagonospora Chenopodii (Westd.) Pk.
  Urophlyctis pulposa (Wallr.) Schrt.
Atriplex polycarpa Watson.
  Pucciniola Atriplicis Arth.
Atriplex rosea L.
  Dicaeoma Sarcobati Arth. I.
  Puccinia Sarcobati (Arth.) Bethel. I.
  Puccinia subnitens Diet. I.
  Uromyces peckianus Farl. I.
Atriplex semibaccata R. Br.
  Coniothyrium olivaceum Bon.

Atriplex Wolfii Watson.
  Dicaeoma Sarcobati Arth. I.
Atriplex sp. indet.
  ⎧ Ascochyta Atriplicis Lasch, var. effusa Ell. &
  ⎱   Kellerm.
  ⎰ Septogloeum Atriplicis Ell. & Ev.
  ⎩ Stagonospora Atriplicis (Westd.) J. Lind.
Suckleya suckleyana (Torr.) Ryd.
  ⎰ Dicaeoma Sarcobati Arth. I.
  ⎱ Puccinia subnitens Diet. I.
Grayia spinosa (Hook.) Moq.
  Uredo Grayiae Arth.
Eurotia lanata (Pursh.) Moq.
  ⎰ Aecidium Eurotiae Ell. & Ev.
  ⎱ Dicaeoma Eurotiae Arth. & Fromme. I.
  Didymella Eurotiae Fairman.
  Phoma exigua Desm.
  ⎧ Micropuccinia Eurotiae (D. Griff.) Arth. &
  ⎱   Jackson.
  ⎩ Puccinia Eurotiae D. Griff.
Kochia scoparia (L.) Schrad.
  ⎰ Dicaeoma Sarcobati Arth. I.
  ⎱ Puccinia subnitens Diet. I.
Kochia trichophylla Hort.
  Rhizoctonia Solani Kühn.
Spirostachys occidentalis Watson.
  Uredo Spirostachydis Arth.
Salicornia ambigua Michx.
  Pleospora Salsolae Fckl.
  ⎰ Nigredo peckiana (Farl.) Arth. l.
  ⎱ Uromyces peckianus Farl. I.
Salicornia europaea L.
  Uromyces peckianus Farl. I.
Salicornia herbacea L.
  Pleospora Salsolae Fckl.
  Protomyces conglomeratus Pk.
  ⎰ Nigredo peckiana (Farl.) Arth. I.
  ⎱ Uromyces peckianus Farl. I.
Salicornia virginica L.
  Pleospora Salsolae Fckl.
Salicornia sp. indet.
  Sphaerella Salicorniae Awd.
Sarcobatus vermiculatus (Hook.) Torr.
  ⎧ Aecidium Sarcobati Pk.
  ⎪ Dicaeoma Sarcobati Arth. I.
  ⎨ Peridermium gracile Hark.
  ⎪ Puccinia Sarcobati (Arth.) Bethel. I.
  ⎩ Puccinia subnitens Diet. I.
  ⎰ Dicaeoma luxuriosum (Syd.) Arthur &
  ⎱   Fromme.
  ⎩ Puccinia luxuriosa Syd. I.
  Eutypella Sarcobati Ell. & Ev.
  Hendersonia heterophragmia Ell. & Ev.
  Septoria Sarcobati Dearness & Barthol.
Suaeda
  (Dondia brevifolia Standley).
Suaeda californica Watson.
Suaeda multiflora Phil.
Suaeda occidentalis Watson.

Suaeda
  (Dondia ramosissima Standley.)
Suaeda suffrutescens Watson.
Suaeda
  (Dondia taxifolia Standley.)
Suaeda torreyana Watson.
  ⎰ Nigredo Chenopodii-fruticosi Arth.
  ⎱ Uromyces Chenopodii Schrt.
Suaeda depressa (Pursh) Watson.
  Dicaeoma Sarcobati Arth. I.
  Metasphaeria anisometra Cke. & Hark.
  Pyrenophora echinella (Cke.) Berl.
Suaeda intermedia Watson.
  Puccinia Dondiae Arth.
Suaeda maritima (L.) Dumort.
  Uromyces peckianus Farl. I.
Suaeda multiflora Phil.
  Uromyces Chenopodii (Duby) Schrt.
Suaeda torreyana Watson.
  Dicaeoma Sarcobati Arth. I.
Salsola Kali L.
  Melanospora Townei Griffiths.
  Pleospora Salsolae Fckl.
  Pyrenophora Salsolae Griffiths.
Salsola pestifer A. Nels.
  ⎧ Dicaeoma Sarcobati Arth. I.
  ⎨ Puccinia Sarcobati (Arth.) Bethcl. I.
  ⎩ Puccinia subnitens Diet. I.
  Coniothyrium olivaceum, var. Salsolae Fair-
    man.
Salsola Tragus L.
  Puccinia subnitens Diet. I.
  Delitschia apiculata Griffiths.
  Melanospora Townei Griffiths.
  Pleospora? Lecanora (Fabre) Rehm.
  Pleurage dakotensis Griffiths.
  Pyrenophora Salsolae Griffiths.
  Sordaria curvicolla Wint.
  Sordaria curvula DBy.
Salsola sp. indet.
  Sordaria pleospora Wint.

AMARANTACEAE

Celosia Huttoni Mart., var. **Thompsonii magni-
  fica** Hort.
  Rhizoctonia Solani Kühn.
Celosia latifolia Steud.
  Uromyces Celosiae Diet. & Holw.
Amaranthus Bigelovii Uline & Bray.
Amaranthus crispus (Lesp. & Thev.) A. Br.
Amaranthus emarginatus Salzm.
Amaranthus Palmeri Watson.
Amaranthus paniculatus L.
Amaranthus Powellii Watson.
Amaranthus tristis L.
Amaranthus viridis L.
  ⎰ Albugo Amaranthi (S.) O. Kuntze.
  ⎱ Albugo Bliti (Biv.) O. Kuntze.

Amaranthus blitoides Watson.
  Aecidium Ellisii Pk.
  Puccinia subnitens Diet. I.
  Albugo Bliti (Biv.) O. Kuntze.
  Cystopus Bliti (Biv.) Lév.

Amaranthus caudatus L.
Amaranthus salicifolius Hort.
  Rhizoctonia Solani Kühn.

Amaranthus graecizans L.
  Aecidium Ellisii Pk.
  Dicaeoma Sarcobati Arth. I.
  Puccinia subnitens Diet. I.
  Albugo Bliti (Biv.) O. Kuntze.
  Cystopus Bliti (Biv.) Lév.
  Fusarium roseum Lk.
  Lophiostoma caulium (Fr.) Ces. & De Not.
  Rhizoctonia Solani Kühn.

Amaranthus hybridus L.
  Albugo Amaranthi (Biv.) O. Kuntze.
  Cystopus Amaranthi (S.) B.
  Cystopus Bliti (Biv.) Lév.
  Phoma Amaranthi Halsted.

Amaranthus paniculatus L.
  Caeoma Amaranthi S.
  Cystopus Amaranthi (S.) B.
  Cystopus Bliti (Biv.) Lév.
  Uredo Amaranthi (S.) B.

Amaranthus retroflexus L.
  Aecidium Ellisii Pk.
  Puccinia subnitens Diet. I.
  Alternaria Amaranthi (Pk.) Hook.
  Alternaria Solani (Ell. & Martin) Jones & Grout.
  Aposphaeria Amaranti Ell. & Barthol.
  Cercospora brachiata Ell. & Ev.
  Corticium vagum B. & C.
  Rhizoctonia Solani Kühn.
  Albugo Amaranthi (S.) O. Kuntze
  Albugo Bliti (Biv.) O. Kuntze.
  Cystopus Amaranthi (S.) B.
  Cystopus Bliti (Biv.) Lév.
  Fusarium roseum Lk.
  Gloeosporium amaranthicola Dearness.
  Macrosporium Amaranthi Pk.
  Phoma longissima (P. ex Fr.) Westd.
  Phyllosticta Amaranthi Ell. & Kellerm.

Amaranthus spinosus L.
  Albugo Amaranthi (S.) O. Kuntze.
  Albugo Bliti (Biv.) O. Kuntze.
  Cystopus Bliti (Biv.) Lév.
  Cercospora brachiata Ell. & Ev.
  Corticium vagum B. & C.
  Rhizoctonia Solani Kühn.
  Gloeosporium Amaranthi Ell. & Ev.

Amaranthus sp. indet.
  Gloeosporium Amaranthi Ell. & Ev.

Heptameria eriophora Cke.
  Heptameria eutypoides (Pk.) Cke.
  Leptosphaeria eriophora (Cke.) Sacc.
  Leptosphaeria eutypoides Pk.
  Pocosphaeria eriophora (Cke.) Berl.
  Sphaeria eriophora Cke.
  Sclerotium Rolfsii Sacc.

Acnida cannabina L.
  Albugo Bliti (Biv.) O. Kuntze.
  Cercospora Acnidae Ell. & Ev.

Acnida tuberculata Moq.
  Albugo Amaranthi (S.) O. Kuntze.
  Albugo Bliti (Biv.) O. Kuntze.
  Cystopus Amaranthi (S.) B.
  Cystopus Bliti (Biv.) Lév.
  Phyllosticta Amaranthi Ell. & Kellerm.

Cyathula achyranthoides (H. B. K.) Moq.
  Uredo Cyathulae Mayor.

Achyranthes aspera L.
  Albugo Bliti Lév.
  Cercospora Achyranthes Syd.

Achyranthes obovata (Mart. & Gab.) Standley.
Achyranthes philoxeroides (Mart.) Standley.
  Dicaeoma (?) obesisporum Arth.
  Puccinia obesispora Arth.
  Uredo nitidula Arth.

Achyranthes Williamsii Standley.
  Uredo maculans Pat. & Gaill.

Guilleminea illecebroides H. B. K.
  Dicaeoma Guillemineae (Diet. & Holw.) Arth.
  Puccinia Guillemineae Diet. & Holw.

Cladothrix lanuginosa Nutt. ex Moq.
  Albugo Bliti (Biv.) O. Kuntze.
  Albugo Froelichiae G. W. Wilson.
  Thecaphora Thornberi Griffiths.

Cladothrix sp. indet.
  Albugo Cladothricis G. W. Wilson.

Froelichia floridana (Nutt.) Moq.
  Cercospora crassoides J. J. Davis.

Froelichia floridana (Nutt.) Moq.
Froelichia gracilis Moq.
  Albugo Bliti Fung. Columb. *2407.*
  Albugo Froelichiae G. W. Wilson.
  Cystopus Froelichiae (G. W. Wilson) Sacc. & Trott.

Pfaffia iresinoides (H. B. K.) O. Kuntze.
  Uredo maculans Pat. & Gaill.

Alternanthera Achyrantha R. Br.
Alternanthera portoricensis O. Kuntze.
  Cercospora Althernantherae Ell. & Langlois.

Alternanthera sessilis R. Br.
  Guignardia Cephalariae Aud., var. Alternantherae Sacc.

Alternanthera sp. indet.
  Rhizoctonia Solani Kühn.
  Torula herbarum Lk.

Iresine augustifolia Euphr.
Iresine elatior Rich.
  Puccinia macropoda Speg.
  { Dicaeoma striolatum Arth.
  { Puccinia striolata Arth.
Iresine calea (Ibanez) Standley.
  Cercospora gonatoclada Syd.
  { Nigredo (?) Celosiae (Diet. & Holw.) Arth.
  { Uromyces Celosiae Diet. & Holw.
Iresine canescens Humb. & Bonpl.
  Uromyces Celosiae Diet. & Holw.
Iresine Celosia L.
  Cercospora Gilbertii Speg.
  { Dicaeoma striolatum Arth.
  { Puccinia macropoda Speg.
  { Puccinia striolata Arth.
  Thecaphora Iresine (Elliott) H. S. Jackson.
  { Nigredo (?) Celosiae (Diet. & Holw.) Arth.
  { Uromyces Celosiae Diet. & Holw.
  Uromyces Iresine Lagerh.
Iresine latifolia Benth. & Hook.
  Uromyces Celosiae Diet. & Holw.
Iresine Pringlei Watson.
  { Nigredo (?) Celosiae (Diet. & Holw.) Arth.
  { Uromyces Celosiae Diet. & Holw.
Iresine sp. indet.
  Rhizoctonia Solani Kühn.

NYCTAGINACEAE

Oxybaphus hirsutus (Pursh) Sweet.
  Cercospora Oxybaphi Ell. & Halsted.
Oxybaphus linearis (Pursh) Robinson.
  Cercospora Oxybaphi Ell. & Halsted.
  Clathrospora permunda (Cke.) Berl.
  Heterosporium Oxybaphi Patterson.
  Pleospora herbarum (Fr.) Rabh.
Oxybaphus nyctagineus (Michx.) Sweet.
  Aposphaeria Oxybaphi Ell. & Ev.
  Ascochyta Oxybaphi Trel.
  Cercospora Oxybaphi Ell. & Halsted.
  Chaetomella atra Fckl.
  Peronospora Oxybaphi Ell. & Kellerm.
Mirabilis Jalapa L.
  Aecidium Mirabilis Diet. & Holw.
  Albugo Bliti (Biv.) O. Kuntze.
  Albugo Platensis (Speg.) Swingle.
  Cercospora mirabilis Tharp.
Mirabilis multiflora Gray.
  Aecidium Mirabilis Diet. & Holw.
  { Aecidium Sarcobati Pk.
  { Dicaeoma Sarcobati Arth. I.
  { Puccinia subnitens Diet. I.
  Leptosphaeria Quamoclidii Fairman.
Allionia comata Small.
  { Aecidium Sarcobati Pk.
  { Dicaeoma Sarcobati Arth. I.
Allionia incarnata L.
  Albugo platensis (Speg.) Swingle.

Boerhaavia anisophylla Torr.
  Albugo platensis (Speg.) Swingle.
Boerhaavia erecta L.
  Albugo candida (P. ex Lév.) O. Kuntze.
  Albugo platensis (Speg.) Swingle.
  Ascochyta Boerhaaviae Tharp.
Boerhaavia hirsuta L.
Boerhaavia paniculata Rich.
Boerhaavia scandens L.
Boerhaavia Sonorae Rose.
Boerhaavia spicata Choisy.
Boerhaavia viscosa Lag. & Rodr.
Boerhaavia Xanti Watson.
  Albugo platensis (Speg.) Swingle.
Boerhaavia sp. indet.
  Thecaphora tunicata G. P. Clinton.
Bougainvillea glabra Choisy, var. **sanderiana**
    Hort.
  Leptostroma Bougainvilleae Fragoso & Ciferri.
Abronia Cycloptera Gray.
Abronia elliptica Nels.
Abronia fragrans Nutt.
Abronia pinetorum Jepson.
Abronia umbellata Lam.
  { Aecidium Abroniae Ell. & Ev.
  { Aecidium biforme Pk.
  { Dicaeoma Sarcobati Arth.
  { Puccinia subnitens Diet. I.
Abronia Crux-maltae Kellogg.
Abronia umbellata Lam.
  Peronospora Oxybaphi Ell. & Kellerm.
Abronia latifolia Esch.
  Heterosporium Abroniae Hark.
Pisonia aculeata L.
  Aecidium Pisoniae Arth. & Johnston.

PHYTOLACCACEAE

Rivina humilis L.
  Cercospora flagellaris Ell. & Martin.
  Darluca Filum (Biv.) Cast.
  { Aecidium Rivinae B. & C.
  { Dicaeoma Rivinae Arth.
  { Puccinia Raunkiaerii Ferdinandsen & Winge.
  { Puccinia Rivinae (Arth.) Speg.
  Septoria Rivinae Pat.
Rivina octandra L.
  { Aecidium Rivinae B. & C.
  { Dicaeoma Rivinae Arth.
  { Endophyllum Rivinae Arth.
  { Puccinia Rivinae (Arth.) Speg.
  Cercospora Trichostigmae F. L. Stevens.
  Linospora Trichostigmae F. L. Stevens.
  Septoria Rivinae Pat.
Petiveria alliacea L.
  Meliola perexigua Gaill.
  Rosellinia bunodes B. & Br.
  Vermicularia atricha Ell. & Ev.

Phytolacca decandra L.

PEZIZINEAE

Lachnella bicolor Pk.
Lachnum leucophaeum (P.) Karst.
{ Peziza pulviscula Cke.
{ Pezizella pulviscula (Cke.) Sacc.

PHACIDIINEAE

Stictis radiata (L.) ex P.

DOTHIDEALES

{ Dothidea Himantia (P.) ex Fr.
{ Sphaeria Himantia P. ex Fr.
{ Asteroma crustaceum (S.) M. A. Curtis.
{ Dothidea crustacea S.
{ Phyllachora crustacea (S.) Sacc.
{ Asteroma elegans (S.) M. A. Curtis.
{ Dothidea elegans S.
{ Phyllachora elegans (S.) Sacc.
{ Asteroma inelegans (S.) M. A. Curtis.
{ Dothidea inelegans S.
{ Phyllachora inelegans (S.) Sacc.
{ Dothidea Phytolaccae S.
{ Phyllachora Phytolaccae (S.) Sacc.

SPHAERIALES

{ Diaporthe aculeata (S.) Sacc.
{ Diaporthe spiculosa N. A. F. *589*.
{ Sphaeria aculeata S.
{ Sphaeria Berkeleii Auct. Amer.
{ Sphaeria spiculosa, var. Phytolaccae C. & E.
{ Didymosphaerella adelphica Cke.
{ Didymosphaeria adelphica (Cke.) Sacc.
{ Sphaeria adelphica Cke.
{ Didymosphaeria cupula (Ell.) Sacc.?
{ Sphaeria cupula Ell.
{ Heptameria clavigera C. & E.
{ Leptosphaeria clavigera (C. & E.) Sacc.
{ Leptosphaeria Vitalbae, var. clavigera (C. &
{   E.) Berl.
{ Sphaeria clavigera C. & E.
Leptosphaeria rubicunda Rehm.
Leptosphaeria variegata Pk.
Sphaeria lilacina S.

HYMENOMYCETINEAE

{ Corticium vagum B. & C.
{ Rhizoctonia Solani Kühn.
Hydnum herbicola Ell.

SPHAEROPSIDALES

Aposphaeria herbicola Ell. & Ev.
Dinemasporium patellum C. & E.
Excipula erumpens B., var. subhispida C. & E.
Phlyctaena orthospora B. & C.
{ Phlyctaena septorioides Sacc.
{ Septoria phlyctaenoides B. & C.

Phlyctaena vagabunda Desm.
Phoma apocrypta Ell. & Ev.
Phoma Phytolaccae B. & C.
Phyllosticta Phytolaccae Cke.
Vermicularia Dematium (P.) ex Fr.

HYPHOMYCETES

Cercospora flagellaris Ell. & Martin.
{ Fusarium incarnatum (Rob.) Sacc.
{ Fusarium pallidoroseum (Cke.) Sacc.
{ Fusisporium pallidoroscum Cke.
Fusarium roseum Lk.
{ Dendryphium nodulosum Sacc.
{ Helminthosporium interseminatum B. & Rav.
{ Hymenella Phytolaccae B. & C.
{ Hymenula Phytolaccae B. & C.
Macrosporium abruptum C. & E.
Macrosporium caudatum C. & E.
Macrosporium cladosporioides Desm.
{ Monilia herbarum P. ex Lk.
{ Torula herbarum (P.) ex Lk.
Periconia pycnospora Fres.

MISCELLANEA

{ Ophiotheca umbrina B. & C.
{ Ophiotheca vermicularis (S.) Macbr.
{ Perichaena variabilis Rostf.
Uredo panamensis Arth.

Phytolacca dioica L.
Uredo panamensis Arth.

Phytolacca icosandra L.
Cercospora flagellaris Ell. & Martin.

AIZOACEAE

Mollugo verticillata L.
Cercospora Molluginis Halsted. 1893.
Cercospora Molluginis J. J. Davis. 1924.
Phyllosticta Molluginis Ell. & Halsted.
Sesuvium sessile P.
{ Dicaeoma Sarcobati Arth.
{ Puccinia Sarcobati (Arth.) Bethel. I.
Trianthema Portulacastrum L.
{ Albugo Trianthemae G. W. Wilson.
{ Cystopus Trianthemae (G. W. Wilson) Sacc.
{   & Trott.
Mesembrianthemum aequilaterale Haworth.
Camarosporium ellipticum Cke. & Hark.
Mesembrianthemum sp. indet.
Gibberella Saubinetii (Mont.) Sacc.
Torula herbarum (P.) ex Lk.

PORTULACACEAE

Calandrinia Breweri Watson.
Ustilago Calandriniae G. P. Clinton.
Calandrinia leana Porter.
Uromyces unitus Pk.

Calandrinia Menziesii Torr. & Gray.
  Peronospora Claytoniae Farl.
  Ustilago Calandriniae G. P. Clinton.
Spraguea multiceps Howell.
Spraguea umbellata Torr.
Calyptridium roseum Watson.
Calyptridium umbellatum Watson.
  Uromyces Spragueae Hark.
Claytonia arctica Adam.
Claytonia asarifolia Bong.
Claytonia caroliniana Michx.
Claytonia lanceolata Pursh.
  Aecidium claytoniatum S.
  Aecidium Mariae-Wilsoni Halsted non G. W.
    Clinton.
  Allodus claytoniata (Pk.) Arth.
  Caeoma claytoniatum S.
  Puccinia claytoniata Pk.
  Puccinia Mariae-Wilsoni G. W. Clinton.
Claytonia caroliniana Michx.
  Uromyces Claytoniae C. & P.
Claytonia linearis Dougl.
  Ustilago Claytoniae Shear.
Claytonia megarrhiza (Gray) Parry.
  Micropuccinia agnita (Arth.) Arth. & Jackson.
  Puccinia agnita Arth.
  Allodus claytoniata (Pk.) Arth.
  Puccinia claytoniata Pk.
Claytonia perfoliata Donn.
  Peronospora Claytoniae Farl.
Claytonia sibirica L.
  Allodus claytoniata (Pk.) Arth.
  Puccinia claytoniata Pk.
Claytonia virginica L.
  Peronospora Claytoniae Farl.
  Aecidium Mariae-Wilsoni Halsted non G. W.
    Clinton.
  Allodus claytoniata (Pk.) Arth.
  Caeoma claytoniatum S.
  Puccinia claytoniata Pk.
  Puccinia Mariae-Wilsoni G. W. Clinton.
Portulaca lanceolata Engelm.
  Albugo Portulacae (DC.) O. Kuntze.
Portulaca oleracea L.
  Corticium vagum B. & C.
  Rhizoctonia Solani Kühn.
  Albugo Portulacae (DC.) O. Kuntze.
  Cystopus Portulacae (DC.) Lév.
  Thielavia basicola (B. & Br.) Zopf.
  Vermicularia oblongispora Ell. & Ev.
Portulaca sp. indet.
  Phoma Stigma Cke. & Hark.
Lewisia columbiana (Howell) B. L. Robinson.
  Uromyces unitus Pk.
Lewisia rediviva Pursh.
  Uromyces Spragueae Hark.
  Uromyces unitus Pk.

CARYOPHYLLACEAE

Stellaria biflora L.
  Pyrenophora comata (Niessl) Sacc.
Stellaria borealis Bigel.
  Melampsorella Cerastii (Wint.) Schrt.
  Melampsorella elatina Arth.
  Micropuccinia Arenariae (Schum.) Arth. &
    Jackson.
  Puccinia Arenariae Wint.
  Ustilago antherarum Fr.
  Ustilago violacea (P.) Fckl.
Stellaria crassifolia Ehrh.
  Sphaerella Stellarinearum Karst.
Stellaria Curtisii (Rydb.) Auct.
  Sorosporium Saponariae Rud.
Stellaria glauca With.
  Puccinia Arenariae Wint.
Stellaria graminea L.
  Melampsorella elatina Arth.
Stellaria humifusa Rottb.
  Ascochyta Dianthi (A. & S.) Lib.
  Leptosphaeria Stellariae Rostr.
  Pleospora herbarum (Fr.) Rabh.
  Septoria Stellariae Rob.
  Sphaerella Stellarinearum Karst.
Stellaria jamesiana Torr.
  Septoria Jamesii Pammel & Hume.
Stellaria long:folia Muhl.
  Melampsorella Caryophyllacearum Schrt.
  Melampsorella elatina Arth.
  Septoria Stellariae Rob.
  Sphaerella Stellarinearum Karst.
Stellaria longipes Goldie.
  Cladosporium herbarum (P.). ex Lk.
  Helotiella erythrostigma (Rehm) Sacc.
  Leptosphaeria Stellariae Rostr.
  Melampsorella elatina Arth.
  Phoma herbarum Westd.
  Pleospora Cerastii Oud.
  Pleospora herbarum (Fr.) Rabh.
  Micropuccinia Arenariae (Wint.) Arth. &
    Jackson.
  Puccinia Arenariae Wint.
  Puccinia Dianthi DC.
  Puccinia Lychnidearum Lk.
  Pyrenophora comata (Niessl.) Sacc.
  Mycosphaerella pachyasca (Rostr.) Vester-
    gren.
  Sphaerella pachyasca Rostr.
  Sphaerella Stellarinearum Karst.
  Trochila Stellariae Rostr.
Stellaria longipes Goldie, var. **laeta** (Richards)
    Watson.
  Micropuccinia Arenariae (Wint.) Arth. &
    Jackson.
Stellaria media (L.) Cyrill.
  Dicaeoma Sarcobati Arth. I.
  Entyloma Alsines Halsted.

Stellaria media (*cont.*)
- Aecidium elatinum A. & S. III.
- Melampsorella Caryophyllacearum Schrt.
- Melampsorella elatina Arth.
- Septoria Stellariae Rob.
- Synchytrium Stellariae Fckl.

Stellaria nitens Nutt.
- Ustilago violacea, var. major G. P. Clinton.

Stellaria ovata Willd.
- Micropuccinia detonsa (Arth. & Holw.) Arth. & Jackson.
- Puccinia detonsa Arth. & Holw.

Stellaria umbellata Turcz.
- Melampsorella Caryophyllacearum Schrt.
- Melampsorella Cerastii (Wint.) Schrt.
- Melampsorella elatina Arth.

Cerastium alpinum L.
- Ascochyta Dianthi (A. & S. ex Fr.) Lib. 1832.
- Ascochyta Dianthi (A. & S. ex Fr.) B. 1860.
- Sphaeria Dianthi A. & S. ex Fr.
- Melampsorella elatina Arth.
- Phoma herbarum Westd.
- Pleospora herbarum (Fr.) Rabh.
- Pleospora vulgaris Niessl.
- Pseudopeziza Cerastiorum (Wallr.) Fckl.
- Micropuccinia Arenariae (Wint.) Arth. & Jackson.
- Puccinia Arenariae Wint.
- Pyrenophora Cerastii (Oud.) J. Lind.
- Pyrenophora chrysospora (Niessl) Sacc.
- Pyrenophora comata (Niessl) Sacc.
- Rhabdospora Drabae (Fckl.) Berl. & Vogl.
- Mycosphaerella pachyasca (Rostr.) Vestergren.
- Sphaerella pachyasca Rostr.
- Sphaerella Stellarinearum Karst.
- Mycosphaerella tassiana (De Not.) Johans.

Cerastium arcticum Lange.
- Pleospora herbarum (Fr.) Rabh.

Cerastium arvense L.
- Melampsora Cerastii (P.) Wint.
- Melampsorella Cerastii Schrt.
- Melampsorella elatina Arth.
- Uredo Caryophyllacearum (Lk.) Johnst.
- Phoma herbarum Westd.
- Puccinia Arenariae Wint.
- Septoria Cerastii Rob. & Desm.
- Sorosporium Saponariae Rud.
- Sphaerella Stellarinearum Karst.

Cerastium campestris Greene.
- Melampsorella elatina Arth.

Cerastium cerastioides (L.) Britton.
- Peronospora Alsinearum Casp.

Cerastium maximum L.
- Mycosphaerella pachyasca (Rostr.) Vestergren.
- Phoma Cerastis-maximi Dearness.
- Pyrenophora comata (Niessl) Sacc.
- Ustilago violacea (P.) Fckl.

Cerastium nutans Raf.
- Peronospora Alsinearum Casp.
- Peronospora tomentosa Fckl.

Cerastium oblongifolium (Torr.) Hollick & Britton.
- Septoria Cerastii Rob. & Desm.

Cerastium occidentale Greene.

Cerastium oreophilum Greene.

Cerastium scopulorum Greene.
- Melampsorella elatina Arth.

Cerastium strictum L.
- Melampsorella elatina Arth.
- Micropuccinia Arenariae (Wint.) Arth. & Jackson.

Cerastium trigynum Vill.
- Calloria erythrostigmoides Rehm.
- Peronospora Alsinearum Casp.
- Phoma herbarum Westd.
- Heteropatella umbilicata (P.) Jaap.
- Septoria cercosperma Rostr.
- Sphaerella Stellarinearum Karst.

Cerastium viscosum L.
- Isariopsis alborosella (Desm.) Sacc.
- Isariopsis pusilla Fres.
- Melampsorella elatina Arth.
- Peronospora Alsinearum Casp.
- Septoria Cerastii Rob. & Desm.

Cerastium vulgatum L.
- Isariopsis alborosella (Desm.) Sacc.
- Isariopsis pusilla Fres.
- Aecidium elatinum A. & S.
- Melampsorella Caryophyllacearum (Lk.) Schrt.
- Melampsorella Cerastii P.
- Melampsorella elatina Arth.
- Peronospora Alsinearum Casp.
- Septoria Cerastii Rob. & Desm.

Cerastium sp. indet.
- Rhizoctonia Solani Kühn.

Sagina nivalis Fries.
- Septoria nivalis Rostr.

Alsine? sp. indet.
- Puccinia obliqua B. & C.

Minuartia rubella Graebn.
- Clathrospora pentamera (Karst.) Berl.
- Coniothyrium olivaceum Bon.
- Pleospora herbarum (Fr.) Rabh.
- Pyrenophora Cerastii (Oud.) J. Lind.
- Pyrenophora chrysospora (Niessl) Sacc.
- Rhabdospora Drabae (Fckl.) Berl. & Vogl.
- Mycosphaerella tassiana (De Not.) Johans.

Arenaria alsinoides Auct.
- Puccinia modica Holw.

Arenaria arctica Stev. ex DC. f. **scapigera.**
- Pyrenophora phaeospora (Duby) Sacc.

Arenaria biflora (L.) Watson.
- Durella groenlandica (Rostr.) Sacc.
- Leptopeziza groenlandica Rostr.
- Pyrenophora comata (Niessl) Sacc.

Arenaria biflora (*cont.*)
    Sphaerella Stellarinearum (Rabh.) Karst.
    Sphaerella tassiana De Not.
Arenaria Burkei Howell.
    Dicaeoma (?) tardissimum (Garrett) Arth.
Arenaria ciliata L.
    Pyrenophora comata Niessl.
    Sphaerella Stellarinearum (Rabh.) Karst.
    Mycosphaerella tassiana (De Not.) Johans.
Arenaria congesta Nutt.
    Micropuccinia hysteriiformis (Pk.) Arth. & Jackson.
    { Dicaeoma (?) tardissimum (Garrett) Arth.
    { Puccinia tardissima Garrett.
    Ustilago Arenariae Ell. & Ev.
Arenaria Fendleri Gray.
    Mycosphaerella tingens Niessl?
    Pleospora herbarum (Fr.) Rabh.
    Puccinia hysteriiformis Pk.
    { Dicaeoma (?) tardissimum (Garrett) Arth.
    { Puccinia tardissima Garrett.
Arenaria glabrescens (Watson) Howell.
    { Nigredo Silenes (Fckl.) Arth.
    { Uromyces Silenes Fckl.
Arenaria groenlandica (Retz.) Spreng.
    Sphaerella Stellarianearum (Rabh.) Karst.
    Ustilago violacea (P.) Fckl.
Arenaria lanuginosa Rohrb.
    { Dicaeoma (?) modicum (Holw.) Arth.
    { Puccinia modica Holw.
Arenaria lateriflora L.
    Pleospora herbarum (Fr.) Rabh.
    Pseudopeziza Cerastiorum (Wallr. ex Fr.) Fckl., var. Arenariae Sacc.
    { Micropuccinia Arenariae (Wint.) Arth. & Jackson.
    { Puccinia Arenariae Wint.
    { Nigredo Polemonii Arth. I.
    { Uromyces Spartinae Farl. I.
    Ustilago violacea (P.) Fckl.
Arenaria laxiflora Rydb.
    Dicaeoma (?) tardissimum (Garrett) Arth.
Arenaria macrocarpa Pursh.
    Pyrenophora comata (Niessl) Sacc.
Arenaria Nuttallii Pax.
    Sphaerella Stellarianearum (Rabh.) Karst.
Arenaria peploides L.
    Laestadia arctica Rostr.
    Phoma herbarum Westd.
    Pleospora herbarum (Fr.) Rabh.
    Pyrenophora chrysospora (Niessl) Sacc.
    Pyrenophora comata (Niessl) Sacc.
    Sphaerella Stellarianearum (Rabh.) Karst.
Arenaria Peyritschii Rohrb.
    Puccinia modica Holw.
Arenaria physodes Fisch.
    { Micropuccinia Arenariae (Wint.) Arth. & Jackson.
    { Puccinia Arenariae Wint.

Arenaria reptans Hemsl.
    Puccinia modica Holw.
Arenaria sajanensis Willd.
    Leptosphaeria Stellariae Rostr.
Arenaria stricta Michx.
    Pleospora herbarum (Fr.) Rabh.
    Micropuccinia Arenariae (Wint.) Arth. & Jackson.
Arenaria subcongesta Rydb.
    Puccinia hysteriiformis Pk.
    Puccinia tardissima Garrett.
Arenaria uintahensis A. Nels.
    { Micropuccinia hysteriiformis (Pk.) Arth. & Jackson.
    { Puccinia hysteriiformis Pk.
Arenaria verna L.
    Mycosphaerella pachyasca (Rostr.) Vestergren.
    Puccinia hysteriiformis Pk.
    Pyrenophora comata (Niessl) Sacc.
    Pleospora herbarum (Fr.) Rabh.
    Sphaerella Stellarianearum (Rabh.) Karst.
Arenaria verna L., var. **hirta** Watson.
    Cladosporium herbarum (P.) ex Lk.
    Hendersonia tenella Schrt.
    Pleospora vulgaris Niessl.
    Sphaerella tassiana DeNot.
Spergula arvensis L.
    Macrosporium parasiticum Thm.
    Peronospora Alsinearum Casp.
    Peronospora obovata Bon.
    { Micropuccinia Arenariae (Wint.) Arth. & Jackson.
    { Puccinia Arenariae Wint.
    { Puccinia Spergulae DC.
Spergularia canadensis (P.) Don.
    { Nigredo Polemonii Arth. I.
    { Uromyces Spartinae Farl. I.
Spergularia Clevelandi B. L. Robinson.
    { Puccinia Sarcobati (Arth.) Bethel. I.
    { Puccinia subnitens Diet. I.
Spergularia macrotheca Heynh.
    Aecidium Tissae Ell. & Ev.
    Nigredo Polemonii Arth. I.
    { Dicaeoma Sarcobati Arth. I.
    { Puccinia subnitens Diet. I.
    Albugo Lepigoni (DBy.) O. Kuntze.
Spergularia marina (L.) Griseb.
    { Albugo Lepigoni (DBy.) O. Kuntze.
    { Cystopus Lepigoni DBy.
    Nigredo Polemonii Arth. I.
Drymaria cordata Willd.
    Physalospora caryophyllinicola F. L. Stevens.
Paronychia chilensis DC.
    Uredo Paronychiae H. S. Jackson.
Scleranthus annuus L.
    Septoria Scleranthi Desm.
Agrostemma Githago L.
    Marssonia Delastrei (Delacr.) Sacc.

Silene acaulis L.
- Leptosphaeria Silenes (De Not.) Rostr.
- Leptosphaeria Silenes-acaulis De Not.
- Pleospora fuckeliana Niessl.
- Pleospora herbarum (Fr.) Rabh.
- Pyrenophora chrysospora (Niessl) Sacc.
- Sphaerella sibirica Thm.
- Sphaerella tassiana De Not.
- Ustilago violacea (P.) Fckl.

Silene antirrhina L.
- Ascochyta Silenes Ell. & Ev.
- Dicaeoma Sarcobati Arth. I.
- Puccinia subnitens Diet. I.
- Peronospora Arenariae (B.) DBy., var. macrospora Farl.
- Peronospora Silenes Wilson.
- Phyllosticta Silenes Pk.
- Septoria dimera Sacc.
- Septoria noctiflorae Ell. & Kellerm.
- Septoria Saponariae (DC.) Sav. & Becc.
- Septoria Silenes Westd.
- Septoria silenicola Ell. & Martin.

Silene Douglasii Hook., var. multicaulis (Nutt.) B. L. Robinson.
- Nigredo Silenes (Schl.) Arth.
- Uromyces pulchellus Ell. & Ev.
- Uromyces Silenes Fckl.

Silene Drummondii Hook.
- Nigredo Suksdorfii (Diet. & Holw.) Arth.

Silene gallica L.
- Pleospora oligomera Sacc. & Speg.

Silene Hallii Watson.
- Nigredo Suksdorfii (Diet. & Holw.) Arth.

Silene Lemmonii Watson.
- Nigredo Silenes (Fckl.) Arth.

Silene Lyallii Watson.
- Ustilago violacea (P.) Fckl.

Silene Menziesii Hook.
- Septoria silenicola Sacc.
- Sorosporium Saponariae Rud.

Silene nivea (Nutt.) Otth.
- Nigredo Silenes (Schl.) Arth.
- Uromyces pulchellus Ell. & Ev.
- Septoria noctiflorae Ell. & Kellerm.

Silene noctiflora L.
- Phyllosticta nebulosa Sacc.
- Phyllosticta pallida Halsted.
- Septoria noctiflorae Ell. & Kellerm.
- Septoria Silenes Ell. & Martin.
- Septoria silenicola Ell. & Martin.
- Nigredo Silenes (Fckl.) Arth.

Silene occidentalis Watson.
- Nigredo Silenes (Fckl.) Arth.
- Nigredo Suksdorfii (Diet. & Holw.) Arth.

Silene oregana Watson.
- Nigredo Suksdorfii (Diet. & Holw.) Arth.
- Uromyces Suksdorfii Diet. & Holw.

Silene pennsylvanica Michx.
- Pleospora herbarum (Fr.) Rabh.

Silene Schafta Gmel. ex Hohen.
- Rhizoctonia Solani Kühn.

Silene Scouleri Hook.
- Nigredo Suksdorfii (Diet. & Holw.) Arth.
- Uromyces Suksdorfii Diet. & Holw.

Silene stellata (L.) Ait. f.
- Macrosporium Saponariae Pk.
- Marssonia Delastrei (Delacr.) Sacc.
- Marssonina Delastrei (Delacr.) Magn.
- Septoria Silenes Westd.
- Septoria silenicola Ell. & Martin.

Silene tetonensis E. Nels.
- Ustilago violacea (P.) Fckl.

Silene verecunda Watson.
- Pucciniola Betheli Arth.
- Uromyces Betheli Arth.
- Nigredo Suksdorfii (Diet. & Holw.) Arth.

Silene Watsoni Robinson & Seaton.
- Ustilago violacea (P.) Fckl.
- Ustilago violacea, var. major G. P. Clinton.

Silene sp. indet.
- Pleospora Silenes Earle.

Lychnis affinis J. Vahl.
- Cladosporium herbarum (P.) ex Lk.
- Pleospora herbarum (Fr.) Rabh.
- Pyrenophora comata (Niessl) Sacc.
- Mycosphaerella pachyasca (Rostr.) Vestergren.
- Sphaerella pachyasca Rostr.
- Sphaerella sibirica Thm.

Lychnis alba Mill.
- Phyllosticta Lychnidis (Fr.) Ell. & Ev.
- Septoria Melandrii Pass.
- Nigredo verruculosa (Schrt.) Arth.
- Uromyces verruculosus Schrt.

Lychnis alpina L.
- Cladosporium herbarum (P.) ex Lk.
- Pleospora herbarum (Fr.) Rabh.
- Sclerotium rufum Rostr.
- Septoria Viscariae Rostr.
- Sphaerella pachyasca Rostr.

Lychnis apetala L.
- Leptosphaeria vanhoeffeniana Allescher.
- Cf. Hendersonia vanhoeffeniana Allescher.
- Niptera Lychnidis (Fckl.) J. Lind.
- Pleospora infectoria Fckl.
- Pleospora vulgaris Niessl.
- Pyrenophora chrysospora (Niessl) Sacc.
- Pyrenophora comata (Niessl) Sacc.
- Pyrenophora Dianthi (De Not.).
- Sphaerella sibirica Thm.
- Mycosphaerella tassiana (De Not.) Johans.
- Ustilago violacea (P.) Fckl.

Lychnis chalcedonica L.
- Septoria Melandrii Pass.

Lychnis Coeli-rosa Desr.
- Rhizoctonia Solani Kühn.

Lychnis dioica Auct.
- Uromyces Lychnidis Tracy & Earle.

Lychnis Drummondii (Hook.) Watson.
Uromyces Lychnidis Tracy & Earle.
Lychnis Flos-cuculi L.
Leptothyrium Lychnidis B. & C.
Lychnis pauciflora Ledeb.
Pleospora infectoria Fckl.
Pyrenophora Dianthi (De Not.).
Mycosphaerella tassiana (De Not.) Johans.
Lychnis triflora R. Br.
Cladosporium herbarum (P.) ex Lk.
Clathrospora pentamera (Karst.) Berl.
Helotium herbarum Fr.
Leptosphaeria Vahlii Rostr.
Marssonia Delastrei (Delacr.) Sacc.
Pleospora herbarum (Fr.) Rabh.
Pyrenophora chrysospora (Niessl) Sacc.
Pyrenophora comata (Niessl) Sacc.
Sphaerella sibirica Thm.
Mycosphaerella tassiana (De Not.) Johans.
Lychnis sp. indet.
Hymenula Lychnidis Pk.
Phoma punctiformis Desm.
{ Ustilago antherarum Fr.
{ Ustilago violacea (P.) Fckl.
Melandrium involucratum Rohrb.
Cladosporium herbarum (P.) ex Lk.
Phoma exserta Thm.
Phoma exserta Thm., var. arctica Allescher.
Pleospora herbarum (Fr.) Rabh.
Pleospora media Niessl.
Pyrenophora chrysospora (Niessl) Sacc.
Pyrenophora comata (Niessl) Sacc.
Sphaerella sibirica Thm.
Gypsophila muralis L.
Gypsophila repens L.
Rhizoctonia Solani Kühn.
Gypsophila sp. indet.
Uromyces caryophyllinus (Schrank) Schrt.
Dianthus Armeria L.
{ Ascochyta Dianthi (A. & S. ex Fr.) Lib.
{ Sphaeria Dianthi A. & S. ex Fr.
Dianthus barbatus L.
{ Micropuccinia Arenariae (Wint.) Arth. &
{ Jackson.
{ Puccinia Arenariae Wint.
{ Puccinia Dianthi DC.
{ Puccinia Lychnidearum Lk.
Rhizoctonia Solani Kühn.
Septoria Dianthi Desm.
{ Nigredo caryophyllina (Schrank) Arth.
{ Uromyces Dianthi Niessl.
Dianthus Caryophyllus L.

UREDINALES

{ Caeomurus caryophyllinus (Schrank) O.
{ Kuntze.
{ Nigredo caryophyllina (Schrank) Arth.
{ Uromyces caryophyllinus (Schrank) Wint.
{ Uromyces Dianthi Niessl.

THELEPHORACEAE

{ Corticium vagum B. & C.
{ Corticium vagum, var. Solani Burt.

SPHAEROPSIDALES

Darluca filum (Biv.) Cast.
Septoria Caryophylli Scalia.
Septoria Dianthi Desm.
Vermicularia herbarum Westd.
Vermicularia subeffigurata S.

MELANCONIALES

Colletotrichum Dianthi Auct.

HYPHOMYCETES

Alternaria Dianthi Stevens & Hall.
Botrytis vulgaris (Lk.) ex Fr.
Fusarium Dianthi Prill. & Delacr.
Fusarium incarnatum (Desm.) Sacc.
{ Fusarium Poae (Pk.) Wr.
{ Sporotrichum anthophilum Pk.
{ Sporotrichum Poae Pk.
Heterosporium echinulatum (B.) Cke.
Macrosporium Dianthemphus Hume.
Macrosporium nobile Vize.
Volutella Dianthi Atk.
Volutella leucotricha Atk.

MISCELLANEA

Ozonium omnivorum Shear.
Pythium debaryanum Hesse.
Sphaerella Caryophylli Pass.
Dianthus chinensis L.
Phytophthora terrestris Sherb.
Rhizoctonia Solani Kühn.
Stilbum fasciculatum B. & Br.
{ Nigredo caryophyllina (Schrank) Arth.
{ Uromyces caryophyllinus (Schrank) Wint.
Vermicularia subeffigurata S., var. dianthi-
cola S.
Dianthus pelviformis Heuff.
Nigredo caryophyllina (Schrank) Arth.
Dianthus plumarius L.
Rhizoctonia Solani Kühn.
Sclerotium Rolfsii Sacc.
Dianthus sp. indet.
Asteroma Dianthi Cke. & Hark.
Botryosporium prorumpens S.
Cladosporium herbarum (P.) ex Lk., var. nodo-
sum B.
Polyactis vulgaris Lk.
{ Laestadia caryophyllea (Cke. & Hark.) Berl. &
{ Vogl.
{ Sphaerella caryophyllea Cke. & Hark.
Saponaria officinalis L.
Cylindrosporium officinale Ell. & Ev.
Macrosporium Saponariae Pk.
Phyllosticta tenerrima Ell. & Ev.
Septoria noctiflorae Ell. & Kellerm.
Sphaeria herbarum Plowr.

Saponaria officinalis (*cont.*)
  Vermicularia compacta C. & E.
  Vermicularia Saponariae Allescher.
Saponaria Vaccaria L.
  Dicaeoma Sarcobati Arth. I.
Saponaria sp. indet.
  ⎰Clathrospora permunda (Cke.) Berl.
  ⎱Pleospora permunda (Cke.) Sacc.
  ⎩Sphaeria permunda Cke.
Caryophyllaceae gen. indet.
  Puccinia Arenariae (Schum.) Schrt.
  Uromyces Polemonii (Pk.) Barthol.

NYMPHAEACEAE

Nelumbo lutea (Willd.) P.
  Cercospora Nelumbonis Tharp.
  Macrosporium Nelumbii Ell. & Ev.
Nelumbo sp. indet.
  Dothiorella Nelumbii Ell. & F. W. Anderson.
Nelumbium speciosum Willd.
  Alternaria Nelumbii Enlows & Rand.
Nymphaea advena Ait.
  ⎰Entyloma Nymphaeae (Cunningh.) Setchell.
  ⎱Entyloma Castaliae Holw.
  Phyllosticta fatiscens Pk.
  ⎰Phyllosticta Orontii Ell. & Martin, var. ad-
  ⎱ vena Ell. & Ev.
  Phyllosticta nymphaeacea Ell. & Ev.
  Phyllosticta nymphaeicola Tehon & Daniels.
  Phyllosticta Orontii Ell. & Martin.
  ⎰Sphaerella paludosa Ell. & Ev.
  ⎱Sphaerella Pontederiae Pk.
Castalia odorata (Ait.) Woodville & Wood.
  Cercospora nymphaeacea C. & E.
  Cercospora Nymphaeae Ell. & Ev.
  ⎰Entyloma Castaliae Holw.
  ⎱Entyloma Nymphaeae (Cunningh.) Setchell.
  ⎩Rhamphospora Nymphaeae Auct. Amer.
  Helicosporium Nymphaearum Rand.
  Phyllosticta fatiscens Pk.
  Sphaerella Pontederiae Pk.
Castalia tuberosa (Paine) Greene.
  Cercospora nymphaeacea C. & E.
  ⎰Entyloma Castaliae Holw.
  ⎱Entyloma Nymphaeae (Cunningh.) Setchell.
  Helicosporium Nymphaearum Rand.
Nymphaeaceae gen. indet.
  Cercospora exotica Ell. & Ev.

RANUNCULACEAE

Hydrastis canadensis L.
  Alternaria panax Whetzel.
Paeonia Brownii Dougl.
  Cladosporium Paeoniae Pass.
Paeonia Moutan Sims.
  Discosia grammita B. & C.
Paeonia officinalis Retz.
  Armillaria mellea (Vahl) ex Fr.
  Botrytis Paeoniae Oud.

Cercospora Paeoniae Tehon & Daniels.
Cercospora variicolor Wint.
Cladosporium Paeoniae Pass.
Cryptostictis Paeoniae Tehon & Daniels.
Discosia Artocreas (Tode) ex Fr.
Periconia pycnospora Fres.
Phyllosticta Commonsii Ell. & Ev.
Sclerotinia libertiana Fckl.
Septoria Paeoniae Westd.
Septoria Paeoniae Westd., var. berolinensis
  Allescher.
? ⎰Cronartium flaccidum Auct.
  ⎱Sphaeria flaccida (A. & S.) ex Wint.
Paeonia sp. indet.
  ⎰Botrytis cinerea P. †
  ⎱Botrytis vulgaris (Lk.) ex Fr.
  ⎩Polyactis vulgaris Lk. ex Fr.
  Cladosporium herbarum (P.) ex Lk.
  ⎰Corticium vagum B. & C.
  ⎱Rhizoctonia Solani Kühn.
  Erysiphe communis Auct. Amer.
  Hypoderma commune (Fr.) Duby.
  Verticillium albo-atrum Reinke & Berthold.
Caltha biflora DC.
  ⎰Dicaeoma areolatum (Diet. & Holw.) O.
  ⎱ Kuntze.
  ⎩Puccinia areolata Diet. & Holw.
  Puccinia Calthae Lk.
  ⎰Micropuccinia gemella (Diet. & Holw.) Arth.
  ⎱ & Jackson.
  ⎩Puccinia gemella Diet. & Holw.
  ⎰Micropuccinia treleasiana (Pazschke) Arth.
  ⎱ & Jackson
  ⎩Puccinia treleasiana Pazschke.
Caltha Howellii Greene.
  ⎰Micropuccinia gemella (Diet. & Holw.) Arth.
  ⎱ & Jackson.
  ⎩Puccinia gemella Diet. & Holw.
Caltha leptosepala DC.
  Aecidium sp. indet.
  Dicaeoma areolatum (Diet. & Holw.)O. Kuntze.
  ⎰Dicaeoma calthicola (Schrt.) Arth.
  ⎱Puccinia Zopfii Wint.
  ⎰Micropuccinia gemella (Diet. & Holw.) Arth.
  ⎱ & Jackson.
  ⎩Puccinia gemella Diet. & Holw.
  ⎰Micropuccinia treleasiana (Pazschke) Arth. &
  ⎱ Jackson.
  ⎩Puccinia treleasiana Pazschke.
Caltha palustris L.
  Acrospermum compressum Tode.
  Aecidium Calthae Grev.
  Fabraea rousseauana Sacc. & Bomm.
  ⎰Dicaeoma Calthae (Lk.) O. Kuntze.
  ⎱Puccinia Calthae Lk.
  ⎰Dicaeoma calthicola (Schrt.) Arth.
  ⎱Puccinia calthicola Schrt.
  ⎩Puccinia Zopfii Wint.
  Ramularia Calthae Lindr.

Caltha rotundifolia (Huth) Greene.
  Dicaeoma areolatum (Diet. & Holw.) O.
    Kuntze.
  ⎰Micropuccinia treleasiana (Pazschke) Arth.
  ⎱ & Jackson.
  ⎱Puccinia treleasiana Pazschke.
Trollius laxus Salisb.
  Pleospora alpestris Ell. & Ev.
  Sphaerella hypsicola Ell. & Ev.
Trollius sp. indet.
  Phompsis Trollii Fairman.
  Urocystis pompholygodes (Schl.) Rabh.
Helleborus niger L.
  Coniothyrium Hellebori Cke. & Massee.
  Verticillium albo-atrum Reinke & Berth.
Eranthis hyemalis (L.) Salisb.
  Aecidium punctatum P.
Isopyrum biternatum (Raf.) T. & G.
  ⎰Aecidium Ranunculacearum Auct. Amer. p. p.
  ⎱Aecidium Thalictri Auct. Amer. p.p.
  ⎰Dicaeoma Clematidis (Lagerh.) Arth. I.
  ⎱Puccinia Clematidis Lagerh.
  Cercospora Merrowi Ell. & Ev.
Coptis asplenifolia Salisb.
  Septoria Coptidis B. & C.
Coptis trifolia (L.) Salisb.
  Phoma herbarum Westd.
  Phyllosticta helleboricola, var. Coptidis Sacc.
    & Scalia.
  ⎰Heteropatella umbilicata (P.) Jaap.
  ⎰Rhabdospora cercosperma (Rostr.) Sacc.
  ⎱Septoria cercosperma Rostr.
  Septoria Coptidis B. & C.
  ⎰Laestadia Coptis (S.) Ell. & Ev.
  ⎰Mycosphaerella Coptis (S.) House.
  ⎰Sphaerella Coptis (S.) Farl.
  ⎱Sphaeria Coptis S.
  Vermicularia coptina Pk.
Zanthorhiza apiifolia L'Her.
  Phyllosticta Xanthorrhizae Ell. & L. W. Nut-
    tall.
Actaea alba (L.) Mill.
  ⎰Aecidium Actaeae Opiz.
  ⎰Aecidium cimicifugatum (S.) B.
  ⎰Dicaeoma Clematidis (Lagerh.) Arth. I.
  ⎱Puccinia Clematidis Lagerh. I.
  Ramularia Actaeae Ell. & Holw.
  ⎰Urocystis Anemones Auct. Amer. p. p.
  ⎱Urocystis carcinodes (B. & C.) Fisch. Wald.
Actaea rubra (Ait.) Willd.
  ⎰Aecidium Actaeae Opiz.
  ⎰Aecidium cimicifugatum (S.) B.
  ⎰Dicaeoma Clematidis (Lagerh.) Arth. I.
  ⎰Puccinia Actaeae-Agropyri Ed. Fisch. I.
  ⎱Puccinia Clematidis Lagerh. I.
  Ascochyta Actaeae (Bres.) J. J. Davis.
Actaea rubra (Ait.) Willd., var. **neglecta** (Gill-
    man) B. L. Robinson.
  Ramularia Actaeae Ell. & Holw.

⎰Leptostroma lineare Pk.
⎱Leptostroma lineatum Sacc.
  Leptostroma vulgare Fr.
  Melanopsamma utahensis Ell. & Ev.
  Phyllactinia corylea (P.) ex Karst.
  Ramularia Actaeae Ell. & Holw.
  Urocystis carcinodes (B. & C.) Fisch. Wald.
Actaea spicata L., var. **arguta** L.
  ⎰Dicaeoma Clematidis (Lagerh.) Arth. I.
  ⎱Puccinia Clematidis Lagerh. I.
Actaea sp. indet.
  Marssonia Actaeae Bres.
Cimicifuga racemosa (L.) Nutt.
  ⎰Aecidium Actaeae Opiz.
  ⎰Aecidium cimicifugatum (S.) B.
  ⎰Caeoma cimicifugatum S.
  ⎰Dicaeoma Clematidis (Lagerh.) Arth. I.
  ⎱Puccinia triticina Erikss. I.
  ⎰Dothidea afflata S.
  ⎰Ectostroma afflatum (S.) Fr.
  ⎱Xyloma afflatum S.
  ⎰Leptosphaeria ogilviensis (B. & Br.) Ces. &
  ⎰ De Not.
  ⎱Sphaeria ogilviensis B. & Br.
  ⎰Leptostroma Actaeae S.
  ⎰Leptostroma vulgare Fr.
  ⎱Xyloma Actaeae S.
  ⎰Phoma Cimicifugae B. & C.
  ⎱Sphaeria Cimicifugae S.
  ⎰Thecaphora carcinodes B. & C.
  ⎱Urocystis carcinodes (B. & C.) Fisch. Wald.
Aquilegia caerulea James.
  Aecidium Aquilegiae P.
  ⎰Aecidium Aquilegiae Auct. Amer. non P.
  ⎰Dicaeoma Clematidis (Lagerh.) Arth. I.
  ⎰Puccinia Agrostidis Plowr. I.
  ⎰Puccinia Clematidis Lagerh. I.
  ⎱Puccinia obliterata Arth. I.
  Dasyscypha tuberculiformis Ell. & Ev.
  Erysiphe Polygoni DC. †
  Excipulina rostrata Syd.
  Kellermania alpina Ell. & Ev.
  ⎰Mycosphaerella caerulea (Ell. & Ev.) Tracy &
  ⎰ Earle.
  ⎱Sphaerella caerulea Ell. & Ev.
  Urocystis sorosporioides Körn.
Aquilegia canadensis L.
  Aecidium dakotense Griffiths.
  Cercospora Aquilegiae Kellerm. & Swingle.
  ⎰Erysiphe communis Auct. Amer.
  ⎱Erysiphe Polygoni DC. †
  Phyllosticta Aquilegiae Tehon & Daniels.
  Rhabdospora clarkeana Sacc.
  ⎰Septoria Aquilegiae Penz. & Sacc.
  ⎱Septoria Aquilegiae Ell. & Kellerm. 1887.
Aquilegia elegantula Greene.
  ⎰Dicaeoma Clematidis (Lagerh.) Arth. I.
  ⎱Puccinia Aquilegiae Lagerh. I.

Aquilegia flavescens Watson.
  Dicaeoma Clematidis (Lagerh.) Arth. I.
  Puccinia Agropyri Ell & Ev. I.
  Puccinia Clematidis Lagerh. I.
  Puccinia obliterata Arth. I.
  Urocystis sorosporioides Körn.

Aquilegia formosa Fisch.
  Aecidium Clematidis DC.
  Dicaeoma Clematidis (Lagerh.) Arth. l.
  Puccinia Agropyri Ell. & Ev. I.
  Puccinia Agrostidis Plowr. I.
  Puccinia Clematidis Lagerh. I.
  Puccinia obliterata Arth. I.
  Aecidium Sommerfeltii Johans.
  Erysiphe Polygoni DC. †

Aquilegia Jonesii Parry.
  Sphaerella Aquilegiae Ell. & Ev.

Aquilegia laramiensis A. Nels.
  Dicaeoma Clematidis (Lagerh.) Arth. I.

Aquilegia vulgaris L.
  Erysiphe communis Auct. Amer.
  Erysiphe Polygoni DC. †
  Septoria Aquilegiae Ell. & Kellerm.

Aquilegia sp. indet.
  Gloeosporium Aquilegiae Thm.
  Helminthosporium tenuissimum Lk.
  Marssonia Aquilegiae Dearness.
  Rhizoctonia Solani Kühn.
  Sclerotinia libertiana Fckl.
  Sclerotinia sclerotiorum (Lib.) Massee.

Delphinium Ajacis L.
  Sclerotium Rolfsii Sacc.

Delphinium azureum Michx.
Delphinium bicolor Nutt.
Delphinium cucullatum A. Nels.
Delphinium depauperatum Nutt.
  Aecidium Clematidis DC.
  Aecidium Delphinii Barthol.
  Aecidium Ranunculacearum Auct. Amer. p. p.
  Dicaeoma Clematidis (Lagerh.) Arth. I.
  Puccinia Delphinii I. Auct. Amer. p. p.

Delphinium elatum L.
  Erysiphe communis Auct. Amer.
  Erysiphe Polygoni DC. †
  Erysiphe communis, var. Delphinii Ell.

Delphinium formosum Boiss. & Huet.
  Erysiphe Polygoni DC. †

Delphinium geraniifolium Rydb.
Delphinium Geyeri Greene.
Delphinium glaucescens Rydb.
  Aecidium Delphinii Barthol.
  Dicaeoma Clematidis (Lagerh.) Arth. I.
  Puccinia Clematidis Lagerh. I.

Delphinium grandiflorum L.
  Sclerotium Rolfsii Sacc.

Delphinium hybridum Hort.
  Sclerotium Delphinii Welch.

Delphinium Menziesii DC.
  Puccinia Clematidis Lagerh. I.

Delphinium multiflorum Rydb.
  Phyllosticta Delphinii Clements.

Delphinium Nelsoni Greene.
  Aecidium Delphinii Barthol.
  Dicaeoma Clematidis (Lagerh.) Arth. I.

Delphinium occidentale Watson.
  Sphaeromyces Delphinii Pk.

Delphinium Penardi Huth.
  Septoria delphinella Sacc.

Delphinium reticulatum A. Nels.
  Dicaeoma Clematidis (Lagerh.) Arth. I.

Delphinium robustum Rydb.
  Aecidium Delphinii Barthol.
  Dicaeoma Clematidis (Lagerh.) Arth. I.
  Puccinia Agropyri Ell. & Ev. I.
  Puccinia Clematidis Lagerh. I.
  Leptosphaeria ogilviensis (B. & Br.) Ces. & DeNot.

Delphinium Sapellonis Cockerell.
  Aecidium Clematidis DC.
  Puccinia Clematidis Lagerh. I.
  Puccinia Delphinii I. Auct. Amer. p. p.

Delphinium scopulorum Gray.
  Aecidium Delphinii Barthol.
  Aecidium Ranunculacearum Auct. Amer. p. p.
  Ramularia Delphinii Dearness & House.

Delphinium tricorne Michx.
  Aecidium Delphinii Barthol.
  Dicaeoma Clematidis (Lagerh.) Arth. I.
  Septoria Staphysagriae Wint.

Delphinium virescens Nutt.
  Aecidium batesianum Barthol.
  Aecidium Delphinii Barthol.
  Dicaeoma Clematidis (Lagerh.) Arth.

Delphinium sp. indet.
  Cercospora Delphinii Thm.
  Chaetophoma myriospora Cke.
  Corticium vagum B. & C.
  Didymella Delphinii Earle.
  Erysiphe Cichoracearum DC. †
  Phoma delphiniicola Tracy & Earle.
  Micropuccinia Delphinii (Diet. & Holw.) Arth. & Jackson.
  Puccinia Delphinii Diet. & Holw.
  Sclerotinia libertiana Fckl.
  Sclerotium Delphinii Welch.
  Mycosphaerella delphiniicola Earle.
  Sphaerella delphiniicola (Earle) Sacc. & Syd.
  Urocystis sorosporioides Körn.

Aconitum columbianum Nutt.
  Aecidium Aconiti-Napelli (DC.) Wint.
  Phoma delphiniicola Tracy & Earle.
  Urocystis sorosporioides Körn.
  Nigredo bifrons (O. Kuntze) Arth.
  Uromyces Aconiti-Lycoctoni (DC.) Wint.

Aconitum delphinifolium DC.
  Aecidium circinans Erikss.
  { Aecidium Clematidis DC.
  { Dicaeoma Clematidis (Lagerh.) Arth. I.
  Pyrenophora comata (Niessl) Sacc.
  Mycosphaerella pachyasca (Rostr.) Vester-
    gren.
Aconitum Fischeri Reichb.
  Aecidium Aconiti-Napelli (DC.) Wint.
  { Uromyces Aconiti Fckl.
  { Uromyces Aconiti-Lycoctoni (DC.) Wint.
Anemonella thalictroides (L.) Spach.
  ?Aecidium Sommerfeltii Johans.
  { Aecidium Ranunculacearum Auct. Amer. p. p.
  { Aecidium Thalictri Auct. Amer.
  { Aecidium Thalictri-flavi Auct. Amer. p. p.
  { Dicaeoma Clematidis (Lagerh.) Arth. I.
  { Puccinia tomipara Trel. I.
  Cercospora Caulophylli Pk.
  { Erysiphe communis Auct. Amer.
  { Erysiphe Polygoni DC. †
  { Urocystis Anemones (P.) Wint.
  { Urocystis pomphylogodes (Schl.) Rabh.
Hepatica acutiloba DC.
  Aecidium hepaticatum S.
  { Aecidium punctatum P.
  { Caeoma hepaticatum S.
  { Puccinia Pruni-spinosae P. I.
  { Tranzschelia punctata Arth. I.
  Gloeosporium acutiloba Dearness & House.
  Gloeosporium Hepaticae Pk.
  Phyllactinia corylea (P.) ex Karst.
  Plasmopara pygmaea (Ung.) Schrt.
  { Plasmopara pygmaea, var. fusca (Pk.) J. J.
    Davis.
  { Protomyces fuscus Pk.
  Septoria Hepaticae Desm.
  { Polycystis Ranunculacearum Desm.
  { Urocystis Anemones (P.) Schrt.
  { Urocystis pompholygod s (Schl.) Rabh.
  Vermicularia Hepaticae Pk.
Hepatica triloba Chaix.
  { Aecidium hepaticatum S.
  { Aecidium punctatum P.
  { Caeoma hepaticatum S.
  { Puccinia Pruni-spinosae P. I.
  Tranzschelia punctata Arth.
  Gloeosporium Hepaticae Pk.
  { Peronospora pygmaea Ung.
  { Plasmopara pygmaea (Ung.) Schrt.
  Protomyces fuscus Pk.
  Urocystis Anemones (P.) Schrt.
Anemone canadensis L.
  { Aecidium Clematidis DC.
  { Aecidium Ranunculacearum Auct. Amer. p. p.
  { Dicaeoma Clematidis (Lagerh.) Arth. I.
  { Puccinia Clematidis Lagerh. I.
  { Dicaeoma magnusianum (Körn.) O. Kuntze. I.
  { Puccinia simillima Arth. I.

  { Didymaria didyma (Ung.) Pound.
  { Didymaria Ungeri Cda.
  { Erysiphe communis Auct. Amer.
  { Erysiphe Polygoni DC. †
  { Peronospora pygmaea Ung.
  { Plasmopara pygmaea (Ung.) Schrt.
  Phyllosticta Anemonis Ell. & Ev.
  Phyllosticta anemonicola Sacc. & Syd.
  { Micropuccinia Anemones-virginianae (S.) Arth.
  {   & Jackson.
  Puccinia Anemones-virginianae S.
  ?Puccinia fusca Relh.
  Ramularia Ranunculi Pk., forma Anemones
    Shear.
  { Polycystis Ranunculacearum Desm.
  { Urocystis Anemones (P.) Wint
  { Urocystis pompholygodes (Schl.) Rabh.
Anemone caroliniana Walt.
  { Aecidium punctatum P.
  { ?Aecidium Ranunculacearum Auct. Amer. p. p.
  { Tranzschelia punctata Arth. I.
  Plasmopara pygmaea (Ung.) Schrt.
  Septoria Anemones Desm.
  Urocystis Anemones (P.) Wint.
Anemone coronaria L.
  Aecidium punctatum P.
Anemone cylindrica Gray.
  { Aecidium Anemones Auct. Amer. p. p.
  Aecidium Clematidis DC.
  Aecidium Ranunculacearum Auct. Amer. p. p.
  Dicaeoma Clematidis (Lagerh.) Arth.
  Puccinia Agropyri Ell. & Ev. I.
  Puccinia Clematidis Lagerh. I.
  Puccinia gigantispora I. Auct. Amer.
  Puccinia magnusiana I. N. Am. Uredinales
    3257.
  Puccinia missouriensis I. Arth.
  Didymaria Ungeri Cda.
  Dothidea Anemones Fr.
  Phleospora Anemones Ell. & Kellerm.
  Phoma vulgaris Sacc.
  { Dasyspora Anemones-virginianae (S.) Arth.
  Dicaeoma Anemones-Virginianae (S.) Arth.
  { Micropuccinia Anemones-virginianae (S.) Arth.
  {   & Jackson.
  { Puccinia Anemones-virginianae S.
  Puccinia compacta Auct. Amer. p. p. non DBy.
  Puccinia missouriensis III. Arth.
  Puccinia solida S.
  { Allodus gigantispora (Bubák) Arth.
  { Puccinia gigantispora Bubák.
  Septoria cylindrica Ell. & Ev.
  Synchytrium Anemones (DC.) Wor.
Anemone decapetala Ard.
  Aecidium punctatum P.
  Plasmopara pygmaea (Ung.) Schrt.
  { Puccinia cohaesa Long.
  { Tranzschelia cohaesa (Long) Arth.
  Urocystis Anemones (P.) Wint.

Anemone Drummondii Watson.
  Micropuccinia Pulsatillae (Kalchbr.) Arth. &
    Jackson.
  Puccinia compacta DBy.
  Puccinia debaryana Thm.
  Pyrenophora comata (Niessl) Sacc.
Anemone globosa Nutt.
  Dicaeoma Clematidis (Lagerh.) Arth. I.
  Puccinia Clematidis Lagerh. I.
  Allodus gigantispora (Bubák) Arth.
  Puccinia Anemones-virginianae Seymour p. p.
    non S.
  Puccinia gigantispora Bubák.
  Allodus opposita C. R. Orton.
  Puccinia opposita (C. R. Orton) Arth. 1921.
  Puccinia opposita (C. R. Orton) Sacc. & Trott.
    1925.
Anemone lithophila Rydb.
  Micropuccinia retecta (Syd.) Arth. & Jackson.
Anemone multifida Poir.
  Aecidium Ranunculacearum Auct. Amer. p. p.
  Dicaeoma Clematidis (Lagerh..) Arth. I.
  Plasmopara pygmaea (Ung.) Schrt.
  ?Puccinia Anemones-virginianae S.
  Puccinia fusca (Relh.) Wint.
  Puccinia Pulsatillae Rostr.
  Puccinia suffusca Holw.
Anemone narcissiflora L.
  Aecidium Anemones Auct. Amer. p. p.
  Allodus gigantispora (Bubák) Arth.
  Puccinia retecta Syd.
  Puccinia vesiculosa W. Am. Fung. *328*.
  Puccinia vesiculosa Schl.
  Rhabdospora camptospora Sacc. & Scalia.
Anemone oregana Gray.
  Polythelis fusca Arth.
Anemone parviflora Michx.
  Pleospora stenospora Schrt.
  Polythelis fusca Arth.
  Micropuccinia Pulsatillae (Kalchbr.) Arth. &
    Jackson.
  Puccinia debaryana Thm.
  Polythelis Pulsatillae (Rostr.) Arth.
  Puccinia Pulsatillae Rostr. non Kalchbr.
  Puccinia suffusca Holw.
  Rhabdospora Drabae (Fckl.) Berl. & Vogl.
  Mycosphaerella confinis (Karst.) Dearness.
  Sphaerella confinis Karst.
Anemone patens L., var. **wolfgangiana** (Bess.)
    Koch.
  Cercosporella filiformis J. J. Davis.
  Mycosphaerella pachyasca (Rostr.) Vestergren.
  Micropuccinia Pulsatillae (Kalchbr.) Arth. &
    Jackson.
  Puccinia Anemones-virginianae Wint. non S.
  Puccinia debaryana Thm.
  Puccinia fusca Auct. Amer. p. p.
  Puccinia Pulsatillae Kalchb. non Rostr.

  Polythelis Pulsatillae (Rostr.) Arth.
  Puccinia fusca Auct. Amer. p. p.
  Puccinia Pulsatillae Rostr.
  Puccinia suffusca Holw.
  Polythelis suffusca (Holw.) Arth.
  Pyrenophora comata (Niessl) Sacc.
  Urocystis Anemones (P.) Schrt.
Anemone Piperi Britt.
  Dicaeoma Clematidis (Lagerh.) Arth. I.
  Polythelis fusca Arth.
Anemone quinquefolia L.
    (Includes A. nemorosa).
  Aecidium Anemones Auct. Amer. p. p.
  ?Aecidium leucospermum Auct. Amer.
  Aecidium Ranunculacearum Auct. Amer. p. p.
  Dicaeoma Clematidis (Lagerh.) Arth. I.
  Puccinia Clematidis Lagerh. I.
  Aecidium punctatum P.
  Aecidium quadrifidum DC.
  Puccinia Pruni-spinosae P. I.
  Tranzschelia punctata Arth. I.
  Dothidea Anemones Fr.
  Entyloma Ranunculi (Bon.) Schrt.
  Peronospora pygmaea Ung.
  Plasmopara pygmaea (Ung.) Schrt.
  Dicaeoma Anemones (P.) Arth.
  Dicaeoma fuscum (Wint.) O. Kuntze.
  Polythelis fusca (Wint.) Arth.
  Puccinia Anemones P.
  Puccinia fusca Wint.
  ?Puccinia Anemones-virginianae S.
  Sclerotinia tuberosa (Hedw. ex Fr.) Fckl.
  Septoria Anemones Desm.
  Synchytrium Anemones (DBy.) Wor.
  Urocystis Anemones (P.) Schrt.
  Urocystis pompholygodes (Schl.) Rabh.
Anemone ranunculoides L.
  Aecidium punctatum P.
  Synchytrium Anemones (DC.) Wor.
Anemone Richardsonii Hook.
  Aecidium Ranunculacearum DC.
  Mycosphaerella pachyasca (Rostr.) Vestergren.
Anemone riparia Fern.
  Dicaeoma Clematidis (Lagerh.) Arth. I.
  Micropuccinia Anemones-virginianae (S.) Arth.
    & Jackson.
Anemone sphenophylla Poepp.
  Tranzschelia cohaesa (Long) Arth.
Anemone tetonensis Porter.
  Pyrenophora ampla Syd.
Anemone tuberosa Rydb.
  Lipospora tucsonensis Arth.
Anemone virginiana L.
  Aecidium Anemones Auct. Amer. p. p.
  Aecidium Ranunculacearum Auct. Amer. p. p.
  Dicaeoma Clematidis (Lagerh.) Arth. I.
  Puccinia Clematidis Lagerh. I.
  Uromyces Dactylidis I. W. A. Orton.

Anemone virginiana (*cont.*)
  Didymaria Didyma (Ung.) Pound.
  Didymaria Ungeri Cda., var. Anemones Holw.
  Dothidea Anemones Fr.
  Erysiphe communis (Wallr.) ex Lk.
  Erysiphe Polygoni DC. †
  Phleospora Anemones Ell. & Kellerm.
  Phyllosticta Ellisiana Lamb. & Fautr.
  Plasmopara pygmaea (Ung.) Schrt.
  Dasyspora Anemones-virginianae (S.) Arth.
  Dicaeoma Anemones-virginianae (S.) Arth.
  Puccinia Anemones-virginianae S.
  Puccinia pallida Tracy.
  Puccinia solida S.
  ?Puccinia fusca Wint.
  Puccinia gigantispora Bubák.
  Sclerotium Anemones S.
  Septoria Anemones Desm.
  Macrobasis platypus (S.) Starb.
  Sphaeria platypus S.
  Synchytrium Anemones (DC.) Wor.
  Urocystis Anemones (P.) Schrt.

Anemone zephyra A. Nels.
  Polythelis retecta (Syd.) Arth.

Anemone sp. indet.
  Phleospora Anemones Ell. & Kellerm.
  Phoma segina Fairman.
  Physalospora borealis Sacc.
  Stagonospora Pulsatillae (Vestergren) Sacc. &
    Scalia.
  Sclerotinia tuberosa (Hedw. ex Fr.) Fckl.

Clematis dioica L.
Clematis Douglasii Hook.
Clematis Drummondii Torr. & Gray.
Clematis Fremonti Watson.
Clematis grossa Benth.
Clematis hirsutissima Pursh.
Clematis Jonesii O.Kuntze.
Clematis lasiantha Nutt.
Clematis ligusticifolia Nutt.
Clematis pauciflora Nutt.
Clematis reticulata Walt.
Clematis Scottii Porter.
Clematis Viorna L.
Clematis virginiana L.
  Aecidium Clematidis DC.
  Aecidium clematitatum S.
  Aecidium Clematis S.
  Aecidium occidentale Arth.
  Caeoma (Aecidium) clematitatum S.
  Dicaeoma Clematidis (Lagerh.) Arth. I.
  Puccinia Agropyri Ell. & Ev. I.
  Puccinia Clematidis Lagerh. I.
  Puccinia tomipara Trel. I.
  Puccinia triticina Erikss. I.
Clematis Drummondii Torr. & Gr.
  Phleospora adusta Heald & Wolf.

Clematis Fremonti Watson.
  Macrosporium Clematidis Pk.
Clematis lasiantha Nutt.
  Micropuccinia Pulsatillae (Kalchbr.) Arth. &
    Jackson.
Clematis ligusticifolia Nutt.
  Aecidium Clematidis DC.
  Arthrobotryum? pestalozzioides Dearness &
    Fairman.
  Cercospora Rubigo Cke. & Hark.
  ?Cercospora squalida Auct. Amer.
  Cercospora squalidula Pk.
  Ceriospora montaniensis (Ell.) Berl.
  Lophiostoma montaniense Ell.
  Cladosporium herbarum (P.) ex Lk.
  Didymaria Clematidis Cke. & Hark.
  Dothidella insculpta (Wallr.) Theiss. & Syd.
  Erysiphe communis Auct. Amer.
  Erysiphe Polygoni DC. †
  Lophiostoma pseudomacrostomum Sacc.
  Otthia Clematitis Earle.
  Otthia fruticola Ell. & Ev.
  Parodiella fruticola Ell. & Ev.
  Clathrospora permunda (Cke.) Berl.
  Pleospora permunda (Cke.) Sacc.
  Pyrenophora Clematidis Earle.
  Ramularia Clematidis Dearness & Barthol.
  Sphaerella applanata Ell. & Ev.
Clematis paniculata Thunb.
  Ascochyta clematidina (Thm.) Gloyer.
  Diplodia hortensis Sacc.
  Hendersonia hortilecta Fairman.
Clematis patens, var. **Jackmani** Hort.
  Cylindrosporium Clematidis Ell. & Ev., var.
    Jackmanii Ell. & Ev.
  Septoria Jackmani Ell. & Ev.
Clematis Scottii Porter.
  Dothiorella phomopsis Fairman.
Clematis Viorna L.
  Cercospora squalidula Pk.
Clematis Viorna L., var. **coccinea** Auct.
  Phyllosticta Clematidis Ell. & Dearness.
Clematis virginiana L.
      See also above.
  Ascochyta clematidina Thm.
  Cercospora squalidula Pk.
  Cylindrosporium Clematidis Ell. & Ev.
  Cylindrosporium Ranunculi (Bon.) Sacc., var.
    Thalictri Ell. & Ev.
  Entyloma Ranunculi (Bon.) Schrt., var.
    Thalictri Farl.
  Entyloma Thalictri Schrt.
  Erysiphe Polygoni DC. †
  Erysiphe tortilis Auct. Amer.
  Haplosporella Clematidis (Dearness & House)
    Petrak & Syd.
  Macroplodia Clematidis Dearness & House.
  Sphaeropsis Clematidis Dearness & House.

Clematis sp. indet.
  Ascochyta Actaeae (Bres.) J. J. Davis.
  Leptosphaeria agminalis Sacc. & Morth.
  Meliola furcata Lév.
  Phleospora adusta Heald & Wolf.
  Physarum melanospermum P.
  Puccinia stromatica B. & C.
  Puccinia Viornae Arth.
  Vermicularia Dematium (P.) Fr.
Atragene occidentalis Hornem.
  Urocystis carcinodes (B. & C.) Fisch. Wald.
Trautvetteria carolinensis (Walt.) Vail.
  Septoria Trautvetteriae Ell. & Ev.
  Vermicularia Trautvetteriae L. W. Nuttall.
Trautvetteria grandis Nutt.
  { Micropuccinia Pulsatillae (Kalchbr.) Arth. &
  { Jackson.
  { Puccinia Pulsatillae Kalchbr.
  Urocystis Anemones (P.) Wint.
Ranunculus abortivus L.
  { Aecidium Ranunculi S.
  { Caeoma ranunculaceatum Lk.
  { Dicaeoma Eatoniae Arth. I.
  { Puccinia Eatoniae Arth. I.
  Ascochyta infuscans Ell. & Ev.
  { Erysiphe communis Auct. Amer.
  { Erysiphe Polygoni DC. †
  Peronospora Ficariae Tul.
  { Ramularia aequivoca (Ces.) Sacc.
  { Septocylindrium Ranunculi Pk.
  Ramularia Ranunculi Pk.
  Septocylindrium Ranunculi Pk.
Ranunculus acris L.
  { Aecidium Clematidis DC.
  { Dicaeoma Clematidis (Lagerh.) Arth. I.
  { Puccinia Clematidis Lagerh. I.
  { Puccinia perplexans Plowr. I.
  Cladosporium herbarum (P.) ex Lk.
  { Didymaria Didyma (Ung.) Pound.
  { Didymaria Ungeri Cda.
  { Erysiphe communis Auct. Amer.
  { Erysiphe Polygoni DC. †
  Fabraea Ranunculi (Fr.) Karst.
  Mollisia atrata (P.) Karst.
  Ovularia decipiens Sacc.
  Peronospora Ficariae Tul.
  Peronospora hiemalis Gäuman.
  Ramularia aequivoca (Ces.) Sacc.
  Ramularia decipiens Ell. & Ev.
  Ramularia Ranunculi Pk.
  Sclerotium rufum Rostr.
  Septocylindrium Ranunculi Pk.
Ranunculus affinis R. Br.
  { Dicaeoma Clematidis (Lagerh.) Arth. I.
  { Puccinia Clematidis Lagerh. I.
  Heterosporium groenlandicum Allescher.
  Leptosphaeria Ranunculi Rostr.
  Pleospora herbarum (Fr.) Rabh.

  Pleospora vulgaris Niessl.
  Puccinia Ranunculi Seym.
  Septoria cercosperma Rostr.
  { Mycosphaerella ootheca (Sacc.) Dearness.
  { Sphaerella ootheca Sacc.
  Sphaerella pachyasca Rostr.
Ranunculus aleophilus A. Nels.
  Dicaeoma Clematidis (Lagerh.) Arth. I.
Ranunculus alismifolius Geyer.
  Uromyces Jonesii Pk.
Ranunculus Andersoni Gray.
  Urocystis sorosporioides Körn.
Ranunculus apetalus Torr.
  Uromyces Alopecuri Seymour. I.
Ranunculus Bolanderi Greene.
  Aecidium indecisum Arth.
Ranunculus bulbosus L.
  Aecidium Ranunculacearum DC. p. p.
  Peronospora Ficariae Tul.
Ranunculus californicus Benth.
  { Aecidium Clematidis DC.
  { Dicaeoma Clematidis (Lagerh.) Arth. I.
  Aecidium indecisum Arth.
  Stigmatea Ranunculi Fr.
  Synchytrium andinum Lagerh.
Ranunculus calthiflorus Greene.
  { Aecidium Ranunculi S.
  { Dicaeoma Eatoniae Arth. I.
Ranunculus cardiophyllus Hook.
  Dicaeoma Clematidis (Lagerh.) Arth. I.
Ranunculus Cymbalaria Pursh.
  { Aecidium Clematidis DC.
  { Aecidium Ranunculacearum Fung. Utah. *126.*
  { Dicaeoma Clematidis (Lagerh.) Arth. I.
  { Puccinia cinerea Arth. I.
  { Puccinia Clematidis Lagerh. I.
  ?Aecidium Ranunculi S.
  { Erysiphe communis Auct. Amer.
  { Erysiphe Polygoni DC. †
  Septoria ficarioides Pk.
Ranunculus delphinifolius Torr.
  Doassansia ranunculina J. J. Davis.
  Entyloma Ranunculi (Bon.) Schrt.
  { Erysiphe communis Auct. Amer.
  { Erysiphe Polygoni DC. †
Ranunculus digitatus Hook.
  Urocystis Anemones (P.) Schrt.
Ranunculus ellipticus Greene.
  Aecidium Ranunculacearum Auct. p. p.
Ranunculus eremogenes Greene.
  Entyloma Ranunculi (Bon.) Schrt.
Ranunculus Eschscholtzii Schlecht.
  { Micropuccinia Ranunculi (A. Blytt) Arth. &
  { Jackson.
  { Puccinia Ranunculi A. Blytt.
  Urocystis Anemones (P.) Wint.

Ranunculus fascicularis Muhl.
 Aecidium Ranunculacearum DC.
 ⎰Didymaria Didyma (Ung.) Pound.
 ⎱Didymaria Ungeri Cda.
 Entyloma microsporum (Ung.) Schrt.
 Peronospora Ficariae Tul.

Ranunculus Ficaria L.
 Synchytrium anomalum Schrt.
 Urocystis Anemones (P.) Schrt.

Ranunculus Flammula L.
 Uromyces Jonesii Pk.

Ranunculus glaberrimus Hook.
 ⎧Aecidium Clematidis DC.
 ⎪Aecidium Ranunculacearum Auct. Amer. p. p.
 ⎨Dicaeoma Clematidis (Lagerh.) Arth. I.
 ⎩Puccinia Clematidis Lagerh. I.
 Micropuccinia Ranunculi (A. Blytt) Arth. &
   Jackson.

Ranunculus Greenei Howell.
 Ramularia aequivoca (Ces.) Sacc.

Ranunculus hebecarpus Hook. & Arn.
 Puccinia Clematidis Lagerh. I.

Ranunculus hispidus Michx.
 Peronospora Ficariae Tul.

Ranunculus Lobbii Gray.
 Aecidium indecisum Arth.

Ranunculus Lyallii Rydb.
 Ramularia Ranunculi-Lyallii Dearness &
   Barthol.
 Septocylindrium Ranunculi Pk.

Ranunculus Macounii Brit.
 ⎰Nigredo Alopecuri (Seym.) Arth. I.
 ⎱Uromyces Alopecuri Seym. I.

Ranunculus macranthus Scheele.
 ⎰Erysiphe communis Auct. Amer.
 ⎱Erysiphe Polygoni DC. †

Ranunculus
    (Cyrtorhyncha neglecta Greene.)
 ⎰Micropuccinia Ranunculi (A. Blytt) Arth. &
 ⎨ Jackson.
 ⎩Puccinia Ranunculi A. Blytt.

Ranunculus nivalis L.
 Cladosporium herbarum (P.) ex Lk.
 Pleospora herbarum (P.) ex Rabh.
 Pleospora media Niessl.
 ⎧Discosia acuta Dearness.
 ⎪Heteropatella umbilicata (P.) Jaap.
 ⎨Rhabdospora cercosperma (Rostr.) Sacc
 ⎩Septoria cercosperma Rostr.
 Sphaerella fusispora Fckl., var. groenlandica
   Allescher.
 Sphaerella pachyasca Rostr.
 Stigmatea Ranunculi Fr.

Ranunculus Nuttallii Gray.
 ⎰Aecidium Ranunculacearum Auct. Amer. p. p.
 ⎱Dicaeoma Clematidis (Lagerh.) Arth. I.

Fabraea litigiosa (R. & D.) Sacc.?
 Puccinia gibberulosa Schrt.?
 ⎧Micropuccinia Ranunculi (A. Blytt) Arth. &
 ⎪ Jackson.
 ⎨Puccinia Nuttallii Ell. & Ev.
 ⎩Puccinia Ranunculi A. Blytt.
 Urocystis Anemones (P.) Wint.

Ranunculus occidentalis Nutt.
 ⎰Aecidium Clematidis DC.
 ⎱Dicaeoma Clematidis (Lagerh.) Arth. I.
 Fabraea Ranunculi (Fr.) Karst.

Ranunculus parviflorus L.
 Erysiphe communis Auct. Amer.

Ranunculus pennsylvanicus L.
 Aecidium Ranunculacearum DC. ?
 ⎧Didymaria Didyma (Ung.) Pound.
 ⎨Didymaria Ungeri Cda.
 ⎩Ramularia Didyma Ung.
 Entyloma Ranunculi (Bon.) Schrt.
 ⎰Erysiphe communis Auct. Amer.
 ⎱Erysiphe Polygoni DC. †
 Fabraea Ranunculi (Fr.) Karst.
 Peronospora Ficariae Tul.
 Phacidium Ranunculi Desm.
 Pseudopeziza singularia (Pk.) J. J. Davis.

Ranunculus pusillus Poir.
 Septoria Ranunculacearum Lév.

Ranunculus pygmaeus Wahl.
 Cladosporium herbarum (P.) ex Lk.
 Entyloma microsporum (Ung.) Schrt., var.
   pygmaea Allescher.
 Phoma complanata (Fr.) Desm.
 Phoma Ranunculorum Desm.
 Phyllosticta pygmaea Allescher.
 Pleospora herbarum (Fr.) Rabh.
 Pyrenophora chrysospora (Niessl) Sacc.
 Rhabdospora caudata (Karst.) Sacc.
 ⎧Mycosphaerella pachyasca (Rostr.) Vestergren.
 ⎨Sphaerella pachyasca Rostr.
 ⎩Mycosphaerella Ranunculi (Karst.) J. Lind.
 Stigmatea Ranunculi Fr.

Ranunculus recurvatus Poir.
 Tranzschelia punctata Arth. I.
 ⎰Didymaria Didyma (Ung.) Pound.
 ⎱Didymaria Ungeri Cda.
 ⎰Erysiphe communis Auct. Amer.
 ⎱Erysiphe Polygoni DC. †
 Peronospora Ficariae Tul.
 Ramularia Ranunculi Pk.
 Synchytrium aureum Schrt.
 ⎰Synchytrium aureum Prov. List 1892.
 ⎱Synchytrium cinnamomeum J. J. Davis.

Ranunculus repens L.
 Peronospora Ranunculi Gäumann.
 ⎰Nigredo Poae (Rabh.) Arth. I.
 ⎱Uromyces Poae Rabh. I.

Ranunculus repens L., var. **hispidus** Torr.
⎰Mollisia singularis (Pk.) Sacc.
⎱Peziza singularis Pk.
⎱Pseudopeziza singularia (Pk.) J. J. Davis.
Ranunculus repens L.? and **Ranunculus repens**
Auct. Amer. p. p. (R. septentrionalis Poir.)
Peronospora Ficariae Tul.
Ramularia gibba Fckl.
Ranunculus rhomboideus Goldie.
Septoria polaris Karst.
Ranunculus sceleratus L.
⎰Aecidium Ranunculacearum Auct. Amer. p. p.
⎱Dicaeoma Clematidis (Lagerh.) Arth. I.
⎰Erysiphe communis Auct. Amer.
⎱Erysiphe Polygoni DC. †
Phacidium Ranunculi Desm.
Pseudopeziza singularia (Pk.) J. J. Davis.
⎰Nigredo Alopecuri (Seym.) Arth. I.
⎱Uromyces Alopecuri Seym. I.
Ranunculus septentrionalis Poir. (see also R.
repens.)
Puccinia Clematidis Lagerh. I.
Cercospora Ranunculi Ell. & Holw.
⎰Didymaria Didyma (Ung.) Pound.
⎪Didymaria Ungeri Cda.
⎱Ramularia Didyma Ung.
⎰Protomyces microsporus Ung.
⎱Entyloma microsporum (Ung.) Schrt.
⎰Erysiphe communis Auct. Amer.
⎱Erysiphe Polygoni DC. †
Peronospora Ficariae Tul.
Pseudopeziza singularia (Pk.) J. J. Davis.
⎰Dasyspora Ranunculi (Seym.) Arth.
⎪Dicaeoma Ranunculi (Seym.) O. Kuntze.
⎱Micropuccinia andina (Diet. & Neger) Arth. &
Jackson.
⎰Puccinia diffusa Holw.
⎱Puccinia Ranunculi Seym.
Ramularia aequivoca (Ces.) Sacc.
Ramularia Ranunculi Pk.
Septocylindrium Ranunculi Pk.
Septoria polaris Karst.
Septoria septentrionalis H. W. Anderson.
Urocystis Anemones (P.) Schrt.
Ranunculus stenolobus Rydb.
⎰Micropuccinia Ranunculi (Blytt) Arth. &
⎱Jackson.
Puccinia Ranunculi Blytt.
Urocystis Anemones (P.) Wint.
Ranunculus Suksdorfii Gray.
⎰Micropuccinia Ranunculi (Blytt) Arth. & Jack-
⎱son.
Puccinia Ranunculi Blytt.
Ranunculus sulphureus Soland.
Mycosphaerella tassiana (De Not.) Johans.
Ranunculus sp. indet.
Ascochyta? infuscans Ell. & Ev.
⎰Excipula conglutinata Ell. & Ev.
⎱Excipulina conglutinata (Ell. & Ev.) Sacc.

Pyrenopeziza compressula Rehm.
Ramularia aequivoca (Ces.) Sacc.
Uromyces Ficariae Lév.
Uromyces Jonesii Pk.

Thalictrum alpinum L.
⎰Aecidium Sommerfeltii Johans.
⎪Dicaeoma Sommerfeltii Arth. I.
⎱Puccinia Sommerfeltii (Arth.) Stevenson. I.
Puccinia septentrionalis Juel. I.
⎰Aecidium Thalictri Auct. Amer. p. p.
⎪Dicaeoma Clematidis (Lagerh.) Arth. I.
⎱Puccinia obliterata Arth. I.
Leptosphaeria Thalictri Wint.
Lizonia Thalictri Rostr.
Septoria semilunaris Johans.
Sphaerella Allescheri Sacc.
Sphaerella Allescheri Sacc., var. arctica Alles-
cher.
Sphaerella pachyasca Rostr.
Urocystis sorosporioides Körn.

Thalictrum canadense Mill.
Dicaeoma Clematidis (Lagerh.) Arth. I.

Thalictrum dasycarpum Fisch & Lall.
⎰Aecidium punctatum P.
⎪Puccinia Pruni-spinosae P. I.
⎱Tranzschelia punctata Arth. I.
⎰Aecidium Thalictri Auct. Amer. p. p.
⎪Dicaeoma Clematidis (Lagerh.) Arth. I.
⎪Puccinia Agropyri Arth. I.
⎪Puccinia Clematidis Lagerh. I.
⎱Puccinia triticina Erikss. I.
⎰Ascochyta Actaeae (Bres.) J. J. Davis.
⎪Ascochyta clematidina Thm., var. Thalictri
⎱ J. J. Davis.
Cercospora fingens J. J. Davis.
Entyloma Ranunculi (Bon.) Schrt.
Erysiphe Polygoni DC. †
Gloeosporium Thalictri J. J. Davis.
Leptosphaeria Thalictri Wint.
Phoma thalictrina Sacc. & Malbr.
Phytophthora Thalictri Wilson & Davis.
⎰Polythelis Thalictri (Chev.) Arth.
⎱Puccinia Thalictri Chev.

Thalictrum dioicum L.
⎰Aecidium Clematidis DC.
⎪Aecidium Thalictri Auct. Amer. p. p.
⎪Aecidium Thalictri-flavi Auct. Amer. p. p.
⎪Dicaeoma Clematidis (Lagerh.) Arth. I.
⎪Puccinia Agropyri Ell. & Ev. I.
⎪Puccinia alternans Arth. I.
⎪Puccinia Clematidis Lagerh. I.
⎱Puccinia triticina Erikss. I.
Puccinia cockerelliana Bethel. I.
⎰Aecidium punctatum P.
⎱Tranzschelia punctata Arth. I.
Ascochyta clematidina Thm., var. Thalictri
J. J. Davis.

Thalictrum dioicum (*cont.*)
Cercospora fingens J. J. Davis.
Cylindrosporium Thalictri (Ell. & Ev.) J. J. Davis.
{ Entyloma Ranunculi (Bon.) Schrt., var. Thalictri Farl.
Entyloma Thalictri Schrt.
Hypoderma tenellum Sacc.
Leptosphaeria houseana Sacc.
?Puccinia Pulsatillae Rostr.
{ Caeoma (Uredo) Thalictri S.
Dicaeoma Thalictri (Chev.) O. Kuntze.
?Puccinia Anemones Auct. Amer. p. p.
Polythelis Thalictri (Chev.) Arth.
Puccinia Thalictri Chev.
Pyrenopeziza Thalictri (Pk.) Sacc.
Sphaerella septorioides Pk.
{ Mycosphaerella Thalictri (Ell. & Ev.) Lindau.
Sphaerella Thalictri Ell. & Ev.

Thalictrum Fendleri Engelm.
{ Dicaeoma cockerellianum (Bethel) Arth. & Fromme. I.
Puccinia cockerelliana Bethel. I.
{ Aecidium Clematidis DC.
Aecidium Thalictri Auct. Amer. p. p.
Aecidium Thalictri-flavi Auct. Amer. p. p.
Dicaeoma Clematidis (Lagerh.) Arth. I.
Puccinia Agropyri Ell. & Ev. I.
Puccinia alternans Arth. I.
Puccinia Clematidis Lagerh. I.
Puccinia persistens Plowr. I.
Aecidium punctatum P.
Aecidium Sommerfeltii Johans?.
Phoma thalictrina Sacc. & Malbr.
{ Polythelis Thalictri (Chev.) Arth.
Puccinia Thalictri Chev.
{ Mycosphaerella Fendleri Tracy & Earle.
Sphaerella Fendleri (Tracy & Earle) Sacc. & Syd.

Thalictrum Lunellii Greene.
Aecidium Thalictri Auct. Amer. p. p.

Thalictrum megacarpum Torr.
{ Aecidium Clematidis DC.
Dicaeoma Clematidis (Lagerh.) Arth. I.
Puccinia Clematidis Lagerh. I.
Polythelis Thalictri (Chev.) Arth.

Thalictrum occidentale Gray.
{ Aecidium Thalictri Auct. Amer. p. p.
Dicaeoma Clematidis (Lagerh.) Arth. I.
Puccinia Agropyri Ell. & Ev. I.
Puccinia alternans Arth. I.
Puccinia Clematidis (DC.) Lagerh. I.
Polythelis Thalictri (Chev.) Arth.

Thalictrum polycarpum Watson.
Dicaeoma Clematidis (Lagerh.) Arth. I.
Leptostroma vulgare Fr.
Phoma nebulosa (P. ex Fr.) B.

Thalictrum polygamum Muhl.
{ Aecidium punctatum P.
Tranzschelia punctata Arth. I.
{ Aecidium Thalictri Auct. Amer. p. p.
Aecidium Thalictri-flavi Auct. Amer. p. p.
Puccinia triticina Erikss. I.
Didymosphaeria Thalictri Ell. & Dearness.
Diplodia herbarum Lév.
{ Diplodia Thalictri Ell. & Dearness.
Microdiplodia Thalictri (Ell. & Dearness) Tassi.
Entyloma Thalictri (Bon.) Schrt.
{ Erysiphe communis Auct. Amer.
Erysiphe Polygoni DC. †
Leptosphaeria Thalictri Wint.
Ophiobolus subolivaceus Pk.
Puccinia Pulsatillae Auct. Amer. p. p.
{ Caeoma (Uredo) Thalictri S.
Polythelis Thalictri (Chev.) Arth.
Puccinia Anemones Auct. Amer. p. p.
Puccinia Thalictri Chev.
Peziza Thalictri Pk.
Pyrenopeziza Thalictri (Pk.) Sacc.
Sphaerella Thalictri Ell. & Ev.
Urocystis sorosporioides Körn.

Thalictrum revolutum DC.
{ Aecidium Aikeni Syd.
Aecidium punctatum P.
Tranzschelia punctata Arth. I.
Aecidium Sommerfeltii Johans.?
{ Aecidium Thalictri Auct. Amer. p. p.
Aecidium Thalictri-flavi Auct. Amer. p. p.
Dicaeoma Clematidis (Lagerh.) Arth. I.
Puccinia persistens Plowr. I.
Cylindrosporium Ranunculi (Bon.) Sacc., var. Thalictri Ell. & Ev.
Dinemasporium hispidulum (Schrad.) Sacc.
{ Entyloma Ranunculi Schrt., var. Thalictri Farl.
Entyloma Thalictri Schrt.
{ Erysiphe communis Auct. Amer..
Erysiphe Polygoni DC. †
Phytophthora Thalictri Wilson & Davis.
Puccinia Pulsatillae Rostr.?
{ Polythelis Thalictri (Chev.) Arth.
Puccinia Thalictri Chev.
Pyrenopeziza Thalictri (Pk.) Sacc.
Septoria Thalictri Ell. & Ev.
Synchytrium Anemones (DC.) Wor.?

Thalictrum sparsiflorum Turcz.
Aecidium Sommerfeltii Johns.
{ Aecidium Thalictri-flavi Auct. Amer. p. p.
Dicaeoma Clematidis (Lagerh.) Arth. I.
Puccinia alternans Arth. I.
Chaetosphaeria Thalictri Clements.
{ Polythelis Thalictri (Chev.) Arth.
Puccinia Pulsatillae Fung. Utah. *113*.
Puccinia Thalictri Chev.
Urocystis sorosporioides Körn.

Thalictrum thyrsoideum Greene.
  Aecidium Thalictri Auct. Amer. p. p.
  Dicaeoma Clematidis (Lagerh.) Arth. I.
  Puccinia montanensis I. Fung. Dak. *104.*
Thalictrum vegetum Greene.
  Aecidium Clematidis DC.
  Aecidium Thalictri Auct. Amer. p. p.
Thalictrum venulosum Trel.
  Aecidium Clematidis DC.
  Dicaeoma Clematidis (Lagerh.) Arth. I.
  Puccinia alternans Arth. I.
  Puccinia Clematidis Lagerh. I.
  Polythelis Thalictri (Chev.) Arth.
Thalictrum Wrightii Gray.
  Polythelis Thalictri (Chev.) Arth.
Thalictrum sp. indet.
  Aulographum subconfluens Pk.
  Gloeosporium Thalictri J. J. Davis.
  Microdiplodia Thalictri Sacc.
  Mollisiopsis subcinerea Rehm.
  Phoma spermoides Dearness.
  Haplosporella Thalictri (Ell. & Fairman)
    Petrak & Syd.
  Sphaeropsis Thalictri Ell. & Fairman.

LARDIZABALACEAE

Akebia quinata Decsne.
  Diplodia Akebiae Fairman.
  Eutypella glandulosa (Cke.) Ell. & Ev.
  Phoma Akebiae Dearness.
  Schizoxylon berkeleyanum (Dur. & Lév.) Fckl.
  Haplosporella subconfluens (Fairman) Petrak
    & Syd.
  Sphaeropsis Akebiae Dearness.
  Sphaeropsis subconfluens Fairman.
  Trichothecium roseum Lk.
  Valsaria Akebiae Ell. & Ev.

BERBERIDACEAE

Podophyllum peltatum L.
  Aecidium podophyllatum S.
  Aecidium Podophylli S.
  Allodus Podophylli Arth.
  Caeoma podophyllatum S.
  Dicaeoma Podophylli (S.) O. Kuntze.
  Puccinia aculeata S.
  Puccinia aurea Spreng.
  Puccinia Podophylli S.
  Glomerella fructigena Sacc.
  Glomerella rufomaculans (B.) Spaulding & v.
    Schrenk.
  Macrosporium Podophylli Ell. & Ev.
  Ascospora Podophylli M. A. Curtis.
  Phyllosticta Podophylli (M. A. Curtis) Wint.
  Gloeosporium podophyllinum Ell. & Ev.
  Septogloeum podophyllinum (Ell. & Ev.) Sacc.
  Septoria podophyllina Pk.
  Vermicularia Podophylli Ell. & Dearness.

Jeffersonia diphylla P.
  Cladosporium herbarum (P.) ex Lk.
Achlys triphylla DC.
  Ascochyta Achlydis Dearness.
  Ascochyta achlyicola Ell. & Ev.
Vancouveria hexandra Decsne.
  Ovularia Vancouveriae Ell. & Ev.
Caulophyllum thalictroides Michx.
  Botrytis streptothrix (C. & E.) Sacc.
  Polyactis streptothrix C. & E.
  Calloria Caulophylli (Ell. & Ev.) Rehm.
  Orbilia Caulophylli Ell. & Ev.
  Cercospora Caulophylli Pk.
  Diaporthe Gladioli Ell. & Ev.?
  Leptostroma vulgare Fr.
  Leptothyrium vulgare (Fr.) Sacc.
  Xyloma Actaeae S.
  Phoma Caulophylli Ell. & Ev.
  Vermicularia compacta C. & E.
  Vermicularia hysteriiformis Pk.
Berberis amurensis Rupr.
Berberis Fendleri Gray.
Berberis Fisheri Hort. ex Koch Dendrol.
Berberis macrophylla Hort.
  Puccinia graminis P. I.
Berberis Aquifolium Pursh.
  Aecidium Berberidis P.
  Dicaeoma poculiforme (Wettst.) O. Kuntze. I.
  Puccinia Fendleri H. S. Jackson.
  Dicaeoma Koeleriae (Arth.) Arth. & Fromme.
    I.
  Puccinia Koeleriae Arth. I.
  Coccomyces dentatus (Schm. ex Fr.) Sacc.
  Dicaeoma Oxalidis (Diet. & Ell.) O. Kuntze. I.
  Puccinia Oxalidis Diet. & Ell. I.
  Puccinia Berberidis Mont.
  Puccinia mirabilissima Pk.
  Uromyces sanguineus Pk.
  Uropyxis mirabilissima (Pk.) Magn.
  Uropyxis sanguinea (Pk.) Arth.
Berberis atrocarpa Schneid.
  Uropyxis sanguinea (Pk.) Arth.
Berberis canadensis Pursh.
  Probably most or all of the specimens so
    named as host plants are B. vulgaris.
  Aecidium Berberidis P.
  Caeoma (Aecidium) berberidatum Lk.
  Dicaeoma poculiforme (Wettst.) O. Kuntze. I.
  Puccinia graminis P. I.
  Puccinia graminis P., var. Poae Erikss. & Henn.
    I.
  Puccinia poculiformis Wettst. I.
  Cucurbitaria Berberidis (P.) ex S. F. Gray.
  Sphaeria Berberidis P. ex Fr.
  Diatrype aequilinearis (S.) M. A. Curtis.
  Eutypella aequilinearis (S.) Starb.
  Sphaeria aequilinearis S.
  Valsa aequilinearis (S.) Ell. & Ev.

Berberis canadensis (*cont.*)
Dothidea Berberidis (Wahlenb.) De Not.
Plowrightia Berberidis (Wahlenb.) Sacc.
Valsaria farlowiana Sacc.
Berberis cerasina Schrad.
Puccinia graminis P. I.
Berberis diversifolia Steud.
Dicaeoma Koeleriae (Arth.) Arth. & Fromme.
I.
Berberis Fendleri Gray.
Aecidium Berberidis P.
Puccinia graminis P. I.
Puccinia graminis P., var. Tritici Erikss. &
Henn. I.
Dicaeoma poculiforme (Wettst.) O. Kuntze. I.
Puccinia Koeleriae Arth. I.
Aecidium Fendleri Tracy & Earle.
Dicaeoma montanense (Ell.) O. Kuntze. I.
Puccinia Fendleri H. S. Jackson. I.
Puccinia montanensis Ell. I.
Cucurbitaria Berberidis (P.) ex S. F. Gray.
Berberis Fremontii Torr.
Berberis haematocarpa Wooton.
Uropyxis wootoniana Arth.
Berberis japonica R. Br.
Phyllosticta japonica Thm.
Berberis nana Greene.
Puccinia mirabilissima Pk.
Berberis nervosa Pursh.
Dicaeoma Koeleriae (Arth.) Arth. & Fromme.
I.
Puccinia Fendleri H. S. Jackson. I.
Puccinia mirabilissima Pk.
Uropyxis sanguinea (Pk.) Arth.
Berberis pinnata Lagasca.
Phacidium coronatum Fr.
Dicaeoma poculiforme (Wettst.) O. Kuntze. I.
Puccinia graminis P. I.
Puccinia Fendleri H. S. Jackson. I.
Puccinia mirabilissima Pk.
Uropyxis mirabilissima (Pk.) Magn.
Uropyxis sanguinea (Pk.) Arth.
Berberis pumila Greene.
Puccinia mirabilissima Pk.
Uropyxis sanguinea (Pk.) Arth.
Berberis regeliana Koehne ex Schneid.
Gloeosporium Berberidis Cke.
Berberis sinensis Desf.
Aecidium Berberidis P.
Dicaeoma poculiforme (Wettst.) O. Kuntze. I.
Berberis Thunbergii DC.
Puccinia graminis P. I.
Mycosphaerella Berberidis Awd.
Verticillium albo-atrum Reinke & Berthold.
Verticillium candidulum Pk.
Berberis trifolia Schultes.
Aecidium Berberidis P.
Dicaeoma poculiforme (Wettst.) O. Kuntze. I.
Puccinia graminis P. I.

Aecidium Maublancii Syd.
Dicaeoma Oxalidis (Diet. & Ell.) O. Kuntze. I.
Puccinia Oxalidis Diet. & Ell. I.
Micropuccinia Berberidis-trifoliae (Diet. &
Holw.) Arth. & Jackson.
Puccinia Berberidis-trifoliae Diet. & Holw.
Puccinia mirabilissima Pk.
Berberis trifoliata Moric.
Aecidium Berberidis P.
Dicaeoma poculiforme (Wettst.) O. Kuntze. I.
Puccinia graminis P. I.
Aecidium butlerianum Rosen & Arth.
Puccinia texana Holw. & Long. I.
Uropyxis texana (Holw. & Long.) Arth.
Berberis vulgaris L.
Aecidium Berberidis P.
Caeoma berberidatum Lk.
Dicaeoma poculiforme (Wettst.) O. Kuntze. I.
Puccinia graminis P. I.
Puccinia graminis, var. Poae Erikss., Henn. &
Levine. I.
Puccinia poculiforme Wettst. I.
Cucurbitaria Berberidis (P.) ex S. F. Gray.
Fumago vagans Fr.
Gloeosporium Berberidis Cke.
Heterochaete Sheari Burt.
Sebacina Sheari Burt.
Phyllactinia Berberidis Auct.
Phyllactinia corylea (P.) ex Karst.
Phyllactinia guttata (Wallr. ex Fr.) Lév.
Stagonospora berberidina Sacc.
Berberis sp. indet.
Botryosphaeria Ribis (Tode ex Fr.) Grossen-
bacher & Duggar, var. chromogena Shear
et al.
Creonectria purpurea (L.) Seaver.
Diaporthe velata (P. ex Fr.) Nits.
Sphaeria velata P. ex Fr.
Diplodia berberidina Sacc.
Diplodia Berberidis Sacc.
Gloeosporium Berberidis Cke.
Phoma melaleucum B. & C.
Phyllosticta mahoniicola Pass.
Rhizoctonia Solani Kühn.
Valsaria cincta Ces. & DeNot.
Valsaria insitiva Ces. & DeNot.
Verticillium albo-atrum Reinke & Berthold.

MENISPERMACEAE

Menispermum canadense L.
Anthostoma Peckii Dearness & House.
Cercospora Menispermi Ell. & Holw.
Cladosporium herbarum (P.) ex Lk.
Colletotrichum sordidum J. J. Davis.
Diaporthe menispermoides Dearness & House.
Diplodia Fairmani Ell. & Ev.
Diplodia hypoxyloides Ell. & Ev.

Menispermum canadense (*cont.*)
Diplodia sarmentorum Fr.
Sphaeria sarmentorum Fr.
Entyloma Menispermi Farl. & Trel.
Ramularia contexta Ell. & Ev.
Microsphaera Alni (DC.) Wint. †
Microsphaera Menispermi Howe.
Microsphaera Ravenelii B.
Phoma Menispermi Pk.
Phomopsis Menispermi (Pk.) Grove.
Phyllosticta menispermicola Tehon & Daniels.
Phyllosticta abortiva Ell. & Kellerm.
Septoria abortiva (Ell. & Kellerm.) Tehon & Daniels.
Sphaeropsis Menispermi Pk.
Tubercularia Menispermi Fr.
Valsa Menispermi Ell. & Holw.

Anamirta Cocculus Wight & Arn.
Leptosphaeria harknessiana Ell. & Ev.

Cocculus Carolinus (L.) DC.
Cercospora Menispermi Ell. & Holw.

Cissampelos Pareira L.
Guignardia sp. indet.
Phyllachora Rickseckeri Ell. & Kelsey.

MAGNOLIACEAE

Magnolia acuminata L.
Collybia conigenoides Ell.
Gymnopus conigenoides (Ell.) Murrill.
Daldinia concentrica (S.) Ces. & DeNot.
Dendrodochium rubellum Sacc., var. microsporum Sacc.
Diaporthe americana Speg.
Diaporthe binoculata (Ell.) Sacc.
Dothidea concaviuscula Ell. & Ev.
Hypoxylon crocatum Mont.
Massaria Magnoliae Ell. & Ev.
Micropeltis alabamensis Earle.
Nummularia clypeus (S.) Fckl.
Phyllactinia corylea (P.) ex Karst.
Phyllactinia guttata (Wallr. ex Fr.) Lév.
Phyllactinia suffulta (Reb.) ex Sacc.
Phyllosticta Cookei Sacc.
Phyllosticta Magnoliae Cke.
Pleurotus atrocoeruleus (Fr.) Sacc. Syll., var. griseus Pk.
Sclerotiopsis concava (Desm.) Shear & Dodge.
Sphaeronema Magnoliae Pk.
Haplosporella grandinea Ell. & Ev.
Sphaeropsis Dearnessii Sacc. & Trott.
Sphaeropsis grandiflora Ell. & Ev.
Sphaeropsis Magnoliae Ell. & Dearness.
Sphaeropsis tulipastri House.
?Valsaria Magnoliae Ell. & Ev.
Sporidesmium fusus B. & C.
Steganosporium formosum Ell. & Ev.
Uncinula Bivonae Lév.

Sphaeria ciliata P. ex Fr.
Valsa ciliata (P.) ex Fr.
Valsa coaperta Cke.
Sphaeria fibrosa P. ex Fr.
Valsa fibrosa (P.) ex Fr.
Sphaeria modesta S.
Valsa modesta (S.) Cke.
Sphaeria stellulata Fr.
Valsa stellulata Fr.
Sphaeria melastroma Fr.
Valsa melastroma Fr.
Valsaria melastroma (Fr.) Sacc.

Magnolia cordata Michx.
Discella Magnoliae B. & C.
Discula Magnoliae (B. & C.) Sacc.
Pleomassaria maxima Ell. & Ev.

Magnolia foetida Sarg.
Fomes fasciatus (Sw. ex Fr.) Cke.
Fomes pinicola (Sw. ex Fr.) Cke.

Magnolia Fraseri Walt.

MYXOMYCETES
Hemiarcyria stipata (S.) Rostf.
Physarum psittacinum Ditm.
Tilmadoche nutans (P.) Rostf.
Tilmadoche viridis (Gmel.)?

PEZIZINEAE
Cenangium albo-atrum Ell. & Ev.
Holwaya Ophiobolus (Ell.) Sacc.
Lachnella virginica Ell. & Ev.
Orbilia xanthostigma Fr.
Tapesia sanguinea (P.) Fckl.

PERISPORIALES
Phyllactinia corylea (P.) ex Karst.
Phyllactinia suffulta (Reb.) ex Sacc.

HYPOCREALES
Creonectria coccinea (P. ex Fr.) Seaver.
Nectria coccinea (P.) ex Fr.
Nectria ditissima Tul.

SPHAERIALES
Bombardia fasciculata Fr.
Diatrype platystoma (S.) M. A. Curtis.
Dilophia Magnoliae Ell. & Ev.
Hypoxylon howeianum Pk.
Hypoxylon Nuttallii Ell. & Ev.
Hypoxylon perforatum (S.) Fr.
Melanomma Pulvis-pyrius (P.) Fckl.
Xylaria corniformis Fr.

HYMENOMYCETINEAE
Calocera viscosa (P.) ex Fr.
Collybia conigenoides (Ell.) Sacc.
Corticium leptaleum Ell. & Ev.
Corticium scutellare B. & C.
Hymenochaete corrugata (Fr.) Lév.
Irpex obliquus (Schrad.) ex Fr.

Magnolia Fraseri (*cont.*)
Naematelia nucleata (S.) Fr.
Phlebia merismoides Fr.
Pilacre Petersii B. & C.
Poria incrassata (B. & C.) Burt.
Poria tomento-cincta B. & Rav. sec. Cke.
Radulum Magnoliae B. & C.

SPHAEROPSIDALES
Cytospora tumulosa Ell. & Ev.
Discosia Artocreas (Tode) ex Fr.
Fusicoccum nervicola Ell. & Ev.
Leptothyrium petiolorum (Cke.) Sacc., var. foliicola Ell. & Ev.
Phoma pedunculi Ell. & Ev.
Phyllosticta Magnoliae Sacc.
Stagonospora pedunculi Ell. & Ev.
Vermicularia subeffigurata S.

HYPHOMYCETES
Botrytis vulgaris (Lk.) Fr.
Cladosporium corynitrichum Ell. & Ev.
Helicoma Mulleri Cda.
Helminthosporium macrocarpon Grev.
Helminthosporium septemseptatum Pk.

MISCELLANEA
Sporidesmium concinnum B.
Zygodesmus tiliaceus Ell. & Ev.
Magnolia grandiflora L.

ASCOMYCETES
⎰Asterina comata B. & Rav.
⎱Trichodothis comata (B. & Rav.) Theissen & Syd.
Asterina granulosa (Klotzsch) Hook. & Arn.
⎰Dasyscypha hystricula (Ell. & Ev.) Sacc.
⎱Peziza hystricula Ell. & Ev.
Diatrype hypophlaea B. & Rav.
⎰Asterinula Langloisii Ell. & Ev.
⎱Leptothyrella Langloisii (Ell. & Ev.) Sacc.
Meliola amphitricha, f. Magnoliae-grandiflorae Rav. Fung. Am. *82*, sec. Speg.
Meliola Magnoliae F. L. Stevens.
⎰Eustegia Magnoliae Rav.
⎱Protostegia Magnoliae Rav.
Sphaeria fructuosa B. & C.

BASIDIOMYCETES
Marasmius bombycirhiza B. & Cke.

FUNGI IMPERFECTI
Campsotrichum circinatum B. & C.
Campsotrichum tenue B. & C.
Coniothyrium olivaceum Bon., var. grandiflorae Sacc.
Diplodia punctipetiolae Cke.
⎰Discosia alnea (P. ex Fr.) B.
⎱Discosia nitida Lév.
⎱Discosia ocellata B. & C.
Exophoma Magnoliae Weedon.

Helminthosporium fumosum Ell. & Martin.
Heterosporium Magnoliae Weedon.
Pestalozzia Guepini Desm.
Phyllosticta Magnoliae Sacc.
Septoria niphostoma B. & C.
Septoria Magnoliae Cke.
Sphaeropsis grandiflora Ell. & Ev.
⎰Sirodesmium stictophyllum Sacc.
⎱Sporidesmium punctiphyllum Cke.
Vermicularia carbonacea B. & C.
Magnolia macrophylla Michx.
⎰Acanthostigma Berenice (B. & C.) Sacc.
⎱Sphaeria Berenice B. & C.
Magnolia mexicana DC.
Haplosporella mexicana Ell. & Ev.
Schizophyllum egelingianum Ell. & Ev.
Magnolia obovata Auct.
Camarosporium Magnoliae Spear.
Pleomassaria Magnoliae Shear.
Magnolia Plumieri Sw.
Auricularia Auricula-judae (L. ex Fr.) Schrt.
Auricularia polytricha (Mont.) Sacc.
Phellinus obliquus (Fr.) Pat., var. antillarum Pat.
Phellinus scruposus Fr.
⎰Polyporus auberianus Mont.
⎱Ungulina auberiana (Mont.) Pat.
Xylaria ianthino-velutina Mont.
Xylaria scopiformis Mont.
Xylaria tabacina B.
Magnolia portoricensis Bello.
Meliola Magnoliae F. L. Stevens.
Magnolia tripetala L.
Discosia Artocreas (Tode) ex Fr.
Peniophora mutata (Pk.) Bres.
Phoma melaleucum B. & C.
Magnolia virginiana L.

PEZIZINEAE
Cenangium Magnoliae B. & C.
Ombrophila albofusca Ell.
⎰Dasyscypha albopileata (Cke.) Sacc.
⎱Peziza albopileata Cke.
⎰Peziza protrusa B. & C.
⎱Pseudopeziza protrusa (B. & C.) Sacc.
⎱Pyrenopeziza protrusa (B. & C.) Sacc.

PHACIDIINEAE
Rhytisma Magnoliae S.

PERISPORIALES
Antennaria semiovata B. & Br.
Apiosporium ? erysiphoides Sacc. & Ell.
Asterina comata B. & Rav.
Asterina granulosa (Klotzsch) Hook. & Arn.
Dimerosporium Magnoliae Tracy & Earle.
Dimerosporium tropicale Speg.
⎰Capnodium pelliculosum B. & Rav.
⎱Limacinia pelliculosa (B. & Rav.) Sacc.
Meliola Araliae (Spreng.) Mont.

Magnolia virginiana (*cont.*)
Micropeltis alabamensis Earle.
Saccardia Martini Ell. & Sacc.
Saccardia Martini Ell. & Sacc., var. major Ell.

DOTHIDEALES
Curreya excavata (C. & E.) Sacc.
Dictyodothis excavata (C. & E.) Theissen & Syd.
Dothidea excavata C. & E.
Dothidea concaviuscula Ell. & Ev.
Dothidella concaviuscula (Ell. & Ev.) Theissen & Syd.
Plowrightia concaviuscula (Ell. & Ev.) Sacc.

HYPOCREALES
Hypocrea armeniaca B. & C.?
Hypocrea corticiicola Ell. & Ev.
Hypocrea minima Sacc. & Ell.
Nectria aureofulva C. & E.
Creonectria coccinea (P. ex Fr.) Seaver.
Nectria coccinea (P.) ex Fr.
Dialonectria conigena Ell. & Ev.
Nectria conigena Ell. & Ev.
Nectria microspora Ell. & Ev.
Nectriella microspora (Ell. & Ev.) Sacc.
Nectria rubicarpa Cke.
Nectria Russellii B. & C.
Sphaerostilbe flammea Tul.
Sphaerostilbe flammea Tul., var. pallida Sacc.

SPHAERIALES
Acanthostigma saccardioides (Ell. & Martin) Sacc.
Venturia saccardioides Ell. & Martin.
Daldinia concentrica (Bolt. ex Fr.) Ces. & De Not.
Daldinia vernicosa (S.) Ces. & DeNot.
Diaporthe americana Speg.
Diaporthe Magnoliae Ell. & Ev.
Diaporthe binoculata (Ell.) Sacc.
Valsa binoculata Ell.
Diatrype asterostoma B. & C.
Diatrype disciformis (Hoffm.) Fr., var. americanum Thm.
Diatrype disciformis (Hoffm.) Fr., var. Magnoliae Thm.
Diatrype tremellophora Ell.
Diatrype Duriaei Mont.
Diatrype minima Ell. & Ev.
Diatrype sphaerophora Ell. & Ev.
Eutypella monticulosa (B. & C.) Sacc.
Valsa monticulosa B. & C.
Gnomonia Magnoliae Ell.
Hypoxylon annulatum (S.) Mont.
Hypoxylon epiphaeum B. & C.
Hypoxylon insidens (S.) Ell. & Ev.
Laestadia Magnoliae (S.) Sacc.
Sphaerella Magnoliae (S.) Ell.
Sphaeria Magnoliae S.

Nummularia clypeus (S.) Cke.
Hypoxylon discretum (S.) B. & C.
Nummularia discreta (S.) Tul.
Sphaeria discreta S.
Anthostoma hypophlaea (B. & Rav.) Sacc.
Diatrype hypophlaea B. & Rav.
Nummularia hypophlaea (B. & Rav.) Cke.
Sphaerella annulata Cke.
Sphaerella glauca Cke.
Valsa ambiens (P.) ex Fr.
Valsaria exasperans (Gerard) Sacc.
Valsaria Magnoliae Ell. & Ev.
Venturia applanata Ell. & Martin.
Xylaria filiformis (A. & S.) ex Fr.
Zignoella Magnoliae Tracy & Earle.

HYMENOMYCETINEAE
Clavaria molaris B.
Corticium laeve P.
Corticium subgiganteum B.
Peniophora subgigantea (B.) Massee.
Exidia glandulosa (Bull.) ex Fr.
Hydnum ciliolatum B. & C.
Hydnum fuscoatrum Fr.
Irpex sinuosus Fr.
Irpex Tulipiferae S.
Peniophora mutata (Pk.) Bres.
Phlebia merismoides Fr.
Polyporus salleanus B.
Polyporus semipileatus Pk.
Poria sinuosa (Fr.) Cke.
Radulum Magnoliae B. & C.
Sebacina cinnamomea Burt.
Solenia sulfurea Sacc. & Ell.

SPHAEROPSIDALES
Actinothyrium Magnoliae S.
Diatrype tremellophora Ell.
Cytospora tremellophora Ell. & Ev.
Discosia Artocreas (Tode) ex Fr.
Haplosporella grandinea Ell. & Ev.
Eustegia Magnoliae Rav.
Protostegia Magnoliae Rav.
Stegia Magnoliae Rav.
Phoma mamillaris (B. & C.) Sacc.
Phyllosticta Cookei Sacc.
Depazea glauca (Cke.) Sacc.
Phyllosticta glauca Cke.
Septoria glauca Cke.
Phyllosticta Magnoliae Sacc.
Sphaeronema rufum Fr.
Sphaeronemella rufa (Fr.) Sacc.
Dothiorella macrospora (B. & C.) Sacc.
Sphaeropsis macrospora B. & C.

MELANCONIALES
Melanconium Magnoliae Ell. & Ev.
Melanconium Monotospora (Cke.) Sacc.
Stilbospora Monotospora Cke.

Magnolia virginiana (*cont.*)

HYPHOMYCETES

Atractium flammeum B. & Rav.
Atractium pallidum B. & C.
Botrytis cinerella Sacc. & Wint.
Cercospora Magnoliae Ell. & Hark.
Cladosporium delectum C. & E.
Cladosporium fasciculatum Cda.
Dictyosporium elegans Cda.
Epicoccum duriaeanum Mont.
Helminthosporium Arbuscula B. & C.
Helminthosporium Arbuscula B. & C., var. trichellum Sacc.
Helminthosporium trichellum Sacc.
Macrosporium Martindalei Ell. & Martin.
Menispora ciliata Cda.
Nematogonium aurantiacum Desm.
Septosporium maculatum C. & E.
Sirodesmium ellipticum (Cke.) Sacc.
Sporidesmium ellipticum Cke.
Sporidesmium maculare B. & C.
Sporidesmium rude Ell.
Volutella conorum Ell. & Ev.

MISCELLANEA

Calocera viscosa (P.) Fr.

Magnolia sp. indet.

PEZIZINEAE

Belonidium introspectum (Cke.) Sacc.
Peziza introspecta Cke.
Belonidium? phlegmaceum (Ell.) Sacc.
Peziza phlegmacea Ell.
Chlorosplenium aeruginosum (Oeder ex Fr.) DeNot.
Dermatea Magnoliae B. & C.
Mollisia fumigata (Ell. & Ev.) Sacc.
Peziza fumigata Ell. & Ev.
Mollisia Glenospora (Ell. & Ev.) Sacc.
Peziza Glenospora Ell. & Ev.
Peziza diaphanula Cke.
Pezizella diaphanula (Cke.) Sacc.
Peziza gracilipes Cke.
Sclerotinia gracilipes (Cke.) Sacc.
Peziza incondita Ell.
Sclerotinia incondita (Ell.) Sacc.

HYSTERIINEAE

?Lophodermium exaridum C. & P.
Hysterium foliicola Fr.
Lophodermium hysterioides (P. ex Fr.) Sacc.
Hysterium maculare Fr.
Lophodermium maculare (Fr.) DeNot.

PERISPORIALES

Asterina picea B. & C.
Capnodium Ellisii Sacc.

DOTHIDEALES

Dothidea Magnoliae Cke.
Homostegia Magnoliae (Cke.) Sacc.

Dothidea Scutula B. & C.
Dothidella Scutula (B. & C.) Sacc.

HYPOCREALES

Nectria applanata Fckl.
Creonectria ochroleuca (S.) Seaver.
Nectria ochroleuca (S.) M. A. Curtis.
Nectria Russellii B. & C.
Nectria Russellii B. & C., var. Magnoliae Sacc.

SPHAERIALES

Acanthostigma decastylum (Cke.) Sacc.
Anthostomella Magnoliae Ell. & Ev.
Botryosphaeria Ribis (Tode ex Fr.) Grossenbacher & Duggar, var. chromogena Shear et al.
Diatrype americana Ell. & Berl.
Diatrype asterostoma B. & C.
Diatrype Duriaei Rav. F. Am. *91, 657.*
Diatrype Stigma (Hoffm.) ex Fr.
Hypoxylon tinctor (B.) Cke.
Lasiosphaeria subvelutina Ell. & Ev.
Physalospora Malorum Shear et al.
Physalospora viscosa (C. & E.) Sacc.
Venturia parasitica Ell. & Ev.
Xylaria carpophila (P.) ex Fr.
Xylaria filiformis Fr., var. foliicola Rehm.
Xylaria ianthino-velutina Mont.
Xylaria polymorpha (P. ex Fr.) Grev.

HYMENOMYCETINEAE

Coniophora fulva Massee.
Fomes geotropus Cke.
Hydnum farinaceum P., var. luxurians Ell. & Ev.
Hymenochaete corticolor B. & Rav.
Kneiffia setigera Fr.
Peniophora heterocystidia Burt.
Corticium glabrum B. & C.
Peniophora sanguinea (Fr.) Bres.
Polyporus adustus (Willd.) ex Fr.
Polyporus cinnabarinus (Jacq.) ex Fr.
Polyporus hemileucus B. & C.
Polyporus plebeius B.
Polyporus spumeus Fr.
Polyporus velutinus (P.) ex Fr.
Poria corticola (Fr.) Sacc. Syll., var. tulipifera Ell. & Ev.
Poria nitida P.
Poria purpurea (Fr.) Cke.

SPHAEROPSIDALES

Aschersonia cubensis B. & C.
Aschersonia tahitensis Mont.
Coniothyrium tephrosporum (M. A. Curtis) Tassi.
Diplodia tephrospora M. A. Curtis.
Sphaeropsis tephrospora (M. A. Curtis) B. & C.
Diplodia Ravenelii Cke.

Magnolia sp. indet. (*cont.*)
  Phoma atomispora Cke.
  Phyllosticta terminalis Ell. & Martin.

MELANCONIALES
  Melanconium ramulorum Cda.
  Naemaspora rufa B. & C.

HYPHOMYCETES
  Acrothecium obovatum C. & E.
  ⎰Botrytis curta (B. & C.) Sacc.
  ⎱Polyactis curta B. & C.
  Dendryphium quadriseptatum Cke.
  Glenospora Curtisii B. & Desm.
  Haplaria chlorina Ell. & Ev.
  ⎰Helicoma velutinum Ell.
  ⎱Helicosporium velutinum (Ell.) Sacc.
  ⎰Illosporium acaroides Sacc.
  ⎱Volutellaria acaroides Sacc.
  ?Illosporium Pezizula Ell. & Sacc.
  Menispora glauconigra C. & E.
  Ovularia monilioides Ell. & Martin.
  Penicillium repens C. & E.
  Polyscytalum sericeum Sacc.
  Spegazzinia ornata Sacc.
  Speira minor Sacc.
  Stachylidium fuscum C. & E.
  ⎰Hypocrea rufa (P.) ex Fr.
  ⎱Sphaeria rufa P. ex Fr.
  ⎰Trichoderma lignorum (Tode) ex Harz.
  ⎱Trichoderma viride P. ex Fr.
  Verticillium candelabrum Bon.
  Virgaria globiger Sacc. & Ell.
  Zygodesmus laevisporus Cke.
  Zygodesmus pannosus B. & C.

MISCELLANEA
  Ozonium omnivorum Shear.

Liriodendron Tulipifera L.

MYXOMYCETES
  ⎰Hemiarcyria clavata (P.) Rostf.
  ⎱Trichia clavata P.
  Hemiarcyria stipata (S.) Rostf.
  Licea biformis Morg.
  ⎰Licea circumscissa P.
  ⎱Perichaena corticalis (Batsch) Rostf.
  ⎰Trichia botrytis P.
  ⎱Trichia fragilis (Sow.) Rostf.

PEZIZINEAE
  ⎰Belonidium Aurelia (P.) DeNot.
  ⎱Peziza Aurelia (P.) Fckl.
  ⎰Lachnea Erinaceus (S.) Sacc.
  ⎱Peziza Erinaceus S.
  ⎰Lecanidion atratum (Hedw. ex Fr.) Rabh.
  ⎱Patellaria atrata (Hedw.) ex fr.
  Orbilia rubella (P.) Karst.
  ⎰Orbilia vinosa (A. & S. ex Fr.) Karst.
  ⎱Peziza vinosa A. & S. ex Fr.

  Peziza villosa P. ex Fr.
  Tapesia epicladotricha Sacc.

PHACIDIINEAE
  ⎰Blitrydium nigrocinnabarinum (S.) Sacc.
  ⎱Patellaria nigrocinnabarina S.
  Propolis faginea (Schrad.) Karst.
  Rhytisma Liriodendri Wallr.
  ⎰Stictis hysterina Fr.
  ⎱Xylogramma hysterinum (Fr.) Rehm.

HYSTERIINEAE
  Glonium parvulum (Gerard) Sacc.
  Glonium stellatum Muhl. ex Fr.
  Hypoderma virgultorum DC.
  Hypoderma virgultorum DC., var. petiolare Cke.
  Hysterographium Mori (S.) Rehm.
  ⎰Hysterium maculare Fr.
  ⎱Lophodermium maculare (Fr.) DeNot.
  Ostropa cinerascens S.

PERISPORIALES
  Apiosporium Salicis Kze. ex Fr.
  Capnodium elongatum B. & Desm.
  Erysiphe Liriodendri S.
  Erysiphe Polygoni DC. †
  ⎰Phyllactinia corylea (P.) ex Karst.
  ⎱Phyllactinia guttata (Wallr. ex Fr.) Lév.
  ⎱Phyllactinia suffulta (Reb.) ex Sacc.

HYPOCREALES
  ⎰Hypocrea rufa (P.) ex Fr.
  ⎱Sphaeria rufa P. ex Fr.
  Nectria coccinea (P.) ex Fr.

SPHAERIALES
  ⎰Anthostoma turgidum (P. ex Fr.) Nits.
  ⎱Sphaeria turgida P. ex Fr.
  ⎱Valsa turgida (P.) ex Fr.
  ⎰Botryosphaeria Liriodendri (Cke.) Sacc.
  ⎱Melogramma Liriodendri Cke.
  ⎰Botryosphaeria Ribis (Tode ex Fr.) Grossen-
  ⎱ bacher & Duggar.
  ⎱Nectria Ribis (Tode ex Fr.) Oud.
  Botryosphaeria Ribis (Tode ex Fr.) Grossen-
    bacher & Duggar, var. chromogena Shear
    et al.
  ⎰Cryptosporella divergens (S.) Berl. & Vogl.
  ⎱Sphaeria divergens S.
  ⎱Valsa divergens (S.) Cke.
  ⎰Cryptospora farinea (Ell.) Ell. & Ev.
  ⎱Cryptosporella farinosa (Ell.) Sacc.
  ⎱Valsa farinosa Ell.
  ⎰Diatrypella Liriodendri (S.) Sacc.
  ⎱Sphaeria Liriodendri S.
  Didymosphaeria phyllogena Wint.
  Endothia parasitica (Murrill) P. J. & H. W. Anderson.

Liriodendron Tulipifera (*cont.*)
{ Diatrype plagia B. & C.
{ Eutypella plagia (B. & C.) Berl.
{ Valsa plagia B. & C.
Hypoxylon fuscopurpureum (S.) B.
Hypoxylon insidens (S.) Ell. & Ev.
Hypoxylon investiens (S.) B.
Hypoxylon rubiginosum (P.) ex Fr.
{ Heptameria stictoides (B. & C.) Cke.
{ Leptosphaeria stictoides (B. & C.) Sacc.
{ Sphaeria stictoides B. & C.
Physalospora Malorum Shear et al.
{ Pleosphaeria microloncha (B. & C.) Sacc.
{ Sphaeria microloncha B. & C.
{ Teichospora microloncha (B. & C.) Ell. & Ev.
Rosellinia Aquila (Fr.) DeNot.
Rosellinia calva (Tode ex Fr.) Sacc.
Rosellinia glanduliformis Ell. & Ev.
{ Rosellinia pulveracea (Ehrh. ex Fr.) Fckl., var.
{   transversalis (S.) Ell. & Ev.
{ Sphaeria transversalis S.
{ Rosellinia subiculata (S.) Sacc.
{ Sphaeria subiculata S.
Sphaerella infuscans Ell. & Ev.
{ Mycosphaerella Liriodendri (Cke.) Coons.
{ Sphaerella Liriodendri Cke.
Sphaeria ditopa Fr.
Sphaeria faginea P.
Sphaeria millegrana S.
Sphaeria mutila S.
Sphaeria ovina P. ex Fr.
Sphaeria personata Fr.
Sphaeria tubiformis Tode ex Fr.
{ Depazea Tulipiferae (S.) M. A. Curtis.
{ Sphaerella Tulipiferae (S.) Cke.
{ Sphaeria Tulipiferae S.
Teichospora tuberculata Ell. & Ev.
{ Valsa albopuncta Ell. & Ev.
{ Valsa albopunctata Ell. & Ev. sec. Sacc. &
{   Lindau.
Valsa nivea (Hoffm.) ex Fr.
Valsa quaternata Fr.
{ Cordyceps mucronata (S.) M. A. Curtis.
{ Sphaeria mucronata S.
{ Xylaria mucronata (S.) Sacc.

Tremellaceae
Tremella dependens B. & C.
Tremella moriformis B.

Thelephoraceae
Corticium subgiganteum B.
?Stereum purpureum P.

Hydnaceae
Hydnum ciliolatum B. & C.
Hydnum cirrhatum P. ex Fr.
Hydnum Halei B. & C.
{ Irpex cinnamomeus Fr.
{ Hydnochaete olivaceum (S.) Banker.

Irpex carneus Fr.
{ Boletus Tulipiferae S.
{ Irpex lacteus Fr.
{ Irpex pallescens Fr.
{ Irpiciporus Tulipiferae (S.) Murrill.
{ Polyporus corticola Fr., var. Tulipiferae Fr.
{ Poria Tulipiferae (S.) Sacc. Syll.
Phlebia radiata Fr.

Polyporaceae
Daedalea extensa Pk.
Fomes applanatus (P. ex Wallr.) Gill.
{ Fomes fulvus (Fr.) Karst.
{ Polyporus fulvus Fr.
Fomes graveolens S.
{ Fomes hemileucus (B. & C.) Cke.
{ Polyporus hemileucus B. & C.
Lenzites sepiaria (Wulf.) ex Fr.
Lenzites trabea P. ex Fr
Merulius atrovirens Burt.
Merulius interruptus Bres.
Polyporus adustus (Willd.) ex Fr.
Polyporus caesius (Schrad.) ex Fr.
Polyporus chartaceus B. & C.
Polyporus sulphureus (Bull.) ex Fr.
Polyporus tephroleucus Fr.
Polyporus zonalis B.
{ Coltriciella dependens (B. & C.) Murrill.
{ Polystictus dependens (B. & C.) Cke.
{ Boletus nigromarginatus S.
{ Coriolus nigromarginatus (S.) Murrill.
{ Polyporus hirsutus (Wulf) ex Fr.
{ Polyporus nigromarginatus S.
{ Polystictus hirsutus (Wulf.) ex Fr.
{ Polystictus nigromarginatus (S.) Cke.
{ Coriolus biformis (Klotzsch) Pat.
{ Polyporus nilgheriensis Mont.
{ Polystictus nilgheriensis (Mont.) Fr.
{ Polystictus pergamenus Fr.
{ Polyporus scarrosus B. & C.
{ Polystictus scariosus (B. & C.) Cke.
Polystictus versicolor (L.) ex Fr.
{ Polyporus cinereus S.
{ Poria cinerea (S.) Cke.
{ Polyporus corticola Fr.
{ Poria corticola (Fr.) Cke.
Poria Medulla-panis P.
Poria semitincta (Pk.) Cke.
Porothelium pezizoides S.
Trametes Morganii Lloyd.
Trametes Peckii Kalchbr.

Agaricaceae
Lentinus lepideus Fr.
Lentinus strigosus (S.) Fr.
Lentinus tigrinus Fr.
Pleurotus glandulosus (Bull.) ex Fr.
Pleurotus ulmarius (Bull.) ex Fr.
{ Schizophyllus alneus (L. ex Fr.) Schrt.
{ Schizophyllum commune Fr.

Liriodendron Tulipifera (*cont.*)

SPHAEROPSIDALES
Asteroma Liriodendri Cke.
Diplodia Liriodendri Pk.
Discosia Artocreas (Tode) ex Fr.
Dothiorella Liriodendri Sacc.
Dothiorella minor Ell. & Ev.
Excipula nitidula S.
Hendersonia pauciseptata B. & C.
Leptothyrium Liriodendri Cke.
Microdiplodia lophiostomoides Dearness & House.
Phoma mixta B. & C.
Phoma Tulipiferae S.
⎰Phyllosticta circumvallata Wint.
⎱Phyllosticta Liriodendri Cke.
⎰Phyllosticta liriodendrica Sacc.
Phyllosticta macrospora Ell. & Ev.
Septoria Liriodendri B. & C.
Stagonospora Liriodendri Ell. & Ev.
Stagonospora pedunculi Ell. & Ev.
Vermicularia albomaculata S.
Vermicularia petalicola Ell. & Ev.

MELANCONIALES
Cylindrosporium cercosporoides Ell. & Ev.
Gloeosporium Liriodendri Ell. & Ev.
⎰Melanconium coloratum Pk.
⎱Myxosporium coloratum (Pk.) Sacc.
Myxosporium Liriodendri Dearness & House.
Myxosporium longisporum Edgerton.

HYPHOMYCETES
Alternaria tenuis Nees.
Cercospora Liriodendri Ell. & Hark.
Dendrochium rubellum Sacc., var. microsporum Sacc.
Epicoccum scabrum Cda.
Helicomyces bellus Morg.
Helicomyces olivaceus (Pk.) Morg.
Macrosporium Martindalei Ell. & Martin.
Monilia aurea Lk.
Monilia aurea, var. aurantiaca S. Syn. Car.
⎰Oospora Tulipiferae Ell. & Martin.
⎱Toruloidea Tulipiferae (Ell. & Martin) Sumstine.
Ramularia Liriodendri Ell. & Ev.
Septonema caespitosum B. & C.
Septonema circinatum B. & C.
Septonema punctiforme B. & C.
Sporidesmium sanguineum Ell. & Ev.
Sporidesmium Sarcinula B. & C.
Sporotrichum incarnatum S.
Stigmina Liriodendri Ell. & Ev.
Stilbum giganteum Pk.
Torula ligniperda (Willk.) Sacc.
Trichoderma globosum S.
Trimmatostroma Liriodendri Atk.

MISCELLANEA
Ectostroma Liriodendri (S.) Fr.
Eurotium herbariorum (Wigg.) ex Lk.
Microascus americanus Sacc.
Illicium floridanum Ellis.
Asteridium Illicii Tracy & Earle.
Laestadia illiciicola Tracy & Earle.
Lembosia illiciicola Tracy & Earle.
Drymis chilensis DC.
Meliola corallina Mont.

CALYCANTHACEAE

Calycanthus floridus L.
Haplosporella Calycanthi Fairman.
Calycanthus sp. indet.
⎰Blitrydium nigrocinnabarinum (S.) Sacc.
⎱Patellaria nigrocinnabarina S.
⎰Botryosphaeria Calycanthi (S.) Sacc.
⎱Sphaeria Calycanthi S.
Cytospora laxa B. & C.
Didymosporium Calycanthi S.
⎰Creonectria purpurea (L.) ex Seaver.
⎱Nectria cinnabarina (Tode) ex Fr.
Phoma Calycanthi S.
Tubercularia Calycanthi S.

ANONACEAE

Oxandra laurifolia Rich.
⎰Leptoporus evolutus (B. & C.) Pat.
⎱Polyporus evolutus B. & C.
Stereum duriusculum B. & Br.
Asimina angustifolia Gray.
Asimina parvifolia Dunal.
⎰Inonotus amplectens Murrill.
⎰Polyporus amplectens (Murrill) Sacc. & Trott.
⎱Polyporus fruticum B. & C.
Asimina grandiflora Dunal.
Macrosporium Asimini Hume.
Asimina pygmaea (Bart.) A. Gray.
Phyllosticta Asiminae Ell. & Kellerm.
Asimina triloba Dunal.
Anthostoma microecium Ell. & Ev.
Capnodium Fuligo B. & Desm.
Cercospora Asiminae Ell. & Kellerm.
Corticium incarnatum Fr.
Cytospora carphosperma Fr.
Dinemasporium hispidulum (Schrad.) M. A. Curtis.
Diplocladium cylindrosporum Ell. & Ev.
Dothiorella aberrans Pk.
Dothiorella Asiminae Ell. & Ev.
⎰Dothidea Annonae S.
⎰Ectostroma Annonae (S.) Fr.
⎱Xyloma Annonae S.
Epicoccum neglectum Desm.
Macrosporium olivaceum Ell. & Ev.

Asimina triloba (*cont.*)
    Mucor Mucedo L. p. p. ex Bref.
    Nectria cinnabarina (Tode) ex Fr.
    Phleospora Asiminae Ell. & Morg.
    Phoma microsporella Karst. & Hariot.
    Phyllosticta Asiminae Ell. & Kellerm.
    Poria punctata Fr.
    Scleroderris rubra Morg.
    Septoria Asiminae Ell. & Ev.
    Sphaerella Asiminae Ell. & Kellerm.
    Sphaeria myriadea DC.
    Sphaeropsis Asiminae Ell. & Ev.
    Sphaeropsis Asiminae Ell. & Ev., var. fructi-
      gena Ell. & Ev.
    Sporocybe byssoides (P.) ex Fr.
    Tubercularia vulgaris Tode ex Fr.
    Valsa ambiens (P.) ex Fr.
    Vermicularia albomaculata S.
Asimina sp. indet.
    ⎰Auricularia scutelliformis B. & C.
    ⎱Hirneola scutelliformis B. & C.
    Cylindrocladium scoparium Massey.
    Polyporus contiguus P.?
Guatteria dolichopoda Donn. Sm.
    Asterina nodulosa Speg.
Guatteria Ouregou Dunal.
    ⎰Coriolus cubensis (B. & C.) Pat.
    ⎱Irpex cubensis B. & C.
    ⎰Coriolus polygrammus (B & C.). Murrill.
    ⎱Polyporus polygrammus B. & C.
Cananga odorata Hook.
    Phyllosticta Canangae Fragoso & Ciferri.
Xylopia frutescens Aubl.
Xylopia grandiflora St. Hil.
    ⎰Dasyspora foveolata B. & C.
    ⎰Puccinia foveolata (B. & C.) Henn.
    ⎱Puccinia gregaria Kze.
Xylopia sp. indet.
    Phyllosticta Xylopiae Sacc.
Anona Cherimolia Mill.
    Bonanseja mexicana Sacc.
    ⎰Colletotrichum gloeosporioides Penz.
    ⎰Gloeosporium rufomaculans (B.) Thm.
    ⎱Glomerella cingulata (Stoneman) Spaulding &
      v. Schrenk.
    Hydnum macrodon P. ex Fr.
    Phyllachora atromaculans Syd.
    Physopella Cherimoliae Arth.
    Sporodesmium trichophilum Syd.
    Uredo Cherimoliae Lagerh.
Anona montana Macf.
    Arthrobotryum caudatum Syd.
    Brachysporium stemphylioides (Cda.) Sacc.
    Meliola longipoda Gaill.
    ⎰Leucoporus dictyoporus Pat.
    ⎱Polyporus dictyoporus (Pat.) Sacc. & Trott.
    ⎰Leucoporus gracilis Klotzsch.
    ⎱Polyporus gracilis Klotzsch.
    Triposporium stelligerum Speg.

Anona mucosa Jacq.
    Hypocrea gelatinosa (Tode) ex Fr.
    Lentinus subcervinus B. & C.
Anona muricata L.
    Colletotrichum anonicola Speg.
    Diplodia natalensis Evans.
    Lentinus albellus Pat.
    Mucidula cheimonophylla (B. & C.) Pat.
    Xerotus rawakensis (P.) Fr., var. diminutus.
Anona reticulata L.
    Meliola Popowiae Doidge.
    Uredo Cherimoliae Lagerh.
Anona Spraguei Safford.
    Aecidium Anonae Henn.
Anona squamosa L.
    Diplodia natalensis Evans.
    ⎰Polyporus contractus B.
    ⎱Ungulina contracta (B.) Pat.
    Uredo Cherimoliae Lagerh.
Anona tripetala Ait.
    Ectostroma Annonae (S.) Fr.
Anona sp. indet.
    Asperisporium Caricae (Speg.) Maubl.
    Morenoella portoricensis Speg.
    Phyllachora atromaculans Syd.
    ⎰Phoma helvolum B. & C.
    ⎱Phyllosticta helvola (B. & C.) Tassi.
    Phyllosticta tuisiensis Speg.
Rollinia multiflora Splitg.
    Uredo Cherimoliae Lagerh.
Rollinia Sieberi A. DC.
    Lentinus tubarius Pat.
Anonaceae gen. indet.
    Meliola varicuspis Stevens & Tehon.

MYRISTICACEAE

Myristica sp. indet.
    Corticium Stevensii Burt.
    Eutypa erumpens Massee.
    Phomopsis Citri H. S. Fawcett.
    Phomopsis vexans (Sacc. & Syd.) Harter.

MONIMIACEAE

Siparuna patelliformis Perk.
    ⎰Cicinnobella asperula Syd.
    ⎱Phaeodimeriella asperula Syd.
    Pyrenostigme Siparunae Syd.

LAURACEAE

Cinnamomum aromaticum J. Grah.
    Gloeosporium ochraceum Patterson.
Cinnamomum Camphora T. Nees & Eberm.
    ?Diplodia Camphorae Tassi.
    Diplodia tubericola (Ell. & Ev.) Taubenhaus.
    Gloeosporium Camphorae Sacc.
    Glomerella cingulata (Stoneman) Spaulding &
      v. Schrenk.
    Lembosia Camphorae Earle.
    Rosellinia bunodes (B. & Br.) Sacc.

Cinnamomum Cassiae Blume.
Gloeosporium Cassiae Patterson.
Cinnamomum zeylanicum Breyn.
Glomerella cingulata (Stoneman) Spaulding &
v. Schrenk.
Meliola zigzag B. & C.
Persea Borbonia (L.) Spreng.

PEZIZINEAE
Cenangium Magnoliae B. & C.
Peziza scutellata L. ex Fr.

HYSTERIINEAE
{Gloniopsis lineolata (Cke.) Sacc.
Hysterium lineolatum Cke.
Hysterium maculare Fr.
Lophodermium maculare (Fr.) DeNot.
Lophium mytilinum (P.) ex Fr.

PERISPORIALES
Asterina delitescens Ell. & Martin.
Asterina tenella Cke.
{Meliola amphitricha Auct. Amer. p. p.
Meliola martiniana Gaill.
Meliola Camelliae (Catt.) Sacc.

HYPOCREALES
Hypocrella epiphylla (Massee) Sacc.

DOTHIDEALES
{Asterina? Lauri-Borboniae (S.) Cke.
Dothidea Lauri-Borboniae S.
Phyllachora Lauri-Borboniae (S.) Sacc.
{Coccoidella Scutula (B. & C.) v. Höhnel.
Dothidea Scutula B. & C.
Dothidella Scutula (B. & C.) Sacc.
Phyllachora Scutula (B. & C.) Cke.
Phyllachora demersa (Cda.) Sacc.

SPHAERIALES
{Anthostoma hypophlaeum (B. & Rav.) Sacc.
Diatrype hypophloea B. & Rav.
Nummularia hypophloea (B. & Rav.) Cke.
Diatrype tenuissima Cke.
{Hypoxylon concentricum Rav. Fung. Am.
Hypoxylon Malleolus B. & Rav.
Hypoxylon Sassafras (S.) B.
{Lasiosphaeria Pezizula (B. & C.) Sacc.
Sphaeria Pezizula B. & C.
Melogramma mutilum, var. Rav. Fung. Am.
{Diatrype microplaca B. & C.
Nummularia microplaca (B. & C.) Cke.
{Hypoxylon subiculosum B.
Rosellinia subiculata (S.) Sacc.
Sphaerella exutans Cke.
Valsa tetraploa B. & C.

HYMENOMYCETINEAE
Corticium effuscatum C. & E.
Hydnum mucidum Gmel. ex Fr.
Kneiffia setigera Fr.

Polyporus cinereus S.
Polyporus crocatus Fr.
{Polyporus fuscocarneus P.
Poria fuscocarnea (P.) Cke.
Polyporus mutabilis B. & C.
Polystictus mutabilis (B. & C.) Cke.
Polyporus rufus (Schrad.) ex Fr.
Poria rufa (Schrad. ex Fr.) Cke.
Anthracophyllum Nigrita (Lév.) Kalchb.
Xerotus Nigrita Lév.

SPHAEROPSIDALES
Ceuthospora Cookei Thm.
{Discosia nitida Lév., var.
Discosia nitidissima B. & C.
Excipula recurvispora B. & C.
Excipulina recurvispora (B. & C.) Sacc.
Phyllosticta micropuncta Cke.
Phyllosticta Perseae Ell. & Martin.

MELANCONIALES
{Pestalozzia laurina Mont.
Pestalozzina laurina (Mont.) Lindau.
Pestalozzia maura Ell. & Ev.

HYPHOMYCETES
{Cercospora Perseae Ell. & Martin.
Cercospora purpurea Cke.
Circinotrichum maculiforme Nees.
Helicotrichum obscurum (Cda.) Sacc.
Helminthosporium fumosum Ell. & Martin.
Helminthosporium velutinum Lk.
Menispora cylindrica Cke.
Sporidesmium velutinum Cke.

MISCELLANEA
Acinula candicans Fr.
Tremella Myricae B. & Cke.
{Trichocoma laevispora Massee.
Trichocoma paradoxum Jungh.
Trichoscytale paradoxa B. p. p.
Persea cordata Mez.
Meliola drepanochaeta Syd.
Persea gratissima Gaertn.
Alternaria Citri Pierce, var. Cerasi C. A.
Rudolph.
Cladosporium Citri Massee.
Cladosporium herbarum (P.) ex Lk.
{Colletotrichum gloeosporioides Penz.
Glomerella cingulata (Stoneman) Spaulding &
v. Schrenk.
Diplodia natalensis Evans.
Endothia havannensis Bruner.
Gloeosporium Mangiferae? Henn.
Hendersonia mexicana Sacc.
Hypoxylon effusum Nits.
Irene Perseae (F. L. Stevens) Toro.
Isaria gossypina Pat.
Meliola amphitrica Fr.
Meliola Perseae F. L. Stevens.

Persea gratissima (*cont.*)
  Meliola Perseae F. L. Stevens, var. setulifera
    Speg.
  Microcyclus scutula (B. & C.) Sacc.
  Mycosphaerella Perseae Miles.
  Nectria Theobromae Massee.
  Penicillium expansum Lk.
  Pestalozzia Guepini Desm.
  Pestalozzia Guepini Desm., var. Vaccinii
    Shear.
  Phyllachora gratissima Rehm.
  Phyllosticta Perseae Ell. & Martin.
  Polycephalum subaurantiacum Pk.
  Pythiacystis californica Sm. & Sm.
  Pythiacystis citrophthora Sm. & Sm.
  Rhizopus nigricans Ehrb. ex Fr.
  Rhytisma Perseae Gandara.
  Rosellinia bunodes (B. & Br.) Sacc.
  Sclerotinia libertiana Fckl.
  Sclerotium Rolfsii Sacc.
  Sphaceloma Fawcettii Jenkins.
  Sphaerostilbe cinnabarina Tul.
  Sporotrichum Citri Butl.
Persea pubescens (Pursh) Sargent.
  ⎰Asterella carnea (Ell. & Martin) Sacc.
  ⎱Asterina carnea Ell. & Martin.
  Asterina delitescens Ell. & Martin.
  Asterina pelliculosa B.
  ⎰Brachysporium fumosum (Ell. & Martin) Sacc.
  ⎱Helminthosporium fumosum Ell. & Martin.
  Cercospora purpurea Cke.
  Coryne gelatinosa (Ell. & Martin) Rehm.
  Glonium macrosporum Tracy & Earle.
  ⎰Coccoidella scutula (B. & C.) v. Höhnel.
  ⎱Dothidea scutula B. & C.
  Helotium maculosum Ell. & Martin.
  Isariopsis clavata Ell. & Martin.
  Lembosia rugispora Tracy & Earle.
  Manginula Perseae Arnaud.
  Meliola manca Ell. & Martin.
  Meliola amphitricha Auct. Amer. p. p.
  Meliola martiniana Gaill.
  ⎰Orbilia gelatinosa (Ell. & Martin) Sacc.
  ⎱Peziza gelatinosa Ell. & Martin.
  Scleroderris concinna (B. & C.) Sacc.
Persea sp. indet.
  Botryosphaeria Ribis (Tode ex Fr.) Grossen-
    bacher & Duggar.
  Capnodium Citri B. & Desm.
  Cenangium Magnoliae B. & C.
  Didymopsis phyllogena Sacc.
  Meliola amphitricha Fr., var. Perseae Rav.
    Fung. Am. *82.*
  Meliola anomala Tracy & Earle.
  Phyllachora uberata Sacc.
  Physalospora rhodina (B. & C.) Cke.
  Septobasidium Schweinitzii Burt.
  Sphaerella exutans Cke.
  Tremella Myricae B. & Cke.

Phoebe costaricana Mez. & Tond.
  Acarella costaricensis Syd.
  Actinodochium concinnum Syd.
  ⎰Aphanopeltis Phoebes Syd.
  ⎱Elachopeltis Phoebes Syd.
  Asterina Phoebes Syd.
  Chaetothyrium permixtum Syd.
  Clinoconidium bullatum Syd.
  Merismella proxima Syd.
  Microcallis Phoebes Syd.
  Micropeltis Phoebes Syd.
  Microthyriella Phoebes Syd.
  Perizomatium lachnoides (Rehm.) Syd.
  Perizomella inquinans Syd.
  ⎰Hysterostomella Phoebes Syd.
  ⎱Phragmopeltis Phoebes Syd.
  Plectopeltis egenula Syd.
  Plenotrichum mirabile Syd.
  Stigmopeltis Phoebes Syd.
  Uleomyces comedens Syd.
Phoebe mollicella Blake.
  Achorodothis poasensis Syd.
Phoebe neurophylla Mez. & Pitt.
  Anariste poliothea Syd.
  Asterina hamata Syd.
  Bolosphaera cyanomela Syd.
  Epicyta ampliata Syd.
  Meliola uncitricha Syd.
  Perizomatium lachnoides (Rehm) Syd.
  ?Perizomella inquinans Syd.
  Stomiopeltis heteromeris Syd.
Phoebe Tonduzii Mez.
  Aschersonia basicystis B. & C., forma typica
    Syd.
  Byssocallis Phoebes Syd.
  Chaetothyrium permixtum Syd.
  Clypeolum exiguum Syd.
  Endocycla Phoebes Syd.
  ⎰Merismella gracilenta Syd.
  ⎱cf Microcallis amadelpha Syd.
  Microcallis consociata Syd.
  Microthyriella costaricensis Syd.
  Myriangina mirabilis (Henn.) v. Höhnel.
  Phyllachora Phoebes Syd.
Ocotea cernua Nees.
  ⎰Ackermannia coccogena Pat.
  ⎱Sclerocystis coccogena (Pat.) v. Höhnel.
  Endogone lignicola Pat.
Ocotea insularis (Meissn.) Mez.
  ⎰Parmulina callista Syd.
  ⎱Phragmopeltis callsita Syd.
Ocotea leucoxylon (Sw.) Mez.
  ⎰Asteridiellina portoricensis (Speg.) Seaver &
  ⎱ Toro.
  Asteridium portoricense Speg.
  Catacauma Ocoteae F. L. Stevens.
  Echidnodes microspora (Chardon) Seaver &
    Chardon.

Ocotea leucoxylon (*cont.*)
Helminthosporium Ocoteae F. L. Stevens.
Lembosia microspora Chardon emend. Toro.
Meliola Ocoteae F. L. Stevens.
Meliola ocoteicola F. L. Stevens.
Morenoella portoricensis Speg.
Phyllachora ocoteicola Stevens & Dalbey.
Uredo farinosa Henn.
Verticillium heterocladum Penz.

Ocotea veraguensis Kl.
Chaetothyrium permixtum Syd.
Cyclostomella oncophora Syd.
{ Metabotryon connatum Syd.
{ Parabotryon connatum Syd.
Metasphaeria occulta Syd.
Perizomatium lachnoides (Rehm) Syd.
Phyllachora microchita Syd.
Phyllachora veraguensis Syd.

Ocotea sp. indet.
Botryoconis pallida Syd.
Cryptobasidium Ocoteae Lendner.
Phyllachora wrightiana Speg.

Oreodaphne sp. indet.
Dothidea coccodes Fr.
Physalospora coccodes (Lév.) Sacc.
Stereum bicolor (P.) ex Fr.

Umbellularia californica Nutt.

PEZIZINEAE

Helotium aureum P. ex Fr.
Helotium pallescens (P.) Fr.
{ Ionomidotis plicata (Phil. & Hark.) Durand.
{ Midotis plicata Phil. & Hark.

HYSTERIINEAE

Acrospermum corrugatum Ell.

PYRENOMYCETINEAE

{ Anthostoma Oreodaphnes Cke. & Hark.
{ Anthostomella Oreodaphnes (Cke. & Hark.)
{   Berl. & Vogl.
{ Sphaeria Oreodaphnes Cke. & Hark.
{ Bertia moriformis (Tode ex Fr.) DeNot.
{ Psilosphaeria moriformis (Tode ex Fr.) Cke.
{ Sphaeria moriformis Tode ex Fr.
Diatrypella decipiens Ell. & Ev.
Hypoxylon rubiginosum (P.) Fr.
Hypoxylon serpens (P.) ex Fr.
{ Leptosphaeria odora (Cke. & Hark.) Berl. &
{   Vogl.
{ Sphaeria odora Cke. & Hark.
Massaria pulchra Hark.
Nummularia Bulliardi Tul.
{ Sphaerella arbuticola Pk.
{ Sphaerella Umbellulariae Cke. & Hark.
Thyridaria californica Rehm.
Valsa americana B. & C.

PERISPORIALES

{ Asterina anomala Cke. & Hark.
{ Dimerosporium anomalum (Cke. & Hark.) Ell.
{   & Ev.
Capnodium Tuba Cke. & Hark.

HYPOCREALES

Nectria cinnabarina (Tode) ex Fr.
{ Dialonectria Umbellulariae (Plowr. & Hark.)
{   Ell. & Ev.
{ Nectria Umbellulariae Plowr. & Hark.

HYMENOMYCETINEAE

Corticium comedens (Nees) ex Fr.
Corticium laeve (P.) ex Fr.
Fomes applanatus (P. ex Wallr.) Gill.
{ Elfvingia Brownii Murrill.
{ Fomes Brownii Murrill.
{ Elfvingia tornata (P.) Murrill.
{ Ganoderma tornatum (P.) A. Ames.
Hydnum Stevensoni B. & Br.
Irpex paradoxus (Schrad.) ex Fr.
Polyporus igniarius (L.) ex Fr.
Radulum molare Fr.

SPHAEROPSIDALES

Ceuthospora foliicola (Lib.) Cke.
Cyclodomus Umbellulariae v. Höhnel.
Diplodia Harknessii Sacc.
Diplodia laurina Cke. & Hark.
Diplodia melaena Lév.
Diplodia Umbellulariae Ell. & Ev.
Hendersonia Umbellulariae Ell. & Ev.

MELANCONIALES

Blennoria Umbellulariae Cke. & Hark.
Pestalozzia coryneoidea Hark.

HYPHOMYCETES

Chalara brachyspora Sacc.
Cladosporium Fumago Lk.
Coniothecium Umbellulariae Ell. & Ev.
Fusarium personatum Cke.
{ Epochnium glaucum Cke. & Hark.
{ Stemphylium glaucum (Cke. & Hark.) Sacc.
Zygodesmus pannosus B. & C.
Nectandra antillana Meissn.
{ Phellinus scruposus (Fr.) Pat.
{ Polyporus scruposus Fr.
Nectandra coriacea Griseb.
Guignardia Nectandrae F. L. Stevens.
{ Phellinus plebeius B. ?
{ Polyporus plebeius B. ?
Nectandra dominicensis Meissn.
{ Microporus sanguineus (L. ex Fr.) O. Kuntze.
{ Polyporus sanguineus (L.) ex Fr.
Nectandra membranacea Griseb.
Favolus caperatus Pat.
Favolus hispidulus B. & C.
Omphalia fibula (Bull.) ex Fr.

Nectandra patens (Sw.) Griseb.
  Arthrobotryum glabroides F. L. Stevens.
  Grallomyces portoricensis F. L. Stevens.
  Helminthosporium Helleri F. L. Stevens.
  Isthmospora glabra F. L. Stevens.
  ⎰Irene glabroides (F. L. Stevens) Toro.
  ⎱Meliola glabroides F. L. Stevens.
  Phyllachora Nectandrae Stevens & Dalbey.
Nectandra reticulata Mez.
  Hormodendrdrum Nectandrae Syd.
  Phyllachora ramonensis Syd.
  Puttemansia brachytricha Syd.
Nectandra sanguinea Rottb.
  Chaetocrea parasitica Syd.
  ⎰Cyclostomella disciformis Pat.
  ⎱Pycnostemma disciforme Syd.
Nectandra sp. indet.
  Coccostroma Puttemansii (Henn.) Theissen
    & Syd.
  ⎰Flammula tenuis Murrill.
  ⎱Gymnopilus tenuis Murrill.
  Verticillium heterocladum Penz.
Sassafras officinalis L.

PHACIDIINEAE

Rhytisma Sassafras S.
⎰Cenangium concinnum B. & C.
⎱Scleroderris concina (B. & C.) Sacc.
Xyloma concentricum S. Syn. Car.

HYSTERIINEAE

Gloniopsis australis (Duby) Sacc.
⎰Glonium graphicum (Fr.) Duby.
⎱Hysterium graphicum Fr.
Glonium stellatum Muhl.
⎰Heterosphaeria Patella (Tode ex Fr.) Grev.
⎱Sphaeria Patella (Tode) ex Fr.
Hysterium acuminatum Fr.
Lophium Sassafras S.

PERISPORIALES

Phyllactinia corylea (P.) ex Karst.

DOTHIDEALES

⎰Dothidea Sassafras S.
⎱Phyllachora Sassafras (S.) Sacc.

HYPOCREALES

Hypocrea olivacea C. & E.
⎰Creonectria verrucosa (S.) Seaver.
⎱Nectria verrucosa (S.) Sacc.
⎱Sphaeria verrucosa S.

SPHAERIALES

Botryosphaeria fuliginosa (M. & N.) Ell. & Ev.
Botryosphaeria quercuum (S.) Sacc.
Clypeosphaeria Hendersoniae (Ell.) Sacc.
Diatrypella Sassafras Ell. & Ev.
Didymella lophospora Sacc. & Speg.
Eriosphaeria alligata (Fr.) Sacc.
Gnomonia Sassafras Ell. & Ev.

⎰Lophiostoma tingens (S.) Ell.
⎱Sphaeria tingens S.
⎰Physalospora eriostega (C. & E.) Sacc.
⎱Sphaeria eriostega C. & E.
  Physalospora Malorum Shear et al.
⎧Sphaeria obducens Fr.
⎨Strickeria obducens (Fr.) Cke.
⎩Teichospora obducens (Fr.) Fckl.
⎧Mycosphaerella Sassafras (Ell. & Ev.) Bubák
⎪ & Kabát.
⎨Sphaerella Sassafras Ell. & Ev.
⎪Pseudovalsa nigrificata (C. & E.) Cke.
⎨Valsa nigrofacta C. & E.
⎩Valsaria nigrificata (C. & E.) Sacc.

VALSACEAE

⎧Anthostoma microplacum (B. & C.) Sacc.
⎨Diatrype microplaca B. & C.
⎩Nummularia microplaca (B. & C.) Cke.
  Cryptovalsa Sassafras (Ell. & Ev.) Berl.
⎰Diaporthe biglobosa (C. & E.) Sacc.
⎱Sphaeria biglobosa C. & E.
  Eutypella glandulosa (Cke.) Ell. & Ev.
⎧Eutypella goniostoma (S.) Sacc.
⎪Eutypella indistincta (S.) Ell. & Ev.
⎪Eutypella pentagona Sacc. p. p.
⎪Sphaeria goniostoma S.
⎨Sphaeria indistincta S.
⎪Sphaeria pentagona S. Syn. Car.
⎪Valsa goniostoma (S.) M. A. Curtis.
⎩Valsa indistincta (S.) Cke.
  Eutypella Sorbi (A. & S. ex Fr.) Sacc.
⎧Sphaeria acclinis S.
⎨Valsa acclinis (S.) M. A. Curtis.
⎩Valsa inclinis (S.) Sacc.
  Valsa laurina C. & E.
  Valsa subclypeata C. & P.

XYLARIACEAE

Hypoxylon perforatum (S.) Fr.
⎰Hypoxylon Sassafras (S.) B.
⎱Sphaeria Sassafras S.
  Nummularia punctulata (B. & Rav.) Sacc.

POLYPORACEAE

Daedalea confragosa (Bolt.) ex Fr.
Fomes conchatus (P. ex Fr.) Karst.
Fomes igniarius (L. ex Fr.) Gill.
Fomes Ribis (Schum. ex Fr.) Cke.
Fomes rubriporus (Quél.) Maneval.
Lenzites corrugata Klotzsch.
Merulius Corium (P.) Fr.
Polyporus licnoides Mont.
Polyporus Lindheimeri B. & C.
⎰Coriolus hirsutulus (S.) Murrill.
⎱Polystictus hirsutulus (S.) Cke.
⎧Boletus ferruginosus Schrad. ex Fr.
⎨Polyporus ferruginosus (Schrad.) ex Fr.
⎩Poria ferruginosa (Schrad. ex Fr.) Cke.

Sassafras officinalis (*cont.*)
{Poria contigua (Fr.) Cke.
{Poria floccosa Auct. Amer.
 Poria inermis Ell. & Ev.
{Fomitiporia Lloydii Murrill.
{Poria Lloydii (Murrill) Sacc. & Trott.
 Poria Radula P. ex Fr.
{Polyporus Sassafras S.
{Poria Sassafras (S.) Cke.
 Trametes sepium B.

Hymeomycetineae Miscellaneae

Armillaria mellea (Vahl) ex Fr.
Corticium ochroleucum Fr., var. crimosum B.
Hymenochaete agglutinans Ell.
Irpex Tulipiferae (S.) Fr.
{Schizophyllum alneum (L. ex Fr.) Schrt.
{Schizophyllum commune Fr.
 Stereum erumpens Burt.
 Stereum versiforme B. & C.

Sphaeropsidales

Actinothyrium gloeosporioides Tehon.
{Cytospora albofarcta (S.) Starb.
{Sphaeria albofarcta S.
 Cytospora phomopsis Sacc.
 Cytospora Sassafras Ell. & Ev.
 Cytospora sassafrasicola Tehon & Daniels.
{Cytospora sphaerocephala (S.) M. A. Curtis.
{Lamyella sphaerocephala (S.) Fr.
{Sphaeria sphaerocephala S.
{Valsa ceratophora Tul.
{Depazea frondicola Fr.
{Sphaeria frondicola Fr.
{Diplodia decorticata C. & E.
{Diplodiella decorticata (C. & E.) Sacc.
 Diplodia multicarpa Pk.
 Diplodia officinalis Ell. & Ev.
 Diplodia subcuticularis Dearness & House.
 Discosia Artocreas Fr.
 Hendersonia officinalis Atk.
 Leptothyrium Kellermani Bubák.
 Microdiplodia laurina Dearness & House.
{Diplodia Sassafras Tracy & Earle.
{Microdiplodia Sassafras (Tracy & Earle) Tassi.
 Phoma Sassafras Ell. & Ev.
 Phyllosticta illinoensis Tehon & Daniels.
 Sphaeropsis Sassafras C. & E.
{Haplosporella seriata (Pk.) Petrak & Syd.
{Sphaeropsis punctata Dearness & House.
{Sphaeropsis seriata Pk.

Melanconiales

{Gloeosporium affine (Ell. & Kellerm.) Ell. &
{ Ev.
{Gloeosporium officinale Ell. & Ev.
 Gloeosporium Sassafras (Cke.) Ell. & Ev.
{Glomerella rufomaculans (B.) Spaulding & v.
{ Schrenk.
{Phyllosticta affinis Ell. & Kellerm.
{Phyllosticta Sassafras Cke.

Melanconium foliicola Pk.
Melanconium Sassafras S.
Pestalozzia funerea Desm.
Pestalozzia Guepini Desm.
Pestalozzia Sassafras Ell. & Ev.

Hyphomycetes

Acremonium fuscum Kze. & Schm. ex Fr.
Cladosporium epiphyllum (P.) ex Fr.
Helicomyces gracilis Morg.
Oidium subramosum (Lk.) ex Fr.
{Actinocladium Penicillus (S.) Fr.
{Coremium concentricum S.
{Dematium Penicillus S.
{Sporocybe concentrica (S.) Sacc.

Miscellanea

Reticularia Lycoperdon Bull.
Sclerotium fuscomaculans S.
Sclerotium Sassafras S.

Litsea geniculata Benth. & Hook.
{Cercospora Berkeleyi Cke.
{Helminthosporium pistillare Cke.

Litsea glaucescens H. B. K.
 Asteroconium Saccardoi Syd.

Litsea? sp. indet.
 Asterina verae-crucis Theissen.
 Englerula mexicana Theissen.

Benzoin aestivale (L.) Nees.

Pezizineae

Cenangium Ellisii Sacc.
Patinella vagans Ell. & Ev.
{Peziza Daedalea S.
{Tapesia Daedalea (S.) Sacc.

Phacidiineae

{Cenangium concinnum B. & C.
{Scleroderris concinna (B. & C.) Sacc.

Perisporiales

{Asterina ramularis Ell.
{Asterula ramularis (Ell.) Sacc.
{Microdothella ramularis (Ell.) Theissen & Syd.
{Myiocopron ramulare (Ell.) Speg.

Hypocreales

Nectria ochroleuca (S.) M. A. Curtis.

Dothideales

Dothidea Linderae Gerard.
{Dothidea lauricola S.
{Phyllachora lauricola (S.) Sacc.

Sphaeriales

{Amphisphaeria conferta (S.) Sacc.
{Byssosphaeria conferta (S.) Cke.
{Sphaeria conferta S. Syn. Car.
{Sphaeria confertula S. Am. bor.

Benzoin aestivale (*cont.*)
 ⎧Anthostoma microplacum (B. & C.) Sacc.
 ⎨Diatrype microplaca B. & C.
 ⎩Nummularia microplaca (B. & C.) Cke.
 ⎧Anthostoma ostiolatum (Ell. & Ev.) Cke.
 ⎩Anthostomella ostiolata Ell. & Ev.
 ⎧Diaporthe sociata (C. & E.) Sacc.
 ⎩Valsa sociata C. & E.
 Diatrype Hystrix (Tode) ex Fr.
 Didymosphaeria Linderae Sacc.
 ⎧Eutypa rivulosa (S.) Ell. & Ev.
 ⎩Sphaeria rivulosa S.
 ⎧Eutypella Linderae (Pk.) Berl.
 ⎩Valsa Linderae Pk.
 Eutypella stellulata (Fr.) Sacc.
 Glomerella rufomaculans Spaulding & v.
   Schrenk.
 ⎧Hypoxylon callostroma (S.) B.
 ⎩Sphaeria callostroma S.
 Hypoxylon fuscum (P.) ex Fr.
 ⎧Hypoxylon callostroma Fung. Columb. *1625.*
 ⎩Hypoxylon Sassafras (S.) B.
 Melanopsamma confertissima (Plowr.) Sacc.
 Physalospora Cydoniae Arnaud.
 Physalospora viscosa (C. & E.) Sacc.
 Pleospora Dearnessii Sacc.
 Rosellinia Linderae Pk.
 ⎧Diplodia insitiva Sacc.
 ⎨Valsaria insitiva Ces. & DeNot., var. Linderae
 ⎩ Sacc.

HYMENOMYCETINEAE

 ⎧Corticium coeruleum (Schrad.) ex Fr.
 ⎨Thelephora caerulea Schrad. ex Fr.
 ⎩Thelephora Indigo S.
 Exidia glandulosa (Bull.) ex Fr.
 Hymenochaete agglutinans Ell.

SPHAEROPSIDALES

Camarosporium Linderae Ell. & Ev.
Diplodia benzoina Sacc.
Hendersonia Linderae Sacc.
Hendersonia pauciseptata B. & C.
⎧Diplodia Linderae Ell. & Ev.
⎨Microdiplodia Linderae (Ell. & Ev.) Tassi
⎪ 1902.
⎨Microdiplodia Linderae (Ell. & Ev.) Dearness
⎩ & House 1925.
Phyllosticta Linderae Ell. & Ev.
Phyllosticta lindericola Ell. & Ev.
Sphaeropsis Linderae Pk.

MELANCONIALES

Gloeosporium falcatum Dearness & House.
Gloeosporium officinale Ell. & Ev.

HYPHOMYCETES

Botrytis peronosporoides Sacc.
Epicoccum neglectum Desm.

⎧Graphium Linderae Ell. & Ev.
⎨Helminthosporium Petersii B. & C. p. p.
⎩Isariopsis Linderae (Ell. & Ev.) Sacc.
Zythia rufa (Fr.) S.

MISCELLANEA

Sclerotium lauricola S.
Aniba perutilis Hemsl.
 Phyllosticta Anibae Massee.
Aniba sp. indet.
 Pholiota scobifera B. & C.
Laurus nobilis L.
 Aschersonia goldiana Sacc. & Ell.
 Gloeosporium nobile Sacc.
Laurus sp. indet.
 Capnodium Citri B. & Desm.
 Cenangium Magnoliae B. & C.
 ⎧Creonectria ochroleuca (S.) Seaver.
 ⎩Nectria ochroleuca (S.) M. A. Curtis.
 Eutypa rivulosa (S.) Ell. & Ev.
 ⎧Diplodia Harknessii Sacc.
 ⎨Diplodia laurina Cke. & Hark.
 ⎩Microdiplodia Harknessii (Sacc.) Tassi.
 Micropeltis applanata Mont.
 Phyllosticta micropuncta Cke.
Lauraceae gen. indet.
   (See also Prunus occidentalis.)
 Antennaria aequatorialis Speg.
 Asterina aemula Syd.
 Asterina verae-crucis Theissen.
 ⎧Diatrype corniculata (Ehrh. ex Fr.) B. & Br.
 ⎩Sphaeria corniculata Ehrh. ex Fr.
 Didymella dominicana Ciferri & Fragoso.
 Englerula mexicana Theissen.
 ⎧Hymenochaete episphaeria (Fr.) Massee.
 ⎩Thelephora episphaeria Fr.
 ⎧Macrophoma erumpens (B. & C.) Berl. & Vogl
 ⎪Phaeodomus erumpens (B. & C.) Petrak & Syd.
 ⎨Phoma erumpens (B. & C.) Sacc.
 ⎩Sphaeria erumpens B. & C.
 Phaeodomus Lauracearum v. Hohnel.
 ⎧Hysterostomella leptospila (B. & C.) v. Höhnel.
 ⎨Pycnocarpon leptospilum (B. & C.) Speg.
 ⎩Rhytisma leptospilum B. & C.
 ⎧Leptodothis atramentaria (B. & C.) Theissen
 ⎪ & Syd.
 ⎨Rhytisma atramentarium B. & C.
 ⎩Wrightiella atramentaria (B. & C.) Speg.

HERNANDIACEAE

Hernandia Sonora L.
 ⎧Acia membranacea (Bull. ex Fr.) Pat.
 ⎩Hydnum membranaceum Bull. ex Fr.
 Hymenochaete Kunzei Massee.
 Hymenochaete tabacina Fr.
 Hypholoma appendiculatum Fr.
 ⎧Leptoporus carneopallens (B.) Pat.
 ⎩Polyporus carneopallens B.

PAPAVERACEAE

Dendromecon rigidum Benth.
Massaria cleistotheca Hark.
Phoma capsularum Cke. & Hark.
Pleosphaerulina californica Berl.
Pleospora argyrospora Hark.
Sphaerella Dendromeconis Cke. & Hark.
Dendromecon sp. indet.
Entyloma Eschscholtziae Hark.
Pocosphaeria Dendromeconis Earle.
Eschscholtzia californica Cham.
Entyloma Eschscholtziae Hark.
Heterosporium Eschscholtziae Hark.
⎰Peziza Eschscholtziae Phil. & Hark.
⎱Phialea Eschscholtziae (Phil. & Hark.) Sacc.
Sanguinaria canadensis L.
Cercospora Sanguinariae Pk.
Cylindrosporium circinans Wint.
Epicoccum neglectum Desm.
Gloeosporium Sanguinariae Ell. & Ev.
Phyllosticta Sanguinariae Wint.
Chelidonium sp. indet.
Septoria Chelidonii Desm.
Bocconia cordata Willd.
⎰Heptameria Bocconiae (C. & E.) Cke.
⎱Leptosphaeria Bocconiae (C. & E.) Sacc.
⎰Sphaeria Bocconiae C. & E.
Glaucium flavum Cranz.
Pleospora herbarum (Fr.) Rabh.
Glaucium sp. indet.
Entyloma fuscum Schrt.
Argemone alba Raf.
Gloeosporium Argemonis Ell. & Ev.
Argemone intermedia Sweet.
Aecidium plenum Arth.
Septoria Argemones Tharp.
Argemone mexicana L.
Cladosporium guanicensis F. L. Stevens.
Septoria Argemones Tharp.
Septoria Chelidonii Desm.
Argemone platyceras Lk. & Otto.
Alternaria lancipes Ell. & Ev.
Gloeosporium Argemonis Ell. & Ev.
⎰Peronospora arborescens (B.) DBy.
⎱Peronospora Corydalis Hume.
Septoria Argemones Tharp.
Papaver nudicaule L.
Cladosporium herbarum (P.) ex Lk.
Diplodina minor Dearness.
Heterosporium groenlandicum Allescher.
Physalospora polaris Rostr.
Pleospora herbarum (Fr.) Rabh.
Pleospora media Niessl.
Pleospora papaveracea (DeNot.) Sacc.
Pleospora vulgaris Niessl.
Pyrenophora chrysospora (Niessl) Sacc.
Pyrenophora comata (Niessl) Sacc.
Pyrenophora paucitricha (Fckl.) Berl. & Vogl.

Rhabdospora cercosperma (Rostr.) Sacc.
Rhabdospora Drabae (Fckl.) Berl. & Vogl.
⎰Mycosphaerella arthropyrenioides (Awd.)
⎱ Dearness.
⎱Sphaerella arthopyrenioides Awd.
Sphaerella karajacensis Allescher.
⎰Mycosphaerella pachyasca (Rostr.) Vestergren.
⎱Sphaerella pachyasca Rostr.
Sphaerella tassiana DeNot.
Thielavia basicola (B. & Br.) Zopf.
Torula herbarum Lk.
Papaver radicatum Rottb.
Clathrospora pentamera (Karst.) Berl.
Leptosphaeria Papaveris Rostr.
Pleospora herbarum (Fr.) Rabh.
Pleospora infectoria Fckl.
Pyrenophora comata (Niessl) Sacc.
Pyrenophora coronata (Niessl) Sacc.
Papaver rhoeas L.
Erysiphe Cichoracearum DC. †
Papaver sp. indet.
Entyloma fuscum Schrt.

FUMARIACEAE

Dicentra canadensis (Goldie) Walp.
Peronospora Corydalis DBy.
Dicentra Cucullaria (L.) Bernh.
⎰Aecidium Dicentrae Trel.
⎱Cerotelium Dicentrae (Trel.) Mains & Ander-
⎱ son.
Aecidium fumariacearum Kellerm. & Swingle.
Peronospora Corydalis DBy.
Dicentra spectabilis DC.
Dendryphium nodulosum Sacc.
Corydalis aurea Willd., var. **occidentalis** Gray.
⎰Aecidium Corydalis Webber.
⎱Aecidium Dicentrae, var. Corydalis Ell. &
⎱ Kellerm.
⎱Aecidium Fumariacearum Kellerm. & Swingle.
⎱Puccinia subnitens Diet. I.
Aecidium Dicentrae Trel.
Peronospora Corydalis DBy.
Corydalis Brandegei Watson.
Dasyscypha Bakeri Earle.
Hymenoscypha cyathoidea Phil.
Niptera (?) coccinea Earle.
⎰Micropuccinia Brandegei (Pk.) Arth. & Jack-
⎱ son.
⎱Puccinia Brandegei Pk.
Corydalis flavula (Raf.) DC.
Peronospora Corydalis DBy.
Corydalis glauca Pursh.
Peronospora Corydalis DBy.
Septoria Corydalis Ell. & Davis.
Corydalis micrantha (Engelm.) Gray.
⎰Aecidium Fumariacearum Kellerm. & Swingle.
⎱Dicaeoma Sarcobati Arth. I.
Peronospora Corydalis DBy.

Corydalis montana Engelm.
  {Aecidium Fumariacearum Kellerm. & Swingle.
  {Dicaeoma Sarcobati Arth. I.
  {Puccinia subnitens Diet. I.
Corydalis Scouleri Hook.
  Micropuccinia Brandegei (Pk.) Arth. & Jackson.

CRUCIFERAE

Stanleya glauca Rydb.
Stanleya pinnata (Pursh) Britt.
  {Aecidium Lepidii Tracy & Gall.
  {Dicaeoma Sarcobati Arth. I.
  {Puccinia subnitens Diet. I.
Schoenocrambe pinnata Greene.
  {Aecidium monoicum Pk.
  {Dicaeoma monoicum (Arth.) Arth. & Fromme. I.
Thelypodium laciniatum Endl.
Thelypodium sagittatum (Nutt.) Endl.
  {Aecidium Lepidii Tracy & Gall.
  {Dicaeoma Sarcobati Arth. I.
  {Puccinia subnitens Diet. I.
Thelypodium linearifolium Watson.
  Dicaeoma monoicum (Arth.) Arth. & Fromme. I.
Thelypodium sp. indet.
  Cercospora Nasturtii Pass., var.? Pass.
Streptanthus sp. indet.
  Puccinia Streptanthi v. Höhnel.
Lepidium alyssoides Gray.
  {Aecidium Lepidii Tracy & Gall.
  {Puccinia subnitens Diet. I.
Lepidium apetalum Willd.
  {Aecidium Lepidii Tracy & Gall.
  {Puccinia Sarcobati (Arth.) Bethel. I.
  {Puccinia subnitens Diet. I.
  {Albugo candida (P. ex Lév.) O. Kuntze.
  {Cystopus candidus (P.) ex Lév.
  Peronospora Lepidii (McAlpine) G. W. Wilson.
  Peronospora parasitica (P.) Fr.
  Plasmodiophora Brassicae Wor.
  Pleospora lepidiicola Earle.
  Septoria lepidiicola Ell. & Martin.
Lepidium campestre (L.) R. Br.
  Cercospora Lepidii Pk.
  {Albugo candida (P. ex Lév.) O. Kuntze.
  {Cystopus candidus (P.) ex Lév.
  Plasmodiophora Brassicae Wor.
Lepidium densiflorum Schrad.
  {Aecidium Lepidii Tracy & Gall.
  {Dicaeoma Sarcobati Arth. I.
  {Puccinia subnitens Diet. I.
  {Albugo candida (P. ex Lév.) O. Kuntze.
  {Cystopus candidus (P.) ex Lév.
  Peronospora parasitica (P.) Fr.

Lepidium hirsutum Rydb.
  {Aecidium Lepidii Tracy & Gall.
  {Puccinia subnitens Diet. I.
  Peronospora parasitica (P.) Fr.
Lepidium lasiocarpum Nutt.
  {Aecidium Lepidii Tracy & Gall.
  {Dicaeoma Sarcobati Arth. I.
  {Puccinia subnitens Diet. I.
Lepidium latifolium L.
  Albugo candida (P. ex Lév.) O. Kuntze.
Lepidium medium Greene.
  {Aecidium Lepidii Tracy & Gall.
  {Puccinia subnitens Diet. I.
Lepidium Menziesii DC.
  Plasmodiophora Brassicae Wor.
Lepidium montanum Nutt.
Lepidium perfoliatum L.
  {Aecidium Lepidii Tracy & Gall.
  {Dicaeoma Sarcobati Arth. I.
  {Puccinia subnitens Diet. I.
Lepidium ruderale L.
  Peronospora Lepidii (McAlpine) G. W. Wilson.
Lepidium sativum L.
  Albugo candida (P. ex Lév.) O. Kuntze.
  {Corticium vagum B. & C., var. Solani Burt.
  {Rhizoctonia Solani Kühn.
  Peronospora Lepidii-sativi G. W. Wilson.
  Peronospora parasitica (P.) Fr.
  Pythium debaryanum Hesse.
Lepidium simile Heller.
  {Dicaeoma Sarcobati Arth. I.
  {Puccinia subnitens Diet. I.
Lepidium virginicum L.
  {Aecidium Lepidii Tracy & Gall.
  {Puccinia subnitens Diet. I.
  Cercospora Lepidii Pk.
  Cylindrosporium Capsellae Ell. & Ev.
  {Albugo candida (P. ex Lév.) O. Kuntze.
  {Cystopus candidus (P.) ex Lév.
  {Heptameria virginica (C. & E.) Cke.
  {Leptosphaeria planiuscula Auct. Amer.
  {Leptosphaeria virginica (C. & E.) Sacc.
  {Sphaeria virginica C. & E.
  Peronospora Lepidii (MacAlpine) G. W. Wilson.
  Peronospora Lepidii-virginici Gäumann.
  Peronospora parasitica (P.) Fr.
  Phoma nebulosa (P. ex Fr.) B.
  Septoria lepidiicola Ell. & Martin.
Coronopus Didymus (L.) Sm.
  ?Peronospora Coronopi? Gäumann.
  Peronospora Lepidii (MacAlpine) G. W. Wilson.
Coronopus sp. indet.
  Albugo candida (P. ex Lév.) O. Kuntze.
Iberis umbellata L.
  Plasmodiophora Brassicae Wor.
Iberis sp. indet.
  Rhizoctonia Solani Kühn.

Thlaspi alpestre L. f., var. **purpurascens** (Rydb.)
   Ostenf.
   Cladosporium herbarum (P.) ex Lk.
   Phoma herbarum Westd.
   Micropuccinia Thlaspeos (Schubert) Arth. &
    Jackson.
Thlaspi arvense L.
   Puccinia subnitens Diet. I.
   Plasmodiophora Brassicae Wor.
Thlaspi coloradense Rydb.
   Puccinia subnitens Diet. I.
   Puccinia Thlaspeos Schubert.
Thlaspi glaucum A. Nels.
   Albugo candida (P. ex Lév.) O. Kuntze.
   { Micropuccinia Thlaspeos (Schubert) Arth. &
     Jackson.
   { Puccinia Thlaspeos Schubert.
   { Micropuccinia utahensis (Garrett) Arth. &
     Jackson.
   { Puccinia utahensis Garrett.
Thlaspi Holboellii Auct.
   { Puccinia Holboellii Rostr.
   { Puccinia Thlaspeos N. A. F. *2891*
Thlaspi Nuttallii Rydb.
   { Albugo candida (P. ex Lév.) O. Kuntze.
   { Cystopus candidus (P.) ex Lév.
   { Uredo candida P. ex Lév.
   Ramularia Armoraciae Fckl.
Cochlearia officinalis L.
   Micropuccinia Drabae (Rudolphi) Arth. &
    Jackson.
   Phoma herbarum Westd.
   Phoma nebulosa (P. ex Fr.) B.
   Puccinia Cochleariae Lindr.
Eutrema Edwardsii R. Br.
   Rhabdospora groenlandica Lind.
   Septoria semilunaris Johans.
   Sphaerella Cruciferarum (Fr.) Sacc.
   { Mycosphaerella pachyasca (Rostr.) Vestergren.
   { Sphaerella pachyasca Rostr.
Sisymbrium altissimum L.
   { Aecidium Lepidii Tracy & Gall.
   { Dicaeoma Sarcobati Arth. I.
   { Puccinia subnitens Diet. I.
   { Albugo candida (P. ex Lév.) O. Kuntze.
   { Cystopus candidus (P.) ex Lév.
   Plasmodiophora Brassicae Wor.
Sisymbrium
   (Sophia andrearum Cockerell.)
   { Aecidium Lepidii Tracy & Gall.
   { Dicaeoma Sarcobati Arth. I.
Sisymbrium canescens Nutt.
   { Aecidium monoicum Pk.
   { Dicaeoma monoicum (Arth.) Arth. & Fromme.
     I.
   { Aecidium Lepidii Tracy & Gall.
   { Puccinia subnitens Diet. I.
   Ascochyta Sisymbrii Ell. & Kellerm.

   { Albugo candida (P. ex Lév.) O. Kuntze.
   { Cystopus candidus (P.) ex Lév.
   Peronospora parasitica (P.) Fr.
   Peronospora Sophiae-pinnatae Gäumann.
Sisymbrium incisum Engelm.
   { Aecidium Lepidii Tracy & Gall.
   { Dicaeoma Sarcobati Arth. I.
   { Puccinia subnitens Diet. I.
   { Aecidium monoicum Pk.
   { Dicaeoma monoicum (Arth.) Arth. & Fromme.
     I.
   { Puccinia monoica Arth. I.
   { Albugo candida (P. ex Lév.) O. Kuntze.
   { Cystopus candidus (P.) ex Lév.
   Peronospora Lepidii (McAlpine) G. W. Wilson.
   Peronospora parasitica (P.) Fr.
   Puccinia consimilis Ell. & Ev.
   Urocystis Sophiae Griffiths.
Sisymbrium
   (Sophia intermedia Rydb.)
   { Dicaeoma Sarcobati Arth. I.
   { Puccinia subnitens Diet. I.
   Peronospora parasitica (P.) Fr.
   Peronospora Sisymbrii, var. intermedii Gáu-
    mann.
Sisymbrium latifolium Nutt.
   Dicaeoma monoicum Arth. & Fromme. I.
Sisymbrium.
   (Sophia leptostyla Rydb.)
   { Aecidium monoicum Pk.
   { Dicaeoma monoicum (Arth.) Arth. & Fromme.
     I.
Sisymbrium linifolium Nutt.
   { Aecidium monoicum Pk.
   { Puccinia consimilis N. Am. Uredinales *835.*
   { Puccinia monoica Arth. I.
   { Albugo candida (P. ex Lév.) O. Kuntze.
   { Cystopus candidus (P.) ex Lév.
   Puccinia aberrans Pk.
   { Allodus consimilis (Ell. & Ev.) C. R. Orton.
   { Puccinia consimilis Ell. & Ev.
   { Micropuccinia Holboellii (Rostr.) Arth. &
     Jackson.
   { Puccinia Holboellii Rostr.
Sisymbrium millefolium Ait.
   Albugo candida (P. ex Lév.) O. Kuntze.
Sisymbrium ochroleucum (Wooton) K. Schum.
   Peronospora parasitica (P.) Fr.
   Puccinia subnitens Diet. I.
Sisymbrium officinale (L.) Scop.
   { Albugo candida (P. ex Lév.) O. Kuntze.
   { Cystopus candidus (P.) ex Lév.
   Cercospora Cruciferarum Ell. & Ev.
   Cercospora Nasturtii Pass.
   Peronospora parasitica (P.) Fr.
   Plasmodiophora Brassicae Wor.
   Septoria Sisymbrii Ell.

Sisymbrium
    (Sophia pinnata Howell).
  Peronospora parasitica (P.) Fr.
  Peronospora Sophiae-pinnatae Gäumann.
Sisymbrium vulgare P.
  Plasmodiophora Brassicae Wor.
Sisymbrium sp. indet.
  Peronospora Sisymbrii, var. officinalis Gäu-
    mann.
  Sphaerella Cruciferarum (Fr.) Sacc.
Cakile edentula (Bigel.) Hook.
  Albugo candida (P. ex Lev.) O. Kuntze.
  Phyllosticta allantospora Ell. & Ev.
Brassica alba (L.) Boiss.
  Albugo candida (P. ex Lév.) O. Kuntze.
  Alternaria fasciculata (C. & E.) Jones & Grout.
  Peronospora parasitica (P.) Fr.
  Plasmodiophora Brassicae Wor.
Brassica arvensis (L.) O. Kuntze.
  Puccinia subnitens Diet. I.
  Cercospora Bloxami B. & Br.
  { Albugo candida (P. ex Lév.) O. Kuntze.
  { Cystopus candidus (P.) ex Lév.
  Ophiobolus porphyrogonus (Tode) Sacc.
  Peronospora parasitica (P.) Fr.
  Plasmodiophora Brassicae Wor.
  Rhizoctonia Solani Kühn.
Brassica campestris L.
    (See also B. Napobrassica.)
  Alternaria Brassicae (B.) Sacc.
  { Alternaria herculea (Ell. & Martin) Elliott.
  { Macrosporium herculeum Ell. & Martin.
  { Cercospora albomaculans Ell. & Ev.
  { Cercosporella albomaculans (Ell. & Ev.) Sacc.
  Cercospora Bloxami B. & Br.
  Colletotrichum higginsianum Sacc.
  { Albugo candida (P. ex Lév.) O. Kuntze.
  { Cystopus candidus (P.) ex Lév.
  Erysiphe Polygoni DC. †
  Macrosporium Brassicae (B.) Sacc.
  Mycosphaerella brassicicola (Duby) Lindau.
  Oospora scabies Thax.
  Periola tomentosa Fr.
  Peronospora parasitica (P.) Fr.
  Phoma lingam (Tode) ex Desm.
  Phoma Napobrassicae Rostr.
  Plasmodiophora Brassicae Wor.
  Sclerotinia libertiana Fckl.
  Sclerotium bataticola Taubenhaus.
Brassica chinensis L. (Pak-choi).
  Alternaria Brassicae (B.) Sacc.
Brassica integrifolia O. E. Schulz.
  Albugo candida (P. ex Lév.) O. Kuntze.
  Cercospora Bloxami B. & Br.
Brassica japonica Siebold.
  Cercospora Bloxami B. & Br.
  { Albugo candida (P. ex Lév.) O. Kuntze.
  { Cystopus candidus (P.) ex Lev.
  Plasmodiophora Brassicae Wor.

Brassica juncea (L.) Cosson.
  Dicaeoma Sarcobati Arth. I.
  Cercospora Bloxami B. & Br.
  { Albugo candida (P. ex Lév.) O. Kuntze.
  { Cystopus candidus (P.) Lév.
  Erysiphe Polygoni DC. †
  Peronospora parasitica (P.) Fr.
  Plasmodiophora Brassicae Wor.
  Pleospora media Niessl.
  Ramularia Armoraciae Fckl.
  Septoria Brassicae Ell. & Ev.
Brassica Napobrassica Mill. (Rutabaga.)
    (See also B. campestris.)
  { Albugo candida (P. ex Lév.) O. Kuntze.
  { Cystopus candidus (P.) ex Lév.
  Oidium balsamii Mont.
  Peronospora parasitica (P.) Fr.
  Rhizopus nigricans Ehrenb.
  Sclerotinia perplexa Lawrence.
Brassica Napus L. (Rape. Colza.)
  Albugo candida (P. ex Lév.) O. Kuntze.
  Cercospora Bloxami B. & Br.
  Erysiphe Polygoni DC. †
  Peronospora parasitica (P.) Fr.
  Plasmodiophora Brassicae Wor.
Brassica nigra (L.) Koch.
  Puccinia subnitens Diet. I.
  Alternaria Brassicae (B.) Sacc.
  Cercospora Bloxami B. & Br.
  { Albugo candida (P. ex Lév.) O. Kuntze.
  { Cystopus candidus (P.) ex Lév.
  Erysiphe Polygoni DC. †
  Peronospora parasitica (P.) Fr.
  Pleospora media Niessl.
Brassica oleracea L.
  Alternaria Brassicae (B.) Sacc.
  Alternaria Brassicae, var. macrospora Sacc.
  Alternaria fasciculata (C. & E.) Jones & Grout.
  { Alternaria herculea (Ell. & Martin) J. A.
  {   Elliott.
  { Macrosporium herculeum Ell. & Martin.
  Alternaria oleracea Milbraith.
  { Botrytis cinerea P. †
  { Botrytis vulgaris (Lk.) ex Fr.
  { Polyactis vulgaris Lk.
  Cercospora Bloxami B. & Br.
  Cercospora Cruciferarum Ell. & Ev.
  Cercosporella albomaculans (Ell. & Ev.) Sacc.
  { Chaetomella Brassicae (S.) Starb.
  { Sphaeria Brassicae S.
  Cladosporium atrum Lk.
  Cladotrichum Brassicae Ell. & Barthol.
  Coprinus Brassicae Pk.
  { Corticium vagum B. & C.
  { Corticium vagum B. & C., var. Solani Burt.
  { Rhizoctonia Solani Kühn.
  Cylindrosporium Brassicae Fautr. & Roum.
  { Albugo candida (P. ex Lév.) O. Kuntze.
  { Cystopus candidus (P.) ex Lév.

Brassica oleracea (*cont.*)
Erysiphe Polygoni DC. †
Fusarium conglutinans Wollenw.
Fusidium torulosum B. & C.
Gloeosporium concentricum Grev.
{Helminthosporium brassicola S.
{Helminthosporium folliculatum Cda.
Humaria deerrata (Karst.) Sacc.
{Heptameria olericola (B. & C.) Cke.
{Leptosphaeria eustoma (Fr.) Sacc., var. oleri-
{ cola Berl.
{Leptosphaeria olericola (B. & C.) Sacc.
{Sphaeria olericola B. & C.
Macrosporium Brassicae B.
Macrosporium Cheiranthi Fr., var. circinans
  B. & C.
Mucor Beaumontii B. & C.
{Dialonectria Brassicae (Ell. & Sacc.) Ell. & Ev.
{Nectria Brassicae Ell. & Sacc.
Oidium Balsamii Mont.
Olpidium Brassicae (Wor.) Dangeard.
{Botrytis parasitica P.
{Peronospora parasitica (P.) Fr.
{Peziza brassicicola B.
{Pezizella brassicicola (B.) Sacc.
Phoma Lingam (Tode) ex Desm.
Phoma oleracea Sacc.
Phyllosticta brassicicola McAlpine.
{Ozonium omnivorum Shear.
{Phymatotrichum omnivorum (Shear) Duggar.
Plasmodiophora Brassicae Wor.
Pythium debaryanum Hesse.
Rhizopus nigricans Ehrenb.
Sclerotinia perplexa Lawrence.
{Sclerotinia libertiana Fckl.
{Sclerotinia sclerotiorum (Lib.) Massee.
Sclerotium Rolfsii Sacc.
Spongospora subterranea (Wallr.) Lagerh.
{Mycosphaerella brassicicola (Fr.) Lindau.
{Sphaerella brassicicola (Fr.) Ces. & DeNot.
Stilbum annulatum B. & C.
Stilbum Spraguei B. & C.
Tubercularia liceoides Fr.

Brassica oleracea L., var. **acephala** DC. (Kales.)
Albugo candida (P. ex Lév.) O. Kuntze.
Alternaria Brassicae (B.) Sacc.
Corticium vagum B. & C.
Fusarium conglutinans Wollenw.
Peronospora parasitica (P.) Fr.
Phoma lingam (Tode) ex Desm.
Plasmodiophora Brassicae Wor.
Sclerotinia libertiana Fckl.
Sclerotinia perplexa Lawrence.
Sclerotium Rolfsii Sacc.
Mycosphaerella brassicicola (Fr.) Lindau.

Brassica oleracea L., var. **botrytis** L.
  (Cauliflower. Broccoli.)
Alternaria Brassicae (B.) Sacc.

Alternaria herculea (Ell. & Martin) J. A. El-
  liott.
Alternaria oleracea Milbraith.
Corticium vagum B. & C.
Fusarium conglutinans Wollenw.
Gloeosporium concentricum Grev.
Mycosphaerella brassicicola (Fr.) Lindau.
Olpidium Brassicae (Wor.) Dangeard.
Peronospora parasitica (P.) Fr.
Phoma lingam (Tode) ex Desm.
Phoma oleracea Sacc.
Plasmodiophora Brassicae Wor.
Sclerotinia sclerotiorum (Lib.) Massee.

Brassica oleracea L., var. **caulorapa** Pasq.
  (Kohlrabi).
Peronospora parasitica (P.) Fr.
Phoma lingam (Tode) ex Desm.
Plasmodiophora Brassicae Wor.
Rhizopus nigricans Ehrenb.
Rhizopus Tritici Saito.
Sclerotinia libertiana Fckl.
Mycosphaerella brassicicola (Fr.) Lindau.

Brassica oleracea L., var. **gemmifera** Zenker.
  (Brussels Sprouts.)
Ascobolus Crouani Boud. non Cke.
Corticium vagum B. & C.
Lophiotrema praemorsum (Lasch) Sacc.
Massarinula Brassicae Dearness & House.
Mycosphaerella brassicicola (Fr.) Lindau.
Peronospora parasitica (P.) Fr.
Phoma lingam (Tode) ex Desm.
Plasmodiophora Brassicae Wor.
Pythium debaryanum Hesse.
Sclerotinia sclerotiorum (Lib.) Massee.
Stereum albobadium S.

Brassica pekinensis Rupr. (Pe-tsai).
Alternaria Brassicae (B.) Sacc., var. macro-
  spora Sacc.
Alternaria herculea (Ell. & Martin) J. A.
  Elliott.
Cercospora Bloxami B. & Br.
Cercosporella albo-maculans (Ell. & Ev.) Sacc.
Cylindrosporium Brassicae Fautr. & Roum.
Plasmodiophora Brassicae Wor.
Sclerotinia sclerotiorum (Lib.) Massee.

Brassica Rapa L. (Turnip).
Actinomyces chromogenus Gasp.
{Actinomyces scabies (Thax.) Güssow.
{Oospora scabies Thax.
Alternaria Brassicae (B.) Sacc.
{Alternaria herculea (Ell. & Martin) J. A. El-
{ liott.
{Macrosporium herculeum Ell. & Martin.
Cercospora Bloxami B. & Br.
Cercosporella albomaculans (Ell. & Ev.) Sacc.
Colletotrichum Brassicae Schulz. & Sacc.
Colletotrichum higginsianum Sacc.
Corticium vagum B. & C.
Cylindrosporium Brassicae Fautr. & Roum.

Brassica Rapa (*cont.*)
  { Albugo candida (P. ex Lév.) O. Kuntze.
  { Cystopus candidus (P.) ex Lév.
  Erysiphe Polygoni DC.†
  Fusarium conglutinans Wollenw.
  Leptosphaeria Napi (Fckl.) Sacc.
  Mycosphaerella brassicicola (Fr.) Lindau.
  Oidium balsamii Mont.
  Oidium erysiphoides Fr.
  Peronospora parasitica (P.) Fr.
  Phoma Napobrassicae Rostr.
  Plasmodiophora Brassicae Wor.
  Rhizoctonia Solani Kühn.
  Rhizopus nigricans Ehrenb.
  { Sclerotinia libertiana Fckl.
  { Sclerotinia sclerotiorum (Lib.) Massee.
  Stilbum vulgare Tod.

Brassica urbaniana O. E. Schulze.
  Albugo candida (P. ex Lév.) O. Kuntze.

Brassica sp. indet.
  Alternaria tenuis Nees ex Fr.
  Aspergillus purpureofuscus S.
  Botrytis lateritia S.
  Dacryomyces capitatus S.
  Gibbera pulicaris Fr.
  { Helotium brassicicola (S.) Sacc.
  { Sarea brassicicola S.
  Sporotrichum sporulosum Lk.
  Stachylidium fulvum S.

Raphanus sativus L.
  Actinomyces chromogenus Gasp.
  { Actinomyces scabies (Thax.) Güssow.
  { Oospora scabies Thax.
  { Dicaeoma Sarcobati Arth. I.
  { Puccinia Sarcobati (Arth.) Bethel. I.
  { Puccinia subnitens Diet. I.
  Alternaria Brassicae (B.) Sacc.
  Alternaria Brassicae, var. macrospora Sacc.
  Alternaria fasciculata (C. & E.) Jones & Grout.
  Aphanomyces laevis DBy.
  Aphanomyces Raphani Kendrick.
  Cercospora atrogrisea Ell. & Ev.
  Cercospora Cruciferarum Ell. & Ev.
  Cladosporium herbarum (P.) ex Lk.
  { Corticium vagum B. & C.
  { Corticium vagum B. & C., var. Solani Burt.
  { Rhizoctonia Solani Kühn.
  { Albugo candida (P. ex Lév.) O. Kuntze.
  { Cystopus candidus (P.) ex Lév.
  Erysiphe Polygoni DC.†
  Macrosporium commune Rabh.
  { Nematosporangium aphanidermatum (Edson) Fitzpatrick.
  { Pythium aphanidermatum (Edson) Fitzpatrick.
  { Rheosporangium aphanidermatum Edson.
  Peronospora parasitica (P.) Fr.
  Plasmodiophora Brassicae Wor.
  Pythium debaryanum Hesse.

  { Sclerotinia libertiana Fckl.
  { Sclerotinia sclerotiorum (Lib.) Massee.
Crambe maritima L.
  Fusarium conglutinans Wollenw.
Barbarea stricta Andrz.
  Plasmodiophora Brassicae Wor.
  Ramularia Barbareae Pk.
Barbarea vulgaris R. Br.
  Albugo candida (P. ex Lév.) O. Kuntze.
  Macrosporium caudatum C. & E.
Iodanthus pinnatifidus (Michx.) Steud.
  { Albugo candida (P. ex Lév.) O. Kuntze.
  { Cystopus candidus (P.) ex Lév.
  Peronospora parasitica (P.) Fr.
Radicula aquatica (Eat.) B. L. Robinson.
  Cercospora Nasturtii Pass.
Radicula Armoracia (L.) B. L. Robinson.
  Alternaria Brassicae (B.) Sacc.
  { Alternaria herculea (Ell. & Martin) J. A. Elliott.
  { Macrosporium herculeum Ell. & Martin.
  Ascochyta Armoraciae Fckl.
  Cercospora Armoraciae Sacc.
  Cercospora Nasturtii Pass.
  { Corticium vagum B. & C.
  { Rhizoctonia Solani Kühn.
  { Albugo candida (P. ex Lév.) O. Kuntze.
  { Cystopus candidus (P.) ex Lév.
  Macrosporium parasiticum Thm.
  Mycosphaerella pachyasca (Rostr.) Vestergren.
  Peronospora parasitica (P.) Fr.
  Phyllosticta anceps Sacc.
  Phyllosticta decidua Ell. & Kellerm.
  Phyllosticta orbicula Ell. & Ev.
  { Ozonium omnivorum Shear.
  { Phymatotrichum omnivorum (Shear) Duggar.
  Ramularia Armoraciae Fckl.
  Septoria Armoraciae Sacc.
  ?Septoria Lactucae Pass.
  Thielavia basicola (B. & Br.) Zopf.
Radicula Nasturtium-aquaticum (L.) Britten & Rendle.
  { Dicaeoma Sarcobati Arth. I.
  { Puccinia subnitens Diet. I.
  Cercospora Nasturtii Pass.
  Pythium debaryanum Hesse.
Radicula obtusa (Nutt.) Greene.
  Cystopus candidus (P.) ex Lév.
  Peronospora parasitica (P.) Fr.
Radicula palustris (L.) Moench.
  Puccinia subnitens Diet. I.
  Cercospora Cruciferarum Ell. & Ev.
  Cercospora Nasturtii Pass.
  { Albugo candida (P. ex Lév.) O. Kuntze.
  { Cystopus candidus (P.) ex Lév.
  Peronospora Lepidii (MacAlpine) G. W. Wilson.
  Ramularia Amoraciae Fckl.
  Septoria Radiculae Dearness.

Radicula palustris (L.) Moench, var. hispida
(Desv.) B. L. Robinson.
  Cercospora Nasturtii Pass.
{ Albugo candida (P. ex Lév.) O. Kuntze.
{ Cystopus candidus (P.) ex Lév.
  Peronospora parasitica (P.) Fr.
Radicula sessiliflora (Nutt.) Greene.
  Cystopus candidus (P.) ex. Lév.
  Peronospora parasitica (P.) Fr.
Radicula sinuata (Nutt.) Greene.
{ Dicacoma Sarcobati Arth. I.
{ Puccinia Sarcobati (Arth.) Bethel. I.
{ Puccinia subnitens Diet. I.
  Albugo candida (P. ex Lév.) O. Kuntze.
  Peronospora parasitica (P.) Fr.
Radicula sylvestris (L.) Druce.
  Cercospora Nasturtii Pass.
Radicula Walteri Greene.
{ Albugo candida (P. ex Lév.) O. Kuntze.
{ Cystopus candidus (P.) ex Lév.
  Peronospora parasitica (P.) Fr.
Radicula sp. indet.
  Zignoella Roripae Rehm.
Cardamine bellidifolia L.
  Cladosporium herbarum (P.) ex Lk.
  Phoma nebulosa (P. ex Fr.) B.
  Phoma oleracea Sacc.
  Phyllosticta Cardamines Allescher.
{ Micropuccinia Cruciferarum (Rud.) Arth. &
{   Jackson.
{ Puccinia Cardamines-bellidifoliae Diet.
{ Puccinia Cruciferarum Rudolphi.
  Pyrenophora Cerastii (Oud.) J. Lind.
  Pyrenophora chrysospora (Niessl) Sacc.
{ Heteropatella umbilicata (P.) Jaap.
{ Rhabdospora cercosperma (Rostr.) Sacc.
{ Septoria cercosperma Rostr.
  Sphaerella Cruciferarum (Fr.) Sacc.
  Mycosphaerella densa (Rostr.) J. Lind.
{ Mycosphaerella pachyasca (Rostr.) Vestergren.
{ Sphaerella pachyasca Rostr.
Cardamine bellidifolia L., var. laxa Lange.
  Pyrenophora comata (Niessl) Sacc.
Cardamine bulbosa (Schreb.) B. S. P.
{ Albugo candida (P. ex Lév.) O. Kuntze.
{ Cystopus candidus (P.) ex Lév.
  Peronospora parasitica (P.) Fr.
  Septoria Dentariae Pk.
Cardamine cordifolia Gray.
{ Micropuccinia Cruciferarum (Rud.) Arth. &
{   Jackson.
{ Puccinia Cardamines-bellidifoliae Diet.
Cardamine Douglassii (Torr.) Britt.
  Albugo candida (P. ex Lév.) O. Kuntze.
  Peronospora parasitica (P.) Fr.
{ Allodus arabicola (Ell. & Ev.) Arth. & Orton.
{ Puccinia arabicola Ell. & Ev.
  Septoria Dentariae Pk.

Cardamine heterophylla Wood.
  Peronospora parasitica (P.) Fr.
Cardamine hirsuta L.
  Cystopus candidus (P.) ex Lév.
  Peronospora parasitica (P.) Fr.
Cardamine laciniata Wood.
Cardamine maxima Wood.
Cardamine parviflora L.
Cardamine pennsylvanica Muhl.
  Peronospora parasitica (P.) Fr.
Cardamine pratensis L.
  Phoma nebulosa (P. ex Fr.) B.
  Sphaerella Cruciferarum (Fr.) Sacc.
Cardamine quinquefolia M. B.
  Peronospora parasitica (P.) Fr.
Dentaria diphylla Michx.
{ Albugo candida (P. ex Lév.) O. Kuntze.
{ Cystopus candidus (P.) ex Lév.
  Septoria Dentariae Pk.
  Septoria Dentariae Pk., var. arida Pk.
Dentaria heterophylla Nutt.
  Peronospora parasitica (P.) Fr.
Dentaria laciniata Muhl.
  Albugo candida (P. ex Lév.) O. Kuntze.
  Chaetomella Stevensonii Ell.
  Peronospora parasitica (P.) Fr.
  Septoria Dentariae Pk.
  Septoria Sisymbrii Ell.
Dentaria maxima Nutt.
  Peronospora parasitica (P.) Fr.
Dentaria polyphylla Waldst. & Kit.
  Albugo candida (P. ex Lév.) O. Kuntze.
Dentaria tenella Pursh.
{ Albugo candida (P. ex Lév.) O. Kuntze.
{ Cystopus candidus (P.) ex Lév.
{ Micropuccinia Dentariae (Fckl.) Arth. &
{   Jackson.
{ Puccinia Dentariae (A. & S.) Fckl.
Lunaria annua L.
  Septoria Lunariae Ell. & Dearness.
Lyrocarpa Coulteri Hook. & Harv.
  Pleospora herbarum (Fr.) Rabh.
Lesquerella alpina (Nutt.) Watson.
  Helminthosporium nanum Nees.
  Phoma punctiformis Desm.
  Pleospora herbarum (Fr.) Rabh.
  Pyrenophora comata (Niessl) Sacc.
{ Heteropatella umbilicata (P.) Jaap.
{ Rhabdospora cercosperma (Rostr.) Sacc.
{ Septoria cercosperma Rostr.
  Septoria Vesicariae Rostr.
  Sphaerella sibirica Thm.
Lesquerella arctica (Richards) Watson.
  Cladosporium herbarum (P.) ex Lk.
  Coniothyrium Lesquerellae J. Lind.
  Micropuccinia Cruciferarum (Rud.) Arth. &
    Jackson.
  Pleospora herbarum (Fr.) Rabh.

Lesquerella arctica (*cont.*)
  Pleospora infectoria Fckl.
  Pleospora platyspora Sacc.
  Pyrenophora Cerastii (Oud.) J. Lind.
  Pyrenophora chrysospora (Niessl) Sacc.
  Pyrenophora setigera (Niessl.) Sacc.
  { Rhabdospora cercosperma (Rostr.) Sacc.
  { Septoria cercosperma Rostr.
  Sphaerella Cruciferarum (Fr.) Sacc.
  Sphaerella Vesicariae-arcticae Henn.

Lesquerella Gordoni (Gray) Watson.

Hutchinsia procumbens (L.) Desv.
  { Dicaeoma Sarcobati Arth. I.
  { Puccinia subnitens Diet. I.

Capsella Bursa-pastoris (L.) Medic.
  { Dicaeoma Sarcobati Arth. I.
  { Puccinia Sarcobati (Arth.) Bethel. I.
  { Puccinia subnitens Diet. I.
  Cylindrosporium Capsellae Ell. & Ev.
  { Albugo candida (P. ex Lév.) O. Kuntze.
  { Cystopus candidus (P.) ex Lév.
  Peronospora Lepidii (MacAlpine) G. W. Wilson.
  Peronospora parasitica (P.) Fr.
  Plasmodiophora Brassicae Wor.

Camelina dentata P.

Camelina sativa (L.) Crantz.
  Albugo candida (P. ex Lév.) O. Kuntze.
  Plasmodiophora Brassicae Wor.

Camelina microcarpa Andrz.
  { Dicaeoma Sarcobati Arth. I.
  { Puccinia Sarcobati (Arth.) Bethel. I.
  { Puccinia subnitens Diet. I.
  Albugo candida (P. ex Lév.) O. Kuntze.
  Plasmodiophora Brassicae Wor.

Neslia paniculata (L.) Desv.
  Albugo candida (P. ex Lév.) O. Kuntze.
  Plasmodiophora Brassicae Wor.

Draba Adamsii Ledeb.
  Pyrenophora Androsaceus (Fckl.) Sacc.
  Pyrenophora Cerastii (Oud.) J. Lind.

Draba alpina L.
  Clathrospora pentamera (Karst.) Berl.
  Heteropatella umbilicata (P.) Jaap.
  Leptostromella Drabae Dearness.
  Phoma nebulosa (Fr.) Mont.
  Pleospora Drabae Schrt.
  Pleospora herbarum (Fr.) Rabh.
  Pleospora infectoria Fckl.
  { Rhabdospora Drabae (Fckl.) Berl. & Vogl.
  { Septoria Drabae (Fckl.) Rostr.
  Sphaerella pachyasca Rost.
  Sphaerella Stellarinearum Karst.
  Mycospherella tassiana (De Not.) Johans.

Draba alpina L., var. **corymbosa** Durand.
  Septoria cercosperma Rostr.
  Sphaerella pachyasca Rostr.

Draba alpina L., var. **glacialis** Dickie.
  Clathrospora pentamera (Karst.) Berl.
  Pleospora Drabae Schrt.
  Pyrenophora Cerastii (Oud.) J. Lind.

Draba androsacea Wahl.
  Hymenula macrospora Sacc. & Roum.
  Phoma nebulosa (P.) B.
  Pleospora Drabae Schrt.
  Pleospora herbarum (Fr.) Rabh.
  Pyrenophora chrysospora (Niessl) Sacc.
  Septoria cercosperma Rostr.
  Septoria pleosporoides Sacc.

Draba arabisans Michx.
  { Micropuccinia Drabae (Rud.) Arth. & Jackson.
  { Puccinia Drabae Rudolphi.
  Pyrenophora hispida (Niessl) Sacc.

Draba arctica Vahl.
  Mycosphaerella pachyasca (Rostr.) Vestergren.

Draba aurea Vahl.
  Aecidium Drabae Tracy & Gall.
  { Aecidium monoicum Pk.
  { Puccinia monoica Arth. I.
  Micropuccinia Drabae (Rud.) Arth. & Jackson.
  Pleospora platyspora Sacc.
  { Rhabdospora cercosperma (Rostr.) Sacc.
  { Septoria cercosperma Rostr.
  Sphaerella pachyasca Rostr.

Draba caroliniana Walt.
  { Albugo candida (P. ex Lév.) O. Kuntze.
  { Cystopus candidus (P.) ex Lév.
  Peronospora Drabae Gäumann.
  Peronospora parasitica (P.) Fr.

Draba cinerea Adams.
  Pleospora infectoria Fckl.
  Pyrenophora Cerastii (Oud.) J. Lind.
  Pyrenophora chrysospora (Niessl) Sacc.
  Rhabdospora Drabae (Fckl.) Berl. & Vogl.
  Mycosphaerella tassiana (De Not.) Johans.

Draba corymbosa R. Br.
  Leptostromella Drabae Dearness.

Draba crassifolia Graham.
  Sphaerella Cruciferarum (Fr.) Sacc.

Draba cuneifolia Nutt.
  { Dicaeoma Sarcobati Arth. I.
  { Puccinia subnitens Diet. I.
  Peronospora parasitica (P.) Fr.

Draba fladnizensis Wulf.
  Cladosporium herbarum (P.) ex Lk.
  Pleospora herbarum (Fr.) Rabh.
  Rhabdospora Drabae (Fckl.) Berl. & Vogl.
  { Mycosphaerella pachyasca (Rostr.) Vestergren.
  { Sphaerella pachyasca Rostr.
  Mycosphaerella tassiana (De Not.) Johans.

Draba glacialis Adams.
  Pyrenophora chrysospora (Niessl) Sacc.

Draba globosa Payson.
  Micropuccinia Drabae (Rud.) Arth. & Jackson.

Draba helleriana Greene.
Puccinia Holboellii Rostr.

Draba hirta L.
Cladosporium herbarum (P.) ex Lk.
Didymosphaeria Drabae Rostr.
⎰Erysiphe communis Auct. Amer.
⎱Erysiphe Polygoni DC. †
Laestadia circumtegens Rostr.
Pleospora Drabae Schrt.
⎰Micropuccinia Drabae (Rud.) Arth. & Jackson.
⎱Puccinia Drabae Rudolphi.
Pyrenophora chrysospora (Niessl) Sacc.
Sphaerella pachyasca Rostr.

Draba hirta L., var. **leiocarpa** Lindbl.
Puccinia Drabae Rud., var. arctica Henn.

Draba incana L.
⎰Dicaeoma Drabae (Rud.) O. Kuntze.
⎰Micropuccinia Drabae (Rud.) Arth. & Jackson.
⎱Puccinia Drabae Rudolphi.
Sphaerella pachyasca Rostr.

Draba incerta Payson.
⎰Micropuccinia Drabae (Rud.) Arth. & Jackson.
⎱Puccinia Drabae Rudolphi.

Draba nemorosa L.
Peronospora Drabae Gäumann.

Draba nivalis DC.
Heteropatella umbilicata (P.) Jaap.
Pleospora Drabae Schrt.
Pleospora Drabae Schrt., var. nuda Dearness.
Rhabdospora Drabae (Fckl.) Berl. & Vogl.
Sphaerella Cruciferarum (Fr.) Sacc.
⎰Mycosphaerella pachyasca (Rostr.) Vestergren.
⎱Sphaerella pachyasca Rostr.

Draba Parryi Rydb.
⎰Aecidium monoicum Pk.
⎰Dicaeoma monoicum (Arth.) Arth. & Fromme.
⎱ I.

Draba pectinata Rydb.
Puccinia Drabae Rudolphi.

Draba spectabilis Greene.
⎰Micropuccinia Holboellii (Rostr.) Arth. &
⎰ Jackson.
⎱Puccinia Holboellii Rostr.

Draba subcapitata Simmons.
Pleospora infectoria Fckl.
Rhabdospora Drabae (Fckl.) Berl. & Vogl.
Sphaerella Cruciferarum (Fr.) Sacc.

Draba vernalis Auct.
Pleospora media Niessl., var. limonium Penz.

Draba Wahlenbergii Hartm.
Sphaerella confinis Karst.

Draba sp. indet.
Phoma Drabae Fckl.
Pleospora hispida Niessl.
Puccinia aberrans Pk.

Smelowskia calycina Meyer.
Aecidium Parryi Pk.
⎰Dicaeoma monoicum (Arth.) Arth. & Fromme.
⎰ I.
⎰Puccinia monoica Arth. I.
⎰Micropuccinia aberrans (Pk.) Arth. & Jackson.
⎱Puccinia aberrans Pk.

Smelowskia Fremontii Watson.
Micropuccinia Holboellii (Rostr.) Arth. &
Jackson.

Smelowskia lobata Rydb.
⎰Micropuccinia aberrans (Pk.) Arth. & Jackson.
⎱Puccinia aberrans Pk.

Arabis albida Stev. in Fisch. Cat. Hort. Gorenk.
Peronospora parasitica (P.) Fr.

Arabis alpina L.
Metasphaeria Arabidis Johans.
Plasmodiophora Brassicae Wor.
⎰Rhabdospora arabidicola (Rostr.) Allescher.
⎱Septoria arabidicola Rostr.
Rhabdospora longissima Sacc.
Sirococcus cylindroides Sacc.
Sphaerella pachyasca Rostr.

Arabis ambigua DC.
⎰Micropuccinia Holboellii (Rostr.) Arth. &
⎰ Jackson.
⎰Puccinia Holboellii Rostr.
⎱Puccinia Thlaspeos Schubert.

Arabis arcuata Gray.
⎰Micropuccinia Holboellii (Rostr.) Arth. &
⎰ Jackson.
⎰Puccinia aberrans Auct. Amer. p. p.
⎰Puccinia Holboellii Rostr.
⎱Puccinia palefaciens Diet. & Holw.

Arabis Bolanderi Watson.
⎰Dicaeoma monoicum(Arth.)Arth.& Fromme. I.
⎱Dicaenma Parryi Arth. I.

Arabis Breweri Watson.
⎰Micropuccinia Holboellii (Rostr.) Arth. &
⎰ Jackson.
⎱Puccinia Holboellii Rostr.

Arabis canadensis L.
Albugo candida (P. ex Lév.) O. Kuntze.

Arabis canescens Nutt.
⎰Aecidium monoicum Pk.
⎰Dicaeoma monoicum (Arth.) Arth. & Fromme.
⎱ I.
Micropuccinia Holboellii (Rostr.) Arth. &
Jackson.

Arabis connexa Greene.
Dicaeoma monoicum (Arth.) Arth. & Fromme.
I.

Arabis Crandallii B. L. Robinson.
Dicaeoma monoicum (Arth.) Arth. & Fromme.
I.
Micropuccinia Holboellii (Rostr.) Arth. &
Jackson.

Arabis Cusickii Watson.
  ⌠Aecidium monoicum Pk.
  ⌡Dicaeoma monoicum (Arth.) Arth. & Fromme. I.
Arabis divaricarpa A. Nels.
  Micropuccinia Holboellii (Rostr.) Arth. &
    Jackson.
Arabis Drummondi Gray.
  ⌠Aecidium monoicum Pk.
  │Dicaeoma monoicum (Arth.) Arth. & Fromme.
  │ I.
  │Puccinia monoica Arth. I.
  │Micropuccinia Holboellii (Rostr.) Arth. &
  │ Jackson.
  ⌡Puccinia Holboellii Rostr.
Arabis exilis A. Nels.
  Micropuccinia Holboellii (Rostr.) Arth. &
    Jackson.
Arabis Fendleri (Watson) Greene.
  ⌠Aecidium monoicum Pk.
  │Dicaeoma monoicum (Arth.) Arth. & Fromme.
  │ I.
  ⌡Puccinia monoica Arth. I.
Arabis furcata Watson.
  Albugo candida (P. ex Lév.) O. Kuntze.
  Belonium arabicola Ell. & Ev.
  ⌠Micropuccinia Holboellii (Rostr.) Arth. &
  │ Jackson.
  ⌡Puccinia Holboellii Rostr.
Arabis glabra (L.) Bernh.
  Cladosporium subsclerotioideum Bubák &
    Dearness.
  ⌠Albugo candida (P. ex Lév.) O. Kuntze.
  ⌡Cystopus candidus (P.) ex Lév.
  Macrosporium mycetophilum Bubák & Dear-
    ness.
  Peronospora parasitica (P.) Fr.
Arabis hirsuta (L.) Scop.
  Peronospora parasitica (P.) Fr.
Arabis Holboellii Hornem.
  ⌠Aecidium Holboellii Hornem.
  │Micropuccinia Holboellii (Rostr.) Arth. &
  │ Jackson.
  │Puccinia aberrans Auct. Amer. p. p.
  │Puccinia Holboellii Rostr.
  │Puccinia palefaciens Diet. & Holw.
  │Aecidium monoicum Pk.
  │Dicaeoma monoicum (Arth.) Arth. & Fromme.
  │ I.
  ⌡Puccinia monoica Arth. I.
  Calloria minutissima Rostr.
  Hendersonia Arabidis Rostr.
  Peronospora parasitica (P.) Fr.
  Phlyctaena Andersoni Ell.
  Pleospora platyspora Sacc.
  Sphaerella pachyasca Rostr.
Arabis Hookeri Lange.
  Cladosporium arcticum Berl. & Vogl.
  Pyrenophora comata (Niessl) Sacc.
  Septoria Arabidis Sacc.

Arabis humifusa Watson.
  Pleospora herbarum (Fr.) Rabh.
Arabis laevigata (Muhl.) Poir.
  Peronospora parasitica (P.) Fr.
Arabis lignifera A. Nels.
  Dicaeoma monoicum (Arth.) Arth. & Fromme.
    I.
Arabis lignipes A. Nels.
  ⌠Micropuccinia Holboellii (Rostr.) Arth. &
  │ Jackson.
  ⌡Puccinia Holboellii Rostr.
Arabis Lyalli Watson.
  ⌠Aecidium monoicum Pk.
  │Dicaeoma monoicum (Arth.) Arth. & Fromme.
  │ I.
  │Cornularia sphaeroidea (Ell.) Sacc.
  │Kellermania sphaeroidea (Ell.) Jacz.
  │Sphaeronema sphaeroideum Ell.
  │Micropuccinia Holboellii (Rostr.) Arth. &
  │ Jackson.
  ⌡Puccinia Holboellii Rostr.
Arabis lyrata L.
  ⌠Aecidium monoicum Pk.
  │Dicaeoma monoicum (Arth.) Arth. & Fromme.
  │ I.
  │Puccinia monoica Arth. I.
  │Albugo candida (P. ex Lév.) O. Kuntze.
  ⌡Sphaerella Cruciferarum (Fr.) Sacc.
Arabis lyrata L., var. **occidentalis** Watson.
Arabis microphylla Nutt.
  Micropuccinia Holboellii (Rostr.) Arth. &
    Jackson.
Arabis Nuttallii B. L. Robinson.
  Puccinia monoica Arth. I.
Arabis oreophila Rydb.
  Micropuccinia Holboellii (Rostr.) Arth. &
    Jackson.
Arabis ovata (Pursh) Poir.
  ⌠Aecidium monoicum Pk.
  │Dicaeoma monoicum (Arth.) Arth. & Fromme.
  │ I.
  ⌡Puccinia monoica Arth. I.
Arabis oxyphylla Greene.
  Peronospora Arabidis-oxyphyllae Gäumann.
  Peronospora parasitica (P.) Fr.
Arabis pedicellata A. Nels.
  Dicaeoma monoicum (Arth.) Arth. & Fromme.
    I.
Arabis pendulocarpa A. Nels.
  Micropuccinia Holboellii (Rostr.) Arth. &
    Jackson.
Arabis perennans Watson.
  ⌠Micropuccinia Holboellii (Rostr.) Arth. &
  │ Jackson.
  │Puccinia aberrans N. A. F. *1834.*
  │Puccinia Holboellii Rostr.
  │Puccinia palefaciens Diet. & Holw.
  ⌡Puccinia Thlaspeos N. A. F. *2891.*

Arabis platysperma Gray.
Arabis Selbyi Rydb.
  { Aecidium monoicum Pk.
  { Dicaeoma monoicum (Arth.) Arth. & Fromme.
    I.
Arabis Suksdorfii Howell.
  Puccinia Arabis M. E. Jones.
  Puccinia Holboellii Rostr.
Arabis virginica (L.) Trel.
  { Albugo candida (P. ex Lév.) O. Kuntze.
  { Cystopus candidus (P.) ex Lév.
  Peronospora Lepidii (McAlpine) G. W. Wilson.
Arabis Whitedii Piper.
  { Aecidium monoicum Pk.
  { Dicaeoma monoicum (Arth.) Arth. & Fromme.
  { I.
  { Puccinia monoica Arth. I.
Arabis sp. indet.
  Aecidium Bahiae B. & C.
  Darluca longiseta Henn.
  Pyrenophora depressa Pk.
Erysimum asperrimum (Greene) Rydb.
  Puccinia subnitens Diet. I.
  Plasmodiophora Brassicae Wor.
Erysimum asperum DC.
  { Dicaeoma Sarcobati Arth. I.
  { Puccinia subnitens Diet. I.
  Peronospora parasitica (P.) Fr.
  Plasmodiophora Brassicae Wor.
  Puccinia aberrans Auct. Amer. p. p.
  Puccinia Holboellii Rostr.
Erysimum asperum DC., var. arkansanum Gray.
  Puccinia aberrans Pk.
Erysimum cheiranthoides L.
  Cercospora Erysimi J. J. Davis.
  Erysiphe Polygoni DC. †
  Peronospora parasitica (P.) Fr.
  Plasmodiophora Brassicae Wor.
  Puccinia Holboellii Rostr.
Erysimum parviflorum Nutt.
  Peronospora parasitica (P.) Fr.
  Phoma herbarum Westd.
  Plasmodiophora Brassicae Wor.
Erysimum perofskianum Fisch. & Mey.
  Plasmodiophora Brassicae Wor.
Erysimum pulchellum J. Gay.
  Rhizoctonia Solani Kühn.
Erysimum repandum L.
  { Dicaeoma Sarcobati Arth. I.
  { Puccinia subnitens Diet. I.
Cheirinia sp. indet.
  Albugo candida (P. ex Lév.) O. Kuntze.
Cheiranthus asper Cham. & Schl.
  Albugo candida (P. ex Lév.) O. Kuntze.
  Pleospora vulgaris Niessl.
Cheiranthus cheiri L.
  Albugo candida (P. ex Lév.) O. Kuntze.
  Ascochyta Cheiranthi Bres.

Cheiranthus Menziesii Benth. & Hook.
  { Aecidium auriellum Pk.
  { Aecidium monoicum Pk.
  { Dicaeoma monoicum (Arth.) Arth. & Fromme.
  { I.
Cheiranthus pacificus Sheldon.
  Albugo candida (P. ex Lév.) O. Kuntze.
Cheiranthus pygmaeus Adams.
  { Puccinia Cheiranthi Ell. & Ev.
  { Puccinia Holboellii Rostr.
Cheiranthus sp. indet.
  { Cystopus candidus (P.) ex Lév.
  { Uredo Cheiranthi P.
  Pleospora quadriseptata Cke. & Hark.
  { Sphaerella Cruciferarum (Fr.) Sacc.
  { Sphaeria Cruciferarum Fr.
Lobularia maritima (L.) Desv.
  Peronospora parasitica (P.) Fr.
  Plasmodiophora Brassicae Wor.
  Rhizoctonia Solani Kühn.
Braya purpurascens Bunge.
  Pleospora Drabae Schrt.
  Pleospora platyspora Sacc.
  Rhabdospora Drabae (Fckl.) Berl. & Vogl.
  Mycosphaerella confinis (Karst.) J. Lind.
  { Mycosphaerella Cruciferarum (Fr.) Dearness.
  { Sphaerella Cruciferarum (Fr.) Sacc.
  Mycosphaerella tassiana (De Not.) Johans.
  Sphaerotheca Humuli (DC.) Burrill, var.
    fuliginea (Schl.) Salmon.
Braya sp. indet.
  Leptosphaeria norvegica Rostr.
Hesperis matronalis L.
  Albugo candida (P. ex Lév.) O. Kuntze.
  Peronospora parasitica (P.) Fr.
  Plasmodiophora Brassicae Wor.
Hesperis Pallasii Torr. & Gray.
  Cladosporium herbarum (P.) ex Lk.
  Pleospora herbarum (Fr.) Rabh.
  Puccinia Thlaspeos Schubert.
  Pyrenophora Androsaces (Fckl.) Sacc.
  Pyrenophora Cerastii (Oud.) J. Lind.
  Pyrenophora comata (Niessl) Sacc.
  Mycosphaerella tassiana (De Not.) Johans.
Matthiola bicornis DC.
  Plasmodiophora Brassicae Wor.
Matthiola incana R. Br.
  Plasmodiophora Brassicae Wor.
  Pleospora quadriseptata Cke. & Hark.
  Rhizoctonia Solani Kühn.
Parrya arctica R. Br.
  Mycosphaerella pachyasca (Rostr.) Vestergren.
  Pleospora herbarum (Fr.) Rabh.
  Pyrenophora chrysospora (Niessl) Sacc.
Parrya macrocarpa R. Br.
  Leptothyrium vulgare, var. Parryae Sacc.
  Pyrenophora chrysospora (Niessl) Sacc.

Parrya nudicaulis Boiss.
  Pyrenophora comata (Niessl) Sacc.
Parrya platycarpa Hook. & F. Thom.
  ⎰Micropuccinia utahensis (Garrett) Arth. &
  ⎱ Jackson.
  ⎰Puccinia Clementis Garrett.
Parrya sp. indet.
  Puccinia monoica Arth. I.
Clausia sp. indet.
  Stictis foliicola B. & C.
Conringia orientalis (L.) Dumort.
  Plasmodiophora Brassicae Wor.
  Septoria peregrina Sacc.
Cruciferae gen. indet.
  Puccinia Barbareae Cke.

CAPPARIDACEAE

Cleome gynandra L.
  Cercospora conspicua Earle.
Cleome lutea Hook.
  Dicaeoma Sarcobati Arth. I.
Cleome pentaphylla ex Stevenson.
  Cercospora conspicua Earle.
Cleome pungens Willd.
  Cercospora Cleomis Ell. & Halsted.
Cleome serrulata Pursh.
  ⎰Aecidium Cleomis Ell. & Anderson.
  ⎟Dicaeoma Sarcobati Arth. I.
  ⎟Puccinia Sarcobati (Arth.) Bethel. I.
  ⎱Puccinia subnitens Diet. I.
  Cercospora Cleomis Ell. & Halsted.
  Heterosporium hybridum Ell. & Ev.
Cleome Sonorae Gray.
  Dicaeoma Sarcobati (Bethel) Arth. I.
Cleome spinosa L.
  Puccinia subnitens Diet. I.
  Cercospora conspicua Earle.
Cleomella angustifolia Torr.
Cleomella Montrosae Payson.
Cleomella parviflora Gray.
  ⎰Aecidium Cleomis Ell. & F. W. Anderson.
  ⎨Dicaeoma Sarcobati Arth. I.
  ⎱Puccinia subnitens Diet. I.
Isomeris arborea Nutt.
  ⎰Aecidium Anisacanthi Pk.
  ⎟Aecidium isomerinum Pk.
  ⎟Dicaeoma Sarcobati Arth. I.
  ⎱Puccinia subnitens Diet. I.
  Thyridium lividum P.
Isomeris sp. indet.
  Cladosporium herbarum (P.) ex Lk.
  Clasterosporium carpophilum (Lév.) Aderh.
Polanisia graveolens Raf.
  Cercospora Cleomis Ell. & Halsted.
Capparis cynophallophora L.
  Asterina radians Ell.

Capparis jamaicensis Jacq.
  ⎰Asteridium lepidigenoides (Ell. & Ev.) Sacc.
  ⎱Asterina lepidigenoides Ell. & Ev.
  Hysterium Capparidis B. & C.
Morisonia americana L.
  ⎰Coriolus polygrammus (B. & C.) Pat.
  ⎱Polyporus polygrammus B. & C.
  Lentinus proximus B. & C.

RESEDACEAE

Reseda odorata L.
  Cercospora Resedae Fckl.
  Cladosporium herbarum (P.) ex Lk., var. fasci-
    culare Cda.
  ⎰Corticium vagum B. & C.
  ⎱Rhizoctonia Solani Kühn.

MORINGACEAE

Moringa pterygosperma Gaertn.
  ⎰Polyporus vinctus B.
  ⎱Trametes vincta (B.) Pat.

SARRACENIACEAE

Sarracenia flava L.
  ⎧Mollisia atrata (P.) Karst.
  ⎪Peziza atrata P.
  ⎨Pyrenopeziza atrata (P.) Fckl.
  ⎪Sphaerella Sarraceniae (S.) Sacc.
  ⎩Sphaeria Sarraceniae S.
Sarracenia purpurea L.
  ⎰Brachysporium Sarraceniae MacMillan.
  ⎱Helminthosporium Sarraceniae MacMillan.
  Discosia Artocreas (Tode) ex Fr.
  ⎰Gloeosporium cinctum B. & C.
  ⎨Glomerella cincta (Stoneman) Spaulding & v.
  ⎩ Schrenk.
  ⎰Heptameria scapophila (Pk.) Ckẻ.
  ⎱Leptosphaeria scapophila (Pk.) Sacc.
  ⎰Sphaeria scapophila Pk.
  Peckia Sarraceniae Pk. & Clinton.
  Pestalozzia aquatica Ell. & Ev.
  Mycosphaerella Pontederiae (Pk.) House.
  ⎰Mycosphaerella Sarraceniae (S.) House.
  ⎨Sphaerella Sarraceniae (S.) Sacc.
  ⎩Sphaeria Sarraceniae S.
Sarracenia rubra Walt.
Sarracenia variolaris Michx.
  ⎰Sphaerella Sarraceniae (S.) Sacc.
  ⎱Sphaeria Sarraceniae S.
Darlingtonia californica Torr.
  Septoria Chrysamphorae Ell. & Ev.
  Septoria Darlingtoniae Dearness & House.

CRASSULACEAE

Sedum acre L.
Sedum album L.
  Vermicularia herbarum Westd.
Sedum anglicum Huds.
  Rhizoctonia Solani Kühn.

Sedum annuum L.
  Cladosporium herbarum (P.) ex Lk.
  Pyrenophora chrysospora (Niessl) Sacc.
  Sphaerella pachyasca Rostr.
Sedum debile Watson.
  ⎰Micropuccinia Rydbergii (Garrett) Arth. &
  ⎱ Jackson.
  ⎩Puccinia Rhodiolae Garrett non B. & Br.
Sedum maximum Suter.
Sedum reflexum L.
  Vermicularia herbarum Westd.
Sedum purpureum Tausch.
  Septoria Sedi (Lib.) Westd.
  Septoria sedicola Pk.
  Vermicularia beneficiens Pk.
  Vermicularia Dematium (P.) Fr.
Sedum reflexum L.
  Vermicularia herbarum Westd.
Sedum rhodanthum Gray.
  Tylostoma Purpusii Henn.
Sedum Rhodiola Coult. non DC.
  ⎰Micropuccinia Blyttii DeToni.
  ⎪Micropuccinia Rhodiolae (B. & Br.) Arth. &
  ⎨ Jackson.
  ⎪Puccinia Blyttii De Toni.
  ⎩Puccinia Rhodiolae B. & Br.
Sedum roseum (L.) Scop.
  Cladosporium herbarum (P.) ex Lk.
  Diaporthe muralis Speg.
  Dothidella thoracella (Rostr.) Sacc.
  Sphaerella confinis Karst.
  Sphaerella pachyasca Rostr.
Sedum spectabile Bor.
  Rhizoctonia Solani Kühn.
  Septoria Sedi (Lib.) Westd.
  Sphaeronema minutulum D. Sacc.
Sedum stenopetalum Pursh.
  ⎰Micropuccinia Rydbergii (Garrett) Arth. &
  ⎨ Jackson.
  ⎩Puccinia Rydbergii Garrett.
Sedum Telephium L.
  ⎰Hypoderma commune (Fr.) Duby.
  ⎱Hysterium commune Fr.
  Septoria Sedi (Lib.) Westd.
Sedum villosum L.
  Pyrenophora chrysospora (Niessl) Sacc., var.
    polaris Karst.
  Septoria Sedi (Lib.) Westd.
Sedum sp. indet.
  Cercospora Sedi Ell. & Ev.
  Coniosporium toruloides Sacc.
  Diplodia sedicola Cke. & Hark.
  Vermicularia Telephii Karst.
Sempervivum punctatum C. Sm.
  Endophyllum Sempervivi (A. & S.) DBy.
Bryophyllum pinnatum Kurz.
  Cladosporium herbarum (P.) ex Lk.
  Stilbella flavida Henn.

Crassula sp. indet.
  Diplodia Crassulae Cke. & Hark.
Penthorum sedoides L.
  Cercospora sedoides Ell. & Ev.

SAXIFRAGACEAE

Saxifraga aizoides L.
  Phyllosticta groenlandica Allescher.
  Phyllosticta Saxifragarum Allescher.
  Pleospora herbarum (Fr.) Rabh.
  Septoria Saxifragae Pass., var arctica Alles-
    cher.
Saxifraga Aizoon Jacq.
  Exobasidium Warmingii Rostr.
  Pleospora herbarum (Fr.) Rabh.
  Pyrenophora comata (Awd. & Niessl) Sacc.
  Sphaerella minor Karst.
Saxifraga Aizoon Jacq., var. **brevifolia** Engler.
  Pyrenophora chrysospora (Niessl) Sacc., var.
    polaris Karst.
  Sphaerella Saxifragae Pass.
Saxifraga arguta D. Don.
  ⎰Micropuccinia Heucherae (Diet.) Arth. &
  ⎪ Jackson.
  ⎪Puccinia Heucherae Diet.
  ⎨Puccinia Saxifragae Schl.
  ⎪Micropuccinia pallidomaculata (Ell. & Ev.)
  ⎪ Arth. & Jackson.
  ⎩Puccinia pallido-maculata Ell. & Ev.
Saxifraga austromontana Wiegand.
  Micropuccinia turrita (Arth.) Arth. & Jackson.
Saxifraga bracteata D. Don.
  Asteroma Saxifragae Ell. & Ev.
  ⎰Caeoma Saxifragarum Auct. Amer.
  ⎱Uredo alpina (Juel) Arth. I.
Saxifraga bracteosa Suksdorf.
  Puccinia Heucherae Diet.
Saxifraga caespitosa L.
  Pleospora herbarum (Fr.) Rabh.
  Pyrenophora chrysospora (Niessl) Sacc.
Saxifraga californica Greene.
  Micropuccinia curtipes (Howe) Arth. & Jack-
    son.
Saxifraga cernua L.
  Cladosporium herbarum (P.) ex Lk.
  Pleospora herbarum (Fr.) Rabh.
  Pleospora infectoria Fckl.
  ⎰Micropuccinia Saxifragae (Schl.) Rostr.
  ⎱Puccinia Saxifragae Schl.
  ⎰Mycosphaerella pachyasca (Rostr.) Vestergren.
  ⎱Sphaerella pachyasca Rostr.
  Synchytrium groenlandicum Allescher.
Saxifraga columbiana Piper.
Saxifraga debilis Engelm.
  ⎰Micropuccinia curtipes (Howe) Arth. & Jack-
  ⎨ son.
  ⎩Puccinia curtipes Howe.

Saxifraga flagellaris Willd.
⎰ Caeoma Saxifragarum Auct. Amer.
⎱ Melampsora alpina Juel. I.
⎩ Uredo alpina (Juel) Arth. I.
　Pleospora infectoria Fckl.
Saxifraga fragosa Suksdorf.
⎰ Micropuccinia Heucherae (Diet.) Arth. &
⎱ Jackson.
　Puccinia Heucherae Diet.
Saxifraga groenlandica ex Rostr.
　Phoma alpina Speg.
　Pleospora herbarum (Fr.) Rabh.
　Pyrenophora coronata (Niessl) Sacc.
Saxifraga heterantha Hook.
　Puccinia Heterisiae H. S. Jackson.
Saxifraga hieraciifolia Waldst. & Kit.
　Pleospora herbarum (Fr.) Rabh.
Saxifraga Hirculus L.
　Dothidella sphaerelloides Dearness.
　Mycosphaerella pachyasca (Rostr.) Vestergren.
　Pleospora herbarum (Fr.) Rabh.
Saxifraga integrifolia Hook.
⎰ Micropuccinia curtipes (Howe) Arth. & Jack-
⎱ son.
　Puccinia curtipes Howe.
Saxifraga Lyallii Engler.
　Puccinia curtipes Howe.
⎰ Micropuccinia pallidomaculata (Ell. & Ev.)
⎱ Arth. & Jackson.
　Puccinia pallidomaculata Ell. & Ev.
　Puccinia Saxifragae Schl.
Saxifraga Marshallii Greene.
　Micropuccinia curtipes (Howe) Arth. & Jack-
　son.
　Puccinia Saxifragae Schl.
Saxifraga mertensiana Bong.
⎰ Micropuccinia Heterisiae (H. S. Jackson) Arth.
⎱ & Jackson.
　Puccinia aspera Diet. & Holw.
　Puccinia Heterisiae H. S. Jackson.
⎰ Micropuccinia Heucherae (Diet.) Arth. &
⎱ Jackson.
　Puccinia Heucherae Diet.
Saxifraga neglecta Bray.
　Puccinia laurentiana Trel.
Saxifraga nelsoniana Don.
⎰ Micropuccinia Heucherae (Diet.) Arth. &
⎱ Jackson.
　Puccinia Heucherae Diet.
　Mycosphaerella minor (Karst.) Dearness.
　Sphaerella minor Karst.
　Sphaerella trichophila Karst., var. Saxifragae
　Dearness.
Saxifraga nivalis L.
　Cladosporium herbarum (P.) ex Lk.
　Leptosphaeria vanhoeffeniana Allescher.
　Phoma Saxifragarum Westd.
　Phoma vanhoeffeniana Allescher.
　Pleospora herbarum (Fr.) Rabh.

　Pleospora infectoria Fckl.
　Pleospora mendax (De Not.) Sacc.
⎰ Micropuccinia curtipes (Howe) Arth. & Jack-
⎱ son.
　Puccinia curtipes Howe.
　Puccinia Saxifragae Schl.
　Pyrenophora chrysospora (Niessl) Sacc.
Saxifraga nootkana Moc.
　Micropuccinia jueliana (Diet.) Arth. & Jack-
　son.
Saxifraga nudicaulis D. Don.
⎰ Micropuccinia laurentiana (Trel.) Arth. &
⎱ Jackson.
　Puccinia laurentiana Trel.
Saxifraga occidentalis Watson.
　Puccinia Heucherae (S.) Diet.
Saxifraga oppositifolia L.
　Cladosporium herbarum (P.) ex Lk.
　Exobasidium Warmingii Rostr.
　Leptosphaeria brachyasca Rostr.
⎰ Melampsora alpina Juel. I.
⎪ Melampsora arctica Rostr. I.
⎨ Uredo alpina (Juel) Arth. I.
⎩ Uredo rostrupiana Arth. I.
　Phyllosticta groenlandica Allescher.
　Pleospora infectoria Fckl.
　Pyrenophora Cerastii (Oud.) J. Lind.
　Pyrenophora chrysospora (Niessl) Sacc.
　Sphaerella minor Karst.
Saxifraga oregana Howells.
⎰ Micropuccinia curtipes (Howe) Arth. & Jack-
⎱ son.
　Puccinia curtipes Howe.
Saxifraga parviflora Biv.
　Laestadia Saxifragae Sacc. & Scalia.
Saxifraga peltata Torr.
　Peziza setigera Phil.
Saxifraga pennsylvanica L.
⎰ Micropuccinia curtipes (Howe) Arth. & Jack-
⎱ son.
　Puccinia curtipes Howe.
⎰ Dasyspora Saxifragae (Schl.) Arth.
⎱ Puccinia Saxifragae Schl.
　Septoria albicans Ell. & Ev.
Saxifraga punctata L.
⎰ Puccinia Chrysoplenii Grev.
⎪ Puccinia curtipes Syd. Ured. *1917.*
⎨ Puccinia Heucherae Diet.
⎩ Puccinia spreta Pk.
　Puccinia pallidomaculata Ell. & Ev.
Saxifraga rhomboidea Greene.
　Micropuccinia curtipes (Howe) Arth. & Jack-
　son.
Saxifraga rivularis L.
　Mycosphaerella pachyasca (Rostr.) Vestergren.
　Phoma vanhoeffeniana Allescher.
　Micropuccinia curtipes (Howe) Arth. & Jack-
　son.

Saxifraga rivularis (*cont.*)
  Micropuccinia Saxifragae (Schl.) Rostr.
  Puccinia congregata Ell. & Hark.
  Puccinia Saxifragae Schl.
  Pyrenophora chrysospora (Niessl) Sacc.
Saxifraga rivularis L., var. **purpurascens** Lange.
  Phoma vanhoeffeniana Allescher.
  Pyrenophora chrysospora (Niessl) Sacc.
Saxifraga stellaris L.
  Pseudopeziza axillaris Rostr.
  Sphaerella pachyasca Rostr.
  Mycosphaerella tassiana (De Not.) Johans.
Saxifraga stellaris L., var. **comosa** Willd.
  Cladosporium herbarum (P.) ex Lk.
  Phyllosticta groenlandica Allescher.
  Pyrenophora Cerastii (Oud.) J. Lind.
  Pyrenophora chrysospora (Niessl) Sacc.
Saxifraga tricuspidata Rottb.
  Cladosporium herbarum (P.) ex Lk.
  Coniothyrium Saxifragae Rostr.
  Puccinia Saxifragae Schl.
  Micropuccinia Saxifragae-tricuspidatae
    (Henn.) Arth. & Jackson.
  Puccinia Saxifragae-tricuspidatae Henn.
Saxifraga virginiensis Michx.
  Erysiphe Polygoni DC. †
  Micropuccinia curtipes (Howe) Arth. & Jackson.
  Puccinia curtipes Howe.
  Puccinia Saxifragae Syd. Ured. *1320*.
  Puccinia Saxifragae, var. curtipes Diet.
  Puccinia striata Cke.
  Puccinia Saxifragae Schl.
Saxifraga sp. indet.
  Septoria Saxifragae Pass.
Tiarella cordifolia L.
  Puccinia curtipes Howe.
  Micropuccinia Heucherae (Diet.) Arth. & Jackson.
  Puccinia Heucherae Diet.
  Puccinia Saxifragae Schl.
  Puccinia spreta Pk.
  Puccinia Tiarellae B. & C.
Tiarella laciniata Hook.
  Puccinia Heucherae Diet.
Tiarella trifoliata L.
  Micropuccinia Heucherae (Diet.) Arth. & Jackson.
  Puccinia Heucherae Diet.
  Puccinia trifoliatae Ell. & Ev.
Tiarella unifoliata Hook.
  Micropuccinia Heucherae (Diet.) Arth. & Jackson.
  Puccinia Heucherae Diet.
Heuchera americana L.
  Cercospora Heucherae Ell. & Martin.
  Cercospora heucheriana F. L. Stevens.
  Erysiphe communis Auct. Amer.
  Erysiphe Polygoni DC. †

UREDINALES
  Micropuccinia curtipes (Howe) Arth. & Jackson.
  Puccinia curtipes Howe.
  Puccinia Saxifragae Pazschke.
  Caeoma Heucherae (S.) Lk.
  Micropuccinia Heucherae (Diet.) Arth. & Jackson.
  Puccinia Heucherae Diet.
  Puccinia Saxifragae Schl.
  Puccinia spreta Pk.
  Uredo Heucherae S.
  Septoria Heucherae Pass.
  Septoria Saxifragae Pass.
  Vermicularia Dematium (P.) ex Fr.

Heuchera bracteata (Torr.) Seringe.
  Micropuccinia curtipes (Howe) Arth. & Jackson.
  Micropuccinia Heucherae (Diet.) Arth. & Jackson.

Heuchera cylindrica Dougl.
  Dothidella Heucherae Ell. & Ev.
  Phyllosticta Heucherae Ell. & Ev. non Brun.
  Micropuccinia curtipes (Howe) Arth. & Jackson.
  Puccinia curtipes Howe.
  Puccinia striatospora Pk.
  Micropuccinia Heucherae (Diet.) Arth. & Jackson.
  Puccinia congregata Ell. & Hark.
  Puccinia Heucherae Diet.
  Puccinia Saxifragae Schl.

Heuchera elegans Abrams.
  Micropuccinia Heucherae (Diet.) Arth. & Jackson.

Heuchera glabella Torr. & Gr.
  Phyllosticta excavata Sacc.
  Micropuccinia curtipes (Howe) Arth. & Jackson.
  Puccinia curtipes Howe.
  Puccinia Heucherae Fung. Columb. *1575.*
  Micropuccinia Heucherae (Diet.) Arth. & Jackson.

Heuchera glabra Willd.
Heuchera Hallii Gray.
  Micropuccinia Heucherae (Diet.) Arth. & Jackson.
  Puccinia Heucherae Diet.
  Puccinia Tiarellae B. & C.

Heuchera hispida Pursh.
  Cercospora Heucherae Ell. & Martin.
  Darluca Filum (Biv.) Cast.
  Micropuccinia curtipes (Howe) Arth. & Jackson.
  Puccinia curtipes Howe.
  Puccinia Heucherae Auct. Amer. p. p.

Heuchera micrantha Dougl.
  Micropuccinia Heucherae (Diet.) Arth. & Jackson.
  Puccinia congregata Ell. & Hark.
  Puccinia Heucherae Diet.
Heuchera ovalifolia Nutt.
  Micropuccinia curtipes (Howe) Arth. & Jackson.
  Puccinia curtipes Howe.
Heuchera parvifolia Nutt.
  Pestalozzia Heucherae Tehon & Daniels.
  Phyllactinia corylea (P.) ex Karst.
  Phyllactinia suffulta (Reb.) ex Sacc.
  Micropuccinia curtipes (Howe) Arth. & Jackson.
  Puccinia curtipes Howe.
  Puccinia Heucherae S.?
  Sphaerotheca Castagnei Lév. (aggregate).
  Sphaerotheca Humuli (DC.) Burrill.
Heuchera punctata Auct.
  Puccinia Heucherae Diet.
Heuchera Richardsonii R. Br.
  Micropuccinia Heucherae (Diet.) Arth. & Jackson.
Heuchera rubescens Torr.
  Micropuccinia curtipes (Howe) Arth. & Jackson.
  Puccinia curtipes Howe.
  Micropuccinia Heucherae (Diet.) Arth. & Jackson.
Heuchera villosa Michx.
  Caeoma Heucherae S.
  Micropuccinia Heucherae (Diet.) Arth. & Jackson.
  Puccinia Heucherae Diet.
  Puccinia spreta Pk.
  Uredo Heucherae S.
Tolmiea Menziesii Torr. & Gr.
  Micropuccinia Heucherae (Diet.) Arth. & Jackson.
  Puccinia Heucherae Diet.
  Sphaerotheca Mors-uvae (S.) B. & C.
Tellima affinis Gray.
  Micropuccinia Heucherae (Diet.) Arth. & Jackson.
  Puccinia Heucherae Diet.
Tellima parviflora Hook.
  Micropuccinia Lithophragmae (Holw.) Arth. & Jackson.
  Puccinia Lithophragmae Holw.
Tellima tenella Watson.
  Urocystis Lithophragmae Garrett.
Mitella Breweri Gray?
  Micropuccinia curtipes (Howe) Arth. & Jackson.
  Puccinia curtipes Howe.
  Micropuccinia Heucherae (Diet.) Arth. & Jackson.
  Puccinia Heucherae Diet.

Mitella caulescens Nutt.
  Micropuccinia Heucherae (Diet.) Arth. & Jackson.
  Puccinia Heucherae Diet.
Mitella diphylla L.
  Cercospora Mitellae Hicks. nom. nud.
  Phyllactinia corylea (P.) ex Karst.
  Phyllosticta Mitellae Pk.
  Caeoma Heucherae Lk.
  Micropuccinia Heucherae (Diet.) Arth. & Jackson.
  Puccinia Heucherae Diet.
  Puccinia spreta Pk.
  Puccinia Tiarellae B. & C.
  Ramularia Mitellae Pk.
  Sclerotium deciduum J. J. Davis.
  Septoria Mitellae Ell. & Ev.
  Sphaerotheca Humuli (DC.) Burrill. †
Mitella grandiflora Pursh.
  Micropuccinia Heucherae (Diet.) Arth. & Jackson.
  Puccinia Heucherae Diet.
  Sphaerotheca Humuli (DC.) Burrill, var. fuliginea (Schl.) Salmon.
Mitella nuda L.
  Aecidium Mitellae Ell. et Ev.
  Micropuccinia Heucherae (Diet.) Arth. & Jackson.
  Puccinia congregata Ell. & Hark.
  Puccinia Heucherae Diet.
  Puccinia spreta Pk.
  Puccinia Tiarellae B. & C.
Mitella ovalis Greene.
  Micropuccinia Heucherae (Diet.) Arth. & Jackson.
  Puccinia Heucherae Diet.
Mitella pentandra Hook.
  ?Puccinia curtipes Howe.
  Micropuccinia Heucherae (Diet.) Arth. & Jackson.
  Puccinia Heucherae Diet.
  Puccinia Saxifragae Schl.
Mitella stauropetala Piper.
  Micropuccinia curtipes (Howe) Arth. & Jackson.
  Puccinia curtipes Howe.
  Micropuccinia Heucherae (Diet.) Arth. & Jackson.
Mitella stenopetala Piper.
  Micropuccinia curtipes (Howe) Arth. & Jackson.
Mitella trifida R. Grah.
  Puccinia curtipes Howe.
  Puccinia Saxifragae Fung. Columb. *1379.*
  ?Puccinia Heucherae Diet.
  ?Septoria Mitellae Ell. & Ev.
Elmera racemosa Rydb.
  Puccinia Heucherae Diet.

Parnassia caroliniana Michx.
- Didymosphaerella Parnassiae (Pk.) Cke.
- Didymosphaeria Parnassiae (Pk.) Sacc.
- Sphaeria Parnassiae Pk.
- Erysiphe communis Auct. Amer.
- Erysiphe Polygoni DC. †
- Erysiphe spathulata in Herb. Mo. Bot. Gard.
- Erysiphopsis Parnassiae Halsted.

Parnassia fimbriata Banks.
- Micropuccinia Parnassiae (Arth.) Arth. & Jackson.
- Puccinia Parnassiae Arth.

Parnassia palustris L.
- Aecidium Parnassiae Graves.
- Dicaeoma Parnassiae Arth. & Kern. I.

Philadelphus coronarius L.
- Cercospora angulata Wint.
- Diplodia microspora B. & C.
- Gibberella pulicaris (Fr.) Sacc.
- Gymnosporangium gracilens Kern & Bethel. I.
- Gymnosporangium speciosum Pk. I.
- Nectria cinnabarina (Tode) ex Fr.
- Phoma landeghemiae (Nits.) Sacc.

Philadelphus ellipticus Rydb.
- Gymnosporangium gracilens Kern & Bethel. I.
- Gymnosporangium speciosum Pk. I.

Philadelphus gordonianus Lindl.
- Ramularia Philadelphi Sacc.

Philadelphus grandiflorus Willd.
- Sarcinella heterospora Sacc.

Philadelphus inodorus L.
- Peziza Philadelphi S.
- Pezicula? Philadelphi (S.) Sacc.
- Stictis Philadelphi S.

Philadelphus Keteleerii Carr.
- Gymnosporangium gracilens Kern & Bethel. I.

Philadelphus Lewisii Pursh.
- ?Curcurbitaria Kelseyi Ell. & Ev.
- Phyllactinia corylea (P.) ex Karst.
- Phyllactinia suffulta (Reb.) ex Sacc.
- Septoria Philadelphi Ell. & Ev.

Philadelphus microphyllus Gray.

Philadelphus occidentalis A. Nels.
- Aecidium gracilens Pk.
- Gymnosporangium gracilens Kern & Bethel. I.
- Gymnosporangium speciosum Pk. I.

Philadelphus sp. indet.
- Cercospora angulata Wint.
- Sphaeropsis Syringae (Fr.) Pk. & G. W. Clinton.

Jamesia americana Torr. & Gr.
- Pleospora Edwiniae Clements.
- Stictis Edwiniae Clements.
- Teichosporella Edwiniae (Clements) Sacc. & D. Sacc.
- Teichosporium Edwiniae Clements.

Fendlera falcata Thornb.
- Gymnosporangium gracilens Kern & Bethel. I.

Fendlera rupicola Engelm. & Gray.
- Aecidium Rusbyi Gerard.
- Dasyscypha allantospora Earle.
- Gymnosporangium gracilens Kern & Bethel. I.
- Gymnosporangium speciosum Pk. I.
- Heterosphaeria fendlericola Earle.
- Melospilea emergens Rehm?
- Strickeria Fendlerae Earle.
- Teichospora Fendlerae (Earle) Sacc. & D. Sacc.

Fendlera tomentella Thornb.

Fendlera Wrightii Heller.
- Gymnosporangium gracilens Kern & Bethel. I.
- Gymnosporangium speciosum Pk. I.

Fendlera sp. indet.
- Otthia fendlericola Tracy & Earle.
- Platystomum hysterioides Earle.
- Trematosphaeria Fendlerae Earle.

Whipplea modesta Torr.
- Peronospora Whippleae Ell. & Ev.

Deutzia gracilis Sieb. & Zucc.
- Cercospora Deutziae Ell. & Ev.
- Phyllosticta Deutziae Ell. & Ev.

Decumaria barbata L.
- Cercospora Decumariae Tracy & Earle.

Hydrangea arborescens L.
- Cercospora arborescentis Tehon & Daniels.
- Diaporthe Hydrangeae Ell. & Ev.
- Hypoderma commune (Fr.) Duby.
- Leptosphaeria vagabunda Sacc.
- Phyllosticta Hydrangeae Ell. & Ev.
- Melampsora Hydrangeae Farl.
- Pucciniastrum Hydrangeae (Farl.) Arth.
- Thecopsora Hydrangeae (Farl.) Magn.
- Uredo Hydrangeae B. & C.
- Peziza fracta B. & C.
- Pyrenopeziza fracta (B. & C.) Sacc.

Hydrangea arborescens L., var. **cordata** Torr. & Gr.
- Peziza Hydrangeae S.
- Pirottaea? Hydrangeae (S.) Sacc.

Hydrangea opuloides Koch.
- Ascochyta Hydrangeae Arnaud & Arnaud.
- Phyllosticta Hydrangeae Ell. & Ev.
- Pucciniastrum Hydrangeae (Farl.) Arth.

Hydrangea paniculata Sieb.
- Sclerotium Rolfsii Sacc.

Hydrangea paniculata Sieb., var. **grandiflora** Sieb.
- Hendersonia Hydrangeae Fairman.

Hydrangea vulgaris Michx.
- Peziza fracta B. & C.

Hydrangea sp. indet.
- Botrytis cinerea Auct.
- Cenangium apertum S.
- Cercospora Hydrangeae Ell. & Ev.
- Cercospora hydrangeana Tharp.

Hydrangea sp. indet. (*cont.*)
- Cytospora sphaerocephala (S.) M. A. Curtis.
- Lamyella sphaerocephala (S.) Fr.
- Rabenhorstia sphaerocephala (S.) Starb.
- Sphaeria sphaerocephala S.
- Ohleria Hydrangeae (S.) Cke.
- Sphaeria Hydrangeae S.
- Oospora pallida (B. & Rav.) Sacc. & Vogl.
- Torula pallida B. & Rav.
- Septoria Hydrangeae Bizz.
- ?Sphaeria Sclerotium S.
- Sphaerobolus sparsus S.
- Stictis sparsa (S.) Sacc.
- Tilmadoche gyrocephala (Mont.) Rostf.

Ribes acerifolium Howell.
- Dicaeoma Grossulariae (Lagerh.) Kern. I.

Ribes acicularis Sm. in Rees Cycl.
- Pseudopeziza Ribis Klebahn.

Ribes alpinum L.
- Dicaeoma Grossulariae (Lagerh.) Kern. I.
- Puccinia Grossulariae Lagerh. I.
- Gloeosporium variabile Laub.

Ribes aureum Pursh.

PEZIZINEAE
Pseudopeziza Ribis Klebahn.

HYPOCREALES
- Creonectria purpurea (L.) ex Seaver.
- Nectria cinnabarina (Tode) ex Fr.
- Sphaeria decolorans P. ex Fr.

ERYSIPHACEAE
Sphaerotheca Humuli (DC.) Burrill. †
Sphaerotheca Mors-uvae (S.) B. & C.

SPHAERIALES
- Coniochaeta penicillata (S.) Cke.
- Sphaeria penicillata S.
- Cucurbitaria Ribis Niessl.
- Diaporthe concrescens (S.) Cke.
- Sphaeria concrescens S.
- Diatrype tumida Ell. & Ev.
- Eutypella brunaudiana, var. Ribis-aurei Fairman.
- Glomerella cingulata (Stoneman) Spaulding & v. Schrenk.
- Mycosphaerella aurea R. E. Stone.
- Septoria aurea Ell. & Ev.
- Septoria aurea Ell. & Ev., var. destruens Ell. & Ev.
- Sphaerella aurea R. E. Stone.
- Mycosphaerella Grossulariae (Fr.) Lindau.
- Valsa ribicola Ell. & Ev.

UREDINALES
- Aecidium Grossulariae Schum.
- Dicaeoma Grossulariae (Lagerh.) Kern. I.
- Puccinia albiperidia Arth. I.
- Dicaeoma micranthum (Griffiths) Arth. & Fromme. I.

- Coleosporium ribicola Arth.
- Uredo Jonesii Pk.
- Uredo ribicola C. & E.
- Cronartium occidentale Hedgc., Bethel, & Hunt.
- Peridermium occidentale Hedgc., Bethel, & Hunt. III.
- Cronartium ribicola Auct. Amer. p. p.
- Cronartium ribicola Fischer.
- Caeoma Ribes-alpini Wint.
- Melampsora confluens H. S. Jackson.
- Uredo confluens P.

SPHAEROPSIDALES
Dothiorella ribicola Ell. & Barthol.
Phyllosticta Grossulariae Sacc.
- Septoria aurea Ell. & Ev.
- Septoria aurea, Ell. & Ev., var. destruens Ell. & Ev.
Septoria Grossulariae (Lib.) Westd.
Septoria Ribis Desm.

MELANCONIALES
- Marssonia ribicola Ell. & Ev.
- Marssonina ribicola (Ell. & Ev.) Magn.

Ribes bracteosum Douglas.
- Aecidium Grossulariae Schum.
- Dicaeoma Grossulariae (Lagerh.) Kern. I.
- Puccinia albiperidia Arth. I.
- Cercospora coalescens J. J. Davis.
- Ceriospora Ribis Henn.
- Cronartium ribicola Fischer.
- Gloeosporium Bartholomaei Dearness.
- Gloeosporium Ribis (Lib.) Mont. & Desm.
- Marssonina bracteosum Dearness & Barthol.
- Melampsora confluens H. S. Jackson. I.
- Mycosphaerella Grossulariae (Fr.) Lindau.
- Septoria Ribis Desm.
- Sphaerotheca Humuli (DC.) Burrill.
- Sphaerotheca Mors-uvae (S.) B. & C.

Ribes cereum Douglas.
- Coleosporium ribicola Arth.
- Cronartium occidentale Hedgc., Bethel, & Hunt.
- Cronartium ribicola Fischer.
- Septoria Grossulariae (Lib.) Westd.
- Sphaerotheca Mors-uvae (S.) B. & C.

Ribes coloradense Coville.
- Coleosporium ribicola Arth.
- Cronartium occidentale Hedgc., Bethel & Hunt.
- Cronartium ribicola Fischer.

Ribes Cynosbati L.
- Aecidium Grossulariae Schum.
- Aecidium Grossulariae DC.
- Dicaeoma Grossulariae (Lagerh.) Kern. I.
- Puccinia albiperidia Arth. I.
- Puccinia Grossulariae Lagerh. I.
- Puccinia pringsheimiana Klebahn. I.
- Coleosporium ribicola Arth.

Ribes Cynosbati (*cont.*)
Cronartium ribicola Fischer.
Gloeosporium Ribis (Lib.) Mont. & Desm.
Mycosphaerella Grossulariae (Fr.) Lindau.
{ Phyllactinia corylea (P.) ex Karst.
{ Phyllactinia guttata Lév.
Phyllosticta Grossulariae Sacc.
Plasmopara ribicola Schrt.
Septoria Ribis Desm.
Septoria sibirica Thm.?
{ Sphaerotheca Mors-uvae (S.) B. & C.
{ Sphaerotheca pannosa, var. Ribis Pk.
Ribes divaricatum Douglas.
{ Aecidium Grossulariae Schum.
{ Dicaeoma Grossulariae (Lagerh.) Kern. I.
{ Puccinia Grossulariae Lagerh. I.
Cronartium occidentale Hedgc., Bethel & Hunt.
Cronartium ribicola Fischer.
Melampsora confluens H. S. Jackson. l.
Mycosphaerella Grossulariae (Fr.) Lindau.
Phyllactinia corylea (P.) ex Karst.
Phyllosticta canescens Ell. & Ev.
{ Plasmopara ribicola Schrt.
{ Rhysotheca ribicola (Schrt.) G. W. Wilson.
Micropuccinia Parkerae (Diet. & Holw.) Arth.
  & Jackson.
{ Sphaerotheca Mors-uvae (S.) B. & C.
{ Sphaerotheca pannosa Auct. Amer. p. p.
Ribes divaricatum Douglas, var. **irriguum** Gray.
Septoria Ribis Desm.
Stictis pelvicula P.
Valsa agnostica Cke. & Hark.
Valsa ribesia Karst.
Ribes floridum L'Her.
Asteroma ribicola Ell. & Ev.
{ Diaporthe recondita (S.) Ell. & Ev.
{ Sphaeria recondita S.
{ Diaporthe Strumella (Fr.) Fckl.
{ Diatrype Strumella Fr.
{ Diatrype ribesia (S.) M. A. Curtis.
{ Diatrypella ribesia (S.) Ell. Ev.
{ Sphaeria ribesia S.
Dothidea ribesia (P.) Fr.
{ Fenestella vestita (Fr.) Sacc.
{ Sphaeria vestita Fr.
{ Valsa vestita Fr.
Gloeosporium Ribis (Lib.) Mont. & Desm.
Graphiothecium vinosum J. J. Davis.
Haplosporella Ribis Sacc.
Microsphaera Grossulariae (Wallr. ex Fr.) Lév.
Nectria Ribis (Tode ex Fr.) Oud.
Phyllosticta Grossulariae Sacc.
Pleonectria berolinensis Sacc.
Rosellinia amphisphaerioides Sacc. & Speg.
Scleroderris ribesia (P.) Karst.
Septoria Ribis Desm.
Sphaerella Grossulariae (Fr.) Awd.
{ Haplosporella ribicola (C. & E.) Petrak & Syd.
{ Sphaeropsis ribicola C. & E.

Sphaerotheca Castagnei Lév.
Sphaerotheca Humuli (DC.) Burrill. †
{ Sphaerotheca Mors-uvae (S.) B. & C.
{ Sphaerotheca pannosa Auct. Amer. p. p.

UREDINALES

{ Aecidium Grossulariae Schum.
{ Dicaeoma Grossulariae (Lagerh.) Kern. I.
{ Puccinia albiperidia Arth. I.
{ Puccinia Grossulariae Lagerh. I.
{ Puccinia pringsheimiana Klebahn. I.
{ Puccinia riparia Holw. I.
Coleosporium ribicola Arth.
{ Cronartium ribicola Dietr. nom. nud. 1856.
{ Cronartium ribicola Fischer. 1872.
Cronartium occidentale Hedgc., Bethel & Hunt.
Ribes gordonianum Lem.
{ Dicaeoma Grossulariae (Lagerh.) Kern. I.
{ Puccinia Grossulariae Lagerh. I.
Ribes gracile Michx.
Clypeopycnis aeruginascens Petrak.
Diplodina Grossulariae Sacc. & Br.
{ Dothidea ribesia (P.) ex Fr.
{ Phragmodothella ribesia (P. ex Fr.) Petrak.
{ Plowrightia ribesia (P. ex Fr.) Sacc.
Gloeosporium Ribis (Lib.) Mont. & Desm.
Phyllosticta Grossulariae Sacc.
Pseudopeziza Ribis Klebahn.
Septoria Ribis Desm.
Mycosphaerella Grossulariae (Fr.) Lindau.
Sphaerotheca Mors-uvae (S.) B. & C.

UREDINALES

{ Aecidium Grossulariae Schum.
{ Dicaeoma Grossulariae (Lagerh.) Kern. I.
{ Puccinia albiperidia Arth. I.
{ Puccinia Grossulariae Lagerh. I.
{ Puccinia pringsheimiana Klebahn. I.
Cronartium occidentale Hedgc., Bethel & Hunt.
Cronartium ribicola Fischer.
Ribes gracillima Coville & Britton.
Cronartium occidentale Hedgc., Bethel & Hunt.
Ribes Grossularia L.

PEZIZINEAE

Pseudopeziza Ribis Klebahn.

ERYSIPHACEAE

Phyllactinia corylea (P.) ex Karst.
Sphaerotheca Mors-uvae (S.) B. & C.
Sphaerotheca pannosa Lév.

SPHAERIALES

{ Botryosphaeria Ribis (Tode ex Fr.) Grossen-
{   bacher & Duggar.
{ Nectria Ribis (Tode ex Fr.) Oud.
Cucurbitaria Ribis Niessl.
{ Diatrype Dearnessii Ell. & Ev.
{ Diatrype Stigma, var. Ell. & Ev.
{ Sphaeria subcutanea Herb. S.

Ribes Grossularia (*cont.*)
Leptosphaeria Coniothyrium (Fckl.) Sacc.
Metasphaeria leiostega (Ell.) Sacc.
Plowrightia ribesia (P.) Sacc.
{ Mycosphaerella Grossulariae (Fr.) Lindau.
{ Sphaerella Grossulariae (Fr.) Awd.

UREDINALES
{ Aecidium Grossulariae Schum.
{ Dicaeoma Grossulariae (Lagerh.) Kern. I.
{ Puccinia albiperidia Arth. I.
{ Puccinia Grossulariae Lagerh. I.
{ Puccinia pringsheimiana Klebahn. I.
Coleosporium ribicola Arth.
Cronartium occidentale Hedgc., Bethel & Hunt.
{ Cronartium ribicola Dietr. nom. nud. 1856.
{ Cronartium ribicola Fischer. 1872.

SPHAEROPSIDALES
Hendersonia Grossulariae Oud.
Phoma Ribis Ell. & Barthol.
Phyllosticta Grossulariae Sacc.
Phyllosticta Ribis Ell. & Ev.
{ Septoria Grossulariae (Lib.) Westd.
{ Septoria Ribis N. A. F. *1148a* nec Desm.
Septoria Ribis Desm.
Septoria sibirica Thm.

HYPHOMYCETES
Botrytis cinerea Auct.
Cercospora angulata Wint.

MISCELLANEA
Armillaria mellea (Vahl) ex Fr.
Plasmopara ribicola Schrt.
Ribes hendersonianum Richards.
Sphaerotheca Mors-uvae (S.) B. & C.
Ribes hesperium McClatchie.
Dicaeoma Grossulariae (Lagerh.) Kern. I.
Cronartium ribicola Fischer.
Ribes hirtellum Michx.
{ Aecidium Grossulariae Schum.
{ Dicaeoma Grossulariae (Lagerh.) Kern. I.
{ Puccinia Grossulariae Lagerh. I.
Coleosporium ribicola Arth.
Cronartium occidentale Hedgc., Bethel & Hunt.
Cronartium ribicola Fischer.
Ribes hudsonianum Richards.
Dicaeoma Grossulariae (Lagerh.) Kern. I.
Peridermium Strobi Kleb. III.
Plowrightia ribesia (P. ex Fr.) Sacc.
Sphaerotheca Mors-uvae (S.) B. & C.
Ribes inebrians Lindley.
{ Dicaeoma Grossulariae (Lagerh.) Kern. I.
{ Puccinia Grossulariae Lagerh. I.
Coleosporium ribicola Arth.
Cronartium occidentale Hedgc., Bethel & Hunt.
Cronartium ribicola Fischer.
Lophiostoma quadrinucleatum Karst.

Platystomum compressum (P.) Trev.
Septoria Ribis Desm.
Ribes inerme Rydb.
Dicaeoma Grossulariae (Lagerh.) Kern. I.
Dicaeoma micranthum (Griffiths) Arth. &
    Fromme. I.
Coleosporium ribicola Arth.
Cronartium occidentale Hedgc., Bethel, & Hunt.
Cronartium ribicola Fischer.
Melampsora confluens H. S. Jackson.
Ribes lacustre (P.) Poir.
Diaporthe Strumella (Fr.) Fckl.
Septoria Grossulariae (Lib.) Westd.
Septoria Grossulariae Fung. Columb. *4478.*
Septoria Ribis Desm.
Sphaerotheca Mors-uvae (S.) B. & C.

UREDINALES
{ Aecidium Grossulariae Schum.
{ Dicaeoma Grossulariae (Lagerh.) Kern. I.
{ Puccinia Grossulariae Lagerh. I.
Coleosporium ribicola Arth.
Cronartium ribicola Fischer.
Melampsora confluens H. S. Jackson.
{ Micropuccinia Parkerae (Diet. & Holw.) Arth.
{   & Jackson.
{ Puccinia Parkerae Diet. & Holw.
Ribes laxiflorum Pursh.
{ Dicaeoma Grossulariae (Lagerh.) Kern. I.
{ Puccinia Grossulariae Lagerh. I.
Diaporthe Strumella (Fr.) Fckl., var. oligo-
    carpa Sacc. & Scalia.
Pseudovalsa ribesia Sacc. & Scalia.
Rhynchophoma raduloides Sacc. & Scalia.
Ribes leptanthum Gray.
{ Aecidium Grossulariae Schum.
{ Dicaeoma Grossulariae (Lagerh.) Kern. I.
{ Puccinia albiperidia Arth. I.
{ Dicaeoma micranthum (Griffiths) Arth. &
{   Fromme. I.
{ Puccinia micrantha Griffiths I.
Coleosporium ribicola Arth.
Cronartium occidentale Hedgc., Bethel, & Hunt.
Cucurbitaria Ribis Niessl.
Melampsora confluens H. S. Jackson.
Ribes Lobbii Gray.
Gloeosporium Ribis (Lib.) Mont. & Desm.
Ribes malvaceum Sm. in Rees Cycl.
{ Dicaeoma Grossulariae (Lagerh.) Kern. I.
{ Puccinia Grossulariae Lagerh. I.
Cronartium occidentale Hedgc., Bethel & Hunt.
Ribes mescalerium Coville.
Ribes montigenum McClatchie.
Coleosporium ribicola Arth.
Ribes nevadense Kellogg.
Coleosporium ribicola Arth.
Melampsora confluens H. S. Jackson.

Ribes nigrum L.
{ Aecidium Grossulariae Schum.
{ Puccinia Grossulariae Lagerh. I.
  Botryosphaeria Ribis (Tode ex Fr.) Grossen-
    bacher & Duggar.
  Coleosporium ribicola Arth.
  Cronartium occidentale Hedgc., Bethel & Hunt.
  Cronartium ribicola Fischer.
{ Gloeosporium Ribis (Lib.) Mont. & Desm.
{ Leptothyrium Ribis Lib.
{ Pseudopeziza Ribis Klebahn.
{ Coniothyrium Fuckelii Sacc.
{ Leptosphaeria Coniothyrium (Fckl.) Sacc.
  Microsphaera Grossulariae (Wallr. ex Fr.) Lév.
  Mycosphaerella Grossulariae (Fr.) Lindau.
  Septoria Ribis Desm.
  Sphaeria (Depazea) ribicola Fr.
  Sphaerotheca Mors-uvae (S.) B. & C.

Ribes oxyacanthoides L.
{ Gloeosporium Ribis (Lib.) Desm. & Mont.
{ Pseudopeziza Ribis Klebahn.
  Glomerella cingulata (Stoneman) Spaulding &
    v. Schrenk.
  Mycosphaerella Grossulariae (Fr.) Lindau.
  Phyllosticta Grossulariae Sacc.
{ Peronospora ribicola Schrt.
{ Plasmopara ribicola Schrt.
{ Rhysotheca ribicola (Schrt.) G. W. Wilson.

UREDINALES

{ Aecidium Grossulariae Schum.
  Dicaeoma Grossulariae (Lagerh.) Kern. I. 1913.
  Dicaeoma Grossulariae (Lagerh.) H. S. Jack-
{   son. I. 1916.
  Puccinia albiperidia Arth. I.
  Puccinia Grossulariae (Schum.) Lagerh. I.
{ Puccinia pringsheimiana Klebahn. I.
  Cronartium ribicola Fischer.
  Puccinia Ribis DC.

Ribes petiolare Dougl.
  Dicaeoma Grossulariae (Lagerh.) Kern. I.
  Melampsora confluens H. S. Jackson.

Ribes pinetorum Nutt.
  Coleosporium ribicola Arth.

Ribes prostratum L'Her.
  Cylindrosporium Ribis J. J. Davis.
{ Gloeosporium Ribis (Lib.) Mont. & Desm.
{ Pseudopeziza Ribis Klebahn.
  Hainesia Lythri (Desm.) v. Höhnel.
  Lachnella albilabra Ell. & Ev.
  Lophiotrema incisum Ell. & Ev.
  Microsphaera Grossulariae (Wallr. ex Fr.) Lév.
  Mycosphaerella Grossulariae (Fr.) Lindau.
  Nectria cinnabarina (Tode) ex Fr.
{ Plasmopara ribicola Schrt.
{ Rhysotheca ribicola (Schrt.) G. W. Wilson.
  Septoria Ribis Desm.

  Septoria sibirica Thm.
  Sphaerotheca Mors-uvae (S.) B. & C.
  Thelephora terrestris (Ehrh.) ex Fr.

UREDINALES

{ Aecidium Grossulariae Schum. 1803.
{ Aecidium Grossulariae DC. 1815.
{ Dicaeoma Grossulariae (Lagerh.) Kern. I.
{ Puccinia albiperidia Arth. I.
{ Puccinia Grossulariae Lagerh. I.
  Cronartium occidentale Hedgc., Bethel & Hunt.
  Cronartium ribicola Fischer.
{ Micropuccinia Ribis (DC.) Rostr.
{ Puccinia Grossulariae Wint. p. p.
{ Puccinia pulchella Pk.
{ Puccinia Ribis DC.

Ribes pumilum Nutt.
Ribes Purpusii Köhne.
  Coleosporium ribicola Arth.

Ribes reclinatum L.
  Cronartium occidentale Hedgc., Bethel & Hunt.
  Cronartium ribicola Fischer.

Ribes Roezli (Regel) Coville & Britton.
  Cronartium ribicola Fischer.

Ribes rotundifolium Michx.
  Cucurbitaria Ribis Niessl.
{ Homostegia Kelseyi Ell. & Ev.
{ Phragmodothella Kelseyi (Ell. & Ev.) Theissen
{   & Syd.
  Microsphaera Grossulariae (Wallr. ex Fr.) Lév.
{ Cucurbitaria Ribis (Tode ex Fr.) O. Kuntze.
{ Nectria Ribis (Tode ex Fr.) Oud.
  Peniophora cinerea Fr.
{ Peronospora ribicola Schrt.
{ Plasmopara ribicola Schrt.
{ Rhysotheca ribicola (Schrt.) G. W. Wilson.
  Phyllosticta Grossulariae Sacc.
{ Rhabdospora ribicola (B. & C.) Sacc.
{ Septoria ribicola B. & C.
  Septoria Ribis Desm.
  Septoria Ribis Desm., var. Ribis-rotundifolii
    Sacc.
{ Mycosphaerella Grossulariae (Fr.) Lindau.
{ Sphaerella Grossulariae (Fr.) Awd.
{ Erysiphe Mors-uvae S.
{ Sphaerotheca Mors-uvae (S.) B. & C.
{ Sphaerotheca pannosa Auct. Amer. p. p.

UREDINALES

{ Aecidium Grossulariae Schum.
{ Caeoma grossulariatum Lk.
{ Dicaeoma Grossulariae (Lagerh.) Kern. I.
{ Puccinia albiperidia Arth. I.
{ Puccinia Grossulariae Lagerh. I.
{ Puccinia pringsheimiana Klebahn. I.
{ Puccinia Ribesii-Caricis Klebahn. I.
  Cronartium ribicola Fischer.

Ribes sanguineum Pursh.
 Cercospora ribicola Ell. & Ev.
 Cucurbitaria Ribis Niessl.
 Microsphaera Grossulariae (Wallr. ex Fr.) Lév.
 Septoria sanguinea Dearness.

UREDINALES

{ Dicaeoma Grossulariae (Lagerh.) Kern. I.
{ Puccinia Grossulariae Lagerh. I.
 Coleosporium ribicola Arth.
 Cronartium occidentale Hedgc.,Bethel,& Hunt.
 Cronartium ribicola Fischer.

Ribes saximontanum E. Nels.
{ Aecidium Grossulariae Schum.
{ Puccinia Grossulariae Lagerh. I.

Ribes saxosum Hook.
 Puccinia Grossulariae Lagerh. I.
 Coleosporium ribicola Arth.
{ Caeoma confluens (P.) Schrt.
{ Melampsora confluens H. S. Jackson.
{ Melampsora Ribesii-purpureae Klebahn.
{ Uredo confluens P.

Ribes setosum Lindley.
{ Aecidium Grossulariae Schum.
{ Dicaeoma Grossulariae (Lagerh.) Kern. I.
{ Puccinia Grossulariae Lagerh.
 Dicaeoma micranthum (D. Griff.) Arth. &
  Fromme. I.
 Cronartium ribicola Fischer.
 Pleonectria Ribis (Rabh.) Karst.

Ribes spectabile Auct.
 Sphaerotheca Humuli (DC.) Burrill.

Ribes tenuiflorum Lindl.
 Cercospora ribicola Ell. & Ev.
 Cronartium occidentale Hedgc., Bethel & Hunt.

Ribes triste Pallas.
 Dicaeoma Grossulariae (Lagerh.) Kern. I.
 Coleosporium ribicola Arth.
 Cronartium ribicola Fischer.
 Cylindrosporium Ribis J. J. Davis.
{ ?Gloeosporidiella Ribis (Lib.) Petrak.
{ Gloeosporium Ribis (Lib.) Desm. & Mont.
 Melampsora confluens H. S. Jackson.
{ Micropuccinia Ribis (DC.) Rostr.
{ Puccinia pulchella Pk.
{ Puccinia Ribis DC.

Ribes triste Pallas, var. **albinervium** (Michx.)
 Fern.
{ Plasmopara ribicola Schrt.
{ Rhysotheca ribicola (Schrt.) G. W. Wilson.

Ribes vallicola Greene.
{ Caeoma confluens (P.) Schrt.
{ Melampsora confluens H. S. Jackson.
{ Melampsora Ribesii-purpureae Klebahn.
{ Uredo confluens P.
 Coleosporium ribicola Arth.

Ribes velutinum Greene.
 Cronartium occidentale Hedgc., Bethel & Hunt.

Ribes viscosissimum Pursh.
 Cercospora ribicola Ell. & Ev.
 Cronartium ribicola Fischer.
 Septoriopsis Ribis J. J. Davis.
Ribes vulgare Lam.
{ Botryosphaeria Ribis (Tode ex Fr.) Grossen-
  bacher & Duggar.
{ Nectria Ribis (Tode ex Fr.) Oud.
{ Sphaeria appendiculata S. Syn. Car.
{ Sphaeria Ribis Tode ex Fr.
{ Tubercularia vulgaris Tode ex Fr.
 Botryosphaeria Ribis (Tode ex Fr.) Grossen-
  bacher & Duggar, var. achromogena Gros-
  senbacher & Duggar.
 Cercospora angulata Wint.
 Cercospora Ribis Earle.
 Cylindrosporium Ribis J. J. Davis.
 Diatrypella ribesia (S.) Ell. & Ev.
{ Gloeosporium Ribis (Lib.) Mont. & Desm.
{ Pseudopeziza Ribis Klebahn.
 Gloeosporium rufomaculans (B.) Thm.
{ Glomerella cingulata (Stoneman) Spaulding &
{ v. Schrenk.
 Haplosporella pennsylvanica (B. & C.) Petrak
  & Syd.
 Hypholoma perplexum Pk.
{ Macrophoma hyalina (B. & C.) Berl. & Vogl.
{ Phoma hyalina (B. & C.) Sacc.
{ Sphaeropsis hyalina B. & C.
 Nectria cinnabarina (Tode) ex Fr.
 Pestalozzia Guepini Desm.
 Phyllosticta Grossulariae Sacc.
 Plasmopara ribicola Schrt.
{ Nectria berolinensis (Sacc.) Cke.
{ Nectria Ribis Niessl.
{ Pleonectria berolinensis Sacc.
{ Pleonectria Ribis (Niessl) Karst.
{ Thyronectria berolinensis (Sacc.) Seaver.
 Plowrightia ribesia (P. ex Fr.) Sacc.
 Septoria Ribis Desm.
 Septoria sibirica Thm.
{ Mycosphaerella Grossulariae (Fr.) Lindau.
{ Sphaerella Grossulariae (Fr.) Awd.
 Sphaerotheca Humuli (DC.) Burrill.
 Sphaerotheca Mors-uvae (S.) B. & C.
 Sphaerotheca pannosa Bessey Prelim. List.

UREDINALES

{ Aecidium albiperidium Arth.
{ Aecidium Grossulariae Schum.
{ Dicaeoma Grossulariae (Lagerh.) Kern. I.
{ Puccinia albiperidia Arth. I.
{ Puccinia Caricis Auct. p. p. I.
{ Puccinia Grossulariae Lagerh. I.
{ Puccinia pringsheimiana Klebahn. I.
{ Puccinia Ribesii-Caricis Klebahn. I.
{ Cronartium ribicola Dietr. nom. nud. 1856.
{ Cronartium ribicola Fischer. 1872.
{ Peridermium Strobi Klebahn. III.

Ribes vulgare (*cont.*)
- Micropuccinia Ribis (DC.) Rostr.
- Puccinia bullata Lk.
- Puccinia Grossulariae Wint. p. p.
- Puccinia pulchella Pk.
- Puccinia Ribis DC.
- Puccinia Ribis DC., var. papillifera Lagerh.

Ribes Wolfii Roth.
- Coleosporium ribicola (C. & E.) Arth.

Ribes (currant).
- Fomes Ribis (Schum. ex Fr.) Cke.
- Fulvifomes Ribis (Schum. ex Fr.) Murrill.
- Polyporus Ribis Schum. ex Fr.
- Pyropolyporus Ribis (Schum. ex Fr.) Murrill.
- Fumago vagans Fr.
- Nectria ditissima Tul.
- Physalospora Cydoniae Arnaud.
- Schizosaccharomyces octosporus Beijerinck.
- Septoria aurea Ell. & Ev., var. destruens Ell. & Ev.

Ribes (gooseberry).
- Gloeosporium ribicola Ell. & Ev.
- Guignardia Vaccinii Shear.
- Hymenoscypha Scutula (P.) Phil., var. Grossulariae Kauffman.

Ribes sp. indet.
- Armillaria mellea (Vahl) ex Fr.
- Botryosphaeria Ribis (Tode ex Fr.) Grossenbacher & Duggar, var. chromogena Shear et al.
- Cenangium Ribis Fr.
- Cladosporium cubisporum B. & C.
- Coniophora corrugis Burt.
- Corticium lacteum Fr.
- Thelephora lactea Fr.
- Diaporthe pungens Nits.
- Diaporthe strumella (Fr.) Fckl.
- ?Diaporthe disciformis (Hoffm. ex Fr.) House, var. ribincola Rehm.
- Diatrype disciformis (Hoffm.) Fr., var. ribincola Rehm.
- Dothidella ribesia (P.) Theissen & Syd.
- Eutypa subcutanea (Wahl. ex Fr.) Sacc.
- Sphaeria subcutanea Wahl. ex Fr.
- Fusarium illosporioides Sacc.
- Coniosporium Fumago (S.) Sacc.
- Fusidium Fumago S.
- Gibberidea Ribis Tracy & Earle.
- Godronia urceolus (A. & S.) Sacc.
- Diplodia Dearnessii Ell. & Ev.
- Microdiplodia Dearnessii (Ell. & Ev.) Tassi.
- Nectria vulgaris Speg.
- Otthia Ribis Tracy & Earle.
- Otthiella Ribis (Tracy & Earle) Sacc. & D. Sacc.
- Corticium incarnatum Fr.
- Peniophora incarnata (P.) Karst.
- Thelephora ribesia S. Am. Bor.
- Peziza vinosa A. & S. ex Fr.

Phoma suspecta Massee.
- Phyllosticta Ellisii Sacc. & Syd.
- Phyllosticta Ribis Ell. & Ev.
- Physalospora Malorum Shear et al.
- Sphaeropsis Malorum B.
- Tubercularia confluens P. ex Fr.
- Xylaria Hypoxylon (L.) ex Fr.

PITTOSPORACEAE

Pittosporum sp. indet.
- Diplodia Pittospori Cke. & Hark.
- Gibberella Saubinetii (Mont.) Sacc.
- Phoma Pittospori Cke. & Hark.
- Sclerotium Rolfsii Sacc.
- Sphaerella Pittospori Cke.
- Stictis moniliferak Phil. & Hark.

BRUNELLIACEAE

Brunellia comocladifolia H. & B.
- Asterina Kernii Toro.
- Phyllachora Massinii Toro.

HAMAMELIDACEAE

Liquidambar Styraciflua L.

PEZIZINEAE

Ciboria Liquidambaris Ell. & Ev.
- Hymenoscypha sacchariferum (B.) Lindau.
- Orbilia rufula (S.) Massee.
- Peziza cruenta S.
- Peziza saccharifera B.
- Pseudohelotium sacchariferum (B.) Sacc.
- Peziza rubella P.
- Peziza sanguinella B. & C.
- Peziza vulgaris Fr., var. sanguinella B.
- Pezizella vulgaris (Fr.) Sacc., var. sanguinella Sacc.

PHACIDIINEAE

- Hysterium cinereum S. Syn. Car.
- Stictis farinosa Fr. El.
- Propolis faginea (Schrad.) ex Karst.

HYSTERIINEAE

Glonium lineare (Fr.) De Not., var. augustissimum De Not.
- Hysterium varium Fr.
- Ostreichnion americanum Duby.
- Ostropa cinerea (P.) ex Fr.

HYPOCREALES

Hypocrea contorta (S.) B. & C.
- Calonectria polythalama (B.) Sacc.
- Nectria polythalama B.
- Scoleconectria polythalama (B.) Seaver.
- Dialonectria rimincola Cke.
- Nectria rimincola Cke.

Liquidambar Styraciflua (*cont.*)

SPHAERIALES

Amphisphaeria atrograna (C. & E.) Sacc.
Sphaeria atrograna C. & E.

Anthostoma amygdalinum (Cke.) Sacc.
Fuckelia amygdalina Cke.
Melanconis amygdalina Cke.

Botryosphaeria Ribis (Tode ex Fr.) Grossenbacher & Duggar.
Botryosphaeria Ribis (Tode ex Fr.) Grossenbacher & Duggar, var. chromogena Shear
   et al.

Ceratostoma caminatum (C. & E.) Sacc.
Sphaeria caminata C. & E.
Xylosphaeria caminata (C. & E.) Cke.

Ceratostomella capillifera Hedgc.
Ceratostomella moniliformis Hedgc.

Cryptospora divergens (S.) Ell. & Ev.
Cryptosporella divergens (S.) Berl. & Vogl.
Sphaeria divergens S.
Valsa divergens (S.) M. A. Curtis.

Endothia gyrosa Auct. Amer. p. p.
Endothia radicalis Farl.
Endothia Ravenelii Note.

Lachnella cinnabarina (S.) Fr.
Melogramma gyrosum (S.) Cke.
Peziza cinnabarina S.
Peziza flammea S.
Sphaeria gyrosa S.

Eutypa limiformis (S.) B.

Eutypella stellulata (Fr.) Sacc.
Valsa stellulata Fr.

Coelosphaeria subconnata (B. & C.) Sacc.
Fracchiaea subcongregata (B. & C.) Ell. & Ev.
Fracchiaea subconnata (B. & C.) Cke.
Nitschkia subconnata (B. & C.) O. Kuntze.
Sphaeria subcongregata B. & C.
Sphaeria subconnata B. & C.

Gnomonia petiolorum (S.) Cke.
Gnomoniella amoena (Nees) Fckl., var. petio-
   lorum (S.) Sacc.
Sphaeria petiolorum S.

Hypoxylon perforatum (S.) Fr.
Sphaeria perforata S.

Lasiosphaeria Pezizula (B. & C.) Sacc.
Sphaeria Pezizula B. & C.

Lasiosphaeria Racodium (P. ex Fr.) Ces. & De
   Not.
Sphaeria Racodium P.

Lophiotrema Nucula (Fr.) Sacc.

Physalospora Malorum Shear et al.

Rosellinia Aquila (Fr.) De Not.
Sphaeria Aquila Fr.

Rosellinia millegrana (S.) Sacc.
Sphaeria millegrana S.

Rosellinia pulveracea (Ehrh. ex Fr.) Fckl.
Sphaeria pulveracea Ehrh. ex Fr.

Hypoxylon subiculosum B.
Rosellinia subiculata (S.) Sacc.
Sphaeria pileata Tode ex Fr.

Sphaeria disseminata B. & C.
Teichospora disseminata (B. & C.) Sacc.

Valsa ambiens (P.) ex Fr.

Hypoxylon erinaceum B. & Rav.
Hypoxylon? Ravenelii Sacc.
Valsa erinacea (B. & Rav.) Cke.

Valsa goniostoma S.?

Sphaeria Liquidambaris S.
Valsa Liquidambaris (S.) M. A. Curtis.

Valsa salicina (P.) Fr.

Valsaria exasperans (Gerard) Sacc.

Hypoxylon gemmatum B. & Rav.
Hypoxylon walterianum B. & Rav.
Melogramma gemmatum (B. & Rav.) Cke.
Valsaria gemmata (B. & Rav.) Sacc.

Diatrype quadrata (S.) B.
Valsaria quadrata (S.) Sacc.

Sphaeria carpophila P. ex Fr.
Xylaria carpophila (P.) Fr.

AURICULARIACEAE

Septobasidium Patouillardii Burt.
Septobasidium pseudopedicellatum Burt.

THELEPHORACEAE

Coniophora olivascens (B. & C.) Massee.
Corticium prasinum B. & C.

Corticium crocicreas Massee.
Corticium chrysocreas B. & C.

Corticium evolvens Fr.
Corticium laeve (P.) ex Fr.
Corticium Liquidambaris B. in Herb.
Eichleriella leveilliana (B. & C.) Burt.
Hymenochaete agglutinans Ell.
Peniophora flavido-alba Cke.

Corticium miniatum B. nom. nud. non Cke.
Corticium sanguineum Fr.
Peniophora sanguinea (Fr.) Bres.

Peziza pruinata S.
Solenia poriiformis (P. ex Fr.) Fckl.
Tapesia pruinata Sacc.

Stereum complicatum Fr.
Stereum fasciatum S.
Stereum fuscum (Schrad. ex Fr.) Quél.

Stereum gausapatum Fr.
Corticium siparium B. & C.

Stereum rugosiusculum B. & C.

Stereum Styracifluum (S.) M. A. Curtis.
Thelephora Styraciflua S.

Stereum subpileatum B. & C.
Thelephora bufonia P.

CLAVARIACEAE

Clavaria Petersii B. & C.
Typhula Grevillei Fr.

Liquidambar Styraciflua *(cont.)*

HYDNACEAE

Grandinia crustosa (P.) Fr.
Hydnum Cookei B.
Hydnum ochraceum P. ex Fr.
{?Hydnum omnivorum Shear.
{Ozonium omnivorum Shear.
{Phymatotrichum omnivorum (Shear) Duggar.
{Creolophus pulcherrimus (B. & C.) Banker.
{Hydnum pulcherrimum B. & C.
{Steccherinum pulcherrimum (B. & C.) Banker.
{Hydnum Rhois S.
{Steccherinum Rhois (S.) Banker.
Hydnum setulosum B. & C.
Irpex obliquus Fr.

POLYPORACEAE

{Daedalea confragosa (Bolt.) ex Fr.
{Lenzites Crataegi B.
Fomes fraxineus (Bull. ex Fr.) Cke.
Fomes geotropus Cke.
{Elfvingia megaloma (Lév.) Murrill.
{Fomes applanatus (P. ex Wallr.) Gill.
{Ganoderma applanatum (P. ex Wallr.) Pat.
Ganoderma Curtisii (B.) Murrill.
{Ganoderma lucidum (Leyss. ex Fr.) Karst.
{Polyporus lucidus (Leyss.) ex Fr.
Lenzites betulina (L.) ex Fr.
Lenzites bicolor Fr.
Lenzites corrugata Klotzsch.
Lenzites Klotzschii B.
Lenzites sepiaria (Wulf.) ex Fr.
Lenzites trabea P. ex Fr.
Lenzites vialis Pk.
Merulius tremellosus Schrad. ex Fr.
{Bjerkandera adusta (Willd. ex Fr.) Karst.
{Polyporus adustus (Willd.) ex Fr.
{Polyporus biformis Fr.
{Polyporus carolinensis B. & C.
{Polystictus biformis Fr.
{Boletus gilvus S.
{Hapalopilus gilvus (S.) Murrill.
{Polyporus gilvus S.
{Polystictus gilvus (S.) Lloyd.
{Leptoporus molluscus (P. ex Fr.) Pat.
{Polyporus molluscus (P.) ex Fr.
{Boletus carpineus, var. b. S. Syn. Car.
{Polyporus rutilans S. Am. Bor.
{Polyporus scruposus Fr.
{Boletus cinnabarinus Jacq. ex Fr.
{Polyporus cinnabarinus (Jacq.) ex Fr.
{Polystictus cinnabarinus (Jacq. ex Fr.) Cke.
Polystictus floridanus (B.) Fr.
{Polyporus hirsutus (Wulf.) ex Fr.
{Polystictus hirsutus (Wulf.) ex Fr.
{Coriolus biformis (Klotzsch) Pat.
{Coriolus prolificans (Fr.) Murrill.
{Polyporus pargamenus Fr.
{Polystictus pergamenus Fr.

{Polystictus sanguineus (L.) Meyer.
{Pycnoporus sanguineus (L.) Murrill.
Polystictus versicolor (L.) ex Fr.
Poria incrassata (B. & C.) Burt.
Poria subacida Pk.
Poria vaporaria (P. ex Fr.) Cke.
Trametes sepium B.

AGARICACEAE

Lentinus Lecomtei Fr.
Lentinus lepideus Fr.
Pleurotus niger (S.) Fr.
Schizophyllum commune Fr.

SPHAEROPSIDALES

Aposphaeria pezizoides Ell. & Ev.
{Diplodia gossypina Cke.
{Physalospora gossypina N. E. Stevens.
Harknessia affinis Ell. & Ev.
Physalospora Malorum Shear et al.
Septoria Liquidambaris Cke. & Ell.
{Haplosporella Liquidambaris (Dearness & House) Petrak & Syd.
{Sphaeropsis Liquidambaris Dearness & House.

MELANCONIALES

Gloeosporium nervisequum (Fckl.) Sacc.
Seiridium inarticulatum M. A. Curtis.
Seiridium Liquidambaris B. & C.

HYPHOMYCETES

Cercospora Liquidambaris C. & E.
Cercospora tuberculans Ell. & Ev.
Clasterosporium subulatum C. & E.
Dendrodochium verticillatum Cke. & Massee.
Dendryphium fasciculare B. & Rav.
Exosporium Liquidambaris Tharp.
Graphium atrovirens Hedgc.
Graphium smaragdinum (A. & S. ex Fr.) Sacc.
{Helicoma finale Herb. Curtis.
{Helicoma Berkeleyi M. A. Curtis.
{Helicosporium Berkeleyi (M. A. Curtis) Sacc.
Helminthosporium asterinum Cke.
Hormiscium gelatinosum Hedgc.
Hormodendron griseum Hedgc.
Monilia aureofulva C. & E.
Penicillium aureum Cda.
Sporidesmium concinnum B.
Torula binale C. & E.

MISCELLANEA

Exidia glandulosa (Bull.) ex Fr.
Hirneola scutelliformis B. & C.
Melampsora Liquidambaris Cke.
Trichia proximella Karst.

Fothergilla Gardeni L.
{Dothidea Fothergillae S.
{Xyloma Fothergillae S.

Hamamelis virginiana L.
Botryosphaeria Hamamelidis Rehm.
Cercospora Hamamelidis Ell. & Ev.
Corticium laeve (P.) Fr.
Cytospora Hamamelidis Ell. & Ev.
Dermatea Rubi (Lib.) Rehm.
Dermatella Hamamelidis (Pk.) Durand.
Lecanidion Hamamelidis (Pk.) Sacc.
Patellaria Hamamelidis Pk.
Diatrype platystoma (S.) B.
Sphaeria platystoma S.
Diplodia Hamamelidis Fairman.
Fomes scutellatus (S.) Cke.
Fomes scutellatus (S.) Cke., forma novebora-
    censis Sacc. Syll.
Polyporus scutellatus S.
Gloeosporium Hamamelidis Cke.
Phyllosticta Hamamelidis Cke. 1881.
Phyllosticta Hamamelidis Pk. 1887.
Phyllostictina Hamamelidis (Cke.) Petrak &
    Syd.
Glonium lineare Fr.
Gonatobotrys maculicola Wint.
Gonatobotryum maculicola (Wint.) Sacc.
Graphium Hamamelidis Hook.
Haplographium apiculatum Pk.
Hyaloceras Hamamelidis Dearness.
Massaria plumigera Ell. & Ev.
Pestalozzia consocia Pk.
Pestalozzia funerea Desm.
Phyllactinia corylea (P.) ex Karst.
Phyllactinia suffulta (Reb.) ex Sacc.
Phyllosticta Paviae Ell. & Ev.
Physalospora Cydoniae Arnaud.
Sphaeropsis Malorum B.
Physalospora erratica C. & E., var. Hamame-
    lidis Rehm.
Podosphaera biuncinata C. & P.
Poria attenuata (Pk.) Cke.
Poria eupora (Karst.) Cke.
Ramularia Hamamelidis Pk.
Sphaeropsis Hamamelidis Tassi.
Stereum versiforme B. & C.
Streptothrix atra B. & C.
Valsa ambiens (P.) ex Fr.
Valsa Liquidambaris (S.) Cke.

PLATANACEAE

Platanus cuneata Willd.
Pseudovalsa haplocystis (B. & Br.) Sacc.
Platanus occidentalis L.

PHACIDIINEAE
Phacidium Platani S.
Propolis faginea (Schrad,) ex Karst.

HYSTERIINEAE
Glonium parvulum Gerard.
Hysterium pulcherrimum Tehon & Young.

Hysterographium Mori (S.) Rehm.
Ostropa mellea Dearness & House.

ERYSIPHACEAE
Microsphaera Alni (DC.) Wint. †
Microsphaera Platani Howe.
Phyllactinia corylea (P.) ex Karst.

SPHAERIALES
Diaporthe fulvopruinata (B.) Sacc.
Sphaeria fulvopruinata B.
Valsa fulvopruinata (B.) Cke.
Valsaria fulvopruinata (B.) Sacc.
Diaporthe medusina (Fr.) Sacc.
Diatrype prominens Howe.
Diatrypella prominens (Howe) Sacc.
Eutypella Platani (S.) Sacc.
Sphaeria Platani S.
Valsa Platani (S.) Cke.
Gloeosporium nervisequum (Fckl.) Sacc.
Gnomonia Platani Edgerton.
Gnomonia veneta (Sacc. & Speg.) Klebahn.
Leptosphaeria platanicola (Howe) Sacc.
Heptameria platanicola (Howe) Cke.
Sphaeria platanicola Howe.
Massaria atroinquinans B. & C.
Massaria Platani Ces.
Melanconis stilbostoma (Fr.) Tul.
Sphaeria platanoides S. Syn. Car.
Sphaeria stilbostoma Fr.
Melanomma sporadicum Ell. & Ev.
Nummularia macula (S.) Cke.
Sphaeria macula S. Syn. Car.
Diatrype? tinctor (B.) Sacc.
Hypoxylon tinctor (B.) Cke.
Nummularia tinctor (B.) Ell. & Ev.
Sphaeria tinctor B.
Melanconis bicornis Cke.
Pseudovalsa bicornis (Cke.) Sacc.
Massariovalsa caudata Ell. & Ev.
Pseudovalsa caudata (Ell. & Ev.) Sacc.
Pseudovalsa hapalocystis (B. & Br.) Sacc.
Valsa hapalocystis (B. & Br.) Cke.
Psilosphaeria millegrana (S.) Rav. Fung. Am.
    672.
Rosellinia millegrana (S.) Sacc.
Rosellinia pulveracea (Ehrh. ex Fr.) Fckl.
Sphaeria millegrana S.
Sphaerella maculiformis (P.) Awd.
Sphaerella Platani Ell. & Martin.
Sphaerella platanifolia Cke.
Sphaeria ceratosperma S. Syn. Car.

THELEPHORACEAE
Coniophora cerebella P.
Coniophora puteana (Schum.) ex Fr., var.
    tuberculosa Pk.

Platanus occidentalis (*cont.*)

⎧ Peniophora albomarginata (S.) Massee.
⎨ Thelephora albomarginata S.
⎩ Stereum albobadium S.
Stereum purpureum P. †

HYDNACEAE

Hydnum coralloides Scop. ex Fr.

POLYPORACEAE

Fomes applanatus (P. ex Wallr.) Gill.
Fomes fasciatus (Sw. ex Fr.) Cke.
Ganoderma sessile Murrill.
⎧ Bjerkandera adusta (Willd. ex Fr.) Karst.
⎨ Polyporus adustus (Willd.) ex Fr.
Polyporus fumosus (P.) ex Fr.
Polyporus gilvus S.
Polyporus hirsutus (Wulf.) ex Fr.
⎧ Polyporus versicolor L. ex Fr.
⎨ Polystictus versicolor (L.) ex Fr.
Poria incrassata (B. & C.) Burt.
Poria purpurea (Fr.) Cke.
Poria subacida (Pk.) Sacc. Syll.
Poria viticola (S.) Cke.

AGARICACEAE

Armillaria mellea (Vahl) ex Fr.
Lentinus tigrinus Fr.
Lenzites betulina (L.) ex Fr.

SPHAEROPSIDALES

Aposphaeria pezizoides Ell. & Ev.
Coniothyrium mixtum Fckl.
Cytospora Platani Fckl.
Dendrophoma therryana Sacc. & Roum.
⎧ Hendersonia Desmazieri Mont.
⎨ Hendersonia Platani Pk.
⎧ Macrophoma petiolata (Cke.) Berl. & Vogl.
⎨ Phoma petiolata (Cke.) Sacc.
⎩ Sphaeropsis petiolata Cke.
Myxofusicoccum Platani Petrak.
Phleospora multimaculans Heald & Wolf.
Phoma limbalis Pass.
Phoma platanicola Dearness & House.
Phoma scabra Sacc.
Phyllosticta platanella Sacc.
⎧ Septoria platanifolia Cke.
⎨ Sphaerella platanifolia Cke.
Sphaeropsis Platani Pk.
Sphaeropsis sphaeroides Ell.

MELANCONIALES

Coryneum corticale S.
⎧ Discella Platani Pk.
⎨ Discula Platani (Pk.) Sacc.
Fusicoccum veronense Massal.
Gloeosporidium Platani (Lév.) v. Höhnel.
⎨ Gloeosporium nervisequum (Fckl.) Sacc.
Gloeosporium Platani (Mont.) Oud.
Gloeosporium valsoideum Sacc.
⎩ Gnomonia veneta (Sacc. & Speg.) Klebahn.

Libertella faginea Desm.
Libertella Platani Ell. & Ev.
⎧ Didymosporium minutissimum S.
⎨ Melanconium minutissimum (S.) Pk.
Pestalozzia funerea Desm.
Pestalozzia stellata B. & C.
Pestalozzia stictica B. & C.

HYPHOMYCETES

Cercospora platanicola Ell. & Ev.
Cladosporium epiphyllum (P.) ex Fr
Exosporium platanorum Tharp.
Helminthosporium corticale S.
Helminthosporium macrocarpum Grev.
Isaria capitata Ell. & Ev.
⎧ Macrosporium Cheiranthi (Lib.) Fr., var. echi-
│   nellum B. & C.
⎨ Macrosporium commune Rabh., var. echinel-
│   lum (B. & C.) Sacc.
⎩ Macrosporium echinellum B. & C. nom. nud.
Rhinotrichum Curtisii B.
Stigmella visianica Sacc.?
⎧ Stigmella Platani Fckl.
⎨ Stigmina Platani (Fckl.) Sacc.
Stilbospora quadriseptata S.
Stilbum flavipes Pk.
Trichothecium roseum Lk.

MISCELLANEA

Achlya racemosa Hildebrand, var.
Dacryomyces Syringae (Schum. ex P.) Fr.?
Eurotium subgriseum Pk.
Tremella mesenterica Retz.
Trichia inconspicua Rostf.

Platanus orientalis L.
Gloeosporium nervisequum (Fckl.) Sacc.
Microsphaera Alni (DC.) Wint.? †
Physalospora Cydoniae Arnaud.
Stigmina Platani (Fckl.) Sacc.

Platanus racemosa Nutt.
Diaporthe scabra Nits.
Diatrypella prominens (Howe) Sacc.
Dictyosporium circinatum Cke. & Hark.
Gloeosporium nervisequum (Fckl.) Sacc.
Lasiosphaeria biformis (P.) Sacc.
Phleospora multimaculans Heald & Wolf.
Sphaerella latebrosa Cke.
⎧ Stigmella Platani Fckl.
⎨ Stigmina Platani (Fckl.) Sacc.
Zygodesmus hydnoides B. & C.
Zygodesmus pannosus B. & C.

Platanus Wrightii Watson.
Armillaria mellea (Vahl.) ex Fr.

Platanus sp. indet.

HYSTERIINEAE

Glonium Ravenelii Cke. & Phil.
⎧ Hysterium angustatum A. & S. ex Fr.
⎨ Hysterium pulicare P. ex Fr., var. angustatum
⎩   (A. & S.) Fr.

Platanus sp. indet. (*cont.*)

HYPOCREALES
- Nectria dematiosa (S.) M. A. Curtis.
- Sphaeria dematiosa S.
- Creonectria ochroleuca (S.) Seaver.
- Nectria ochroleuca (S.) M. A. Curtis.
- Hypocrea sublobata (S.) Sacc.
- Sphaeria sublobata S.
- Sphaerostilbe gracilipes Tul.

SPHAERIALES
- Amphisphaeria Platani Ell. & Ev.
- Caryospora callicarpa (Curr.) Nits.
- Ceuthocarpon leucospilum (B. & C.) Berl.
- Linospora leucospila (B. & C.) Sacc.
- Sphaeria leucospila B. & C.
- Diatrype corniculata Rav. Fung. Car.
- Sphaeria corniculata Ehrh. ex Fr.
- Diatrype Hystrix (Tode) ex Fr.
- Didymella psoriella (B. & C.) Cke.
- Eurotium subgriseum Pk.
- Eutypella aleurina (B. & C.) Berl. & Vogl.
- Valsa aleurina B. & C. in Herb. B.
- Eutypella tumidula (C. & P.) Sacc.
- Valsa tumidula C. & P.
- Hypoxylon coccineum Bull. †
- Sphaeria fragiformis P. ex Fr.
- Hypoxylon illitum (S.) Sacc.
- Sphaeria illita S.
- Hypoxylon rubiginosum (P.) ex Fr.
- Sphaeria rubiginosa P. ex Fr.
- Laestadia albocrustata (S.) Sacc.
- Sphaerella albocrustata (S.) Cke.
- Sphaeria albocrustata S.
- Lasiosphaeria canescens (P. ex Fr.) Karst.
- Lasiosphaeria strigosa (A. & S. ex Fr.) Ell. & Ev.
- Lasiosphaeria strigosa (A. & S. ex Fr.) Ell. & Ev., var. canescens (P. ex Fr.) Berl.
- Sphaeria canescens P. ex Fr.
- Massaria circumscissa (P. ex Fr.) M. A. Curtis.
- Sphaeria circumscissa P. ex Fr.
- Massaria Pupula (Fr.) Tul.
- Sphaeria Pupula Fr.
- Steganosporium pyriforme (Hoffm. ex Fr.) Cda.
- Massaria semitecta (B. & C.) Sacc.
- Sphaeria semitecta B. & C.
- Hypoxylon nummularium Bull. ex Fr.
- Nummularia Bulliardi Tul.
- Nummularia rumpens Cke.
- Physalospora Malorum Shear et al.
- Pseudovalsa convergens (Tode ex Fr.) Sacc.
- Sphaeria convergens Tode ex Fr.
- Rosellinia aquila (Fr.) DeNot.
- Sphaeria aquila Fr.
- Coniochaeta Rattus (S.) Cke.
- Rebentischia ranella (B. & Rav.) Sacc.
- Rosellinia Rattus (S.) Ell. & Ev.
- Sphaeria ranella B. & Rav.

- Sphaeria epitephra B. & C.
- Trichosphaeria incisa Morg.
- Valsa salicina (P.) ex Fr.
- Sphaeria stellulata Fr.
- Valsa stellulata Fr.

PROTOBASIDIOMYCETES
- Dacryomyces minor Pk.
- Exidia repanda Fr.
- Exidia spiculata S.

HYMENOMYCETINEAE
- Armillaria mellea (Vahl) Fr.
- Coniophora fumosa (Fr.) Karst.
- Hypochnus fumosus Fr.
- Corticium lacteum Fr.
- Crepidotus putrigenus B. & C.
- Daedalea Aesculi (S.) Murrill.
- Daedalea ambigua B.
- Hydnum Erinaceus Bull. ex Fr.
- Hydnum gelatinosum Scop.
- Corticium echinosporum Ell.
- Hypochnus echinosporus (Ell.) Burt.
- Marasmius felix Morg.
- Peniophora albomarginata (S.) Massee.
- Peniophora nuda (Fr.) Bres.
- Peniophora ochracea (Fr.) Massee.
- Peniophora pubera (Fr.) Sacc.
- Polyporus distortus S.
- Polyporus smaragdinus Lloyd.
- Polystictus lacteus Fr.
- Boletus juglandinus S.
- Polyporus juglandinus S.
- Poria juglandina (S.) Cke.
- Poria vaporaria (P. ex Fr.) Cke.

SPHAEROPSIDALES
- Coniothyrium Platani Sacc.
- Diplodia Aceris Fckl.
- Diplodia fulvella Cke.
- Discosia Artocreas (Tode) ex Fr.
- Coccularia stictica B.
- Phoma stictina (B.) Sacc.
- Phyllosticta Platani Sacc. & Speg.

HYPHOMYCETES
- Arthrobotryum didymium (Cke.) Pound & Clements.
- Didymobotryum Cookei Sacc.
- Stilbum didymum Cke.
- Botrytis rosea Lk.
- Campsotrichum simplex Cke.
- Clasterosporium atrum (Lk. ex Fr.) Sacc.
- Clasterosporium sticticum (B. & C.) Sacc.
- Sporidesmium sticticum B. & C.
- Harpographium fasciculatum Sacc.
- Helicoma ambiguum Morg.
- Helicomyces elegans Morg.
- Helicotrichum obscurum (Cda.) Sacc.

Platanus sp. indet. (*cont.*)
{ Oedemium sparsum B. & Rav.
{ Oedemium subsparsum Sacc.
Septoria platanifolia Cke.
Sporidesmium epicoccoides B. & C.
Sporidesmium stygium B. & C.
Triposporium Ravenelii Cke.

MISCELLANEA
Sclerotium Platani S.

CROSSOSOMATACEAE
Crossosoma californicum Nutt.
Eutypa lata (P. ex Fr.) Tul.
Peniophora velutina (DC.) Cke.
Stereum heterosporum Burt.

ROSACEAE
Physocarpus opulifolius (L.) Maxim.

PEZIZINEAE
Belonidium Spiraeae Dearness & House.
{ Cenangium Spiraeae (S.) B.
{ Dermea Spiraeae S.
{ Dermatea Spiraeae (S.) Cke.
{ Peziza Opulifoliae S.
{ Trichopeziza Opulifoliae (S.) Sacc.

ERYSIPHACEAE
{ Sphaerotheca Castagnei Lév. p. p.
{ Sphaerotheca Humuli (DC.) Burrill.

SPHAERIALES
{ Anthostomella Closterium (B. & C.) Sacc.
{ Sphaeria Closterium B. & C.
Botryosphaeria quercuum (S.) Sacc.
Diaporthe Neilliae Pk.
Diaporthe spiculosa (A. & S.) ex Nits.
Diatrype Stigma (Hoffm.) ex Fr.
Didymella Physocarpi Ell. & Ev.
Leptosphaeria vagabunda Sacc.
{ Lophiosphaera Spiraeae (Pk.) Cke.
{ Lophiostoma Spiraeae Pk.
{ Lophiotrema Spiraeae (Pk.) Sacc.
{ Sphaeria crenata, var. Spiraeae S.
{ Metasphaeria saepincola (Fr.) Sacc.
{ Sphaeria saepincola Fr.
Microdiplodia spiraeicola Dearness & House.
Valsa ambiens (P.) ex Fr.
Valsa Opulifoliae Pk.

HYMENOMYCETINEAE
Corticium confluens Fr.
Peniophora incarnata Fr.
{ Fomitiporia laminata Murrill.
{ Poria laminata (Murrill) Sacc. & Trott.

SPHAEROPSIDALES
Cytospora globifera Fr.
Diplodia spiraeina Sacc.
Excipula epidermis S.

Phoma leucostoma Lév.
Phoma Spiraeae Desm.?
Sphaeronema Physocarpi Ell. & Ev.
Sphaeropsis Neilliae Ell. & Ev.
Sphaeropsis Physocarpi Ell. & Ev.

MELANCONIALES
Marssonia Lonicerae Hark.
{ Gloeosporium Neilliae (Hark.) Ell. & Ev.
{ Marssonia Neilliae Hark.
{ Marssonina Neilliae (Hark.) Magn.
Pestalozzia Jefferisii Ell.?
Pestalozzia monochaetoidea Sacc. & Ell.
Pestalozzia monochaetoidea Sacc. & Ell., var. parasitica Dearness & House.

HYPHOMYCETES
{ Clasterosporium nitens (S.) Sacc.
{ Sporidesmium nitens S.
Ramularia Spiraeae Pk.
Ramularia Ulmariae Cke.
Sporidesmium moriforme Pk.
Stagonospora Physocarpi Ell. & Ev.
Physocarpus Torreyi Max.
Metasphaeria Opulastri Clements.
Spiraea alba Du Roi.
Septoria salicifoliae (Trel.) Ell. & Ev.
Spiraea corymbosa Raf.
Cylindrosporium spiraeicola Ell.
Podosphaera Oxyacanthae (DC.) DBy.
?Rhopalidium cercosporelloides Dearness.
Septoria salicifoliae (Trel.) Ell. & Ev.
Spiraea densiflora Auct.
{ Cylindrosporium salicifoliae (Trel.) J. J. Davis.
{ Septoria salicifoliae (Trel.) Ell. & Ev.
Spiraea discolor Pursh.
Creonectria purpurea (L.) ex Seaver.
Cylindrosporium ariifolium Ell. & Ev.
Cylindrosporium Filipendulae Thm.
Leptosphaeria Sambuci Fautr.
Metasphaeria anisometra (Cke. & Hark.) Sacc.
Phyllactinia corylea (P.) ex Karst.
Podosphaera Oxyacanthae (DC.) DBy.
Valsa clavigera Dearness & Barthol.
Valsa holodiscina Fairman.
Spiraea Douglasii Hook.
Cylindrosporium spiraeicola Ell. & Ev.
{ Podosphaera Oxyacanthae (DC.) DBy., var. tridactyla (Wallr.) Salmon.
{ Podosphaera tridactyla (Wallr.) DBy.
Spiraea Douglasii Hook., var. **dumosa** Watson.
{ Microsphaera fulvofulcra Cke.
{ Podosphaera Oxyacanthae (DC.) DBy.
Spiraea
      (Sericotheca franciscana Rydb.)
Schizoxylon insigne (De Not.) Bres.
Spiraea hypericifolia Sieb. & Zucc.
{ Diplodia spiraeicola Ell. & Ev.
{ Microdiplodia spiraeicola (Ell. & Ev.) Tassi.

Spiraea latifolia Borkh.
Here probably belong many or all of the entries
under Spiraea salicifolia L.
Belonidium Spiraeae Dearness & House.
Gnomonia papillostoma Dearness & House.
Podosphaera Oxyacanthae (DC.) DBy. †
Sphaeropsis Physocarpi Ell. & Ev.

Spiraea lucida Dougl.
Podosphaera Oxyacanthae (DC.) DBy. †

Spiraea Menziesii Hook.
Belonidium Macounii Dearness.
Camarosporium Coronillae Sacc. & Speg., var.
Spiraeae Bäuml.
Diaporthe Macounii Dearness.
Diplodia constricta Dearness.
Rhopalidium cercosporelloides Dearness.
Stagonospora Spiraeae Dearness.

Spiraea pyramidata Greene.
Phleospora mellea Sacc.
{ Ascochyta salicifoliae Trel.
{ Phleospora salicifoliae (Trel.) Petrak.

Spiraea salicifolia L.   See also **S. latifolia** Borkh.
Cercospora Rubigo Cke. & Hark.
Cucurbitaria Rosae Sacc. & Wint.
Cylindrosporium fairmanianum Sacc.
Cylindrosporium Filipendulae Thm.
{ Ascochyta salicifoliae Trel.
{ Cylindrosporium salicifoliae (Trel.) J. J. Davis.
{ Septoria salicifoliae (Trel.) Ell. & Ev. 16 Mar.
{ 1886.
{ Septoria salicifoliae (Trel.) Berl. & Vogl.   31
Dec. 1886.
{ Dimerosporium Collinsii (S.) Thm.
{ Sphaeria Collinsii S.
Hendersonia anceps Sacc.
Phleospora Dearnessii Bubák.
{ Microsphaera fulvofulcra Cke.
{ Podosphaera Kunzei Lév.
{ Podosphaera minor Howe.
{ Podosphaera Oxyacanthae (DC.) DBy. †
{ Sphaerotheca Humuli (DC.) Burrill. †
Tapesia cinerella Rehm.

Spiraea tomentosa L.
{ Cylindrosporium spiraeicola Ell. & Ev.
{ Septoria salicifoliae J. J. Davis p. p. non (Trel.)
{ Ell. & Ev.
{ Microsphaera fulvofulcra Cke.
{ Podosphaera Kunzei Lév.
{ Podosphaera minor Howe.
{ Podosphaera Oxyacanthae (DC.) DBy. †

Spiraea sp. indet.
Diaporthe Neilliae Pk.
Leptostroma Spiraeae Fr.
{ Monochaetia monochaetoidea (Sacc. & Ell.)
{ Allescher.
{ Pestalozzia monchaetoidea Sacc. & Ell.
Podosphaera leucotricha (Ell. & Ev.) Salmon.

Ozonium omnivorum Shear.
Peziza Schumacheri Fr.
Phyllosticta filipendulina Sacc. & Speg.
Ramularia Ulmariae Cke.
Septogloeum Schizonoti Dearness.
Sphaerotheca Castagnei Lév.
Sporidesmium spiraeicola Cke.
Trichopeziza Opulifoliae (S.) Sacc.

Aruncus sylvester Kostl.
?Cercospora Rubigo Cke. & Hark.
Leptosphaeria Arunci Zeller.

Gillenia stipulata (Muhl.) Trel.
{ Gymnosporangium externum Arth. & Kern. I.
{ Roestelia lacerata Fung. Eur. *3323*.

Cotoneaster horizontalis DC.
Phyllosticta horizontalis G. H. Martin, Jr.,
nom. nud.
Tubercularia vulgaris Tode ex Fr.

Cotoneaster tomentosa Lindl.
Fabraea maculata Atk.

Cotoneaster vulgaris Lindl.
Gymnosporangium clavariiforme (Jacq. ex P.)
DC.

Cydonia "japonica" et affin.
Cercospora Cydoniae Ell. & Ev.
Coryneum Cydoniae Dearness & House.
Cylindrosporium Pomi Brooks.
Diatrypella xanthostroma Ell. & Ev.
Hendersonia Cydoniae Cke. & Ell.
Ozonium omnivorum Shear.
{ Aecidium blasdaleanum Diet. & Holw.
{ Gymnosporangium blasdaleanum Kern. I.
{ Gymnosporangium clavipes C. & P. I.
{ Gymnosporangium germinale Kern. I.
{ Roestelia aurantiaca Pk.
Roestelia pyrata (S.) Thax.
Sclerotinia fructigena Schrt.
Sphaeropsis Cydoniae C. & E.

Cydonia oblonga Mill.

ASCOMYCETES
{ Entomosporium maculatum Lév.
{ Fabraea maculata Atk.
{ Glomerella cingulata (Stoneman) Spaulding &
{ v. Schrenk.
{ Glomerella fructigena (G. P. Clinton) Sacc.
{ Glomerella rufomaculans Spaulding &
{ v. Schrenk.
Gnomoniopsis fructigena G. P. Clinton.
Nectria cinnabarina (Tode) ex Fr.
Nectria ditissima Tul.
Nectria mammoidea Phil. & Plowr.
Phyllactinia corylea (P.) ex Karst.
Physalospora Cydoniae Arnaud.
{ Podosphaera Oxyacanthae (DC.) DBy.
{ Podosphaera tridactyla (Wallr.) DBy.

Cydonia oblonga (*cont.*)
- Monilia fructigena Auct. Amer. p. p.
- Sclerotinia americana (Wormald) Norton & Ezekiel.
- Sclerotinia cinerea Schrt.
- Sclerotinia fructicola (Wint.) Rehm.
- Sclerotinia fructigena Norton.
- Valsa leucostoma (P.) ex Fr.

UREDINALES
- Gymnosporangium aurantiacum Pk. I.
- Gymnosporangium clavipes C. & P. I.
- Gymnosporangium germinale Kern. I.
- Roestelia aurantiaca Pk.
- Aecidium blasdaleanum Diet. & Holw.
- Gymnosporangium aurantiacum Syd. I.
- Gymnosporangium blasdaleanum Kern. I.
- Gymnosporangium Libocedri (Henn.) Kern. I.
- Gymnosporangium clavariiforme (Jacq. ex P.) DC. I.
- Gymnosporangium globosum Farl. I.
- Gymnosporangium koreaense H. S. Jackson. I.
- Roestelia koreaense Henn.
- Gymnosporangium Nelsoni Arth. I.
- Gymnosporangium Nidus-avis Thax. I.

THELEPHORACEAE
- Corticium Stevensii Burt.
- Hypochnus ochroleuca Noack.
- Stereum purpureum P. †

SPHAEROPSIDALES
- Hendersonia Cydoniae C. & E.
- Phyllohendersonia Cydoniae (C. & E.) Tassi.
- Phoma Cydoniae Sacc. & Schulz.
- Sphaeropsis Cydoniae C. & E.
- Sphaeropsis Malorum B.
- Sphaeropsis Malorum Pk.
- Sphaeria pomorum S.
- Sphaeropsis pomorum (S.) Cke.

MELANCONIALES
- Cylindrosporium Pomi (Pass.) Brooks.
- Phoma Pomi Pass.
- Blastesis tridens Zabriskie.
- Entomosporium maculatum Lév.
- Entomosporium maculatum Lév., var. Cydoniae C. & E.
- Fabraea maculata Atk.
- Morthiera Mespili (DC.) Fckl., var. Cydoniae C. & E.
- Entomosporium Mespili (DC.) Sacc.
- Gloeosporium Cydoniae Mont.
- Gloeosporium fructigenum B.
- Gloeosporium phomoides Sacc.
- Glomerella cingulata (Stoneman) Spaulding & v. Schrenk.

HYPHOMYCETES
- Cephalothecium roseum Cda.
- Fumago vagans Fr.

Fusicladium dendriticum (Wallr.) Fckl.?
Monilia oregonensis Barss & Posey.

MISCELLANEA
- Ozonium omnivorum Shear.
- Penicillium glaucum Lk.
- Mucor stolonifer Ehrenb. ex Fr.
- Rhizopus nigricans Ehrenb. ex Fr.

Cydonia sp. indet.
- Botrytis vulgaris (Lk.) ex Fr.
- Coniothyrium pyrina (Sacc.) Sheldon.
- Corticium Stevensii Burt.
- Dermea Cydoniae Cke.
- Gloeosporium malicorticis Cordley.
- Neofabraea malicorticis H. S. Jackson.
- Gymnosporangium haraeanum Syd. I.
- Gymnosporangium macropus Lk. I.
- Leptothyrium pomi (Mont. & Fr.) Sacc.
- Pestalozzia concentrica B. & Rav.
- Pestalozzia zonata Ell. & Ev.
- ?Plowrightia morbosa (S.) Sacc.
- Podosphaera leucotricha (Ell. & Ev.) Salmon.
- Sphaerella Pyri Awd.
- Sphaerella sentina (Fr.) Sacc.
- Trichothecium roseum Lk.

Pyrus americana DC.

ASCOMYCETES
- Cenangium Aucupariae (P.) Fr.
- Tympanis Aucupariae (P.) Wallr.
- Coronophora gregaria (Lib.) Fckl.
- Cucurbitaria Sorbi (Cda.) Rabh.
- Dasyscypha bicolor (Bull.) Fckl.
- Diaporthe congesta Ell. & Ev.
- Diaporthe impulsa (C. & P.) Sacc.
- Valsa impulsa C. & P.
- Fenestella superficialis (Pk. & Clinton) Sacc.
- Melogramma superficialis Pk. & Clinton.
- Lophodermium petiolicola Fckl.
- Lophodermium tumidum (Fr.) Rehm.
- Metasphaeria Semen (C. & P.) Sacc.
- Sphaeria Semen C. & P.
- Mollisia cinerea (Batsch) Karst.
- Nummularia discreta (S.) Tul.
- Nummularia repanda (Fr.) Nits.
- Numulariola repanda (Fr.) House.
- Physalospora Cydoniae Arnaud.
- Rosellinia pulveracea (Ehrh. ex Fr.) Fckl.
- Valsa leucostoma (P.) ex Fr.
- Valsa Sorbi Fr.
- Venturia inaequalis (Cke.) Wint.

UREDINALES
- Gymnosporangium Betheli Kern. I.
- Gymnosporangium Davisii Kern. I.
- Gymnosporangium globosum Farl. I.
- Roestelia lacerata Auct. Amer. p. p.

Pyrus americana (*cont.*)

Aecidium cornutum P.

Gymnosporangium cornutum Arth. I.

Gymnosporangium Juniperi Lk. I.

Roestelia cornuta (P.) Fr.

Gymnosporangium juniperinum (L.) ex Mart.
I.

Gymnosporangium Sorbi Kern. I.

HYMENOMYCETINEAE

Pleurotus atrocoeruleus, var. griseus Pk.

Polystictus hirsutus (Wulf.) ex Fr.

Radulum tomentosum Fr.

Stereum hirsutum (Willd.) ex Fr.

FUNGI IMPERFECTI

Atractium flammeum B. & Rav.

Coniothyrium olivaceum Bon.

Cytospora microspora (Cda.) Rabh.

Cytospora rubescens Fr.

Diplodia maura C. & E., var. americana Ell.

Dothiora pyrenophora B. an Fr.?

Dothiorella pyrenophora (Karst.) Sacc.

Entomosporium maculatum Lév., var. domesticum Sacc.

Fusicladium dendriticum (Wallr.) Fckl.

Venturia inaequalis (Cke.) Wint.

Graphium Sorbi Pk.

Melanostroma Sorbi Rostr.

Phoma hysteroidea B. & Br.

Phoma pallida (Pk.) Jacz.

Sphaeronema pallidum Pk.

Phoma Sorbi (Lasch) Sacc.

Phyllosticta Sorbi Westd.

Ramularia destruens Pk.

Septoria inaequalis Sacc. & Roum.

Steganosporium cellulosum Cda.

Pyrus angustifolia Ait.

Gymnosporangium globosum Farl. I.

Gymnosporangium clavariiforme (Jacq. ex P.)
DC. I.

Roestelia lacerata (Sow.) Fr.

Gymnosporangium Juniperi-virginianae S. I.

Roestelia penicillata Auct. Amer.

Roestelia pyrata (S.) Thax.

Pyrus arbutifolia (L.) L. f.

See also Aronia monstrosa Zabel.

Ascochyta pyrina Pegl.

Asteroma atramentarium B.

Calosphaeria princeps Tul.

Calosphaeria pulchella (P. ex Fr.) Schrt. 1897.

Calosphaeria pulchella (P. ex Fr.) House. 1921.

Valsa pulchella (P.) ex Fr.

Cercospora Pyri Farl.

Entomosporium Thuemenii (Cke.) Sacc.

Massaria inquinans (Tode) ex Fr.

Mycosphaerella arbutifoliae (Pk.) House.

Phyllosticta arbutifolia Ell. & Martin.

Physalospora viscosa (C. & E.) Sacc.

Valsa excorians C. & E.

UREDINALES

Gymnosporangium clavipes C. & P. I.

Gymnosporangium germinale Kern. I.

Roestelia aurantiaca Pk.

Roestelia cornuta (P.) Fr.

Gymnosporangium Davisii Kern. I.

Gymnosporangium effusum Kern. I.

Gymnosporangium fraternum Kern. I.

Gymnosporangium clavariiforme (Jacq. ex
P.) DC. I.

Aecidium transformans (Ell.) Pazschke.

Gymnosporangium transformans Kern. I.

Roestelia transformans Ell.

Roestelia transformans Ell., var. fructigena
Thm.

Pyrus arbutifolia (L.) l. f., var. **atro-purpurea**
(Britton) B. L. Robinson.

Gymnosporangium clavipes C. & P. I.

Gymnosporangium germinale Kern. I.

Gymnosporangium Davisii Kern. I.

Gymnosporangium fraternum Kern. I.

Pyrus arbutifolia, var. **erythrocarpa** Michx.

Cercospora Mali Ell. & Ev.

Pyrus Aucuparia L.

Entomosporium maculatum Lév., var. Cydoniae Sacc.

Fomes applanatus (P. ex Wallr.) Gill.

Gymnosporangium blasdaleanum Kern. I.

Gymnosporangium cornutum Arth. I.

Nummularia repanda (Fr.) Nits.

Pyrus baccata L.

Gymnosporangium blasdaleanum Kern. I.

Gymnosporangium globosum Farl. I.

Gymnosporangium Juniperi-virginianae S. I.

Phyllactinia corylea (P.) ex Karst.

Phyllosticta solitaria Ell. & Ev.

Physalospora Malorum Shear et al.

Podosphaera Oxyacanthae (DC.) DBy.

Venturia inaequalis (Cke.) Wint.

Pyrus betulifolia Bunge.

Gymnotelium nootkatense (Trel.) Syd.

Pyrus

(Sorbus californica Greene.)

Coryneum Sorbi Pk.

Pyrus chinensis.

Aecidium blasdaleanum Diet. & Holw.

Pyrus communis L.

PHYCOMYCETES

Mucor amethysteus Bon.

Phytophthora Cactorum (Loeb. & Cohn) Schrt.

Pythiacystis citrophthora Sm. & Sm.

PEZIZINEAE

Fabraea maculata Atk.

Sclerotinia cinerea Auct. Amer.

Sclerotinia fructigena Auct. Amer.

HYSTERIINEAE

Acrospermum viridulum B. & C.

Pyrus communis (*cont.*)

PERISPORIALES

Capnodium elongatum B. & Desm.
{ Podosphaera leucotricha (Ell. & Ev.) Salmon.
{ Sphaerotheca leucotricha Ell. & Ev.
Podosphaera Oxyacanthae (DC.) DBy.

HYPOCREALES

Nectria cinnabarina (Tode) ex Fr.
{ Cylindrocarpon Mali (All.) Wollenw.
{ Nectria galligena Bres.
Sphaerostilbe coccophila Tul.

DOTHIDEALES

{ Gloeodes pomigena (S.) Colby.
{ Phyllachora pomigena (S.) Sacc.

SPHAERIALES

Botryosphaeria Ribis (Tode ex Fr.) Grossen-
  bacher & Duggar.
Chaetomium globosum Kze.
{ Diatrype irregularis C. & E.
{ Diatrypella irregularis (C. & E.) Sacc.
{ Glomerella cingulata (Stoneman) Spaulding &
{   v. Schrenk.
{ Glomerella rufomaculans Spaulding & v.
{   Schrenk.
Lophiostoma scelestum C. & E.
Massaria Pyri Otth.
{ Melanomma Pulvis-pyrius (P. ex Fr.) Fckl.
{ Sphaeria Pulvis-pyrius P. ex Fr.
{ Conisphaeria subcutanea (C. & E.) Cke.
{ Endophlaea subcutanea (C. & E.) Cke.
{ Leptosphaeria subcutanea (C. & E.) Ell.
{ Metasphaeria subcutanea (C. & E.) Sacc.
{ Sphaeria subcutanea C. & E.
Nummularia discreta (S.) Tul.
Physalospora Cydoniae Arnaud.
Physalospora Malorum Shear et al.
Pleospora herbarum (Fr.) Rabh.
{ Dibotryon morbosum (S.) Theissen & Syd.
{ Plowrightia morbosa (S.) Sacc.
{ Sphaerella sentina N. A. F. *597* nec Fr.
{ Sphaerella pyrina Ell. & Ev.
{ Mycosphaerella sentina (Fr.) Schrt.
{ Sphaerella Pyri Awd.
{ Sphaerella sentina (Fr.). Fckl.
Valsa leucostoma (P.) ex Fr.
{ Fusicladium pyrinum (Lib.) Fckl.
{ Venturia ditricha, var. Pyri Aderh.
{ Venturia pyrina Aderh.
Xylaria digitata (L. ex Fr.) Grev.

MYRIANGIACEAE

Myriangium Duriaei Mont. & B.

DACRYOMYCETINEAE

Dacryomyces syringicola B. & C.
{ Dacryomyces destructor B. & Rav.
{ Hypsilophora destructor (B. & Rav.) B.

UREDINALES

{ Gymnosporangium clavipes C. & P. I.
{ Roestelia aurantiaca Pk.
Aecidium blasdaleanum Diet. & Holw.
Gymnosporangium blasdaleanum Kern. I.
{ Gymnosporangium Libocedri (Henn.) Kern. I.
{ Aecidium cancellatum Gmel. ex P.
{ Gymnosporangium Sabinae (Dicks.) Wint. I.
{ Roestelia cancellata (Gmel. ex P.) Reb.
Gymnosporangium clavariiforme (Jacq. ex P.)
  DC. I.
{ Caeoma Roestelites S. Am. Bor. 2900. p.p.[2]
{ Gymnosporangium globosum Farl. I.
Gymnosporangium kernianum Bethel. I.
Gymnosporangium Nelsoni Arth. I.
Gymnosporangium Nidus-avis Thax. I.
{ Aecidium pyratum S.
{ Gymnosporangium Juniperi-virginianae S. I.
{ Puccinia Juniperi-virginianae (S.) Arth. I.
{ Roestelia pyrata (S.) Thax.

AURICULARIALES

{ Septobasidium pedicellatum Auct. Amer. p. p.
{ Septobasidium pseudopedicellatum Burt.
{ Thelephora pedicellata Auct. Amer. p. p.
Septobasidium retiforme (B. & C.) Pat.

THELEPHORACEAE

{ Corticium ochroleucum (Noack) Burt.
{ Corticium Stevensii Burt.
{ Hypochnus ochroleucus Noack.
Corticium salmonicolor B. & Br.
Stereum purpureum P. †

POLYPORACEAE

Polyporus squamosus (Huds.) ex Fr.
Polyporus sulphureus (Bull.) ex Fr.
Polyporus versicolor (L.) ex Fr.
Polyporus zonatus Fr.

AGARICACEAE

Armillaria mellea (Vahl) ex Fr.
Hypholoma incertum Pk.
Lentinus chaetophorus Lév.
Marasmius pyrinus Ell.
Schizophyllum commune Fr.

SPHAEROPSIDALES

Ascochyta pyrina Peglion.
Diplodia maura C. & E.
{ Discella effusa B. & C.
{ Discula effusa (B. & C.) Sacc.
Glutinium macrosporum Zeller.
Hendersonia Cydoniae C. & E.
Hendersonia foliorum Fckl.
Leptothyrium carpophilum Pass.
Leptothyrium pomi (Mont. & Fr.) Sacc.
Macrophoma Malorum (B.) Berl. & Vogl.
Phoma ambigua Sacc.
Phoma Mali Schulz. & Sacc.
Phoma pyrina (Fr.) Cke.
Phoma Radula B. & Br.

Pyrus communis (*cont.*)
Phoma simillima Pk.
Phyllosticta pyrina Sacc.
Phyllosticta Pyrorum Cke.
Septoria nigerina Fckl.
Septoria pyricola Desm.
Mycosphaerella sentina (Fr.) Schrt.
Sphaeropsis Malorum Pk.

MELANCONIALES

? { Colletotrichum lindemuthianum (Sacc. & Magn.) Scribner.
Colletotrichum Lycopersici Chester.
Coryneum foliicola Fckl.
Coryneum longestipitatum Berl. & Bres.
{ Entomosporium maculatum Lév.
Fabraea maculata Atk.
{ Blastesis tridens Zabriskie.
{ Entomosporium Mespili (DC.) Sacc.
Morthiera Mespili (DC.) Fckl.
{ Gloeosporium fructigenum B.
Gloeosporium gallarum Ch. Rich.
{ Glomerella cingulata (Stoneman) Spaulding & v. Schrenk.
Gnomoniopsis fructigena G. P. Clinton.
Gloeosporium hyalinum Ell. & Ev.
{ Gloeosporium malicorticis Cordley.
Neofabraea malicorticis H. S. Jackson.
Gloeosporium melanconioides Pk.
Gloeosporium perennans Zeller & Childs.
Gloeosporium phomoides Sacc.
Gloeosporium piperatum Ell. & Ev.
Myxosporium corticola Edgerton.
Myxosporium microsporum Cke. & Hark.

HYPHOMYCETES
Botrytis cinerea P. †
Botrytis vulgaris (Lk.) ex Fr.
Cephalothecium roseum Cda.
Cercospora minima Tracy & Earle.
Cercospora Pyri Farl.
Cladosporium carpophilum Thm.
Cladosporium herbarum (P.) ex Lk.
Coniothecium intricatum Pk.
Dendrodochium subeffusum Ell. & Gall.
Epochnium monilioides Lk.
Fumago vagans Fr.
Fusarium acuminatum Ell. & Ev. em. Wr.
Fusarium Equiseti (Cda.) Sacc.
Fusarium herbarum (Cda.) Fr.
Fusarium polymorphum Matr.
Fusarium pyrinum (Fr.) Sacc.
{ Cladosporium dendriticum Auct. p. p.
Fusicladium dendriticum Auct. p. p.
Fusicladium pyrinum (Lib.) Fckl.
Fusicladium pyrinum (Lib.) Fckl., var. cladophilum Ell. & Ev.
Helminthosporium Pyrorum Lib.
Venturia inaequalis Auct. p. p.
Venturia pyrina Aderh.

Macrosporium Pyrorum Cke.
Macrosporium sydowianum Farneti.
{ Monilia fructigena Auct. Amer.
Oidium fructigenum Auct. Amer.
Monilia oregonensis Barss & Casey.
Penicillium expansum Lk. ex Thom.
Ramularia obtusispora (Cke. & Hark.) Wr.
{ Sirodesmium Fumago (Cke.) Sacc.
Sporidesmium Fumago Cke.

MISCELLANEA
Ozonium auricomum Lk.
Ozonium omnivorum Shear.

Pyrus coronaria L.
Acrosporium pyrinum (Ell. & Ev.) Sumstine.
Anthostoma discincola (S.) Sacc.
Cenangium pyrinum S.
Cercosporella persicae Sacc.
{ Cercospora pyrina Ell. & Ev.
Cercosporella pyrina Ell. & Ev.
Cladosporium extorre Sacc.
Cryptovalsa pyrina Ell. & Ev.
Fusicladium dendriticum (Wallr.) Fckl.
Hysterium Prostii Duby.
Hysteropatella elliptica (Fr.) Rehm.
{ Ascochyta coronaria Ell. & Davis.
{ Marssonia coronariae Sacc. & Dearness.
Marssonina coronaria (Ell. & Davis) J.J.Davis.
Nummularia discreta (S.) Tul.
Oidium pyrinum Ell. & Ev.
Phyllosticta pyrina Sacc.
Phyllosticta solitaria Ell. & Ev.
Physalospora Cydoniae Arnaud.
Physalospora Malorum Shear et al..
Podosphaera Oxyacanthae (DC.) DBy.
{ Septoria Pyri Cast.
Septoria pyricola Desm.
Venturia Pomi (Fr.) Wint.

UREDINALES
Gymnosporangium Nidus-avis Thax. I.
{ Aecidium pyratum S.
Caeoma (Roestelia) Cylindrites, var. Mali S.
Caeoma pyratum S.
Gymnosporangium Juniperi-virginianae S. I.
Gymnosporangium macropus Lk. I.
Puccinia Juniperi-virginianae Arth. I.
Roestelia penicillata Auct. Amer.
Roestelia pyrata (S.) Thax.

Pyrus floribunda Lindl.
Aecidium blasdaleanum Diet. & Holw.

Pyrus germanica Hook. f.
Fabraea maculata Atk.

Pyrus glauca Auct.
Gymnosporangium Juniperi-virginianae S. I.

Pyrus glaucescens (Rehder) L. H. Bailey.
Gymnosporangium globosum Farl. I.

Pyrus hybrida Hort.
Gymnosporangium blasdaleanum Diet & Holw. I.
Gymnosporangium cornutum Arth. I.

Pyrus ioensis (Wood) L. H. Bailey.
Cercosporella pyrina Ell. & Ev.
⎰Fusicladium dendriticum (Wallr.) Fckl.
⎱Venturia inaequalis (Cke.) Wint.
Venturia Pomi (Fr.) Wint.
Marssonia coronariae Sacc. & Dearness.
Phyllosticta zonata Ell. & Ev.

Uredinales
Gymnosporangium blasdaleanum Kern. I.
Gymnosporangium Nidus-avis Thax. I.
⎰Gymnosporangium Juniperi-virginianae S. I.
⎱Gymnosporangium macropus Lk. I.
Roestelia pyrata (S.) Thax.

Pyrus Malus L.

Phycomycetes
Blastocladia Pringsheimii Reinsch.
Gonapodya siliquiformis (Reinsch) Thax.
Mucor varians Povah nom. nud.
Phytophthora Cactorum (Lib. & Cohn) Schrt.
Pythiacystis citrophthora Sm. & Sm.
⎰Mucor stolonifer Ehrenb. ex Fr.
⎱Rhizopus nigricans Ehrenb. ex Fr.

Protoascineae
Endomyces Mali C. E. Lewis.

Helvellineae
Roesleria hypogaea Thm. & Pass.

Pezizineae
⎰Cenangium prunastri (P.) Fr., var. rigidum
⎱ (S.) Fr.
Cenangium rigidum S.
Dermatea fascicularis (A. & S.) ex Fr.
Helotium citrinum (Hedw.) ex Fr.
Lachnea scutellata (P. ex Fr.) Gill.
Neofabraea malicorticis H. S. Jackson.
⎰Patinella inquinans (Cke.) Sacc.
⎱Peziza inquinans Cke.
⎰Peziza cruenta S.
⎱Orbilia rufula Massee.
Peziza regalis C. & E.
Pezizella Lythri Shear & Dodge.
Sclerotinia aestivalis Pollock.
Monilia oregonensis Barss & Posey.
⎰Monilia fructigena Auct. Amer.
⎱Sclerotinia americana (Wormald) Norton & Ezekiel.
Sclerotinia cinerea Auct. Amer.
Sclerotinia fructicola (Wint.) Rehm.
Sclerotinia fructigena Auct. Amer.
⎰Monilia urediniformis Ell. & Ev.
⎱Sclerotinia (?uredoformis) Demaree.
Tympanis conspersa Fr.

Phacidiineae
⎰Scleroderris gyrosa (B. & C.) Massee.
⎱Tympanis gyrosa B. & C.

Hysteriineae
Glonium lineare (Fr.) De Not.
Hysterographium cookeianum (Gerard) Ell. & Ev.
Hysterographium Mori (S.) Rehm.

Plectascineae
Gliocladium agaricinum Cda. & Massee.
Gliocladium penicilloides Cda.

Perisporiales
Capnodium elongatum B. & Desm.?
Capnodium pomorum B. & C.
Erysiphe Polygoni DC. †
⎰Albigo leucotricha O. Kuntze.
⎢Podosphaera leucotricha (Ell. & Ev.) Salmon.
⎨Podosphaera Oxyacanthae Fairchild.
⎢Sphaerotheca leucotricha Ell. & Ev.
⎩Sphaerotheca Mali (Duby) Burrill.
⎰Podosphaera Kunzei Lév.
⎢Podosphaera Oxyacanthae (DC.) DBy.
⎩Podosphaera tridactyla (Wallr.) DBy.
?Sphaerotheca Mors-uvae (S.) Lév.
?Sphaerotheca pannosa Auct.

Hypocreales
⎰Hypocrea contorta (S.) B. & C.
⎱Sphaeria contorta S.
Nectria cinnabarina (Tode) ex Fr.
⎰Creonectria coccinea (P.) Seaver.
⎨Nectria coccinea (P.) ex Fr.
⎩Nectria ditissima " Tul." Auct. Amer.
Creonectria purpurea (L.) Seaver.
Nectria ditissima Tul.
Nectria galligena Bres.
Nectria mammoidea Phil. & Plowr.
Nectria sanguinea (Sibth.) ex Fr.
Dialonectria vulpina Cke.

Dothideales
⎰Dothidea fructigena S.
⎱Phyllachora fructigena (S.) Sacc.
⎰Dothidea pomigena S.
⎨Gloeodes pomigena (S.) Colby.
⎩Phyllachora pomigena (S.) Sacc.

Sphaeriales
⎰Amphisphaeria bisphaerica (C. & E.) Sacc.
⎱Sphaeria bisphaerica C. & E.
Botryosphaeria Ribis (Tode ex Fr.) Grossenbacher & Duggar.
Botryosphaeria Ribis (Tode ex Fr.) Grossenbacher & Duggar, var. chromogena Shear et al.
Ceratostomella Mali Ell. & Ev.
Cryptosporella viticola (Reddick) Shear.

Pyrus Malus (*cont.*)

Daldinia concentrica (Bolt. ex Fr.) Ces. & DeNot.

{Diaporthe Murrayi (B. & C.) Sacc.
 Sphaeria Murrayi B. & C.

Anthostoma discincola Sacc.

{Diatrype discincola M. A. Curtis.
 Nummularia discincola Cke.
 Sphaeria discincola S. p. p.[1]

{Diatrype discreta (S.) M. A. Curtis.
 Hypoxylon discretum (S.) B. & C.
 Nummularia discreta (S.) Tul.
 Sphaeria discincola S. p. p.[2]
 Sphaeria discreta S.

Dichaena Pyri Dearness & Barthol.

Didymella Mali Ell. & Ev.

Eutypa leioplaca (Fr.) Cke.

Eutypella prunastri (P. ex Fr.) Sacc.

Fenestella vestita (Fr.) Sacc.

Gibberella baccata (Wallr.) Sacc.

Glomerella cingulata (Stoneman) Spaulding & v. Schrenk.

Hypoxylon atramentosum Fr.

Hypoxylon coccineum Bull. †

Hypoxylon Morsei B. & C.

Leptosphaeria concentrica Ell. & Ev.

Leptosphaeria Coniothyrium (Fckl.) Sacc.

Leptosphaeria pomona Sacc.

Lophiostoma scelestum C. & E.

{Massaria excussa (S.) M. A. Curtis.
 Metasphaeria excussa (S.) Starb.
 Sphaeria excussa S.

Massaria Pyri Otth.

Massaria vomitoria B. & C.

Melanconis stilbostoma (Fr.) Tul.

Melanopsamma improvita Karst.

Metasphaeria subcutanea (C. & E.) Sacc.

Otthia amica Sacc.

Physalospora Cydoniae Arnaud.

Physalospora erratica (C. & E.) Sacc.

Physalospora Malorum Shear et al.

{Melogramma fuliginosum Ell. p. p.
 Physalospora viscosa (C. & E.) Sacc.
 Sphaeria viscosa C. & E.

{Sphaerella collapsa (S.) Cke.
 Sphaeria collapsa S.

Sphaerella sentina (Fr.) Fckl.

{Sphaerella subbullans (S.) Cke.
 Sphaeria subbullans S.

Sphaeria pyramidalis S.

Sphaeria pyrina Fr.

Sphaerostilbe coccophila Tul.

Valsa ambiens (P.) ex Fr.

Valsa americana B. & C.

Valsa leucostoma (P.) ex Fr.

Valsa leucostomoides Pk.

{Sphaeria nivea Hoffm. ex Fr.
 Valsa nivea (Hoffm.) ex Fr.

Valsa stellulata Fr.

Valsaria rubricosa (Fr.) Sacc.

{Sphaeria melastoma Fr.
 Valsa melastoma Fr.
 Valsella melastoma (Fr.) Sacc.

Valsella papyriferae (S.) Berl. & Vogl.

{Venturia inaequalis (Cke.) Wint..
 ?Venturia Pomi Auct.

Xylaria digitata (L.) ex Grev.

Xylaria hypoxylon (L.) ex Grev.

Xylaria longiana Rehm.

Xylaria polymorpha (P.) ex Grev.

UREDINALES

{Gymnosporangium clavipes C. & P. I.
 Gymnosporangium germinale Kern. I.
 Roestelia aurantiaca Pk.

Aecidium blasdaleanum Diet. & Holw.

{Gymnosporangium blasdaleanum Kern. I.
 Gymnosporangium globosum Farl. I.
 Gymnosporangium juniperinum (L.) ex Mart. I.

{Aecidium laceratum Sow.
 Gymnosporangium clavariiforme (Jacq. ex P.) DC.
 Roestelia clavariiforme (Jacq. ex P.) O. Kuntze.
 Roestelia lacerata (Sow.) Fr.

Gymnosporangium Nidus-avis Thax. I.

{Aecidium pyratum S.
 Caeoma (Roestelia) Cylindrites, var. Mali S.
 Caeoma Roestelites S. Am. Bor. 2900. p. p.[1]
 Gymnosporangium Juniperi-virginianae S. I.
 Gymnosporangium macropus Lk. I.
 Puccinia Juniperi-virginianae (S.) Arth. I.
 Roestelia penicillata Auct. Amer.
 Roestelia pyrata (S.) Thax.

{Myxosporium colliculosum B.
 Roestelia sp. indet.

PHRAGMOBASIDIOMYCETES

{Dacryomyces violaceus (Relh.) ex Fr.
 Tremella violacea Relh. ex Fr.

Exidia recisa Fr.

Exidia truncata Fr.

{Tremella fragiformis S. Syn. Car.
 Hormomyces aurantiacus Sacc., nec Bon.
 Hypsilophora fragiformis Cke.

Sebacina polyschista B. & C.

{Septobasidium pedicellatum Auct. Amer. p. p.
 Septopedicellatum pseudopedicellatum Burt.
 Thelephora pedicellata Auct. Amer. p. p.

{Septobasidium retiforme (B. & C.) Pat.
 Thelephora retiformis B. & C.

THELEPHORACEAE

Coniophora sistotremoides (S.) Massee.

Corticium atrovirens B.

{Corticium galactinum (Fr.) Burt.
 Thelephora galactina Fr.

Corticium laetum Karst.

Corticium Litschaueri Burt.

Pyrus Malus (*cont.*)

Corticium ochroleucum (Noack) Burt.
Corticium Stevensii (Noack) Burt.
Hypochnus ochroleucus Noack.
Corticium salmonicolor B. & Br.
Cyphella fasciculata (S.) B. & C.
Cyphella marginata McAlpine.
Hymenochaete agglutinans Ell.
Peniophora cinerea (P. ex Fr.) Cke.
Stereum cinerascens (S.) Massee.
Stereum hirsutum (Willd.) ex Fr.
Stereum purpureum P. †
Thelephora fusca (P.) Fr.

HYDNACEAE

Hericium croceum Banker p. p.
Hydnum croceum Fr.
Hydnum mucidum P.
Hydnum ochraceum P. ex Fr.
Ozonium omnivorum Shear.
Phymatotrichum omnivorum (Shear) Duggar.
Hydnum Schiedermayeri Heufler.
Irpex canescens Fr.
Irpex lacteus Fr.
Irpex sinuosus Fr.
Irpex Tulipiferae S.
Irpex obliquus Fr.
Irpiciporus mollis (B. & C.) Murrill.
Radulum aterrimum Fr.

POLYPORACEAE

Daedalea confragosa (Bolt.) ex Fr.
Daedalea unicolor Fr.
Fomes applanatus (P. ex Wallr.) Gill.
Fomes Everhartii (Ell. & Gall.) v. Schrenk.
Fomes fomentarius (L. ex Fr.) Gill.
Fomes fulvus (Scop. ex Fr.) Gill.
Fomes igniarius (L. ex Fr.) Gill.
Polyporus igniarius (L.) ex Fr.
Pyropolyporus igniarius (L. ex Fr.) Murrill.
Fomes pinicola (Sw. ex Fr.) Cke.
Merulius porinoides Fr.
Ganoderma Curtisii (B.) Murrill.
Polyporus Curtisii B.
Polyporus admirabilis Pk.
Polyporus adustus (Willd.) ex Fr.
Polyporus benzoinus Fr.
Polyporus caesius (Schrad.) ex Fr.
Polyporus distortus (S.) Fr.
Polyporus fissilis B. & C.
Spongipellis fissilis (B. & C.) Murrill.
Polyporus fumosus (P.) ex Fr.
Polyporus galactinus B.
Spongipellis galactinus (B.) Pat.
Coriolus nigromarginatus (S.) Murrill.
Polyporus hirsutus (Wulf.) ex Fr.
Polystictus hirsutus (Wulf.) ex Fr.
Polyporus obtusus B.
Polyporus spumeus (Sow.) ex Fr.

Polyporus sulphureus (Bull.) ex Fr.
Polystictus hirsutellus S.
Polystictus hirsutus (Wulf.) ex Fr.
Polyporus lacteus Fr.
Polystictus lacteus Fr.
Polyporus versicolor (L.) ex Fr.
Polystictus versicolor (L.) ex Fr.
Poria floccosa Fr.
Poria latifer Pk.
Poria spissa (S.) Cke.
Solenia anomala (P. ex Fr.) Fckl., var. orbicularis Pk.
Trametes gibbosa (P.) ex Fr.
Coriolellus malicola (B. & C.) Murrill.
Polyporus populinus S.
Polyporus spumeus, var. malicola (B. & C.) Lloyd.
Trametes malicola B. & C.

AGARICACEAE

Armillaria mellea (Vahl) ex Fr.
Clitocybe parasitica Wilcox.
Clitocybe monadelpha Morg.
Clitopilus conissans Pk.
Crepidotus fulvotomentosus Pk.
Hypholoma appendiculatum (Bull.) ex Fr.
Lenzites betulina Fr.
Lenzites vialis Pk.
Mycena corticola (Schum.) ex Fr.
Panus laevis B. & C.
Panus strigosus B. & C.
Pholiota adiposa Fr.
Pleurotus dryinus (P.) ex Fr.
Pleurotus pometi (Paul.) Fr.
Pleurotus pulvinatus (P.) ex Fr.
Pleurotus serotinus Fr.
Pleurotus ulmarius Fr.
Schizophyllus alneus (L. ex Fr.) Schrt.
Schizophyllum commune Fr.
Schizophyllum commune Fr., var. palmatum Debeaux.

SPHAEROPSIDALES

Aposphaeria collabens Sacc.
Ascochyta Mali Ell. & Ev.
Camarosporium Mali Ell. & Ev.
Camarosporulum Mali (Ell. & Ev.) Tassi.
Coniothyrium Fuckelii Sacc.
Coniothyrium pyrinum (Sacc.) Sheldon.
Cornularia pyramidalis (S.) Starb.
Sphaeria pyramidalis S.
Cylindrocarpon angustum Wollenw.
Cytospora ambiens Sacc.
Cytospora carphosperma Sacc.
Cytospora leucosticta Ell. & Barthol.
Cytospora leucostoma Sacc.
Cytospora rubescens Fr.
Diplodia maura C. & E.
Diplodia natalensis Evans.
Diplodia pseudo-diplodia Fckl.

Pyrus Malus (*cont.*)
Diplodia Pyri Ell. & Martin.
{ Diplodia pyrenophora (B.) M. A. Curtis.
{ Dothiora pyrenophora B. an Fr.?
Discosia maculicola Gerard.
{ Discella effusa B. & C.
{ Discula effusa (B. & C.) Sacc.
Dothiorella berengeriana Sacc.
Dothiorella divergens Pk.
Dothiorella Mali Ell. & Ev.
Fusicoccum Pyrorum Chupp & Clapp.
Glutinium macrosporum Zeller.
Haplosporella Malorum Sacc.
Hendersonia Cydoniae C. & E.
Hendersonia diplodioides Ell. & Ev.
Hendersonia foliorum Fckl.
{ Hendersonia Mali Thm.
{ Pleospora Mali Hesler.
Leptostroma fructigenum S.
{ Labrella Pomi Mont. & Fr.
{ Leptothyrium Pomi (Mont. & Fr.) Sacc.
{ Microsticta Pomi (Mont. & Fr.) Desm.
Leptothyrium Pyri Sacc.
Macrophoma curvispora Pk.
Phlyctaena Mali Ell. & Ev.
Phoma ambigua (Nits.) Sacc.
Phoma enteroleuca Sacc.
Phoma Mali Schulz. & Sacc.
Phoma pomi Pass.
Phoma pomorum W. A. Orton.
Phoma pyricola Ell. & Ev.
{ Sphaeria pyrina S. Herb. nec Fr.
{ Phoma pyrina Ell. & Ev.
Phomopsis Mali Roberts.
Phyllosticta clypeata Ell. & Ev.
Phyllosticta limitata Pk.
Phyllosticta Mali Prill. & Delacr.
Phyllosticta Paulowniae Sacc.
Phyllosticta prunicola (Opiz) Sacc.
Phyllosticta pyrina Sacc.
Phyllosticta? pyriseda? Hartley.
Phyllosticta solitaria Ell. & Ev.
{ Aposphaeria fuscomaculans Sacc.
{ Plenodomus fuscomaculans (Sacc.) Coons.
Pyrenochaeta collabens Pk.
Rhabdospora rhoina (Pk.) O. Kuntze.
Scolecosporium pedicellatum Dearness & Overholts.
{ Mycosphaerella sentina (Fr.) Schrt.
{ Septoria Pyri Cast.
{ Septoria pyricola Desm.
Sphaeronema conforme Pk.
{ Macroplodia cinerea C. & E.
{ Sphaeropsis cinerea (C. & E.) Sacc.
Sphaeropsis Mali (Westd.) Sacc.
{ Botryodiplodia Malorum (B.) Petrak & Syd.
{ Macrophoma Malorum (B.) Berl. & Vogl.
{ Phoma Malorum (B.) Sacc.
{ Sphaeropsis Malorum B.

Sphaeropsis Malorum B., var. foliicola Ell. & Ev.
Haplosporella Mali (Westd.) Petrak & Syd.
Sphaeropsis Malorum Pk.
{ Sphaeria pomorum S.
{ Sphaeropsis pomorum (S.) Cke.
{ Sphaeropsis pseudo-diplodia (Fckl.) Delacr.
{ Sphaeropsis rhoina (S.) Starb.
Stagonospora biformis Ell.
{ Hendersonia prominula B. & C.
{ Stagonospora prominula (B. & C.) Sacc.
Vermicularia pomicola Pk.
Vermicularia pomona Sacc.

MELANCONIALES

{ Colletotrichum fructus (Stevens & Hall) Sacc.
{ Volutella fructi Stevens & Hall.
Colletotrichum gloeosporioides Penz.
Gloeosporium fructigenum B.
Gloeosporium rufomaculans (B.) Thm.
Gloeosporium versicolor B. & C.
{ Glomerella cingulata (Stoneman) Spaulding & v. Schrenk.
Glomerella fructigena (G. P. Clinton) Sacc.
Glomerella rufomaculans Spaulding & v. Schrenk.
Gnomoniopsis fructigena G. P. Clinton.
{ Coryneum foliicola Fckl.
{ cf. Hendersonia Mali Thm.
Coryneum longestipitatum Berl. & Bres.
Cylindrosporium Padi Auct.
{ Cylindrosporium pomi Brooks.
{ Mycosphaerella pomi Walton & Orton.
Entomosporium maculatum Lév.
Entomosporium pomi Brooks.
{ Gloeosporium malicorticis Cordley.
{ Neofabraea malicorticis H. S. Jackson.
Gloeosporium melanconioides Pk.
Gloeosporium melongenae Ell. & Halsted.
Gloeosporium perennans Zeller & Childs.
Gloeosporium phomoides Sacc.
Gloeosporium piperatum Ell. & Ev.
Gloeosporium Riessii Schl. & Sacc.
Melanconium fuligineum (Scribn. & Viala) Cavara.
Myxosporium corticola Edgerton.
Pestalozzia brevipes Cke.
Pestalozzia breviseta Sacc.
Pestalozzia concentrica B. & Br.
Pestalozzia funerea Desm.
Pestalozzia Guepini Desm.
{ Monochaetia Mali (Ell. & Ev.) Sacc.
{ Pestalozzia Mali Ell. & Ev.
Pestalozzia rostrata Zabriskie.

HYPHOMYCETES

MUCEDINACEAE

Aspergillus niger van Tiegh.
Aspergillus ovalispermus Lk.

Pyrus Malus (*cont.*)

Botrytis cinerea P. †
Botrytis vulgaris (Lk.) ex Fr.
Cephalothecium roseum (Fr.) Cda.
Coniothecium chromatosporium Cda.
Monilia cinerea Bon.
Monilia oregonensis Barss & Posey.
Nematogonium aurantiacum Desm.
Penicillium commune Thom.
Penicillium expansum (Lk.) ex Thom.
?Penicillium glaucum Auct. Amer. p. p.
Penicillium luteum Zukal.
Penicillium pinophilum Hedgcock.
Ramularia macrospora Fres.
Rhinotrichum repens Preuss.
Sporotrichum cinereum Pk.
Sporotrichum Peckii Sacc.
Sporotrichum luteoalbum S. Am. Bor.
Sporotrichum Thuemenii Sacc.
Trichoderma Koningi Oud.
Dactylium roseum (Lk.) B.
Trichothecium roseum Lk.

DEMATIACEAE

Alternaria Citri Pierce, var. Cerasi B. A.
  Rudolph.
Alternaria fasciculata (C. & E.) Jones & Grout.
Alternaria Mali J. W. Roberts.
Cercospora Mali Ell. & Ev.
Cercospora Pyri Farl.
Cheiromyces Beaumontii B. & C. in N. A. F.
Cladosporium herbarum (P.) ex Lk.
Cladosporium stenosporum B. & C.
Dematium propullans DBy.
Epochnium monilioides Lk.
Cladosporium dendriticum Wallr.
Fusicladium dendriticum (Wallr.) Fckl.
Spilocaea fructigena S. Am. Bor.
Spilocaea Pomi Fr.
Venturia chlorospora, var. Mali Aderh. 1894.
Venturia inaequalis (Cke. p. p.?) Wint. 1880.
Venturia inaequalis (Cke. p. p.?) Wint., var.
  Pyri-Mali Thm. 1880.
Venturia inaequalis Aderh. 1897.
?Venturia Pomi Auct.
Fusicladium dendriticum, var. orbiculatum
  (Desm.) Sacc.
Helicoma Mulleri Cda.
Helminthosporium carpophilum Lév.
Macrosporium sarcinula B.
Sporidesmium fructigenum Ell. & Ev.
Sporidesmium melanopum (Ach.) B. & Br.
Sporidesmium melanopodum Sacc.
Sporidesmium moriforme Pk.

STILBACEAE

Periconia truncata C. & P.
Sporocybe truncata (C. & P.) Sacc.

TUBERCULARIACEAE

Epicoccum granulatum Penz.
Fusarium acuminatum Ell. & Ev. em. Wr.
Fusarium arcuatum B. & C.
Fusarium avenaceum (Fr.) Sacc.
Fusarium bulbigerum Cke. & Massee.
Fusarium graminum Cda.
Fusarium Helianthi C. E. Lewis.
Fusarium lateritium Nees ex Fr.
Fusarium oxysporum Schl.
Fusarium pyrinum S.
Fusarium pyrinum (Fr.) Sacc.
Fusarium putrefaciens Osterw.
Fusarium radicicola Woll.
Fusarium rhizogenum Pound & Clements.
Fusarium Urticacearum (Cda.) Sacc.
Gibberella moricola (Ces. & De Not.) Sacc.
Illosporium malifoliorum Sheldon.
Microcera coccophila Desm.
Tubercularia nigricans (Bull.) ex Lk.
Volutella fructi Stevens & Hall.

MISCELLANEA

Dendrophagus globosus Toumey.
Lycoperdon gemmatum Batsch ex Fr.
Ozonium auricomum Lk.
Sclerotium bataticola Taubenhaus.
Sclerotium Rolfsii Sacc.

Pyrus melanocarpa (Michx.) Willd.

Acrotheca dearnessiana Sacc.
Cercospora Pyri Farl.
Cercospora pyrina Ell. & Ev.
Cercosporella pyrina Ell. & Ev.
Diaporthe melanocarpa Dearness.
Entomosporium maculatum Lév.
Gymnosporangium Davisii Kern. I.
Gymnosporangium fraternum Kern. I.
Gymnosporangium germinale Kern. I.
Gymnosporangium transformans Kern. I.
Hendersonia vagans Fckl.
Phyllosticta leucocarpae Atk.
Podosphaera Oxyacanthae (DC.) DBy.
Sydowia dothideoides Dearness & Barthol.

Pyrus occidentalis Watson.

Gymnosporangium juniperinum (L.) ex Mart.
  I.
Roestelia fimbriata Arth.
Gymnosporangium Nelsoni Arth. I.
Aecidium Sorbi Arth.
Gymnosporangium Sorbi Kern. I.
Gymnotelium nootkatense (Arth.) Syd.

Pyrus pinnatifida Ehrh.

Gymnosporangium blasdaleanum Kern. I.

Pyrus prunifolia Willd.

Fusicladium dendriticum (Wallr.) Fckl.

Pyrus pulcherrima Aschers. & Graebn.

Gymnosporangium Juniperi-virginianae S. I.

Pyrus rivularis Dougl.
  Armillaria mellea, var. bulbosa? Pk.
  {Entomosporium maculatum Lév.
  {Fabraea maculata Atk.
  Fomes applanatus (P. ex Wallr.) Gill.
  Phyllactinia corylea (P.) ex Karst.

UREDINALES

  {Aecidium blasdaleanum Diet. & Holw.
  {Gymnosporangium blasdaleanum Kern. I.
  Gymnosporangium Nelsoni Arth. I.
  {Aecidium Sorbi Arth.
  {Gymnosporangium nootkatensis Arth. I.
  {Gymnosporangium Sorbi Kern. I.
  {Gymnotelium nootkatense (Arth.) Syd.
Pyrus sambucifolia Cham. & Schl.
  Aecidium blasdaleanum Diet. & Holw.
  {Diaporthe impulsa (C. & P.) Sacc.
  {Valsa impulsa C. & P.
  Pseudopeziza Pyri Pk.
  Septoria Sorbi Lasch.
Pyrus scopulina Greene.
  Cytospora chrysosperma (P.) ex Fr.
  Diaporthe impulsa (C. & P.) Sacc.
  {Gymnosporangium cornutum Arth. I.
  {Roestelia cornuta (P.) ex Fr.
  Gymnosporangium juniperinum (L.) ex Mart.
    I.
  Gymnosporangium Nelsoni Arth. I.
  Gymnosporangium nootkatense Arth. I.
  {Aecidium Sorbi Arth.
  {Gymnosporangium Sorbi Kern. I.
  Sphaeronema pallidum Pk.
Pyrus Sieboldi Regel.
  Sphaerotheca Mali (Duby) Burrill.
Pyrus sinensis Lindl.
  Entomosporium maculatum Lév.
  Gymnosporangium blasdaleanum Kern. I.
  {Gymnosporangium koreaense H. S. Jackson. I.
  {Roestelia koreaensis Henn.
Pyrus sitchensis (Roem.) Piper.
  {Entomosporium maculatum Lév.
  {Fabraea maculata Ath.
  Entomosporium maculatum Lév., var. domes-
    ticum Sacc.
  {Gymnosporangium cornutum Arth. I.
  {Roestelia cornuta (P.) ex Fr.
  Gymnosporangium juniperinum (L.) ex Mart. I.
  Gymnosporangium Nelsoni Arth. I.
  {Gymnosporangium nootkatensis (Trel.) Arth.
    I.
  {Gymnotelium nootkatense (Arth.) Syd. I.
  Gymnosporangium Sorbi Kern. I.
  Phyllosticta globigera Sacc.
  Polystictus hirsutus (Wulf.) ex Fr.
  Rhabdospora inaequalis Sacc.
Pyrus Soulardi L. H. Bailey.
  Venturia inaequalis (Cke.) Wint.
  Venturia Pomi (Fr.) Wint.

Pyrus spectabilis Hort., var.
  Gymnosporangium Juniperi-virginianae S. I.
Pyrus sylvestris S. F. Gray.
  Cercospora Mali Ell. & Ev.
  Clitocybe monadelpha (Morg.) Sacc.
  Glomerella cingulata (Stoneman) Spaulding &
    v. Schrenk.
  Podosphaera leucotricha Ell. & Ev.
  Sphaeropsis Malorum Pk.
  Xylaria Hypoxylon (L.) ex Grev.
Pyrus (Aronia) monstrosa Zabel.
  {Gymnosporangium clavipes C. & P. I.
  {Gymnosporangium germinale Kern. I.
Pyrus (Aronia) sp. indet.
  Cercospora Mali Ell. & Ev.
  Pestalozzia longiseta Speg.
  Phyllosticta arbutifolia Ell. & Martin.
Pyrus (Sorbus) sp. indet.
  Cytospora chrysosperma (P.) ex Fr.
  Cytospora " leucostroma."
  Diaporthe Aucupariae Hazsl.
  Diaporthe impulsa (C. & P.) Sacc.
  Fomes applanatus (P. ex Wallr.) Gill.
  Gymnosporangium nootkatensis Arth.
  Hypoxylon multiforme Fr.
  Karschia melaspileoides Rehm.
  Nummularia discreta (S.) Tul.
  Physalospora Malorum Shear et al.
Pyrus (" flowering crab ").
  Sphaeropsis Malorum Pk.
Pyrus sp. indet. (" wild crab ").
  Septoria Rosarum Westd.
Pyrus sp. indet.
  Cenangium enteroxanthum S.
  Cladosporium stenosporum B. & C.
  {Thelephora polygonia P.
  {Corticium polygonium Fr.
  Entoleuca callimorpha Syd.
  Eutypa Acharii Tul.
  Gymnosporangium haraeanum Syd. I.
  Gymnosporangium japonicum Syd. I.
  Hysteropatella elliptica (Fr.) Rehm.
  Illosporium malifoliorum Sheldon.
  Monilia punctans S.
  Nectria cinnabarina (Tode) ex Fr.
  {Diatrype subaffixa (S.) Cke.
  {Nummularia subaffixa (S.) Sacc.
  {Sphaeria subaffixa S.
  {Septoria Oxyacanthae Kze.
  {Phloeospora Oxyacanthae (Kze.) Wallr.
  Phyllosticta leucocarpae Atk.
  Polyporus connatus Fr.
  {Boletus marginatus P. ex Fr.
  {Polyporus marginatus (P.) ex Fr.
  Sclerotinia Johnsonii (Ell. & Ev.) Rehm.
  Sclerotium pyrinum Fr.
  Septoria nigerrima Fckl.
  Sphaeronema pyriforme (P.) Fr.
  Sporotrichum fructigenum Lk.

Eriobotrya japonica Lindl.
  Armillaria mellea (Vahl) ex Fr.
  Capnodium caespitosum Ell. & Ev.
  ⎰Fusicladium dendriticum (Wallr.) Fckl., var.
     Eriobotryae Scalia.
  ⎱Fusicladium Eriobotryae Scalia.
  Glomerella cingulata (Stoneman) Spaulding &
    v. Schrenk.
  Phyllosticta Eriobotryae Thm.
  Rhizoctonia Solani Kühn.
  Septoria Photiniae B. & C.
  Sphaeropsis Malorum Pk.

Heteromeles arbutifolia Roem.
  Capnodium Heteromeles Cke. & Hark.
  Cercospora Heteromeles Hark.
  Ceuthospora brevispora Cke. & Hark.
  Corticium arachnoideum B.
  Dasyscypha cerina (P.) Fckl.
  Diplodia heteromelina Fairman.
  Discosia poikilomera Fairman.
  Embolus ochreatus Sacc.
  ⎰Entomosporium maculatum Lév.
  ⎱Fabraea maculata (Lév.) Atk.
  Eutypella ceranata Fairman.
  Fusicladium dendriticum (Wallr.) Fckl., var.
    Eriobotryae Scalia.
  Fusicladium photinicola McClain.
  Gloniopsis insignis (Cke. & Hark.) Berk. &
    Vogl.
  Glonium parvulum (Gerard) Sacc.
  Hadrotrichum Heteromelis Ell. & Ev.
  Helotiella microspora Burt.
  Hypoxylon annulatum (S.) Mont.
  Hypoxylon rubiginosum (P.) ex Fr.
  Hysterographium Bakeri Earle.
  Hysterographium prominens (Phil. & Hark.)
    Berl. & Vogl.
  ⎰Hypoderma Heteromeles Phil. & Hark.
  ⎱Lophodermium Heteromeles (Phil. & Hark.)
    Ell. & Ev.
  ⎰Meliola Heteromeles (Cke. & Hark.) Berl. &
    Vogl.
  ⎱Meliolopsis Heteromeles Cke. & Hark.
  Peniophora Allescheri Bres.
  Phacidium Heteromeles Phil. & Hark.
  Phoma Heteromeles Cke. & Hark.
  Phyllosticta Heteromeles Cke. & Hark.
  Physalospora heteromelina Fairman.
  Pleosporopsis Heteromeles Cke. & Hark.
  ⎰Pleurotus applicatus (Batsch) ex Fr.
  ⎱Resupinatus applicatus (Batsch) ex S. F. Gray.
  Pleurotus septicus Fr.
  Poria rhodella (Fr.) Cke.
  ⎰Peziza Heteromeles Phil. & Hark.
  ⎱Pyrenopeziza Heteromeles (Phil. & Hark.)
    Sacc.
  Septoria Photiniae B. & C.
  Septoria rhabdocarpa Ell. & Barthol.

  Stictis radiata (L.) ex P.
  Tremella mesenterica Retz.

Peraphyllum ramosissimum Nutt.
  Gymnosporangium inconspicuum Kern. I.
  Gymnosporangium Nelsoni Arth. I.
  Septoria Peraphylli Pk.

Amelanchier alnifolia Nutt.
  Calosphaeria princeps Tul.
  Cylindrosporium Aroniae Sacc.
  Diatrype Stigma (Hoffm.) ex Fr.
  ⎰Dimerosporium Collinsii (S.) Thm.
  ⎱Plowrightia phyllogona Hark.
  ⎱Sphaeria Collinsii S.
  ⎰Entomosporium maculatum Lév.
  ⎱Fabraea maculata Atk.
  ⎰Erysiphe communis Auct. Amer. p.p.
  ⎱Erysiphe Polygoni DC. †
  Eutypa scabrosa (Bull. ex Fr.) Awd.
  Fomes scutellatus (S.) Cke.
  Hymenochaete tabacina (Sow. ex Fr.) Lév.
  Lophodermium tumidum (Fr.) Rehm.
  Nectria cinnabarina (Tode) ex Fr.
  Patinella brenckleana Sacc.
  ⎰Dermatea pruinosa (Farl.) Petrak.
  ⎰Lagynodella pruinosa (Pk.) Petrak.
  ⎱Pezicula pruinosa (Pk.) Farl.
  ⎱Sphaeronema pruinosum Pk.
  ⎰Phyllactinia corylea (P.) ex Karst.
  ⎱Phyllactinia suffulta (Reb.) ex Sacc.
  Phyllosticta innumerabilis Pk.
  Phyllosticta paupercula Pk.
  ?Plowrightia morbosa (S.) Sacc.
  Valsa cincta Fr.

UREDINALES

  ⎰Aecidium blasdaleanum Diet. & Holw.
  ⎱Gymnosporangium aurantiacum Syd. I.
  ⎱Gymnosporangium blasdaleanum Kern. I.
  ⎰Gymnosporangium clavipes C. & P. I.
  ⎰Gymnosporangium germinale Kern. I.
  ⎱Roestelia aurantiaca Pk.
  Gymnosporangium corniculans Kern. I.
  Roestelia Ellisii Pk.
  ⎰Gymnosporangium globosum Farl. I.
  ⎱Roestelia lacerata Auct. Amer. p. p.
  ⎰Gymnosporangium harknessianum Kern. I.
  ⎱Roestelia harknessiana Ell. & Ev.
  ⎰Gymnosporangium inconspicuum Kern. I.
  ⎰Roestelia harknessiana Fung. Columb. *1293.*
  ⎱Roestelia harknessianoides Kern.
  Gymnosporangium kernianum Bethel. I.
  ⎰Gymnosporangium juvenescens Kern. I.
  ⎱Roestelia Nelsoni Auct. Amer. p. p.
  ⎰Gymnosporangium clavariiforme (Jacq. ex
    P.) DC. I.
  ⎱Roestelia lacerata (Sow.) Fr.
  ⎰Gymnosporangium Nelsoni Arth. I.
  ⎱Roestelia Nelsoni Arth.

Amelanchier alnifolia (*cont.*)
Gymnosporangium Nidus-avis Thax. I.
{ Gymnosporangium speciosum Pk. I.
{ Tremella speciosa (Pk.) Arth. I.

Amelanchier amelanchier Degen.
Gymnosporangium biseptatum Ell. I.
{ Gymnosporangium fraternum Kern. I.
{ Roestelia transformans Ell.

Amelanchier Bakeri Greene.
Gymnosporangium inconspicuum Kern. I.
Gymnosporangium juvenescens Kern. I.
Gymnosporangium Nelsoni Arth. I.

Amelanchier bartramiana (Tausch.) Roem.
Gymnosporangium germinale Kern. I.
Sphaeronema pruinosum Pk.
Valsa cincta Fr.

Amelanchier canadensis (L.) Medic.
Anthostoma gastrinum (Fr.) Sacc.
{ Anthostoma phaeospermum (Ell.) Sacc.
{ Diatrype phaeosperma Ell.
{ Fuckelia phaeosperma (Ell.) Cke.
Diaporthe oncostoma (Duby) Fckl.
{ Valsa punctostoma Ell.
{ Diaporthe stictostoma (Ell.) Sacc.
{ Valsa stictostoma (Ell.) Cke.
{ Valsa tuberculosa Ell.
{ Diaporthe tuberculosa (Ell.) Sacc.
Diaporthe tuberculosa (Ell.) Sacc., var. dispersa Pk.
Diatrype disciformis (Hoffm.) ex Fr.
{ Gymnosporangium Nidus-avis Thax. I.
{ Tremella Nidus-avis (Thax.) Arth. I.
{ Apiosporina Collinsii (S.) Höhnel.
Dimerosporium Collinsii (S.) Thm.
Dothidea Collinsii (S.) Ell.
Lasiosphaeria papilionacea (B. & C.) Sacc.
{ Lasiosphaeria Russellii (B. & C.) Sacc.
Plowrightia phyllogona Hark.
{ Sphaeria Collinsii S.
{ Sphaeria papilionacea B. & C.
{ Sphaeria Russellii B. & C.
Discella canadensis Pk.
Entomosporium maculatum Lév.
Entomosporium maculatum Lév., var. Cydoniae C. & E.
Hypoxylon coccineum Bull. †
Massaria vomitoria B. & C.
Morthiera Mespili (DC.) Fckl.
{ Metasphaeria Peckii (Speg.) Sacc.
{ Sphaerella Peckii Speg.
{ Sphaerulina Peckii (Speg.) Cke.
Mycosphaerella maculiformis (P. ex Fr.) Schrt.
Nummularia discreta (S.) Tul.
Oidium destruens Pk.
Peniophora cinerea (P. ex Fr.) Cke.
Peniophora heterocystidia Burt.
{ Pezicula pruinosa Farl.
{ Sphaeronema pruinosum Pk.

{ Phyllosticta destruens Desm.
{ Phyllosticta virginiana (Ell. & Halsted) Seaver
Plowrightia morbosa (S.) Sacc.
Podosphaera Oxyacanthae (DC.) DBy.
Polyporus elegans (Bull.) ex Fr.
Poria ferruginosa (Schrad. ex Fr.) Cke.
Poria incrassata (B. & C.) Burt.
{ Monilia Amelanchieris Reade.
{ Sclerotinia Amelanchieris Reade.
{ Haplosporella Amelanchieris (Dearness) Petrak & Syd.
{ Sphaeropsis Amelanchieris Dearness.
Stysanus Stemonitis Cda.
Valsa ambiens (P.) ex Fr.
Valsa ceratophora Tul.
Valsa cincta Fr.

UREDINALES

{ Caeoma Botryapites S.
{ Gymnosporangium biseptatum Ell. I.
{ Gymnosporangium Botryapites Kern. I.
{ Roestelia Botryapites (S.) C. & E.
{ Gymnosporangium clavariiforme (Jacq. ex P.) DC. I.
{ Roestelia lacerata (Sow.) Fr.
{ Roestelia lacerata *x* Thax.
{ Gymnosporangium clavipes C. & P. I.
{ Gymnosporangium germinale Kern. I.
{ Roestelia aurantiaca Pk.
{ Gymnosporangium corniculans Kern. I.
{ Roestelia cornuta, var. Amelanchieris E. F. 248a.
Roestelia cornuta Auct. Amer. p. p.
{ Gymnosporangium fraternum Kern. I.
{ Roestelia transformans Ell.
Gymnosporangium inconspicuum Kern. I.
Gymnosporangium juvenescens Kern. I.
{ Gymnosporangium Nelsoni Arth. I.
{ Roestelia Nelsoni Arth.
Gymnosporangium Nidus-avis Thax. I.

Amelanchier canadensis (L.) Medic., var. **Botryapium** (L. f.) Torr. & Gr.
Fabraea maculata Atk.
Podosphaera Oxyacanthae (DC.) DBy.
{ Gymnosporangium biseptatum Ell.
{ Roestelia botryapites (S.) C. & E.
{ Gymnosporangium corniculans Kern.
{ Roestelia Amelanchieris N. A. F. 2715.
{ Gymnosporangium Nelsoni Arth. I.
{ Roestelia Nelsoni Arth.

Amelanchier Cusickii Fern.
Sclerotinia gregaria Dana.

Amelanchier elliptica A. Nels.
Gymnosporangium Nelsoni Arth. I.

Amelanchier erecta Blanchard.
Gymnosporangium clavariiforme (Jacq. ex P.) DC. I.
{ Gymnosporangium clavipes C. & P. I.
{ Gymnosporangium germinale Kern. I.

Amelanchier erecta (*cont.*)
  {Gymnosporangium corniculans Kern. I.
  {Gymnosporangium juniperinum Auct. Amer.
  { p. p.
  Gymnosporangium inconspicuum Kern. I.
  {Gymnosporangium Nelsoni Arth. I.
  {Roestelia Nelsoni Arth.
  Gymnosporangium Nidus-avis Thax. I.

Amelanchier florida Lindl.
  Dimerosporium Collinsii (S.) Thm.
  Phyllactinia corylea (P.) ex Karst.
  {Aecidium blasdaleanum Diet. & Holw.
  {Gymnosporangium aurantiacum Syd. I.
  {Gymnosporangium blasdaleanum Kern. I.
  Gymnosporangium clavariiforme (Jacq. ex
    P.) DC. I.
  Gymnosporangium juvenescens Kern. I.
  Gymnosporangium Nelsoni Arth. I.
  Gymnosporangium nootkatensis Arth.

Amelanchier intermedia Spach.
  {Gymnosporangium biseptatum Ell. I.
  {Gymnosporangium Botryapites Kern. I.
  Gymnosporangium clavariiforme (Jacq. ex P.)
    DC. I.
  {Gymnosporangium clavipes C. & P. I.
  {Gymnosporangium germinale Kern. I.
  Gymnosporangium corniculans Kern. I.
  {Gymnosporangium fraternum Kern. I.
  {Roestelia transformans Ell.
  Gymnosporangium juvenescens Kern. I.
  Gymnosporangium Nelsoni Arth I.
  Gymnosporangium Nidus-avis Thax. I.

Amelanchier jonesiana C. R. Schneider.
  Gymnosporangium inconspicuum Kern. I.
  Gymnosporangium juvenescens Kern. I.
  Gymnosporangium Nelsoni Arth. I.

Amelanchier laevis × humilis.
  Gymnosporangium germinale Kern. I.

Amelanchier mormonica C. R. Schneider.
  Gymnosporangium juvenscens Kern. I.
  Gymnosporangium Nelsoni Arth. I.

Amelanchier nana Nutt.
  Gymnosporangium clavariiforme (Jacq. ex
    P.) DC. I.
  Roestelia Nelsoni Arth.

Amelanchier oblongifolia (Torr. & Gr.) Roem.
  Dimerosporium Collinsii (S.) Thm.
  Gymnosporangium Botryapites (O. Kuntze)
    Kern. I.
  Gymnosporangium clavariiforme (Jacq. ex P.)
    DC. I.
  {Gymnosporangium clavipes C. & P. I.
  {Gymnosporangium germinale Kern. I.
  Gymnosporangium corniculans Kern. I.
  Gymnosporangium Nidus-avis Thax. I.
  Oidium destruens Pk.

Amelanchier oligocarpa (Michx.) Roem.
  {Gymnosporangium clavipes C. & P. I.
  {Gymnosporangium germinale Kern. I.
  {Roestelia aurantiaca Pk.

Amelanchier oreophila A. Nels.
  Dimerosporium Collinsii (S.) Thm.
  Gymnosporangium clavariiforme (Jacq. ex P.)
    DC. I.
  Roestelia harknessianoides Kern.
  Gymnosporangium inconspicuum Kern. I.
  Gymnosporangium juvenescens Kern. I.
  Gymnosporangium kernianum Bethel. I.
  Gymnosporangium Nelsoni Arth. I.

Amelanchier pallida Greene.
  {Aecidium blasdaleanum Diet. & Holw.
  {Gymnosporangium aurantiacum Syd. I.
  {Gymnosporangium blasdaleanum Kern. I.

Amelanchier polycarpa Greene.
  Dimerosporium Collinsii (S.) Thm.
  Gymnosporangium clavariiforme (Jacq. ex P.)
    DC. I.
  Gymnosporangium juvenescens Kern. I.
  Gymnosporangium Nelsoni Arth. I.

Amelanchier prunifolia Greene.
  Gymnosporangium inconspicuum Kern. I.

Amelanchier pumila Nutt.
  Gymnosporangium clavariiforme (Jacq. ex P.)
    DC. I.
  Gymnosporangium juvenescens Kern. I.
  Gymnosporangium Nelsoni Arth. I.

Amelanchier sanguinea DC.
  Gymnosporangium corniculans Kern. I.

Amelanchier spicata (Lam.) C. Koch.
  {Entomosporium maculatum Lév.
  {Fabraea maculata Atk.
  Entomosporium maculatum Lév., var. do-
    mesticum Sacc.
  Fenestella vestita (Fr.) Sacc.
  Gymnosporangium clavariiforme (Jacq. ex P.)
    DC. I.
  {Gymnosporangium clavipes C. & P. I.
  {Gymnosporangium germinale Kern. I.
  {Gymnosporangium corniculans Kern. I.
  {Gymnosporangium juniperinum I. Fung. Co-
    lumb. *1827*.
  Gymnosporangium juvenescens Kern. I.
  Gymnosporangium Nelsoni Arth. I.
  Metasphaeria Peckii (Speg.) Sacc.
  Sphaeronema pruinosum Pk.

Amelanchier utahense Koehne.
  Gymnosporangium inconspicuum Kern. I.
  Gymnosporangium juvenescens Kern. I.
  Gymnosporangium Nelsoni Arth. I.

Amelanchier vulgaris Moench.
  {Aecidium blasdaleanum Diet. & Holw.
  {Gymnosporangium aurantiacum Syd. I.
  {Gymnosporangium Libocedri (Henn.) Kern. I.
  Gymnosporangium inconspicuum Kern. I.

Amelanchier vulgaris (*cont.*)
  Gymnosporangium kernianum Bethel. I.
  Gymnosporangium Nelsoni Arth. I.
  Gymnosporangium Nidus-avis Thax. I.

Amelanchier spp. indet.
  Armillaria mellea (Vahl) ex Fr.
  Asteroma atramentarium B.
  Botryodiplodia Amelanchieris Ell. & Fairman.
  Cenangium Aucupariae (P.) Fr.
  Coryneum longestipitatum Berl. & Bres.
  Diatrype asterostoma B. & C.
  Eutypella glandulosa (Cke.) Ell. & Ev.
  Eutypella stellulata (Fr.) Sacc.
  Hysterographium incisum Ell. & Ev.
  { Lophiostoma pallidum Ell.
  { Lophiotrema pallidum (Ell.) Berl. & Vogl.
  { Zignoella pallida Ell.
  Lophium leptothecium Earle.
  Melospilea emergens Rehm.?
  Nummularia discreta (S.) Tul.
  { Pezicula pruinosa Farl.
  { Sphaeronema pruinosum Pk.
  Phyllactinia corylea (P.) ex Karst.
  Platystomum Amelanchieris Tracy & Earle.
  Platystomum hysterioides Earle.
  Poria ambigua Bres.
  { Sclerotinia cinerea Auct. Amer.
  { Sclerotinia fructigena Auct. Amer.
  Stereum ochraceoflavum S.
  { Strickeria Amelanchieris Earle.
  { Teichospora Amelanchieris (Earle) Sacc. & D.
    Sacc.
  Tryblidium occidentale Earle.

Crataegus acutiloba Sarg.
Crataegus alnorum Sarg.
Crataegus ancisa Beadle.
Crataegus Anduennae Sarg.
Crataegus anomala Sarg.
Crataegus apposita Sarg., var. **Bissellii** (Sarg.)
  Eggl.
  Gymnosporangium globosum Farl. I.
Crataegus arborescens Ell.
  Septobasidium Langloisii Pat.
Crataegus arcuata Ashe.
Crataegus asperifolia Sarg.
Crataegus biltmoreana Beadle.
  Gymnosporangium globosum Farl. I.
Crataegus bipinnatifida Auct.
  Roestelia pyrata (S.) Thax.
Crataegus Boyntoni Beadle.
Crataegus Brainerdi Sarg.
Crataegus Buckleyi Beadle.
  Gymnosporangium globosum Farl. I.
Crataegus cerronis A. Nels.
  { Gymnosporangium aurantiacum Syd. I.
  { Gymnosporangium Libocedri (Henn.) Kern. I.
  { Gymnosporangium Betheli Kern. I.
  { Roestelia Betheli Kern.

  { Gymnosporangium clavariiforme (Jacq. ex P.)
    DC. I.
  Gymnosporangium trachysorum Kern. I.
  Podosphaera Oxycanthae (DC.) DBy.

Crataegus champlainensis Sarg.
Crataegus Chapmani Ashe.
  Gymnosporangium globosum Farl. I.

Crataegus chrysocarpa Ashe.
  Diatrype Stigma (Hoffm.) ex Fr.
  Eutypa lata (P.) Tul.
  Gymnosporangium Betheli Kern. I.
  Gymnosporangium germinale Kern. I.
  Gymnosporangium globosum Farl. I.
  Gymnosporangium Nelsoni Arth. I.
  Gymnosporangium tubulatum Kern. I.
  Otthia Crataegi Fckl.
  Phyllosticta crataegicola Sacc.
  Schizoxylon insigne (De Not.) Bres.
  Valsa ambiens (P.) ex Fr., var. Crataegi Rehm.

Crataegus clara Beadle.
  Gymnosporangium hyalinum Kern. I.

Crataegus coccinea L.
  { Clasterisporium curvatum (B. & C.) Sacc.
  { Sporidesmium curvatum B. & C.
  ?Cylindrosporium Crataegi Ell. & Ev.
  { Entomosporium Thuemenii (Cke.) Sacc.
  { Morthiera Thuemenii Cke.
  Fomes applanatus (P. ex Wallr.) Gill.
  Gymnosporangium Betheli Kern. I.
  { Caeoma germinale S.
  { Gymnosporangium clavipes C. & P. I.
  { Gymnosporangium germinale Kern. I.
  { Roestelia aurantiaca Pk.
  Gymnosporangium floriforme Thax. I.
  { Gymnosporangium globosum Farl. I.
  { Puccinia globosa O. Kuntze. I.
  { Roestelia globosa Thax.
  { Aecidium Crataegi, var. Oxyacanthae S.
  { Gymnosporangium clavariiforme (Jacq. ex P.)
    DC. I.
  { Roestelia lacerata (Sow.) Fr.
  ?Roestelia pyrata (S.) Thax.
  Gymnosporangium trachysorum Kern. I.
  Hirudinaria macrospora Ces.
  { Phyllactinia corylea (P.) ex Karst.
  { Phyllactinia suffulta (Reb.) ex Sacc.
  { Podosphaera Kunzei Lév.
  { Podosphaera Oxyacanthae (DC.) DBy.
  Valsa ambiens (P.) ex Fr.

Crataegus coccinioides Ashe.
  Gymnosporangium germinale Kern. I.
  Gymnosporangium globosum Farl. I.

Crataegus collina Chapman.
  Gymnosporangium globosum Farl. I.

Crataegus colonica Beadle.
  { Gymnosporangium clavipes C. & P. I.
  { Gymnosporangium germinale Kern. I.

Crataegus colorata Sarg.
Crataegus conjuncta Sarg.
Crataegus conspicua Sarg.
Crataegus consueta Sarg.
Crataegus corusca Sarg.
 Gymnosporangium globosum Farl. I.
Crataegus Crus-galli L.
 Clasterosporium curvatum (B. & C.) Sacc.
 Corticium nudum Fr.
 Crepidotus rufolateritius Bres.
 Entomosporium Thuemenii (Cke.) Sacc.
 Gloeosporium crataeginum Sacc.
 Hysterium angustatum (A. & S.) ex Fr.
 {Phyllactinia corylea (P.) ex Karst.
 {Phyllactinia suffulta (Reb.) ex Sacc.
 Podosphaera Oxyacanthae (DC.) DBy.
 {Gymnosporangium clavipes C. & P. I.
 {Gymnosporangium germinale Kern. I.
 Roestelia aurantiaca Pk.
 {Gymnosporangium globosum Farl. I.
 {Puccinia globosa O. Kuntze. I.
 {Roestelia globosa Shear.
 {Roestelia lacerata Auct. Amer. p. p.
 {Roestelia penicillata Auct. Amer.
 {Roestelia pyrata (S.) Thax.
 Valsa Hoffmanni Nits.
Crataegus cyclophylla Sarg.
Crataegus decorata Sarg.
Crataegus delecta Sarg.
Crataegus delectabilis Sarg.
Crataegus delucida Sarg.
Crataegus demissa Sarg.
Crataegus disjuncta Sarg.
 Gymnosporangium globosum Farl. I.
Crataegus dispar Beadle.
 {Aecidium blasdaleanum Diet. & Holw.
 {Gymnosporangium aurantiacum Syd. I.
 {Gymnosporangium blasdaleanum Kern. I.
 {Gymnosporangium Libocedri Kern. I.
 {Gymnosporangium clavipes C. & P. I.
 {Gymnosporangium germinale Kern. I.
 Gymnosporangium globosum Farl. I.
 Gymnosporangium hyalinum Kern. I.
 Lenzites sepiaria (Wulf.) ex Fr.
 Phyllactinia corylea (P.) ex Karst.
 Xylaria digitata (L.) ex Grev.
 Xyloschizon atratum Syd.
Crataegus dispersa Ashe.
Crataegus dissimilis Sarg.
Crataegus dissona Sarg.
 Gymnosporangium globosum Farl. I.
Crataegus Douglasii Lindl.
 {Cylindrosporium brevispina Dearness.
 {Cylindrosporium Crataegi Ell. & Ev., var.
 { brevispina Dearness.
 Gloeosporium Crataegi Dearness & Barthol.
 Gymnosporangium germinale Kern. I.
 Gymnosporangium Betheli Kern. I.
 Gymnosporangium tubulatum Kern. I.

Crataegus dumetosa Sarg.
Crataegus Eamesii Sarg.
 Gymnosporangium globosum Farl. I.
Crataegus egens Beadle.
 Gymnosporangium hyalinum Kern. I.
Crataegus Egglestoni Sarg.
 Gymnosporangium globosum Farl. I.
Crataegus egregia Beadle.
 Gymnosporangium hyalinum Kern. I.
Crataegus Engelmanni Sarg.
 Gymnosporangium globosum Farl. I.
Crataegus erythropoda Ashe.
 Gymnosporangium Betheli Kern. I.
 Phyllosticta Crataegi (Cke.) Sacc.
 Platystomum compressum (P. ex Fr.) Trevisan.
 Schizoxylon insigne (De Not.) Bres.
Crataegus festiva Sarg.
 Gymnosporangium globosum Farl. I.
Crataegus flava Ait.
 {Entomosporium Thuemenii (Cke.) Sacc.
 {Morthiera Thuemenii Cke.
 {Gymnosporangium clavipes C. & P. I.
 {Gymnosporangium germinale Kern. I.
 {Hendersonia crataegicola Atk.
 {Phyllohendersonia crataegicola (Atk.) Tassi.
 ?Hendersonia Cydoniae C. & E.
Crataegus flavocarnis Ashe.
 Gymnosporangium trachysorum Kern. I.
Crataegus Forbesae Sarg.
Crataegus fretalis Sarg.
Crataegus genialis Sarg.
Crataegus glaucophylla Sarg.
Crataegus Harbisoni Beadle.
 Gymnosporangium globosum Farl. I.
Crataegus holmesiana Ashe.
 Gymnosporangium germinale Kern. I.
 Gymnosporangium globosum Farl. I.
 Phyllosticta Crataegi (Cke.) Sacc.
Crataegus Jesupi Sarg.
 Gymnosporangium germinale Kern. I.
 Gymnosporangium globosum Farl. I.
Crataegus Jonesae Sarg.
 {Gymnosporangium clavipes C. & P. I.
 {Gymnosporangium germinale Kern. I.
Crataegus lasiantha Sarg.
Crataegus leiophylla Sarg., var. maineana (Sarg.)
 Eggl.
Crataegus McGeeae Ashe.
Crataegus macilentia Beadle.
 Gymnosporangium globosum Farl. I.
Crataegus macracantha Lodd.
 Cladosporium carpophilum Thm.
 Roestelia Betheli Kern.
 Gymnosporangium globosum Farl. I.
Crataegus macracantha Lodd, var. succulenta
 (Schrad.) Eggl.

Crataegus macrosperma Ashe.
Crataegus Margaretta Ashe.
  ⎰ Gymnosporangium clavipes C. & P. I.
  ⎱ Gymnosporangium germinale Kern. I.
   Roestelia aurantiaca Pk.
  Gymnosporangium globosum Farl. I.
Crataegus Marshallii Eggl.
  Cercospora apiifoliae Tharp.
  Gymnosporangium clavariiforme (Jacq. ex P)
    DC. I.
  Gymnosporangium trachysorum Kern. I.
Crataegus membranacea Sarg.
  Gymnosporangium globosum Farl. I.
Crataegus mexicana Moc. & Sessé.
  Gymnosporangium germinale Kern. I.
Crataegus Michauxii P.
  Gymnosporangium hyalinum Kern. I.
Crataegus Mohri Beadle.
  Gymnosporangium globosum Farl. I.
Crataegus mollis (Torr. & Gr.) Scheele.
  Ceratostoma graphidioides Sacc.
  Cladosporium carpophilum Thm.
  Cucurbitaria conglobata, var. Crataegi Rehm.
  Cucurbitaria Crataegi (S.) Ell. & Ev.
  Fomes conchatus (P.) ex Fr.
  Hendersonia Crataegi Brenckle.
  Myriangium tuberculans Miles.
  Otthia Crataegi Fckl.
  Phyllosticta crataegicola Sacc.
  Pleosphaerulina corticola (Fckl.) Rehm, var.
    Crataegi Rehm.
  Podosphaera Oxyacanthae (DC.) DBy.
  Schizoxylon insigna (De Not.) Bres.
  Septoria Crataegi Kickx.
  Valsa ambiens (P.) ex Fr., var. Crataegi Rehm.

UREDINALES

  ⎰ Gymnosporangium clavipes C. & P. I.
  ⎱ Gymnosporangium germinale Kern. I.
  ⎰ Aecidium globosum Farl.
  ⎱ Gymnosporangium globosum Farl. I.
  ⎰ Roestelia globosa (Farl.) Shear.
   Roestelia lacerata y Thax.
  ⎱ Gymnosporangium Juniperi-virginianae S. I.
  ⎰ Gymnosporangium macropus Lk. I.
  ⎱ Roestelia lacerata Thax.
Crataegus monogyna Jacq.
  Gymnosporangium clavariiforme (Jacq. ex P.)
    DC. I.
  Gymnosporangium globosum Farl. I.
  Gymnosporangium trachysorum Kern. I.
Crataegus munda Beadle.
  ⎰ Gymnosporangium hyalinum Kern. I.
  ⎱ Roestelia hyalina Cke.
Crataegus neofluvialis Ashe.
  Gymnosporangium germinale Kern. I.
  Gymnosporangium globosum Farl. I.
Crataegus neolondinensis Sarg.
  Gymnosporangium globosum Farl. I.

Crataegus nigra Pall.
  Gymnosporangium clavariiforme (Jacq. ex P.)
    DC. I.
Crataegus occidentalis Brit.
  ⎰ Gymnosporangium Betheli Kern. I.
  ⎱ Roestelia Betheli Kern.
Crataegus Oxyacantha L.
  Dothiorella Crataegi Ell. & Ev.
  Entomosporium Mespili (DC. ex Fckl.) Sacc.
  Entomosporium Thuemenii (Cke.) Sacc.
  ⎰ Gymnosporangium clavariiforme (Jacq. ex P.)
    DC. I.
  ⎱ Roestelia lacerata (Sow.) Fr.
  ⎰ Gymnosporangium clavipes C. & P. I.
  ⎱ Roestelia aurantiaca Pk.
  ⎰ Caeoma Cylindrites Lk. *g.*
  ⎱ Gymnosporangium trachysorum Kern. I.
  Physalospora Cydoniae Arnaud.
  Podosphaera Oxyacanthae (DC.) DBy.
  Polystictus versicolor (L.) ex Fr.
  Septoria Crataegi Kickx.
  Sphaeropsis demersa (Bon.) Sacc.
Crataegus pausiaca Ashe.
  Gymnosporangium germinale Kern. I.
Crataegus peckiella Sarg.
Crataegus pequotorum Sarg.
  Gymnosporangium globosum Farl.
Crataegus pentandra Sarg.
Crataegus pertomentosa Ashe.
  Gymnosporangium globosum Farl. I.
Crataegus pexa Beadle.
  Gymnosporangium hyalinum Kern. I.
Crataegus phaenopyrum (L. f.) Medic.
  Botryosphaeria melathroa B. & C.
  Gymnosporangium germinale Kern. I.
  ⎰ Gymnosporangium Betheli Kern. I.
  ⎱ Roestelia Betheli Kern.
  ⎰ Gymnosporangium globosum Farl. I.
  ⎱ Roestelia lacerata y Thax.
  Gymnosporangium trachysorum Kern. I.
Crataegus pinguis Sarg.
  Gymnosporangium globosum Farl. I.
Crataegus Piperi Brit.
  Phyllactinia corylea (P.) ex Karst.
Crataegus pisifera Sarg.
  Gymnosporangium globosum Farl. I.
Crataegus praecox Sarg.
  Gymnosporangium globosum Farl. I.
  Phyllosticta grisea Pk.
Crataegus Pringlei Sarg.
  Gymnosporangium Betheli Kern. I.
  ⎰ Aecidium blasdaleanum Diet. & Holw.
  ⎱ Gymnosporangium aurantiacum Syd. I.
  ⎱ Gymnosporangium Libocedri (Henn.) Kern. I.
  Gymnosporangium exiguum Kern. I.
  Gymnosporangium globosum Farl. I.
  Gymnosporangium Nidus-avis Thax. I.

Crataegus pruinosa (Wendl.) C. Koch.
Gymnosporangium globosum Farl. I.
Crataegus punctata Jacq.
Entomosporium Thuemenii (Cke.) Sacc.
Phoma leprosa Pk.
Phyllactinia suffulta (Reb.) ex Sacc.
Plagiorhabdus Crataegi Shear.
Podosphaera Oxycanthae (DC.) DBy.
⎰Ciboria Johnsoni Ell. & Ev.
⎱Monilia Crataegi Diedicke.
⎱Sclerotinia Johnsoni (Ell. & Ev.) Rehm.
Septoria Crataegi Kickx.

UREDINALES
Gymnosporangium Betheli Kern. I.
Gymnosporangium clavariiforme (Jacq. ex P.)
DC. I.
⎰Gymnosporangium clavipes C. & P.
⎱Gymnosporangium germinale Kern. I.
⎱Roestelia aurantiaca Pk.
⎰Caeoma Cylindrites Lk. *a.*
Gymnosporangium globosum Farl. I.
⎰Puccinia globosa O. Kuntze. I.
⎱Roestelia globosa (Farl.) Shear.
Roestelia lacerata Auct. Amer. p. p.
⎰Gymnosporangium Juniperi-virginianae S. I.
⎱Gymnosporangium macropus Lk. I.
Gymnosporangium trachysorum Kern. I.
Crataegus Pyracantha P.
Gymnosporangium clavariiforme (Jacq. ex P.)
DC. I.
Podosphaera Oxyacanthae (DC.) DBy.
Crataegus quasita Beadle.
Gymnosporangium hyalinum Kern. I.
Crataegus quinebaugensis Sarg.
Gymnosporangium globosum Farl. I.
Crataegus Reverchoni Sarg.
⎰Gymnosporangium clavipes C. & P. I.
⎱Gymnosporangium germinale Kern. I.
Gymnosporangium globosum Farl. I.
Crataegus rhombifolia Sarg.
Gymnosporangium globosum Farl. I.
Crataegus rivularis Nutt.
Gymnosporangium Betheli Kern. I.
⎰Aecidium blasdaleanum Diet. & Holw.
⎱Gymnosporangium blasdaleanum Kern. I.
Gymnosporangium globosum Farl. I.
Cercosporella mirabilis Pk.
Dasyscypha allantospora Earle.
Phyllactinia suffulta (Reb.) ex Sacc.
Podosphaera Oxyacanthae (DC.) DBy.
Crataegus roanensis Ashe.
Gymnosporangium globosum Farl. I.
Crataegus rotundifolia Moench.
Entomosporium Thuemenii (Cke.) Sacc.
⎰Gymnosporangium clavipes C. & P. I.
⎱Gymnosporangium germinale Kern. I.
Gymnosporangium globosum Farl. I.

Crataegus saligna Greene.
⎰Gymnosporangium Betheli Kern. I.
⎱Gymnosporangium globosum I. West Am.
⎱ Fung. *333.*
⎱Roestelia Betheli Kern.
Crataegus sanguinea ex Kansas.
Phyllosticta rubra Pk.
Roestelia pyrata (S.) Thax.?
Crataegus scabrida Sarg.
Crataegus schweinitziana Sarg.
Crataegus silvicola Beadle, var. **Beckwithae**
(Sarg.) Eggl.
Gymnosporangium globosum Farl. I.
Crataegus spathulata Michx.
Podosphaera Oxyacanthae (DC.) DBy.

UREDINALES
⎰Gymnosporangium clavipes C. & P. I.
⎱Gymnosporangium germinale Kern. I.
⎱Roestelia aurantiaca Pk.
⎰Aecidium flaviforme (Atk.) Farl.
⎱Gymnosporangium flaviforme Earle. I.
⎱Gymnosporangium floriforme Thax. I.
⎱Roestelia flaviformis Atk.
⎰Gymnosporangium clavariiforme I. Myc.
⎱ Exch. *33d.*
⎱Gymnosporangium globosum Farl. I.
⎰Gymnosporangium macropus Lk. I.
⎱Roestelia pyrata (S.) Thax.
Crataegus straminea Beadle.
Gymnosporangium germinale Kern. I.
Gymnosporangium globosum Farl. I.
Crataegus submollis Sarg.
Gymnosporangium globosum Farl. I.
Crataegus subvillosus Schrad.
Podosphaera Oxyacanthae (DC.) DBy.
⎰Gymnosporangium globosum Farl. I.
⎱Puccinia globosa O. Kuntze. I.
⎱Roestelia lacerata Auct. Amer. p. p.
Crataegus succulenta Schrad.
Gymnosporangium Betheli Kern. I.
Gymnosporangium globosum Farl. I.
Crataegus sucida Sarg.
Gymnosporangium globosum Farl. I.
Crataegus tanacetifolia Webb.
Gymnosporangium clavariiforme (Jacq. ex P.)
DC. I.
Crataegus tecta Beadle.
Crataegus tenella Ashe.
Crataegus tetrica Beadle.
Gymnosporangium globosum Farl. I.
Crataegus Thayeri Sarg.
Venturia inaequalis (Cke.) Wint..
Crataegus tomentosa L.
⎰Cenangium Crataegi S.
⎱Sphaeronema longirostre Clements.
Crepidotus distans Pk.
⎰Daedalea confragosa (Bolt.) ex Fr.
⎱Lenzites Crataegi B.

Crataegus tomentosa (*cont.*)
Diatrypella quercina (P.) Nits.
Entomosporium Thuemenii (Cke.) Sacc.
Macrosporium stilbosporoideum B. & C.
Pestalozzia Crataegi Ell. & Ev.
{ Phyllactinia corylea (P.) ex Karst.
{ Phyllactinia suffulta (Reb.) ex Sacc.
{ Cheilaria Crataegi Cke.
{ Phyllosticta? Crataegi (Cke.) Sacc.
Phyllosticta rubra Pk.
{ Podosphaera Oxyacanthae (DC.) DBy.
{ Podosphaera tridactyla (Wallr.) DBy.
Septoria Crataegi Kickx.
Stigmella Crataegi Ell. & Ev.
Valsa ambiens (P.) ex Fr.

UREDINALES
{ Gymnosporangium clavipes C. & P. I.
{ Roestelia aurantiaca Pk.
{ Gymnosporangium aurantiacum Syd. I.
Gymnosporangium Libocedri (Henn.) Kern. I.
{ Gymnosporangium clavariiforme Auct. Amer.
{   p. p. I.
{ Gymnosporangium globosum Farl. I.
{ Gymnosporangium macropus I. Fung. Eur.
{   *3416* p. p., *4316.*
Roestelia globosa (Farl.) Shear.
Roestelia lacerata Auct. Amer. p. p.
Crataegus Tracyi Ashe.
Gymnosporangium exiguum Kern. I.
Crataegus Treleasei Sarg.
Gymnosporangium globosum Farl. I.
Crataegus viridis L.
Gymnosporangium globosum Farl. I.
{ Caeoma Cylindrites Lk. *b.*
{ Gymnosporangium hyalinum Kern. I.
{ Roestelia hyalina Cke.
Crataegus visenda Beadle.
{ Gymnosporangium hyalinum Kern. I.
{ Roestelia hyalina Cke.
Crataegus Williamsii Eggl.
Gymnosporangium tubulatum Kern. I.
Crataegus sp. indet.

PEZIZINEAE
Cenangium Crataegi S.
Ciboria Johnsoni Ell. & Ev.
Dasyscypha allantospora Earle.
Dermatea crataegicola Durand.
Dermatea olivascens Rehm.
Fabraea maculata Atk.
Helotium citrinum (Hedw.) ex Fr.

PHACIDIINEAE
{ Blitrydium nigrocinnabarinum (S.) Sacc.
{ Patellaria nigrocinnabarina S.

MYRIANGIACEAE
Myriangium Duriaei Mont. & B.

PERISPORIALES
Podosphaera leucotricha (Ell. & Ev.) Salmon.
Saccardoella canadensis Ell. & Ev.

HYPOCREALES
Creonectria Coryli (Fckl.) Seaver.
Scoleconectria Atkinsonii (Rehm) Seaver.
Sphaerostilbe flammea (B. & Rav.) Tul.

SPHAERIALES
{ Botryosphaeria Crataegi (S.) Sacc.
{ Cucurbitaria Crataegi (S.) Ell. & Ev.
{ Sphaeria Crataegi S.
{ Valsa Crataegi (S.) Cke.
Diaporthe aliena Ell. & Ev.
Diatrype albopruinosa (S.) C. & E.
Diatrypella quercina (P. ex Fr.) Nits.
Eutypella stellulata (Fr.) Sacc.
{ Eutypella tumidula (C. & P.) Sacc.
{ Valsa tumidula C. & P.
Fenestella princeps Tul.
Glomerella cingulata (Stoneman) Spaulding &
  v. Schrenk.
Hypoxylon albocinctum Ell. & Ev.
Lophidium compressum (P. ex Fr.) Sacc.
Lophidium diminuens (P. ex Fr.) Ces. & DeNot.
Massaria inquinans (Tode) ex Fr.
Physalospora Cydoniae Arnaud.
Physalospora Malorum Shear et al.
Physalospora rhodina B. & C.
Pseudovalsa canadensis Ell. & Ev.
Rosellinia subsimilis Sacc.
Thyridaria aurata Rehm.
Valsa ceratophora Tul.
Valsa ceratophora Tul., var. Crataegi C. & E.
Valsa clausa C. & E.

HYMENOMYCETINEAE
Corticium confluens Fr.
Corticium crustaceum (Karst.) v. Höhnel &
  Litschauer.
{ Corticium vagum B. & C.
{ Rhizoctonia Solani Kühn.
Crepidotus rufolateritius Bres.
Crepidotus tiliophilus Pk.
Daedalea confragosa (Bolt.) ex Fr.
{ Fomes conchatus (P. ex Fr.) Karst.
{ Pyropolyporus conchatus (P. ex Fr.) Murrill.
Fomes fulvus (Scop. ex Fr.) Gill.
{ Fomes Langloisii (Murrill) Sacc. & D. Sacc.
{ Pyropolyporus Langloisii Murrill.
Fomes pomaceus (P.) Lloyd, var. Crataegi
  Baxter.
Peniophora cinerea (P. ex Fr.) Cke.
Poria ferruginosa (Schrad. ex Fr.) Cke.
Poria inermis Ell. & Ev.
{ Septobasidium pseudopedicellatum Burt.
{ Thelephora pedicellata Auct. Amer. pl. p.
Stereum purpureum P. †

Crataegus sp. indet. (*cont.*)
- Trametes Abietis Auct. p. p. ?
- Trametes piceinus Pk.
- Trametes Pini Auct. p. p. ?

SPHAEROPSIDALES

Cytospora microspora (Cda.) Rabh.
Discosia Artocreas (Tode) ex Fr.
Hendersonia Crataegi Brenckle.
- Hendersonia discosioides Ell. & Dearness.
- Phyllohendersonia discosioides (Ell. & Dearness) Tassi.
Hendersonia foliorum Fckl.
- Macrophoma fusigera (B. & C.) Berl. & Vogl.
- Phoma fusigera (B. & C.) Sacc.
- Sphaeropsis fusiger B. & C.
Phleospora Oxyacanthae (Kze. & Schm.) ex Wallr.
- Cercosporella mirabilis Pk.
- Phleospora Crataegi J. J. Davis.
- Phleospora Oxyacanthae Ell. ex J. J. Davis.
Phoma semi-immersa Sacc.
Phyllosticta Crataegi (Cke.) Sacc.
Phyllosticta solitaria Ell. & Ev.
Septoria Crataegi Kickx.
Sphaeropsis foliicola (B. & Rav.) Sacc.
Sphaeropsis Malorum Pk.

MELANCONIALES

Coryneum foliicola Fckl.
Cylindrosporium brevispina Dearness.
Cylindrosporium Crataegi Ell. & Ev.
- Entomosporium maculatum Lév.
- Fabraea maculata Atk.
Gloeosporium Crataegi Dearness & Barthol.
- Gloeosporium fructigenum B.
- Glomerella cingulata (Stoneman) Spaulding & v. Schrenk.
- Morthiera Thuemenii Cke., var. sphaerocysta Pk.
Pestalozzia concentrica B. & Rav.
Pestalozzia turgida Atk.

HYPHOMYCETES

Aspergillus glaucus (L.) ex Lk.
Cercospora Crataegi Heald & Wolf.
Cercosporella mirabilis Pk.
Epicoccum neglectum Desm.
Exosporium melampsoroides Sacc.
Monilia Crataegi Diedicke.
Monilia linhartiana Sacc.
- Monilia linhartiana J. J. Davis, no. 527, p. p.
- Sclerotinia Johnsonii (Ell. & Ev.) Rehm.
- Sirodesmium Fumago (Cke.) Sacc.
- Sporidesmium Fumago Cke.
Sporidesmium quadratum Atk.
Streptothrix atra B. & C.
Tubercularia difformis S.

MISCELLANEA

Aecidium purpusiorum Henn.
Hypodendrum limonellum (Pk.) Murrill.
Rhodotypos kerrioides Sieb. & Zucc.
Ascochyta Rhodotypi H. W. Anderson.
Kerria japonica DC.
- Calonectria flavitecta (B. & C.) Sacc.
- Nectria auriger B. & Rav., var. flavitecta B. & C.
- Sphaeria flavitecta B. & C.
- Coccomyces Kerriae V. B. Stewart.
- Cylindrosporium Kerriae V. B. Stewart.
- Diplodia Corchori (Desm.) Kickx.
- Phoma japonica Sacc.
- Stictis glaucoma B. & C.
- Cesatia turbinata B. & C.
- Trullula turbinata (B. & C.) Sacc.
- Valsa decorticans Fr.

Rubus. Note: It is evidently impossible to refer fungi reported in earlier years on Rubus species to host plants of names now approved.

Rubus abbrevians Blanchard.
- Kuehneola albida (Kühn) Magn.
- Kuehneola Uredinis Arth.

Rubus aboriginum Rydb.
Kunkelia nitens Arth.

Rubus acaulis Michx.
Gymnoconia interstitialis (Trans.) Lagerh.
Pucciniastrum arcticum Tranz.

Rubus adenotrichus Schl.
- Spirechina pittieriana (Henn.) Arth.
- Uredo ochraceo-flavus Henn.
- Uromyces pittierianus Henn.
- Spirechina Rubi (Diet. & Holw.) Arth.

Rubus allegheniensis Porter.
Cercospora Rubi Sacc.
- Gloeosporium Rubi Ell. & Ev.
- Tuberculina argillacea J. J. Davis.
- Gloeosporium venetum Speg.
- Plectodiscella veneta Burkh.
Gnomonia Rubi Rehm.
- Gymnoconia interstitialis (Tranz.) Lagerh.
- Gymnoconia peckiana (Howe) Arth.
- Kunkelia nitens Arth.
- Kuehneola albida (Kühn) Magn.
- Kuehneola Uredinis Arth.
Peronospora Rubi Rabh.
Pyrenopeziza Rubi Rehm.
Septoria comitata J. J. Davis.
- Mycosphaerella Rubi Roark.
- Septoria Rubi Westd.
Sphaerotheca Humuli (DC.) Burrill. †

Rubus andrewsianus Blanchard.
Gymnoconia interstitialis (Tranz.) Lagerh.
Kuehneola Uredinis Arth.
Kunkelia nitens Arth.

Rubus arcticus L.
  Helotium epiphyllum (P.) Fr., var. praeponens
    Nyl.
  Pucciniastrum arcticum Tranz.
Rubus argutus Lk.
  ⎧Chrysomyxa albida Kühn.
  ⎩Kuehneola Uredinis Arth.
  Glonium macrosporum Tracy & Earle.
  Gymnoconia interstitialis (Tranz.) Lagerh.
  Kunkelia nitens Arth.
  Meliola manca Ell. & Martin.
Rubus arizonicus (Greene) Rydb.
  Phragmidium imitans Arth.
Rubus Boyntonii Ashe.
  Kunkelia nitens Arth.
Rubus canadensis L.
  Early reports under this name should probably
    be referred to R. villosus or elsewhere.
  Ascochyta Rubi Lasch.
  Asterina rubicola Ell. & Ev.
  Botrytis cinerea Auct.
  Cercospora Rubi Sacc.
  Cercospora septorioides Ell. & Ev.
  Coccochora Rubi J. J. Davis.
  Coniothyrium Fuckelii Sacc.
  Hendersonia platypus Ell. & Ev.
  Marssonina Potentillae-tormentillae Trail.
  Peronospora Rubi Rabh.
  Phoma lethalis Ell. & Martin.
  ⎧Septoria Rubi Westd. 1854.
  ⎩Septoria Rubi B. & C. 1874.
  Septoria Rubi Westd., var. alba Pk.
  Sphaerotheca Humuli (DC.) Burrill.
  Tuberculina persicina Ditm.
  ⎧?Sphaeria subclypeata B. & C.
  ⎩Valsa subclypeata (B. & C.) C. & P.

UREDINALES

  ⎧Gymnoconia interstitialis Auct. p. p.
  ⎨Puccinia peckiana Auct. p. p.
  ⎩Uredo Caeoma-nitens DeToni.
  ⎧Caeoma luminatum Lk.
  ⎨Caeoma nitens Auct. Amer. p.p.
  ⎩Kunkelia nitens Arth.
  ⎧?Uredo luminata (Lk.) M. A. Curtis.
  ⎩?Uredo nitens (S.) M. A. Curtis.
  Kuehneola Uredinis Arth.
Rubus canadensis, var. **roribaccus** L. H. Bailey.
  Gloeosporium necator Ell. & Ev.
Rubus carpinifolius Rydb.
  Kunkelia nitens Arth.
Rubus Chamaemorus L.
  Leptostroma virgultorum Sacc., var. rubinum
    Karst.
  Leptothyrium clypeosphaerioides Sacc.
  Leptothyrium Rubi (Duby) Sacc.
  Phoma herbarum Westd.
  Phragmidium Rubi-Idaei Auct. p. p.

  Pucciniastrum arcticum Tranz.
  Sphaerella Chamaemori Karst.
Rubus cuneifolius Pursh.
  Cercospora Rubi Sacc.
  ⎧Chrysomyxa albida Kühn.
  ⎩Kuehneola Uredinis Arth.
  Coleosporium Rubi Ell. & Holw.
  Phragmidium Rubi-Idaei Auct. p. p.
  ⎧Gymnoconia interstitialis (Tranz.) Lagerh.
  ⎨Puccinia interstitialis Tranz.
  ⎩Puccinia peckiana Howe.
  ⎧Kunkelia nitens Arth.
  ⎩?Uredo Caeoma-nitens DeToni.
Rubus deliciosus James.
  Metasphaeria rubicola Ell. & Ev.
  ⎧Lecythea deliciosa H. I. error.
  ⎪Lecythea speciosa Pk.
  ⎪Phragmidium occidentale Auct. p. p.
  ⎨Phragmidium peckianum Arth.
  ⎪Phragmidium Rubi Auct. Amer. p. p.
  ⎪Uredo ribicola Fung. Columb. *877.*
  ⎩Uredo speciosa Pk.
  Teichospora nitida Ell. & Ev.
Rubus floridus Tratt.
  Kuehneola Uredinis Arth.
  Kunkelia nitens Arth.
Rubus frondosus Bigel.
  Puccinia peckiana Howe.
  Kuehneola Uredinis Arth.
  Kunkelia nitens Arth.
Rubus fruticosus L.
  Cercospora Rubi Sacc.
  Gloeosporium necator Ell. & Ev.
Rubus glandicaulis Blanchard.
  Gymnoconia interstitialis (Tranz.) Lagerh.
Rubus glaucus Benth.
  Kuehneola albida Kern.
  ⎧Spirechina Rubi (Diet & Holw.) Arth.
  ⎩Uromyces Rubi Diet. & Holw.
Rubus guyanensis Focke (?).
  ⎧Spirechina Arthuri (Syd.) Arth.
  ⎩Uromyces Arthuri Syd.
Rubus hispidus L.
  Coccochora Rubi J. J. Davis.
  ⎧Coniothyrium Fuckelii Sacc.
  ⎨Leptosphaeria Coniothyrium (Fckl.) Sacc.
  ⎩Leptosphaeria fuscella Fung. Dak. *384.*
  Darluca Filum (Biv.) Cast.
  Macrosporium Rubi Ell.
  Marssonina Potentillae-tormentillae Trail.
  Peronospora Rubi Rabh.
  Rhytisma Blakei M. A. Curtis.
  ⎧Mycosphaerella Rubi Roark.
  ⎩Septoria Rubi Westd.
  Septoria Rubi Westd., var. brevispora Sacc.
  Septoria Rubi Westd., var. pallida Ell. & Holw.
  ⎧Sphaerotheca Castagnei Lév. p. p.
  ⎩Sphaerotheca Humuli (DC.) Burrill. †
  Synchytrium aureum Schrt.

Rubus hispidus (*cont.*)

UREDINALES

Caeoma nitens S.
Kunkelia nitens Arth.
?Uredo Caeoma-nitens De Toni.
Chrysomyxa albida Kühn.
Kuehneola albida (Kühn) Magn.
Kuehneola Uredinis Arth.
Uredo Muelleri Schrt.
Gymnoconia interstitialis Tranz.
Gymnoconia peckiana (Howe) Trotter.
Puccinia interstitialis (Tranz.) Lagerh.
Puccinia peckiana Howe.
Phragmidium Rubi Wint.
Phragmidium Rubi-idaei Karst.

Rubus idaeus L.

Coniothecium Rubi Pk.
Gloeosporium necator Ell. & Ev.
Gloeosporium venetum Speg.
Plectodiscella veneta Burkholder.
Pezizella Lythri Shear & Dodge.
Mycosphaerella rubina (Pk.) House.
Sphaerella rubina Pk.
Sphaeria caespitulans S.
Sphaerotheca Humuli (DC.) Burrill. †
Thecopsora deformans Dur. & Mont.

UREDINALES

Gymnoconia peckiana (Howe) Trotter.
Caeoma ruborum S. Am. Bor.
Kuehneola Uredinis Arth.
Caeoma gyrosum S. Am. Bor.?
Phragmidium imitans? Arth.

Rubus idaeus L., var. **aculeatissimus** [C. A. Mey.] Regel & Filing.

PLECTODISCELLAE

Plectodiscella veneta Burkholder.

PEZIZINEAE

Dasyscypha clandestina (Bull. ex Fr.) Fckl.
Peziza clandestina Bull. ex Fr.
Dermatea Rubi (Fr.) Rehm.
Helotium herbarum (P.) Fr., var. Rubi Ell. & Ev.
Pseudohelotium ceracellum (Fr.) Sacc.
Pyrenopeziza Rubi (Fr.) Rehm.

PHACIDIINEAE

Coccomyces rubicola Ell. & Dearness.

HYSTERIINEAE

Hypoderma Rubi (P. ex Fr.) De Not.
Hypoderma virgultorum DC. ex Fr.
Hysterium Rubi P. ex Fr.
Hysterium virgultorum (DC. ex Fr.) Rob. & Desm.

PYRENOMYCETINEAE

Asterina rubicola Ell. & Ev.
Ceratostoma subrufum Ell. & Ev.

Coniochaeta caespitulans (S.) Cke.
Sphaeria caespitulans S.
Diaporthe obscura (Pk.) Sacc.
Didymosphaeria manitobiensis Ell. & Ev..
Gnomonia Rubi Rehm.
Laestadia rubicola Ell. & Ev.
Leptosphaeria Coniothyrium (Fckl.) Sacc.
Leptosphaeria fuscella (B. & Br.) Ces. & De-Not.
Sphaeria fuscella B. & Br.
Clypeosphaeria Hendersoniae (Ell.) Sacc.
Leptosphaeria Hendersoniae (Ell.) Cke.
Sphaeria Hendersonia Ell.
Sphaeria melantera Pk.
Lophiotrema praemorsum (Lasch) Sacc.
Mycosphaerella rubina (Pk.) Jacz.
Sphaerella rubina Pk.
Phyllactinia corylea (P.) ex Karst.
Physalospora minima Ell. & Ev.
Physalospora vagans Ell. & Ev.
Sphaerotheca Humuli (DC.) Burrill. †
Valsa ambiens (P.) ex Fr.
Valsa sepincola Fckl.
Sphaeria tumida S.
Sphaeria syngenesia Fr.
Valsa syngenesia Fr.

UREDINALES

Kuehneola albida Magn.
Phragmidium gracile Arth.
Phragmidium imitans Arth.
Phragmidium occidentale Auct. Amer. p. p.
Phragmidium Rubi Auct. Amer. p. p.
Phragmidium Rubi-idaei Auct. Amer. p. p.
Uredo gyrosa Reb.
Aecidium nitens Auct. p. p.
Caeoma luminatum Auct. p. p.
Gymnoconia interstitialis Auct. p. p.
Puccinia peckiana Howe.
Phragmidium Rubi-idaei E. F. *32*.
Pucciniastrum americanum (Farl.) Arth.
Pucciniastrum arcticum Arth. p. p.
Pucciniastrum arcticum, var. americanum Farl.

SPHAEROPSIDALES

Coniothyrium Fuckelii Sacc.
Leptosphaeria Coniothyrium (Fckl.) Sacc.
Coniothyrium olivaceum Bon.
Cytospora ambiens Sacc.
Cytospora Rubi S.
Diplodia Rubi Fr.
Leptothyrium Pomi (Mont. & Fr.) Sacc.
Phoma perminuta Sacc.
Phyllosticta Ruborum Sacc.
Rhabdospora Rubi Ell.
Mycosphaerella Rubi Roark.
Septoria Rubi Westd.
Sphaeropsis Rosarum C. & E.

Rubus idaeus var. **aculeatissimus** (*cont.*)
⎰ Diplodia Ruborum (S.) Cke.
⎟ Sphaeria Ruborum S.
⎨ Sphaeropsis rubicola C. & E.
⎟ Sphaeropsis Ruborum (S.) Ell. & Ev.
⎱ Vermicularia compacta C. & E.

MELANCONIALES

⎰ Ascospora Rubi Zeller.
⎟ Ascospora Ruborum Zeller.
⎨ Coryneum Ruborum Oud.
⎱ Hendersonia Rubi Westd.
Coryneum microstictum B. & Br.
Cylindrosporium Rubi Ell. & Morg.
Gloeosporium Rubi Ell. & Ev.
⎰ Colletotrichum rubicola Ell. & Ev.
⎟ Gloeosporium rubicola Ell. & Ev.
⎨ Glomerella rubicola (Stoneman) Spaulding &
⎟   v. Schrenk.
⎱ Gnomoniopsis rubicola Stoneman.
⎰ Gloeosporium necator Ell. & Ev.
⎨ Gloeosporium venetum Speg.
⎱ Plectodiscella veneta Burkholder.
⎰ Hainesia Lythri (Desm.) v. Höhnel.
⎨ Pezizella Lythri Shear & Dodge.
⎱ Sclerotiopsis concava (Desm.) Shear & Dodge.
Melanconium griseum S.
Pestalozzia monochaetoidea Sacc. & Ell., var.
    Rubi Ell. & Ev.
Pestalozzia truncata, var. Rubi Karst.

HYPHOMYCETES

Botrytis patula Sacc. & Berl.
Botrytis vulgaris (Lk.) ex Fr.
⎰ Graphium eumorphum Sacc.
⎨ Sporotrichum vellereum Sacc. & Speg.
Graphium gracile Pk.
⎰ Graphium pruinosipes (Pk.) Sacc.
⎨ Stilbum pruinosipes Pk.

MISCELLANEA

Peniophora cinerea (P. ex Fr.) Cke.
Peronospora Rubi Rabh.

Rubus jamaicensis Sw.
Meliola manca Ell. & Martin.

Rubus jeckylanus Blanchard.
Kuehneola Uredinis Arth.

Rubus laxus Rydb.
⎰ Spirechina Rubi (Diet. & Holw.) Arth.
⎨ Uromyces Rubi Diet. & Holw.

Rubus leucodermis Dougl.
Coleroa Chaetomium (Kze.) Rabh., var. ame-
    ricana Petrak.
Peronospora Rubi Rabh.
⎰ Phragmidium imitans Arth.
⎨ Phragmidium Rubi-idaei Auct. Amer. p. p.
Pyrenopeziza Rubi (Fr.) Rehm.
Septoria Rubi Westd.

Rubus lucidus Rydb.
Kuehneola Uredinis Arth.
Kunkelia nitens Arth.

Rubus macropetalus Dougl.
Gymnoconia interstitialis (Tranz.) Lagerh.
Kunkelia nitens Arth.
Peronospora Rubi Rabh.
Septoria Rubi Westd.

Rubus melanolasius Focke.
Phragmidium imitans Arth.
Pucciniastrum americanum (Farl.) Arth.

Rubus Millspaughi Brit.
Gymnoconia interstitialis (Tranz.) Lagerh.
Kuehneola Uredinis Arth.

Rubus multiformis Blanchard.
Kuehneola Uredinis Arth.

Rubus neglectus Pk.
⎰ Gloeosporium venetum Speg.
⎨ Plectodiscella veneta Burkholder.
Phragmidium imitans Arth.
⎰ Pucciniastrum americanum (Farl.) Arth.
⎨ Pucciniastrum arcticum Tranz., var. ameri-
⎱   canum Farl.
Pucciniastrum arcticum Tranz.
Sphaerella rubina Pk.

Rubus neomexicanus Gray.
Phragmidium peckianum Arth.
Aregma mucronatum Fr. in herb.
Phragmidium Rubi Auct. p. p.

Rubus nigricans Rydb.
Gymnoconia interstitialis (Tranz.) Lagerh.

Rubus occidentalis L.
Acrostalagmus caulophagus Lawrence.
Asterina rubicola Ell. & Ev.
Cercospora Rubi Sacc.
⎰ Clypeosphaeria Hendersoniae (Ell.) Sacc.
⎨ Sphaeria Hendersonia Ell.
⎰ Coniothyrium Fuckelii Sacc.
⎨ Leptosphaeria Coniothyrium (Fckl.) Sacc.
Cylindrosporium Rubi Ell. & Morg.
⎰ Gloeosporium Rubi Ell. & Ev.
⎨ Tuberculina argillacea J. J. Davis.
⎰ Gloeosporium necator Ell. & Ev.
⎨ Gloeosporium venetum Speg.
⎱ Plectodiscella veneta Burkholder.
Glomerella cingulata (Stoneman) Spaulding &
    v. Schrenk.
Gnomonia Rubi Rehm.
Macrosporium punctiforme B.
⎰ Monilia fructigena P. ex Fr.
⎨ Sclerotinia fructigena Norton.
Oidium ruborum Rabh.
Peronospora Rubi Rabh.
Pezizella Lythri Shear & Dodge.
Phyllosticta rubicola Rabh.
⎰ Physalospora eriostega (C. & E.) Sacc., var.
⎨   glabrata Sacc.
⎱ Sphaeria eriostega C. & E.

Rubus occidentalis (*cont.*)
⎰ Mycosphaerella Rubi Roark.
⎱ Septoria Rubi Westd.
Septosporium praelongum Sacc.
Sphaerella rubina Pk.
Sphaeropsis rubicola C. & E.
Sphaerulina intermixta (B. & Br.) Sacc.
Venturia rubicola Ell. & Ev.
Vermicularia compacta C. & E.
Verticillium albo-atrum Reinke & Berthold.

UREDINALES

⎰ Gymnoconia interstitialis (Tranz.) Lagerh.
⎱ Gymnoconia peckiana (Howe) Trotter.
⎰ Puccinia interstitialis Tranz.
⎱ Puccinia tripustulata Pk.
⎰ Chrysomyxa albida Kühn.
⎱ Kuehneola albida Magn.
⎰ Kuehneola Uredinis Arth.
⎱ Uredo Muelleri Schrt.
⎰ Aecidium nitens S.
⎱ Caeoma luminatum Lk.
⎰ Caeoma nitens Auct. Amer. p. p.
⎱ Kunkelia nitens Arth.
⎰ Uredo luminata (Lk.) M. A. Curtis.
⎱ Uredo nitens (S.) M. A. Curtis.
⎰ Phragmidium gracile Auct. Amer. p. p.
⎱ Phragmidium imitans Arth.
⎰ Phragmidium incrassatum, var. gracile Farl.
⎱ Phragmidium Rubi-idaei Auct. Amer. p. p.
⎱ Uredo gyrosa Fung. Columb. *1386.*
Phragmidium violaceum Auct.
⎰ Pucciniastrum americanum (Farl.) Arth.
⎱ Pucciniastrum arcticum Tranz., var. americanum Farl.

Rubus odoratus L.
Diaporthe obscura (Pk.) Sacc.
Diaporthe rostellata (Fr.) Nits.
⎰ Gnomonia melanostyla (DC.) Fckl.
⎱ Sphaeria melanostyla DC.
Lophiostoma bicuspidatum Cke.
Lophiotrema praemorsum (Lasch) Sacc.
Oidium erysiphoides Fr.
Periconia pyrenospora Fres.
⎰ ?Phragmidium gracile Auct. Amer. p. p.
⎱ ?Phragmidium Rubi (P.) Wint.
⎰ Phragmidium Rubi-idaei (P.) Wint.
⎱ Phragmidium Rubi-odorati Diet.
⎰ Phyllosticta bicolor Pk.
⎱ Phyllosticta variabilis Pk.
Physalospora obtusa (S.) Sacc.
⎰ Peziza lacerata C. & P.
⎱ Pyrenopeziza lacerata (C. & P.) Sacc.
Septoria Rubi Westd.
Sphaerotheca Humuli (DC.) Burrill. †
⎰ Peziza subochracea C. & P.
⎱ Trichopeziza subochracea (C. & P.) Sacc.
Vermicularia compacta C. & E.

Rubus parviflorus Nutt.
Aposphaeria major Syd.
⎰ Dasyscypha bicolor (Bull. ex Fr.) Fckl.
⎱ Peziza bicolor Bull. ex Fr.
⎰ Dasyscypha scabrovillosa (Phil.) Sacc.
⎱ Peziza scabrovillosa Phil.
Diaporthe rostellata (Fr.) Nits.
Lachnum crystalligerum Sacc.
Peziza acutipila Karst.
Phacidium Rubi Fr.
⎰ Mycosphaerella Rubi Roark.
⎱ Septoria Rubi Westd.
Sphaerotheca Humuli (DC.) Burrill. †

UREDINALES

Kunkelia nitens Arth.
⎰ Phragmidium gracile Auct. Amer. p. p.
⎱ Phragmidium occidentale Arth.
⎱ Phragmidium Rubi-idaei Auct. Amer. p. p.
Phragmidium Rubi Auct.
Rubus pedatus Sm.
Venturia Kunzei Sacc.
Rubus pergratus Blanchard.
⎰ Kuehneola albida (Kühn) Magn.
⎱ Kuehneola Uredinis Arth.
Rubus phoenicolasius Maxim.
Phomopsis rubiseda Fairman.
Rubus poliophyllus Focke.
Kuehneola albida (Kühn) Magn.
Spirechina Rubi (Diet. & Holw.) Arth.
Rubus Pringlei Rydb.
⎰ Spirechina Rubi (Diet. & Holw.) Arth.
⎱ Uromyces Rubi Diet. & Holw.
Rubus Randii (L. H. Bailey) Rydb.
Gymnoconia interstitialis (Tranz.) Lagerh.
Rubus roesbergianus Blanchard.
Kuehneola Uredinis Arth.
Rubus rubicundus Woot. & Standl.
Phragmidium peckianum Arth.
Rubus rubrisetus Rydb.
Kuehneola Uredinis Arth.
Rubus sativus (L. H. Bailey) Brainerd.
Gloeosporium venetum Speg.
Gnomonia Rubi Rehm.
⎰ Gymnoconia interstitialis (Tranz.) Lagerh.
⎱ Gymnoconia peckiana (Howe) Trotter.
⎰ Kuehneola albida (Kühn) Magn.
⎱ Kuehneola Uredinis Arth.
Kunkelia nitens Arth.
Rubus saxatilis L.
Pucciniastrum arcticum Tranz.
Rubus schiedeanus Steud.
⎰ Spirechina Arthuri (Syd.) Arth.
⎱ Uromyces Arthuri Syd.
Rubus setosus Bigel.
Gymnoconia interstitialis (Tranz.) Lagerh.
Kuehneola albida (Kühn) Magn.
Pezizella Lythri Shear & Dodge.

Rubus spectabilis Pursh.
Botrytis cinerea P. †
Septoria Rubi Westd.
Sphaerotheca Humuli (DC.) Burrill. †
Sphaerotheca pannosa (Wallr.) Lév.
Rubus stellatus Smith.
Gymnoconia interstitialis (Trans.) Lagerh.
Leptothyrium vulgare (Fr.) Sacc.
⎰Earlea alaskana Arth.
⎱Phragmidium alaskanum (Arth.) Syd.
Phragmidium Rubi Auct.
Pucciniastrum arcticum Tranz.
Venturia Kunzei Sacc., var. ramicola Sacc. &
  Scalia.
Rubus trichomallus Schl.
Spirechina loeseneriana (Henn.) Arth.
⎰Spirechina Rubi (Diet. & Holw.) Arth.
⎱Uromyces Rubi Diet. & Holw.
Rubus triflorus Richards.
Discosia Artocreas (Tode) ex Fr.
Marssonina Potentillae, var. Tormentillae
  Trail.
Phyllosticta Dearnessii Sacc.
Septoria Rubi Westd.
⎰Sphaerotheca Castagnei Lév. p. p.
⎱Sphaerotheca Humuli (DC.) Burrill. †
Sphaerotheca Humuli (DC.) Burrill, var. Rubi
  Rehm.
Sphaerotheca pannosa (Wallr.) Lév.
Synchytrium aureum Schrt.

UREDINALES

⎰Gymnoconia interstitialis (Tranz.) Lagerh.
⎱Puccinia peckiana Howe.
Kuehneola Uredinis Arth.
⎰Caeoma luminatum Lk.
⎱Kunkelia nitens Arth.
Phragmidium imitans Arth.
⎰Pucciniastrum americanum (Farl.) Arth.
⎱Pucciniastrum arcticum Tranz., var. ameri-
  canum Farl.
Pucciniastrum articum Tranz.
Rubus trilobus (Moc. & Sesse) Seringe.
Phragmidium occidentale Arth.
Rubus trivialis Michx.
Cercospora Rubi Sacc.
⎰Gloeosporium rufomaculans (B.) Thm.
⎱Glomerella cingulata (Stoneman) Spaulding &
  v. Schrenk.
Kuehneola Uredinis Arth.
⎰Caeoma interstitiale Auct. Amer. p. p.
⎱Gymnoconia interstitialis N. Am. Ured. *1504.*
⎰Caeoma nitens Auct. Amer. p. p.
⎱Kunkelia nitens Arth.
⎰Meliola manca Ell. & Martin.
⎱Meliola sanguinea Ell. & Ev.
Puccinia peckiana Howe.
Septoria Rubi Westd.
Septoria Rubi Westd., var. alba Pk.

Sphaerotheca Humuli (DC.) Burrill. †
Tubercularia persicina Ditm.
⎰Spirechina epiphylla Arth.
⎱Uromyces epiphyllus (Arth.) Sacc. & Trott.
Rubus ursinus Cham. & Schl.
⎰Diaporthe rostellata (Fr.) Nits.
⎱Sphaeria rostellata Fr.
⎰Hendersonia Rubi (C. & E.) Sacc.
⎱Hendersonia sarmentorum Westd., var. Rubi
  C. & E.
Kuehneola Uredinis Arth.
Libertella Rosae Desm.
Septoria Rubi Westd.
Sphaerotheca Humuli (DC.) Burrill. †
Rubus villosus Auct. Amer. p. p. (previous to
  1908 approximately.)
Cercospora rosicola Pass.
Cercospora Rubi Sacc.
⎰Chrysomyxa albida Kühn.
⎱Coleosporium Rubi Ell. & Holw.
Lecythea tripustulata Cke. in Rav. Fung. Am.
  491.
Phragmidium albidum (Kühn) Ludw.
Uredo Muelleri Schrt.
⎰Clypeosphaeria Notarisii Fckl.
⎱Sphaeria clypeata Nees.
⎰Sphaeria gallophila Ell.
⎱Diaporthe gallophila (Ell.) Ell. & Ev.
Diaporthe obscura (Pk.) Sacc.
⎰Diaporthe rostellata (Fr.) Nits.
⎱Sphaeria rostellata Fr.
Didymosphaeria manitobiensis Ell. & Ev.
Diplodia Rubi Fr.
⎰Fusarium? Rubi (Wint.) Berl. & Vogl.
⎱Fusisporium? Rubi Wint.
Gloeosporium Rubi Ell. & Ev.
Gloeosporium venetum Speg.
Glonium macrosporum Tracy & Earle.
⎰Aecidium nitens S.
⎱Caeoma luminatum Lk.
Caeoma nitens Auct. Amer. p. p.
Uredo Caeoma-nitens DeToni.
⎰Gymnoconia interstitialis (Tranz.) Lagerh.
⎱Gymnoconia peckiana (Howe) Trotter. I.
Puccinia peckiana Howe.
Puccinia tripustulata Pk.
Hendersonia platypus Ell. & Ev.
Hypoderma Rubi (P.) DeNot.
⎰Hysterium viticola C. & P. p. p.
⎱Hysterographium viticola Rehm, var. Ru-
  borum Cke.
Isariopsis grayiana Ell.
Mollisia alabamensis Ell. & Ev.
⎰Patellaria rhabarbarina B.
⎱Pezicula rhabarbarina (B.) Tul.
Peronospora Rubi Rabh.
Phoma lethalis Ell. & Martin.
Phyllosticta Ruborum Sacc.

Rubus villosus (*cont.*)
Physalospora carpogena Atk.
⎰ Physalospora obtusa (S.) Sacc.
⎱ Sphaeria obtusa S.
Septoria Rubi Westd.
Spegazzinia trichophila Atk.
Sphaeropsis rubicola C. & E.
Sphaerotheca Humuli (DC.) Burrill. †
Stictis Rubi S.
Teichospora nitida Ell. & Ev.
Triposporium elegans Cda.
⎰ Tubercularia carpogena Pk.
⎱ Tubercularia decolorans Pk.
⎰ Valsa Rubi Fckl. 1869.
⎱ Valsa Rubi Pk. 1876.

Rubus villosus Ait. (after 1907.)
Cercospora Rubi Sacc.
Cercospora septorioides Ell. & Ev.
⎰ Fusarium Rubi Wint.
⎱ Fusisporium (?) Rubi Wint.
Ramularia Rubi (Wint.) Wr.
⎰ Kuehneola albida (Kühn) Magn
⎱ Kuehneola Uredinis Arth.
⎰ Caeoma nitens Auct. p. p. non S.
⎜ Gymnoconia interstitialis I. N. Am. Uredinales
⎜   *1411.*
⎱ Kunkelia nitens Arth.
Peronospora Rubi Rabh.
Phomopsis vepris (Nits.) Traverso.
Sclerotiopsis concava (Desm.) Shear & Dodge.
Septoria Rubi Westd.
Septoria Rubi Westd., var. brevispora Sacc.
Sphaeropsis rubicola C. & E.
Synchytrium aureum Schrt.

Rubus villosus Ait., var. **humifusus** Torr. & Gr.
See also **R. canadensis.**
Gymnoconia interstitialis (Tranz.) Lagerh.
Hypoderma virgultorum DC.
⎰ Caeoma luminatum Lk.
⎱ Kunkelia nitens Arth.
Peronospora Rubi Rabh.
Scleroderris rhabarbarina (B.) Ell. & Ev.

Rubus vitifolius Cham. & Schl.
Armillaria mellea (Vahl) ex Fr.
Gloeosporium venetum Speg.
Kuehneola Uredinis Arth.
⎰ Gymnoconia interstitialis Syd. Ured. *1785.*
⎱ Kunkelia nitens Arth.
Septoria Rubi Westd.

Rubus vitifolius Cult. (Loganberry).
⎰ Acrostalagmus caulophagus Lawrence.
⎜ Verticillium caulophagum (Lawrence) Carpen-
⎱   ter.
Corticium vagum B. & C.
Fusarium Rubi Wint.
⎰ Gloeosporium venetum Speg.
⎱ Plectodiscella veneta Burkholder.

Gnomonia Rubi Rehm.
Gnomonia setacea (P. ex Fr.) Ces. & De Not.
Kunkelia nitens Arth.
Leptosphaeria Coniothyrium Sacc.
Leptosphaeria thomasiana Sacc. & Roum.
Mycosphaerella rubina (Pk.) Jacz.
?Puccinia peckiana Howe.
⎰ Mycosphaerella Rubi Roark.
⎱ Septoria Rubi Westd.
Sphaerotheca Humuli (DC.) Burrill. †

Rubus (blackberry).
Acrostalagmus caulophagus Lawrence.
Aleurodiscus botryosus Burt.
Armillaria mellea (Vahl) ex Fr.
Cercospora Bliti Tharp.
Cercospora Rubi Sacc.
Coniothyrium Fuckelii Sacc.
Corticium galactinum (Fr.) Burt.
Corticium vagum B. & C.
Cylindrosporium Rubi Ell. & Morg.
Fusisporium Rubi Wint.
⎰ Gloeosporium venetum Speg.
⎱ Plectodiscella veneta Burkholder.
Gloeosporium naviculisporum Stoneman.
Gloeosporium phaeosorum Sacc.
Gnomonia Rubi Rehm.
Lachnella rufo-olivacea (A. & S. ex Fr.) Phil.
?Leptothyrium pomi (Mont. & Fr.) Sacc.
⎰ Gloeodes pomigena (S.) A. S. Colby.
⎱ Phyllachora pomigena (S.) Sacc.
Pycnochytrium globosum Schrt.
⎰ Mycosphaerella Rubi Roark.
⎱ Septoria Rubi Westd.
Sphaerotheca Humuli (DC.) Burrill, var. fuli-
  ginea (Schl.) Salmon.
Tuberculina persicina (Ditm.) Sacc.

Rubus (dewberry.)
⎰ Gloeosporium venetum Speg.
⎱ Plectodiscella veneta Burkholder.
?Leptothyrium pomi (Mont. & Fr.) Sacc.
Mycosphaerella Rubi Roark.
Peronospora Potentillae DBy.
Peronospora Rubi Rabh.
Phyllosticta Ruborum Sacc.
⎰ Phyllostictina carpogena Shear.
⎱ Physalospora carpogena Atk.
Sphaerotheca Humuli (DC.) Burrill.

Rubus (raspberry).
Acrostalagmus caulophagus Lawrence.
Armillaria mellea (Vahl) ex Fr.
Ascospora Ruborum Zeller.
Botryosphaeria Ribis (Tode ex Fr.) Grossen-
  bacher & Duggar, var. chromogena Shear
  et al.
Clypeosphaeria Hendersoniae (Ell.) Sacc.
Corticium vagum B. & C.
Cylindrosporium Rubi Ell. & Morg.
Cytospora Rubi S.

Rubus (raspberry) (*cont.*)
- Colletotrichum gloeosporioides Penz.
- Colletotrichum rubicola (Ell. & Ev.) Stoneman.
- Glomerella fructigena (G. P. Clinton) Sacc.
- Glomerella rubicola (Stoneman) Spaulding & v. Schrenk.
- Colletotrichum venetum (Speg.) Halsted.
- Gloeosporium venetum Speg.
- Plectodiscella veneta Buckholder.
- Discosia Artocreas (Tode) ex Fr.
- Fusisporium Rubi Wint.
- Coremium Fragariastrum S.
- Graphiothecium Fragariastri Sacc.
- Helotium herbarum Fr., var. Rubi Ell. & Ev.
- Lecanidion atratum (Hedw. ex Fr.) Rabh.
- Leptosphaeria Coniothyrium (Fckl.) Sacc.
- Leptothyrium pomi (Mont. and Fr.) Sacc.
- Pestalozzia longiseta Speg.
- Phyllosticta bicolor Pk.
- Rhabdospora Rubi Ell.
- Rhizopus nigricans Ehrenb.
- Sphaerotheca Humuli (DC.) Burrill, var. fuliginea (Schl.) Salmon.
- Stigmatea Tonduzi Speg.
- Valsa leucostoma (P.) ex Fr.
- Verticillium albo-atrum Reinke & Berthold.
- Verticillium ovatum G. H. Berkeley & A. B. Jackson.

Rubus sp. indet.

PEZIZINEAE
- Dermatea Rubi (Lib.) Rehm.
- Patellaria rhabarbarina B.
- Pezicula rhabarbarina (B.) Tul.
- Fabraea cincta Sacc. & Scalia.
- Lachnella rufo-olivacea (A. & S. ex Fr.) Sacc.
- Peziza rufo-olivacea A. & S. ex Fr.
- Orbilia vinosa (A. & S. ex Fr.) Karst.
- Peziza vinosa A. & S. ex Fr.
- Peziza compressa P., var. rubicola C. & E.
- Cenangium Rubi (Fr.) Duby.
- Excipula Rubi Fr.
- Pyrenopeziza Rubi (Fr.) Rehm.
- Tympanis conspersa Fr.

HYSTERIINEAE
- Aulographum confluens Earle.
- Hypoderma Rubi Schrt.
- Hysterium confluens S.
- Hysterographium levanticum Rehm.
- Hysterographium Ruborum Cke.
- Lophodermium rubicola Earle.

PLECTASCINEAE
- Arachniotus trachyspermus Shear.
- Meliola Puiggarii Speg.

SPHAERIALES
- Botryosphaeria quercuum (S.) Sacc., var.
- Clypeosphaeria Hendersoniae (Ell.) Sacc.

- Diaporthe gallophila Ell.
- Diaporthe obscura (Tk.) Sacc.
- Diatrypella rubincola (S.) Starb.
- Sphaeria rubincola S.
- Valsa rubincola (S.) Cke.
- Didymosphaeria manitobiensis Ell. & Ev.
- Sphaeria clypeata Nees ex Fr.
- Leptosphaeria Doliolum (P. ex Fr.) DeNot.
- Sphaeria Doliolum P. ex Fr.
- Leptosphaeria fuscella (B. & Br.) Ces. & DeNot.
- Lophiostoma Jerdoni B. & Br.
- Lophiostoma praemorsum (Lasch) Sacc.
- Endophlaea anisometra Cke. & Hark.
- Metasphaeria anisometra (Cke. & Hark.) Sacc.
- Sphaeria anisometra Cke. & Hark.
- Physalospora Malorum Shear et al.
- Pleospora herbarum (Fr.) Rabh.
- Schizoparme straminea Shear.
- Sphaeria sapincola Fr.
- Stigmatea Chaetomium (Kze.) ex Fr.
- Teichospora nitida Ell. & Ev.
- Cf. "Sphaeria rostellata Fr." S.
- Sphaeria rostellata S. Herb.
- Trematosphaeria Schweinitzii Ell. & Ev.
- Valsa subclypeata C. & P.

UREDINALES
- Spirechina loeseneriana Arth.
- Uredo loeseneriana Henn.
- Uromyces loesenerianus (Arth.) Syd.

HYMENOMYCETINEAE
- Corticium Rubi B. & C.
- Corticium rubicola B. & C.
- ?Corticium Sambuci P.
- Cyphella porrigens Burt.
- Marasmius ramealis Fr.
- Peniophora isabellina Burt.
- Typhula rubincola S.

FUNGI IMPERFECTI
- Ascochyta Rubi Lasch.
- Botrytis patula Sacc. & Berl.
- Cylindrosporium Rubi Ell. & Morg.
- Diplodia Rubi Fr.
- Diplodia Ruborum (S.) Sacc.
- Gloeosporium naviculisporum Stoneman.
- Helminthosporium glabroides F. L. Stevens.
- Hymenella nigra Fr.
- Leptostroma vulgare Fr.
- Myxormia atroviridis B. & Br.
- Pestalozzia longiseta Speg.
- Sphaeropsis rubicola C. & E.
- Tubercularia nigricans (Bull.) ex Lk.
- Vermicularia effusa S.

MISCELLANEA
- Capnodium elongatum B. & Desm.
- Creonectria purpurea (L.) ex Seaver.

Dalibarda repens L.
  {Dothidea Dalibardae Pk.
  {Phyllachora Dalibardae (Pk.) Sacc.
  Septoria Dalibardae Pk.
Fragaria chiloensis Duchesne.
  Patellina Fragariae Stevens & Peterson.
  {Mycosphaerella Fragariae (Tul.) Lindau.
  {Ramularia Tulasnei Sacc.
  {Sphaerella Fragariae (Tul.) Sacc.
  Sphaerotheca Humuli (DC.) Burrill. †
Fragaria elatior Ehrh.
  Sphaerella Fragariae (Tul.) Sacc.
Fragaria glauca (Watson) Rydb.
  Ramularia Tulasnei Sacc.
  Sphaerotheca Castagnei Lév.
Fragaria grandiflora Ehrh.
  Leptothyrium macrothecium Fckl.
  Oospora pilularis Sacc.
  Phyllosticta fragaricola Desm. & Rob.
  Ramularia Tulasnei Sacc.
  Trichothecium roseum Lk.
Fragaria mexicana Schl.
  {Hainesia Lythri (Desm.) v. Höhnel.
  {Sclerotiopsis concava (Desm.) Shear & Dodge.
Fragaria ovalis (Lehm) Rydb.
  Sphaerella Fragariae (Tul.) Sacc.
Fragaria platypetala Rydb.
  Mycosphaerella Fragariae (Tul.) Lindau.
  Sphaerotheca Humuli (DC.) Burrill. †
Fragaria vesca L.
  Ascochyta colorata Pk.
  Cercospora vexans C. Massal.
  Rhizopus nigricans Ehrenb. ex Fr.
  {Mycosphaerella Fragariae (Tul.) Lindau.
  {Ramularia Fragariae Pk.
  {Ramularia Tulasnei Sacc.
  {Sphaerella Fragariae (Tul.) Sacc.
  Sphaerella earliana Wint.
Fragaria virginiana Duchesne.
  {Ascochyta colorata Pk.
  {Ascochyta Fragariae Sacc.
  {Cercospora vexans C. Massal.
  {Ramularia modesta J. J. Davis.
  {Hainesia Lythri (Desm.) v. Höhnel.
  {Pezizella Lythri Shear & Dodge.
  {Sclerotiopsis concava (Desm.) Shear & Dodge.
  {Ramularia Fragariae Pk.
  {Ramularia Tulasnei Sacc.
  Mycosphaerella Fragariae (Tul.) Lindau.
  Synchytrium aureum Schrt.
  Mycorrhiza of Legumes F. R. Jones.
Fragaria sp. indet.
  Armillaria mellea (Vahl) ex Fr.
  Botrytis cinerea P. †
  Botrytis vulgaris (Lk.) ex Fr.
  Botrytis vulgaris (Lk.) ex Fr., var. Fragariae
    Sacc.
  {Corticium vagum B. & C., var. Solani Burt.
  {Rhizoctonia Solani Kühn.

{Diachea elegans Fr.
{Diachea leucopoda (Bull.) Rostf.
  Fuligo varians Sommf.
  Fusarium Rubi Wint.
  ?Gymnoconia interstitialis (Tranz.) Lagerh.
{Diplocarpon earlianum (Ell. & Ev.) Wolf.
{Gloeosporium Fragariae (Lib.) Mont.
{Gloeosporium Potentillae (Desm.) Oud.
{Leptothyrium Fragariae Lib.
{?Marssonia Fragariae (Lib.) Sacc.
{Marssonia Potentillae (Desm.) Fischer.
{Marssonia Potentillae, var. Fragariae Sacc.
{Marssonina Potentillae (Desm.) Magn.
{Mollisia earliana (Ell. & Ev.) Sacc.
{Peziza earliana Ell. & Ev.
  Leptosphaeria Coniothyrium (Fckl.) Sacc.
  Mucilago spongiosa (Leyss.) Morg.
  Oidium Fragariae Harz.
  Patellina Fragariae Stevens & Peterson.
  Peronospora Fragariae Roze & Cornu.
  Pestalozzia Guepini Desm.
  Phyllosticta fragaricola Rob.
{Dendrophoma obscurans (Ell. & Ev.) H. W.
    Anderson.
{Phoma obscurans Ell. & Ev.
{Phyllosticta obscurans (Ell. & Ev.) Tassi.
{Physarum cinereum (Batsch) P.
{Didymium cinereum (Batsch.) Fr., var.
  Physarum vernum Sommf.
  Phytophthora Cactorum (Leb. & Cohn.) Schrt.
  Pycnochytrium globosum Schrt.
  Rhabdospora Fragariae Atk.
  Rhizopus nigricans Ehrenb. ex Fr.
  Schizoparme straminea Shear.
{Sclerotinia libertiana Fckl.
{Sclerotinia sclerotiorum (Lib.) Massee.
  Sclerotium Rolfsii Sacc.
  Septoria aciculosa Ell. & Ev.
  Sphaerella earliana Wint.
  Sphaeria Fragariae S.
  Sphaeronemella Fragariae Stevens & Peterson.
  Sphaeropsis Malorum B.
{Sphaerotheca Castagnei Lév. p. p.
{Sphaerotheca Humuli (DC.) Burrill. †
  Sphaerotheca Humuli (DC.) Burrill, var. fuli-
    ginea (Schl.) Salmon.
  Spumaria alba DC.
  Thelephora fimbriata S.
Duchesnea indica (Andr.) Focke.
  Hainesia Lythri (Desm.) Shear & Dodge.
  Peronospora Potentillae DBy.
{Frommea Duchesneae Arth.
{Kuehneola Duchesneae Arth.
{Phragmidium Duchesneae (Arth.) Syd.
{Phragmidium obtusum Auct. p.p.
{Phragmidium Potentillae-canadensis Fung.
    Columb. *3050*
Potentilla Andersonii Greene.
  Phragmidium Andersoni Shear.

Potentilla Anserina L.
Gloeosporium Potentillae (Desm.) Oud.
Marssonia Potentillae (Desm.) Fischer.
Marssonina Potentillae (Desm.) Magn.
Ramularia arvensis Sacc.
Ramularia punctiformis Sacc.
Sphaerotheca Humuli (DC.) Burrill. †
Trochila Potentillae Rostr.

Potentilla arachnoidea Dougl.
Phragmidium Potentillae (P.) Karst.

Potentilla argentea L.
Gloeosporium Potentillae (Desm.) Oud.
Mollisia Dehnii (Rabh.) Karst.
Peziza Dehnii Rabh.

Potentilla arguta Pursh.
Marssonina Potentillae (Desm.) Magn.
Phragmidium Fragariastri (DC.) Schrt.
Septoria purpurascens Ell. & Martin.
Taphrina Potentillae (Farl.) Johans.

Potentilla Baileyi (Watson) Greene.
Phragmidium Jonesii Diet.

Potentilla Bakeri Rydb.
Phragmidium affine Syd.
Phragmidium Ivesiae Syd.

Potentilla biennis Greene.

Potentilla bipinnatifida Dougl.
Phragmidium Potentillae (P.) Karst.

Potentilla blaschkeana Turcz.
Phragmidium affine Syd.
Phragmidium Fragariastri Auct. Amer. p. p.
Phragmidium Ivesiae Syd.
Sphaerotheca Humuli (DC.) Burrill.

Potentilla Breweri Watson.
Phragmidium Ivesiae Syd.

Potentilla californica Greene.
Marssonia Potentillae (Desm.) Fischer.

Potentilla canadensis L.
Darluca Filum (Biv.) Cast.
Hainesia Lythri (Desm.) v. Höhnel.
Sclerotiopsis concava (Desm.) Shear & Dodge.
Ascomyces Potentillae (Farl.) Phil.
Exoascus deformans, var. Potentillae Farl.
Exoascus Potentillae (Farl.) Sacc.
Magnusiella Potentillae (Farl.) Sadebeck.
Taphrina Potentillae (Farl.) Johans.
Marssonia Potentillae (Desm.) Fischer.
Marssonina Potentillae (Desm.) Magn.
Marssonina Potentillae (Desm.) Magn., var.
Tormentillae Trail.
Peronospora Potentillae DBy.
Rhysotheca Potentillae (DBy.) G. W. Wilson.
Phyllachora Potentillae (S.) Pk.
Sphaeria Potentillae S.
Physalospora Potentillae Rostr.
Pyrenopeziza coloradensis Ell. & Ev.
Ramularia arvensis Sacc.
Rhizoctonia Solani Kühn.
Sclerotium fallax Sacc.
?Sphaeria Solidaginis S.

Dothidea Potentillae Fr.
Stigmatea Potentillae Fr.
Synchytrium aureum Schrt.
Synchytrium Myosotidis, var. Potentillae
Schrt.

UREDINALES
Aregma Fragariae Arth. Ind. Acad.
Aregma obtusatum Auct. Amer. p. p.
Aregma triarticulatum B. & C.
Caeoma (Uredo) Potentillarum S. Am. Bor.
2834.
Frommea obtusa Arth.
Kuehneola canadensis Fung. Columb. *3634.*
Kuehneola obtusa Arth.
Kuehneola Potentillae (S.) Arth.
Phragmidium Fragariae Arth. Ind. Acad.
Phragmidium Fragariastri Auct. Amer. p. p.
Phragmidium obtusum Auct. Amer. p. p.
Phragmidium obtusum, var. Potentillae- cana-
densis Myc. Univ. *1735.*
Phragmidium Potentillae Auct. Amer. p. p.
Phragmidium Potentillae-canadensis Diet.
Phragmidium Tormentillae Auct. Amer.
Phragmidium triarticulatum (B. & C.) Farl.
Puccinia Potentillae S.
Uredo Alchemillae S. Syn. Car.
Uredo obtusa Auct. p. p.
Uredo Potentillae Auct. Amer. p. p.
Uredo Potentillarum Auct. Amer. p. p.
Uredo Potentillarum, var. Potentillae-cana-
densis Myc. Univ. *1445.*

Potentilla coloradensis Rydb.

Potentilla concinna Richards.
Phragmidium Ivesiae Syd.

Potentilla Convallaria Rydb.
Sphaerotheca Humuli (DC.) Burrill. †

Potentilla divisa Rydb.
Phragmidium Potentillae (P.) Karst.

Potentilla dichroa Rydb.

Potentilla diversifolia Lehm.

Potentilla effusa Dougl.

Potentilla Elmeri Rydb.
Phragmidium affine Syd.
Phragmidium Ivesiae Syd.

Potentilla emarginata Pursh.
Chaetosphaeria byssiseda Rostr.
Coniothecium asperulum Dur. & Mont.
Leptostroma Potentillae (Fr.) Karst.
Leptothyrium arcticum (Fckl.) J. Lind.
Mollisia atrata (P.) Karst.
Pyrenopeziza atrata (P.) Fckl.
Phoma potentillica Allescher.
Pleospora herbarum (Fr.) Rabh.
Pleospora vulgaris Niessl.
Pyrenophora chrysospora (Niessl) Sacc.
Trochila Potentillae Rostr.

Potentilla fastigiata Nutt.
Phragmidium affine Syd.
Phragmidium Ivesiae Syd.

Potentilla filipes Rydb.
{ Phragmidium affine Syd.
{ Phragmidium Ivesiae Syd.
　Pleospora herbarum (Fr.) Rabh.
Potentilla fissa Nutt.
　Magnusiella Potentillae (Farl.) Sadebeck.
Potentilla flabellifolia Hook.
{ Earlea bilocularis (Diet. & Holw.) Arth.
{ Phragmidium biloculare Diet. & Holw.
Potentilla flabelliformis Lehm.
{ Phragmidium affine Syd.
{ Phragmidium Ivesiae Syd.
Potentilla fruticosa L.
{ Phragmidium Andersoni Shear.
{ Phragmidium Potentillae Auct. Amer. p. p.
　Phragmidium bulbosum Auct.
　?Phragmidium Potentillae (P.) Karst.
　Sphaeropezia coloradensis Ell. & Ev.
　Zignoella Potentillae Tracy & Earle.
Potentilla glabrella Rydb.
　Phragmidium Potentillae (P.) Karst.
Potentilla glandulosa Lindl.
　Marssonia Potentillae (Desm.) Fischer.
　Phragmidium Ivesiae Syd.
　Sphaerotheca Humuli (DC.) Burrill. †
{ Dothidea Potentillae Fr.
{ Stigmatea Potentillae Fr.
Potentilla glaucophylla Lehm.
Potentilla glomerata A. Nels.
{ Phragmidium affine Syd.
{ Phragmidium Ivesiae Syd.
Potentilla Gordoni Greene.
{ Earlea Horkeliae (Garrett) Arth.
{ Phragmidium Horkeliae Garrett.
{ Phragmidium affine Syd.
{ Phragmidium Ivesiae Syd.
　Phragmidium Jonesii Diet.
Potentilla gracilis Dougl.
{ Phragmidium affine Syd.
{ Phragmidium Fragariae N. A. F. *2881.*
{ Phragmidium Fragariastri Auct. Amer. p p.
{ Phragmidium Ivesiae Syd.
{ Phragmidium Potentillae Fung. Columb. *3731,*
　?Phragmidium Potentillae (P.) Karst.
　Sphaerotheca Humuli (DC.) Burrill. †
Potentilla grandiflora L.
　Peronospora Potentillae DBy.
Potentilla grosseserrata Rydb.
Potentilla Hallii Rydb.
{ Phragmidium affine Syd.
{ Phragmidium Ivesiae Syd.
Potentilla hippiana Lehm.
{ Phragmidium affine Syd.
{ Phragmidium Ivesiae Syd.
　Phragmidium Potentillae (P.) Karst.
Potentilla maculata Pourret.
　Laestadia Potentillae Rostr.
　Microthyrium arcticum Oud.
　Mollisia atrata (P.) Karst.

Physalospora Potentillae Rostr.
{ Catharinea vitrea (Rostr.) Sacc.
{ Pleosphaerulina vitrea (Rostr.) Berl.
{ Pleospora vitrea Rostr.
　Pleospora herbarum (Fr.) Rabh.
　Pleospora vulgaris Niessl.
　Sclerotium durum P. ex Fr.
　Septoria potentillica Thm.
　Sphaerella pachyasca Rostr.
　Sphaerella punctiformis (P. ex Fr.) Rabh.
Potentilla monspeliensis L.
　Gloeosporium Fragariae (Lib.) Mont.
　Peronospora Potentillae DBy.
{ Phragmidium affine Syd.
{ Phragmidium Ivesiae Syd.
　Phragmidium Potentillae (P.) Karst.
　Mycosphaerella Fragariae (Tul.) Lindau.
　Sphaerotheca Humuli (DC.) Burrill. †
Potentilla monspeliensis L., var. norvegica (L.)
　　Rydb.
{ Beloniella Dehnii (Rabh.) Rehm.
{ Mollisia Dehnii (Rabh.) Karst.
{ Peziza Dehnii Rabh.
{ Pseudopeziza Dehnii (Rabh.) Fckl.
　Oidium erysiphoides Fr.
　Peronospora Potentillae DBy.
　?Phragmidium Fragariae (DC.) Wint.
　Ramularia arvensis Sacc.
　Septoria purpurascens Ell. & Martin.
Potentilla nepalensis Hook.
　Peronospora Potentillae DBy.
Potentilla nivea L.
　Chaetosphaeria Potentillae Rostr.
　Phoma potentillica Allescher.
　Pleospora herbarum (Fr.) Rabh.
　Pyrenophora Cerastii (Oud.) J. Lind.
　Pyrenophora comata (Niessl) Sacc.
　Rhabdospora cercosperma (Rostr.) Sacc.
　Septoria semilunaris Johanson.
　Trochila Potentillae Rostr.
Potentilla nivea L., var. prostrata Lehm.
　Laestadia Potentillae Rostr.
　Orbilia arctica Allescher.
{ Pleospora Allescheri Sacc. & Syd.
{ Pleospora leptosphaerioides Allescher.
　Pleospora media Niessl.
Potentilla Nuttallii Lehm.
{ Phragmidium affine Syd.
{ Phragmidium Fragariastri Auct. Amer. p. p.
{ Phragmidium Ivesiae Syd.
{ Earlea bilocularis (Diet. & Holw.) Arth.
{ Phragmidium biloculare Diet. & Holw.
Potentilla palustris (L.) Scop.
　Cercospora Comari Pk.
{ Gloeosporium Potentillae (Desm.) Oud.
{ Marssonina Potentillae (Desm.) Magn.
　Mycosphaerella innumerella (Karst.) Schrt.
　Mycosphaerella pachyasca (Rostr.) Vesterg.

Potentilla palustris (*cont.*)
Septogloeum Potentillae Allescher.
Sphaerotheca Humuli (DC.) Burrill. †
Potentilla paradoxa Nutt.
Mollisia Dehnii (Rabh.) Karst.
⎰Phragmidium affine Syd.
⎱Phragmidium Fragariastri Auct. Amer. p. p.
⎰Phragmidium Ivesiae Syd.
Potentilla Parishii Rydb.
Phragmidium Ivesiae Syd.
Potentilla pectinata Fisch.
Phragmidium Potentillae (P.) Karst.
Potentilla Pedersenii Ryd.
Pleospora herbarum (Fr.) Rabh.
Mycosphaerella tassiana (De Not) Johans.
Potentilla pennsylvanica L.
Phragmidium Potentillae (P.) Karst.
⎰Aregma triarticulatum B. & C.
⎱Phragmidium triarticulatum (B. & C.) Farl.
Potentilla puberula Greene.
Marssonia Potentillae (Desm.) Fischer.
Potentilla pulchella R. Br.
Cladosporium herbarum (P.) ex Lk.
Pleospora herbarum (Fr.) Rabh.
Pyrenopeziza atrata (P.) Fckl.
Pyrenophora chrysospora (Niessl) Sacc.
Pyrenophora comata (Awd. & Niessl) Sacc.
Rhabdospora cercosperma (Rostr.) Sacc.
Potentilla pulchella R. Br., var. **humilis** Auct.
Cladosporium arcticum Berl. & Vogl.
Potentilla rivalis Nutt., var. **pentandra** (Engelm.)
Watson.
Peronospora Potentillae DBy.
Ramularia arvensis Sacc.
Potentilla rubricaulis Bourg. ex Watson.
Coniothecium asperulum Dur. & Mont.
Pyrenophora chrysospora (Niessl) Sacc.
Trochila Potentillae Rostr.
Potentilla rubripes Rydb.
Phragmidium affine Syd.
Potentilla santolinoides Bail. ex Watson.
Typhula sclerotioides (P.) Fr.
Potentilla sericoleuca Rydb.
Phragmidium Ivesiae Syd.
Potentilla setosa Watson.
Phragmidium Jonesii Diet.
Potentilla strigosa Pall.
Phragmidium Potentillae (P.) Karst.
Potentilla tridentata Ait.
⎰Phragmidium Fragariastri Auct. Amer. p. p.
⎱Phragmidium Ivesiae Syd.
Phyllosticta potentillica Sacc.
Pucciniastrum Potentillae Komarov.
Trochila Potentillae Rostr.
Potentilla trina A. Nels.
Earlea bilocularis (Diet. & Holw.) Arth.
Potentilla unguiculata (Gray) Greene.
Phragmidium Ivesiae Syd.

Potentilla vahliana Lehm.
Coniothecium asperulum Dur. & Mont.
Mollisia atrata (P.) Karst.
Pyrenophora chrysospora (Niessl) Sacc.
Potentilla villosa Pall.
Phragmidium Ivesiae Syd.
Potentilla viridescens Rydb.
Peronospora Potentillae DBy.
⎰Phragmidium affine Syd.
⎱Phragmidium Ivesiae Syd.
Sibbaldia procumbens L.
Botrytis cinerea P. †
Laestadia Potentillae Rostr.
Sphaerella innumerella Karst.
Waldsteinia fragarioides (Michx.) Trattinick.
⎰Micropuccinia Waldsteiniae (M. A. Curtis)
⎱ Arth. & Jackson.
⎱Puccinia Waldsteiniae M. A. Curtis.
Ramularia Waldsteiniae Ell. & Davis.
Septoria Waldsteiniae Pk. & Clinton.
⎰Urocystis Waldsteiniae Pk.
⎱Ustilago Waldsteiniae (Pk.) Pazschke.
Waldsteinia idahoensis Piper.
Micropuccinia Waldsteiniae (M. A. Curtis)
Arth. & Jackson.
Geum canadense Jacq.
Peronospora Potentillae DBy.
Phyllosticta decidua Ell. & Kellerm.
Septoria Gei Rob. & Desm.
⎰Sphaerotheca Castagnei Lév. p. p.
⎱Sphaerotheca Humuli (DC.) Burrill. †
Sphaerotheca pannosa (Wallr.) Lév.
Synchytrium aureum Schrt.
Geum macrophyllum Willd.
Erysiphe Polygoni DC. †
Peronospora Potentillae DBy.
Septoria Gei Rob. & Desm.
Sphaerotheca Humuli (DC.) Burrill. †
Geum oregonense Rydb.
Marssonia adunca Sacc.
Geum Peckii Pursh.
Cylindrosporium Gei Farl.
Geum rivale L.
Peronospora Potentillae DBy.
Sphaerotheca Humuli (DC.) Burrill. †
Geum Rossii Seringe.
⎰Patinella Crandallii Sacc.
⎱Patinella macrospora Ell. & Ev.
⎱Patinella monticola Ell. & Ev.
Geum strictum Ait.
Diaporthe obscura (Pk.) Sacc.
Marssonia adunca Sacc.
Peronospora Potentillae DBy.
Septoria Gei Rob. & Desm.
Sphaerotheca Humuli (DC.) Burrill.
Synchytrium aureum Schrt.
Geum triflorum Pursh.
⎰Urocystis Gei Ell. & Ev.
⎱Urocystis Waldsteiniae Pk.

Geum turbinatum Rydb.
[Micropuccinia Sieversiae (Arth.) Arth. &
{ Jackson.
[Puccinia Sieversiae Arth.
Patinella Crandallii Sacc.
Geum virginianum L.
Septoria Gei Rob.
Sphaerotheca Humuli (DC.) Burrill. †
Synchytrium aureum Schrt.
Geum sp. indet.
Eurotium herbariorum (Wigg.) ex Lk.
[Puccinia simplex Pk.
{Puccinia solitaria Syd.
Ramularia Gei (Elias) v. Höhnel.
Dryas Drummondii Richards.?
Laestadia rhytismoides (B.) Sacc.
Dryas integrifolia Vahl.
[Carlia rhytismoides (B.) O. Kuntze.
{Hypospila rhytismoides (B.) Niessl.
[Laestadia rhytismoides (B.) Sacc.
[Macrophoma Dryadis (Allescher) Tassi.
{Phoma Dryadis Allescher.
Massarina Dryadis Rostr.
Melasmia Dryadis Rostr.
[Didymosphaeria Dryadis (Fckl.) Berl. & Vogl.
{Pleospora Dryadis Fckl.
Pleospora herbarum (Fr.) Rabh.
Pyrenophora Cerastii (Oud.) J. Lind.
Septoria semilunaris Johans.
Dryas octopetala L.
Didymosphaeria Dryadis (Fckl.) Berl. & Vogl.
[Carlia rhytismoides (B.) O. Kuntze.
{Laestadia rhytismoides (B.) Sacc.
Massarina Dryadis Rostr.
Melanomma Dryadis Johans.
Pleospora Dryadis Fckl.
Pleospora herbarum (Fr.) Rabh.
Sphaerella Dryadis Awd.
[Mycosphaerella ootheca (Sacc.) Stevenson.
{Sphaerella ootheca Sacc.
[Mycosphaerella pachyasca (Rostr.) Vestrg.
{Sphaerella pachyasca Rostr.
Stictis mollis P.
Cercocarpus betulifolius Nutt.
Gloeosporium Cercocarpi Ell. & Ev.
Glonium parvulum (Gerard) Sacc.
Hypoxylon rubiginosum (P.) ex Fr.
Hysterographium Mori (S.) Rehm.
Cercocarpus ledifolius Nutt.
Dothidea Cercocarpi Ell. & Ev.
Leptosphaeria Cercocarpi Syd.
Melaspilea emergens Rehm?
Cercocarpus montanus Raf.
Diatrype Standleyi Fairman.
Hysterographium Bakeri Earle.
Lophiotrema Cercocarpi Earle.
Schizostoma Cercocarpi Earle.
[Strickeria Cercocarpi Earle.
{Teichospora Cercocarpi (Earle) Sacc. & D. Sacc.

Cercocarpus parvifolius Nutt.
Gloeosporium Cercocarpi Ell. & Ev.
Cercocarpus sp. indet.
Fomes abramsianus Murrill.
Tryblidium occidentale Earle.
Adenostoma fasciculatum Hook. & Arn.
Eutypella domicalis Fairman.
Exidia recisa (Ditm.) ex Fr.
Hypoxylon californicum Ell. & Ev.
Hysterographium prominens (Phil. & Hark.)
Berl. & Vogl.
Patellea californica Rehm.
Polystigma Adenostomatis Farl.
Stereum heterosporum Burt.
Schizoxylon insigne (DeNot.) Bres.
Stereum hirsutum (Willd.) ex Fr.
Adenostoma sp. indet.
[Corticium cinereum P. ex Fr.
{Peniophora cinerea (P. ex Fr.) Cke.
Corticium scutellare B. & C.
Filipendula hexapetala Gilib.
Pezizella lanceolata, var. paraphysata Rehm.
Filipendula Ulmaria (L.) Maxim.
Hendersonia lirella Cke.
Septoria Ulmariae Oud.
Filipendula sp. indet.
Cylindrosporium Filipendulae Thm.
Alchemilla alpina L.
Sphaerella melanoplaca (Desm.) Awd.
Alchemilla pratensis F. W. Schmidt.
Coleroa Alchemillae (Grev.) Wint.
Trachyspora Alchemillae (P.) Fckl.
Alchemilla vulgaris L.
Coleroa Alchemillae (Grev.) Wint.
Laestadia Alchemillae Rostr.
Phoma herbarum Westd.
[Trachyspora Alchemillae (P.) Fckl.
{Uromyces intrusus (Grev.) Lév.
Venturia Alchemillae (Grev.) B. & Br.
Alchemilla sp. indet.
Uromyces Alchemillae (Fckl.) Lév.
Agrimonia gryposepala Wallr.
Peronospora Potentillae DBy.
Phyllosticta decidua Ell. & Kellerm.
Septoria Agrimoniae Roum.
Septoria Agrimoniae-Eupatorii Bomm. &
Rouss.
Sphaerotheca Humuli (DC.) Burrill. †

UREDINALES
[Caeoma (Uredo) Agrimoniae S.
|Coleosporium ochraceum Bon.
|Melampsora Agrimoniae (Diet.) Lagerh.
|Pucciniastrum Agrimoniae (Diet.) Tranz.
|Thecopsora Agrimoniae Diet.
|Uredo Agrimoniae (DC.) Schrt.
|Uredo Agrimoniae-Eupatoriae (DC.) Wint.
[Uredo Rosae S. Syn. Car.

Agrimonia incisa Torr. & Gr.
Agrimonia microcarpa Wallr.
  Pucciniastrum Agrimoniae (Diet.) Tranz.
Agrimonia mollis (Torr. & Gr.) Brit.
  Peronospora Potentillae DBy.
  {Caeoma Agrimoniae S.
  {Pucciniastrum Agrimoniae (Diet.) Tranz.
  {Uredo Agrimoniae (DC.) Schrt.
  Septoria Agrimoniae Roum.
  Septoria Agrimoniae-Eupatorii Bomm. & Rouss.
  Sphaerotheca Humuli (DC.) Burrill. †
  Uropyxis Agrimoniae Arth.
Agrimonia parviflora Ait.
  Peronospora Potentillae DBy.
  {Caeoma (Uredo) Agrimoniae S.
  {Coleosporium ochraceum Bon.
  {Pucciniastrum Agrimoniae (Diet.) Tranz.
  {Pucciniastrum Agrimoniae-Eupatorii Tranz.
  {Uredo Agrimoniae Schrt.
Agrimonia rostellata Wallr.
  Pucciniastrum Agrimoniae (Diet.) Tranz.
Agrimonia striata Michx.
  Leptosphaeria dumetorum Niessl.
  Peronospora Potentillae DBy.
  Phoma herbarum Westd.
  Phyllosticta decidua Ell. & Kellerm.
  {Caeoma Agrimoniae S.
  {Pucciniastrum Agrimoniae (Diet.) Tranz.
  {Uredo Agrimoniae Schrt.
  {Uredo Potentillae Rav. Fung. Car.
  Septoria Agrimoniae-Eupatorii Bomm. & Rouss.
  Sphaerotheca Humuli (DC.) Burrill. †
Sanguisorba canadensis L.
  Ovularia bulbigera (Fckl.) Sacc.
  Gloeosporium Sanguisorbae Fckl.
  Podosphaera Oxyacanthae (DC.) DBy.
  Sphaerotheca Humuli (DC.) Burrill. †
Sanguisorba latifolia Coville.
  Phragmidium minor (Arth.) Syd.
Sanguisorba microcephala Presl.
  {Phragmidium minor (Arth.) Syd.
  {Xenodochus minor Arth.
Sanguisorba minor Scop.
  Ovularia bulbigera (Fckl.) Sacc.
Polylepis sp. indet.
  Frommea Polylepidis Arth.
Acaena tridactyla Presl.
  {Phragmidium affine Syd.
  {Phragmidium Ivesiae Syd.
  {Uredo Acaenae Ell. & Ev.
Rosa acicularis L.
  {Phragmidium disciflorum (Tode) ex J. F. James.
  {Phragmidium Rosae-acicularis Liro.
  {Phragmidium Rosa-arkansanae Diet.
  {Phragmidium subcorticium Auct. Amer. p. p.
  {Uredo miniata Auct. Amer. p. p.

  Phragmidium montivagum Arth.
  {Ameris rosicola (Ell. & Ev.) Arth.
  {Uromyces rosicola Ell. & Ev.
Rosa aciculata (Cockerell) Rydb.
  Phragmidium montivagum Arth.
Rosa alba L.
  {Aregma disciflora Arth. p. p.
  {Phragmidium americanum Fung. Columb. 2745.
  {Phragmidium disciflorum (Tode) ex J. F. James.
Rosa arkansana Auct. non Porter. See Rosa pratincola Greene.
Rosa Bakeri Rydb.
  Phragmidium montivagum Arth.
Rosa blanda Ait.
  {Actinonema Rosae (Lib.) Fr.
  {Diplocarpon Rosae (S.) Wolf.
  Cercospora rosicola Pass.
  Hysterographium praelongum (S.) Ell. & Ev.
  {Phragmidium americanum Diet.
  {Phragmidium disciflorum J. J. Davis p. p.
  {Phragmidium mucronatum, var. americanum Pk.
  {Phragmidium Rosae-alpinae E. F. 36.
  {Phragmidium subcorticium Auct. Amer.
  Sphaeropsis Rosarum C. & E.
  Sphaerotheca pannosa (Wallr.) Lév.
  {Diatrype tristicha DeNot.
  {Valseutypella tristicha (DeNot.) v. Höhnel.
  Phragmidium montivagum Arth.
  Phragmidium Rosae-arkansanae Diet.
  {Earlea speciosa (Fr.) Arth.
  {Phragmidium speciosum (Fr.) Bon.
Rosa bourgeauiana Crépin.
  Phragmidium Rosae-acicularis Liro.
Rosa californica Cham. & Schl.
  {Actinonema Rosae (Lib.) Fr.
  {Asteroma Rosae Lib.
  Cercospora rosicola Pass.
  Diaporthe Rosae B. & C.
  Peronospora sparsa B.
  Phragmidium Rosae-californicae Diet.
Rosa canina L.
  Phragmidium disciflorum (Tode) ex J.F. James.
  Physalospora Cydoniae Arnaud.
Rosa carolina L.
  {Calosphaeria expers (S.) Ell. & Ev.
  {Sphaeria expers S.
  {Valsa expers (S.) Cke.
  Cenangium Rosae S.
  Cercospora rosicola Pass.
  Cytospora Rosae S. Am. Bor.
  Dacryomyces difformis S.
  Phoma rhodophila Sacc.
  Phragmidium americanum Diet.
  {Aregma disciflorum Arth. p. p.
  {Phragmidium Rosae-setigerae Diet.
  {?Phragmidium subcorticium Auct. Amer. p. p.

Rosa carolina (*cont.*)

{ Aregma speciosa Fr.
Earlea speciosa (Fr.) Arth.
Phragmidium speciosum (Fr.) Bon.

Phyllachora Rosae (S.) Sacc.

{ Pseudovalsa convergens (Tode ex Fr.) Sacc.
Sphaeria convergens (Tode) ex Fr.
Valsa convergens (Tode) ex Fr.

Sphaeria palliolata S.

Sphaerotheca pannosa (Wallr.) Lév.

Valsa ambiens (P.) ex Fr.

Rosa chrysocarpa Rydb.

Phragmidium Rosae-californicae Diet.

Rosa cinnamomea L.

Cercospora rosicola Pass.

Diaporthe simulans Sacc.

Phragmidium subcorticium Auct. Amer. p. p.

Rosa damascena Mill.

Phragmidium disciflorum (Tode) ex J. F. James.

Rosa Eglanteria L.

{ Phragmidium disciflorum Fung. Columb. *3643*.
Phragmidium Rosae-pimpinellifoliae Diet.
?Phragmidium subcorticium Auct. Amer. p. p.

Rosa Fendleri Crépin.

Actinonema Rosae (Lib.) Fr.

Phragmidium montivagum Arth.

Phragmidium Rosae-arkansanae Diet.

{ Earlea speciosa (Fr.) Arth.
Phragmidium speciosum Fr.
Phragmidium subcorticium Auct. Amer. p. p. I.

Uromyces rosicola Ell. & Ev.

Rosa foliosa Leman.

{ Earlea speciosa (Fr.) Arth.
Phragmidium speciosum (Fr.) Bon.

Rosa gallica L.

Olpitrichum macrosporum (Farl.) Sumstine.

Phragmidium disciflorum (Tode) ex J. F. James.

Rosa glauca Pourr.

Phragmidium speciosum (Fr.) Bon.

Rosa grosseserrata E. Nels.

Phragmidium montivagum Arth.

Rosa gymnocarpa Nutt.

Actinonema Rosae (Lib.) Fr.

{ Caeoma Rosae-gymnocarpae Diet.
Gymnoconia Rosae-gymnocarpae Arth.
Kunkelia Rosae-gymnocarpae Arth.

Phragmidium Rosae-californicae Diet.

{ Phragmidium montivagum Arth.
?Phragmidium subcorticium Auct. Amer. p. p.

Phragmidium Rosae-acicularis Liro.

{ Earlea speciosa (Fr.) Arth.
Phragmidium speciosum (Fr.) Bon.

Phyllactinia corylea (P.) ex Karst.

Rosa hemisphaerica Herrm.

Phragmidium Rosae-acicularis Liro.

Phragmidium Rosae-pimpinellifoliae Diet.

Phragmidium subcorticium Wint.

Rosa hugonis Hemsl.

Sphaeronemella Rosae Ell. & Ev.

Rosa humilis Marsh.

{ Actinonema Rosae (Lib.) Fr.
Diplocarpon Rosae (S.) Wolf.

Cercospora rosicola Pass., var. undosa J. J. Davis.

Phyllosticta Rosae Desm.

Sphaerotheca pannosa (Wallr.) Lév.

UREDINALES

Phragmidium americanum Diet.

{ Aregma disciflora Arth. p. p.
Phragmidium disciflorum (Tode) ex J. F. James.
Phragmidium subcorticium Auct. Amer. p. p.

{ Aregma speciosa Fr.
Earlea speciosa (Fr.) Arth.
Phragmidium speciosum (Fr.) Bon.
Uredo miniata Auct. Amer .p. p.

Rosa laevigata Michx.

{ Cryptosphaeria inordinata (B. & C.) Sacc.
Sphaeria inordinata B. & C.

Rosa Macdougali Holz.

Phragmidium Rosae-acicularis Liro.

Rosa Macounii Greene.

Phragmidium montivagum Arth.

{ Earlea speciosa (Fr.) Arth.
Phragmidium speciosum (Fr.) Bon.

Rosa manca Greene.

Phragmidium montivagum Arth.

Rosa melina Greene.

Phragmidium speciosum (Fr.) Bon.

Rosa minutifolia Parry.

Phragmidium Rosae-californicae Diet.

Rosa multifida Hort.

{ Phragmidium americanum Diet.
Phragmidium subcorticium Fung. Columb. *2132*.

Rosa multiflora Thunb.

Sphaerotheca pannosa (Wallr.) Lév.

Rosa neomexicana Cockerell.

Phragmidium montivagum Arth.

Rosa nitida Willd.

Cercospora rosicola Pass.

{ Aregma speciosum Fr.
Phragmidium speciosum (Fr.) Bon.

Rosa nutkana Presl.

Phragmidium Rosae-acicularis Liro.

Phragmidium Rosae-californicae Diet.

{ Phragmidium montivagum Arth.
Phragmidium subcorticium Auct. Amer. p. p.

Rosa parviflora Ehrh.

Phragmidium disciflorum (Tode) ex J. F. James.

Phragmidium speciosum (Fr.) Bon.

Rosa pecosensis Cockerell.

{ Earlea speciosa (Fr.) Arth.
Phragmidium speciosum (Fr.) Bon.

Rosa pilifera Rydb.
Phragmidium Rosae-californicae Diet.

Rosa pisocarpa Gray.
Phragmidium montivagum Arth.
Phragmidium Rosae-acicularis Liro.
Phragmidium Rosae-californicae Diet.
{ Earlea speciosa (Fr.) Arth.
{ Phragmidium speciosum Fr.
Phyllactinia corylea (P.) ex Karst.

Rosa pratincola Greene.
Actinonema Rosae (Lib.) Fr.
Cercospora rosicola Pass.
Phoma sepincola (Kickx) Sacc.
Sphaerotheca Humuli (DC.) Burrill. †
{ Oidium leucoconium Auct.
{ Sphaerotheca pannosa Auct.
Trimmatostroma Brencklei Sacc.
Valsa ambiens (P.) ex Fr., var. Rosae Rehm.

UREDINALES

{ Phragmidium americanum Syd. Ured. *2282*.
{ Phragmidium Rosae-acicularis Liro.
{ Phragmidium mucronatum Auct. Amer. p. p.
{ Phragmidium Rosae-arkansanae Diet.
{ Phragmidium tuberculatum Carl. Ured. *15*.
{ Caeoma miniata West. Am. Fung. *12b*.
{ Earlea speciosa (Fr.) Arth.
{ Phragmidium speciosum (Fr.) Bon.

Rosa puberulenta Rydb.

Rosa pyrifera Rydb.
Phragmidium montivagum Arth.

Rosa rubiginosa L.
{ Actinonema Rosae (Lib.) Fr.
{ Asteroma Rosae Lib.
{ Diplocarpon Rosae (S.) Wolf.
{ Dothidea Rosae S.
{ Phyllachora Rosae (S.) Sacc.
Phragmidium montivagum Arth.
{ Phragmidium Rosae-pimpinellifoliae Diet.
{ Phragmidium subcorticium Fung. Columb.
{   *2545*.)
Phragmidium Rosae-setigerae Diet.
{ Physalospora rhodina (B. & C.) Cke.
{ Sphaeria rhodina B. & C.
{ Laestadia spinicola (Ell. & Ev.) Sacc.
{ Sphaerella spinicola Ell. & Ev.
Stictis glaucoma B. & C.

Rosa rugosa Thunb.
Cephalothecium roseum Cda.
{ Hainesia Lythri (Desm.) v. Höhnel.
{ Sclerotiopsis concava (Desm.) Shear & Dodge.
Phragmidium disciflorum (Tode) ex James.
Phragmidium Rosae-acicularis Liro.
{ Earlea speciosa (Fr.) Arth.
{ Phragmidium speciosum Fr.
Schizoparme straminea Shear.
Sphaerotheca Humuli (DC.) Burrill. †
Sphaerotheca pannosa (Wallr.) Lév.

Rosa Sayi S.
{ Phragmidium americanum (Pk.) Diet.
{ Phragmidium mucronatum, var. Americanum
{   Pk.
{ Phragmidium montivagum Arth.
{ Phragmidium subcorticium Auct. Amer. p. p.
Phragmidium Rosae-acicularis Liro.
{ Earlea speciosa (Fr.) Arth.
{ Phragmidium speciosum Fr.

Rosa setigera Michx.
Cercospora rosicola Pass.
{ Diaporthe umbrina A. E. Jenkins.
{ Myxosporium Rosae Sheldon an Fckl.
Diplocarpon Rosae Wolf.
{ ?Aregma disciflorum Arth. p. p.
{ Phragmidium Rosae-setigerae Diet.
{ Phragmidium subcorticium Auct. Amer. p. p.
Phragmidium speciosum Fr.
{ Phragmidium Rosae-setigerae Diet.
{ Phragmidium speciosum Fung. Columb. *2544*.
Phyllosticta rosae Desm.

Rosa setipoda Hemsl. & E. H. Nils.
{ Apiospora rhodophila Sacc.
{ Apiosporella rhodophila (Sacc.) Petrak.
Botryosphaeria Ribis (Tode ex Fr.) Grossen-
  bacher & Duggar.
Botryosphaeria Ribis (Tode ex Fr.) Grossen-
  bacher & Duggar, var. chromogena Shear
  et al.

Rosa sonomensis Greene.
Phragmidium Rosae-californicae Diet.

Rosa spinosissima L.
{ Phragmidium Rosae-pimpinellifoliae Diet.
{ Phragmidium subcorticium Auct. Amer. p.p.

Rosa subnuda Lunell.
{ Diatrype tristicha De Not.
{ Valseutypella tristicha (De Not.) v. Höhnel.
Pezicula Rosae Sacc.
Phragmidium Rosae-arkansanae Diet.

Rosa suffulta Greene.
Phragmidium Rosae-acicularis Liro.

Rosa Underwoodii Rydb.
Phragmidium montivagum Arth.

Rosa virginiana L.
Phragmidium americanum Diet.
Phragmidium mucronatum, var. americanum
  Pk.
{ Phragmidium disciflorum Auct. Amer. p. p.
{ Phragmidium Rosae-arkansanae Diet.
{ Phragmidium subcorticium Myc. Exch. *50d*.
{ Earlea speciosa (Fr.) Arth.
{ Phragmidium speciosum (Fr.) Bon.
{ Seiridium marginatum S.
{ Phoma Ellisii Jacz.
{ Sphaeronemella Rosae Ell. & Ev.
Sphaerotheca Humuli (DC.) Burrill. †
Sphaerotheca pannosa (Wallr.) Lév.

Rosa Woodsii Lindl.
  Phragmidium montivagum Arth.
  Phragmidium Rosae-arkansanae Diet.
  ⎰Earlea speciosa (Fr.) Arth.
  ⎱Phragmidium speciosum (Fr.) Bon.
  Pleosphaerulina corticola (Fckl.) Rehm, var.
    Rosae Rehm.
  Rosellinia Rosarum Niessl.
  Sphaerotheca Humuli (DC.) Burrill. †
  Sphaerotheca pannosa (Wallr.) Lév.

Rosa sp. indet.
                PHYCOMYCETES
  ⎰Leptothyrium chromospermum Pk.
  ⎱Pilobolus crystallinus (Wigg.) Tode. †
  Pilobolus Oedipus Mont.

                PEZIZINEAE
  ⎰Peziza Rosae P.
  ⎱Tapesia Rosae (P.) Fckl.
  ⎰Peziza Curtisii Cke.
  ⎱Peziza umbilicata B. & C.
  ⎱Trichopeziza umbilicata (B. & C.) Sacc.

                PERISPORIALES
  Perisporium speireum Fr.
  Sphaerella gallae Ell. & Ev.
  ⎰Sphaerotheca Humuli (DC.) Burrill. †
  ⎱Sphaerotheca pannosa E. F. *131a*.
  Sphaerotheca Humuli (DC.) Burrill, var. fuli-
    ginea (Schl.) Salmon.
  ⎰Erysiphe pannosa Lév.
  ⎱Microsphaera pannosa Auct.
  ⎱Sphaerotheca pannosa (Wallr.) Lév.
  Sphaerotheca pannosa (Wallr.) Lév., var.
    Rosae Wor.
  Sphaerotheca pruinosa C. & P.

                SPHAERIALES
  Botryosphaeria dothidea Ces. & De Not.
  ⎰Clypeosphaeria Notarisii Fckl.
  ⎱Sphaeria clypeata Nees.
  ⎰Cryptosphaeria fissicola (C. & E.) Sacc.
  ⎱Sphaeria fissicola C. & E.
  Cucurbitaria Rosae Wint. & Sacc.
  Diaporthe exiguestroma Dearness.
  Diaporthe gallophila Ell.
  Diaporthe oligocarpoides Rehm.
  ⎰Diaporthe rostellata (Fr.) Nits.
  ⎱Sphaeria rostellata Fr.
  Diatrype incarcerata B. & Br.
  Didymella nigrificans Karst.
  ⎰Didymella Rauii (Ell. & Ev.) Sacc.
  ⎱Endophlaea Rauii (Ell. & Ev.) Cke.
  ⎱Sphaeria Rauii Ell. & Ev.
  Hypoxylon epirhodium E. & Rav.
  Leptosphaeria Coniothyrium (Fckl.) Sacc.
  Leptosphaeria fuscella (B. & Br.) Ces. & De
    Not.
  ⎰Lophiostoma auctum Sacc.
  ⎱Lophiotrema auctum Sacc.

  ⎰Endophlaea brachytheca (B. & C.) Cke.
  ⎱Metasphaeria brachytheca (B. & C.) Sacc.
  ⎱Sphaeria brachytheca B. & C.
  ⎰Endophlaea leiostega (Ell.) Cke.
  ⎱Metasphaeria leiostega (Ell.) Sacc.
  ⎱Sphaeria leiostega Ell.
  Metasphaeria Macounii Dearness.
  Phaeotrype Brencklei Sacc.
  Phomatospora Rosae Rehm.
  Physalospora Cydoniae Arnaud.
  ⎰Physalospora erratica (C. & E.) Sacc.
  ⎱Sphaeria erratica C. & E.
  ⎰Physalospora Malorum Shear et al.
  ⎱Sphaeropsis Malorum Pk.
  ⎰Mycosphaerella rosigena (Ell. & Ev.) Lindau.
  ⎱Sphaerella rosigena Ell. & Ev.
  Sphaeria fissa P.?
  Sphaeria Rosae S.
  Sphaeria saepincola Fr.
  Sphaerulina corticola (Fckl.) Rehm.
  Valsa leucostoma (P.) ex Fr.
  Valsa Rosarum De Not.
  ⎰?Sphaeria subclypeata B. & C.
  ⎱Valsa subclypeata (B. & C.) C. & P.

                BASIDIOMYCETES
  Corticium Rosae Burt.
  Corticium Stevensii Burt.
  Fomes Ribis (Schum. ex Fr.) Cke.
  Pyropolyporus Ribis (Schum. ex Fr.) Murrill.
  ⎰Caeoma (Peridermium) germinale Auct. p. p.
  ⎱Coleosporium pingue Auct. Amer.
  ⎱Phragmidium sp. indet.

                SPHAEROPSIDALES
  Asteroma geographicum (DC. ex Fr.) Desm.
  Asteroma punctiforme B.
  ⎰Coniothyrium Fuckelii Sacc.
  ⎱Leptosphaeria Coniothyrium (Fckl.) Sacc.
  Coniothyrium pyrinum (Sacc.) Sheldon.
  Coniothyrium Rosarum Cke. & Hark.
  Coniothyrium Wernsdorffiae Laubert.
  ⎰Diplodia rhodocarpa Sacc.
  ⎱Diplodia rosicarpa Cke.
  ⎱Diplodia Rosae B. & C.
  ⎱Microdiplodia Rosae (B. & C.) Tassi.
  Discosia Artocreas (Tode) ex Fr.
  Hendersonia hypocarpa Fairman.
  ⎰Hendersonia longipes B. & C., var. Rosarum
  ⎰ Cke.
  ⎱Hendersonia Rosae Kickx.
  Leptothyrium Rosarum Cke.
  Phoma rhodocarpa Sacc.
  Phyllosticta erratica Ell. & Ev.
  Phyllosticta rosicola Massal.
  Septoria Rosae Desm.
  Septoria Rosae-arvensis Sacc.
  Sphaeropsis rhodocarpa Fairman.
  ⎰Sphaeria Rosae S. p. p.
  ⎱Sphaeropsis Rosarum C. & E.

Rosa sp. indet. (*cont.*)

MELANCONIALES

Coryneum microstictum B. & Br.
Dicoccum (Marssonia) Rosae Bon.
{ Gloeosporium Rosae Halsted.
{ Glomerella cincta (Stoneman) Spaulding & v.
    Schrenk.
Marssonia Rosae (Lib.) Trail.
{ Naemaspora erythraea B. & C.
{ Naemaspora erythrella B. & C.
Pestalozzia compacta Sacc.
Pestalozzia discosioides Ell. & Ev.
Pestalozzia foliorum Ell. & Ev., var. Rosa
    Ell. & Ev.
Pestalozzia Guepini Desm.
Pestalozzia Rosae Westd.
Pestalozzia suffocata Ell. & Ev.

HYPHOMYCETES

Botrytis cinerea P. †
Polyactis vulgaris Lk.
Cercospora rosigena Tharp.
Cladosporium fuscum Lk.
Coniosporium limoniforme Syd.
Cylindrocladium parvum P. J. Anderson.
{ Cylindrocladium scoparium Morg.
{ Diplocladium cylindrosporum Ell. & Ev.
Heydenia americana Sacc & Ell.
Macrosporium Cheiranthi (Lib.) Fr.
Ramularia macrospora Fres.
Sporotrichum elaeochroum Fr.
Stysanus Stemonitis (P.) Cda.

MISCELLANEA

Ozonium omnivorum Shear.
Nuttallia cerasiformis Torr. & Gr.
{ Cylindrosporium conservans Pk.
{ Cylindrosporium Nuttallii (Hark.) Dearness.
{ Gloeosporium Nuttallii (Hark.) Ell. & Ev.
{ Septogloeum Nuttallii Hark.
Diaporthe columbiensis Ell. & Ev.
Diplodia Nuttalliae Dearness.
Gloeosporium Osmaroniae Dearness.
Nectria subcoccinea Sacc. & Ell.
Nuttallia pumila (Nutt.) Greene.
Dicaeoma Sarcobati Arth. I.
Nuttallia Rusbyi Rydb.
Leptosphaeria dumetorum Niessl.
Dicaeoma Sarcobati Arth. I.

Prunus americana Marshall.

EXOASCACEAE

Exoascus Cerasi (Fckl.) Sadebeck.
{ Ascomyces Pruni Auct. Amer.
{ Exoascus communis Sadebeck.
{ Exoascus Pruni Auct. Amer. p. p.
{ Taphrina communis (Sadebeck) Giesenhagen.
{ Taphrina Pruni Auct. Amer p. p.
{ Exoascus decipiens Atk.
{ Taphrina decipiens (Atk.) Giesenhagen.

{ Exoascus decipiens Atk., var. superficialis Atk
{ Taphrina decipiens (Atk.) Giesenhagen, var
{   superficialis (Atk.) Giesenhagen.
Exoascus deformans Fckl.
{ Exoascus longipes Atk.
{ Taphrina longipes (Atk.) Giesenhagen.
{ Exoascus mirabilis Atk.
{ Taphrina mirabilis (Atk.) Giesenhagen.
Exoascus mirabilis, var. tortilis Atk.
{ Exoascus Pruni Fckl.
{ Taphrina Pruni (Fckl.) Tul.

PEZIZINEAE

Cenangium prunastri (P.) Fr.

PHACIDIINEAE

Coccomyces hiemalis Higgins.
Coccomyces prunophorae Higgins.

HYSTERIINEAE

{ Gloniopsis stictoidea (Lk.) Sacc.
{ Hysterium stictoideum C. & E.

PYRENOMYCETINEAE

Calosphaeria princeps Tul.
Cryptospora pennsylvanica (B. & C.) Ell. &
    Ev.
Diatrype tumida Ell. & Ev., var. Pruni Rehm.
Eutypa lata (P. ex Fr.) Tul.
Eutypella microsperma Kalchbr. & Malbr.
{ Eutypella prunastri (P. ex Fr.) Sacc.
{ Valsa prunastri (P.) ex Fr.
Hypoxylon commutatum Nits.
Lophiostoma Pruni Ell. & Ev.
Massaria conspurcata (Wallr.) Sacc.
{ Cucurbitaria morbosa (S.) Ell.
{ Dibotryon morbosum (S.) Theissen & Syd.
{ Gibbera morbosa (S.) Cke.
{ Otthia morbosa (S.) Cke.
{ Plowrightia morbosa (S.) Sacc.
{ Sphaeria morbosa S.
{ Enslinia Schweinitzii Cke.
{ Sphaeria intermedia S.
Sphaeria rhytostoma Fr.
Teichospora Pruni-americanae Rehm.
Valsa americana B. & C.
Valsa leucostoma (P.) ex Fr.

PERISPORIALES

Capnodium pelliculosum B. & Rav.
Phyllactinia corylea (P.) ex Karst
{ Podosphaera Oxyacanthae (DC.) DBy. †
{ Podosphaera tridactyla (Wallr.) DBy.

UREDINALES

{ Puccinia Pruni DC.
{ Puccinia Pruni-spinosae P.
{ Puccinia Prunorum Lk.
{ Tranzschelia punctata Arth.
{ Uromyces Prunorum Fckl.

Prunus americana (*cont.*)

POLYPORACEAE
{ Fomes fulvus (Scop. ex Fr.) Gill.
Pyropolyporus fulvus (Scop. ex Fr.) Murrill.
{ Fomes igniarius (L. ex Fr.) Gill.
Polyporus igniarius L. ex Fr.
{ Pyropolyporus igniarius (L. ex Fr.) Murrill.
Fomes pomaceus (P. ex Fr.) Lloyd.
{ Irpex lacteus Fr.
{ Irpex sinuosus Fr.
Polyporus gilvus S.
Polystictus hirsutus (Wulf.) ex Fr.
{ Coriolus prolificans (Fr.) Murrill.
{ Polystictus pargamenus Fr.
Polystictus versicolor (L.) ex Fr.
Poria laminata (Murrill) Sacc. & Trott.

SPHAEROPSIDALES
{ Cornicularia Persicae (S.) Sacc.
{ Sphaeronema Persicae (S.) Ell.
{ Micropera spuria (Fr.) v. Höhnel.
{ Sphaeronema spuria (Fr.) Sacc.
Phyllosticta circumscissa Cke.
{ Phyllosticta destruens Desm.
{ Phyllosticta virginiana (Ell. & Halsted) Tassi.
Septoria cerasina Pk.
Septoria Pruni Ell.
Septoria purpureocincta Ell. & Ev.
Sphaeropsis Peckii Sacc.

MELANCONIALES
Cylindrosporium Padi Karst.
Melanconium effusum Lk.

HYPHOMYCETES
Cercospora circumscissa Sacc.
Cercospora Persicae Sacc.
Cercospora prunicola Ell. & Ev.
Cladosporium carpophilum Thm.
Dematium fimbriatum S.
Fusicladium cerasi (Rabh.) Sacc.
{ Monilia cinerea Auct. Amer.
Monilia fructigena Auct. Amer.
Sclerotinia americana (Wormald) Norton &
  Ezekiel.
{ Sclerotinia cinerea Auct. Amer.
Sclerotinia cinerea, var. americana Wormald.
Sclerotinia fructicola (Wint.) Rehm.
Sclerotinia fructigena Auct. Amer.
{ Knyaria fatiscens (S.) O. Kuntze.
{ Tubercularia fatiscens S.

Prunus angustifolia Marsh.

EXOASCACEAE
Taphrina deformans (B.) Tul.
{ Exoascus mirabilis Atk.
{ Taphrina mirabilis (Atk.) Giesenhagen.
{ Taphrina Pruni Gall.
Exoascus mirabilis Atk., var. tortilis Atk.
{ Exoascus Pruni Fckl.
{ Taphrina Pruni (Fckl.) Tul.

PYRENOMYCETINEAE
Capnodium pelliculosum B. & Rav.
{ Cucurbitaria morbosa (S.) Ell.
{ Plowrightia morbosa (S.) Sacc.
{ Sphaeria morbosa S.
Podosphaera Oxyacanthae (DC.) DBy. †

UREDINALES
{ Puccinia Pruni DC.
{ Puccinia Pruni-spinosae P.
{ Tranzschelia punctata Arth.
{ Uromyces Prunorum Fckl.

POLYPORACEAE
Fomes supinus S.
Polyporus supinus Sw. sec. Fr.

FUNGI IMPERFECTI
Cladosporium carpophilum Thm.
Cylindrosporium Padi Karst.

Prunus armeniaca L.

PHYCOMYCETES
Pythiacystis citrophthora Sm. & Sm.

HELOTIACEAE
{ Sclerotinia cinerea Auct. Amer.
{ Sclerotinia fructicola (Wint.) Rehm.
{ Sclerotinia libertiana Fckl.
{ Sclerotinia sclerotiorum (Lib.) Schrt.

HYPOCREALES
Nectria coccinea (P.) Fr.

PYRENOMYCETINEAE
Physalospora Cydoniae Arnaud?
Plowrightia morbosa (S.) Sacc.
Rosellinia pulveracea (Ehrh. ex Fr.) Fckl., var.
  microspora Sacc.
{ Cytospora rubescens Nits.
{ Valsa leucostoma (P.) ex Fr.
Valsa leucostoma (P.) ex Fr., var. rubescens
  F. M. Rolfs.

UREDINALES
{ Puccinia Pruni DC.
{ Puccinia Pruni-spinosae P.
{ Tranzschelia punctata Arth.

HYMENOMYCETINEAE
Armillaria mellea (Vahl) ex Fr.
Irpex lacteus Fr.
Ozonium omnivorum Shear.
Stereum purpureum P. †

SPHAEROPSIDALES
Cytospora eutypelloides Sacc.
Diplodia Amygdali Cke. & Hark.
Phyllosticta circumscissa Cke.
Phyllosticta prunicola Sacc.
Septoria cerasina Pk.
Septoria Pruni Ell.

Prunus armeniaca (*cont.*)

MELANCONIALES

Coryneum Beyerinckii Oud.
Cylindrosporium Padi Auct.
Monochaetia rosenwaldia A. Khazanoff.

HYPHOMYCETES

Botrytis cinerea P. †
Cladosporium carpophilum Thm.
Clasterosporium carpophilum (Lév.) Aderh.
⎧Monilia fructigena Auct. Amer.
⎪Sclerotinia americana (Wormald) Norton &
⎪   Ezekiel.
⎨Sclerotinia cinerea Schrt. ?
⎪Sclerotinia fructicola (Wint.) Rehm.
⎩Sclerotinia fructigena Auct. Amer.
Verticillium [innominatum] Czarnecki.

Prunus avium L.

Alternaria Citri Pierce, var. Cerasi B. A.
    Rudolph.
Armillaria mellea (Vahl) ex Fr.
Cercospora cerasella Sacc.
Cercospora circumscissa Sacc.
Coryneum Beyerinckii Oud.
⎧Coccomyces hiemalis Higgins.
⎨Cylindrosporium hiemalis Higgins.
⎩Cylindrosporium Padi Auct. Amer. p. p.
Cylindrosporium Padi Karst.?
Dermatea Cerasi (P.) Fr.
Exoascus Cerasi (Fckl.) Sadebeck.
Exoascus communis Sadebeck.
Exoascus Pruni Fckl.
Fomes applanatus (P. ex Wallr.) Gill.
Gloeophyllum hirsutum (Schaeff.) ex Murrill.
Micropera Drupacearum Lév.
Phlebia merismoides Fr.
Physalospora Cydoniae Arnaud.?
Physalospora Malorum Shear et al
Plowrightia morbosa (S.) Sacc.
Podosphaera Oxyacanthae (DC.) DBy. †
Polyporus lacteus Fr.
⎧Puccinia Pruni-spinosae P.
⎨Tranzschelia punctata Arth.
⎧Sclerotinia cinerea Auct. Amer.
⎨Sclerotinia fructicola (Wint.) Rehm.
⎩Sclerotinia fructigena Auct. Amer.

Prunus Besseyi L. H. Bailey.

Exoascus deformans Fckl.
Exoascus Pruni Fckl.
Plowrightia morbosa (S.) Sacc.
Podosphaera Oxyacanthae (DC.) DBy. †
⎧Puccinia Pruni DC.
⎨Tranzschelia punctata Arth.
⎧Sclerotinia cinerea Auct. Amer.
⎨Sclerotinia fructigena Auct. Amer.
Valsella Laschii Nits.

Prunus Capollin Zucc.

Taphrina Reichei Auct.

Prunus caroliniana Ait.

⎧Asteroma Cerasi Cke.
⎨Asteroma cerasicola Sacc.
Ceuthospora Cookei Thm.
⎧Cytospora leucophthalma B. & C.
⎨Cytospora nivosa B. & C.
Diplodia natalensis Evans.
Discosia Artocreas (Tode) ex Fr.
Phyllachora Beaumontii (B. & C.) Cke.
Septoria Ravenelii Thm.
Sphaerella lenticula Cke.

Prunus cerasifera Ehrh.

Tranzschelia punctata Arth.

Prunus Cerasus L.

EXOASCACEAE

⎧Taphrina Cerasi (Fckl.) Sadeb. 1891.
⎨Exoascus Cerasi (Fckl.) Sacc. 1892.
⎩Exoascus Cerasi (Fckl.) Sadeb. 1893.
Exoascus communis Sadebeck.

PEZIZINEAE

⎧Cenangium Cerasi (P.) Fr.
⎨Dermatea Cerasi (P.) Fr.

PHACIDIINEAE

Coccomyces hiemalis Higgins.

PERISPORIALES

⎧?Podosphaera Cerasi Pk. an Lév.
⎪Podosphaera Kunzei Lév.
⎨Podosphaera Oxyacanthae (DC.) DBy. †
⎪Podosphaera tridactyla (Wallr.) DBy.
⎪Podosphaera Oxyacanthae (DC.) DBy., var.
⎩   tridactyla (Wallr.) Salmon.

SPHAERIALES

Amphisphaeria apiosporoides Rehm.
Botryosphaeria Cerasi (C. & E.) Sacc.
Calosphaeria princeps Tul.
Hypoxylon multiforme Fr.
⎧Plowrightia morbosa (S.) Sacc.
⎨Sphaeria morbosa S.
Sphaerella cinerascens Fckl.
Sphaeria varia P.
Teichospora interstitialis (C. & P.) Sacc.
Valsa leucostoma (P.) ex Fr.

BASIDIOMYCETES

⎧Cerrena unicolor (Bull. ex Fr.) Murrill.
⎨Daedalea unicolor (Bull.) ex Fr.
⎧Irpex Tulipiferae S.
⎨Irpiciporus Tulipiferae (S.) Murrill.
Phlebia radiata Fr.
Polyporus cinnabarinus (Jacq.) ex Fr.
Polyporus sulfureus (Bull.) ex Fr.
⎧Coriolus versicolor (L. ex Fr.) Quél.
⎨Polystictus versicolor (L.) ex Fr.
Puccinia Pruni DC.

Prunus Cerasus (*cont.*)

FUNGI IMPERFECTI

Cercospora cerasella Sacc.
Cercospora circumscissa Sacc.
Cladosporium carpophilum Thm.
{ Cornularia Persicae (S.) Sacc.
{ Sphaeronema Persicae (S.) Ell.
{ Sporocybe Persicae (S.) Fr.
{ Coccomyces hiemalis Higgins.
{ Cylindrosporium hiemale Higgins.
Cylindrosporium Padi Karst.
Cytospora cincta Sacc.
Cytosporina ludibunda Sacc.
Fumago vagans Fr.
Fusicladium Cerasi (Rabh.) Sacc.
Micropera Drupacearum Lév.
Micropera rubida B. & C.
{ Monilia fructigena Auct. Amer.
{ Sclerotinia cinerea Auct. Amer.
{ Sclerotinia fructicola (Wint.) Rehm.
{ Sclerotinia fructigena Auct. Amer.
Penicillium glaucum Lk.
Phyllosticta prunicola Sacc.
Septoria cerasina Pk.

Prunus communis (L.) Fritsch.

Armillaria mellea (Vahl) ex Fr.
Botryosphaeria Ribis (Tode ex Fr.) Grossen-
    bacher & Duggar.
Cercospora circumscissa Sacc.
Cladosporium carpophilum Thm.
Coryneum Beyerinckii Oud.
Cyphella marginata McAlpine.
Diplodia Pruni Fckl.
Fumago salicina Tul.
Gloeosporium amygdalinum Brizi.
Phoma ramealis Desm.
Physalospora Malorum Shear et al.
{ Puccinia Pruni DC.
{ Puccinia Pruni-spinosae P.
{ Tranzschelia punctata Arth.
{ Uredo Castagnei Rav. Fung. Car.
Pythiacystis citrophthora Sm. & Sm.
{ Sclerotinia cinerea Auct. Amer.
{ Sclerotinia fructicola (Wint.) Rehm.
Trichopeltis (?) reptans (B. & C.) Speg.
Valsa leucostoma (P.) ex Fr.

Prunus cuneata Raf.

Cylindrosporium hiemale Higgins.
Exoascus communis Sadebeck.
Harpographium magnum Sacc.
{ Puccinia Pruni-spinosae P.
{ Tranzschelia punctata Arth.

Prunus demissa (Nutt.) Walp.

{ Cercospora Cerasae Duggar.
{ Cercospora cerasella Sacc.
Coccomyces lutescens Higgins.
Corticium evolvens Fr.

{ Cylindrosporium Nuttallii (Hark.) Dearness.
{ Septogloeum Nuttallii Hark.
Cylindrosporium Padi Karst.
Cytospora chrysosperma (P.) ex Fr.
{ Diplodia Pruni Ell. & Barthol.
{ Diplodina Pruni Ell. & Barthol.
{ Diplodinula Pruni (Ell. & Barthol.) Tassi.
Fomes igniarius (L. ex Fr.) Gill.
Lenzites sepiaria (Wulf.) ex Fr.
Lenzites trabea (P.) ex Fr.
Lophiostoma acervatum Karst.
Melanconium cerasinum Pk.
Merulius Corium (P.) Fr.
Phyllactinia corylea (P.) ex Karst.
Phyllosticta circumscissa Cke.
{ Phoma virginiana Ell. & Halsted.
{ Phyllosticta destruens Desm.
{ Phyllosticta virginica Ell. & Ev.
Phyllosticta prunicola Sacc.
{ Otthia morbosa (S.) Cke.
{ Plowrightia morbosa (S.) Sacc.
{ Podosphaera Kunzei Lév.
{ Podosphaera Oxyacanthae (DC.) DBy. †
{ Podosphaera tridactyla (Wallr.) DBy.
Septoria Pruni Ell.
{ Exoascus Cerasi Patterson p. p.
{ Exoascus varius Atk.
{ Taphrina Farlowii Sadebeck.
{ Nectria cinnabarina (Tode) ex Fr.
{ Tubercularia vulgaris Tode ex Fr.
Valsa Auerswaldii Nits.
Valsa leucostoma (P.) ex Fr.

Prunus domestica L.

See also Prunus (prune).

ASCOMYCETES

Coccomyces hiemalis Higgins.
Coccomyces prunophorae Higgins.
Eutypella prunastri (P. ex Fr.) Sacc.
Eutypella scoparia Ell. & Ev.
Exoascus communis Sadebeck.
Physalospora Cydoniae Arnaud.
{ Dibotryon morbosum (S.) Theissen & Syd.
{ Otthia morbosa (S.) Cke.
{ Plowrightia morbosa (S.) Sacc.
{ Sphaeria morbosa S.
Podosphaera Oxyacanthae (DC.) DBy. †
Taphrina mirabilis Atk.
{ Exoascus Pruni Fckl.
{ Taphrina Pruni (Fckl.) Tul.

BASIDIOMYCETES

Armillaria mellea (Vahl) ex Fr.
Fomes pomaceus (P.) Lloyd.
{ Puccinia Pruni DC.
{ Puccinia Pruni-spinosae P.
{ Puccinia Prunorum Lk.
{ Tranzschelia punctata Arth.

Prunus domestica (*cont.*)

FUNGI IMPERFECTI

Alternaria Citri Pierce, var. Cerasi B. A.
  Rudolph.
Aposphaeria putaminum (Speg.) Sacc.
Aspergillus ovalispermus Lk.
Cercospora circumscissa Sacc.
Cladosporium carpophilum Thm.
Coryneum Beyerinckii Oud.
Cylindrosporium Padi Karst.
{ Coccomyces Prunophorae Higgins.
{ Cylindrosporium Prunophorae Higgins.
Cytospora leucostoma Sacc.
{ Cytospora rubescens Nits.
{ Valsa leucostoma (P.) ex Fr.
Monilia oregonensis Barss and Posey.
{ Monilia fructigena Auct. Amer.
{ Oidium fructigenum Auct. Amer.
{ Oospora fructigena Auct. Amer.
{ Sclerotinia cinerea Auct. Amer.
{ Sclerotinia fructicola (Wint.) Rehm.
{ Sclerotinia fructigena Auct. Amer.
Pestalozzia adusta Ell. & Ev.
Phyllosticta pyrina Sacc.
Septoria Cerasi Pass.
Septoria cerasina Pk.
Sphaeropsis Peckii Sacc.
Sporotrichum parasiticum Pk.

Prunus Dussii Krug & Urb.
Stereum cupulatum Pat.

Prunus emarginata Walp.
Armillaria mellea, var. bulbosa Pk.
Cylindrosporium Padi Karst.
Cylindrosporium Padi Karst., var. fructicola
  Sacc.
Cylindrosporium simile Pk., var. pruninum Pk.
Dermatea Cerasi (P.) Fr.
Exoascus Cerasi (Fckl.) Sadebeck.
Exoascus Pruni Fckl.
Fomes igniarius (L. ex Fr.) Gill.
Fomes pomaceus (P.) Lloyd.
Micropera Drupacearum Lév.
{ Creonectria purpurea (L.) ex Seaver.
{ Nectria cinnabarina (Tode) ex Fr.
Plowrightia morbosa (S.) Sacc.
{ Podosphaera Oxyacanthae (DC.) DBy. †
{ Podosphaera Oxyacanthae, var. tridactyla
  Wallr.

Prunus Fremonti Watson.
Septoria magnospora Pk.

Prunus hortulana L. H. Bailey.
Cladosporium carpophilum Thm.
Coccomyces Prunophorae Higgins.
Cornularia Persicae (S.) Sacc.
Diaporthe Pruni Ell. & Ev.
Exoascus Cerasi (Fckl.) Sadebeck.
{ Exoascus mirabilis Atk.
{ Taphrina mirabilis (Atk.) Giesenhagen.

Phyllosticta congesta Heald & Wolf.
{ Puccinia Pruni-spinosae P.
{ Tranzschelia punctata Arth.
{ Sclerotinia cinerea Auct. Amer.
{ Sclerotinia fructicola (Wint.) Rehm.
{ Sclerotinia fructigena Auct. Amer.

Prunus hortulana L. H. Bailey, var. **Mineri** L. H.
  Bailey.
Cladosporium carpophilum Thm.

Prunus ilicifolia Walp.
Cercospora circumcissa Sacc.

Prunus insititia L.
Coccomyces Prunophorae Higgins.
Cylindrosporium Padi Karst.

Prunus japonica Thunb.
Puccinia Pruni DC.
Sphaeropsis Persicae Ell. & Barthol.
Valsa leucostoma (P.) ex Fr.

Prunus Lauro-Cerasus L.
Cercospora cladosporioides Sacc.
Chaetasterina anomala (Cke. & Hark.) Bubák.
Phyllosticta Laurocerasi Sacc. & Speg.
Physalospora Cydoniae Arnaud.

Prunus Lyoni Sudworth.
Discosia poikilomera Fairman.
Pleurotus salignus (P.) ex Fr.
Propolis faginea (Schrad.) ex Karst.
Schizoxylon insigne (DeNot.) Bres.
Stereum heterosporum Burt.

Prunus Mahaleb L.
{ Botryosphaeria Cerasi (C. & E.) Sacc.
{ Dothidea Cerasi C. & E.
{ Melogramma fuliginosum Ell. p. p.
{ Coccomyces lutescens Higgins.
{ Cylindrosporium lutescens Higgins.
Cylindrosporium Padi Karst.
Diaporthe rhoina (C. & E.) Ell. & Ev.
Diatrype Stigma (Hoffm.) ex Fr.
{ Eutypella tetraploa (B. & C.) Sacc.
{ Valsa stellulata Fr.
{ Valsa tetraploa B. & C.
Exoascus communis Sadebeck.
Sphaerella cerasina Cke.
Valsa Mahaleb C. & E.

Prunus maritima Wang.
Hysterographium putaminum (Cke.) Sacc.
{ Plowrightia morbosa (S.) Sacc.
{ Sphaeria morbosa S.
Puccinia Pruni-spinosae P.
{ Exoascus communis Sadebeck.
{ Taphrina communis (Sadebeck) Giesenhagen.
{ Taphrina Pruni Auct. Amer. p. p.
Taphrina Pruni (Fckl.) Tul.

Prunus melanocarpa (A. Nels.) Rydb.
Cenangium populneum (P.) ex Rehm., var.
Cercospora circumscissa Sacc.
Cucurbitaria elongata (Fr.) Grev.

Prunus melanocarpa (*cont.*)
Cylindrosporium Padi Karst.
Diatrype asterostoma B. & Cke.
⎧Diatrype Stigma (Hoffm.) ex Fr.
⎩Eutypa lata Fung. Dak. *379.*
Exoascus deformans Fckl.
Exoascus Pruni Fckl.
Fomes pomaceus (P.) Lloyd.
Fusicoccum dakotense Sacc. & Syd.
Lophiostoma Pruni Ell. & Ev.
Lophiostoma Starbaeckii Karst.
Melanconium botryosum Sacc.
Melanconium cerasinum Pk.
Monilia angustior Reade.
Creonectria purpurea (L.) ex Seaver.
⎧Nectria cinnabarina (Tode) ex Fr.
⎩Tubercularia vulgaris Tode ex Fr.
Nitschkea crustacea (Karst.) Sacc.
Patellaria atrata (Hedw.) ex Fr.
Peroneutypa corniculata (Ehrh. ex Fr.) Berl.
Phyllosticta destruens Desm.
⎧Otthia morbosa (S.) Ell. & Ev.
⎩Plowrightia morbosa (S.) Sacc.
Podosphaera Oxyacanthae (DC.) DBy. †
Polystictus hirsutus (Wulf.) ex Fr.
Schizoxylon compositum Ell. & Ev.
Sclerotinia cinerea Auct. Amer.
Sphaeronema polymorphum Awd.
Valsa cincta Pk.
Valsa leucostoma (P.) ex Fr.
Volutella nectrioides Sacc.
Prunus mexicana Watson.
Tranzschelia punctata Arth.
Prunus microphylla Hemsl.
Taphrina mexicana Syd.
Prunus mume Sieb. & Zucc.
Puccinia Pruni DC.
Prunus munsoniana W. F. Wright & Hedrick.
Coccomyces Prunophorae Higgins.
Sclerotinia cinerea Auct. Amer.
Prunus nigra Ait.
Cladosporium carpophilum Thm.
⎧Exoascus communis Sadebeck.
⎨Taphrina communis (Sadebeck) Giesenhagen.
⎩Taphrina Pruni Auct. Amer. p. p.
Exoascus Pruni Fckl.
Phyllosticta prunicola (Opiz?) Sacc.
Plowrightia morbosa (S.) Sacc.
Puccinia Pruni-spinosae P.
Sclerotinia cinerea Auct. Amer.
Prunus occidentalis Sw.
Ganoderma australe (Fr.) Pat.
Heliomyces foetens Pat.
Marasmius holophaeus Mont.
Rhytisma leptospilum B. & C.
     "on Lauraceae" may belong here.
Prunus orthosepala Köhne.
Tranzschelia punctata Arth.

Prunus Padus L.
Cylindrosporium Padi Karst.
Monilia linhartiana Sacc.
Plowrightia morbosa (S.) Sacc.
Taphrina Farlowii Sadebeck.
Prunus pennsylvanica L. f.

EXOASCACEAE
⎧Exoascus Cerasi Patterson p. p.
⎪Exoascus Insititiae Sadebeck.
⎨Taphrina deformans E. F. *15.*
⎩Taphrina Insititiae (Sadebeck) Johans.
Exoascus Pruni Fckl.

PEZIZINEAE
⎧Cenangium Cerasi (P.) Fr.
⎩Dermatea Cerasi (P.) Fr.
Tympanis conspersa Fr.

PHACIDIINEAE
Coccomyces hiemalis Higgins.

HYSTERIINEAE
Glonium Pruni Dearness & House.

PYRENOMYCETINEAE
Calosphaeria pulchella (P.) House.
⎧Calospora pennsylvanica (B. & C.) Sacc.
⎪Diaporthe cylindrospora Pk.
⎨Valsa pennsylvanica B. & C.
⎩Valsa prunicola Pk.
Diatrype tumidella Pk.
Diatrypella prunicola Ell. & Ev.
Massariella bufonia (B. & Br.) Speg.
Mycosphaerella nigristigma Higgins.
Physalospora Cydoniae Arnaud.
Physalospora Malorum Shear et al.
⎧Otthia morbosa (S.) Cke.
⎨Plowrightia morbosa (S.) Sacc.
⎩Sphaeria morbosa S.
Podosphaera Oxyacanthae (DC.) DBy. †
Valsa leucostoma (P.) ex Fr.
Valsa microstoma (P.) ex Fr.

BASIDIOMYCETES
Corticium colliculosum B. & C.
Gloeophyllum hirsutum (Schaeff.) ex Murrill.
?Guepinia Spathularia (S.) Fr.
Irpex paradoxus (Schrad.) ex Fr.
Merulius Pruni Pk.
Odontia Pruni Lasch.
Peniophora cinerea (P. ex Fr.) Cke.
Peniophora incarnata (Fr.) Massee.
Phlebia radiata Fr.
Poria incrassata (B. & C.) Burt.
Poria latemarginata (Dur. & Mont.) Sacc.
⎧Fomitiporia prunicola Murrill.
⎨Poria prunicola (Murrill) Sacc. & Trott.
⎪Puccinia Pruni DC.
⎩Tranzschelia punctata Arth.
Stereum rameale S.

Prunus pennsylvanica (*cont.*)

FUNGI IMPERFECTI
Cercospora circumscissa Sacc.
Cornularia Persicae (S.) Sacc.
Cylindrosporium hiemale Higgins.
Cylindrosporium Padi Karst.
Cylindrosporium Padi, var. cerasina Pk. nom.
    nud.
Monilia fructigena Auct. Amer.
Phyllosticta congesta Heald & Wolf.
Septoria cerasina Pk.

Prunus persica (L.) Stokes.

PHYCOMYCETES
Choanephora persicaria E. D. Eddy.
Pythiacystis citrophthora Sm. & Sm.
Rhizopus nigricans Ehrenb. ex Fr.

EXOASCACEAE
⎰ Ascomyces deformans B.
⎱ Exoascus deformans (B.) Fckl.
⎱ Taphrina deformans (B.) Tul.

PEZIZINEAE
Sclerotinia fructicola (Wint.) Rehm.

PHACIDIINEAE
Coccomyces hiemalis Higgins.
Lichenopsis sphaeroboloidea S.

HYSTERIINEAE
⎰ Hysterium Gerardi C. & P.
⎱ Hysterographium Gerardi (Cke.) Sacc.
⎰ Hysterium putaminum Cke.
⎱ Hysterographium putaminum (S.) Sacc.

PERISPORIALES
Capnodium elongatum B. & Desm.
⎰ Oidium Crataegi Grognot.
⎱ Podosphaera Oxyacanthae (DC.) DBy. †
Podosphaera Oxyacanthae, var. tridactyla
    Wallr.
Sphaerotheca Mors-uvae Auct.
⎰ Oidium leucoconium Desm.
⎱ Sphaerotheca pannosa (Wallr.) Lév.
Sphaerotheca pannosa (Wallr.) Lév., var. per-
    sicae Wor.

HYPOCREALES
Sphaerostilbe aurantiicola B. & Br.
Sphaerostilbe coccophila Tul.

SPHAERIALES
⎰ Amphisphaeria putaminum (S.) Cke.
⎱ Caryospora putaminum (S.) DeNot.
⎱ Sphaeria putaminum S.
⎰ Botryosphaeria Ribis (Tode ex Fr.) Grossen-
⎱ bacher & Duggar.
⎱ Nectria Ribis (Tode ex Fr.) Oud.

Botryosphaeria Ribis (Tode ex Fr.) Grossen-
    bacher & Duggar, var. chromogena Shear
    et al.
⎰ Calosphaeria princeps Tul.
⎱ Sphaeria pulchella P. ex Fr.
⎱ Valsa pulchella (P.) ex Fr.
Cucurbitaria delitescens Sacc.
Didymosphaeria epidermidis (Fr.) Fckl.
⎰ Eutypella microcarpa (Ell. & Ev.) Sacc.
⎱ Peroneutypella microcarpa (Ell. & Ev.) Berl.
⎱ Valsa microcarpa Ell. & Ev.
Hypoxylon coccineum Bull. †
Hypoxylon commutatum Nits.
Hypoxylon effusum Nits.
⎰ Gloeodes pomigena (S.) Colby.
⎱ Phyllachora pomigena (S.) Sacc.
Physalospora Cydoniae Arnaud.
Physalospora Malorum Shear et al.
⎰ Massaria Seiridia B. & C.
⎱ Pseudovalsa profusa (Fr.) Cke.
⎰ Mycosphaerella sentina (Fr.) Schrt.
⎱ Sphaerella sentina Fr.
Valsa leucostoma (P.) ex Fr., var. cincta
    F. M. Rolfs.
⎰ Sphaeria microstoma P. ex Fr.
⎱ Valsa microstoma (P.) ex Fr.
Xylaria Hypoxylon (L.) ex Fr.
⎰ Sphaeria persicaria S.
⎱ Xylaria persicaria (S.) M. A. Curtis.
Xylaria polymorpha (P. ex Fr.) Grev.

MYRIANGIACEAE
Myriangium Duriaei Mont. & B.

UREDINALES
⎰ Puccinia Pruni DC.
⎱ Puccinia Pruni-spinosae P.
⎱ Transzchelia punctata Arth.
⎱ Uredo Prunastri DC.
⎰ Uromyces Prunorum Fckl.
⎱ Uromyces Prunorum Fckl., var. Amygdali
⎱   Vize.

BASIDIOMYCETES
Armillaria mellea (Vahl) ex Fr.
⎰ Clitocybe monadelpha Morg.
⎱ Clitocybe parasitica Wilcox.
Cyphella marginata McAlpine.
Dacryomyces Ellisii Coker.
Fomes fraxineus (Bull. ex Fr.) Cke.
⎰ Fomes igniarius (L. ex Fr.) Gill.
⎱ Polyporus igniarius (L.) ex Fr.
Fomes pinicola (Sw. ex Fr.) Cke.
Fomes roseus (A. & S. ex Fr.) Cke.
Lenzites sepiaria (Wulf.) ex Fr.
Panus stypticus (Bull.) ex Fr.
Peniophora albomarginata (S.) Massee.
⎰ Boletus conchatus P. ex Fr.
⎱ Polyporus conchatus (P.) ex Fr.

Prunus persica (*cont.*)

{ Boletus marginatus P.
{ Polyporus marginatus (P.) Fr.
 Polyporus supinus Swartz.
{ Boletus cervinus S.
{ Polyporus cervinus (S.) Fr.
{ Polystictus cervinus (S.) Cke
{ Polyporus cinnabarinus (Jacq.) ex Fr.
{ Polystictus cinnabarinus (Jacq. ex Fr.) Cke.
{ Pycnoporus cinnabarinus (Jacq. ex Fr.) Karst.
{ Polyporus hirsutus (Wulf.) ex Fr.
{ Polystictus hirsutus (Wulf.) ex Fr.
 Polystictus lacteus Fr.
{ Coriolus prolificans (Fr.) Murrill.
{ Polyporus pargamenus Fr.
{ Coriolus versicolor (L. ex Fr.) Quél.
{ Polyporus versicolor (L.) ex Fr.
{ Polystictus versicolor (L.) ex Fr.
{ Coriolus sericeohirsutus (Klotzsch) Murrill.
{ Polystictus villosus (Sw. ex Fr.) Cke.
{ Schizophyllum alneum (L.) ex Schrt.
{ Schizophyllum commune Fr.
{ Septobasidium retiforme (B. & C.) Pat.
{ Thelephora retiformis B. & C.
 Stereum hirsutum (Willd.) ex Fr.
 Stereum purpureum P. †
 Stereum rameale (S.) Reddick.
 Trametes carnea Lloyd.

SPHAEROPSIDALES

{ Cornularia persicae (S.) Sacc.
{ Isariopsis pilosa Earle.
{ Periconia persicae S.
{ Sphaeronema persicae (S.) Ell.
{ Sporocybe persicae (S.) Fr.
 Cytospora leucostoma Sacc.
 Cytospora persicae S.
{ Cytospora rubescens Nits.
{ Valsa leucostoma (P.) ex Fr.
{ Sphaeria leucostoma P. ex Fr.
 Diplodia natalensis Evans.
 Fusicoccum persicae Ell. & Ev.
 Haplosporella amygdalina Dearness & Barthol.
{ Haplosporella demersa (Bon.) Petrak & Syd.,
{   var. missouriensis (Bubák) Petrak & Syd.
{ Haplosporella missouriensis Bubák.
 Leptothyrium Pomi (Mont. & Fr.) Sacc.
{ Macrophoma persicina (B. & C.) Berl. & Vogl.
{ Phoma persicina (B. & C.) Sacc.
{ Sphaeropsis persicina B. & C.
 Phoma persicae Sacc.
 Phoma potomeana Sacc.
 Phyllosticta circumscissa Cke.
 Phyllosticta persicae Sacc.
 Phyllosticta prunicola (Opiz?) Sacc.
 Septoria cerasina Pk.
 Septoria pyricola Desm.
 Sphaeropsis persicae Ell. & Barthol.

MELANCONIALES

 Coryneum Beyerinckii Oud.
 Cylindrosporium Padi Karst.
 Entomosporium maculatum Lév.
{ Gloeosporium fructigenum B.
{ Gloeosporium laeticolor B.
{ Gloeosporium rufomaculans (B.) Thm.
{ Gloeosporium versicolor B. & C.
{ Glomerella cingulata (Stoneman) Spaulding &
{   v. Schrenk.
{ Glomerella rufomaculans Spaulding & v.
{   Schrenk.
{ Gnomoniopsis fructigena G. P. Clinton.
{ Gloeosporium malicorticis Cordley.
{ Neofabraea malicorticis H. S. Jackson.
 Naemaspora crocea P. ex Fr.
 Pestalozzia Guepini Desm.

HYPHOMYCETES

 Alternaria Citri Pierce, var. Cerasi C. A.
    Rudolph.
 Aspergillus flavus Lk.
 Aspergillus glaucus (L.) ex Lk.
{ Aspergillus niger van Tiegh.
{ Sterigmatocystis nigra van Tiegh.
 Botrytis cinerea P. †
 Botrytis vulgaris (Lk.) ex Fr.
 Cephalothecium roseum Cda.
 Cercospora circumscissa Sacc.
{ Cercospora consobrina Ell. & Ev.
{ Cercospora rubritincta Ell. & Ev.
{ Cercospora persica Sacc.
{ Cercosporella persica Sacc.
 Cladosporium carpophilum Thm.
 Cladosporium phyllophilum McAlpine.
 Fusarium gemmiperda Aderh.
 Fusarium pyrinum Fr.
 Fusarium sarcochroum (Desm.) Sacc.
 Fusarium Solani (Mart. p. p.) App. & Wr.
 Fusarium sticticum B. & C.
 Helminthosporium carpophilum Lév.
 Helminthosporium rhabdiferum B.
 Macrosporium commune Rabh.
 Monilia oregonensis Barss & Posey.
{ Ciboria fructicola Wint.
{ Monilia cinerea Auct. Amer.
{ Monilia fructigena Auct. Amer.
{ Oidium fructigenum Auct. Amer.
{ Oospora fructigena Auct. Amer.
{ Sclerotinia americana (Wormald) Norton &
{   Ezekiel.
{ Sclerotinia cinerea Auct. Amer.
{ Sclerotinia fructicola (Wint.) Rehm.
{ Sclerotinia fructigena Auct. Amer.
 Monilia peckiana Sacc. & Vogl., var. angustior
    Sacc.
 Penicillium expansum (Lk.) Thom.
 Trichothecium roseum Lk.
 Verticillium alboatrum Reinke & Berthold.

Prunus persica (*cont.*)

MISCELLANEA

Ozonium omnivorum Shear.
Sclerotium pyrinum Fr.
Tremella ustulata Bull. ex Fr.
Sclerotium Rolfsii Sacc.
Sphinctrina Cerasi B. & C.
Sphinctrina gummae B. & Mont.

Prunus pumila L.

Exoascus Pruni Fckl.
Taphrina Pruni (Fckl.) Tul.
Exoascus communis Sadebeck.
Exoascus Pruni Auct. Amer. p. p.
Taphrina communis (Sadebeck) Giesenhagen.
Taphrina Pruni Auct. Amer. p. p.
Monilia fructigena Auct. Amer.
Plowrightia morbosa (S.) Sacc.
Podosphaera Oxyacanthae (DC.) DBy. †
Podosphaera tridactyla (Wallr.) DBy.
Puccinia Pruni DC.
Puccinia Pruni-spinosae P.

Prunus salicifolia H. B. K.

Heterochaete gelatinosa (B. & C.) Pat.

Prunus salicina Lindl.

Sclerotinia cinerea Auct. Amer.

Prunus serotina Ehrh.

EXOASCACEAE

Exoascus Cerasi (Fckl.) Sadebeck.
Taphrina deformans Auct Amer.
Taphrina deformans, var. Wiesneri (Ráthay) Farl.
Exoascus Farlowii (Sadebeck) Sacc.
Exoascus Pruni Auct. Amer.
Exoascus varius Atk.
Taphrina deformans E. F. *128.*
Taphrina Farlowii Sadebeck.
Taphrina Pruni Auct. Amer.

PEZIZINEAE

Cenangium Cerasi (P.) Fr.
Cenangium clavatum Fr.
Peziza Cerasorum S.
Durella minutissima Rehm.
Hainesia Lythri (Desm.) v. Höhnel.
Pezizella Lythri Shear & Dodge.
Sclerotiopsis concava (Desm.) Shear & Dodge.
Sclerotinia fructicola (Wint.) Rehm.
Sclerotinia fructigena Auct. Amer.
Sclerotinia Seaveri Rehm.

PHACIDIINEAE

Coccomyces hiemalis Higgins.
Coccomyces lutescens Higgins.

HYSTERIINEAE

Glonium macrosporum Tracy & Earle.
Hysterographium Mori Rehm.

PYRENOMYCETINEAE

Coelosphaeria exilis (A. & S. ex Fr.) Sacc.
Lasiosphaeria exilis (A. & S. ex Fr.) Cke.
Sphaeria exilis A. & S. ex Fr.
Cryptospora pennsylvanica (B. & C.) Ell. & Ev.
Diaporthe Pruni Ell. & Ev.
Diaporthe tuberculosa (Ell.) Sacc., var. Pruni Dearness & House.
Eutypella prunastri (P. ex Fr.) Sacc.
Sphaeria prunastri P. ex Fr.
Valsa prunastri (P.) ex Fr.
Lophiostoma Pruni Ell. & Ev.
Lophodermium petiolicola (Fr.) Fckl.
Massaria conspurcata (Wallr.) Sacc.
?Physalospora pustulata Sacc.
Plowrightia morbosa (S.) Sacc.
Sphaeria morbosa S.
Podosphaera Oxyacanthae (DC.) DBy. †
Valsa leucostoma (P.) ex Fr.
Valsa leucostoma (P.) ex Fr., var. cincta Rolfs.
Sphaeria microstoma P. ex Fr.
Valsa microstoma (P.) ex Fr.

UREDINALES

Puccinia Pruni DC.
Puccinia Pruni-spinosae P.
Puccinia Prunorum Lk.
Tranzchelia punctata Arth.

BASIDIOMYCETES

Armillaria mellea (Vahl) ex Fr.
Corticium cremoricolor B. & C.
Exidia gelatinosa (Bull.) ex Fr.
Grandinia corrugata Fr.
Odontia Pruni Lasch.
Peniophora cinerea (P. ex Fr.) Cke.
Phlebia radiata Fr.
Phlebia strigosozonata (S.) Kauffman.
Schizophyllum commune Fr.
Stereum erumpens Burt.
Stereum purpureum P. †
Trogia crispa Fr.

POLYPORACEAE

Daedalea confragosa (Bolt.) ex Fr.
Fomes fomentarius (L. ex Fr.) Gill.
Fomes pinicola (Sw. ex Fr.) Cke.
Gloeoporus conchoides Mont.
Irpex lacteus Fr.
Irpex Tulipiferae S.
Polyporus Tulipiferae (S.) Fr.
Merulius ambiguus B.
Polyporus chioneus Fr.
Hapalopilus gilvus (S.) Murrill.
Polyporus gilvus S.
Polyporus marmoratus B. & C.
Polyporus plebeius B.
Polyporus nidulans Fr.

Prunus serotina (*cont.*)
{ Hapalopilus rutilans (P. ex Fr.) Murrill.
{ Polyporus rutilans (P.) ex Fr.
Polyporus salicinus Fr.
{ Laetiporus speciosus (Batarr.) ex Murrill.
{ Polyporus sulphureus (Bull.) ex Fr.
{ Polyporus cinnabarinus (Jacq.) ex Fr.
{ Polystictus cinnabarinus (Jacq. ex Fr.) Cke.
{ Pycnoporus cinnabarinus (Jacq. ex Fr.) Karst.
{ Trametes cinnabarina (Jacq.) ex Fr.
Polystictus hirsutus (Wulf.) ex Fr.
{ Coriolus prolificans (Fr.) Murrill.
{ Polystictus pargamenus Fr.
Polystictus pubescens (Schum. ex Fr.) Lloyd.
Polystictus versicolor (L.) ex Fr.
Poria ferruginosa (Schrad. ex Fr.) Cke.
Poria incrassata (B. & C.) Burt.
Poria laevigata Fr.
Poria prunicola (Murrill) Sacc. & Trott.
Poria spissa Fr.
Poria vaporaria (P. ex Fr.) Cke.

SPHAEROPSIDALES
{ Asteroma geographicum (DC. ex Fr.) Desm.
{ Dothidea geographica (DC.) ex Fr.
Diplodia natalensis Evans.
Discosia Artocreas (Tode) ex Fr.
Dothichiza serotina Atk.
Phoma prunicola S.
Phyllosticta prunicola Sacc.?
{ Phyllosticta prunicola Auct. Amer. p. p.
{ Phyllosticta serotina Cke.
Phyllosticta Treleasei Berl. & Vogl.
Phyllosticta virginiana (Ell. & Halsted) Seaver.
Septoria cerasina Pk.
Septoria Ravenelii Thm.
Sphaeronema minutissimum Pk.
Sphaeropsis cerasina Pk.

MELANCONIALES
Cryptosporium prunicola Ell. & Ev.
{ Coccomyces lutescens Higgins.
{ Cylindrosporium lutescens Higgins.
Cylindrosporium Padi Karst.
Cylindrosporium prunicola Ell. & Ev.
Gloeosporium ovalisporum Ell. & Ev.
Gloeosporium serotinum Ell. & Ev.
Leptothyrium cinctum Cke.
Pestalozzia adusta Ell. & Ev.

HYPHOMYCETES
Cercospora cerasella Sacc.
{ Cercospora circumscissa Sacc.
{ Cercospora graphioides Ell.
Helminthosporium Pruni B. & C.
Monilia angustior (Sacc.) Reade.
{ Monilia linhartiana J. J. Davis p. p.
Monilia Seaveri Reade.
Oidium destruens Pk. p. p. [2]
Oospora linhartiana (Sacc.) Sumstine.
{ Sclerotinia Seaveri Rehm.

Tubercularia granulata P. ex Fr.
Zygodesmus avellaneus Sacc.

MISCELLANEA
{ Sphinctrina Cerasi B. & C. nom. nud.
{ Sphinctrina gummae B. & Mont.
Prunus Simonii Carr.
{ Puccinia Pruni DC.
{ Tranzschelia punctata Arth.
{ Exoascus Pruni Fckl.
{ Taphrina Pruni (Fckl.) Tul.
Prunus sphaerocarpa Swartz.
Auerswaldiella puccinioides (Speg.) Theissen & Syd.
Phyllachora Beaumontii (B. & C.) Cke.
Prunus spinosa L.
Cladosporium carpophilum Thm.
Cylindrosporium Padi Karst.
Cylindrosporium prunophorae Higgins.
Prunus subcordata Benth.
{ Ascomyces Pruni Auct. Amer.
{ Exoascus communis Sadebeck.
{ Taphrina communis (Sadebeck) Giesenhagen.
{ Taphrina Pruni Auct. Amer. p. p.
Exoascus Pruni-subcordatae Zeller.
Prunus triflora Roxb.
Alternaria Citri Pierce, var. Cerasi Rudolph.
Cercospora circumscissa Sacc.
Exoascus deformans (B.) Fckl.
{ Exoascus rhizipes Atk.
{ Taphrina rhizipes (Atk.) Giesenhagen.
Phyllosticta congesta Heald & Wolf.
Physalospora Cydoniae Arnaud.
Plowrightia morbosa (S.) Sacc.
Tranzschelia punctata Arth.
Sclerotinia fructigena Auct. Amer.
Trematosphaeria pertusa (P. ex Fr.) Fckl.
Valsa leucostoma (P.) ex Fr.
Valsa leucostoma (P.) ex Fr., var. rubescens F. M. Rolfs.
Prunus triloba Lindl.
Plowrightia morbosa (S.) Sacc.
Prunus umbellata Ell.
Diplodia natalensis Evans.
Diplodia Pruni Fckl.
Exoascus communis Sadebeck.
Plowrightia morbosa (S.) Sacc.
Podosphaera Oxyacanthae (DC.) DBy. †
{ Puccinia Pruni-spinosae P.
{ Tranzschelia punctata Arth.
Sclerotinia cinerea Auct. Amer.
Prunus virginiana L.

EXOASCACEAE
{ Exoascus Cerasi (Fckl.) Sadebeck.
{ Taphrina deformans Auct. Amer. p. p.
Exoascus communis Sadeb.
{ Exoascus cecidomophilus Atk.
{ Exoascus confusus Atk.
{ Taphrina confusa (Atk.) Giesenhagen.

Prunus virginiana (*cont.*)
{ Exoascus Farlowii (Sadebeck) Sacc.
{ Exoascus varius Atk.
Exoascus Pruni Fckl.
Exoascus unilateralis Pk.

PEZIZINEAE
Cenangium populneum (P.) Rehm, var. pruni-
cola Rehm.
Lachnella flammea (A. & S.) ex Fr.
{ Sclerotinia americana (Wormald) Norton &
} Ezekiel.
{ Sclerotinia cinerea Auct. Amer.
{ Sclerotinia fructicola (Wint.) Rehm.
Sclerotinia demissa Dana.
Sclerotinia Seaveri Rehm.

PHACIDIINEAE
Coccomyces hiemalis Higgins.
Coccomyces lutescens Higgins.
Coccomyces prunophorae Higgins.

PYRENOMYCETINEAE
{ Calosphaeria vibratilis (Fr.) Nits.
{ Sphaeria vibratilis Fr.
Diaporthe Pruni Ell. & Ev.
Diatrype patella Rehm.
Eurotium herbariorum Lk.
Eutypella prunastri (P. ex Fr.) Sacc.
Massaria conspurcata (Wallr.) Sacc.
Melanospora sphaerophila Sacc.
Peroneutypa corniculata (Ehrh.) Berl.
Phyllactinia corylea (P.) ex Karst.
{ Physalospora Cydoniae Auct. Amer.
{ Physalospora Malorum Shear et al.
{ Otthia morbosa (S.) Cke.
{ Plowrightia morbosa (S.) Sacc.
{ Sphaeria morbosa S.
{ Podosphaera Kunzei Lév.
{ Podosphaera Oxyacanthae (DC.) DBy. †
{ Podosphaera tridactyla (Wallr.) DBy.
Sphaeria ocellata Fr.
Teichospora helenae Ell. & Ev.
Valsa cincta Fr.
Winteria tuberculifera Ell. & Ev., var. caespi-
tosa Ell. & Ev.

UREDINALES
{ Puccinia Pruni DC..
{ Puccinia Pruni-spinosae P.
{ Tranzschelia punctata Arth.

BASIDIOMYCETES
Cyphella fasciculata (S.) B. & C.
Daedalea quercina (L.) ex Fr.
Favolus canadensis Klotzsch.
Fomes pomaceus (P.) Lloyd.
Hymenochaete Curtisii (B.) Morg.
Irpex paradoxus (Schrad.) ex Fr.
Irpex sinuosus Fr.
Peniophora cinerea (P. ex Fr.) Cke.

Peniophora occidentalis Ell. & Ev.
Polyporus chioneus Fr.
{ Poria contigua (Fr.) Cke.
{ Poria floccosa Auct. Amer. an Fr.
Poria laminata Murrill.
Solenia ochracea Hoffm. ex Fr.
Stereum purpureum P. †
Stereum versiforme B. & C.
Thelephora lilacina S.

SPHAEROPSIDALES
Cytospora leucosperma (P.) ex Fr.
{ Cytospora Pruni Ell. & Dearness.
{ Diaporthe Pruni Ell. & Ev.
{ Cytospora rubescens Nits.
{ Valsa leucostoma (P.) Fr.
Dendrophoma cytosporoides Sacc., var. Pruni-
virginianae Sacc.
Dichomera prunicola Ell. & Dearness.
Fusicoccum dakotense Sacc. & Syd.
{ Phoma peckiana Jacz.
{ Sphaeronema minutissimum Pk.
Phoma Pruni Pk.
Phoma prunicola S.
{ Phoma virginiana Ell. & Halsted.
{ Phyllosticta destruens Desm.
{ Phyllosticta virginiana (Ell. & Halsted) Tassi.
Phyllosticta Padi Brunaud.
Phyllosticta prunicola Sacc.
Septoria cerasina Pk.
Septoria Pruni Ell.
Sphaeropsis cerasina Pk.
Sphaeropsis Peckii Sacc.

MELANCONIACEAE
{ Coccomyces lutescens Higgins.
{ Cylindrosporium lutescens Higgins.
Cylindrosporium tubeufianum Allescher.
Gloeosporium prunicola Ell. & Ev.
Melanconium cerasinum Pk.
Myxosporium necans Pk.
Pestalozzia adusta Ell. & Ev.
Septogloeum Nuttallii Hark.

HYPHOMYCETES
Cercospora cerasella Sacc.
Cercospora circumscissa Sacc.
Cercospora circumscissa Sacc., var. virginiana
Sacc.
Dendryphium muricatum Ell. & Ev.
Helminthosporium Pruni B. & C.
{ Monilia angustior (Sacc.) Reade.
{ Monilia linhartiana J. J. Davis p. p.
{ Monilia peckiana, var. angustior Sacc.
{ Sclerotinia angustior Reade.
Monilia linhartiana Sacc.

MISCELLANEA
Sclerotium Prunorum S.

Prunus (Cherry).

EXOASCACEAE

Exoascus Cerasi (Fckl.) Sadebeck.
Taphrina Cerasi (Fckl.) Sadebeck.
Exoascus Wiesneri Ráthay.
Taphrina deformans Auct. p. p.
Taphrina Pruni (Fckl.) Tul.

ASCOMYCETES

Calosphaeria princeps Tul.
Valsa pulchella (P.) ex Fr.
Clathrospora permunda (Cke.) Berl.
Coccomyces hiemalis Higgins.
Coccomyces lutescens Higgins.
Didymella fructigena Ell. & Ev.
Discina orbicularis Pk
Lecanidion atratum (Hedw. ex Fr.) Rabh.
Mycosphaerella cerasella Aderh.
Nectria cinnabarina (Tode) ex Fr.
Nectria ditissima Tul.
Phomatospora phomatospora (B. & Br.) Schrt.
Phyllachora Beaumontii (B. & C.) Cke.
Physalospora coccodes (Lév.) Sacc.
Physalospora pustulata (Cke.) Sacc.
Sphaeria pustulata Cke.
Plowrightia morbosa (S.) Sacc.
Sphaeria morbosa S.
Podosphaera leucotricha (Ell. & Ev.) Salmon.
Podosphaera Oxyacanthae Fairchild non (DC.) DBy.
Podosphaera Oxyacanthae (DC.) DBy. †
Sclerotinia fructicola (Wint.) Rehm.
Sphaeria epidermidis Fr., var. microscopica Desm.
Sphaeria interstitialis C. & P.
Teichospora interstitialis (C. & P.) Sacc.
Valsa leucostoma (P.) ex Fr., var. cincta F. M. Rolfs.
Valsaria quadrata (S.) Sacc.
Venturia Cerasi Aderh.
Xylaria polymorpha (P. ex Fr.) Grev.

HYMENOMYCETINEAE

Armillaria mellea (Vahl.) ex Fr.
Clitocybe parasitica Wilcox.
Corticium lacteum Fr.
Corticium scutellare B. & C.
Exidia glandulosa (Bull.) ex Fr.
?Fomes applanatus (P. ex Wallr.) Gill.
Hydnum amplissimum B. & C.
Hydnum ochraceum P. ex Fr.
Hymenochaete tabacina (Sow. ex Fr.) Lév.
Irpex lacteus Fr.
Lentinus patulus Lév.
Lenzites sepiaria (Wulf.) ex Fr.
Merulius tremellosus Schrad. ex Fr.
Peniophora albomarginata (S.) Massee.
Polyporus brumalis (P.) ex Fr.

Polyporus connatus Fr.
Polyporus sulphureus (Bull.) ex Fr.
Polyporus zonatus Fr.
Polystictus hirsutus (Wulf.) ex Fr.
Polystictus lacteus Fr.
Poria nitida P. ex Fr.
Poria subacida (Pk.) Sacc.
Schizophyllum commune Fr.
Trametes sepium B.

SPHAEROPSIDALES

Aposphaeria nucicola Ell. & Ev.
Asteroma geographicum (DC. ex Fr.) Desm
Coniosporium atrum S.
Haplosporella Peckii (Sacc.) House.
Hendersonula morbosa Sacc.
Phomopsis padina (Sacc.) Diedicke.
Phyllosticta Laurocerasi Sacc. & Speg.
Phyllosticta prunicola Sacc.
Rhabdospora baculum, var. nucimaculans Fairman.
Vermicularia putaminicrustans Fairman.

MELANCONIALES

Coryneum Beyerinckii Oud.
Cryptosporium cerasinum Pk.
Cylindrosporium Padi Karst.
Entomosporium maculatum Lév.
Gloeosporium malicorticis Cordley.
Neofabraea malicorticis H. S. Jackson.
Pestalozzia longiseta Speg.

HYPHOMYCETES

Cercospora cerasella Sacc.
Cercospora circumscissa Sacc.
Cercospora rosicola Pass.
Cladosporium carpophilum Thm.
Fusarium roseum Lk.
Fusicladium dendriticum (Wallr.) Fckl.
Helicotrichum obscurum (Cda.) Sacc.
Micropera rudida B. & C.
Monilia Cerasi Tracy & Earle.
Oospora Cerasi (Tracy & Earle) Sumstine.
Monilia oregonensis Barss & Posey.
Monilia fructigena Auct. Amer.
Oospora cinerea Auct. Amer.
Oidium fructigenum Auct. Amer.
Sclerotinia cinerea Auct. Amer.
Sclerotinia fructicola (Wint.) Rehm.
Sclerotinia fructigena Norton.
Rhinotrichum ramosisimum B. & C.
Tubercularia vulgaris Tode ex Fr.

MISCELLANEA

Arcyria denudata Macbr.
Badhamia hyalina (P.) B.
Lycoperdon pyriforme Schaeff. ex Fr.
Rhizopus nigricans Ehrb.
Tranzschelia punctata Arth.

Prunus (Japan Plum).
  Exoascus mirabilis Atk.
  Plowrightia morbosa (S.) Sacc.
  {Taphrina Pruni Benton.
  {Cf. Taphrina rhizipes (Atk.) Giesenhagen.
Prunus (Plum).

PHYCOMYCETES

Mucor ambiguum Vuill.
Pythiacystis citrophthora Sm. & Sm.

EXOASCACEAE

{Exoascus communis Sadebeck.
{Exoascus Pruni Auct. Amer. p. p.
{Taphrina communis (Sadebeck) Giesenhagen.
{Taphrina Pruni Auct. Amer. p. p.
{Exoascus decipiens Atk.
{Taphrina decipiens (Atk.) Giesenhagen.
Exoascus deformans (B.) Fckl.
Exoascus mirabilis Atk.

ASCOMYCETES

Calosphaeria princeps (P.) Tul.
Caryospora putaminum (S.) DeNot.
Hypoxylon commutatum Nits.
Lasiodiplodia triflorae Higgins.
Massaria conspurcata (Wallr.) Sacc.
Nectria ditissima Tul.
Neofabrea malicorticis H. S. Jackson.
Podosphaera leucotricha (Ell. & Ev.) Salmon.
Podosphaera Oxyacanthae (DC.) DBy. †
Sphaerostilbe coccophila Tul.
Valsa prunastri (P.) ex Fr.
{Diatrype quadrata (S.) B.
{Valsaria quadrata (S.) Sacc.

BASIDIOMYCETES

Armillaria mellea (Vahl) ex Fr.
Fomes applanatus (P. ex Wallr.) Gill.
{Fomes fulvus (Scop. ex Fr.) Gill.
{Pyropolyporus fulvus (Scop. ex Fr.) Murrill.
Fomes pinicola (Sw. ex Fr.) Cke.
{Corticium Stevensii Burt.
{Hypochnus ochroleucus Noack.
Lenzites sepiaria Fr.
Polystictus hirsutus (Wulf.) ex Fr.
Polystictus lacteus Fr.
Poria inermis Ell. & Ev.
Rhizoctonia Solani Kühn.
Schizophyllum commune Fr.
Septobasidium pedicillatum (B. & C.) Pat.
Septobasidium retiforme (B. & C.) Pat.
Solenia anomaloides Pk.
Stereum purpureum P. †
Trametes carnea Nees ex Fr.
Trogia crispa Fr.

FUNGI IMPERFECTI

Cladosporium carpophilum Thm.
Cladosporium cucumerinum Ell. & Arth. ?
Coniothecium saccharium Pk.

Coniothecium sociale Pk.
Coniothyrium pyrinum (Sacc.) Sheldon.
Cornularia Persicae (S.) Sacc.
Coryneum Beyerinckii Oud.
Cytospora carphosperma Fr.
Diplodia Pruni Fckl.
Fumago vagans Fr.
Micropera Drupacearum Lév.
Monilia linhartiana Sacc.
Pestalozzia adusta Ell. & Ev.
Phyllosticta circumscissa Cke.
Phyllosticta congesta Heald and Wolf.
Phyllosticta prunicola Sacc.
Septoria cerasina Pk.
Septoria Pruni Ell.

MISCELLANEA

Ozonium omnivorum Shear.
Prunus (Prune).
  See also Prunus domestica.
  Armillaria mellea (Vahl) ex Fr.
  Cladosporium carpophilum Thm.
  Coryneum Beyerinckii Oud.
  Exoascus communis Sadebeck.
  Exoascus Pruni Fckl.
  Fomes applanatus (P. ex Wallr.) Gill.
  Fomes fraxinophilus (Pk.) Sacc.
  Fomes pinicola (Sw. ex Fr.) Cke.
  Gloeosporium malicorticis Cordley.
  Lasiodiplodia triflorae Higgins.
  Lenzites sepiaria (Wulf.) ex Fr.
  Leptothyrium pomi (Mont. & Fr.) Sacc.
  Polyporus chioneus Fr.
  Tranzschelia punctata Arth.
  Sclerotinia fructicola (Wint.) Rehm.
  Stereum hirsutum (Willd.) ex Fr.
  Trametes carnea Nees ex Fr.
Prunus sp. indet.

PEZIZINEAE

Dermatea prunastri (P.) Fr.
Helotium rhizogenum Ell. & Ev.
Mollisia cinerea (Batsch ex P.) Karst., var. luteola Sacc.
{Peziza plicatocrenata S.
{Phacidium plicatum Fr.
{Tympanis plicatocrenata (S.) Fr.

PYRENOMYCETINEAE

Amphisphaeria xera Fairman.
Auerswaldia puccinioides (Speg.) Theissen & Syd.
Calosphaeria barbirostris (Dufour) Ell. & Ev
{Chilonectria Cucurbitula (Curr.) Sacc.
{Nectria Cucurbitula (Curr.) Cke.
{Cryptospora corylina (Tul.) Fckl.
{Sphaeria versatilis Fr.
{Cryptospora vasculosa (Fr.) Cke.
{Sphaeria vasculosa Fr.
{Valsa vasculosa Fr.

Prunus sp. indet. (*cont.*)
  Cucurbitaria Pruni-mahaleb Allescher.
  ⎧ Berlesiella echinata (Ell. & Ev.) Berl.
  ⎪ Berlesiella setosa (Ell. & Ev.) Sacc.
  ⎨ Cucurbitaria echinata Ell. & Ev.
  ⎩ Cucurbitaria setosa Ell. & Ev.
  Diaporthe tuberculosa (Ell.) Sacc.
  Diatrype albopruinosa (S.) Cke.
  Eutypa manura (Fr.) Sacc.
  ⎧ Fenestella hormospora Cke.
  ⎨ Fenestella ulmicola Ell. & Ev.
  ⎩ Fenestella vestita (Fr.) Sacc.
  ⎧ Sphaeria conjuncta S. Am. Bor. 1383.
  ⎪ Sphaeria vestita Fr.
  ⎨ Valsa conjuncta Cke.
  ⎪ Valsa hormospora B. & C. in Herb.
  ⎩ Valsa vestita Fr.
  Hypocrea contorta (S.) B. & C.
  Hypoxylon fuscum (P.) ex Fr.
  Hysterium pulicare (P.) ex Fr.
  ⎧ Hysterium flexuosum S.
  ⎨ Hysterographium flexuosum (S.) Rehm.
  ⎧ Apiosporium pelliculosum (B. & Rav.) Millsp.
  ⎨ Limacinia pelliculosa (B. & Rav.) Sacc.
  ⎧ Nummularia excavata (S.) Ell. & Ev.
  ⎨ Sphaeria excavata S.
  Podosphaera leucotricha (Ell. & Ev.) Salmon.
  Podosporium rigidum S.
  Schizoparme straminea Shear.
  Trimmatostroma americanum Thm.
  Valsa ambiens (P.) ex Fr.
  ⎧ Sphaeria ciliata P. ex Fr.
  ⎨ Valsa ciliata (P.) ex Fr.
  ⎧ Sphaeria monadelpha Fr.
  ⎨ Valsa monadelpha Fr.
  ⎧ Sphaeria scutellata P.
  ⎨ Valsa scutellata (P.) M. A. Curtis.
  Valsaria exasperans (Gerard) Sacc.
  Venturia Cerasi Aderh.
  ⎧ Winterella tuberculigera (Ell. & Ev.) Berl.
  ⎨ Winteria tuberculifera Ell. & Ev.

BASIDIOMYCETES
  Auricularia sambucina Mart. ex Fr.
  Coniophora arida Fr.
  Coniophora cerebella P.
  ⎧ Corticium albulum Atk. & Burt. nom. nud.
  ⎨ Peniophora albula Atk. & Burt.
  ⎧ Irpex paradoxus (Schrad.) ex Fr.
  ⎨ Sistotrema Cerasi (P.) ex Fr.
  Irpex sinuosus Fr.
  Peniophora violaceolivida (Sommerf.) Bres.
  Poria ferruginosa (Schrad. ex Fr.) Cke.
  Poria inermis Ell. & Ev.
  Poria Medulla-panis (P. ex Fr.) Cke.
  Poria prunicola Murrill.
  ⎧ Boletus superficialis S.
  ⎨ Poria superficialis (S.) Cke.

  Radulum orbiculare Fr.
  Solenia anomala (P. ex Fr.) Fckl.
  Solenia anomaloides Pk.

SPHAEROPSIDALES
  Cytospora ocellata Fckl.
  Helicopsis punctata Pk.
  Libertella faginea Desm.
  Libertella prunicola Atk.
  ⎧ Cytospora Pruni Ell. & Dearness.
  ⎨ Phomopsis Pruni (Ell. & Dearness) Wehmeyer.
  Phyllosticta sanguinea Desm.
  Phyllosticta solitaria Ell. & Ev.
  Septoria gemmigena Ell. & Ev.
  ⎧ Sphaeropsis anomala Pk.
  ⎨ Sphaeropsis Peckii Sacc.

MELANCONIALES
  Microgloeum Pruni Petrak.

HYPHOMYCETES
  Cephalothecium roseum Cda.
  Coniothecium saccharinum Pk.
  Coniothecium sociale Pk.
  Dendryphium corticale Ell. & Ev.
  Fusicladium Cerasi Sacc.
  Volutella ciliata (Lk.) Fr.

MISCELLANEA
  ?Amaurochaete minor Sacc. & Ell.
  Mucor ambigua Vuillemin.
  Physarum atrum S.

Chrysobalanus Icaco L.
  Asterina Schroeteri (Rehm) Theissen.
  Leprieurina radiata Toro.
  Mycosphaerella Chrysobalani Miles.
  Pestalozzia funerea Desm.
  Tremella nucleata S.

Chrysobalanus oblongifolius Michx.
  Cercospora Chrysobalani Ell. & Ev.
  Glomerella cingulata (Stoneman) Spaulding &
    v. Schrenk.

Chrysobalanus pellocarpus G. F. W. Mey.
  Asterina Schroeteri (Rehm) Theissen.

Hirtella triandra Sw.
  Asterina inaequalis Mont.

Couepeia polyandra (H. B. K.) Rose.
  Uredo Licaniae Henn.

Lyonothamnus floribundus Gray.
  Agyrium rufum (P.) Fr.
  Hymenochaete tabacina (Sow. ex Fr.) Lév.
  Hysterographium Mori (S.) Rehm.
  Hysterographium prominens (Phil. & Hark.)
    Berl. & Vogl.
  Poria incrustans B. & C.
  Sebacina podlachia Bres.
  Stereum gausapatum Fr.
  Stereum hirsutum Fr.
  Strikeria Catalinae Fairman.

CONNARACEAE

Rourea glabra H. B. K.
  Arcangelia Roureae Fragoso & Ciferri.
  Micropeltis aeruginescens Rehm.
  Phyllachora Rourea Syd.
Rourea surinamensis Miq.
  Micropeltis aeruginascens Rehm.

LEGUMINOSAE

Inga dulcis Willd.
  Ceratiomyxa arbuscula (B. & Br.) Pat.
Inga edulis Mart.
  Phthora vastatrix d'Herelle.
  Ravenelia Ingae Arth.
Inga ingoides Willd.
  Nectria saccharina B. & C.
Inga Inicuil Cham. & Schl.
  ⎰ Ravenelia Ingae Arth.
  ⎱ Uredo excipulata Syd.
Inga laurifolia Bong. ex Benth.
  Clavaria cristata Fr.
  Ungulina hornoderma (Mont.) Pat.
  Hypoxylon multiforme Fr.
  Kretzschmaria heliscus (Mont.) Pat.
  Leptoporus fumosus (Fr.) Quél.
  Lophiosphaera antillarum Pat.
  ⎰ Poria Dussii Pat.
  ⎱ Porogramme Dussii Pat.
  Ptychogaster cubensis Pat.
Inga laurina Willd.
  Ciboria caespitosa Seaver.
  Crepidotus mollis (Schaeff.) ex Fr.
  Hypocrella guaranitica Speg.
  Melasmia Ingae F. L. Stevens.
  Meliola toruloidea F. L. Stevens.
  Microstroma ingaicola Lamkey.
  Perisporium truncatum F. L. Stevens.
  Ravenelia Ingae Arth.
Inga leptopoda Benth.
  Ravenelia Ingae Arth.
Inga marginata Willd.
  Eriomycopsis tenuis Syd.
  Parodiopsis Stevensii Arnaud.
  Scolecopeltis Ingae Toro.
  Septoidium Stevensii Arnaud.
  Stereum caperatum Massee.
  Stilbum flavidum Cke.
  Trichosporium tomentosum (B. & C.) Pat.
Inga martinicensis Presl.
  Isaria Albizziae Pat.
  Isaria gossypina Pat.
Inga Preussii Harms.
  Perisporium truncatum Stevenson.
  Ravenelia Ingae Arth.
Inga Swartzii Auct.
  Auricularia polytricha (Mont.) Sacc.
  Mycobonia brunneoleuca (B. & C.) Pat.

Inga vera Willd.
  ⎧ Antennularia (?) tenuis Earle.
  ⎨ Phaeosaccardinula tenuis (Earle) Scaver &
  ⎩   Chardon.
  Calothyrium Ingae Ryan.
  Chaetothyrium permixtum Syd.
  Diatractium Ingae (Rehm) Syd.
  Meliola toruloidea F. L. Stevens.
  Microstroma ingaicola Lamkey.
  Microthyrium Ingae (Ryan) Toro.
  Mycosphaerella maculiformis (P. ex Fr.) Schrt.
  Parodiopsis Stevensii Arnaud.
  Perisporium truncatum F. L. Stevens.
  Pestalozzia funerea Desm.
  Phyllachora ingicola Syd.
  ⎰ Ravenelia Ingae Arth.
  ⎱ Ravenelia Whetzelii Arth.
  Scolecopeltis Ingae Toro.
  ⎰ Stilbella flavida (Cke.) Henn.
  ⎱ Stilbum flavidum Cke.
  Uredo curvata Arth.
Inga sp. indet.
  Hypoplegma viridescens (Rehm) Theissen &
    Syd., var. Ingarum Henn.
  Maravalia Ingae Syd.
  Maravalia utriculata Syd.
  Phyllachora amphibola Syd.
  Rosellinia bunodes B. & Br.
  Rosellinia necatrix (R. Hartig) Berl.
Enterolobium cyclocarpum (Sw.) Griseb.
  Ravenelia havanensis Arth.
Pithecolobium brevifolium Benth.
  Ravenelia gracilis Arth.
Pithecolobium dulce Benth.
  Prospodium Amphilophii (Diet. & Holw.) Arth.
Pithecolobium flexicaule (Benth.) Coult.
  Ravenelia Siderocarpi Long.
Pithecolobium jupunba Urban.
  Meliola Pithecolobii Stevens & Tehon.
Pithecolobium latifolium (L.) Benth.
  Maravalia pallida Arth. & Thax.
Pithecolobium Saman Benth.
  Fomes lucidus (Leyss. ex Fr.) Cke.
  Microstroma Pithecolobii Lamkey.
Pithecolobium tortum Mart.
  Ravenelia Pithecolobii Arth.
Pithecolobium Unguis-cati Benth.
  Colletotrichum Erythrinae Ell. & Ev.
  Fomes lucidus (Leyss. ex Fr.) Cke.
  Hysterographium Pithecolobii Seaver.
  Pestalozzia funerea Desm.
  Phyllosticta Pithecolobii E. Young.
  Phyllosticta Pithecolobii E. Young, var. mo-
    nensis E. Young.
  Ravenelia Pithecolobii Arth.
Albizzia Lebbek Benth.
  Ganoderma Dussii Pat.
  ⎰ Graphium Albizziae Pat.
  ⎱ Isaria Albizziae Pat.

Albizzia Lebbek (*cont.*)
Guepiniopsis spathularius Fr.
Phoma lathyrina Sacc.
Phyllosticta divergens Sacc.
Coriolus vinosus (B.) Pat.
Microporus sanguineus (L. ex Fr.) O. Kuntze.
Trichosporium tomentosum (B. & C.) Pat.

Calliandra gracilis Klotzsch.
Ravenelia ectypa Arth. & Holw.

Calliandra grandiflora Benth.
Ravenelia mexicana Tranz.

Calliandra Houstoni Benth.
Ravenelia bizonata Arth. & Holw.

Calliandra humilis Benth.
Ravenelia reticulatae Long.

Calliandra mexicana Brandg.
Ravenelia mexicana Tranz.

Calliandra petiolaris ex Duss.
Microstelium hyalinum Pat.

Calliandra portoricensis Benth.
Phellinus scruposus (Fr.) Pat.

Calliandra purpurea Benth.
Favolus tessellatus Mont.

Calliandra reticulata Gray.
Ravenelia reticulatae Long.

Calliandra similis Sprague & Riley.
Camptomeris Calliandrae Syd.

Lysiloma acapulcensis Benth (?).
Ravenelia sololensis Arth. & Holw.

Lysiloma bahamensis Benth.
Ravenelia annulata Long.
Ravenelia Lysilomae Arth.
Ravenelia sololensis Arth. & Holw.

Lysiloma latisiliqua Benth.
Ravenelia annulata Long.

Lysiloma tergemina Benth.
{ Dendroecia Lysilomae Arth.
{ Ravenelia Lysilomae Arth.

Acacia amentacea DC.
Phyllachora Acaciae Henn.

Acacia angustissima (Mill.) O. Kuntze.
Ravenelia igualica Arth.
Ravenelia Leucaenae-microphyllae Diet.

Acacia anisophylla Watson.
{ Dendroecia farlowiana (Diet.) Arth.
{ Ravenelia farlowiana Diet.
Ravenelia indica B.

Acacia bursaria Schrenk.
Ravenelia inquirenda Arth. & Holw.

Acacia cochliacantha Humb. & Bonpl.
Dendroecia farlowiana (Diet.) Arth.
Ravenelia Acaciae-pennatulae Diet.
Ravenelia expansa Diet. & Holw.

Acacia constricta Benth., var. **paucispina** Wooton
& Standley.
Ravenelia thornberiana Long.

Acacia crassifolia Gray.
{ Dendroecia farlowiana (Diet.) Arth.
{ Ravenelia farlowiana Diet.
Ravenelia indica B.

Acacia farnesiana (L.) Willd.
Aecidium sp. indet.
Phyllachora Acaciae Henn.
{ Ravenelia australis Diet. & Neg.
{ Ravenelia verrucosa Arth. *5314* non C. & E.
{ Cystingophora Hieronymi (Speg.) Arth.
{ Pleoravenelia Hieronymi (Speg.) Long.
Ravenelia siliquae Long.

Acacia filiculoides (Cav.) Trel.
{ Ravenelia expansa Fung. Columb. *2473*.
{ Ravenelia igualica Arth.

Acacia flexicaulis Benth.
Fomes rimosus (B.) Cke.
Ravenelia Siderocarpi Long.

Acacia Greggii Gray.
Cucurbitaria arizonica Ell. & Ev.
Fomes badius (B.) Cke.
{ Ravenelia decidua Holw.
{ Ravenelia versatilis (Pk.) Diet.
{ Uredo versatilis Diet.
{ Uromyces versatilis Pk.

Acacia julibrissin Willd.
Fusarium aurantiacum Cda.
Pachnocybe subulata (Nees) B.
{ Verticicladium pulvinatum (B. & C.) Sacc.
{ Verticillium pulvinatum B. & C.

Acacia macrantha Thumb.
Mucidula cheimonophylla (B. & C.) Pat.

Acacia melanoxylon R. Br.
Schizophyllum commune Fr.

Acacia micrantha Benth.
Ravenelia Acaciae-micranthae Diet.
{ Dendroecia farlowiana (Diet.) Arth.
{ Ravenelia farlowiana Diet.

Acacia nudiflora Willd.
Corticium calceum Fr.
Lenzites applanata Fr.
Xerotus lateritius B. & C.

Acacia pennatula Benth.
Ravenelia Acaciae-pennatulae Diet.
Ravenelia siliquae Long.

Acacia riparia H. B. K.
{ Coriolus actinobolus (Mont.) Pat.
{ Polyporus atypus Lév.
Ravenelia Stevensii Arth.

Acacia roemeriana Scheele.
Fomes rimosus (B.) Cke.
Ravenelia roemerianae Long.

Acacia stricta Willd.
{ Pyropolyporus Robiniae Murrill.
{ Polyporus igniarius Auct. p. p.
{ Polyporus rimosus Auct. p. p.

Acacia subtortuosa Shafer.
{ Neoravenelia subtortuosae (Long) Arth.
{ Ravenelia subtortuosa Long.

Acacia suffrutescens Rose.
Ravenelia Gooddingii Long.

Acacia tequilana Watson.
Ravenelia expansa Diet. & Holw.

Acacia Wrightii Benth.
Phyllachora texana Tharp.

Acacia sp. indet.
⎰Aposphaeria librincola (Cke. & Hark.) Sacc.
⎱Phoma librincola Cke. & Hark.
⎰Badhamia nodulosa (Cke. & Balf.) Massee.
⎱Physarum nodulosum Cke. & Balf.
Coniothyrium decipiens Cke. & Hark.
Coniothyrium punctum Cke. & Hark.
Diaporthe gorgonoidea Cke. & Hark.
Diplodia decorticata C. & E.
Diplodia lata Cke. & Hark.
Diplodia mutila (Fr.) Mont.
Diplodia Phyllactiniae Cke. & Hark.
Diplodia phyllodiae Cke. & Hark.
Diplodia vulgaris Lév.
⎰Diplodia millegrana Cke. & Hark.
⎱Diplodiella millegrana (Cke. & Hark.) Sacc.
Fomes applanatus (Wallr. ex Fr.) Gill.
Fomes lucidus (Leyss. ex Fr.) Cke.
Fusarium Acaciae Cke. & Hark.
Fusarium cataleptum Cke. & Hark.
Fusarium obtusisporum Cke. & Hark.
⎰Fusarium leguminum (Cke.) Sacc.
⎨Fusarium Salicis Fckl.
⎩Fusisporium leguminum Cke.
Helminthosporium atro-olivaceum Cke. & Hark.
⎰Gloniopsis insigne (Cke. & Hark.) Berl. & Vogl.
⎱Hysterographium insigne Cke. & Hark.
Nectria ditissima Tul.
Nectria infusaria Cke. & Hark.
Pachnocybe subulata (Nees) B.
Phoma lignicola Rabh.
Pleospora gummipara Oud.
Poria vincta (B.) Cke.
Rhabdospora decorticata Cke. & Hark.
Septoria mortolensis Penz.
Septosporium praelongum Sacc.
Sphaerella Acaciae Cke. & Hark.
⎰Sphaeria personata Cke. & Hark.
⎨Thyridium personatum (Cke. & Hark.) Berl. &
⎩ Vogl.
Volutella ciliata (Lk.) Fr.
⎰Psilosphaeria eunotiispora (Cke. & Hark.)
⎨ Cke.
⎨Sphaeria eunotiispora Cke. & Hark.
⎩Wallrothiella eunotiispora (Cke. & Hark.)
   Berl. & Vogl.

Leucaena diversifolia Benth.

Leucaena esculenta Benth.
Ravenelia Leucaenae Long.

Leucaena glauca (L.) Benth.
Exosporium Leucaenae Stevens & Dalbey.

Leucaena lanceolata Watson.
⎰Dendroecia verrucosa (C. & E.) Arth.
⎱Ravenelia verrucosa C. & E.

Leucaena pulverulenta Benth.
Ravenelia Leucaenae Long.

Schrankia uncinata Willd.
Cercospora Morongiae Tracy & Earle.
Macrosporium caespitulum Cke.
Pleospora herbarum (Fr.) Rabh., var. Allii Rabh.
Ravenelia Morongiae Long.

Mimosa albida H. B. K.
Ravenelia mainsiana Arth. & Holw.
Ravenelia Mimosae-albidae Diet.
Ravenelia Mimosae-sensitivae Henn.

Mimosa asperata L.
⎰Diabole cubensis Arth.
⎱Uromycladium (?) cubense Arth.

Mimosa biuncifera Benth.
Ravenelia fragrans Long.

Mimosa caerulea Rose.
Ravenelia Mimosae-caeruleae Diet.

Mimosa ceratonia L.
Meliola bicornis Wint.
⎰Ravenelia Caesalpiniae Arth.
⎱Uromyces Caesalpiniae Arth.

Mimosa fragrans Gray.
Ravenelia fragrans Long.

Mimosa Galeottii Benth.
Ravenelia Mimosae-sensitivae Henn.

Mimosa pigra L.
⎰Diabole cubensis Arth.
⎱Uromycladium (?) cubense Arth.
Dicheirinia binata (B. & C.) Arth.

Mimosa polyanthoides Willd.

Mimosa stipitata B. L. Robinson.
Ravenelia mimosicola Arth.

Mimosa pudica L.
Ramularia Mimosae Stevens & Dalbey.

Mimosaceae gen. indet.
Ravenelia distans Arth. & Holw.
Ravenelia gracilis Arth.

Desmanthus acuminatus Benth.

Desmanthus Jamesii Torr. & Gray.
Ravenelia texensis Ell. & Gall.

Desmanthus illinoensis (Michx.) MacM.
⎰Cercospora condensata Ell. & Kellerm., var.
⎨ Desmanthi Ell. & Kellerm.
⎩Cercospora Desmanthi Ell. & Kellerm.
Erysiphe communis Auct. Amer.

Dichrostachys nutans Benth.
Corticium portentosum B. & C.
Ganoderma pulverulentum Murrill.
Hypoxylon rubiginosum (P.) ex Fr.
Polyporus opacus B. & Mont.
Polystictus pinsitus Auct. Amer.
Tryblidiella rufula (Spreng.) Sacc.

Dichrostachys nutans (*cont.*)
Trametes rigida B. & Mont.
Ustulina vulgaris Tul.
Ustulina zonata (Lév.) Sacc.
Prosopis glandulosa Torr.
Asterella Prosopidis Ell. & Ev.
Cercospora Prosopidis Heald & Wolf.
Diatrypella Underwoodii Pk.
Didymosphaeria cryptosphaerioides Rehm.
Eichleriella Schrenkii Burt.
Fomes Everhartii (Ell. & Gall.) v. Schrenk.
Fomes rimosus (B.) Cke.
Lenzites protracta Fr.
Napicladium prosopodium Tharp.
⎰ Inonotus texanus Murrill.
⎱ Polyporus texanus (Murrill) Sacc. & Trott.
Polystictus Lindheimeri B. & C.
Ravenelia arizonica Ell. & Ev.
Neoravenelia Holwayi (Diet.) Long.
Schizophyllum commune Fr.
Scleropycnium aureum Heald & Lewis.
Stereum albobadium S.
Stereum leveillianum Fr.
Uncinula Prosopodis Speg.
Prosopis juliflora (Sw.) DC.
Asterella Prosopidis Ell. & Ev.
Fomes rimosus (B.) Cke.
Phyllosticta juliflora Ell. & Barthol.
Polyporus texanus (Murrill) Sacc. & Trott.
Pyropolyporus Everhartii (Ell. & Gall.) Murrill.
Ravenelia arizonica Ell. & Ev.
Ravenelia decidua (Pk.) Holw.
⎰ Neoravenelia Holwayi (Diet.) Long.
⎱ Ravenelia Holwayi Diet.
⎰ Ravenelia arizonica Fung. Columb. *2681.*
⎱ Ravenelia Prosopidis Long.
⎰ Haplosporella Prosopidis (Dearness & Barthol.) Petrak & Syd.
⎱ Sphaeropsis Prosopodis Dearness & Barthol.
Prosopis pubescens Benth.
⎰ Ravenelia decidua (Pk.) Holw.
⎱ Uromyces deciduus Pk.
Prosopis velutina Wooton.
⎰ Ravenelia arizonica Ell. & Tracy.
⎱ Ravenelia decidua Fung. Columb. *1481.*
Prosopis sp. indet.
⎰ Discella leguminum Cke.
⎱ Discula leguminum (Cke.) Sacc.
  Gloeosporium leguminum (Cke.) Sacc.
⎰ Fomes sublinteus (Murrill) Sacc. & Trott.
⎱ Pyropolyporus sublinteus Murrill.
Hirneolina Schenkii (Burt.) Sacc.
Polyporus pinsitus Fr.
Adenanthera pavonina L.
⎰ Leptoporus albogilvus (B. & C.) Pat.
⎱ Polyporus albogilvus B. & C.
Piptadenia peregrina Benth.
Ravenelia Cebil Speg.

Entada polystachya DC.
Ravenelia Entadae Lagerh. & Diet.
Pentaclethra sp. indet.
Hypocrella nectrioides Thax.
Saraca indica L.
Asteridium moniliferum Ell. & Ev.
Hymenaea Courbaril L.
Hypoxylon marginatum S.
Odontia Wrightii (B. & C.) Pat.
⎰ Coriolus vinosus (B.) Pat.
⎰ Polystictus vinosus (B.) Cke.
⎱ Leucoporus Warmingii (B.) Pat.
⎱ Polyporus Warmingii B.
Rosellinia Pepo Pat.
Stilbum cinnabarinum Mont.
Uredo Hymenaeae Mayor.
Xylaria multiplex Fr.
Amherstia sp. indet.
Corticium salmonicolor B. & Br.
Cercis canadensis L.
Acrospermum Ravenelii B. & C.
⎰ Auerswaldia Cercidis (Cke.) Theissen & Syd.
⎰ Bagnisiella Cercidis (Cke.) Berl. & Vogl.
⎱ Dothidea Cercidis Cke.
Cercospora cercidicola Ell.
⎰ Cercospora chionea Ell. & Kellerm.
⎱ Cercosporella chionea (Ell. & Kellerm.) Sacc.
Diplodia Cercidis Ell. & Ev.
Discosia Artocreas (Tode) ex Fr.
Hainesia Lythri (Desm.) v. Höhnel.
Haplosporella Cercidis Ell. & Barthol.
⎰ Hypoxylon durissimum (S.) Fr.
⎱ Sphaeria durissima S.
⎰ Cyphella cinereofusca (S.) Sacc.
⎰ Lachnella cinereofusca (S.) Sacc.
⎱ Peziza cinereofusca S.
Nummularia repanda (Fr.) Nitz.
Phyllosticta cercidicola Ell. & Ev.
Phyllosticta siliquastri Sacc. & Speg.
Poria ferruginosa (Schrad. ex Fr.) Cke.
Rosellinia medullaris (Wallr.) Ces. & DeNot.
Sarcinella heterospora Sacc.
Sphaerella cercidicola Ell. & Kellerm.
Sphaeropsis Cercidis Dearness & Barthol.
⎰ Corticium leveillianum B. & C.
⎱ Stereum leveillianum B. & C.
Cercis japonica Siebold.
Cercospora cercidicola Ell.
Cercospora chionea Ell. & Kellerm.
Diplodia Cercidis Ell. & Ev.
Phoma cercidicola Fairman.
Cercis occidentalis Torr.
Cercospora cercidicola Ell.
Cercis sp. indet.
⎰ Durella Lecideola (Fr.) Rehm.
⎰ Patellaria Lecideola Fr.
⎱ Peziza Lecideola Fr.
⎰ Hypoxylon discretum (S.) B. & C.
⎱ Nummularia discreta (S.) Tul.

Cercis sp. indet. (*cont.*)
  Nummularia repanda (Fr.) Nits.
  Nummularia tinctor (B.) Ell. & Ev.
  Ovularia Cercidis S. Cam.
  Physalospora Malorum Shear et al.

Bauhinia divaricata L.
  Ramularia Bauhiniae Ell. & Ev.
  ⎰Teleutospora jamaicensis (Vestergren) Arth. &
  ⎱ Bisby.
  Uromyces jamaicensis Vestergren.

Bauhinia heterophylla Kunth.
  Uredo bauhiniicola Henn.

Bauhinia inermis P.
  Uromyces guatemalensis Vestergren.

Bauhinia Krugii Urb.
  Marasmius stenophyllus Mont.

Bauhinia pauletia P.

Bauhinia porrecta Sw.
  ⎰Teleutospora jamaicensis (Vestergren) Arth. &
  ⎱ Bisby.
  Uromyces jamaicensis Vestergren.

Bauhinia Pringlei Watson.
  ⎧Telospora bauhiniicola Arth.
  ⎨Teleutospora bauhiniicola (Arth.) Arth. &
  ⎩ Bisby.
  Uromyces bauhiniicola Arth.

Bauhinia ungulata L.
  Uromyces guatemalensis Vestergren.

Bauhinia sp. indet.
  Cladosporium herbarum (P.) ex Lk.
  ⎰Dothidea tenuis B. & C.
  ⎱Phyllachora tenuis (B.) Sacc.
  Podosporium rigidum S.
  Rhytisma Bauhiniae T. F. Nees ex Fr.
  ⎧Uredo Bauhiniae B. & C.
  ⎨Uromyces Bauhiniae (B. & C.) Vestergren.
  ⎩Uromyces imperfectus Arth.

Ceratonia Siliqua L.
  Uredo Hymenaeae Mayor.

Cassia Absus L.
  Ravenelia indica B.

Cassia acutifolia Gray.
  Cercospora nigricans Cke.

Cassia Aeschynomene DC.
  Erysiphe Polygoni DC. (?).
  Ravenelia cassiicola Atk.

Cassia alata L.
  Asterina elaeocarpi Syd.
  Cercospora Chamicristae Ell. & Kellerm.
  Cercospora simulata Ell. & Ev.

Cassia angustisiliqua Torr. & Gray.
  Ravenelia papillifera Syd.

Cassia
   (Chamaefistula antillana Britton & Rose.)
  Irene toruloidea (F. L. Stevens) Stevens &
   Tehon.
  Meliola toruloidea F. L. Stevens.
  Uredo lutea Arth.

Cassia aspera Muhl.
  Ravenelia cassiicola Atk.

Cassia bacillaris L. f.
  Uredo ramonensis Syd.
  Volutella uredinophila Syd.

Cassia bauhinioides Gray.
  Ravenelia mesillana Ell. & Barthol.

Cassia biflora L.
  Ravenelia spinulosa Diet. & Holw.

Cassia Chamicrista L.
  Aecidium Cassiae Ell. & Kellerm.
  Aecidium Chamicristae Arth.
  Cercospora Chamicrista Ell. & Kellerm.
  ⎰Erysiphe communis Auct. Amer.
  ⎱Erysiphe Polygoni DC. †
  Pestalozzia lateripes Ell. & Ev.
  Phytomyxa Leguminosarum (Frank) Schrt.
  ⎰Coriolus vinosus (B.) Pat.
  ⎱Polyporus vinosus B.
  Ravenelia cassiicola Atk.
  Septoria cassiicola Kellerm. & Swingle.
  Thielavia basicola (B. & Br.) Zopf.

Cassia Covesii Gray.
  Ravenelia Cassii-covesii Long & Gooding.

Cassia diphylla L.
  Erysiphe Polygoni DC. † (?).

Cassia emarginata L.
  ⎰Ravenelia Arthuri Long.
  ⎱Ravenelia portoricensis Arth.

Cassia fistula L.
  Ganoderma Dussii Pat.
  Phyllachora canafistulae Stevens & Dalbey.
  Phyllachora Cassiae Henn.

Cassia galeottiana Martens.
  Ravenelia spinulosa Diet. & Holw.

Cassia glandulosa L.
  Meliola Chamicristae Earle.
  Ravenelia cassiicola Atk.

Cassia grandis L.
  Phyllachora canafistulae Stevens & Dalbey.

Cassia granulata (Urb.) Britton.
  Meliola chamicristicola F. L. Stevens.

Cassia hispidula Vahl.
  Ravenelia indica B.

Cassia lindheimeriana Schl.
  ⎰Ravenelia papillifera Syd.
  ⎱Ravenelia spinosa Fung. Columb. *1672*.

Cassia marilandica L.
  Cercospora nigricans Cke.
  Cercospora simulata Ell. & Ev.
  Helminthosporium Cassiae Gerard.
  Vermicularia Dematium (P.) ex Fr.

Cassia multiflora Mart. & Gal.
  Ravenelia spinulosa Diet. & Holw.

Cassia multipinnata (Pollard) Greene.
  Ravenelia cassiicola Atk.

Cassia nictitans L.
  Cercospora pinnulicola Atk.

Cassia occidentalis L.
  Cercospora atromaculans Ell. & Ev.
  Cercospora Chamicristae Ell. & Kellerm.
  Cercospora nigricans Cke.
  ⎰Cercospora occidentalis Cke.
  ⎪Cercospora personata (B. & C.) Sacc., var.
  ⎨ Cassiae-occidentalis Sacc.
  ⎪Cladosporium personatum B. & C., var. Cas-
  ⎱ siae Thm.
  Cercospora personata (B. & C.) Ell. & Ev.
  Cicinnobolus Cesatii DBy.
  Erysiphe Polygoni DC. † (?).
  Macrosporium cassiicola Thm.
  Macrosporium commune Rabh.
  Macrosporium leguminum Cke.
  Macrosporium Ravenelii Thm.
  Phoma Cassiae Sacc.
  Ramularia cassiicola (Ell. & Kellerm.) Heald
    & Wolf.
  Ravenelia longiana Syd.
Cassia oxyphylla Kunth.
  Cercospora greciana Syd.
  Phyllachora deviata Syd.
Cassia quinquangulata L. C. Rich.
  Helminthosporium glabroides F. L. Stevens.
  Helminthosporium Helleri F. L. Stevens.
  Meliola toruloidea F. L. Stevens.
Cassia reticulata Willd.
  Pleosphaerulina Cassiae Henn.
Cassia robiniifolia Benth.
  Ravenelia cubensis Arth. & Johnston.
Cassia roemeriana Scheele.
  ⎰Ravenelia longiana Syd.
  ⎱Ravenelia mesillana Ell. & Barthol.
Cassia Tora L.
  Cercospora atromaculans Ell. & Ev.
  Cercospora nigricans Cke.
  Cercospora Torae Tharp.
  Cicinnobolus Cesatii DBy.
  Erysiphe Polygoni DC. † (?)
  Metasphaeria Carveri Ell. & Ev.

Cassia sp. indet.
  Botryosphaeria Ribis (Tode ex Fr.) Grossen-
    bacher & Duggar, var. chromogena Shear
    et al.
  Helminthosporium cassiicola B. & C.
  Hypoderma commune Duby.
  Irene cubitella Stevens & Tehon.
  Leptosphaeria cassiicola Ell. & Ev.
  Meliola toruloidea F. L. Stevens.
  Mystrosporium polytrichum Cke.
  Physalospora Cassiae (Lév.) Sacc.
  Pleospora Cassiae Ell. & Ev.
  ?Ravenelia inconspicua Arth.
  Sphaeria Cathartocarpi Lév.
Krameria glandulosa Rose & Painter.
Krameria parvifolia Benth.
  Uromyces Krameriae Long.

Gleditsia triacanthos L.

ASCOMYCETES

  ⎰Botryosphaeria rhizogena (B.) Sacc.
  ⎨Melogramma rhizogenum B.
  ⎱Sphaeria rhizogena B.
  ⎰Calloria rubrococcinea Rehm & Wint.
  ⎱Orbilia rubrococcinea (Rehm & Wint.) Sacc.
  Eutypa ludibunda Sacc.
  Eutypella Gleditschiae Berl.
  Glomerella cingulata (Stoneman) Spaulding &
    v. Schrenk.
  ⎰Hysterium flexuosum S.
  ⎱Hysterographium flexuosum (S.) Sacc.
  ⎰Hysterium Lesquereuxii Duby.
  ⎱Hysterographium Lesquereuxii (Duby) Sacc.
  ⎰Calocladia Ravenelii (B.) Rehm.
  ⎨Microsphaera Alni (DC.) Wint. †
  ⎱Microsphaera Ravenelii B.
  Myriangium Curtisii B. & Mont.
  Nummularia discreta (S.) Tul.
  ⎰Chilonectria sphaerospora (Ell. & Ev.) Sacc.
  ⎱Nectria sphaerospora Ell. & Ev.
  Thyronectria sphaerospora (Ell. & Ev.) Seaver.
  ⎰Pleonectria denigrata Wint.
  ⎱Thyronectria denigrata (Wint.) Seaver.
  Valsaria insitiva Ces. & De Not.
  Xylaria polymorpha (P. ex Fr.) Grev.

BASIDIOMYCETES

  Daedalea confragosa (Bolt.) ex Fr.
  ⎰Fomes connatus (Weinm.) Gill.
  ⎨Fomes Meliae (Underw.) Murrill.
  ⎱Polyporus connatus Weinm.
  Hirneola Auricula-Judae (L. ex Fr.) B.
  ⎰Irpex lacteus Fr.
  ⎨Irpex Tulipiferae (S.) Fr.
  ⎱Irpiciporus lacteus (Fr.) Murrill.
  Polyporus albus (Huds.) ex Fr.
  Polyporus sulphureus (Bull.) ex Fr.
  Polyporus versicolor (L.) ex Fr.
  ⎰Fuscoporia ferruginea Fung. Columb. *4420.*
  ⎱Poria ferruginosa (Schrad. ex Fr.) Cke.
  Poria incrassata (B. & C.) Burt.
  Poria vaporaria Fr.
  ⎰Dendroecia opaca (Diet.) Arth.
  ⎨Ravenelia indica, var. opaca Seymour & Earle.
  ⎱Ravenelia opaca Diet.
  Schizophyllum commune Fr.

FUNGI IMPERFECTI

  ⎰Cercospora Berkeleyi Cke.
  ⎪Cercospora olivacea (B. & Rav.) Wint.
  ⎨Cercospora seymouriana Wint.
  ⎱Helminthosporium olivaceum B. & Rav.
  Cercospora condensata Ell. & Kellerm.
  Ceuthospora Gleditschiae Ell. & Barthol.
  Cytospora Gleditschiae (Ell. & Barthol.)
    Ferdinandsen & Winge.

Gleditsia triacanthos (*cont.*)
 Cylindrocladium scoparium Morg.
 Diplocladium cylindrosporum Ell. & Ev.
 Discosia Artocreas (Tode) ex Fr.
 Fusarium gleditsiicola Dearness & Barthol.
 Glenospora Curtisii B. & Desm.
 Haplosporella gleditschiicola (Cke.) Ell. &
   Ev. 1896.
 Haplosporella gleditschiicola (Cke.) Petrak &
   Syd. 1926.
 Sphaeropsis gleditschiicola Cke.
 Sphaeropsis triacanthi Ell. & Barthol.
 Libertella Gleditschiae Wint.
 Leptostroma hypophyllum B. & Rav.
 Melasmia Gleditschiae (Lév.) Ell. & Ev.
 Melasmia hypophylla (B. & Rav.) Sacc.
 Sacidium Gleditschiae Lév.
 Pestalozzia monorhyncha (Speg.) Sacc.
 Phomopsis occidentalis Sacc., var. irregularis
   Trav.
 Tubercularia vulgaris Tode ex Fr.

MISCELLANEA

 Didymium rugulosum B.
Gleditsia sp. indet.
 Acontium minus Morg.
 Cladosporium Gleditschiae Cke.
 Cucurbitaria elongata (Fr.) Grev.
 Botryosphaeria Gleditschiae (S.) Sacc.
 Cucurbitaria Gleditschiae (S.) B. & C.
 Cucurbitaria recuperata Theissen.
 Melogramma Gleditschiae (S.) M. A. Curtis.
 Sphaeria Gleditschiae S.
 Valsaria Gleditschiae (S.) Ell. & Ev.
 Dothidea Encoelium S.
 Eutypella conseptata (S.) Ell. & Ev.
 Sphaeria conseptata S.
 Valsa conseptata (S.) Cke.
 Fomes applanatus (P. ex Wallr.) Gill.
 Polyporus lucidus (Leyss.) ex Fr.
 Fusarium anomalum B. & C.
 Helotium discretum Karst.
 Hysterium lineare B. nec Fr.
 Hysterium lineariforme Sacc.
 Hysterographium Mori (S.) Rehm.
 Kalmusia aspera Morg.
 Lachnella cinereofusca (S.) Sacc.
 Peziza cinereofusca S.
 Macrophoma mamillaris (B. & C.) Tassi.
 Phoma mamillaris (B. & C.) Sacc.
 Sphaeropsis mamillaris B. & C.
 Macrophoma triacanthi (Sacc.) Berl. & Vogl.
 Phoma triacanthi Sacc.
 Sphaeropsis Gleditschiae Cke.
 Nectria nigrescens Cke.
 Poria ambigua Bres.
 Poria Medulla-panis (P. ex Fr.) Cke.
 Sphaeria amorphostoma S.
 Valsa amorphostoma (S.) Cke.

 Sphaeria Notarisii Mont.
 Valsa Notarisii Mont.
 Valsaria Notarisii (Mont.) Sacc.
Gymnocladus dioica (L.) Koch.
 Amerosporium subclausum Ell. & Kellerm.
 Cercospora Gymnocladi Ell. & Kellerm.
 Cercospora superflua Ell. & Holw.
 Coniothyrium olivaceum Bon., v. Gymnocladi
   Hollos.
 Phyllosticta Gymnocladi Tehon & Daniels.
 Vermicularia albomaculata S. ?
Parkinsonia aculeata L.
 Corticium tephrum B. & C.
 Cylindrosporium Parkinsoniae Heald.
 Dimerosporium Parkinsoniae Heald & Wolf.
 Phyllosticta Parkinsoniae Ell. & Ev.
Parkinsonia torreyana Watson.
 Asteroma Parkinsoniae Ell. & Ev.
Haematoxylon campechianum L.
 Coriolus pinsitus (Fr.) Pat.
 Fomes Haematoxyli (Murrill) Sacc. & D. Sacc.
 Pyropolyporus Haematoxyli Murrill.
 Ganoderma subincrustatum Murrill.
 Peniophora citrinella (B. & C.) Burt.
Poinciana regia Boj. ex Hook.
 Botryosphaeria Ribis (Tode ex Fr.) Grossen-
   bacher & Duggar.
 Diatrypella verruciformis, var. spegazziniana
   Sacc.
Hoffmanseggia oxycarpa Benth.
 Ravenelia Hoffmanseggiae Long.
Caesalpinia bahamensis Lam.
 Ravenelia humphreyana Henn.
Caesalpinia Bonduc Wight & Arn.
 Peziza striata Bert.
 Phyllosticta Bonduc F. L. Stevens.
Caesalpinia coriacea Poit.
 Fomes lucidus (Leyss. ex Fr.) Cke.
Caesalpinia Crista L.
 Cercospora guanicensis E. Young.
 Phyllosticta guanicensis E. Young.
Caesalpinia exostemma Moc. & Sesse.
 Ravenelia inconspicua Arth.
Caesalpinia pulcherrima Sw.
 Botryosphaeria Ribis (Tode ex Fr.) Grossen-
   bacher & Duggar, var. chromogena Shear
   et al.
 Pestalozzia funerea Desm.
 Ravenelia humphreyana Henn.
 Ravenelia pulcherrima Arth.
Caesalpinia sp. indet.
 Uredo bauhiniicola Henn.
Swartzia sp. indet.
 Phyllachora copeyensis Henn.
Ateleia cubensis Griseb.
 Phyllachora Ateleiae Seaver.
Dussia martinicensis Krug & Urban.
 Catacauma Dussiae Syd.
 Mycobonia flava (B.) Pat.

Ormosia dasycarpa Jacks.
{ Leptoporus Braunii (Rabh.) Pat.
{ Polyporus rufoflavus B. & C.
Ormosia Kingii Urb.
{ Dicaeoma Ormosiae Arth.
{ Puccinia Ormosiae Arth.
Ormosia mexicana Standl.
Dermatella mirabilis Syd.
Pleurophomella mirabilis Syd.
Castanospermum australe A. Cunn. & Fraser.
Clethris Castanospermi Ciferri & Fragoso.
Sophora japonica L.
Microsphaera Alni (DC.) Wint. †
Ozonium omnivorum Shear.
Sophora sericea Nutt.
{ Klebahnia hyalina (Pk.) Arth.
{ Telospora hyalina (Pk.) Arth.
{ Uromyces hyalinus Pk.
{ Uromyces Sophorae Pk.
Sophora speciosa Torr.
Phyllosticta Sophorae Ell. & Ev.
Sophora secundiflora Lag.
Phyllosticta Sophorae Ell. & Ev.
Sophora sp. indet.
Microsphaera Sophorae Gandara.
Thermopsis arenosa A. Nels.
Cercospora Thermopsidis Earle.
Thermopsis californica Watson.
Stigmina Thermopsidis Hark.
Thermopsis divaricarpa A. Nels.
Erysiphe Polygoni DC. †
Thermopsis montana Nutt.
{ Erysiphe communis Auct. Amer.
{ Erysiphe Polygoni DC. †
Ramularia sphaerioides Ell. & Ev.
Thermopsis pinetorum Greene.
Coniothyrium olivaceum, var. Thermopsidis Fairman.
Phoma herbarum Westd.
Thermopsis rhombifolia Richard.
Phoma Thermopsidis Ell. & Gall.
Baptisia australis (L.) R. Br.
Aecidium Kellermanii De Toni.
Aecidium Onobrychidis Burrill.
Cercospora velutina Ell. & Kellerm.
Erysiphe Polygoni DC. †
Baptisia bracteata (Muhl.) Ell.
{ Aecidium amphigenum Ell. & Kellerm.
{ Aecidium Kellermannii De Toni.
Aecidium Onobrychidis Burrill.
Cercospora velutina Ell. & Kellerm.
Microsphaera Alni (DC.) Wint. †
Sphaerella leucophaea Ell. & Kellerm.
Baptisia leucantha Torr. & Gr.
Aecidium Kellermannii De Toni.
Ascochyta Baptisiae J. J. Davis.
Cercospora velutina Ell. & Kellerm.
{ Marssonia Baptisiae Ell. & Ev.
{ Marssonina Baptisiae (Ell. & Ev.) Magn.

{ Mycosphaerella baptisiicola (Cke.) Earle.
{ Sphaerella baptisiicola (Cke.) Sacc.
{ Sphaeria baptisiicola Cke.
Baptisia perfoliata R. Br.
{ Anthostomella Bapisiae (Cke.) Sacc.
{ Sphaeria Baptisiae Ctke.
{ Coniothyrium Baptisiae (Thm.) Roum.
{ Sphaeropsis Baptisiae Thm.
Haplosporella Baptisiae Petrak & Syd.
Macrosporium Baptisiae Thm.
Phoma Baptisiae Cke.
Septoria Baptisiae Cke.
Baptisia tinctoria R. Br.
Diaporthe Baptisiae Rehm.
{ Erysiphe Martii Lév.
{ Erysiphe Polygoni DC. †
{ Heptameria comatella (C. & E.) Cke.
{ Leptosphaeria comatella (C. & E.) Sacc.
{ Sphaeria comatella C. & E.
Mollisia plicata (Rehm) Sacc., var. Baptisiae Dearness & House.
{ Mycosphaerella baptisiicola (Cke.) Earle.
{ Sphaerella baptisiicola (Cke.) Sacc.
{ Sphaeria baptisiicola Cke.
Sphaerella granulata Ell. & Ev.
Crotalaria guatemalensis Benth.
Cercosporina josensis Syd.
Crotalaria longirostrata Arth.
Crotalaria maypurensis H. B. K.
{ Hapalopyxis Crotalariae (Arth.) Syd.
{ Uropyxis Crotalariae Arth.
Crotalaria retusa L.
Microsphaera diffusa C. & P.
{ Dimerium grammodes (Kze. ex B. & C.) P. Garman.
{ Dothidella grammodes (Kze. ex B. & C.) Sacc.
{ Parodiella grammodes (Kze. ex B. & C.) Cke.
{ Parodiella perisporioides (B. & C.) Speg.
Crotalaria rotundifolia (Walt.) Poir.
Parodiella paraguayensis Speg.
Crotalaria sagittalis L.
Cercospora demetrioniana Wint.
Crotalaria sericea Retz.
{ Sporidesmium polymorphum Cda.
{ Stemphylium polymorphum (Cda.) Thm.
Crotalaria usaramoensis E. G. Baker.
Sclerotium rolfsii Sacc.
Crotalaria verrucosa L.
{ Sporidesmium polymorphum Cda.
{ Stemphylium polymorphum (Cda.) Thm.
Crotalaria vitellina Ker.
Hapalopyxis Crotalariae (Arth.) Syd.
{ Nigredo (?) decorata (Syd.) Arth.
{ Uromyces decoratus Syd.
Crotalaria sp. indet.
{ Corticium vagum B. &C.
{ Rhizoctonia Solani Kühn.
Oidium erysiphoides Fr., var. Crotalariae Ciferri & Fragoso.

Lupinus aduncus Greene.
  Phoma Lupini Ell. & Ev.
  Nigredo Lupini (B. & C.) Arth.
  Nigredo substriata (Syd.) Arth.
Lupinus albifrons Benth.
  Hadrotrichum Lupini Ell. & Ev.
  Phyllosticta ferax Ell. & Ev.
  { Nigredo Lupini (B. & C.) Arth.
  { Uromyces Lupini B. & C.
Lupinus ammophilus Greene.
  { Nigredo occidentalis (Diet.) Arth.
  { Uromyces occidentalis Diet.
Lupinus amplus Greene.
  Nigredo Lupini (B. & C.) Arth.
Lupinus arboreus Sims.
  Armillaria mellea (Vahl) ex Fr.
  Collybia velutipes Fr.
  { Dialonectria depallens Cke. & Hark.
  { Nectria depallens (Cke. & Hark.) Berl. & Vogl.
  Diaporthe Lupini Hark.
  { Didymella Lupini (Cke. & Hark.) Berl. & Vogl.
  { Sphaeria Lupini Cke. & Hark.
  Diplodia Lupini Cke. & Hark.
  Hymenula Lupini Cke. & Hark.
  { Macrophoma Lupini (Cke. & Hark.) Berl. & Vogl.
  { Phoma Lupini Cke. & Hark.
  Metasphaeria Lathyri Sacc.
  Pleospora leguminum (Wallr.) Rabh.
  { Pleurage Brassicae (Klotzsch) O. Kuntze.
  { Podospora Brassicae (Klotzsch) Wint.
  { Sphaeria Brassicae Klotzsch.
  Sordaria lanuginosa Sacc.
  Sphaeropsis Lupini Cke. & Hark.
  Stictis decipiens Karst.
  Stictis Lupini Phil. & Hark.
  Nigredo occidentalis (Diet.) Arth.
  Valsa Lupini Cke. & Hark.
Lupinus argenteus Pursh.
  Aecidium Onobrychidis Burrill.
  Uromyces Lupini B. & C.
  Nigredo occidentalis (Diet.) Arth.
  { Nigredo substriata (Syd.) Arth.
  { Uromyces Genistae-tinctoriae Auct. Amer. p. p.
  { Uromyces striatus Auct. Amer. p. p.
  { Uromyces substriatus Syd.
Lupinus argenteus Pursh., var. **argophyllus** Watson.
  { Erysiphe communis Auct. Amer. p. p.
  { Erysiphe Polygoni DC. †
Lupinus arcticus Watson.
  Dendrophoma Lupini-arctici Dearness.
Lupinus Bakeri Greene.
  Uromyces occidentalis Diet.
Lupinus Bridgesii (Watson) Greene.
  Nigredo Lupini (B. & C.) Arth.
Lupinus caespitosus Nutt.
  { Nigredo occidentalis (Diet.) Arth.
  { Uromyces occidentalis Diet.

Lupinus campestris Cham. & Schl.
  Nigredo Lupini (B. & C.) Arth.
Lupinus Chamissonis Esch.
  Hendersonia Lupini Cke. & Hark.
  Nigredo Lupini (B. & C.) Arth.
Lupinus Clarkiae Oerst.
  Chrysocelis Lupini Lagerh. & Diet. I.
Lupinus decumbens Torr.
  Nigredo Lupini (B. & C.) Arth.
Lupinus densiflorus Benth.
  Septoria Lupini Hark.
Lupinus diffusus Nutt.
  Cercospora Lupini Cke.
  Septosporium Lupini Thm.
Lupinus Douglasii Agardh.
  { Uredo Lupini B. & C.
  { Uromyces Lupini B. & C.
  { Nigredo occidentalis (Diet.) Arth.
  { Uromyces occidentalis Diet.
Lupinus elegans H. B. K.
  { Nigredo Lupini (B. & C.) Arth.
  { Uromyces Lupini B. & C.
Lupinus formosus Greene.
  Phyllosticta ferax Ell. & Ev.
  Uromyces Lupini B. & C.
Lupinus Hallii Rusby.
  Cladosporium herbarum (P.) ex Lk., var.
  Pleospora infectoria Fckl.
Lupinus hirsutus L.
  Thielavia basicola (B. & Br.) Zopf.
Lupinus holosericeus Nutt.
  Nigredo Lupini (B. & C.) Arth.
  { Nigredo occidentalis (Diet.) Arth.
  { Uromyces occidentalis Diet.
Lupinus humicola A. Nels.
  Hadrotrichum Lupini Ell. & Ev.
Lupinus ingratus Greene.
  Leptosphaeria lupinicola Earle.
  Phoma [innominata] Fairman.
Lupinus Kingii Watson.
  Tuberculina Lupini Farl.
  Uromyces Lupini B. & C.
  Uromyces occidentalis Diet.
Lupinus latifolius Lindl. ex Agardh.
  Cylindrosporium Lupini Ell. & Ev.
  Uromyces occidentalis Diet.
Lupinus laxiflorus Dougl.
  Uromyces Lupini B. & C.
  { Nigredo substriata (Syd.) Arth.
  { Puccinia Lupini West Am. Fung. *279.*
  { Uromyces Lupini West Am. Fung *279.*
Lupinus leptophyllus Benth.
  { Nigredo occidentalis (Diet.) Arth.
  { Uromyces occidentalis Diet.
Lupinus leucophyllus Dougl.
  Erysiphe Polygoni DC. †
  Nigredo Lupini (B. & C.) Arth.

Lupinus Losani Rose.
Nigredo Lupini (B. & C.) Arth.
Lupinus Lyallii Gray.
Nigredo occidentalis (Diet.) Arth.
Lupinus mexicanus H. B. K.
{ Pucciniola montana Arth.
Telospora montana Arth.
Uromyces montanus Arth.
Lupinus montanus H. B. K.
Uromyces montanus Arth.
Lupinus monticola Ryd.
Nigredo substriata (Syd.) Arth.
Lupinus nootkatensis Donn., var. **Kjellmanii** ex
J. Lind.
Phoma herbarum Westd.
Pleospora Anthyllidis Awd.
Lupinus ornatus Dougl.
Stictochorella Lupini Syd.
Lupinus Palmeri Watson.
Nigredo occidentalis (Diet.) Arth.
Nigredo substriata (Syd.) Arth.
Lupinus parviflorus Nutt.
Erysiphe communis (Wallr.) Schl.
Uromyces occidentalis Diet.
Lupinus perennis L.
Aecidium Lupini Pk.
Aecidium Onobrychidis Burrill.
Ascochyta Pisi Lib.
Ascochyta Pisi Lib., var. Lupini Sacc.
Cercospora filispora Pk.
{ Cercospora longispora Pk.
Cercoseptoria longissima (Pk.) Petrak.
Cylindrosporium longisporum Ell. & Dearness.
{ Erysiphe communis Auct. Amer.
Erysiphe Martii Lév.
Erysiphe Polygoni DC. †
Peronospora Trifoliorum DBy.
Sclerotinia sclerotiorum (Lib.) Massee.
Septogloeum Lupini Ell. & Ev.
Septoria lupinicola Dearness.
Tuberculina persicina (Ditm. ex Fr.) Sacc.
Lupinus plattensis Watson.
Phoma Lupini Ell. & Ev.
{ Uredo Lupini B. & C.
Uromyces Astragali (Opiz) Sacc., var. Lupini
De Toni.
Uromyces Lupini B. & C.
Lupinus polyphyllus Lindl.
Uromyces Lupini B. & C.
Uromyces Orobi Fckl.
Lupinus pulcherrimus Ryd.
{ Nigredo occidentalis (Diet.)Arth.
Uromyces lupinicola Auct. Amer. p. p.
Uromyces occidentalis Diet.
Uromyces rugosus Arth.
Lupinus pusillus Pursh.
Nigredo occidentalis (Diet.) Arth.

Lupinus rivularis Dougl.
Cylindrosporium Lupini Ell. & Ev.
{ Nigredo Lupini Arth.
Uredo Lupini B. & C.
Uromyces Anthyllidis Fung. Columb. 2290.
Uromyces Lupini B. & C.
Lupinus sericeus Pursh.
{ Erysiphe communis Auct. Amer.
Erysiphe Polygoni DC. †
Nigredo Lupini (B. & C.) Arth.
Nigredo substriata (Syd.) Arth.
Lupinus sparsiflorus Benth.
Placosphaeria Lupini Syd.
Lupinus Stiveri Kellogg.
{ Hadrotrichum globiferum (Ell. & Ev.) J. J.
Davis.
Ovularia? globifera Ell. & Ev.
Lupinus Suksdorfii B. L. Robinson.
Lupinus sulphureus Dougl.
{ Nigredo Lupini (B. & C.) Arth.
Uromyces Lupini B. & C.
Lupinus texensis Hook.
Cercospora texensis Tharp 1917 non Ell. &
Gall. 1898.
Erysiphe Polygoni DC. †
Lupinus villosus Willd.
Cercospora longispora Pk.
Lupinus sp. indet.
Botrytis cinerea P. †
Cryptosporium Lupini Cke.
Gloeosporium lupinicola Dearness.
Leptosphaeria foeniculacea H. Fabr., var.
lupina Sacc. & Scalia.
Mastigosporium Lupini (Sor.) Cav.
Nectria coccinea (P.) ex Fr.
Nectria Peziza (Tode) ex Fr.
Ovularia sphaeroidea Sacc.
Penicillium glaucum Lk.
Phoma lupinicola Earle.
Phytophthora terrestris Sherbakoff.
Pleospora amplispora Ell. & Ev.
Pleospora herbarum (Fr.) Rabh.
Ramularia Lupini J. J. Davis.
Sorosporium Astragali Pk.
Trematosphaeria Lupini Earle.
Trichopeziza earoleuca (B. & Br.) Sacc.
Genista tinctoria L.
{ Diatrype collecta (S.) Cke.
Dothidea collecta (S.) Ell. & Ev.
Dothidea crystallophora B. & C.
Dothidea Lonicerae Cke.
Dothidea tetraspora B. & Br.
Parodiella tetraspora (B. & Br.) Kellerm. &
Carleton.
Sphaeria collecta S.
Genista sp. indet.
?Eutypa ludibunda Sacc.
Laburnum sp. indet.
Stereum purpureum P. †

Ulex europaeus L.
Thielavia basicola (B. & Br.) Zopf.
Cytisus scoparius (L.) Lk.
Diaporthe Sarothamni Nits.
Diplodia Sarothamni Cke. & Hark.
{ Leptosphaeria californica (Cke. & Hark.) Berl.
& Vogl.
{ Metasphaeria californica (Cke. & Hark.) Berl.
{ Sphaeria californica Cke. & Hark.
Pestalozzia polychaeta Cke. & Hark.
Phoma Sarothamni Cke.
Thielavia basicola (B. & Br.) Zopf.
Cytisus sp. indet.
Ceratophorum setosum Kirch.
Trigonella foenum-graecum L.
Thielavia basicola (B. & Br.) Zopf.
Medicago arabica Huds.
Cercospora Medicaginis Ell. & Ev.
Colletotrichum Trifolii Bain.
Pseudoplea Medicaginis Miles.
Sphaerulina Trifolii Rostr.
Medicago arborea L.
Phyllosticta bonanseana Sacc.
Medicago falcata L.
{ Nigredo Medicaginis (Sacc.) Arth.
{ Uromyces striatus Schrt.
Urophlyctis Alfalfae (Lagerh.) Magn.
Medicago hispida Gaertn.
Cercospora Medicaginis Ell. & Ev.
Colletotrichum Trifolii Bain.
Thielavia basicola (B. & Br.) Zopf.
{ Nigredo Medicaginis (Sacc.) Arth.
{ Uromyces Medicaginis Sacc.
{ Uromyces Medicaginis-falcatae Wint.
{ Uromyces striatus Schrt.
?Medicago indica Auct.
Entyloma Meliloti McAlpine.
Medicago lupulina L.
Cercospora helvola Sacc.
Cercospora Medicaginis Ell. & Ev.
Peronospora Trifoliorum DBy.
Pseudopeziza Medicaginis (Lib.) Sacc.
{ Gloeosporium Medicaginis (Rob. & Desm.)
Ell. & Kellerm.
{ ?Septogloeum Medicaginis (Rob. & Desm.) Ell.
& Ev.
{ Septoria Medicaginis Rob. & Desm.
{ Ascochyta Medicaginis (Voss) Bres.
{ Stagonospora Medicaginis (Voss) Bubák.
{ Nigredo Medicaginis (Pass.) Arth.
{ Uromyces Medicaginis Pass.
{ Uromyces Medicaginis-falcatae Wint.
{ Uromyces striatus Schrt.
Medicago sativa L.

PHYCOMYCETES

Aphanomyces euteiches Drechsler.
Asterocystis radicis DeWilld.
Olpidium Brassicae (Wor.) Dangeard.

Peronospora aestivalis Syd.
Peronospora Trifoliorum DBy.
Pythium debaryanum Hesse.
Urophlyctis Alfalfae (Lagerh.) Magn.

PEZIZINEAE

{ Phacidium Medicaginis Lib.
{ Pseudopeziza Medicaginis (Lib.) Sacc.
{ Ascobolus Trifolii Biv.
{ Phacidium Trifolii (Biv.) Boud.
{ Pseudopeziza Trifolii (Biv.) Fckl.
Pseudopeziza Trifolii, var. Medicaginis Auct.
Pyrenopeziza Medicaginis Fckl.
{ Sclerotinia libertiana Fckl.
{ Sclerotinia sclerotiorum (Lib.) Massee.
Sclerotinia Trifoliorum Erikss.

PYRENOMYCETINEAE

{ Erysiphe Martii Lév.
{ Erysiphe Polygoni P. †
Erysiphe Trifolii Grev.
Gibberella Saubinetii (Mont.) Sacc.
Pleospora Alfalfae Auct.
Pleospora herbarum (Fr.) Rabh.
Pleospora hyalospora Ell. & Ev.
Sphaerella Tulasnei Jancz.
Sphaerulina Trifolii Rostr.

BASIDIOMYCETES

{ Corticium vagum B. & C.
{ Rhizoctonia Solani Kühn.
Tilletia glomerulata Cocconi & Morini.
Uromyces appendiculatus Lk.
{ Nigredo Medicaginis (Pass.) Arth.
{ Uromyces Medicaginis Pass.
{ Uromyces Medicaginis-falcatae Wint.
{ Uromyces striatus Schrt.
{ Uromyces Trifolii Auct. Amer. p. p.

SPHAEROPSIDALES

Ascochyta imperfecta Pk.
Ascochyta Medicaginis (Voss) Bres.
Ascochyta Pisi Lib.
Ascochyta Pisi Lib., var. Medicaginis Sacc.
Diplodina Medicaginis Oud.
Phoma herbarum Westd., var. Medicaginis
Rabh.
{ Phyllosticta Medicaginis (Fckl.) Sacc.
{ Sporonema phacidioides Desm.
{ Rhabdospora allantoidea (B. & C.) Sacc.
{ Septoria allantoidea B. & C.
Stagonospora carpathica Bäumler.

MELANCONIALES

Colletotrichum Trifolii Bain.
Gloeosporium Medicaginis Ell. & Kellerm.
Gloeosporium Morianum Sacc.
Marssonia Medicaginis (Voss) Magn.
Septogloeum Medicaginis (Rob. & Desm.) Ell.
& Ev.

Medicago sativa (*cont.*)

HYPHOMYCETES

Cercospora helvola Sacc.
Cercospora helvola Sacc., var. Medicaginis Chester.
Cercospora Medicaginis Ell. & Ev.
Fusarium radicicola Wr.
Fusarium roseum Lk.
Haplographium toruloides (Fres.) Sacc.
Macrosporium commune Rabh.
{ Macrosporium sarciniforme Cav.
Thyrospora sarciniforme (Cav.) Tehon & Daniels.
Macrosporium Sarcinula B.
?Ovularia Medicaginis Briosi & Cav.
Periconia pycnospora Fres.
{ Ozonium omnivorum Shear.
Phymatotrichum omnivorum (Shear) Duggar.
Pionnotes rhizophila (Cda.) Sacc.
Sporotrichum globuliferum Speg.
Volutella gilva (P.) Sacc.

MISCELLANEA

Didymium difforme (P.) Duby.
Mycorrhiza of Legumes F. R. Jones.
Ozonium auricomum Lk.
{ Rhizoctonia Crocorum (P. ex Fr.) DC.
Rhizoctonia Medicaginis DC.
Rhizoctonia violacea Auct. Amer.
Sclerotium Rolfsii Sacc.
Thielavia basicola (B. & Br.) Zopf.

Medicago tuberculata Willd.
Nigredo Medicaginis (Sacc.) Arth.

Melilotus alba Desr.
Ascochyta Abelmoschi Harter.
Ascochyta caulicola Laubert.
Cercospora Davisii Ell. & Ev.
Colletotrichum Trifolii Bain.
Corticium vagum B. & C.
Diaporthe Phaseolorum (C. & E.) Sacc.
Fusarium eumartii C. W. Carpenter.
Fusarium hyperoxysporum Wr.
Fusarium vasinfectum, var. inodoratum Wollen.
Gloeosporium caulivorum Kirch.
Gloeosporium vexans Atk.
Leptosphaeria dumetorum Niessl.
Macrosporium Meliloti Pk.
{ Ascochyta caulicola Laubert.
Ascochyta lethalis Ell. & Barthol.
Ascochyta Meliloti (Trel.) J. J. Davis.
Gloeosporium Meliloti Trel.
Marssonia Meliloti (Trel.) Sacc.
Marssonina Meliloti (Trel.) Magn.
Mycosphaerella lethalis R. E. Stone.
Mycorrhiza of Legumes F. R. Jones.
Ozonium omnivorum Shear.
Peronospora Trifoliorum DBy.

Phoma Meliloti Allescher.
Phoma oleracea Sacc.
Phoma oleracea, var. Meliloti Sacc.
Phoma tuberosa Melhus et al.
Plenodomus destruens Harter.
Pleospora kansensis Ell. & Ev.
Pleospora Meliloti Rabh.
Pseudopeziza Medicaginis (Lib.) Sacc.
Sclerotinia Trifoliorum Erikss.
Sphaerella linhartiana Niessl.
Sphaerulina Trifolii Rostr.
Stagonospora Meliloti (Lasch) Petrak.
Stagonospora Meliloti Dearness & House. 1921.
Thielavia basicola (B. & Br.) Zopf.
Vermicularia Dematium (P.) ex Fr., var. Meliloti Pk.

Melilotus indica All.
Ramularia Meliloti Ell. & Ev.
Thielavia basicola (B. & Br.) Zopf.

Melilotus officinalis (L.) Lam.
{ Ascochyta lethalis Ell. & Barthol.
Mycosphaerella lethalis R. E. Stone.
Mycorrhiza of Legumes F. R. Jones.
Sphaerulina Trifolii Rostr.

Melilotus sp. indet.
{ Cyphina lanuginosa (Pk.) Sacc.
Excipula lanuginosa Pk.
Didymium xanthopus (Ditm.) Fr.
Erysiphe Polygoni DC. †
Fusarium Batatas Wollenw.
{ Heptameria viridella (Pk.) Cke.
Leptosphaeria viridella (Pk.) Sacc.
Sphaeria viridella Pk.
Periconia pycnospora Fres.
Sclerotinia Trifoliorum Erikss.

Trifolium agrarium L.
Cercospora zebrina Fung. Columb. *461.*

Trifolium albopurpureum Torr. & Gr.
{ Pucciniola oblonga (Vize) Arth.
Uromyces minor Schrt.
Uromyces oblongus Vize.

Trifolium amabile H. B. K.
Uromyces Trifolii (Hedw. f.) Lév.

Trifolium amphianthum Torr. & Gr.
Uromyces minor Schrt.
{ Nigredo Trifolii (Hedw. f.) Arth.
Uromyces Trifolii (Hedw. f.) Lév.

Trifolium andinum Nutt.
Pucciniola oblonga (Vize) Arth.

Trifolium arvense L.
Cercospora helvola Sacc.

Trifolium bifidum Gray.
Trifolium Breweri Watson.
Pucciniola oblonga (Vize) Arth.

Trifolium carolinianum Michx.
Peronospora Trifoliorum DBy.
⎰Aecidium elegans B. & C.
⎱Aecidium Orobi, var. elegans B.
⎰Uromyces elegans Lagerh.
⎱Uromyces Trifolii Auct. Amer. p. p.
⎰Uromyces Medicaginis-falcatae Wint.
⎱Uromyces striatus Schrt.

Trifolium ciliatum Nutt.
Pucciniola oblonga (Vize) Arth.
Uromyces elegans Lagerh.
Uromyces Trifolii (Hedw. f.) Lév.

Trifolium dasyphyllum Torr. & Gr.

Trifolium depauperatum Desv.
⎰Pucciniola oblonga (Vize) Arth.
⎪Uromyces minor Schrt.
⎪Uromyces oblongus Vize.
⎱Uromyces Trifolii Fung. Columb. *1797.*

Trifolium dubium Sibth.
Cercospora zebrina Pass.
Erysiphe Polygoni DC. †
⎰Pucciniola oblonga (Vize) Arth.
⎪Uromyces minor Schrt.
⎱Uromyces oblongus Vize.

Trifolium eriocephalum Nutt.
⎰Pucciniola oblonga (Vize) Arth.
⎱Uromyces oblongus Vize.

Trifolium Fendleri Greene.
Phyllachora Trifolii (P. ex Fr.) Fckl.
Polythrincium Trifolii Kze.
Pucciniola oblonga (Vize) Arth.

Trifolium gracilentum Torr. & Gr.

Trifolium gymnocarpon Nutt.

Trifolium Hallii Howell.
⎰Pucciniola oblonga (Vize) Arth.
⎪Uromyces minor Schrt.
⎪Uromyces oblongus Vize.
⎱Uromyces Trifolii Syd. Ured. *860.*

Trifolium hybridum L.
Cercospora zebrina Pass.
Colletotrichum Trifolii Bain.
Corticium vagum B. & C.
⎰Erysiphe Martii Lév.
⎱Erysiphe Polygoni DC. †
Macrosporium sarciniforme Cav.
Mycorrhiza of Legumes F. R. Jones.
Phyllachora Trifolii (P. ex Fr.) Fckl.
Polythrincium Trifolii Kze.
Sclerotinia Trifoliorum Erikss.
Sphaerulina Trifolii Rostr.
Stagonospora Trifolii Ell. & Dearness.
Thielavia basicola (B. & Br.) Zopf.
⎰Caeomurus Trifolii (Hedw. f.) S. F. Gray.
⎪Nigredo Trifolii (Hedw. f.) Arth.
⎪Uromyces hybridi W. H. Davis.
⎪Uromyces Trifolii (Hedw. f.) Lév.
⎱Uromyces Trifolii-repentis Liro.

Trifolium incarnatum L.
Cercospora helvola Sacc., var. Medicaginis Chester.
Cercospora Medicaginis Ell. & Ev.
Colletotrichum Trifolii Bain.
Corticium vagum B. & C.
Gloeosporium caulivorum Kirch.
Phyllachora Trifolii (P. ex Fr.) Fckl.
Polythrincium Trifolii Kze.
Sclerotinia libertiana Fckl.
Sclerotinia Trifoliorum Erikss.
Sclerotium Rolfsii Sacc.
Sphaerulina Trifolii Rostr.
Thielavia basicola (B. & Br.) Zopf.
⎰Nigredo fallens (Kern.) Arth.
⎱Uromyces fallens Kern.
⎰Nigredo Trifolii (Hedw. f.) Arth.
⎪Uromyces Trifolii (Hedw. f.) Lév.
⎱Uromyces Trifolii-repentis Liro.

Trifolium involucratum Willd.
⎰Erysiphe communis Auct. Amer.
⎱Erysiphe Polygoni DC. †
Phyllachora Trifolii (P. ex Fr.) Fckl.
⎰Uromyces minor Schrt.
⎱Uromyces Trifolii West Am. Fung. *365.*

Trifolium Kingii Watson.
Leptosphaeria monticola Ell. & Ev.
Uromyces oblongus Vize.

Trifolium Logani House.
Nigredo Trifolii (Hedw. f.) Arth.

Trifolium longipes Nutt.
⎰Erysiphe communis Auct. Amer.
⎱Erysiphe Polygoni DC. †

Trifolium Macraei Hook. & Arn.
⎰Pucciniola oblonga (Vize) Arth.
⎪Uromyces oblongus Vize.
⎱?Uromyces Trifolii Auct. Amer. p. p.

Trifolium macrocephalum Poir.
Uromyces Trifolii (Hedw. f.) Lév.

Trifolium medium L.
⎰Nigredo fallens Arth.
⎱Uromyces Trifolii Fung. Columb. *2997.*

Trifolium megacephalum Nutt.
⎰Nigredo Trifolii (Hedw. f.) Arth.
⎱Uromyces oblongus N. Am. Uredinales *294.*

Trifolium michelianum Savi.
Polythrincium Trifolii Kze.

Trifolium microcephalum Pursh.
⎰Pucciniola oblonga (Vize) Arth.
⎪Uromyces oblongus Vize.
⎱Uromyces Trifolii Auct. Amer. p. p.

Trifolium microdon Hook. & Arn.
Pseudopeziza Trifolii (Biv.) Fckl.
⎰Pucciniola oblonga (Vize) Arth.
⎪Uromyces minor Schrt.
⎱Uromyces oblongus Vize.

Trifolium monanthum Gray.
⎰Erysiphe communis Auct. Amer.
⎱Erysiphe Polygoni DC. †

Trifolium nanum Torr.
  Pleospora herbarum (Fr.) Rabh.

Trifolium obtusiflorum Hook.
  ⎰Uromyces minor Schrt.
  ⎱Uromyces oblongus Vize.
  ?Uromyces Trifolii (Hedw. f.) Lév.

Trifolium oliganthum Steud.
Trifolium olivaceum Greene.
Trifolium Parryi Gray.
  ⎰Pucciniola oblonga (Vize) Arth.
  ⎱Uromyces oblongus Vize.

Trifolium pratense L.
  Cercospora helvola Sacc., var. Medicaginis
    Chester.
  Cercospora Medicaginis Ell. & Ev.
  Cercospora zebrina Pass.
  Cicinnobolus Cesatii D.By.
  Colletotrichum destructivum O'Gara.
  Colletotrichum Trifolii Bain.
  Erysiphe Polygoni DC. †
  Fusarium roseum Lk.
  Gloeosporium caulivorum Kirch.
  Gloeosporium Trifolii Pk.
  Macrosporium sarciniforme Cav.
  Macrosporium sarcinula B.
  ⎰Metasphaeria bucera (C. & E.) Sacc.
  ⎱Sphaeria bucera C. & E.
  Mycorrhiza of Legumes F. R. Jones.
  ⎰Ophiobolus collapsus (Ell.) Ell. & Sacc.
  ⎱Raphidospora collapsa (Ell.) Cke.
  ⎱Sphaeria collapsa Ell.
  Periconia pycnospora Fres.
  Peziza Sphaerella Pk. & Clinton.
  Phyllachora Trifolii (P. ex Fr.) Fckl.
  ⎰Pleospora denotata (C. & E.) Sacc.
  ⎱Sphaeria denotata C. & E.
  Polythrincium Trifolii Kze. ex Fr.
  ⎰Phacidium Trifolii (Biv.) Boud.
  ⎱Pseudopeziza Trifolii (Biv.) Fckl.
  Pseudopeziza Trifoliorum H. S. Jackson nom.
    nud.
  ⎰Rhabdospora Trifolii (Ell.) Sacc.
  ⎱Septoria Trifolii Ell.
  Rhizoctonia Crocorum (P. ex Fr.) DC.
  Rhizoctonia Solani Kühn.
  Sclerotinia Trifoliorum Erikss.
  Septoria Trifolii Ell.
  Sphaerella nebulosa (P. ex Fr.) Sacc.
  Sphaerulina Trifolii Rostr.
  Stictis pustulata Ell.
  Thielavia basicola (B. & Br.) Zopf.
  ⎰Caeomurus Trifolii Auct. Amer. p. p.
  ⎱Nigredo fallens (Kern) Arth.
  ⎰Nigredo Trifolii Auct. Amer. p. p.
  ⎱Uromyces fallens Kern.
  ⎱Uromyces Trifolii Auct. Amer. p. p.
  Verticillium dichotomum Ell. & Ev.
  Volutella flexuosa C. & E.

Trifolium procumbens L.
  Erysiphe Polygoni DC. †
  ⎰Pucciniola oblonga (Vize) Arth.
  ⎱Uromyces oblongus Vize
  ⎱Uromyces Trifolii Auct. Amer. p. p.

Trifolium reflexum L.
  Erysiphe Polygoni DC. †
  Polythrincium Trifolii Kze.

Trifolium repens L.
  Brachysporium Trifolii C. H. Kauffman.
  Cercospora helvola Sacc.
  Cercospora zebrina Pass.
  Corticium vagum B. & C.
  Erysiphe Polygoni DC. †
  Gloeosporium Trifolii Pk.
  Mycorrhiza of Legumes F. R. Jones.
  Peronospora Trifoliorum DBy.
  ⎰Dothidea Trifolii (P.) ex Fr.
  ⎱Phyllachora Trifolii (P. ex Fr.) Fckl.
  Physarum cinereum (Batsch) P.
  ⎰Phytomyxa Leguminosarum (Frank) Schrt.
  ⎱Schinzia Leguminosarum Frank.
  Polythrincium Trifolii Kze. ex Fr.
  ⎰Phacidium Trifolii (Biv.) Boud.
  ⎱Pseudopeziza Trifolii (Biv.) Fckl.
  Sclerotinia Trifoliorum Erikss.
  Sphaerulina Trifolii Rostr.
  Stagonospora carpathica Bäuml.
  ⎰Stagonospora Dearnessii Sacc.
  ⎱Stagonospora Trifolii Ell. & Ev.
  Thielavia basicola (B. & Br.) Zopf.
  ⎰Uromyces flectens Lagerh.
  ⎱Uromyces nerviphila (Grognot) Hotson.
  ?Uromyces Medicaginis-falcatae (DC.) Wint.
  ⎰Uromyces minor Schrt.
  ⎱Uromyces oblongus Vize.
  ⎱Uromyces Trifolii J. J. Davis p. p.
  ?Aecidium Orobi Auct. Amer. p. p.
  Aecidium Trifolii-repentis Cast.
  Caeomurus Trifolii Arth. p. p.
  Nigredo Trifolii (Hedw. f.) Arth.
  ⎰Uromyces apiculatus N. A. F. 244.
  ⎱Uromyces apiculosa Auct. Amer. p. p.
  ⎱Uromyces fallens Auct. Amer. p. p.
  ⎱Uromyces striatus Thax.
  ⎱Uromyces Trifolii (Hedw. f.) Lév.
  ⎱Uromyces Trifolii-repentis Liro.

Trifolium Rydbergii Greene.
  Erysiphe Polygoni DC. †
  Phyllachora Trifolii (P. ex Fr.) Fckl.
  ⎰Pucciniola oblonga (Vize) Arth.
  ⎱Uromyces oblongus Vize.

Trifolium scariosum A. Nels.
Trifolium stenophyllum Nutt.
  ⎰Pucciniola oblonga (Vize) Arth.
  ⎱Uromyces oblongus Vize.

Trifolium stenolobum Rydb.
  Pleospora herbarum (Fr.) Rabh.

Trifolium stoloniferum Muhl.
　　Erysiphe Polygoni DC. †
Trifolium suaveolens Willd.
　　⎰Helminthosporium fragile Sorokin.
　　⎱Thielavia basicola Zopf.
Trifolium tridentatum Lindl.
　　Erysiphe Polygoni DC. †
　　Thecaphora deformans Dur. & Mont.
　　⎰Pucciniola oblonga (Vize) Arth.
　　⎱Uromyces oblongus Vize.
Trifolium variegatum Nutt.
　　⎧Pucciniola oblonga (Vize) Arth.
　　⎨Uromyces minor Schrt.
　　⎩Uromyces oblongus Vize.
Trifolium variegatum Nutt., var. **major** Loja.
　　⎰Erysiphe communis Auct. Amer. p. p.
　　⎱Erysiphe Polygoni DC. †
Trifolium Wormskioldii Lehm.
　　Phyllachora umbilicata Theissen & Syd.
　　Pucciniola oblonga (Vize) Arth.
Trifolium sp. indet.
　　Actinothyrium graminis Kze. ex Fr.
　　Ascochyta caulicola Laub.
　　Ascochyta imperfecta Pk.
　　Colletotrichum cereale Manns.
　　Darluca Filum (Biv.) Cast.
　　Gibberella Saubinetii (Mont.) Sacc.
　　Lophiostoma caulium (Fr.) Ces. & De Not.
　　Lophiostoma insidiosum (Desm.) Ces. & De Not.
　　⎧Catharinia americana (Ell. & Ev.) Sacc.
　　⎪Pleospora americana Ell. & Ev.
　　⎨Pleospora hyalospora Ell. & Ev.
　　⎩Pleosphaerulina hyalospora (Ell. & Ev.) Berl.
　　Pseudopeziza Medicaginis (Biv.) Fckl.
　　Pythium debaryanum Hesse.
　　Sclerotinia ciborioides Rehm.
　　Sclerotinia libertiana Fckl.
　　Streptothrix glauca Ell. & Ev.
Hosackia americana (Nutt.) Piper.
　　Alternaria tenuis Nees ex Fr.
　　Epicoccum neglectum Desm.
　　Erysiphe Cichoracearum DC. †
　　⎰Erysiphe communis Auct. Amer.
　　⎱Erysiphe Polygoni DC. †
　　Mycorrhiza of Legumes F. R. Jones.
　　Ovularia lotophaga Ell. & Ev.
　　Pleospora Leguminum (Wallr.) Rabh.
　　Ramularia Schulzeri Bauml.
Hosackia argophylla Gray.
　　Erysiphe Polygoni DC. †
　　Nigredo Medicaginis (Sacc.) Arth.
Hosackia denticulata Drew.
　　Erysiphe Polygoni DC. †
Hosackia glabra Torr.
　　Pestalozzia Moorei Hark.
　　Phoma Hosackiae Cke. & Hark.
　　Nigredo Medicaginis (Sacc.) Arth.
　　Uromyces punctatus Schrt.

Hosackia Ornithopus Greene.
　　Uromyces Loti Blytt.
　　Nigredo Medicaginis (Sacc.) Arth.
Hosackia parviflora Benth.
　　Erysiphe Polygoni DC. †
　　Thecaphora deformans Dur. & Mont.
Hosackia strigosa Nutt.
　　Septoria Hosackiae Hark.
Hosackia Torreyi Gray.
　　Erysiphe Polygoni DC. †
　　Ovularia lotophaga Ell. & Ev.
Hosackia sp. indet.
　　⎰Ditopella Hosackiae (Cke. & Hark.) Sacc.
　　⎨Physalospora Hosackiae (Cke. & Hark.) Cke.
　　⎩Sphaerella (?) Hosackiae Cke. & Hark.
Lotus eriophorus (Vogel) Greene.
　　Uromyces punctatus Schrt.
Lotus corniculatus L.
Lotus villosus Burm.
　　Thielavia basicola (B. & Br.) Zopf.
Cyamopsis tetragonoloba Taub.
　　Sclerotium Rolfsii Sacc.
Indigofera Anil L.
　　Ravenelia Indigoferae Tranz.
Indigofera caroliniana Walt.
　　⎧Dothidea perisporioides B. & C.
　　⎨Dothidella grammodes (Kze. ex B. & C.) Sacc.
　　⎩Parodiella perisporioides (B. & C.) Speg.
Indigofera Conzattii Rose.
Indigofera cuernavacana Rose.
　　Ravenelia Indigoferae Tranz.
Indigofera densiflora Mart. & Gal.
Indigofera jaliscensis Rose.
　　⎰Pleoravenelia laevis (Diet. & Holw.) Long.
　　⎱Ravenelia laevis Diet. & Holw.
Indigofera leptosepala Nutt. in Torr. & Gr.
　　Uromyces appendiculatus Lk.?
　　⎰Nigredo Indigoferae (Diet. & Holw.) Arth.
　　⎱Uromyces Indigoferae Diet. & Holw.
Indigofera mexicana Benth.
Indigofera miniata Orteg.
　　⎰Nigredo Indigoferae (Diet. & Holw.) Arth.
　　⎱Uromyces Indigoferae Diet. & Holw.
Indigofera mucronata Spreng.
　　Ravenelia Indigoferae Tranz.
　　Uromyces Indigoferae Diet. & Holw.
Indigofera Palmeri Watson.
　　⎰Pleoravenelia Indigoferae (Tranz.) Long.
　　⎱Ravenelia Indigoferae Tranz.
Indigofera sp. indet.
　　Neocosmospora vasinfecta Erw. Sm.
Psoralea argophylla Pursh.
　　Cercospora latens Ell. & Ev.
　　⎰Parodiella grammodes (Kze. ex B. & C.) Cke.
　　⎱Parodiella perisporioides (B. & C.) Speg.
　　Ramularia Psoraleae Ell. & Ev.
　　Septoria argophylla Ell. & Kellerm.

Psoralea argophylla (*cont.*)
- Aecidium porosum Auct. Amer. p. p.
- Aecidium Psoraleae Pk.
- Pucciniola argophyllae (Seym.) Arth.
- Uromyces argophyllae Seym.
- Uromycopsis porosa Brenckle p. p.

Psoralea Bigelovii (Rydb.) Tidestr.
- Pucciniola argophyllae (Seym.) Arth.

Psoralea collina Rydb.
- Aecidium Psoraleae Pk.
- Pucciniola argophyllae (Seym.) Arth.
- ?Uromyces Psoraleae Auct. p. p.

Psoralea digitata Nutt.
- Actinonema Psoraleae Ell. & Ev.

Psoralea esculenta Pursh.
- Gloeosporium Psoraleae Pk.

Psoralea lanceolata Pursh.
- Aecidium Psoraleae Pk.
- Uromyces Psoraleae Pk.

Psoralea linearifolia Torr. & Gr.
- Pucciniola argophyllae (Seym.) Arth.

Psoralea macrostachya DC.
- Calloria myriospora Phil. & Hark.
- Orbilia myriospora (Phil. & Hark.) Sacc.
- Ramularia Psoraleae Ell. & Ev.

Psoralea Onobrychis Nutt.
- Aecidium Onobrychidis Burrill.

Psoralea orbicularis Lindl.
- Leptosphaeria doliolum (P. ex Fr.) DeNot.

Psoralea physodes Dougl.
- Microsphaera diffusa C. & P.
- Teleutospora abbreviata (Arth.) Arth. & Bisby.
- Uromyces abbreviatus Arth.
- Uromyces Psoraleae Pk.

Psoralea Purshii Vail.
- Teleutospora abbreviata (Arth.) Arth. & Bisby.
- Uromyces abbreviatus Arth.
- Uromyces Psoraleae West Am. Fung. *390.*
- Uromyces Psoraleae Pk.

Psoralea tenuiflora Pursh.
- Dicoccum Psoraleae Ell. & Barthol.
- Diplodina Psoraleae Ell. & Barthol.
- Diplodinula Psoraleae (Ell. & Barthol.) Tassi.
- Erysiphe communis Auct. Amer.
- Erysiphe Polygoni DC. †
- Parodiella Griffithsii Theissen & Syd.
- Dothidea perisporioides B. & C.
- Parodiella grammodes (Kze. ex B. & C.) Cke.
- Parodiella perisporioides (B. & C.) Speg.
- Pyrenophora chrysospora, var. polaris Karst.
- Aecidium Orobi Auct. Amer. p. p.
- Aecidium Psoraleae Pk.
- Pucciniola argophyllae (Seym.) Arth.
- Uromyces argophyllae Seym.
- Uromyces Psoraleae Auct. Amer. p. p.
- ? Uromyces Fabae (P.) DBy.
- Uromyces Orobi Fckl.

Psoralea sp. indet.
- Phoma Psoraleae Cke.
- Phyllosticta Psoraleae (Cke.) Tassi.

Amorpha californica Nutt.
- Puccinia Amorphae M. A. Curtis.
- Uropyxis Amorphae (M. A. Curtis) Schrt.
- Valsa Amorphae Ell. & Ev.
- Valsaria insitiva (Tode ex Fr.) Ces. & DeNot.

Amorpha canescens Pursh.
- Aecidium fluxum Arth.
- Camarosporium Amorphae Sacc.
- Cercospora passaloroides Wint.
- Erysiphe Polygoni DC. †
- Puccinia Amorphae M. A. Curtis.
- Uropyxis Amorphae (M. A. Curtis) Schrt.

Amorpha fruticosa L.
- Cercospora passaloroides Wint.
- Cucurbitaria Amorphae (Wallr.) Fckl.
- Curcurbitaria elongata (Fr.) Grev.
- Cytospora Amorphae Ell. & Barthol.
- Diaporthe Amorphae Ell. & Ev.
- Diatrype tumida Ell. & Ev.
- Diplodia Amorphae (Wallr.) Sacc.
- Eutypella Amorphae Ell. & Ev.
- Phoma biformis Ell. & Barthol.
- Aecidium Amorphae Cke.
- Puccinia Amorphae M. A. Curtis.
- Uredo kansensis Kellerm. & Swingle.
- Uropyxis Amorphae (M. A. Curtis) Schrt.
- Quaternaria dissepta (Fr.) Tul.
- Sphaeria dissepta Fr.
- Valsa dissepta Fr.
- Rosellinia Bigeloviae Ell. & Ev.
- Rosellinia Bigeloviae Ell. & Ev., var. Amorphae Ell. & Ev. sec. Sacc. & D. Sacc.
- Sphaeropsis Amorphae Ell. & Barthol.
- Stagonospora cytisporoides Ell. & Barthol.
- Valsaria insitiva (Tode ex Fr.) Ces. & DeNot.

Amorpha herbacea Walt.
- Cladosporium Amorphae Thm.
- Puccinia Amorphae M. A. Curtis.
- Uropyxis Amorphae (M. A. Curtis) Schrt.

Amorpha laevigata Nutt.

Amorpha microphylla Pursh.

Amorpha montana Boynton.

Amorpha nana Nutt.

Amorpha occidentalis Abrams.

Amorpha virgata Small.
- Uropyxis Amorphae (M. A. Curtis) Schrt.

Amorpha sp. indet.
- Creonectria purpurea (L.) ex Seaver.
- Nectria cinnabarina (Tode) ex Fr.

Eysenhardtia adenostylis Baill.
- Calliospora Holwayi Arth.

Eysenhardtia amorphoides H. B. K.
- Calliospora Holwayi Arth.
- ? Uromyces apiculatus (Str.) Lév.
- Uropyxis Eysenhardtiae (Diet. & Holw.) Lindau & Syd.

Eysenhardtia orthocarpa (Gray) Watson.
Eysenhardtia polystachya (Ortega) Sarg.
  Calliospora Holwayi Arth.
  { Puccinia Eysenhardtiae Diet. & Holw.
  { Uropyxis Eysenhardtiae (Diet. & Holw.) Lin-
    dau & Syd.
Dalea acutifolia Moc. & Sesse.
  { Puccinia Daleae Diet. & Holw.
  { Uropyxis Daleae (Diet. & Holw.) Lindau &
    Syd.
Dalea alopecuroides Willd.
  Phytomyxa Leguminosarum (Frank) Schrt.
  Uropyxis Daleae (Diet. & Holw.) Lindau &
    Syd.
Dalea citriodora Willd.
  Puccinia Daleae Diet. & Holw.
Dalea diffusa Moric.
  Uropyxis Daleae (Diet. & Holw.) Lindau &
    Syd.
Dalea domingensis DC.
  Calliospora Farlowii Arth.
  Uropyxis Daleae (Diet. & Holw.) Lindau &
    Syd.
Dalea enneandra Nutt.
  { Aecidium Daleae Kellerm. & Swingle.
  { Aecidium Onobrychidis Burrill.
Dalea Holwayi Rose.
Dalea mutabilis Willd.
Dalea nutans Willd.
Dalea trifoliata Zucc.
  { Puccinia Daleae Diet. & Holw.
  { Uropyxis Daleae (Diet. & Holw.) Lindau &
    Syd.
Petalostemum candidum Michx.
  { Aecidium Onobrychidis Burrill.
  { Aecidium Petalostemonis Kellerm. & Carl.
  { Puccinia Petalostemonis Farl.
  { Uropyxis Petalostemonis (Farl.) De Toni.
Petalostemum compactum (Spreng.) Swezey.
  Uropyxis Petalostemonis (Farl.) De Toni.
Petalostemum multiflorum Nutt.
  Aecidium Petalostemonis Kellerm. & Carl.
  { Puccinia Petalostemonis Farl.
  { Uropyxis Petalostemonis (Farl.) De Toni.
Petalostemum oligophyllum (Torr.) Rydb.
  { Aecidium Onobrychidis Burrill.
  { Aecidium Petalostemonis Kellerm. & Carl.
  { Uropyxis Petalostemonis I. Fung. Columb.
    2497.
  Calliospora Petalostemonis Arth.
  Hendersonia Petalostemonis Fairman.
  Pyrenophora comata (Awd. & Niessl) Sacc.
  Uropyxis Petalostemonis (Farl.) De Toni.
Petalostemum purpureum (Vent.) Rydb.
  { Aecidium Petalostemonis Kellerm. & Carl.
  { Aecidium Onobrychidis Burrill.
  { Uropyxis Petalostemonis Fung. Columb. *2296.*
  Mycorrhiza of Legumes F. R. Jones.

  { Puccinia Petalostemonis Farl.
  { Uropyxis Petalostemonis (Farl.) De Toni.
Petalostemum villosum Nutt.
  { Aecidium Onobrychidis Burrill.
  { Aecidium Petalostemonis Kellerm. & Carl.
Brongniartia foliosa Benth.
Brongniartia intermedia Moric.
  { Pleoravenelia Brongniartiae (Diet. & Holw.)
    Long.
  { Ravenelia Brongniartiae Diet. & Holw.
Brongniartia nudiflora Watson.
  Ravenelia similis (Long) Arth.
Brongniartia podalyrioides H. B. K.
  Ravenelia Brongniartiae Diet. & Holw.
  ?Ravenelia epiphylla (S.) Diet.
  { Ravenelia similis (Long) Arth.
  { Pleoravenelia similis Long.
Brongniartia sericea Schl.
  Ravenelia Brongniartiae Diet. & Holw.
Tephrosia ambigua (Curtis) O. Kuntze.
  Ravenelia epiphylla (S.) Diet.
Tephrosia candida DC.
  Neocosmospora vasinfecta Erw. Sm.
Tephrosia cinerea (L.) P.
  Phragmopyxis deglubens (B. & C.) Diet.
  Ravenelia caulicola Arth.
Tephrosia hispidula (Michx.) (L.) P.
  Cercospora Tephrosiae Atk.
  { Pleoravenelia epiphylla (S.) Long.
  { Ravenelia epiphylla (S.) Diet.
Tephrosia macrantha Watson.
  Ravenelia irregularis Arth.
  Ravenelia talpa (Long) Arth.
Tephrosia spicata (Walt.) Torr. & Gr.
  { Pleoravenelia epiphylla (S.) Long.
  { Ravenelia epiphylla (S.) Diet.
  { Ravenelia glanduliformis B. & C.
Tephrosia talpa Watson.
  Ravenelia epiphylla (S.) Diet.
  { Pleoravenelia talpa Long.
  { Ravenelia talpa (Long) Arth.
  Uropyxis roseana Arth.
Tephrosia virginiana (L.) P.
  Helotium consanguineum Ell. & Ev.
  Hendersonia anomala C. & E.
  { Leptosphaeria Tephrosiae (C. & E.) Sacc.
  { Sphaeria Tephrosiae C. & E.
  { Pleoravenelia epiphylla (S.) Long.
  { Ravenelia epiphylla (S.) Diet.
  { Ravenelia glanduliformis B. & C.
  { Ravenelia glandulosa B.
  { Ravenelia sessilis B.
  { Sphaeria epiphylla S.
  Thielavia basicola (B. & Br.) Zopf.
Wisteria chinensis DC.
  Botryosphaeria Wisteriae (Rehm) Sacc.
  { Hendersonia Wistariae Cke.
  { Hendersonulina Wistariae (Cke.) Tassi.

Wisteria chinensis (*cont.*)
Septoria Wistariae Tharp.
Sphaerella Wistariae Cke.

Wisteria frutescens (L.) Poir.
Phomatospora Wistariae Ell. & Ev.

Wisteria sp. indet.
Camarosporium wistarianum Fairman.
Haplosporella Maclurae Ell. & Barthol.
{ Haplosporella Wistariae Ell. & Barthol.
{ Sphaeropsis wistariana Fairman.
{ Macrophoma fusigera (B. & C.) Berl. & Vogl.
{ Phoma fusigera (B. & C.) Sacc.
{ Sphaeropsis fusiger B. & C.
Phyllosticta Wistariae Sacc.

Robinia hispida L.
Macrosporium heteronemum (Desm.) Sacc.

Robinia neomexicana Gray.
Fomes Robiniae (Murrill) Sacc. & D. Sacc.
Macrosporium heteronemum (Desm.) Sacc.
Peniophora limonia Burt.
Phyllosticta neomexicana Bubák & Kabát.

Robinia Pseudo-acacia L.

ASCOMYCETES

{ Aglaospora profusa (Fr.) DeNot.
{ Massaria seiridia B. & C.
{ Pseudovalsa profusa (Fr.) Cke.
{ Sphaeria profusa Fr.
{ Valsa profusa Fr.
Belonidium Aurelia De Not.
{ Coniochaeta intonsa (S.) Cke.
{ Sphaeria intonsa S.
{ Curcurbitaria elongata (Fr.) Grev.
{ Sphaeria elongata Fr.
{ Diaporthe oncostoma (Duby) Fckl.
{ Diaporthe personata (C. & E.) Sacc.
{ Valsa oncostoma Duby.
{ Valsa personata C. & E.
{ Diatrype Robiniae (S.) M. A. Curtis.
{ Sphaeria Robiniae S.
{ Valsaria Robiniae (S.) Cke.
{ Diatrype tumida Ell. & Ev.
{ Eutypa ludibunda Sacc.
{ Valsa ludibunda Sacc.
Eutypella longirostris Pk.
Eutypella scoparia (S.) Ell. & Ev.
Eutypella stellulata (Fr.) Sacc.
{ Eutypella venusta (Ell.) Sacc.
{ Valsa venusta Ell.
{ Herpotrichia diffusa (S.) Ell.
{ Herpotrichia rhodomphala (B.) Sacc.
Hypoxylon Ravenelii Rehm.
Hypoxylon rubiginosum (P.) ex Fr.
Hysterium pulicare P. ex Fr.
Hysterium truncatum P. ex Fr.
Leptosphaeria eustoma (Fr.) Sacc., var. leguminosa Fairman.
Leptosphaeria lyndonvillae Fairman.

Metasphaeria leguminosa Fairman.
Metasphaeria lyndonvillae Fairman.
Mollisia melaleuca (Fr.) Sacc.
{ Creonectria purpurea (L.) ex Seaver.
{ Nectria cinnabarina (Tode) ex Fr.
{ Creonectria coccinea (P. ex Fr.) Seaver.
{ Nectria coccinea (P.) ex Fr.
Nectria ditissima Tul.
?Peroneutypella heteracantha (Sacc.) Berl.
Pleospora aureliana Fairman.
Pseudovalsa irregularis (DC.) Schrt.
Rosellinia pulveracea (Ehrh. ex Fr.) Fckl.
Rosellinia subiculata (S.) Sacc.
Sporormia leguminosa Fairman.
Thielavia basicola (B. & Br.) Zopf.
Valsa ceratophora Tul.
Valsaria insitiva (Tode ex Fr.) Ces. & De Not.

THELEPHORACEAE

{ Corticium muscigenum Sacc. p. p.
{ Stereum muscigenum Cke.
{ Stereum rugosiusculum B. & C.
Corticium mutatum Pk.
Hymenochaete rubiginosa (Schrad. ex Fr.) Lév.
Peniophora incarnata Pk.
Sebacina calcea (P.) Bres.

POLYPORACEAE

Fomes applanatus (P. ex Wallr.) Gill.
{ Fomes rimosus (B.) Cke.
{ Polyporus rimosus B.
{ Fomes Robiniae (Murrill) Sacc. & D. Sacc.
{ Fulvifomes Robiniae Murrill.
{ Polyporus igniarius S. p. p.
{ Pyropolyporus Robiniae Murrill.
Polyporus gilvus S.
Polyporus leucoxanthus Bres.
Polyporus obtusus B.
Polyporus resinosus (Schrad.) ex Fr.
{ Bjerkandera robiniophila Murrill.
{ Polyporus robiniophilus (Murrill) Lloyd.
{ Trametes robiniophila Murrill.
{ Laetiporus speciosus Batarr. ex Murrill.
{ Polyporus sulphureus (Bull.) ex Fr.
{ Fuscoporia viticola Murrill p. p.
{ Poria contigua (P.) Cke.
Poria ferruginosa (Schrad. ex Fr.) Bres.
Poria incrassata (B. & C.) Burt.
Poria Medulla-panis (P. ex Fr.) Cke.
Poria pulchella S.
Poria umbrina Fr.

AGARICACEAE

?Agaricus spectabilis Fr.
Armillaria mellea (Vahl) ex Fr.
Coprinus radians (Desm.) Fr.
Mycena corticola (Schum.) ex Fr.

Robinia Pseudo-acacia (*cont.*)

SPHAEROPSIDALES

Camarosporium Robiniae (Westd.) Sacc.
Camarosporium subfenestratum (B. & C.) Sacc.
Hendersonia pubens (S.) Herb. Curtis.
Hendersonia Robiniae Westd.
Hendersonia Sartwellii Herb. Curtis.
Hendersonia subfenestrata B. & C.
Sphaeria pubens S.
Cornularia macrospora (B. & C.) Sacc.
Pseudographium macrosporum (B. & C.) Jacz.
Sphaeronema macrosporum B. & C.
Cytospora coccinea (Reb.) Fr.
Cytospora leucosperma (P.) ex Fr.
Naemaspora leucosperma P. ex Fr.
Cytospora orthospora B. & C.?
Cytospora parva B. & C.
Dinemasporium Robiniae Gerard.
Diplodia profusa DeNot.
Diplodia vulgaris Lév.
Diplodina Robiniae Pk.
Diplodiopsis Robiniae Dearness & Barthol.
Dothiorella glandulosa (Cke.) Sacc.?
Haplosporella chlorostoma Speg.
Hendersonia Pseudacaciae Ell. & Barthol.
Leptothyrella Lathami Dearness.
Leptothyrella Robiniae Dearness & Barthol.
Macrophoma numerosa Pk.
Microdiplodia valvuli Fairman.
Phleospora Robiniae (Lib.) v. Höhnel.
Phoma leguminum Westd.
Phomopsis epicarpa Sacc.
Septoria curvata (Rabh. & A. Br.) Sacc.
Sphaeropsis conspersa (S.) Archer.
Haplosporella Robiniae (Ell. & Barthol.) Petrak & Syd.
Sphaeropsis Robiniae Ell. & Barthol.
Sporonema Robiniae Sacc.
Vermicularia petiolorum S.

MELANCONIALES

Coryneum trimerum Sacc.
Cryptosporium Robiniae Dearness & House.
Cylindrosporium solitarium Heald & Wolf.
Gloeosporium revolutum Ell. & Ev.
Melanconium viscosum S.?
Myxosporium Russellii (B. & C.) Sacc.
Naemaspora Russellii B. & C.

HYPHOMYCETES

Cladosporium epiphyllum (P.) ex Fr.
Cladosporium nigrellum Ell. & Ev.
Epicoccum duriaeanum Mont.
Fusarium lateritium Nees ex Fr.
Fusicladium Robiniae Shear.

Isaria rosea (B. & C.) Sacc.
Pachnocybe rosea B. & C.
Pachnocybe rosella B. & C.
Tubercularia granulata P. ex Fr.
Tubercularia vulgaris Tode ex Fr.

MISCELLANEA

Dictydiaethalium plumbeum (Schum.) Rostf.
Ozonium omnivorum Shear.
Trichia favoginea (Batsch) P.

Robinia viscosa Vent.

Anthostoma tuberculosum (S.) Ell. & Ev.
Sphaeria tuberculosa S.
Camarosporium Robiniae (Westd.) Sacc.
Cucurbitaria elongata (Fr.) Grev.
Cytospora orthospora B. & C.
Melanconium viscosum S.
Diplodia conspersa (S.) Cke.
Microdiplodia conspersa (S.) Tassi.
Sphaeria conspersa S.
Cornularia macrospora (B. & C.) Sacc.
Pseudographium macrosporum (B. & C.) Jacz.
Sphaeronema macrosporum B. & C.
Rhytisma Robiniae S.

Robinia sp. indet.

ASCOMYCETES

Amphisphaeria applanata (Fr.) Ces. & De Not.
Sphaeria applanata Fr. p. p.
Ceratostomella stricta (P.) Sacc.
Sphaeria stricta P.
Cucurbitaria parasitans (S.) Cke.
Sphaeria parasitans S.
Diaporthe enteroleuca (Fr.) Sacc.
Valsa enteroleuca Fr.
Diatrypella prorumpens (Wallr. ex Fr.) Ell. & Ev.
Sphaeria prorumpens Wallr. ex Fr.
Diatrype verruciformis (Ehrh.) ex Fr.
Diatrypella affinis Cke.
Diatrypella informis Ell. & Ev.
Diatrypella subglobata Cke. & Gerard.
Diatrypella tocciiana De Not., var. subeffusa Ell. & Ev.
Diatrypella verruciformis (Ehrh. ex Fr.) Nits.
Sphaeria verruciformis Ehrh. ex Fr.
Dothidea Robiniae S.
Eutypa allostoma (S.) Cke.
Sphaeria allostoma S.
Valsa allostoma (S.) Cke.
Eutypella glandulosa (Cke.) Ell. & Ev.
Eutypella innumerabilis (Pk.) Sacc.
Gloniopsis fibriseda (Gerard) Sacc.
Hysterium fibrisedum Gerard.
Helotium aciculare (Bull.) ex P.
Leotia acicularis (Bull.) ex P.
Peziza acicularis (Bull.) Fr.
Sarea acicularis (Bull.) S.

Robinia sp. indet. (*cont.*)
  Massaria vomitoria B. & C.
  ⎰Byssosphaeria lanuginosa (B. & C.) Cke.
  ⎮Herpotrichia lanuginosa (B. & C) Ell. & Ev.
  ⎱Melanopsamma lanuginosa (B. & C.) Sacc.
  Sphaeria lanuginosa B. & C.
  ⎰Endophlaea anisometra (Cke. & Hark.) Cke.
  ⎨Metasphaeria anisometra (Cke. & Hark.) Sacc.
  ⎱Sphaeria anisometra Cke. & Hark.
  Peziza clavata P.
  ⎰Pseudovalsa convergens (Tode ex Fr.) Sacc.
  ⎱Sphaeria convergens Tode ex Fr.
  Rosellinia aquila (Fr.) De Not.
  Schizoxylon tuberculatum S.
  Sphaerella petiolicola (Desm.) Awd.
  ⎰Sphaeria nigrobrunnea S.
  ⎱Teichospora nigrobrunnea (S.) Starb.
  ⎧Strickeria Kochii Körb.
  ⎨Teichospora Kochii (Körb.) Ell. & Ev.
  ⎩Teichospora pezizoides Sacc. & Speg.
  ⎰Sphaeria anomia S. nec Fr ?
  ⎱Valsa anomia (S. nec Fr.?) Cke.
  Valsa ceratophora Tul.
  Valsa subscripta (Fr.) Cke.
  ⎧Sphaeria Notarisii Mont.
  ⎨Valsa Notarisii Mont.
  ⎩Valsaria Notarisii (Mont.) Sacc.

BASIDIOMYCETES

  Cyphella minutissima Burt.
  Hericium Erinaceus Bull. ex Fr.
  ⎰Irpex mollis B. & C.
  ⎱Irpiciporus mollis (B. & C.) Murrill.
  Polyporus adustus (Willd.) ex Fr.
  ⎧Boletus triqueter S. Syn. Car.
  ⎨Polyporus conchatus (P.) ex Fr.
  ⎩Polyporus cuticularis S. Am. bor.
  Polyporus fumosus (P.) ex Fr.
  Polyporus hirsutus (Wulf.) ex Fr.
  Polyporus versicolor (L.) ex Fr.
  Stereum cinerascens (S.) Massee.
  Tremella carneoalba Coker.

SPHAEROPSIDALES

  Cytospora Robiniae S.
  ⎰Dothidea Robiniae S.
  ⎱Haplosporella Robiniae (S.) Ell. & Ev.
  ⎰Cytospora abnormis B. & C.
  ⎱Phoma abnormis (B. & C.) Sacc.
  Phoma capsularum Cke. & Hark.
  ⎰Rhabdospora breviuscula (B. & C.) Sacc.
  ⎱Septoria breviuscula B. & C.
  Sphaeronema Robiniae B. & C.

MELANCONIALES

  Gloeosporium Leguminis Cke. & Hark.
  ⎰Myxormia convexula C. & E.
  ⎱Trullula convexula (C. & E.) Sacc.

HYPHOMYCETES

  ⎧Coniosporium Pseudacaciae (S.) Sacc.
  ⎮Cryptosporium Pseudacaciae S.
  ⎮Fusarium ciliatum Sacc. non Lk.
  ⎨Fusarium scolecoides Sacc. & Ell.
  ⎮Microcera Massariae Pass.
  ⎮Periconia Robiniae S.
  ⎩Sporocybe Robiniae (S.) Fr.
  Trichothecium roseum Lk.
  Volutella comata Ell.

MISCELLANEA

  ⎰Physarum lividum Rostf.
  ⎱Spumaria licheniformis S.
Gliricidia sepium Steud.
  Corticium koleroga (Cke.) v. Höhnel.
Diphysa robinioides Benth.
Diphysa suberosa Watson.
  Calliospora Diphysae Arth.
Sabinea punicea Urban.
  Uromyces Sabineae Arth.
Coursetia glandulosa Gray.
  ⎰Phragmopyxis acuminata (Long) Syd.
  ⎱Tricella acuminata Long.
Benthamantha cinerea (L.) O. Kuntze.
Benthamantha Edwardsii Rose.
Benthamantha fruticosa Rose.
  Phragmopyxis deglubens (B. & C.) Diet.
Sesbania grandiflora Poir.
  Cladosporium herbarum (P.) ex Lk.
Sesbania macrocarpa Muhl.
  ⎰Phomatospora Sesbaniae (Ell. & Ev.) Sacc.
  ⎱Physalospora Sesbaniae Ell. & Ev.
  Sphaerella Sesbaniae Ell. & Ev.
Sesbania vesicaria Elliott.
  Erysiphe Polygoni DC. †
  Gloeosporium Glottidii Ell. & Martin.
  Macrosporium floridanum Cke.
  Phoma clitoricarpa (Cke.) Sacc.
  Phoma Leguminum Westd.
Sesbania sp. indet.
  Botryosphaeria minor Ell. & Ev.
  ⎰Erysiphe Cichoracearum DC. †
  ⎱Erysiphe Montagnei Lév.
Glottidium floridanum DC.
  Cercospora glotidiicola Tracy & Earle.
  Gloeosporium Glottidii Ell. & Martin.
  Macrosporium floridanum Cke.
Colutea arborescens L.
  Berlesiella nigerrima (Blox.) Sacc.
  Botryosphaeria fuliginosa (M. & N.) Ell. & Ev.
  ⎰Camarosporium Coluteae (Pk. & Clinton) Sacc.
  ⎱Hendersonia Coluteae Pk. & Clinton.
  Cryptosporium fusarioides Sacc.
  ⎰Cucurbitaria Coluteae (Rabh.) Awd.
  ⎱Curcubitaria elongata (Fr.) Grev.

Colutea arborescens (*cont.*)

Dinemasporium hispidulum (Schrad. ex P.) M. A. Curtis. 1867.
Dinemasporium hispidulum (Schrad. ex P.) Sacc. 1881.
Diplodia Coluteae Schnabe.
Eutypa ludibunda Sacc.
Eutypella Laburni Allescher.
Fenestella canadica Rehm.
Coniothyrium insitivum Sacc.
Haplosporella insitiva Sacc.
Microsphaera Euphorbiae (Pk.) B. & C.
Phoma Coluteae Sacc. & Roum.
Robertomyces mirabilis Starb.
Sphaeropsis Coluteae Sacc.
Thyridaria minor Sacc.
Tremella moriformis B.
Nigredo Coluteae Arth.
Uromyces Coluteae Arth.
Uromyces Genistae-tinctoriae Auct. Amer. p. p.
Valsaria insitiva (Tode ex Fr.) Ces. & De Not., var. Coluteae Sacc.

Colutea sp. indet.
Dothidea Coluteae B. & C.

Caragana arborescens Lam.
Phyllosticta gallorum Thm.

Astragalus aboriginorum Richards.
Nigredo punctata (Schrt.) Arth.

Astragalus adsurgens Pall.
Erysiphe communis Auct. Amer.
Erysiphe Polygoni DC. †
Microsphaera Alni (DC.) Wint. †
Microsphaera Ravenelii B.
Microsphaera Euphorbiae (Pk.) B. & C.
Microsphaera Ravenelii Auct. Amer. p. p.
Physalospora aurantia Ell. & Ev.
Physalospora megastoma (Pk.) Sacc.
Physalosporina megastoma (Pk.) Woronichin.
Uromyces astragalicola Henn.
Nigredo punctata (Schrt.) Arth.
Uromyces Astragali Sacc.
Uromyces punctatus Schrt.

Astragalus albiflorus A. Nels.
Nigredo punctata (Schrt.) Arth.
Uromyces punctatus Schrt.

Astragalus alpinus L.
Mycosphaerella pachyasca (Rostr.) Vestergren.
Phoma Astragali-alpini Oud.
Pucciniola carnea Arth.
Uromyces Astragali Sacc.

Astragalus amphioxus Gray.

Astragalus argophyllus Nutt.
Uromyces Astragali Sacc.
Uromyces punctatus Schrt

Astragalus arizonicus Gray.

Astragalus atratus Watson, var. **arctus** E. P. Sheldon.

Astragalus Bigelowii Gray.
Nigredo punctata (Schrt.) Arth.
Uromyces Astragali Sacc.

Astragalus bisulcatus Gray.
Laestadia megastoma (Pk.) Cke.
Physalospora megastoma (Pk.) Sacc.
Physalosporina megastoma (Pk.) Woronichin.
Sphaerella megastoma Pk.
Sorosporium Astragali Pk.
Thecaphora deformans Dur. & Mont.

Astragalus Bourgovii Gray.
Pyrenophora fenestrata Pk.

Astragalus caespitosus Gray.
Erysiphe communis Auct. Amer.
Nigredo punctata (Schrt.) Arth.

Astragalus canadensis L.
Didymaria Astragali (Ell. & Holw.) Sacc.
Ramularia Astragali Ell. & Holw.
Didymella Astragali Ell. & Ev.
Erysiphe communis Auct. Amer.
Erysiphe Martii Lév.
Erysiphe Polygoni DC. †
Gloeosporium Astragali J. J. Davis.
Microsphaera diffusa C. & P.
Peronospora Trifoliorum DBy.
Phoma herbarum Westd.
Phytomyxa Leguminosarum (Frank) Schrt.
Nigredo punctata (Schrt.) Arth.
Uredo Oxytropidis De Toni.
Uromyces Astragali Sacc.
Uromyces punctatus Schrt.

Astragalus candolleanus (H. B. K.) E. P. Sheldon.
Nigredo punctata (Schrt.) Arth.

Astragalus caryocarpus Ker.
Colletotrichum carpophilum Kellerm. & Swingle.
Erysiphe communis Auct. Amer.
Erysiphe Polygoni DC. †
Nigredo punctata (Schrt.) Arth.
Uromyces Astragali Sacc.

Astragalus Chamaeleuce Gray.
Napicladium Astragali Ell. & Ev.

Astragalus crotalariae (Benth.) Gray.

Astragalus cyaneus Gray.
Nigredo punctata (Schrt.) Arth.
Uromyces Astragali Sacc.

Astragalus decumbens (Nutt.) Gray.
Erysiphe communis Auct. Amer.
Erysiphe Polygoni DC. †
Nigredo punctata (Schrt.) Arth.

Astragalus diphysus Gray.
Uromyces Astragali (Opiz) Schrt.

Astragalus Drummondii Dougl.
Microsphaera Astragali Auct. Amer.
Microsphaera Euphorbiae (Pk.) B. & C.
Physalospora megastoma (Pk.) Sacc.
Sorosporium Astragali Pk.
Thecaphora Astragali (Pk.) Wor.
Volutella occidentalis Ell. & F. W. Anderson.

Astragalus eucosmus B. L. Robinson.
{ Erysiphe communis Auct. Amer.
{ Erysiphe Polygoni DC.†
Mycosphaerella pachyasca (Rostr.) Vestergren.
Nigredo punctata (Schrt.) Arth.
Astragalus flexuosus Dougl.
Dendryphium nubilosum Ell. & Ev.
Physalospora megastoma (Pk.) Sacc.
{ Pucciniola carnea (Nees) Arth.
{ Uromyces lapponicus Lagerh.
{ Uromyces carneus (Nees) Hariot.
{ Uromycopsis lapponica (Lagerh.) Arth.
Nigredo punctata (Schrt.) Arth.
Volutella occidentalis Ell. & F. W. Anderson.
Astragalus frigidus Gray.
Euryachora frigida (Rostr.) Theissen & Syd.
Pleospora vulgaris Niessl.
Pucciniola carnea (Hariot) Arth.
{ ?Aecidium sp. indet.
{ Uromyces Phacae-frigidae (Wahl.) Hariot.
Astragalus frigidus Gray, var. americanus Watson.
{ Erysiphe communis Auct. Amer.
{ Erysiphe Polygoni DC.†
Astragalus frigidus Gray, var. littoralis Watson.
Erysiphe Polygoni DC.†
Mycosphaerella pachyasca (Rostr.) Vestergren.
Pyrenophora comata (Awd. & Niessl) Sacc.
Astragalus glareosus Dougl.
{ Nigredo punctata (Schrt.) Arth.
{ Uromyces punctatus Schrt.
Astragalus goniatus Nutt.
Phoma Astragali Cke. & Hark.
{ Physalospora megastoma (Pk.) Sacc.
{ Physalosporina megastoma (Pk.) Woronichin.
Nigredo punctata (Schrt.) Arth.
Astragalus guatemalensis Hemsl.
Astragalus Hornii Gray.
Astragalus Hosackiae Greene.
Astragalus Humboldtii Gray.
Astragalus humistratus Gray.
{ Nigredo punctata (Schrt.) Arth.
{ Uromyces Astragali Sacc.
{ Uromyces punctatus Schrt.
Astragalus hypoglottis L.
{ Erysiphe communis Auct. Amer.
{ Erysiphe Polygoni DC. †
Fusicladium brevipes Ell. & Ev.
Physalospora megastoma (Pk.) Sacc.
Uromyces punctatus Schrt.
Astragalus involutus Nels.
Astragalus junceus Gray.
{ Erysiphe communis Auct. Amer.
{ Erysiphe Polygoni DC.†
Astragalus lentiginosus Dougl.
Erysiphe Polygoni DC.†
Nigredo punctata (Schrt.) Arth.

Astragalus leptocarpus Gray
Astragalus leucophyllus Torr. & Gr.
Astragalus leucopsis Torr.
Astragalus Lindheimeri Engelm.
{ Nigredo punctata (Schrt.) Arth.
{ Uromyces Astragali Sacc.
{ Uromyces punctatus Schrt.
Astragalus lotiflorus Hook.
Peronospora Trifoliorum DBy.
Uromyces Astragali Sacc.
Astragalus Macounii Rydb.
{ Pucciniola carnea (Hariot) Arth.
{ Uromyces splendens Blytt.
Astragalus Menziesii Gray.
Phoma Astragali Cke. & Hark.
{ Nigredo punctata (Schrt.) Arth.
{ Uredo Oxytropidis De Toni.
{ Uromyces Astragali Sacc.
Astragalus missouriensis Nutt.
Thecaphora deformans Dur. & Mont.
Astragalus microlobus Gray.
Astragalus mollissimus Torr.
{ Nigredo punctata (Schrt.) Arth.
{ Uredo Oxytropidis De Toni.
{ Uromyces Astragali Sacc.
{ Uromyces punctatus Schrt.
Astragalus Mortoni Nutt.
Microsphaera Euphorbiae (Pk.) B. & C.
Astragalus nebraskensis Bates.
{ Nigredo punctata (Schrt.) Arth.
{ Uredo Oxytropidis De Toni.
{ Uromyces Astragali Sacc.
Astragalus neglectus (Torr. & Gr.) E. P. Sheldon.
{ Microsphaera Astragali (DC.) Trev.†
{ Microsphaera Euphorbiae (Pk.) B. & C.
{ Microsphaera holosericea Auct. Amer.
Astragalus nitidus Dougl.
{ Nigredo punctata (Schrt.) Arth.
{ Uredo Oxytropidis De Toni.
Astragalus nuttallianus DC.
Nigredo punctata (Schrt.) Arth.
Thecaphora deformans Dur. & Mont.
Astragalus oreophilus Rydb.
Phoma Astragali Cke. & Hark.
Astragalus parviflorus (Pursh) MacM.
Mycorrhiza of Legumes F. R. Jones.
Astragalus pectinatus Dougl.
Peronospora Viciae (B.) DBy., var. Astragali Sacc.
Physalospora Astragali (Lasch) Sacc., var. caulicola Sacc.
{ Physalospora aurantia Ell. & Ev.
{ Physalosporina aurantia (Ell. & Ev.) Sacc.
Septoria psammophila Sacc.
Astragalus plattensis Nutt.
{ Nigredo punctata (Schrt.) Arth.
{ Uromyces Astragali Sacc.

Astragalus Preussii Gray.
Astragalus Purshii Dougl.
Astragalus pycnostachys Gray.
- Nigredo punctata (Schrt.) Arth.
- Uredo Oxytropidis De Toni.
- Uromyces Astragali Sacc.
- Uromyces punctatus Schrt.

Astragalus scopulorum Porter.
  Sorosporium Astragali Pk.
Astragalus sinicus L.
  Thielavia basicola (B. & Br.) Zopf.
Astragalus Sonorae Gray.
Astragalus sulphurescens Rydb.
Astragalus tennesseensis Gray.
- Nigredo punctata (Schrt.) Arth.
- Uromyces punctatus Schrt.

Astragalus tenellus Pursh.
- Erysiphe communis Auct. Amer.
- Erysiphe Polygoni DC. †
  Thecaphora deformans Dur. & Mont.

Astragalus Thompsonae Watson.
  Thecaphora deformans Dur. & Mont.
Astragalus Thurberi Gray.
Astragalus Tracyi Greene.
- Nigredo punctata (Schrt.) Arth.
- Uromyces Astragali Sacc.

Astragalus tridactylicus Gray.
Astragalus triflorus Gray.
- Nigredo punctata (Schrt.) Arth.
- Uromyces Astragali Sacc.
- Uromyces punctatus Schrt.

Astragalus triphyllus Pursh.
- Erysiphe communis Auct. Amer.
- Erysiphe Polygoni DC. †
- Nigredo punctata (Schrt.) Arth.
- Uromyces punctatus Schrt.

Astragalus uintensis M. E. Jones.
Astragalus utahensis Torr. & Gr.
Astragalus viridis (Nutt.) E. P. Sheldon, var. **impensus** E. P. Sheldon.
Astragalus Wardii Gray.
- Nigredo punctata (Schrt.) Arth.
- Uromyces Astragali Sacc.
- Uromyces punctatus Schrt.

Astragalus Wootoni E. P. Sheldon.
  Thecaphora deformans Dur. & Mont.
- Nigredo punctata (Schrt.) Arth.
- Uromyces Astragali Sacc.

Astragalus sp. indet.
  Aecidium Astragali Thm.
  Aecidium Astragali-Alpini Erikss.
  Colletotrichum carpophilum Kellerm. & Swingle.
- Cucurbitaria Astragali Ell. & Ev.
- Cucurbitaria Ellisii Sacc. & Syd.
  Phoma Astragali Cke. & Hark.
  Phyllosticta Astragali Pk.

Physalosporina Astragali (Lasch) Woronichin.
Ramularia Desmodii Cke.
- Fusidium ravenelianum Thm.
- Ramularia Desmodii Cke., var. epiphylla Ell.
  Septoria astragalicola Pk.
- Sphaerella Astragali (Curr.) Cke.
- Sphaeria Astragali Curr.

Oxytropis albiflorus Bunge.
  Uromyces Astragali Sacc.
Oxytropis arctobia Bunge.
  Pyrenophora chrysospora (Niessl) Sacc.
Oxytropis campestris DC., var. **melanocephala** Hook.
  Pyrenophora chrysospora (Niessl) Sacc.
  Pyrenophora comata (Niessl) Sacc.
Oxytropis campestris DC., var. **sordida** Willd.
  Pleospora arctica Fckl.
Oxytropis campestris, var. **spicata** Hook.
Oxytropis deflexa (Pall.) DC.
- Nigredo punctata (Schrt.) Arth.
- Uromyces punctatus Schrt.

Oxytropis Lamberti Pursh.
- Erysiphe communis Auct. Amer.
- Erysiphe Polygoni DC. †
  Phleospora Oxytropidis Ell. & Gall.
- Nigredo punctata (Schrt.) Arth.
- Trichobasis Oxytropidis Pk.
- Uredo Oxytropidis (Pk.) De Toni.
- Uromyces Astragali Sacc.
- Uromyces punctatus Schrt.

Oxytropis monticola Gray.
  Pleospora herbarum (Fr.) Rabh.
Oxytropis nigrescens (Pall.) Fisch.
  Pleospora oblongata Niessl.
  Pyrenophora chrysospora (Niessl) Sacc.
Oxytropis podocarpa Gray.
  Nigredo punctata (Schrt.) Arth.
Oxytropis Roaldi Ostenf.
  Pleospora herbarum (Fr.) Rabh.
Oxytropis sericeus Nutt.
- Nigredo punctata (Schrt.) Arth.
- Uredo Oxytropidis (Pk.) De Toni.

Oxytropis spicatus Hook.
  Nigredo punctata (Schrt.) Arth.
Oxytropis uralensis DC.
  Ascochyta Oxytropidis Schrt.
Oxytropis uralensis DC., var. **arctica** Ledeb.
  Pleospora herbarum (Fr.) Rabh.
Glycyrrhiza glutinosa Watson.
- Klebahnia Glycyrrhizae (Magn.) Arth.
- Uromyces Glycyrrhizae Magn.

Glycyrrhiza lepidota (Nutt.) Pursh.
  Cylindrosporium Glycyrrhizae Hark.
- Erysiphe communis Auct. Amer.
- Erysiphe Polygoni DC. †
  Microsphaera diffusa C. & P.
  Septoria Glycyrrhizae Ell. & Kellerm.

Glycyrrhiza lepidota (*cont.*)
  Klebahnia Glycyrrhizae (Magn.) Arth.
  Uromyces Glycyrrhizae Magn.
  Uromyces Trifolii Auct. Amer. p. p.
  Uromyces Trifolii, var. Glycyrrhizae Ell. &
    Kellerm.
Ornithopus sativus Brot.
  Rhizoctonia Solani Kühn.
  Thielavia basicola (B. & Br.) Zopf.
Hedysarum boreale Nutt.
  Pucciniola Hedysari-obscuri (DC.) Arth.
  Uromyces borealis Pk.
  Uromyces Hedysari Surv. Pl. D. Can.
  ?Uromyces Hedysari-paniculati Auct. p. p.
  Uromyces Hedysari-obscuri (DC.) Carest. &
    Picc.
Hedysarum flavescens Regel & Schmalh.
  Uromyces Hedysari-obscuri (DC.) Carest. &
    Picc.
Hedysarum Mackenzii Richardson.
  Pyrenophora comata (Niessl) Sacc.
  Uromyces borealis Pk.
  Uromyces Hedysari-obscuri (DC.) Carest. &
    Picc.
Hedysarum marginatum Greene.
Hedysarum occidentale Greene.
Hedysarum pabulare A. Nels.
Hedysarum sulphurescens Rydb.
Hedysarum utahense Rydb.
  Pucciniola Hedysari-obscuri (DC.) Arth.
  Uromyces borealis Pk.
  Uromyces Hedysari-obscuri (DC.) Carest. &
    Picc.
Hedysarum sp. indet.
  Sphaeria Aegopodii P. ex Fr.
Onobrychis viciifolia Scop.
  Thielavia basicola (B. & Br.) Zopf.
Nissolia confertifolia Watson.
Nissolia fruticosa Jacq.
Nissolia hirsuta DC.
Nissolia laxior Rose.
Nissolia multiflora Rose.
  Puccinia Nissoliae Diet. & Holw.
  Uropyxis Nissoliae (Diet. & Holw.) Magn.
Brya Ebenus DC.
  Glomerella cingulata (Stoneman) Spaulding &
    v. Schrenk.
Aeschynomene americana L.
  Darluca Filum (Biv.) Cast.
  Phakopsora Aeschynomenis Arth.
  Physopella Aeschynomenis Arth.
  Uredo Aeschynomenis Arth.
Aeschynomene sensitiva Sw.
  Phakopsora Aeschynomenis Arth.
  Physopella Aeschynomenis Arth.
  Dothidea Gramma (S.) Fr.
  Phoma Gramma (S.) Starb.
  Sphaeria Gramma S.
  Phyllosticta phaseolina Sacc.

Stylosanthes biflora (L.) B. S. P.
  Cercospora Commonsii Sacc.
  Cercospora Stylosanthis Ell. & Ev.
  Cladosporium stenosporum B. & C.
  Coryneum Hedysari S.
  Parodiella perisporioides (B. & C.) Speg.
Chapmania floridana Torr. & Gr.
  Parodiella reticulata (Ell. & Ev.) Theissen &
    Syd.
Arachis hypogaea L.
  Aspergillus flavus Lk.
  Aspergillus niger Van Tiegh.
  Cercospora personata (B. & C.) Ell. & Ev.
  Cladosporium personatum B. & C.
  Corticium vagum B. & C.
  Darluca Filum (Biv.) Cast.
  Fusarium vasinfectum Atk.
  Macrosporium commune Rabh., var. Arachidis
    Sacc.
  Neocosmospora vasinfecta Erw. Sm.
  Ozonium omnivorum Shear.
  Bullaria (?) Arachidis (Speg.) Arth. & Mains.
  Puccinia Arachidis Speg.
  Uredo Arachidis (Speg.) Lagerh.
  Uromyces Arachidis (Speg.) Henn.
  Sclerotium Rolfsii Sacc.
  Thielavia basicola (B. & Br.) Zopf.
Zornia bracteata (Walt.) Gmel.
  Bullaria (?) Zorniae (McAlpine) Arth.
  Puccinia offuscata Arth.
  Uredo Zorniae Diet.
Zornia diphylla (L.) P.
  Parodiella perisporioides (B. & C.) Speg.
  Bullaria (?) Zorniae (McAlpine) Arth.
  Puccinia offuscata Arth.
  Puccinia Zorniae McAlpine.
  Uredo Zorniac Dict.
Desmodium adscendens DC.
  Dimerium grammodes (Kze. ex B. & C.) P.
    Garman.
  Parodiella perisporioides (B. & C.) Speg.
  Meliola bicornis Wint.
  Microsphaera diffusa C. & P.
  Phyllosticta desmodiiphila Speg.
Desmodium affine Schl.
  Uromyces Hedysari-paniculati (S.) Farl.
Desmodium amplifolium Hemsl.
Desmodium angustifolium (H. B. K.) O. Kuntze.
  Nigredo Hedysari-paniculati (S.) Arth.
  Uromyces Hedysari-paniculati (S.) Farl.
Desmodium axillaris DC.
  Meliola bicornis Wint.
  Meliola Desmodii Karst. & Roum.
  Nigredo Hedysari-paniculati (S.) Arth.
  Uromyces Hedysari-paniculati (S.) Farl.
Desmodium barbatum Benth. & Oerst.
  Dimerium grammodes (Kze. ex B. & C.) P.
    Garman.

Desmodium Barclayi Benth.
  Nigredo Hedysari-paniculati (S.) Arth.
Desmodium bracteosum (Michx.) DC.
  Microsphaera diffusa C. & P.
  Uromyces Hedysari-paniculati (S.) Farl.
Desmodium callilepis Hemsl.
  Nigredo Hedysari-paniculati (S.) Arth.
Desmodium canadense (L.) DC.
  Microsphaera diffusa C. & P.
  {Dothidea perisporioides B. & C.
  {Dothidea seminata B. & Rav.
  {Parodiella grammodes (Kze. ex B. & C.) Cke.
  {Parodiella perisporioides (B. & C.) Speg.
  {Phyllachora perisporioides (B. & C.) Pk.
  {Sphaeria perisporioides B. & C.
  {Stigmatea seminata (B. & Rav.) Sacc.
  {Phyllactinia corylea (P.) ex Karst.
  {Phyllactinia suffulta (Reb.) ex Sacc.
  Ramularia Desmodii Cke.
  {Caeomurus Hedysari-paniculati (S.) Arth.
  {Nigredo Hedysari-paniculati (S.) Arth.
  {Uromyces Hedysari-paniculati (S.) Farl.
  Vermicularia herbarum Westd.
Desmodium canescens (L.) DC.
  {Erysiphe communis Auct. Amer.
  {Erysiphe Polygoni DC.†
  Microsphaera diffusa C. & P.
  Parodiella paraguayensis Speg.
  {Dothidea perisporioides B. & C.
  {Parodiella perisporioides (B. & C.) Speg.
  Phyllosticta Desmodii Ell. & Ev.
  Ramularia Desmodii Cke.
  Sphaerella Desmodii Wint.
  Synchytrium decipiens Farl.
  {Caeomurus Hedysari-paniculati (S.) Arth.
  {Nigredo Hedysari-paniculati (S.) Arth.
  {Uromyces Desmodii Thm.
  {Uromyces Hedysari-paniculati (S.) Farl.
Desmodium canum Gmel.
  Meliola Desmodii Karst. & Roum.
Desmodium Conzattii Greenm.
  {Nigredo Hedysari-paniculati (S.) Arth.
  {Uromyces Desmodii Thm.
  {Uromyces Hedysari-paniculati (S.) Farl.
Desmodium Dillenii Darl.
  {Microsphaera diffusa C. & P.
  {Microsphaera Lycii Auct. Amer.
  {Microsphaera Mougeotii Auct. Amer.
  {Phyllosticta Desmodii Atk. non Ell. & Ev.
  {Phyllosticta macroguttata Earle.
  {Caeomurus Hedysari-paniculati (S.) Arth.
  {Nigredo Hedysari-paniculati (S.) Arth.
  {Uromyces Hedysari-paniculati (S.) Farl.
Desmodium elegans DC.
Desmodium Ghiesbrechtii Hemsl.
  Nigredo Hedysari-paniculati (S.) Arth.
Desmodium grandiflorum (Walt.) DC.
  Cercospora Desmodii Ell. & Kellerm.
  Cercospora melaleuca Ell. & Ev.

Microsphaera diffusa C. & P.
  {Dothidea perisporioides B. & C.
  {Parodiella perisporioides (B. & C.) Speg.
  {Phyllactinia corylea (P.) ex Karst.
  {Phyllactinia suffulta (Reb.) ex Sacc.
  Phytomyxa Leguminosarum (Frank) Schrt.
  Thecaphora deformans Dur. & Mont.
  {Sorosporium Desmodii Pk.
  {Thecaphora Desmodii (Pk.) Wor.
  {Nigredo Hedysari-paniculati (S.) Arth.
  {Uromyces Hedysari-paniculati (S.) Farl.
Desmodium hirsutum Mart. & Gal.
  Nigredo mexicana (Diet. & Holw.) Arth.
Desmodium illinoense Gray.
  Ramularia Desmodii Cke.
  {Nigredo Hedysari-paniculati (S.) Arth.
  {Uromyces Hedysari-paniculati (S.) Farl.
Desmodium infractum DC.
Desmodium jaliscanum Watson.
Desmodium laevigatum (Nutt.) DC.
  {Caeomurus Hedysari-paniculati (S.) Arth.
  {Nigredo Hedysari-paniculati (S.) Arth.
  {Uromyces Hedysari-paniculati (S.) Farl.
Desmodium leiocarpum G. Don.
  Cercospora desmodiicola Ell. & Kellerm., var.
    leiocarpi Fragoso & Ciferri.
Desmodium lineatum (Mich.) DC.
  {Cercosporella raveneliana (Thm.) Sacc.
  {Fusidium ravenelianum Thm.
  {Fusisporium pubescens B. & C.
  Ramularia Desmodii Cke.
  {Dothidea Desmodii M. A. Curtis.
  {Dothidea simillima B. & Rav.
  {Parodiella simillima (B. & Rav.) Cke.
  {Phyllachora simillima (B. & Rav.) Sacc.
Desmodium longifolium Nutt.
Desmodium marilandicum F. Boott.
  {Nigredo Hedysari-paniculati (S.) Arth.
  {Uromyces Hedysari-paniculati (S.) Farl.
Desmodium molle DC.
  Cercospora Desmodii Ell. & Kellerm.
  Macrosporium Ravenelii Thm.
Desmodium nudiflorum (L.) DC.
  Cercospora Desmodii Ell. & Kellerm.
  Microsphaera diffusa C. & P.
  {Sorosporium Desmodii Pk.
  {Thecaphora Desmodii (Pk.) Wor.
  Vermicularia uncinata B. & C.
Desmodium obtusum (Muhl.) DC.
  Ramularia Desmodii Cke.
  {Nigredo Hedysari-paniculati (S.) Arth.
  {Uromyces Hedysari-paniculati (S.) Farl.
Desmodium orbiculare Schl.
  Nigredo Hedysari-paniculati (S.) Arth.
Desmodium paniculatum (L.) DC.
  Cercospora Desmodii Ell. & Kellerm.
  Microsphaera Alni (DC.) Wint., var. ludens
    Salmon.
  Microsphaera diffusa C. & P.

Desmodium paniculatum (*cont.*)
{ Parodiella grammodes (Kze. ex B. & C.) Cke.
{ Parodiella perisporioides (B. & C.) Speg.
  Ramularia Desmodii Cke.
  Tuberculina flavogranulata Dearness & Barthol.
{ Caeomurus Hedysari-paniculati (S.) Arth.
{ Phragmidium Hedysari S.
{ Puccinia Hedysari-paniculati S.
{ Uromyces Desmodii Thm.
{ Uromyces Hedysari-paniculati (S.) Farl.
{ Uromyces solida B. & C.
Desmodium pauciflorum (Nutt.) DC.
Desmodium prehensile Schl.
  Uromyces Hedysari-paniculati (S.) Farl.
Desmodium rhombifolium DC.
Desmodium rigidum (Ell.) DC.
{ Nigredo Hedysari-paniculati (S.) Arth.
{ Uromyces Hedysari-paniculati (S.) Farl.
Desmodium rotundifolium (Michx.) DC.
  Phyllosticta Desmodii Ell. & Kellerm.
  Sclerotium Desmodii Thm.
{ Nigredo Hedysari-paniculati (S.) Farl.
{ Uromyces Desmodii Thm.
{ Uromyces Hedysari-paniculati (S.) Farl.
{ Uromyces solida B. & C.
Desmodium scorpiurus Desv.
  Microsphaera diffusa C. & P.
  Parodiella perisporioides (B. & C.) Speg.
{ Nigredo Hedysari-paniculati (S.) Arth.
{ Uromyces Hedysari-paniculati (S.) Farl.
Desmodium sessilifolium (Torr.) Torr. & Gr.
  Microsphaera diffusa C. & P.
{ Caeomurus Hedysari-paniculati (S.) Arth.
{ Nigredo Hedysari-paniculati (S.) Arth.
{ Uromyces Hedysari-paniculati (S.) Farl.
Desmodium spirale Auct.
  Nigredo mexicana (Diet. & Holw.) Arth.
Desmodium strictum (Pursh) DC.
  Cladosporium infuscans Thm.
{ Coryneum Hedysari S.
{ Didymosporium Hedysari S.
  Hypoderma virgultorum DC.
{ Leptosphaeria comatella (C. & E.) Sacc.
{ Sphaeria comatella C. & E.
{ Leptosphaeria dissiliens (C. & E.) Ell.
{ Metasphaeria dissiliens (C. & E.) Sacc.
{ Sphaeria dissiliens C. & E.
  Pistillaria clavulata Ell.
{ Coryneum Hedysari Roum. Fung. Sel. *4895.*
{ Nigredo Hedysari-paniculati (S.) Arth.
{ Uromyces Desmodii Cke.
{ Uromyces Hedysari-paniculati (S.) Farl.
{ Uromyces solida B. & C.
Desmodium strobilaceum Schl.
{ Nigredo Hedysari-paniculati (S.) Arth.
{ Uromyces Hedysari-paniculati (S.) Farl.
{ Nigredo tenuistipes (Diet. & Holw.) Arth.
{ Uromyces tenuistipes Diet. & Holw.

Desmodium supinum DC.
  Arthrobotryum caudatum Syd.
  Calonectria erubescens (Rob.) Sacc.
  Dimerium piceum (B. & C.) Theissen.
  Isthmospora glabra F. L. Stevens.
  Meliola bicornis Wint.
  Microsphaera diffusa C. & P.
{ Phakopsora Meibomiae Arth.
{ Phacopsora Meibomiae (Arth.) Trott.
{ Physopella Meibomiae Arth.
Desmodium
    (Meibomia tenuipes Blake.)
  Nigredo Hedysari-paniculati (S.) Arth.
Desmodium tortuosum DC.
  Cercospora melaleuca Ell. & Ev.
  Microsphaera diffusa C. & P.
  Phakopsora Meibomiae Arth.
  Sclerotium Rolfsii Sacc.
{ Stagonospora Desmodii Ell. & Ev.
{ Stagonosporina Desmodii (Ell. & Ev.) Tassi.
  Thielavia basicola (B. & Br.) Zopf.
  Uredo Desmodii-tortuosi Henn.
  Uromyces Hedysari-paniculati (S.) Farl.
Desmodium
    (Meibomia umbrosa Britt.)
  Nigredo Hedysari-paniculati (S.) Arth.
Desmodium uncinatum DC.
  Nigredo Hedysari-paniculati (S.) Arth.
{ Nigredo mexicana (Diet. & Holw.) Arth.
{ Uromyces mexicanus Diet. & Holw.
Desmodium viridiflorum (L.) Beck.
{ Caeomurus Hedysari-paniculati (S.) Arth.
{ Nigredo Hedysari-paniculati (S.) Arth.
{ Uromyces Hedysari-paniculati (S.) Farl.
Desmodium sp. indet.
  Aecidium Orobi P. 1794.
  Aecidium Orobi DC. ? 1815.
  Aschersonia viridans (B. & C.) Pat.
{ Diaporthe desmodiana (C. & E.) Sacc.
{ Sphaeria desmodiana C. & E.
{ Diaporthe Desmodii (Pk.) Sacc.
{ Sphaeria Desmodii Pk.
  Diaporthe micromegala Ell. & Ev.
{ Didymosphaeria cupula (Ell.) Sacc.
{ Sphaeria cupula Ell. & Ev.
  Meliola Meibomiae Stevens & Tehon.
  Meliola trinidadensis Stevens & Tehon.
{ Heptameria distributa (C. & E.) Cke.
{ Leptosphaeria distributa (C. & E.) Sacc.
{ Metasphaeria distributa (C. & E.) Berl.
{ Sphaeria distributa C. & E.
{ Mollisia atrocinerea (Cke.) Phil.
{ Peziza atrocinerea Cke.
  Patellaria ferruginea C. & E.
  Phyllosticta Desmodii Ell. & Ev.
{ Physalospora phomopsis (C. & E.) Sacc.
{ Sphaeria phomopsis C. & E.
  Sclerotium Rolfsii Sacc.
  Vermicularia compacta C. & E.

Lespedeza angustifolia (Pursh) Ell.
Aecidium leucostictum B. & C.
Aecidium Orobi, var. leucostictum B.
Nigredo Lespedezae-procumbentis (S.) Arth.
Uromyces Lespedezae-procumbentis (S.) M.
  A. Curtis.
Lespedeza capitata Michx.
Cercospora flagellifera Atk. ?
Cercospora latens Ell. & Ev.
Cercospora Lespedezae Ell. & Dearness.
Leptosphaeria microspora Ell. & Ev.
Microsphaera diffusa C. & P.
Dothidea Lespedezae (S.) B.
Phyllachora Lespedezae (S.) Sacc.
Sphaeria Lespedezae S.
Sphaeria Trifolii S. Syn. Car.
Aecidium leucostictum B. & C.
Nigredo Lespedezae-procumbentis (S.) Arth.
Uromyces Lespedezae (S.) ex Pk.
Uromyces Lespedezae-procumbentis (S.) M. A.
  Curtis.
Uromyces macrosporus B. & C.
Lespedeza frutescens (L.) Britt.
Cercospora flagellifera Atk.
Caeomurus Lespedezae-procumbentis (S.) Arth.
Nigredo Lespedezae-procumbentis (S.) Arth.
Uromyces Lespedezae (S.) ex Pk.
Uromyces Lespedezae-procumbentis (S.) M.
  A. Curtis.
Lespedeza hirta (L.) Hornem.
Cercospora Lespedezae Ell. & Dearness.
Microsphaera diffusa C. & P.
Phyllachora Lespedezae (S.) Sacc.
Aecidium leucostictum B. & C.
Caeomurus Lespedezae-procumbentis (S.)
  Arth.
Nigredo Lespedezae-procumbentis (S.) Arth.
Puccinia Lespedezae-procumbentis S.
Puccinia Lespedezae-violaceae S.
Uromyces Lespedezae (S.) ex Pk.
Uromyces Lespedezae-procumbentis (S.) M.
  A. Curtis. 1867.
Uromyces Lespedezae-procumbentis (S.)
  Lagerh. 1895.
Lespedeza leptostachya Engelm.
Lespedeza Nuttallii Darl.
Lespedeza procumbens Michx.
Nigredo Lespedezae-procumbentis (S.) Arth.
Puccinia Lespedezae-procumbentis S.
Uromyces Lespedezae (S.) ex Pk.
Uromyces Lespedezae-procumbentis (S.) M. A.
  Curtis.
Lespedeza repens (L.) Bart.
Phyllachora Lespedezae (S.) Sacc.
Aecidium leucostictum B. & C.
Puccinia Lespedezae-procumbentis S.
Uromyces Lespedezae (S.) ex Pk.
Uromyces Lespedezae-procumbentis (S.) M. A.
  Curtis.

Lespedeza striata (Thunb.) Hook. & Arn.
Erysiphe communis Auct. Amer.
Erysiphe Polygoni DC. †
Microsphaera diffusa C. & P.
Thielavia basicola (B. & Br.) Zopf.
Lespedeza Stuvei Nutt.
Lespedeza texana Britt.
Nigredo Lespedezae-procumbentis (S.) Arth.
Uromyces Lespedezae (S.) ex Pk.
Uromyces Lespedezae-procumbentis (S.) M.
  A. Curtis.
Lespedeza violacea (L.) P.
Microsphaera diffusa C. & P.
Phyllachora Lespedezae (S.) Sacc.
Nigredo Lespedezae-procumbentis (S.) Arth.
Puccinia Lespedezae-polystachyae S.
Puccinia Lespedezae-procumbentis S.
Puccinia Lespedezae-violaceae S.
Uredo Lespedezae (S.) ex Thm.
Uromyces Lespedezae (S.) ex Pk.
Uromyces Lespedezae-procumbentis (S.) M. A.
  Curtis. 1867.
Uromyces Lespedezae-procumbentis (S.)
  Lagerh. 1895.
Uromyces Lespedezae-violaceae (S.) M. A.
  Curtis.
Uromyces macrosporus B. & C.
Lespedeza virginica (L.) Britt.
Microsphaera diffusa C. & P.
Caeomurus Lespedezae-procumbentis (S.)
  Arth.
Nigredo Lespedezae-procumbentis (S.) Arth.
Uromyces Lespedezae (S.) ex Pk.
Uromyces Lespedezae-procumbentis (S.) M. A.
  Curtis.
Lespedeza sp. indet.
Darluca Filum (Biv.) Cast.
Nectria Papilionacearum Seaver.
Dothidea perisporioides B. & C.
Parodiella perisporioides (B. & C.) Speg.
Ramularia Desmodii Cke.
Septoria Lespedezae Ell. & Ev.
Dalbergia Amerimnum Benth.
Sphaerophragmium Dalbergiae Diet.
Dalbergia Monetaria L.
Helminthosporium parathesicola F. L. Stevens.
Meliola bicornis Wint.
Machaerium Seemanni Benth.
Lasmenia Machaerii Henn.
Lasmeniella Melacherii (Henn.) Petrak & Syd.
Pseudothis Machaerii (Rehm) Theissen & Syd.
Drepanocarpus lunatus G. F. W. Mey.
Trabutia conica Chardon.
Pterocarpus Ecastophyllus L.
Physalospora Ecastophylli (Lév.) Sacc.
Sphaeria Ecastophylli Lév.
Pterocarpus sp. indet.
Asterina yucatanensis Ell. & Ev.

Lonchocarpus glaucifolius Urb.
Meliola bicornis Wint.
Trametes rufitincta (B.) Bres.
Lonchocarpus latifolius H. B. K.
Lonchocarpus salvadorensis Pittier.
Ravenelia Lonchocarpi Lagerh. & Diet.
Lonchocarpus violaceus H. B. K.
Phoma leguminum Westd.
Xylaria anisopleura Mont.
Piscidia erythrina L.
Cercospora Ichthyomethiae Dearness & Barthol.
Cercospora Piscidiae Henn.
Matruchotia varians Boulanger.
Ravenelia Piscidiae Long.
Andira excelsa H. B. K.
Polystigma pusillum Syd.
Andira inermis H. B. K.
Calonectria graminicola F. L. Stevens.
Cercospora Stevensii E. Young.
Dothidella andiricola Speg.
Meliola Andirae Earle.
Physalospora Andirae F. L. Stevens.
Andira racemosa Lam.
Radulum calceum Pat.
Dipteryx odorata Willd.
Anthostomella abdita (B. & C.) Sacc.
Sphaeria abdita B. & C.
Diatrype ruficarnis B. & C.
Diplodia vulgaris Lév.
Fusarium pallidum B. & C.
Gymnosporium decipiens B. & C.
Helminthosporium molle B. & C.
Helminthosporium vinosum B. & C.
Hymenochaete paupercula B. & C.
Monotospora sphaerophora B. & C.
Botryodiplodia dlavuligera (B. & C.) Petrak & Syd.
Phoma clavuligera (B. & C.) Sacc.
Sphaeropsis clavuligera B. & C.
Septonema curtum B. & C.
Septonema brevi-articulatum B. & C.
Sirodesmium brevi-articulatum (B. & C.) Sacc.
Sporocybe byssoides (P.) ex Fr.
Dipteryx punctata ex Fragoso & Ciferri.
Phyllosticta dipterixicola Fragoso & Ciferri.
Cicer sp. indet.
Neocosmospora vasinfecta Erw. Sm.
Vicia americana Muhl.
Ascochyta Pisi Lib.
Cylindrosporium Glycyrrhizae Hark.
Erysiphe communis Auct. Amer.
Erysiphe Polygoni DC.†
Gloeosporium Davisii Ell. & Ev.
Gloeosporium americanum Ell. & Ev.
Gloeosporium Everhartii Sacc. & Syd.
Microdiplodia Viciae Pk.
Microsphaera Alni (DC.) Wint. †

Microsphaera Alni., var. ludens Salmon.
Microsphaera diffusa Auct. Amer.
Microsphaera Alni, var. Vaccinii (S.) Salmon.
Microsphaera diffusa C. & P.
Microsphaera penicillata, var. ludens Salmon.
Peronospora Trifoliorum DBy.
Peronospora Viciae Auct. Amer.
Peronospora Viciae, var. americana J. J. Davis.
Phleospora reticulata Ell. & Ev.
Septoria Astragali Rob. & Desm.
Thecaphora deformans Dur. & Mont.
Synchytrium Jonesii Pk.
Tuberculina Jonesii (Pk.) Sacc.
Aecidium porosum Pk.
Pucciniola porosa Arth.
Uromyces albus Diet. & Holw.
Uromyces coloradensis Ell. & Ev.
Uromyces Fabae Fung. Columb. 1894.
Uromyces porosus (Arth.) H. S. Jackson.
Uromycopsis porosa Arth.
Aecidium album G. W. Clinton.
Caeoma leguminosorum S. Am. Bor. 2847.
Caeomurus Orobi Arth.
Caeomurus Pisi Auct. Amer.
Nigredo Fabae (DBy.) Arth.
Uromyces Fabae DBy.
Uromyces Orobi Fckl.
Uromyces polymorphus Pk. & Clinton.
Vicia americana Muhl., var. angustifolia Nees.
Erysiphe communis Auct. Amer.
Erysiphe Polygoni DC. †
Microdiplodia Viciae Pk.
Microsphaera Alni (DC.) Wint. †
Microsphaera Alni, var. ludens Salmon.
Erysiphe communis Kelsey Jour. Myc. 5: 83.
Microsphaera diffusa C. & P.
Microsphaera Ravenelii B.
Peronospora Viciae Fung. Columb. 1836.
Peronospora Viciae, var. americana J. J. Davis.
Aecidium album West Am. Fung. 84, 84a.
Aecidium porosum Pk.
Pucciniola porosa Arth.
Uromyces albus Diet. & Holw.
Uromyces porosus (Arth.) H. S. Jackson.
Uromycopsis porosa Arth.
Aecidium album G. W. Clinton.
Nigredo Fabae (DBy.) Arth.
Uromyces Fabae DBy.
Uromyces polymorphus Pk.
Vicia americana Muhl., var. truncata (Nutt.) Brewer.
Microsphaera Alni (DC.) Wint., var. ludens Salmon.
Microsphaera diffusa C. & P.
Thecaphora deformans Dur. & Mont.
Aecidium porosum Pk.
Pucciniola porosa Arth.
Uromyces albus Diet. & Holw.
Uromyces porosus (Arth.) H. S. Jackson.

Vicia americana var. **truncata** (*cont.*)
- Nigredo Fabae (DBy.) Arth.
- Aecidium album G. W. Clinton.
- Uromyces Fabae DBy.

Vicia angustifolia L.
- Nigredo Fabae (DBy.) Arth.

Vicia angustifolia (L.) Richards, var. **segetalis** (Thuillier) Koch.
- Ascochyta Pisi Lib.
- Pleospora americana Ell. & Ev.
- Pleospora hyalospora Ell. & Ev.

Vicia californica Greene.
- Pucciniola porosa Arth.
- Uromyces albus Diet. & Holw.
- Nigredo Fabae (DBy.) Arth.
- Uromyces Fabae DBy.

Vicia caroliniana Walt.
- Ascochyta Pisi Lib.
- Cercospora Viciae Ell. & Holw.
- Nigredo Fabae (DBy.) Arth.
- Thecaphora deformans Dur. & Mont.

Vicia Cracca L.
- Cercospora Viciae Ell. & Holw.
- Microsphaera Ravenelii B.
- Nigredo Fabae (DBy.) Arth.
- Uromyces Fabae DBy.

Vicia dasycarpa Tenore.
- Protocoronospora nigricans Atk. & Edgerton emend. Wolf.
- Thielavia basicola (B. & Br.) Zopf.

Vicia dissitifolia (Nutt.) Rydb.
- Nigredo Fabae (DBy.) Arth.

Vicia Faba L.
- Ascochyta Pisi Lib.
- Corticium vagum B. & C.
- Fusarium culmorum W. G. Sm.
- Fusarium trichothecioides Wollenw.
- Peronospora Viciae (B.) DBy.
- Rosellinia Pepo Pat.
- Sclerotium Rolfsii Sacc.
- Caeoma Leguminosorum S. Am. Bor. 2847.
- Nigredo Fabae (DBy.) Arth.
- Puccinia Fabae Lk. ex S.
- Uredo Leguminosarum Curt. Cat.
- Uromyces Fabae DBy.
- Uromyces Orobi Fckl.
- Uromyces Viciae-Fabae Schrt.

Vicia gigantea Hook.
- Hadrotrichum Blasdalei Sacc.
- Uredo (?) californica Ell. & Ev.

Vicia melilotoides Wooton & Standley.
- Nigredo Fabae (DBy.) Arth.

Vicia oregana Nutt.
- Nigredo Fabae (DBy.) Arth.

Vicia sativa L.
- Ascochyta Pisi Lib.
- Ascochyta Viciae Trail.
- Cercospora Viciae Ell. & Holw.
- Nigredo Fabae (DBy.) Arth.

- Peronospora Viciae Auct. Amer.
- Peronospora Viciae-sativae Gäuman.
- Protocoronospora nigricans Atk. & Edgerton, emend. Wolf.
- Mycosphaerella pinodes (B. & Blox.) R. E. Stone.

Vicia sepium L.
- Peronospora Viciae Auct. Amer.

Vicia tetrasperma (L.) Moench.
- Phoma melaena (Fr.) Mont. & Dur.

Vicia trifida D. Dietr.
- Pucciniola porosa Arth.
- Thecaphora deformans Dur. & Mont.
- Thecaphora Viciae Bubák.

Vicia truncata Nutt.
- Nigredo Fabae (DBy.) Arth.

Vicia villosa Roth.
- Ascochyta Pisi Lib.
- Ascochyta Viciae Lib.
- Corticium vagum B. & C.
- Protocoronospora nigricans Atk. & Edgerton emend. Wolf.
- Pseudopeziza Medicaginis (Lib.) Sacc.
- Mycosphaerella pinodes (B. & Blox.) R. E. Stone.
- Thielavia basicola (B. & Br.) Zopf.

Vicia sp. indet.
- Colletotrichum Viciae Dearness & Overholts.
- Pleospora herbarum (Fr.) Rabh.
- Sclerotinia libertiana Fckl.
- Sclerotinia Trifoliorum Erikss.
- Sphaerotheca Humuli (DC.) Burrill. †
- Uromyces appendiculatus Fr.

Lens esculenta Moench.
- Thielavia basicola (B. & Br.) Zopf.

Lathyrus arizonicus Britt.

Lathyrus bijugatus T. G. White.

Lathyrus Bolanderi Watson.

Lathyrus coriaceus T. G. White.
- Nigredo Fabae (DBy.) Arth.
- Uromyces Fabae DBy.
- Uromyces Orobi Fckl.

Lathyrus decaphyllus Pursh.
- Erysiphe communis Auct. Amer.
- Erysiphe Polygoni DC. †
- Septoria emaculata Pk. & Clinton.
- Nigredo Fabae (DBy.) Arth.
- Uromyces Fabae DBy.
- Uromyces Orobi Fckl.

Lathyrus Jepsonii Greene.

Lathyrus laetivirens Greene.
- Nigredo Fabae (DBy.) Arth.
- Uromyces Fabae DBy.

Lathyrus latifolius L.
- Cercospora lathyrina Ell. & Ev.
- Didymella lathyrina (B. & C.) Sacc.
- Sphaerella lathyrina (B. & C.) Cke.
- Sphaeria lathyrina B. & C.
- Septoria Lathyri Ell. & Ev.

Lathyrus leucanthus Rydb.
  Erysiphe Polygoni DC. †
  { Nigredo Fabae (DBy.) Arth.
  { Uromyces Fabae DBy.
Lathyrus maritimus (L.) Bigel.
  Cercospora Lathyri Dearness & House.
  Erysiphe Polygoni DC. †
  Leptosphaeria dumetorum Niessl.
  Phoma herbarum Westd.
  Phyllosticta orobella Sacc.
  Septoria Astragali Rob. & Desm.
  Septoria emaculata Pk. & Clinton.
Lathyrus Nuttallii Watson.
Lathyrus obovatus (Torr.) T. G. White.
  { Nigredo Fabae (DBy.) Arth.
  { Uromyces Fabae DBy.
Lathyrus ochroleucus Hook.
  Aecidium Orobi P.
  Cercospora Viciae Ell. & Holw.
  Dicoccum lathyrinum Ell. & Gall.
  { Erysiphe communis Auct. Amer.
  { Erysiphe Polygoni DC. †
  { Microsphaera Alni (DC.) Wint. †
  { Microsphaera diffusa Trel. p. p.
  Microsphaera diffusa C. & P.
  Phleospora reticulata Ell. & Ev.
  Phyllosticta orobella Sacc.
  Septoria Astragali Rob. & Desm.
  { Nigredo Fabae (DBy.) Arth.
  { Uromyces Fabae DBy.
  { Uromyces Orobi Fckl.
  { Uromyces polymorphus Pk. & Clinton.
Lathyrus odoratus L.
  Chaetomium spirochaete Palliser.
  Cladosporium album Dowson. ?
  Colletotrichum Pisi Pat.
  { Corticium vagum B. & C.
  { Rhizoctonia Solani Kühn.
  Erysiphe Polygoni DC. †
  Fusarium Lathyri Taubenhaus.
  Fusarium Martii, var. Pisi F. R. Jones.
  Fusarium vasinfectum Atk.
  Gloeosporium piperatum Ell. & Ev.
  { Colletotrichum nigrum Ell. & Halsted.
  { Colletotrichum phomoides (Sacc.) Chester.
  { Gloeosporium Diospyri Ell. & Ev.
  { Gloeosporium fructigenum B.
  { Gloeosporium gallarum Rich.
  { Gloeosporium officinale Ell. & Ev.
  { Glomerella cingulata (Stoneman) Spaulding &
  {   v. Schrenk.
  { Glomerella rufomaculans (B.) Spaulding & v.
  {   Schrenk.
  Glomerella Gossypii Edgerton.
  Microsphaera Alni (DC.) Wint. †
  Microsphaera diffusa C. & P.
  Microsphaera Ravenelii B.
  Mycosphaerella pinodes (B. & Blox.) R. E.
    Stone.

Mycorrhiza of Legumes F. R. Jones.
  Ozonium omnivorum Shear.
  Phytophthora Cactorum (Leb. & Cohn) Schrt.
  Pythium debaryanum Hesse.
  { Sclerotinia libertiana Fckl.
  { Sclerotinia sclerotiorum (Lib.) Schrt.
  Sclerotium Rolfsii Sacc.
  Sphaerotheca pannosa (Wallr.) Lév.
  Thielavia basicola (B. & Br.) Zopf.
Lathyrus oregonensis T. G. White.
Lathyrus ornatus Nutt.
  { Aecidium porosum Pk.?
  { Nigredo Fabae (DBy.) Arth.
  { Uromyces Fabae DBy.
  { Uromyces Orobi Fckl.
Lathyrus palustris L.
  Alternaria fasciculata (C. & E.) Jones & Grout.
  Ascochyta Pisi Lib.
  Cercospora Viciae Ell. & Holw.
  { Erysiphe communis Auct. Amer.
  { Erysiphe Polygoni DC. †
  { Microsphaera Alni (DC.) Wint. †
  { Microsphaera Ravenelii B.
  Microsphaera Alni, var. ludens Salmon.
  Phleospora reticulata Ell. & Ev.
  Septoria emaculata Pk. & Clinton.
  { Nigredo Fabae (DBy.) Arth.
  { Uromyces Fabae DBy.
  { Uromyces Orobi Fckl.
Lathyrus palustris L., var. **myrtifolius** (Muhl.)
    Gray.
  Erysiphe Polygoni DC. †
  Microsphaera Alni (DC.) Wint. †
  Microsphaera diffusa C. & P.
  { Nigredo Fabae (DBy.) Arth.
  { Uromyces Fabae DBy.
Lathyrus parvifolius Watson.
Lathyrus pauciflorus Fernald.
  { Nigredo Fabae (DBy.) Arth.
  { Uromyces Fabae DBy.
Lathyrus polyphyllus Nutt.
  Erysiphe Polygoni DC. †
  { Nigredo Fabae (DBy.) Arth.
  { Uromyces Fabae DBy.
Lathyrus sativus L.
  { Pleosphaerulina hyalospora (Ell. & Ev.) Berl.
  { Pleospora americana Ell. & Ev. p. p.[2]
  { Pleospora hyalospora Ell. & Ev.
  Mycosphaerella ontarioensis R. E. Stone.
Lathyrus strictus Nutt.
  Nigredo Fabae (DBy.) Arth.
Lathyrus sulphureus Brewer.
  Erysiphe Polygoni DC. †
  { Nigredo Fabae (DBy.) Arth.
  { Uromyces Fabae DBy.
Lathyrus tingitanus L.
  Mycorrhiza of Legumes F. R. Jones.

Lathyrus Torreyi Gray.
⌠Nigredo Fabae (DBy.) Arth.
⌡Uromyces Fabae DBy.

Lathyrus utahensis M. E. Jones.
Thecaphora deformans Dur. & Mont.
⌠Nigredo Fabae (DBy.) Arth.
⎨Uromyces Fabae DBy.
⌡Uromyces Orobi Fckl.

Lathyrus venosus Muhl.
Aecidium porosum Pk.?
Cercospora Lathyri Dearness & House.
Cercospora Viciae Ell. & Holw.
⌠Didymosphaerella vizeana Cke.
⎨Didymosphaeria vizeana (Cke.) Sacc.
⌡Sphaeria vizeana Cke.
⌠Erysiphe communis Auct. Amer.
⌡Erysiphe Polygoni DC. †
Gloeosporium Davisii Ell. & Ev.
⌠Microsphaera Alni (DC.) Wint. †
⌡Microsphaera Ravenelii B.
Phleospora reticulata Ell. & Ev.
Septoria Astragali Rob. & Desm.
Septoria Astragali Rob. & Desm., var. Brenck-
klei Sacc.
⌠Nigredo Fabae (DBy.) Arth.
⎪Uromyces Fabae DBy.
⎨Uromyces Orobi Fckl.
⌡Uromyces polymorphus Pk. & Clinton.

Lathyrus violaceus Greene.
Lathyrus Watsoni T. G. White.
⌠Nigredo Fabae (DBy.) Arth.
⌡Uromyces Fabae DBy.

Lathyrus sp. indet.
Aecidium Orobi P.
Pleococcum pezizoideum Cke.
Torula herbarum Lk.
Urophlyctis Lathyri (Bjorn.) Palm.

Pisum sativum L.
Alternaria Brassicae (B.) Sacc., var. Phaseoli
Bruner.
Ascochyta Pisi Lib.
Botrytis vulgaris (Lk.) ex Fr.
Cercospora Pisi-sativae Stevenson.
Cladosporium herbarum (P.) ex Lk.
Cladosporium (?) myriosporum Ell. & Dearness.
Colletotrichum lindemuthianum (Sacc. &
Magn.) Briosi & Cav.
Colletotrichum Pisi Pat.
⌠Corticium vagum B. & C.
⎨Corticium vagum, var. Solani Burt.
⌡Rhizoctonia Solani Kühn.
Erysiphe Cichoracearum DC. †
⌠Erysiphe communis Auct. Amer.
⎨Erysiphe Martii Lév.
⌡Erysiphe Polygoni DC. †
Fabraea maculata Lév.
Fusarium Martii, var. minus Sherbakoff.

Fusarium Martii, var. Pisi F. R. Jones.
Fusarium orthoceras Appel & Wr.
Fusarium oxysporum Schl.
Fusarium redolens Wr.
Fusicladium brevipes Ell. & Ev.
Fusicladium pisicola Linford.
Isariopsis griseola Sacc.
Macrosporium caudatum C. & E.
Nectriella tracheiphila Erw. Sm.
Ozonium omnivorum Shear.
Phoma subcircinata Ell. & Ev.
Phytomyxa Leguminosarum (Frank) Schrt.
⌠Catharinia americana Sacc. p. p.[2]
⎪Pleosphaerulina americana Berl.
⎨Pleospora americana Ell. & Ev. p. p.[2]
⌡Pleospora hyalospora Ell. & Ev. p. p.[2]
⌠Pleospora herbarum (Fr.) Rabh.
⎪Pleospora Pisi (Sow.) Fckl.
⌡Sphaeria Pisi Sow.
⌠Sclerotinia libertiana Fckl.
⌡Sclerotinia sclerotiorum (Lib.) Massee.
Sclerotium Rolfsii Sacc.
Septoria flagellifera Ell. & Ev.
Septoria irregularis Pk.
Septoria Pisi Westd.
⌠Mycosphaerella pinodes (B. & Blox.) R. E.
⎪ Stone.
⌡Sphaerella pinodes (B. & Blox.) Niessl.
Thielavia basicola (B. & Br.) Zopf.
⌠Uredo appendiculata P.?
⌡Uromyces appendiculatus Lév?
⌠Nigredo Fabae (DBy.) Arth.
⎨Uromyces Fabae DBy.
⌡Uromyces Pisi Auct. Amer. p. p.

PHYCOMYCETES
⌠Aphanomyces euteiches Drechsler.
⌡Pythium debaryanum Auct. Amer. p. p.
Peronospora Trifoliorum DBy.
Peronospora Viciae (B.) DBy.
Phytophthora Cactorum (Cohn & Loeb.)
Schrt.
Phytophthora terrestris Sherbakoff.
⌠Artotrogus debaryanus (Hesse) Atk.
⌡Pythium debaryanum Hesse.

Clitoria arborescens Ait.
Klebahnia yurinaguascensis. (Henn.) Arth.

Clitoria cajanifolia Benth.
Clitoria guianensis (Aubl.) Benth.
⌠Nigredo Neurocarpi (Diet.) Arth.
⎨Uromyces insularis Arth.
⌡Uromyces Neurocarpi Diet.

Clitoria mariana L.
Cercospora Clitoriae Atk.

Clitoria mexicana Lk.
⌠Nigredo Clitoriae Arth.
⌡Uromyces Clitoriae Arth.

Clitoria rubiginosa Juss.
⎰Nigredo Neurocarpi (Diet.) Arth.
⎱Uromyces Neurocarpi Diet.

Clitoria ternatea L.
Cercospora cruenta Sacc.

Clitoria triandra
Cercospora Clitoridis Fragoso & Ciferri.
Cladosporium herbarum (P.) ex Lk.
Macrosporium commune Rabh.
Melanconiella Clitoridis Fragoso & Ciferri.

Bradburya angustifolia (H. B. K.) O. Kuntze.
Meliola cookeana Sacc.

Bradburya pubescens (Benth.) O. Kuntze.
Cercospora Bradburyae E. Young.
Meliola bicornis Wint.
⎰Nigredo Neurocarpi (Diet.) Arth.
⎱Uromyces Neurocarpi Diet.

Centrosema virginiana (L.) Benth.
Cercospora Clitoriae Atk.
Meliola bicornis Wint.
Meliola Desmodii Karst. & Roum.
Phyllachora Lathyri (Lév.) Theissen.

Amphicarpa monoica (L.) Ell.
Aecidium leguminosatum Auct Amer. p. p.
⎰Aecidium Falcatae Arth.
⎱Aecidium Onobrychidis Burrill.
Aecidium Orobi P.
Cercospora monoica Ell. & Holw.
Cercospora simulans Ell. & Kellerm.
⎰Erysiphe communis Auct. Amer.
⎱Erysiphe Martii Lév.
Erysiphe Polygoni DC. †
⎰Leptostroma scandentium S.
⎱Xyloma scandentium S.
Microsphaera diffusa C. & P.
Mycorrhiza of Legumes F. R. Jones.
⎰Dothidea Glycineos S.
⎱Phyllachora Glycineos (S.) Sacc.
Phytomyxa Leguminosarum (Frank) Schrt.
⎰Stilbum candidum Pk.
⎱Stilbum Peckii Sacc.
⎰Synchytrium aecidioides (Pk.) Lagerh.
|Synchytrium decipiens Farl.
|Synchytrium fulgens, var. decipiens Farl.
|Uredo aecidioides Pk.
|Uredo Fabae Herb. Curt.
|Uredo Leguminosarum Herb. Curt.
|Uredo Peckii Thm.
⎱Woroninella aecidioides (Pk.) Syd.
⎰Uromyces appendiculatus Fr.
⎱Uromyces Phaseoli (Reb.) Wint.

Amphicarpa Pitcheri Torr. & Gr.
Cercospora monoica Ell. & Holw.
Erysiphe Polygoni DC. †
⎰Synchytrium aecidioides (Pk.) Lagerh.
⎱Synchytrium decipiens Farl.
Trichosporium Falcatae Dearness & Barthol.

Cologania affinis Mart. & Gal.
Cologania congesta Rose.
Cologania glabrior Rose.
Cologania pulchella H. B. K.
⎰Nigredo Cologaniae Arth.
⎱Uromyces Cologaniae Arth.

Glycine Max Merr.
Alternaria atrans Gibson.
Botryodiplodia pallida Ell. & Ev.
Botrytis cinerea Auct.
Cercospora cruenta Sacc.
Cercospora daizu Miura.
Corticium vagum B. & C.
Glomerella cingulata (Stoneman) Spaulding &
v. Schrenk.
⎰Colletotrichum Glycines Hori.
⎱Glomerella Glycines (Hori) Lehman & Wolf.
Diaporthe Sojae Lehman.
Erysiphe Polygoni DC. †
Fusarium tracheiphilum (Erw. Sm.) Wr.
Metasphaeria Carveri Ell. & Ev.
Mycorrhiza of Legumes F. R. Jones.
Ozonium omnivorum Shear.
Peronospora manshurica (Naoumoff) Syd. in lit.
Peronospora Sojae Lehman & Wolf.
Peronospora Trifoliorum DBy.
Phomopsis Sojae Lehman.
Phyllosticta glycineum Tehon & Daniels.
Pythium debaryanum Hesse.
Rhizoctonia Solani Kühn.
Sclerotinia sclerotiorum (Lib.) Massee.
Sclerotium Rolfsii Sacc.
Septoria Glycines T. Hemmi.
Thielavia basicola (B. & Br.) Zopf.

Teramnus uncinatus (L.) Sw.
Cercospora maricaoensis E. Young.
Meliola bicornis Wint.
⎰Physopella concors Arth.
⎱Uredo concors Arth.
⎰Phakopsora Vignae Arth.
⎱Uredo Vignae Bres.
Uromyces Cologaniae Arth.

Erythrina breviflora Moc & Sesse.
Septoria bonanseana Sacc.

Erythrina Corallodendron L.
Trichoscypha tricholoma Mont.

Erythrina Crista-galli L.
Cercospora Erythrinae Ell. & Ev.
Dicheirinia binata (B.) Arth.
Phyllosticta australis Speg.?

Erythrina glauca Willd.
Diabole cubensis Arth.
⎰Dicheirinia binata (B.) Arth.
⎱Uredo cabreriana Kern & Kellerm.
Phaeosaccardinula seaveriana Toro.
Trichoscypha tricholoma Mont.

Erythrina herbacea L.
Cercospora erythrinicola Tharp.
Colletotrichum Erythrinae Ell. & Ev.
Sporocybe byssoides (P.) ex Fr.

Erythrina indica Zoll.
Discina hirneoloides (B. & C.) Pat., var. car-
minea Pat.
⎧Podoscypha macrorhiza (Lév.) Pat.
⎨Stereum macrorhiza (Lév.) Lloyd.
⎩Thelephora macrorhiza Lév.

Erythrina Lithosperma Blume.
Phyllosticta Erythrinae Petch.

Erythrina micropteryx Poepp.
⎧Dicheirinia binata (B.) Arth.
⎩Uredo Cabreriana Kern & Kellerm.
Meliola bicornis Wint.
Phyllosticta erythrinicola E. Young.

Erythrina umbrosa H. B. K.
Dicheirinia binata (B.) Arth.

Erythrina sp. indet.
Aschersonia turbinata B.
Colletotrichum Erythrinae Ell. & Ev.
Fumago vagans Fr.
Rosellinia (paraguayensis Starb.?).

Rudolphia volubilis Willd.
Belonidium leucorrhodinum (Mont.) Sacc.
Meliola Rudolphiae F. L. Stevens.
Triposporium stelligerum Speg.

Apios tuberosa Moench.
Aecidium leguminosatum Auct. Amer. p. p.
⎧Aecidium Falcatae Arth.
⎩Aecidium Onobrychidis Burrill.
Aecidium Orobi P.
Alternaria tenuis Nees ex Fr.
⎧Cercospora glaucescens Wint.
⎩Cercospora tuberosa Ell. & Kellerm.
⎧Erysiphe communis Auct. Amer.
⎪Erysiphe Polygoni DC. †
⎪Microsphaera Alni (DC.) Wint. †
⎨Microsphaera Ravenelii B.
⎪Microsphaera diffusa C. & P.
⎩Microsphaera Lycii Auct. Amer.
Mollisia apiophila Dearness.
Periconia pycnospora Fres.
?Synchytrium decipiens Farl.
⎧Uromyces appendiculatus Fr.
⎩Uromyces Phaseoli (Reb.) Wint.
Uromyces Fabae DBy.

Mucuna andreana Micheli.
Uromyces illotus Arth. & Holw.

Mucuna sp. indet.
Cercospora Mucunae Syd.
Cercospora Stizolobii Syd.
Phyllosticta Mucunae Ciferri & Fragoso. 1925.

Stizolobium aterrimum Piper & Tracy.
Cercospora Mucunae Syd.

Stizolobium deeringianum Bort.
Amerosporium oeconomicum Ell. & Tracy.
Cercospora Mucunae Syd.
Cercospora Stizolobii Syd.
Corticium vagum B. & C.
Phyllosticta Mucunae Ell. & Ev. 1900.
Sclerotium Rolfsii Sacc.

Stizolobium pruriens Medic.
Cercospora Mucunae Syd.
Cercospora Stizolobii Syd.
Mycosphaerella Mucunae F. L. Stevens.

Stizolobium urens P.
Cercospora Mucunae Syd.

Stizolobium utile Piper & Tracy.
Didymella Ricini Ell. & Ev., var. Mucunae
Ell. & Ev.
Metasphaeria Carveri Ell. & Ev.
Phyllosticta Mucunae Ell. & Ev.
Sclerotium Rolfsii Sacc.

Calopogonium galactoides Benth.
Meliola bicornis Wint., var. Calopogonii F. L.
Stevens.

Calopogonium orthocarpum Urb.
Cercospora boringuensis E. Young.
Meliola bicornis Wint., var. Calopogonii F. L.
Stevens.

Galactia dubia DC.
Meliola bicornis Wint., var. Galactiae F. L.
Stevens.

Galactia Nuttallii Ell.
Cercospora Galactiae Ell. & Ev.

Galactia rudolphioides (Griseb.) Benth. & Hook.
Phyllachora Galactiae Earle.

Galactia striata Urb.
Phyllachora Galactiae Earle.
Phyllachora Lathyri (Lév.) Theissen & Syd.

Galactia volubilis (L.) Britt.
Cercospora flagellifera Atk.
Uromyces Phaseoli (Reb.) Wint.

Galactia sp. indet.
Thielavia basicola (B. & Br.) Zopf.

Pueraria thunbergiana Benth.
Diplodia Puerariae Barthol.

Canavalia ensiformis DC.
⎧Cerotelium Canavaliae Arth.
⎩Dietelia Canavaliae (Arth.) Syd.
Phakopsora Vignae (Bres.) Arth.

Canavalia gladiata DC.
⎧Cerotelium Canavaliae Arth.
⎩Dietelia Canavaliae (Arth.) Syd.

Canavalia maritima (Aubl.) Thore.
Cladosporium herbarum (P.) ex Lk.
Colletotrichum Canavaliae Fragoso & Ciferri.

Canavalia villosa Benth.
Cerotelium Canavaliae Arth.
Phakopsora Vignae (Bres.) Arth.

Canavalia sp. indet.
Rosellinia Pepo Pat.

Cajanus Cajan Millsp.
  Acanthonitschkea argentinensis Speg.
  Alternaria Brassicae (B.) Sacc., var. Phaseoli
    Brun.
  Botryosphaeria xanthocephala (Syd. & Butler)
    Theissen & Syd.
  Cercospora Cajani Henn.
  Colletotrichum Cajani Rangel.
  Cladosporium Citri Massee.
  { Corticium lilacinofuscum Auct.
  { Corticium salmonicolor B. & Br.
  Gloeosporium ampelophagum Auct.
  Megalonectria pseudotrichia (S.) Speg.
  { Creonectria grammicospora (Ferdinandsen &
  {   Winge) Seaver.
  { Nectria grammicospora Ferdinandsen & Winge.
  Neocosmospora vasinfecta Erw. Sm.
  { Pleonectria megalospora Speg.
  { Thyronectria megalospora (Speg.) Seaver &
  {   Chardon.
  Rosellinia Pepo Pat.
  Septobasidium Langloisii Pat.
  Sphaerostilbe cinnabarina Tul.
  { Nigredo Dolicholi Arth.
  { Uredo Cajani Syd.
  { Uromyces Dolicholi Arth.
Rhynchosia cinerea Nash.
  Parodiella paraguayensis Speg.
Rhynchosia erecta (Walt.) DC.
  Phyllosticta Rhynchosiae Miles.
Rhynchosia minima DC.
  ?Erysiphe Polygoni DC. †
  { Nigredo Dolicholi Arth.
  { Uromyces Dolicholi Arth.
Rhynchosia reticulata DC.
  Meliola bicornis Wint.
  Parodiella perisporioides (B. & C.) Speg.
  { Synchytrium decipiens Farl.
  { Woroninella Dolicholi (Cke.) Syd.
  { Nigredo appendiculata Arth. p. p.
  { Nigredo Dolicholi Arth.
  { Uromyces appendiculatus Arth. p. p.
  { Puccinia Dolichi Arth.
  { Uredo Dolichi Arth.
  { Uromyces Dolicholi Arth.
Rhynchosia simplicifolia (Walt.) Wood.
  Ascochyta Rhynchosiae (Thm.) Sacc.
Rhynchosia texana Torr. & Gr.
  { Nigredo Dolicholi Arth.
  { Uromyces Dolicholi Arth.
Rhynchosia tomentosa Hook. & Arn.
  { Ascochyta Rhynchosiae (Thm.) Sacc.
  { Depazea Rhynchosiae Thm.
  Nectria Peziza (Tode) ex Fr.
  { Coryneum Hedysari S. p. p.
  { Dothidea perisporioides B. & C.
  { Parodiella grammodes (Kze. ex B. & C.) Cke.
  { Parodiella perisporioides (B. & C.) Speg.
  { Sphaeria perisporioides B. & C.

Rhynchosia sp. indet.
  Graphium hyalosporum B. & Rav.
  Graphium leguminum Cke.
  Nectria Papilionacearum Seaver.
Eriosema crinitum G. Don.
  Phakopsora Vignae Arth.
Phaseolus acutifolius Gray.
  Ascochyta Bornmullerii Syd.
  Ozonium omnivorum Shear.
  Thielavia basicola (B. & Br.) Zopf.
Phaseolus acutifolius Gray, var. latifolius Free-
  man.
  Fusarium Martii Appel & Wr., var. Phaseoli
    Burkholder.
  Uromyces appendiculatus Fr.
Phaseolus adenanthus G. F. W. Meyer.
  Erysiphe Polygoni DC. †
  { Hyponectria Phaseoli F. L. Stevens.
  { Zythia Phaseoli F. L. Stevens.
  { Nigredo appendiculata (Fr.) Arth.
  { Uromyces appendiculatus Fr.
Phaseolus angularis W. F. Wight.
  Amerosporium oeconomicum Ell. & Tracy.
  Fusarium Martii Appel & Wr., var. Phaseoli
    Burkholder.
  Fusarium vasinfectum Atk.
  Neocosmospora vasinfecta Erw. Sm.
Phaseolus anisotrichus Schl.
Phaseolus atropurpureus DC.
  { Nigredo appendiculata (Fr.) Arth.
  { Uromyces appendiculatus Fr.
  { Uromyces Phaseoli (Reb.) Wint.
Phaseolus aureus Roxb.
  Sclerotinia sclerotiorum (Lib.) Massee.
Phaseolus coccineus Jacq.
  Colletotrichum lindemuthianum (Sacc. &
    Magn.) Briosi & Cav.
  Fusarium Martii Appel & Wr., var. Phaseoli
    Burkholder.
  { Nigredo appendiculata (Fr.) Arth.
  { Uromyces appendiculatus Fr.
Phaseolus disophyllus Benth.
  { Nigredo appendiculata (Fr.) Arth.
  { Uromyces appendiculatus Fr.
Phaseolus lathyroides L.
  { Nigredo appendiculata Fr.
  { Uromyces appendiculatus Fr.
Phaseolus lunatus L.
  Ascochyta Phaseolorum Sacc.?
  Cercospora Apii Fres.
  Cercospora canescens Ell. & Martin.
  Cercospora cruenta Sacc.
  Cercospora Phaseolorum Cke.
  Cladosporium herbarum (P.) ex Lk.
  Colletotrichum lindemuthianum (Sacc. &
    Magn.) Briosi & Cav.
  { Corticium vagum B. & C.
  { Rhizoctonia Solani Kühn.

Phaseolus lunatus (*cont.*)
  { Diaporthe Phaseolorum (C. & E.) Sacc.
  { Sphaeria Phaseolorum C. & E.
  Dimerium grammodes (Kze. ex B. & C.) P.
    Garman.
  Epicoccum duriaeanum Mont.
  Erysiphe Polygoni DC. †
  Fusarium Martii, Appel & Wr., var. Phaseoli
    Burkholder.
  Fusarium roseum Lk.
  Glomerella rufomaculans Spaulding & v.
    Schrenk.
  Isariopsis griseola Sacc.
  Microsphaera Euphorbiae (Pk.) B. & C.
  Nematospora Phaseoli S. A. Wingard.
  Ozonium omnivorum Shear.
  { Phakopsora Vignae Arth.
  { Physopella concors Arth.
  { Uredo concors Arth.
  Phoma subcircinata Ell. & Ev.
  Phyllachora Phaseoli (Henn.) Theissen & Syd.
  Phyllosticta phaseolina Sacc.
  { Peronospora Phaseoli (Thax.) Comes.
  { Phytophthora Phaseoli Thaxter.
  Septoria Petroselini Desm.
  { Nigredo appendiculata (Fr.) Arth.
  { Uromyces appendiculatus Fr.
  Vermicularia polytricha Cke.

Phaseolus multiflorus Willd.
  Colletotrichum lindemuthianum (Sacc. &
    Magn.) Briosi & Cav.

Phaseolus nanus L.
  Colletotrichum lindemuthianum (Sacc. &
    Magn.) Briosi & Cav.
  Macrosporium fasciculatum C. & E.
  { Nigredo appendiculata (Fr.) Arth.
  { Uromyces appendiculatus Fr.

Phaseolus obvallatus Schl.
Phaseolus pauciflorus Benth.
  { Nigredo appendiculata (Fr.) Arth.
  { Uromyces appendiculatus Fr.
  { Uromyces Phaseoli (Reb.) Wint.

Phaseolus polystachyus (L.) B. S. P.
  { Erysiphe communis Auct. Amer.
  { Erysiphe Polygoni DC. †
  Microsphaera diffusa C. & P.
  Phyllosticta phaseolina Sacc.
  { Nigredo appendiculata (Fr.) Arth.
  { Uromyces appendiculatus Fr.

Phaseolus retusus Benth.
Phaseolus sinuatus Nutt.
  { Nigredo appendiculata (Fr.) Arth.
  { Uromyces appendiculatus Fr.

Phaseolus truxillensis H. B. K.
  { Nigredo appendiculata (Fr.) Arth.
  { Uromyces appendiculatus Fr.
  Nigredo Vignae (Barcl.) Fromme.

Phaseolus vulgaris L.
  Acrostalagmus albus Preuss.
  { Alternaria fasciculata (C. & E.) Jones &
  {   Grout.
  { Macrosporium fasciculatum C. & E.
  Botrytis cinerea Auct.
  Cercospora canescens Ell. & Martin.
  Cercospora columnaris Ell. & Ev.
  Cercospora cruenta Sacc.
  Colletotrichum caulicola Heald & Wolf.
  { Colletotrichum lindemuthianum (Sacc. &
  {   Magn.) Briosi & Cav.
  { Gloeosporium lindemuthianum Sacc. & Magn.
  Colletotrichum lindemuthianum (Sacc. &
    Magn.) Briosi & Cavara, var. alpha Barrus.
  { Corticium vagum B. & C.
  { Corticium vagum B. & C., var. Solani Burt.
  { Rhizoctonia Solani Kühn.
  { Diaporthe Phaseolorum (C. & E.) Sacc.
  { Sphaeria Phaseolorum C. & E.
  Dimerium grammodes (Kze. ex B. & C.) P.
    Garman.
  Erysiphe Polygoni DC. †
  Fusarium aduncisporum Weimer & Harter.
  Fusarium macroceras Wr. & Reink.
  Fusarium Martii Appel & Wr.
  Fusarium Martii, var. Phaseoli Burkholder.
  Glomerella cingulata (Stoneman) Spaulding &
    v. Schrenk.
  Isariopsis griseola Sacc.
  { Graphium laxum Ell.
  { Isariopsis laxa (Ell.) Sacc.
  Leptosphaeria Phaseolorum Ell.
  Microsphaera diffusa C. & P.
  Mycorrhiza of Legumes F. R. Jones.
  Nematospora Phaseoli S. A. Wingard.
  Oedocephalum roseum Cke.
  Ozonium omnivorum Shear.
  Phoma subcircinata Ell. & Ev.
  Phyllachora Phaseoli (Henn.) Theissen & Syd.
  Phyllosticta phaseolina Sacc.
  Physarum cinereum (Batsch) P.
  Phytophthora terrestris Sherbakoff.
  Pythium debaryanum Hesse.
  Rhizoctonia microsclerotia Matz.
  { Sclerotinia libertiana Fckl.
  { Sclerotinia sclerotiorum (Lib.) Schrt.
  Sclerotium Rolfsii Sacc.
  Thielavia basicola (B. & Br.) Zopf.
  { Caeomurus Phaseoli (Reb.) Arth.
  { Nigredo appendiculata (Fr.) Arth.
  { Puccinia Phaseoli Reb.
  { Trichobasis rubrum Bon.
  { Uredo Leguminosarum Herb. Peters.
  { Uredo Phaseoli DC.
  { Uromyces appendiculatus Fr.
  { Uromyces Fabae Fung. Columb. *651.*
  { Uromyces obscurus Diet. & Holw.
  { Uromyces Phaseoli (Reb.) Wint.

Phaseolus Wrightii Gray.
 {Dothidea perisporioides B. & C.
 {Parodiella perisporioides (B. & C.) Speg.
Phaseolus sp. indet.
 Aspergillus flavus Lk.
 * Aspergillus niger van Tiegh.
 Cephalothecium roseum Cda.
 Cercospora Mucunae Syd.
 Colletotrichum lagenarium (Pass.) Ell. & Halsted.
 Corticium pezizoideum Ell. & Ev.
 Epicoccum micropus Cda.
 Fusarium oxysporum Schl.
 {Gloeosporium fructigenum B.
 {Gloeosporium phomoides Sacc.
 Glomerula repens Bain.
 {Leptosphaeria comatella (C. & E.) Sacc.
 {Sphaeria comatella C. & E.
 Macrophoma Phaseoli Maubl.
 Mystrosporium polytrichum Cke.
 {Creonectria seminicola Seaver.
 {Nectria seminicola Seaver.
 Nectria umbrina (B.) Fr.
 Polyactis vulgaris Lk.
 Rhizoctonia dimorpha Matz.
 Rhizopus nigricans Ehrh.
 Typhula tenuissima M. A. Curtis.
 Vermicularia truncata S.
Strophostyles helvola (L.) Brit.
 {Erysiphe communis Auct. Amer.
 {Erysiphe Polygoni DC. †
 Phyllosticta phaseolina Sacc.
 Thielavia basicola (B. & Br.) Zopf.
 {Caeomurus Phaseoli (Reb.) Arth.
 {Nigredo appendiculata (Fr.) Arth.
 {Puccinia Phaseoli-trilobi S.
 {Uredo appendiculata P.
 {Uromyces appendiculatus Fr.
 {Uromyces Phaseoli (Reb.) Wint.
 {Uromyces Phaseolorum (DC.) Tul.
Strophostyles pauciflora (Benth.) Watson.
 Phyllosticta phaseolina Sacc.
 {Nigredo appendiculata (Fr.) Arth.
 {Uromyces appendiculatus Fr.
Strophostyles umbellata (Muhl.) Britton.
 {Nigredo appendiculata (Fr.) Arth.
 {Uromyces appendiculatus Fr.
 {Uromyces Phaseoli (Reb.) Wint.
Vigna Catjang Walp.
 Cercospora Vignae Ell. & Ev.
 Fusarium vasinfectum, var. tracheiphilum Erw. Sm.
 Spermophthora Gossypii Ashby & Nowell.
Vigna lutea Gray.
 {Phakopsora Vignae Arth.
 {Uredo Vignae Bres.
Vigna luteola Benth.
 Cercospora canescens Ell. & Martin.
 Cercospora Vignae Ell. & Ev.

 {Coscinaria Langloisii Ell. & Ev.
 {Oomyces Langloisii Ell. & Ev.
Vigna repens (L.) O. Kuntze.
 Dimerium grammodes (Kze. ex B. & C.) P. Garman.
 ?Erysiphe Polygoni DC. †
 Myriosticta portoricensis Pat.
 Nigredo Vignae (Barcl.) Fromme.
 {Nigredo appendiculata (Fr.) Arth.
 {Uromyces appendiculatus Fr.
 {Uromyces Phaseoli (Reb.) Wint.
Vigna sesquipedalis Wight.
 Cladosporium Vignae Gardner.
Vigna sinensis (L.) Endl.
 Alternaria atrans Gibson.
 Amerosporium oeconomicum Ell. & Tracy.
 Aspergillus niger van Tiegh.
 Blakeslea trispora Thax.
 Botrytis Rileyi Farl.
 {Cercospora cruenta Sacc.
 {Cercospora Dolichi Ell. & Ev.
 Cercospora Vignae Ell. & Ev. 1887.
 Cercospora Vignae Racib. 1898.
 Cladosporium Vignae Gardner.
 Colletotrichum Gossypii Southw.
 {Colletotrichum lindemuthianum (Sacc. & Magn.) Briosi & Cav.
 {Glomerella lindemuthiana Shear.
 {Corticium vagum B. & C.
 {Rhizoctonia Solani Kühn.
 Erysiphe Polygoni DC. †
 Fusarium Martii, var. Phaseoli Burkholder.
 Fusarium vasinfectum Atk.
 {Fusarium vasinfectum, var. tracheiphilum Erw. Sm.
 {Fusarium tracheiphilum (Erw. Sm.) Wr.
 Gloeosporium fructigenum B.
 Helminthosporium molle B. & C.
 Macrophoma subconica Ell. & Ev.
 Macrosporium leguminum Cke.
 Microsphaera Alni (DC.) Wint. †
 Microsphaera Euphorbiae (Pk.) B. & C.
 Nectriella tracheiphila Erw. Sm.
 Nematospora Phaseoli Wingard.
 Neocosmospora vasinfecta Erw. Sm.
 Neocosmospora vasinfecta Erw. Sm., var. tracheiphila Erw. Sm.
 Ozonium omnivorum Shear.
 Periconia pycnospora Fres.
 Phoma lathyrina Sacc.
 Phyllosticta phaseolina Sacc.
 Pleospora americana Ell. & Ev.
 Pythium aphanidermatum (Edson) Fitzpatrick
 Pythium myriotylum Drechsler.
 Rhizoctonia dimorpha Matz.
 Rhizoctonia microsclerotia Matz.
 Rhizoctonia Solani Kühn.
 Sclerotium Rolfsii Sacc.

Vigna sinensis (*cont.*)
  Thielavia basicola (B. & Br.) Zopf.
  ⎰Caeomurus Phaseoli (Reb.) Arth.
  ⎰Nigredo appendiculata (Fr.) Arth.
  ⎱Uromyces appendiculatus Fr.
  ⎰Uromyces Phaseoli (Reb.) Wint.
  ⎰Nigredo Vignae (Barcl.) Fromme.
  ⎱Uromyces Vignae Barcl.

Vigna strobilophora B. L. Robinson.
  Nigredo appendiculata (Fr.) Arth.
  Uromyces punctiformis Syd.
  Uromyces Vignae Barcl. ?

Vigna unguiculata (L.) Walp.
  Cercospora canescens Ell. & Martin.
  Cercospora cruenta Sacc.
  Cercospora Vignae Racib.
  Erysiphe Polygoni DC. †
  Ozonium omnivorum Shear.
  Physarum cinereum (Batsch) P.
  Uromyces appendiculatus Fr.

Vigna vexillata A. Rich.
  Hyponectria Phaseoli F. L. Stevens.
  Phyllachora Phaseoli (Henn.) Theissen & Syd.
  ⎰Nigredo appendiculata (Fr.) Arth.
  ⎱Uromyces appendiculatus Fr.

Vigna sp. indet.
  Fusarium oxysporum Schl.
  Pythium debaryanum Hesse.

Dolichos biflorus L.
  Erysiphe Polygoni DC. (?)

Dolichos eninimus (L.) Medic.
  Uromyces Dolicholi Arth.

Dolichos Lablab L.
  Cercospora canescens Ell. & Martin.
  ⎰Phakopsora Vignae (Bres.) Arth.
  ⎰Physopella concors Arth.
  ⎱Uredo concors Arth.
  Phytophthora terrestris Sherbakoff.
  Thielavia basicola (B. & Br.) Zopf.
  ⎰Nigredo Vignae (Barcl.) Fromme.
  ⎱Uromyces Vignae Barcl.

Dolichos melanophthalmus DC.
  Cercospora Dolichi Ell. & Ev.
  Septoria melanophthalmi B. & C.
  ⎰Nigredo appendiculata (Fr.) Arth.
  ⎱Uredo Dolichi Arth.
  ⎰Uromyces appendiculatus Fr.
  ⎱Uromyces Phaseoli (Reb.) Wint.

Dolichos sp. indet.
  Acrospermum compressum Tode ex Fr.
  Amerosporium Dolichi Ell. & Ev.
  Cercospora cruenta Sacc.
  Colletotrichum lindemuthianum (Sacc. & Magn.) Briosi & Cav.
  Helminthosporium molle B. & C.
  ⎰Phomatospora phlyctanoides (B. & C.) Cke.
  ⎰Physalospora phlyctanoides (B. & C.) Sacc.
  ⎱Sphaeria phlyctanoides B. & C.
  Septoria Dolichi B. & C.

Leguminosae gen. indet.
  Cystomyces costaricensis Syd.
  Elfvingia tornata (P.) Murrill.
  Meliola polyodonta Syd.
  Phoma punctulata Cke.
  ⎰Phragmidium? deglubens (B. & C.) De Toni.
  ⎱Triphragmium deglubens B. & C.
  Pleospora herbarum (Fr.) Rabh.
  Xylaria tentaculata B. & Br.

GERANIACEAE

Geranium Bicknellii Britton.
  Plasmopara Geranii (Pk.) Berl. & De Toni.
  Puccinia Polygoni-amphibii P. I.

Geranium caespitosum James.
  Sphaerotheca Humuli (DC.) Burrill. †

Geranium carolinianum L.
  Aecidium geraniatum Lk.
  Botrytis pellucida S.
  Cercospora Geranii Kellerm. & Swingle.
  Cylindrosporium Geranii Ell. & Ev.
  ⎰Peronospora Geranii Pk.
  ⎰Plasmopara Geranii (Pk.) Berl. & De Toni.
  ⎱Rhysotheca Geranii (Pk.) G. W. Wilson.
  Pestalozziella subsessilis Sacc. & Ell.
  Phyllosticta Geranii Ell. & Ev.
  Septoria expansa Niessl.
  Sphaerotheca Humuli (DC.) Burrill. †
  Stigmatea Geranii Fr.
  Synchytrium Geranii Clendenin.
  Venturia glomerata Cke.

Geranium columbinum L.
  Dicaeoma Polygoni-amphibii (P.) Arth. I.

Geranium dissectum L.
  Rhysotheca Geranii (Pk.) G. W. Wilson.

Geranium erianthum DC.
  Aecidium violascens Trel.
  ⎰Micropuccinia Leveillei (Mont.) Arth. & Jackson.
  ⎱Puccinia Geranii-silvatici Karst.
  Nigredo Geranii (Fr.) Arth.
  Venturia circinans (Fr.) Sacc.

Geranium Fremontii Torr.
  Cercospora Geranii Kellerm. & Swingle.
  ⎰Micropuccinia Leveillei (Mont.) Arth. & Jackson.
  ⎱Puccinia Leveillei Mont.

Geranium incisum Nutt.
  Dicaeoma Polygoni-amphibii (P.) Arth. I.
  ⎰Erysibe communis (Wallr.) Lk.
  ⎱Erysiphe Polygoni DC. †
  ⎰Micropuccinia Leveillei (Mont.) Arth. & Jackson.
  ⎰Puccinia Geranii-silvatici Karst.
  ⎱Puccinia Leveillei Mont.
  ⎰Sphaerotheca Castagnei Lév. p. p.
  ⎱Sphaerotheca Humuli (DC.) Burrill. †
  Sphaerotheca Humuli, var. fuliginea Schl.

Geranium maculatum L.
- Aecidium Geranii Auct. Amer.
- Aecidium Geranii-maculati S.
- Aecidium sanguinolentum Lindr.
- Dicaeoma Polygoni-amphibii (P.) Arth. I.
- Puccinia Polygoni-amphibii P. I.
- Uromyces Geranii Auct. Amer. I.
- Botrytis pellucida S.
- Cercospora Geranii Kellerm. & Swingle.
- Erysiphe communis Auct. Amer.
- Erysiphe Polygoni DC. †
- Peronospora Geranii Pk.
- Peronospora nivea, var. Geranii Farl.
- Plasmopara Geranii (Pk.) Berl. & De Toni.
- Plasmopara nivea, var. Geranii Farl.
- Rhysotheca Geranii (Pk.) G. W. Wilson.
- Pestalozziella subsessilis Ell. & Ev.
- ?Puccinia Geranii Cda.
- Ramularia Geranii (Westd.) Fckl.
- Sclerotinia Geranii Seaver & Horne.
- Sphaerotheca Castagnei Lév. p. p.
- Sphaerotheca Humuli (DC.) Burrill. †
- Sphaerotheca Mors-uvae (S.) B. & C.
- ?Uromyces Geranii Auct. Amer.
- Vermicularia herbarum Westd.
- Vermicularia petiolicola Brun.

Geranium mexicanum H. B. K.
- Uredo unilateralis Arth.

Geranium nervosum Rydb.
- Micropuccinia Leveillei(Mont.)Arth. & Jackson
- Puccinia Geranii Lév.
- Puccinia Geranii-silvatici Karst.
- Puccinia Leveillei Mont.

Geranium pusillum Burm. f.
- Rhysotheca Geranii (Pk.) G. W. Wilson.

Geranium Richardsonii Fisch. & Trautv.
- Erysiphe communis Auct. Amer.
- Erysiphe Polygoni DC. †
- Puccinia Geranii-silvatici Karst.
- Puccinia Leveillei Mont.
- Rhysotheca Geranii (Pk.) G. W. Wilson.
- Sphaerotheca Castagnei Lév. p. p.
- Sphaerotheca Humuli (DC.) Burrill. †

Geranium Robertianum L.
- Peronospora Geranii Pk.
- Plasmopara Geranii (Pk.) Berl. & De Toni.
- Rhysotheca Geranii (Pk.) G. W. Wilson.
- Dothidea Robertiani Fr.
- Stigmatea Robertiani Fr.

Geranium sibiricum L.

Geranium texanum Heller.
- Peronospora Geranii Pk.
- Plasmopara Geranii (Pk.) Berl. & De Toni.

Geranium viscosissimum Fisch. & Mey.
- Micropuccinia Leveillei (Mont.) Arth. & Jackson.
- Puccinia Geranii-silvatici Karst.
- Puccinia Leveillei Mont.
- Sphaerotheca Castagnei Lév.

Geranium sp. indet.
- Amerosporium Geranii Cke. & Hark.
- Botrytis cinerea P. †
- Cercospora Brunkii Ell. & Gall.
- Leptosphaeria culmifraga (Fr.) Ces. & De Not.
- Physalospora Geranii Cke. & Hark.

Erodium cicutarium (L.) L'Her.
- Synchytrium papillatum Farl.

Pelargonium capitatum Ait.
- Hainesia Lythri (Desm.) v. Höhnel.

Pelargonium graveolens L'Her.
- Cercospora Brunkii Ell. & Gall.

Pelargonium hortorum Bailey.
- Botrytis cinerea P. †

Pelargonium peltatum Ait.
- Cercospora Brunkii Ell. & Gall.

Pelargonium zonale Willd.
- Amerosporium Geranii Cke. & Hark.
- Diaporthe elephantina Cke. & Hark.
- Diaporthe Geranii Cke. & Hark.
- Hainesia Lythri (Desm.) v. Höhnel.
- Heptameria subcaespitosa (Cke. & Hark.) Cke.
- Leptosphaeria subcaespitosa Cke. & Hark.
- Macrosporium Pelargonii Ell. & Ev.
- Phomatospora Geranii Cke.
- Physalospora Geranii Cke. & Hark.
- Rhizoctonia Solani Kühn.
- Tubercularia Geranii Cke. & Hark.
- Tubercularia sphaeroidea Cke. & Hark.

Pelargonium sp. indet.
- Botrytis (Polyactis) doryphora Pound & Clements.
- Botrytis vulgaris (Lk.) ex Fr.
- Macrosporium Pelargonii Ell. & Ev.
- Pythium complectens H. Braun.
- Pythium debaryanum Hesse.
- Pythium debaryanum Hesse, var. Pelargonii H. Braun.
- Pythium splendens H. Braun.
- Sclerotinia fuckeliana (DBy.) Fckl.

OXALIDACEAE

Oxalis Acetosella L.
- Didymium oxalinum Pk.
- Ramularia Oxalidis Farl.
- Septoria Acetosella Dearness & House.

Oxalis corniculata L.
Including O. corniculata and O. stricta Auct. Amer. p. p. non L., and O. cymosa Small. These names as applied to host plants can not be accurately segregated.
- Aecidium Oxalidis Thm.
- Dicaeoma Sorghi (S.) O. Kuntze. I.
- Puccinia Maydis Béreng. I.
- Puccinia Sorghi S. I.
- Microsphaera Russellii G. W. Clinton.
- Phyllachora oxalina Ell. & Ev.

Oxalis corniculata (*cont.*)
Phyllosticta guttulatae Halsted.
Ramularia Oxalidis Farl.
Sphaerella depazeiformis (Awd.) Ces. & De Not.
Thielavia basicola (B. & Br.) Zopf.
Ustilago Oxalidis Ell. & Tracy.

Oxalis Hayi Kunth.
{ Argomyces? Oxalidis (Diet. & Ell.) Arth.
{ Dicaeoma Oxalidis (Diet. & Ell.) O. Kuntze.

Oxalis filipes Small.

Oxalis Langloisii (Small).
Dicaeoma Sorghi (S.) O. Kuntze. I.

Oxalis latifolia H. B. K.

Oxalis martiana Zucc.
{ Dicaeoma Oxalidis (Diet. & Ell.) O. Kuntze.
{ Puccinia Oxalidis Diet. & Ell.

Oxalis oregana Nutt.
Ramularia Oxalidis Farl.

Oxalis pumila Nutt.

Oxalis recurva Elliott.
Microsphaera Russellii G. W. Clinton.

Oxalis stricta L.
Puccinia of Andropogon furcatus.
{ Aecidium Oxalidis Thm.
{ Dicaeoma Sorghi (S.) O. Kuntze. I.
{ Puccinia Sorghi S. I.
Microsphaera Russellii G. W. Clinton.
Phyllachora oxalina Ell. & Ev.
Phyllosticta guttulata Halsted.
Phyllosticta Oxalidis Sacc.
Sphaerulina Oxalidis Rehm.
Ustilago Oxalidis Ell. & Tracy.

Oxalis Suksdorfii Trel.
Microsphaera Russellii G. W. Clinton.

Oxalis
(Ionoxalis tetraneuris Small.)

Oxalis
(Ionoxalis trinervis Small.)

Oxalis vallicola (Rose) Kunth.
{ Argomyces Oxalidis (Lév.) Arth.
{ Dicaeoma Oxalidis (Lév.) O. Kuntze.

Oxalis violacea L.
{ Aecidium Oxalidis Thm.
{ Dicaeoma Sorghi (S.) O. Kuntze. I.
Microsphaera Russellii G. W. Clinton.
{ Argomyces? Oxalidis (Diet. & Ell.) Arth.
{ Dicaeoma Oxalidis (Diet. & Ell.) O. Kuntze.
{ Puccinia Oxalidis Diet.& Ell.
{ Uredo Oxalidis Lév.
Ramularia Oxalidis Farl.

Oxalis sp. indet.
Didymium squamulosum Fr.
Phyllosticta oxalicola Speg.
Phyllosticta oxalidicola Henn.

Averrhoa Bilimbi L.
Xerotus martinicensis Pat.

TROPAEOLACEAE

Tropaeolum majus L.
{ Dicaeoma Sarcobati Arth. I.
{ Puccinia subnitens Diet. I.
Albugo candida (P.) O. Kuntze.
{ Didymosphaeria sarmenti (Cke. & Hark.) Berl. & Vogl.
{ Sphaeria sarmenti Cke. & Hark.
Pleospora herbarum (Fr.) Rabh.
Pleospora Tropaeoli Halsted.

Tropaeolum sp. indet.
Cercospora Tropaeoli Atk.

LINACEAE

Linum arkansanum Osterh.
Linum australe Heller.
Linum Berlandieri Hook.
Linum Breweri Pursh.
Linum congestum Gray.
Linum digynum Gray.
Linum drymarioides Curran.
Linum Kingii Watson.
Linum medium (Planch.) Britt.
Linum micranthum Gray.
Linum perenne L.
Linum rigidum Pursh.
{ Melampsora Lini Desm.
{ Uredo Lini (P.) Schum. II.
{ Uredo Lini (Desm.) Arth. III.

Linum grandiflorum Desf., var. **rubrum** Hort.
Rhizoctonia Solani Kühn.

Linum humile Mill.
Fusarium Lini Bolley.

Linum Lewisii Pursh.
Melampsora Lini Desm.
Pyrenopeziza californica Sacc.

Linum sulcatum Riddell.
Cercospora Lini Ell. & Ev.
{ Peronospora Lini Schrt.? 1886.
{ Peronospora Lini Ell. & Kellerm. 1887.
{ Melampsora Lini Desm. 1850.
{ Uredo Lini (P.) Schum. II. 1803.
{ Uredo Lini (Desm.) Arth. III. 1907.

Linum usitatissimum L.
Fusarium Lini Bolley.
{ Melampsora Lini Desm.
{ Uredo Lini (P.) Schum. II.
{ Uredo Lini (Desm.) Arth. III.
Phlyctaena linicola Speg

Linum virginianum L.
Aecidium Lini Dearness & House.
Cercospora Lini Ell. & Ev.
{ Melampsora Lini Desm.
{ Uredo Lini (P.) Schum. II.
{ Uredo Lini (Desm.) Arth. III.

Linum sp. indet.
  Colletotrichum Lini Bolley.
  Colletotrichum linicola Peth. & Laf.
  Polyspora Lini Lafferty.

ERYTHROXYLACEAE

Erythroxylon areolatum L.
Erythroxylon brevipes DC.
Erythroxylon havanense Jacq.
  Uredo Erythroxylonis Grazian.
Erythroxylon ovatum Cav.
  Trametes Medulla-panis (P. ex Fr.) Pat.

ZYGOPHYLLACEAE

Guaiacum officinale L.
  Meliola woodiana Sacc. & Syd.
  Phyllosticta Guayaci Ciferri & Fragoso.

RUTACEAE

Zanthoxylum americanum Mill.
  Aecidium Xanthoxyli Pk.
  Cercospora Xanthoxyli Cke.
  Dermatea Xanthoxyli Pk.
  Diplodia natalensis Evans.
  {Fenestella Xanthoxyli (Pk.) Sacc.
  {Pseudovalsa Xanthoxyli (Pk.) Sacc.
  {Thyronectria Xanthoxyli (Pk.) Ell. & Ev.
  {Valsa Xanthoxyli Pk.
  Gloeosporium dearnessianum Sacc.
  Hysterographium Fraxini (P. ex Fr.) De Not.
  {Lophidium obtectum (Pk.) Sacc.
  {Lophiostoma obtectum Pk.
  {Massaria Xanthoxyli (Pk.) Petrak.
  {Massariella Xanthoxyli Pk.
  Phorcys Xanthoxyli (Pk.) House.
  {Phyllactinia corylea (P.) ex Karst.
  {Phyllactinia suffulta (Reb.) ex Sacc.
  Septoria pachyspora Ell. & Holw.
  Thyridium americanum Ell. & Ev.
  Valsaria insitiva Ces. & De Not.
Zanthoxylum aromaticum Willd.
  Irene trachylaena Syd.
  Phyllachora applanata Wint.
  Stereum ferreum B.
Zanthoxylum carolinianum, var. **fruticosum**
  Gray.
  Aecidium Xanthoxyli Pk.
Zanthoxylum Clava-Herculis L.
  Aecidium Xanthoxyli Pk.
  Cercospora Xanthoxyli Cke.
  Fumago vagans Fr.
  Septoria pachyspora Ell. & Holw.
  Valsaria Xanthoxyli Ell. & Ev.
Zanthoxylum fagara L.
  Irene obesa (Speg.) Theissen & Syd.
Zanthoxylum martinicense (Lam.) DC.
  Phyllachora Zanthoxyli Wint.
  Trabutia Zanthoxyli Chardon.

Zanthoxylum microcarpum Griseb.
  Ovulariopsis farinosa Syd.
  Phyllachora Winteri Sacc. & Syd.
Zanthoxylum procerum Donn. Sm.
  Meliola aterrima Syd.
  Meliola macropoda Syd.
  Sphaerulina concinna Syd.
Zanthoxylum sp. indet.
  Discula Xanthoxyli Ell. & Ev.
  {Eutypella stellulata (Fr.) Sacc.
  {Valsa stellulata Fr.
  Fomes igniarius (L. ex Fr.) Gill.
  Macrophoma Xanthoxyli Ell. & Ev.
  Thyronectria pyrrhochlora (Awd.) Sacc.
Dictamnus Fraxinella P.
  Excipula Dictamni Fairman.
  Phyllosticta Dictamni Fairman.
Pilocarpus racemosus Vahl.
  Meliola Pilocarpi F. L. Stevens.
  Porothelium reviviscens B. & C.
Ptelea trifoliata L.
  {Aecidium Pteleae B. & C.
  {Dicaeoma Windsoriae (S.) O. Kuntze. I.
  {Puccinia Windsoriae S. I.
  Alternaria tenuis Nees ex Fr.
  Cercospora afflata Wint.
  Cercospora Pteleae Wint.
  Phleospora Pteleae Tharp.
  Phyllosticta pteleicola Tehon & Daniels.
  Septoria Pteleae Ell. & Ev.
Casimiroa edulis La Llave.
  Cercospora coleroides Sacc.
Amyris elemifera L.
  Calonectria melioloides Speg.
  Helminthosporium glabroides F. L. Stevens.
  Helminthosporium Helleri F. L. Stevens.
  Meliola monensis F. L. Stevens.
  Micropeltidium monense Speg.
  Stevensula monensis Speg.
Amyris sp. indet.
  Meliola amphitricha Fr.
Murraya exotica L.
  {Crinipellis asperifolius Pat.
  {Marasmius asperifolius Pat.

Citrus aurantifolia (Christm.) Swingle.
  (Lime.)
  Cladosporium Citri Massee.
  Colletotrichum gloeosporioides Penz.
  Diaporthe Citri Wolf.
  Gloeosporium limetticola Clausen.
  Phytophthora terrestris Sherbakoff.
  Rosellinia bunodes (B. & Br.) Sacc.
  Rosellinia Pepo Pat.
  Sphaeropsis tumefaciens Hedges.
  {Sphaceloma Fawcettii A. E. Jenkins.
  {Sporotrichum Citri Butler.

Citrus Aurantium L.   (Sour orange.)

PHYCOMYCETES

Phytophthora terrestris Sherbakoff.
{ Phytophthora citrophthora (Sm. & Sm.) Leonian.
  Pythiacystis citrophthora Sm. & Sm.

ASCOMYCETES

Angelina nigrocinnabarina B. & C.
Capnodium Citri B. & Desm.
{ Cryptovalsa citricola (Ell. & Ev.) Berl.
  Diatrypella citricola Ell. & Ev.
Capnodium Citri Mont. p. p.
{ Meliola Camelliae (Catt.) Sacc.
Capnodium Citri B. & Desm. p. p.
{ Meliola Penzigi Sacc.
Mycosphaerella lageniformis Rehm.
Myriangium Curtisii B. & Mont.
Myriangium Duriaei Mont. & B.
Myriangium floridanum (Ell. & Gall.) Rehm.
Nectria vulgaris Speg.
Pleospora media Niessl, var. Limonum Sacc.
Rosellinia bunodes (B. & Br.) Sacc.
Rosellinia Pepo Pat.
Scleroderris gigaspora Massee.
Scleroplea Aurantiorum Rehm.
{ Sclerotinia libertiana Fckl.
  Sclerotinia sclerotiorum (Lib.) Schrt. 1893.
{ Sclerotinia sclerotiorum (Lib.) Massee 1895.
  Sclerotinia sclerotiorum (Lib.) Sacc. & Trott. 1913.
Scoleconectria coccicola (Ell. & Ev.) Seaver.
Sphaerostilbe aurantiicola B. & Br.
Sphaerostilbe cinnabarina Tul.
Sphaerostilbe coccophila Tul.
Ustulina vulgaris Tul.

HYMENOMYCETINEAE

Armillaria mellea (Vahl) ex Fr.
Corticium dendriticum Henn.
{ Corticium koleroga (Cke.) v. Höhnel.
  Pellicularia koleroga Cke.
Corticium salmonicolor B. & Br.
Crepidotus parvulus Murrill.
Hypochnus albocinctus Mont. (Lichen).
Hypochnus rubrocinctus Ehrenb. (Lichen).
Polyporus igniarius (L.) ex Fr.
Fomes marmoratus B.
Ganoderma Oerstedii (Fr.) Murrill.
Peniophora albofarcta Burt.
Polyporus annosus Fr.
Inonotus fruticum (B. & C.) Murrill.
Polyporus hispidus Fr.
Poria cocos Wolf.
Poria undata (P.) Bres.
Poria vincta (B.) Cke.
Rhodophyllus miniatus Pat.
{ Schizophyllum alneum (L. ex Fr.) Schrt.
  Schizophyllum commune Fr.

Septobasidium pedicellatum Pat.
Septobasidium pseudopedicellatum Burt.

SPHAEROPSIDALES

Aschersonia Aleyrodis Webber.
{ Aschersonia flavocitrina Auct. Amer.
  Aschersonia goldiana Sacc. & Ell.
Aschersonia Pittieri Henn.
Aschersonia tahitensis Mont.
Aschersonia turbinata B.
Botryodiplodia diplocarpa Ell. & Ev.
Chaetophoma Citri Sacc.
Chaetophoma Citri Sacc., var. hainensis Ciferri & Fragoso.
Diplodia hesperidica Speg.
Diplodia natalensis Evans.
Phoma socia Wolf.
Phomopsis Citri Fawcett.
{ Phyllosticta aurantiicola (B. & C.) Sacc.
  Sphaeropsis aurantiicola B. & C.
Sphaeropsis placenta B. & C.
Sphaeropsis tumefaciens Hedges.

MELANCONIALES

{ Colletotrichum adustum (Ell. & Martin) Ell.
  Phyllosticta adusta Ell. & Martin.
{ Colletotrichum gloeosporioides Penz.
  Gloeosporium Psidii Sheldon.
{ Glomerella cingulata (Stoneman) Spaulding & v. Schrenk.
Gloeosporium Citri Massee.
Gloeosporium hysterioides Ell. & Ev.
Hainesia Aurantii Henn.

HYPHOMYCETES

Aegerita Webberi Fawcett.
Alternaria Citri Pierce.
Cercospora aurantia Heald & Wolf.
Cladosporium Citri Massee.
Cladosporium elegans Penz.
Cladosporium herbarum (P.) ex Lk.
Cladosporium herbarum, (P.) ex Lk., var. citricola Fawcett & Burger.
Fumago salicina Tul.
Fumago vagans Fr.
Fusarium Aurantii Auct.
{ Fusarium Limonis (Briosi) Sacc.
  Fusisporium Limoni Briosi.
Fusarium sarcochroum (Desm.) Sacc.
Fusarium Solani Auct.
Oospora Citri-aurantii (Ferr.) Sacc. & Syd.
{ Oidium fasciculatum B.
  Oospora fasciculata (B.) Sacc. & Vogl.
Penicillium digitatum (Fr.) Sacc.
Penicillium glaucum Lk.
Penicillium italicum Wehmer.
{ Sphaceloma Fawcettii A. E. Jenkins.
  Sporotrichum Citri Butler.
Stemphylium Citri Patterson & Charles.
Stilbella flavida (Cke.) Henn.

Citrus Aurantium (*cont.*)
Stilbum cinnabarinum Mont.
Trichoderma lignorum (Tode) ex Harz.
Triposporium Aurantii Henn.
Verticillium heterocladum Penz.

MISCELLANEA

Dematophora necatrix Hartig.
Pseudomicrocera Henningsii (Koord.) Petch.
Citrus Aurantium L., var. **amara** Auct.
Cladosporium Citri Massee.
Citrus Aurantium L., var. **vulgaris** Wright & Arn.
Diplodia hesperidica Speg.
Citrus Limetta Risso. (Citron.)
Atichia dominicana Cotton.
Cladosporium Citri Massee.
Cladosporium elegans? Penz.
Colletotrichum gloeosporioides Penz.
Corticium salmonicolor B. & Br.
Cyathus striatus Hoffm.
Diplodia natalensis Auct. Amer.
Physalospora rhodina Cke.
Fomes lucidus (Leyss. ex Fr.) Cke.
Gloeosporium limetticola Clausen.
Hypocrella oxyspora Massee.
Lasiodiplodia Theobromae (Pat.) Griffon & Maublanc.
Myriangium Duriaei Mont. & B.
Nectria vulgaris Spreng.
Ophionectria coccicola Ell. & Ev.
Polystictus hirsutus Fr.
Rosellinia bunodes (B. & Br.) Sacc.
Rosellinia Pepo Pat.
Sphaeropsis tumefaciens Hedges.
Sphaerostilbe coccophila Tul.
Sphaerostilbe repens B. & Br.
Thelephora pedicellata S. ?
Citrus Limonia Osbeck. (Lemon.)
Alysidium fasciculatum (B.) Pound & Clements.
Oidium fasciculatum B.
Armillaria mellea (Vahl) ex Fr.
Botryosphaeria Ribis (Tode ex Fr.) Grossenbacher & Duggar.
Dothiorella Ribis Fawcett non Sacc.
Botrytis cinerea Auct.
Botrytis vulgaris (Lk.) ex Fr.
Capnodium Citri B. & Desm.
Cladosporium Citri Massee.
Colletotrichum gloeosporioides Penz.
Glomerella cingulata (Stoneman) Spaulding & v. Schrenk.
Coprinus atramentarius Fr.
Coryneum Beyerinckii Oud.
Crepidotus Citri Pat.
Diplodia natalensis Evans.
Fumago salicina Tul.
Fusisporium Limoni Briosi.

Gloeosporium limetticola Clausen.
Gloeosporium Spegazzinii Sacc.
Meliola Camelliae (Catt.) Sacc.
Meliola Penzigi Sacc.
Mycosphaerella lageniformis Rehm.
Myriangium Duriaei Mont. & B.
Oospora Citri-aurantii Ferraris.
Penicillium digitatum (Fr.) Sacc.
Penicillium glaucum Lk.
Penicillium italicum Wehmer.
Penicillium roseum Lk.
Phomopsis californica Fawcett.
Phomopsis Citri Fawcett.
Phyllosticta adusta Ell. & Martin.
Phyllosticta Hesperidearum (Catt.) Penz.
Phytophthora parasitica Dastur.
Phytophthora terrestris Sherb.
Phytophthora citrophthora (Sm. & Sm.) Leonian.
Pythiacystis citrophthora Sm. & Sm.
Pleospora herbarum (Fr.) Rabh., var. citrorum Sacc.
Polystictus versicolor (L.) ex Fr.
Rhizopus nigricans Ehrenb. ex Fr.
Scleroplea aurantiorum Rehm.
Sclerotinia libertiana Fckl.
Sclerotinia sclerotiorum (Lib.) Schrt.
Sphaceloma Fawcettii A. E. Jenkins.
Sporotrichum Citri Butler.
Stemphylium Citri Patterson.
Stilbum atrofuscum Mont.
Trichoderma lignorum (Tode) ex Harz.
Citrus maxima (Burm.) Merrill.
(C. grandis, C. decumana, Pummelo, Grapefruit.)

PHYCOMYCETES

Phytophthora terrestris Sherbakoff.
Pythiacystis citrophthora Sm. & Sm.
Rhizopus nigricans Ehrenb. ex Fr.

ASCOMYCETES

Capnodium Citri B. & Desm.
Chaetothyrium hawaiiense Mendoza.
Daldinia concentrica (Bolt.) Ces. & DeNot.
Glomerella cingulata (Stoneman) Spaulding & v. Schrenk.
Nectria coccicola Ell. & Ev.
Ophionectria coccicola (Ell. & Ev.) Berl. & Vogl.
Podonectria coccicola (Ell. & Ev.) Petch.
Scoleconectria coccicola (Ell. & Ev.) Seaver.
Diplodia natalensis Auct. Amer.
Physalospora rhodina Cke.
Sphaerostilbe coccophila Tul.
Ustulina vulgaris Tul.

HYMENOMYCETINEAE

Corticium salmonicolor B. & Br.
Peniophora cinerea (Fr.) Cke.

Citrus maxima (*cont.*)
Fomitiporia jamaicensis Murrill.
Schizophyllum commune Fr.
Septobasidium lilacinum Burt.
Septobasidium Spongia (B. & C.) Pat.

SPHAEROPSIDALES
Aschersonia cubensis B. & C.
Chaetothyrium hawaiiense Mendoza.
Phoma socia Wolf.
Phomopsis caribaea Horne.
{ Diaporthe Citri Wolf.
{ Phomopsis Citri Fawcett.
Sphaeropsis tumefaciens Hedges.

MELANCONIALES
{ Colletotrichum adustum (Ell. & Martin) Ell.
{ Phyllosticta adusta Ell. & Martin.
{ Colletotrichum gloeosporioides Penz.
{ Glomerella cingulata (Stoneman) Spaulding &
    v. Schrenk.

HYPHOMYCETES
Cladosporium gloeosporioides Penz.
Fumago Citri P.
Fusarium Limonis (Briosi) Sacc.
Microcera Fujikuroi Miy. & Sav.
Penicillium digitatum (Fr.) Sacc.
Penicillium glaucum Lk.
Penicillium italicum Wehmer.
Spegazzinia ornata Sacc.
Cladosporium Citri Massee.
{ Sphaceloma Fawcettii A. E. Jenkins.
{ Sporotrichum Citri Butler.
Tubercularia coccicola Stevenson.

MISCELLANEA
Sclerotium Rolfsii Sacc.
Citrus medica L., var. **genuina.**
Cladosporium Citri Massee.
Citrus nobilis Lour.
    (Mandarin orange.)
Alternaria Citri Pierce, var. Cerasi C. A.
    Rudolph.
Aschersonia turbinata B.
Cladosporium Citri Massee.
Glomerella cingulata (Stoneman) Spaulding &
    v. Schrenk.
Oidium tingitaninum Carter.
Phoma socia Wolf.
{ Diaporthe Citri Wolf.
{ Phomopsis Citri Fawcett.
Sphaceloma Fawcettii A. E. Jenkins.
Citrus nobilis Lour, var. **unshiu** Swingle.
    (Satsuma orange).
Alternaria Citri Pierce.
{ Colletotrichum gloeosporioides Penz.
{ Glomerella cingulata (Stoneman) Spaulding &
    v. Schrenk.
Diplodia natalensis Evans.

Penicillium digitatum (Fr.) Sacc.
Penicillium italicum Wehmer.
Phomopsis Citri Fawcett.
Citrus sinensis P.   (Sweet orange.)
Alternaria Citri Pierce.
Alternaria tenuis Nees ex Fr., var. chalaroides
    Sacc.
Camarosporium pulchellum Speg.
Cercospora aurantia Heald & Wolf.
Cladosporium Citri Massee.
Cladosporium furfuraceum MacAlpine.
{ Colletotrichum gloeosporioides Penz.
{ Glomerella cingulata (Stoneman) Spaulding &
    v. Schrenk.
Corticium salmonicolor B. & Br.
{ Diplodia natalensis Auct. Amer.
{ Physalospora rhodina Cke.
Fusarium Limonis (Briosi) Sacc.
Hainesia aurantii Henn.
Leptothyrium pomi (Mont. & Fr.) Sacc.
Microcera Fujikuroi Miy. & Sav.
Penicillium digitatum (Fr.) Sacc.
Phomopsis californica Fawcett.
{ Diaporthe Citri Wolf.
{ Phomopsis Citri Fawcett.
Phyllosticta adusta Ell. & Martin.
{ Phytophthora parasitica Dastur.
{ Phytophthora terrestris Sherbakoff.
Pseudocamptoum Citri Fragoso & Ciferri.
Pythiacystis citrophthora Sm. & Sm.
Rosellinia bunodes Sacc.
Rosellinia Pepo Pat.
Septobasidium Spongia (B. & C.) Pat.
{ Sphaceloma Fawcettii A. E. Jenkins.
{ Sporotrichum Citri Butler.
Stemphylium Citri Patterson & Charles.
Stilbella flavida (Cke.) Henn.

Citrus trifoliata L.   (Trifoliate orange.)
Colletotrichum gloeosporioides Penz.
?Didymella Citri Noak.
Diplodia Aurantii Catt.
Myriangium Duriaei Mont. & B.
Phoma socia Wolf.
Phomopsis Citri Fawcett.
Pythiacystis citrophthora Sm. & Sm.
Sphaeropsis Malorum Pk.

Citrus sp. indet.

ASCOMYCETES
Capnodium citricola McAlpine.
Capnodium elongatum B. & Desm.
Creonectria ochroleuca (S.) Seaver.
Glonium parvulum (Gerard) Sacc.
Hypoxylon fuscopurpureum B.
{ Lecanidion cyaneum (Cke.) Sacc.
{ Patellaria cyanea Cke.
Meliola Penzigi Sacc.
Nectria diploa B. & C.
Nectria episphaeria (Tode) ex Fr.

Citrus sp. indet. (*cont.*)
Nectria tuberculariae Petch.
Physalospora fusca N. E. Stevens.
Physalospora Malorum Shear et al.
Physalospora rhodina Cke.
Sphaerostilbe gracilipes Tul.
Sphaerostilbe repens B. & Br.
Stictis radiata P.

HYMENOMYCETINEAE

Corticium confluens Fr.
Crepidotus Citri Pat.
Fomes fasciatus (Sw. ex Fr.) Cke.
{ Fomes lucidus (Leyss. ex Fr.) Cke.
{ Ganoderma lucidum (Leyss. ex Fr.) Karst.
Marasmius praeacutus Ell.
Peniophora cinerea (P. ex Fr.) Cke.
Peniophora Roumeguerii Bres.
Polyporus gilvus S.
Poria vaporaria (P. ex Fr.) Cke.
Rhizoctonia Solani Kühn.
Septobasidium pedicillatum (B. & C.) Pat.
Stereum albobadium (S.) Fr.
Stereum coffearum B. & C.
Trametes hydnoides (Sw.) ex Fr.

SPHAEROPSIDALES

Aschersonia marginata Ell. & Ev.
Botryodiplodia diplocarpa Ell. & Ev.
{ Discella Citri Cke.
{ Discula Citri (Cke.) Sacc.
Leptothyrium Pomi (Mont. & Fr.) Sacc.
Phyllosticta citricola Hori.
Phyllosticta longispora MacAlpine.

MELANCONIALES

Gloeosporium intermedium Sacc.
Gloeosporium Mangiferae Henn.?
Pestalozzia Guepini Desm.

HYPHOMYCETES

Aegerita Webberi Fawcett.
Aspergillus flavus Lk.
Aspergillus niger van Tiegh.
Cephalosporium Lecanii Zimm.
Cercospora fumosa Penz.
?Cladosporium brunneo-atrum McAlpine.
?Cladosporium elegans Penz.
Cladosporium herbarum, var. citricola Fawcett.
Fusarium Aleyrodis Petch.
Fusarium lateritium Nees ex Fr.
Fusarium Limonis (Briosi) Sacc.
Myrothecium Verrucaria (A. & S.) ex Fr.
Oidium tingitaninum Carter.
Oospora hyalinula Sacc.
Oospora lactis (Fres.) Sacc.
{ Oospora pallida (B. & Rav.) Sacc. & Vogl.
{ Torula pallida B. & Rav.
Penicillium stoloniferum Thom.

MISCELLANEA

Mucor clavatus Lk.
Sclerotium Rolfsii Sacc.
Fortunella margarita (Lour) Swingle.
(Kumquat.)
Pestalozzia Guepini Desm.
Phoma socia Wolf.
Sphaeropsis citricola McAlpine.
Cladosporium Citri Massee.

SIMARUBACEAE

Simaruba amara Aubl.
Corticium chartaceum Pat.
{ Leucoporus labiatus Pat.
{ Polyporus labiatus (Pat.) Sacc. & D. Sacc.
{ Leucoporus Xalapensis (B.) Pat.
{ Polyporus Xalapensis B.
Simaruba tulae Urb.
Isthmospora glabra F. L. Stevens.
Meliola glabroides F. L. Stevens.
Simaba Cedron Planch. in Hook.
Phyllachora Simabae-Cedronis Henn.
Ailanthus glandulosa Desf.

MYXOMYCETES

{ Badhamia hyalina (P.) B.
{ Didymium simulans Howe.
{ Chondrioderma albulum (Howe) Cke.
{ Diderma albulum Howe.

ASCOMYCETES

Ceratostoma corticola Ell. & Ev.
Cucurbitaria Ravenelii Cke. & Massee.
Dasyscypha clandestina (Bull. ex Fr.) Fckl.
{ Diaporthe Ailanthi Sacc.
{ ?Eutypella Ailanthi (Sacc.) Fairman.
{ Phomopsis Ailanthi (Sacc.) Trav.
{ Chorostate Ailanthi (Sacc.) Trav., var. megaceraphora (Fairman) Sacc.
{ Diaporthe Ailanthi Sacc., var. megaceraphora Fairman.
Diatrype cornuta Ell. & Ev.
Diatrype tumida Ell. & Ev.
Didymella Ricini Ell. & Ev.
Didymella Ricini Ell. & Ev., var. Ailanthi Ell. & Ev.
Eutypa heteracantha Sacc.
{ Eutypella clavulata (Cke.) Sacc.
{ Eutypella glandulosa (Cke.) Ell. & Ev.
{ Peroneutypella clavulata (Cke.) Berl.
{ Valsa clavulata Cke.
{ Valsa glandulosa Cke.
Eutypella stellulata (Fr.) Sacc.
{ Eutypella ventriosa (C. & E.) Sacc.
{ Valsa ventriosa C. & E.
Hypoderma virgultorum DC.
Leptosphaeria doliolum (P. ex Fr.) De Not.
Massariella bispora (Cke.) Sacc.

Ailanthus glandulosa (*cont.*)

  { Creonectria purpurea (L.) ex Seaver.
  { Nectria cinnabarina (Tode) ex Fr.
  Rosellinia limoniispora Ell. & Ev.
  Mycosphaerella Ailanthi (Cke.) House.
  { Sphaerella Ailanthi Cke.

BASIDIOMYCETES

  Collybia platyphylla Fr.
  Collybia velutipes (W. Curtis) ex Fr.
  Daedalea ambigua B.
  { Irpex lacteus Fr.
  { Irpex sinuosus Fr.
  Pleurotus sapidus Kalchb.
  Polyporus brumalis (P.) ex Fr.
  Polyporus contiguus (P.) ex Fr.
  { Abortiporus distortus (S.) Murrill.
  { Polyporus distortus (S.) Fr.
  Polyporus hirsutus Wulf. ex Fr.
  Polystictus lacteus (Fr.). Auct.
  { Schizophyllum alneum (L. ex Fr.) Schrt.
  { Schizophyllum commune Fr.
  Typhula gyrans (Batsch) ex Fr.

SPHAEROPSIDALES

  { Botryodiplodia Ailanthi (Cke.) Sacc.
  { Diplodia Ailanthi Cke.
  { Camarosporium berkeleyanum (Lév.) Sacc.
  { Hendersonia berkeleyana Lév.
  { Camarosporium subfenestratum (B. & C.) Sacc.
  { Hendersonia Sartwellii Herb. Curt.
  { Hendersonia subfenestrata B. & C.
  Cytospora Ailanthi B. & C.
  Cytosporina Ailanthi Sacc.
  { Dothiorella glandulosa (Cke.) Sacc.
  { Sphaeropsis glandulosa Cke.
  { Haplosporella Ailanthi Ell. & Ev.
  { Haplosporella dothideoides Ell. & Barthol.
  { Haplosporella Ellisii Syd.
  { Sphaeropsis Ailanthi Ell. & Barthol.
  Sphaeropsis melanconioides Pk.
  { Leptostroma petiolorum Cke.
  { Leptothyrium petiolorum (Cke.) Sacc.
  { Macrophoma tertia (Cke.) Berl. & Vogl.
  { Phoma tertia (Cke.) Sacc.
  { Sphaeropsis tertia Cke.
  Phoma Ailanthi Sacc.
  Phoma glandulosum Cke.
  Vermicularia Dematium (P.) ex Fr.
  Vermicularia petiolicola Brun.

MELANCONIALES

  Gloeosporium Ailanthi Dearness & Barthol.

HYPHOMYCETES

  Cercospora glandulosa Ell. & Kellerm.
  Cladosporium delectum C. & E.
  Fusarium lateritium Nees ex Fr.
  Monilia aurantiaca Pk. & Sacc.

  { Periconia epiphylla S.
  { Sporocybe epiphylla (S.) Sacc.
  { Tubercularia Ailanthi Cke.
  { Tubercularia vulgaris Tode ex Fr.

Picramnia bonplandiana Tul.

  Ascochytella cryptica Syd.
  Diaporthe bicincta (Bomm. & Rouss.) Syd.
  { Dothidella Picramniae Syd.
  { Endodothella Picramniae Syd.
  Phomopsis bicincta Syd.
  Pseudophyllachora Tonduzi Speg.
  Telimena bicincta (Bomm. & Rous.) Theissen
    & Syd.

BURSERACEAE

Tetragastris balsamifera Sw.

  Meliola amphitricha Fr.
  Meliola evanida Gaill.

Canarium sp. indet.

  Anthomycetella Canarii Syd.

Dacryodes hexandra Griseb.

  Rhodophyllus miniatus Pat.

Bursera balsamifera P.

  Hypoxylon rubiginosum (P.) ex Fr.
  Hypoxylon serpens (P.) ex Fr.

Bursera gummifera L.

  Cladosporium herbarum (P.) ex Lk.
  Daedalea Burserae Pat.
  Henningsinia caespitosa Pk.
  Hormodendron cladosporioides (Fres.) Sacc.
  Hymenochaete tenuissima B.
  Hypoxylon fossulatum Mont.
  Macrophoma Burserae Pk.
  Panus eugrammus Mont.
  Physopella Burserae Syd.
  { Leptoporus molluscus (P. ex Fr.) Pat.
  { Polyporus molluscus (P.) ex Fr.
  { Polyporus portoricensis Fr.
  { Trametes portoricensis (Fr.) Pat.

MELIACEAE

Cedrela odorata L.

  Dimerosporium urbanianum Henn.
  Doassansia Sintenisii Bres.
  { Fomes Cedrelae (Murrill) Sacc. & Trott.
  { Fulvifomes Cedrelae Murrill.
  { Pyropolyporus Cedrelae Murrill.
  { Fomes sclerodermus (Lév.) Cke.
  { Elfvingia fasciata (Sw.) Murrill.
  Parodiopsis melioloides (B. & C.) Maubl.
  Phoma Cedrelae Pat.
  { Dendrophagus Colossus (Fr.) Murrill.
  { Polyporus Colossus Fr.
  { Tomophagus Colossus (Fr.) Murrill.
  { Leucoporus fibrillosoradians (Mont.) Pat.
  { Polyporus fibrosoradians Mont.

Cedrela odorata (*cont.*)
Polyporus scabellus (Pat.) Sacc. & Syd.
{ Leucoporus virgatus (B. & C.) Pat.
{ Polyporus virgatus B. & C.
{ Leptoporus carneopallens (B.) Pat.
{ Poria carneopallens (B.) Cke.
Sphaerobolus stellatus Tode ex Fr.
Cedrela sinensis Juss.
Schizophyllum commune Fr.
Cedrela Tonduzii C. DC.
Phyllachora Balansae Speg.
Cedrela sp. indet.
Daedalea juniperina Murrill.
Parodiopsis melioloides (B. & C.) Maubl.,
var. Meliaceae Arnaud.
Swietenia mahagoni Jacq.
{ Fulvifomes Swieteniae Murrill.
{ Fomes Swieteniae (Murrill) Lloyd.
Polystictus sanguineus (L.) ex Fr.
Melia Azadirachta L.

PHYCOMYCETES

{ Peronoplasmopara portoricensis Lamkey.
{ Pseudoperonospora   portoricensis (Lamkey)
{   Seaver & Chardon.

HYSTERIINEAE

{ Hysterium nigrocinnabarinum (S.) Rehm.
{ Hysterium rufulum Spreng.
{ Patellaria nigrocinnabarina S.
{ Tryblidiella rufula (Spreng.) Sacc.
Tryblidiella rufula, var. microspora Underw. &
  Earle.

PERISPORIALES

Meliola Wrightii B. & C.

HYPOCREALES

{ Botryosphaeria Ribis (Tode ex Fr.) Grossen-
{   bacher & Duggar.
{ Nectria Ribis (Tode ex Fr.) Oud.
Hypocrea jecorina B. & Br.
{ Chilonectria Cucurbitula (Tode ex Fr.) Sacc.
{ Nectria Cucurbitula (Tode) ex Fr.
{ Sphaeria Cucurbitula Tode ex Fr.
{ Creonectria purpurea (L.) ex Seaver.
{ Nectria cinnabarina Tode ex Fr.
{ Creonectria coccinea (P. ex Fr.) Seaver.
{ Nectria coccinea (P.) ex Fr.
Nectria ditissima Tul.
Nectria lactea Ell. & Morg.
Nectria Meliae Earle.
{ Creonectria verrucosa (S.) Seaver.
{ Nectria verrucosa (S.) Sacc.
{ Sphaeria verrucosa S.
Sphaerostilbe gracilipes Tul.

SPHAERIALES

{ Calospora aculeans (S.) Sacc.
{ Valsa aculeans (S.) B. & C.
Cucurbitaria cupularis (P.) Cke.

{ Endoxyla eutypoides Ell. & Ev.
{ Thyridaria eutypoides Ell. & Ev.
{ Diatrype Azedarachtae Cke.
{ Eutypella Azedarachae (Cke.) Berl.
{ Eutypella glandulosa Underw. & Earle, non
{   (Cke.) Ell. & Ev.
{ Valsa heteracantha Ell.
{ Eutypella stellulata (Fr.) Sacc.
{ Valsa stellulata Fr.
{ Fracchiaea pauridia (B. & C.) Berl.
{ Nitschkea pauridia (B. & C.) Cke.
Hypoxylon effusum Nits.
Hypoxylon platystomum Ell. & Ev.
Hypoxylon rubricosum (Fr.) Mont.
{ Melanconis stilbostoma (Fr.) Tul.
{ Valsa stilbostoma (Fr.) Kickx.
{ Melogramma fuliginosum Ell. p. p.
{ Botryosphaeria fuliginosa Ell. & Ev. p. p.
{ Botryosphaeria Meliae (S.) Sacc.
{ Melogramma fuliginosum Ell. p. p.
{ Melogramma Meliae (S.) B. & C.
{ Sphaeria Meliae S.
Melogramma Meliae Herb. Curtis.
Physalospora Malorum Shear et al.
Sphaeria appendiculata P. ex Fr.
Valsaria insitiva (Tode ex Fr.) Ces. & De Not.

BASIDIOMYCETES

Corticium comedens (Nees) ex Fr.
Corticium Stevensii Burt.
Mycena corticola (Schum.) ex Fr.
{ Mycena meliigena B. & Cke.
{ Prunulus meliigena (B. & Cke.) Murrill.
{ Fomes Meliae (Underw.) Murrill.
{ Polyporus Meliae Underw.
Peniophora galachroa Bres.

SPHAEROPSIDALES

{ Botryodiplodia Meliae Ell. & Ev.
{ Diplodia Langloisii Sacc. & Syd.
{ Diplodia Meliae Ell. & Ev.
Macrophoma subconica Ell. & Ev.
Phoma petiolorum Desm.
Phyllosticta Azedarachis Thm.
Phyllosticta Meliae Ell. & Ev.
Vermicularia rectispora Cke.

HYPHOMYCETES

Cercospora leucosticta Ell. & Ev.
Cercospora Meliae Ell. & Ev.
{ Fusarium azedarachinum (Thm.) Sacc.
{ Fusarium lateritium Nees ex Fr.
{ Fusisporium azedarachinum Thm.
Fusarium oxysporum Schl.
Fusarium sarcochroum (Desm.) Sacc.
Ozonium omnivorum Shear.
Pachnocybe rosella B. & C.
Tubercularia Ailanthi Cke.

Guarea simplicifolia ex Duss.
Collybia irrorata Pat.
Guarea Swartzii Macfad.
Xylaria filiformis (A. & S.) ex Fr.
Guarea trichilioides L.
Coniothyrium glabroides F. L. Stevens.
Grallomyces portoricensis F. L. Stevens.
Helminthosporium guareicola F. L. Stevens.
Helminthosporium Helleri F. L. Stevens.
Meliola Guareae Speg.
Meliola guareicola F. L. Stevens.
Phyllosticta Guareae Henn.
Clausena Wampi Oliver.
Gloeosporium Clausenae Patterson.
Trichilia havannensis Jacq.
Asterina guaranitica Speg.
{ Dothidea explanata Lév.
{ Phyllachora explanata (Lév.) Sacc.
Trichilia oerstediana C. DC.
Asterina guaranitica Speg.
Phaeodimeriella exigua Syd.
Phyllachora? explanata (Lév.) Sacc.
Trichilia pallida Sw.
Trichilia trinitensis A. Juss.
Uredo Trichiliae Arth.

MALPIGHIACEAE

Mascagnia sepium (Juss.) Griseb.
Parodiopsis megalospora (Sacc. & Berl.) Arnaud.
Tetrapteris mexicana Hook. & Arn.
Asteridium moniliforme Ell. & Ev.
Tetrapteris Seemanni Triana & Planch.
Parodiopsis megalospora (Sacc. & Berl.) Arnaud.
Puccinia trachytela Syd.
Gaudichaudia schiedeana A. Juss.
Uromyces standleyanus Arth.
Banisteria laurifolia L.
Calonectria erubescens (Rob.) Sacc.
Helminthosporium parathesicola F. L. Stevens.
Meliola rectangularis F. L. Stevens.
Nectria portoricensis F. L. Stevens.
{ Bullaria barbatula (Arth. & Johnston) Arth. & Mains.
{ Puccinia barbatula Arth. & Johnston.
Banisteria portillana (Watson) C. B. Robinson.
{ Bullaria rubricans (Holw.) Arth. & Mains.
{ Puccinia rubricans Holw.
Puccinia sanguinolenta Henn.
Banisteria tomentosa Desf.
Phyllachora Banisteriae Stevens & Dalbey.
Stigmaphyllon lingulatum (Poir.) Small.
Meliola crenato-furcata Syd.
Puccinia inflata Arth.

Stigmaphyllon periplocifolium A Juss.
Stigmaphyllon sagraeanum A. Juss.
{ Bullaria inflata (Arth.) Arth. & Mains.
{ Puccinia inflata Arth.
Stigmaphyllon sp. indet.
{ Bullaria (?) circinata (Arth.) Arth. & Mains.
{ Puccinia circinata Arth.
Morenoella decalvans (Pat.) Th., var. Stigmatophylli Ryan.
Echinopterys Lappula A. Juss.
{ Bullaria Echinopteridis (Holw.) Arth. & Mains.
{ Puccinia Echinopteridis Holw.
Galphimia humboldtiana Bartl. in L.
{ Nigredo Galphimiae (Diet. & Holw.) Arth.
{ Uromyces Galphimiae Diet. & Holw.
Malpighia glabra L.
{ Asterina indecora Syd.
{ Asterostomella indecora Syd.
Meliola xenoderma Syd.
Malpighia urens L.
{ Coriolus brunneolus (B.) Pat.
{ Polyporus brunneolus B.
Puccinia insueta Wint.
Trametes hydnoides Fr.
Bunchosia glandulosa DC.
Porogramme aurantiotingens (Ell. & Macbr.) Pat., var. separans Pat.
Byrsonima crassifolia H. B. K.
{ Aecidium Byrsonimae Kern & Kellerm.
{ Aecidium Byrsonimatis Henn.
{ Aecidium singulare (Diet. & Holw.) Arth.
{ Cronartium notatum (Arth.) Arth. & Johnston.
{ Crossopsora notata Arth.
{ Uredo notata Arth.
Meliola stuhlmanniana Henn.
Byrsonima lucida (Sw.) L. Cl. Rich.
Isthmospora spinosa F. L. Stevens.
Meliola Byrsonimae F. L. Stevens.
Byrsonima sericea DC.
Aecidium singulare (Diet. & Holw.) Arth.
Byrsonima spicata Rich ex Juss.
Clavaria laeticolor B. & C.
Erinella cyphelloides Pat.
{ Favolus caperatus Pat.
{ Hexagona caperata (Pat.) Murrill.
Rosellinia Aquila (Fr.) DeNot.
Stereum hirsutum (Willd.) ex Fr.
Trametes occidentalis Fr.
Trametes occidentalis Fr., var. myriadoporus Pat.
Xylaria polymorpha (P. ex Fr.) Grev.
Byrsonima variabilis A. Juss.
Byrsonima verbascifolia Rich. ex Juss.
{ Aecidium Byrsonimatis Henn.
{ Aecidium singulare (Diet. & Holw.) Arth.
Malpighiaceae gen. indet.
Puccinia circinata (S.) Arth.

POLYGALACEAE

Polygala acicularis Oliver.
Polygala americana Mill.
  Uredo peribebuyensis Speg.
Polygala cruciata L.
  Cercospora grisea C. & E.
Polygala grandiflora Walter.
  { Dothidea Polygalae S.
  { Phyllachora Polygalae (S.) Sacc.
Polygala longa Blake.
  Aecidium renatum Arth.
Polygala lutea L.
Polygala nana DC.
  { Cercospora grisea C. & E.
  { Cercospora minuta Sacc.
Polygala paucifolia Willd.
  Aecidium polygalinum Pk.
  { Micropuccinia Pyrolae (Cke.) Arth. & Jackson.
  { Puccinia Polygalae Pazschke.
  { Puccinia Pyrolae Cke.
  Septoria Polygalae Pk. & Clinton.
Polygala polygama Walt.
  Gloeosporium ramosum Ell. & Ev.
Polygala sanguinea L.
  { Cercospora grisea C. & E.
  { Cercospora minuta Sacc.
  Gloeosporium ramosum Ell. & Ev.
Polygala Senega L.
  Aecidium polygalinum Pk.
  Septoria consocia Pk.
Polygala Watsoni Chod.
  Uredo peribebuyensis Speg.
Polygala sp. indet.
  { Gibbera Saubinetii Mont.
  { Gibberella Saubinetii (Mont.) Sacc.
  Phoma Polygalae Cke. & Hark.
  Phomatospora Berkeleyi Sacc.
Securidaca virgata Sw.
  Phyllachora perforans (Rehm) Sacc. & Syd.
  { Phyllachora perforans P. Garman.
  { Phyllachora Securidacae Henn.
Securidaca volubilis L.
  Meliola bicornis Wint.
  Morenoella Whetzelii Toro.

EUPHORBIACEAE

Savia sessiliflora (Sw.) Willd.
  Uredo Saviae Arth. & Johnston.
Amanoa caribaea Krug & Urb.
  { Leucoporus tricholoma (Mont.) Pat.
  { Polyporus tricholoma Mont.
  { Poria borbonica Pat.
  { Trametes borbonica Pat.
Phyllanthus acidus (L.) Skeels.
  Aecidium albicans Arth. & Holw.

Phyllanthus acuminatus Vahl.
  Aecidium albicans Arth. & Holw.
  Aecidium favaceum Arth.
  Ravenelia appendiculata Lagerh. & Diet.
  Uredo Phyllanthi Henn.
Phyllanthus distichus (L.) Müll.-Arg.
  { Phakopsora fenestrala Arth.
  { Schroeteriaster fenestrala Arth.
  { Uredo fenestrala Arth.
Phyllanthus galeottianus Baill.
  Ravenelia appendiculata Lagerh. & Diet.
Phyllanthus grandifolius L.
Phyllanthus Niruri L.
  { Phakopsora fenestrala Arth.
  { Schroeteriaster fenestrala Arth.
  { Uredo fenestrala Arth.
Phyllanthus nobilis Müll.
  Aecidium favaceum Arth.
  Stereum cinereobadium Klotzsch.
Drypetes alba Poit.
  { Coriolus gibberulosus (Lév.) Pat.
  { Polyporus gibberulosus Lév.
Drypetes glauca Vahl.
  Phyllachora drypeticola Stevens & Dalbey.
Drypetes lateriflora (Sw.) Urb.
  Asterina Drypetis Ryan.
  Phyllachora drypeticola Stevens & Dalbey.
Drypetes sp. indet.
  { Asterina reptans B. & C.
  { Trichopeltis (?) reptans (B. & C.) Speg.
  Meliola glabra B. & C.
  { Microthyrium reptans Pat.
  { Peltistroma juruanum Henn.
Richeria grandis Vahl.
  Amphisphaeria aterrima Pat.
  { Crinipellis nidulus (B. & C.) Pat.
  { Marasmius nidulus B. & C.
  Erinella subcorticalis Pat.
  { Grammothele grisea B. & C.
  { Kneiffia grisea B. & C.
  { Phellinus extensus (Lév.) Pat.
  { Polyporus extensus Lév.
  { Poria Richeriae (Pat.) Sacc. Syll.
  { Porogramme Richeriae Pat.
  Pterula laxa Pat.
Croton argyranthemus Michx.
  { Bubakia Crotonis (Burrill) Arth.
  { Schroeteriaster Crotonis (Burrill) Diet.
Croton Astroites Dryand.
  Phyllachora Crotonis (Cke.) Sacc.
Croton californicus Müll.-Arg.
  Bubakia Crotonis (Burrill) Arth.
  Cercospora Crotonis Ell. & Ev.
  Phyllachora Crotonis (Cke.) Sacc.
Croton calvescens Watson.
  { Bubakia mexicana Arth.
  { Melampsora mexicana (Arth.) Sacc. & Trott.
  { Phakopsora mexicana Arth.
  { Schroeteriaster mexicanus (Arth.) Syd.

Croton capitatus Michx.
  Bubakia Crotonis (Burrill) Arth.
  Melampsora Crotonis Burrill.
  Phakopsora Crotonis (Burrill) Arth.
  Pucciniastrum Crotonis (Burrill) De Toni.
  Cercospora capitati Tharp.

Croton ciliatoglanduliferus Ortega.
  Pucciniastrum Crotonis (Burrill) De Toni.

Croton discolor Willd.
  Asterina diplocarpa Cke.
  Asterina solanicola B. & C.
  Asterina triloba Earle.

Croton Engelmannii Ferguson.
  Bubakia Crotonis Arth.

Croton flavens L.
  Phyllachora Tragiae (B. & C.) Sacc.

Croton fruticulosus Torr.
  Cercospora crotonicola Ell. & Barthol.

Croton glandulosus L.
  Cercospora crotonifolia Cke.
  Melampsora Crotonis Burrill.

Croton gossypiifolius Vahl.
  Asterina crotonicola Pat.
  Meliola cladophaga Syd.
  Phakopsora Crotonis (Burrill) Arth.

Croton hirtus L'Her.
  Phakopsora Crotonis (Burrill) Arth.

Croton lobatus L.
  Cercospora Tiglii Henn.

Croton lucidus L.
  Phyllachora Tragiae (B. & C.) Sacc.
  Phyllosticta portoricensis E. Young.

Croton maritimus Walt.
  Cercospora maritima Tracy & Earle.

Croton monanthogynus Michx.
  Aecidium Crotonopsidis Burrill.
  Aecidium splendens Wint.
  Bubakia Crotonis (Burrill) Arth.
  Melampsora Crotonis Burrill.
  Phakopsora Crotonis (Burrill) Arth.
  Pucciniastrum Crotonis (Burrill) De Toni.
  Schroeteriaster Crotonis (Burrill) Diet.
  Trichobasis Crotonis Cke.
  Trichobasis Wrightii B. & C. in Herb. Fr.
  Uredo Wrightii B. & C. nom. nud.

Croton procumbens Jacq.

Croton punctatus Jacq.
  Bubakia Crotonis (Burrill) Arth.
  Pucciniastrum Crotonis (Burrill) De Toni.
  Schroeteriaster Crotonis (Burrill) Diet.
  Trichobasis Crotonis Cke.

Croton texensis (Klotzsch) Müll.-Arg.
  Cercospora Crotonis Ell. & Ev.
  Bubakia Crotonis (Burrill) Arth.
  Melampsora Crotonis Burrill.
  Pucciniastrum Crotonis (Burrill) De Toni.

Croton sp. indet.
  Corticium koleroga (Cke.) Höhnel.
  Pellicularia koleroga Cke.
  Fumago vagans Fr.
  Phyllachora Crotonis (Cke.) Sacc.

Crotonopsis linearis Michx.
  Bubakia Crotonis (Burrill) Arth.
  Melampsora Crotonis Burrill.
  Pucciniastrum Crotonis (Burrill) De Toni.
  Schroeteriaster Crotonis (Burrill) Diet.
  Nigredo graminicola (Burrill) Atk. I.

Eremocarpus setigerus Benth.
  Melampsora Piscariae H. S. Jackson.

Chiropetalum schiedeanum (Müll.-Arg.) Pax.
  Aecidium Argithamniae Arth.

Argithamnia mercurialina Müll.-Arg.
  Cercospora Argythamniae Dearness & House.

Mercurialis perennis L.
  Synchytrium Mercurialis (Lib.) Fckl.

Adelia Bernardia L.
  Cercospora Bernardiae F. L. Stevens.

Mallotus japonicus Müll.
  Cercospora Malloti Ell. & Ev.

Alchornea latifolia Sw.
  Olivea capituliformis (Henn.) Arth.
  Ravenelia capituliformis Henn.
  Uredo capituliformis Henn.

Acalypha bisetosa Bert.
  Coniothyrium glabroides F. L. Stevens.
  Appendiculella arecibensis (F. L. Stevens)
    Toro.
  Meliola arecibensis F. L. Stevens.

Acalypha gracilens Gray.
  Cercospora Acalyphae Pk.

Acalypha laevigata Sw.
  Ophiotrichum Acalyphae Thm.

Acalypha Lindheimeri Müll. Arg.
  Ramularia Acalyphae Tharp.

Acalypha macrostachya Jacq., var .hirsutissima
    (Willd.) Müll.-Arg.
  Asterina Acalyphae Syd.
  Cicinnobella asperula Syd.
  Ophiotexis perpusilla (Speg.) Theissen.

Acalpha marginata Spreng.
  Botryosphaeria Ribis (Tode ex Fr.) Grossen-
    bacher & Duggar, var. chromogena Shear
    et al.

Acalypha musaica Hort.
  Rosellinia bunodes (B. & Br.) Sacc.
  Xylaria Hypoxylon (L.) ex Fr.

Acalypha ostryifolia Riddell.
  Cercospora Acalyphae Pk.
  Cercospora Acalypharum Tharp.
  Volutella Acalyphae Atk.

Acalypha virginica L.
Cercospora Acalyphae Pk.
{ Peronospora Euphorbiae J. J. Davis.
{ Plasmopara Acalyphae G. W. Wilson.
{ Rhysotheca Acalyphae G. W. Wilson.
Synchytrium aureum Schrt.
Synchytrium cellulare J. J. Davis.
Acalypha wilkesiana Müll.
Rhizoctonia Solani Kühn.
Tragia nepetifolia Cav.
Cercospora euphorbiicola, var. Tragiae Tharp.
Ricinus communis L.
Alternaria Brassicae (B.) Sacc.
Botryosphaeria Ribis (Tode ex Fr.) Grossen-
bacher & Duggar.
Botryosphaeria Ribis (Tode ex Fr.) Grossen-
bacher & Duggar, var. chromogena Shear
et al.
Botrytis cinerea Auct.
{ Cercospora albidomaculans Wint.
{ Cercospora ricinella Sacc. & Berl.
Cercospora canescens Ell. & Martin, var.
Ricini Ell. & Ev.
Cladosporium solutum Lk.
Corticium vagum B. & C.
Didymella Ricini Ell. & Ev.
Epicoccum nigrum Lk.
{ Macrophoma Ricini (Cke.) Berl. & Vogl.
{ Phoma Ricini (Cke.) Sacc.
{ Sphaeropsis Ricini Cke.
Macrosporium compactum Cke.
Mucor botryoides Lendner.
Ozonium omnivorum Shear.
Phytophthora terrestris Sherbakoff.
Sclerotinia Ricini Godfrey.
Sclerotium Rolfsii Sacc.
Aleurites Fordii Hemsl.
Corticium Stevensii (Noack) Burt.
Joannesia princeps Vell.
Uredo maceiensis Henn.
Jatropha angustifolia Griseb.
Uredo jatrophicola Arth.
Jatropha Curcas L.
Uredo jatrophicola Arth.
Schizophyllum commune Fr.
Jatropha gossypifolia L.
Uredo jatrophicola Arth.
Jatropha hernandifolia Vent.
Meliola Jatrophae F. L. Stevens.
Jatropha multifida L.
{ Nigredo Janiphae Arth.
{ Uromyces Jatrophae Diet. & Holw.
Jatropha spathulata Müll.-Arg.
Aecidium Mozinnae Arth.
Jatropha stimulosa Michx.
Cercospora Jatrophae Atk.
Septoria Jatrophae Heald & Wolf.
Uromyces agnatus Arth.

Jatropha urens L.
Uromyces oaxacanus Diet. & Holw.
Hevea brasiliensis Müll.-Arg.
Botryodiplodia Elasticae Petch.
Corticium lilacinofuscum B. & C.
Corticium salmonicolor B. & Br.
Diplodia cacaoicola Henn.
Diplodia rapax Massee.
Eutypa caulivora Massee.
Eutypa erumpens Massee.
{ Gloeosporium Elasticae Ckc. & Massee.
{ Gloeosporium intermedium, var. brevipes Sacc.
Helminthosporium Heveae Petch.
Irpex flavus Klotzsch.
Meliola Heveae Vincens.
Pestalozzia Guepini Desm.
Phyllosticta Heveae Zimm.
Phytophthora Faberi Delacr. & Maubl.
Sphaeronema fimbriatum Ell. & Halsted.
Thyridaria tarda Bancroft.
Xylaria platypoda (Lév.) Fr.
Manihot carthagenensis Müll.
{ Alternaria fasciculata (C. & E.) Jones & Grout.
{ Macrosporium fasciculatum C. & E.
Ascochyta carthagenensis Sacc.
Dothiorella botrya Sacc.
{ Macrophoma Janiphae (Thm.) Berl. & Vogl.
{ Phoma Janiphae (Thm.) Sacc.
{ Sphaeropsis Janiphae Thm.
Manihot utilissima Pohl.
Cercospora cassavae Ell. & Ev.
Cercospora Henningsii Allescher.
Cercospora Jatrophae Atk.
Cercospora Manihotis Henn.
Dimerosporium Pellicula Syd.
Gloeosporium ampelophagum Auct.
Gloeosporium Manihot Earle.
Microsphaera Euphorbiae (Pk.) B. & C. ?.
Rhizoctonia Solani Kühn.
Rosellinia bunodes (B. & Br.) Sacc.
Rosellinia Pepo Pat.
{ Nigredo Janiphae Arth.
{ Uromyces Janiphae Arth.
{ Uredo Janiphae Wint.
Codiaeum variegatum Blume.
Corticium Stevensii Burt.
Gloeosporium sorauerianum Allescher.
Sphaeropsis Codiaei Ciferri & Fragoso.
Codiaeum sp. indet.
Cordyceps peltata Wakefield.
Corticium koleroga (Cke.) v. Höhnel.
Gloeosporium Crotonis Delacr.
Omphalea sp. indet.
Phyllosticta Omphaleae Dearness & House.
Stillingia acutifolia Benth. & Hook.
Physalospora Kellermanii Rehm.
Stillingia angustifolia (Torr.) Watson.
Nigredo graminicola (Burrill) Arth. I.

Stillingia aquatica Chapm.
  Aecidium Stillingiae Tracy & Earle.
Stillingia ligustrina Michx.
  Aecidium Stillingiae Tracy & Earle.
  Nigredo graminicola (Burrill) Arth. I.
Stillingia sebifera Michx.
  Cercospora Stillingiae Ell. & Ev.
  Phyllosticta Stillingiae Ell. & Ev.
Stillingia sylvatica L.
  Nigredo graminicola (Burrill) Arth. I.
Sapium aucuparium Jacq.
  ⌠Coriolus brunneolus (B.) Pat.
  ⌡Polyporus brunneolus B.
Sapium biglandulosum Müll.-Arg.
Sapium macrocarpum Müll.-Arg.
  ⌠Nigredo (?) globosa (Diet. & Holw.) Arth.
  ⌡Uromyces globosus Diet. & Holw.
Hippomane Mancinella L.
  Ganoderma pulverulentum Murrill.
Gymnanthes lucida Sw.
  Helminthosporium Helleri F. L. Stevens.
  Meliola gymnanthicola F. L. Stevens.
Hura crepitans L.
  Cercospora Hurae F. L. Stevens.
  Colletotrichum curvisetum F. L. Stevens.
  Hypholoma tuberculatum Pat.
  Lentinus strigellus B. & C.
  Leptosphaeria Hurae Pat.
  Mucidula cheimonophylla (B. & C.) Pat.
  ⌠Leptoporus pallidocervinus (S.) Pat.
  ⌡Polyporus pallidocervinus S.
  Puccinia Huberi F. L. Stevens.
Euphorbia adenoptera Bertol.
  ⌠Nigredo proëminens (Pass.) Arth.
  ⌡Uromyces proëminens Pass.
Euphorbia albomarginata Torr. & Gr.
  Aecidium Euphorbiae S.
  ⌠Nigredo proëminens (Pass.) Arth.
  ⌡Uromyces proëminens Pass.
  Uromyces striatus Ell. & Varney.
Euphorbia arizonica Engelm.
  Nigredo proëminens (Pass.) Arth.
Euphorbia arkansana Engelm. & Gray.
  Nigredo dictyosperma (Ell. & Ev.) Arth.
Euphorbia barbellata Engelm.
  ⌠Nigredo proëminens (Pass.) Arth.
  ⌡Uromyces proëminens Pass.
Euphorbia bicolor Engelm. & Gray.
  Darluca Filum (Biv.) Cast.
  ⌠Nigredo prëminens (Pass.) Arth.
  ⌡Uromyces Euphorbiae C. & P.
  ⌡Uromyces Myristica B. & C.
Euphorbia biformis Watson.
Euphorbia bilobata Engelm.
Euphorbia Blodgettii Engelm.
  ⌠Nigredo proëminens (Pass.) Arth.
  ⌡Uromyces proëminens Pass.

Euphorbia brasiliensis Lam.
  Microsphaera Euphorbiae (Pk.) B. & C. ?
  ⌠Nigredo proëminens (Pass.) Arth.
  ⌡Uromyces proëminens Pass.
Euphorbia calyculata H. B. K.
  Puccinia Euphorbiae Henn.
  ⌠Allodus intumescens (Syd.) Arth. & Orton.
  ⌡Puccinia Euphorbiae, var. intumescens Syd.
  ⌡Puccinia intumescens (Syd.) Holw.
Euphorbia campestris Cham. & Schl.
  Melampsora Euphorbiae (Schubert) Cast.
Euphorbia caracasana Boiss.
  ⌠Bullaria longipes (Syd.) Arth. & Mains.
  ⌡Puccinia Euphorbiae, var. longipes Syd.
  Puccinia Euphorbiae Henn.
Euphorbia Chamaesula Boiss.
  Aecidium Euphorbiae Auct. Amer. p. p.
  Nigredo occidentalis (Diet.) Arth.
  Teleutospora Tranzschelii (Syd.) Arth. &
    Bisby.
Euphorbia commutata Engelm.
  Aecidium Cyparissiae DC.
  ⌠Aecidium Euphorbiae N. Am. Uredinales 703.
  ⌡Aecidium Tithymali Arth.
  Melampsora Euphorbiae-gerardianae W. Müll.
Euphorbia cordata Meyen.
  ⌠Puccinia velata Arth.
  ⌡Uredo velata Ell. & Ev.
Euphorbia cordifolia Ell.
  Peronospora Esulae Gäumann.
  Peronospora Euphorbiae Fckl.
  ⌠Uromyces Euphorbiae C. & P.
  ⌡Uromyces proëminens Pass.
Euphorbia corollata L.
  Aecidium Euphorbiae S.
  ⌠Aecidium Pammelii Trel.
  ⌡Dicaeoma Pammelii Arth. I.
  ⌡Puccinia Pammelii Arth. I.
  ⌡Puccinia Panici Diet. I.
  Cercospora Euphorbiae Kellerm. & Swingle.
  Cercospora heterospora Ell. & Ev.
  Microsphaera diffusa C. & P.
  ⌠Erysiphe Euphorbiae C. & P.
  ⌡Microsphaera Euphorbiae (Pk.) B. & C.
  Microsphaera Russellii G. W. Clinton. ?
  Passalora fasciculata (C. & E.) Earle.
Euphorbia cotinifolia L.
  Puccinia Euphorbiae Henn.
  ⌠Bullaria longipes (Syd.) Arth. & Mains.
  ⌡Puccinia Euphorbiae, var. longipes Syd.
Euphorbia cuphosperma Engelm.
Euphorbia cyathophora Murr.
  Nigredo proëminens (Pass.) Arth.
Euphorbia Cyparissias L.
  Melampsora Euphorbiae (Schubert) Cast.
  Uromyces Pisi Auct. Amer.
  Uromyces striatus Ell. & Varney.

Euphorbia densiflora Klotzsch.
  {Nigredo proëminens (Pass.) Arth.
  {Uromyces proëminens Pass.
Euphorbia dentata Michx.
  {Aecidium Euphorbiae Auct. p. p.
  {Caeomurus Euphorbiae (C. & P.) O. Kuntze.
  {Nigredo proëminens (Pass.) Arth.
  {Uromyces ellisianus Henn.
  {Uromyces Euphorbiae C. & P.
  {Uromyces Euphorbiae C. & P., var. subcirci-
    nata Ell. & Ev.
  {Uromyces Poinsettiae Tranz.
  {Uromyces proëminens Pass.
Euphorbia dictyosperma Fisch. & Mey.
  Aecidium Tithymali Arth.
  {Nigredo dictyosperma (Ell. & Ev.) Arth.
  {Uromyces dictyospermus Ell. & Ev.
  Uromyces scutellatus (Schrank) Lév.
  Uromyces tuberculatus Fckl.?
Euphorbia Esula L.
  Alternaria Brassicae (B.) Sacc.
  Peronospora Esulae Gäumann.
Euphorbia Fendleri Torr. & Gr.
Euphorbia Geyeri Engelm.
  {Nigredo proëminens (Pass.) Arth.
  {Uromyces Euphorbiae C. & P.
  {Uromyces proëminens Pass.
Euphorbia glyptosperma Engelm.
  Peronospora Chamaesycis G. W. Wilson.
  {Peronospora Cyparissiae DBy.
  {Peronospora Euphorbiae Auct. Amer.
  Peronospora Euphorbiae Fckl.
  Peronospora Euphorbiae, var. glyptospermae
    Gäuman.
  {Nigredo proëminens (Pass.) Arth.
  {Uromyces Euphorbiae C. & P.
  {Uromyces proëminens Pass.
Euphorbia graminea Jacq.
Euphorbia Greenei Millsp.
Euphorbia havanensis Willd.
  Uromyces proëminens (DC.) Pass.
Euphorbia heterophylla L.
  {Aecidium Euphorbiae Auct. p. p.
  {Nigredo proëminens (Pass.) Arth.
  {Uromyces Euphorbiae C. & P.
  {Uromyces Poinsettiae Tranz.
  {Uromyces proëminens Pass.
Euphorbia hexagona Nutt.
  {Aecidium Pammelii Trel.
  {Dicaeoma Pammelii Arth. I.
  {Puccinia Panici Diet. I.
  Nigredo proëminens (Pass.) Arth.
Euphorbia hirsuta (Torr.) Wiegand.
  Peronospora Esulae Gäumann.
  Peronospora Euphorbiae Fckl.
  {Nigredo proëminens (Pass.) Arth.
  {Uromyces proëminens Pass.

Euphorbia hirta L.
  Oidium Cyparissiae Syd.
  {Aecidium Euphorbiae Auct. Amer.
  {Nigredo proëminens (Pass.) Arth.
  {Uromyces euphorbiicola Tranz.
  {Uromyces proëminens Pass.
Euphorbia hirtula Engelm.
  Peronospora Euphorbiae Fckl.
Euphorbia humistrata Engelm.
  Peronospora Euphorbiae Fckl.
  {Caeomurus Euphorbiae (C. & P.) O. Kuntze.
  {Nigredo proëminens (Pass.) Arth.
  {Uromyces Euphorbiae C. & P.
  {Uromyces euphorbiicola Tranz.
  {Uromyces proëminens Pass.
Euphorbia hypericifolia L.
  Cercoseptoria Chamaesyceae (Stevens & Dal-
    bey) Petrak.
Euphorbia hyssopifolia L.
  Nigredo proëminens (Pass.) Arth.
Euphorbia Ipecacuanhae L.
  Dicaeoma Pammelii Arth. I.
  Fusicladium fasciculatum C. & E.
Euphorbia lancifolia Schl.
  Aecidium seriatum Arth. & Holw.
Euphorbia lasiocarpa Klotzsch.
Euphorbia lata Engelm.
  {Nigredo proëminens (Pass.) Arth.
  {Uromyces Euphorbiae C. & P.
  {Uromyces proëminens Pass.
Euphorbia leiococcus (Engelm.) Small.
  Aecidium Tithymali Arth.
Euphorbia leptocera Engelm.
  Melampsora monticola Mains.
Euphorbia lurida Engelm.
  Aecidium Euphorbiae Auct. Amer. p. p.
Euphorbia macropodoides Rob. & Greenm.
  Nigredo occidentalis (Diet.) Arth.
  Nigredo proëminens (Pass.) Arth.
Euphorbia maculata L.
  Peronospora Euphorbiae Fckl.
  {Peronospora Cyparissiae DBy.
  {Peronospora Euphorbiae Auct. Amer. p. p.
  Sclerotinia Trifoliorum Erikss.
  {Aecidium Euphorbiae Auct. Amer.
  {Caeoma punctuosum S. Am. Bor. 2846.
  {Caeomurus Euphorbiae (C. & P.) O. Kuntze.
  {Nigredo proëminens (Pass.) Arth.
  {Trichobasis euphorbiicola B. & C.
  {Uredo Euphorbiae S. Syn. Car.
  {Uredo euphorbiicola (B. & C.) De Toni.
  {Uromyces Euphorbiae C. & P.
  {Uromyces Euphorbiae, var. minor Arth.?
  {Uromyces euphorbiicola Tranz.
  {Uromyces macounianus Ell. & Ev.
  {Uromyces proëminens Pass.

Euphorbia marginata Pursh.
  Alternaria tenuis Nees ex Fr.
  Botrytis cinerea P. †
  Cladosporium solutum Lk.
  Helminthosporium herbarum Lk.
  Macrosporium Euphorbiae Barthol.
  Microsphaera Euphorbiae (Pk.) B. & C.
  ⌠ Phoma euphorbiicola (S.) Starb.
  ⌡ Sphaerella euphorbiicola (S.) Ell. & Ev.
  ⌡ Sphaeria euphorbiicola S.
  Pyrenophora calvescens (Fr.) Sacc.
  ⌠ Tubercularia persicina Ditm. ex Fr.
  ⌡ Tuberculina persicina (Ditm. ex Fr.) Sacc.

UREDINALES

  ⌠ Aecidium Pammelii Trel.
  │ Dicaeoma Pammelii Arth. I.
  │ Puccinia Pammelii Arth. I.
  ⌡ Puccinia Panici Diet. I.
  ⌠ Aecidium Euphorbiae Auct. Amer. p. p.
  │ Nigredo proëminens (Pass.) Arth.
  │ Uromyces ellisianus Henn.
  │ Uromyces Euphorbiae C. & P.
  ⟨ Uromyces Euphorbiæ, var. minor Arth. ?
  │ Uromyces marginatus Ell. & Ev.
  │ Uromyces myristica B. & C.
  │ Uromyces proëminens Pass.
  ⌡ Uromyces pulvinatus N. A. F. *3046*.

Euphorbia missouriensis Norton.
  Aecidium Tithymali Arth.
  Nigredo dictyosperma (Ell. & Ev.) Arth.

Euphorbia montana Engelm.
  See also Euphorbia robusta.
  ⌠ Teleutospora Tranzschelii (Syd.) Arth. &
  │   Bisby.
  ⟨ Uromyces excavatus Diet. p. p.
  │ Uromyces scutellatus Auct. Amer.
  ⌡ Uromyces Tranzschelii Syd.

Euphorbia Myrsinites L.
  Gloeosporium Euphorbiae Halsted.

Euphorbia nudiflora Jacq.
  Uredo Euphorbiae-nudiflorae Henn.
  Nigredo proëminens (Pass.) Arth.

Euphorbia obtusata Pursh.
  ⌠ Aecidium Euphorbiae Auct. Amer.
  ⟨ Uromyces Euphorbiae C. & P.
  Nigredo dictyosperma (Ell. & Ev.) Arth.

Euphorbia oregonensis Millsp.
  ⌠ Nigredo proëminens (Pass.) Arth.
  ⌡ Uromyces proëminens Pass.

Euphorbia Palmeri Engelm.
  Melampsora monticola Mains.
  Uromyces co-ordinatus Arth. I.
  ⌠ Teleutospora Tranzschelii (Syd.) Arth. &
  │   Bisby.
  ⌡ Uromyces Tranzschelii Syd.

Euphorbia petaloides Engelm.
  Fusicladium fasciculatum C. & E.
  ⌠ Nigredo proëminens (Pass.) Arth.
  ⟨ Uromyces Euphorbiae C. & P.
  ⌡ Uromyces proëminens Pass.

Euphorbia petiolaris Sims.
  ⌠ Bullaria velata (Ell. & Ev.) Arth. & Mains.
  ⟨ Puccinia Euphorbiae Auct. p. p.
  ⌡ Puccinia Euphorbiae, var. minor Holw.

Euphorbia polycarpa Benth.

Euphorbia polygonifolia L.

Euphorbia potosina Fern.
  ⌠ Aecidium Euphorbiae Auct. Amer.
  │ Nigredo proëminens (Pass.) Arth.
  ⟨ Uromyces Euphorbiae C. & P.
  │ Uromyces euphorbiicola Tranz.
  ⌡ Uromyces proëminens Pass.

Euphorbia Preslii Guss.
  ⌠ Cercosporidium Euphorbiae (Tracy & Earle)
  │   Earle.
  │ Piricularia Euphorbiae Atk.
  ⌡ Scolecotrichum? Euphorbiae Tracy & Earle.
  Fusicladium fasciculatum C. & E.
  ⌠ Erysiphe Euphorbiae Pk.
  ⌡ Microsphaera Euphorbiae (Pk.) B. & C.
  Peronospora Esulae Gäumann.
  Peronospora Euphorbiae Fckl.
  ⌠ Aecidium Euphorbiae Auct. Amer.
  │ Caeoma Euphorbiae-hypericifoliae S.
  │ Caeoma punctuosum S. Am. Bor.
  │ Caeomurus Euphorbiae (C. & P.) O. Kuntze.
  │ Nigredo proëminens (Pass.) Arth.
  │ Uredo Euphorbiae S. Syn. Car.
  │ Uredo punctuosum Curt. Cat.
  ⟨ Uredo scutellata S. Syn. Car.
  │ Uromyces apiculosus Curt. Cat. p. p.
  │ Uromyces Euphorbiae C. & P.
  │ Uromyces Myristica B. & C.
  ⌡ Uromyces proëminens Pass.

Euphorbia procumbens Mill.
  Uromyces Euphorbiae C. & P.

Euphorbia prostrata Ait.
  Peronospora Euphorbiae Fckl.
  ⌠ Nigredo proëminens (Pass.) Arth.
  │ Uromyces Euphorbiae C. & P.
  ⟨ Uromyces euphorbiicola Tranz.
  ⌡ Uromyces proëminens Pass.

Euphorbia pulcherrima Willd.
  ⌠ Botrytis cinerea P. †
  ⌡ Botrytis vulgaris (Lk.) ex Fr.
  Cercospora pulcherrimae Tharp.
  Cercospora pulcherrimae Tharp., var. minima
    Tharp.
  Cladosporium herbarum (P.) ex Lk.
  Clitocybe tabescens Bres.
  Gloeosporium intermedium Sacc., var. Poin-
    settiae Sacc.
  Ozonium omnivorum Shear.
  Pestalozzia funerea Desm.

Euphorbia pulcherrima (*cont.*)
  Ravenelia humphreyana Henn.
  Rhizoctonia Solani Kühn.
Euphorbia robusta (Engelm.) Small.
  See also Euphorbia montana.
  {Aecidium Euphorbiae Auct. p. p.
  {Uromyces andinus Fung. Utah *96*.
  Aecidium Tithymali Arth.
  {Melampsora Euphorbiae-gerardianae Fung.
  { Columb. *4938*.
  {Melampsora monticola Mains.
  Pucciniola coordinata Arth.
  Nigredo occidentalis (Diet.) Arth.
  {Teleutospora Tranzschelii (Syd.) Arth. &
  { Bisby.
  {Uromyces andinus Fung. Utah *97*.
  {?Uromyces scutellatus Auct. Amer. p. p.
  {Uromyces Tranzschelii Syd.
Euphorbia rugulosa (Engelm.) Rydb.
  Uromyces proëminens Pass.
Euphorbia Schlechtendahlii Boiss.
Euphorbia Scotanam Schl.
  {Bullaria velata (Arth.) Arth. & Mains.
  {Puccinia Euphorbiae Henn., var. minor Holw.
  {Puccinia velata Arth.
Euphorbia serpens H. B. K.
  Peronospora Euphorbiae Fckl.
  {Nigredo proëminens (Pass.) Arth.
  {Uromyces Euphorbiae C. & P.
  {Uromyces proëminens Pass.
  {Teleutospora Tranzschelii (Syd.) Arth. &
  { Bisby.
  {Uromyces Tranzschelii Syd.
Euphorbia serpyllifolia P.
  Passalora fasciculata (C. & E.) Earle.
  Peronospora Cyparissiae DBy.
  Peronospora Euphorbiae Fckl.
  {Aecidium Euphorbiae Auct. Amer.
  {Nigredo proëminens (Pass.) Arth.
  {Uromyces Euphorbiae C. & P.
  {Uromyces proëminens Pass.
Euphorbia stictospora Engelm.
  Peronospora Chamaesycis G. W. Wilson.
  Peronospora Cyparissiae DBy.
  Peronospora Euphorbiae Fckl.
  {Nigredo proëminens (Pass.) Arth.
  {Uromyces proëminens Pass.
Euphorbia stricticaulis Auct.
Euphorbia strigosa Hook. & Arn.
  {Nigredo proëminens (Pass.) Arth.
  {Uromyces Euphorbiae C. & P.
Euphorbia texana Boiss.
  Aecidium Tithymali Arth.
Euphorbia Tracyi Small.
  Nigredo proëminens (Pass.) Arth.
Euphorbia zygophylloides Boiss.
  {Nigredo proëminens (Pass.) Arth.
  {Uromyces Euphorbiae C. & P.
  {Uromyces proëminens Pass.

Euphorbia sp. indet.
  {Botryosphaeria Ribis (Tode ex Fr.) Grossen-
  { bacher & Duggar.
  {Nectria Ribis (Tode ex Fr.) Oud.
  Botryosporium prorumpens S.
  Cercospora euphorbiicola Atk.
  Cladosporium Chaetomium Cke.
  Gloeosporium Euphorbiae Halsted.
  Oidium Cyparissiae Syd.
  Peronospora Chamaesycis G. W. Wilson.
  Uromyces globosus Diet. & Holw.

BUXACEAE

Pachysandra procumbens Michx.
  Phyllosticta Pachysandrae Dearness & House.
Buxus bahamensis (Baker) Britton.
  Ophiodothis Bahamensis Seaver.
Buxus citrifolia Spreng.
  Helminthosporium martinicense Thm.
Buxus sempervirens L.
  {Fusarium lateritium Nees ex Fr.
  {Fusarium pyrochroum (Desm.) Sacc.
  Laestadia Buxi (Desm.) Sacc.
  {Diplodia Buxi (DC.) Fr.
  {Macrophoma Candollei (B. & Br.) Berl. &
  { Vogl.
  {Phoma Candollei (B. & Br.) Sacc.
  {Sphaeria Buxi DC.
  {Sphaeropsis Candollei B. & Br.
  Penicillium roseum Cke. non Lk.
  Phoma stictica B. & Br.
  Phyllosticta Auerswaldii Allescher.
  Phyllosticta buxina Sacc.
  Septoria Negundinis Ell. & Ev.
  Sphaeria buxicola S. Am. Bor. 1810.
  {Fusidium Buxi Schm. ex Fr.
  {Fusisporium Buxi (Schm.) ex Fr.
  {Verticillium Buxi (Schm. ex Fr.) Awd. &
  { Fleisch.
  {Nectria rousselliana Tul.
  {Volutella Buxi (Cda.) B.

CORIARIACEAE

Coriaria myrtifolia L.
  {Dothiorella macrospora (B. & C.) Sacc.
  {Sphaeropsis macrospora B. & C.

EMPETRACEAE

Corema Conradii Torr.
  Cucurbitaria Coremae Ell. & Ev.
  Diaporthe Conradii Ell.
Empetrum nigrum L.
  Ascochyta Baccae Rostr.
  {Chrysomyxa Empetri (Karst.) Schrt.
  {Melampsoropsis Empetri (Karst.) Arth.
  {Uredo Empetri P.

Empetrum nigrum (*cont.*)
  Cladosporium herbarum (P.) ex Lk.
  { Clithris Empetri (Rostr.) Ell. & Ev.
  { Sporomega Empetri Rostr.
  Didymosphaeria Empetri (Fr.) Sacc.
  Metasphaeria Empetri (Fr.) Sacc.
  Physalospora Crepiniana Sacc. & March.
  Septoria Empetri Rostr.

LIMNANTHACEAE

Floerkea proserpinacoides Willd.
  Entyloma Floerkeae Holw.
  Peronospora Floerkeae Kellerm.

ANACARDIACEAE

Mangifera indica L.
  Agaricus cheimonophyllus B. & C.
  Aleurodiscus candidus (S.) Burt.
  Aschersonia cubensis B. & C.
  Bresadolia Mangiferae Pat.
  Cephalosporium Lecanii Zimm.
  Cladoderris dendritica P.
  { Capnodium mangiferum Cke. & Br.
  { Dimerosporium mangiferum (Cke. & Br.) Sacc.
  Diplodia cacaoicola Henn.
  Diplodia Mangiferae Koord.
  Endothia havanensis Bruner.
  { Fomes Mangiferae (Lév.) Cke.
  { Ganoderma Mangiferae (Lév.) Pat.
  Fumago vagans Fr.
  Ganoderma argillaceum Murrill.
  Ganoderma perzonatum Murrill.
  { Gloeoporus conchoides Mont.
  { Leptoporus conchoides (Mont.) Pat.
  Gloeosporium Mangiferae Henn.
  Gloeosporium Raciborskii Henn.
  { Colletotrichum gloeosporioides Penz.
  { Glomerella cingulata (Stoneman) Spaulding &
  {   v. Schrenk.
  Grammothele polygramma B. & C.
  Hypocrella turbinata (B.) Petch.
  Kretzschmaria clavus Fr.
  Kretzschmaria coenopus Mont.
  Lasiodiplodia Theobromae (Pat.) Griffon &
    Maubl.
  Lasiodiplodia tubericola Ell. & Ev.
  Lentinus Lecomtei Fr.
  Lophodermium Mangiferae Koord.
  Meliola brasiliensis Speg.
  Meliola Mangiferae Earle.
  Microthyrium Mangiferae Bomm. & Rouss.
  Nectria Theobromae Massee.
  Pestalozzia funerea Desm.
  Pestalozzia Guepini Desm.
  Pestalozzia scirrofaciens N. A. Brown.
  Pholiota martinicensis Pat.
  Phyllosticta Mortoni Fairman.

  Poria borbonica Pat.
  Septobasidium penicillatum (B. & C.) Pat.
  Stilbella flavida (Cke.) Henn.
  Stilbum stromaticum B.
  Valsa congesta Pat.
Anacardium excelsum Skeels.
  Asterina carbonacea Speg., var. Anacardii
    Ryan.
Anacardium occidentale L.
  Hypholoma appendiculatum Fr.
Spondias cytherea Tuss.?
  { Corticium Murrayi (B. & C.) Pat.
  { Thelephora Murrayi B. & C.
Spondias dulcis Forst.
  Capnodium Citri B. & Desm.
  Colletotrichum falcatum Went.
Spondias mombin L.
  { Cerotelium alienum (Syd. & Butler) Arth.
  { Cerotelium Spondiadis Arth.
  Endothia havanensis Bruner.
  Helminthosporium Helleri F. L. Stevens.
  Meliola Comocladiae F. L. Stevens.
  Panus eugrammus (Mont.) Fr.
  Trametes sepium B.
Spondias purpurea L.
  Kretzschmaria clavus Fr.
  Meliola nicaraguensis Speg.
  Podoscypha nitidula B. & C.
Pistacia chinensis Bunge.
  Corticium Stevensii (Noack) Burt.
Pistacia mexicana H. B. K.
  Sphaerella Pistaciae Cke.
Pistacia vera L.
  Corticium Stevensii Burt.
Mauria glauca Donn. Sm.
  Aspergillopsis tropicalis Speg.
  Uredo Mauriae Syd. II.
Schinus molle L.
  Armillaria mellea (Vahl) ex Fr.
  Fomes applanatus (P. ex Wallr.) Gill.
  Ganoderma polychromum (Copeland) Murrill.
  Ozonium omnivorum Shear.
  Phleospora bonanseana Sacc.
  { Inonotus Schini J. G. Brown.
  { Trametes Schini (J. G. Brown) G. A. Martin.
Comocladia glabra Spreng.
  Amphinectria portoricensis Speg.
  Helminthosporium glabroides F. L. Stevens.
  Meliola Comocladiae F. L. Stevens.
  Micropeltidium portoricense Speg.
Rhus
    (Schmalzia Bakeri Greene.)
  Lachnella flammea (A. & S.) ex Fr.
  Teichospora rhoina (Earle) Fairman.
Rhus canadensis Marsh.
  Cercospora rhoina C. & E.
  Cladosporium aromaticum Ell. & Ev.
  Exoascus purpurascens (Ell. & Ev.) Sacc.
  Hysterographium incisum Ell. & Ev.

Rhus canadensis (*cont.*)
Uromyces brevipes (B. & Rav.) Pazschke.
{ Pileolaria effusa Pk.
{ Uromyces effusus (Pk.) De Toni.
Rhus canadensis Marsh., var. **trilobata** (Nutt.)
Gray.
{ Camarosporium rhoinum (Cke. & Hark.) Sacc.
{ Dichomera rhoina Cke. & Hark.
Cylindrosporium Toxicodendri (Ell. & Martin) Ell. & Ev.
Dasyscypha allantospora Earle.
Diplodia rhoina Cke. & Hark.
Lachnella rhoina Earle.
{ Diplodia resurgens Cke. & Hark.
{ Microdiplodia resurgens (Cke. & Hark.) Tassi.
{ Strickeria rhoina Earle.
{ Teichospora rhoina (Earle) Sacc. & D. Sacc.
Rhus choriophylla Woot. & Standl.
Pileolaria mexicana Arth.

Rhus copallina L.

ASCOMYCETES

{ Aponectria inaurata (B. & Br.) Sacc.
{ Nectria inaurata B. & Br.
{ Botryosphaeria ambigua (S.) Sacc.
{ Melogramma ambiguum (S.) Rav.
{ Calospora aculeans (S.) Sacc.
{ Cryptospora aculeans (S.) Ell. & Ev.
{ Diaporthe albovelata (B. & C.) Sacc.
{ Sphaeria aculeans S.
{ Valsa aculeans (S.) B.
{ Valsa albovelata B. & C.
{ Valsa rufescens (S.) M. A. Curtis.
Cucurbitaria stenocarpa Ell. & Ev.
Diaporthe rhoina (C. & E.) Ell. & Ev.
Didymella lophospora Sacc. & Speg.
Eurotium herbariorum Lk.
{ Cucurbitaria brevibarbata B. & C.
{ Fracchiaea brevibarbata (B. & C.) Sacc.
Hypoxylon rubiginosum (P.) ex Fr.
Metasphaeria varia Dearness & House.
{ Dothidea Rhois (S.) Fr.
{ Phyllachora Rhois (S.) Sacc.
{ Xyloma Rhois S.
{ Sphaerotheca Humuli (DC.) Burrill. †
{ Sphaerotheca pruinosa C. & P.
{ Ascomyces deformans, var. purpurascens Ell.
& Ev.
{ Exoascus deformans, var. Farl.
{ Exoascus purpurascens (Ell. & Ev.) Sacc.
{ Taphrina purpurascens (Ell. & Ev.) B. L. Robinson.
{ Diatrype quadrata (S.) B.
{ Sphaeria quadrata S.
{ Valsaria quadrata (S.) Sacc.
{ Winteria rhoina (Ell. & Ev.) Berl. & Vogl.
{ Winterina rhoina (Ell. & Ev.) Sacc.
Xylaria corniformis Fr.

BASIDIOMYCETES

Hydnum Rhois S.
Pleurotus niger S.
{ Polyporus cupuliformis B. & C.
{ Polyporus Pocula (S.) B. & C.
{ Porodisculus pendulus (S.) Murrill.
Stereum ochraceoflavum (S.) M. A. Curtis.
Stereum sericeum (S.) Morg.

FUNGI IMPERFECTI

Cercospora copallina Cke.
Cercospora rhoina C. & E.
{ Cornularia Rhois (B. & C.?) Karst.
{ Sphaeronema Rhois B. & C.?
Cylindrosporium Toxicodendri Ell. & Ev.
Diplodia Rhois Sacc.
{ Gonatobotrys maculicola Wint.
{ Gonatobotryum maculicola (Wint.) Sacc.
Helminthosporium Arbuscula B. & C.
Hendersonia hyalopus B. & C.
Patellina Fragariae Stevens & Petersen.
{ Hainesia Lythri (Desm.) v. Höhnel.
{ Sclerotiopsis concava (Desm.) Shear & Dodge.
Septoria irregularis Pk.
Septoria rhoina B. & C.
{ Phoma pulchella (B. & C.) Sacc.
{ Sphaeropsis pulchella B. & C.
{ Sporocybe Rhois B. & C. (Lichen).
{ Stilbum Rhois B. & C.
Stemphylium copallinum Ell. & Ev.
Rhus coriaria L.
Septoria rhoina (B. & C.) Sacc.
Rhus cotinoides Nutt.
{ Septoria rhoina Sacc.
{ Septoria Rhois B. & C.
Rhus Cotinus L.
Cercospora rhoina C. & E.
Hainesia rhoina Ell. & Sacc.
{ Hainesia Lythri (Desm.) v. Höhnel.
{ Pezizella Lythri Shear & Dodge.
{ Sclerotiopsis concava (Desm.) Shear & Dodge.
Septoria rhoina Sacc.
Rhus diversiloba Torr. & Gr.
Botryosphaeria ambigua (S.) Sacc.
Cercospora Toxicodendri Ell.
Cucurbitaria stenocarpa Ell. & Ev.
{ Cylindrosporium Toxicodendri (M. A. Curtis)
Ell. & Ev.
{ Septoria irregularis Pk.
{ Diatrype Rhois (S.) Cke.
{ Diatrypella Rhois (S.) Ell. & Ev.
Diplodia resurgens Cke. & Hark.
Diplodia rhoina Cke. & Hark.
Lachnella rhizophila Ell. & Ev.
Marssonina Toxicodendri (M. A. Curtis ex
Martin) Magn.
{ Ophiocarpella tarda (Hark.) Theissen & Syd.
{ Ophiodothis tarda Hark.

Rhus diversiloba (*cont.*)
  Peniophora decorticans Purt.
  Stictis radiata (L.) ex. P.
  Strumella corynoidea Auct. Amer.
  ⎰Tryblidiella rufula (Spreng. ex Fr.) Sacc.
  ⎱Tryblidium rufulum (Spreng. ex Fr.) Cke.
  Pileolaria Toxicodendri (B. & Rav.) Arth.
  Uromyces brevipes (B. & Rav.) Pazschke.
  ⎰Uromyces punctatostriatus Cke. & Hark.
  Uromyces Terebinthi Wint. p. p.
  Uromyces Toxicodendri B. & Rav.
  Valsonectria virens Hark.
Rhus
     (Schmalzia Emoryi Greene).
  ⎰Pileolaria patzcuarensis (Holw.) Arth.
  ⎱Uromyces patzcuarensis Holw.
Rhus floridana Mearns.
  ⎰Pileolaria Toxicodendri (B. & Rav.) Arth.
  ⎱Uromyces Toxicodendri B. & Rav.
Rhus glabra L.

EXOASCACEAE
Taphrina purpurascens B. L. Robinson.

PEZIZINEAE
Cenangium Rhois S.
⎰Hainesia Lythri (Desm.) v. Höhnel.
⎱Pezizella Lythri Shear & Dodge.
Sclerotiopsis concava (Desm.) Shear & Dodge.
Tapesia Rhois Fairman.

HYSTERIINEAE
Gloniopsis cookeana (Gerard) Sacc.
Lophodermium petiolicola Fckl.

PERISPORIALES
Microthyrium microscopicum Desm.
⎰Sphaerotheca Humuli (DC.) Burrill. †
⎱Sphaerotheca pruinosa C. & P.

DOTHIDEALES
⎰Dothidea Rhois (S.) Fr.
Phyllachora Rhois (S.) Sacc.
⎱Xyloma Rhois S.

SPHAERIALES
⎰Anthostoma atrofuscum (B. & C.) Berl. &
   Vogl.
Diatrype atrofusca (B. & C.) Cke.
Fuckelia atrofusca Herb. Berk.
Melogramma atrofuscum B. & C.
Rosellinia atrofusca (B. & C.) Starb.
⎱Sphaeria atrofusca B. & C.
Botryosphaeria berengeriana De Not.
Calospora aculeans (S.) Sacc..
Didymosphaeria major Ell. & Ev.
Didymosphaeria rhoina Ell. & Ev.
Dimerosporium pulchrum Sacc.
⎰Eutypa elevans (S.) Cke.
Eutypella elevans (S.) Berl.
⎱Sphaeria elevans S.

Leptosphaeria rhoina Ell. & Ev.
Lophidium confertum Ell. & Ev.
Physalospora Cydoniae Arnaud.
⎰Physalospora subsimplex (S.) Sacc.
⎱Sphaeria subsimplex S.
Pleonectria virens Hark., var. chrysogramma
   Ell. & Ev.
⎰Quaternaria Persoonii Tul., var. americana
   (Fr.) Farl.
⎱Sphaeria quaternata P., var. americana Fr.
Rosellinia ligniaria (Grev.) Nits.
⎰Sphaerella nigredo (S.) Cke.
⎱Sphaeria nigredo S.
Sphaeria Aucupariae, var. *g* S.
Sphaeria Rhois S.
Thyridium pallidum Ell. & Ev.
Valsa ambiens (P.) ex Fr.

SPHAEROPSIDALES
Aposphaeria fuscomaculans Sacc.
Cytospora rhoina Fr.
Diplodia natalensis Evans.
Diplodia Rhois Sacc.
Diplodia subsolitaria (S.) Curr.
⎰Botryosphaeria Sumachi (S.) Cke.
Haplosporella Sumachi (S.) Ell. & Ev.
Sphaeria rhoina S.
Sphaeria Sumachi S.
Sphaeropsis rhoina (S.) Starb.
Sphaeropsis Sumachi (S.) C. & E.
⎰Haplosporella rhoina Dearness & Barthol.
Haplosporella Sumachi (S.) Ell. & Ev. var.
   microspora Petrak & Syd.
Hendersonia glabra Cke.
⎰Phoma pulchella (B. & C.) Sacc.
⎱Sphaeropsis pulchella B. & C.
⎰Septoria rhoina Sacc.
⎱Septoria Rhois B. & C.
Sphaeronema pruinosum Pk.
Sphaeropsis Frostii B. & C.

MELANCONIALES
Hainesia rhoina Ell. & Sacc.
Leptostroma rhoina S.
Libertella olivacea Patterson.
⎰Myxosporium Rhois Sacc.
⎱Naemaspora Rhoidis B. & C.
Pestalozzia fibriseda Ell. & Barthol.

HYPHOMYCETES
Ceratosporium fuscescens S.
Cercospora Bartholomaei Ell. & Kellerm.
Cercospora rhoina C. & E.
Cladosporium aromaticum Ell. & Ev.
Cryptocoryneum fasciculatum Fckl.
Sarcinella heterospora Sacc.
⎰Sporocybe Rhois B. & C.
⎱Stilbum Rhois B. & C.
Stemphylium Fuligo B. & C.

Rhus glabra (*cont.*)

MISCELLANEA

Calocera palmata Schum. ex Fr.
Exidia applanata S.
Irpiciporus lacteus (Fr.) Murrill.
Sclerotium petiolorum S.

Rhus integrifolia Benth. & Hook.

Didymosporium Rhoinum Ell. & Ev.
Harknessia rhoina Ell. & Ev.
{ Homostegia rhoina Ell. & Ev.
{ Telimena rhoina (Ell. & Ev.) Theissen & Syd.
Phaeangium sphaeroides Ell. & Ev.
Phyllosticta rhoiseda Fairman.

Rhus lanceolata (Gray) Britt.

Cercospora rhoina Ell. & Ev.

Rhus laurina Nutt.

Hysterographium prominens (Phil. & Hark.)
    Berl. & Vogl.
Metasphaeria anisometra (Cke. & Hark.)
    Sacc.
Phaeangium sphaeroides Ell. & Ev.
Poria vaporaria Fr.
{ Briardia nigerrima Ell. & Ev.
{ Xylogramma nigerrimum (Ell. & Ev.) Rehm.

Rhus

(Schmalzia malacophylla Greene.)
Pileolaria Toxicodendri (B. & Rav.) Arth.

Rhus mexicana Gray.

{ Pileolaria extensa Arth.
{ Uromyces extensus (Arth.) Syd.

Rhus mollis H. B. K.

{ Pileolaria mexicana Arth.
{ Uromyces propinquus Syd.
Uromyces patzcuarensis Holw.

Rhus pumila Michx.

Cercospora rhoina C. & E.

Rhus rhomboidea Small.

Discospora effusa (Pk.) Arth.

Rhus schmideloides Schl.

Pileolaria patzcuarensis (Holw.) Arth.

Rhus Toxicodendron L.

(Including Rhus radicans).

ASCOMYCETES

{ Botryosphaeria ambigua (S.) Sacc.
{ Melogramma ambiguum (S.) Rav.
{ Sphaeria ambigua S.
Botryosphaeria berengeriana De Not.
{ Calospora gemmata (B. & C.) Sacc.
{ Cryptospora gemmata (B. & C.) Ell. & Ev.
{ Valsa gemmata B. & C.
{ Diaporthe Peckii Sacc.
{ Diaporthe sparsa Pk.
Diaporthe rhoina (C. & E.) Ell. & Ev.
Diatrype Maclurae Ell. & Ev.
{ Diatrype Rhois (S.) Cke.
{ Diatrypella Rhois (S.) Ell. & Ev.
{ Sphaeria Rhois S.
Dothidea rhoina S.

{ Dothidea Toxici S.
{ Ectostroma Toxici (S.) M. A. Curtis.
{ Xyloma Toxicodendri S.
Hypoxylon discoideum Ell. & Ev.
{ Lophiostoma radicans Ell. & Ev.
{ Lophiostoma vagabundum Ell. & Ev.
{ Lophiotrema radicans (Ell. & Ev.) Sacc.
{ Lophiotrema vagabundum, var. radicans (Ell.
    & Ev.) Berl.
Phyllactinia corylea (P.) ex Karst.
{ Rosellinia aquila (Fr.) De Not.
{ Sphaeria aquila Fr.
Sphaerostilbe cinnabarina Tul.
{ Hysterium rufulum Spreng.
{ Tryblidiella rufula (Spreng.) Sacc.
Melogramma Toxici (S.) Cke.
Sphaeria Toxici S.
Valsa Toxici (S.) B.
Valsaria Toxici (S.) Sacc.

UREDINALES

{ Caeomurus Terebinthi O. Kuntze p. p.
{ Pileolaria brevipes B. & Rav.
{ Pileolaria Terebinthi Auct. Amer.
{ Pileolaria Toxicodendri (B. & Rav.) Arth.
{ Trichobasis Toxicodendri B. & Rav.
{ Uredo Terebinthi Auct. Amer.
{ Uredo Toxicodendri B. & Rav.
{ Uromyces brevipes (B. & Rav.) Pazschke.
{ Uromyces Terebinthi Auct. Amer.
{ Uromyces Toxicodendri B. & Rav.
Discospora effusa (Pk.) Arth.

BASIDIOMYCETES

Exidia glandulosa (Bull.) ex Fr.
{ Hydnum Rhois S.
{ Steccherinum Rhois (S.) Banker.
Irpex lacteus Fr.
{ Polyporus dryadeus (P.) ex Fr.
{ Polyporus scruposus Fr.
Polyporus floridanus B.
Polyporus gilvus S.
Poria inermis Ell. & Ev.
Xerotus nigrita Lév.

SPHAEROPSIDALES

Botryodiplodia compressa (Cke.) Sacc., var.
    Toxicodendri Dearness.
Dothiorella radicans Ell. & Ev.
Dothiorella toxica Ell. & Ev.
Haplosporella Burnhami Dearness.
Phlyctaena albocincta Ell. & Ev.
Phyllosticta Iridis Ell. & Ev.
Phyllosticta rhoicola Ell. & Ev.
Phyllosticta toxica Ell. & Martin.
Phyllosticta Toxicodendri Thm.
Septoria rhoina B. & C.
Vermicularia toxica Ell. & Ev. nom. nud.
Zythia rhoina Ell. & Ev.

Rhus Toxicodeendron (*cont.*)

MELANCONIALES

Coryneum Rhois Halsted.
{ Cylindrosporium irregulare (Pk.) Dearness.
{ Cylindrosporium Toxicodendri (Ell. & Martin) Ell. & Ev.
Gloeosporium Toxicodendri Ell. & Martin.
Marssonia Toxicodendri (Ell. & Martin) Sacc.
{ Marssonina Toxicodendri (Ell. & Martin) Magn.
Phleospora irregularis (Pk.) Bubák.
Septoria irregularis Pk.
{ Septoria Toxicodendri M. A. Curtis nom. nud.
{ Septoria Toxicodendri (Ell. & Martin) Martin.
Didymosporium corticale S.
{ Hainesia Lythri (Desm.) v. Höhnel.
{ Pezizella Lythri Shear & Dodge.
{ Sclerotiopsis concava (Desm.) Shear & Dodge.
Hainesia rhoina (Sacc.) Ell. & Sacc.
Melanconium cellulosum B. & C.
Pestalozzia toxica Ell. & Ev.

HYPHOMYCETES

Cercospora Bartholomaei Ell. & Kellerm.
Cercospora rhoina C. & E.
Cercospora Toxicodendri Ell.
{ Dematium crucigerae S.
{ Podosporium rigidum S.
Exosporium pallidum Ell. & Ev.
Macrosporium commune Rabh.
Tubercularia Rhois Halsted.
Tubercularia vulgaris Tode ex Fr.

Rhus typhina L.

ASCOMYCETES

{ Calospora aculeans (S.) Sacc.
{ Cryptospora aculeans (S.) Ell. & Ev.
{ Diaporthe inornata Pk.
{ Sphaeria aculeans S.
{ Valsa aculeans (S.) B.
{ Valsa stilbostoma Fung. Car.
Calospora rhoina (C. & E.) Sacc.
{ Cryptosporella leptasca (Pk. & Clinton) Sacc.
{ Flageoletia leptasca (Pk. & Clinton) v. Höhnel.
{ Valsa leptasca Pk. & Clinton.
Cucurbitaria typhina Ell. & Ev.
Endothia parasitica (Murrill) P. J. & H. W. Anderson.
{ Eutypa Acharii Tul.
{ Sphaeria eutypa Fr.
Exoascus purpurascens (Ell. & Ev.) Sadebeck.
Hysterium Rhois S.
Nectria cinnabarina (Tode) ex Fr.
Physalospora Cydoniae Arnaud.
{ Physalospora Cydoniae Auct. Amer.
{ Physalospora Malorum Shear et al.
Sphaeria mucida Fr., var. rostellata S.

{ Sphaerotheca Humuli (DC.) Burrill. †
{ Sphaerotheca pruinosa C. & P.
Thyridium pallidum Ell. & Ev.

BASIDIOMYCETES

Irpex lacteus Fr.
{ Bjerkandera adusta (Willd.) Karst.
{ Polyporus adustus (Willd.) Fr.
Poria incrassata (B. & C.) Burt.
{ Schizophyllum alneum (L.) ex Schrt.
{ Schizophyllum commune Fr.

FUNGI IMPERFECTI

Ceratosporium fuscescens S.
Cercospora rhoina C. & E.
Cladosporium herbarum (Lk.) ex Fr.
Cladosporium nervale Ell. & Dearness.
Coryneum Rhois Halsted.
Cytospora grandis Pk.
Cytospora rhoina Fr.
Cytospora Rhois-hirtae L. W. Nutt.
{ Hainesia Lythri (Desm.) v. Höhnel.
{ Sclerotiopsis concava (Desm.) Shear & Dodge.
Helminthosporium Arbuscula B. & C.
{ Myxosporium Rhois (B. & C.) Sacc.
{ Naemaspora Rhois B. & C.
Phoma pulchella (B. & C.) Sacc.
Phyllosticta Iridis Ell. & Ev.
Rhabdospora rhoina Pk.
Septoria irregularis Pk.
{ Septoria rhoina Sacc.
{ Septoria Rhois B. & C.
Sphaeropsis pallida Pk.
Sphaeropsis Sambuci Pk.
{ Haplosporella Sumachi (S.) Ell. & Ev.
{ Sphaeropsis Sumachi (S.) C. & E.
{ Sporocybe Rhois B. & C. (Lichen.)
{ Stilbum Rhois B. & C.
Torula dimidiata Penz.
Tubercularia floccosa Lk.
Tubercularia vulgaris Tode ex Fr.

Rhus Vernix L.
{ Aposphaeria fibriseda (C. & E.) Sacc.
{ Phoma fibriseda C. & E.
{ Botryosphaeria venenata (C. & E.) Sacc.
{ Dothidea venenata C. & E.
Melogramma fuliginosum Ell. p. p.
{ Calospora aculeans (S.) Sacc.
{ Diaporthe albovelata (B. & C.) Sacc.
{ Sphaeria aculeans S.
{ Sphaeria rufescens S.
{ Valsa aculeans (S.) B.
{ Valsa albovelata B. & C.
{ Valsa rhoiphila C. & E.
{ Valsa rufescens (S.) M. A. Curtis.
{ Calospora rhoina (C. & E.) Sacc.
{ Diaporthe confusa Ell. & Ev.
{ Diaporthe rhoina (C. & E.) Ell. & Ev.
{ Diatrype rhoina C. & E.

Rhus Vernix (*cont.*)
  Cercospora infuscans Ell. & Ev.
  Cercospora rhoina C. & E.
  Corticium colliculosum B. & C.
  Diatrype Duriaei Mont.
  {Eutypella goniostoma (S.) Sacc.
  {Valsa goniostoma (S.) M. A. Curtis.
  {Fuckelia Morsei (B. & C.) Cke.
  {Hypoxylon Morsei B. & C.
  {Lachnella theioidea (C. & E.) Sacc.
  {Peziza thcioidca C. & E.
  Phyllosticta rhoina Kalchbr. & Cke.
  Polyporus pargamenus Fr.
  Polyporus versicolor L. ex Fr.
  Radulum orbiculare Fr.
  Schizophyllum commune Fr.
  {Dermatea carnea C. & E., var. pallida Ell.
  {Dermatea pallida Cke. in N. A. F.
  {Dermatea pallidula Cke.
  {Scleroderris pallidula (Cke.) Sacc.
  Scoriomyces Cragini Ell. & Sacc.
  Sphaeronema pruinosum Pk.
  Sphaeropsis fibriseda C. & E.
  Stereum rameale S.
  Zygodesmus rudis Ell.

Rhus virens Lindheim.
  Coniothyrium Rhois Tharp.

Rhus sp. indet.
  ?{Botryodiplodia compressa (Cke.) Sacc.
  {Diplodia compressa Cke.
  Botryosphaeria fuliginosa (M. & N.) Ell. & Ev.
  Calonectria chlorinella (Cke.) Sacc.
  Corticium lacteum Fr.
  {Dendrophoma pruinosum (Fr.) Sacc.
  {Sphaeria Ligustri S.
  {Sphaeria pruinosa Fr.
  Dicoccum minutissimum Cda.
  Diplodia fibriseda (C. & E.) Fll.
  Eutypella stellulata (Fr.) Sacc.
  Gloeosporium rhoinum Sacc.
  Hypoxylon perforatum (S.) Fr.
  Hypoxylon quadratum (S.) Ell. & Ev.
  Hysterium pulicare P. ex Fr.
  Hysterographium Mori (S.) Rehm.
  Lophiostoma triseptatum Pk.
  Lophium leptothecium Earle.
  Macrophoma rhoina (S.) Sacc.
  Microcera coccophila Desm.
  {Chilonectria Coryli (Fckl.) Ell. & Ev.
  {Creonectria Coryli (Fckl.) Seaver.
  {Nectria Cucurbitula N. A. F. *159.*
  {Chilonectria Cucurbitula (Tode ex Fr.) Sacc.
  {Nectria Cucurbitula (Tode) ex Fr.
  Peziza triformis Fr.
  {Diplodia subsolitaria (S.) Curr.
  {Physalospora subsolitaria (S.) Sacc.
  {Sphaeria subsolitaria S.
  Poria cocos Wolf.

  Poria Medulla-panis (P. ex Fr.) Cke.
  Pseudovalsa subrufa Ell. & Ev.
  {Radulum orbiculare Fr.
  {?Sistrema digitatum S. Syn. Car. 958.
  Rosellinia pulveracea (Ehrh. ex Fr.) Fckl.
  Schizoparme straminea Shear.
  Teichospora rhypodes Ell. & Ev.
  {Sphaeria livida (P.) ex Fr.
  {Thyridium lividum (P. ex Fr.) Sacc.
  Thyronectria virens Hark.
  Tryblidium occidentale Earle.
  Tubercularia dubia Lk.

Amphipterygium amplifolium Hemsl. & Rose.
  Phyllactinia corylea (P.) ex Karst.
  Phyllosticta Amphipterygii Ricker.

CYRILLACEAE

Cliftonia ligustrina Bank.
  {Lembosia Cliftoniae Tracy & Earle.
  {Morenoella Cliftoniae (Tracy & Earle) Theis-
  { sen.
  Pestalozzia Cliftoniae Tracy & Earle.

Cyrilla racemiflora L.
  Aecidium Cyrillae Arth.
  {Botryosphaeria abrupta B. & C. in Herb. B.
  { sec. Cke.
  {Sphaeria abrupta B. & C.
  {Chaetosphaeria flavidocompta (B. & C.) Sacc.
  {Sphaeria flavidocompta B. & C.
  {Diatrype leioplaca Fr.
  {Eutypa leioplaca (Fr.) Cke.
  Glenospora Curtisii B. & Desm.
  {Glonium chlorinum (B. & C.) Sacc.
  {Glonium Cyrillae (B. & C.) Sacc.
  {Hysterium chlorinum B. & C.
  {Hysterium Cyrillae B. & C.
  {Byssosphaeria rhodospila (B. & C.) Cke.
  {Heterotrichia rhodospila (B. & C.) Sacc.
  {Sphaeria rhodospila B. & C.
  Hypocrea citrina (P.) ex Fr.
  Lophodermium cyrillicola Tracy & Earle.
  Phyllosticta Cyrillae Ell. & Martin.
  {Polyporus contiguus (P.) ex Fr.
  {Poria contigua (P. ex Fr.) Karst.
  {Hypoxylon mammiforme (P. ex Fr.) B.
  {Rosellinia mammiformis (P. ex Fr.) Ces. &
  { De Not.
  {Sphaeria mammiformis P. ex Fr.
  Sphaeria assecla S.
  Stilbum cinereorubrum B. & C.
  Torula aequalis B. & C.
  {Conisphaeria cyrillicola (B. & C.) Cke.
  {Melanomma cyrillicola (B. & C.) Sacc.
  {Sphaeria cyrillicola B. & C.
  {Zignoella cyrillicola (B. & C.) Berl.

AQUIFOLIACEAE

Ilex brasiliensis Loes.
    Puccinia infuscans Arth. & Holw.

Ilex Cassine L.
    Aschersonia columnifera Petch.
    Aschersonia cubensis B. & C.
    Asterina orbicularis Ell.
    Phyllosticta terminalis Ell. & Martin.

Ilex Cassine L., var. **myrtifolia** (Walt.) Sarg.
    Dimerosporium ilicinum Cke.

Ilex decidua Walt.
    Amerosporium ilicinum Ell. & Ev.
    { Cenangella Ravenelii (B. & C.) Sacc.
    { Tympanis Ravenelii B. & C.
    { Diatrype friabilis (P. ex Fr.) M. A. Curtis.
    { Diatrypella friabilis (P. ex Fr.) Ell. & Ev.
    { Sphaeria friabilis P. ex Fr.
    Fusarium helotioides B. & C.
    Microsphaera Alni (DC.) Wint. †
    Phyllactinia suffulta (Reb.) ex Sacc.
    Phyllosticta concomitans Ell. & Ev.
    { Rhytisma ilicincola (S.) Fr.
    { Xyloma ilicincola S.
    { Rhytisma velatum (S.) Fr.
    { Xyloma velatum S.

Ilex glabra (L.) Gray.
    { Asterina Ilicis Ell.
    { Microphyma Ilicis (Ell.) Speg.
    Capnodium Citri B. & Desm.
    Capnodium elongatum B. & Desm.
    Cenangium tuberculiforme Ell. & Ev.
    Cercospora Ilicis Ell.
    Dermatea olivacea Ell.
    { Diaporthe Badhami (Curr.) Sacc.
    { Diatrype Badhami Curr.
    { ?Diaporthe ocularia (C. & E.) Sacc.
    { ?Valsa ocularia C. & E.
    { Lembosia Ilicis Tracy & Earle.
    { Morenoella Ilicis (Tracy & Earle) Theissen.
    Nectria punicea (Schm.) ex Fr.
    { Creonectria rubicarpa (Cke.) Seaver.
    { Nectria rubicarpa Cke.
    Phacidium sphaeroideum C. & E.
    Sphaerella Ilicis Ell.
    Sphaerella Prini Cke.
    { Sphaerographium stellatum (Ell.) Sacc.
    { Sphaeronema stellatum Ell.
    Stereum ochraceoflavum (S.) M. A. Curtis.
    Valsa cercophora Ell.

Ilex laevigata (Pursh) Gray.
    { Dermatella Ravenelii (B. & C.) Pazschke.
    { Tympanis Ravenelii B. & C.

Ilex idluca (Ait.) Torr. & Gr.
    { Asterina orbicularis B. & C.
    { Dimerosporium orbiculare (B. & C.) Martin.
    { Englerulaster orbicularis (B. & C.) v. Höhnel.
    Asterina pelliculosa B.
    Capnodium elongatum B. & Desm.

Dimerium nigrosporum Miles.
{ Aulographum angustiforme (Tracy & Earle)
    Theissen.
{ Lembosia angustiformis Tracy & Earle.
{ Morenoella angustiformis (Tracv & Earle)
    Theissen.
{ Lembosia prinoides Tracy & Earle.
{ Morenoella prinoides (Tracy & Earle) Theis-
    sen.
Patellaria cyanea Ell. & Martin nec Cke.
{ Poria albocincta Cke. & Massee.
{ Poria Fuligo B. & Br., var. aurantiotingens Ell.
    & Macbr.
{ Tinctoporia albocincta (Cke. & Massee) Mur-
    rill.
Porogramme aurantiotingens (Ell. & Macbr.)
    Pat., var. crassa Pat.
{ Peltistroma juruanum Henn.
{ Rhytisma atramentarium B. & C.
{ Winteria lobata Tracy & Earle.
{ Winterina lobata (Tracy & Earle) Sacc. & Syd.

Ilex montana Griseb.
    { Dictyopanus subpulverulentus (B. & C.) Pat.
    { Polyporus subpulverulentus B. & C.

Ilex monticola Gray, var. **mollis** (Gray) Brit.
    Microsphaera Alni (DC.) Wint. †
    Ramularia Prini Pk.
    { Rhytisma Prini (S.) Fr.
    { Xyloma Prini S.

Ilex nitida (Vahl) Maxim.
    Englerulaster asperulispora (Gaill.) Theissen.
    Helminthosporium glabroides F. L. Stevens.
    Meliola maricaensis F. L. Stevens.

Ilex opaca Ait.

PEZIZINEAE

Cenangium microspermum Sacc. & Ell.
{ Peziza Aquifoliae C. & E.
{ Pezizella Aquifoliae (C. & E.) Sacc.
Tympanis picastra B. & C.

PHACIDIINEAE

{ Phacidium elegantissimum B. & C.
{ Tridens elegantissimum (B. & C.) Massee.
Phacidium Ilicis Lib.
Phacidium multivalve (DC.) ex Fr.
Peltistroma juruanum Henn.
Rhytisma atramentarium B. & C.
Rhytisma Curtisii B. & Rav.
Rhytisma Ilicis B. & Rav.
Rhytisma Ilicis-canadensis S.
Rhytisma velatum (S.) Fr.

HYSTERIINEAE

Aulographum vagum Desm.

HEMISPHAERIACEAE

{ Asterina cuticulosa Cke.
{ Microthyriella cuticulosa (Cke.) v. Höhnel.
{ Microthyrium cuticulosum (Cke.) v. Höhnel.

Ilex opaca (*cont.*)
Asterina Ilicis Ell.
{ Asterina orbicularis B. & C.
{ Dimerosporium orbiculare (B. & C.) Martin.
{ Englerulaster orbicularis (B. & C.) v. Höhnel.
Asterina pelliculosa B.

ERYSIPHACEAE

Phyllactinia corylea (P.) ex Karst.
Saccardia Martini Ell. & Sacc.

SPHAERIALES

{ Amerodothis Ilicis (Cke.) Theissen & Syd.
{ Bagnisiella Ilicis (Cke.) Sacc.
{ Dothidea Ilicis Cke.
{ Calosphaeria subcuticularis (C. & E.) Ell. & Ev.
{ Valsa didymospora Ell.
{ Valsa subcuticularis C. & E.
{ Diaporthe cercophora (Ell.) Sacc.
{ Valsa cercophora Ell.
{ Diatrypella nigro-annulata (Grev.) Nits.
{ Valsa angulata Fr.
{ Diatrype opaca Cke.
{ Diatrypella opaca Cke.
Hypoxylon fuscum (P.) ex Fr.
Hypoxylon perforatum (S.) Fr.
Metasphaeria Ilicis Ell. & Ev.
{ Diplodia ilicicola Desm.
{ Diplodia Ilicis (Schleich.) ex Fr.
{ Phoma ilicicola (Desm.) Sacc.
{ Phyllosticta ilicicola (Desm.) Ell. & Ev.
{ Physalospora Ilicis (Schleich. ex Fr.) Sacc.
{ Sphaeria Ilicis (Schleich.) ex Fr.
{ Laestadia philoprina (B. & C.) Cke.
{ Physalospora philoprina (B. & C.) Sacc.
{ Sphaeria philoprina B. & C.
Sphaerella ilicella Cke.
Valsa dissepta Fr.

BASIDIOMYCETES

Clitocybe tabescens (Scop.) Bres.
{ Aecidium ilicinum Ell. & Ev.
{ Melampsoropsis ilicinum Arth.
Pilacre Petersii B. & C.
Polyporus dibaphus B. & C.
{ Coriolus ilicincola (B. & C.) Murrill.
{ Polyporus ilicicola B. & C.
{ Polystictus ilicicola (B. & C.) Cke.
Poria incrassata (B. & C.) Burt.

FUNGI IMPERFECTI

Cercospora ilicicola Maubl.
Cercospora Ilicis Maubl.
Cercospora pulvinata C. & E.
Chaetophoma ilicifolia Cke.
Discosia deflectens Sacc.
Discosia minima B. & C.
Fusicoccum ilicinum Ell. & Ev.

Heliscus lugdunensis Sacc.
Leptothyrium foraminulatum Sacc. & Ell.
{ Macrophoma phacidiella (C. & E.) Berl. & Vogl.
{ Phoma phacidiella (C. & E.) Sacc.
{ Sphaeropsis phacidiella C. & E.
Pestalozzia stellata B. & C.
Phoma Ilicis Desm., var. Ilicis-opacae Sacc.
Phyllosticta opaca Ell. & Ev.
Phyllosticta terminalis Ell. & Martin.
{ Septoria stemmatea (Fr.) B.
{ Sphaeria stemmatea Fr.
Sporonema Ilicis Earle.
Ilex paraguayensis Hook.
Acanthonitschkea argentinensis Speg.
Ilex verticillata (L.) Gray.
Diaporthe binoculata (Ell.) Sacc.
Diaporthe binoculata (Ell.) Sacc., var. Ilicis Ell. & Ev.
{ Diaporthe epimicta Ell. & Ev.
{ Diatrype Badhami N. A. F. *495.* nec Curr.
Diaporthe ocularia (C. & E.) Sacc.
Diaporthe oxyspora (Pk.) Sacc.
Glenospora Curtisii B. & Desm.
Gloeosporium niveum J. J. Davis.
Hormomyces aurantiacus Bon.
Hypoxylon callostroma (S.) B.
Irpex lacteus Fr.
Micropera caespitosa (Pk.) Archer.
Micropera endoleuca Sacc.
Microsphaera Alni (DC.) Wint. †
Peniophora cinerea (P. ex Fr.) Cke.
Phyllosticta Haynaldi Roum.
Phyllosticta Prini Pk.
Poria ferruginosa (Schrad. ex Fr.) Cke.
Poria inermis Ell. & Ev.
Ramularia Alaterni Thm.
Ramularia Prini Pk.
Rhytisma concavum Ell. & Kellerm.
Rhytisma Ilicis-canadensis S.
Rhytisma Ilicis-canadensis S., var. verticillata Ell. & Ev.
Rhytisma Prini (S.) Fr.
{ Rosellinia prinicola (B. & C.) Sacc.
{ Sphaeria prinicola B. & C.
Sphaeronema caespitosum Pk.
Trichothecium roseum Lk.
Tympanis stictica B. & C.
Ilex vomitoria Ait.
Tryblidium hysterinum Duf.
Ilex sp. indet.
{ Alternaria fasciculata (C. & E.) Jones & Grout.
{ Macrosporium fasciculatum C. & E.
{ Amerosporium microsporum (C. & E.) Sacc.
{ Excipula microspora C. & E.
{ Anthostomella nigrotecta (B. & Rav.) Sacc.
{ Sphaeria nigrotecta B. & Rav.
Aschersonia basicystis B. & C.
Aschersonia goldiana Sacc. & Ell.
Belonium consanguineum Ell. & Ev.

Ilex sp. indet. (*cont.*)
  Coniothyrium ilicinum Ell. & F. W. Anderson.
  Corticium cremoricolor B. & C.
  Cytospora leucosperma (P.) ex Fr.
  Dactylium roseum (Lk.) B.
  Dothiora asterinospora (Ell. & Ev.) Sacc.
  Lembosia brevis Tracy & Earle.
  Mystrosporium orbiculare C. & E.
  Nectria ditissima Tul.
  Pestalozzia annulata B. & C.
  Phoma ilicina Ell. & F. W. Anderson.
  { Diplodia gossypina Cke.
  { Physalospora gossypina N. E. Stevens.
  Septoria examinans B. & C.
  Septoria ilicifolia C. & E.
  Sporoschisma Tracyi Earle.
  Valsa ceratophora Tul.

Nemopanthus mucronata (L.) Trel.
  { Cenangium peckianum Rehm.
  { Tympanis Nemopanthis N. A. F. *3042.*
  Curreya peckiana Sacc.
  Diaporthe binoculata (Ell.) Sacc., var. Ilicis
    Ell. & Ev.
  { Diaporthe oxyspora (Pk.) Sacc.
  { Valsa oxyspora Pk.
  { Godronia Nemopanthis (Pk.) Sacc.
  { Tympanis Nemopanthis Pk.
  Microsphaera Nemopanthis Pk.
  Poria inermis Ell. & Ev.
  Ramularia Nemopanthis Pk.
  { Rhytisma canadensis Pk.
  { Rhytisma Ilicis-canadensis S.
  { Sphaeronema caespitosum Pk.
  { Sphaeronema Nemopanthes Ell. & Ev.
  { Sphaeronema Peckii Sacc. & Syd.
  Stemphylium Nemopanthes Dearness.
  Stigmella Nemopanthis Dearness.

CELASTRACEAE

Evonymus americanus L.
  Cercospora Euonymi Ell.
  Phyllosticta Euonymi Sacc.
  Verticillium heterocladum Penz.

Evonymus atropurpureus Jacq.
  Cercospora Euonymi Ell.
  Diaporthe Euonymi Dearness.
  Haplosporella Euonymi Ell. & Ev.
  Hendersonia staphylea Ell. & Ev.
  Marasmius concinnus Ell. & Ev.
  { Marssonia thomasiana Sacc.
  { Marssonina thomasiana (Sacc.) Magn.
  { Septogloeum thomasianum (Sacc.) v. Höhnel.
  Microsphaera Alni (DC.) Wint. †
  Microsphaera Euonymi (DC.) Sacc. †
  Phoma weldiana Fairman.
  Phyllosticta Euonymi Sacc. 1878.
  Phyllosticta Euonymi Tharp. 1917.
  Ramularia Euonymi Ell. & Kellerm.

Septoria atropurpurei Tehon.
Septoria Evonymi Rabh.
Solenia ochracea Hoffm. ex Fr.
Uncinula macrospora Pk.?

Evonymus europaeus L.
  Diplodia Euonymi Westd.
  Phyllosticta pallens Ell. & Ev.
  Septoria Evonymi Rabh.

Evonymus japonicus Thunb.
  Cercospora destructiva Rav.
  { Ceuthospora foliicola Lib.
  { Cytospora foliicola, var. Euonymi Cke.
  Cicinnobolus Cesatii DBy.
  Cladosporium fasciculatum Cda., var. densum
    Cke.
  Cladosporium punctulatum Sacc. & Ell.
  Colletotrichum griseum Heald & Wolf.
  Diplodia Euonymi Westd.
  Exosporium concentricum Heald & Wolf.
  Gibberella pulicaris Sacc.
  Oidium Euonymi-japonici (Arcang.) Sacc.
  { Pestalozzia Euonymi Vize.
  { Pestalozzia Planimi Vize.
  Zygosporium oscheoides Mont.

Evonymus occidentalis Nutt.
  Ramularia Euonymi Ell. & Kellerm.

Evonymus vulgaris Scop.
  Cercospora Euonymi Ell.

Evonymus sp. indet.
  Exosporium concentricum Heald & Wolf.
  Gibberella Euonymi (Fckl.) Sacc.
  Gloeosporium frigidum Sacc.
  { Metasphaeria californica (Cke. & Hark.) Berl.
  { Sphaeria californica Cke. & Hark.
  { Creonectria purpurea (L.) Seaver.
  { Nectria cinnabarina (Tode) ex Fr.
  { Cucurbitaria seriata Pk.
  { Otthia seriata (Pk.) Sacc.
  Ozonium omnivorum Shear.
  { Phyllosticta Euomymi N. A. F. *2675* non Sacc.
  { Septoria spiculispora Ell. & Ev.
  Septoria evonymella Pass.
  { Sirodesmium Fumago (Cke.) Sacc.
  { Sporidesmium Fumago Cke.

Celastrus scandens L.
  { Asteridium Celastri (Ell. & Kellerm.) Sacc.
  { Asterina Celastri Ell. & Kellerm.
  { Microthyriella (?) Celastri (Ell. & Kellerm.)
    Theissen.
  { Botryodiplodia Celastri (Cke.) Sacc.
  { Diplodia Celastri Cke.
  Botryosphaeria Hibisci (S.) Sacc.
  { Camarosporium abnormale (Pk.) Sacc.
  { Hendersonia abnormalis Pk.
  Cercospora melanochaeta Ell. & Ev.
  { Clypeosphaeria mamillana (Fr.) Lambotte.
  { Sphaeria mamillana Fr.
  Coniosporium subcorticale Dearness & Barthol.
  Corticium comedens B. & C.

Celastrus scandens (*cont.*)
Cortinarius rubripes Kauffman.
Coryneum pithoideum Dearness & House.
Cytospora Celastri Clements.
Cytospora celastrina Ell. & Barthol.
Diaporthe celastrina Ell. & Barthol.
Diatrype celastrina Ell. & Ev.
Diatrype subconfluens (S.) Cke.
Sphaeria subconfluens S.
Didymosporium erumpens S.
Diplodia celastrina Ell. & Ev.
Dothidea collecta (S.) Ell. & Ev.
Dothiorella Celastri Pk.
Exidia lurida S.
Cytoplea propullans (S.) Starb.
Haplosporella propullans (S.) Petrak & Syd.
Sphaeria propullans S.
Sphaeropsis celastrina Pk.
Sphaeropsis propullans (S.) Pk.
Haplosporella propullans (S.) Petrak & Syd.,
  var. velata Ell. & Barthol.
Haplosporella velata Ell. & Barthol.
Labrella Celastri Dearness & House.
Leptothyrium Celastri B. & C.
Melanconis dolosa (Fr.) Sacc.
Sphaeria dolosa Fr.
Valsaria dolosa (Fr.) De Not.
Microsphaera Alni (DC.) Wint. †
Nectria Celastri (S.) Pk.
Sphaeria Celastri S.
Aponectria inaurata (B. & Br.) Sacc.
Nectria inaurata B. & Br.
Phoma pallens B. & C.
Phyllactinia corylea (P.) ex Karst.
Phyllactinia guttata (Wallr. ex Fr.) Lév.
Phyllactinia suffulta (Reb.) ex Sacc.
Phyllosticta Celastri Ell. & Ev.
Physalospora Cydoniae Arnaud.
Ramularia Celastri Ell. & Martin. Dec 1882.
Ramularia Celastri Pk. June 1883.
Sphaeria sarmentorum Fr.
Tubercularia Celastri S.
Tubercularia nigricans (Bull.) ex Lk.

Celastrus sp. indet.
Creonectria purpurea (L.) ex Seaver.
Nectria cinnabarina (Tode) ex Fr.

Maytenus elongata (Urban) Britton.
Scolecopeltis Chardonii Toro.

Gymnosporia spinosa Merrill & Rolfe.
Meliola Gymnosporiae Syd.

?Pachistima Canbyi Gray.
Melasmia alnea Lév.

Pachistima Myrsinites Raf.
Mycosphaerella Pachystimae Dearness.

Elaeodendron xylocarpum DC.
Fumago vagans Fr.

Rhacoma Crossopetalum L.
Meliola compacta Earle.
Meliola conferta Tehon.
Meliola tehoniana Trotter.
Schaefferia frutescens Jacq.
Microthyrium Urbani Bres.

HIPPOCRATEACEAE

Hippocratea volubilis L.
Asterina Hippocrateae Ryan.
Asterinella Hippeastri Ryan.
Calothyrium Hippocratea Ryan.
Pestalozzia funerea Desm.
Botryorhiza Hippocrateae Whetzel & Olive.
Uromyces Hippocrateae (Whetzel & Olive)
  Sacc. & Trott.

STAPHYLEACEAE

Staphylea trifolia L.
Cenangium Staphyleae S.
Clasterosporium ontariense Sacc.
Comatricha Persoonii Rostf.
Stemonitis oblonga Fr.
Coniothyrium Staphyleae Pk.
Creonectria atrofusca (S.) Seaver.
Melogramma atrofuscum (S.) Cke.
Nectria atrofusca (S.) Ell. & Ev.
Pseudodiplodia atrofusca (S.) Starb.
Sphaeria atrofusca S.
Valsaria atrofusca (S.) Sacc.
Diaporthe albocarnis Ell. & Ev.
Diaporthe robergeana (Desm.) Niessl.
Diaporthe staphylina Ell. & Ev.
Didymella lophospora Sacc. & Speg.
Eutypella Staphyleae Dearness & House.
Haplosporella staphylina Ell. & Dearness.
Hendersonia Staphyleae Ell. & Ev.
Hysterium staphylina (Pk.) Dearness & House.
Leptosphaeria rubrotincta Ell. & Ev.
Lophiostoma roseotinctum Ell. & Ev.
Metasphaeria Staphyleae Dearness & House.
Endophlaea staphylina (Pk.) Cke.
Metasphaeria staphylina (Pk.) Sacc.
Sphaeria staphylina Pk.
Ophiobolus staphylinus Ell. & Ev.
Oidium irregulare Pk.
Ovularia irregularis (Pk.) Trelease.
Ovularia isarioides (Ell. & Ev.) Sacc.
Ramularia isarioides Ell. & Ev.
Phyllosticta Staphyleae Dearness.
Otthia staphylina Ell. & Ev.
Otthiella staphylina (Ell. & Ev.) Dearness &
  House.
Plowrightia staphylina Ell. & Ev.
Sacidium vegetans S.
Septoria cirrhosa Wint.
Sphaerella Staphyleae (S.) Cke.
Sphaeria Staphyleae S.

Staphylea trifolia (*cont.*)
  Sphaerella staphylina Ell. & Ev.
  Sphaeropsis Staphyleae Brun.
  ⎰Periconia gracilis S.
  ⎱Sporocybe gracilis (S.) Sacc.
  Stemphylium magnusianum Sacc.
  Stilbospora Staphyleae S.
  Valsaria staphylina Ell. & Ev.
  Vermicularia Staphyleae S.

Turpinia paniculata Vent.
  Helminthosporium Helleri F. L. Stevens.
  Meliola Guignardi Gaill.

ACERACEAE

Acer circinatum Pursh.
  Armillaria mellea (Vahl) ex Fr., var. bullosa?
    Pk.
  Cytospora chrysosperma (P.) ex Fr.
  ⎰Creonectria coccinea (P. ex Fr.) Seaver.
  ⎱Nectria coccinea (P.) ex Fr.
  Nectria galligena Bres.
  Septoria Aceris-macrophylli Pk.
  ⎰Cylindrosporium acerinum Tracy & Earle.
  ⎱Septoria circinata Ell. & Ev.

Acer glabrum Torr.
  Barya parasitica Fckl.
  Cylindrosporium acerinum Tracy & Earle.
  Cylindrosporium consociatum Dearness.
  Cytospora chrysosperma (P.) ex Fr.
  Diatrype bullata (Hoffm.) ex Fr.
  Fomes igniarius (L. ex Fr.) Gill.
  Helotium citrinum (Hedw.) ex Fr.
  Hymenochaete tabacina (Sow. ex Fr.) Lév.
  Lenzites sepiaria (Wulf.) ex Fr.
  Ophiogloea linospora Clements.
  Phyllosticta minima (B. & C.) Underw. &
    Earle.
  Phyllosticta minutissima Ell. & Ev.
  Platystomum Aceris Tracy & Earle.
  Polyporus brumalis (P.) ex Fr.
  Polyporus floridanus Quél.
  Polystictus cinnabarinus (Jacq. ex Fr.) Cke.
  Poria semisupina (B. & C.) Weir.
  Septoria acerina Pk.
  ⎰?Cylindrosporium acerinum Tracy & Earle.
  ⎮?Phleospora curvispora (Ell. & Ev.) Petrak.
  ⎮Septoria circinata Ell. & Ev.
  ⎱Septoria curvispora Ell. & Ev.
  Septoria saccharina, var. occidentalis Ell. & Ev.
  Septoria samarae Pk.
  Uncinula circinata C. & P.

Acer grandidentata Nutt.
  Exoascus Aceris Dearness & Barthol.
  Helminthosporium repente Dearness & Barthol.

Acer interior Brit.
  Septoria Negundinis Ell. & Ev.

Acer macrophyllum Pursh.
  Armillaria mellea (Vahl) ex Fr., var. bulbosa
    Pk.
  Botryosphaeria berengeriana De Not.
  ⎰Botryosphaeria berengeriana (De Not.), var.
  ⎮ acerina Rehm.
  ⎮Botryosphaeria trames (B. & C.) Sacc.
  ⎨Lasiosphaeria trames (B. & C.) Cke.
  ⎮Sphaeria millegrana S. in Herb. Kew.
  ⎮Sphaeria trames B. & C.
  ⎱Trichosphaeria trames (B. & C.) Ell. & Ev.
  Cercosporella Aceris Dearness & Barthol.
  Cercosporella albopunctata Ell. & Ev.
  Chaetophoma atriella Cke. & Hark.
  Diatrypella Frostii Pk.
  Diplodia extensa Cke. & Hark.
  Diplodia subtecta Fr.
  Fomes applanatus (P. ex Wallr.) Gill.
  Fomes igniarius (L. ex Fr.) Gill.
  Hypochnus cervinus Burt.
  Hypocrea contorta (S.) B. & C.
  Hypoderma commune (Fr.) Duby.
  Hypoxylon concurrens B. & C.
  Illosporium maculicola Sacc.
  Massaria inquinans (Tode) ex Fr.
  Melanconium acerinum Ell. & Ev.
  Melanconium magnum B.
  ⎰Melanconium Monotospora (Cke.) Sacc.
  ⎱Stilbospora Monotospora Cke.
  Myriococcum sparsum Hark.
  ⎰Creonectria purpurea (L.) ex Seaver.
  ⎱Nectria cinnabarina (Tode) ex Fr.
  Nectria galligena Bres.
  Peniophora decorticans Burt.
  ⎰Bjerkandera adusta (Willd. ex Fr.) Karst.
  ⎱Polyporus adustus (Willd) ex Fr.
  Polyporus dryadeus (P.) ex Fr.
  Poria contigua (P. ex Fr.) Cke.
  Poria incrassata (B. & C.) Burt.
  ⎰Ceratostoma tinctum Ell. & Ev.
  ⎱Rhynchostoma tinctum (Ell. & Ev.) Berl. &
    Vogl.
  Rhytisma acerinum (P.) ex Fr.
  ⎰Rhytisma punctatum (P.) ex Fr.
  ⎱Rhytisma punctiforme Mayr.
  Septoria Aceris-macrophylli Pk.
  Septoria circinata Ell. & Ev.
  Septoria samarae-Aceris Dearness & Barthol.
  Septoria samarae-macrophylli Dearness &
    Barthol.
  Sphaerella maculiformis (P. ex Fr.) Awd.
  ⎰Steganosporium ovatum (P. ex Fr.) v. Keissler.
  ⎮Steganosporium pyriforme (Hoffm. ex Fr.) Cda.
  ⎱Stilbospora ovata P. ex Fr.
  Thelephora terrestris Ehrh. ex Fr.
  Trichaegum opacum Cke. & Hark.
  Valsa clavigera Dearness & Barthol.
  Valsa exigua Nits.
  Valsaria rubricosa (Fr.) Sacc.

Acer Negundo L.

MYXOMYCETES

Badhamia hyalina (P.) B.
Comatricha pulchella (Bab.) Rostf.
Physarum polymorphum (Mont.) Rostf.
Trichia contorta (Ditm.) Rostf., var. inconspicua (Rostf.) Lister.

PEZIZINEAE

Lachnea setosa (Nees ex Fr.) Sacc.
Patellaria atrata (Hedw.) ex Fr.

PHACIDIINEAE

Phacidium Negundinis Tehon & Daniels.
Rhytisma acerinum (P.) ex Fr.
Rhytisma punctatum (P.) ex Fr.
Stictis linearis C. & E.
Stictis phacidioides (Desm.) Fr.

PYRENOMYCETINEAE

Capnodium salicinum Mont.
{ Cucurbitaria elongata (Fr.) Grev.
{ Cucurbitaria Negundinis Wint.
Diatrype Hochelagae Ell. & Ev.
Dimerosporium pulchrum Sacc. ?
Eutypella angulosa Nits., var. Negundinis Rehm.
Hypoxylon perforatum (S.) Fr.
{ Lophionema crenatum Ell. & Ev.
{ Sphaeria cristata S. Syn. Car. 136.
{ Lophiostoma excipuliforme (Fr.) Ces. & De Not.
{ Sphaeria excipuliformis Fr.
Nectria cinnabarina (Tode) ex Fr.
{ Creonectria verrucosa (S.) Seaver.
{ Nectria verrucosa (S.) Sacc.
Nectria verrucosa (S.) Sacc., var. Aceris Rehm.
{ Coelosphaeria cupularis (P. ex Fr.) Sacc.
{ Cucurbitaria cupularis (P. ex Fr.) Cke.
{ Nitschkia cupularis (P. ex Fr.) Karst.
{ Sphaeria cupularis P. ex Fr.
{ Phyllactinia corylea (P.) ex Karst.
{ Phyllactinia suffulta (Reb.) ex Sacc.
Physalospora Cydoniae Arnaud.
Rosellinia Bigeloviae Ell. & Ev.
Rosellinia Bigeloviae Ell. & Ev., var. Negundinis Ell. & Ev.
Rosellinia Kellermanii Ell. & Ev.
Sphaeria rhodoglea B. & C.
Teichospora clavispora Ell. & Ev.
Teichospora helenae Ell. & Ev.
Teichospora Negundinis Ell. & Ev.
Teichospora pygmaea Ell. & Ev.
{ Valsaria allantospora Ell. & Ev.
{ Valsaria coloradensis Ell. & Ev.
Valsaria moroides (C. & P.) Sacc., var. Aceris Rehm.

HYMENOMYCETINEAE

Fomes annosus (Fr.) Cke.
Fomes applanatus (P. ex Wallr.) Gill.
Fomes scutellatus (S.) Cke.
Ganoderma Curtisii (B.) Murrill.
Lentinus lepideus Fr.
Marasmius Rotula (Scop.) ex Fr.
Mycena corticola (Schum.) ex Fr.
Peniophora cinerascens (S.) Sacc.
Pleurotus ostreatus (Jacq.) ex Fr.
Pleurotus ulmarius (Bull.) ex Fr.
{ Bjerkandera adusta (Willd. ex Fr.) Karst.
{ Polyporus adustus (Willd.) ex Fr.
Polyporus Farlowii Lloyd.
Polyporus Rheades P.
Polyporus squamosus (Huds.) ex Fr.
Polystictus hirsutus (Wulf.) ex Fr.
Polystictus versicolor (L.) ex Fr.
Poria corticola (Fr.) Cke.
Poria pulchella (S.) Cke.
Poria tomentocincta B. & Rav.
Schizophyllum commune Fr.
{ Septobasidium pedicellatum Auct. Amer. non Pat.
{ Septobasidium pseudopedicellatum Burt.
Stereum purpureum P. †
Stereum versicolor (Sw.) ex Fr.
Thelephora terrestris Ehrh. ex Fr.
Trametes Pini (Brot.) ex Fr.
Trametes sepium B.

SPHAEROPSIDALES

Camarosporulum Negundinis (Ell. & Ev.) Tassi.
Coniothyrium Negundinis Tehon & Daniels.
Cytospora annulata Ell. & Ev.
Cytospora hyalosperma Fr.
Cytospora Negundinis Ell. & Ev.
Dinemasporium decipiens (De Not.) Sacc.
Dinemasporium hispidulum (Schrad. ex Fr.) M. A. Curtis.
Diplodia atrata (Desm.) Sacc.
Diplodia lophiostomoides Ell. & Barthol.
Dothiorella Negundinis Ell. & Barthol.
Haplosporella Negundinis Ell. & Barthol.
{ Labrella scripta S.
{ Leptostroma scriptum (S.) Fr.
Leptothyrium maximum Tehon & Daniels.
Macrophoma Negundinis Ell. & Ev.
{ Phleospora Aceris (Lib.) Sacc.
{ Septoria Aceris (Lib.) B. & Br.
Phoma fumosa Ell. & Ev.
Phoma negundinicola Thm.
Phoma negundinicola Thm., var. ramicola Ell. & Ev.
Phyllosticta arida Earle.
Phyllosticta minima (B. & C.) Ell. & Ev.
Phyllosticta Negundinis Sacc. & Speg.

Acer Negundo (*cont.*)
Phyllosticta platanoidis Sacc.
Piggotia Negundinis Ell. & Dearness.
{ Septoria acerella Sacc.
{ Septoria Negundinis Ell. & Ev.
Septoria marginata Heald & Wolf.
Septoria saccharina Ell. & Ev.
Septoria Samarae Pk.
Sphaeronema canum Ell. & Ev.
Sphaeronema Negundinis Ell. & Ev.
Sphaeronema nitidum B. & C.
{ Haplosporella Clintonii (Pk.) Petrak & Syd.
{ Sphaeropsis albescens Ell. & Ev.
{ Sphaeropsis Clintonii Pk.
Sphaeropsis Negundinis Tehon & Daniels.

MELANCONIALES

Coryneum Negundinis B. & C.
Coryneum septosporioides Sacc. & Syd.
Cylindrosporium Negundinis Ell. & Ev.
Gloeosporium apocryptum Ell. & Ev.
{ Gloeosporium apocryptum Ell. & Ev., var.
{   ramicola Ell. & Ev.
Gloeosporium Negundinis Ell. & Ev.
Septogloeum acerinum (Pass.) Sacc.
Septomyxa Negundinis G. H. Martin nom.
  nud.

HYPHOMYCETES

Alternaria Citri Pierce, var. Cerasi C. A.
  Rudolph. ?
Cercospora Negundinis Ell. & Ev.
Coniothecium epidermis Cda.
Dendrodochium nigrescens Ell. & Ev.
{ Fusarium cinnabarinum (B. & C.) Sacc.
{ Fusisporium cinnabarinum B. & C.
Fusarium Negundi Sherbakoff.
Fusarium pyrochroum (Desm.) Sacc.
Fusarium sarcochroum (Desm.) Sacc.
Helminthosporium subcuticulare Ell. & Ev.
Macrosporium negundinicola Ell. & Barthol.
Stilbum aleuriatum B. & C.
Trimmatostroma americanum Thm.
Tubercularia vulgaris Tode ex Fr.

MISCELLANEA

Ozonium omnivorum Shear.
Acer negundo L., var. **californicum** Sarg.
Gloeosporium Negundinis Ell. & Ev.
Phleospora Aceris (Lib.) Sacc.
Phleospora californica Ell. & Ev.
Phoma Lebiseyi Sacc.
Septoria marginata Heald & Wolf.
Acer neomexicanum Greene.
Diatrype albopruinosa (S.) C. & E.
Acer palmatum Thunb.
Polyporus igniarius (L.) ex Fr.
Nectria cinnabarina (Tode) ex Fr.
Phoma Palmarum Sacc.
Rhytisma acerinum (P.) ex Fr.

Acer pennsylvanicum L.
Botryodiplodia acerina Ell. & Ev.
Cylindrosporium acerinum Tracy & Earle.
Cylindrosporium pennsylvanicum Ell. & Ev.
Cytospora exasperans Ell. & Ev.
{ Didymella sphaerellula (Pk.) Sacc.
{ Endophlaea sphaerellula (Pk.) Cke.
{ Sphaeria sphaerellula Pk.
{ Discella obscura B. & C.
{ Discula obscura (B. & C.) Sacc.
Endothia parasitica (Murrill) P. J. & H. W.
  Anderson.
{ Fomes igniarius (L. ex Fr.) Gill.
{ Polyporus igniarius (L.) ex Fr.
Gloeosporium acerinum Westd., var. fructi-
  genum Ell. & Ev.
Gloeosporium apocryptum Ell. & Ev.
Gloeosporium vagans Syd.
Helminthosporium Phomatae Dearness &
  House.
{ Hypoderma rufilabrum (B. & C.) Duby.
{ Hysterium rufilabrum B. & C.
Hypoxylon cohaerens (P.) ex Fr.
{ Irpex laeteus Fr.
{ Polyporus tulipiferus (S.) Lloyd.
Lentinus haematopus B.
Leptostroma acerinum S.
{ Macrosporium concinnum B. & Br.
{ Sporidesmium concinnum (B. & Br.) B.
{ Diaporthe subaquila (B. & C.) Sacc.
{ Melogramma subaquilum B. & C.
{ Myrmaecium subaquilum (B. & C.) Ell. & Ev.
Nectria coccinea (P.) ex Fr.
Phleospora Aceris (Lib.) Sacc.
Phleospora canadensis Bubák & Dearness.
Phoma pennsylvanica Ell. & Ev.
Phoma samararum Desm.
{ Phyllosticta acericola C. & E.
{ Sphaeropsis minima B. & C.
Phyllosticta minutissima Ell. & Ev.
Phyllosticta saccharina Ell. & Martin.
Rhytisma acerinum (P.) ex Fr.
{ Rhytisma punctatum (P.) ex Fr.
{ Xyloma punctatum P. ex Fr.
Septoria acerina Pk.
Sphaeria corticis S.
Trichia reniformis Pk.
Uncinula circinata C. & P.

Acer platanoides L.
Cladosporium epiphyllum (P.) ex Fr., var.
  acerinum Sacc.
Diatrype bullata (Hoffm.) ex Fr.
Gloeosporium apocryptum Ell. & Ev.
{ Macroplodia simillima (Pk.) Dearness & House.
{ Sphaeropsis simillima Pk.
Nectria cinnabarina (Tode) ex Fr.
Nectria coccinea (P.) ex Fr. ?
Phyllosticta acericola C. & E.

Acer platanoides (*cont.*)
  Phyllosticta minima (B. & C.) Underw. &
    Earle.
  Phyllosticta platanoides Sacc.
  Phyllosticta saccharina Ell. & Martin.
  Pleospora papillata Karst.
  Polyporus squamosus (Huds.) ex Fr.
  Rhytisma acerinum (P.) ex Fr.
  Schizophyllum commune Fr.
  Steganosporium pyriforme (Hoffm. ex Fr.) Cda.
  Taphrina Cerasi (Fckl.) Sadebeck.
  Tubercularia vulgaris Tode ex Fr.

Acer Pseudo-platanus L.
  Dendrodochium acerinum Dearness & House.
  Polyporus igniarius (L.) ex Fr.
  Lentinus lepideus Fr.
  Lentinus tigrinus Fr.
  Lenzites sepiaria (Wulf.) ex Fr.
  Lenzites trabea P. ex Fr.
  Nectria athroa Ell. & Ev.
  Nectria cinnabarina Fr.
  Phyllosticta minima (B. & C.) Underw. &
    Earle.
  ⎰Inonotus perplexus (Pk.) Murrill.
  ⎱Polyporus perplexus Pk.
  Rhytisma acerinum (P.) ex Fr.
  Rhytisma punctatum (P.) ex. Fr.
  ⎧Steganosporium acerinum Pk.
  ⎨Steganosporium cellulosum Cda.
  ⎩Steganosporium pyriforme (Hoffm. ex Fr.) Cda.

Acer rubrum L.
Pezizineae
  Angelina maura Ell.
  Cenangella Aceris (Hazsl.) Sacc.
  Chlorosplenium aeruginosum (Oeder ex Fr.)
    De Not.
  Dermatea acericola Pk.
  ⎧Dermatea acerina (Pk.) Rehm.
  ⎨Phaeangium Peckianum Sacc.
  ⎩Scleroderris acerina (Pk.) Sacc.
  Dermatea carnea C. & E.
  Dermatea simillima Ell. & Ev.
  ⎰Erinella miniopsis (Ell.) Sacc.
  ⎱Peziza miniopsis Ell.
  Helotium epiphyllum (P.) Fr., var. Ellisii
    Rehm.
  Holwaya gigantea Durand.
  ⎧Patellaria lurida (Phil.) B. & C.
  ⎨Patinella lurida (Phil.) Massee.
  ⎩Phacidium luridum Phil.
  Pezicula acericola Pk., var. gregaria Pk.
  Peziza turbinulata S.

Phacidiineae
  Cryptodiscus melanocinctus Rehm.
  ⎰Rhytisma acerinum (P.) ex Fr.
  ⎱Xyloma acerinum P. ex Fr.
  Tympanis picastra B. & C.

Hysteriineae
  Gloniopsis fibriseda (Gerard) Sacc.
  Hysterium pulicare P. ex Fr.
  ⎰Hysterium flexuosum S.
  ⎱Hysterographium flexuosum (S.) Sacc.

Hypocreales
  ⎰Broomella Ravenelii (B.) Sacc.
  ⎱Hypocrea Ravenelii B.
  Hypocrea scutelliformis B. & Rav.
  Hypocrea citrina Fr.
  Nectria cinnabarina (Tode) ex Fr.
  Sphaerostilbe flammea Tul.

Erysiphaceae
  Uncinula circinata C. & P.

Sphaeriales
  ⎰Diatrype Hystrix (Tode) ex Fr.
  ⎱Sphaeria Hystrix Tode ex Fr.
  Diatrype Macounii Ell. & Ev.
  Diatrype platystoma (S.) B.
  Endothia parasitica (Murrill) P. J. & H. W.
    Anderson.
  ⎰Cucurbitaria brevibarbata B. & C.
  ⎱Fracchiaea brevibarbata (B. & C.) Sacc.
  Gnomonia emarginata Fckl.?
  ⎰Gnomonia tenella Ell. & Ev.
  ⎱Gnomoniella tenella (Ell. & Ev.) Sacc.
  Gnomonia veneta (Sacc. & Speg.) Klebahn. ?
  ⎧Depazea brunnea B. & C.
  ⎨Laestadia brunnea (B. & C.) Sacc.
  ⎩Sphaerella brunnea (B. & C.) Cke.
  ⎰Laestadia glaucescens (Cke.) Sacc.
  ⎱Sphaerella glaucescens Cke.
  Lasiosphaeria viridicoma (C. & P.) Sacc.
  ⎧Massaria sudans B. & C.
  ⎨Massariella sudans (B. & C.) Sacc.
  ⎩Massariovalsa sudans (B. & C.) Sacc.
  Massaria vomitoria B. & C.
  Sphaeria myriocarpa Fr.
  Valsaria acericola Ell. & Fairman.
  ⎧Diatrype obesa B. & C.
  ⎨Diatrype quadrata B.
  ⎩Valsaria quadrata (B.) Sacc.
  Zignoella Magnoliae Tracy & Earle.

Valsaceae
  ⎰Diaporthe Aceris Nits.
  ⎧Diaporthe myinda C. & E.
  ⎩Valsa myinda (C. & E.) Sacc.
  ⎰Diaporthe sphendamnina (B. & C.) Sacc.
  ⎱Diatrype sphendamnina B. & C.
  ⎧Eutypella corynostoma (B. & Rav.) Sacc.
  ⎨Peroneutypella corynostoma (B. & Rav.) Berl.
  ⎩Valsa corynostoma B. & Rav.
  ⎰Eutypella rugiella (C. & E.) Sacc.
  ⎱Valsa rugiella C. & E.
  Valsa ambiens (P.) ex Fr.
  Valsa etherialis Ell. & Ev.
  Valsa grisea Pk.

Acer rubrum (*cont.*)
  Valsa multiplex C. & E.
  Valsa pauperata C. & E.
  Valsa quaternata Fr.
  { Sphaeria stellulata Fr.
  { Valsa stellulata Fr.

XYLARIACEAE
  Hypoxylon annulatum (S.) Mont.
  Hypoxylon coccineum Bull. †
  Hypoxylon florideum B. & C.
  Hypoxylon fuscum (P.) ex Fr.
  Hypoxylon jecorinum B. & Rav.
  Hypoxylon marginatum (S.) B.
  Hypoxylon rubiginosum (P.) ex Fr.
  Hypoxylon serpens (P.) ex Fr.
  { Hypoxylon nummularium Bull. ex Fr.
  { Nummularia Bulliardi Tul.
  { Nummularia Clypeus (S.) Cke.
  { Sphaeria Clypeus S.
  Ustulina vulgaris Tul.
  Xylaria corniformis Fr.
  Xylaria hypoxylon (L.) ex Grev.

AURICULARIACEAE
  Septobasidium fumigatum Burt.
  Septobasidium pedicellatum Auct. Amer.
    non Pat.

THELEPHORACEAE
  Corticium centrifugum Lév.
  Corticium confluens Fr.
  Corticium investiens Bres.
  Corticium ochroleucum Fr., var. resupinatum
    Ell. & Ev.
  Corticium scutellare B. & C.
  Corticium stramineum Bres.
  Corticium subgiganteum B.
  Hymenochaete agglutinans Ell.
  Hymenochaete rubiginosa (Schrad. ex Fr.) Lév.
  Hymenochaete tabacina (Sow. ex Fr.) Lév.
  { Corticium aschistum B.
  { Peniophora aschista (B.) Cke.
  Peniophora eichleriana Bres.
  { Peniophora neglecta Pk.
  { Stereum neglectum Pk.
  Stereum purpureum P. †
  Stereum rameale (S.) Reddick.
  Stereum rugosum P. ex Fr.

HYDNACEAE
  { Irpex mollis B. & C.
  { Irpiciporus mollis (B. & C.) Murrill.
  Odontia acerina Pk.
  Radulum Bennettii B. & C.

POLYPORACEAE
  Fomes conchatus (Fr.) Karst.
  { Fomes connatus (Weinm.) Gill.
  { Fomes populinus Auct. Amer.
  { Poria obducens Auct. Amer. p. p.

  { Fomes igniarius (L. ex Fr.) Gill.
  { Polyporus igniarius (L.) ex Fr.
  { Pyropolyporus igniarius (L. ex Fr.) Murrill.
  { Fomes applanatus (P. ex Wallr.) Gill.
  { Fomes leucophaeus (Mont.) Cke.
  { Ganoderma applanatum (P. ex Wallr.) Pat.
  { Polyporus applanatus (P.) ex Wallr.
  { Polyporus leucophaeus Mont.
  { Fomes lucidus (Leyss. ex Fr.) Cke.
  { Fomes sessilis (Murrill) Sacc. & D. Sacc.
  { Ganoderma sessile Murrill.
  { Polyporus lucidus (Leyss.) ex Fr.
  { Polyporus sessilis (Murrill) Lloyd.
  Fomes roseus (Fr.) Cke.
  Lenzites albida Fr.
  Mucronoporus Andersoni Ell. & Ev.
  Mucronoporus ferruginosus (Schrad.) Ell. &
    Ev.
  { Ischnoderma fuliginosum (Scop. ex Fr.) Mur-
    rill.
  { Polyporus fuliginosus (Scop.) ex Fr.
  { Hapalopilus gilvus (S.) Murrill.
  { Polyporus gilvus S.
  Polyporus glomeratus Pk.
  Polyporus pachycheiles Ell. & Ev.
  Polyporus semipileatus Pk.
  Polystictus hirsutus (Wulf.) ex Fr.
  { Polyporus biformis Auct. p. p.
  { Polyporus elongatus B.
  { Polyporus pargamenus Fr.
  { Polystictus pargamenus Fr.
  { Sistotrema violaceum S. Syn. Car.
  Poria floccosa Fr.
  Poria purpurea (Hall. ex Fr.) Cke.
  Poria salmonicolor (B. & C.) Cke.
  Poria setigera Pk.
  Poria spissa (Fr.) Cke.
  Poria subacida (Pk.) Sacc. Syll.

AGARICACEAE
  Collybia dryophila Fr.
  Flammula alnicola Fr., var. marginalis Pk.
  Flammula expansa Pk.
  Pholiota adiposa Fr.
  Pleurotus applicatus (Batsch) ex Fr.
  Pleurotus approximans Pk.
  Schizophyllum commune Fr.
  Volvaria bombycina (Schaeff.) ex Fr.

SPHAEROPSIDALES
  Cytospora chrysosperma (P.) ex Fr.
  Cytospora exasperans Ell. & Ev.
  Cytospora hyalosperma Fr.
  { Diplodia stenospora B. & C.
  { Diplodina stenospora (B. & C.) Sacc.
  Discosia Artocreas (Tode) ex Fr.
  { Discella rugosa B. & C.
  { Discula rugosa (B. & C.) Sacc.

Acer rubrum (*cont.*)

{ Macrophoma albifructua (Pk.) Berl. & Vogl.
{ Phoma albifructua Pk.
Melasmia acerina Lév.
Phleospora Aceris (Lib.) Sacc.
Phyllosticta acericola Ell. & Ev.
{ Phoma minima (B. & C.) Sacc.
{ Sphaeropsis minima B. & C.
{ Phyllosticta minima (B. & C.) Underw. &
  Earle. 1897.
Phyllosticta minima (B. & C.) Ell. & Ev. 1900.
Phyllosticta minima (B. & C.) Tassi. 1902.
{ Naemosphaera acerina (Pk.) v. Höhnel.
{ Sphaeronema acerinum Pk.
{ Sphaeronema nigripes Ell.
{ Rhynchophoma Radula (B. & C.) Sacc.
{ Sphaeronema Radula B. & C.
Sphaeropsis simillima Pk.
Stagonospora collapsa (C. & E.) Sacc.

MELANCONIALES

Cylindrosporium saccharinum Ell. & Ev.
Gloeosporium Aceris Cke.
Gloeosporium decolorans Ell. & Ev.
{ Gloeosporium nervisequum (Fckl.) Sacc.
{ Gnomonia veneta (Sacc. & Speg.) Klebahn?
{ Hainesia Lythri (Desm.) v. Höhnel.
{ Pezizella Lythri Shear & Dodge.
{ Sclerotiopsis concava (Desm.) Shear & Dodge.
Libertella acerina Westd.
Melanconium intermedium Pk.
{ Steganosporium pyriforme (Hoffm. ex Fr.) Cda.
{ Stilbospora ovata P. ex Fr.

HYPHOMYCETES

Cheiromyces Beaumontii B. & C. in Ellis.
Cladosporium humile J. J. Davis.
Coniothecium applanatum Sacc.
Exosporium sociatum Ell. & Ev.
Glenospora Curtisii B. & Desm.
{ Helicoön auratum (Ell.) Morg.
{ Helicosporium auratum Ell.
Helminthosporium Arbuscula B. & C.
Helminthosporium pedunculatum (Pk.) House.
Helminthosporium persistens Cke.
Helminthosporium subolivaceum Ell. & Ev.
{ Hymenella rhabdophora B. & Rav.
{ Hymenula rhabdophora (B. & Rav.) Sacc.
Microcera fujikuroi Miy. & Sav.
Ramularia lethalis Ell. & Ev.
{ Dematium salicinum A. & S.
{ Sporotrichum salicinum (P.) ex Fr.
Stachybotrys elongata Pk.
Trichoderma lignorum (Tode) ex Harz.

MISCELLANEA

Pilacre Petersii B. & Br.
Trichia reniformis Pk.

Acer saccharinum L.

Including Acer dasycarpum Ehrh. Some belonging here may perhaps be found under Acer saccharum Marsh.

PEZIZINEAE

Erinella miniopsis (Ell.) Sacc.

PHACIDIINEAE

{ Rhytisma acerinum (P.) ex Fr.
{ Rhytisma Aceris-eriocarpae S.
Rhytisma acerinum (P.) ex Fr., var. Dasycarpi Rehm.
Rhytisma punctatum (P.) ex Fr.
Scleroderris pallidula (Cke.) Sacc.

HYSTERIINEAE

Hysterographium gloniopsis (Gerard) Ell. & Ev.

PYRENOMYCETINEAE

Calospora allantospora Ell. & Ev.
Diaporthe robusta Pk.
Diatrype platystoma (S.) M. A. Curtis.
Diatrypella Frostii Pk.
Eutypa maura (Fr.) Sacc.
Leptosphaeria inquinans Pk.
Lophodermium petiolicola Fckl.
Massaria inquinans (Tode) ex Fr.
{ Melanconis dasycarpa Ell. & Kellerm.
{ Melanconis Everhartii Ell.
{ Chilonectria Coryli (Fckl.) Ell. & Ev.
{ Nectria Coryli Fckl.
Nummularia Bulliardi Tul.
Phyllactinia corylea (P.) ex Karst.
Physalospora Cydoniae Arnaud.
Sphaerella maculiformis Awd.
Thyridium stilbostomum Ell. & Ev.
Trichosphaeria interpilosa Fairman.
Uncinula circinata C. & P.
Valsa ceratophora Tul.
Valsa etherialis Ell. & Ev.
Valsa saccharina Rehm.

BASIDIOMYCETES

Coniophora byssoidea (P.) ex Fr.
{ Elfvingia megaloma Murrill.
{ Fomes applanatus (P. ex Wallr.) Gill.
Fomes connatus (Weinm. ex Fr.) Gill.
{ Elfvingiella fomentaria (L. ex Fr.) Murrill.
{ Fomes fomentarius (L. ex Fr.) Gill.
{ Polyporus fomentarius (L.) ex Fr.
{ Fomes igniarius (L. ex Fr.) Gill.
{ Polyporus igniarius (L.) ex Fr.
{ Fomes marginatus (P. ex Fr.) Gill.
{ Fomes pinicola (Sw. ex Fr.) Cke.
{ Fomes ungulatus (Schaeff. ex Fr.) Sacc.
Fomes populinus (Schum. ex Fr.) Cke.
Gloeophyllum hirsutum (Schaeff.) ex Murrill.
Hypochnus isabellinus Fr.

Acer saccharinum (*cont.*)
  Irpex mollis B. & C.
  Leptonia acericola Murrill.
  Mycena corticola (Schum.) ex Fr.
{ Merulius tremellosus Fung. Columb. *2844.*
{ Phlebia radiata Fr.
  Pholiota adiposa Fr.
  Polyporus delectans Pk.
  Polyporus gilvus S.
  Polyporus obtusus B.
  Polyporus squamosus (Huds.) ex Fr.
  Polystictus pergamenus Fr.
{ Coriolus versicolor (L. ex Fr.) Quél.
{ Polystictus versicolor (L.) ex Fr.
  Poria aurea Pk.
  Poria incrassata (B. & C.) Burt.
  Schizophyllum commune Fr.
  Stereum acerinum (P.) ex Fr.
  Trametes Peckii Kalchb.
  Volvaria bombycina (Schaeff.) ex Fr.

SPHAEROPSIDALES

  Cytospora leucosperma (P.) ex Fr.
  Diplodina fusispora Pk.
  Phleospora Aceris (Lib.) Sacc.
  Phyllosticta acericola C. & E.
  Phyllosticta minima (B. & C.) Ell. & Ev.
  Phyllosticta minutissima Ell. & Ev.
  Septoria acerina Pk.
  Septoria Aceris (Lib.) B. & Br.
  Septoria Salliae W. R. Gerard.
  Sphaeronema acerinum Pk.
{ Haplosporella acerina (Ell. & Barthol.) Ell. &
{   Ev.
{ Haplosporella Clintonii (Pk.) Petrak & Syd.
{ Sphaeropsis acerina Ell. & Barthol.
  Sphaeropsis simillima Pk.
  Stagonospora collapsa (C. & E.) Sacc.
  Vermicularia Dematium (P.) Fr., var. micro-
    spora Hook.

MELANCONIALES

  Gloeosporium acerinum Westd.
{ Gloeosporium acerinum Pass.
{ Septogloeum acerinum (Pass.) Sacc.
  Gloeosporium Aceris Cke.
  Gloeosporium apocryptum Ell. & Ev.
  Gloeosporium multipunctatum Dearness.
  Gloeosporium saccharinum Ell. & Ev.
  Libertella acerina Westd.
  Melanconiopsis inquinans Ell. & Ev.
  Myxosporium acerinum Pk.
  Steganosporium acerinum Pk.
  Steganosporium cellulosum Cda.
{ Steganosporium pyriforme (Hoffm. ex Fr.) Cda.
{ Stilbospora ovata P. ex Fr.
{ Stilbospora pyriforme Hoffm. ex Fr.
  Steganosporium pyriforme (Hoffm. ex Fr.) Cda.,
    var. majus Ell. & Ev.

HYPHOMYCETES

  Alternaria tenuis Nees. ex Fr., var. condensata
    Sacc.
  Bispora effusa Pk.
  Cladosporium humile J. J. Davis.
  Fusarium sarcochroum (Desm.) Sacc.
  Helicoma ambiens Morg.
{ Helicoma polysporum Morg.
{ Helicosporium polysporum (Morg.) Sacc.
{ Helicoma repens Morg.
{ Helicosporium repens (Morg.) Sacc.
  Septonema breviusculum B. & C.
  Trichothecium subgriseum Pk.
  Tubercularia vulgaris Tode ex Fr.
  Zygodesmus fulvus Sacc.

MISCELLANEA

  Dematophora necatrix Hartig.
  Lycogala flavofuscum (Ehrenb.) Rostf.
  Ozonium auricomum Lk.
  Physarum nefroideum Rostf.

Acer saccharum Marsh.
  Including Acer saccharinum Wang. non L.,
    and some reported above as Acer saccha-
    rinum L.

PEZIZINEAE

  Bulgaria inquinans (P.) ex Fr.
{ Dermatea acerina (Pk.) Rehm.
{ Phaeangium peckianum Sacc.
  Helotium fraternum Pk.
  Lecanidion acericola Atk.
{ Lecanidion leptospermum (Pk.) Sacc.
{ Patellaria leptosperma Pk.

PHACIDIINEAE

  Rhytisma acerinum (P.) ex Fr.
{ Rhytisma punctatum (P.) ex Fr.
{ Rhytisma punctiforme Mayr.
  Scleroderris pallidula (Cke.) Sacc.

PYRENOMYCETINEAE

  ?Antennaria pinophila Nees ex Fr.
  Calospora allantospora Ell. & Ev.
  Capnodium expansum B. & Desm.
  Cucurbitaria Fraxini Ell. & Ev.
  Diaporthe Aceris Fckl.
  Diaporthe microstroma Ell. & Ev.
  Diaporthe robusta Pk.
  Diaporthe subcongrua Ell. & Ev.
  Diatrype cercidicola B. & C.
  Diatrype platystoma (S.) M. A. Curtis.
  Diatrypella Frostii P.
{ Eutypa spinosa (P. ex Fr.) Tul.
{ Sphaeria horrida S.
{ Sphaeria spinosa P. ex Fr.
  Gnomonia petiophila (Pk.) Berl. & Vogl.
  Hypocrea rufa (P.) ex Fr.
  Hypoxylon fuscum (P.) ex Fr.
  Hypoxylon suborbiculare Pk.

Acer saccharum (*cont.*)
Laestadia acerifera (Cke.) Sacc.
Leptosphaeria inquinans Pk.
Lophiostoma macrostomum (Tode ex Fr.) Ces.
   & De Not.
Lophodermium petiolicola Fckl.
Lophodermium petiolicola Fckl., var. aceri-
   num Pk.
{Massaria inquinans (Tode) ex Fr.
{Massaria vomitaria Michigan list.
{Nectria cinnabarina (Todo) ex Fr.
{Creonectria purpurea (L.) ex Seaver.
Nectria coccinea (P.) ex Fr.
{Phyllactinia corylea (P.) ex Karst.
{Phyllactinia suffulta (Reb.) ex Sacc.
Pseudovalsa minima Ell. & Ev.
Rosellinia aquila (Fr.) De Not.
Mycosphaerella septorioides (Desm.) Lindau.
Uncinula circinata C. & P.
Valsa coronata (Hoffm.) ex Fr.
Valsa leucostomoides Pk.
Xylaria castorea B.
Xylaria digitata (L. ex Fr.) Grev., var. tenuis
   Pk.
Xylaria polymorpha (P. ex Fr.) Grev.

BASIDIOMYCETES

Corticium subgiganteum B.
{Cynophallus caninus Fr.
{Mutinus caninus W. Curtis ex P.
{Hymenochaete corrugata (Fr.) Lév.
{Hymenochaete insularis B.
Naematelia nucleata (S.) Fr.
Physalacria inflata (S.) Pk.
Pilacre Petersii B. & C.
Stereum rugosum P. ex Fr.
Stereum tuberculosum Fr.

HYDNACEAE

Hydnum nudum B. & C.
{Hydnum Peckii (Banker) Lloyd.
{Steccherinum Peckii Banker.
Hydnum septentrionale Fr.
{Hydnoporia fuscescens (S.) Murrill.
{Irpex fuscescens S.
{Irpex mollis B. & C.
{Irpiciporus mollis (B. & C.) Murrill.
Irpex tabacinus B. & C.
Irpex tulipiferae (S.) Fr.
Phlebia acerina Pk.

POLYPORACEAE

{Daedalea ambigua B.
{Daedalea glaberrima B. & C.
{Lenzites glaberrima B. & C.
{Trametes ambigua (B.) Fr.
{Trametes incana B.
{Trametes lactea B.

{Cerrena unicolor (Bull. ex Fr.) Murrill.
{Daedalea unicolor (Bull.) ex Fr.
{Elfvingia megaloma (Lév.) Murrill.
{Fomes applanatus (P. ex Wallr.) Gill.
{Polyporus applanatus (P.) ex Wallr.
{Fomes conchatus (Fr.) Karst.
{Pyropolyporus conchatus (Fr.) Murrill.
{Fomes connatus (Fr.) Cke.
{Polyporus connatus Fr.
Fomes fomentarius (L. ex Fr.) Gill.
{Fomes fuliginosus (Scop. ex Fr.) Cke.
{Ischnoderma fuliginosum (Scop. ex Fr.) Mur-
   rill.
Fomes igniarius (L. ex Fr.) Gill.
{Fomes pinicola (Sw. ex Fr.) Cke.
{Polyporus pinicola Sw. ex Fr.
Fomes populinus (Schum. ex Fr.) Cke.
Ganoderma sessile Murrill.
Gloeophyllum trabeum (P.. ex Fr.) Murrill.
Lenzites betulina (L.) ex Fr.
Merulius Corium (P.) Fr.
Merulius molluscus Fr.
Polyporus admirabilis Pk.
Polyporus bombycinus Fr.
{Polyporus borealis Fr.
{Spongipellis borealis (Fr.) Murrill.
Polyporus cuticularis (Bull.) ex Fr.
Polyporus frondosus (Dicks.) ex Fr.
Polyporus gilvus S.
Polyporus glomeratus Pk.
Polyporus hirsutus (Wulf.) ex Fr.
Polyporus obtusus B.
{Polyporus pubescens (Schum.) ex Fr.
{Polystictus pubescens (Schum. ex Fr.) Lloyd.
Polyporus resinosus (Schrad.) ex Fr.
Polyporus sinuosus Fr.
Polyporus sulphureus (Bull.) ex Fr.
Polyporus versicolor (L.) ex Fr.
Polyporus violaceus Fr.
{Polyporus cinnabarinus (Jacq.) ex Fr.
{Polystictus cinnabarinus (Jacq. ex Fr.) Cke.
{Pycnoporus cinnabarinus (Jacq. ex Fr.) Karst.
{Trametes cinnabarina (Jacq.) ex Fr.
{Hapalopilus licnoides (Mont.) Murrill.
{Polystictus licnoides (Mont.) Cke.
{Coriolus prolificans (Fr.) Murrill.
{Polystictus pergamenus Fr.
{Inonotus radiatus (Sow. ex Fr.) Karst.
{Polyporus radiatus Sow. ex Fr.
{Polystictus radiatus (Sow. ex Fr.) Cke.
{Coriolopsis rigida (B. & Mont.) Murrill.
{Polystictus rigidus (B.) Cke.
Poria aurea Pk.
{Polyporus purpureus Fr.
{Poria purpurea (Fr.) Cke.
Trametes mollis (Sommf.) ex Fr.
Trametes pallidofulva (B.) Fr.

Acer saccharum (*cont.*)

AGARICACEAE

Armillaria mellea (Vahl) ex Fr.
Clitocybe truncicola Pk.
Collybia velutipes Wm. Curtis.
Cortinarius rubipes Kauffman.
Hebeloma appendiculatum Murrill.
Hypholoma saccharinophilum Pk.
Lepiota acerina Pk.
{ Leptonia acericola Murrill.
{ Leptoniella acericola Murrill.
Mycena corticola (Schum.) ex Fr.
Omphalia striipilea (Fr.) Sacc. Syll., var. albogrisea Pk.
Pholiota acericola Pk.
Pholiota adiposa Fr.
Pholiota albocrenulata Pk.
Pholiota lutea Pk.
{ Crepidotus ostreatus (Jacq. ex Fr.) S. F. Gray.
{ Pleurotus ostreatus (Jacq.) ex Fr.
Pleurotus ulmarius (Bull.) ex Fr.
Schizophyllum commune Fr.

SPHAEROPSIDALES

Asteroma Aceris Rob.
Cytospora leucosperma (P.) ex Fr.
Dinemasporium Robiniae Gerard.
Diplodia subtectoides Pk.
{ Phleospora Aceris (Lib.) Sacc.
{ Septoria Aceris (Lib.) B. & Br.
Phyllosticta acericola Ell. & Ev.
Phyllosticta minima (B. & C.) Underw. & Earle.
Phyllosticta minutella Bubák & Dearness.
Phyllosticta minutissima Ell. & Ev.
Phyllosticta saccharina Ell. & Martin.
Septoria belonidium Ell. & Ev.
Septoria flavescens Ell. & Halsted.
{ Septoria acerina N. A. F. *2951*.
{ Septoria saccharina Ell. & Ev.
Septoria Salliae Gerard.
Sphaeronema acerinum Pk.
Sphaeropsis simillima Pk.

MELANCONIALES

Coryneum Negundinis B. & C.
Cylindrosporium saccharinum Ell. & Ev.
Gloeosporium alboferrugineum Ell. & Ev.
Gloeosporium apocryptum Ell. & Ev.
Gloeosporium hysterioideum Dearness & Barthol.
Gloeosporium oblongisporum Ell. & Dearness.
Gloeosporium saccharinum Ell. & Ev.
Gloeosporium tuberculoides Sacc.
Libertella acerina Westd.
Melanconium magnum B.
Myxosporium acerinum Pk.
Naemaspora microsperma Ell. & Ev.
Septogloeum acerinum (Pass.) Sacc.

Steganosporium cellulosum Cda.
Steganosporium cellulosum Cda., var. major Ell. & Ev.
Steganosporium pyriforme (Hoffm. ex Fr.) Cda.

HYPHOMYCETES

Helminthosporium macrocarpon Grev.

MISCELLANEA

Lycogala flavofuscum (Ehrh.) Rostf.

Acer saccharum Marsh., var. **nigrum** (Michx. f.) Britt.

Calonectria chlorinella (Cke.) Ell. & Ev.
Capnodium expansum B. & Desm.
Cytodiplospora parallela Dearness.
Dermatea carnea C. & E.
Dermatea carnea C. & E., var. seriata Rehm.
Diaporthe ontariensis Ell. & Ev.
{ Fomes applanatus (P. ex Wallr.) Gill.
{ Polyporus applanatus (P.) ex Wallr.
Gloeosporium saccharinum Ell. & Ev.
{ Haplosporella Clintonii (Pk.) Petrak & Syd.
{ Sphaeropsis grandinea Ell. & Ev.
Massaria vomitaria B. & C.
Phyllosticta saccharina Ell. & Martin.
Polyporus frondosus (Schrank.) ex Fr.
Polyporus resinosus (Schrad.) ex Fr.
Rhytisma punctatum (P.) ex Fr.
Sphaeropsis lineata Ell. & Dearness.
Uncinula circinata C. & P.
Valsaria exasperans (Gerard) Ell. & Ev., var. Aceris Rehm.

Acer spicatum Lam.

Acrospermum cuneolum Dearness & House.
Agaricus variabilis P. ex Fr.
Amphisphaeria applanata (Fr.) Ces. & De Not.
Capnodium expansum B. & Desm.
Cenangium griseum Dearness & House.
Corticium viticola S.
Cylindrosporium acerinum Tracy & Earle.
Cylindrosporium canadense Bubák.
Cylindrosporium saccharinum Ell. & Ev.
{ Dermatea acericola (Pk.) Cke.
{ Nodularia acericola Pk.
{ Pezicula acericola Pk.
{ Diaporthe acerina (Pk.) Sacc.
{ Diaporthe albocincta (C. & P.) Sacc.
{ Diaporthe myinda (C. & E.) Sacc.
{ Diaporthe spicata Ell. & Ev.
{ Valsa acerina Pk.
{ Valsa albocincta C. & P.
{ Valsa myinda C. & E.
Diaporthe disciformis (Hoffm.) ex Fr.
Discella obscura B. & C.
Exidia glandulosa (Bull.) ex Fr.
{ Fomes applanatus (P. ex Wallr.) Gill.
{ Fomes leucophaeus (Mont.) Cke.
{ Fomes igniarius (L. ex Fr.) Cke.
{ Polyporus igniarius (L.) ex Fr.

Acer spicatum (*cont.*)
Gloeosporium saccharinum Ell. & Ev.
{ Gnomonia petiolophila (Pk.) Berl. & Vogl.
{ Gnomoniella petiolophila (Pk.) Sacc.
{ Sphaeria petiolophila Pk.
Helminthosporium macrocarpon Grev.
{ Herpotrichia albidostoma (Pk.) Sacc.
{ Herpotrichia incisa Ell. & Ev.
{ Herpotrichia leucostoma Pk.
{ Sphaeria albidostoma Pk.
Hydnum sulphurellum Pk.
Hypoderma rufilabrum (B. & C.) Duby.
Hypoxylon perforatum S.
Hysterium virgultorum (DC.) ex Rob. &
    Desm., var. Aceris Desm.
Leptothyrella Aceris Dearness & House.
Marasmius acerinus Pk.
Metasphaeria microecia Ell. & Ev.
Montagnella acerina Ell. & Ev.
Ombrophila setulata Dearness & House.
Peniophora cinerea (P. ex Fr.) Cke.
Pezicula spicata Ell. & Ev.
{ Phyllosticta acericola C. & E.
{ Phyllosticta minima (B. & C.) Ell. & Ev.
Phyllosticta platanoides Sacc.
{ Polyporus aureonitens Pat.
{ Polystictus aureonitens (Pat.) Sacc.
Polyporus semipileatus Pk.
Pseudovalsa stylospora Ell. & Ev.
Rhytisma acerinum (P.) ex Fr.
Rhytisma punctatum (P.) ex Fr.
Septoria acerina Pk.
Sphaeria peliospora B. & C.
{ Ascomyces letifer Pk.
{ Taphrina letifer (Pk.) Sacc.
Uncinula circinata C. & P.
Valsella Laschii (Nits.) Sacc.
Valsella Laschii (Nits.) Sacc., var. acerina Pk.
Zignoella pulviscula (Curr.) Sacc.

Acer texanum Pax.
Septoria marginata Heald & Wolf.

Acer sp. indet.

Myxomycetes

Arcyria magna Rex.
Comatricha crypta (S.) Morg.
Leocarpus fragilis (Dicks.) Rostf.
Perichaena depressa Lib.
Reticularia Lycoperdon Bull.
Stemonitis Morgani Pk.

Pezizineae

Agyrium rufum (P.) Fr.
Bulgaria sarcoides (Jacq.) ex Fr.
{ Cenangium bicolor (Ell.) Sacc.
{ Tympanis bicolor Ell.
Cenangium patellatum Cke.
Cenangium prunastri (P.) ex Fr.
Chlorosplenium versiforme (P.) De Not.

Ciboria luteovirescens (Rob.) Sacc.
Coryne sarcoides (Jacq. ex Fr.) Tul.
{ Durella compressa (P.) Tul.
{ Peziza compressa P.
{ Godronia rhabdospora (B. & C.) Sacc.
{ Tympanis rhabdospora B. & C.
Helotium albovirens Cke.
Helotium epiphyllum (P.) Fr.
Helotium fraternum Pk.
Helotium imberbe (Bull.) ex Fr.
Helotium naviculisporum Ell.
Lachnella flammea (A. & S.) ex Fr.
Midotis irregularis (S.) Sacc.
{ Mollisia aureofulva (Cke.) Sacc.
{ Peziza aureofulva Cke.
{ Mollisia paullopuncta (C. & E.) Sacc.
{ Peziza paullopuncta C. & E.
{ Ombrophila aurata (B. & Rav.) Phil.
{ Peziza aurata B. & Rav.
Lecanidion atratum (Hedw. ex Fr.) Rabh.
Patellaria atrata (Hedw.) ex Fr.
{ Patellaria cylindrospora Ell.
{ Scutularia cylindrospora (Ell.) Sacc.
Patellaria nigrovirens Ell. & Sacc.
Pezicula acericola Pk.
Peziza aeruginosa P.
Peziza atrovirens P.
Peziza Erinaceus S.
Peziza rubella P.
Peziza vinosa A. & S. ex Fr., var. minor C. & E.
{ Peziza floriformis Pk.
{ Pezizella floriformis (Pk.) Sacc.
{ Peziza simulata Ell.
{ Phialea simulata (Ell.) Sacc.
{ Peziza acerina C. & E.
{ Trichopeziza acerina (C. & E.) Sacc.
{ Tympanis conspersa Fr.
{ Tympanis rhabdospora B. & C.

Phacidineae

Propolis faginea (Schrad.) ex Karst.
Propolis lobata C. & E.
?Rhytisma Pseudoplatani Müller.
Schizoxylon aeruginosum Fckl.
Stictis linearis C. & E.
{ Scleroderris acerina (Pk.) Sacc.
{ Tympanis acerina Pk.

Hysteriineae

Hysterium acerinum Frost.?
{ Hysterium Prostii Duby.
{ Hysterium ellipticum N. A. F. *461.*
Hysterium Gerardi C. & P.
Hysterium stictoideum C. & E.
Hysterium vulvatum S.
Hysterographium cookeanum (Gerard) Ell. &
    Ev.
{ Hysterium xylomoides Chev.
{ Lophodermium hysterioides (P. ex Fr.) Sacc.

Acer sp. indet. (*cont.*)

HYPOCREALES

Chilonectria cucurbitula (Curr.) Sacc.
Nectria cucurbitula (Curr.) Cke.
Dialonectria vulpina Cke.
Nectriella vulpina (Cke.) Berl. & Vogl.
Hypocrea alutacea (P. ex Fr.) Ces. & De Not.
Hypocrea gelatinosa (Tode) ex Fr.
Hypocrea sulphurea (S.) Sacc.
Nectria ditissima Tul.
Nectria mammoidea Phil. & Plowr.
Nectria sanguinea (Sibth.) ex Fr.
Scoleconectria Atkinsonii (Rehm) Seaver.
Sphaerostilbe flammea (B. & Rav.) Tul.
Thyronectria pyrrhochlora (Awd.) Sacc.

SPHAERIALES

Anthostomella eructans Ell. & Ev.
Anthostoma picaceum C. & E.
Anthostomella picaceum (C. & E.) Sacc.
Bertia moriformis (Tode ex Fr.) De Not.
Botryosphaeria fuliginosa (M. & N.) Ell.&Ev.
Byssosphaeria acanthostroma (Mont.) Cke.
Sphaeria acanthostroma Mont.
Trichosphaeria acanthostroma (Mont.) Sacc.
Byssosphaeria subiculata (S.) Cke.
Ceratostoma caminatum (C. & E.) Sacc.
Sphaeria caminata C. & E.
Calosphaeria barbirostris (Dufour) Ell. & Ev.
Ceratostomella barbirostris (Dufour) Sacc.
Sphaeria barbirostris Dufour.
Calospora allantospora Ell. & Ev.
Ceratostomella echinella Ell. & Ev.
Ceratostomella rostrata (Fr.) Sacc.
Chaetomium pannosum Wallr.
Chaetomium velutinum Ell. & Ev.
Chaetosphaeria ludens Morg.
Cryptosporella Niesslii (Kze.) Sacc.
Cucurbitaria echinata Ell. & Ev.
Enchnosphaeria hispida Morg.
Gnomonia veneta (Sacc. & Speg.) Klebahn.
Lasiosphaeria pezizula (B. & C.) Sacc.
Sphaeria pezizula B. & C.
Leptospora stictochaetophora Fairman.
Lophidium tingens (Ell.) Sacc.
Lophiostoma tingens Ell.
Lophiostoma excipuliforme (Fr.) Ces. & De Not.
Lophiostoma macrostoma (Tode ex Fr.) Ces. & De Not.
Lophiostoma microstoma C. & E.
Lophiostoma scelestum C. & E.
Lophiostoma rhizophilum (B. & C.) Sacc.
Lophiostoma rhopaloides Sacc., var. pluriseptatum Fairman.
Lophiostoma triseptatum Pk., var. acutum Fairman.
Lophiostoma triseptatum Pk., var. pluriseptatum Ell. & Ev.

Massaria bispora Cke.
Massariella bispora (Cke.) Sacc.
Massaria inquinans (Tode) ex Fr.
Sphaeria inquinans Tode ex Fr.
Melanconis stilbostoma (Fr.) Tul.
Valsa stilbostoma Fr.
Melanomma Pulvis-pyrius (P. ex Fr.) Fckl.
Amphisphaeria papilla (S.) Sacc.
Melanopsamma papilla (S.) Sacc.
Sphaeria papilla S.
Melogramma campylosporum Fr.
Nitschkia tristis (P. ex Fr.) Fckl.
Ophiobolus porphyrogonus (Tode ex Fr.) Sacc.
Otthia Aceris Wint.
Physalospora Malorum Shear et al.
Protoventuria vancouverensis Dearness.
Massaria seiridia B. & C.
Pseudovalsa profusa (Fr.) Cke.
Rosellinia mammiformis (P. ex Fr.) Ces. & De Not.
Rosellinia megalocarpa (Plowr.) Sacc.
Sphaeria megalocarpa Plowr.
Rosellinia obtusissima (B. & C.) Sacc.
Sphaeria obtusissima B. & C.
Rosellinia subiculata (S.) Sacc.
Sphaeria subiculata S.
Philocopra lutea Ell. & Ev.
Sordaria lutea Ell. & Ev.
Sphaerella alarum Ell. & Halsted.
Mycosphaerella latebrosa (Cke.) Schrt.
?Sphaerella septorioides (Desm.) Niessl.
Sphaeria culcitella B. & Rav.
Sphaeria gyrosa Torrey.
Sphaeria pilulifera Fr.
Sphaeria trames B. & C.
Sphaeria vetusta Ell.
Strickeria vetusta (Ell.) Sacc.
Teichospora vetusta (Ell.) Sacc.
Trichosphaeria solaris (C. & E.) Ell. & Ev.
Valsaria exasperans (Gerard) Sacc.
Valsaria insitiva (Tode ex Fr.) Ces. & DeNot.
Sphaeria atriella C. & E.
Zignoella atrella (C. & E.) Sacc.

VALSACEAE

Anthostoma acerinum Ell. & Fairman.
Anthostoma saprophilum Ell. & Ev.
Diaporthe magnispora (Ell. & Ev.) Sacc.
Valsa magnispora Ell. & Ev.
Diaporthe tuberculosa (Ell.) Sacc.
Endoxyla acericola Ell. & Ev.
Eutypa spinosa (P. ex Fr.) Tul.
Eutypa velutina (Wallr.) Sacc.
Thyridaria Cajugae Rehm.
Diaporthe Aceris Nits.
Valsa Aceris (Nits.) Cke.
Valsa decorticans Fr.
Sphaeria pugillus S.
Valsa pugillus (S.) Cke.

Acer sp. indet. (*cont.*)
Valsa rhodospora Sacc.
Valsa thelebola Fr.

DIATRYPACEAE
Calosphaeria acerina Ell. & Ev.
{ Calosphaeria microtheca (C. & E.) Sacc.
Physalospora microtheca (C. & E.) Sacc.
Sphaeria microtheca C. & E.
{ Allescherina eutypiformis (Sacc.) Berl.
Cryptovalsa eutypiformis Sacc.
Diatrype quercina (P.) ex Fr., var. lignicola C. & E.
{ Diatrype stigma (Hoffm.) ex Fr.
Sphaeria stigma Hoffm. ex Fr.
{ Quaternaria Persoonii Tul.
Quaternaria quaternata (P. ex Fr.) Schrt.

XYLARIACEAE
Daldinia concentrica (Bolt. ex Fr.) Ces. & De Not.
{ Hypoxylon Aceris (C. & E.) Sacc.
Melogramma Aceris C. & E.
Hypoxylon Caries (S.) Sacc.
?Hypoxylon commutatum Nits., var. holwayanum Sacc. & Ell.
Hypoxylon howeianum Pk.
{ Hypoxylon insidens (S.) Ell. & Ev.
Hypoxylon serpens N. A. F. *164*.
Hypoxylon multiforme Fr., var. effusum C. & E.
Hypoxylon regale Morg.
Hypoxylon rubiginosum (P.) ex Fr.
Nummularia discreta (S.) Tul.
Nummularia lateritia Ell. & Ev.
Nummularia nummularia (Bull. ex Fr.) Atk.
Nummularia tinctor (B.) Ell. & Ev.
Xylaria corniformis Fr.
Xylaria digitata (L. ex Fr.) Grev.
Xylaria Hypoxylon (L.) ex Grev.

AURICULARIACEAE
Hirneola Auricula-judae (L. ex Fr.) B.

PILACRACEAE
Pilacre faginea (Fr.) B. & Br.

TREMELLACEAE
Tremella lutescens (P.) ex Fr.
Tremella violacea Morg.

DACRYOMYCETINEAE
Calocera cornea (Batsch) ex Fr.
Dacryomyces Ellisii Coker.
Dacryomyces moriformis Fr.

THELEPHORACEAE
{ Aleurodiscus acerinus (P. ex Fr.) v. Höhnel & & Litschauer.
Stereum acerinum (P.) ex Fr.
Aleurodiscus candidus (S.) Burt.

{ Aleurodiscus Oakesii (B. & C.) Cke.
Corticium Oakesii B. & C.
{ Artocreas Micheneri B. & C.
Michenera Artocreas B. & C.
Coniophora capnoides Ell. & Ev.
Corticium bombycinum (Sommerf.) Bres.
Corticium confluens Fr.
Corticium crustaceum (Karst.) v. Höhnel & Litschauer.
Corticium effuscatum C. & E.
Corticium epigaeum Ell. & Ev.
Corticium evolvens Fr.
Corticium galactinum (Fr.) Burt.
Corticium incanum Burt.
Corticium investiens (S.) Bres.
Corticium roseum (P.) ex Fr.
Cyphella pezizoides Zopf.
Hymenochaete avellana Fr.
Hymenochaete cinnamomea (P.) Bres.
{ Hymenochaete Curtisii (B.) Morg.
Stereum Curtisii B.
Peniophora albula Atk. & Burt.
Peniophora candida (P. ex Fr.) Lyman.
Peniophora carnosa Burt.
{ Corticium cinereum Fr.
Peniophora cinerea (Fr.) Cke.
Peniophora flavido-alba Cke.
Peniophora guttulifera (Karst.) Sacc.
Peniophora heterocystidia Burt.
Peniophora nuda (Fr.) Bres.
Peniophora velutina (DC. ex Fr.) Cke.
Peniophora viticola (S.) v. Höhnel & Litschauer.
Solenia ochracea Hoffm. ex Fr.
Solenia poriiformis (P. ex Fr.) Fckl.
Stereum cinerascens (S.) Massee.
Stereum complicatum Fr.
Stereum fasciatum S.
Stereum fuscum (Schrad. ex Fr.) Quél.
Stereum lilacinofuscum (B. & C.) Burt.
Stereum Murrayi (B. & C.) Burt.
Stereum ochraceoflavum S.
Stereum spadiceum Fr.
{ Corticium ochroleucum B. & C. non Fr.
Stereum spumeum Burt.
Stereum tuberculosum Fr.

HYDNACEAE
Hydnum alutaceum Fr.
Hydnum Caput-ursi Fr.
Hydnum Caput-ursi Fr., var. brevispineum Pk.
Hydnum chlorinum Cke.
Hydnum ciliolatum B. & C.
Hydnum coralloides Scop. ex Fr.
Hydnum gelatinosum Scop. ex Fr., var. viride Auct.
{ Hydnum ochraceum P. ex Fr.
Steccherinum ochraceum (P. ex Fr.) S. F. Gray.

Acer sp. indet. (*cont.*)

Hydnum pulcherrimum B. & C.

{ Creolophus septentrionalis (Fr.) Banker.
Hydnum septentrionale Fr.
Steccherinum septentrionale (Fr.) Banker.

Irpex cinnamomeus Fr.

Irpex lacteus Fr.

Irpex Tulipiferae S.

Lentodium squamulosum Morg.

Odontia fimbriata (P.) ex Fr.

?Phlebia vaga Fr.

POLYPORACEAE

Daedalea confragosa (Bolt.) ex Fr.

Favolus europaeus Fr.

Favolus tesselatus Mont.

Fomes Everhartii (Ell. & Gall.) v. Schrenk.

Fomes geotropus Cke.

{ Fomes graveolens (S.) Cke.
Globifomes graveolens (S.) Murrill.

Fomes nigricans (Fr.) Cke.

Fomes ohiense B.

Fomes pomaceus (P.) Lloyd.

Ganoderma Curtisii (B.) Murrill.

Gleoporus conchoides Mont.

Hexagona striatula (Ell. & Ev.) Murrill.

Merulius incarnatus S.

Merulius tremulosus Schrad. ex Fr.

{ Daedalea Aesculi (S.) Murrill.
Daedalea ambigua B.
Polyporus Aesculi S.

{ Polyporus aurantiacus Pk.
Polyporus fibrillosus Karst.
Polystictus aurantiacus (Pk.) Cke.
Pycnoporellus fibrillosus (Karst.) Murrill.

Polyporus aureonitens Pat.

Polyporus benzoinus Fr.

Polyporus caesius (Schrad.) ex Fr.

Polyporus caudicinus (Scop. ex Fr.) Murrill.

{ Polyporus chioneus Fr.
Tyromyces chioneus (Fr.) Karst.

Polyporus contiguus (P.) ex Fr.

{ Polyporus cutifractus Murrill.
Tyromyces cutifractus Murrill.

{ Polyporus delectans Pk.
Spongipellis delectans (Pk.) Murrill.

{ Gloeoporus dichrous (Fr.) Kauffman.
Polyporus dichrous Fr.

Polyporus epileucus Fr.

Polyporus fimbriatellus Pk.

Polyporus floriformis Quél.

Polyporus fumosus (P.) ex Fr.

Polyporus giganteus (P.) ex Fr.

{ Boletus gilvus S.
Polyporus gilvus S.

{ Polyporus nidulans Fr.
Polyporus rutilans (P.) ex Fr.

{ Polyporus nitidus (P.) Fr.
Poria nitida (P. ex Fr.) Cke.

Polyporus resinosus Schrad ex Fr.

Polyporus robiniophilus (Murrill) Lloyd.

{ Abortiporus distortus (S.) Murrill.
Polyporus rufescens (P.) ex Fr.

Polyporus picipes Fr., var. castaneus Lloyd.

{ Polyporus semisupinus B. & C.
Tyromyces semipileatus (Pk.) Murrill.
Tyromyces semisupinus (B. & C.) Murrill.

Polyporus spumeus (Sow.) ex Fr.

Polyporus sulphureus (Bull.) ex Fr.

{ Polyporus unicolor S.
Spongipellis unicolor (S.) Murrill.
Trametes unicolor (S.) Murrill.

Polyporus vaporarius Fr.

{ Polyporus picipes Fr.
Polyporus varius Fr.

Polyporus vulgaris Fr.

{ Polyporus abietinus (Dicks.) ex Fr.
Polystictus abietinus (Dicks. ex Fr.) Cke.

Polystictus biformis Fr.

Polystictus lacteus Fr.

Poria Amesii Murrill.

Poria Calkinsii Murrill.

Poria candidissima (S.) Cke.

{ Poria eupora (Karst.) Cke.
Poria attenuata (Pk.) Cke.

{ Mucronoporus ferruginosus (Schrad. ex Fr.) Ell. & Ev.
Polyporus ferruginosus (Schrad.) ex Fr.
Poria ferruginosa (Schrad. ex Fr.) Cke.

Poria fimbriatella (Pk.) Sacc. Syll.

Poria Medulla-panis (P. ex Fr.) Cke.

Poria punctata Fr.

{ Polyporus semitinctus Pk.
Poria semitincta (Pk.) Cke.

{ Polyporus sinuosus Fr.
Poria sinuosa (Fr.) Cke.

Poria subincarnata (Pk.) Murrill.

Porothelium confusum B. & Br.

Trametes malicola B. & C.

{ Antrodia mollis (Sommerf. ex Fr.) Karst.
Trametes mollis (Sommerf.) ex Fr.

Trametes Peckii Kalchb.

Trametes sepium B.

AGARICACEAE

Coprinus atramentarius (Bull.) ex Fr., var. sylvaticus Pk.

Coprinus radians (Desm.) Fr.

Coprinus soboliferus Fr.

Cortinarius maculatus Johnson.

Crepidotus fulvotomentosus Pk.

Crepidotus herbarum Pk.

Flammula ludoviciana (Murrill) Sacc. & Trott.

Flammula subfulva Pk.

Hypholoma hirtosquamulosum Pk.

Lentinus haematopus B.

Lentinus suavissimus Fr.

Lentinus vulpinus Sow. ex Fr.

Acer sp. indet. (*cont.*)
Leptonia subeuchroa Kauffm.
Marasmius fagineus Morg.
Marasmius Rotula Fr.
Marasmius spondoleucus B. & Br.
⎰Mycena adirondackensis Murrill.
⎱Prunulus adirondackensis Murrill.
⎰Mycena niveipes Murrill.
⎱Prunulus niveipes Murrill.
Mycena sanguinolenta Fr.
⎰Omphalia curvipes Pk.
⎱Prunulus curvipes (Pk.) Murrill.
Panus strigosus B. & C.
Panus stypticus (Bull.) ex Fr.
Pholiota adiposa Fr.
Pholiota aegerita Brigant.
Pholiota albocrenulata Pk.
Pholiota aurivella Batsch.
Pholiota squarrosoides Pk.
Pleurotus atrocaeruleus Fr.
Pleurotus corticatus Fr.
Pleurotus lignatilis (P.) ex Fr.
Pleurotus petaloides (Bull.) ex Fr.
Pleurotus sapidus Kalchbr.
Pleurotus striatulus (P.) ex Fr.
Pleurotus subareolatus Pk.
Pleurotus subpalmatus Fr.
Pluteolus expansus Pk.

SPHAEROPSIDALES

Aposphaeria pezizoides Ell. & Ev.
Camarosporium acerinum Ell. & Ev.
Cytospora ambiens Sacc.
Dinemasporium acerinum Pk.
Diplodina anomala Sacc.
Discella pilosula Ell. & Ev.
Haplosporella acerina (Ell. & Barthol.) Ell. & Ev.
Macrophoma albifructa (Pk.) Berl. & Vogl.
Melanconium crinigerum Ell. & Ev.
Naemosphaera Fairmani Sacc.
Phoma consorta C. & E.
⎰Phoma consors (C. & E.) Sacc. Syll.
⎱Phoma pustulata Sacc.
Phyllosticta Aceris Sacc.
Septoria pseudoplatani Rob. & Desm.
Sirothecium nigrum Morg.
⎰Sphaeronema carnea (Ell. & Ev.) Jacz.
⎱Sphaeronemella carnea Ell. & Ev.
Sphaeropsis conspicua House.
Sporonema pallidum Ell. & Ev.
⎰Hendersonia collapsa C. & E.
⎱Stagonospora collapsa (C. & E.) Sacc.
Vermicularia ochrochaeta Ell. & Ev.

MELANCONIALES

Gloeosporium tremellinum Sacc.
Libertella acerina Westd.
Myxosporium seriatum Ell. & Ev.
Myxosporium Tulasnei Sacc.
Naemaspora crocea Auct. Amer.

HYPHOMYCETES
MUCEDINACEAE

Acontium album Morg.
Botrytis fuliginosa C. & E.
Botrytis griseola Sacc.
Botrytis olivascens Ell. & Ev.
Botrytis pannosa Ell. & Ev.
⎰Chromosporium lateritium Cke. & Hark.
⎱Chromosporium Cookei Sacc.
Helicomyces elegans Morg.
⎰Helicomyces fuscus (B. & C.) Morg.
⎱Helicosporium fuscum B. & C.
⎰Helicomyces olivaceus (Pk.) Morg.
⎱Helicosporium olivaceum Pk.
Helicöon aureum (Ell. & Ev.) Morg.
Menispora glauconigra C. & E.
Papulospora sporotrichoides Hotson.
Rhinotrichum ramosissimum B. & C.

DEMATIACEAE

Brachysporium canadense Ell. & Ev.
Cephalothecium roseum Cda.
Clasterosporium caespitulosum Ell. & Ev.
⎰Coniosporium corticola Ell. & Ev.
⎱Goniosporium corticale Ell. & Ev.
⎰Coniothecium effusum Cda.
⎱Sporidesmium Lepraria B.
Dendryphium Ellisii Cke.
Dendryphium? intermixtum Fairman.
Fumago vagans Pers.
Helicoma Berkeleyi M. A. Curtis.
⎰Helicoma Muelleri Cda.
⎱Helicosporium Mulleri (Cda.) Sacc.
?Helminthosporium attenuatum C. & P.
Helminthosporium brachytrichum C. & E.
Helminthosporium dendroideum B.
Helminthosporium macrocarpon Grev.
Helminthosporium persistens Cke.
Helminthosporium septemseptatum Pk.
⎰Hormiscium uniforme (Pk.) Sacc.
⎱Torula uniformis Pk.
Ramularia magnusiana (Sacc.) Lindau.
Septonema breviusculum B. & C.
⎰Speira effusa (Pk.) Sacc.
⎱Synphragmidium effusum Pk.
Sporoschisma mirabile B. & Br.
Sporidesmium antiquum Cda.
Sporidesmium aurantiacum B. & C.
Sporidesmium compositum B. & Rav.
Sporidesmium hysterioideum C. & E.
⎰Epochnium macrosporoideum B. & Br.
⎱Stemphylium macrosporoideum (B. & Br.)
  Sacc.
Streptothrix atra B. & C.
Torula ligniperda (Willk.) Sacc.
Torula saccharina Heald & Poole.
Zygodesmus limoniisporus Ell. & Ev.

Acer sp. indet. (*cont.*)

STILBACEAE

Arthrobotryum robustum C. & E.
Arthrosporium compositum Ell.
Atractium flammeum B. & Rav., var. minor Rav.
{ Graphium giganteum (Pk.) Sacc.
{ Stilbum giganteum Pk.
Septosporium velutinum C. & E.
Stilbum aeruginosum Desm.
Stilbum aleuriatum B. & C.
Stilbum atrocephalum Ell.
Stilbum cinnabarinum Mont.
Stilbum parvulum C. & E.

TUBERCULARIACEAE

Dendrodochium pallidum Pk.
Fusarium Macounii Dearness.
Fusarium platanoides Oud.
Tubercularia confluens P. ex Fr.
Tubercularia nigricans (Bull.) ex Lk.

MISCELLANEA

Bactridium Ellisii B.
Pycnochytrium globosum Schrt.
Rhizoctonia aurantiaca Ell. & Ev.
Uncinula Aceris (DC.) Sacc.?

HIPPOCASTANEAE

Aesculus californica Nutt.
Cladosporium herbarum (P.) ex Lk.
Diaporthe Aesculi Cke. & Hark.
Diatrype asterostoma B. & C.
Eutypella aesculina Ell. & Ev.
Gloeosporium carpigenum Cke.
Nectria cinnabarina (Tode) ex Fr.
Nectria zealandica Cke.
Phyllactinia corylea (P.) ex Karst.
Polystictus hirsutus (Wulf.) ex Fr.
Septoria Aesculi (Lib.) Westd.
Septoria aesculina Thm.
{ Ascomyces deformans Hark.
{ Ascomyces deformans, var. Aesculi Ell. & Ev.
{ Exoascus Aesculi (Ell. & Ev.) Patterson.
{ Taphrina Aesculi (Ell. & Ev.) Giesenhagen.
Valsaria majuscula Cke. & Hark.

Aesculus glabra Willd.
Aecidium Aesculi Ell. & Kellerm.
Aspergillus glaucus Lk.
Berlesiella hispida Morg.
Cucurbitaria erratica Pk.
Eurotium herbariorum (Wigg.) ex Lk.
Nectria cinnabarina (Tode) ex Fr.
{ Guignardia Aesculi (Pk.) V. B. Stewart.
{ Phyllosticta Aesculi Ell. & Martin.
{ Phyllosticta aesculicola Sacc.
{ Phyllosticta Paviae Desm.
Phyllosticta sphaeropsoidea Ell. & Ev.

Sclerotium Aesculi S.
Septoria Aesculi (Lib.) Westd.
Septoria glabra Ell. & Ev.
Uncinula flexuosa Pk.
Aesculus glabra Willd., var. **arguta** (Buckley) B. L. Robinson.
Aecidium Aesculi Ell. & Kellerm.
Guignardia Aesculi (Pk.) V. B. Stewart.
Macrosporium baccatum Ell. & Kellerm.
Nectria cinnabarina (Tode) ex Fr.
{ Phyllosticta aesculicola Sacc.
{ Phyllosticta Paviae Desm.
Septoria Aesculi (Lib.) Westd.
Uncinula flexuosa Pk.
Aesculus Hippocastanum L.
Aecidium Aesculi Ell. & Kellerm.
Agaricus comosus Fr., var. albus Pk.
Botryosphaeria Ribis (Tode ex Fr.) Grossenbacher & Duggar.
Botryosphaeria Ribis (Tode ex Fr.) Grossenbacher & Duggar, var. chromogena Shear et al.
Collybia velutipes Wm. Curtis.
Diplodia Aesculi Lév.
Dothiorella Hippocastani Ell. & Ev.
Fomes applanatus (P. ex Wallr.) Gill.
Fusarium roseum Lk.
Fusidium candidulum Sacc.
Glomerella cingulata (Stoneman) Spaulding & v. Schrenk.
{ Guignardia Aesculi (Pk.) V. B. Stewart.
{ Laestadia Aesculi Pk.
{ Phyllosticta aesculicola Sacc.
{ Phyllosticta Paviae Desm.
Haplosporella Aesculi (Faut. & Roum.) Fairman.
Haplosporella Hippocastani Ell. & Ev.
Helotium humile Sacc.
Phomopsis coneglanensis (Sacc.) Traverso.
{ Macrophoma sphaeropsoidea (Ell. & Ev.) Tassi.
{ Phyllosticta sphaeropsoidea Ell. & Ev.
Monochaetia Desmazierii Sacc.
Mycena corticola (Schum.) ex Fr.
Nectria cinnabarina (Tode) ex Fr.
Phoma Clintonii Pk.
Phomopsis carposchiza Fairman.
Phyllosticta Aesculi Ell. & Martin.
Pleurotus sapidus Kalchbr.
Pleurotus ulmarius (Bull.) ex Fr.
Polyporus caudicinus (Scop. ex Fr.) Murrill.
Polyporus squamosus (Huds.) ex Fr.
Rhabdospora baculum Grove.
Schizophyllum alneum (L. ex Fr.) Schrt.
Schizothyrella Hippocastani Ell. & Ev.
Septoria Aesculi (Lib.) Westd.
Septoria Hippocastani B. & Br.
Tubercularia carpigena Cda.
Tubercularia vulgaris Tode ex Fr.

Aesculus Hippocastanum (*cont.*)
Uncinula flexuosa Pk.
Volvaria bombycina (Schaeff.) ex Fr.
Aesculus octandra Marsh.
Cercospora aesculina Ell. & Kellerm.
Corticium scutellare B. & C.
⎰Guignardia Aesculi (Pk.) V. B. Stewart.
⎱Phyllosticta Aesculi Ell. & Martin.
│Phyllosticta aesculicola Sacc.
Phyllosticta sphaeropsoidea Ell. & Ev.
⎰Agaricus Aesculi (Fr.) Murrill.
⎱Boletus Aesculi-flavae S.
│Polyporus Aesculi Fr.
Poria incrassata (B. & C.) Burt.
Uncinula flexuosa Pk.
Aesculus octandra Marsh, var. **hybrida** (DC.)
Sarg.
Phyllosticta Paviae Ell. & Ev.
Aesculus Pavia L.
Diplodia Aesculi Lév.
⎰Guignardia Aesculi (Pk.) V. B. Stewart.
⎱Phyllosticta Aesculi Ell. & Martin.
│Phyllosticta aesculicola Sacc.
Phyllosticta Paviae Desm.
Phyllosticta sphaeropsoidea Ell. & Ev.
Uncinula flexuosa Pk.
Aesculus sp. indet.
Diatrype disciformis (Hoffm.) ex Fr.
⎰Gibberella Saubinetii (Mont.) Sacc.
⎱Sphaeria Saubinetii Mont.
Hymenochaete agglutinans Ell.
⎰Arcyria globosa S.
⎱Lachnobolus globosus (S.) Rostf.
Patellaria congregata B. & C.
Peziza furfuracea Fr.
Pleurotus salignus (P.) ex Fr.
Sphaerella maculiformis (P. ex Fr.) Awd.
Sphaerella punctiformis (P.) ex Fr.
Sphaeria aesculicola Fr.
Stereum complicatum Fr.
Trichia varia P.
Vermicularia involucri S.
Vermicularia petiolorum S.
⎰?Leotia circinans Burt.
⎱Vibrissea lutea Pk.

SAPINDACEAE

Serjania caracasana Willd.
Coniothyrium insuetum Syd.
Dicoccum Cupaniae Syd.
Meliola Serjaniae F. L. Stevens.
Nectria prodigiosa Syd.
Phyllachora insueta Syd.
Micropuccinia Arechavaleteae (Speg.) Arth. &
Jackson.
Serjania polyphylla (L.) Radlk.
Meliola ambigua Pat. & Gaill.

Meliola Serjaniae F. L. Stevens.
Phyllachora serjaniicola Chardon.
Serjania racemosa Schum.
Fusarium Serjaniae Syd.
⎰Micropuccinia Arechavaletae (Speg.) Arth. &
⎱Jackson.
│Puccinia Arechavaletae Speg.
Puccinia Serjaniae Ell. & Ev.
Serjania trifoliolata Radlk.
Puccinia Arechavaletae Speg.
Paullinia pinnata L.
Acremonium Meliola F. L. Stevens.
Calonectria melioloides Speg.
Dexteria pulchella F. L. Stevens.
Helminthosporium glabroides F. L. Stevens.
Helminthosporium Helleri F. L. Stevens.
Meliola Hessii F. L. Stevens.
Meliola Paulliniae F. L. Stevens.
Perisporium Paulliniae F. L. Stevens.
Urvillea seriana (L.) H. B. K.
Puccinia Arechavaletae Speg.
Cardiospermum coluteoides H. B. K.
Cardiospermum grandiflorum Sw.
⎰Micropuccinia Arechavaletae (Speg.) Arth. &
⎱Jackson.
Puccinia Arechavaletae Speg.
Cardiospermum Halicacabum L.
Aecidium Reichei Diet.
⎰Micropuccinia Arechavaletae (Speg.) Arth. &
⎱Jackson.
Puccinia Arechavaletae Speg.
Cardiospermum microcarpum H. B. K.
⎰Micropuccinia Arechavaletae (Speg.) Arth. &
⎱Jackson.
│Puccinia Arechavaletae Speg.
Puccinia Serjaniae Ell. & Ev.
Thouinia acuminata Watson.
Thouinia Pringlei Watson.
Melasmia Thouiniae Syd.
Thouinia striata Rad.
Cercospora Thouiniae F. L. Stevens.
Meliola Thouiniae Earle.
Thouinia sp. indet.
Cladosporium hypophloeum B. & C.
Allophyllus cominia (L.) Sw.
Meliola ambigua Pat. & Gaill.
Allophyllus crassinervis Radlk.
Meliola Thouiniae Earle.
Thouinidium decandrum H.B.K.
Skierka Holwayi Arth.
Sapindus Drummondi Hook. & Arn.
Cylindrosporium griseum Heald & Wolf.
Uncinula circinata C. & P.
Sapindus marginatus Willd.
⎰Anthostoma confusa (B. & C.) Sacc.
⎱Sphaeria appendiculosa B. & C.
Cylindrosporium griseum Heald & Wolf.
Uncinula circinata C. & P.

Sapindus mukorossi Gaertn., var. **carinatus** Auct.
Corticium Stevensii (Noack) Burt.
Sapindus Saponaria L.
Odontia crustosa P. ex Fr., var. lutescens Pat.
Sapindus sp. indet.
Cylindrosporium griseum Heald & Wolf.
Glomerella cingulata (Stoneman) Spaulding & v. Schrenk.
Uncinula circinata C. & P.
Melicocca bijuga L.
Ascochytella Melicoccae Fragoso & Ciferri.
⎰Amauroderma flaviporum Murrill.
⎱Ganoderma flaviporum (Murrill) Sacc. & Trott.
Meliola Sapindacearum Speg.
⎰Podoscypha decolorans (B. & C.) Pat.
⎱Thelephora decolorans B. & C.
Septoria Melicoccae Fragoso & Ciferri.
Stereum fasciatum Fr.
Tubulina stipitata (B. & Rav.) E. P. Sheldon.
Cupania americana L.
Calonectria erubescens (Rob.) Sacc.
Cionothrix Cupaniae Arth.
Meliola Cupaniae F. L. Stevens.
Meliola praetervisa Gaill.
Meliola Thouiniae Earle.
⎰Ctenoderma cristatum Syd.
⎱Uromyces Cupaniae Arth. & Johnston.
Cupania glabra Sw.
Cionothrix Cupaniae Arth.
Cupania guatemalensis Radlk.
Cercospora Cupaniae Syd.
Dicoccum Cupaniae Syd.
Irene glabroides (F. L. Stevens) Toro.
Cupania macrophylla Rich.
⎰Ctenoderma cristatum Syd.
⎱Uromyces Cupaniae Arth. & Johnston.
Blighia sapida Koen.
Colletotrichum gloeosporioides Penz.
Tryblidium hysterineum Dufour.
Koelreuteria paniculata Laxm.
Nectria cinnabarina (Tode) ex Fr.
Hypelate trifoliata Sw.
Meliola glabra B. & C.
Sapindaceae gen. indet.
Botrytis seriata Ell. & Ev.
Catacauma cubense Theissen & Syd.
Cladosporium hypophloeum B. & C.
Dothidea repens B.
Melasmia Sapindacearum Henn.
Meliola Wrightii B. & C.

SABIACEAE

Meliosma Herbertii Rolfe.
Podoscypha radicans (B. & C.) Duss.
⎰Melanopus marasmioides Pat.
⎱Polyporus marasmioides (Pat.) Sacc. & D. Sacc.
⎩Polyporus marasmioides (Pat.) Murrill.

Meliosma Pardonii King & Urb.
⎰Podoscypha radicans (B. & C.) Duss.
⎱Thelephora radicans B. & C.

BALSAMINACEAE

Impatiens Balsamina L.
Fusarium acuminatum Ell. & Ev. emend. Wr.
Puccinia Impatientis Arth. I.
Rhizoctonia Solani Kühn.
Septoria nolitangere Gerard.
Vermicularia Balsamitae S.
Impatiens biflora Walt.
⎰Aecidium impatientatum S.
⎱Aecidium Impatientis S.
⎱Caeoma impatientatum S.
⎱Dicaeoma Impatientis Arth. I.
⎱Puccinia Elymi-Impatientis J. J. Davis. I.
⎱Puccinia Impatientis Arth. I.
⎱Puccinia Impatientis-Elymi Klebahn. I.
⎱Puccinia perminuta Arth. I.
⎩Uredo schweinitziana Spreng.
?Puccinia procera Diet. & Holw. I.
Gloeosporium Impatientis H. W. Anderson.
Leptosphaeria subconica (C. & P.) Sacc.
Naevia canadica Rehm.
Ophiobolus porphyrogonus (Tode ex Fr.) Sacc.
⎰Peronospora Impatientis Ell. & Ev.
⎱Peronospora obducens Schrt.
⎱Plasmopara Impatientis (Ell. & Ev.) Berl.
⎱Plasmopara obducens Schrt.
⎩Rhysotheca obducens (Schrt.) G. W. Wilson.
Phoma pleosporoides Sacc.
Physarum sinuosum (Bull.) Weinm.
⎰Dicaeoma argentatum (Wint.) O. Kuntze.
⎱Dicaeoma nolitangeris (Cda.) Arth.
⎱Puccinia argentata Wint.
⎩Puccinia nolitangeris Cda.
Ramularia Impatientis Pk.
⎰Septoria nolitangere Gerard.
⎱Septoria nolitangere Thm.
⎰Mycosphaerella Impatientis (Pk. & Clinton) House.
⎩Sphaerella Impatientis Pk. & Clinton.
Tuberculina persicina (Ditm.) Sacc.
Vermicularia subeffigurata S., var. Impatientis Sacc.
Impatiens pallida Nutt.
⎰Aecidium Impatientis S.
⎱Caeoma impatientatum S.
⎱Dicaeoma Impatientis Arth. I.
⎩Puccinia Impatientis Arth. I.
?Puccinia procera Diet. & Holw. I.
Helotium herbarum (P.) Fr.
Peronospora Corydalis DBy. ?
⎰Peronospora Impatientis Ell. & Ev.
⎱Peronospora obducens Schrt.
⎱Plasmopara Impatientis (Ell. & Ev.) Berl.
⎱Plasmopara obducens Schrt.
⎩Rhysotheca obducens (Schrt.) G. W. Wilson.

Impatiens pallida (*cont.*)
- Dicaeoma nolitangeris (Cda.) Arth.
- Puccinia argentata Wint.
- Puccinia nolitangeris Cda.
- Ramularia Impatientis Pk.
- Septoria nolitangere Gerard.
- Sphaerella Impatientis Pk. & Clinton.

Impatiens sp. indet.
- Leptosphaeria agnita (Desm.) DeNot.
- Leptosphaeria dumetorum Niessl.
- Phialea cyathoidea (Bull. ex Fr.) Gill., var. albidulum Hedw.
- Phialea scutula (P.) Gill.
- Pythium debaryanum Hesse.
- Rhizoctonia Solani Kühn.
- Trichopeziza sulfurea (P.) Fckl.

RHAMNACEAE

Berchemia scandens (Hill) Trel.
- Aecidium pulcherrimum Rav.
- Aecidium Rhamni P.
- Dicaeoma Rhamni (Wettst.) O. Kuntze. I.
- Puccinia coronata Cda. I.
- Eutypella Berchemiae (Cke.) Sacc.
- Valsa Berchemiae Cke.
- Glonium medium (Cke.) Sacc.
- Hysterium medium Cke.
- Helminthosporium lanceolatum Cke.
- Peziza earoleuca Rav. Fung. Am.
- Hendersonia sp. indet.
- Sphaeria Berchemiae B. & Rav.
- Tryblidiella rufula (Spreng. ex Fr.) Sacc.
- Tryblidium rufulum (Spreng.) ex Fr.

Rhamnus alnifolia L'Her.
- Aecidium crassum P.
- Aecidium Rhamni P.
- Dicaeoma Rhamni (Wettst.) O. Kuntze. I.
- Puccinia coronata Cda. I.
- Puccinia Rhamni Wettst. I.
- Cercospora Rhamni Fckl.
- Microsphaera Alni (DC.) Wint.†
- Sphaerographium niveum Dearness & House.

Rhamnus californica Eschsch.
- Capnodium Rhamni Cke. & Hark.
- Diplodia Frangulae Fckl.
- Phoma communis Rob.
- Phoma rhamnicola Cke. & Hark.
- Pleospora Frangulae Fckl.
- Micropuccinia mesnieriana (Thm.) Arth. & Jackson.
- Puccinia mesnieriana Thm.
- Septoria Rhamni-catharticae Ces.
- Tympanis Frangulae Fr.

Rhamnus caroliniana Walt.
- Dicaeoma Rhamni (Wettst.) O. Kuntze. I.
- Puccinia coronata Cda. I.

Rhamnus cathartica L.
- Aecidium crassum P.
- Dicaeoma Rhamni (Wettst.) O. Kuntze. I.
- Puccinia coronata Cda. I.
- Puccinia Lolii Nielsen. l.
- Puccinia Rhamni Wettst. I.
- Cercospora Rhamni Fckl.
- Torula ligniperda (Willk.) Sacc.

Rhamnus crocea Nutt.
- Puccinia coronata Cda. I.
- Ceuthospora foliicola (Lib.) Cke.
- Cytospora foliicola Lib.
- Micropuccinia mesnieriana (Thm.) Arth. & Jackson.
- Puccinia digitata Ell. & Hark.
- Puccinia digitata Ell. & Hark., var. ramicola Henn.

Rhamnus insularis Kellogg.
- Hymenochaete rubiginosa (Fr.) Lév.
- Phaenangium sphaeroides Ell. & Ev.
- Puccinia mesnieriana Thm.

Rhamnus lanceolata Pursh.
- Aecidium crassum P.
- Aecidium Rhamni P.
- Dicaeoma Rhamni (Wettst.) O. Kuntze. I.
- Puccinia coronata Cda. I.
- Puccinia coronifera Klebahn. I.
- Puccinia Rhamni Wettst. I.
- Cercospora aeruginosa Cke.
- Cercospora Rhamni Fckl.
- Dacryomyces deliquescens (Bull.) ex Duby.
- Hysterographium elongatum (Wahl.) Cda.
- Melanomma alpinum Speg.
- Polyporus subspadiceus Fr.
- Speira toruloides Cda.

Rhamnus latifolia L'Her.
- Puccinia mesnieriana Thm.
- Puccinia Rhamni Wettst. I.

Rhamnus purshiana DC.
- Aecidium Rhamni P.
- Puccinia coronata Cda. I.
- Puccinia Rhamni Wettst. I.
- Coniophora olivacea (Fr.) Bres.
- Cylindrosporium Rhamni Ell. & Ev.
- Fomes igniarius (L. ex Fr.) Gill.
- Marssonia Rhamni Ell. & Ev.
- Marssonina Rhamni (Ell. & Ev.) Magn.
- Phyllosticta rhamnigena Sacc.
- Septoria Blasdalei Sacc. & Syd.
- Septoria variegata Ell. & Ev.

Rhamnus Smithii Greene.
- Dicaeoma Rhamni (Wettst.) O. Kuntze. I.
- Puccinia Rhamni Wettst. I.

Rhamnus tomentella Benth.
- Ovularia rhamnigena Ell. & Ev.
- Ovularia rhamnigera Ell. & Ev. sec. Sacc.

Rhamnus sp. indet.
    Hypoxylon atropurpureum Fr.
    Nectria Cucurbitula (Tode) ex Fr.
    Sphaeropsis Rhamni Cke.

Krugiodendron ferreum (Vahl) Urb.
    Meliola Thouiniae Earle.

Ceanothus americanus L.
    Puccinia Ceanothi Arth. I.
    Cercospora Ceanothi Kellerm. & Swingle.
    Cucurbitaria Ceanothi Dearness & House.
    Diaporthe minuta Dearness & House.
    Didymosphaeria Housei Dearness.
    {Discella microspora B. & C.
    {Discula microspora (B. & C.) Sacc.
    Frankia Ceanothi Atk.
    {Macrophoma Ceanothi Dearness & House.
    {Macrophoma peckiana Dearness & House.
    Microdiplodia Ceanothi Dearness & House.
    {Erysiphe Ceanothi S.
    {Microsphaera Alni (DC.) Wint. †
    {Microsphaera Ceanothi (S.) Pk.
    Oospora candidula Sacc., var. carpogena Sacc.
    Phyllosticta Ceanothi Miles.
    Physalospora ceanothina (Pk.) Sacc.
    {Haplosporella Ceanothi (Dearness & House)
      Petrak & Syd.
    Sphaeropsis Ceanothi Dearness & House.
    Thyridium Ceanothi Dearness & House.
    Valsa ambiens (P.) ex Fr.

Ceanothus arboreus Greene.
    Cercospora catalinae Ell. & Ev.
    Cercospora fuliginosa Ell. & Ev.
    Cylindrosporium Ceanothi Ell. & Ev.

Ceanothus azureus Desf.
    {Dicaeoma Ceanothi (Arth.) Arth. & Fromme. I.
    {Puccinia Ceanothi Arth. I.

Ceanothus californicus Kellogg.
    Cylindrosporium Ceanothi Ell. & Ev.

Ceanothus integerrimus Hook & Arn.
    Stictis chrysopsis Ell. & Ev.

Ceanothus ovatus Desf.
    {Aecidium Ceanothi Ell. & Kellerm.
    {Dicaeoma Ceanothi (Arth.) Arth. & Fromme.
      I.
    {Puccinia Ceanothi Arth. I.
    Cercospora Ceanothi Kellerm. & Swingle.
    Diplodia Ceanothi Ell. & Barthol.
    Valsa ambiens (P.) ex Fr.

Ceanothus pubescens (Torr. & Gr.) Rydb.
    {Dicaeoma Ceanothi (Arth.) Arth. & Fromme.
      I.
    {Puccinia Ceanothi Arth. I.

Ceanothus sanguineus Pursh.
    Cylindrosporium Ceanothi Ell. & Ev.
    Cylindrosporium simile Pk.
    Microsphaera Alni (DC.) Wint., var. divari-
      cata M. E. Jones, nom. nud.

Ceanothus thyrsiflorus Esch.
    Cylindrosporium Ceanothi Ell. & Ev.
    Schizophyllum commune Fr.

Ceanothus velutinus Dougl.
    Cenangium aureum Ell. & Ev.
    Cenangium furfuraceum (Roth) De Not.
    Cylindrosporium Ceanothi Ell. & Ev.
    Harknessia aggregata Syd.

Ceanothus sp. indet.
    Cytospora Ceanothi S.
    Didymosphaeria Ceanothi (Cke. & Hark.)
      Berl. & Vogl.
    {Diatrype Ceanothi Cke. & Hark.
    {Eutypella Ceanothi (Cke. & Hark.) Berl.
    Gloniopsis connivens (Cke. & Hark.) Pazschke.
    {Hysterium Ceanothi Phil. & Hark.
    {Hysterographium Ceanothi (Phil. & Hark.)
      Berl. & Vogl.
    {Hysterographium prominens (Phil. & Hark.)
      Berl. & Vogl.
    Peniophora Peckii Burt.
    {Polyporus igniarius (L.) ex Fr.
    {Pyropolyporus igniarius (L. ex Fr.) Murrill.
    Sphaeria vacciniicola S.?
    {Leptosphaeria Ceanothi (Cke. & Hark.) Berl.
      & Vogl.
    {Sphaerulina Ceanothi (Cke. & Hark.) Berl.
    Thyridium tuberculatum Rehm.
    Valsa Ceanothi Rehm. 1911.
    {Sphaeria Ceanothi S.
    {Valsa Ceanothi (S.) Cke. 1877.

Colubrina reclinata (L'Her.) Brongn.
    Amerosporium Colubrinae Fragoso & Ciferri.
    {Asterina Colubrinae Ell. & Kelsey.
    {Dictyopeltis Colubrinae (Ell. & Kelsey)
      Theissen.
    {Dictyothyrium Colubrinae (Ell. & Kelsey)
      Theissen.
    Phyllosticta Colubrinae Fragoso & Ciferri.

Adolphia infesta Meisn.
    Cytosporina Adolphiae Turconi.
    Phyllachora Adolphiae Ell. & Kellerm.
    Phyllachora mexicana Turconi.

Gouania lupuloides (L.) Urb.
    Catacaumella Gouaniae F. L. Stevens.
    Meliola tenuissima F. L. Stevens.
    Phacellula Gouaniae Syd.
    {Bullaria Gouaniae (Holw.) Arth.
    {Puccinia Gouaniae Holw.
    {Uredo Gouaniae Lagerh.
    {Bullaria invaginata (Arth. & Johnston) Arth.
      & Mains.
    {Puccinia invaginata Arth. & Johnston.
    {Uredo Gouaniae Ell. & Kelsey.
    {Nigredo Gouaniae (Kern) Arth.
    {Uromyces Gouaniae Kern.

Gouania polygama (Jacq.) Urb.
    Catacaumella Gouaniae F. L. Stevens.

Gouania polygama (*cont.*)
- Bullaria Gouaniae (Holw.) Arth.
- Puccinia Gouaniae Holw.
- Bullaria invaginata (Arth. & Johnston) Artn.
- Puccinia invaginata Arth. & Johnston.
- Uredo Gouaniae Ell. & Kelsey.

Gouania tomentosa Jacq.
- Catacauma contractum Syd.
- Catacaumella Gouaniae F. L. Stevens.
- Darluca Filum (Biv.) Cast.
- Dendrodochium Gouaniae Syd.
- Eudarluca australis Speg.
- Meliola tenuissima F. L. Stevens.
- Phacellula Gouaniae Syd.
- Puccinia Gouaniae Holw.

VITACEAE

Vitis species variae.
- Ascochyta Ellisii Thm.
- Depazea labruscae Engelm.
- Macrophoma Ampelopsidis (C. & E.) Berl. & Vogl.?
- Naemaspora ampelicida Engelm.
- Phoma Ampelopsidis (C. & E.) Sacc.?
- Phoma ustulatum B. & C.
- Phoma uvarum (B. & C.) Sacc.
- Phoma uvicola B. & C.
- Phoma uvicola B. & C., var. labruscae (Engelm.) Thm.
- Phyllosticta Ampelopsidis Ell. & Martin.
- Phyllosticta labruscae (Engelm.) Thm.
- Phyllosticta viticola (B. & C.) Thm.
- Sacidium viticola (B. & C.) Cke.
- Septoria viticola B. & C.
- Sphaeropsis Ampelopsidis C. & E.?
- Sphaeropsis uvarum B. & C.

- Carlia Bidwellii (Ell.) Magn.
- Guignardia Bidwellii (Ell.) Viala & Ravaz.
- Laestadia Bidwellii (Ell.) Viala & Ravaz.
- Physalospora Bidwellii (Ell.) Sacc.
- Sphaeria Bidwellii Ell.

Vitis aestivalis Michx.
- Aleurodiscus botryosus Burt.
- Cladosporium viticola Ces.
- Corticium crocicreas B. & C.
- Corticium viticola Fr.
- Peniophora viticola (S.) v. Höhnel & Litschauer.
- Thelephora viticola Fr.
- Diplodia viticola Desm.
- ?Diplodia Vitis Desm.
- Discosia Artocreas (Tode) ex Fr., var. viticola Cke.
- Excipula viticola S.
- Exidia glandulosa (Bull.) ex Fr.
- Gnomonia pruina (S.) Cke.
- Sphaeria pruina S.

- Hendersonia ampelina Thm.
- Hydnum luteopallidum S.
- Hymenochaete corrugata (Fr.) Lév.
- Leptothyrium longisporum Thm.
- Macrophoma longispora (Thm.) Berl. & Vogl.
- Phoma longispora (Thm.) Cke.
- Naematelia nucleata (S.) Fr.
- Peniophora cinerea (P. ex Fr.) Cke.
- Pestalozzia pezizoides De Not.
- Coniothyrium ampelinum Cke.
- Phoma ampelina (Cke.) Sacc.
- Phoma ustulata B. & C.
- Phoma uvicola B. & C.
- Phomopsis viticola Sacc.
- Dothidea picea B. & C.
- Phyllachora picea (B. & C.) Sacc.
- Phyllosticta labruscae Thm.
- Pistillaria viticola Pk.
- Peronospora viticola (B. & C.) DBy.
- Plasmopara viticola (B. & C.) Berl. & DeToni.
- Rhysotheca viticola (B. & C.) G. W. Wilson.
- Pyrenochaeta Vitis Viala & Sauvageau.
- Rhytisma monogramme B. & C. p. p
- Rhytisma Vitis S. p. p.
- Septoria ampelina B. & C.
- Solenia poriiformis (P. ex Fr.) Fckl.
- Sphaerella sparsa (Wallr.) Awd.
- Sporocybe byssoides (P.) ex Fr.
- Oidium Tuckeri B.
- Uncinula Ampelopsidis Pk.
- Uncinula necator (S.) Burrill.
- Uncinula spiralis B. & C.

Vitis arborea L.
- Diatrype Vitis (Ell. & Ev.) Sacc.
- Diatrypella Vitis Ell. & Ev.
- Podosporium rigidum S.

Vitis arizonica Engelm.
- Peronospora viticola (B. & C.) DBy.

Vitis Berlandieri Planch.
- Coniothyrium Berlandieri Viala & Sauvageau.
- Rhytisma monogramme B. & C. p. p.
- Rhytisma Vitis S. p. p.
- Pyrenochaeta Vitis Viala & Sauvageau.

Vitis bicolor Le Conte.
- Eutypa viticola Sacc. non S.
- Eutypella viticola (Sacc.) Berl.
- Eutypella Vitis (S.) Ell. & Ev.
- Valsa Vitis (S.) M. A. Curtis.
- Plasmopara viticola (B. & C.) Berl. & De Toni.
- Rhysotheca viticola (B. & C.) G. W. Wilson.
- Sphaerobolus stellatus Tode ex Fr.

Vitis californica Benth.
- Cercospora Roesleri (Catt.) Sacc.
- Septosporium Fuckelii Thm.
- Cercospora viticola (Ces.) Sacc.
- Cladosporium viticola Ces.
- Fusicladium minutulum Sacc.
- Macrosporium caudatum C. & E.

Vitis californica (*cont.*)
{ Peronospora viticola (B. & C.) DBy.
{ Rhysotheca viticola (B. & C.) G. W. Wilson.
  Phoma Vitis Bon.
{ Septosporium Fuckelii Scribner nec Thm.
{ Septosporium heterosporum Ell. & Gall.
  Uncinula necator (S.) Burrill.

Vitis candicans Engelm.
  Coniothyrium Berlandieri Viala & Sauvageau.
{ Guignardia Bidwellii (Ell.) Viala & Ravaz.
{ Laestadia Bidwellii (Ell.) Viala & Ravaz.
  Pyrenochaeta Vitis Viala & Sauvageau.

Vitis caribaea DC.
  Capnodinula Tonduzi Speg.
  Fumago vagans Fr.
{ Phakopsora Vitis Syd.
{ Physopella Vitis Arth.
{ Uredo Vialae Lagerh.
{ Uredo Vitis Thm.
  Rhysotheca viticola (B. & C.) G. W. Wilson.

Vitis cinerea Engelm.
  Coniothyrium Berlandieri Viala & Sauvageau.
  Guignardia Bidwellii (Ell.) Viala & Ravaz.
{ Plasmopara viticola (B. & C.) Berl. & DeToni.
{ Rhysotheca viticola (B. & C.) G. W. Wilson.
{ Uncinula Ampelopsidis Pk.
{ Uncinula necator (S.) Burrill.

Vitis Coignetiae Puliat.

Vitis doaniana Sweet.
  Guignardia Bidwellii (Ell.) Viala & Ravaz.

Vitis cordifolia Michx.
  Ascochyta ampelina Sacc.
  Cercospora viticola (Ces.) Sacc.
  Corticium calceum (P.) Fr.
{ Guignardia Bidwellii (Ell.) Viala & Ravaz.
{ Laestadia Bidwellii (Ell.) Viala & Ravaz.
{ Phoma ustulatum B. & C. (?).
{ Phoma uvicola B. & C.
{ Phyllosticta labruscae Thm.
{ Phyllosticta viticola (B. & C.) Thm.
  Lophiostoma stenostomum Ell. & Ev.
  Sclerotiopsis concava (Desm.) Shear & Dodge.
{ Peronospora viticola (B. & C.) DBy.
{ Plasmopara viticola (B. & C.) Berl. & De Toni.
{ Rhysotheca viticola (B. & C.) G. W. Wilson.
  Phoma ustulata B. & C.
  Pyrenochaeta Vitis Viala & Sauvageau.
  Sacidium Vitis Ell. & Ev.
  Septoria kellermaniana Thm.
{ Uncinula americana Howe.
{ Uncinula necator (S.) Burrill.
{ Uncinula spiralis B. & C.

Vitis flexuosa Thunb.
  Uncinula necator (S.) Burrill.

Vitis indivisa Willd.
  Cercospora truncata Ell. & Ev.
  Cercospora viticola (Ces.) Sacc

Vitis labrusca L.

PHYCOMYCETES
{ Botrytis viticola B. & C.
{ Peronospora viticola (B. & C.) DBy.
{ Plasmopara viticola (B. & C.) Berl. & De Toni.
{ Rhysotheca viticola (B. & C.) G. W. Wilson.

PEZIZINEAE
{ Calloria vinosa (A. & S.) ex Fr.
{ Orbilia vinosa (A. & S. ex Fr.) Karst.
{ Peziza vinosa A. & S. ex Fr.
{ Cenangium viticola (S.) Fckl.
{ Peziza viticola S.
  Tympanis viticola (S.) Fr.
  Helotium pullatum Gerard.
{ Lachnella ascoboloidea (S.) Fr.
{ Peziza ascoboloidea S.
{ Patellaria viticola (P.) Sacc.
{ Peziza viticola P.
{ Propolis prominula (S.) Cke.
{ Stictis prominula S.
{ Peziza penicillata S.
{ Trichopeziza penicillata (S.) Sacc.
{ Peziza Vitis S.
{ Trichopeziza Vitis (S.) Sacc.

HYSTERIINEAE
{ Gloniopsis australis (Duby) Sacc.
{ Hysterium australe Duby.
{ Hypoderma commune (Fr.) Duby.
{ Hysterium commune Fr.
{ Hypoderma Rubi (P. ex Fr.) DeNot.
{ Hysterium Rubi P. ex Fr.
{ Hysterium viticola C. & P.
{ Hysterographium viticola (C. & P.) Rehm.

PERISPORIALES
{ Erysiphe necator S.
{ Uncinula americana Howe.
{ Uncinula Ampelopsidis Pk.
{ Uncinula necator (S.) Burrill.
{ Uncinula spiralis B. & C.
{ Uncinula subfusca B. & C.
  Uncinula spiralis B. & C., var. racemorum
    Thm.

DOTHIDEALES
{ Dothidea viticola S.
{ Phyllachora viticola (S.) Sacc.

SPHAERIALES
  Acrospermum compressum Tode ex Fr.
  Acrospermum foliicola B.
  Acrospermum Ravenelii B. & C.
{ Cryptosphaeria propagata (Plowr.) Sacc.
{ ?Diatrype Vitis (S.) B. & C.
{ Eutypa viticola Sacc.
{ Sphaeria propagata Plowr.
{ Sphaeria Vitis S.
{ Valsa Vitis (S.) B. & C.

Vitis labrusca (*cont.*)

Leptostroma sphaeroides Fr.

{ Lophiostoma sexnucleatum Cke.
Lophiotrema peckiana (Sacc.) House.
Lophiotrema sexnucleatum (Cke.) Sacc., var. peckianum Sacc.

Physalospora baccae Cavara.

{ Sphaerella sentina (Fr.) Sacc.
Sphaeria sentina Fr.

Sphaeria ampelos S.

{ Diatrype insitiva (Tode) ex Fr.
Sphaeria insitiva Tode ex Fr.
Valsaria insitiva (Tode ex Fr.) Ces. & De Not.

BASIDIOMYCETES

{ Corticium albidocarneum (S.) Rav.
Thelephora albidocarnea S.

Cyathus striatus Willd. ex P.

{ Cyphella villosa (P. ex Fr.) Karst.
Peziza villosa P. ex Fr.

Dacryomyces viticola S.

Ditiola sulcata (Tode) ex Fr.

Marasmius viticola B. & C.

Merulius Corium Fr.

{ Boletus papyraceus S.
Polyporus papyraceus S.
Polyporus vaporarius, var. b. Fr.
Polyporus vaporarius, var. papyraceus (S.) Fr.
Poria papyracea (S.) Cke.

{ Polyporus viticola S.
Poria viticola (S.) Cke.

Uredo Vitis Thm.

SPHAEROPSIDALES

{ Ascochyta Ellisii Thm.
Carlia Bidwellii (Ell.) Magn.
Depazea labruscae Engelm.
Guignardia Bidwellii (Ell.) Viala & Ravaz.
Laestadia Bidwellii (Ell.) Viala & Ravaz.
Naemaspora Ampelicida Engelm.
Phoma uvicola B. & C.
Phoma uvicola B. & C., var. labruscae Thm.
Phyllosticta Ampelopsidis Ell. & Martin.
Phyllosticta labruscae Thm.
Phyllosticta viticola (B. & C.) Thm.
Sacidium viticola (B. & C.) Cke.
Septoria viticola B. & C.
Sphaerella Bidwellii Ell.

Cytospora coryneoides B. & C.

{ Diplodia sclerotiorum Viala & Sauvageau.
Rhytisma monogramme B. & C. p. p.
Rhytisma Vitis S. p. p.

Diplodia viticola Desm.

Fusicoccum viticola Reddick.

Haplosporella fabiformis (Pass. & Thm.) Petrak & Syd.

{ Macrophoma farlowiana (Viala & Sauvageau) Tassi.
Phoma farlowiana Viala & Sauvageau.
Rhytisma monogramme B. & C. p. p.
Rhytisma Vitis S. p. p.

{ Macrophoma peckiana (Thm.) Berl. & Vogl.
Phoma peckiana (Thm.) Sacc.
Sphaeropsis peckiana Thm.

Phyllosticta macrospora Ell. & Ev.

{ Melanopsamma subfasciculata (S.) Sacc.
Psilosphaeria subfasciculata (S.) Cke.
Sphaeria subfasciculata S.
Sphaeropsis subfasciculata (S.) Starb.

Vermicularia herbarum (P.) Fr.

MELANCONIALES

{ Gloeosporium ampelophagum Atk. non Pass.
Gloeosporium fructigenum B.
Gloeosporium rufomaculans Thm.
Glomerella cingulata (Stoneman) Spaulding & v. Schrenk.
Glomerella fructigena (G. P. Clinton) Sacc.
Glomerella rufomaculans Spaulding & v. Schrenk.
Gnomoniopsis fructigena G. P. Clinton.

{ Greeneria fuliginea Scribner & Viala.
Melanconium fuligineum (Scribner & Viala) Cavara.

Pestalozzia pezizoides De Not.

HYPHOMYCETES

Alternaria tenuis Nees ex Fr.

{ Cercospora viticola (Ces.) Sacc.
Cladosporium ampelinum Pass.
Cladosporium viticola Ces.
Graphium clavisporum B. & C.
Helminthosporium Vitis Pirotta.
Isariopsis clavispora (B. & C.) Sacc.

Epochnium monilioides Lk.

Gonytrichum caesium Nees ex Fr.

Myrothecium convexum B. & C.

Sporotrichum alutaceum S.

Tubercularia subdiaphana S.

Volutella ciliata (A. & S.) ex Fr.

Vitis monticola Buckley.

Guignardia Bidwellii (Ell.) Viala & Ravaz.

Vitis munsoniana J. H. Simpson.

Phakopsora Vitis Syd.

Phyllosticta viticola (B. & C.) Thm.

Vitis palmata Vahl.

Cercospora viticola (Ces.) Sacc.

Vitis Piasezkii Maxim.

Guignardia Bidwellii (Ell.) Viala & Ravaz.

Vitis quadrangularis Wall. Cat.

Schizonella Colemani Gyngar & Marasiman.

Vitis quinquefolia Lam.

Uncinula necator (S.) Burrill.

Vitis Romaneti Romanet.
  Peronospora viticola (B. & C.) DBy.

Vitis rotundifolia Michx.
  Cercospora brachypus Ell. & Ev.
  Chaetosphaeria pannicola (B. & C.) Sacc.
  ⎰Eutypella Vitis (S.) Cke.
  ⎱Sphaeria Vitis S.
  Exidia gelatinosa (Bull. ex Fr.) Duby.
  ⎰Exidia truncata Fr.
  ⎱Ulocolla foliacea Ala. Bull.
  Fusarium miniatum (B. & C.) Sacc.
  ⎰Cryptosporella viticola Shear.
  ⎱Fusicoccum viticola Reddick.
  Glonium macrosporum Tracy & Earle.
  ⎰Guignardia Bidwellii (Ell.) Viala & Ravaz.
  ⎱Phyllosticta labruscae Thm.
  Hysterographium viticola C. & P.
  Hysterographium vulvatum (S.) Rehm.
  ⎰Plasmopara viticola (B. & C.) Berl. & De Toni.
  ⎱Rhysotheca viticola (B. & C.) G. W. Wilson.
  Rosellinia pulveracea (Ehrh. ex Fr.) Fckl.
  Valsaria viticola (S.) Sacc.

Vitis rupestris Scheele.
  Guignardia Bidwellii (Ell.) Viala & Ravaz.
  Trematosphaeria vitigena Ell. & Ev.
  Uncinula necator (S.) Burrill.

Vitis Simpsoni Munson.
  Phyllosticta viticola (B. & C.) Thm.

Vitis Slavinii Auct.
Vitis Treleasei Munson.
  Guignardia Bidwellii (Ell.) Viala & Ravaz.

Vitis vinifera L.
  Cenangium viticola Fckl.
  ⎰Cercospora viticola (Ces.) Sacc.
  ⎱Helminthosporium Vitis Pirotta.
  Cladochytrium viticola Prunet.
  Cytospora Vitis Mont.
  ⎰Dialonectria viticola (B. & C.) Cke.
  ⎱Nectria viticola B. & C.
  Diplodia viticola Desm.
  ⎰Eutypa viticola Sacc.
  ⎱Sphaeria Vitis S.
  ⎰Fusarium Schweinitzii Ell. & Hark. N. A. F.
  ⎱ *539.*
  ⎰Gloeosporium crassipes Speg.
  ⎰Guignardia Bidwellii (Ell.) Viala & Ravaz.
  ⎱Laestadia Bidwellii (Ell.) Viala & Ravaz.
  ⎰Phoma uvicola B. & C.
  ⎱Septoria viticola B. & C.
  Helminthosporium siliquosum B. & C.
  Hendersonia longipes B. & C.
  ⎰Hysterium viticola C. & P.
  ⎱Hysterographium viticola (C. & P.) Rehm.
  Melanconium fuligineum (Scrib. & Viala)
    Cavara.
  Micropera ampelina Sacc. & Fairman.

  ⎰Calloria vinosa (A. & S.) ex Fr.
  ⎱Orbilia vinosa (A. & S. ex Fr.) Karst.
  Peziza vinosa A. & S. ex Fr. 1803, 1822.
  Peziza vinosa P. 1822.
  ⎰Patellaria viticola (P.) Sacc.
  ⎱Peziza viticola P.
  Pestalozzia pezizoides De Not.
  ⎰Peronospora viticola (B. & C.) DBy.
  ⎰Plasmopara viticola (B. & C.) De Toni.
  ⎱Rhysotheca viticola (B. & C.) G. W. Wilson.
  Peziza penicillata S.
  ⎰Pleospora antiqua Ell. & Ev.
  ⎱Sphaeria antiqua Ell. & Ev.
  Thyridium antiquum Ell. & Ev.
  Phoma ampelina B. & C.
  Phoma confluens B. & C.
  ⎰Physalospora uvisarmenti (Cke.) Sacc.
  ⎱Sphaeria uvisarmenti Cke.
  ⎰Phakopsora Vitis Syd.
  ⎰Physopella Vitis (Syd.) Arth.
  ⎱Uredo Vitis Thm.
  Septoria ampelina B. & C.
  ⎰Rhabdospora falx (B. & C.) Sacc.
  ⎱Septoria falx B. & C.
  Sphaeronema viticola B. & C.
  Uncinula necator (S.) Burrill.
  Vermicularia compacta C. & E.

Vitis vulpina L.
  Ascochyta ampelina Sacc.
  ⎰Cercospora viticola (Ces.) Sacc.
  ⎱Cladosporium viticola Ces.
  Cercospora vulpina Ell. & Kellerm.
  Chlorosplenium salvicolor Ell. & Ev.
  ⎰Eutypa viticola Sacc.
  ⎱Valsa Vitis (S.) B. & C.
  Guignardia Bidwellii (Ell.) Viala & Ravaz.
  Phoma uvarum (B. & C.) Sacc.
  Phoma uvicola B. & C.
  Phyllosticta labruscae Thm.
  Phyllosticta viticola (B. & C.) Sacc.
  Sphaeropsis uvarum B. & C.
  ⎰Haplosporella fabiformis (Pass. & Thm.)
  ⎱ Petrak & Syd.
  ⎱Sphaeropsis viticola Pass.
  Sphaeropsis vitigena Ell. & Ev.
  Helminthosporium siliquosum B. & C.
  Humaria vitigena Massee & Morg.
  ⎰Hysterium flexuosum S.
  ⎱Hysterographium flexuosum (S.) Rehm.
  ⎰Hysterium vulvatum S.
  ⎱Hysterographium vulvatum (S.) Rehm.
  Irpex lacteus Fr.
  ⎰Lachnella cinereofusca (S.) Sacc.
  ⎱Peziza cinereofusca S.
  ⎰Lecanidion atrofuscum (B. & C.) Sacc.
  ⎱Patellaria atrofusca B. & C.
  ⎰Macrophoma farlowiana (Viala & Sauv.)
  ⎱ Tassi.
  ⎱Phoma farlowiana Viala & Sauvageau.

Vitis vulpina (*cont.*)
Pestalozzia Jefferisii Ell.
Pestalozzia pezizoides De Not.
Pestalozzia quadriciliata Bubák & Dearness.
⎰ Peronospora viticola (B. & C.) DBy.
⎱ Plasmopara viticola (B. & C.) Berl. & DeToni.
⎱ Rhysotheca viticola (B. & C.) G. W. Wilson.
⎰ Phyllosticta spermoides Pk.
⎱ Phyllosticta turmalis Ell. & Ev.
Phyllosticta vitea Sacc.
Propolis faginea (Schrad.) ex Karst.
Pseudovalsa viticola Ell. & Ev.
⎰ Pyrenochaeta Vitis Viala & Sauvageau.
⎱ Rhytisma monogramme B. & C. p. p.
⎱ Rhytisma Vitis S. p. p.
Rosellinia pulveracea (Ehrh. ex Fr.) Fckl.
Septoria ampelina B. & C.
Septoria kellermaniana Thm.
Thyridium Vitis Ell. & Ev.
⎰ Erysiphe necator S.
⎪ Uncinula americana Howe.
⎨ Uncinula necator (S.) Burrill.
⎩ Uncinula spiralis B. & C.
⎰ Diatrype viticola (S.) B. & C.
⎨ Sphaeria viticola S.
⎩ Valsaria viticola (S.) Sacc.
⎰ Xerotus lateritius B. & Rav. nec B. & C.
⎱ Xerotus viticola B. & C.

Vitis sp. indet.

Myxomycetes

Lamproderma arcyrioides (Sommf.) Rostf.,
  var. iridea Cke.
Plasmodiophora californica Viala & Sauvageau.
Plasmodiophora Vitis Viala & Sauvageau.

Phycomycetes

Ascophora Mucedo Tode ex Fr.
Chytridium viticola Prunet.
Mucor griseolilacinus Povah.
Pythium hydnosporum (Mont.) Schrt.
Rhizopus nigricans Ehrenb. ex Fr.

Helvellineae

⎰ Roesleria hypogaea Thm. & Pass.
⎨ Vibrissea hypogaea (Thm. & Pass.) Rich & Le
⎩ Mon.

Pezizineae

⎰ Calloria occulta Rehm.
⎨ Orbilia occulta (Rehm) Sacc.
⎩ Peziza occulta Rehm.
Dasyscyphella Vitis (S.) Rehm.
Dermatea puberula Durand.
Dermatella viticola Ell. & Ev.
Helotium ochraceum (Grev.) Phil.
Helotium sarmentorum DeNot.
Helotium vitigenum DeNot.
Lachnella corticalis (P.) Fr.
Patellaria atrata (Hedw.) ex Fr.

Peziza cinerea Batsch ex Fr.
⎰ Peziza pruinata S.
⎱ Tapesia pruinata (S.) Sacc.
Peziza scutula P.
⎰ Helotium virgultorum (Vahl) ex Fr.
⎱ Phialea virgultorum (Vahl ex Fr.) Sacc.
Sclerotinia fuckeliana (DBy.) Fckl.

Hysteriineae

⎰ Gloniella Curtisii (Duby) Sacc.
⎨ Hysterium Curtisii Duby.
⎩ Hysteroglonium Curtisii (Duby) Earle.
Hysterium pulicare P.
Hysterographium Ruborum Cke., forma Vitis
  Rehm.

Pyrenomycetineae

Botryosphaeria Quercuum Sacc.
Botryosphaeria Ribis (Tode ex Fr.) Grossen-
  bacher & Duggar.
Capnodium elongatum B. & Desm.
Diatrype nigerrima Ell. & Ev.
Didymella lophospora Sacc. & Speg.
Didymosphaeria bacchans Pass.
⎰ Didymosphaeria Sarmenti (Cke. & Hark.)
⎨   Berl. & Vogl.
⎩ Sphaeria Sarmenti Cke. & Hark.
Endothia gyrosa (S.) Farl.
Endothia radicalis (S.) De Not.
Eutypella capitata Ell. & Ev.
Hypoxylon perforatum (S.) Fr.
Lophidium nitidum Ell. & Ev.
Lophiostoma pustulatum Ell. & Ev.
Lophiostoma rhopalosporum Ell. & Ev.
⎰ Lophiostoma pseudomacrostomum Sacc.
⎱ Lophiostoma sexnucleatum N. A. F. *1695*.
Meliola asterinoides Wint.
Meliola furcata Lév.
Nummularia clypeus (S.) Cke.
Physalospora Cydoniae Arnaud.
⎰ Diplodia gossypina Cke.
⎱ Physalospora gossypina N. E. Stevens.
Rosellinia aquila (Fr.) De Not.
Rosellinia Langloisii Ell. & Ev.
Schizosaccharomyces octosporus Beyerinck.
Valsa americana B. & C.
Valsa vitigera Cke.

Hymenomycetineae

Armillaria mellea (Vahl) ex Fr.
Asterostroma corticola Massee.
⎰ Clitocybe monadelpha (Morg.) Sacc.
⎱ Clitocybe tabescens (Scop.) Bres.
Corticium albidocarneum (S.) Massee.
⎰ Corticium armeniacum Thm.
⎨ Corticium ceraceum B. & Rav.
⎩ Corticium molle B. & C.
Corticium confluens Fr.
Corticium hypopyrrhinum B. & C.
Corticium Petersii B. & C.

Vitis sp. indet. (*cont.*)
 Corticium pilosum Burt.
{ Corticium vagum B. & C.
{ Rhizoctonia Solani Kühn.
 Cyphella virgultorum Cke.
{ Eichleriella leveilliana (B. & C.) Burt.
{ Stereum leveilleanum B. & C.
{ Fomes conchatus (P. ex Fr.) Karst.
{ Pyropolyporus conchatus (P. ex Fr.) Murrill.
 Hydnum udum Fr.
{ Hydnum mucidum Gmel., var. viticola S.
{ Hydnum viticola S.
 Hydnum stipatum Fr.
 Hymenochaete corrugata (Fr.) Lév.
 Irpex viticola C. & P.
 Marasmius Vaillantii Fr.
{ Hydnum fimbriatum (P.) ex Fr.
{ Odontia fimbriata (P.) ex Fr.
 Mucronoporus ferruginosus (Schrad. ex Fr.)
  Ell. & Ev.
 Mycena corticola (Schum.) ex Fr.
 Peniophora flavido-alba Cke.
{ Corticium viticola (S.) Fr.
{ Peniophora viticola (S.) v. Höhnel & Litsch-
{ auer.
 Pleurotus applicatus (Batsch) ex Fr.
 Pleurotus applicatus (Batsch,) ex Fr., var.
  sarmenticius Sacc.
 Plicatura lateritia (B. & C.) Murrill.
{ Coriolus versicolor (L. ex Fr.) Quél.
{ Polystictus versicolor (L.) ex Fr.
{ Polyporus barbiformis B. & C.
{ Poria barbiformis (B. & C.) Sacc.
 Stereum cristatum B. & C.
 Stereum ochraceoflavum (S.) M. A. Curtis.

SPHAEROPSIDALES
{ Camarosporium viticola (Cke. & Hark.) Sacc.
{ Camarosporulum viticola (Cke. & Hark.) Tassi.
{ Dichomera viticola Cke. & Hark.
{ Coniothyrium ampelos (S.) Tassi.
{ Sphaeria ampelos S.
{ Sphaeropsis ampelos (S.) Cke.
 Cytospora coryneoides B. & C.
 Diplodia ampelina Cke.
 Diplodia cacaoicola Henn.
 Diplodia natalensis Evans.
 Diplodia viticola Desm.
 Discella albomaculans Pk.
 Discosia Artocreas (Tode) ex Fr.
 Hendersonia corticalis Ell. & Ev.
 Hendersonia sarmentorum Westd.
 ?Leptothyrium pomi (Mont. & Fr.) Sacc.
 Macrophoma flaccida (Viala & Ravaz) Cavara.
 Macrophoma rimiseda (Sacc.) Berl. & Vogl.
{ Macrophoma viticola (Cke.) Berl. & Vogl.
{ Phoma viticola (Cke.) Sacc.
{ Sphaeropsis viticola Cke.
 Phoma longipes B. & C.

 Phoma pallens B. & C.
 Septoria Vitis B. & C.
 Sphaeropsis Malorum B.

MELANCONIALES
{ Charrinia Diplodiella (Speg.) Viala & Ravaz.
{ Coniothyrium Diplodiella (Speg.) Sacc.
 Gloeosporium Physalosporae Cavara.
 Pestalozzia compacta B. & C.
 Pestalozzia funerea Desm.
 Pestalozzia menenzesiana Bres. & Torrend.
 Pestalozzia tremelloides Ell. & Ev.
 Pestalozzia uniseta Tracy & Earle.
 Pestalozzia uvicola Speg.
{ Gloeosporium ampelophagum (Pass.) Sacc.
{ Manginia ampelina (DBy.) Viala & Pacottet.
{ Sphaceloma ampelinum DBy.
{ Steganosporium viticola Ell. & Ev.

HYPHOMYCETES
 Acrosporium Tuckeri (B.) Sumstine.
 Aspergillus glaucus Lk.
 Botrytis acinorum P.
 Botrytis cinerea P. †
{ Brachysporium oosporum (Cda.) Sacc.
{ Helminthosporium oosporum Cda.
 Cladosporium Fumago Lk.
 Cladosporium herbarum (P.) ex Lk.
 Dendryphium acinorum Ell. & Ev.
 Dendryphium Harknessii Ell., var. leptaleum
  Ell.
 Fumago vagans Fr.
 Fusarium Schweinitzii Ell. & Hark.
 Fusarium viticola Thm., var. uvicola Pk.
 Ozonium omnivorum Shear.
 Penicillium glaucum Lk.
 Septosporium heterosporium Ell. & Gall.
 Sporidesmium antiquum Cda.
 Sporidesmium Rauii Ell. & Hark.
 Sporotrichum Himantiae S.
 Tubercularia ciliata Lk.

MISCELLANEA
 Dematophora necatrix Hartig.
Psedera quinquefolia (L.) Greene.
 Botryosphaeria Quercuum (S.) Sacc.
 Cercospora Ampelopsidis Pk.
 Cercospora psedericola Tehon.
 Cercospora pustula Cke.
 Cladosporium herbarum P. ex Lk.
 Coniothyrium Fuckelii Sacc.
 Corticium Stevensii Burt.
{ Cryptosporella Ampelopsidis (Ell.) Sacc.
{ Valsa Ampelopsidis Ell.
 Cytospora Ampelopsidis Massee.
 Hendersonia sarmentorum Westd.
{ Gloeosporium Ampelopsidis Ell. & Ev.
{ Phleospora Ampelopsidis (Ell. & Ev.) Bubák.
{ Septogloeum Ampelopsidis (Ell. & Ev.) Sacc.
{ Septoria Ampelopsidis (Ell. & Ev.) Ell.

Psedera quinquefolia (*cont.*)
Phoma pallens B. & C.
Periconia pycnospora Fres.
⎰Guignardia Bidwellii (Ell.) Viala & Ravaz.
⎱Laestadia Bidwellii (Ell.) Viala & Ravaz.
Macrophoma Ampelopsidis (C. & E.) Berl. & Vogl.?
⎰Phoma Ampelopsidis (C. & E.) Sacc.?
⎱Phoma uvicola B. & C.
Phyllosticta Ampelopsidis Ell. & Martin.
Phyllosticta labruscae (Engelm.) Thm.
Phyllosticta viticola (B. & C.) Thm.
Sphaeropsis Ampelopsidis C. & E.?
⎰Peronospora viticola (B. & C.) DBy.
⎱Plasmopara viticola (B. & C.) Berl. & DeToni.
Rhysotheca viticola (B. & C.) G. W. Wilson.
Plowrightia neomexicana Earle.
Podosporium rigidum S.
Septogloeum Ampelopsidis (Ell. & Ev.) Sacc.
Septoria Ampelopsidis Ell.
Sphaeronema Ampelopsidis B. & C.
Sphaeropsis Ampelopsidis Daniels.
Stagonospora heterospora Sacc.
⎰Uncinula Ampelopsidis Pk.
Uncinula necator (S.) Burrill.
Uncinula spiralis B. & C.
Uncinula subfusca B. & C.
⎱Uncinula Wallrothii Auct. Amer.
⎰Sphaeria capsularis P.
Valsa ambiens (P.) ex Fr.
⎱Valsa capsularis (P.).
Vermicularia compacta C. & E.
Psedera vitacea (Knerr.) Greene.
Phyllosticta labruscae Thm.
Psedera sp. indet.
Creonectria purpurea (L.) Seaver.
Nectria cinnabarina Fr.
Phakopsora Vitis (Arth.) Syd.
Septoria Hederae Desm.
Parthenocissus tricuspidata Planch.
Armillaria mellea (Vahl) ex Fr.
Cercospora Ampelopsidis Pk.
Cladosporium herbarum (P.) ex Lk.
Guignardia Bidwellii (Ell.) Viala & Ravaz.
⎰Hainesia Lythri (Desm.) v. Höhnel.
⎱Sclerotiopsis concava (Desm.) Shear & Dodge.
Naematelia nucleata (S.) Fr.
⎰Peronospora viticola (B. & C.) DBy.
Plasmopara viticola (B. & C.) Berl. & DeToni.
⎱Rhysotheca viticola (B. & C.) G. W. Wilson.
⎰Phyllosticta Ampelopsidis Ell. & Martin.
⎱Phyllosticta labruscae (Engelm.) Thm.
Phyllosticta viticola (B. & C.) Thm.
Uncinula necator (S.) Burrill.
Cissus arborea (L.) Des Moulins.
Cercospora arboriae Tharp.
Cercospora viticola (Ces.) Sacc.
Diatrypella Vitis Ell. & Ev.
Fusarium Volutella Ell. & Ev.

⎰Guignardia Bidwellii (Ell.) Viala & Ravaz.
⎱Laestadia Bidwellii (Ell.) Viala & Ravaz.
Cissus acida L.
Cissus erosa L.
⎰Mykosyrinx Cissi (DC.) G. Beck.
⎱Schroeteria Cissi (DC.) DeToni.
Cissus incisa (Nutt.) Des Moulins.
Aecidium Clemensae Arth.
Aecidium mexicanum Diet. & Holw.
Cissus rhombifolia Vahl.
⎰Cronartium wilsonianum Arth. & Johnston.
⎱Crossopsora wilsoniana (Arth. & Johnston) Arth.
Cissus sicyoides L.
⎰Aecidium circumscriptum S.
Aecidium Cissi Wint.
Endophyllum circumscriptum Whetzel & Olive.
⎱Endophyllum guttatum Syd.
Meliola Merrillii Syd.
⎰Geminella exotica, var. Candollei Fisch. Wald.
Mykosyrinx Cissii (DC.) G. Beck.
Mykosyrinx Cissi (DC.) G. Beck., var. Candollei (Fisch. Wald.) Note.
Puccinia incarcerata Lév.
Schroeteria Cissi (DC.) De Toni.
⎱Uredo Cissi DC.
Phyllosticta cissicola Speg.

ELAEOCARPACEAE

Sloanea berteriana Choisy.
Clavaria inaequalis Fr.
Trametes lactea Fr.
Sloanea caribaea ex Duss.
⎰Aleurodiscus mancinianus (Sacc. & Cub.) Pat.
⎱Stereum mancinianum Sacc. & Cub.
Aleurodiscus strumosus (Fr.) Burt.
Galera martiana B. & C.
⎰Acia pyramidata (B. & C.) Pat.
⎱Hydnum pyramidatum B. & C.
⎰Androsaceus Bulliardi (Quél.) Pat.
⎱Marasmius Bulliardi Quél.
Physarum globuliferum Fr.
Sloanea faginea Standl.
Irene amoena Syd.
Sloanea Massoni Sw.
Aleurodiscus mancinianus (Sacc. & Cub.) Pat.
⎰Armillaria umbilicata (Pat.) Sacc. & Syd.
⎱Armillariella umbilicata Pat.
Auricularia mesenterica Fr.
Fomitella supina (S.) Murrill.
Helotium Sloaneae Pat.
⎰Podoscypha nitidula (B. & C.) Pat.
⎱Stereum nitidulum B. & C.
Coriolus cubensis (B. & C.). Pat.
⎰Polyporus hemileucus B. & C.
⎱Ungulina hemileuca (B. & C.). Pat.

Solanea Massoni (*cont.*)
  Torrubiella rubra Pat.
  Xylaria grammica Mont.
Sloanea sinemariensis Aubl.
  ⎰ Agaricus cheimonophylla B. & C.
  ⎱ Mucidula cheimonophylla (B. & C.) Pat.
Sloanea surinamensis ex Duss.
  Trametes hydnoides Fr.
Sloanea sp. indet.
  Rosellinia bunodes B. & Br.
Elaeocarpaceae gen. indet.
  Cercospora poasensis Syd.

TILIACEAE

Corchorus hirsutus L.
  Asterina sidicola Ryan.
  Dimerosporium zonatum Seaver.
Tilia americana L.

MYXOMYCETES

Cribraria violacea Rex.
Dictydiaethalium plumbeum (Schum.) Rostf.
Stemonitis ferruginea Ehrenb.
Stemonitis maxima S.

PEZIZINEAE

Sarcoscypha floccosa (S.) Cke.
Sclerotinia Seaveri Rehm.?
Sclerotinia Tiliae Reade.
Trichopeziza candida Clements.

PYRENOMYCETINEAE

⎰ Amphisphaeria phileura (C. & P.) Sacc.
⎱ Sphaeria phileura C. & P.
⎰ Cryptospora femoralis (Pk.) Sacc.
⎱ Valsa femoralis Pk.
  Cryptospora Tiliae Pk.
⎰ Chorostate atropuncta (Pk.) Sacc. & Trott.
⎱ Diaporthe atropuncta Pk.
  Diaporthe farinosa Pk.
⎰ Diaporthe velata (P. ex Fr.) Nits.
⎱ Sphaeria velata P. ex Fr.
  Eutypella stellulata (Fr.) Sacc.
  Eutypella Tiliae Ell. & Ev.
⎰ Gnomonia melanostyla (DC. ex Fr.) Fckl.
⎰ Gnomoniella melanostyla (DC. ex Fr.) Sacc.
⎱ Ophiognomonia melanostyla (DC. ex Fr.) Sacc.
⎱ Sphaeria melanostyla DC. ex Fr.
  Hypocrea citrina (P.) ex Fr.
  Hypoxylon anthracodes (Fr.) Mont.
  Hypoxylon atropurpureum Fr.
  Lasiosphaeria ovina (P. ex Fr.) Fckl., var.
    aureliana Fairman.
⎰ Massaria Curreyi Tul.
⎱ Massariella Curreyi (Tul.) Sacc.
⎱ Phorcys Tiliae (Curr.) Schrt.
  Massariella Curreyi (Tul.) Sacc., var. ameri-
    cana Pk.

Microsphaera Alni (DC.) Wint. †
Nectria coccinea (P.) ex Fr.
⎰ Nummularia anthracina (Schm. ex Fr.) Trav.,
⎱   var. tiliicola Rehm.
  Nummularia Bulliardi Tul., var. tiliicola
    (Rehm) Sacc. & Trott.
⎰ Physalospora citrispora (B. & C.) Sacc.
⎱ Sphaeria citrispora B. & C.
  Physalospora Cydoniae Arnaud.
  Sphaeria maculiformis P. ex Fr.
  Sphaeria nobilis B. & C.
  Uncinula Clintonii Pk.
  Valsa ambiens (P.) ex Fr.
⎰ Sphaeria variolaria S.
⎱ Valsa variolaria (S.) Cke.
⎰ Diatrype angularis Pk.
⎱ Valsaria angularis (Pk.) Sacc.

TREMELLACEAE

⎰ Naematelia nucleata (S.) Fr.
⎱ Tremella nucleata S.
  Tremella nigricans (Fr.) Sacc.

THELEPHORACEAE

Sebacina helvelloides (S.) Burt.
Corticium basale Pk.
Corticium laeve (P.) ex Fr.
Corticium vellereum Ell. & Cragin.
Cyphella pezizoides Zopf.
⎰ Cyphella Tiliae (Pk.) Cke.
⎱ Peziza Tiliae Pk.
⎱ Trichopeziza Tiliae (Pk.) Sacc.
  Hypochnus isabellinus Fr.
  Peniophora Allescheri Bres.
  Solenia anomala (P. ex Fr.) Fckl.

HYDNACEAE

Irpex mollis B. & C.
Radulum pendulum Fr.

POLYPORACEAE

Daedalea confragosa (Bolt.) ex Fr.
Daedalea unicolor (Bull.) ex Fr.
⎰ Fomes applanatus (P. ex Wallr.) Gill.
⎱ Polyporus applanatus (P.) ex Wallr.
  Fomes conchatus (P. ex Fr.) Karst.
  Fomes populinus (Schum. ex Fr.) Cke.
  Gloeoporus dichrous Fr.
  Lenzites sepiaria (Wulf.) ex Fr.
  Lenzites vialis Pk.
  Lenzites trabea P. ex Fr.
  Merulius sulcatus Pk.
  Merulius tremulosus Schrad. ex Fr.
⎰ Bjerkandera adusta (Willd. ex Fr.) Karst.
⎱ Polyporus adustus (Willd.) ex Fr.
  Polyporus arcularius (Batsch) ex Fr.
  Polyporus benzoinus Fr.
  Polyporus brumalis (P.) ex Fr.
  Polyporus fumosus (P.) ex Fr.

Tilia americana (*cont.*)
Polyporus gilvus S.
Polyporus hirsutus (Wulf.) Fr.
Polyporus resinosus (Schrad.) ex Fr.
{ Polyporus tiliophilus (Murrill) Sacc. & Trott.
Tyromyces tiliophila Murrill.
Polyporus versicolor (L.) ex Fr.
Poria punctata Fr.
Trametes sepium B.

AGARICACEAE

Collybia colorea Pk.
Crepidotus tiliophilus Pk.
Flammula praecox Pk.
Lentinus lepideus Fr.
Lentinus tigrinus Fr.
Pholiota adiposa Fr.
Pholiota aurivella (Batsch) ex Fr.
Pholiota curvipes Fr.
Pleurotus ostreatus (Jacq.) ex Fr.
Pleurotus ulmarius (Bull.) ex Fr.
Russula subpunctata Kauffman.
{ Schizophyllum alneum (L. ex Fr.) Schrt.
Schizophyllum commune Fr.

SPHAEROPSIDALES

Actinonema Tiliae Allescher.
Asteroma canadense Bubák & Dearness.
Asteroma Tiliae Rud.
Asteroma vagans Desm.
Coniothyrium Tiliae Lasch.
Cytospora carnea Ell. & Ev.
Dendrophoma Tiliae Pk.
Dothiorella Tiliae Sacc.
{ Haplosporella tiliacea (Pk.) Petrak.
Haplosporella Tiliae Pk.
Sphaeropsis tiliacea Pk.
{ Hercospora Tiliae (P. ex Fr.) Tul.
Rabenhorstia Tiliae (P.) ex Fr.
Sphaeria Tiliae P. ex Fr.
{ Diatrype tiliacea Ell.
Hercospora tiliacea (Ell.) Sacc.
Melanconis tiliacea (Ell.) Ell. & Ev.
Macrophoma tiliacea Pk.
Phlyctaena verrucarioides Sacc.
Phyllosticta bacteriospora Vuill.
Phyllosticta Tiliae Sacc.
Sphaeronema Robiniae B. & C.
Sphaeropsis americana Sacc.

MELANCONIALES

Coryneum disciforme Nees ex Fr.
Coryneum Kunzei Cda.
Gloeosporium Tiliae Oud.
Melanconium Tiliae Pk.
Myxosporium fumosum Ell. & Ev.
Myxosporium Tiliae Dearness.

HYPHOMYCETES

{ Cercospora microsora Sacc.
Cercospora Tiliae Pk.
Chaetopsis grisea Ehrenb.
Cladosporium herbarum (P.) ex Lk.
{ Coryneum pulvinatum Kze. & Schm. ex Fr.
Exosporium Tiliae Lk.
Helminthosporium Tiliae Fr.
Fusarium erubescens B. & C.
Fusicoccum Tiliae Ell. & Ev.
Helicosporium Tiliae Pk.
Helminthosporium macrocarpon Grev.
Ozonium auricomum Lk.
Sporotrichum sulfureum Grev.
Tilia americana L., var. **pubescens** Loud.
Discosia minima B. & C.
Tilia europea L.
Cercospora microsora Sacc.
Polyporus squamosus (Huds.) ex Fr.
Pythium debaryanum Hesse.
Sphaeronema Robiniae B. & C.
Tilia heterophylla Vent.
Hercospora Tiliae (Fr.) Tul.
Tilia Michauxii Nutt.
Discosia minima B. & C.
Tilia ulmifolia Scop.
Pythium debaryanum Hesse.
Tilia vulgaris Heyne.
Exosporium Tiliae Lk.
Melanconis tiliacea (Ell.) Ell. & Ev.
Sphaeronema Robiniae B. & C.
Tilia sp. indet.

MYXOMYCETES

Arcyria cinerea (Bull.) P.
Badhamia utricularis (Bull.) B.
Ceratiomyxa plumosa Atk.
{ Comatricha friesiana (DBy.) Rostf.
Stemonitis obtusata Fr.
Stemonitis ovata P.
Lycogala exiguum Morg.

PEZIZINEAE

Chlorosplenium canadense Ell. & Ev.
{ Coryne Ellisii B.
Dacryopsis ellisiana Massee.
Holwaya tiliacea Ell. & Ev.
Lachnea setosa (Nees ex Fr.) Sacc.
Peziza clypeata S.

HYSTERIINEAE

Hysterium Fraxini P. ex Fr.

PYRENOMYCETINEAE

Amphisphaeria aeruginosa Fairman.
{ Ascotricha pusilla (Ell. & Ev.) Chivers.
Chaetomium pusillum Ell. & Ev.
Chaetomium sphaerospermum C. & E.
Chaetosphaeria longipila Pk.

Tilia sp. indet. (*cont.*)

{ Diaporthe furfuracea (Fr.) Sacc.
Sphaeria furfuracea Fr.
Valsa furfuracea Fr.

Diaporthe Woolworthii (Pk.) Sacc.
Hypocrea sulphurea (S.) Sacc.
Hypoxylon commutatum Nits.

{ Creonectria purpurea (L.) ex Seaver.
Nectria cinnabarina (Tode) ex Fr.

Nectria ditissima Tul.

{ Nummularia Clypeus (S.) Cke.
Sphaeria Clypeus S.

Phyllactinia suffulta (Reb.) ex Sacc.
Scoleconectria Atkinsonii (Rehm) Seaver.

{ Sphaerella incanescens (S.) Cke.
Sphaeria incanescens S.

Sphaerella sparsa (Wallr.) Awd.
Sphaeria barbata P. ex Fr.

{ ?Diatrype texensis Ell. & Ev.
Pseudovalsa texensis Ell. & Ev.
?Thyridaria texensis (Ell. & Ev.) Berl. & Vogl.

THELEPHORACEAE

Corticium bombycinum (Sommerf.) Bres.
Peniophora albula Atk. & Burt.
Peniophora mutata (Pk.) Bres.
Solenia ochracea Hoffm. ex Fr.
Stereum cinerascens (S.) Massee.

HYDNACEAE

Hydnum septentrionale Fr.
Phlebia radiata Fr.
Phlebia zonata B. & C.
Radulum Bennettii B. & C.

POLYPORACEAE

{ Antrodia mollis (Sommf.) Karst.
Daedalea mollis Sommf.

Merulius haedinus B. & C.
Fomes connatus (Weinm. ex Fr.) Gill.
Polyporus connatus Fr.
Polyporus elegans Bull. ex Fr.
Polyporus fragilis Fr.
Polyporus frondosus (Schrank) ex Fr.

{ Ischnoderma fuliginosum (Scop. ex Fr.)Murrill.
Polyporus fuliginosus (Scop.) ex Fr.

Polyporus squamosus (Huds.) ex Fr.
Polyporus sulphureus (Bull.) ex Fr.
Polystictus cinnabarinus (Jacq. ex Fr.) Cke.
Polystictus pergamenus Fr.
Polystictus versicolor (L.) ex Fr.
Poria attenuata (Pk.) Cke.
Poria eupora (Karst.) Cke.
Poria Medulla-panis (P. ex Fr.) Cke.
Poria spissa (S.) Cke.

AGARICACEAE

Annularia Fenzlii Schulz.
Collybia velutipes Wm. Curtis.

Coprinus quadrifidus Pk.
Crepidotus albidus Ell. & Ev.
Crepidotus calolepis Fr.
Gomphidius viscidus Fr.
Lentinus vulpinus Sow. ex Fr.
Pilosace eximia Pk.
Pleurotus subareolatus Pk.

SPHAEROPSIDALES

Aposphaeria aranea Pk.
Diplodia paraphysata Ell. & Ev.

{ Discosia placentula (S.) Ell.
Rhytisma Juglandis S.
Sphaeria placentula S.

MELANCONIALES

Gloeosporium Tiliae Oud.
Oedemium atrum Lk.
Pestalozzia strictica B. & C.

HYPHOMYCETES

Cladosporium lignicola Cda.

{ Fusarium obtusisporum Cke. & Hark.
Ramularia obtusispora (Cke. & Hark.) Wr.

Sacidium lignarium Pk.
Torula ligniperda (Willk.) Sacc.

MISCELLANEA

Guepinia spathularia S.
Epidochium nigricans Fr.
Fumago vagans Fr.
Myriococcum consimile Ell. & Ev.
Naematelia atrata Pk.

Triumfetta Bartramia L.
Triumfetta grandiflora Vahl.
    Pucciniosira pallidula (Speg.) Lagerh.
Triumfetta Lappula L.

{ Aecidiella Triumfettae Ell. & Kelsey.
Pucciniosira pallidula (Speg.) Lagerh.

    Rhysotheca heliocarpa (Lagerh.) G. W. Wilson.

Triumfetta polyandra DC.
    Aecidium Triumfettae Henn.

Triumfetta rhomboidea Jacq.
    Pucciniosira pallidula (Speg.) Lagerh.

Triumfetta semitriloba Jacq.

{ Asterina isothea Syd.
Asterostomella isothea Syd.

    Meliola Triumfettae F. L. Stevens.
    Phyllosticta Stevensii E. Young.

{ Micropuccinia Triumfettae (Diet. & Holw.) Arth. & Jackson.
Puccinia Triumfettae Diet. & Holw.

    Pucciniosira pallidula (Speg.) Lagerh.

Triumfetta speciosa Seem.
    Pucciniosira pallidula (Speg.) Lagerh.

MALVACEAE

Malope sp. indet.
  Puccinia Malvacearum Bert.
Abutilon hybridum Voss, var. **Savitzii.**
  Rhizoctonia Solani Kühn.
Abutilon abutiloides (Jacq.) Garcke.
Abutilon Berlandieri Gray.
Abutilon Calderoni Standley.
Abutilon crispum Don.
Abutilon discissum Schl.
Abutilon giganteum (Jacq.) Presl.
Abutilon hemsleyanum Rose.
Abutilon hirtum Don.
Abutilon holosericeum Scheele.
Abutilon Holwayi Rose.
Abutilon imberbe G. Don.
Abutilon incanum (Lk.) Sweet.
Abutilon indicum Sweet.
Abutilon parvulum Gray.
Abutilon pauciflorum St. Hil.
Abutilon permolle (Willd.) Sweet.
Abutilon sidoides Hemsl.
Abutilon texense Torr. & Gr.
  Micropuccinia heterospora (B. & C.) Arth. & Jackson.
  Puccinia heterospora B. & C.
  Uromyces pulcherrimus B. & C.
Abutilon Theophrasti Medic.
  Alternaria Abutilonis Speg.
  Cercospora Abutilonis Tehon & Daniels.
  Cercospora althaeina Sacc.
  Cladosporium herbarum (P.) ex Lk.
  Fusisporium roseum Lk.
  Macrosporium Abutilonis Speg.
  Phyllosticta althaeina Sacc.
  Micropuccinia heterospora (B. & C.) Arth. & Jackson.
  Puccinia heterospora B. & C.
Abutilon umbellatum Sweet.
  Phyllosticta hibiscina Ell. & Ev.
  Micropuccinia heterospora (B. & C.) Arth. & Jackson.
Abutilon sp. indet.
  Asterina diplocarpa Cke.
  Asterina sidicola Ryan.
  Dicaeoma hibisciatum (Kellerm.) Arth.
  Meliola amphitricha Fr.
  Puccinia Malvacearum Bert.
  Puccinia heterospora Fung. Columb. *2453.*
  Uromyces pictus Thm.
  Verticillium atro-album Reinke & Berthold.
Wissadula amplissima (L.) R. E. Fries.
Wissadula Fadyenii R. E. Fries.
Wissadula periplocifolia (L.) Preah.
Wissadula rostrata (Schum. & Thonn.) Planch.
  Micropuccinia heterospora (B. & C.) Arth. & Jackson.
  Puccinia heterospora B. & C.

Sphaeralcea ambigua Gray.
  Puccinia interveniens Bethel.
  Puccinia sherardiana Körn.
Sphaeralcea angustifolia (Cav.) G. Don.
  Aecidium Sphaeralceae Ell. & Ev.
Sphaeralcea arcuata (Greene) Arth.
Sphaeralcea arenaria Woot. & Standley.
Sphaeralcea arizonica Heller.
Sphaeralcea cuspidata (Gray) Britton.
Sphaeralcea dissecta (Nutt.) Rydb.
Sphaeralcea elata (Baker f.) Rydb.
Sphaeralcea fasciculata (Nutt.) Arth.
  Micropuccinia sherardiana (Körn.) Arth. & Jackson.
  Puccinia sherardiana Körn.
  Puccinia Sphaeralceae Ell. & Ev.
Sphaeralcea Fendleri Gray.
Sphaeralcea grossulariifolia Rydb.
Sphaeralcea incana Torr.
Sphaeralcea lobata Woot.
  Aecidium Napaeae Arth. & Holw.
  Dicaeoma hibisciatum (Kellerm.) Arth. I.
  Puccinia Muhlenbergiae Arth. & Holw. I.
  Puccinia tosta Arth. I.
  Micropuccinia sherardiana (Körn.) Arth. & Jackson.
  Puccinia Sphaeralceae Ell. & Ev.
Sphaeralcea marginata York.
  Puccinia sherardiana Körn.
  Puccinia Sphaeralceae Ell. & Ev.
Sphaeralcea munroana (Dougl.) Spach.
  Aecidium Malvastri Ell. & Tracy.
  Micropuccinia sherardiana (Körn.) Arth. & Jackson.
  Puccinia sherardiana Körn.
  Puccinia Sphaeralceae Ell. & Ev.
Sphaeralcea Orcuttii Rose.
  Micropuccinia lobata (B. & C.) Arth. & Jackson.
Sphaeralcea pedata Torr.
Sphaeralcea subrhomboidea Rydb.
  Micropuccinia sherardiana (Körn.) Arth. & Jackson.
  Puccinia sherardiana Körn.
Sphaeralcea ? sp. indet.
  Sphaerella stenospora Ell. & Ev.
Modiola caroliniana (L.) G. Don.
  Cercospora althaeina Sacc.
  Cercospora althaeina Sacc., var. Modiolae Atk.
  Cercospora Modiolae Tharp.
Lavatera arborea L.
  Micropuccinia Malvacearum (Bert.) Arth. & Jackson.
  Puccinia Malvacearum Bert.
  Rhizoctonia Solani Kühn.

Lavatera assurgentiflora Kellogg.
   Micropuccinia Malvacearum (Bert.) Arth. &
    Jackson.
   Puccinia Malvacearum Bert.
   Valsa Lavaterae Cke. & Hark.
Lavatera cretica L.
Lavatera maritima Gouan.
Lavatera plebeia Sims.
Lavatera sylvestris Brot.
   Micropuccinia Malvacearum (Bert.) Arth. &
    Jackson.
   Puccinia Malvacearum Bert.
Lavatera sp. indet.
   Colletotrichum Malvarum (A. Br. & Casp.)
    Southworth.
   Torula quaternata B. & C.
Althaea cannabina L.
   Ascochyta althaeina Sacc. & Bizz.
Althaea ficifolia Cav.
   Micropuccinia Malvacearum (Bert.) Arth. &
    Jackson.
   Puccinia Malvacearum Bert.
Althaea rosea L.
   Aecidium malvicola Arth.
   Aecidium Napaeae Arth. & Holw.
   Dicaeoma hibisciatum (Kellerm.) Arth. I.
   Puccinia hibisciata Kellerm. I.
   Ascochyta althaeina Sacc. & Bizz.
   Ascochyta parasitica Fautr.
   Cercospora althaeina Sacc.
   Cercospora Kellermani Bubák.
   Cercospora Malvarum Sacc.
   Cercospora nebulosa Sacc.
   Colletotrichum Althaeae Southworth.
   Colletotrichum Malvarum (A. Br. & Casp.)
    Southworth.
   Steirochaete Malvarum A. Br. & Casp.
   Aecidium tuberculatum Ell. & Kellerm.
   Endophyllum tuberculatum Arth. & Fromme.
   Ozonium omnivorum Shear.
   Phyllosticta althaeina Sacc.
   Micropuccinia heterospora (B. & C.) Arth. &
    Jackson.
   Micropuccinia lobata (B. & C.) Arth. & Jack-
    son.
   Puccinia lobata B. & C.
   Dasyspora Malvacearum (Bert.) Arth.
   Dicaeoma Malvacearum (Bert.) O. Kuntze.
   Micropuccinia Malvacearum (Bert.) Arth. &
    Jackson.
   Puccinia Malvacearum Bert.
   Micropuccinia sherardiana (Körn.) Arth. &
    Jackson.
   Puccinia Malvastri Pk.
   Puccinia sherardiana Körn.
   Rhizoctonia microsclerotia Matz.
   Septoria Fairmani Ell. & Ev.
   Septoria malvicola Ell. & Martin.

Althaea sp. indet.
   Sphaeropsis lyndonvillae Sacc.
Malva Alcea L.
   Sphaeria malvicola S.
Malva borealis Wallm.
   Puccinia Malvacearum Mont., var. Malvastri
    Farl.
   Puccinia Malvastri Pk.
Malva moschata L.
Malva oxyloba Boiss.
   Micropuccinia Malvacearum (Bert.) Arth. &
    Jackson.
   Puccinia Malvacearum Bert.
Malva parviflora L.
   Micropuccinia Malvacearum (Bert.) Arth. &
    Jackson.
   Puccinia Malvacearum Bert.
   Steirochaete Malvarum A. Br. & Casp.
Malva rotundifolia L.
   Cercospora althaeina Sacc.
   Cercospora malvicola Ell. & Martin.
   Cercospora Malvarum Sacc.
   Colletotrichum magnusianum Bres.
   Macrosporium Malvae Thm.
   Phoma lyndonvillensis Fairman.
   Dasyspora Malvacearum (Bert.) Arth.
   Micropuccinia Malvacearum (Bert.) Arth. &
    Jackson.
   Puccinia Malvacearum Bert.
   Septoria destruens Auct. Amer.
   Septoria heterochroa Desm.
   Septoria malvicola Ell. & Martin.
   Steirochaete Malvarum A. Br. & Casp.
Malva sylvestris L.
   Micropuccinia heterospora (B. & C.) Arth. &
    Jackson.
   Puccinia heterospora B. & C.
   Micropuccinia Malvacearum (Bert.) Arth. &
    Jackson.
   Puccinia Malvacearum Bert.
   Septoria malvicola Ell. & Martin.
Malva verticillata L.
   Micropuccinia Malvacearum (Bert.) Arth. &
    Jackson.
   Puccinia Malvacearum Bert.
Malva sp. indet.
   Aecidium Callirrhoes Ell. & Kellerm.
   Capillaria Malvacearum S.
Callirhoe alcaeoides (Michx.) Gray.
   Aecidium Napaeae Arth. & Holw.
   Dicaeoma hibisciatum (Kellerm.) Arth. I.
   Aecidium tuberculatum Ell. & Kellerm.
   Aecidium roestelioides Ell. & Ev.
   Allodus interveniens Bethel.
   Dicaeoma interveniens (Bethel) Arth. &
    Fromme.
Callirhoe digitata Nutt.
   Dicaeoma hibisciatum (Kellerm.) Arth. I.

Callirhoe digitata (*cont.*)
{ Aecidium roestelioides Ell. & Ev.
{ Allodus interveniens Bethel.
{ Dicaeoma interveniens (Bethel) Arth. &
    Fromme.
Callirhoe involucrata (Torr. & Gr.) Gray.
{ Aecidium Callirhoes Ell. & Kellerm.
{ Aecidium malvicola Arth.
{ Aecidium Napaeae Arth. & Holw.
{ Dicaeoma hibisciatum (Kellerm.) Arth. I.
{ Puccinia Muhlenbergiae Arth. & Holw. I.
{ Puccinia Schedonnardi Kellerm. & Swingle. I.
    Cercospora althaeina Sacc.
{ Aecidium tuberculatum Ell. & Kellerm.
{ Endophyllum tuberculatum Arth. & Fromme.
    Pistillaria Bartholomei Ell. & Ev.
    Pistillaria Batesii Pk.
    Synchytrium australe Speg.
    Vermicularia sparsipila Ell. & Kellerm.
Callirhoe triangularis (Leavenworth) Gray.
    Cercospora althaeina Sacc., var. praecincta J.
        J. Davis.
Sidalcea asprella Greene.
{ Allodus interveniens Bethel.
{ Dicaeoma interveniens (Bethel) Arth. &
    Fromme.
{ Puccinia interveniens Bethel.
Sidalcea candida Gray.
{ Aecidium interveniens (Pk.) Farl.
{ Allodus interveniens Bethel.
{ Dicaeoma interveniens (Bethel) Arth. &
    Fromme.
{ Aecidium Napaeae Arth. & Holw.
{ Aecidium Sphaeralceae Ell. & Ev.
{ Dicaeoma hibisciatum (Kellerm.) Arth. I.
{ Aecidium tuberculatum Ell. & Kellerm.
{ Endophyllum tuberculatum Arth. & Fromme.
    Ramularia sidalceae Ell. & Ev.
Sidalcea diploscypha (Torr. & Gr.) Gray.
    Micropuccinia Malvacearum (Bert.) Arth. &
        Jackson.
Sidalcea glaucescens Greene.
    Micropuccinia Sidalceae (Holw.) Arth. & Jack-
        son.
Sidalcea humilis Gray.
    Aecidium interveniens (Pk.) Farl.
Sidalcea malviflora (Moc. & Sessé) Gray.
    Aecidium tuberculatum Ell. & Kellerm.
{ Aecidium interveniens (Pk.) Farl.
{ Aecidium roestelioides Ell. & Ev.
{ Allodus interveniens Bethel.
{ Dicaeoma interveniens (Bethel) Arth. &
    Fromme.
{ Puccinia Burnettii N. Am. Uredinales *1932*.
{ Puccinia interveniens Bethel.
    Puccinia sherardiana Körn.
{ Micropuccinia Sidalceae (Holw.) Arth. &
    Jackson.
{ Puccinia Sidalceae Holw.

Septoria destruens Auct. Amer.
Sphaerella sidicola Ell. & Ev.
Sidalcea neomexicana Gray.
{ Aecidium tuberculatum Ell. & Kellerm.
{ Endophyllum tuberculatum Arth. & Fromme.
    Phoma Sidalceae Fairman.
{ Aecidium roestelioides Ell. & Ev.
{ Allodus inteveniens Bethel. I.
{ Dicaeoma interveniens (Bethel) Arth. &
    Fromme.
{ Puccinia interveniens Bethel.
Sidalcea nervata A. Nels.
{ Aecidium roestelioides Ell. & Ev.
{ Dicaeoma interveniens (Bethel) Arth. &
    Fromme.
    Monilia Sidalceae Pk.
Sidalcea oregana Gray.
    Puccinia interveniens Bethel.
    Micropuccinia sherardiana (Körn.) Arth. &
        Jackson.
{ Micropuccinia Sidalceae (Holw.) Arth. &
    Jackson.
{ Puccinia Sidalceae Holw.
{ Puccinia? Sphaeralceae Syd. Ured. *1782*.
Sidalcea rivularis (Dougl.) Torr.
{ Aecidium interveniens (Pk.) Farl.
{ Allodus interveniens Bethel.
{ Dicaeoma interveniens (Bethel) Arth. &
    Fromme. I.
{ ?Puccinia Burnettii Auct. non Griffiths.
{ Puccinia interveniens Bethel.
Sidalcea spicata Greene.
{ Micropuccinia sherardiana (Körn.) Arth. &
    Jackson.
{ Puccinia sherardiana Körn.
    Micropuccinia Sidalceae (Holw.) Arth. &
        Jackson.
Sidalcea virgata Howell.
{ Micropuccinia sherardiana (Körn.) Arth. &
    Jackson.
{ Puccinia sherardiana Körn.
Sidalcea sp. indet.
    Puccinia Malvacearum Bert.
    Puccinia Sphaeralceae Ell. & Ev.

Napaea dioica L.
{ Aecidium Napaeae Arth. & Holw.
{ Dicaeoma hibisciatum (Kellerm.) Arth. I.
    Erysiphe Cichoracearum DC. †
Malvastrum ambiguum ex Blasdale.
    Puccinia interveniens Bethel.
Malvastrum coccineum (Pursh) Gray.
    Aecidium Malvastri Ell. & Tracy.
{ Aecidium malvicola Arth.
{ Aecidium Napaeae Arth. & Holw.
{ Dicaeoma hibisciatum (Kellerm.) Arth. I.
{ Puccinia Muhlenbergiae Arth. & Holw. I.
{ Puccinia Schedonnardi Kellerm. & Swingle. I.

Malvastrum coccineum (*cont.*)

  Micropuccinia sherardiana (Körn.) Arth. &
    Jackson.
  Puccinia Malvacearum, var. Malvastri (Pk.)
    Farl.
  Puccinia Malvastri Pk.
  Puccinia sherardiana Körn.
  Puccinia Sphaeralceae Ell. & Ev.
  Roestelia interveniens Pk.
  Stemphylium botryosum Wallr., var. Ulocla-
    dium (Preuss) Sacc.

Malvastrum Cockerelli A. Nels.

Malvastrum corchorifolium (Desv.) Brit.

  Micropuccinia Malvacearum (Bert.) Arth. &
    Jackson.
  Puccinia Malvastri Pk.

Malvastrum dissectum A. Nels.

Malvastrum elatum (Baker) A. Nels.

  Micropuccinia sherardiana (Körn.) Arth. &
    Jackson.
  Puccinia sherardiana Körn.

Malvastrum fasciculatum (Nutt.) Greene.

  Aecidium Napaeae Arth. & Holw.
  Dicaeoma hibisciatum (Kellerm.) Arth.
  Dicaeoma interveniens (Bethel) Arth. &
    Fromme. I.
  Puccinia sherardiana Körn.

Malvastrum marrubioides Dur. & Hilg.

  Aecidium interveniens (Pk.) Farl.
  Dicaeoma interveniens (Bethel) Arth. &
    Fromme. I.
  Puccinia Malvacearum Mont., var. Malvas-
    tri (Pk.) Farl.
  Puccinia Malvastri Pk.

Malvastrum splendens Kellogg.

  Puccinia sherardiana Körn.

Malvastrum Thurberi Gray.

  Metasphaeria anisometra (Cke. & Hark.) Sacc.
  Puccinia Malvastri Pk.
  Puccinia sherardiana Körn.
  Puccinia interveniens Bethel.
  Roestelia interveniens Pk.

Malvastrum tricuspidatum Gray.

  Micropuccinia heterospora (B. & C.) Arth. &
    Jackson.
  Micropuccinia Malvacearum (Bert.) Arth. &
    Jackson.
  Puccinia Malvacearum Bert.

Sida acuta Burm.

Sida angustifolia Lam.

  Micropuccinia heterospora (B. & C.) Arth. &
    Jackson.
  Puccinia heterospora B. & C.

Sida carpinifolia L.

  Asterina diplocarpa Cke.
  Asterina Sidae Earle.
  Asterina sidicola Ryan.
  Dimerosporium appendiculatum Earle.

Sida cordifolia L.

  Puccinia heterospora B. & C.

Sida glabra Mill.

  Nitschkia cupularis Karst.

Sida glutinosa Commerson.

Sida hastata St.-Hil.

  Micropuccinia heterospora (B. & C.) Arth.
    & Jackson.
  Puccinia heterospora B. & C.

Sida hederacea (Dougl.) Torr.

  Aecidium Napaeae Arth. & Holw.
  Dicaeoma hibisciatum (Kellerm.) Arth. I.
  Puccinia Muhlenbergiae Arth. & Holw. I.
  Micropuccinia lobata (B. & C.) Arth. &
    Jackson.
  Puccinia lobata B. & C.
  Puccinia Malvacearum Bert.
  Puccinia Sidae Pat.
  Puccinia Sphaeralceae Ell. & Ev.

Sida hederifolia Cav.

Sida Holwayi Baker & Rose.

Sida humilis Cav.

  Micropuccinia heterospora (B. & C.) Arth. &
    Jackson.
  Puccinia heterospora B. & C.

Sida lepidota Gray.

  Micropuccinia lobata (B. & C.) Arth. & Jack-
    son.
  Puccinia lobata B. & C.

Sida Lindheimeri Engelm. & Gray.

Sida physocalyx Gray.

Sida procumbens Sw.

  Micropuccinia heterospora (B. & C.) Arth. &
    Jackson.
  Puccinia heterospora B. & C.

Sida rhombifolia L.

  Cercospora densissima Speg.
  Puccinia heterospora B. & C.

Sida salviifolia Presl.

  Puccinia heterospora B. & C.

Sida spinosa L.

  Cercospora sidicola Ell. & Ev.
  Ozonium auricomum Lk.
  Phyllosticta spinosa Ell. & Kellerm.
  Micropuccinia heterospora (B. & C.) Arth. &
    Jackson.
  Puccinia heterospora B. & C.
  Puccinia Thwaitesii (B. & Br.) Wint.
  Micropuccinia Malvacearum (Bert.) Arth. &
    Jackson.
  Puccinia sherardiana Körn.
  Vermicularia platyspora Ell. & Ev.

Sida supina L'Her.

Sida texana (Torr. & Gr.) Small.

  Micropuccinia heterospora (B. & C.) Arth. &
    Jackson.
  Puccinia heterospora B. & C.

Sida urens L.
  Meliola molleriana Wint.
  ⎰ Micropuccinia heterospora (B. & C.) Arth. &
  ⎱ Jackson.
  Puccinia heterospora B. & C.
  Uromyces Malvacearum Speg.
  Tuberculina Malvacearum Speg.

Sida sp. indet.
  Cercospora densissima Speg.
  Cicinnobolus Cesatii DBy.
  Cladosporium Sidae Ciferri & Fragoso.
  Colletotrichum Malvarum (A. Br. & Casp.)
    Southworth.
  Erysiphe communis Auct. Amer.
  Septoria heterochroa Desm.

Gaya occidentalis (Griseb.) Sweet.
  ⎰ Micropuccinia heterospora (B. & C.) Arth. &
  ⎱ Jackson.
  Puccinia heterospora B. & C.

Bastardia viscosa (L.) H. B. K.
  Micropuccinia heterospora (B. & C.) Arth. &
    Jackson.

Anoda acerifolia Cav.
Anoda hastata Cav.
  ⎰ Micropuccinia Anodae (Syd.) Arth. & Jack-
  ⎱ son.
  Puccinia Anodae Syd.
  ⎰ Micropuccinia heterospora (B. & C.) Arth. &
  ⎱ Jackson.
  Puccinia heterospora B. & C.

Anoda cristata (L.) Schl.
Anoda incarnata H. B. K.
Anoda indicum Sweet.
Anoda lavateroides Medic.
Anoda permollis (Willd.) Sweet.
  ⎰ Micropuccinia heterospora (B. & C.) Arth. &
  ⎱ Jackson.
  Puccinia heterospora B. & C.

Malachra capitata L.
  Cercospora Malachrae Heald & Wolf.

Malachra rotundifolia Schrank.
  ⎰ Cercospora Malachrae Heald & Wolf. 1911.
  ⎱ Cercospora Malachrae E. Young. 1916.

Pavonia lasiopetala Scheele.
  Kuehneola malvicola Arth.

Pavonia racemosa Sw.
  Kuehneola malvicola Arth.
  Uromyces Pavoniae Arth.

Pavonia rosea Schl.
  ⎰ Micropuccinia exilis (Syd.) Arth. & Jackson.
  ⎱ Puccinia exilis Syd.

Pavonia speciosa H. B. K.
  Kuehneola malvicola Arth.

Pavonia spinifex (L.) Cav.
  Asterina solanicola B. & C.

Pavonia sp. indet.
  Pucciniosira pallidula (Speg.) Lagerh.

Malache scabra B. Vogl.
  Kuehneola malvicola Arth.
  ⎰ Micropuccinia heterospora (B. & C.) Arth. &
  ⎱ Jackson.
  Puccinia heterospora B. & C.
  Uromyces Pavoniae Arth.

Malvaviscus acerifolius Presl.
  Dicaeoma hibisciatum (Kellerm.) Arth.

Malvaviscus arboreus Cav.
  Kuehneola malvicola Arth.
  ⎰ Micropuccinia heterospora (B. & C.) Arth. &
  ⎱ Jackson.
  Puccinia heterospora B. & C.
  Phyllachora Malvavisci Syd.

Malvaviscus Drummondii Torr. & Gr.
  ⎰ Kuehneola Hibisci Arth.
  | Kuehneola malvicola Arth.
  | Uredo Hibisci Syd.
  ⎱ Puccinia heterospora B. & C.

Malvaviscus mollis DC.
  Kuehneola malvicola Arth.

Malvaviscus palmatus Pitt. & Donn.
  Micropuccinia heterospora (B. & C.) Arth. &
    Jackson.

Malvaviscus sagraeanus Rich.
  Aschersonia viridula Sacc.
  ⎰ Kuehneola malvicola Arth.
  ⎱ Uredo malvicola Speg.

Hibiscus brasiliensis L.
  Colletotrichum dominicanum Fragoso & Ci-
    ferri.
  Colletotrichum dominicanum, var. ramulicola
    Fragoso & Ciferri.

Hibiscus coccineus Walt.
  Choanephora Cucurbitarum (B. & Rav.) Thax.

Hibiscus domingensis Jacq.
  Olivea Petitiae Arth.
  Septoria Petitiae P. Garman.

Hibiscus esculentus L.
  Acrostalagmus albus Preuss.
  Aecidium hibisciatum S.
  Ascochyta Abelmoschi Harter.
  Botrytis hortensis Ell. & Ev.
  Cercospora Abelmoschi Ell. & Ev.
  Cercospora althaeina Sacc.
  Cercospora brachypoda Speg.
  Cercospora Hibisci Tracy & Earle.
  Choanephora Cucurbitarum (B. & Rav.) Thax.
  Cyphella virgultorum Cke.
  Didymella Ricini, var. Hibisci Ell. & Ev.
  Erysiphe Cichoracearum DC. †
  Fusarium Malvacearum Taubenhaus.
  Fusarium tracheiphila Atk.
  Fusarium vasinfectum Atk.
  Fusarium vasinfectum, var. inodoratum Wr.
  Herpotrichia diffusa (S.) Ell. & Ev.
  Macrosporium abruptum C. & E.
  Macrosporium canificans Thm.
  Macrosporium hibiscinum Thm.

Hibiscus esculentus (*cont.*)
  Macrosporium spadiceum Thm.
  Meliola Hibisci (Spreng. ex Fr.) Fragoso &
    Ciferri.
  Mystrosporium polytrichum Cke.
  Neocosmospora vasinfecta Erw. Sm.
  Ophiobolus consimilis Ell. & Ev.
  Ozonium omnivorum Shear.
  Phoma Okra Cke.
  Phyllosticta hibiscina Ell. & Ev.
  Phyllosticta Syriaca Sacc.
  { Corticium vagum B. & C.
  { Rhizoctonia Solani Kühn.
  Trichothecium subfulvum Ell. & Ev.
  Verticillium albo-atrum Reinke & Berth.
Hibiscus grandiflorus Michx.
  { Aecidium hibisciatum S.
  { Caeoma hibisciatum S.
  Periconia pycnospora Fres.
Hibiscus lasiocarpus Cav.
  Ascochyta Gossypii Syd.
  Dicaeoma hibisciatum (Kellerm.) Arth. I.
Hibiscus Manihot L.
  Vermicularia hibiscina Ell. & Ev.
Hibiscus militaris Cav.
  { Aecidium hibisciatum S.
  { Caeoma hibisciatum S.
  { Dicaeoma hibisciatum (Kellerm.) Arth. I.
  { Puccinia hibisciata Kellerm. I.
  Ascochyta Gossypii Syd.
  { Dothidea hibiscicola S.
  { Phyllachora hibiscicola (S.) Sacc.
  { Rhabdospora hibiscicola (S.) Starb.
  { Sphaeria hibiscicola S.
Hibiscus Moscheutos L.
  { Aecidium Hibisci M. A. Curtis.
  { Aecidium hibisciatum S.
  { Caeoma hibisciatum S.
  { Dicaeoma hibisciatum (Kellerm.) Arth. I.
  { Puccinia dochmia Auct. Amer. p. p. I.
  { Puccinia Muhlenbergiae Arth. & Holw. I.
  Diaporthe Arctii Lasch.
  Phoma ochra Cke.
  Phyllosticta Hibisci Pk.
  Phyllosticta hibiscina Ell. & Ev.
  Sphaeria hibiscicola S.
Hibiscus mutabilis L.
  Phyllosticta hibiscina Ell. & Ev.
Hibiscus rosa-sinensis L.
  Rosellinia bunodes (B. & Br.) Sacc.
  Fusarium bullatum Sherbakoff, var. brevius
    Wollenw. & Reink.
  Puccinia Malvacearum Bert.
Hibiscus roseus Thor.
  { Botryosphaeria Hibisci (S.) Sacc.
  { Sphaeria Hibisci S.
  { Diaporthe tenella (S.) Starb.
  { Sphaeria tenella S.
  Dothidea atra Fr.

Hibiscus Sabdariffa L.
  Microsphaera Euphorbiae (Pk.) B. & C.
  Phytophthora terrestris Sherbakoff.
Hibiscus syriacus L.
  Camarosporium lyndonvillae Sacc.
  Choanephora conjuncta Couch.
  Choanephora Cucurbitarum (B. & Rav.) Thax.
  Fusarium Berkelei Mont.
  Gibbera pulicaris Fr.
  Kuehneola malvicola Arth.
  { Melogramma Hibisci (S.) B. & C.
  { Sphaeria Hibisci S.
  { Nectria offuscata B. & C.
  { Nectriella offuscata (B. & C.) Sacc.
  Peziza alboviolascens A. & S. ex Fr.
  Phyllosticta Syriaca Sacc.
  Physalospora Cydoniae Arnaud.
  { Haplosporella Hibisci (B.) Petrak & Syd.
  { Sphaeropsis Hibisci Cke.
  { Sphaeropsis lyndonvillae Sacc.
  Sphaerostilbe gracilipes Tul.
  Torula brevissima B. & C.
  Uredo Hibisci Syd.
  Uromyces heterogenus Cke.?
Hibiscus tiliaceus L.
  Cercospora Hibisci Tracy & Earle.
  Cercospora hibiscina Ell. & Ev.
  Meliola Triumfettae F. L. Stevens.
  Phyllachora minuta Henn.
Hibiscus Trionum L.
  Cercospora althaeina Sacc.
  Fusarium roseum Lk.
Hibiscus sp. indet.
  Colletotrichum Hibisci Poll.
  Diaporthe ophites Sacc.
  Diplodia hibiscina C. & E.
  Hendersonia collapsa C. & E.
  { Corticium koleroga (Cke.) v. Höhnel.
  { Pellicularia koleroga Cke.
  Peziza variecolor Fr.
  Stilbum cinereorubrum B. & C.
Gossypium acuminatum Roxb.
  { Cerotelium Gossypii Arth.
  { Kuehneola Gossypii Arth.
Gossypium album Ham.
  { Botryosphaeria subconnata (S.) Cke.
  { Sphaeria subconnata S.
  { Thuemenia valsarioides Rehm.
Gossypium arboreum L.
  Cercospora gossypina Cke.
  { Cerotelium Gossypii Arth.
  { Kuehneola Gossypii Arth.
Gossypium barbadense L.
  Dicaeoma hibisciatum (Kellerm.) Arth. I.
  Cercospora gossypina Cke.
  { Cerotelium desmium Arth.
  { Cerotelium Gossypii Arth.
  { Kuehneola Gossypii Arth.
  { Uredo Gossypii Lagerh.

Gossypium barbadense (*cont.*)
  Corticium vagum B. & C., var. Solani Burt.
  Darluca Filum (Biv.) Cast.
  Fusarium vasinfectum Atk.
  Fusarium vasinfectum (Atk.), var. inodoratum
    Wollenw.
  Helminthosporium Gossypii Tucker.
  Mycosphaerella gossypina (Atk.) Earle.
  Ovulariopsis Gossypii Wakefield.
  Phyllosticta Malkoffii Bubák.
  Ramularia areola Atk.
  Rosellinia bunodes (B. & Br.) Sacc.

  Reported in Bull. U. S. Agr. 1366. 1926
    on either or both the following hosts.
Gossypium barbadense L.
Gossypium hirsutum L.
  Ascochyta Gossypii Syd.
  Cercospora althaeina Sacc.
  Diplodia gossypina Cke.
  Macrosporium nigricantium Atk.
  Olpitrichum carpophilum Atk.
  Ozonium omnivorum Shear.
  Phlyctaena gossypina Ell. & Martin.
  Pythium debaryanum Hesse.
  Thielavia basicola (B. & Br.) Zopf.
  Verticillium albo-atrum Reinke & Berth.
Gossypium brasiliense Macfad.
  ⎰Cerotelium desmium Arth.
  ⎱Kuehneola Gossypii Arth.
Gossypium hirsutum L.
  Including Gossypium herbaceum Auct. Amer.
    and "cotton," which is presumably G. hir-
    sutum in most cases.

PHYCOMYCETES

  Acrosporium Gossypii Sumstine.
  Choanephora Cucurbitarum (B. & Rav.) Thax.
  Mucor Mucedo L.
  ⎰Cunninghamella echinulata Thax.
  ⎱Oedocephalum echinulatum Thax.
  Papulospora polyspora Hotson.
  Phytophthora parasitica Dastur.
  Pythium debaryanum Hesse.
  Rhizopus nigricans Ehrenb. ex Fr.

PYRENOMYCETINEAE

  Amphisphaeria separans Ell. & Ev.
  Botryosphaeria berengeriana De Not.
  Botryosphaeria fuliginosa (M. & N.) Ell. & Ev.
  ⎧Botryosphaeria horizontalis (B. & C.) Sacc.
  ⎪Botryosphaeria subconnata (S.) Cke.
  ⎨Melogramma horizontalis B. & C.
  ⎪Sphaeria subconnata S.
  ⎩Thuemenia valsarioides Rehm.
  Botryosphaeria Ribis (Tode ex Fr.) Grossen-
    bacher & Duggar.
  Botryosphaeria Ribis (Tode ex Fr.) Grossen-
    bacher & Duggar, var. chromogena Shear
    et al.

  Chaetomium olivaceum C. & E.
  Gibberella pulicaris (Fr.) Sacc. (?).
  ⎰Hyponectria? Gossypii (S.) Sacc.
  ⎱Sphaeria Gossypii S.
  Nectria Brassicae Ell. & Sacc.
  Neocosmospora vasinfecta Erw. Sm.
  Neocosmospora vasinfecta Erw. Sm., var.
    tracheiphila Erw. Sm.
  Ophiobolus porphyrogonus (Tode ex Fr.) Sacc.
  ⎰Pleosphaeria hyphasmatis (Ell. & Ev.) Berl.
  ⎱Pyrenophora hyphasmatis Ell. & Ev.
  ⎰Pleospora nigricans Atk.
  ⎱Pleospora nigricantia Atk.
  Rosellinia subcompressa Ell. & Ev.
  ⎰Mycosphaerella gossypina (Atk.) Earle.
  ⎱Sphaerella gossypina Atk.
  Sphaeria millegrana S.
  Thielavia basicola (B. & Br.) Zopf.
  Valsa gossypina Cke.
  ⎧Catharinia funicola (Ell.) Berl.
  ⎪Psilosphaeria funicola (Ell.) Cke.
  ⎨Sphaeria funicola Ell.
  ⎩Zignoella funicola (Ell.) Sacc.

UREDINALES

  ⎧Aecidium Gossypii Ell. & Ev.
  ⎪Puccinia Gossypii Kellerm. I.
  ⎨Aecidium Napaeae Arth. & Holw.
  ⎩Dicaeoma hibisciatum (Kellerm.) Arth. I.
  ⎧Cerotelium desmium Arth.
  ⎨Kuehneola Gossypii Arth.
  ⎩Uredo Gossypii Lagerh.

HYMENOMYCETINEAE

  ⎧Corticium vagum B. & C.
  ⎨Corticium vagum B. & C., var. Solani Burt.
  ⎩Rhizoctonia Solani Kühn.
  Marasmius Sacchari Wakker.
  Schizophyllum alneum (L.) ex Schrt.

SPHAEROPSIDALES

  Ascochyta Gossypii Syd.
  Botryodiplodia Gossypii Ell. & Barthol.
  Darluca Filum (Biv.) Cast.
  Diplodia gossypina Cke.
  Diplodia herbarum (Cda.) Lév.
  Diplodia herbarum (Cda.) Lév., var. Gossypii
    Sacc.
  ?Diplodia natalensis Evans.
  Diplodiella striispora Ell. & Barthol.
  Dothiorella botryosphaerioides Sacc.
  Dothiorella major Ell. & Ev.
  Lasiodiplodia tubericola Ell. & Ev.
  Phoma canescens Ell. & Barthol.
  Phoma corvina Rav.
  Phoma Gossypii Sacc.
  Phoma subconnata B. & C.
  Phyllosticta gossypina Ell. & Martin.

Gossypium hirsutum (*cont.*)
Phyllosticta Roumii Auct.
Phyllosticta subconnata B. & C.
⎰ Phlyctaena Gossypii Sacc.
⎱ Septoria arcuata (B.) Sacc., var. Gossypii Sacc.
Septoria gossypina Cke.

Melanconiales

Colletotrichum falcatum Went.
Gloeosporium carpigenum Cke. & Hark.
⎰ Colletotrichum Gossypii Southworth.
⎱ Glomerella Gossypii Edgerton.
⎰ Colletotrichum Gossypii Southworth, var.
⎮   barbadense Lewton-Brain.
⎮ Glomerella Gossypii Edgerton, var. barba-
⎱   dense Lewton-Brain.
Pestalozziella gossypina Atk.

Hyphomycetes

Alternaria tenuis Nees ex Fr.
Alternaria gossypii Auct.
Aspergillus niger van Tiegh.
Cercospora althaeina Sacc.
⎰ Cercospora gossypina Cke.
⎱ Sphaerella gossypina Atk.
Cladosporium herbarum (P.) ex Lk.
⎰ Fusarium aurantiacum (Lk.) Sacc.
⎱ Fusisporium aurantiacum Lk.
Fusarium eumartii C. W. Carpenter.
Fusarium oxysporum Schl.
Fusarium radicicola Wollenw.
Fusarium roseum Lk.
Fusarium vasinfectum Atk.
Fusarium vasinfectum Atk., var. inodoratum
  Wollenw.
Macrosporium gossypinum Thm.
⎰ Macrosporium nigricans (Atk.) Sacc.
⎱ Macrosporium nigricantium Atk.
Mystrosporium polytrichum Cke.
Olpitrichum carpophilum Atk.
Ovulariopsis Gossypii Wakefield.
Ozonium auricomum Lk.
⎰ Ozonium omnivorum Shear.
⎱ Phymatotrichum omnivorum (Shear) Duggar.
Penicillium glaucum Lk.
Penicillium spiculisporum Lehman.
Ramularia areola Atk.
Rhinotrichum tenellum B. & C.
Rhinotrichum macrosporum Farl.
Sporotrichum chlorinum Lk.
Trichothecium roseum Lk.
Verticillium albo-atrum Reinke & Berthold.
Verticillium rexianum Sacc.

Miscellanea

Eremothecium cymbalariae Borzi.
Licea Lindheimeri B.
Nematospora Coryli Peglion.
Nematospora Gossypii Ashby & Nowell.

Sclerotium Rolfsii Sacc.
Spermophthora Gossypii Ashby & Nowell.
Gossypium mexicanum Tod.
Gossypium microcarpon Tod.
Gossypium peruvianum Cav.
Kuehneola Gossypii Arth.
Malvaceae gen. indet.
⎰ Belonidium leucorrhodinum (Mont.) Sacc.
⎱ Peziza leucorrhodina Mont.
Cladosporium anomalum B. & C.
Periconia byssoides P.

BOMBACACEAE

Montezuma speciosissima Moc. & Sesse.
Cerotelium desmium Arth.
Ochroma lagopus Sw.
Cicinnobella costaricensis Syd.
Dimerium costaricense Syd.

STERCULIACEAE

Fremontia californica Torr.
Ascochyta Fremontiae Hark.
Moluchia tomentosa (L.) Brit.
Cercospora Melochiae Henn.
Buettneria carthagenensis Jacq.
Bionectria Tonduzi Speg.
Haplolepis polyadelpha Syd.
Hypostigme polyadelpha Syd.
⎰ Micropuccinia filopes (Arth. & Holw.) Arth.
⎮   & Jackson.
⎱ Puccinia filopes Arth. & Holw.
Puiggarina costaricensis Speg.
Buettneria lateralis Presl.
⎰ Micropuccinia filopes (Arth. & Holw.) Arth. &
⎮   Jackson.
⎱ Puccinia filopes Arth. & Holw.
Theobroma cacao L.

Phycomycetes

Phytophthora Cactorum (Lib. & Cohn) Schrt.
Phytophthora Faberi Maubl.
Phytophthora infestans (Mont.) DBy.
Phytophthora Meadii MacRae.
Phytophthora omnivora DBy.
Phytophthora palmivora Butler.
Phytophthora parasitica Dastur.
Phytophthora Theobromae Coleman.
Pythium debaryanum Hesse.
Vasculomyces Xanthosomae Ashby.

Ascomycetes

Eutypa erumpens Massee.
Exoascus Theobromae Ritzema Bos.
Helotium miniatum Pat.
Lophodermium Theobromae Pat.
Melanomma henriquesianum Bres. & Roum.
Penzigia dealbata (B. & C.) Sacc. & Paol.

Theobroma cacao (*cont.*)
Rosellinia bunodes (B. & Br.) Sacc.
Rosellinia Hartii Massee.
Rosellinia necatrix (R. Hartig) Berl.
Rosellinia paraguayensis Starb.
Rosellinia Pepo Pat.
Saccharomyces apiculatus Reess.
Saccharomyces ellipsoideus Reess.
Saccharomyces Theobromae Preyer.
Calonectria flavida Massee.
Calonectria tetraspora (Seaver) Sacc. & Trott.
⎰Creonectria Bainii (Massee) Seaver.
⎱Nectria Bainii Massee.
Nectria cinnabarina (Tode) ex Fr.
Nectria discophora Mont.
Nectria ditissima Tul.
Nectria striatospora Zimm.
Nectria Theobromae Massee.
Ophionectria Theobromae Pat.
Sphaerostilbe Musarum Ashby.
Sphaerostilbe ochracea Pat.

BASIDIOMYCETES

Auricularia polytricha (Mont.) Sacc.
Corticium laeve Fr.
⎰Corticium lilacinofuscum Auct. p. p.
⎱Corticium salmonicolor B. & Br.
Corticium Stevensii Burt.
Hymenochaete leonina B. & C.
Hymenochaete noxia B.
Hypochnus Sacchari Speg.
Marasmius equicrinus Müll.
Marasmius perniciosus Stahel.
⎰Marasmius sarmentosus B.
⎱Polymarasmius sarmentosus (B.) Murrill.
Marasmius theobromicola Murrill.
Marasmius Underwoodii Murrill.
⎰Polyporus Korthalsii Lév.
⎱Xanthochrous Korthalsii (Lév.) Pat.
Leptoporus microstomus (B. & C.) Pat.
⎰Polyporus microstomus B. & C.
⎱Rigidoporus microstomus (B. & C.) Murrill.
⎰Leptonia hypoporphyrinus B. & C.
⎱Rhodophyllus hypoporphyrinus (B. & C.) Pat.
Septobasidium Spongia (B. & C.) Pat.
⎰Corticium lilacinofuscum B. & C.
⎱Stereum roseocarneum (S.) Fr.

SPHAEROPSIDALES

Asterostomella paraguayensis Speg.
⎰Botryodiplodia elasticae Petch.
⎱Botryodiplodia Theobromae Pat.
Diplodia cacaoicola Henn.
Diplodia Theobromae (Pat.) Taubenhaus.
Lasiodiplodia Theobromae (Pat.) Griff. & Maubl.
Macrophoma vestita Prill. & Delacr.
Thyridaria tarda Bancoft.

MELANCONIALES

Colletotrichum brachytrichum Delacr.
Colletotrichum Cradwickii Bancroft.
Colletotrichum incarnatum Zimm.
Colletotrichum luxificum van Hall.
⎰Colletotrichum theobromicola Delacr.
⎱Glomerella cingulata (Stoneman) Spaulding & v. Schrenk.
Stilbospora Cacao Massee.

HYPHOMYCETES

Acrostalagmus Vilmorinii, var. Thomensis Guéguen.
Aspergillus Delacroixii Sacc. & Syd.
Aspergillus olivaceus Delacr.
Cercospora Kophei Krüger.
Didymostilbe coccinea Massee.
Fusarium camptoceras Wr. & Reink.
Fusarium Theobromae Lutz.
Hartiella coccinea Massee.
Pellicularia koleroga Cke.
Ramularia necator Massee.
Spicaria colorans De Jonge.
Sporotrichum globuliferum Speg.
Sterigmatocystis nigra van Tiegh.
Stilbum nanum Massee (?).
Thielaviopsis paradoxa (De Seynes) v. Höhnel.

MISCELLANEA

Sclerotium Rolfsii Sacc.
Guazuma tomentosa H. B. K.
Cyphella eruciformis (Batsch) Fr.
Pachytrichum Guazumae Syd.
Trichosporium tomentosum (B. & C.) Pat.
Guazuma ulmifolia Lam.
Nectria flavella Pat.
Phoma macromphala Pat.
Scleromeris Guazumae Syd.
Sphaeronemella mirabilis Speg.
Trabutia Guazumae Chardon.
Helicteres jamaicensis Jacq.
Cercospora trichophila F. L. Stevens.
Guignardia Helicteres F. L. Stevens.
Phyllosticta borinquensis E. Young.
Sterculia caribaea R. Br.
Calocera cornea Fr.
Dictyopanus subpulverulentus Pat.
Hypocrea cupularis Pat.
⎰Leptoporus carneopallens (B. & C.) Pat.
⎱Polyporus carneopallens B. & C.
⎰Leptoporus nigrellus Pat.
⎱Polyporus nigrellus (Pat.) Sacc. & D. Sacc.
⎰Cladoderris caperata (B. & Mont.) Pat.
⎱Stereum caperatum (B. & Mont.) Massee.
Thelephora caperata B. & Mont.
Sterculia carthaginensis Cav.
Phyllosticta sterculicola Trav., var. carthaginensis Fragoso & Ciferri.
Cola vera K. Schum.
Leptostroma Colae Ciferri & Fragoso.

DILLENIACEAE

Tetracera volubilis L.
- ⎰Coccomyces Tetracerae (Rud.) Sacc.
- ⎱Phacidium Tetracerae Rud.
- Harknessia (?) Tetracerae Ell. & Ev.

Actinidia polygama Franch. & Sav.
- Rhizoctonia Solani Kühn.

Saurauja Conzatti Buscalioni.
- ⎰Micropuccinia hiascens (Arth.) Arth. & Jackson.
- ⎱Puccinia aucta Arth. & Holw.
- Puccinia hiascens Arth.

Saurauja pauciserrata Hemsl.
- Puccinia vergrandis Arth. & Holw.

Saurauja smithiana Buscalioni.
- ⎰Micropuccinia hiascens (Arth.) Arth. & Jackson.
- ⎱Puccinia aucta Arth. & Holw.
- Puccinia hiascens Arth.

OCHNACEAE

Sauvagesia erecta L.
- Meliola glabra B. & C.
- ⎰Irene glabroides (F. L. Stevens) Toro.
- ⎱Meliola glabroides F. L. Stevens.
- Uredo Sauvagesiae Arth.

MARCGRAVIACEAE

Marcgravia nepenthoides Seem.
- Meliola ramonensis Syd.

Marcgravia rectiflora Tr. & Planch.
- Meliola Marcgraviae Tehon.

THEACEAE
(TERNSTROEMIACEAE)

Thea bohea L.
- Colletotrichum Camelliae Massee.
- Colletotrichum Carveri Ell. & Ev.
- Corticium salmonicolor B. & Br.
- Darluca Filum (Biv.) Cast.
- Glomerella cingulata (Stoneman) Spaulding & v. Schrenk.
- Sphaeria orthogramma B. & C.
- Stilbum nanum Massee.

Thea sp. indet.
- Phyllosticta erratica Ell. & Ev.

Camellia japonica L.
- Exobasidium Camelliae Shirai.
- Hendersonia subalbicans Gerard.
- Meliola Camelliae Sacc.
- Monochaetia Camelliae Miles.
- Pestalozzia Guepini Desm.
- Pestalozzia inquinans Cke. & Hark.
- Sporonema Camelliae Earle.

Gordonia lasiantha L.
- Cystospora Gordoniae B.
- Isariopsis penicillata Ell. & Ev.

Meliola cryptocarpa Ell. & Martin.
Phyllosticta Gordoniae Ell. & Martin.
Sphaerella Gordoniae Cke.

Ternstroemia elliptica Sw.
- ⎰Cyclomyces iodinus (Mont.) Pat.
- ⎱Polyporus iodinus Mont.

Freziera undulata Willd.
- ⎰Podoscypha petalodes (B. & C.) Pat.
- ⎱Stereum petalodes B. & C.

HYPERICACEAE

Ascyrum hypericoides L.
- Fusicladium ascyrinum Ell. & Ev.
- ⎰Aecidium hypericatum (Lk.) S.
- ⎱Nigredo Hyperici-frondosi Arth.

Ascyrum stans Michx.
- Cladosporium gloeosporioides Atk.

Hypericum adpressum Bart.
- Cercospora Hyperici Tehon & Daniels.

Hypericum anagalloides Cham. & Schl.

Hypericum Ascyron L.
- ⎰Nigredo Hyperici-frondosi Arth.
- ⎨Uromyces Hyperici M. A. Curtis.
- ⎩Uromyces Hyperici-frondosi Arth.

Hypericum aureum Barton?
- Didymosporium complanatum Nees.
- Fusarium effusum S.

Hypericum boreale (Britton) Bicknell.

Hypericum canadense L.

Hypericum ellipticum Hook.

Hypericum fasciculatum Lam.

Hypericum kalmianum L.

Hypericum majus (Gray) Brit.
- ⎰Aecidium hypericatum (Lk.) S.
- ⎪Aecidium Hyperici-frondosi S.
- ⎪Aecidium Hypericorum B. & C.
- ⎪Aecidium oblongum Bon.
- ⎪Caeoma hypericatum Lk.
- ⎨Caeomurus Hyperici-frondosi Arth.
- ⎪Nigredo Hyperici-frondosi Arth.
- ⎪Uredo Hyperici Spreng.
- ⎪Uromyces Hyperici M. A. Curtis.
- ⎪Uromyces Hyperici-frondosi Arth.
- ⎩Uromyces triqueter Cke.

Hypericum mutilum L.
- Colletotrichum cladosporioides (Ell. & Ev.) Atk.
- ⎰Cladosporium gloeosporioides Atk.
- ⎱Gloeosporium cladosporioides Ell. & Halsted.
- Septoria sphaerelloides Ell. & Kellerm.
- ⎰Aecidium hypericatum (Lk.) S.
- ⎪Aecidium minutissimum Gerard.
- ⎪Caeoma Hyperici S.
- ⎨Caeomurus Hyperici-frondosi Arth.
- ⎪Nigredo Hyperici-frondosi Arth.
- ⎪Uromyces Hyperici M. A. Curtis.
- ⎪Uromyces Hyperici-frondosi Arth.
- ⎩Uromyces triqueter Cke.

Hypericum opacum Torr. & Gray.
Hypericum paludosum Choisy.
  Nigredo Hyperici-frondosi Arth.
  Uromyces Hyperici M. A. Curtis.
Hypericum perforatum L.
  Leptostroma Hyperici S.
  Aecidium hypericatum (Lk.) S.
  Nigredo Hyperici-frondosi Arth.
  Uromyces Hyperici M. A. Curtis.
  Uromyces triqueter Cke.
Hypericum petiolatum Walt.
Hypericum pratense Schl. & Cham.
  Nigredo Hyperici-frondosi Arth.
  Uromyces Hyperici-frondosi Arth.
Hypericum prolificum L.
  Botryosphaeria Hypericorum Cke.
  Leptosphaeria vagabunda Sacc.
  Sphaerella hypericina Ell.
  Sphaeria Hyperici S.
  Caeoma hypericatum Lk.
  Uromyces Hyperici M. A. Curtis.
  Uromyces Hyperici-frondosi Arth.
Hypericum punctatum Lam.
  Septoria sphaerelloides Ell. & Kellerm.
  Aecidium Hyperici-frondosi S.
  Nigredo Hyperici-frondosi Arth.
  Trichobasis Hyperici (M. A. Curtis) Gerard.
  Uromyces Hyperici M. A. Curtis.
  Uromyces Hyperici-frondosi Arth.
Hypericum pyramidatum Ait.
  Aecidium hypericatum (Lk.) S.
  Uromyces Hyperici M. A. Curtis.
  Uromyces Hyperici-frondosi Arth.
Hypericum Sarothra Michx.
  Mollisia atrocinerea (Cke.) Phil.
  Peziza atrocinerea Cke.
Hypericum Scouleri Coulter.
Hypericum submontanum Rose.
  Nigredo Hyperici-frondosi Arth.
  Uromyces Hyperici-frondosi Arth.
Hypericum virginicum L.
  Cladosporium gloeosporioides Atk.
  Ramularia ontariensis Sacc.
  Caeomurus Hyperici-frondosi Arth.
  Nigredo Hyperici-frondosi Arth.
  Uromyces Hyperici M. A. Curtis.
  Uromyces Hyperici-frondosi Arth.
  Uromyces triqueter Cke.
Hypericum sp. indet.
  Phomatospora hypericina (B. & C.) Cke.
  Physalospora hypericina (B. & C.) Sacc.
  Sphaeria hypericina B. & C.
  Sphaeria Hyperici S.
Vismia ferruginea H. B. K.
  Cercospora Vismiae Syd.
Vismia sp. indet.
  Dothidella Vismiae Bomm. & Rouss.
  Endodothella Vismiae (Bomm. & Rouss.)
    Theissen & Syd.

GUTTIFERAE

Mammea americana L.
  Anthostomella Mammeae Fragoso & Ciferri.
  Aulographum melioloides Cke. & Massee.
  Corticium chelidonium Pat.
  Daldinia concentrica (Bolt. ex Fr.) Ces. &
    DeNot.
  Echidnodes Mammeae Ryan.
  Ganoderma guadelupense Pat.
  Grallomyces portoricensis F. L. Stevens.
  Meliola Paulliniae F. L. Stevens.
  Phyllosticta mammeicola Ciferri & Fragoso.
Calophyllum antillanum Brit.
  Appendiculella Calophylli (F. L. Stevens) Toro.
  Meliola Calophylli F. L. Stevens.
  Helminthosporium glabroides F. L. Stevens.
  Lembosia Sepotae Ryan.
  Marasmius fibrosipes B. & C.
  Melanopus varius (Fr.) Pat.
  Polyporus varius Fr.
  Meliolidium portoricense Speg.
  Perisporina portoricensis (F. L. Stevens)
    Seaver & Toro.
  Perisporium portoricense F. L. Stevens.
Calophyllum sp. indet.
  Microthyrium Calophylli Ryan.
Clusia alba Jacq.
  Aschersonia oxyspora B.
Clusia Gundlachi Stahl.
  Asterina solanicola B. & C.
  Guignardia Clusiae F. L. Stevens.
  Meliola Clusiae F. L. Stevens.
  Mycosphaerella Guttiferae Miles.
Clusia krugiana Urb.
  Parodiopsis melioloides (B. & C.) Maubl.
Clusia minor L.
  Grallomyces portoricensis F. L. Stevens.
  Meliola Clusiae F. L. Stevens.
Clusia "parasitica" Auct.
  Dothidella millepunctata (B. & C.) Sacc.
  Coccomyces limitatus (B. & C.) Sacc.
  Phacidium limitatum B. & C.
  Coccomyces pluridens (B. & C.) Sacc.
  Phacidium pluridens B. & C.
  Glonium Clusiae B. & C.
  Sporidesmium Millegrana B. & C.
Clusia rosea Jacq.
  Coccomyces Clusiae (Lév.) Sacc.
  Dimerium melioloides (B. & C.) P. Garman.
  Ellisiella portoricensis F. L. Stevens.
  Favolus brasiliensis Fr.
  Mycosphaerella Clusiae F. L. Stevens.
  Pestalozzia funerea Desm.
  Phyllosticta Clusiae F. L. Stevens.
  Uredo Clusiae Arth.
  Xylaria aristata Mont.
Clusia venosa Jacq.
  Corticium auberianum Mont.

Clusia venosa (*cont.*)
  {Leucoporus stipitarius (B. & C.) Pat.
  {Polyporus stipitarius B. & C.
Clusia sp. indet.
  Asterina connata B. & C.
  Aulographum ciliatum B. & C.
  Lophodermium platyplacum B. & C.
  Stictis foliicola B. & C.
  {Asterina reptans Fung. Cub. 409 (p. p.?).
  {Trichothyrium dubiosum (Bomm. & Rouss.)
  {   Theissen.
Rheedia edulis Planch. & Triana.
  Asterina tropicalis Speg.
  Meliola glabroides F. L. Stevens.
  Phyllachora peregrina Syd.
Garcinia mangostana L.
  {Corticium koleroga (Cke.) v. Höhnel.
  {Pellicularia koleroga Cke.
  Pestalozzia Espaillatii Ciferri & Fragoso.
Moronobea coccinea Aubl.
  {Corticium diminuens B. & C.
  {Corticium portentosum B. & C.
  Mycena corticola (Schum.) ex Fr.
  Pluteus leoninus (Schaeff.) ex Fr.
  {Poria aurantiotingens Ell. & Macbr.
  {Porogramme aurantiotingens (Ell. & Macbr.)
  {   Pat.

TAMARICACEAE
Tamarix africana Poir.
  Pyrenopeziza Tamaricis (Roum.) Sacc.
Tamarix gallica L.
  {Bagnisiella Tamaricis (Cke.) Sacc.
  {Dothidea Tamaricis Cke.
  Botryosphaeria Tamaricis (Cke.) Theissen &
    Syd.
Tamarix parviflora DC.
  Diplodia tamariscina Sacc.
Tamarix sp. indet.
  {Leptosphaeria Tamaricis (Grev.) Sacc.
  {Sphaeria Tamaricis Grev.
  Ozonium omnivorum Shear.

FOUQUIERIACEAE
Fouquieria splendens Engelm.
  Aecidium Cannonii D. Griff.

CISTACEAE
Helianthemum canadense (L.) Michx.
Helianthemum majus BSP.
  Cylindrosporium eminens J. J. Davis.
Helianthemum mutabile Moench.
  Lophiostoma simillimum Karst.
Hudsonia tomentosa Nutt.
  Cucurbitaria Coremae Ell. & Ev.
  Diaporthe Conradii Ell.
Lechea intermedia Leggett.
  Septoria Chamaecisti Vestergren.

BIXACEAE
Bixa orellana L.
  Cercospora Bixae Allescher & Noack.
  Phyllosticta bixina E. Young.
  Rosellinia necatrix (R. Hartig) Berl.
  Uredo Bixae Arth.

KOEBERLINIACEAE
Koeberlinia spinosa Zucc.
  Diplodina Koerberliniae Ell. & Ev.

CANELLACEAE
Canella alba Murr.
  Helminthosporium Helleri F. L. Stevens.
  Meliola Thouiniae Earle.
  Scolecopeltis portoricensis Speg.
  Triposporium stelligerum Speg.
Canella winterana (L.) Gaertn.
  Meliola Thouiniae Earle.
  Scolecopeltis portoricensis Speg.

VIOLACEAE
Hybanthus concolor (Forster) Spreng.
  Cercospora columbiensis Ell. & Ev.
Viola affinis Le Conte.
  Aecidium Mariae-Wilsoni Pk.
  Puccinia effusa Diet. & Holw.
  {Dicaeoma Violae (DC.) O. Kuntze.
  {Puccinia Violae DC.
Viola arenaria DC.
  {Aecidium Violae Schum.
  {Dicaeoma Violae (DC.) O. Kuntze.
  {Puccinia Violae DC.
Viola blanda Willd.
  {Aecidium Mariae-Wilsoni Pk.
  {Puccinia ellisiana Thm. I.
  Cercospora granuliformis Ell. & Holw.
  Cercospora Violae Sacc.
  Puccinia Fergussoni B. & Br.
  {Aecidium Violae Schum.
  {Dicaeoma Violae (DC.) O. Kuntze.
  {Puccinia Violae DC.
  Septoria cercosperma Rostr.
  Septoria hyalina Ell. & Ev.
  Septoria Violae Westd.
  Septoria Violae Westd., var. oligocarpa Pk.
  Sphaerella pachyasca Rostr.
  Sphaerotheca Humuli (DC.) Burrill. †
Viola brittoniana Pollard.
  Dicaeoma Violae (DC.) O. Kuntze.
Viola canadensis L.
  Puccinia ellisiana Thm. I.
  Puccinia alpina Fckl.
  {Micropuccinia ornatula (Holw.) Arth. &
  {   Jackson.
  {Puccinia ornatula Holw.

Viola canadensis (*cont.*)
- Aecidium Violae Schum.
- Dicaeoma Violae (DC.) O. Kuntze. I.
- Puccinia Violae DC. I.
- Ramularia ionophila J. J. Davis.
- Septoria Violae Westd.
- Sphaerotheca Humuli (DC.) Burrill. †

Viola canina L.
- Puccinia Violae DC.
- Septoria cercosperma Rostr.

Viola cognata Greene.
- Puccinia Violae DC.

Viola conspersa Reichenb.
- Cercospora Violae Sacc.
- Dicaeoma Violae (DC.) O. Kuntze.
- Septoria Violae Westd.
- Synchytrium aureum Schrt.

Viola cucullata Ait.
- Aecidium Mariae-Wilsoni Pk.
- Puccinia ellisiana Thm. I.
- Nigredo pedatata (J. Sheldon) Arth. I.
- Uromyces Andropogonis Tracy. I.
- Alternaria Violae Gall. & Dorsett.
- Ascochyta Violae Sacc. & Speg.
- Cercospora granuliformis Ell. & Holw.
- Cercospora murina Ell. & Kellerm.
- Cercospora Violae Sacc.
- Marssonia Violae (Pass.) Sacc.
- Phyllosticta Violae Desm.
- Aecidium Violae Schum.
- Caeoma violatum Lk.
- Dicaeoma Violae (DC.) O. Kuntze.
- Puccinia Violae DC.
- Septoria Violae Westd.
- Sphaerotheca Humuli (DC.) Burrill.†
- Sphaerotheca Humuli (DC.) Burrill, var. fuliginea (Schl.) Salmon.
- Vermicularia Peckii Sacc.
- Vermicularia Violae Ell. & Ev.
- Colletotrichum Violae-rotundifoliae (Sacc.) H. W. Anderson.
- Vermicularia Violae-rotundifoliae (Sacc.) House.
- Volutella Violae Stoneman.

Viola cucullata, var. prionosepala (Greene) Brainerd.
- Dicaeoma Violae (DC.) O. Kuntze.

Viola delphinifolia Nutt.
- Aecidium Mariae-Wilsoni Pk.
- Aecidium Petersii B. & C.
- Aecidium Violae Schum.
- Puccinia Violae DC.

Viola emarginata LeConte.
- Puccinia ellisiana Thm. I.

Viola eriocarpa S.
- Colletotrichum Violarum J. J. Davis.
- Vermicularia Violae-rotundifoliae (Sacc.) House.
- Dicaeoma Mariae-Wilsoni Arth. & Fromme. I.

- Aecidium Violae Schum.
- Dicaeoma Violae (DC.) O. Kuntze.
- Puccinia Violae DC.

Viola fimbriatula J. E. Sm.
- Aecidium pedatatum S.
- Dicaeoma Mariae-Wilsoni Arth. & Fromme.
- Puccinia ellisiana Thm. I.
- Dicaeoma Violae (DC.) O. Kuntze.
- Puccinia Violae DC.

Viola glabella Nutt.
- Puccinia densa Diet. & Holw.
- Micropuccinia ornatula (Holw.) Arth. & Jackson.
- Puccinia ornatula Holw.
- Dicaeoma Violae (DC.) O. Kuntze.
- Puccinia Violae DC.

Viola Grahami Benth.
- Dicaeoma Violae (DC.) O. Kuntze.

Viola hastata Michx.
- Puccinia Fergussoni B. & Br., var. hastata (Cke.) DeToni.
- Puccinia hastata Cke.
- Aecidium Violae Schum.
- Caeoma violatum Lk.
- Dicaeoma Violae (DC.) O. Kuntze.
- Puccinia Violae DC.
- Septoria Violae Westd.

Viola hirsutula Brainerd.
- Puccinia ellisiana Thm. I.
- Dicaeoma Violae (DC.) O. Kuntze.

Viola Howellii Gray.

Viola incognita Brainerd.
- Dicaeoma Violae (DC.) O. Kuntze.
- Puccinia Violae DC.

Viola labradorica Schrank.
- Phyllactinia corylea (P.) ex Karst.
- Puccinia Violae DC.

Viola lanceolata L.
- Dicaeoma Mariae-Wilsoni Arth. & Fromme. I.
- Puccinia ellisiana Thm. I.
- Dicaeoma Violae (DC.) O. Kuntze.
- Puccinia Violae DC.
- Uredo Violarum DC.
- Septoria hyalina Ell. & Ev.
- Septoria Violae Westd.
- Nigredo pedatata (J. L. Sheldon) Arth. I.
- Uromyces pedatatus J. L. Sheldon. I.

Viola Langsdorfii Fisch.
- Micropuccinia Fergussoni (B. & Br.) Arth. & Jackson.
- Puccinia Fergussoni B. & Br.
- Dicaeoma Violae (DC.) O. Kuntze.

Viola lobata Benth.
- Allodus effusa (Diet. & Holw.) Arth.
- Puccinia effusa Diet. & Holw.
- Dicaeoma Violae (DC.) O. Kuntze.

Viola longipes Nutt.
- Puccinia Violae DC.
- Urocystis Violae (Sow.) Fisch. Wald.

Viola Lunellii Greene.
  Puccinia ellisiana Thm. I.
Viola Macloskeyi F. E. Lloyd.
  Micropuccinia Fergussoni (B. & Br.) Arth. &
    Jackson.
  Puccinia Violae DC.
Viola missouriensis Greene.
  { Dicaeoma Violae (DC.) O. Kuntze.
  { Puccinia Violae DC.
Viola montanensis Rydb.
  { Dicaeoma Violae (DC.) O. Kuntze.
  { Puccinia Violae DC.|
  Sphaerotheca Humuli (DC.) Burrill. †
Viola monticola Rydb.
Viola nannei Polak.
  { Dicaeoma Violae (DC.) O. Kuntze.
  { Puccinia Violae DC.
Viola nephrophylla Greene.
  { Micropuccinia Fergussoni (B. & Br.) Arth. &
  {   Jackson.
  { Puccinia Fergussoni B. & Br.
  { Dicaeoma Violae (DC.) O. Kuntze.
  { Puccinia Violae DC.
Viola Nuttallii Pursh.
  { Dicaeoma Mariae-Wilsoni Arth. & Fromme. I.
  { Puccinia ellisiana Thm. I.
  { Aecidium pedatatum S.
  { Uromyces Andropogonis Tracy. I.
  Puccinia effusa Diet. & Holw.
  Puccinia Violae DC
  Urocystis Violae (Sow.) Fisch. Wald.
Viola ocellata Torr. & Gr.
  { Dicaeoma Violae (DC.) O. Kuntze.
  { Puccinia effusa Auct. Amer. p. p.
  { Puccinia Violae DC.
  Ramularia ionophila J. J. Davis.
Viola odorata L.
  Alternaria Violae Gall. & Dorsett.
  Ascochyta Violae Sacc. & Speg.
  Cercospora Violae Sacc.
  Colletotrichum Violae-tricoloris R. E. Sm.
  { Corticium vagum B. & C.
  { Rhizoctonia Solani Kühn.
  Gloeosporium Violae B. & Br.
  { Marssonia Violae (Pass.) Sacc.
  { Marssonina Violae (Pass.) Magn.
  Peronospora Violae DBy.
  Phyllosticta Violae Desm.
  Sclerotium Rolfsii Sacc.
  { Thielavia basicola (B. & Br.) Zopf.
  { Torula basicola B. & Br.
  Urocystis Violae (Sow.) Fisch. Wald.
  Zygodesmus albidus Ell. & Halsted.
Viola orbiculata Geyer.
  { Micropuccinia canadensis (Arth.) Arth. &
  {   Jackson.
  { Puccinia canadensis Arth.
Viola Painteri Rose & House.
  Dicaeoma Violae (DC.) O. Kuntze.

Viola pallens (Banks) Brainerd.
  Cercospora granuliformis Ell. & Holw.
  Dicaeoma Violae (DC.) O. Kuntze.
  Synchytrium aureum Schrt.
Viola palmata L.
  { Dicaeoma Mariae-Wilsoni Arth. & Fromme. I.
  { Puccinia ellisiana Thm. I.
  Cercospora Violae Sacc.
  { Aecidium Violae Schum.
  { Dicaeoma Violae (DC.) O. Kuntze.
Viola palustris L.
  { Micropuccinia Fergussoni (B. & Br.) Arth. &
  {   Jackson.
  { Puccinia Fergussoni B. & Br.
  Dicaeoma Violae (DC.) O. Kuntze.
  Septoria hyalina Ell. & Ev.
Viola papilionacea Pursh.
  { Dicaeoma ellisiana (Thm.) O. Kuntze. I.
  { Dicaeoma Mariae-Wilsoni Arth. & Fromme. I.
  { Puccinia ellisiana Thm. I.
  { Puccinia Mariae-Wilsoni (Arth. & Fromme)
  {   Barthol. I.
  Nigredo pedatata (J. L. Sheldon) Arth. I.
  Cercospora granuliformis Ell. & Holw.
  Cercospora Violae Sacc.
  { Aecidium Violae Schum.
  { Dicaeoma Violae (DC.) O. Kuntze.
  { Puccinia Violae DC.
Viola pedata L.
  Dicaeoma Mariae-Wilsoni Arth. & Fromme. I.
  { Aecidium Mariae-Wilsoni Auct. Amer. p. p.
  { Aecidium pedatatum S.
  { Aecidium Petersii B. & C.
  { Caeoma pedatatum S.
  { Nigredo pedatata (J. L. Sheldon) Arth. I.
  { Uromyces pedatatus J. L. Sheldon. I.
  Aecidium Violae Schum.
Viola pedatifida G. Don.
  { Aecidium pedatatum S.
  { Uromyces Andropogonis Tracy. I.
  { Dicaeoma Mariae-Wilsoni Arth. & Fromme. I.
  { Puccinia ellisiana Thm. I.
  { Dicaeoma Violae (DC.) O. Kuntze.
  { Puccinia Violae DC.
Viola praemorsa Dougl.
  Allodus effusa (Diet. & Holw.) Arth.
Viola pratincola Greene.
  Dicaeoma Violae (DC.) O. Kuntze.
Viola primulifolia L.
  Dicaeoma Mariae-Wilsoni Arth. & Fromme. I.·
  { Aecidium pedatatum S.
  { Uromyces Andropogonis Tracy. I.
  { Uromyces pedatatus J. L. Sheldon. I.
  Puccinia hastata Cke.
  { Dicaeoma Violae (DC.) O. Kuntze.
  { Puccinia Violae DC.
  Septoria hyalina Ell. & Ev.
  Septoria Violae Westd.

Viola pubescens Ait.
  Puccinia ellisiana Thm. I.
  Ascochyta Violae Sacc. & Speg.
  Cercospora granuliformis Ell. & Holw.
  Cercospora murina Ell. & Kellerm.
  Darluca Filum (Biv.) Cast.
  Phyllosticta Violae Desm.
  {Aecidium Violae Schum.
  {Dicaeoma Violae (DC.) O. Kuntze.
  {Puccinia Violae DC.
  {Puccinia Violarum Lk.
  Sclerotium nervale (A. & S.) ex Fr.
  Septoria Violae Westd.
  Synchytrium aureum Schrt.

Viola purpurea Kellogg.
  Allodus effusa (Diet. & Holw.) Arth.

Viola Rafinesquii Greene.
  {Bremiella megasperma (Berl.) G. W. Wilson.
  {Peronospora megasperma Berl.
  {Peronospora Violae N. A. F. *2007*.
  {Plasmopara megasperma Berl.
  Peronospora Violae DBy.
  Phyllosticta Rafinesquii H. W. Anderson.
  Urocystis kmetiana Magn.

Viola renifolia Gray.
  {Aecidium Violae Schum.
  {Dicaeoma Violae (DC.) O. Kuntze.
  {Puccinia Violae DC.

Viola retusa Greene.
  Sphaerotheca Humuli (DC.) Burrill. †

Viola rostrata Pursh.
  Dicaeoma Mariae-Wilsoni Arth. & Fromme. I.
  {Dicaeoma Violae (DC.) O. Kuntze.
  {Puccinia Violae DC.

Viola rotundifolia Michx.
  {Aecidium Violae Schum.
  {Puccinia Violae DC.
  {Vermicularia concentrica Pk. & Clinton.
  {Vermicularia Peckii Sacc.
  {Vermicularia Peckii, var. Violae-rotundifoliae
  { Sacc.
  {Vermicularia Violae-rotundifoliae (Sacc.)
  { House.

Viola rugulosa Greene.
  Micropuccinia ornatula (Holw.) Arth. & Jackson.
  {Dicaeoma Violae (DC.) O. Kuntze.
  {Puccinia Violae DC.

Viola Rydbergii Greene.
  Puccinia effusa Diet. & Holw.
  Puccinia Violae DC. ·

Viola sagittata Ait.
  Cercospora granuliformis Ell. & Holw.
  {Dicaeoma Mariae-Wilsoni Arth. & Fromme. I.
  {Puccinia ellisiana Thm. I.
  {Dicaeoma Violae (DC.) O. Kuntze.
  {Puccinia Violae DC.

  Septoria Violae Westd.
  {Aecidium pedatatum S.
  {Caeoma sagittatum S.
  {?Puccinia pedatata Overholts. I.
  {Uromyces pedatatus J. L. Sheldon. I.
Viola scopulorum (Gray) Greene.
Viola Selkirkii Pursh.
  {Dicaeoma Violae (DC.) O. Kuntze.
  {Puccinia Violae DC.
Viola septentrionalis Greene.
  Dicaeoma Mariae-Wilsoni Arth. & Fromme. I.
  Cercospora granuliformis Ell. & Holw.
  Marssonina Violae (Pass.) Magn.
  {Dicaeoma Violae (DC.) O. Kuntze.
  {Puccinia Violae DC.
Viola sororia Willd.
  {Dicaeoma Mariae-Wilsoni Arth. & Fromme. I.
  {Puccinia ellisiana Thm. I.
  {Nigredo pedatata (J. L. Sheldon) Arth. I.
  {Uromyces Andropogonis Tracy. I.
  Cercospora granuliformis Ell. & Holw.
  {Aecidium Violae Schum.
  {Dicaeoma Violae (DC.) O. Kuntze.
  {Puccinia Violae DC.
Viola striata Ait.
  {Aecidium pedatatum S.
  {Nigredo pedatata (J. L. Sheldon) Arth. I.
  {Dicaeoma Violae (DC.) O. Kuntze.
  {Puccinia Violae DC.
Viola tricolor L.
  {Dicaeoma Mariae-Wilsoni Arth. & Fromme. I.
  {Puccinia ellisiana Thm. I.
  {Aecidium pedatatum S.
  {Nigredo pedatata (J. L. Sheldon) Arth. I.
  {Uromyces pedatatus J. L. Sheldon. I.
  Alternaria Violae Gall. & Dorsett.
  Ascochyta Violae Sacc.
  Cercospora macrospora Osterw.
  Cercospora Violae Sacc.
  Colletotrichum Violae-tricoloris R. E. Sm.
  {Corticium vagum B. & C.
  {Rhizoctonia Solani Kühn.
  Fusarium Violae Wolf.
  Peronospora Violae DBy.
  Phyllosticta Violae Desm.
  Pleospora americana Ell. & Ev. (p. p.?).
  Puccinia Violae DC.
  Pythium debaryanum Hesse.
  Ramularia lactea (Desm.) Sacc.
  Sphaerotheca Humuli (DC.) Burrill. †
  Sphaerotheca Humuli (DC.) Burrill, var.
    fuliginea (Schl.) Salmon.
  Thielavia basicola (B. & Br.) Zopf.
Viola triloba S.
  Puccinia ellisiana Thm. I.
Viola villosa Walt.
  Cercospora Violae Sacc.
  {Dicaeoma Violae (DC.) O. Kuntze.
  {Puccinia Violae DC.

Viola vittata Greene.
  Dicaeoma Violae (DC.) O. Kuntze.
Viola sp. indet.
  Cryptostictis Violae Tehon & Daniels.
  Cylindrosporium Violae Sacc.
  Erysiphe communis Auct. Amer.
  Mycorrhiza of Legumes F. R. Jones.
  Ramularia lactea (Desm.) Sacc.
  ⎰ Pycnochytrium globosum Schrt.
  ⎱ Synchytrium globosum Schrt.
  ⎰ Thelephora Micheneri Herb. Peters.
  ⎱ Thelephora sebacea P.
  Urocystis Violae (Sow.) Fisch. Wald.

FLACOURTIACEAE

Myroxylon martinicense Krug. & Urban.
  Favolus caperatus Pat.
  ⎰ Leptoporus concrescens (Mont.) Pat.
  ⎱ Polyporus concrescens Mont.
  Stereum fasciatum (S.) Fr.
Xylosma Salzmanni Eichl.
  Capnodiastrum tropicum Speg.
  Dendryphium? costaricense Speg.
  Diblastospermella aequatorialis Speg.
  Meliola Tonduzi Speg.
  Opasterinella Tonduzi Speg.
  ⎰ Phyllachora costaericae Trotter.
  ⎱ Phyllachora Pittieri Speg.
  Phyllosticta Tonduzi Speg.
  Uredo recondita Speg.
Xylosma velutina Triana & Karst.
  ⎰ Asterina Tonduzi Syd.
  ⎱ Asterostomella Tonduzi Syd.
  Phyllachora Pittieri Speg.
Flacourtia cataphracta Roxb.
  Valsa Flacourtiae Pat.
Casearia aculeata Jacq.
  Meliola Paulliniae F. L. Stevens.
  Myriangiella arcuata Toro.
  Scolecopeltis micropeltiformis Toro.
Casearia arborea (L. Cl. Rich.) Urb.
  Helminthosporium Melastomacearum F. L.
    Stevens.
  Meliola Paulliniae F. L. Stevens.
Casearia guianensis J. R. Johnston.
  Asterina juruana Henn.
  Cercospora Caseariae F. L. Stevens.
  Meliola ambigua Pat. & Gaill.
  Meliola Paulliniae F. L. Stevens.
  Micropeltis albo-ostiolata Henn.
Casearia ramiflora Vahl.
  Arthrobotryum caudatum Syd.
  Cercospora Caseariae F. L. Stevens.
  Dimerium piceum (B. & C.) Theissen.
  Meliola Paulliniae F. L. Stevens.
Casearia sylvestris Sw.
  Calonectria melioloides Speg.
  Cercospora Caseariae F. L. Stevens.

  ⎰ Chaetothyrium concinnum Syd.
  ⎱ Merismella concinna Syd.
  Chaetothyrium permixtum Syd.
  Endocycla Phoebes Syd.
  Fusarium meliolicola F. L. Stevens.
  Helminthosporium Melastomacearum F. L.
    Stevens.
  Meliola Paulliniae F. L. Stevens.
  Merismella oligomera Syd.
  Nectria meliolicola F. L. Stevens.
  Scolecopeltis micropeltiformis Toro.
  Stigmopeltella costaricana Syd.
Casearia sp. indet.
  Aschersonia turbinata B.
  Septoria costaricensis Speg.

TURNERACEAE

Turnera ulmifolia L.
  Asterina solanicola B. & C.
  Bagnisiella eutypoides Ell. & Ev.
  Cercospora Turnerae Ell. & Ev.

PASSIFLORACEAE

Passiflora adenopoda DC.
  Asterina megalospora B. & C.
Passiflora biflora Lam.
  Aecidium passifloricola Henn.
Passiflora foetida L.
  Helminthosporium Stahlii F. L. Stevens.
Passiflora incarnata L.
  Cercospora biformis Pk.
  Cercospora fuscovirens Sacc.
  Cercospora truncatella Atk.
Passiflora lutea L.
  ⎰ Cercospora fuscovirens Sacc.
  ⎱ Erineum Passiflora-luteae S.
Passiflora multiflora L.
  Asterina arnaudia Ryan.
Passiflora rubra L.
  ⎰ Aecidium passifloricola Henn.
  ⎰ Dicaeoma Scleriae (Pazschke) Arth. I.
  ⎱ Puccinia Scleriae (Pazschke) Arth. I.
  Asterina megalospora B. & C.
  Asterina passifloricola Ryan.
Passiflora sexflora A. Juss.
  Asterina arnaudia Ryan.
  Asterina tacsonia Pat., var. Passiflorae Ryan.
  Cercospora biformis Pk.
  Phyllosticta superficiale F. L. Stevens.
Passiflora tuberosa Jacq.
  Aecidium passifloricola Henn.
  Asterina Tacsoniae Pat., var. Passiflorae
    Ryan.
  ⎰ Dicaeoma Scleriae (Pazschke) Arth. I.
  ⎱ Puccinia Scleriae (Pazschke) Arth. I.
Passiflora sp. indet.
  ⎰ Asterina confertissima Speg.
  ⎱ Asterina perconferta Trott.

Passiflora sp. indet. (*cont.*)
 Asterina megalospora B. & C.
 Asterina passifloricola Ryan.
 Asterina platasca B. & C.
 Cercospora regalis Tharp.
 Cladosporium oxysporum B. & C.
 Helminthosporium molle B. & C.
 Meliola aristata Toro.
 {Septoria fructicola B. & C.
 {Septoria fructigena B. & C.

CARICACEAE

Carica Papaya L.
 Asperisporium Caricae (Speg.) Maubl.
 Asterinella Papayae Fragoso & Ciferri.
 Chaetothyrium Caricae Syd.
 Cicinnobolus Cesatii DBy.
 Colletotrichum falcatum Went.
 Didymella Caricae Tassi.
 Epiclinium Cumminsii Massee.
 Gloeosporium cingulatum Atk.
 Gloeosporium Papayae Henn.
 Oidium Caricae Noack.
 Ovulariopsis Papayae van der Bijl.
 Phomopsis Papayae Fragoso & Ciferri.
 Pucciniopsis Caricae Earle.
 Pythium debaryanum Hesse.
 Scolecotrichum Caricae Ell. & Ev.
 {?Mycosphaerella (Caricae?)
 {Sphaerella Caricae Maubl.
 Zygosporium oscheoides Mont.

LOASACEAE

Petalonyx Thurberi Gray.
 Camarosporium Petalonycis Henn.

Mentzelia albicaulis Dougl.
Mentzelia congesta Nutt.
 Dicaeoma Sarcobati Arth. I.

Mentzelia cordata Kellogg.
 Coleosporium Mentzeliae (Diet. & Holw.) Arth.
 Uredo floridana Syd.

Mentzelia decapetala (Pursh) Urban & Gilg.
 Diplodina Stevensii Sacc.
 Septoria Mentzeliae Ell. & Kellerm.

Mentzelia floridana Nutt.
 Uredo floridana Syd.

Mentzelia hispida Willd.
 {Coleosporium Mentzeliae (Diet. & Holw.) Arth.
 {Stichopsora Mentzeliae Diet. & Holw.

Mentzelia laevicaulis Torr. & Gr.
 Septoria Mentzeliae Ell. & Kellerm.

Mentzelia Lindleyi Torr. & Gr.
 Rhizoctonia Solani Kühn.

Mentzelia multiflora (Nutt.) Gray.
 Puccinia subnitens Diet. I.
Mentzelia nuda (Pursh) Torr. & Gr.
 {Dicaeoma Sarcobati Arth. I.
 {Puccinia subnitens Diet. I.
 Phyllosticta Mentzeliae Ell. & Kellerm.
 Septoria Mentzeliae Ell. & Kellerm.
Mentzelia ornata Torr. & Gr.
 Lecanidion atratum (Hedw. ex Fr.) Rabh.
 Phyllosticta Mentzeliae Ell. & Kellerm.
 Septoria Mentzeliac Ell. & Kellerm.
Mentzelia pumila Nutt.
Mentzelia Rusbyi Wooton.
 Dicaeoma Sarcobati Arth. I.

DATISCACEAE

Datisca glomerata Benth. & Hook.
 Phomatospora Datiscae Hark.
 Rhabdospora Datiscae Earle.
 Septoria Datiscae Ell. & Ev.

BEGONIACEAE

Begonia gracilis Benth.
 Coleosporium Begoniae Arth.
Begonia rubra Blume.
Begonia semperflorens Link & Otto.
 Thielavia basicola (B. & Br.) Zopf.
Begonia sp. indet.
 Gloeosporium Begoniae Magn.
 Glomerella cincta (Stoneman) Spaulding & v. Schrenk.
 Rhizoctonia Solani Kühn.
 Septoria Begoniae Ell. & Ev.
 Sphaeropsis begoniicola Ell. & Ev.
 Stilbella flavida (Cke.) Henn.

CACTACEAE

Cereus geometrizans Mart.
 Anthostomella bonanseana Sacc.
 Fusarium candidulum Sacc.
 Phoma bonanseana Sacc.
Cereus giganteus Engelm.
 {Camarosporium Cerei (Pk.) Sacc.
 {Hendersonia Cerei Pk.
 Xylaria digitata (L. ex Fr.) Grev.
Cereus triangularis Mill.
 Colletotrichum Cerei Earle.
Cereus sp. indet.
 Dendrodochium verticillioides Sacc.
 Gloeosporium Cerei Pass.
 Trematosphaeria Cactorum Earle.
Phyllocactus latifrons Walp.
 Colletotrichum Phyllocacti Ell. & Ev.
Echinocactus sp. indet.
 Naemaspora pruinosa B. & C.
Mammillaria retusa Hort. Belg. ex Pfeiff.
 Phoma moreliana Sacc.

Mammillaria vivipara Haworth.
  Phoma Mamillariae Ell. & Ev.
Cactus sp. indet.
  Asterina Wrightii B. & C.
  Didymium trochus Lister.
  Gloeosporium Cactorum Stoneman.
  Gloeosporium lunatum Ell. & Ev.
  Perisporium Wrightii B. & C.
  Phoma Opuntiae Ell.
  Phytophthora terrestris Sherb.
  Pythium debaryanum Hesse.
  Sphaeria opulenta De Not.
Rhipsalis cassytha Gaertn.
  Corynelia pteridicola F. L. Stevens.
  Phaeospora cacticola F. L. Stevens.
Opuntia arborescens Engelm.
  Phyllosticta Cacti (B.) Archer.
  Teichospora Opuntiae Ell. & Ev.
Opuntia brasiliensis Haw.
  Gloeosporium Opuntiae Ell. & Ev.
Opuntia Dillenii (Ker-Gawl) Haw.
  Gloeosporium lunatum Ell. & Ev.
  Perisporium Wrightii B. & C.
  Septoria Fici-indicae Vogl.
  ⎰Haplosporella Opuntiae (Fairman)▪ Petrak &
  ⎱ Syd.
  ⎰Sphaeropsis Opuntiae Fairman.
Opuntia echinocarpa Engelm.
  Teichospora mammoides Ell. & Ev., var.
    Opuntiae Dearness & Barthol.
Opuntia Engelmanni Salm.
  ⎰Anthostomella Cacti (S.) Sacc.
  ⎱Sphaeria Cacti S.
  ⎱Vermicularia Cacti (S.) Starb.
Opuntia ferruginispora D. Griffiths.
  Gloeosporium lunatum Ell. & Ev.
Opuntia Ficus-indica Mill.
  Hendersonia Opuntiae Ell. & Ev.
  ⎰Hyponectria Cacti (Ell. & Ev.) Seaver.
  ⎱Nectriella Cacti Ell. & Ev.
Opuntia jamaicensis Britton & Harris.
  Gloeosporium lunatum Ell. & Ev.
Opuntia Lindheimeri Engelm.
  Gloeosporium lunatum Ell. & Ev.
  Perisporium Wrightii B. & C.
  ⎰Mycosphaerella Opuntiae (Ell. & Ev.) Dear-
  ⎱ ness.
  ⎱Sphaerella Opuntiae Ell. & Ev.
Opuntia macrorhiza Engelm.
  ⎰Ceratocarpia Wrightii (B. & C.) Toro.
  ⎱Perisporiopsis Wrightii (B. & C.) F. L. Stevens.
  ⎱Perisporium Wrightii B. & C.
Opuntia Opuntia (L.) Coult.
  ⎰Mycosphaerella Opuntiae (Ell. & Ev.) Dear-
  ⎱ ness.
  ⎱Sphaerella Opuntiae Ell. & Ev.
Opuntia polyacantha Haw.
  Phoma Mamillariae Ell. & Ev.
  Sphaerella Opuntiae Ell. & Ev.

Opuntia Rafinesquii Engelm.
  Perisporium Wrightii B. & C.
Opuntia Tuna Mill.
  ⎰Diplotheca Tunae (Spreng.) Starb.
  ⎱Sphaeria Tunae Spreng.
  Gloeosporium lunatum Ell. & Ev.
  Macrophoma opuntiicola (Speg.) Sacc. & Syd.,
    var. Tunae Ciferri & Fragoso.
  Macrosporium opuntiicola Fragoso & Ciferri.
  Perisporium Wrightii B. & C.
  Pestalozzia opuntiicola Ciferri & Fragoso.
Opuntia vulgaris Mill.
  Lembosia Cactorum Tracy & Earle.
Opuntia sp. indet.
  Badhamia macrocarpa (Ces.) Rostf.
  Diplodia Opuntiae Sacc.
  Gibbera pulicaris Fr.
  Gloeosporium Cactorum Stoneman.
  Gloeosporium Opuntiae Ell. & Ev.
  Macrosporium commune Rabh.
  Neotiella sericeovillosa Rehm.
  Phyllosticta concava Seaver.
  Phyllosticta Opuntiae Sacc. & Speg.
  Phyllosticta Opuntiae Sacc. & Speg., var. mic-
    roscopica Ciferri.
  Rhytisma Cacti S.
  Vermicularia Dematium (P.) ex Fr.

THYMELAEACEAE

Daphnopsis caribaea Griseb.
  ⎰Hymenochaete Kunzei Massee.
  ⎱Hymenochaete luteobadia (Fr.) v. Höhnel &
  ⎱ Litschauer.
  ⎱Stereum luteobadium Fr. p. p.
  Irene aibonitensis (F. L. Stevens) Toro.
  Phaeoradulum guadalupense Pat.
  Stilbocrea Dussii Pat.
  Stilbum Daphnopsidis Pat.
Daphne Mezereum L.
  Dothidea Mezerei Fr.
  Fusarium inseptatum S.
  Sphaeria Daphnidis S.
Daphne sp. indet.
  Sclerotium Rolfsii Sacc.
Edgeworthia papyrifera Sieb. & Zucc.
  Sclerotium Rolfsii Sacc.
Dirca palustris L.
  Aecidium hydnoideum B. & C.
  Diaporthe Dircae Ell. & Ev.
  Fusarium lateritium Nees ex Fr.
  Phyllosticta Dircae Ell. & Dearness.
  Sphaerella Dircae Ell. & Ev.
  Sphaeropsis Dircae Ell. & Ev.

ELAEAGNACEAE

Shepherdia argentea Nutt.
  Aecidium Allenii G. W. Clinton.
  Cercospora manitobana J. J. Davis.

Shepherdia argentea (*cont.*)
Cucurbitaria occulta Oud.
{ Cucurbitaria Shepherdiae Ell. & Ev.
{ Curreya Shepherdiae Ell. & Ev.
{ Fomes circumstans (Morg.) Sacc.
{ Fomes ellisianus F. W. Anderson.
{ Fomes fraxinophilus Auct. Amer. p. p.
{ Polyporus circumstans Morg.
{ Polyporus ellisianus (Anderson) Underw.
Fomes lobatus (S.) Cke.
Phyllactinia corylea (P.) ex Karst.
Pleospora Shepherdiae Pk.
?Puccinia coronata Cda. I.
Sphaerotheca Castagnei Lév.
Sphaerotheca Humuli (DC.) Burrill. †
Valsa ambiens (P.) ex Fr., var. Shepherdiae Sacc.
Valsa Lepargyreae Earle.

Shepherdia canadensis (L.) Nutt.
{ Aecidium Allenii G. W. Clinton.
{ Dicaeoma Allenii (G. W. Clinton) Arth. & Fromme. I.
{ Puccinia Caricis-Shepherdiae J. J. Davis. I.
{ Dicaeoma Rhamni (Wettst.) O. Kuntze. I.
{ Puccinia apocrypta I. Auct. p. p.
{ ? Puccinia coronata Cda. I.
{ Puccinia Rhamni Wettst. I.
Cladosporium herbarum (P.) ex Lk.
Cylindrosporium Shepherdiae Sacc.
Fomes ellisianus F. W. Anderson.
Septoria Shepherdiae (Sacc.) Dearness.
{ ?Sphaerotheca Castagnei Auct. Amer. p. p.
{ Sphaerotheca Humuli (DC.) Burrill. †
{ Sphaerotheca Shepherdiae Selby MS.
Valsa ambiens (P.) ex Fr.

Elaeagnus angustifolia L.
Aecidium arctoum Arth.
Camarosporium elaeagnellum Fairman.
Cercospora Carrii Barthol.
Cercospora elaeagni Heald & Wolf.
{ Cucurbitaria Caraganae, var. Elaeagni Rehm.
{ Cucurbitaria elongata (Fr.) Grev.
Septoria argyrea Sacc.
Sphaeropsis elaeagnina Fairman.

Elaeagnus argentea Pursh.
Aecidium Allenii G. W. Clinton.
{ Cucurbitaria Caraganae, var. Elaeagni Rehm.
{ Cucurbitaria elongata (Fr.) Grev.
Puccinia coronata Cda. I. ?
Valsa ambiens (P.) ex Fr., var. Elaeagni Rehm.

Elaeagnus commutata Bernh.
Aecidium Allenii G. W. Clinton.
? { Dicaeoma Rhamni (Wettst.) O. Kuntze.
{ Puccinia Rhamni Wettst. I.

Elaeagnus longifolia P.
Phyllosticta argyrea Speg.

Elaeagnus longipes Gray.
Camarosporium elaeagnellum Fairman.

Diaporthe Elaeagni Rehm, var. americanum Fairman.
Plasmodiophora Elaeagni Schrt.
{ Haplosporella elaeagnina (Fairman) Petrak & Syd.
{ Sphaeropsis elaeagnina Fairman.
Elaeagnus sp. indet.
Corticium vagum B. & C.

LYTHRACEAE

Ammannia coccinea Rottb.
Cercospora Ammanniae Tharp.
Lythrum alatum Pursh.
Cercospora Lythri (Westd.) Niessl.
Leptosphaeria Lythri Pk.
Septoria lythrina Pk.
Lythrum Salicaria L.
{ Hainesia Lythri (Desm.) v. Höhnel.
{ Sclerotiopsis Lythri (Desm.) Shear & Dodge.
Septoria lythrina Pk.
Lythrum sp. indet.
Rhizoctonia Solani Kühn.
Cuphea aequipetala Cav.
Cuphea cyanea Moc. & Sesse.
Cuphea hookeriana Walp.
Cuphea nitidula H. B. K.
{ Micropuccinia Cupheae (Holw.) Arth. & Jackson.
{ Puccinia Cupheae Holw.
{ Puccinia jaliscensis Holw.
Cuphea infundibulum Köhne.
Asterina Cupheae Syd.
Cuphea Balsamona Cham. & Schl.
Cuphea parsonsia R. Br.
Uredo Cupheae Henn.
Cuphea petiolata (L.) Koehne.
{ Erysiphe communis Auct. Amer. p. p.
{ Erysiphe Polygoni DC. †
{ Septoria maculifera Sacc.
{ Septoria maculosa Gerard nec Lév.
Cuphea platycentra Benth.
Rhizoctonia Solani Kühn.
Cuphea procumbens Cav.
Cuphea squamuligera Koehne
{ Micropuccinia Cupheae (Holw.) Arth. & Jackson.
{ Puccinia Cupheae Holw.
{ Puccinia jaliscensis Holw.
Decodon verticillatus (L.) Ell.
{ Aecidium Nesaeae Gerard.
{ Dicaeoma minutissimum (Arth.) H. S. Jackson. I.
{ Puccinia minutissima Arth. I.
{ Puccinia Nesaeae I Auct. Amer. p. p.
Cercospora Decodontis Tehon & Daniels.
Cercospora Nesaeae Ell. & Ev.
{ Peziza cyathoidea Bull. ex P.
{ Phialea cyathoidea (Bull. ex P.) Gill.

Decodon verticillata *(cont.)*
Phyllosticta Nesaeae Pk.
{ Peziza subatra C. & P.
{ Pyrenopeziza subatra (C. & P.) Sacc.
Ginoria americana Jacq.
Uredo Cupheae Henn.
Lagerstroemia indica L.
Botryodiplodia varians Ell. & Langlois.
Cercospora Lythracearum Heald & Wolf.
Corticium caeruleum (Schrad.) ex Fr.
Dacryomyces minor Pk.
Hendersonia pauciseptata B. & C.
Peniophora cinerea (P. ex Fr.) Cke.
Pestalozzia Guepini Desm.
Phoma Lagerstroemiae Speg., var. foliicola
Ell. & Ev.
Phyllosticta Lagerstroemia Ell. & Ev.
Platygloea caroliniana Coker.
Uncinula australiana McAlpine.

PUNICACEAE

Punica Granatum L.
Aspergillus niger van Tiegh.
Cercospora Lythracearum Heald & Wolf.
Corticium Stevensii Burt.
Rhizoctonia Solani Kühn.
Sterigmatocystis castanea Patterson.

LECYTHIDACEAE

Bertholletia excelsa Humb. & Bonpl.
Actinomyces brasiliensis Spencer.
Aspergillus umbrinus Patterson.
Cephalosporium bertholletianum Spencer.
Chaetomium funicola Cke.
Circinella spinosa van Tiegh. & Le Monn.
Cunninghamella Bertholletiae Blakeslee.
Mucor christianiensis Hagem.
Mucor plumbeus Bon.
Mucor spinescens Lendner.
Pellioniella macrospora Spencer.
Phomopsis bertholletianum Spencer.
Rhizopus nigricans Ehrenb.
Bertholletia nobilis Miers.
Actinomyces brasiliensis Spencer.
Cephalosporium bertholletianum Spencer.
Pellioniella macrospora Spencer.

RHIZOPHORACEAE

Rhizophora Mangle L.
Anthostomella Rhizomorphae (Kze.) Berl. &
Vogl. 1886.
Anthostomella Rhizomorphae F. L. Stevens
ex Stevenson. 1918.
Anthostomella Rhizophorae Vizioli.
Pestalozzia Guepini Desm.
Rhizophora sp. indet.
Ascochytella rhizophoropsis Ciferri & Fragoso.

COMBRETACEAE

Bucida Buceras L.
Trabutia Bucidae Chardon.
Terminalia Catappa L.
Coprinus plicatilis Fr.
Lenzites striata Fr.
Psathyrella tigrina Pat.
Buchenavia capitata (Vahl) Eichl.
Uredo Buchenaviae Kern & Whetzel.
Conocarpus erectus L.
Helminthosporium glabroides F. L. Stevens.
Meliola Lagunculariae Earle.
Conocarpus sericea Forst.
Acanthostigma Conocarpi Tracy & Earle.
Laguncularia racemosa (L.) Gaertn.
Botryosphaeria Ribis (Tode ex Fr.) Grossen-
bacher & Duggar.
Botryosphaeria Ribis (Tode ex Fr.) Grossen-
bacher & Duggar, var. chromogena Shear
et al.
Helminthosporium glabroides F. L. Stevens.
{ Irene Lagunculariae (Earle) Toro.
{ Meliola Lagunculariae Earle.
Meliola nigra F. L. Stevens.
Micropeltis Lagunculariae Wint.
Microthyrium Lagunculariae Wint.
Physalospora Lagunculariae Rehm.

MYRTACEAE

Myrtus communis L.
Sclerotium Rolfsii Sacc.
Psidium Guajava L.
Aegerita Webberi Fawcett.
Aschersonia Aleyrodis Webber.
Aschersonia cubensis B. & C.
Aschersonia turbinata B.
Asterella crustacea Ell. & Ev.
Asterina Psidii Ryan.
Caudella Psidii Ryan.
Cephalosporium Lecanii Zimm.
{ Clitocybe monadelpha (Morg.) Sacc.
{ Clitocybe tabescens (Scop.) ex Fr..
Corticium laeve Fr.
{ Colletotrichum gloeosporioides Penz.
{ Gloeosporium Psidii Delacr.
{ Glomerella cingulata (Stoneman) Spaulding &
v. Schrenk.
{ Glomerella Psidii J. L. Sheldon.
{ Glomerella rufomaculans (S.) Spaulding & v.
Schrenk.
Hypocrella epiphylla (Massee) Sacc.
Hypocrella turbinata (B.) Petch.
Isthmospora spinosa F. L. Stevens.
Meliola horrida Ell. & Ev.
{ Meliola amphitricha Fragoso & Ciferri.
{ Meliola Psidii Fr.
Mucidula cheimonophylla (B. & C.) Pat.
{ Panellus cantharelloides (Mont.) Murrill.
{ Panus cantharelloides Mont.

Psidium Guajava (*cont.*)
{ Melanopus infernalis (B.) Pat.
{ Polyporus infernalis B.
  Porothelium reviviscens B. & C.
{ Bullaria (?) Psidii (Wint.) Arth. & Mains.
{ Puccinia Psidii Wint.
  Seuratia coffeicola Pat.
  Trichomerium portoricense Speg.

Psidium sp. indet.
  Antennaria Guava Cke.
  Daldinia vernicosa Ces. & De Not.
{ Flammula lateritia Pat.
{ Gymnopilus lateritius (Pat.) Murrill.
{ Fomes jamaicensis (Murrill) Sacc. & D. Sacc.
{ Pyropolyporus jamaicensis Murrill.
{ Fusarium salmonicolor B. & C.
{ Fusidium salmonicolor (B. & C.) Wollenw.
{ Stilbum byssisedum B. & C.
{ Stilbum byssogenum B. & Br.

Pimenta acris Kostel.
  Glomerella cingulata (Stoneman) Spaulding &
    v. Schrenk.
  Panus Leprieurii Mont.
  Rostrella Coffeae Zimm.

Amomis caryophyllata (Jacq.) Krug & Urb.
  Meliola amomicola F. L. Stevens.

Myrcia citrifolia (Aubl.) Urb.
  Catacauma Myrciae (Lév.) Theissen & Syd.

Myrcia deflexa DC.
  Helminthosporium Helleri F. L. Stevens.
  Meliola Helleri Earle.
{ Coriolus sector (Ehrenb. ex Fr.) Pat.
{ Polyporus sector (Ehrenb.) ex Fr.
  Trichosporium stelligerum Speg.

Myrcia leptoclada DC.
{ Androsaceus Myrciae Pat.
{ Marasmius Myrciae Pat.
{ Prunulus Myrciae (Pat.) Murrill.
  Lentinus scyphoides Pat.
  Nummularia Bulliardi Tul.

Myrcia monticola. ex Duss.
  Lentinus Wrightii B. & C.

Myrcia octopleura ex Duss.
  Clavaria laeticolor B. & C.
{ Hypocrea phyllogena Mont.
{ Hypocrella phyllogena (Mont.) Speg.
  Polyporus rugulosus Lév.

Myrcia oerstediana Berg.
  Puccinia Jambosae Henn.

Myrcia splendens DC.
  Asterina Myrciae Ryan.
  Echidnodella Myrciae Ryan.
  Isthmospora spinosa F. L. Stevens.
  Meliola Helleri Earle.
  Stereum lobatum Fr.
  Stereum papyrinum Mont.

Myrcia sp. indet.
  Grallomyces portoricensis F. L. Stevens.

Calyptranthes Krugii Kiaersk.
  Catacauma urbanianum (Allescher & Henn.)
    Theiss. & Syd.

Calyptranthes pallens Griseb.
  Tremellodon hirneoloides B. & C.

Calyptranthes Tonduzii Donn. Sm.
  Phyllachora gentilis Speg., var. Calyptran-
    this Pat.

Calyptranthes sp. indet.
  Daldinia vernicosa Ces. & De Not.

Eugenia buxifolia Willd.
  Asterina Fawcetti Ryan.
  Phyllosticta Eugeniae E. Young.

Eugenia caryophyllata Thun.
{ Polyporus cubensis Mont.
{ Ungulina cubensis (Mont.) Pat.
  Polyporus hirsutus (Wulf.) ex Fr.
  Puccinia Arenariae (Schum.) Wint.

Eugenia Dussii Krug. & Urb.
  Erinella cognata Pat.
{ Phellinus ferruginosus (Schrad. ex Fr.) Pat.
{ Polyporus ferruginosus (Schrad.) ex Fr.

Eugenia Jambos L.
  Aschersonia turbinata B.
  Clitocybe tabescens (Scop. ex Fr.) Bres.
  Herpotrichia pezizula B. & C.
  Hypoxylon annulatum S.
  Pestalozzia Guepini Desm.
{ Hainesia Lythri (Desm.) v. Höhnel.
{ Sclerotiopsis concava (Desm.) Shear & Dodge.
{ Crepidopus Eugeniae (Earle) Murrill.
{ Pleurotus Eugeniae Earle.
{ Bullaria (?) Psidii (Wint.) Arth. & Mains.
{ Puccinia Psidii Wint.
  Rosellinia bunodes (B. & Br.) Sacc.
  Septobasidium atratum Pat.
  Tremella Janus B. & C.
  Verticillium heterocladum Penz.
  Xylaria dichotoma Mont.

Eugenia malaccensis L.
  Agaricus guadelupensis Pat.

Eugenia montana Wight.
  Septobasidium frustulosum (B. & C.) Pat.

Eugenia monticola (Sw.) DC.
  Meliola Helleri Earle.

Eugenia oerstediana Berg.
  Puccinia Jambosae Henn.

Eugenia rhombea (Berg.) Krug & Urb.
  Phyllachora biareolata Speg.

Eugenia Stahlii (Kiser.) Krug & Urb.
  Grallomyces portoricensis F. L. Stevens.
  Helminthosporium Helleri F. L. Stevens.
  Meliola Helleri Earle.

Eugenia sp. indet.
  Aschersonia turbinata B.
  Asterina Myrciae Ryan.
  Asterinella cylindrotheca (Speg.) Theissen.
{ Asterina Eugeniae Mont.
{ Dothidea (Asteroma) Eugeniae Mont.

Eugenia sp. indet. (*cont.*)
  Marasmius picipes Murrill.
  Melophia Eugeniae Ferdinandsen & Winge.
  Phyllachora rimulosa Speg.
  Phyllachora Whetzelii Chardon.
  Rhytisma gyrosum Mont.
  Uredo flavidula Wint.
Syzygium calyptranthus ex Duss.
  Asterina pelliculosa B.
Eucalyptus botryoides Sm.
  Endothia havanensis Bruner.
Eucalyptus globulus Labill.

PEZIZINEAE

{ Mollisia subcornea (Phil. & Hark.) Sacc.
{ Peziza subcornea Phil. & Hark.
{ Calloria Eucalypti Phil. & Hark.
{ Orbilia Eucalypti (Phil. & Hark.) Sacc.
{ Peziza emergens Phil. & Hark.
{ Pyrenopeziza emergens (Phil. & Hark.) Sacc.

SPHAERIALES

{ Acrospermum corrugatum Ell.
{ Acrospermum fultum Hark.
  Diaporthe Eucalypti Hark.
  Diatrype Eucalypti Cke. & Hark.
  Diatrype linearis Ell. & Ev.
{ Didymosphaerella circinans (Hark.) Cke.
{ Didymosphaeria circinans Hark.
{ Didymosphaeria Cupula (Ell.) Sacc.
{ Sphaeria Cupula Ell.
  Eriosphaeria investans (Cke.) Sacc.
  Physalospora suberumpens Ell. & Ev.
  Sphaerella molleriana Thm.
  Valsa Eucalypti Cke. & Hark.

HYMENOMYCETINEAE

  Fomes applanatus (P.) Wallr.
  Polyporus Schweinitzii Fr.
  Stereum albobadium (S.) Fr.

SPHAEROPSIDALES

{ Harknessia Eucalypti Cke.
{ Harknessia longipes Hark.
{ Harknessia uromycoides Speg.
  Hendersonia eucalypticola A. R. Davis.
{ Macrophoma molleriana (Thm.) Berl. & Vogl.
{ Phoma molleriana (Thm.) Sacc.
{ Sphaeropsis molleriana Thm.
  Phoma Eucalypti Cke. & Hark.
  Phyllosticta extensa Sacc. & Syd.

MELANCONIACEAE

  Cryptosporium Eucalypti Cke. & Hark.
{ Hainesia Lythri (Desm.) v. Höhnel.
{ Pezizella Lythri Shear & Dodge.
{ Sclerotiopsis concava (Desm.) Shear & Dodge.

HYPHOMYCETES

  Camposporium antennatum Hark.
  Chalara montellica Sacc.
  Cladosporium epiphyllum (P.) ex Fr.
{ Cladosporium Fumago Lk.
{ Fumago vagans Fr.
  Heterosporium Eucalypti Ell. & Ev.
  Thecospora bifida Hark.
  Triposporium elegans Cda.

MISCELLANEA

  Cleistosoma purpureum Hark.
  Inzengaea erythrospora Borzi.
Eucalyptus microphylla Willd.
Eucalyptus occidentalis Endl.
Eucalyptus robusta Sm.
Eucalyptus rostrata Schl.
  Endothia havanensis Bruner.
Eucalyptus odorata Behr.
{ Harknessia longipes Hark.
{ Harknessia uromycoides Speg.?
Eucalyptus sp. indet.

PEZIZINEAE

{ Lachnella rufo-olivacea (A. & S. ex Fr.) Sacc.
{ Peziza rufo-olivacea A. & S. ex Fr.
  Lachnum atropurpureum Durand.
  Peziza cerina P.
  Peziza luteorubella Nyl.
{ Peziza carneorosea Cke. & Hark.
{ Pezizella carneorosea (Cke. & Hark) Sacc.
  Pezizella Lythri Shear & Dodge.

PHACIDIINEAE

{ Propolis faginea (Schrad.) ex Karst.
{ Propolis versicolor Fr.
{ Dermatea Eucalypti Cke. & Hark.
{ Scleroderris Eucalypti (Cke. & Hark.) Sacc.
  Stictis radiata (L.) ex P.
  Hypoderma Eucalypti Cke. & Hark.
  Hysterium Eucalypti Phil. & Hark.
  Hysterium pulicare P. ex Fr.

HYPOCREALES

  Hypocrea consimilis Ell.
{ Byssonectria chrysocoma Cke. & Hark.
{ Nectria chrysocoma (Cke. & Hark.) Berl. & Vogl.
{ Dialonectria Eucalypti Cke. & Hark.
{ Nectria Eucalypti (Cke. & Hark.) Berl. & Vogl.

SPHAERIALES

  Acanthostigma spinosum (Hark.) Ell. & Ev.
  Bagnisiopsis Eucalypti Dearness & House.
  Botryosphaeria Ribis (Tode ex Fr.) Grossenbacher & Duggar.
  Cerastostomella echinella Ell. & Ev.
  Chaetosphaeria ornata Hark.

Eucalyptus sp. indet. (*cont.*)
  Diaporthe cubensis Bruner.
  Diaporthe eucalyptica Hark.
  Lasiosphaeria ovina (P. ex Fr.) Ces. & De Not.
  { Endophlaea anismometra Cke. & Hark.
  { Metasphaeria anismometra (Cke. & Hark.)
      Sacc.
  { Sphaeria anismometra Cke. & Hark.
  { Endophlaea plagarum Cke. & Hark.
  { Metasphaeria plagarum (Cke. & Hark.) Berl.
      & Vogl.
  { Sphaeria plagarum Cke. & Hark.
  Phragmodothidea Eucalypti Dearness & Bar-
      thol.
  Physalospora eucalyptina Fairman.
  Physalospora latitans Sacc.
  Rosellinia spinosa Hark.
  Schizoparme straminea Shear.
  Sphaeria mutila S., var. Eucalypti Cke. &
      Hark.
  { Sphaeria Eucalypti Cke. & Hark.
  { Teichospora Eucalypti (Cke. & Hark.) Berl. &
      Vogl.
  { Pleosphaeria modesta Hark.
  { Teichospora modesta (Hark.) Ell. & Ev.
  Valsa Eucalypti Cke. & Hark.
  Valsaria Eucalypti (Kalchb. & Cke.) Sacc.

BASIDIOMYCETES

  Clitocybe tabescens (Scop. ex Fr.) Bres.
  Coniophora cerebella P.
  Coniophora puteana (Schum.) Fr.
  Corticium colliculosum B. & C.
  Corticium epiphyllum (P.) Cke.
  Dacryomyces deliquescens (Bull.) ex Duby.
  Fomes applanatus (P. ex Wallr.) Gill.
  Fomes robustus (S.) Cke.
  Mycena saccharifera B. & Br.
  Peniophora Roumeguerii Bres.
  Peniophora stratosa Burt.
  Pistillaria ovata Fr.
  Pleurotus ostreatus (Jacq.) ex Fr.
  { Hapalopilus gilvus (S.) Murrill.
  { Polyporus gilvus S.
  Stereum heterosporum Burt.
  Tubaria Eucalypti Earle.

SPHAEROPSIDALES

  { Aposphaeria macrosperma (Cke. & Hark.)
      Sacc.
  { Sphaeropsis macrosperma Cke. & Hark.
  { Coniothyrium leprosum Fairman.
  { Fairmaniella leprosa (Fairman) Petrak & Syd.
  Diplodia Eucalypti Cke. & Hark.
  { Diplodia microspora Sacc. nec B. & C.
  { Diplodia microsporella Sacc.
  { Diplodia tenuis Cke. & Hark.
  { Diplodinula tenuis (Cke. & Hark.) Tassi.

Hendersonia coryneoidea Cke. & Hark.
  Hendersonia Eucalypti Cke. & Hark.
  Macrophoma molleriana (Thm.) Berl.
  { Phyllosticta Eucalypti Ell. & Ev. nec Thm.
  { Phyllosticta extensa Ell. & Ev.
  { Cryptosporium ceuthosporoides Cke. & Hark.
  { Septoria ceuthosporoides (Cke. & Hark.) Sacc.
  Septoria mortolensis Penz. & Sacc.
  Sphaeronema Eucalypti Cke. & Hark.
  Sphaeropsis stictoides Earle.

MELANCONIALES

  Cylindrosporium (scoparium?)
  Gloeosporium capsularum Cke. & Hark.
  Gloeosporium Eucalyptorum Turconi.
  Melanconium globosum Cke. & Hark.
  Pestalozzia funerea Desm.
  Pestalozzia inquinans Cke. & Hark.
  Pestalozzia monochaeta Desm.
  { Pestalozzia truncata Lév.
  { Pestalozzia truncatula (Cda.) Fckl.
  Stilbospora angustata P. ex Fr.

HYPHOMYCETES

  { Botrytis fusca (Cke. & Hark.) Sacc.
  { Polyactis fusca Cke. & Hark.
  Chaetopsis fusca Cda.
  Chalara fusidioides Cda.
  Circinotrichum maculiforme Nees ex Fr.
  { Bactrodesmium clavatum Cke. & Hark.
  { Clasterosporium clavatum (Cke. & Hark.)
      Sacc.
  Coremium glaucum Lk.
  { Cylindrocephalum hyalinum (Cke. & Hark.)
      Sacc.
  { Menispora hyalina Cke. & Hark.
  Epidochium Eucalypti Cke.
  { Fusarium albidocarneum (Cke. & Hark.) Sacc.
  { Fusidium albidocarneum Cke. & Hark.
  Fusarium Eucalyptorum Cke. & Hark.
  Fusarium mesentericum Cke. & Hark.
  { Helicoma Berkeleyi M. A. Curtis
  { Helicosporium Berkleyi Sacc.
  Helminthosporium obovatum B. & Br.
  Monilia viridiflava Cke. & Hark.
  { Mystrosporium Curtisii B.
  { Mystrosporium Spraguei B. & C. in Herb.
  Septonema multiplex B. & C.
  Septosporium scyphophorum Cke. & Hark.
  Speira toruloides Cda.
  Stysanus Stemonitis (P.) Cda.
  Torula ligniperda (Willk.) Sacc.
  Tubercularia Eucalypti Cke. & Hark.
  Volutella coronata Cke. & Hark.

MISCELLANEA

  Reticularia Lycoperdon Bull.
Myrtaceae gen. indet.
  Gibberella cyanospora Bomm. & Rouss.

Myrtaceae gen. indet. (*cont.*)
 Meliola Helleri Earle.
 Parapeltella mediocris Speg.
 Puccinia Rompelii Magn.

MELASTOMATACEAE

Chaetogastra lanceolata DC.
 Sphaeria melastomatum Lév.
Melastoma sp. indet.
 Lembosia melastomatum Mont.
Rhexia ciliosa Michx.
 Phyllosticta Rhexiae Dearness & House.
Rhexia mariana L.
 Cercospora erythrogena Atk.
Rhexia virginica L.
 Cercospora erythrogena Atk.
 Colletotrichum Rhexiae Ell. & Ev.
Conostegia lanceolata Cogn.
 Meliola brachycera Syd.
 Trichothyrium dubiosum (Bomm. & Rouss.)
  Theissen.
Conostegia subhirsuta DC.
 Stereum duriusculum B. & Br.
Tetrazygia elaeagnoides (Sw.) DC.
 Asterina dilabens Syd.
 Asterina Tetrazygiae Ryan.
 {Dothidina peribebuyensis (Speg.) Chardon.
 {Phyllachora peribebuyensis Speg.
 Guignardia Tetrazygiae F. L. Stevens.
 Phyllachora graminis (P. ex Fr.) Fckl.
Tetrazygia sp. indet.
 Nectria saccharina B. & C.
 Physalacria Langloisii Ell.
Miconia angustifolia Griseb.
 {Leptoporus stereinus (B. & C.) Pat.
 {Polyporus stereinus B. & C.
Miconia argentea (Sw.) DC.
 Colletotrichum Melastomacearum (Speg.) Syd.
 Dothidina scabrosa Syd.
 Episphaerella trichophila Syd.
 Mycosphaerella Miconiae Syd.
Miconia Beurlingii Triana.
 Araneomyces acariferus v. Höhnel.
 Dothidina Fiebrigii (Henn.) Theissen & Syd.
 Hyalosphaeria Miconiae F. L. Stevens.
 Paranectria juruana Henn.
 Paranectria Miconiae F. L. Stevens.
Miconia flavida Cogn.
 Belonidium spilogenum Syd.
Miconia furfuracea Griseb.
 Dothidina amadelpha Syd.
Miconia guianensis Cogn.
 Asterina guianensis Ryan.
Miconia impetiolaris D. Don.
 Asterina Melastomacearum Ryan.
 {Hydnum decurrens B. & C.
 {Mycoleptodon decurrens (B. & C.) Pat.
 Meliola Melastomacearum Speg.

Morenoella dothideoides (Ell. & Ev.) v. Höhnel,
  var. impetiolaris Ryan.
 Septoria Miconiae P. Garman.
Miconia laevigata (L.) DC.
 Arthrobotryum caudatum Syd.
 Asterina Chrysophylli Henn.
 Aulographum culmigenum Ell.
 Blastotrichum Miconiae F. L. Stevens.
 Borinquenia Miconiae F. L. Stevens.
 Echidnodella Miconiae Ryan.
 Hyalosphaera Miconiae F. L. Stevens.
 {Irene Melastomacearum (Speg.) Toro.
 {Meliola Melastomacearum Speg.
 Meliola Miconiae F. L. Stevens.
 Microclava Miconiae F. L. Stevens.
 Morenoella giganteae Ryan.
 Morenoella pothodei, var. laevigatae Ryan.
 Phyllachora peribebuyensis Speg.
 Septoria Miconiae P. Garman.
Miconia longifolia (Aubl.) DC.
 Hysterostomina costaricensis Syd.
Miconia martinicensis Cogn.
 {Coriolus velutinus (P. ex Fr.) Quél.
 {Polyporus velutinus (P.) ex Fr.
Miconia prasina (Sw.) DC.
 Asterina Chrysophylli Henn.
 Asterina correacola Cke. & Massee.
 {Lembosia diffusa Wint.
 {Lembosia Melastomatum Mont.
 {Irene Melastomacearum (Speg.) Toro.
 {Meliola Melastomacearum Speg.
 Meliola Miconiae F. L. Stevens.
 Morenoella dothideoides (Ell. & Ev.) v.
  Höhnel, var. impetiolaris Ryan.
 Morenoella Miconiae Ryan.
 Morenoella miconicola Ryan.
 {Dothidina Miconiae (Henn.) Theissen & Syd.
 {Dothidina peribebuyensis (Speg.) Chardon.
 {Phyllachora peribebuyensis Speg.
Miconia racemosa (Aubl.) DC.
 Arthrobotryum caudatum Syd.
 Asterina Melastomacearum Ryan.
 Asterina miconicola Ryan.
 Asterina racemosae Ryan.
 {Asterina Miconiae Ryan.
 {Asterina spathulata Seaver & Toro.
 Asterina transiens Theissen.
 Helminthosporium Melastomacearum F. L.
  Stevens.
 Meliola Melastomacearum Speg.
 {Asteridium dothideoides Ell. & Ev.
 {Morenoella dothideoides (Ell. & Ev.) v. Höh-
  nel.
Miconia rubiginosa (Bonpl.) DC.
 Asterina theissenia Ryan.
 Echidnodella Melastomacearum Ryan.
Miconia Sintenisii Cogn.
 Meliola miconicola F. L. Stevens.

Miconia Sintenisii (*cont.*)
- Dothidina peribebuyensis (Speg.) Chardon.
- Phyllachora peribebuyensis Speg.

Miconia splendens Griseb.
- Asterina Camelliae Syd. & Butler.

Miconia thomasiana DC.
- Asterina Miconiae Ryan.
- Asterina spathulata Seaver & Toro.
- Protoscypha pulla Syd.
- Sucinaria minuta Syd.

Miconia triandra ex Duss.
- Aschersonia turbinata B.
- Marasmius subcoracinus B. & C.

Miconia sp. indet.
- Asterina Camelliae Syd. & Butler.
- Auerswaldia Miconiae Henn.
- Aulographum culmigenum Ell.
- Byssocallis Phoebes Syd.
- Discina hirneoloides, var. contorta Pat.
- Antennaria tropicicola Speg.
- Euantennaria tropicicola Speg.
- Cordyceps brevipes Mont.
- Hypocrea brevipes (Mont.) Sacc.
- Hypocrella Tamoneae Earle.
- Lembosia Melastomatum Mont.
- Lembosia Rolliniae Rehm.
- Lembosia Sclerolobii Henn.
- Monogrammia Miconiae F. L. Stevens.
- Napicladium Fumago Speg.
- Paranectria Miconiae F. L. Stevens.
- Phyllachora mexicana Sacc.
- Phyllachora neomexicana Trott.
- Phyllachora miconiicola Speg.
- Phyllachora peribebuyensis Speg.
- Rosellinia bunodes (B. & Br.) Sacc.
- Tremella inflata Pat.
- Trichothecium fusaroides F. L. Stevens.
- Triposporium stelligerum Speg.

Tamonea sp. indet.
- Hypocrella Tamoneae Earle.

Heterotrichum cymosum (Wendl.) Urb.
- Guignardia Heterotrichi F. L. Stevens.
- Meliola Melastomacearum Speg.
- Phyllachora Heterotrichi Stevens & Dalbey.
- Dothidina peribebuyensis (Speg.) Chardon.
- Phyllachora peribebuyensis Speg.

Heterotrichum umbellatum (Mill.) Urb.
- Asterina Melastomatis Lév.

Clidemia dentata D. Don.
- Asterina schlechteriana Syd.

Clidemia hirta (L.) D. Don.
- Asterina Melastomatis Kellerm.
- Isthmospora glabra F. L. Stevens.
- Irene Melastomacearum (Speg.) Toro.
- Meliola Melastomacearum Speg.
- Trichothyrium dubiosum (Bomm. & Rouss.) Theissen.

Clidemia strigillosa (Sw.) DC.
- Meliola Melastomacearum Speg.

Topobea durandiana Cogn.
- Phyllachora stenocarpa Syd.

Melastomaceae gen. indet.
- Asterina Chrysophylli Henn.
- Asterina correacola Cke. & Massee.
- Asterina hypophylla (S.) B.
- Asterina Melastomatis Lév.
- Asterinella Melastomacearum Ryan.
- Bagnisiopsis peribebuyensis (Speg.) Theissen & Syd.
- Echidnodella Melastomacearum Ryan.
- Hyalotexis pellucida Syd.
- Lophodermium platyplacum (B. & C.) Sacc.
- Morenoella Melastomacearum Ryan.
- Stictis foliicola B. & C.
- Synostomella costaricensis Syd.

ONAGRACEAE

Jussiaea angustifolia Lam.
- Uredo guaynabensis Kern & Whetzel.

Jussiaea californica (Watson) Jepson.
- Aecidium Betheli Arth.

Jussiaea decurrens (Walt.) DC.
- Cercospora Jussiaeae Atk.
- Colletotrichum Jussiaeae Earle.

Jussiaea diffusa Forsk.
- Septoria Jussiaeae Ell. & Kellerm.

Jussiaea leptocarpa Nutt.
- Cercospora Jussiaeae Atk.
- Septoria confusa Atk.
- Septoria Jussiaeae Ell. & Kellerm. 1888.
- Septoria Jussiaeae Ell. & Ev. 1897.

Jussiaea peruviana L.
- Uredo guaynabensis Kern. & Whetzel.

Jussiaea pilosa H.B.K.
- Septoria Jussiaeae Ell. & Kellerm. 1888.
- Septoria Jussiaeae Ell. & Ev. 1897.

Jussiaea sp. indet.
- Puccinia sphaeroidea Henn.

Ludvigia alternifolia L.
- Aecidum Epilobii DC.
- Aecidium Ludwigiae Ell. & Ev.
- Allodus Jussiaeae (Speg.) Arth. & Orton.
- Allodus Ludwigiae (Holw.) C. R. Orton.
- Puccinia Ludwigiae Holw.
- Cercospora Ludwigiae Atk.
- Pezizella Lythri Shear & Dodge.
- Septoria Ludwigiae Cke.

Ludvigia glandulosa Walt.

Ludvigia hirtella Raf.

Ludvigia natans Ell.
- Aecidium Ludwigiae Ell. & Ev.
- Allodus Jussiaeae (Speg.) Arth. & Orton.
- Allodus Ludwigiae (Holw.) C. R. Orton.
- Puccinia Ludwigiae Holw.

Ludvigia polycarpa Short & Peter.
⎰Aecidium Ludwigiae Ell. & Ev.
⎢Allodus Jussiaeae (Speg.) Arth. & Orton.
⎢Allodus Ludwigiae (Holw.) C. R. Orton.
⎨Puccinia Jussiaeae Speg.
⎢Puccinia Ludwigiae Holw.
⎣Puccinia Nesaeae Ell. & Ev.
　Phyllosticta Ludwigiae Pk.
　Septoria Ludwigiae Cke.
Ludvigia palustris (L.) Ell.
Ludvigia sphaerocarpa Ell.
⎰Aecidium Isnardiae Lagerh.
⎢Aecidium Ludwigiae Ell. & Ev.
⎨Allodus Jussiaeae (Speg.) Arth. & Orton.
⎢Puccinia Ludwigiae Holw.
⎣Puccinia Nesaeae Ell. & Ev.
　Phyllosticta Ludwigiae Pk.
　Septoria Ludwigiae Cke.
Ludvigia repens Sw.
⎰Allodus Jussiaeae (Speg.) Arth. & Orton.
⎱Puccinia Ludwigiae Holw.
Ludvigia virgata Michx.
⎰Aecidium Ludwigiae Ell. & Ev.
⎱Allodus Jussiaeae (Speg.) Arth. & Orton.
Ludvigia sp. indet.
⎰Phomatospora Ludwigiae Cke.
⎨Physalospora Ludwigiae (Cke.) Sacc.
⎩Sphaeria Ludwigiae Cke.
Zauschneria californica Presl.
⎰Dicaeoma Epilobii-tetragoni (Wint.) Arth.
⎢Puccinia Clarkiae Pk.
⎢Puccinia Epilobii Auct.
⎨Puccinia Epilobii-tetragoni Wint.
⎢Puccinia Oenotherae Vize.
⎢Puccinia Zauschneriae Syd.
⎢Synchytrium Jonesii Pk.
⎣Tuberculina Jonesii (Pk.) Sacc.
Zauschneria Garrettii A. Nels.
⎰Dicaeoma Epilobii-tetragoni (Wint.) Arth.
⎨Puccinia Epilobii-tetragoni Wint.
⎩Puccinia Zauschneriae Syd.
Epilobium adenocaulon Hausskn.
　Puccinia Veratri Duby. I.
⎰Cercospora montana (Speg.) Sacc.
⎱Ramularia montana Speg.
⎰Dicaeoma Epilobii-tetragoni (Wint.) Arth.
⎨Puccinia Epilobii-tetragoni Wint.
⎩Puccinia pulverulenta Grev.
　Pucciniastrum Abieti-Chamaenerii Klebahn.
⎰Pucciniastrum Epilobii (Chaill.) Otth.
⎱Pucciniastrum pustulatum (Schrt.) Diet.
　Ramularia Karstenii Sacc.
　Septoria Epilobii Westd.
⎰Sphaerotheca Epilobii (Lk.) Sacc.
⎱Sphaerotheca Humuli (DC.) Burrill. †
　Synchytrium fulgens Schrt.
Epilobium adenocaulon Hausskn., var. **occidentale** Trel.

Cercospora Epilobii Schneid.
Pucciniastrum Epilobii Otth.
Epilobium affine Bong.
　Puccinia Epilobii-tetragoni Wint.
　Pucciniastrum Abieti-Chamaenerii Klebahn.
　Pucciniastrum pustulatum (Schrt.) Diet.
　Sphaerotheca Humuli (DC.) Burrill. †
Epilobium alpinum L.
⎰Dicaeoma Veratri (Duby) O. Kuntze. I.
⎱Puccinia Veratri Duby. I.
　Cercospora Epilobii Schneid.
　Doassansia Epilobii Farl.
⎰Micropuccinia Epilobii (DC.) Rostr.
⎱Puccinia Epilobii DC.
⎰Aecidium Epilobii DC.
⎨Caeoma Epilobii Schl.
⎩Puccinia Epilobii-tetragoni Wint.
　Puccinia scandica Johans.
　Pucciniastrum pustulatum (Schrt.) Diet.
　Sphaerotheca Epilobii (Lk.) Sacc.
Epilobium alsineifolium Wirtg.
　Botrytis cinerea P. †
⎰Micropuccinia Epilobii (DC.) Rostr.
⎱Puccinia Epilobii DC.
　Puccinia pulverulenta Grev.
　Septoria cercosperma Rostr.
Epilobium americanum Hausskn.
　Dicaeoma Epilobii-tetragoni (Wint.) Arth.
　Pucciniastrum pustulatum (Schrt.) Diet.
Epilobium anagallidifolium Lam.
⎰Dicaeoma Veratri (Duby) O. Kuntze. I.
⎱Puccinia Veratri Duby. I.
⎰Micropuccinia Epilobii (DC.) Rostr.
⎱Puccinia Epilobii DC.
　Pucciniastrum Abieti-Chamaenerii Klebahn.
⎰Pucciniastrum Epilobii Otth.
⎱Pucciniastrum pustulatum (Schrt.) Diet.
Epilobium angustifolium L.
　Dicaeoma Peckii (Kellerm.) Arth. I.
　Asterella Chamaenerii Rostr.
⎰Asteroma Epilobii Fr.
⎱Dothidea Epilobii Fr.
　Cercospora Epilobii Schneid.
　Cercospora montana (Speg.) Sacc.
　Clavaria typhuloides Pk.
⎰Diaporthe racemula (C. & P.) Sacc.
⎱Sphaeria racemula C. & P.
　Didymella fenestrans (Duby) Wint.
　Discosia kriegeriana Bres.
　Gnomonia fenestrans (Duby) Sacc.
⎰Hainesia Lythri (Desm.) v. Höhnel.
⎨Sclerotiopsis concava (Desm.) Shear & Dodge.
⎢Helotium herbarum (P.) Fr.
⎣Peziza herbarum P.
　Hyaloceras kriegerianum (Bres.) Died.
　Laestadia Epilobii (Wallr.) Sacc.
⎰Marssonia Chamaenerii Rostr.
⎱Marssonina Chamaenerii (Rostr.) Magn.
　Mollisia atrata (P.) Karst.

Epilobium angustifolium (*cont.*)
  Pestalozzia kriegeriana Bres.
  Micropuccinia Epilobii (DC.) Rostr.
  { Micropuccinia gigantea (Karst.) Arth. & Jack-
    son.
  { Puccinia annulata Ell. & Ev.
  { Puccinia gigantea Karst.
  Pucciniastrum Abieti-Chamaenerii Klebahn.
  { Melampsora Epilobii (Otth) Fckl.
  { Pucciniastrum Epilobii Otth.
  { Pucciniastrum pustulatum (Schrt.) Diet.
  { Uredo pustulata P.
  Ramularia cercosporoides Ell. & Ev.
  Ramularia Chamaenerii Rostr.
  Ramularia punctiformis (Schl.) v. Höhnel.
  Sclerotium Rolfsii Sacc.
  Sphaerella adusta Niessl.
  Sphaerella microspila (B. & Br.) Cke.
  Sphaerella minor Karst.
  Trochila Epilobii Karst.

Epilobium Bongardi Hausskn.
  Dicaeoma Epilobii-tetragoni (Wint.) Arth.
  Sphaerella adusta Niessl.

Epilobium boreale Hausskn.
  Sphaerella adusta Fckl.

Epilobium brevistylum Barbey.

Epilobium californicum Hausskn.
  Pucciniastrum Abieti-Chamaenerii Klebahn.
  Pucciniastrum pustulatum (Schrt.) Diet.

Epilobium clavatum Trel.
  { Dicaeoma Epilobii-tetragoni (Wint.) Arth.
  { Puccinia Epilobii-tetragoni Wint.
  { Micropuccinia scandica (Johans.) Arth. &
    Jackson.
  { Puccinia scandica Johans.
  Pucciniastrum pustulatum (Schrt.) Diet.

Epilobium coloratum Muhl.
  { Cercospora montana (Speg.) Sacc.
  { Ramularia montana Speg.
  Gloeosporium Bowmani Ell. & Dearness.
  { Melampsora Epilobii (Otth) Fckl.
  { Pucciniastrum Epilobii Otth.
  { Pucciniastrum pustulatum (Schrt.) Diet.
  Ramularia punctiformis (Schl.) v. Höhnel.
  Septoria Epilobii Westd.
  { Sphaerotheca Epilobii (Lk.) Sacc.
  { Sphaerotheca Humuli (DC.) Burrill. †

Epilobium densum Raf.
  { Melampsora Epilobii (Otth) Fckl.
  { Pucciniastrum pustulatum (Schrt.) Diet.

Epilobium Drummondii Hausskn.
  Puccinia Veratri Duby. I.
  Pucciniastrum pustulatum (Schrt.) Diet.

Epilobium franciscanum Barbey.
  { Dicaeoma Epilobii-tetragoni (Wint.) Arth.
  { Puccinia Epilobii-tetragoni Wint.
  Pucciniastrum pustulatum (Schrt.) Diet.

Epilobium glandulosum Lehm.
  Dicaeoma Epilobii-tetragoni (Wint.) Arth.

Epilobium hirsutum L.
  { Pucciniastrum Epilobii Otth.
  { Pucciniastrum pustulatum (Schrt.) Diet.
  { Uredo pustulata P.

Epilobium holosericeum Trel.
  Pucciniastrum pustulatum (Schrt.) Diet.

Epilobium Hornemanni Reich.
  { Dicaeoma Veratri (Duby) O. Kuntze. I.
  { Puccinia Veratri Duby. I.
  Puccinia scandica Johans.
  Pucciniastrum pustulatum (Schrt.) Diet.

Epilobium jucundum Gray.
  Dicaeoma Epilobii-tetragoni (Wint.) Arth.
  Sphaerotheca Humuli (DC.) Burrill. †

Epilobium latifolium L.
  { Dicaeoma Veratri (Duby) O. Kuntze. I.
  { Puccinia Veratri Duby. I.
  { Asterella Chamaenerii Rostr.
  { Asterina Chamaenerii (Rostr.) Ell. & Ev.
  Cladosporium arcticum Berl. & Vogl.
  { Didymella nivalis (Fckl.) Berl. & Vogl.
  { Sphaeria nivalis Fckl.
  Gloeosporium Bowmani Ell. & Dearness.
  Gloeosporium Chamaenerii Allescher.
  Gloeosporium Epilobii Pass.
  Gnomonia fenestrans (Duby) Sacc.
  Leptosphaeria Doliolum (P. ex Fr.) De Not.
  Marssonia Chamaenerii Rostr.
  Phoma Chamaenerii Brunaud.
  Plasmopara Epilobii (Rabh.) Schrt.
  Pleospora arctica Fckl.
  Pleospora herbarum (Fr.) Rabh.
  Pleospora platyspora Sacc.
  { Dicaeoma Epilobii-tetragoni (Wint.) Arth.
  { Puccinia Epilobii-tetragoni Wint.
  Pyrenophora chrysospora (Niessl) Sacc.
  Pyrenophora chrysospora (Niessl) Sacc., **var.**
    polaris Karst.
  Ramularia Chamaenerii Rostr.
  Rhabdospora cercosperma (Rostr.) Sacc.
  Sphaerella minor Karst.
  { Mycosphaerella pachyasca (Rostr.) Vestergren.
  { Sphaerella pachyasca Rostr.
  Mycosphaerella tassiana Johans.
  Torula herbarum (P.) ex Lk.
  Trochila Epilobii Karst.

Epilobium latifolium L., **var. tenuiflora**
  Phoma Epilobii Preuss.

Epilobium minutum Lindl.
  { Dicaeoma Epilobii-tetragoni (Wint.) Arth.
  { Puccinia Epilobii-tetragoni Wint.

Epilobium neomexicanum Hausskn.
  Pucciniastrum Abieti-Chamaenerii Klebahn.
  Pucciniastrum pustulatum (Schrt.) Diet.

Epilobium occidentale Rydb.

Epilobium palustre L.
  Sphaerotheca Humuli (DC.) Burrill. †

Epilobium palustre L., var. **lineare** Gray.
  Melampsora Epilobii (Otth) Fckl.
Epilobium paniculatum Nutt.
  ⎰Dicaeoma Veratri (Duby) O. Kuntze. I.
  ⎱Puccinia Veratri Duby. I.
  ⎰Micropuccinia Epilobii (DC.) Rostr.
  ⎱Puccinia Epilobii DC.
  Aecidium Epilobii DC.
  Dicaeoma Epilobii-tetragoni (Wint.) Arth.
  ⎰Puccinia Epilobii-tetragoni Wint.
  ⎱Puccinia intermedia Diet. & Holw.
  Puccinia pulverulenta Grev.
  Sphaerotheca Humuli (DC.) Burrill. †
Epilobium Parishii Trel.
  Cercospora Epilobii Schneid.
  Pucciniastrum Epilobii Otth.
Epilobium perplexans Trel.
  Puccinia Epilobii-tetragoni Wint.
Epilobium platyphyllum Rydb.
  Puccinia Epilobii-tetragoni Wint.
  Pucciniastrum pustulatum (Schrt.) **Diet.**
Epilobium rigidum Hausskn.
  Puccinia Epilobii-tetragonii Wint.
Epilobium rubescens Rydb.
Epilobium rubricaule Rydb.
  ⎰Dicaeoma Veratri (Duby) O. Kuntze. I.
  ⎱Puccinia Epilobii-tetragoni Auct. Amer. p. p. I.
  Puccinia Veratri Duby. I.
Epilobium stramineum Rydb.
  Puccinia Veratri Duby. I.
  Pucciniastrum pustulatum (Schrt.) Diet.
Epilobium tetragonum L.
  Uredo Epilobii DC.
Epilobium sp. indet.
  Cladosporium herbarum (P.) ex Lk.
  Erysiphe Polygoni DC. †
  Ramularia Epilobii Allescher.
  Venturia Johnstoni (B. & Br.) Sacc. ?
Boisduvalia densiflora (Lindl.) Watson.
Boisduvalia glabella (Nutt.) Walp.
Boisduvalia parviflora Heller.
Boisduvalia salicina (Nutt.) Rydb.
Boisduvalia sparsiflora A. Heller.
Boisduvalia stricta (Gray) Greene.
Boisduvalia Torreyi Watson.
  ⎰Dicaeoma Epilobii-tetragoni (Wint.) Arth.
  ⎱Puccinia Boisduvaliae Pk.
  Puccinia Epilobii-tetragoni Wint.
  Puccinia glabella Holw.
  Puccinia Oenotherae Vize.
Clarkia amoena (Lehm.) Nelson & Macbr.
Clarkia elegans Dougl.
Clarkia epilobioides (Nutt.) Nelson & Macbr.
Clarkia grandiflora Greene.
Clarkia pulchella Pursh.
Clarkia rhomboidea Dougl.
Clarkia superba Nelson & Macbr.

  ⎰Aecidium Clarkiae Diet. & Holw.
  ⎱Dicaeoma Epilobii-tetragoni (Wint.) Arth.
  ⎰Puccinia Clarkiae Pk.
  ⎱Puccinia Epilobii-tetragoni Wint.
  Puccinia Oenotherae Vize.
Godetia amoena G. Don.
Godetia biloba Watson.
Godetia Bottae Spach.
Godetia epilobioides Watson.
Godetia grandiflora Lindl.
Godetia rubicunda Lindl.
  ⎰Puccinia Clarkiae Pk.
  ⎱Puccinia Epilobii-tetragoni Wint.
  Puccinia Oenotherae Vize.
Godetia sp. indet.
  Rhizoctonia Solani Kühn.
Oenothera alyssoides H. & A.
Oenothera andina Nutt.
  ⎰Dicaeoma Epilobii-tetragoni (Wint.) Arth.
  ⎱Puccinia Epilobii-tetragoni Wint.
Oenothera biennis L.
  Ceratostoma subulatum Ell.
  Cercospora didymospora Ell. & Barthol.
  Cercospora Oenotherae Ell. & Ev.
  ⎰Erysiphe communis Auct. Amer.
  ⎱Erysiphe Polygoni DC. †
  ⎰Leptosphaeria Doliolum (P. ex Fr.) De Not.
  ⎱Sphaeria Doliolum P. ex Fr.
  Leptosphaeria ellisiana Berl.
  ⎰Leptosphaeria subconica N. A. F. 697.
  ⎱Leptosphaeria subconica (C. & P.) Sacc.
  ⎱Sphaeria subconica C. & P.
  Leptothyrium protuberans (Lév.) Sacc.
  Leptothyrium vulgare (Fr.) Sacc.
  ⎰Lophionema vermisporum (Ell.) Sacc.
  ⎱Lophiostoma vermisporum Ell.
  ⎰Lophiostoma Oenotherae Ell. & Ev.
  ⎱Lophiotrema Oenotherae Ell. & Ev.
  ⎰Lophiotrema vagabundum Sacc., var. Oeno-
  ⎱   therae (Ell. & Ev.) Rehm.
  Macrophoma Oenotherae-biennis Dearness.
  Metasphaeria gaurina Ell. & Ev.
  Mollisia astericola (C. & E.) Sacc.
  Myxosporium Oenotherae Dearness.
  ⎰Ophiotheca umbrina B. & C.
  ⎱Perichaena variabilis Rostf.
  Peronospora Arthuri Farl.
  Pestalozzia Oenotherae Ell. & Barthol.
  ⎰Hainesia Lythri (Desm.) v. Höhnel.
  ⎱Pezizella Lythri Shear & Dodge.
  ⎱Sclerotiopsis concava (Desm.) Shear & Dodge.
  ⎰Peziza Oenotherae C. & E.
  ⎱Pezizella Oenotherae (C. & E.) Sacc.
  Phlyctaena arcuata B.
  Phlyctaena vagabunda Desm.
  Phoma herbarum Westd.
  Phoma infuscans Ell. & Ev.
  ⎰Septoria Oenotherae Westd. 1861?
  ⎱Septoria Oenotherae B. & C. 1867.

Oenothera biennis (*cont.*)
  Sphaerella Oenotherae Ell. & Ev.
  Sphaeronema corneum C. & E.
  Sphaeropsis Oenotherae Ell. & Ev.
  Synchytrium fulgens Schrt.
  Synchytrium Mercurialis (Lib.) Fckl.
  Vermicularia Dematium (P.) ex Fr.

UREDINALES
  Aecidium Oenotherae Mont.?
  ⎧Aecidium Oenotherae Pk.
  ⎪Aecidium Peckii De Toni.
  ⎪Dicaeoma Peckii (Kellerm.) Arth. I.
  ⎨Puccinia ludibunda Ell. & Ev. I.
  ⎪Puccinia Peckii Kellerm. I.
  ⎩?Uromyces Peckii Kellerm. & Werner.
  ?Aecidium Epilobii DC.
  ?Puccinia Epilobii DC.
  ⎧Aecidium Epilobii E. F. *281*.
  ⎨Nigredo plumbaria (Pk.) Arth.
  ⎩Uromyces plumbarius Pk.
Oenothera bistorta Nutt.
Oenothera Boothii Dougl.
  ⎧Dicaeoma Epilobii-tetragoni (Wint.) Arth.
  ⎪Puccinia Clarkiae Pk.
  ⎨Puccinia Epilobii-tetragoni Wint.
  ⎩Puccinia Oenotherae Vize.
Oenothera brachycarpa Gray.
  Aecidium Oenotherae Mont.?
  ⎧Nigredo plumbaria (Pk.) Arth.
  ⎨Uromyces plumbarius Pk.
Oenothera breviflora (Nutt.) Gray.
  ⎧Dicaeoma Epilobii-tetragoni (Wint.) Arth.
  ⎨Puccinia Epilobii-tetragoni Wint.
Oenothera caespitosa Nutt.
  Aecidium Oenotherae Mont.
  Uromyces plumbarius Pk.
Oenothera cardiophylla Torr.
  Uromyces Oenotherae Burrill.
Oenothera cheiranthifolia Hornem.
  ⎧Dicaeoma Sarcobati Arth. I.
  ⎨Puccinia subnitens Diet. I.
Oenothera contorta Dougl.
  ⎧Dicaeoma Epilobii-tetragoni (Wint.) Arth.
  ⎪Puccinia Epilobii-tetragoni Wint.
  ⎩Puccinia Oenotherae Vize.
Oenothera coronopifolia Torr & Gr.
  Cryptostictis utensis Fairman.
  Erysiphe Polygoni DC. †
  Microdiplodia Anograe Fairman.
  Synchytrium fulgens Schrt.
Oenothera densiflora Lindl.
Oenothera dentata Cav.
  ⎧Dicaeoma Epilobii-tetragoni (Wint.) Arth.
  ⎨Puccinia Epilobii-tetragoni Wint.
  ⎩Puccinia Oenotherae Vize.
Oenothera flava A. Nels.
  Septoria Oenotherae Westd.

Oenothera Fremontii Watson.
  Cercospora didymospora Ell. & Barthol.
  Puccinia Oenotherae Vize.
  ⎧Nigredo plumbaria (Pk.) Arth.
  ⎪Uromyces Fremonti Syd.
  ⎨Uromyces Oenotherae Burrill.
  ⎩Uromyces plumbarius Pk.
Oenothera fruticosa L.
  ⎧?Aecidium Epilobii Auct.
  ⎨Puccinia Peckii Kellerm. I.
  Septoria Oenotherae Westd.
  Synchytrium fulgens Schrt.
Oenothera gauriflora Torr. & Gr.
Oenothera graciliflora Hook. & Arn.
  ⎧Dicaeoma Epilobii-tetragoni (Wint.) Arth.
  ⎪Puccinia Epilobii-tetragoni Wint.
  ⎨Puccinia heterantha Ell. & Ev.
  ⎩Puccinia Oenotherae Vize.
Oenothera heterantha Nutt.
  Aecidium Oenotherae Mont. ?
  ⎧Dicaeoma Epilobii-tetragoni (Wint.) Arth.
  ⎨Puccinia Epilobii-tetragoni Wint.
  ⎩Puccinia heterantha Ell. & Ev.
Oenothera
    (Chylisma hirta A. Nels.)
Oenothera hirtella Greene.
  ⎧Dicaeoma Epilobii-tetragoni (Wint.) Arth.
  ⎨Puccinia Epilobii-tetragoni Wint.
  ⎩Puccinia Oenotherae Vize.
Oenothera Hookeri Torr. & Gr.
  ⎧Dicaeoma Peckii (Kellerm.) Arth. I.
  ⎨Puccinia Peckii Kellerm. I.
  Septoria Oenotherae Westd.
Oenothera humifusa Nutt.
  Septoria Oenotherae Westd.
Oenothera
    (Sphaerostigma implexa A. Nels.).
  Puccinia Epilobii-tetragoni Wint.
Oenothera laciniata Hill.
  Aecidium Epilobii DC. ?
  Cercospora Oenotherae-sinuatae Atk.
  ⎧Erysibe communis Auct. Amer. p. p.
  ⎨Erysiphe Polygoni DC. †
  Peronospora Arthuri Farl.
  ⎧Phomatospora Oenotherae (B. & C.) Cke.
  ⎨Physalospora Oenotherae (B. & C.) Sacc.
  Sphaeria Oenotherae B. & C.
  ⎧Aecidium Oenotherae Pk.
  ⎪Aecidium Peckii De Toni.
  ⎨Dicaeoma Peckii (Kellerm.) Arth. I.
  ⎩Puccinia Peckii Kellerm. I.
  Septoria Oenotherae Westd.
  Sphaeronema corneum C. & E.
  Synchytrium fulgens Schroet.
  ⎧Nigredo plumbaria (Pk.) Arth.
  ⎨Uromyces plumbarius Pk.
Oenothera linifolia Nutt.
  ⎧Nigredo plumbaria (Pk.) Arth.
  ⎨Uromyces Oenotherae Burrill.

Oenothera
  (Pachylophus macroglottis Rydb.).
  Dicaeoma Peckii (Kellerm.) Arth. I.
  Uromyces plumbarius Pk.
Oenothera marginata Nutt.
  Uromyces plumbarius Pk.
Oenothera micrantha Hornem.
  { Dicaeoma Epilobii-tetragoni (Wint.) Arth.
  { Puccinia Epilobii-tetragoni Wint.
  { Puccinia Oenotherae Vize.
Oenothera missouriensis Sims.
  Peronospora Arthuri Farl.
Oenothera montana Nutt.
Oenothera muricata L.
  { Nigredo plumbaria (Pk.) Arth.
  { Uromyces plumbarius Pk.
Oenothera Nuttallii Torr. & Gr.
  Aecidium Anograe Arth.
  { Dicaeoma Epilobii-tetragoni (Wint.) Arth.
  { Puccinia Epilobii-tetragoni Wint.
Oenothera ovata Nutt.
  { Dicaeoma Epilobii-tetragoni (Wint.) Arth.
  { Puccinia Epilobii-tetragoni Wint.
  { Puccinia heterantha Ell. & Ev.
  { Puccinia Oenotherae Vize.
  Septoria Oenotherae Westd.
  Nigredo plumbaria (Pk.) Arth.
Oenothera pallida Lindl.
  Aecidium Anograe Arth.
  { Erysibe communis Auct. Amer. p. p.
  { Erysiphe Polygoni DC. †
  Septoria Oenotherae Westd.
Oenothera procera Woot. & Standley.
  Erysiphe Polygoni DC.?
Oenothera pumila L.
  Dicaeoma Peckii (Kellerm.) Arth. I.
  Septoria Oenotherae Westd.
Oenothera rhombipetala Nutt.
  { Dicaeoma Peckii (Kellerm.) Arth. I.
  { Puccinia Peckii Kellerm. I.
  Septoria Oenotherae Westd.
Oenothera
  (Anogra runcinata Small.)
  Uromyces plumbarius Pk.
Oenothera scapoidea Nutt.
  Dicaeoma Epilobii-tetragoni (Wint.) Arth.
  Dicaeoma Sarcobati Arth. I.
Oenothera serrulata Nutt.
  { Aecidium Oenotherae Pk.
  { Aecidium Peckii De Toni. I.
  { Dicaeoma Peckii (Kellerm.) Arth. I.
  { Puccinia Peckii Kellerm. I.
  Septoria Oenotherae Westd.
  Synchytrium fulgens Schrt.
Oenothera speciosa Nutt.
  Aecidium Peckii De Toni.
  Cercospora Oenotherae Ell. & Ev.
  Peronospora Arthurii Farl.

Oenothera spiralis Lehm.
  { Dicaeoma Epilobii-tetragoni (Wint.) Arth.
  { Puccinia Epilobii Schrt.
  { Puccinia Epilobii-tetragoni Wint.
  { Puccinia Oenotherae Vize.
  { Uromyces plumbarius N. Am. Uredinales 295.
Oenothera strigosa Ryd.
  { Dicaeoma Peckii (Kellerm.) Arth. I.
  { Puccinia Peckii Kellerm. I.
  Leptosphaeria Onagrae Rehm.
  Peronospora Arthuri Farl.
  { Dicaeoma Epilobii-tetragoni (Wint.) Arth.
  { Puccinia Epilobii-tetragoni Wint.
  { Puccinia Oenotherae Vize.
  Septoria Oenotherae Westd.
Oenothera strigulosa Torr. & Gr., var. **pubens**
  Watson.
  { Dicaeoma Epilobii-tetragoni (Wint.) Arth.
  { Puccinia Epilobii-tetragoni Wint.
  { Puccinia Oenotherae Vize.
Oenothera tanacetifolia Torr. & Gr.
  Nigredo plumbaria (Pk.) Arth.
Oenothera triloba Nutt.
  Dicaeoma Peckii (Kellerm.) Arth. I.
Oenothera utahensis (Small) Garrett.
  Puccinia Oenotherae Vize.
Oenothera viridescens Lehm.
  { Dicaeoma Epilobii-tetragoni (Wint.) Arth.
  { Puccinia Epilobii-tetragoni Wint.
  { Puccinia Oenotherae Vize.
Oenothera
  (Anogra Vreelandii Rydb.)
  Aecidium Anograe Arth.
Oenothera sp. indet.
  { Didymella lophospora (Sacc. & Speg.) Ell.
  { Sphaeria lophospora Ell.
  Lophiostoma insidiosum (Desm.) Ces. & De
    Not.
Eulobus californicus Nutt.
  { Dicaeoma Epilobii-tetragoni (Wint.) Arth.
  { Puccinia Epilobii-tetragoni Wint.
  { Puccinia Eulobi Diet. & Holw.
  { Puccinia Oenotherae Vize.
  Pucciniastrum pustulatum (P.) Diet.
Gayophytum caesium Torr. & Gray.
  { Dicaeoma Epilobii-tetragoni (Wint.) Arth.
  { Puccinia Epilobii-tetragoni Wint.
  { Puccinia Gayophyti Pk.
  Ustilago Gayophyti Hark.
Gayophytum diffusum Torr. & Gray.
  Cercospora Gayophyti Ell. & Ev.
  { Dicaeoma Epilobii-tetragoni (Wint.) Arth.
  { Puccinia Epilobii-tetragoni Wint.
  { Puccinia Gayophyti Billings. 1871.
  { Puccinia Gayophyti Pk. 1882.
Gayophytum Helleri Rydb.
  Dicaeoma Epilobii-tetragoni (Wint.) Arth.

Gayophytum intermedium Rydb.
Puccinia Gayophyti Billings.
Ustilago Gayophyti Hark.

Gayophytum lasiospermum Greene.
Gayophytum Nuttallii Torr. & Gray.
Gayophytum pumilum Watson.
Gayophytum racemosum Torr. & Gr.
Dicaeoma Epilobii-tetragoni (Wint.) Arth.
Puccinia Epilobii Fung. Columb. *1289.*
Puccinia Epilobii-tetragoni Wint.
Puccinia Gayophyti Billings. 1871.
Puccinia Gayophyti Pk. 1882.

Gayophytum ramosissimum Torr. & Gr.
Aecidium Gayophyti Vize.
Dicaeoma Epilobii-tetragoni (Wint.) Arth.
Puccinia Epilobii-tetragoni Wint.
Puccinia Gayophyti Billings. 1871.
Puccinia Gayophyti Pk. 1882.
Ustilago Gayophyti Hark.

Gaura augustifolia Michx.
Nigredo plumbaria (Pk.) Arth.

Gaura biennis L.
?Puccinia Peckii Kellerm. I.
Cercospora Gaurae Kellerm. & Swingle.
Peronospora Arthuri Farl.
Hainesia Lythri (Desm.) v. Höhnel.
Pezizella Lythri Shear & Dodge.
Sclerotiopsis concava (Desm.) Shear & Dodge.
Sphaerella granulata Ell. & Ev.
Caeomurus gaurinus (Snyder) Arth.
Caeomurus plumbarius (Pk.) O. Kuntze.
Uromyces gaurinus Snyder.
Nigredo plumbaria (Pk.) Arth.
Uredo gaurina (Pk.) DeToni.
Uromyces plumbarius Pk.

Gaura brachycarpa Small.
Puccinia ludibunda Ell. & Ev. I.

Gaura coccinea Pursh.
Septoria gaurina Ell. & Kellerm.
Aecidium gaurinum Pk.
Nigredo plumbaria (Pk.) Arth.
Trichobasis gaurina Pk.
Uredo gaurina (Pk.) DeToni.
Uromyces gaurinus Snyder.
Uromyces plumbarius Pk.

Gaura glabra Lehm.
Nigredo plumbaria (Pk.) Arth.
Uromyces plumbarius Pk.

Gaura induta (Woot.) Standl.
Rhabdospora gauracea Fairman.
Septoria gaurina Ell. & Kellerm.
Nigredo plumbaria (Pk.) Arth.
Uromyces gaurinus Snyder.
Uromyces plumbarius Pk.

Gaura marginata Lehm.
Gaura neomexicana Wooton.
Nigredo plumbaria (Pk.) Arth.

Gaura parviflora Dougl.
Aecidium Gaurae Ell. & Ev.
Dicaeoma Peckii (Kellerm.) Arth. I.
Puccinia Peckii Kellerm. I.
Erysiphe Polygoni DC. †
Metasphaeria gaurina Ell. & Ev.
Peronospora Arthuri Farl.
Septoria gaurina Ell. & Kellerm.
Nigredo plumbaria (Pk.) Arth.
Uromyces gaurinus Snyder.

Gaura sinuata Nutt.
Dicaeoma Peckii (De Toni) Arth. I.
Nigredo plumbaria (Pk.) Arth.
Uromyces gaurinus Snyder.
Uromyces plumbarius Pk.

Stenosiphon linifolius (Nutt.) Brit.
Septoria Stenosiphonis Ell. & Kellerm.

Fuchsia microphylla H. B. K.
Fuchsia parviflora Zucc.
Fuchsia thymifolia H. B. K.
Micropuccinia Fuchsiae (Syd. & Holw.) Arth. & Jackson.
Puccinia Fuchsiae Syd. & Holw.

Fuchsia splendens Zucc.
Uredo Fuchsiae Arth. & Holw.

Fuchsia sp. indet.
Didymella Fuchsiae Cke. & Hark.
Diplodia Fuchsiae Cke. & Hark.

Lopezia hirsuta Jacq.
Micropuccinia Fuchsiae (Syd. & Holw.) Arth. & Jackson.
Puccinia Fuchsiae Syd. & Holw.
Uredo Fuchsiae Arth. & Holw.

Circaea alpina L.
Circaea intermedia Ehrh.
Micropuccinia Circaeae (P.) Arth. & Jackson.
Puccinia Circaeae P.
Puccinia nolitangeris Fung. Columb. *1286.*

Circaea lutetiana L.
Phyllactinia corylea (P.) ex Karst.
Dasyspora Circaeae (P.) Arth.
Dicaeoma Circaeae (P.) O. Kuntze.
Micropuccinia Circaeae (P.) Arth. & Jackson.
Puccinia Circaeae P.

Circaea pacifica Asch. & Magn.
Puccinia Circaeae P.

Onagraceae gen. indet.
Synchytrium rugulosum Diet.

HALORAGIDACEAE

Proserpinaca palustris L.
Proserpinaca pectinata Lam.
Proserpinaca platycarpa Small.
Aecidium Proserpinacae B. & C.
Dicaeoma Proserpinacae (Farl.) Arth.
Puccinia Epilobii, var. Proserpinacae Farl.
Puccinia Proserpinacae Farl.

HIPPURIDACEAE

Hippuris vulgaris L.
  Physoderma Hippuridis Rostr.

ARALIACEAE

Sciadophyllum capitatum Griseb.
  Chaetophoma macrospora Karst. & Hariot.
  {Leucoporus Tricholoma (Mont.) Pat.
  {Polyporus Tricholoma Mont.
Sciadophyllum sp. indet.
  Xylaria axifera Mont.
Oreopanax capitatum Dcne. & Planch.
  Coprinus ephemerus Fr.
Gilibertia arborea (L.) E. Marsh.
  Helminthosporium glabroides F. L. Stevens.
  Meliola amphitricha Fr.
  {Amphitrichum Araliae Spreng.
  {Meliola Araliae (Spreng.) Mont.
  {Sphaeria? amphitricha, var. Araliae Fr.
  Meliola Didymopanacis Henn.
  Mycosphaerella Didymopanacis Miles.
  Phyllosticta araliana E. Young.
Gilibertia laurifolia (Dcne. & Planch.) E. Marsh.
  Arthrobotryum caudatum Syd.
  Meliola Didymopanacis Henn.
Hedera Helix L.
  {Camarosporium Hederae Ell. & Ev.
  {Camarosporulum Hederae (Ell. & Ev.) Tassi.
  Cladosporium punctulatum Sacc. & Ell.
  Colletotrichum gloeosporioides Penz., var.
    Hederae Pass.
  Colletotrichum hedericola Taubenhaus.
  Gloeosporium hedericola Maubl.
  Gloeosporium paradoxum (De Not.) Fckl.
  Glomerella cingulata (Stoneman) Spaulding &
    v. Schrenk.
  {Metasphaeria hederifolia (Cke.) Sacc.
  {Sphaerulina hederifolia Cke.
  {Metasphaeria helicicola (Desm.) Sacc.
  {Sphaerulina helicicola Cke.
  {Phyllosticta concentrica Sacc.
  {Phyllostictina concentrica (Sacc.) v. Hohnel.
  Phyllosticta concentrica Sacc., var. sparsa Ell.
    & Ev.
  Phyllosticta decipiens Ell. & Ev.
  Phyllosticta hedericola Dur. & Mont.
  {Phomatospora Eunotia (B. & C.) Cke.
  {Physalospora Eunotia (B. & C.) Sacc.
  Ramularia hedericola Heald & Wolf.
  Sphaeropsis Hederae Ell. & Ev.
  {Haplosporella hedericola Speg.
  {Sphaeropsis hedericola (Speg.) Sacc.
  Vermicularia trichella Fr.
Acanthopanax aculeatum Seem.
  Sphaerella Acanthopanacis Ciferri & Fragoso.
Didymopanax Morototoni Dcne. & Planch.
  Mycosphaerella Didymopanacis Miles.
  Triposporium stelligerum Speg.

Aralia californica Watson.
  Septoria Araliae Ell. & Ev.
Aralia cordata Thunb.
  Sclerotinia libertiana Fckl.
  Verticillium albo-atrum Reinke & Berthold.
Aralia hispida Vent.
  {Cercospora leptosperma Pk.
  {Cylindrosporium leptospermum Pk.
  Triphragmium clavellosum B.
Aralia nudicaulis L.
  Ascochyta marginata J. J. Davis.
  Leptostroma virgultorum Sacc.
  Phyllactinia corylea (P.) ex Karst.
  Ramularia repens Ell. & Ev.
  Sclerotium deciduum J. J. Davis.
  {Cercospora leptosperma Pk.
  {Cercoseptoria leptosperma (Pk.) Petrak.
  {Cercosporella leptosperma (Pk.) J. J. Davis.
  {Cylindrosporium leptospermum Pk.
  {Septoriopsis leptosperma (Pk.) J. J. Davis.
  {Nyssopsora clavellosa (B.) Arth.
  {Triphragmium clavellosum B.
  Triphragmium echinatum Lév.
  Vermicularia herbarum (P.) ex Fr.
Aralia racemosa L.
  Belonidium minimum Ell. & Ev.
  Phyllosticta decidua Ell. & Kellerm.
  Ramularia repens Ell. & Ev.
Aralia spinosa L.
  Botryosphaeria Araliae M. A. Curtis.
  Cercospora atromaculans Ell. & Ev.
  Diaporthe Araliae Ell. & Ev.
  Eutypella densissima Ell. & Ev.
  Haplosporella Araliae Ell. & Ev.
  Hypoderma commune (Fr.) Duby.
  Hypoderma variegatum (B. & C.) Duby.
  Hypoderma virgultorum DC. ex Fr.
  Hypoxylon coccineum Bull. †
  Lecanidion atratum (Hedw. ex Fr.) Rabh.
  Leptothyrium vulgare (Fr.) Sacc.
  Macrosporium commune Rabh.
  Naematelia nucleata (S.) Fr.
  {Creonectria purpurea (L.) ex Seaver.
  {Nectria cinnabarina (Tode.) ex Fr.
  Phoma melaleuca B. & C.
  Phyllosticta Araliae Ell. & Ev.
  Phyllosticta Everhartii Sacc. & Syd.
  Physarum sinuosum (Bull.) Rostf.
  Stagonospora petiolorum Ell. & Ev.
  Tubercularia vulgaris Tode ex Fr.
  Valsa ambiens (P.) ex Fr.
  Vermicularia petiolorum S.
Aralia sp. indet.
  {Didymella commanipula (B. & Br.) Sacc.
  {Sphaeria commanipula B. & Br.
  Leptosphaeria comatella (C. & E.) Sacc.
  Meliola Araliae Mont.
  Physalospora Araliae Pat.
  Rhizoctonia Solani Kühn.

Aralia sp. indet. (*cont.*)
    Lachnum setigerum (Phil.) Rehm.
    Peziza setigera Phil.
    Trichopeziza setigera (Phil.) Sacc.
Panax plumatum Hort.
    Rosellinia bunodes (B. & Br.) Sacc.
Panax quinquefolium L.
    Acrostalagmus albus Preuss.
    Acrostalagmus panax Rankin.
    Alternaria panax Whetzel.
    Corticium vagum B. & C.
    Fusarium ferruginosum Sherbakoff.
    Fusarium vasinfectum Atk.
    Neocosmospora vasinfecta Erw. Sm.
    Neocosmospora vasinfecta, var. nivea Erw.
        Sm.
    Pestalozzia funerea Desm.
    Phytophthora Cactorum (Leb. & Cohn) Schrt.
    Phytophthora omnivora DBy.
    Pythium debaryanum Hesse.
    Ramularia destructans Zinssmeister.
    Ramularia panacicola Zinssmeister.
    Sclerotinia libertiana Fckl.
    Sclerotinia sclerotiorum (Lib.) Massee.
    Sclerotinia Panacis Rankin.
    Sclerotinia smilacina Durand.
    Thielavia basicola (B. & Br.) Zopf.
    Vermicularia Dematium (P.) ex Fr.
    Verticillium albo-atrum Reinke & Berth.
Panax trifolium L.
    Micropuccinia Araliae (Ell. & Ev.) Arth. &
        Jackson.
    Puccinia Araliae Ell. & Ev.
    Septoria Araliae Ell. & Ev.
Araliaceae gen. indet.
    Linochora Lagerheimii Petrak.
    Phyllachora Araliae (Pat.) Petrak.
    Physalospora Araliae Pat.

UMBELLIFERAE

Hydrocotyle americana L.
    Cercospora Hydrocotyles Ell. & Ev.
    Septoria Hydrocotyles Desm.
    Septoria pallidula Dearness & House.
    Synchytrium aureum Schrt.
Hydrocotyle australis Coult. & Rose.
    Nigredo Scirpi (Burrill) Arth. I.
Hydrocotyle bonariensis Lam.
    Puccinia Hydrocotyles Cke.
Hydrocotyle Canbyi Coult. & Rose.
    Uromyces Scirpi Burrill. I.
    Cercospora Hydrocotyles Ell. & Ev.
    Bullaria Hydrocotyles (Cke.) Arth. & Mains.
Hydrocotyle Hazeni Rose.
    Puccinia Hydrocotyles Cke.
Hydrocotyle mexicana Cham. & Schl.

Hydrocotyle prolifera Kellogg.
    Bullaria Hydrocotyles (Cke.) Arth. & Mains.
    Puccinia Hydrocotyles Cke.
    Trichobasis Hydrocotyles (Lk.) Cke.
    Uredo Hydrocotyles (Lk.) Bert.
Hydrocotyle ranunculoides L. f.
    Bullaria Hydrocotyles (Cke.) Arth. & Mains.
    Uredo Hydrocotyles (Lk.) Bert.
Hydrocotyle umbellata L.
Hydrocotyle verticillata Thunb.
    Nigredo Scirpi (Burrill) Arth. I.
    Uromyces Scirpi (Cast.) Burrill. I.
    Cercospora Hydrocotyles Ell. & Ev.
    Bullaria Hydrocotyles (Cke.) Arth. & Mains.
    Puccinia Hydrocotyles Cke.
    Trichobasis Hydrocotyles (Lk.) Cke.
    Uredo Hydrocotyles (Lk.) Bert.
Centella asiatica (L.) Urb.
    Septoria asiaticae Speg.
    Septoria Hydrocotyles Desm.
Sanicula canadensis L.
    Entyloma Saniculae Pk.
    ?Aecidium Saniculae Auct. Amer.
    Dicaeoma marylandicum (Lindr.) Arth.
    Dicaeoma Saniculae Auct. Amer.
    Puccinia marylandica Lindr.
    Puccinia Saniculae Auct. Amer.
Sanicula floridana Bicknell.
    Dicaeoma marylandicum (Lindr.) Arth.
Sanicula gregaria Bicknell.
    Ascochyta Thaspii, var. Saniculae J. J. Davis.
    Cercospora Saniculae J. J. Davis.
    Entyloma Saniculae Pk.
    Phyllosticta vexans Bubák & Dearness.
    Puccinia marylandica Lindr.
    Synchytrium pluriannulatum (B. & C.) Farl.
Sanicula marilandica L.
    Ascochyta Saniculae J. J. Davis.
    Ascochyta Thaspii Ell. & Ev., var. Saniculae
        J. J. Davis.
    Entyloma Saniculae Pk.
    Allodus lacerata C. R. Orton.
    Puccinia lacerata ("Doidge") Sacc. & Trott.
    Dicaeoma marylandicum (Lindr.) Arth.
    Puccinia marylandica Lindr.
    Puccinia Saniculae Auct.
    Septoria Saniculae Ell. & Ev.
    Synchytrium pluriannulatum (B. & C.) Farl.
    Urophlyctis pluriannulata (B. & C.) Farl.
Sanicula Menziesii Hook. & Arn.
    Entyloma Saniculae Pk.
    Synchytrium pluriannulatum (B. & C.) Farl.
    Urophlyctis pluriannulata (B. & C.) Farl.
Sanicula nevadensis Watson.
Sanicula trifoliata Bickn.
Sanicula tuberosa Torr.
    Dicaeoma marylandicum (Lindr.) Arth.
Sanicula sp. indet.
    Colletotrichum Saniculae Dearness.

Eryngium yuccifolium Michx.
  Cylindrosporium Eryngii Ell. & Kellerm.
  Dasyscypha eryngiicola Ell. & Ev.
  Entyloma Eryngii (Cda.) DBy.

Chaerophyllum procumbens (L.) Crantz.
Chaerophyllum Teinturieri Hook.
  ⎰ Aecidium Osmorrhizae Pk.
  ⎰ Caeoma Chaerophylli S.
  ⎱ Dicaeoma Pimpinellae (Mart.) O. Kuntze.
  ⎱ Puccinia Myrrhis S.
  ⎱ Puccinia Pimpinellae Mart.
  ⎱ Uredo Chaerophylli (S.) Pk.

Osmorhiza ambigua (Gray) Coult. & Rose.
Osmorhiza brachypoda Torr.
  ⎰ Dicaeoma Pimpinellae (Mart.) O. Kuntze.
  ⎱ Puccinia Pimpinellae Mart.

Osmorhiza brevipes (Coult. & Rose) Suksdorf.
  Mycosphaerella Washingtoniae Rehm.
  ⎰ Dicaeoma Pimpinellae (Mart.) O. Kuntze.
  ⎰ Puccinia Osmorrhizae Ds.
  ⎱ Puccinia Pimpinellae Mart.

Osmorhiza Claytoni (Michx.) Clarke.
  ⎰ Aecidium Osmorrhizae Pk.
  ⎰ Aecidium Pimpinellae Kirchner.
  ⎰ Dicaeoma Pimpinellae (Mart.) O. Kuntze.
  ⎰ Puccinia Myrrhis S.
  ⎱ Puccinia Osmorrhizae C. & P.
  ⎱ Puccinia Pimpinellae Mart.
  ⎱ Ramularia reticulata Ell. & Ev.
  Septoria Aegopodii Desm.
  ⎰ Septoria Aegopodii J. J. Davis, non Desm.
  ⎱ Septoria Osmorrhizae Pk.
  Vermicularia compacta C. & E.

Osmorhiza divaricata Nutt.
  ⎰ Dicaeoma Pimpinellae (Mart.) O. Kuntze.
  ⎰ Puccinia Osmorrhizae C. & P.
  ⎱ Puccinia Pimpinellae Mart.
  ⎱ Ramularia reticulata Ell. & Ev.

Osmorhiza intermedia (Rydb.) Blankinship.
Osmorhiza Leibergii (Coult. & Rose) Blankin-
  ship.
  Dicaeoma Pimpinellae (Mart.) O. Kuntze.
  Puccinia Pimpinellae Mart.

Osmorhiza longistylis (Torr.) DC.
  Cercospora Osmorrhizae Ell. & Ev.
  ⎰ Aecidium Osmorrhizae Pk.
  ⎰ Aecidium Pimpinellae Kirchner.
  ⎰ Caeoma Anemones S.
  ⎰ Caeoma Chaerophylli S.
  ⎰ Dicaeoma Chaerophylli S.
  ⎱ Puccinia Osmorrhizae C. & P.
  ⎱ Puccinia Pimpinellae Mart.
  ⎱ Ramularia reticulata Ell. & Ev.
  Septoria Aegopodii Desm.
  Septoria Osmorrhizae Pk.
  Septoria Podagrariae Lasch.

Osmorhiza nuda Torr.

Osmorhiza obtusa (Coult. & Rose) Fern.
  ⎰ Aecidium Osmorrhizae Pk.
  ⎰ Caeoma Chelidonii S.
  ⎰ Dicaeoma Pimpinellae (Mart.) O. Kuntze.
  ⎱ Puccinia Osmorrhizae C. & P.
  ⎱ Puccinia Pimpinellae Mart.

Osmorhiza occidentalis (Nutt.) Torr.
  ⎰ Dicaeoma Pimpinellae (Mart.) O. Kuntze.
  ⎰ Puccinia Osmorrhizae C. & P.
  ⎱ Puccinia Pimpinellae Mart.
  Septoria Osmorrhizae Pk.
  ⎰ Mycosphaerella Glycosmae Tracy & Earle.
  ⎰ Sphaerella Glycosmae (Tracy & Earle) Sacc.
  ⎱   & Syd.

Osmorhiza sp. indet.
  Cercospora Osmorrhizae Ell. & Ev.
  Metasphaeria Washingtoniae Earle.
  Septoria micropuncta Ell. & Ev.
  Sphaerodothis Neowashingtoniae Shear.

Erigenia bulbosa (Michx.) Nutt.
  Aecidium Aegopodii Reb.
  ⎰ Allodus Erigeniae C. R. Orton.
  ⎰ Puccinia Erigeniae (C. R. Orton.) Arth. 1921.
  ⎰ Puccinia Erigeniae ("Doidge") Sacc. & Trott.
  ⎱   1925.
  ⎱ Puccinia Osmorrhizae Auct. Amer. p. p.
  ⎱ Puccinia Pimpinellae N. A. F. *1040* (*b*).

Neonelsonia ovata Coult. & Rose.
  ⎰ Dicaeoma obscuratum (Arth. & Holw.) Arth.
  ⎱ Puccinia obscurata Arth. & Holw.

Conium maculatum L.
  Puccinia Conii Fckl.

Musineon divaricatum (Pursh) Nutt.
  ⎰ Aecidium mutum Arth.
  ⎰ Dicaeoma Sarcobati I. Arth. p. p.
  ⎱ Puccinia Jonesii I. Auct. p. p.
  Allodus Jonesii (Pk.) Arth.

Musineon Hookeri (Torr. & Gr.) Nutt.
  ⎰ Allodus Jonesii (Pk.) Arth.
  ⎱ Puccinia Jonesii Pk.

Musineon tenuifolium Nutt.
  ⎰ Allodus Musenii (Ell. & Ev.) C. R. Orton.
  ⎰ Micropuccinia Musenii (Ell. & Ev.) Arth. &
  ⎱   Jackson.
  ⎱ Puccinia Jonesii Seymour non Pk.
  ⎱ Puccinia Musenii Ell. & Ev.
  ⎱ Puccinia Seymourii Lindr.

Deweya arguta Torr. & Gray.
  Fusicladium depressum (B. & Br.) Sacc.
  ⎰ Puccinia Jonesii N. Am. Ured. *349*.
  ⎰ Puccinia Jonesii Auct. Amer. p. p.
  ⎱ Puccinia Lindrothii Syd.
  ⎱ Puccinia sphalerocondra Lindr.

Drudeophytum Hartwegi (Gray) Coult. & Rose.
  ⎰ Allodus Lindrothii (Syd.) C. R. Orton.
  ⎰ Puccinia Jonesii Auct. Amer. p. p.
  ⎰ Puccinia Oreoselini Fung. Columb. *343*.
  ⎱ Puccinia Lindrothii Syd.

Drudeophytum Parishii Coulter & Rose.
  Allodus Jonesii (Pk.) Arth.
  Allodus Lindrothii (Syd.) C. R. Orton.
Arracacia bracteata Coult. & Rose.
  ⎧ Dicaeoma Arracacharum Arth.
  ⎩ Puccinia Arracacharum Arth.
Arracacia multifida Watson.
  ⎧ Allodus imperspicua (Syd.) C. R. Orton.
  ⎩ Puccinia imperspicua Syd.
Arracacia xanthorrhiza Bancr.
  Erysiphe Polygoni DC. (?).
Apium graveolens L.
  Botrytis cinerea P. †
  Cercospora Apii Fres.
  Cercospora beticola Sacc.
  Cercospora Petroselini Desm., var. Apii Briosi
    & Cav.
  ⎧ Corticium vagum B. & C.
  ⎩ Rhizoctonia Solani Kühn.
  Fusarium orthocreas App. & Wr.
  Mycorrhizal Fungus.
  Phoma apiicola Speg.
  Phyllosticta Apii Halsted.
  Physarum gyrosum Rostf.
  Plasmopara pygmaea (Ung.) Schrt.
  Puccinia bullata Schrt.
  Pythium debaryanum Hesse.
  Rhizoctonia alba Matz.
  Sclerotinia libertiana Fckl.
  Sclerotinia minor Jagger.
  Sclerotiorum (Lib.) Massee.
  ⎧ Phlyctaena magnusiana (Allescher) Bres.
  | Septoria Apii (Bri. & Cav.) Chester.
  ⎨ Septoria Apii Rostr.
  | Septoria Petroselini Desm., var. Apii Briosi &
  ⎩   Cav.
  Septoria Petroselini Desm.
Petroselinum hortense Hoffm.
  Ozonium omnivorum Shear.
  Pleospora diaportheoides Ell. & Ev.
  Sclerotinia libertiana Fckl.
  Septoria Petroselini Desm.
  Septoria Petroselini Desm., var. Apii Br. & Cav.
Zizia aurea (L.) Koch.
  Ascochyta Thaspii Ell. & Ev.
  Cercospora Ziziae Ell. & Ev.
  Bullaria bullata (Schrt.) Arth.
  Puccinia Ziziae Ell. & Ev.
  Urophlyctis pluriannulata (B. & C.) Farl.
Zizia cordata (Walt.) DC.
  Cercospora Ziziae Ell. & Ev.
  Cylindrosporium Ziziae Ell. & Ev.
  Oidium erysiphoides Fr.
  ⎧ Bullaria Ziziae (Ell. & Ev.) Arth.
  ⎩ Puccinia Ziziae Ell. & Ev.
  Septoria Ziziae Ell. & Ev.
Cicuta Bolanderi Watson.
  ⎧ Dicaeoma Cicutae (Lasch) O. Kuntze.
  ⎩ Puccinia Cicutae Lasch.

Cicuta bulbifera L.
  ⎧ Aecidium Sii-latifolii Wint.
  ⎩ Uromyces Scirpi Burrill. I.
  Septoria Sii Rob. & Desm.
Cicuta californica Gray.
Cicuta Curtisii Coult. & Rose.
  ⎧ Dicaeoma Cicutae (Lasch) O. Kuntze.
  ⎩ Puccinia Cicutae Lasch.
Cicuta maculata L.
  ?Aecidium Pimpinellae Farl. & Seym. H. I. 48.
  ⎧ Nigredo Scirpi (Burrill) Arth. I.
  ⎩ Uromyces Scirpi Burrill. I.
  Ascochyta Thaspii Ell. & Ev.
  Botrytis vulgaris (Lk.) Fr.
  Cylindrosporium Cicutae Ell. & Ev.
  Helminthosporium interseminatum B. & Rav.
  Macrosporium commune Rabh.
  ⎧ Peziza cyathoidea Bull. ex P.
  ⎩ Phialea cyathoidea (Bull. ex P.) Gill.
  Plasmopara nivea (Ung.) Schrt.
  Protomyces macrosporus Ung.
  ⎧ Dicaeoma Cicutae (Lasch.) Kuntze.
  ⎩ Puccinia Cicutae Lasch.
  Septoria Sii Rob.
  Septoria Umbelliferarum Kalchb.
Cicuta occidentalis Greene.
Cicuta vagans Greene.
  ⎧ Dicaeoma Cicutae (Lasch) O. Kuntze.
  ⎨ Puccinia Cicutae Lasch.
  ⎩ Puccinia Pimpinellae West Am. Fung. *376.*
Cryptotaenia canadensis (L.) DC.
  ⎧ Allodus Cryptotaeniae (Pk.) Arth.
  | Micropuccinia Cryptotaeniae (Pk.) Arth. &
  | Jackson.
  ⎨ Puccinia Astrantiae B. & C.
  | Puccinia Cryptotaeniae Pk.
  ⎩ Puccinia enormis N. A. F. *1450.*
  ⎧ Allodus microica (Ell.) C. R. Orton.
  ⎩ Puccinia microica Ell.
  Puccinia Pimpinellae Mart.
  ⎧ Septoria Cryptotaeniae Ell. & Rau.
  ⎩ Septoria Saniculae Ell. & Ev.
  Sphaeria Myrrhis S.
Carum Gairdneri Gray.
Carum Garrettii A. Nels.
  ⎧ Micropuccinia Ligustici (Ell. & Ev.) Arth. &
  ⎨   Jackson.
  ⎩ Puccinia Ligustici Ell. & Ev.
Taenidia integerrima (L.) Drude.
  Cercospora platyspora Ell. & Holw.
  Fusicladium depressum (B. & Br.) Sacc.
  ⎧ Bullaria bullata (Schrt.) Arth.
  | Puccinia Angelicae Fckl.
  ⎨ Puccinia bullata Schrt.
  ⎩ Puccinia Pimpinellae Fung. Columb. *1771.*
  Septoria Pimpinellae Ell.
Eulophus Parishii Coult. & Rose.
  Micropuccinia Musenii (Ell. & Ev.) Arth. &
     Jackson.

Sium cicutifolium Schrank.
⎰Aecidium Sii-latifolii Wint.
⎰Nigredo Scirpi (Burrill) Arth. I.
⎱Uromyces Scirpi Burrill. I.
  Cercospora Sii Ell. & Ev.
  Fuscicladium depressum B. & Br.
  Physoderma vagans Schrt.
  Septoria Sii Rob. & Desm.
  Sphaerotheca Humuli (DC.) Burrill. †
Oenanthe californica Watson.
⎰Nyssopsora echinata (Lév.) Arth.
⎱Triphragmium echinatum Lév.
  Uromyces Scirpi Burrill.
Oenanthe sarmentosa Presl.
  Nyssopsora echinata (Lév.) Arth.
  Septoria Oenanthis Ell. & Ev.
Foeniculum vulgare Hill.
  Calonectria Umbelliferarum Seaver.
  Cladosporium herbarum (P.) ex Lk.
  Cyphella Capula Holmsk. ex Fr.
⎰Metasphaeria brunnea (Cke.) Sacc.
⎱Pleospora brunnea Cke.
  Pleospora herbarum (Fr.) Rabh.
  Pleurotus cyphelliformis B.
Anethum graveolens L.
⎰Cercospora (Cercosporina) Anethi Sacc.
⎱Cercosporella Anethi Sacc. nom. nud.
  Phoma Anethi Sacc.
Selinum capitellatum Benth. & Hook.
  Bullaria Cynomarathri (Holw.) Arth. & Mains.
Ligusticum apiifolium Gray.
⎰Dicaeoma Polygoni-vivipari (Dietr.) Arth. I.
⎰Puccinia Polygoni-vivipari Dietr. I.
⎰Micropuccinia Ligustici (Ell. & Ev.) Arth. &
⎱ Jackson.
⎱Puccinia Ligustici Ell. & Ev.
  Urophlyctis pluriannulatus (B. & C.) Farl.
Ligusticum Cusickii Coult. & Rose.
Ligusticum Leibergii Coult. & Rose.
⎰Micropuccinia Ligustici (Ell. & Ev.) Arth. &
⎰ Jackson.
⎰Puccinia Ligustici Ell. & Ev.
⎰Nyssopsora echinata (Lév.) Arth.
⎱Triphragmium echinatum Lév.
Ligusticum filicinum Watson.
  Allodus Jonesii (Pk.) Arth.
⎰Micropuccinia Ligustici (Ell. & Ev.) Arth. &
⎰ Jackson.
⎱Puccinia Ligustici Ell. & Ev.
  Triphragmium echinatum Lév.
Ligusticum Grayi Coult. & Rose.
  Micropuccinia Ligustici (Ell. & Ev.) Arth. &
    Jackson.
Ligusticum Porteri Coult. & Rose.
  Leptosphaeria rubrotincta Ell. & Ev.
  Micropuccinia Ligustici (Ell. & Ev.) Arth. &
    Jackson.
⎰Nyssopsora echinata (Lév.) Arth.
⎱Triphragmium echinatum Lév.

Ligusticum purpureum Coult. & Rose.
⎰Nyssopsora echinata (Lév.) Arth.
⎱Triphragmium echinatum Lév.
Ligusticum scothicum L.
  Aecidium Ligustici Ell. & Ev.
  Heterosphaeria Patella (Tode) ex Grev.
  Phoma complanata (Tode ex Fr.) Desm.
  Triphragmium echinatum Lév.
Ligusticum sp. indet.
  Pleospora aurea Ell.
Coelopleurum Gmelini (DC.) Ledeb.
  Dicaeoma Bistortae (DC.) O. Kuntze.
  Puccinia bullata Schrt.?
⎰Bullaria Coelopleuri (Arth.) Arth. & Mains.
⎱Puccinia Coelopleuri Arth.
Coelopleurum lucidum (L.) Fern.
  Capillaria caulincola (P.) Lk.
⎰Sphaerella Angelicae-lucidae (S.) Cke.
⎱Sphaeria Angelicae-lucidae S.
  Sclerotium convexulum S.
Oreoxis humilis Raf.
⎰Allodus Musenii (Ell. & Ev.) C. R. Orton.
⎰Micropuccinia Musenii (Ell. & Ev.) Arth. &
⎰ Jackson.
⎱Puccinia Musenii Ell. & Ev.
Thaspium aureum Nutt., var. **trifoliatum** Coult.
    & Rose.
  Cercospora Thaspii Ell. & Ev.
Thaspium barbinode (Michx.) Nutt.
  Ascochyta Thaspii Ell. & Ev.
Conioselinum Gmelini (Bray) Steud.
  Cercospora Apii Fres., var. Selini-Gmelini Sacc.
    & Scalia.
Conioselinum pacificum (Watson) Coult. & Rose.
⎰Nyssopsora echinata (Lév.) Arth.
⎱Triphragmium echinatum Lév.
Conioselinum scopulorum (Gray) Coult. & Rose.
  Acanthostigma scopulorum Ell. & Ev.
  Puccinia bullata Schrt.?
⎰Micropuccinia Ligustici (Ell. & Ev.) Arth. &
⎰ Jackson.
⎱Puccinia Ligustici Ell. & Ev.
  Septoria Petroselini Desm., var. treleasiana
    Sacc. & Scalia.
⎰Nyssopsora echinata (Lév.) Arth.
⎱Triphragmium echinatum Lév.
Angelica ampla A. Nels.
⎰Micropuccinia Ligustici (Ell. & Ev.) Arth. &
⎰ Jackson.
⎱Puccinia Ligustici Ell. & Ev.
Angelica Archangelica L.
  Asteroma Robergei Desm.
  Botrytis cinerea P. †
  Coniothyrium conoideum Sacc.
  Cudoniella fructigena Rostr.
  Dothidella Angelicae (Fr.) Rostr.
  Helotium aciculare (Bull.) ex Fr.

Angelica Archangelica (*cont.*)
- Helotium cyathoideum (Bull. ex P.) Karst.
- Peziza cyathoidea Bull. ex P.
- Phialea cyathoidea (Bull. ex P.) Gill.
- Heterosphaeria Patella (Tode) ex Grev.
- Laestadia Archangelicae Rostr.
- Leptosphaeria Doliolum (P. ex Fr.) De Not.
- Leptosphaeria modesta (Desm.) Karst.
- Mollisia atrata (P.) Karst.
- Mollisia cinerea (Batsch ex Fr.) Karst.
- Ombrophila Archangelicae Rostr.
- Calloria minutissima Rostr.
- Orbilia minutissima (Rostr.) Sacc.
- Phoma complanata (Tode ex Fr.) Desm.
- Pyrenophora phaeocomes (Reb.) ex Fr.
- Pyrenophora phaeocomoides Sacc.
- Sclerotinia libertiana Fckl.
- Sclerotium Oxyriae Rostr.
- Sclerotium rufum Rostr.
- Rhabdospora cercosperma (Rostr.) Sacc.
- Septoria cercosperma Rostr.

Angelica atropurpurea L.
- Didymella Angelicae (Ell. & Ev.) Sacc.
- Sphaerella Angelicae Ell. & Ev.
- Dothidea stipata Fr.
- Cercospora platyspora Ell. & Holw.
- Cladosporium depressum B. & Br.
- Didymaria platyspora Ell. & Holw.
- Fusicladium Angelicae Ell. & Ev.
- Fusicladium depressum (B. & Br.) Sacc.
- Passalora depressa (B. & Br.) Sacc.
- Leptostromella Angelicae Dearness & House.
- Mollisia Angelicae Dearness.
- Piggotia depressa Dearness.
- Bullaria bullata (Schrt.) Arth.
- Puccinia Angelicae Fckl.
- Puccinia bullata Schrt.
- Puccinia Umbelliferarum DC.
- Septoria Dearnessii Ell. & Ev.

Angelica Breweri Gray.
- Phyllosticta Angelicae Sacc.
- Bullaria (?) Ellisii (De Toni) Arth. & Mains.

Angelica dilatata A. Nels.
- Micropuccinia poromera (Holw.) Arth. & Jackson.
- Puccinia poromera Holw.

Angelica genuflexa Nutt.
- Fusicladium depressum (B. & Br.) Sacc.
- Bullaria bullata (Schrt.) Arth.
- Puccinia Angelicae Fckl.
- Bullaria (?) Ellisii (De Toni) Arth. & Mains.
- Puccinia Angelicae Ell. & Ev.
- Puccinia Ellisii De Toni.
- Puccinia Oreoselini Diet. p. p.

Angelica Grayi Coult. & Rose.
- Micropuccinia Ligustici (Ell. & Ev.) Arth. & Jackson.
- Puccinia Ligustici Ell. & Ev.

Angelica Lyallii Watson.
- Cylindrosporium Angelicae Dearness.
- Fusicladium depressum (B. & Br.) Sacc.
- Phyllosticta Angelicae Sacc.
- Piggotia depressa Dearness.
- Bullaria bullata (Schrt.) Arth.
- Puccinia Angelicae Fckl.

Angelica mexicana Vatke.
- Asterina Pittieri Bomm. & Rouss.

Angelica tomentosa Watson.
- Bullaria (?) Ellisii (De Toni) Arth. & Mains.
- Puccinia Ellisii De Toni.

Angelica villosa (Walt.) B. S. P.
- Cercospora Thaspi Ell. & Ev.
- Bullaria bullata (Schrt.) Arth.

Angelica sp. indet.
- Cercospora Apii Fres., var. Angelicae Sacc. & Scalia.
- Sclerotium Oxyriae Rostr.
- Septogloeum Angelicae (Cke.) Sacc.
- Xylaria filiformis (A. & S.) ex Fr., var. caulincola Rehm.

Phellopterus montanus Nutt.
- Allodus Jonesii (Pk.) Arth.
- Puccinia Cymopteri Diet. & Holw.

Phellopterus purpurascens (Gray) Coult. & Rose.
Coriophyllus Betheli (Osterhout) Rydb.
Pteryxia calcarea (M. E. Jones) Coult. & Rose.
Pteryxia terebinthina (Hook.) Coult. & Rose.
Aulospermum longipes (Watson) Coult. & Rose.
Aulospermum purpureum (Watson) Coult. & Rose.
- Allodus Cymopteri (Diet. & Holw.) Barthol.
- Allodus Jonesii (Pk.) Arth.
- Puccinia Cymopteri Diet. & Holw.
- Puccinia Jonesii Pk.
- Puccinia traversiana Syd.

Cymopterus acaulis (Pursh) Rydb.
- Aecidium Cymopterorum Cockerell.
- Allodus Jonesii (Pk.) Arth.
- Puccinia Cymopteri Diet. &Holw.

Cymopterus Fendleri Gray.
Cymopterus lapidosus M. E. Jones.
- Allodus Jonesii (P.) Arth.
- Puccinia Cymopteri Diet. & Holw.
- Puccinia Jonesii Pk.

Pseudocymopterus anisatus (Gray) Coult. & Rose.
- Allodus Musenii (Ell. & Ev.) C. R. Orton.
- Micropuccinia Musenii (Ell. & Ev.) Arth. & Jackson.
- Puccinia Musenii Ell. & Ev.
- Puccinia Pseudocymopteri Holw.

Pseudocymopterus bipinnatus (Watson) Coult. & Rose.
- Pleospora herbarum (Fr.) Rabh.

Pseudocymopterus bipinnatus (*cont.*)
{ Allodus Musenii (Ell. & Ev.) C. R. Orton.
{ Micropuccinia Musenii (Ell. & Ev.) Arth. &
{   Jackson.
{ Puccinia Jonesii Seymour non Pk.
{ Puccinia Musenii Ell. & Ev.
{ Puccinia Seymourii Lindr.
  Dicaeoma Pseudocymopteri (Holw.) Arth.
Pseudocymopterus montanus (Gray) Coult. &
  Rose.
  Aecidium Osmorrhizae Pk.?
{ Dicaeoma Pseudocymopteri (Holw.) Arth.
{ Puccinia Pseudocymopteri Holw. 1913.
{ Puccinia Pseudocymopteridis Holw. ex Garrett.
{   1914.
Pseudocymopterus multifidus Rydb.
Pseudocymopterus Tidestromii Coult. & Rose.
{ Dicaeoma Pseudocymopteri (Holw.) Arth.
{ Puccinia Pseudocymopteri Holw.
{ Puccinia Pseudocymopteridis Holw.
Prionosciadium dissectum Coult. & Rose.
Prionosciadium linearifolium (Wats.) Coult. &
  Rose.
Prionosciadium Nelsoni Coult. & Rose.
Prionosciadium serratum Coult. & Rose.
Prionosciadium Watsoni Coult. & Rose.
Coulterophytum Holwayi Rose.
Coulterophytum laxum B. L. Robinson.
{ Bullaria (?) Prionosciadii (Lindr.) Arth. &
{   Mains.
{ Puccinia Coulterophyti Diet & Holw.
{ Puccinia Prionosciadii Lindr.
Bonannia resinifera Guss.
  Puccinia bullata Auct. p. p. sec. Lindr.
Polytaenia Nuttallii DC.
  Cercospora Polytaeniae Ell. & Kellerm.
Myrrhidendron Donnellsmithii Coult. & Rose.
  Cercosporina Donnell-Smithii Speg.
Oxypolis Fendleri (Gray) A. Heller.
{ Micropuccinia Ligustici (Ell. & Ev.) Arth. &
{   Jackson.
{ Puccinia Ligustici Ell. & Ev.
Oxypolis rigidior (L.) Coult. & Rose.
  Septoria Umbelliferarum Kalchb.
Leptotaenia dissecta Nutt.
{ Allodus asperior (Ell. & Ev.) C. R. Orton.
{ Puccinia aspera N. Am. Ured. *1219.*
{ Puccinia asperior Ell. & Ev.
{ Puccinia oregonensis Earle.
Leptotaenia Eatoni Coult. & Rose.
{ Allodus Jonesii (Pk.) Arth.
{ Puccinia Jonesii Pk.
  Dicaeoma Pseudocymopteri (Holw.) Arth.
Leptotaenia filicina M. E. Jones.
  Puccinia asperior Ell. & Ev.
  Puccinia Jonesii Pk.
Leptotaenia multifida Nutt.
{ Aecidium Aethusae Ell. & Ev. non Kirch.
{ Aecidium Leptotaeniae Lindr.

Comoclathris lanata Clements.
{ Allodus Jonesii (Pk.) Arth.
{ Puccinia Jonesii Pk.
Leptotaenia purpurea (Watson) Coult. & Rose.
  Allodus Jonesii (Pk.) Arth.
Peucedanum foeniculaceum Nutt.
  Aecidium anisotomes Reichardt.
{ Allodus Jonesii (Pk.) Arth.
{ Puccinia Jonesii Pk.
  Puccinia Pimpinellae Mart.
Peucedanum Gormani Howell.
  Puccinia Jonesii Pk.
Peucedanum sp. indet.
  Puccinia asperior Ell. & Ev.
Lomatium ambiguum (Nutt.) Coult. & Rose.
Lomatium dasycarpum (T. & G.) Coult. & Rose.
Lomatium daucifolium (Nutt.) Coult. & Rose.
{ Allodus Jonesii (Pk.) Arth.
{ Puccinia Jonesii Pk.
Lomatium
    (Peucedanum Geyeri Watson).
  Micropuccinia Ligustici (Ell. & Ev.) Arth. &
    Jackson.
Lomatium Grayi Coult. & Rose.
Lomatium macrocarpum (Nutt.) Coult. & Rose.
Lomatium nevadense (Watson) Coult. & Rose.
Lomatium orientale Coult. & Rose.
{ Allodus Jonesii (Pk.) Arth.
{ Puccinia Jonesii Pk.
Lomatium platycarpum (Torr.) Coult. & Rose.
  Fusicladium Peucedani Ell. & Holw.
{ Allodus Jonesii (Pk.) Arth.
{ Puccinia Jonesii Pk.
Lomatium purpureum A. Nels.
Lomatium Suksdorfii (Watson) Coult. & Rose.
Lomatium triternatum (Pursh) Nutt.
{ Allodus Jonesii (Pk.) Arth.
{ Puccinia Jonesii Pk.
Euryptera Hassei Coult. & Rose.
  Allodus Jonesii (Pk.) Arth.
  Allodus Lindrothii (Syd.) C. R. Orton.
Euryptera lucida Nutt.
  Allodus Lindrothii (Syd.) C. R. Orton.
Euryptera parvifolia (Hook. & Arn.) Coult. &
  Rose.
  Allodus Jonesii (Pk.) Arth.
  Dicaeoma marylandicum (Lindr.) Arth.
Cynomarathrum Eastwoodae Coult. & Rose.
  Puccinia Cymopteri Diet. & Holw.
Cynomarathrum Nuttallii (Gray) Coult. & Rose.
  Heterosphaeria Patella (P.) ex Grev.
Cynomarathrum Parryi (Watson) Coult. & Rose.
{ Bullaria Cynomarathri (Holw.) Arth. & Mains.
{ Puccinia Cynomarathri Holw.
{ Puccinia Ellisii Fung. Utah *9, 51.*
  Allodus Jonesii (Pk.) Arth.
Pastinaca sativa L.
{ Actinomyces scabies (Thax.) Güssow.
{ Oospora scabies Thax.

Pastinaca sativa (*cont.*)
  Cercospora Apii Fres.
  ⎰Cercospora Apii Fres., var. Pastinacae Sacc.
  ⎱Cercospora Pastinacae (Sacc.) Pk.
  Cercosporella Pastinacae Karst.
  ⎰Corticium vagum B. & C., var. Solani Burt.
  ⎱Rhizoctonia Solani Kühn.
  Cylindrosporium crescentum Barthol.
  Diaporthe Arctii (Lasch) Nits.
  Ophiobolus Bardanae Fckl.
  Ozonium omnivorum Shear.
  ?Peronospora nivea Ung.
  ⎰Helotium pastinacinum Cke.
  ⎱Pezizella Pastinacae (S.) Sacc.
  Phoma nebulosa (P.) Mont.
  Phomopsis canadensis Bubák & Dearness.
  Phomopsis Diachenii Sacc.
  Pleospora diaporthoides Ell. & Ev.
  ⎰Ramularia Pastinacae (Karst.) Lindr. &
  ⎮   Vestergren. 1902.
  ⎱Ramularia Pastinacae Bubák. 1903.
  Rhabdospora pastinacina (Sacc.) Allescher.
  Rhizopus nigricans Ehrenb. ex Fr.
  ⎰Sclerotinia libertiana Fckl.
  ⎱Sclerotinia sclerotiorum (Lib.) Massee.
  Septoria pastinacina Sacc.
  Stictis Umbellatarum (S.) Sacc.
  Thielavia basicola (B. & Br.) Zopf.

Heracleum lanatum Michx.
  Cylindrosporium Heraclei Ell. & Ev.
  Diaporthe Arctii (Lasch) Nits.
  Didymella exigua (Niessl) Sacc.
  ⎰Gloeosporium achaeniicola Rostr.
  ⎮Phoma herbarum Westd., var. epicarpina J. J.
  ⎱ Davis.
  Heterosphaeria patella (Tode) Grev.
  Leptosphaeria Doliolum (P.) De Not.
  Leptosphaeria Simmonsii Sacc.
  Leptothyrium nitidum Patterson.
  Naevia stenospora Sacc.
  ⎰Ophiobolus porphyrogonus (Tode ex Fr.) Sacc.
  ⎱Sphaeria rubella P. ex Fr.
  Phoma asteriscus B.
  Phoma complanata (Tode ex Fr.) Desm.
  Phoma Heraclei Earle.
  Phoma oleracea Sacc., var. Heraclei-lanati Sacc.
  Phyllachora Heraclei (Fr.) Fckl.
  Phyllosticta Heraclei Ell. & Dearness.
  Puccinia bakeriana Arth.
  Ramularia Heraclei (Oud.) Sacc.
  Rhabdospora Heraclei Earle.
  Sclerotium varium P. ex Fr.
  Septoria Heraclei (Lib.) Desm.
  Septoria pastinacina Sacc.
  Sirococcus americanus Sacc.
  Sphaerographium abditum Sacc. & Scalia.
  Vermicularia Dematium (P.) ex Fr.

Daucus Carota L.
  Actinomyces scabies (Thax.) Güssow.
  Alternaria radicina Meier, Drechs. & Reddy.
  Aspergillus niger van Tiegh.
  Botrytis vulgaris (L.) ex Fr.
  Cercospora Apii Fres.
  Cercospora Apii Fres., var. Carotae Pass.
  Clathrospora permunda (Cke.) Berl.
  ⎰Corticium vagum B. & C., var. Solani Burt.
  ⎱Rhizoctonia Solani Kühn.
  ⎰Leptosphacria comatella (C. & E.) Sacc.
  ⎱Sphaeria comatella C. & E.
  Macrosporium Carotae Ell. & Langlois.
  Mucor ramannianus Moeller.
  Ozonium omnivorum Shear.
  ⎰Pleospora herbarum (Fr.) ex Rabh.
  ⎱Sphaeria herbarum Fr.
  Rhizoctonia Crocorum DC.
  Rhizoctonia microsclerotia Matz.
  Rhizopus nigricans Ehrenb. ex Fr.
  Sclerotinia intermedia Ramsey.
  ⎰Sclerotinia libertiana Fckl.
  ⎱Sclerotinia sclerotiorum (Lib.) Massee.
  Sclerotium Rolfsii Sacc.

Daucus pusillus Michx.
  Pleospora diaporthoides Ell. & Ev.

Umbelliferae gen. indet.
  ⎰Aegerita decolorans (S.) Sacc.
  ⎱Dermosporium decolorans S.
  ⎰Diaporthe aculeata (S.) Sacc.
  ⎱Sphaeria aculeata S.
  ⎰Diaporthe umbellatum (S.) Ell. & Ev.
  ⎱Sphaeria umbellatum (S.)
  Hendersonia cylindrospora Ell. & Ev.
  ⎰Lachnella extricata (B. & C.) Sacc.
  ⎱Peziza extricata B. & C.
  ⎰Heptameria tenera (Ell.) Cke.
  ⎱Leptosphaeria tenera Ell.
  Leptosphaeria utahensis Ell. & Ev.
  Metasphaeria seriata Ell. & Ev.
  Metasphaeria Thwaitesii (B. & Br.) Sacc.
  Ophiobolus purpureus Ell. & Ev.
  Puccinia luteobasis Ell. & Ev.
  Rhabdospora Umbelliferarum Earle.
  Rhysotheca Umbelliferarum (Casp.) G. W.
    Wilson.
  Vermicularia Eryngii (Cda.) Fckl.

CORNACEAE

Garrya elliptica Dougl.
  Cercospora Garryae Hark.
  Cercospora glomerata Hark.
  ⎰Dasyscypha tautilla (Phil. & Hark.) Sacc.
  ⎱Pezizella tautilla Phil. & Hark.
  ⎰Harknessiella purpurea (Phil. & Hark.) Sacc.
  ⎱Phillipsiella purpurea Phil. & Hark.
  ⎰Aulographum lucens Hark.
  ⎱Lembodia lucens (Hark.) Sacc.

Garrya elliptica (*cont.*)
  Peltosphaeria Garryae (Cke. & Hark.) Berl.
  Sphaeria Garryae Cke. & Hark.
  Thyridium Garryae (Cke. & Hark.) Berl. &
    Vogl.
  Phyllosticta Garryae Cke. & Hark.
Garrya Lindheimeri Torr.
  Phyllosticta Garryae Cke. & Hark.
Garrya Veatchii Kellogg.
  Podosporiella humilis Ell. & Ev.
Garrya sp. indet.
  Tryblidaria Garryae (Earle) Sacc. & Trott.
  Tryblidium Garryae Earle.
Nyssa aquatica L.
  Aplopsora Nyssae (Ell. & Tracy) Mains.
  Uredo Nyssae Ell. & Tracy.
  Isothea Nyssae B. & C.
  Phoma nyssicarpae Cke.
  Phyllosticta Nyssae Cke.
  Sphaerella nyssicola Cke.?
  Valsa Nyssae Cke.
  Valsa praestans B. & C.
Nyssa capitata Walt.
  Phyllosticta Nyssae Cke.
  Uredo Nyssae Ell. & Tracy.
Nyssa sylvatica Marsh.
  Cercospora Nyssae Tharp.
  Ciboria nyssigena (Ell.) Sacc.
  Peziza nyssigena Ell.
  Daedalea confragosa (Bolt.) ex Fr., var. rube-
    scens Pk.
  Diaporthe paulula (C. & E.) Sacc.
  Diatrypella subfulva (B. & C.) Sacc.
  Didymella segna (C. & E.) Sacc.
  Endophlaea segna (C. & E.) Cke.
  Fomes applanatus (P. ex Wallr.) Gill.
  Hainesia Lythri (Desm.) v. Höhnel.
  Sclerotiopsis concava (Desm.) Shear & Dodge.
  Hydnum Caput-ursi Fr.
  Leptothyrium dryinum Sacc.
  Lophiostoma subcollapsum Ell. & Ev.
  Trematosphaeria subcollapsa Ell. & Ev.
  Melanconiella nyssigena Ell. & Ev.
  Melanconis nyssigena Ell. & Ev.
  Phyllosticta Nyssae Cke.
  Pirostoma Nyssae Tehon.
  Delacourea thuridonta (C. & E.) Sacc.
  Pleospora thuridonta (C. & E.) Sacc.
  Sphaeria thuridonta C. & E.
  Polyporus cinnabarinus (Jacq.) ex Fr.
  Polyporus versicolor (L.) ex Fr.
  Polyporus hirsutus Wulf. ex Fr.
  Polystictus hirsutus (Wulf.) ex Fr.
  Polystictus pargamenus Fr.
  Poria incrassata (B. & C.) Burt.
  Cornularia hispidula (Ell.) Sacc.
  Pseudographium hispidulum (Ell.) Jacz.
  Sphaeronema hispidulum Ell.

  Scoleconectria scolecospora (Bref.) Seaver.
  Stereum hirsutum (Willd.) ex Fr.
  Stereum sericeum (S.) Morg.
  Stereum striatum Fr.
  Thelephora sericea S.
  Thelephora striata Fr.
  Tulasnella violea (Quél.) Bourdot & Galzin.
  Valsa apatosa C. & E.
  Valsaria apatosa (C. & E.) Sacc.
  Valsa Nyssae Grev.
  Zignoella nyssigena Ell. & Ev.
Nyssa sp. indet.
  Amphisphaeria Papilla (S.) Sacc.
  Amphisphaeria pelorospora Dearness.
  Chilonectria Coryli (Fckl.) Ell. & Ev.
  Nectria Coryli Fckl.
  Nectria Cucurbitula N. A. F. *159.*
  Corticium Nyssae B. & C.
  Fomes geotropus Cke.
  Glenospora Curtisii B. & Desm.
  Hydnum pulcherrimum B. & C.
  Hydnum Rhois S.
  Steccherinum Rhois (S.) Banker.
  Hydnum septentrionale Fr.
  Steccherinum septentrionale (Fr.) Banker.
  Hysterium hiascens B. & C.
  Karschia lignyota (Fr.) Sacc.
  Patellaria lignyota Fr.
  Myriangium Duriaei Mont. & B.
  Phyllactinia Candollei Lév.
  Phyllactinia corylea (P.) ex Karst.
  Rhizoctonia moniliformis Ell. & Ev.
  Septobasidium Patouillardi Burt.
  Septobasidium pseudopedicellatum Burt.
  Sirothecium fragile Morg.
  Sporidesmium adscendens B.
  Stereum purpureum P. †
  Torula bigemina C. & E.
  Valsaria exasperans (Gerard) Sacc.
Cornus alternifolia L. f.
  Calosphaeria cornicola Ell. & Ev.
  Togninia cornicola (Ell. & Ev.) Berl.
  Calospora allantospora Ell. & Ev.
  Coryneum cornicola Ell. & Ev.
  Diaporthe Corni Fckl.
  Fracchiaea callista (B. & C.) Sacc.
  Hendersonia alternifoliae Ell. & Ev.
  Microsphaera Alni (DC.) Wint. †
  Myxosporium nitidum B. & C.
  Sphaeria mamillana S. Am. Bor. 1850.
  Pezicula rhabarbarina (B.) Tul.
  Phyllactinia corylea (P.) ex Karst.
  Phyllosticta cornicola (DC. ex Fr.) Rabh.
  Ramularia gracilipes J. J. Davis.
  Septoria cornicola Desm.
  Zythia aurantiaca (Pk.) Sacc.
Cornus Amomum Mill.
  Ascochyta cornicola Sacc.

Cornus Amomum (*cont.*)
{ Dermatea Rubi (Lib.) Rehm.
{ Patellaria rhabarbarina B.
{ Pezicula rhabarbarina (B.) Tul.
Dimerosporium pulchrum Sacc.
Microsphaera Alni (DC.) Wint. †
{ Phyllactinia corylea (P.) ex Karst.
{ Phyllactinia suffulta (Reb.) ex Sacc.
Phyllosticta cornicola (DC. ex Fr.) Rabh.
Septoria cornicola Desm.
Cornus asperifolia Michx.
Calosphaeria cornicola Ell. & Ev.
Cytospora Corni Westd.
Fenestella princeps Tul.
Valsa cornina Pk.
Cornus canadensis L.
Glomerularia Corni Pk.
Helminthosporium macrocarpum Grev.
Pezizella Lythri Shear & Dodge.
Phyllactinia corylea (P.) ex Karst.
{ Micropuccinia porphyrogenita (M. A. Curtis)
{   Arth. & Jackson.
{ Puccinia acuminata Pk.
{ Puccinia porphyrogenita M. A. Curtis.
Septoria canadensis Pk.
Venturia Clintoni Pk.
Cornus circinata L'Her.
{ Macrophoma cornina (Pk.) Sacc.
{ Sphaeropsis cornina Pk.
{ Monilia Corni Reade.
{ Sclerotinia Corni Reade.
Myxosporium nitidum B. & C.
Phoma Corni Fckl.
{ Phyllactinia corylea (P.) ex Karst.
{ Phyllactinia suffulta (Reb.) ex Sacc.
Phyllosticta cornicola (DC. ex Fr.) Rabh.
Valsa ambiens (P.) ex Fr.
Cornus disciflora Moc. & Sessé.
Episphaerella Corni Syd.
Cornus florida L.
{ Catharinia olivispora (B. & C.) Berl.
{ Heptameria olivispora (B. & C.) Cke.
{ Leptosphaeria olivispora (B. & C.) Sacc.
{ Sphaeria olivispora B. & C.
Cercospora cornicola Tracy & Earle.
Coelosphaeria exilis (A. & S. ex Fr.) Sacc.
Daedalea confragosa (Bolt.) ex Fr.
Discosia Artocreas (Tode) ex Fr.
{ Eriosphaeria xestothele (B. & C.) Dearness &
{   House.
{ Herpotrichia xestothele (B. & C.) Berl.
{ Lasiosphaeria xestothele (B. & C.) Sacc.
Melogramma gyrosum Tul.
{ Mollisia miltophthalma (B. & C.) Sacc.
{ Peziza miltophthalma B. & C.
{ Myxosporium Corni Ell. & Ev.
{ Myxosporium Everhartii Sacc. & Syd.
Nummularia Bulliardi Tul.
Ozonium omnivorum Shear.

{ Mollisia exidiella (B. & C.) Massee.
{ Peziza exidiella B. & C.
{ Pezizella exidiella (B. & C.) Sacc.
Peniophora affinis Burt.
Peniophora cinerea (P. ex Fr.) Cke.
Phoma florida Dearness & House.
{ Phyllactinia corylea (P.) ex Karst.
{ Phyllactinia guttata (Wallr. ex Fr.) Lév.
{ Phyllactinia suffulta (Reb.) ex Sacc.
{ Phyllosticta Corni Starb.
{ Sphaeria Corni S. p. p.
Phyllosticta cornicola (DC. ex Fr.) Rabh.
Phyllosticta Fraxini Ell. & Martin.
Phyllosticta globifera Ell. & Ev.
Phyllosticta Starbaeckii Sacc. & Syd.
Septoria cornicola Desm.
Septoria Corni-Maris Sacc.
Septoria floridae Tehon & Daniels.
{ Solenia poriiformis (DC.) Fckl.
{ Tapesia pruinata (S.) Sacc.
{ Sphaerella Corni (S.) Cke.
{ Sphaerella cornifolia Cke.
{ Sphaeria Corni S.
{ Haplosporella parallela (Dearness & House)
{   Petrak & Syd.
{ Sphaeropsis parallela Dearness & House.
Sporodesmium toruloides Ell. & Ev.
Tremella virens S.
{ Peziza roseoalba S.
{ Trichopeziza roseoalba (S.) Sacc.
Valsa ambiens (P.) ex Fr.
Xylaria carpophila (P.) ex Fr.
Xylaria persicaria (S.) M. A. Curtis.
Cornus instolonea A. Nels.
Macrophoma cornina (Pk.) Sacc.
Phoma Corni-sueciae (Fr.) Sacc.
Cornus Nuttallii Audubon.
Fomes igniarius (L. ex Fr.) Gill.
{ Nectria cinnabarina (Tode) ex Fr.
{ Creonectria purpurea (L. ex Fr.) Seaver.
Nectria coccinea (P.) ex Fr.
Nectria galligena Bres.
{ Phyllactinia corylea (P.) ex Karst.
{ Phyllactinia suffulta (Reb.) ex Sacc.
Placosphaeria cornicola Dearness.
Cornus occidentalis Coville.
Helminthosporium macrocarpum Grev.
Phyllactinia corylea (P.) ex Karst.
Cornus paniculata L'Her.
{ Calosphaeria cornicola Ell. & Ev.
{ Togninia cornicola (Ell. & Ev.) Berl.
Cercospora Corni J. J. Davis.
Diaporthe cornicola Ell. & Holw.
Dimerosporium pulchrum Sacc.
{ Macrophoma paniculatae (Ell. & Dearn.)
{   Sacc. & Syd.
{ Phoma paniculata Ell. & Dearness.
Meliola nidulans (S.) Cke.
Microsphaera Alni (DC.) Wint. †

Cornus paniculata (*cont.*)
  Monilia Corni Reade.
  { Phyllactinia corylea (P.) ex Karst.
  { Phyllactinia suffulta (Reb.) ex Sacc.
  { Phyllosticta cornicola (DC. ex Fr.) Rabh.
  { Phyllosticta globifera Ell. & Ev.
  Sarcinella heterospora Sacc.
  { Phyllosticta cornicola N. A. F. *2833*.
  { Septoria cornicola Desm.
  Valsa ambiens (P.) ex Fr.

Cornus pubescens Nutt.
  Phyllactinia corylea (P.) ex Karst.

Cornus sanguinea L.
  Erysiphe tortilis (Wallr.) ex Fr.
  Phyllactinia corylea (P.) ex Karst.
  Physalospora Cydoniae Arnaud.
  Ramularia stolonifera Ell. & Ev.
  Septoria cornicola Desm.

Cornus sibirica Lodd.
  Septoria Convolvuli Desm.

Cornus stolonifera Michx.
  Amphisphaeria decolorans Rehm.
  Diaporthe crassicollis Nits.
  Didymosphaeria decolorans Rehm, var. americana Sacc.
  Diplodia mamillana Fr.
  Eutypa leioplaca (Fr.) Cke.
  Helotium serotinum (P.) ex Fr.
  Hymenochaete corrugata (Fr.) Lév.
  Hysterium Prostii Duby.
  Hysterographium Mori (S.) Rehm.
  Melanopsamma pomiformis (P. ex Fr.) Sacc.
  { Microsphaera Alni (DC.) Wint. †
  { Microsphaera Corni Mayr.
  { Podosphaera Corni Mayr.
  Mycosphaerella cornicola Tehon & Daniels.
  Myxosporium nitidum B. & C.
  Patellaria nigrovirens Sacc. & Ell.
  Pezicula Corni Petrak.
  Phoma Corni-suecicae (Fr.) Sacc.
  { Phyllactinia corylea (P.) ex Karst.
  { Phyllactinia guttata (Wallr. ex Fr.) Lév.
  { Phyllactinia suffulta (Reb.) ex Sacc.
  Phyllosticta Corni Westd.
  Physalospora Cydoniae Arnaud.
  Ramularia stolonifera Ell. & Ev.
  Sarcinella heterospora Sacc.
  Septoria cornicola Desm.
  Stictis radiata (L.) ex P.
  Valsa ambiens (P.) ex Fr.
  Valsa cornina Pk.

Cornus stricta Lam.
  Phyllactinia corylea (P.) ex Karst.

Cornus suecica L.
  Hypoderma commune (Fr.) Duby.
  Leptostroma herbarum (Fr.) Lk.
  { Patellaria applanata B. & C.
  { Patinella applanata (B. & C.) Sacc.

{ Patellaria rhabarbarina B.
{ Pezicula rhabarbarina (B.) Tul.
Puccinia porphyrogenita M. A. Curtis.
Cornus sp. indet.

ASCOMYCETES

Acrospermum compressum Tode ex Fr., var. foliicola (B.) Riddle.
Anthostomella cornicola Ell. & Ev.
{ Cenangella flavocinerea (Phil.) Sacc.
{ Dermatea flavocinerea Phil.
Cenangium contortum B. & C.
{ Cryptomyces maximus (Fr.) Rehm.
{ Rhytisma maximum Fr.
Dermatea Corni Phil. & Hark.
Diaporthe albocarnis Ell. & Ev.
{ Diatrype aspera Fr.
{ Diatrypella aspera (Fr.) Nits.
Didymosphaeria epidermis (Fr.) Fckl.
Didymosphaeria oblitescens (B. & Br.) Sacc.
{ Eutypa atomospora (Cke.) Sacc.
{ Eutypa heteracantha Sacc.
{ Eutypella atomispora (Cke.) Sacc.
{ Valsa atomispora Cke.
Helotium propinquum Sacc. & Ell.
Lichenopsis sphaeroboloidea S.
Lophidium diminuens (P. ex Fr.) Ces. & De Not.
Lophiostoma prominens Pk.
Lophiostoma quadrinucleatum Karst.
Lophiostoma triseptatum Pk.
Metasphaeria Fiedleri (Niessl) Sacc.
Myrmaecium harperianum Rehm.
Nectria ditissima Tul.
Nummularia repanda (Fr.) Nits.
{ Dothidea subcuticularis S.
{ Phyllachora subcuticularis (S.) Sacc.
{ Physalospora Corni Sacc.
{ Physalospora Corni Ell. & Ev.
{ Physalospora Everhartii Sacc. & Syd.
Pleospora atromaculans Rehm.
Stictis stigma C. & E.
Valsa ceratophora Tul.
Valsa munda B. & C.
Valsa scutellata (P. ex Fr.) M. A. Curtis.
Valsaria cornicola Ell. & Ev.

BASIDIOMYCETES

Corticium ceraceum B. & Rav.
Corticium incarnatum Fr.
Corticium molle B. & C.
Corticium subcinereum Burt.
Dacryomyces minor Pk.
{ Daedalea corrugata Klotzsch.
{ Lenzites corrugata (Klotzsch) B. & C.
{ Septobasidium pseudopedicellatum Burt.
{ Thelephora pedicellata Auct. Amer. p. p.
Solenia ochracea Hoffm. ex Fr.

Cornus sp. indet. (*cont.*)

FUNGI IMPERFECTI

Diplodina macrospora Ell. & Ev.
Fusarium Berkelei Mont.
{ Diplodia papillosa Ell. & Ev.
{ Microdiplodia papillosa (Ell. & Ev.) Tassi.
Sporidesmium toruloides Ell. & Ev.
{ Hendersonia pallida B. & C.
{ Stagonopsis pallida (B. & C.) Sacc.
Stagonospora cornicola Earle.

Aucuba sp. indet.
Rhizoctonia Solani Kühn.

ERICACEAE

Clethra alnifolia L.
{ Cenangella urceolata (Ell.) Sacc.
{ Cenangium urceolatum Ell.
Sphaeronema clethrincola Ell.
{ Dasyscypha albopileata (Cke.) Sacc., var.
  subaurata (Ell.) Sacc.
{ Lachnella albopileata (Cke.) Phil., var. subau-
  rata Ell.
{ Diaporthe binoculata (Ell.) Sacc., var. Cle-
  thrae Dearness.
Dichomera Clethrae Dearness.
Melanomma Pulvis-pyrius (P. ex Fr.) Fckl.
{ Dialonectria depauperata Cke.
{ Nectria depauperata Cke.
{ Peziza virginea Batsch, var. clethricola Ell. &
  Ev.
Phyllosticta clethricola Ell. & Martin.
{ Steganosporium fenestratum (Ell. & Ev.) Sacc.
{ Stilbospora fenestrata Ell. & Ev.
Synchytrium Vaccinii Thomas.
{ Dendrophoma pruinosa (Fr.) Sacc.
Sphaeria Ligustri S.
{ Sphaeria pruinosa Fr.
Valsa Cypri Tul.
Valsa obtecta C. & E.
{ Valsa clethricola C. & E.
{ Valsaria clethricola (C. & E.) Sacc.

Clethra sp. indet.
{ Cenangium Urceolus (A. & S.) ex Fr.
{ Godronia Urceolus (A. & S. ex Fr.) Sacc.
{ Creonectria ochroleuca (S.) Seaver.
{ Nectria ochroleuca (S.) M. A. Curtis.
{ Physalospora viscosa (C. & E.) Sacc.
{ Sphaeria viscosa C. & E.
{ Sphaeronema rufum Fr.
{ Sphaeronemella rufa (Fr.) Sacc.
Sphaeropsis clethricola C. & E.
Valsa americana B. & C.

Chimaphila corymbosa Pursh.
Pucciniastrum Pyrolae (Karst.) Diet.

Chimaphila maculata (L.) Pursh.
{ Pucciniastrum Pyrolae (Karst.) Diet.
{ Uredo Chimaphilae Pk.
Septoria Chimaphilae Ell. & Ev.

Chimaphila occidentalis Rydb.
Pucciniastrum Pyrolae (Karst.) Diet.

Chimaphila umbellata (L.) Nutt.
{ Pucciniastrum Pyrolae (Karst.) Diet.
{ Uredo Chimaphilae Pk.
Depazea Pyrolae (Ehrenb. ex Fr.) Rabh.
Mycosphaerella chimaphilina (Sacc.) House.
Phoma Pyrolae (Ehrenb. ex Fr.) Rostr.
Sphaerella Chimaphilae Pk. Nov. 1894.
Sphaerella chimaphilina Sacc.
Sphaeria Pyrolae Ehrenb. ex Fr.
Stigmatea? Pyrolae (Ehrenb. ex Fr.) Schrt.
Sphaerella Chimaphilae Ell. & Ev. 27 Feb.
  1894.

Moneses reticulata Nutt.
Melampsoropsis Pyrolae (Rostr.) Arth.

Moneses uniflora (L.) Gray.
{ Chrysomyxa Pyrolae Rostr.
{ Melampsoropsis Pyrolae (Rostr.) Arth.
Pucciniastrum Pyrolae (Karst.) Diet.

Pyrola americana Sweet.
{ Chrysomyxa Pyrolae Rostr.
{ Melampsoropsis Pyrolae (Rostr.) Arth.
Pucciniastrum Pyrolae (Karst.) Diet.

Pyrola asarifolia Michx.
Cladosporium herbarum (P.) ex Lk.
Melampsoropsis Pyrolae (Rostr.) Arth.
Phoma Pyrolae (Ehrenb. ex Fr.) Rostr.
Pucciniastrum Pyrolae (Karst.) Diet.
Pyrenophora comata (Niessl) Sacc.
Septoria pyrolata Rostr.
Sphaerella Pyrolae Rostr.

Pyrola asarifolia Michx., var. **incarnata** (Fisch.)
  Fernald.
{ Caeoma pyrolatum S.
{ Chrysomyxa Pyrolae Rostr.
{ Melampsoropsis Pyrolae (Rostr.) Arth.
Pucciniastrum Pyrolae (Karst.) Diet.

Pyrola bracteata Hook.
{ Chrysomyxa Pyrolae Rostr.
{ Melampsoropsis Pyrolae (Rostr.) Arth.

Pyrola chlorantha Swartz.
{ Chrysomyxa Pyrolae Rostr.
{ Melampsoropsis Pyrolae (Rostr.) Arth.
Pucciniastrum Pyrolae (Karst.) Diet.

Pyrola elliptica Nutt.
{ Aecidium pyrolatum S.
Caeoma pyrolatum S.
{ Chrysomyxa Pyrolae Rostr.
Chrysomyxa pyrolata Wint.
{ Melampsoropsis Pyrolae (Rostr.) Arth.
Ovularia Pyrolae Trel.
Phyllosticta Pyrolae Ell. & Ev.
{ Melampsora Pyrolae (Karst.) Schrt.
Pucciniastrum Pyrolae (Karst.) Diet.
{ Trichobasis Pyrolae (P.) B.
{ Uredo Pyrolae (P.) Mart.

Pyrola grandiflora Radius.
⎰ Chrysomyxa Pyrolae Rostr.
⎱ Melampsoropsis Pyrolae (Rostr.) Arth.
Phoma Pyrolae (Ehrenb.) Rostr.
Pucciniastrum Pyrolae (Karst.) Diet.
Pyrenophora Cesatii (Oud.) J. Lind.
Septoria pryolata Rostr.

Pyrola minor L.
⎰ Chrysomyxa Pyrolae Rostr.
⎱ Melampsoropsis Pyrolae (Rostr.) Arth.
Pucciniastrum Pyrolae (Karst.) Diet.

Pyrola picta Sm.
Melampsoropsis Pyrolae (Rostr.) Arth.
Pucciniastrum Pyrolae (Karst.) Diet.

Pyrola rotundifolia L.
⎧ Aecidium pyrolatum S.
⎪ Caeoma pyrolatum S.
⎪ Chrysomyxa Pyrolae Rostr.
⎨ Chrysomyxa pyrolata Wint.
⎪ Melampsoropsis Pyrolae (Rostr.) Arth.
⎩ Uredo pyrolata (S.) Körn.
Phyllosticta Pyrolae Ell. & Ev.
⎰ Ovularia Pyrolae Trel.
⎱ Ramularia Pyrolae (Trel.) Ell. & Ev.
Zygodesmus Pyrolae Ell. & Halsted.

Pyrola secunda L.
⎧ Chrysomyxa Pyrolae Rostr.
⎪ Chrysomyxa pyrolata Wint.
⎪ Chrysomyxa Ramischiae Lagerh.
⎪ Melampsoropsis Pyrolae (Rostr.) Arth.
⎪ Leptosphaeria marginata Niessl.
⎨ Melampsora Pyrolae Schrt.
⎪ Pucciniastrum Pyrolae (Karst.) Diet.
⎪ Thecopsora Pyrolae Karst.
⎪ Trichobasis Pyrolae (P.) B.
⎩ Uredo Pyrolae (P.) Mart.
Septoria Pyrolae Ell. & Martin.

Pyrola sp. indet.
Sphaerella pachyasca Rostr.
Stigmatea? Pyrolae (Ehrenb. ex Fr.) Schrt.

Monotropa uniflora L.
Vermicularia Dematium (P.) ex Fr.

Monotropa sp. indet.
⎰ Hypoderma plantarum (S.) Cke.
⎱ Hysterium plantarum S.

Ledum decumbens Lodd.
Melampsoropsis abietina Arth.
Melampsoropsis ledicola (Lagerh.) Arth.

Ledum glandulosum Nutt.
⎰ Chrysomyxa Ledi DBy.
⎱ Melampsoropsis abietina Arth.
Microsphaera diffusa C. & P.

Ledum groenlandicum Oeder.
Ascochyta Ledi Rostr.
Aulographum Ledi Pk.
⎰ Clithris lactea (C. & P.) Ell. & Ev.
⎱ Colpoma lacteum C. & P.

⎧ Chrysomyxa Ledi DBy.
⎪ Melampsoropsis abietina Arth.
⎪ Melampsoropsis Ledi Arth.
⎨ Uredo Ledi A. & S.
⎩ Caeoma ledicola (Pk.) Diet.
⎰ Chrysomyxa ledicola Lagerh.
⎱ Melampsoropsis ledicola (Lagerh.) Arth.
⎰ Puccinia Ledi B. & C.
⎱ Uredo ledicola Pk.
Coryneum triseptatum Pk.
⎰ Hysterium sphaerioides A. & S. ex Fr.
⎱ Lophodermium sphaerioides (A. & S. ex Fr.)
Duby.
Phyllosticta Ledi Rostr.

Ledum palustre L.
Lophodermium sphaerioides (A. & S. ex Fr.)
Duby.
⎰ Melampsoropsis ledicola (Lagerh.) Arth.
⎱ Uredo ledicola Pk.

Ledum sp. indet.
Gloeosporium Ledi Schrt.
Lophodermium maculare (Fr.) De Not.

Rhododendron albiflorum Hook.
Exobasidium Vaccinii (Fckl.) Wor.

Rhododendron arboreum Sm.
Sphaeria Kalmiarum S.

Rhododendron atlanticum Rehder.
Exobasidium Vaccinii (Fckl.) Wor.

Rhododendron californicum Hook.
⎰ Caeoma piperianum (Arth.) Sacc. & Trott.
⎨ Chrysomyxa piperiana (Arth.) Sacc. & Trott.
⎩ Melampsoropsis piperiana Arth.
Coryneum Rhododendri S.
Exobasidium Vaccinii (Fckl.) Wor.
Lophodermium Rhododendri (S.) Pk.
Sporocybe Azaleae (Pk.) Sacc.
Uredo Arbuti Diet. & Holw.

Rhododendron canadense (L.) B. S. P.
Exobasidium Vaccinii (Fckl.) Wor.
⎧ Caeoma Vacciniorum (DC.) Lk.
⎪ Peridermium Peckii Thm. III.
⎨ Pucciniastrum minimum Arth.
⎪ Pucciniastrum Myrtilli (Karst.) Arth.
⎪ Thekopsora minima (Arth.) Syd.
⎩ Uredo Vacciniorum DC.

Rhododendron catawbiense Michx.
⎰ Hendersonia concentrica Ell. & Ev.
⎱ Phyllohendersonia concentrica (Ell. & Ev.)
Tassi.
Lophodermium melaleucum (Fr.) De Not.
Melampsoropsis Roanensis Arth.
Pestalozzia Guepini Desm.
⎰ Phyllosticta maxima Ell. & Ev.
⎱ Phyllosticta Rhododendri Westd.

Rhododendron indicum Sweet.
⎰ Exobasidium Azaleae Pk.
⎱ Exobasidium Vaccinii (Fckl.) Wor.
Septoria Azaleae Vogl.

Rhododendron kamtschaticum Pall.
  Melasmia Rhododendri Sacc.
  Rhytisma? Rhododendri Fr.
Rhododendron lapponicum (L.) Wahlenb.
  Antennatula arctica Rostr.
  Dimerosporium oreophilum Speg.
  Helminthosporium Rhododendri Rostr.
  Torula Rhododendri Kze.
Rhododendron maximum L.
  Cenangium palmatum S.
  Cephalotrichum rigescens Lk.
  Coryneum Rhododendri S.
  Coryneum triseptatum Pk.
  { Cryptostictis Mariae (G. W. Clinton) Sacc.
  { Dochmolopha Clintonii Cke.
  { Pestalozzia Mariae G. W. Clinton.
  Dermatea lobata Ell.
  Eomycenella echinocephala Atk.
  { Eutypa denigrata (S.) Cke.
  { Sphaeria denigrata S.
  { Exobasidium Rhododendri Cramer.
  { Exobasidium Vaccinii (Fckl.) Wor.
  Grandinia crustosa (P.) ex Fr.
  Helotium castaneum Sacc. & Ell.
  Hendersonia concentrica Ell. & Ev.
  Hypocrea virginiensis Ell. & Ev.
  Hypocreopsis Rhododendri Thax.
  Hypoxylon colliculosum (S.) M. A. Curtis.
  { Coccomyces Rhododendri (S.) Cke.
  { Hysterium Rhododendri S.
  { Lophodermium Rhododendri (S.) Pk.
  { Phacidium Rhododendri S.
  Marasmius opacus B. & C.
  Metasphaeria californica (Cke. & Hark.) Berl.
  Mycosphaerella clintoniana House.
  { Ohleria inconstans (S.) Cke.
  { Sphaeria inconstans S.
  Omphalia Rhododendri Pk.
  Pestalozzia Guepini Desm.
  Phyllosticta maxima Ell. & Ev.
  { Polyporus Rhododendri S.
  { Poria Rhododendri (S.) Cke.
  Sphaerella oblivia Cke.
  Sphaerella Rhododendri Cke.
  Sporocybe Azaleae (Pk.) Sacc.
  Stereum triste B. & C.
  Tremella frondosa Fr.
Rhododendron molle G. Don.
  Phomopsis ericaceana Fairman.
Rhododendron nudiflorum (L.) Torr.
  { Colpoma Azaleae (S.) Cke.
  { Hysterium abietinum S. Syn. Car. p. p.
  { Hysterium Azaleae S.
  { Sporomega Andromedae Duby p. p.
  Dacryomyces Azaleae S.
  Dendrophoma Azaleae Dearness & House.
  Exobasidium Azaleae Pk.
  Exobasidium discoideum Ell.
  Exobasidium Vaccinii (Fckl.) Wor.

  { Microsphaera Alni (DC.) Wint. †
  { Microsphaera Platani Howe.
  Phyllosticta Rhododendri Westd.
  { Caeoma Azaleae S.
  { Melampsora Vacciniorum (Karst.) Schrt.
  { Pucciniastrum minimum Arth.
  { Pucciniastrum Myrtilli Arth.
  { Pucciniastrum Vacciniorum (Karst.) Diet.
  { Thekopsora minima (Arth.) Syd.
  { Uredo Azaleae (S.) M. A. Curtis.
  { Uredo minima S.
  Ramularia angustata Pk.
  { Periconia Azaleae Pk.
  { Sporocybe Azaleae (Pk.) Sacc.
  { Sphaeria Azaleae S.
  { Teichosporella Azaleae (S.) Cke.
Rhododendron occidentale Gray.
  Diatrype asterostoma B. & C.
  Exobasidium decolorans Hark.
  { Leptosphaeria californica (Cke. & Hark.) Berl.
  {   & Vogl.
  { Sphaeria californica Cke. & Hark.
  Septoria solitaria Ell. & Ev.
Rhododendron punctatum Andr.
  Melampsoropsis roanensis Arth.
Rhododendron viscosum (L.) Torr.
  Clithris Andromedae (S.) Ell. & Ev.
  Colletotrichum Azaleae Ell. & Ev.
  { Exobasidium Azaleae Pk.
  { Exobasidium discoideum Ell.
  { Exobasidium Vaccinii (Fckl.) Wor.
  { Exobasidium Vaccinii, var. discoideum Ell.
  { Hypocrea consimilis Ell.
  { Hypocreopsis consimilis (Ell.) Seaver.
  Pestalozzia Guepini Desm.
  { Melogramma fuliginosum Ell. p. p.
  { Physalospora viscosa (C. & E.) Sacc.
  { Sphaeria viscosa C. & E.
  { Caeoma Azaleae S.
  { Peridermium Peckii Thm. III.
  { Pucciniastrum minimum (S.) Arth.
  { Pucciniastrum Myrtilli Arth.
  { Uredo Azaleae (S.) M. A. Curtis.
  { Rosellinia xylarispora (C. & E.) Sacc.
  { Sphaeria xylariispora C. & E.
  { Sphaerographium hystricinum (Ell.) Sacc.
  { Sphaeronema hystricinum Ell.
  Sporocybe Azaleae (Pk.) Sacc.
  Synchytrium Vaccinii Thomas.
  { Sphaeria rhizina S.
  { Valsa decidua C. & E.
  { Valsa delicatula C. & E.
  { Valsa rhizina (S.) Cke.
Rhododendron sp. indet.
  { Amphisphaeria aperta (S.) Cke.
  { Sphaeria aperta S.
  { Aposphaeria Rhododendri (S.) Sacc.
  { Sphaeronema Rhododendri S.
  Armillaria mellea (Vahl) ex Fr.

Rhododendron sp. indet. (*cont.*)
Botrytis laxa S.
Cheiromyces comatus Ell. & Ev.
Coccomyces dentatus (Kze. & Schum.) Sacc.
Colletotrichum Azaleae Ell. & Ev.
Corticium vagum B. & C.
Coryneum depressum Kze. & Schm.
Dacrina hydnoideum S. Am. Bor.
Dacryobolus sudans (A. & S.) ex Fr.
Hydnum sudans A. & S. ex Fr.
Thelebolus sudans (A. & S.) ex Fr.
Diatrype asterostoma B. & C., var. minor Cke. & Hark.
Elfvingia megaloma Murrill.
Fomes applanatus (P. ex Wallr.) Gill.
Hysterium abbreviatum S.
Hysterium teres S.
Irpex cinnamomeus Fr.
Irpex fuscescens S.
Laestadia Rhodorae Berl. & Vogl.
Microthyrium microscopicum Desm.
Patellaria Rhododendri S.
Pestalozzia funerea Desm.
Pestalozzia Guepini Desm., var. Vaccinii Shear.
Phacidium corticale S.
Phyllosticta Saccardoi Thm.
Physarum caespitosum S.
Pleospora decipiens Ell. & Ev.
Ramularia angustata Pk.
Sarcosoma cyttarioides Rehm.
Schizoxylon Persoonii S.
Dermatea crypta Cke.
Scleroderris crypta (Cke.) Sacc.
Septoria Rhododendri Cke.
Mycosphaerella Rhododendri (Cke.) G. H. Martin.
Sphaerella Rhododendri Cke.
?Sphaeria strigosa A. & S. ex Fr.
Sphaeria truncata Fr.
Sphaerographium echinatum (B. & C.) Sacc.
Sphaeronema echinatum B. & C.
Sphaeronema cladoniscus Fr.
Stereum purpureum P.†
Sphaeria ambleia C. & E.
Thyridium ambleia (C. & E.) Sacc.
Torula opaca Cke.
Agyrium herbarum Fr.
Tremella Stictis A. & S. non P.
Valsa clypeata C. & P.
Valsa subclypeata C. & P.
Venturia Rhododendri Tengwall.
Phyllodoce coerulea (L.) Bab.
Antennaria arctica (Rostr.) Sacc.
Antennatula arctica Rostr.
Phyllodoce empetriformis D. Don.
Herpotrichia nigra Hartig.
Neopeckia Coulteri (Pk.) Sacc.

Phyllodoce glanduliflora Rydb.
Antennaria rectangularis Sacc.
Cassiope hypnoides (L.) Don.
Ascochyta Cassandrae Pk.
Cassiope lycopodioides Don.
Hysterium gracile Ehrenb. ex Fr.
Lophodermium gracile (Ehrenb. ex Fr.) Sacc.
Hysterium orbiculare Ehrenb. ex Fr.
Lophodermium orbiculare (Ehrenb. ex Fr.) Sacc.
Sphaerella punctiformis (P. ex Fr.) Rabh.
Sphaeria punctiformis P. ex Fr.
Cassiope mertensiana Don.
Exobasidium Cassiopes Pk.
Exobasidium Vaccinii (Fckl.) Wor.
Cassiope tetragona (L.) Don.
Cenangium arcticum (Ehrenb.) ex Fr.
Tryblidium arcticum Ehrenb. ex Fr.
Coryneum Cassiopes Rostr.
Didymella hyperborea (Karst.) Sacc.
Didymosphaeria Cassiopes Rostr.
Exobasidium Vaccinii (Fckl.) Wor.
Leptosphaeria Andromedae (Awd.) Sacc.
Sphaerulina Andromedae (Awd.) Cke.
Leptosphaeria hyperborea (Fckl.) Berl. & Vogl.
Pleospora hyperborea Fckl.
Leptosphaeria inconspicua (Rostr.) Berl.
Metasphaeria Cassiopes Rostr.
Mycosphaerella immersa Dearness.
Sclerotinia Cassiopes Rostr.
Septonema arcticum Allescher.
Sphaerella Andromedae Awd.
Mycosphaerella inconspicua (Schrt.) Dearness.
Sphaerella inconspicua Schrt.
Mycosphaerella pachyasca (Rostr.) Vestrgn.
Sphaerella pachyasca Rostr.
Sphaeria Hederae Fr.
Venturia Myrtilli Cke.?
Andromeda acuminata Ait.
Asterina diplodioides B. & C.
Andromeda ferruginea Walt.
Asteridium dothideoides Ell. & Ev.
Maurodothella dothideoides (Ell. & Ev.) Arnaud.
Asteridium lepidigenum (Ell. & Martin) Sacc.
Asterina lepidigena Ell. & Martin.
Ceuthocarpon ferrugineum (Ell. & Martin) Berl.
Linospora ferruginea Ell. & Martin.
Septoria pulchella B. & C.
Andromeda glaucophylla Lk.
Exobasidium Vaccinii (Fckl.) Wor.
Rhytisma Andromedae (P.) ex Fr.
Venturia Cassandrae Pk.
Andromeda polifolia L.
Exobasidium Andromedae Pk.

Andromeda polifolia (*cont.*)
{ Exobasidium Karstenii Sacc. & Trott.
{ Exobasidium Vaccinii (Fckl.) Wor.
Microsphaera Alni (DC.) Wint., var. Vaccinii (S.) Salmon.
Rhytisma Andromedae (P.) ex Fr.
Sphaerella polifolia Ell. & Ev.
Venturia Cassandrae Pk.

Andromeda sp. indet.

PEZIZINEAE

Cenangium urceolatum Ell.
{ Dasyscypha fuscidula (Cke.) Sacc.
{ Peziza fuscidula Cke.
{ Patinella mauriata (C. & E.) Sacc.
{ Peziza mauriata C. & E.
{ Peziza marginata Cke.
{ Trichopeziza marginata (Cke.) Sacc.

PHACIDIINEAE

Clithris degenerans (Fr.) Rehm.
Phacidium nigrum Cke.
{ Dermatea crypta Cke.
{ Scleroderris crypta (Cke.) Sacc.

PYRENOMYCETINEAE

{ Asterella clavuligera (Cke.) Sacc.
{ Asterina clavuligera Cke.
Dimerosporium clavuligerum (Cke.) Martin.
{ Calosphaeria microtheca (C. & E.) Sacc.
{ Jattaea microtheca (C. & E.) Berl.
{ Physalospora microtheca (C. & E.) Sacc.
{ Sphaeria microtheca C. & E.
{ Valsa microtheca (C. & E.) Cke.
Capnodium Citri B. & Desm.
{ Dimerosporium Ellisii (Ell.) Sacc.
{ Meliola maculosa Ell.
{ Venturia maculosa Ell.
Dothidea collecta (S.) Ell. & Ev.
{ Endophlaea sublanosa Cke.
{ Lasiosphaeria sublanosa (Cke.) Berl.
{ Leptosphaeria sublanosa (Cke.) Ell.
{ Metasphaeria sublanosa (Cke.) Sacc.
{ Sphaeria sublanosa Cke.
{ Creonectria ochroleuca (S.) Seaver.
{ Nectria ochroleuca (S.) M. A. Curtis.
{ Rosellinia arctispora (C. & E.) Sacc.
{ Sphaeria arctispora C. & E.
{ Rosellinia xylarispora (C. & E.) Sacc.
{ Sphaeria detonsa Cke.
{ Sphaeria xylariispora C. & E.
{ Sphaeria Andromedae Rav. Fung. Amer.
{ Sphaeria Andromedarum S.
{ Sphaeria kalmicola Rav. Fung. Amer.
? { Sphaeria salicina P.
{ Valsa salicina Fr.
Valsa delicatula C. & E.

THELEPHORACEAE

Hymenochaete agglutinans Ell.
Stereum ochraceoflavum (S.) Rav.

Chamaedaphne calyculata (L.) Moench.
Ascochyta Cassandrae Pk.
Cenangium Cassandrae Pk.
Cenangium pezizoides Pk.
{ Caeoma Cassandrae Gobi.
{ ?Caeoma Vacciniorum Auct. Amer. p. p.
{ Chrysomyxa Cassandrae Tranz.
{ Melampsoropsis Cassandrae (Tranz.) Arth.
{ Uredo Cassandrae Pk. & Clinton.
Cucurbitaria Cassandrae Ell. & Ev.
Dendrophoma phyllogena Sacc.
Discella arida Pk.
Dothichiza Cassandrae Ell. & Ev.
{ Exobasidium Cassandrae Pk.
{ Exobasidium Vaccinii (Fckl.) Wor.
Gloeosporium Chamaedaphnis Dearness.
Godronia Cassandrae Pk.
Hypoderma Cassandrae Ell. & Ev.
Hysterium maculare Fr.
Lophodermium orbiculare Ell. & Ev.
Synchytrium Vaccinii Thomas.
Venturia Cassandrae Pk.
Venturia pulchella C. & P.

Menziesia ferruginea Sm.
Exobasidium Vaccinii (Fckl.) Wor.
Melasmia Menziesiae Dearness & Barthol.
Tremella (?) phyllachoroidea Sacc.

Menziesia glabella Gray.
{ Exobasidium Andromedae Pk.
{ Exobasidium Vaccinii (Fckl.) Wor.
Rhytisma Arbuti Phil.

Menziesia pilosa (Michx.) P.
{ Pucciniastrum minimum Arth.
{ Pucciniastrum Myrtilli (Karst.) Arth.
{ Thekopsora minima (Arth.) Syd.

Loiseleuria procumbens (L.) Desv.
Phoma herbarum Westd.
Sphaerella inconspicua Schrt.

Kalmia angustifolia L.
Clavaria pallescens Pk.
{ Discella Kalmiae Pk.
{ Discula Kalmiae (Pk.) Sacc.
{ Dothidea Kalmiae Pk.
{ Dothidella Kalmiae (Pk.) Sacc.
Leptosphaeria Kalmiae Pk.
{ Hysterium exaridum C. & P.
{ Lophodermium exaridum C. & P.
{ Septoria kalmiicola N. A. F. *2661* non (S.) B. & C.
{ Septoria angustifolia Ell. & Ev.
{ Depazea kalmicola (S.) Rav.
{ Sphaerella colorata Pk.
{ Sphaeria kalmiicola S.

Kalmia angustifolia (*cont.*)
{ Dermatea Kalmiae (Pk.) Cke.
{ Pezicula Kalmiae (Pk.) Sacc.
{ Peziza Kalmiae Pk.
{ Trichopeziza Kalmiae (Pk.) Sacc.
Synchytrium Vaccinii Thomas.
Venturia Kalmiae Pk.

Kalmia latifolia L.
Antennaria semiovata B. & Br.
{ Arthrobotryum atrocephalum (Ell.) Sacc.
{ Stilbum atrocephalum Ell.
{ Asterina exasperans (S.) B. & C.
{ Phacidium exasperans S.
Cercospora Kalmiae Ell. & Ev.
Cercospora sparsa Cke.
{ Ceuthospora foliicola (Lib.) Cke., var. Kalmiae Sacc.
{ Cytospora foliicola Lib., var. Kalmiae Sacc.
Corticium alboflavescens Ell. & Ev.
Corticium Kalmiae Pk.
Dacryomyces deliquescens (Bull.) ex Duby.
Dacryomyces minor Pk.?
Hebeloma kalmicola Murrill.
Hendersonia kalmicola Ell. & Barthol.
Hymenochaete unicolor B. & C.
{ Hypocreopsis lichenoides (Tode ex Fr.) Seaver.
{ Hypocreopsis riccioidia (Bolt. ex Fr.) Karst.
Hysterium Kalmiae S.?
Lophodermium exaridum C. & P.
{ Ophioceras longisporum (Ell.) Sacc.
{ Sphaeria longispora Ell.
Pestalozzia kalmicola Ell. & Ev.
Phomopsis Kalmiae Enlows.
Phyllosticta kalmicola (S.) Ell. & Ev., var. berolinensiformis Fairman.
Phyllosticta latifolia Ell. & Ev.
Poria sinuosa (Fr.) Cke.
{ Rhabdospora Kalmiae (S.) Ell. & Ev.
{ Sphaeria Kalmiarum S.
Septoria angustifolia Ell. & Ev.
Septoria kalmiicola (S.) B. & C.
{ Asteromella kalmicola (S.) Petrak.
{ Depazea kalmiicola (S.) Rav.
Mycosphaerella colorata (Pk.) Earle. 1901.
Mycosphaerella colorata (Pk.) House. 1921.
{ Phyllosticta kalmiicola (S.) Cke.
Sphaerella colorata Pk.
Sphaerella kalmiicola (S.) Cke.
Sphaeria Kalmiarum S.
Sphaeria kalmiicola S.
Sphaeria Andromedarum S.
Sphaeria kalmiicola Rav. Fung. Amer.
{ Pseudovalsa Peckii (Howe) Cke.
{ Valsa Peckii Howe.
{ Valsaria Peckii (Howe) Sacc.
Venturia Kalmiae Pk.
{ Psilosphaeria atrella (C. & E.) Cke.
{ Sphaeria atriella C. & E.
{ Zignoella atrella (C. & E.) Sacc.

Kalmia microphylla Heller.
Venturia Kalmiae Pk.
Kalmia polifolia Wang.
Dothidella Kalmiae (Pk.) Sacc.
{ Laestadia haematodes (B. & C.) Cke.
{ Sphaerella haematodes B. & C.
Microsphaera Alni (DC.) Wint., var. Vaccinii Salmon.
Microsphaera Vaccinii (S.) C. & P.
Rhytisma Andromedae (P.) ex Fr.
Septoria angustifolia Ell. & Ev.
{ Coleroa Kalmiae (Pk.) Rehm.
{ Venturia Kalmiae Pk.
Kalmia sp. indet.
Arthrosporium compositum Ell.
Cylindrocolla lactea Sacc. & Ell.
Endoxyla macrostoma Fckl.
Helminthosporium subopacum C. & E.
{ Lasiosphaeria strigosa (A. & S. ex Fr.) Sacc.
{ Sphaeria strigosa A. & S. ex Fr.
{ Lophiosphaera hysterioides (S.) Cke.
{ Lophiostoma hysterioides (S.) Sacc.
{ Sphaeria hysterioides S.
Phacidium sphaeroideum C. & E.
{ Dothidea chalybea S.
{ Phyllachora chalybaea (S.) Sacc.
{ Dothidea denigrans S.
{ Phyllachora denigrans (S.) Sacc.
Sarcosoma cyttarioides Rehm.
{ Philocopra lutea Ell. & Ev.
{ Sordaria lutea Ell. & Ev.
Sphaeria atrovirens A. & S. ex Fr.
{ Peziza subiculata S
{ Tapesia subiculata (S.) Sacc.
Xyloma sphaerioides S. Syn. Car.
Leucothoë acuminata D. Don.
{ Hypoderma variegatum (B. & C.) Duby.
{ Hysterium variegatum B. & C.
{ Macrophoma Leucothoes (Ell. & Martin) Tassi.
{ Phyllosticta Leucothoes Ell. & Martin.
Sphaeria atrovirens A. & S. ex Fr.
Xyloma sphaerioides S. Syn. Car.
Leucothoë axillaris (Lam.) D. Don.
Exobasidium Leucothoes Henn.
Mycosphaerella Leucothoes Miles.
{ Hysterium Andromedae S.
{ Sporomega Andromedae (S.) Duby p. p.
{ Laestadia Leucothoes (Cke.) Sacc.
{ Sphaerella Leucothoes Cke.
{ Hysterium foliicola Fr.
{ Lophodermium hysterioides (P. ex Fr.) Sacc.
{ Xyloma hysterioides P. ex Fr.
Phoma Andromedae S.
{ Sphaerella Andromedae (S.) Cke.
{ Sphaeria Andromedae S.
{ Sphaeria Andromedarum S.
Leucothoë Catesbaei (Walt.) Gray.
Asterina diplodioides B. & C.

Leucothoë racemosa (L.) Gray.
  Clithris Andromedae (S.) Ell. & Ev.
  Hysterium Andromedae S.
  Sporomega Andromedae (S.) Duby p. p.
  Dermatea lobata Ell.
  Dialonectria depauperata Cke.
  Dimerosporium Ellisii Sacc.
  Peziza subiculata S.
  Ramularia Andromedae Ell. & Martin.
  Rhytisma decolorans Fr.
  Hysterium Vaccinii Carm.
  Sporomega cladophila (Lév.) Duby.
  Valsa delicatula C. & E.
  Venturia pezizoides Sacc. & Ell.

Leucothoë sp. indet.
  Phyllosticta terminalis Ell. & Martin.

Lyonia ferruginea Nutt.
  Exobasidium Vaccinii (Fckl.) Wor.

Lyonia jamaicensis D. Don.
  Exobasidium Fawcettii Massee.
  Exobasidium Vaccinii (Fckl.) Wor.

Lyonia ligustrina (L.) DC.
  Cryptosphaeria vexata (C. & E.) Sacc.
  Sphaeria vexata C. & E.
  Cucurbitaria longitudinalis Pk.
  Diaporthe ligustrina Ell. & Ev.
  Didymosphaeria grumata (Cke.) Rehm.
  Sphaeria grumata Cke.
  Exobasidium Andromedae Pk.
  Exobasidium Vaccinii (Fckl.) Wor., var. Andromedae Ell.
  Exobasidium Vaccinii (Fckl.) Wor.
  Gloniopsis cookeana (Gerard) Sacc.
  Hypocrea rufa (P.) Fr.
  Microsphaera Alni (DC.) Wint. †
  Microsphaera penicillata (Wallr.) Lév.
  Microsphaera Alni, var. Vaccinii (S.) Salmon.
  Microsphaera Vaccinii (S.) C. & P.
  Melogramma fuliginosum Ell. p. p.
  Physalospora entaxia (C. & E.) Sacc.
  Sphaeria entaxia C. & E.
  Polyporus gilvus S.
  Polystictus velutinus (P. ex Fr.) Cke.
  Poria vaporaria (P.) ex Fr.
  Poria viticola (S.) Cke.
  Rhytisma Andromedae Fr.
  Rhytisma Andromedae-ligustrinae (S.) Wilson & Seaver.
  Rhytisma decolorans Fr.
  Xyloma Andromedae-ligustrinae S.
  Rosellinia arctispora (C. & E.) Sacc.
  Schizoxylon microstomum Ell. & Ev.
  Sphaerella punctiformis (P. ex Fr.) Rabh.
  Sphaeria punctiformis P. ex Fr.
  Hysterium Vaccinii Carm.
  Sporomega cladophila (Lév.) Duby.
  ?Stereum Underwoodii Burt.
  Valsa ligustrina Cke.

  Caeoma Vacciniorum (DC.) Lk.
  Melampsora Vaccinii Wint.
  Melampsoropsis Cassandrae Arth. p. p.
  Pucciniastrum minimum Arth.
  Pucciniastrum Myrtilli Arth.
  Thekopsora Vacciniorum Karst.
  Uredo Andromedae N. A. F. *2717.*
  Uredo Vacciniorum DC.

Lyonia mariana (L.) D. Don.
  Exobasidium Peckii Halsted.
  Exobasidium Vaccinii (Fckl.) Wor.
  Melampsoropsis Cassandrae Arth. p. p.
  Pucciniastrum Myrtilli Arth.
  Uredo Andromedae Auct. p. p.
  Ramularia cylindriopsis Pk.

Lyonia nitida (Bartr.) Fern.
  Corticium calceum (P.) Fr.
  Hysterium Andromedae S.
  Sporomega Andromedae (S.) Duby p. p.
  Hypoderma variegatum Duby.
  Hysterium variegatum (B. & C.) Duby.
  Sporomega Andromedae Duby p. p.
  Lembosia Andromedae Tracy & Earle.
  Melampsoropsis Cassandrae Arth. p. p.
  Pucciniastrum Myrtilli Arth.
  Uredo Andromedae Auct. p. p.
  Sphaerella Andromedae Tracy & Earle.
  Sphaerella Andromedae (S.) Cke.
  Sphaeria Andromedae S.

Lyonia paniculata Nutt.
  Microsphaera Alni (DC.) Wint.†
  Microsphaera Alni (DC.) Wint., var. Vaccinii (S.) Salmon.

Oxydendrum arboreum (L.) DC.
  Cenangium Andromedae (S.) Fr.
  Peziza Andromedae S.
  Tympanis Andromedae (S.) Fr.
  Cercospora Oxydendri Tracy & Earle.
  Dematium ramosum S.
  Oedemium ramorum Fr.
  Racodium ramosum S.
  Discosia maculicola Gerard.
  Exidia recisa (Ditm.) ex Fr.
  Peziza gelatinosa (Bull.) ex Fr.
  Fusarium Oxydendri Ell. & Ev.
  Godronia rugosa Ell. & Ev.
  Hydnum olivaceum (S.) Fr.
  Sistotrema olivaceum S.
  Hysterium flexuosum S.
  Hypoderma variegatum (B. & C.) Duby.
  Hysterium variegatum B. & C.
  Phyllosticta Oxydendri Ell. & Ev.
  Scleroderris pallidula (Cke.) Sacc.
  Sphaerella caroliniana Wolf.
  Sphaerulina polyspora Wolf.
  Hysterium Vaccinii Carm.
  Sporomega cladophila (Lév.) Duby.
  Stictis radiata (L.) ex P.
  Venturia Oxydendri Wolf.

Epigaea repens L.
{ Cercospora Epigaeae Ell. & Dearness.
{ Cercospora epigaeina J. J. Davis.
Discosia Artocreas (Tode) ex Fr.
{ Erysiphe Vaccinii S.
{ Microsphaera Alni (DC.) Wint., var. Vaccinii
{   (S.) Salmon.
Microsphaera Vaccinii (S.) C. & P.
Phyllosticta Epigaeae Pk.
Ramularia Epigaeae Ell.
Gaultheria odorata Willd.
Seynesia costaricensis Speg.
Gaultheria procumbens L.
{ Asterella Gaultheriae (M. A. Curtis) Sacc.
{ Asterina Gaultheriae M. A. Curtis.
Cercospora Gaultheriae Ell. & Ev.
Discosia maculicola Gerard.
{ Hainesia Lythri (Desm.) v. Höhnel.
{ Sclerotiopsis Lythri (Desm.) Shear & Dodge.
Hypocrea tenerrima Ell. & Ev.
Phyllosticta Gaultheriae Ell. & Ev.
{ Mycosphaerella Gaultheriae (C. & E.) House.
{ Sphaerella Gaultheriae C. & E.
Synchytrium Vaccinii Thomas.
Venturia Gaultheriae Ell. & Ev.
Gaultheria Shallon Pursh.
{ Dasyscypha Gaultheriae (Ell. & Ev.) Sacc.
{ Peziza Gaultheriae Ell. & Ev.
Leptosphaeria Gaultheriae Dearness.
Mollisia Gaultheriae Ell. & Ev.
Pestalozzia gibbosa Hark.
Phacidium Gaultheriae Dearness.
Phyllosticta Gaultheriae Ell. & Ev.
{ Mycosphaerella Gaultheriae (C. & E.) House.
{ Sphaerella Gaultheriae C. & E.
Gaultheria sp. indet.
Pestalozzia Gaultheriae Dearness & House.
Pernettya coriacea Kl.
{ Botryodiplodia Pernettyae (Dearness & House)
{   Petrak & Syd.
{ Macrophoma Pernettyae Dearness & House.
Chiogenes hispidula (L.) Torr. & Gr.
{ Chrysomyxa Chiogenis Diet.
{ Melampsoropsis Chiogenis (Diet.) Arth.
Didymium melanospermum (P.) Macbr., var.
  minus (Lister) Dearness & House.
Arbutus densiflorus H. B. K.
{ Pucciniastrum sparsum (Wint.) E. Fischer.
{ Uredo Arbuti Diet. & Holw.
Arbutus Menziesii Pursh.
Aleurodiscus succineus Bres.
Ascochyta Hanseni Ell. & Ev.
Ascochyta Menziesii Ell. & Ev.
Corticium calceum (P.) Fr.
Cryptosporium punctiforme Cke. & Hark.
Cyphella Ravenelii B.
{ Diatrype prominens Howe.
{ Diatrypella prominens (Howe) Sacc.

Diplodia maculata Cke. & Hark.
Discosia minima B. & C.
Exobasidium Vaccinii (Fckl.) Wor.
Grandinia ocellata Fr.
{ Macrophoma maculiformis (Cke. & Hark.)
{   Sacc.
{ Sphaeropsis maculiformis Cke. & Hark.
Phacidium Arbuti Cke. & Hark.
Phacidium quadratum Schm. ex Fr.
{ Dothidea rugodisca Cke. & Hark.
{ Homostegia rugodisca (Cke. & Hark.) Sacc.
{ Phyllachora rugodisca Cke. & Hark.
Phyllosticta fimbriata Ell. & Ev.
{ Pucciniastrum sparsum (Wint.) E. Fischer.
{ Uredo Arbuti Diet. & Holw.
{ Melasmia arbuticola Vize.
{ Rhytisma Arbuti Phil.
{ Mycosphaerella arbuticola (Pk.) House.
{ Sphaerella arbuticola Pk.
{ Sphaerella Umbellulariae Cke. & Hark.
Sphaerella maculiformis (P. ex Fr.) Awd.
{ Coniothyrium asterinum (Cke. & Hark.)
{   Tassi.
{ Macroplodia asterina Cke. & Hark.
{ Sphaeropsis asterina (Cke. & Hark.) Sacc.
Stictis radiata (L.) ex P.
Trametes carnea Nees ex Fr.
Valsa delicatula C. & E.
Arbutus sp. indet.
Fumago salicina Tul.
Septoria hiascens Sacc.
Arctostaphylos alpina (L.) Spreng.
Asteroma alpinum Sacc.
{ Melampsora sparsa Wint.
{ Pucciniastrum sparsum (Wint.) E. Fischer.
Arctostaphylos bicolor Gray.
Asteridium bicolor Ell. & Ev.
Arctostaphylos columbiana Piper.
Pucciniastrum sparsum (Wint.) E. Fischer.
Arctostaphylos diversifolia Parry.
Phaeangium sphaeroides Ell. & Ev.
Arctostaphylos glandulosa Eastw.
Exobasidium Vaccinii (Fckl.) Wor.
Arctostaphylos glauca Lindl.
{ Botryosphaeria Arctostaphyli (Plowr.) Sacc.
{ Coniothyrium Arctostaphyli (Vize) Tassi.
{ Macroplodia Arctostaphyli Vize.
{ Sphaeria Arctostaphyli Plowr.
{ Sphaeropsis Arctostaphyli (Vize) Sacc.
Patellaria californica Rehm.
Arctostaphylos Hookeri Don.
Pucciniastrum sparsum (Wint.) E. Fischer.
Arctostaphylos Manzanita Parry.
Exobasidium Vaccinii (Fckl.) Wor.
Phyllosticta amicta Ell. & Ev.
Pucciniastrum sparsum (Wint.) E. Fischer.
Arctostaphylos nevadensis Gray.
Exobasidium Vaccinii (Fckl.) Wor.

Arctostaphylos nevadensis (*cont.*)
Hypoderma tunicatum Ell. & Ev.
Melanomma alpestre Ell. & Ev.
Placosphaeria Arctostaphyli Ell. & Ev.
⎰Pucciniastrum sparsum (Wint.) E. Fischer.
⎱Thekopsora sparsa (Wint.) Magn.
Uredo Copelandi Syd.
Arctostaphylos patula Greene.
⎰Pucciniastrum sparsum (Wint.) E. Fischer.
⎱Uredo Copelandi Syd.
Arctostaphylos Pringlei Parry.
Fomes Arctostaphyli Long.
Arctostaphylos pumila Nutt.
Venturia Arctostaphyli Cke. & Hark.
Arctostaphylos pungens HBK.
⎰Exobasidium Arctostaphyli Hark.
⎱Exobasidium Vaccinii (Fckl.) Wor.
Fomes Arctostaphyli Long.
Glonium stellatum Muhl.
Hysterium vulvatum S.
Macroplodia Arctostaphyli Vize.
⎰Peziza labrosa Phil. & Hark.
⎱Trichopeziza labrosa (Phil. & Hark.) Sacc.
Arctostaphylos tomentosa Lindl.
Curreya rimosa Ell. & Ev.
Exobasidium Arctostaphyli Hark.
Gloeosporium apiosporium Sacc.
Phyllosticta amicta Ell. & Ev.
Arctostaphylos Uva-ursi (L.) Spreng.
Asterina Gaultheriae M. A. Curtis.
⎧Asterina conglobata B. & C.
⎨Dimerosporium conglobatum (B. & C.) Ell. &
⎩ Ev.
Exobasidium Arctostaphyli Hark.
Exobasidium Vaccinii (Fckl.) Wor.
⎧Chrysomyxa Arctostaphyli Diet.
⎨Melampsora sparsa J. J. Davis non Wint.
⎩Melampsoropsis Arctostaphyli (Diet.) Arth.
Arctostaphylos viscida Parry.
Phyllosticta amicta Ell. & Ev.
Arctostaphylos sp. indet.
⎧Anthostoma sustentum (Plowr.) Sacc.
⎨Sphaeria sustenta Plowr.
⎩Xylosphaeria sustenta (Plowr.) Cke.
Bagnisiella Arctostaphyli (Plowr.) Theissen.
Cryptosporium falcatum Cke. & Hark.
⎰Diaporthe spiculosa (A. & S.) ex Nits.
⎱Sphaeria spiculosa A. & S. ex Nits.
Fomes igniarius (L. ex Fr.) Gill.
Harknessia Arctostaphyli Cke. & Hark.
⎧Sirodesmium Fumago (Cke.) Sacc., var. um-
⎨ brinum (Cke. & Hark.) Sacc.
⎨Sporidesmium Fumago Cke., var. umbrinum
⎩ Cke. & Hark.
Sporidesmium induratum Cke.
Gaylussacia baccata (Wang.) C. Koch.
Exobasidium Vaccinii (Fckl.) Wor.
Melampsora goeppertiana (Kühn.) Wint.

Melampsora Vaccinii Wint.
Peridermium Peckii Thm. I.
Pucciniastrum Myrtilli Arth.
Pucciniastrum Vacciniorum (Karst.) Diet.
Microsphaera Alni, var. Vaccinii (S.) Salmon.
Microsphaera Vaccinii (S.) C. & P.
Monilia peckiana Sacc. & Vogl.
Peziza venturioides Ell. & Ev.
Ramularia effusa Pk.
Sclerotinia baccarum (Schrt.) Rehm.
Synchytrium Vaccinii Thomas.
Valsa delicatula C. & E.
Valsa tenera Ell. & Ev.
Gaylussacia dumosa (Andr.) Torr. & Gr.
⎰Peziza venturioides Ell. & Ev.
⎱Trichopeziza venturioides (Ell. & Ev.) Sacc.
Gaylussacia dumosa (Andr.) Torr. & Gr., var.
hirtella (Ait. f.) Gray.
Dimerosporium Ellisii Sacc.
Gaylussacia frondosa (L.) Torr. & Gr.
⎧Clithris Vaccinii (S.) Ell. & Ev.
⎨Hysterium abietinum S. Syn. Car. p. p.
⎩Hysterium Vaccinii S.
Exobasidium Vaccinii (Fckl.) Wor.
Microsphaera Vaccinii (S.) C. & P.
⎧Rhytisma Vaccinii Fr.
⎨Xyloma Andromedae-ligustrinae S., var. Vac-
⎩ cinii S.
Valsa delicatula C. & E.
Gaylussacia sp. indet.
Guignardia Vaccinii Shear.
Phaeochora densa (B. & Br.) Theissen & Syd.
Vaccinium alaskense Howell.
⎰Pucciniastrum minimum Arth.
⎱Pucciniastrum Myrtilli Arth.
Vaccinium arboreum Marshall.
⎰Dasyscypha albocitrina (Cke.) Sacc.
⎱Peziza albocitrina Cke.
⎰Corticium simulans B. & Rav.
⎱Hymenochaete arida Karst.
Phyllosticta Vaccinii Earle.
Podosporium praelongum B. & C.
Rhytisma Vaccinii (S.) Fr.
Septoria albopunctata Cke.
Sphaerella Vaccinii Cke.
Vaccinium atrococcum (Gray) Heller.
Dothidella vacciniicola Dearness & House.
Hysterographium Vaccinii (S.) Fairman.
Pucciniastrum Myrtilli Arth.
Vaccinium caespitosum Michx.
Calyptospora columnaris Kühn.
Exobasidium Vaccinii (Fckl.) Wor.
Pucciniastrum Myrtilli Arth.
Vaccinium canadense Kalm.
⎧Calyptospora columnaris Kühn.
⎨Calyptospora goeppertiana Kühn.
⎩Melampsora goeppertiana (Kühn) Wint.
⎰Microsphaera Alni., var. Vaccinii (S.) Salmon.
⎱Microsphaera Vaccinii (S.) C. & P.

Vaccinium canadense (*cont.*)
  Piggotia Vaccinii J. J. Davis.
  { Melampsora Vacciniorum (Karst.) Schrt.
  { Pucciniastrum Myrtilli Arth.
  Ramularia effusa Pk.
  Ramularia Vaccinii Pk.
  Sclerotinia baccarum (Schrt.) Rehm.
  Synchytrium Vaccinii Thomas.
Vaccinium Chandleri Jepson
  { Calyptospora columnaris Kühn.
  { Calyptospora goeppertiana Kühn.
Vaccinium corymbosum L.

Pezizineae

  Agyrium rufum (P.) Fr.
  { Cenangium asterinosporum Ell. & Ev.
  { Dothiora asterinospora (Ell. & Ev.) Sacc.
  { Dermatea Kalmiae (Pk.) Cke.
  { Peziza Kalmiae Pk.
  Sclerotinia Vaccinii Wor.
  { Monilia Vaccinii-corymbosi Reade.
  { Sclerotinia Vaccinii Longyear.
  { Sclerotinia Vaccinii-corymbosi Reade.
  ?Helminthosporium humile Sacc.
  { Peziza mollisioides S.
  { Tapesia mollisioides (S.) Sacc.

Phacidiineae

  { Clithris degenerans (Fr.) Rehm.
  { Hysterium degenerans Fr.
  { Sporomega degenerans (Fr.) Cda.
  Gloniella vaccinicola Dearness & House.
  Lophodermium melaleucum (Fr.) De Not.
  Rhytisma Vaccinii (S.) Fr.
  { Hysterium Vaccinii Carm.
  { Sporomega cladophila (Lév.) Duby.

Pyrenomycetineae

  { Chaetosphaeria nidulans (S.) Rehm.
  { Meliola Ellisii Roum.
  { Meliola nidulans (S.) Cke.
  { Sphaeria nidulans S.
  { Cryptosphaeria vexata (C. & E.) Sacc.
  { Sphaeria vexata C. & E.
  { Diaporthe corymbosa (C. & E.) Sacc.
  { Valsa corymbosa C. & E.
  { Diatrype concolor (S.) Cke.
  { Sphaeria concolor S.
  { Eutypella quadrifida (S.) Ell. & Ev.
  { Sphaeria quadrifida S.
  { Valsa quadrifida (S.) Cke.
  { Hypocrea citrinella Ell.
  { Hypomyces citrinellus (Ell.) Seaver.
  Microsphaera Alni (DC.) Wint. †
  { Microsphaera Alni, var. Vaccinii (S.) Salmon.
  { Microsphaera Friesii, var. Vaccinii (S.) C. & P.
  { Microsphaera Vaccinii (S.) C. & P.
  Sphaerella Gallae Ell. & Ev.

  { Mycosphaerella Vaccinii (Cke.) Schrt.
  { Sphaerella Vaccinii Cke.
  Sphaerella Vaccinii Cke., var. corymbosi Sacc.
  Valsa delicatula C. & E.
  { Pseudovalsa Peckii (Howe) Cke.
  { Valsa Peckii Howe.
  { Valsaria Peckii (Howe) Sacc.
  { Conisphaeria paecilostoma (B. & Br.) Cke.
  { Sphaeria paecilostoma B. & Br.
  { Zignoella paecilostoma (B. & Br.) Sacc.

Uredinales

  { Calyptospora columnaris Kühn.
  { Calyptospora goeppertiana Kühn.
  { Melampsora goeppertiana (Kühn) Wint.
  { Caeoma Vacciniorum (DC.) Lk.
  { Melampsora Vacciniorum (Karst.) Schrt.
  { Pucciniastrum Myrtilli Arth.
  { Pucciniastrum Vacciniorum (Karst.) Diet.
  { Thecopsora Vacciniorum Karst.
  { Uredo Vacciniorum DC.

Fungi Imperfecti

  { Coniothyrium vaccinicola (S.) Starb.
  { Sphaeria vaccinicola S.
  Micropera Vaccinii Ell. & Ev.
  Phoma houseana Sacc.
  Phoma Vaccinii Dearness & House.
  Phyllosticta Cyanococci Dearness & House.
  Ramularia Andromedae Ell. & Martin.
  Ramularia Vaccinii Pk.
  Septoria difformis C. & P.

Miscellanea

  Marasmius cucullatus Ell.
  Synchytrium Vaccinii Thomas.
Vaccinium deliciosum Piper.
  Exobasidium Vaccinii, var. Myrtilli (Fckl.)
    Juel.
Vaccinium densiflorum Benth.
  Antennularia Robinsonii (B. & Mont.) De
    Wildem.
Vaccinium erythrococcum Rydb.
  Calyptospora columnaris Kühn.
  { Pucciniastrum minimum Arth.
  { Pucciniastrum Myrtilli Arth.
Vaccinium globulare Rydb.
  Pucciniastrum Myrtilli Arth.
Vaccinium intermedium Ruth.
  Exobasidium Oxycocci Rostr.
Vaccinium macrocarpon Ait.

Ascomycetes

  Acanthorhynchus Vaccinii Shear.
  Anthostomella destruens Shear.
  { Anthostoma picaceum C. & E.
  { Anthostomella? picacea (C. & E.) Sacc.
  { Sphaeria picacea C. & E.
  { Xylosphaeria picacea C. & E.

Vaccinium macrocarpon (*cont.*)
Arachniotus trachyspermus Shear.
Exobasidium Oxycocci Rostr.
Exobasidium Vaccinii (Fckl.) Wor.
Gibbera Vaccinii (Sow.) ex Fr.
Guignardia Bidwellii (Ell.) Viala & Ravaz.
Guignardia Vaccinii Shear.
Hainesia Lythri (Desm.) v. Höhnel.
Pezizella Lythri Shear & Dodge.
Sclerotiopsis Lythri (Desm.) Shear & Dodge.
Sclerotinia Oxycocci Wor.
Sclerotinia Vaccinii Wor.
Sphaerella maculiformis (P. ex Fr.) Awd.
Mycosphaerella Oxycocci Dearness & House.
Valsa delicatula C. & E.
Sphaeria cincinnata Fr.
Venturia cincinnata (Fr.) Rostr.
Venturia compacta Pk.

SPHAEROPSIDALES
Ceuthospora lunata Shear.
Discosia Artocreas (Tode) ex Fr.
Fusicoccum putrefaciens Shear.
Leptothyrium Oxycocci Shear.
Leptothyrium Pomi (Mont. & Fr.) Sacc.
Phyllosticta putrefaciens Shear.
Plagiorhabdus Crataegi Shear.
Plagiorhabdus Oxycocci Shear.
Rhabdospora Oxycocci Shear.
Septoria longispora Shear.
Septoria sheareana Sacc. & Trott.
Sphaeronema pomorum Shear.
Sporonema epiphyllum Shear.
Sporonema Oxycocci Shear.
Sporonema pulvinatum Shear.

MELANCONIALES
Gloeosporium minus Shear.
Glomerella cingulata (Stoneman) Spaulding & v. Schrenk.
Glomerella rufomaculans Spaulding & v. Schrenk.
Gloeosporium cingulatum Atk., var. Vaccinii Shear.
Glomerella cingulata (Stoneman) Spaulding & v. Schrenk, var. Vaccinii Shear.
Glomerella fructigena (G. P. Clinton) Sacc., var. Vaccinii Shear.
Glomerella rufomaculans Spaulding & v. Schrenk, var. Vaccinii Shear.
Pestalozzia Guepini Desm.
Pestalozzia Guepini Desm., var. Vaccinii Shear.

HYPHOMYCETES
Cladosporium Oxycocci Shear.
Helminthosporium inaequalis Shear.
Penicillium glaucum Lk.
Plectothrix globosa Shear.

MISCELLANEA
Chondrioderma simplex Schrt.
Pucciniastrum minimum Arth.
Pucciniastrum Myrtilli Arth.
Synchytrium Vaccinii Thomas.
Vaccinium macrophyllum (Hook.) Piper.
Calyptospora columnaris Kühn.
Pucciniastrum minimum Arth.
Pucciniastrum Myrtilli Arth.
Vaccinium membranaceum Dougl.
Calyptospora columnaris Kühn.
Calyptospora goeppertiana Kühn.
Exobasidium Vaccinii (Fckl.) Wor.
Exobasidium Vaccinii, var. uliginosi Boud.
Pucciniastrum Myrtilli Arth.
Trichopeziza coarctata Ell. & Ev.
Vaccinium microphyllum Rydb.
Calyptospora columnaris Kühn.
Exobasidium Vaccinii (Fckl.) Wor.
Microsphaera Vaccinii C. & P.
Pucciniastrum Myrtilli Arth.
Vaccinium Myrsinites Lam.
Pucciniastrum Myrtilli Arth.
Thecopsora Vacciniorum Karst.
Vaccinium Myrtillus L.
Calyptospora columnaris Kühn.
Calyptospora goeppertiana Kühn.
Microsphaera Alni, var. Vaccinii (S.) Salmon.
Microsphaera Vaccinii (S.) C. & P.
Pucciniastrum Myrtilli Arth.
Vaccinium oreophilum Rydb.
Calyptospora columnaris Kühn.
Calyptospora goeppertiana Kühn.
Exobasidium Vaccinii (Fckl.) Wor.
Pucciniastrum Myrtilli Arth.
Vaccinium ovalifolium Sm.
Calyptospora columnaris Kühn.
Calyptospora goeppertiana Kühn.
Exobasidium parvifolii Hotson.
Exobasidium Vaccinii (Fckl.) Wor.
Pucciniastrum minimum Arth.
Pucciniastrum Myrtilli Arth.
Stictis Vaccinii Ell. & Ev.
Vaccinium ovatum Pursh.
Calyptospora columnaris Kühn.
Calyptospora goeppertiana Kühn.
Ceuthospora minima Cke. & Hark.
Coccomyces albus (Phil. & Hark.) Sacc.
Phacidium album Phil. & Hark.
Lophodermium maculare De Not.
Pucciniastrum Myrtilli Arth.
Venturia Vaccinii Ell. & Ev.
Vaccinium Oxycoccos L.
Acanthorhynchus Vaccinii Shear.
Exobasidium Oxycocci Rostr.
Exobasidium Vaccinii (Fckl.) Wor.
Leocarpus fragilis (Dicks.) Rostf.
Leptothyrium Oxycocci Shear.
Lophodermium Oxycocci (Fr.) Karst.

Vaccinium Oxycoccos (*cont.*)
　Lophodermium Oxycocci (Fr.) Karst., var.
　　hypophyllum Dearness & House.
　Phoma Vaccinii Ell. & Ev.
　Ramularia multiplex Pk.
　Synchytrium Vaccinii Thomas.
　Venturia cincinnata Fr.
Vaccinium parvifolium Sm.
　Calyptospora goeppertiana Kühn.
　Exobasidium parvifolii Hotson.
　Microsphaera Alni (DC.) Wint., var. Vaccinii
　　(S.) Salmon.
　{Pucciniastrum minimum Arth.
　{Pucciniastrum Myrtilli Arth.
Vaccinium pennsylvanicum Lam.
　{Calyptospora columnaris Kühn
　{Calyptospora goeppertiana Kühn.
　Melampsora goeppertiana (Kühn) Wint.
　Exobasidium Vaccinii (Fckl.) Wor.
　Lophodermium cladophilum (Lév.) Rehm.
　Lophodermium maculare (Fr.) De Not.
　{Erysiphe Vaccinii S.
　{Microsphaera Alni, var. Vaccinii (S.) Salmon.
　{Microsphaera Friesii, var. Vaccinii (S.) C. & P.
　{Microsphaera Vaccinii (S.) C. & P.
　Monilia peckiana Sacc. & Vogl.
　{Melampsora Vacciniorum (Karst.) Schrt.
　{Pucciniastrum Myrtilli Arth.
　{Pucciniastrum Vaccinii Crypt.Farl. Herb. *280a.*
　Ramularia effusa Pk.
　Ramularia Vaccinii Pk.
　Sclerotinia baccarum (Schrt.) Rehm.
　Septoria difformis C. & P.
　Valsa delicatula C. & E.
Vaccinium scoparium Lieb.
　Calyptospora columnaris Kühn.
　{Pucciniastrum minimum Arth.
　{Pucciniastrum Myrtilli Arth.
Vaccinium stamineum L.
　Exobasidium Vaccinii (Fckl.) Wor.
　Pestalozzia gibbosa Hark.
　{Phyllactinia corylea (P.) ex Karst.
　{Phyllactinia suffulta (Reb.) ex Sacc.
　{Rhytisma Vaccinii (S.) Fr.
　{Xyloma punctatum S. Syn. Car. p. p.
　{Monilia Polycodii Reade.
　{Sclerotinia Polycodii Reade.
Vaccinium uliginosum L.
　{Antennaria arctica (Rostr.) Sacc.
　{Antennatula arctica Rostr.
　Cenangella pruinosa Rostr.
　Exobasidium Vaccinii (Fckl.) Wor.
　Lophodermium maculare (Fr.) De Not.
　Mycosphaerella Vaccinii (Cke.) Schrt.
　{Phoma cymbispora (B. & C.) Sacc.
　{Sphaeropsis cymbispora B. & C.
　Phoma leptidea (Fr.) Sacc.
　{Podosphaera myrtillina Kze.
　{Podosphaera Oxyacanthae (DC.) DBy.

　{Melampsora Vacciniorúm (Karst.) Schrt.
　{Pucciniastrum Myrtilli Arth.
　{Pucciniastrum Vaccinii Crypt.Farl. Herb. *280b.*
　{Pucciniastrum Vacciniorum (Karst.) Diet.
　{Thecopsora Vacciniorum Karst.
　{Dothidella Vaccinii Rostr.
　{Pyrenobotrys conferta (Fr.) Theissen & Syd.
　{Hysterium degenerans Fr.
　{Sporomega degenerans (Fr.) Cda.
　Venturia Myrtilli Cke.
Vaccinium vacillans Kalm.
　Calyptospora columnaris Kühn.
　{Leptothyrium conspicuum Dearness & House.
　{Piggotia Vaccinii J. J. Davis.
　{Microsphaera Alni DC., var. Vaccinii (S.)
　　Salmon.
　{Microsphaera Vaccinii (S.) C. & P.
　{Pucciniastrum minimum Arth.
　{Pucciniastrum Myrtilli Arth.
　Sclerotinia baccarum (Schrt.) Rehm
Vaccinium virgatum Ait.
　Meliola nidulans (S.) Cke.
　{Pucciniastrum minimum Arth.
　{Pucciniastrum Myrtilli Arth.
　Rhytisma Vaccinii (S.) Fr.
Vaccinium Vitis-Idaea L.
　Acanthorhynchus Vaccinii Shear.
　{Calyptospora columnaris Kühn.
　{Calyptospora goeppertiana Kühn.
　{Melampsora goeppertiana (Kühn.) Wint.
　{Dothiorella latitans (Fr.) Sacc.
　{Phyllachora latitans (Fr.) Sacc.
　Exobasidium Vaccinii (Fckl.) Wor.
　Fusicoccum putrefaciens Shear.
　Gibbera Vaccinii (Sow.) ex Fr.
　Leptostroma punctiforme Wallr.
　Lophodermium melaleucum (Fr.) De Not.
　Phacidium Vaccinii Fr.
Vaccinium sp. indet.
　{Asterella clavuligera (Cke.) Sacc.
　{Asterina clavuligera Cke.
　{Dimerosporium clavuligerum (Cke.) Martin.
　Corticium cinereum P. ex Fr.
　Corticium roseolum Massee.
　{Dasyscypha virginella (Cke.) Sacc.
　{Peziza virginella Cke.
　Dimerosporium Ellisii Sacc.
　Helminthosporium arctisporum C. & E.
　Hendersonia delicatula C. & E.
　Hymenochaete agglutinans Ell.
　{Corticium epichlorum B. & C.
　{Hymenochaete epichlora (B. & C.) Cke.
　Irpex cinnamomeus Fr.
　{Endophlaea leiostega (Ell.) Cke.
　{Metasphaeria leiostega (Ell.) Sacc.
　{Sphaeria leiostega Ell.
　Oidium compactum C. & E.
　Peziza fusca P.
　Podosphaera leucotricha (Ell. & Ev.) Salmon.

Vaccinium sp. indet. (*cont.*)
  Polyporus brumalis (P.) ex Fr.
  Rhytisma decolorans Fr.
  Sclerotinia urnula (Weinm.) Rehm.
  Speira punctulata C. & E.
  Sphaeria punctulata C. & E.
  {Peziza subiculata S.
  {Tapesia subiculata (S.) Sacc.
  Uredo Bigelowii (Thm.) Arth. ?
  {Stictis linearis C. & E.
  {Xylogramma lineare (C. & E.) Sacc.
  {Conisphaeria subvestita (Ell. & Ev.) Cke.
  {Sphaeria subvestita Ell. & Ev.
  {Zignoella subvestita (Ell. & Ev.) Berl. & Vogl.

Erica arborea L.
  Torula ligniperda (Willk.) Sacc.

Ericaceae gen. indet.
  Endophyllum singulare Diet. & Holw.
  Leptosphaeria subconica (C. & P.) Sacc.

DIAPENSIACEAE

Diapensia lapponica L.
  Ascochyta Diapensiae Rostr.
  Excipula Diapensiae Rostr.
  Septoria Diapensiae Karst.
  Sphaerella pachyasca Rostr.
  {Stictis phacidioides Fr.
  {Trochila phacidioides (Fr.) Karst.

Shortia galacifolia Torr. & Gr.
  Sclerotiopsis concava (Desm.) Shear & Dodge.

Galax aphylla L.
  {Asterina Leemingii Ell. & Ev.
  {Clypeolella Leemingii (Ell. & Ev.) Theissen.
  Dimerosporium Galactis Ell. & Ev.
  Glenospora melioloides M. A. Curtis.
  Laestadia galactina Dearness & House.
  Phoma Galactis Dearness & House.
  Phyllosticta Galactis (Cke.) Ell. & Ev.
  Sclerotiopsis concava (Desm.) Shear & Dodge.

THEOPHRASTACEAE

Jacquinia armillaris L.
  {Asterella paupercula (Ell. & Ev.) Sacc.
  {Asterina paupercula Ell. & Ev.
  Lizonia Jacquiniae Briard & Hariot.
  Penicillium glaucum Lk.
  Phyllachora conspicua Ferdinandsen & Winge.

Jacquinia aurantiaca Ait.
  Phyllachora Jacquiniae Rehm.

Jacquinia Barbasco Mez.
  Dimerina Jacquiniae P. Garman.
  Dimerina Monenses F. L. Stevens.
  Lizonia Jacquiniae Briard & Hariot.

Jacquinia Berterii Spreng.
  {Dothidea inclusa B. & C.
  {Phyllachora inclusa (B. & C.) Sacc.

Jacquinia sp. indet.
  {Inonotus pusillus Murrill.
  {Polyporus pusillus (Murrill) Sacc. & Trott.

MYRSINACEAE

Ardisia compressa H. B. K.
  {Teleutospora Myrsines (Diet.) Arth. & Bisby.
  {Uromyces Myrsines Diet.

Ardisia guadalupensis Duchess.
  Helminthosporium Helleri F. L. Stevens.
  Meliola Myrsinacearum F. L. Stevens.

Ardisia laurifolia A. D C.
  {Androsaceus atrorubens (B.) Pat.
  {Marasmius atrorubens B.

Ardisia Pickeringii Torr. & Gr.
  Hysterostomella floridana Tracy & Earle.

Parathesis serrulata (Sw.) Mez.
  Helminthosporium parathesicola F. L. Stevens.
  Meliola parathesicola F. L. Stevens.

Wallenia aurifolia Sw.
  Dimerina dominicana Toro.

Myrsine coriacea R. Br.
  Erinella cognata Pat.

Myrsine sp. indet.
  {Hendersonia nitida Ell. & Ev.
  {Phyllohendersonia nitida (Ell. & Ev.) Tassi.
  Phyllachora Pittieri Theissen & Syd.
  Phyllachora Tonduzii Henn.
  {Melanopus scabellus Pat.
  {Polyporus scabellus (Pat.) Murrill.

Rapanea pellucidopunctata (Oerst.) Mez.
  Chaetosphaeria meliolicola Syd.
  Dimerina epidochica Syd.
  Trichodochium disseminatum Syd.

Rapanea sp. indet.
  Lembosia Rapaneae Ryan.

PRIMULACEAE

Primula acaulis Hill.
  Ramularia Primulae Thm.

Primula angustifolia Torr.
  Hendersonia foliorum Fckl.

Primula egaliksensis Wormsk. ex Hornem.
  Phoma herbarum Westd.
  Pleospora herbarum (Fr.) Rabh.
  Sphaerella pachyasca Rostr.

Primula malacoides Franch.
  Rhizoctonia Solani Kühn.

Primula mistassinica Michx.
  Cladosporium herbarum (P.) ex Lk.

Primula obconica Hance.
  Botrytis vulgaris (Lk.) ex Fr.

Primula polyantha Mill.
  Ramularia Primulae Thm.

Primula sinensis Sabine.
  Ascochyta Primulae Trail.
  Phyllosticta primulicola Desm.

Primula suffrutescens Gray.
　⎰Teleutospora nevadensis (Hark.) Arth. &
　⎱　Bisby.
　Uromyces nevadensis Hark.
Primula sp. indet.
　Uromyces acuminatus Arth. I.
　Ascochyta Primulae Trail.
　Asteroma garrettianum Syd.
　⎰Botrytis cinerea P. †
　⎱Botrytis vulgaris (Lk.) ex Fr.
　Colletotrichum Primulae Halsted.
　Phyllosticta primulicola Desm.
　Ramularia Primulae Thm.
　Sclerotinia fuckeliana (DBy.) Fckl.
Androsace Chamaejasme Host.
　Pleospora Crandallii Ell. & Ev.
Androsace Chamaejasme Host., var. **arctica**
　Kunth.
　Pyrenophora helvetica (Niessl) Sacc.
Androsace diffusa Small.
　Mycosphaerella Primulae (Awd. & Heufl.)
　　Schrt.
Androsace officinalis Pursh.
Androsace occidentalis Pursh.
　⎰Peronospora Androsaces Niessl.
　⎱Peronospora candida Fckl.
Samolus Valerandi L.
　Pleospora herbarum (Fr.) Rabh.
Lysimachia lanceolata Pursh.
　Aecidium Lysimachiae (Schl.) Wallr.
Lysimachia quadrifolia L.
　⎰Aecidium Lysimachiae S.
　｜Aecidium Lysimachiae (Schl.) Wallr.
　｜Caeoma lysimachiatum Lk.
　⎨Dicaeoma Lysimachiae O. Kuntze.
　｜Puccinia Lysimachiae Kern. I.
　｜Puccinia lysimachiata Kern. I.
　⎩Uredo Lysimachiae Spreng.
　Septoria conspicua Ell. & Martin.
Lysimachia terrestris (L.) BSP.
　⎰Aecidium Lysimachiae S.
　｜Aecidium Lysimachiae (Schl.) Wallr.
　｜Caeoma lysimachiatum Lk.
　⎨Dicaeoma Lysimachiae O. Kuntze. I.
　｜Puccinia lysimachiata Kern. I.
　⎩Uredo Lysimachiae Spreng.
　Cercospora Lysimachiae Ell. & Halsted.
　Ramularia Lysimachiae Thm.
　Synchytrium aureum Schrt.
Lysimachia thyrsiflora L.
　⎰Aecidium Lysimachiae S.?
　｜Aecidium Lysimachiae (Schl.) Wallr.
　｜Caeoma Lysimachiae Schl.
　⎨Dicaeoma Lysimachiae O. Kuntze.
　｜Puccinia limosae Magn. I.
　⎩Puccinia lysimachiata Kern. I.
　Ramularia Lysimachiae Thm.
Steironema ciliatum (L.) Raf.
　Aecidium Lysimachiae (Schl.) Wallr.

　⎰Dicaeoma Distichlidis (Ell. & Ev.) O. Kuntze.
　⎱　I.
　Puccinia Distichlidis Ell. & Ev. I.
　Uromyces acuminatus Arth. I.
　Uromyces Polemonii Barthol. I.
　Uromyces Spartinae Farl. I.
　Uromyces Steironematis Arth. I.
　Leptosphaeria dumetorum Niessl.
　Leptosphaeria Steironematis Ell. & Ev.
　⎰Peziza Dearnessii Ell. & Ev.
　⎱Phialea Dearnessii Ell. & Ev.
　⎰Hainesia Lythri (Desm.) v. Höhnel.
　⎱Pezizella Lythri Shear & Dodge.
　Sclerotiopsis concava (Desm.) Shear & Dodge.
　Phyllosticta decidua Ell. & Kellerm.
　Phyllosticta Steironematis Dearness & House.
　⎰Dasyspora Dayi (G. W. Clinton) Arth.
　｜Dicaeoma Dayi (G. W. Clinton) O. Kuntze.
　⎨Micropuccinia Dayi (G. W. Clinton) Arth. &
　｜　Jackson.
　⎩Puccinia Dayi G. W. Clinton.
　Puccinia Lysimachiae Karst.
　Ramularia Lysimachiae Thm.
　Sclerotium deciduum J. J. Davis.
　Septoria conspicua Ell. & Martin.
　Septoria Lysimachiae Ell. & Halsted.
　Septoria Steironematis Ell. & Ev.
　⎰Mycosphaerella ciliata (Ell. & Ev.) House.
　⎱Sphaerella ciliata Ell. & Ev.
Steironema lanceolatum (Walt.) Gray.
　Aecidium Lysimachiae (Schl.) Wallr.?
　⎰Uromyces acuminatus Arth. I.
　｜Uromyces Spartinae Farl. I.
　⎨Micropuccinia Dayi (G. W. Clinton) Arth. &
　｜　Jackson.
　⎩Puccinia Dayi G. W. Clinton.
　Ramularia Lysimachiae Thm.
　Septoria conspicua Ell. & Martin.
Steironema Lunellii Greene.
　⎰Nigredo Polemonii (Barthol.) Arth. I.
　⎨Uromyces acuminatus Arth. I.
　⎩Uromyces Spartinae Farl. I.
Steironema quadriflorum (Sims.) Hitchc.
　Septoria conspicua Ell. & Martin.
　Septoria Lysimachiae Westd.
Steironema sp. indet.
　Cylindrosporium Steironematis Atk.
Trientalis arctica Fisch.
　Dicaeoma Trientalis Arth. & Kern. I.
　Tuburcinia Trientalis B. & Br.
Trientalis borealis Raf.
　⎰Aecidium Trientalis Tranz.
　｜Dicaeoma Trientalis Arth. & Kern. I.
　｜Puccinia karelica Tranz. I.
　⎨Puccinia Trientalis (Arth. & Kern) House. I.
　｜Ramularia candida (Ehrh.) Wr.
　⎨Ramularia magnusiana (Sacc.) Lindau.
　⎩Septocylindrium magnusianum Sacc.
　Septoria increscens Pk.

Trientalis europaea L.
Trientalis latifolia Hook.
{ Sorosporium Trientalis (B. & Br.) Wor.
{ Tuburcinia Trientalis B. & Br.

Glaux maritima L.
Aecidium Glaucis Dozy & Molkenb.?
{ Dicaeoma Sarcobati (Pk.) Arth. I.
{ Puccinia subnitens Diet. I.
{ Dicaeoma Distichlidis (Ell. & Ev.) O. Kuntze.
{   I.
{ Puccinia Distichlidis Ell. & Ev. I.
Micropuccinia Dayi (G. W. Clinton) Arth. &
  Jackson.
Puccinia Glaucis Arth.
{ Nigredo Scirpi (Burrill) Arth. I.
{ Uromyces Scirpi Burrill. I.

Anagallis arvensis L.
Septoria Anagallidis Ell. & Halsted.

Cyclamen persicum Mill.
Colletotrichum Cyclamenae Halsted.
Glomerella rufomaculans Spaulding & v.
  Schrenk, var. Cyclaminis Patterson &
  Charles.
Phoma Cyclamenae Halsted.
Thielavia basicola (B. & Br.) Zopf.

Cyclamen sp. indet.
Botrytis cinerea Auct.
Glomerella cingulata (Stoneman) Spaulding &
  v. Schrenk.
Phyllosticta cyclamenicola Trel.
Ramularia cyclamenicola Trel.

Dodecatheon alpinum Greene.
{ Dicaeoma Ortonii (H. S. Jackson) Arth.
{ Puccinia Ortonii H. S. Jackson.

Dodecatheon cruciatum Greene.
Allodus melanconioides (Ell. & Hark.) Arth.

Dodecatheon frigidum Cham. & Schl.
Dicaeoma Ortonii (H. S. Jackson) Arth.
Mycosphaerella minor (Karst.) Dearness.
Pyrenophora comata (Awd. & Niessl) Sacc.

Dodecatheon Hendersoni Gray, var. leptophylla
  Suksdorf.
{ Dicaeoma Ortonii (H. S. Jackson) Arth.
{ Puccinia Ortonii H. S. Jackson.

Dodecatheon Jeffreyi Moore.
Puccinia melanconioides Ell. & Hark.
{ Dicaeoma Ortonii (H. S. Jackson) Arth.
{ Puccinia Ortonii H. S. Jackson.

Dodecatheon latifolium (Hook.) Piper.
{ Allodus melanconioides (Ell. & Hark.) Arth.
{ Puccinia melanconioides Ell. & Hark.

Dodecatheon Meadia L.
Phyllosticta Dodecathei Trelease.
Puccinia melanconioides Ell. & Hark.
Nigredo Polemonii (Barthol.) Arth. I.

Dodecatheon puberulum (Nutt.) Piper.
Puccinia melanconioides Ell. & Hark.

Dodecatheon tetrandrum Suksdorf.
Puccinia melanconioides Ell. & Hark.
Puccinia Ortonii H. S. Jackson.

Dodecatheon thornense Lunell.
{ Nigredo Polemonii (Barthol.) Arth. I.
{ Uromyces Steironematis Arth. I.

PLUMBAGINACEAE

Statice Armeria L.
Phyllosticta Armeriae Allescher.
Sphaerella pachyasca Rostr.
{ Nigredo Armeriae (Lév.) Arth.
{ Uromyces Armeriae Lév.
{ Aecidium Statices Desm.
{ Nigredo Limonii (DC.) Arth.
{ Uredo Statices De Toni.
{ Uromyces Limonii (DC.) Lév.

Statice Armeria L., var. sibirica (Turcz.)
  Simm.
Cladosporium herbarum (P.) ex Lk.
Gloeosporium Armeriae Allescher.
Hendersonia vanhoeffeniana Allescher.
Leptostroma herbarum (Fr.) Lk.
Phoma Armeriae-sibericae Allescher.
Phyllosticta Armeriae Allescher.
Pleospora herbarum (Fr.) Rabh.
{ Clathrospora platyspora (Sacc.) Dearness.
{ Pleospora platyspora Sacc.
Pleospora vulgaris Niessl.
Rhabdospora cercosperma (Rostr.) Sacc.
Septoria Armeriae Allescher.
Sphaerella pachyasca Rostr.
Vermicularia herbarum Westd.

Statice plantaginea Ait.
Septoria Armeriae Allescher & Henn.

Statice sp. indet.
?Puccinia sclerotioidea Cke.

Limonium californicum (Boiss.) Small.
{ Nigredo Limonii (DC.) Arth.
{ Uromyces Limonii (DC.) Lév.

Limonium carolinianum (Walt.) Britton.
Fusicladium Staticis Ell. & Ev.
Phyllosticta Staticis Petrak.
{ Laestadia Wrightii (B. & C.) Cke.
{ Physalospora Wrightii (B. & C.) Sacc.
{ Sphaeria Wrightii B. & C.
{ Aecidium Limonii Pk.
{ Aecidium Statices Desm.
{ Nigredo Limonii (DC.) Arth.
{ Uredo Statices De Toni.
{ Uromyces Limonii (DC.) Lév.
{ Uromyces Statices B. & C.

Limonium limbatum Small.
{ Nigredo Limonii (DC.) Arth.
{ Uromyces Limonii (DC.) Lév.

SAPOTACEAE

Achras Sapota L.
  Cephalosporium Lecanii Zimm.
  Colletotrichum gloeosporioides Penz.
  Phyllosticta Sapotae Sacc.
  Ptychogaster cubensis Pat.
  ⌠Podoscypha aurantiaca (P.) Pat.
  ⌡Thelephora aurantiaca P.
  Torrubiella Lecanii Johnston.
  Uredo Sapotae Arth. & Johnston.

Sapota sp. indet.
  Lembosia Sapotae Ryan.

Lucuma mammosa Gaertn.
  Diplodia " natalensis "? Evans.
  Linochora advena Syd.
  Pestalozzia scirrofaciens N. A. Brown.
  Phyllachora advena Syd.
  Stilbella flavida (Cke.) Henn.

Lucuma multiflora A. DC.
  Meliola Lucumae F. L. Stevens.
  Pestalozzia Lucumae Tehon.

Lucuma nervosa DC.
  Uredo Lucumae Arth. & Johnston.

Lucuma sp. indet.
  Physalospora Malorum Shear & al.

Sideroxylon foetidissimum (L.) A. DC.
  Halstedia portoricensis F. L. Stevens.
  Puccinia Johnstonii Arth.

Siderocarpos flexicaulis (Benth.) Small.
  Ravenelia Siderocarpi Long.

Micropholis sp. indet.
  Asterina sydowiana Ryan.

Dipholis salicifolia (L.) A. DC.
  Helminthosporium Helleri F. L. Stevens.
  Meliola Dipholidis F. L. Stevens.
  Puccinia Johnstonii Arth.
  Scolecopeltella portoricensis Speg.

Bumelia lanuginosa (Michx.) P.
  Cercospora lanuginosa Heald & Wolf.
  Fumago vagans Fr.
  Phyllosticta bumeliifolia Heald & Wolf.
  Phyllosticta Curtisii (Sacc.) Ell. & Ev.
  ⌠Dothidea Bumeliae S.
  ⌡Polystigma (?) Bumeliae (S.) Sacc.

Bumelia lycioides (L.) P.
  ⌠Phoma Bumeliae House.
  ⎮Phoma maculans (B. & C.) Sacc.
  ⎮Phyllosticta Bumeliae Underw. & Earle.
  ⌡Sphaeropsis maculans B. & C.
  Phyllosticta bumeliifolia Heald & Wolf.
  Septoria Bumeliae Sacc. 1878.
  Septoria Bumeliae Miles. 1926.

Bumelia sp. indet.
  Phoma circumscripta Cke.
  Sphaerella Bumeliae Cke.

Chrysophyllum argenteum Jacq.
  Empusa Fresenii Nowak.

Chrysophyllum bicolor Poir.
  Meliola ocoteicola F. L. Stevens.

Chrysophyllum Cainito L.
  Hypocrella oxyspora Massee.
  Uredo amicosa Arth.

Chrysophyllum glabrum Jacq.
  Thelephora tentaculata Pat.
  Trametes borbonica Pat.

Chrysophyllum olivifo:me L.
  Asterina Chrysophylli Henn.

Chrysophyllum sp. indet.
  Asterina Chrysophylli Henn.
  Asterina sydowiana Ryan.
  ⌠Favolus fragilis (Murrill) Sacc. & D. Sacc.
  ⎮Hexagona fragilis Murrill.
  ⎮Androsaceus glaucopus Pat.
  ⌡Marasmius glaucopus (Pat.) Sacc.

Mimusops balata Crueg.
  ⌠Phellinus lichnoides (Mont.) Pat.
  ⌡Polyporus lichnoides Mont.
  Trametes hydnoides Fr.

Mimusops hahnianum ex Duss.
  Stereum lobatum Fr.

EBENACEAE

Diospyros Kaki L. f.
  Capnodium Citri B. & Desm.
  Cercospora Diospyri Thm.
  Cercospora fuliginosa Ell. & Kellerm.
  Cercospora Kaki Ell. & Ev.
  Ozonium omnivorum Shear.
  Phyllosticta biformis Heald & Wolf.
  Physalospora Cydoniae Arnaud?

Diospyros texana Scheele.
  Phyllosticta biformis Heald & Wolf.

Diospyros virginiana L.
  Aposphaeria turmalis Ell. & Ev.
  ⌠Asteroma Diospyri (S.) M. A. Curtis.
  ⎮Dothidea Diospyri (S.) Fr.
  ⌡Xyloma Diospyri S.
  ⌠Botryosphaeria Persimon (Fr.) Sacc.
  ⎮Dothidea parsimons Fr.
  ⎮Melogramma Persimmons (Fr.) M. A. Curtis.
  ⌡Sphaeria Persimmons (Fr.) S.
  ⌠Cercospora atra Ell. & Ev.
  ⎮Cercospora fuliginosa Ell. & Kellerm.
  ⎮Cercospora Diospyri Thm.
  ⎮Cercospora Diospyri, var. ferruginea Atk.
  ⎮Cercospora flexuosa Tracy & Earle.
  ⌡Helminthosporium Diospyri Thm.
  Cercospora virginiana Thm.
  Corticium Stevensii Burt.
  Crepidotus alabamensis Murrill.
  Dendrina Diospyri B. & C.
  Dothiorella Diospyri Petrak & Syd.
  Fusarium roseum Lk.
  Gloeosporium Diospyri Ell. & Ev.

Diospyros virginiana (*cont.*)

{ Gloeosporium fructigenum B.
  Glomerella rufomaculans Spaulding & v.
  Schrenk.

Gloeosporium piperatum Ell. & Ev.
Hirneola Auricula-judae (L. ex Fr.) B.
Isariopsis Linderae (Ell. & Ev.) Sacc.
Lasiosphaeria Pezizula (B. & C.) Sacc.
Leptothyrium pomi (Mont. & Fr.) Sacc.
Macrophoma Diospyri Earle.
Myxormia hypospila Cke.
Ozonium auricomum Lk.
Ozonium omnivorum Shear.
Pestalozzia foliorum Ell. & Ev.
Pestalozzia Guepini Desm.
Phoma Diospyri Sacc.

{ Dothidea orbiculata (S.) Fr.
  Phyllachora orbiculata (S.) Sacc.
  Xyloma orbiculatum S.

Phyllosticta Asiminae Ell. & Kellerm.
Physalospora Cydoniae Arnaud.
Physalospora Malorum Shear et al.
Podosphaera leucotricha (Ell. & Ev.) Salmon.
Podosphaera Oxyacanthae (DC.) DBy.
Rhizopus nigricans Ehrenb. ex Fr.

{ Haplosporella Diospyri (Dearness & Barthol.)
  Petrak & Syd.
  Sphaeropsis Diospyri Dearness & Barthol.

Valsa Diospyri Ell. & Ev.

{ Diatrype Diospyri (S.) M. A. Curtis.
  Sphaeria Diospyri S.
  Valsaria Diospyri (S.) De Not.

Diospyros sp. indet.

Capnodium Citri B. & Desm.
Diplodia Diospyri (S.) Sacc. & Trav.
Mucor Mucedo L.

{ Mycena meliigena (B. & Cke.) Sacc.
  Prunulus meliigena (B. & Cke.) Murrill.

{ Polyporus rigidus (B. & Mont.) Rav.
  Polystictus rigens Sacc. & Cub.
  Polystictus rigidus (B. & Mont.) Cke.
  Trametes rigida B. & Mont.

Stilbomyces Berenice Ell. & Ev.
Xylaria Hypoxylon (L.) ex Fr.

STYRACACEAE

Halesia carolina L.

Cytospora Halesiae Ell. & Ev.
Diaporthe Halesiae Ell. & Ev.
Diaporthe tetraptera Ell. & Ev.
Lophiotrema Halesiae Fairman.
Phoma Halesiae Fairman.
Polyporus Halesiae B. & C.
Sirococcus Halesiae Ell. & Ev.
Steccherinum Rhois (S.) Banker.

Styrax glabrum Sw.

Hymenochaete dura B.

Styrax polyneura Perk.

Asterina styracina Syd.

Styrax sp. indet.

{ Dothidea pulverulenta B. & C.
  Monopus pulverulentus (B. & C.) Theissen &
  Syd.

Symplocos martinicensis Jacq.

Erinella subcorticalis Pat.

{ Poria lateritia Pat.
  Porogramme lateritia Pat.

Symplocos tinctoria L'Her.

Exobasidium Symploci Ell. & Martin.

{ Corticium epichlorum B. & C.
  Hymenochaete epichlora (B. & C.) Cke.
  Leptothyrium Symploci (Cke.) Tassi.
  Sacidium Symploci Cke.

Septoria stigma B. & C.
Septoria Symploci Ell. & Martin.
Septoria tinctoria Dearness & House.

OLEACEAE

Fraxinus americana L.

PEZIZINEAE

{ Cenangium Fraxini (S.) Tul.
  Durandia Fraxini (S.) Rehm.
  Peziza Fraxini S.
  Sphaeria Fraxini (S.) Fr.
  ?Sphaerographium Fraxini (S.) Pk.
  Tympanis Fraxini (S.) Fr.

Helotium sulfurellum Ell. & Ev.

PHACIDIINEAE

Phacidium fraxineum S.

HYSTERIINEAE

{ Hysterium Fraxini P. ex Fr.
  Hysterographium Fraxini (P. ex Fr.) De Not.

Lophodermium petiolicola Fckl.

PYRENOMYCETINEAE

Acanthostigma Fraxini Ell.
Botryosphaeria fuliginosa (M. & N.) Ell. & Ev.
Cucurbitaria Fraxini Ell. & Ev.

{ Chorostate peckiana Sacc.
  Diaporthe peckiana Sacc.
  Diaporthe spiculosa (A. & S. ex Fr.) Nits.
  Sphaeria spiculosa A. & S. ex Fr.

Endoxyla Fraxini Ell. & Ev.

{ Eutypella fraxinicola (C. & P.) Sacc.
  Valsa fraxinicola C. & P.

Hypoxylon annulatum (S.) Mont.
Hypoxylon argillaceum Auct. an B.
Hypoxylon rubricosum Fr.

{ Depazea fraxinicola M. A. Curtis.
  Laestadia fraxinicola (M. A. Curtis) Sacc.

Leptosphaeria Fraxini Ell. & Ev.

Fraxinus americana (*cont.*)

Phyllactinia corylea (P.) ex Karst.
Phyllactinia suffulta (Reb.) ex Sacc.
Physalospora Cydoniae Arnaud.
Rosellinia subiculata (S.) Sacc.
Mycosphaerella effigurata (S.) House.
Sphaerella effigurata (S.) Cke.
Sphaerella fraxinea Pk.
Mycosphaerella fraxinicola (S.) House.
Sphaerella fraxinicola (S.) Cke.
Sphaeria fraxinicola S.
Sphaerella maculiformis (P. ex Fr.) Awd.
Sphaeria maculiformis P. ex Fr.
Sphaerella punctiformis (P. ex Fr.) Rabh.
Valsa ambiens (P.) ex Fr.
Valsa fraxinina Pk.
Valsa grisea Pk.
Xylaria clavulata (S.) B. & C.

UREDINALES

Aecidium Fraxini S.
Caeoma Fraxinites S.
Dicaeoma Fraxini Arth.
Puccinia fraxinata Arth.
Puccinia peridermiospora Arth.
Puccinia sparganioides Ell. & Barthol.

HYMENOMYCETINEAE

Aleurodiscus acerinus (P. ex Fr.) v. Höhnel & Litschauer.
Corticium basale Pk.
Daedalea confragosa (Bolt.) ex Fr., var. rubescens Pk.
Fomes applanatus (P. ex Wallr.) Gill.
Fomes conchatus (P. ex Fr.) Karst.
Mucronoporus conchatus (P. ex Fr.) Ell. & Ev.
Polyporus conchatus (P.) ex Fr.
Pyropolyporus conchatus (P. ex Fr.) Murrill.
Fomes fraxineus (Bull. ex Fr.) Cke.
Polyporus fraxineus (Bull.) ex Fr.
Fomes fraxinophilus (Pk.) Sacc.
Polyporus fraxinophilus Pk.
Hypholoma sublateritium (Schaeff.) ex Fr.
Lenzites vialis Pk.
Sesia pallidofulva (B.) Murrill.
Pholiota adiposa Fr.
Polyporus admirabilis Pk.
Polyporus picipes Fr.
Polyporus salicinus Fr.
Polystictus pargamenus Fr.
Polystictus versicolor (L.) ex Fr.

SPHAEROPSIDALES

Cytospora annularis Ell. & Ev.
Cytospora fugax (Bull.) ex Fr.
Cytospora minuta Thm.
Cytospora minuta Thm., var. americana Sacc.
Dendrophoma crassicollis Schulz. & Sacc.

Diplodia inquinans Westd.
Discosia magna Pk.
Micropera Fraxini Ell. & Ev.
Phoma fraxinea Sacc.
Phoma samararum Desm.
Sphaeria samarae S. p. p.
Phyllosticta Coryli Westd.
Phyllosticta Fraxini Ell. & Martin.
Phyllosticta fraxinicola (Curr.) Sacc.
Phyllosticta variegata Ell. & Ev.
Phyllosticta viridis Ell. & Kellerm.
Piggotia Fraxini B. & C.
Septoria Besseyi Pk.
Septoria Fraxini Westd.
Septoria leucostoma Ell. & Ev.
Septoria submaculata Wint.
Ceratostoma spina (S.) Sacc.
Sphaeria spina S.
Sphaerographium Fraxini (Pk.) Sacc.
Sphaeronema Fraxini Pk.
Sphaeronema spina (S.) B. & Rav.
Diplodia infuscans Ell. & Ev.
Haplosporella pennsylvanica (B. & C.) Petrak & Syd.
Macrophoma hyalina (B. & C.) Berl. & Vogl.
Macroplodia phomatella (Pk.) O. Kuntze.
Microdiplodia infuscans (Ell. & Ev.) Tassi.
Phoma hyalina (B. & C.) Sacc.
Sphaeropsis biformis Pk.
Sphaeropsis fertilis Pk.
Sphaeropsis hyalina B. & C.
Sphaeropsis phomatella Pk.
Sphaeria samarae S. p. p.
Sphaeropsis samarae Starb.
Vermicularia Dematium (P.) ex Fr.
Vermicularia herbarum Westd.

MELANCONIALES

Cylindrosporium Fraxini (Ell. & Kellerm.) Ell. & Ev.
Cylindrosporium fraxinicola Dearness & House.
Gloeosporium aridum Ell. & Holw.
Gloeosporium irregulare Ell. & Ev.
Gloeosporium decipiens Ell. & Ev.
Gloeosporium Everhartii Ell.
Gloeosporium punctiforme Ell. & Ev.

HYPHOMYCETES

Botrytis affinis Ell. & Ev.
Cercospora fraxinites Ell. & Ev.
Dicoccum nebulosum Ell. & Ev.
Coryneum clavisporum Pk.
Exosporium clavisporum (Pk.) Sacc.
Exosporium Tiliae Lk.
Hormodendron griseum Hedgc.
Ramularia fraxinea J. J. Davis.
Epochnium quadratum Cke.
Stemphylium quadratum (Cke.) Sacc.
Torula ligniperda (Willk.) Sacc.

Fraxinus americana (*cont.*)

MISCELLANEA

Hemiarcyria rubiformis (P.) Rostf.
Ozonium auricomum Lk.

Fraxinus campestris Brit.
{ Aecidium Fraxini S.
{ Dicaeoma Fraxini Arth. I.
{ Puccinia fraxinata Arth. I.
Cylindrosporium minus Ell. & Kellerm.
Hysterographium Fraxini (P. ex Fr.) De Not.
Piggotia Fraxini B. & C.
Sphaerella fraxinicola (S.) Cke.

Fraxinus caroliniana Mill.
Dicaeoma Fraxini (S.) Arth. I.
Cylindrosporium minus Ell. & Kellerm.
Phyllactinia suffulta (Reb.) ex Sacc.
Septoria Fraxini Westd.

Fraxinus excelsior L.
{ Durandia Fraxini (S.) Rehm.
? { Sphaerographium Fraxini (S.) Pk.
{ Tympanis Fraxini (S.) Fr.
Polyporus squamosus Huds. ex Fr.

Fraxinus nigra Marsh.
{ Aecidium Fraxini S.
{ Dicaeoma Fraxini Arth. I.
{ Puccinia fraxinata Arth. I.
{ Anthostoma cercidicola (B. & C.) Sacc.
{ Diatrype cercidicola B. & C.
{ Hypoxylon suborbiculare Pk.
{ Nummularia lateritia Ell. & Ev.
Asterella fraxinina Dearness & House.
Ciboria? tabacina Ell. & Holw.
Coprinus laniger Pk.
Coprinus radians (Desm.) Fr.
Cordyceps clavulata (S.) Ell. & Ev.
Cytispora annularis Ell. & Ev.
Daldinia concentrica (Bolt. ex Fr.) Ces. & De Not.
Dasyscypha sulphuricolor Pk.
{ Cytophoma pruinosa (Fr.) v. Höhnel.
{ Dendrophoma pruinosa (Fr.) Sacc.
{ Sphaeria pruinosa Fr.
Diaporthe artospora Dearness & House.
Diaporthe spiculosa (A. & S.) ex Nits.
{ Endoxyla Fraxini Ell. & Ev.
{ Thyridaria Fraxini Ell. & Ev.
Gloeosporium aridum Ell. & Holw.
Hymenochaete arida Karst.
Hypoxylon fuscopurpureum (S.) B.
{ Marssonia Fraxini Ell. & Davis.
{ Marssonina Fraxini Ell. & Davis.
Michenera Artocreas B. & C.
Peniophora ludoviciana Burt.
Peziza subvernalis Pk.
Phoma samarum Desm.
{ Phyllactinia corylea (P.) ex Karst.
{ Phyllactinia suffulta (Reb.) ex Sacc.
Piggotia Fraxini B. & C.

{ Fomes conchatus (P. ex Fr.) Karst.
{ Pyropolyporus conchatus (P. ex Fr.) Murrill.
Polyporus cuticularis (Bull.) ex Fr.
Poria ferruginosa (Schrad. ex Fr.) Cke.
Poria pissa (S.) Cke.
Poria subacida Pk.
Poria undata (P.) Bres.
Septoria Fraxini Westd.
Tubercularia hirtissima Pk.

Fraxinus oregana Nutt.
Corticium spretum Burt.
Cylindrosporium californicum Earle.
Cylindrosporium Fraxini (Ell. & Kellerm.) Ell. & Ev.
Cylindrosporium minus Ell. & Kellerm.
{ Gloeosporium Fraxini (Hark.) Ell. & Ev.
{ Septogloeum Fraxini Hark.
Phoma samarum Desm.
Phyllosticta viridis Ell. & Kellerm.

Fraxinus pennsylvanica Marsh.
{ Aecidium Fraxini S.
{ Dicaeoma Fraxini Arth. I.
{ Puccinia fraxinata Arth. I.
{ Puccinia peridermiospora Arth. I.
Cercosporella trichophila J. J. Davis.
Cladosporium simplex S.
Cytospora ceratophora Sacc.
{ Cytospora minuta Thm.
{ Phoma infossa Ell. & Ev.
Diplodia inquinans Westd.
Discosia Artocreas (Tode) ex Fr.
{ Enslinia candida (S.) Fr.
{ Poronia candida (S.) M. A. Curtis.
{ Sphaeria candida S.
Fomes igniarius (L. ex Fr.) Gill.
Gloeosporium aridum Ell. & Holw.
Gloeosporium fraxineum Pk.
Hypoxylon rubiginosum (P.) ex Fr.
Hysterographium Fraxini (P. ex Fr.) De Not.
Phyllactinia corylea (P.) ex Karst.
Phyllosticta fraxinicola (Curr.) Sacc.
Phyllosticta viridis Ell. & Kellerm.
Piggotia Fraxini B. & C.
Ramularia fraxinea J. J. Davis.
Sphaeropsis biformis Pk.
Sphaeropsis hyalina B. & C.

Fraxinus pennsylvanica Marsh, var. **lanceolata** (Borkh.) Sarg.

PYRENOMYCETINEAE

Anthostoma picaceum (C. & E.) Ell. & Ev.
Blitrydium megalosporum Clements.
{ Chilonectria crinigera Ell. & Ev.
{ Chilonectria sphaerospora (Ell. & Ev.) Sacc.
{ Nectria sphaerospora Ell. & Ev.
Cryptosphaeria millepunctata Grev.
Cucurbitaria Fraxini Ell. & Ev.
Diatrypella Fraxini Ell. & Ev.
Eutypa Fraxini (Nits.) Sacc.

Fraxinus pennsylvanica var. **lanceolata** (*cont.*)
Eutypa scabrosa (Bull. ex Fr.) Awd.
Eutypella angulosa Nits., var. Fraxini Rehm.
Haplosporella pennsylvanica (B. & C.) Fetrak & Syd.
Hysterographium Fraxini (P. ex Fr.) De Not.
Lophidium confertum Ell. & Ev.
Lophiostoma macrostomoides De Not.
Lophiostoma speciosum Ell. & Ev.
Lophiostoma triseptatum Pk., var. Fraxini Rehm.
Lophiotrema Fraxini Ell. & Ev.
Melanomma Pulvis-pyrius (P. ex Fr.) Fckl., var. Fraxini Rehm.
Myrmaecium fraxineum Ell. & Ev.
Phyllactinia corylea (P.) ex Karst.
Phyllactinia guttata (Wallr. ex Fr.) Lév.
Phyllactinia suffulta (Reb.) ex Sacc.
Pleospora saccardiana Roum.
Schizoxylon compositum Ell. & Ev.
Teichospora gregaria Ell. & Ev.
Teichospora obducens (Fr.) Fckl.
Teichospora piriospora Ell. & Ev.
Cytosporina Fraxini Ell. & Ev.
Thyridaria Fraxini Ell. & Ev.
Trematosphaeria Fraxini Ell. & Ev.
Trematosphaeria hyalopus Ell. & Ev.
Uncinula circinata C. & P.
Valsa ambiens (P.) ex Fr.
Valsa fraxinea Pk.
Valsa leucopsis Ell. & Ev.

UREDINALES

Aecidium Fraxini S.
Caeoma fraxinatum Lk.
Caeoma fraxinites S.
Puccinia fraxinata Arth. I.
Puccinia peridermiospora Arth. I.
Roestelia Fraxini (S.) M. A. Curtis.
Uredo Fraxini (S.) Spreng.

HYMENOMYCETINEAE

Favolus europaeus Fr.
Fomes fraxinophilus (Pk.) Sacc.
Irpex lacteus Fr.
Polyporus dichrous Fr.

SPHAEROPSIDALES

Diplodia inquinans Westd.
Diplodia rhizogena Ell. & Barthol.
Dothiorella concaviuscula Ell. & Barthol.
Hendersonia Fraxini Ell. & Barthol.
Hendersonulina Fraxini (Ell. & Barthol.) Tassi.
Phoma viridis Ell. & Barthol.
Phyllosticta Fraxini Ell. & Martin.
Phyllosticta fraxinicola Curr.
Phyllosticta viridis Ell. & Kellerm.
Piggotia Fraxini B. & C.

Schizothyrella Fraxini Ell. & Ev.
Septoria Besseyi Pk.
Septoria Fraxini Desm.
Sphaeropsis fertilis Pk.
Sphaeropsis nubilosa Ell. & Barthol.

MELANCONIALES

Cercospora Fraxini Ell. & Kellerm.
Cercosporella Fraxini Ell. & Kellerm.
Cylindrosporium Fraxini (Ell. & Kellerm.) Ell. & Ev.
Cylindrosporium minus Ell. & Kellerm.
Cylindrosporium Orni (Pass.) Pegl.
Cylindrosporium viride Ell. & Ev.
Gloeosporium Fraxini (Hark.) Ell. & Ev.
Septogloeum Fraxini Hark.
Gloeosporium decipiens Ell. & Ev.

HYPHOMYCETES

Cercospora texensis Ell. & Gall.
Ramularia fraxinea J. J. Davis.

MISCELLANEA

Dematophora necatrix Hartig.
Fraxinus profunda Bush.
Dicaeoma Fraxini Arth. I.
Puccinia fraxinata Arth. I.
Sphaeropsis profundae Tehon & Daniels.
Fraxinus quadrangulata Michx.
Aecidium Fraxini S.
Dicaeoma Fraxini Arth. I.
Phyllactinia corylea (P.) ex Karst.
Phyllactinia suffulta (Reb.) ex Sacc.
Sphaerella quadrangulata Ell. & Ev.
Sphaerella Sapindi Ell. & Ev.
Fraxinus velutina Torr.
Fomes fraxinophilus Pk.
Fraxinus sp. indet.

MYXOMYCETES

Arcyria pomiformis (Leers) Rostf.
Didymium eximium Pk.
Perichaena angulata Fr.
Trichia angulata S.

PEZIZINEAE

Ciboria sulphurella (Ell. & Ev.) Rehm.
Dasyscypha puberula (B. & C.) Sacc.
Peziza puberula B. & C.
Dermatella Fraxini Ell. & Ev.
Gorgoniceps turbinata (Phil.) Sacc.
Gorgoniceps vibrisseoides (Pk.) Sacc.
Helotium vibrisseoides Pk.
Vibrissea turbinata Phil.
Gyromitra infula (Schaeff. ex Fr.) Quél.
Karschia lignyota (Fr.) Sacc.
Karschia taveliana Rehm.
Lecanidion atratum (Hedw. ex Fr.) Rabh.

Fraxinus sp. indet. (*cont.*)

Lecanidion tetraspora (Massee & Morg.) Seaver.
Orbilia delicatula Karst.
Patellaria indigota C. & P.
Peziza atrata P.
Schizoxylon occidentalis Ell. & Ev.
Stictis radiata (L.) ex P.

PERISPORIACEAE

{ Dimerosporium pulchrum Sacc.
{ Sarcinella heterospora Sacc.

MICROTHYRIACEAE

Microthyrium microscopicum Desm.

HYPOCREALES

Calonectria Dearnessii Ell. & Ev.
{ Calonectria aurigera (B. & Rav.) Sacc.
{ Calonectria polythalama (B.) Sacc.
{ Nectria aurigera B. & Rav.
{ Nectria polythalama B.
{ Scoleconectria polythalama (B.) Seaver.
Nectria chlorinella Cke.
{ Creonectria coccinea (P. ex Fr.) Seaver.
{ Nectria coccinea (P.) ex Fr.
Nectria ditissima Tul.
Thyronectria pyrrhochlora (Awd.) Sacc.
Thyronectria sphaerospora (Ell. & Ev.) Seaver.
Thyronectria virens Hark.

SPHAERIALES

{ Acrospermum foliicola B.
{ Acrospermum Ravenelii Fung. Am. *735.*
{ Byssosphaeria euomphala (B. & C.) Cke.
{ Nitschkia euomphala (B. & C.) Ell. & Ev.
{ Sphaeria euomphala B. & C.
Ceratostomella pilifera (Fr.) Wint.
Chaetomium elatum Kze. ex Fr.
{ Diatrype corniculata (Ehrh. ex Fr.) B. & Br.
{ Peroneutypa corniculata (Ehrh. ex Fr.) Berl.
{ Sphaeria corniculata Ehrh. ex Fr.
{ Valsa corniculata (Ehrh. ex Fr.) M. A. Curtis.
{ Diatrypella angulata Ces. & De Not.
{ Diatrypella nigroannulata (Grev.) Nits.
{ Valsa angulata Fr.
Didymosphaeria accedens Sacc.
{ Fracchiaea heterogenea Sacc.
{ Sphaeria polycocca B. & Rav.
Gnomonia veneta (Sacc. & Speg.) Klebahn.
{ Gnomonia amoena (Nees) Fckl., var. petiolorum (S.) Cke.
{ Gnomoniella amoena, var. petiolorum Sacc.
{ Sphaeria amoena Auct. Amer.
{ Sphaeria petiolorum S.
Leptosphaeria borealis Ell. & Ev.
Massaria vomitoria B. & C.
Melanomma deciduum Ell. & Ev.

Otthia Hypoxylon (Ell. & Ev.) Shear.
{ Melanomma Ellisii Berl.
{ Pleospora pustulans Ell. & Ev.
{ Rosellinia aquila (Fr.) De Not.
{ Sphaeria aquila Fr.
Rosellinia glandiformis Ell. & Ev.
Rosellinia ligniaria (Grev.) Nits.
Rosellinia limoniispora Ell. & Ev.
{ Rosellinia myriocarpa (Fr.) Cke.
{ Sphaeria myriocarpa Fr.
Sphacria foveolaris S. Am. Bor.
{ Sphaeria obducens Cke.
{ Strickeria obducens Cke.
{ Conisphaeria Friesii (Nits.) Cke.
{ Melomastia Friesii Nits.
{ Sphaeria albicans S. Syn. Car.
{ Sphaeria mastoidea Fr.
{ Trematosphaeria mastoidea (Fr.) Wint.
{ Melogramma grandinea B. sec. Cke.
{ Melogramma insidens B. nec S.
{ Valsaria grandinea Berl. & Vogl.
Valsaria purpurea Pk.

XYLARIACEAE

Daldinia vernicosa S.
Hypoxylon atropurpureum Fr.
{ Hypoxylon colliculosum Rav. Fung. Am.
{ ?Hypoxylon insidens (S.) Ell. & Ev.
Hypoxylon concentricum (Bolt.) ex Grev.
{ Hypoxylon enteromelum (S.) B.
{ Sphaeria enteromela S.
Hypoxylon fuscopurpureum (S.) B. & C.
Hypoxylon perforatum (S.) Fr.
Hypoxylon rubricosum (Fr.) Mont.
{ Anthostoma rumpens (Cke.) Sacc.
{ Diatrype rumpens Cke.
{ Nummularia rumpens Cke.
Xylaria digitata (L. ex Fr.) Grev.

VALSACEAE

Diaporthe congenera Ell. & Ev.
{ Diaporthe Crataegi (Curr.) Nits.
{ Valsa Crataegi Curr.
{ Calosphaeria hylodes (Ell. & Ev.) Berl. & Vogl.
{ Diatrype corniculata Fung. Car. **4:** *43.*
{ Eutypa atomispora (Cke.) Sacc.
{ Eutypa echinata Ell. & Ev.
{ Eutypa heteracantha Sacc.
{ Valsa atomispora Cke.
{ Valsa heteracantha Sacc.
{ Valsa hylodes Ell. & Ev.
Eutypella fraxinicola (C. & P.) Sacc., var. lignicola Berl.
{ Eutypella stellulata (Fr.) Sacc.
{ Valsa stellulata Fr.

AURICULARIINEAE

{ Auricularia mesenterica (Dicks.) ex P.
{ Phlebia mesenterica (Dicks. ex P.) Fr.

Fraxinus sp. indet. (*cont.*)
Septobasidium frustulosum (B. & C.) Pat.
Septobasidium Patouillardii Burt.
Septobasidium pedicellatum (B. & C.) Pat.
Septobasidium pseudopedicellatum Burt.
⎰Tremella albida Huds. ex Fr.
⎱Exidia albida (Huds. ex Fr.) Brefeld.
Tremella colorata Pk.

THELEPHORACEAE

⎧Aleurodiscus amorphus (P.) Rabh.
⎪Corticium amorphum (P.) Fr.
⎨Peziza amorpha P.
⎩Thelephora amorpha (P.) Fr.
Aleurodiscus candidus (S.) Burt.
Aleurodiscus macrodens Coker.
⎰Aleurodiscus Oakesii (B. & C.) Cke.
⎱Corticium Oakesii B. & C.
Corticium hepaticum B. & C.
Corticium macrosporum Ell. & Ev.
Corticium tuberculatum Karst.
Corticium vellereum Ell. & Cragin.
Peniophora argentea Ell. & Ev. in Burt.
Peniophora canadensis Burt.
Peniophora cinerea (P. ex Fr.) Cke.
Peniophora incarnata (P. ex Fr.) Massee.
Peniophora ludoviciana Burt.
Peniophora violaceolivida (Sommerf.) Bres.
Stereum purpureum P. †

HYDNACEAE

Hydnum coralloides Scop. ex Fr.
Hydnum strigosum Swartz.
Irpex Tulipiferae (S.) Fr.
Phlebia pileata Pk.
Phlebia radiata Fr.

POLYPORACEAE

Daedalea confragosa (Bolt.) ex Fr.
Fomes igniarius (L. ex Fr.) Gill.
Fomes Meliae (Underw.) Murrill.
Ganoderma Curtisii (B.) Murrill.
Gloeophyllum hirsutum (Schaeff.) Murrill.
Polyporus adustus (Willd.) ex Fr.
Polyporus Berkeleyi Fr.
Polyporus corticola Fr., var. b.
Polyporus fumosus (P.) ex Fr.
Polyporus guttulatus Pk.
Polyporus hirsutus (Wulf.) ex Fr.
Polyporus hispidus (Bull.) ex Fr.
Polyporus immitis Pk.
⎧Enslinia pocula (S.) Fr.
⎪Polyporus pendulus (S.) Ell.
⎨Polyporus pocula (S.) B. & C.
⎪Porodiscus pendulus (S.) Murrill.
⎩Sphaeria pocula S.
⎰Abortiporus distortus (S.) Murrill.
⎱Polyporus rufescens (P.) ex Fr.

Polyporus spumeus (Sow.) ex Fr.
⎰Laetiporus speciosus (Batarr.) ex Murrill.
⎱Polyporus sulphureus (Bull.) ex Fr.
Polystictus biformis Fr.
Polystictus hirsutus (Wulf.) ex Fr.
Polystictus pubescens (Schum.) ex Fr.
Poria inermis Fr.
Poria Medulla-panis (P. ex Fr.) Cke.
⎰Polyporus molluscus (P.) ex Fr.
⎱Poria mollusca (P. ex Fr.) Cke.
Poria nitida (P. ex Fr.) Cke.
Poria salmonicolor Ell. & Ev.
Poria semitincta Pk.
Poria spissa (S.) Cke.
⎰Polyporus subspadiceus Fr.
⎱Poria subspadicea (Fr.) Cke.
Trametes sepium B.

AGARICACEAE

Coprinus fuscescens (Schaeff.) ex Fr.
Crepidotus fraxinicola Murrill.
Crepidotus haerens Pk.
Lentinus cochleatus Fr.
Lentinus Dunallii (DC.) ex Fr.
Lentinus vulpinus Sow. ex Fr.
Marasmius minutulus Pk.
Marasmius subvenosus Pk.
Panus dealbatus B.
Panus stypticus Fr.
Panus torulosus Fr.
Pleurotus dryinus (P.) ex Fr.
Pleurotus serotinus (Schrad.) ex Fr.
Pleurotus subpalmatus Fr.
Schizophyllum commune Fr.

SPHAEROPSIDALES

Aposphaeria pezizoides Ell. & Ev.
Coniothecium perplexum Pk.
Cytospora Micheneri B. & C.
Cytospora minuta Thm.
⎰Dichomera sphaerosperma (B. & C.) Cke.
⎱Hendersonia sphaerosperma B. & C.
Diplodia sarmentorum Fr.
⎰Dothiorella Everhartii Sacc. & Syd.
⎱Dothiorella Fraxini Ell. & Ev.
Dothiorella fraxinicola Ell. & Ev.
Phyllosticta osteospora Sacc.
Phyllosticta variegata Ell. & Ev.
Pyrenochaeta fraxinina Fairman.
Septoria submaculata Wint.
⎧Phoma sphaeropsideum Jacz.
⎨Sphaeronema sphaeropsideum Ell. & Ev.
⎪Sphaeronema carnea Jacz.
⎩Sphaeronemella carnea (Jacz.) Ell. & Ev.
⎰Haplosporella pennsylvanica (B. & C.) Petrak
⎨   & Syd.
⎱Sphaeropsis pennsylvanica B. & C.

Fraxinus sp. indet. (*cont.*)

MELANCONIALES

Cylindrosporium californicum Earle.
{ Melanconium magnum (Grev.) B.
{ Nemaspora magna Grev.
{ Stilbospora magna (Grev.) B.

HYPHOMYCETES

Cercospora fraxinites Ell. & Ev.
Cercospora lumbricoides Turconi & Maffei.
Cercospora superflua Ell. & Holw.
Cercospora texensis Ell. & Gall. 1898 non
 Tharp 1917.
Cladosporium acutum Ell. & Dearness.
Cladosporium epiphyllum (P.) C. Martius.
Cladosporium simplex S.
Epidochium olivaceum Ell. & Ev.
{ Helicoma Berkeleyi M. A. Curtis.
{ Helicosporium Berkeleyi (M. A. Curtis) Sacc.
Helminthosporium macrocarpum Grev.
Helminthosporium reticulatum Cke.
Sporidesmium compactum B. & C.
Tubercularia dubia Lk.
Tubercularia nigricans (Bull.) ex Lk.

MISCELLANEA

Ozonium omnivorum Shear.
Sclerotium reniforme S.
Forsythia suspensa Vahl.
Alternaria Forsythiae Harter.
Forsythia viridissima Lindl.
Phyllosticta terminalis Ell. & Martin.
Sclerotinia libertiana Fckl.
Forsythia sp. indet.
Discosia maculicola Gerard.
{ Phyllosticta discincola Ell. & Ev.
{ Phyllostictella discincola (Ell. & Ev.) Tassi.
Syringa chinensis Willd.
Microsphaera Alni (DC.) Wint. †
Syringa persica L.
Cercospora lilacis (Desm.) Sacc.
Microsphaera Alni (DC.) Wint. †
Syringa vulgaris L.
Aleurodiscus botryosus Burt.
Ascochyta Syringae Bres.
{ Botryosphaeria Syringae (S.) Cke.
{ Sphaeria Syringae S. Am. Bor.
Botrytis cinerea P. †
Cercospora lilacis (Desm.) Sacc.
Corticium Stevensii Burt.
Cyphella alboviolascens (A. & S. ex Fr.) Karst.
Cytospora ambiens Sacc.
{ Dacryomyces syringicola B. & C.
{ Hypsilophora syringicola (B. & C.) B.
Dendrophoma albomaculans (S.) Starb.
Dendrophoma Syringae Dearness.
Fomes conchatus (P. ex Fr.) Karst.
{ Fomes scutellatus (S.) Cke.
{ Polyporus scutellatus S.

Hymenochaete agglutinans Ell.
{ Hysterium Syringae S.
{ Hysterographium Syringae (S.) Sacc.
{ Pseudographis dealbata (Gerard) Sacc.
{ Tryblidium dealbatum Gerard.
{ Tryblidium Syringae (S.) Cke.
{ Macrophoma Halstedii (Ell. & Ev.) Tassi.
{ Phyllosticta Halstedii Ell. & Ev.
{ Erysiphe penicillata Rav. Fung. Car. p. p.
{ Erysiphe Syringae S.
{ Microsphaera Alni (DC.) Wint. †
{ Microsphaera Friesii Lév.
{ Microsphaera Friesii Lév., var. Syringae (S.)
{ C. & P.
{ Microsphaera Hedwigii Lév.
{ Microsphaera Syringae (S.) Magn.
Monochaetia Syringae Oud.
Myxosporium depressum Sacc.
Peniophora caesia Bres.
Phoma Syringae B. & C.
Phomopsis depressa Latham.
Phyllosticta Porteri Tehon & Daniels.
Phyllosticta Syringae Westd.
Physalospora Cydoniae Arnaud.
{ Coriolus versicolor (L. ex Fr.) Quél.
{ Polyporus versicolor L. ex Fr.
{ Polystictus versicolor (L.) ex Fr.
Sphaeropsis Syringae Pk. & Clinton.
Stereum purpureum P. †
Uncinula Clintonii Pk.
Uncinula macrospora Pk.

Syringa sp. indet.
{ Amphisphaeria albomaculans (S.) Cke.
{ Sphaeria albomaculans S.
Cercospora macromaculans Heald & Wolf.
Corticium subcinereum Burt.
{ Cryptospora leucopis (Fr.) Ell. & Ev.
{ Sphaeria leucopis Fr.
{ Valsa leucopis Fr.
Dacryomyces Syringae (Schum.) Fr.
Hymenochaete agglutinans Ell.
Lichenopsis sphaeroboloidea S.
Myrothecium roridum Tode ex Fr..
Phoma herbarum Westd.
Phoma Syringae B. & C.
Phyllosticta Halstedii Ell. & Ev.
Sporotrichum nitens (P.) Lk.
Thyridium Syringae Ell. & Ev.
{ Sphaeria decorticans Fr.
{ Valsa decorticans Fr.
Valsa salicina (P.) ex Fr.

Osmanthus americana Benth. & Hook.
Asterina discoidea Ell. & Martin.
{ Asterella oleina (Cke.) Sacc.
{ Asterina oleina Cke.
{ Asteridium purpureum (Ell. & Martin) Sacc.
{ Asterina purpurea Ell. & Martin.
{ Zukalia purpurea (Ell. & Martin) Theissen.

Osmanthus americana (*cont.*)
  {Calonectria erubescens (Rob.) Sacc.
  {Dialonectria erubescens (Rob.) Cke.
  Capnodium elongatum B. & Desm.
  Fumago salicina (P. ex Fr.) Tul.
  Helotium castaneum Sacc. & Ell.
  Lembosia Oleae Tracy & Earle.
  Meliola amphitricha Fr.
  {Dothidea coccodes (Lév.) B. & C.
  {Phyllachora coccodes (Lév.) Ell. & Ev.
  Phyllosticta Oleae Ell. & Martin.
  {Phyllosticta oleina Cke.
  {Sphaerella oleina Cke.
  Phyllosticta sinuosa Ell. & Martin.
  Venturia formosa Ell. & Martin.
Osmanthus sp. indet.
  Phyllosticta terminalis Ell. & Martin.
Adelia acuminata Michx.
  Microsphaera Alni (DC.) Wint. †
Adelia ligustrina Michx.
  Coleosporium minutum Hedgc. & Hunt.
Adelia
  (Forestiera phillyreoides Torr.).
Adelia porulosa Michx.
Adelia segregata O. Kuntze.
  {Dicaeoma Fraxini Arth. I.
  {Puccinia fraxinata Arth. I.
Mayepea domingensis Krug. & Urb.
  Englerodothis kilimandscharica (Henn.)
    Theissen & Syd.
  Meliola Mayepeae F. L. Stevens.
  Meliola mayepeicola F. L. Stevens.
  Phyllachora Mayepeae Stevens & Dalby.
Chionanthus virginica L.
  {Botryosphaeria pyriospora (Ell.) Sacc.
  {Melogramma fuliginosum Ell. p. p.
  {Sphaeria pyriospora Ell.
  {Calonectria polythalama (B.) Sacc.
  {Nectria aurigera B. & Rav.
  {Scoleconectria polythalama (B.) Seaver.
  Cercospora Chionanthi Ell. & Ev.
  Dermatea Chionanthi Ell. & Ev.
  Microsphaera Alni (DC.) Wint. †
  {Phoma diatrypea (C. & E.) Sacc.
  {Sphaeropsis diatrypea C. & E.
  Phyllactinia corylea (P.) ex Karst.
  Phyllosticta Chionanthi Thm.
  Septoria Chionanthi Cke.
  Septoria eleospora Sacc.
  Valsa ceratophora Tul.
  Valsa Chionanthi Ell. & Ev.
Olea europaea L.
  Antennaria elaeophila Mont.
  Armillaria mellea (Vahl) ex Fr.
  Capnodium Citri (P.) B. & Desm.
  Cycloconium oleaginum Cast.
  Fumago vagans Fr.
  Gloniopsis australis (Duby) Sacc.
  Ozonium omnivorum Shear.

Olea fragrans Thunb.
  Cladosporium aeruginosum Patterson.
  Gloeosporium Oleae Patterson.
Olea sp. indet.
  Armillaria mellea (Vahl) ex Fr.
  Fumago salicina (P. ex Fr.) Tul.
  Septoria serpentaria Ell. & Martin.
Ligustrum Ibota Sieb.
  Diaporthe ligustrina Ell. & Ev.
  Phoma ligustrina Sacc.
Ligustrum japonicum Thunb.
  Cercospora Ligustri Roum.
Ligustrum ovalifolium Hassk.
  Cercospora adusta Heald & Wolf.
  Corticium caeruleum (Schrad.) ex Fr.
  Periconia pycnospora Fres.
  Phyllosticta ovalifolii Brun.
  Valsa Ligustri (S.) Schrt.
Ligustrum sinense Lour.
  Dacryomyces minor Pk.
  Peniophora violaceolivida (Sommerf.) Bres.
  Tremella auricularia Möller.
Ligustrum vulgare L.
  Exosporium concentricum Heald & Wolf.
  {Gloeosporium cingulatum Atk.
  {Glomerella cingulata (Stoneman) Spaulding &
    v. Schrenk.
  {Gnomoniopsis cingulata Stoneman.
  Hysterographium Mori (S.) Rehm.
  Microsphaera Alni (DC.) Wint. †
  Ozonium omnivorum Shear.
  Poria Cokeri Murrill.
  Stictis Ligustri S.
  {Dendrophoma pruinosa (Fr.) Sacc.
  {Sphaeria Ligustri S.
  {Sphaeria pruinosa Fr.
  {Valsa Cypri Tul.
Ligustrum sp. indet.
  Armillaria mellea (Vahl) ex Fr.
  Phyllosticta ovalifolii Brunaud.
  Polystictus versicolor (L.) ex Fr.
  Rhizoctonia Solani Kühn.
  Septobasidium pseudopedicellatum Burt.
  Stereum rameale S.
  Tremella carneoalba Coker.
  Tremella lutescens (P.) ex Fr.
Menodora scoparia Engelm.
  Coniothecium erumpens Sacc. & Syd.
Jasminum fruticans L.
  Haplosporella Jasmini Ell. & Ev.
Jasminum Sambac Soland.
  Choanephora infundibulifera (Curr.) Cunn.
Jasminum simplicifolium Forst.
  Xylaria aristata Mont.
Jasminum sp. indet.
  Rhabdospora Jasmini (S.) Cke.
  Uromyces comedens Syd.

Oleaceae gen. indet.
  Puccinia plagiopus Mont.
  Trichothyrium Oleaceae Fragoso & Ciferri.

LOGANIACEAE

Gelsemium sempervirens (L.) Ait. f.
  Asterina stomatophora Ell. & Martin.
  Capnodium grandisporum Ell. & Martin.
  Cladosporium maculans S.
  {Creonectria rubicarpa (Cke.) Seaver.
  {Nectria rubicarpa Cke.
  Phyllosticta Gelsemii Ell. & Ev.
  {Rhabdospora Jasmini (S.) Cke.
  {Sphaeria Jasmini S.
  Saccardia Martini Ell. & Sacc.
Gelsemium sp. indet.
  {Physalospora gelsemiata (Cke.) Sacc.
  {Sphaeria gelsemiata Cke.
  {Rosellinia aquila (Fr.) De Not.
  {Sphaeria aquila Fr.
Spigelia Anthelmia L.
Spigelia humboldtiana Cham. & Schl.
  Coleosporium Spigeliae Arth.
Spigelia sp. indet.
  Cylindrosporium Spigeliae Dearness & House.
  Septoria Spigeliae Henn.
Cynoctonum Mitreola (L.) Britton.
  Cercospora torta Tracy & Earle.

GENTIANACEAE

Sabatia angularis (L.) Pursh.
  {Cercospora grisea C. & E.
  {Cercospora minuta Sacc.
  Cercospora Sabbatiae Ell. & Ev.
Centaurium calycosum (Buckl.) Fern.
  {Dicaeoma Sarcobati (Pk.) Arth.
  {Puccinia subnitens Diet.
Centaurium macrantha B. L. Robinson.
  Septoria Erythraeae Dearness & House.
Gentiana Amarella L., var. **acuta** (Michx.) Herder.
  Puccinia Gentianae Lk.
  Uromyces Gentianae Arth.
Gentiana affinis Griseb.
Gentiana Bigelovii Gray.
Gentiana frigida Haenke.
Gentiana interrupta Greene.
Gentiana Menziesii Griseb.
Gentiana Newberryi Gray.
Gentiana oregana Engelm.
Gentiana Parryi Engelm.
Gentiana plebeia Cham.
Gentiana sceptrum Griseb.
Gentiana spathacea H. B. K.
  {Dicaeoma Gentianae (Lk.) O. Kuntze.
  {Puccinia Gentianae Lk.

Gentiana Hartwegi Benth.
Gentiana mexicana Griseb.
Gentiana propinqua Richardson.
Gentiana quinquefolia L., var. **occidentalis** (Gray) Hitchc.
Gentiana strictiflora A. Nels.
  {Nigredo Gentianae Arth.
  {Uromyces Gentianae Arth.
Gentiana Andrewsii Griseb.
  Cercospora Gentianae Pk.
  {Asteroma Gentianae Auct. Amer. nec Fckl.
  {Depazea gentianicola Auct. Amer. nec (DC. ex Fr.) Rabh.
  {Leptothyrium gentianicola Auct. Amer. nec (DC. ex Fr.) Baeumler.
  {Phyllosticta gentianicola Auct. Amer. nec (DC. ex Fr.) Ell. & Ev.
  {Leptothyrium gentianicola Fung. Dak. *385*.
  {Sphaerella Andrewsii Sacc.
  {Dicaeoma Gentianae (Lk.) O. Kuntze.
  {Puccinia Gentianae Lk.
Gentiana calycosa Griseb.
  {Micropuccinia Haleniae (Arth. & Holw.) Arth. & Jackson.
  {Puccinia Haleniae Arth. & Holw.
Gentiana crinita Froel.
  Cercospora gentianicola Ell. & Ev.
  Phyllosticta gentianicola (DC.) Ell. & Ev.
Gentiana flavida Gray.
  Phyllosticta gentianicola (DC.) Ell. & Ev.
Gentiana heterosepala Engelm.
  Puccinia Gentianae Lk.
  {Nigredo Gentianae Arth.
  {Uromyces Gentianae Arth.
Gentiana linearis Froel.
  Cercospora Gentianae Pk.
  Dicaeoma Gentianae (Lk.) O. Kuntze.
Gentiana nivalis L.
  Botrytis cinerea P. †
  Pyrenophora chrysospora (Niessl) Sacc.
  Septoria cercosperma Rostr.
  Sphaerella pachyasca Rostr.
Gentiana puberula Michx.
  Asteroma Gentianae Fckl.
  {Dicaeoma Gentianae (Lk.) O. Kuntze.
  {Puccinia Gentianae Lk.
Gentiana quinquefolia L.
  Puccinia Gentianae Lk.
  Septoria Gentianae Dearness & House.
  Septoria gentianoides Dearness & House.
  Uromyces Gentianae Arth.
Gentiana Saponaria L.
  {Mycosphaerella Gentianae (Niessl) Lindau.
  {Sphaerella Gentianae Niessl?
Gentiana serrata Gunner.
  Phoma californica Ell. & Ev.
  Pyrenophora chrysospora (Niessl) Sacc.

Gentiana tenella Rottb.
  Pleospora platyspora Sacc.

Gentiana villosa L.
  { Dothidea Gentianae S.
  { Phyllachora Gentianae (S.) Sacc.

Gentiana sp. indet.
  Macrosporium compactum Cke.?
  Pseudopeziza Holwayi Henn.
  Septoria tosevi Bubák.

Pleurogyne rotata (L.) Griseb.
  Sphaerella pachyasca Rostr.
  Nigredo Gentianae Arth. I.

Swertia Fritillaria Rydb.
Swertia ovalifolia Greene.
Swertia palustris A. Nels.
Swertia perennis L.
Swertia scopulina Greene.
  { Aecidium Fraserae Trel.
  { Allodus Swertiae (Wint.) C. R. Orton.
  { Puccinia Swertiae Wint.

Frasera fastigiata A. A. Heller.
  Ascochyta Fraserae Sacc.

Frasera speciosa Dougl.
  Ascochyta Fraserae Ell. & Ev.
  Capnodium puccinioides Ell. & Ev.
  { Cercospora Fraserae Ell. & Ev.
  { Cercosporella Fraserae (Ell. & Ev.) Sacc.
  Leptosphaeria Fraserae Ell. & Ev.
  ?Uromyces Fraserae Arth. & Ricker.
  { Nigredo (?) speciosa (Holw.) Arth.
  { Uromyces speciosus Holw.
  { Didymochaete americana Sacc. & Ell.
  { Vermiculariella americana (Sacc. & Ell.) Syd.

Frasera stenosepala Rydb.
  { Nigredo (?) speciosa (Holw.) Arth.
  { Uromyces speciosus Holw.

Frasera thyrsiflora Hook.
  Asteroma Fraserae Ell. & Ev.
  Marssonia Fraserae Ell. & Ev.

Frasera sp. indet.
  Aecidium Fraserae Trel.
  { Ascochyta Fraserae Ell. & Ev.
  { Diplodina Fraserae (Ell. & Ev.) Tracy & Earle.
  { Heptameria harknessiana (Ell. & Ev.) Cke.
  { Leptosphaeria harknessiana Ell. & Ev.
  Phyllosticta Fraserae Ell. & Ev.

Halenia deflexa (J. E. Sm.) Griseb.
  Cercospora gentianicola Ell. & Ev.
  { Micropuccinia Haleniae (Arth. & Holw.) Arth.
    & Jackson.
  { Puccinia Haleniae Arth. & Holw.
  Synchytrium aureum Schrt.

Lisianthus exsertus Sw.
  Phyllosticta Lisianthi Syd.
  Puccinia Lisianthi Syd.

Eustoma Andrewsii Nels.
  Cercospora Eustomae Pk.

Eustoma russellianum Griseb.
  Cercospora Eustomae Pk.
  Cercospora nephaloides Ell. & Holw.

Eustoma silenifolium Salisb.
  Cercospora nephaloides Ell. & Holw.

Menyanthes trifoliata L.
  Ascochyta Menyanthis Oud.
  { Cladochytrium Menyanthis DBy.
  { Physoderma Menyanthis DBy.
  { Protomyces Menyanthis DBy.
  Septoria Menyanthis (Lib.) Desm.

Nymphoides grayanum (Griseb.) Arth.
  Aecidium Nymphaiarum DC.
  Aecidium Nymphoidis DC.
  { Dicaeoma Scirpi (DC.) S. F. Gray.
  { Puccinia Scirpi DC.

Nymphoides lacunosum (Vent.) Fern.
  { Burrillia decipiens (Wint.) G. P. Clinton.
  { Doassansia decipiens Wint.

APOCYNACEAE

Allamanda neriifolia Hook.
  Colletotrichum gloeosporioides Penz.

Plumiera alba L.
Plumiera obtusa L.
  Coleosporium Plumierae Pat.
  Septoria Plumeriae Sacc. & Syd.

Plumiera emarginata Griseb.
Plumiera lutea Ruiz. & Pav.
Plumiera rubra L.
  { Coleosporium domingensis Arth.
  { Coleosporium Plumierae Pat.
  { Uredo domingensis B.

Plumiera Krugii Urb.
  Coleosporium Plumierae Pat.
  Meliola Tabernaemontanae Speg.

Amsonia angustifolia Michx.
  Coleosporium apocynaceum Cke.
  Torula microsora Thm.

Amsonia ciliata Walt.
  Coleosporium apocynaceum Cke.

Amsonia Tabernaemontana Walt.
  Aecidium Apocyni S.
  { Aecidium obesum Arth.
  { Dicaeoma Cephalanthi H. S. Jackson. I.
  { Coleosporium Amsoniae (Cke.) Underw. &
    Earle.
  { Coleosporium apocynaceum Cke.
  { Trichobasis Amsoniae Cke.
  { Uredo Amsoniae (Cke.) De Toni.

Vinca major L.
  Botryosporium pulchrum Cda.
  { Bullaria Vincae (B.) Arth.
  { Puccinia Berkeleyi Pass.
  { Puccinia Vincae B.

Vinca major (*cont.*)
Rhizoctonia Solani Kühn.
Septoria Vincae Desm.
Sphaeropsis Vincae Sacc. & Wint.

Vinca minor L.
Cladosporium herbarum (P.) ex Lk.
Cladosporium Vincae Fairman.
Microthyrium microscopicum Desm.
Phyllosticta minor Ell. & Ev.
Phyllosticta Vincae-majoris Allescher.
⎰Diplodia Vincae Sacc. & Wint.
⎱Sphaeropsis Vincae Sacc. & Wint.
Stictis Vincae Ell.
Strumella Vincae Cke. & Hark.
Volutella Vincae Fairman.

Vinca rosea L.
Phytophthora Colocasiae Rac.

Tabernaemontana citrifolia Jacq.
Meliola isothea Syd.
Meliola Tabernaemontanae Speg.

Tabernaemontana longipes Donn. Sm.
Calonectria Adianthi Rehm.
Irene escharoides Syd.
Nectria pipericola Henn.
Neostomella Tabernaemontanae Syd.

Tabernaemontana oppositifolia (Spreng.) Urb.
Meliola isothea Syd.
Meliola Tabernaemontanae Speg.

Tabernaemontana Sananho Ruiz & Pav.
Calloriopsis gelatinosa (Ell. & Martin) Syd.
Calonectria inconspicua Wint.
⎰Cicinnobella consimilis Syd.
⎱Dimerium consimile Syd.
Irene escha oides Syd.
Neostomella Tabernaemontanae Syd.
Paranectria meliolicola F. L. Stevens.

Tabernaemontana sp. indet.
Meliola Tabernaemontanae Speg.

Rauwolfia nitida Jacq.
Meliola Tabernaemontanae Speg.
Meliola vicina Syd.

Rauwolfia tetraphylla L.
Meliola Tabernaemontanae Speg.

Tanghinia venenifera Poir.
Hendersonula Cerberae Tassi.
Laestadia Cerberae Tassi.

Thevetia cuneifolia A. DC.
Aecidium Thevetiae Sacc.
Puccinia ametableta Syd.

Thevetia nereifolia Juss.
Diplodia aegyptiaca Tassi, var. incrustans Tassi.
Leptothyrium Thevetiae Tassi.
Meliola modesta Syd.
Puccinia ametableta Syd.

Thevetia venenifera (Steud.) Tassi.
Fusarium Thevetiae Tassi.

Echites Brownei J. Müll.
Meliola simillima Ell. & Ev.

Echites tomentosa Raf.
Crossopsora Stevensii Syd.

Macrosiphonia brachysiphon Gray.
Aecidium leporinum Arth.

Mandevilla tomentosa (Vahl) O. Kuntze.
Uredo Mandevillae Mayor.

Urechites lutea (L.) Brit.
Phyllosticta glaucispora Delacr.

Trachelospermum difforme (Walt.) Gray.
Cercospora repens Ell. & Ev.

Apocynum androsaemifolium L.
Aecidium Apocyni S.
⎰Cercospora Apocyni Ell. & Kellerm.
⎱Cercosporella Apocyni (Ell. & Kellerm.) Trel.
Cylindrosporium Apocyni Ell. & Ev.
⎰Phyllosticta Apocyni Trel. Nov. 1884.
⎪Phyllosticta Apocyni Ell.&Martin. Dec. 1884.
⎨Phyllosticta Apocyni-androsaemifolii Bubák & Dearness.
Pyrenopeziza Dearnessii Rehm.
Septoria littorea Sacc.
⎰Dearnessia Apocyni Bubák.
⎪Gloeosporium Apocyni (Pk.) Ell. & Ev.
⎨Septogloeum Apocyni Pk.
⎱Stagonospora Apocyni (Pk.) J. J. Davis.

Apocynum cannabinum L.
⎰Aecidium Apocyni S.
⎪Caeoma apocynatum Lk.
⎨Aecidium Apocyni Fung. Columb. *1295*, Micr. Sel. *1101*.
⎧Aecidium obesum Arth.
⎪Dicaeoma Cephalanthi H. S. Jackson. I.
⎩Puccinia seymouriana Arth. I.
⎰Cercospora Apocyni Ell. & Kellerm.
⎱Cercosporella Apocyni (Ell. & Kellerm.) Trel.
Cylindrosporium Apocyni Ell. & Ev.
Nectria Apocyni Pk.
Pestalozziella Andersoni Ell. & Ev.
⎰Phyllosticta Apocyni Trel.
⎱Phyllosticta Asclepiadearum Desm.
Septoria littorea Sacc.
⎰Gloeosporium Apocyni (Pk.) Ell. & Ev.
⎨Septogloeum Apocyni Pk.
⎱Stagonospora Apocyni (Pk.) J. J. Davis.
Uromyces demetrianus Pazschke.

Apocynum cannabinum L., var. **hypericifolium** (Ait.) Gray.
Aecidium obesum Arth.
Cercospora Apocyni Ell. & Kellerm.
Didymosphaeria brunneola Niessl.
Laestadia Apocyni Ell. & Ev.
Schizoxylon decipiens Karst.

Apocynum cannabinum L., var. **pubescens** R. Br.
Aecidium Apocyni S.

Apocynum sibiricum Jacq.
  Aecidium obesum Arth.
  { Dicaeoma Cephalanthi H. S. Jackson. I.
  { Puccinia Cephalanthi (H. S. Jackson) Bar-
      thol. I.
  Cercospora Apocyni Ell. & Kellerm.
  Cylindrosporium sibiricum Dearness & Bisby.
Apocynum sp. indet.
  Didymosphaeria epidermidis (Fr.) Fckl., var.
      herbicola Ell. & Ev.
  { Erysiphe Cichoracearum DC. †
  { Erysiphe Montagnei Lév.
  Gloeosporium Apocyni Dearness & Overholts.
Nerium Oleander L.
  Capnodium Citri B. & Desm.
  { Capnodium elongatum B. & Desm., var. Nerii
  {   (Rabh.) Cke.
  { Capnodium Nerii Rabh.
  Cercospora neriella Sacc.
  Chaetophoma foeda Sacc.
  Cladosporium microsporum Rabh.
  Corticium salmonicolor B. & Br.
  Dicranidion fragile Hark.
  Diplodia Nerii Speg.
  Gloeosporium Oleandri Sacc.
  Haplosporella Nerii Sacc.
  Macrosporium Nerii Cke.
  Meliola Camelliae (Catt.) Sacc.
  Pestalozzia stellata B. & C., var. Nerii Cke.
  Phyllosticta Nerii Westd.
  { Inonotus fruticum (B. & C.) Murrill.
  { Polyporus fruticum B. & C.
  Septoria oleandrina Sacc.
  Thecospora lateralis Hark.
  Uredo Vincetoxici DC.
Forsteronia corymbosa (Jacq.) Mey.
  Meliola Tabernaemontanae Speg., var. Fors-
      teroniae F. L. Stevens.
Thenardia galeottiana Baill.
  Aecidium Thenardiae Arth.
Prestonia ipomoeifolia A. DC.
  Hysterostomina polyadelpha Syd.

ASCLEPIADACEAE

Macroscepis congestiflora J. D. Sm.
  { Micropuccinia obliqua (B. & C.) Arth. &
  {   Jackson.
  { Puccinia obliqua B. & C.
Philibertella clausa (Jacq.) Vail.
  { Micropuccinia obliqua (B. & C.) Arth. &
  {   Jackson.
  { Puccinia Gonolobi Rav.
  { Puccinia obliqua B. & C.
Philibertella crassifolia Hemsl.
  { Puccinia Cynanchi Lagerh.
  { Puccinia obliqua B. & C.

Philibertella Hartwegii Vail.
  { Aecidium Brandegei Pk.
  { Dicaeoma jamesianum Arth. I.
Philibertia cynanchoides Gray.
Philibertia hirtella Vail.
Philibertia linearis Gray.
Philibertia viridifolia Britton & Rusby.
  { Micropuccinia obliqua (B. & C.) Arth. & Jack-
  {   son.
  { Puccinia Gonolobi Rav.
  { Puccinia Gonolobi Rav., var. Philibertiae Pk.
  { Puccinia obliqua B. & C.
  { Puccinia Philibertiae Ell. & Ev.
Acerates floridana (Lam.) Hitchc.
  { Aecidium jamesianum Pk.
  { Dicaeoma jamesianum Arth. I.
  { Puccinia Bartholomaei Diet. I.
Acerates viridiflora Ell.
  { Aecidium jamesianum Pk.
  { Dicaeoma jamesianum Arth. I.
  { Puccinia Bartholomaei Diet. I.
  { Puccinia jamesiana Arth. I.
  Cercospora Briareus Ell. & Ev.
Schizonotus discolor Raf.
  Septogloeum Schizonoti Dearness.
  Valsa clavigera Dearness & Barthol.
Asclepiodora decumbens Gray.
  { Aecidium jamesianum Pk.
  { Puccinia Bartholomaei Diet. I.
  { Puccinia jamesiana Arth. I.
  Uromyces Howei Pk.
Asclepiodora viridis Gray.
  { Aecidium jamesianum Pk.
  { Dicaeoma jamesianum Arth. I.
  { Cercospora Asclepiadorae Ell. & Kellerm.
  { Cercospora fraxinea Ell. & Ev.
  { Nigredo (?) Howei (Pk.) Arth.
  { Uromyces Howei Pk.
Asclepias amplexicaulis Sm.
  Cercospora clavata (Gerard) Cke.
  Macrosporium asclepiadeum Cke.
  { Nigredo (?) Howei (Pk.) Arth.
  { Uromyces Howei Pk.
Asclepias arenaria Torr.
  { Aecidium Brandegei Pk.
  { Aecidium jamesianum Pk.
  { Dicaeoma jamesianum Arth. I.
  { Puccinia Bartholomaei Diet. I.
  { Puccinia jamesiana Arth. I.
  { Cercospora Asclepiadis Ell.
  { Cercospora clavata (Gerard) Pk.
  { Uromyces Howei Pk.
Asclepias brachystephana Engelm.
  { Dicaeoma jamesianum Arth. I.
  { Puccinia jamesiana Arth. I.

Asclepias Curassavica L.
  Cercospora venturioides Pk.
  Nematospora Gossypii Ashby & Nowell.
  { Micropuccinia concrescens (Ell. & Ev.) Arth.
     & Jackson.
  Puccinia compacta Kze.
  Puccinia concrescens Ell. & Ev.
  Sphaeria Curassavicae S.
  Uromyces Howei Pk.

Asclepias ecornuta Kellogg.
  Cercospora Hanseni Ell. & Ev.

Asclepias eriocarpa Benth.
  Scolecotrichum Asclepiadis Ell. & Ev.

Asclepias fasciculata Hemsl.
  Uromyces Howei Pk.

Asclepias galioides H. B. K.
  { Aecidium Brandegei Pk.
  { Dicaeoma jamesianum Arth. I.
  { Puccinia jamesiana Arth. I.

Asclepias guatemalensis J. D. Sm.
  { Nigredo (?) Howei (Pk.) Arth.
  { Uromyces Howei Pk.

Asclepias incarnata L.
  { Aecidium jamesianum Pk.
  { Puccinia Bartholomaei Diet. I.
  Alternaria fasciculata (C. & E.) Jones & Grout.
  { Cercospora Asclepiadis Ell.
  { Cercospora clavata (Gerard) Cke.
  { Cercospora venturioides Pk.
  { Cercosporella clavata (Gerard) Underw.
  { Helminthosporium clavatum Gerard.
  { Virgasporium clavatum (Gerard) Cke.
  Cercospora incarnata Ell. & Ev.
  { Clathrospora ellisiana Berl.
  { Pleospora diplospora Ell. & Ev. p. p.[2]
  { Dothidea ornans S.
  { Phyllachora ornans (S.) Sacc.
  Phyllosticta tuberosa Ell. & Martin.
  Septoria asclepiadicola Ell. & Ev.
  Septoria Cryptotaeniae Ell. & Ev.
  Septoria incarnata Ell. & Barthol.
  { Caeomurus Howei (Pk.) O. Kuntze.
  { Nigredo (?) Howei (Pk.) Arth.
  { Uromyces Asclepiadis Cke.
  { Uromyces Howei Pk.

Asclepias incarnata L., var. pulchra (Ehrh.) P.
  { Dicaeoma Cephalanthi H. S. Jackson. I.
  { Puccinia seymouriana Arth. I.
  Uromyces Howei Pk.

Asclepias Jamesii Torr.
  { Aecidium jamesianum Pk.
  { Puccinia Bartholomaei Diet. I.
  Cercospora Asclepiadis Ell.
  Cercospora Asclepiadorae Ell. & Kellerm.

Asclepias Kotolo Eastw.
  Scolecotrichum Asclepiadis Ell. & Ev.

Asclepias latifolia (Torr.) Raf.
  { Dicaeoma jamesianum Arth. I.
  { Puccinia jamesiana Arth. I.
  Nigredo (?) Howei (Pk.) Arth.

Asclepias Meadii Torr.
  { Aecidium jamesianum Pk.
  { Puccinia Bartholomaei Diet. I.
  Cercospora clavata (Gerard) Pk.

Asclepias nivea L.
  { Micropuccinia concrescens (Ell. & Ev.) Arth.
     & Jackson.
  { Puccinia concrescens Ell. & Ev.
  Nigredo (?) Howei (Pk.) Arth.

Asclepias ovalifolia Decne.
  { Aecidium jamesianum Pk.
  { Dicaeoma jamesianum Arth. I.
  { Puccinia Bartholomaei Diet. I.
  { Puccinia jamesiana Arth. I.

Asclepias phytolaccoides Pursh.
  Cercospora clavata (Gerard.) Cke.

Asclepias pumila (Gray) Vail.
  Aecidium Brandegei Pk.
  Rhodochytrium Spilanthidis Lagerh.
  Rhodochytrium Spilanthidis Lagerh., var.
     Asclepiadis Farl.

Asclepias purpurascens L.
Asclepias quadrifolia Jacq.
Asclepias Rolfsii Brit.
  { Caeomurus Howei (Pk.) O. Kuntze.
  { Nigredo (?) Howei (Pk.) Arth.
  { Uromyces Howei Pk.

Asclepias rubra L.
  Septoria asclepiadicola Ell. & Ev.

Asclepias speciosa Torr.
  { Dicaeoma Cephalanthi H. S. Jackson. I.
  { Puccinia seymouriana Arth. I.
  { Aecidium jamesianum Pk.
  { Dicaeoma jamesianum Arth. I.
  { Puccinia Bartholomaei Diet. I.
  { Puccinia jamesiana Arth. I.
  { Cercospora clavata (Gerard) Cke.
  { Cercospora elaeochroma Sacc.
  Colletotrichum salmonicolor O'Gara.
  Gloeosporium fusarioides Ell. & Kellerm.
  Phoma asclepiadea Ell. & Ev.
  Phoma rostrata O'Gara.
  Trichothecium roseum Lk.
  Uromyces Howei Pk.

Asclepias subverticillata Vail.
  Aecidium Brandegei Pk.

Asclepias syriaca L.
  { Aecidium jamesianum Pk.
  { Dicaeoma jamesianum Arth. I.
  { Puccinia Bartholomaei Diet. I.
  { Aecidium obesum Arth.
  { Dicaeoma Cephalanthi H. S. Jackson. I.
  { Puccinia seymouriana Arth. I.
  Alternaria tenuis Nees ex Fr.

Asclepias syriaca (*cont.*)
Ascochyta Asclepiadis Ell. & Ev.
{ Asterella capnoides (Ell.) Sacc.
Asterina capnoides Ell.
Asteroma capnoides Ell.
Calyptra capnoides (Ell.) Theissen.
Dimerosporium capnoides (Ell.) Martin.
Botrytis hypophylla Ell. & Kellerm.
{ Cercospora Asclepiadis Ell.
Cercospora clavata (Gerard) Cke.
Cercospora venturioides Pk.
Cercospora elaeochroma Sacc.
Cercospora illinoensis Barthol.
Colletotrichum salmonicolor O'Gara.
{ Coniothyrium sphaerosporum (Pk.) Tassi.
Sphaeropsis sphaerospora Pk.
Diaporthe Asclepiadis Ell. & Ev.
Didymella cornuta Ell. & Ev.
Erysiphe Cichoracearum DC. †
Fusarium roseum Lk.
{ Colletotrichum fusarioides (Ell. & Kellerm.)
  O'Gara.
Colletotrichum salmonicolor O'Gara.
Gloeosporium fusarioides Ell. & Kellerm.
Glomerella fusarioides Edgerton.
Hysterium librincola S.
{ Laestadia cinerascens (S.) Sacc.
Sphaerella cinerascens (S.) Cke.
Sphaeria cinerascens S.
Macrosporium asclepiadeum Cke.?
Mollisia Asclepiadis Ell. & Ev.
Phoma asclepiadea Ell. & Ev.
{ Dothidea Asclepiadis S.
Phyllachora Asclepiadis (S.) Sacc.
{ Dothidea cinerascens S.
Phyllachora cinerascens (S.) Sacc.
Phyllactinia corylea (P.) ex Karst.
Phyllactinia guttata (Wallr. ex Fr.) Lév.
Phyllosticta Cornuti Ell. & Kellerm.
Pleospora permunda Cke.
Scolecotrichum Asclepiadis Ell. & Ev.
Septoria asclepiadicola Ell. & Ev., var. syriaca
  Dearness.
Septoria Cryptotaeniae Ell. & Ev.
Sphaeria lactescentium S.
Sphaeria lilacina S.
Stagonospora zonata J. J. Davis.
{ Caeomurus Howei (Pk.) O. Kuntze.
Nigredo (?) Howei (Pk.) Arth.
Trichobasis Howei Pk.
Uromyces Asclepiadis Cke.
Uromyces Howei Pk.
{ Sphaeria Asclepiadis S.
Vermicularia asclepiadea Pass.
Asclepias tuberosa L.
{ Aecidium jamesianum Pk.
Dicaeoma jamesianum Arth. I.
Puccinia Bartholomaei Diet. I.
Puccinia jamesiana Arth. I.

Cercospora Asclepiadorae Ell. & Kellerm.
Cercospora clavata (Gerard) Cke.
Diaporthe Asclepiadis Ell. & Ev.
Nectria Apocyni Pk.
Phyllosticta tuberosa Ell. & Martin.
{ Nigredo (?) Howei (Pk.) Arth.
Uromyces Howei Pk.
Volutella flexuosa C. & E.

Asclepias variegata L.
Erysiphe Cichoracearum DC.
Phyllosticta tuberosa Ell. & Martin.

Asclepias verticillata L.
{ Aecidium Brandegei Pk.
Dicaeoma jamesianum Arth. I.
Leptothyrium pazschkeanum Bubák.
Nectria Apocyni Pk.
Pestalozziella Andersoni Ell. & Ev.
Phomopsis missouriensis Bubák.
Rhabdospora demetriana Bubák.
Rhizoctonia Solani Kühn.
{ Nigredo (?) Howei (Pk.) Arth.
Uromyces Asclepiadis Cke.
Uromyces Howei Pk.
Vermicularia compacta C. & E.

Asclepias sp. indet.
Cladosporium molle Cke.
Diplodia asclepiadea C. & E.
Gloeosporium mollerianum Thm., var. ascle-
  piadeum Sacc.
Leptosphaeria distributa (C. & E.) Sacc.
Lophiostoma imperfectum Ell. & Fairman.

Calotropis procera R. Br.
Cercospora Calotropidis Ell. & Ev.
Cercospora microsora Pat.
Cercospora Patouillardi Sacc. & D. Sacc.
Cladosporium Calotropidis F. L. Stevens.
Placosphaeria Calotropidis Fragoso & Ciferri.

Metastelma angustifolia Turcz.
Metastelma bahamense Griseb.
Metastelma barbigerum Scheele.
Metastelma lineare Bello.
Metastelma palustre Schl.
Metastelma parviflorum R. Br.
Metastelma penicillatum Griseb.
{ Micropuccinia obliqua (B. & C.) Arth. & Jack-
  son.
Puccinia Gonolobi Rav.
Puccinia obliqua B. & C.
Puccinia Philibertiae Ell. & Ev.
Puccinia sphaerospora Syd. & Henn.

Metastelma Schlechtendalii Dcne.
{ Puccinia obliqua B. & C.
Puccinia sphaerospora Syd. & Henn.

Metastelma sp. indet.
Phyllachora Metastelmae Stevens & Dalby.

Funastrum hirtellum (Gray) Schleich.
  Micropuccinia obliqua (B. & C.) Arth. &
    Jackson.
  Puccinia Cynanchi Lagerh.
Cynanchum parviflorum Sw.
  Puccinia Cynanchi Lagerh.
Vincetoxicum bifidum (Hemsl.) Arth.
Vincetoxicum erianthum (Dcne.) Arth.
  ⎰Micropuccina obliqua (B. & C.) Arth. & Jack-
  ⎱ son.
  ⎰Puccinia obliqua B. & C.
Vincetoxicum gonocarpos Walt.
  ⎰Micropuccinia obliqua (B. & C.) Arth. &
  ⎱ Jackson.
  Puccinia Gonolobi Rav.
  Rhysotheca Gonolobi (Lagerh.) G. W. Wilson.
  Nigredo (?) Howei (Pk.) Arth.
Vincetoxicum hirsutum (Michx.) Brit.
  Cercospora Vincetoxici Ell. & Ev.
  ⎰Micropuccinia obliqua (B. & C.) Arth. &
  ⎱ Jackson.
  Puccinia Gonolobi Rav.
  Rhysotheca Gonolobi (Lagerh.) G. W. Wilson.
Vincetoxicum mexicanum Watson.
Vincetoxicum palustre Gray.
Vincetoxicum productum (Torr.) Vail.
  ⎰Micropuccinia obliqua (B. & C.) Arth. &
  ⎱ Jackson.
  Puccinia Gonolobi Rav.
  Puccinia obliqua B. & C.
Vincetoxicum Shortii (Gray) Brit.
  Nigredo (?) Howei (Pk.) Arth.
Vincetoxicum uniflorum (H. B. K.) Arth.
  ⎰Micropuccinia obliqua (B. & C.) Arth. &
  ⎱ Jackson.
  Puccinia obliqua B. & C.
Vincetoxicum sp. indet.
  Cercospora Bellynckii (Westd.) Sacc.
  Plasmopara Vincetoxici Ell. & Ev.
  Puccinia jamesiana Arth. I.
Sarcostemma swartziana Schult.
  Puccinia Araujae Lév.
Stephanotis floribunda Brongn.
  Macrophoma Stephanotidis Tassi.
Hoya carnosa R. Br.
  Gloeosporium sphaerelloides Sacc.
Marsdenia mexicana Dcne.
  Puccinia Marsdeniae Diet. & Holw.
Marsdenia propinqua Hemsl.
  Neostomella ditissima Syd.
Metalepis cubensis Griseb.
  Micropuccinia obliqua (B. & C.) Arth. & Jack-
    son.
Ibatia maritima (Jacq.) Dcne.
  Uromyces Howei Pk.
Gonolobus bifidus Hemsl.
  ⎰Puccinia Gonolobi Rav.
  ⎱Puccinia obliqua B. & C.

Gonolobus edulis Hemsl.
  Fumago vagans Fr.
Gonolobus erianthus Dcne.
  Puccinia Gonolobi Rav.
Gonolobus laevis Michx.
  ⎰Peronospora Gonolobi Lagerh.
  ⎰Plasmopara Gonolobi (Lagerh.) Swingle.
  ⎰Micropuccinia obliqua (B. & C.) Arth. &
  ⎱ Jackson.
  Puccinia Gonolobi Rav.
Gonolobus maritimus R. Br.
  ⎰Nigredo (?) Howei (Pk.) Arth.
  ⎰Uromyces Asclepiadis Cke.
  ⎱Uromyces Howei Pk.
Gonolobus suberosus R. Br.
  ⎰Peronospora Gonolobi Lagerh.
  ⎰Plasmopara Gonolobi (Lagerh.) Swingle.
  ⎰Rhysotheca Gonolobi (Lagerh.) G. W. Wilson.
  ⎰Micropuccinia obliqua (B. & C.) Arth. &
  ⎱ Jackson.
  Puccinia Gonolobi Rav.
Gonolobus uniflorus H. B. K.
  Puccinia Gonolobi Rav.
Gonolobus sp. indet.
  ⎰Didymium obrusseum B. & C.
  ⎰Physarum obrusseum (B. & C.) Rostf.
  ⎰Meliola bidentata Cke.
  ⎱Meliola furcata N. A. F. *1297b.*

CONVOLVULACEAE

Cuscuta Gronovii Willd.
  Protomyces Martindalei Pk.
Cuscuta sp. indet.
  Stagonospora carpathica Baeuml.
Dichondra carolinensis Michx.
Dichondra repens Forst.
Dichondra sericea Sw.
  ⎰Micropuccinia Dichondrae (Mont.) Arth. &
  ⎱ Jackson.
  Puccinia Dichondrae Mont.
Dichondra sp. indet.
  Meliola malacotricha Speg.
Evolvulus argenteus Pursh.
Evolvulus nummularius L.
Evolvulus nuttallianus R. & S.
Evolvulus sericeus Sw.
  ⎰Dicaeoma Lithospermi (Ell. & Kellerm.) O.
  ⎰ Kuntze.
  ⎰Dicaeoma tuyutense (Speg.) Arth.
  ⎱Puccinia Lithospermi Ell. & Kellerm.
Evolvulus sp. indet.
  Aecidium Cressae DC.
  Cercospora Balansae Speg., var. hainensis
    Ciferri & Fragoso.
  Uredo Evolvuli Speg.

Cressa aphylla A. Heller.
Cressa Cretica L.
Cressa depressa Goodding.
Cressa erecta Rydb.
Cressa truxillensis HBK.
   Aecidium Cressae DC.
   Dicaeoma Cressae (Lagerh.) O. Kuntze.
   Puccinia Cressae Lagerh.
   Puccinia cretica Holw.
Breweria humistrata (Walt.) Gray.
   Cercospora Stylismae Tracy & Earle.
Jacquemontia cayensis Brit.
   Albugo Ipomoeae-panduranae (Farl.) Swingle.
Jacquemontia confusa Meissn.
   Albugo Ipomoeae-panduranae (Farl.) Swingle.
   Uromyces gemmatus B. & C.
Jacquemontia nodiflora (Desv.)
   Klebahnia gemmata (B. & C.) Arth.
Jacquemontia pentantha G. Don.
   Aecidium Jacquemontiae Ell. & Ev.
   Albugo Ipomoeae-panduranae (Farl.) Swingle.
Jacquemontia tamnifolia Griseb.
   Coleosporium Ipomoeae Burrill.
   Albugo Ipomoeae-panduranae (Farl.) Swingle.
Thyella hirtiflora (Mart. & Gall.) House.
   Aecidium Jacquemontiae Ell. & Ev.
Convolvulus acetosifolius Steud.
   Cercospora Convolvuli Tracy & Earle.
Convolvulus arvensis L.
   Dicaeoma Convolvuli (Cast.) O. Kuntze.
   Puccinia Convolvuli Cast.
   Rhizoctonia Solani Kühn.
   Septoria Convolvuli Desm.
   Septoria Convolvuli Auct. p. p.
   Septoria septulata W. S. Beach.
Convolvulus atriplicifolius House.
   Dicaeoma Convolvuli (Cast.) O. Kuntze.
   Puccinia Convolvuli Cast.
Convolvulus californicus Choisy.
   Curreya Harknessii Ell. & Ev.
   Dicaeoma Convolvuli (Cast.) O. Kuntze.
   Puccinia Convolvuli Cast.
Convolvulus dissectus Jacq.
   Uredo Operculinae Arth.
Convolvulus hermannioides Gray.
Convolvulus incanus Vahl.
   Albugo Ipomoeae-panduranae (Farl.) Swingle.
Convolvulus interior House.
Convolvulus malacophyllus Greene.
   Dicaeoma Convolvuli (Cast.) O. Kuntze.
Convolvulus luteolus Gray.
   Albugo Ipomoeae-panduranae (Farl.) Swingle.
   Dothidea Calystegiae Cke. & Hark.
   Plowrightia Calystegiae (Cke. & Hark.) Berl.
    & Vogl.
   Puccinia Convolvuli Cast.

Convolvulus nodiflorus Desr.
   Klebahnia gemmata (B. & C.) Arth.
   Puccinia Convolvuli Auct. p. p.
   Uredo gemmata B. & C., var.
   Uromyces gemmatus B. & C.
Convolvulus occidentalis Gray.
   Dicaeoma Convolvuli (Cast.) O. Kuntze.
   Puccinia Convolvuli Cast.
   Septogloeum Convolvuli Ell. & Ev.
Convolvulus polymorphus Greene.
Convolvulus purpuratus Greene.
Convolvulus retusus Colla.
   Cystopus Convolvulacearum Zalewski.
Convolvulus sepium L.
   Cercospora tuberculella J. J. Davis.
   Coleosporium Ipomoeae Burrill.
   Coniothyrium sepium Fairman.
   Albugo Ipomoeae-panduranae (Farl.) Swingle.
   Cystopus cubicus Auct. Amer. p. p.
   Diplodia Convolvuli Dearness & House.
   Mazzantia sepium Sacc. & Penz.
   Ozonium omnivorum Shear.
   Dothidea Calystegiae Cke. & Hark.
   Dothidella Calystegiae (Cke. & Hark.) Theis-
    sen & Syd.
   Plowrightia Calystegiae (Cke. & Hark.) Berl.
    & Vogl.
   Aecidium Calystegiae Cast.
   Aecidium dubium G. W. Clinton.
   Dicaeoma Convolvuli (Cast.) O. Kuntze.
   Puccinia Convolvuli Cast.
   Septoria Calystegiae Westd.
   Septoria Convolvuli Desm.
   Septoria flagellaris Ell. & Ev.
   Septoria Convolvuli Desm., var. dolichospora
    Sacc.
   Stagonospora Convolvuli Dearness & House.
Convolvulus spithamaeus L.
   Puccinia Convolvuli Cast.
   Septogloeum Convolvuli Ell. & Ev.
   Septoria Convolvuli Desm.
   Septoria flagellaris Ell. & Ev.
Convolvulus Soldanella L.
   Dicaeoma Convolvuli (Cast.) O. Kuntze.
   Puccinia Convolvuli Cast.
Convolvulus subacaulis Gray.
Convolvulus villosus Gray.
   Puccinia Convolvuli Cast.
Convolvulus sp. indet.
   Clasterosporium Convolvuli Fragoso & Ciferri.
   Dothiorella Convolvuli Fragoso & Ciferri.
   Guignardia Convolvuli Fragoso & Ciferri.
   Macrophoma Convolvuli Fragoso & Ciferri.
   Metasphaeria Convolvuli Fragoso & Ciferri.
   Mystrosporium polytrichum Cke.
   Phomatospora Convolvuli Fragoso & Ciferri.
   Phyllosticta Batatas (Thm.) Cke.

Convolvulus sp. indet. *(cont.)*
  Septogloeum Convolvuli Ell. & Ev.
  { Sphaerella brachytheca Cke. & Hark.
  { Sphaerella Harknessii Sacc.
  Thecaphora hyalina Fingerh.
Operculina dissecta (Jacq.) House.
  Uredo laeticolor Arth.
  Uredo Operculariae Arth.
Ipomoea acuminata (Vahl) Roem. & Schult.
  Coleosporium Ipomoeae Burrill.
Ipomoea aegyptia L.
  Albugo Ipomoeae-panduranae (Farl.) Swingle.
Ipomoea angustifolia Jacq.
  Coleosporium Ipomoeae Burrill.
Ipomoea arborescens (H. & B.) G. Don.
  { Allodus megalospora C. R. Orton.
  { Puccinia megalospora (C. R. Orton) Arth. &
     Johnston.
  { Allodus superflua (Holw.) C. R. Orton.
  { Puccinia superflua Holw.
Ipomoea barbigera Sweet.
  Coleosporium Ipomoeae Burrill.
Ipomoea Batatas (L.) Lam.

MYXOMYCETES

{ Acrocystis Batatas Ell. & Halsted.
{ Cystospora batata (Ell. & Halsted) Elliott.
Fuligo violacea P. ex Fr.
Physarum plumbeum Fr.

PHYCOMYCETES

Ascophora nucuum Cda.
{ Albugo Ipomoeae-panduranae (Farl.) Swingle.
{ Cystopus Convolvulacearum Zalewski.
{ Cystopus cubicus Auct. p. p.
{ Cystopus Ipomoeae-panduranae Farl.
Mucor Mucedo (L. p. p.) ex Bref.
Mucor racemosus Fres.
Pythium debaryanum Hesse.
Rhizopus Artocarpi Racib.
Rhizopus batatas Nakazawa.
Rhizopus Maydis Bruderl.
Rhizopus nigricans Ehrenb. ex Fr.
Rhizopus Oryzae Went. & Pr. Geerligs.
Rhizopus reflexus Bain.
Rhizopus Tritici Saito.

ASCOMYCETES

Gibberella Saubinetii (Mont.) Sacc.
Melanospora globosa Berl.
Meliola clavulata Wint.
Meliola Ipomoeae Earle.
Nectria Brassicae Ell. & Sacc.
{ Calonectria Ipomoeae (Halsted) Seaver.
{ Hypomyces Ipomoeae (Halsted) Wr.
{ Nectria Ipomoeae Halsted.
Neocosmospora vasinfectum Atk.
Rostrella Coffeae Zimm.
Sclerotinia libertiana Fckl.
Sclerotinia minor? Jagger.

BASIDIOMYCETES

Coleosporium Ipomoeae Burrill.
{ Corticium vagum B. & C.
{ Corticium vagum, var. Solani Burt.
{ Rhizoctonia Solani Kühn.
Marasmius Sacchari Walker.
{ Schizophyllum alneum (L. ex Fr.) Schrt.
{ Schizophyllum commune Fr.

SPHAEROPSIDALES

Aschersonia Aleyrodis Webber.
Diplodia bataticola Harter & Weimer.
Diplodia Gossypii Taubenhaus.
Diplodia Maclurae Speg.
Diplodia natalensis Evans.
{ Diplodia tubericola (Ell. & Ev.) Taubenhaus.
{ Lasiodiplodia tubericola Ell. & Ev.
{ Diaporthe batatatis Harter & Field.
{ Phoma Batatae Ell. & Halsted.
{ Phomopsis Batatae (Ell. & Halsted) Harter &
   Field.
{ Depazea Batatas Thm.
{ Phyllosticta Batatas (Thm.) Cke.
Phyllosticta bataticola Ell. & Martin.
Plenodomus destruens Harter.
Septoria bataticola Taubenhaus.
{ Ceratocystis Batatae E. M. Wilcox.
{ Ceratocystis fimbriata Ell. & Halsted.
{ Cerastostomella fimbriata Elliott.
{ Sphaeronema fimbriatum (Ell. & Halsted) Sacc.

MELANCONIALES

Pestalozzia Batatae Ell. & Ev.

HYPHOMYCETES

Actinomyces chromogenus Gasp.
Actinomyces poolensis Taubenhaus.
Botrytis cinerea P. †
Botrytis nivosa Cke.
Botrytis vulgaris (Lk.) ex Fr.
Monosporium uredinicola F. L. Stevens.
{ Oospora lactis (Fres.) Sacc.
{ Oosporoidea lactis (Fres.) Sumstine.
Penicillium expansum Lk.
Penicillium luteum Zuk.
Ramularia Coleosporii Sacc.
Trichoderma Köningi Oud.
Trichoderma lignorum (Tode) ex Harz.
Trichothecium roseum Lk.
Verticillium atro-album Reinke & Berthold.
Verticillium cinnabarinum (Cda.) Reinke &
   Berthold.

DEMATIACEAE

Cercospora batatae Zimm.
Cladosporium tuberum Cke.
Coniosporium epiphyllum Sacc.
Macrosporium Solani Ell. & Martin.
Mystrosporium polytrichum Cke.

Ipomoea Batatas (*cont.*)

TUBERCULARIACEAE

Fusarium acuminatum Ell. & Ev.
Fusarium batatatis Wollenw.
Fusarium caudatum Wollenw.
Fusarium caudatum Wr., var. volutum **Wr.**
Fusarium conglutinans Wr.
Fusarium culmorum (W. G. Sm.) Sacc.
Fusarium discolor App. & Wollenw.
Fusarium discolor, var. sulphureum (Schl.)
    App. & Wollenw.
Fusarium falcatum App. & Wollenw.
⌠Fusarium flocciferum Cda.
⌡Fusarium tuberum Cke.
Fusarium gibbosum App. & Wollenw.
Fusarium hyperoxysporum Wollenw.
Fusarium incarnatum (Rob.) Sacc.
Fusarium Lycopersici Sacc.
Fusarium metachroum App. & Wollenw.
Fusarium niveum E. F. Sm.
Fusarium orthoceras App. & Wollenw.
Fusarium orthoceras App. & Wollenw., var. tri-
    septatum Wollenw.
Fusarium oxysporum Schl.
Fusarium putrefaciens Ostw.
Fusarium radicicola Wollenw.
Fusarium redolens Wollenw.
Fusarium rubiginosum App. & Wollenw.
Fusarium sclerotium Wollenw.
Fusarium Solani (Mart.) Sacc.
Fusarium subulatum App. & Wollenw.
Fusarium tracheiphilum Erw. Sm.
Fusarium vasinfectum Atk.

MISCELLANEA

Monilochaetes infuscans Ell. & Halsted.
Monilochaetes nigricans Ehr.
Ozonium auricomum Lk.
⌠Ozonium omnivorum Shear.
⌡Phomatrichum omnivorum (Shear) Duggar.
⌠Rhizoctonia Batatas Fr.
⌡Sclerotium Batatas S. ined.
Sclerotium bataticola Taubenhaus.
Sclerotium Rolfsii Sacc.
Typhula gyrans (Batsch) Fr.

Ipomoea Bona-nox L.
Coleosporium Ipomoeae Burrill.
Albugo Ipomoeae-panduranae Swingle.

Ipomoea carolina L.
Coleosporium Ipomoeae Burrill.
Albugo Ipomoeae-panduranae (Farl.) Swingle.
⌠Allodus crassipes (B. & C.) Arth.
⌡Puccinia crassipes B. & C.
⌠Allodus megalospora C. R. Orton.
⌡Puccinia megalospora (C. R. Orton) Arth. &
    Johnston.
Puccinia megalospora ("Doidge") Sacc. &
    Trott.

Ipomoea cathartica Poir.
Coleosporium Ipomoeae Burrill.
Albugo Ipomoeae-panduranae (Farl.) Swingle.
Meliola caymanensis Ell. & Ev.
Meliola clavulata Wint.
Meliola Ipomoeae Earle non Rehm.
Meliola quadrispina Racib.
⌠Allodus crassipes (B. & C.) Arth.
⌡Puccinia crassipes B. & C.

Ipomoea coccinea L.
Coleosporium Ipomoeae Burrill.
Albugo Ipomoeae-panduranae (Farl.) Swingle.
Thielavia basicola (B. & Br.) Zopf.
Vermicularia Ipomoearum S.

Ipomoea commutata Roem. & Schult.
⌠Aecidium Ipomoeae B.
⎪Albugo Ipomoeae-panduranae (Farl.) Swingle.
⎨Cystopus cubicus Auct. p. p.
⎪Cystopus Ipomoeae-panduranae Farl.
⌡Cystopus Tragopogonis Auct. p. p.
Puccinia crassipes B. & C.

Ipomoea crassicaulis (Benth.) B. L. Robinson.
Coleosporium Ipomoeae Burrill.
Puccinia nocticolor Holw.

Ipomoea digitata L.
Coleosporium Ipomoeae Burrill.

Ipomoea dissecta (Jacq.) Pursh.
Coleosporium Ipomoeae Burrill.
Uredo laeticolor Arth.

Ipomoea dubia Hemsl.
Coleosporium Ipomoeae Burrill.

Ipomoea fistulosa Mart.
Coleosporium Ipomoeae Burrill.
⌠Allodus nocticolor (Holw.) C. R. Orton.
⌡Puccinia nocticolor Holw.
⌠Allodus rubicunda (Holw.) Arth. & Orton.
⌡Puccinia rubicunda Holw.

Ipomoea glabra (Aubl.) Choisy.
Coleosporium Ipomoeae Burrill.

Ipomoea glabriuscula House.
Coleosporium Ipomoeae Burrill.
⌠Allodus crassipes (B. & C.) Arth.
⌡Puccinia crassipes B. & C.

Ipomoea hederacea Jacq.
Cercospora Ipomoeae Wint.
Coleosporium Ipomoeae Burrill.
⌠Albugo Ipomoeae-panduranae (Farl.) Swingle.
⎨Cystopus Convolvulacearum Zalewski.
⌡Cystopus Ipomoeae-panduranae Farl.
Fusarium Batatas Wollenw.
Fusarium hyperoxysporum Wollenw.

Ipomoea hirsutula Jacq.

Ipomoea incarnata Choisy.
Albugo Ipomoeae-panduranae (Farl.) Swingle.
Coleosporium Ipomoeae Burrill.

Ipomoea intrapilosa Rose.
Aecidium Ipomoeae Speg.
⌠Allodus nocticolor (Holw.) C. R. Orton.
⌡Puccinia nocticolor Holw.

Ipomoea intrapilosa (*cont.*)
- Allodus megalospora C. R. Orton.
- Puccinia megalospora (C. R. Orton) Arth. & Johnston.

Ipomoea jalapa (L.) Pursh.
- Cystopus cubicus Auct. p. p.
- Cystopus Ipomoeae-panduranae Farl.
- Cystopus Tragopogonis Auct. p. p.
- Aecidium jalapense Holw.
- Dicaeoma jalapense Arth.
- Puccinia jalapense (Arth.) Barthol.

Ipomoea lacunosa L.
- Cercospora Ipomoeae Wint.
- Coleosporium Ipomoeae Burrill.
- Albugo Ipomoeae-panduranae (Farl.) Swingle.
- Cystopus Ipomoeae-panduranae Farl.

Ipomoea laeta Gray.
- Coleosporium Ipomoeae Burrill.

Ipomoea leptophylla Torr.
- Comoclathris Ipomoeae Clements.
- Pyrenophora Ipomoeae Crypt. Form. Colo. *450*.
- Albugo Ipomoeae-panduranae (Farl.) Swingle.
- Cystopus Convolvulacearum Zalewski.
- Cystopus cubicus Auct. p. p.
- Cystopus Ipomoeae-panduranae Farl.

Ipomoea littoralis Blume.

Ipomoea macrocalyx (Ruiz. & Pav.) Choisy.

Ipomoea microsepala Benth.
- Coleosporium Ipomoeae Burrill.

Ipomoea microsticta Hallier.
- Puccinia crassipes B. & C.

Ipomoea muricata Roem. & Schult.
- Coleosporium Ipomoeae Burrill.

Ipomoea murucoides Roem. & Schult.
- Allodus megalospora C. R. Orton.
- Puccinia megalospora (C. R. Orton) Arth. & Johnston.
- Puccinia nocticolor Holw.
- Puccinia superflua Holw.

Ipomoea mutabilis Lindl.
- Coleosporium Ipomoeae Burrill.

Ipomoea pandurata (L.) G. F. W. Meyer.
- Botrytis vulgaris (Lk.) ex Fr.
- Cercospora Ipomoeae Wint.
- Caeoma Ipomoeae (S.) Lk.
- Coleosporium Ipomoeae Burrill.
- Uredo Ipomoeae S.
- ?Aecidium Convolvuli M. A. Curtis.
- Aecidium Ipomoeae B.
- Aecidium Ipomoeae-panduranae S.
- Aecidium rutilum Bon.
- Albugo Ipomoeae-panduranae (Farl.) Swingle.
- Caeoma convolvulatum Lk.
- Cystopus Convolvulacearum Zalewski.
- Cystopus cubicus Auct. Amer. p. p.
- Cystopus Ipomoeae-panduranae Farl.
- Cystopus Tragopogonis Auct. Amer. p. p.
- Uredo Convolvuli Spreng.
- Pestalozzia funerea Desm.

Phlyctaena Ipomoeae Ell. & Ev.
Phyllosticta Ipomoeae Ell. & Kellerm.
Sphaeropsis Ipomoeae Ell. & Ev.
Trichoderma Koenigii Oud.

Ipomoea parasitica Don.
- Albugo Ipomoeae-panduranae (Farl.) Swingle.
- Puccinia crassipes B. & C.

Ipomoea Pes-caprae Roth.

Ipomoea Pes-tigridis L.
- Albugo Ipomoeae-panduranae (Farl.) Swingle.
- Cystopus Convolvulacearum Zalewski.
- Cystopus Ipomoeae-panduranae Farl.

Ipomoea Petri Donn. Sm.
- Coleosporium Ipomoeae Burrill.

Ipomoea purga (Lindl.) Hayne.
- Coleosporium Ipomoeae Burrill.
- Allodus crassipes (B. & C.) Arth.
- Puccinia crassipes B. & C.

Ipomoea purpurea (L.) Roth.
- Cercospora alabamensis Atk.
- Cercospora viridula Ell. & Ev.
- Chaetophoma capsularum (S.) Starb.
- Phoma capsularum (S.) Cke.
- Sphaeria capsularum S.
- Coleosporium Ipomoeae Burrill.
- Albugo Ipomoeae-panduranae (Farl.) Swingle.
- Cystopus Convolvulacearum Zalewski.
- Cystopus Ipomoeae-panduranae Farl.
- Mycorrhiza of Legumes F. R. Jones.
- Allodus crassipes (B. & C.) Arth.
- Puccinia crassipes B. & C.
- Puccinia Ipomoeae Cke.
- Puccinia Ipomoeae-panduranae Auct.
- Septoria Convolvuli Desm.
- Vermicularia Ipomoearum S.

Ipomoea Quamoclit L.
- Albugo Ipomoeae-panduranae (Farl.) Swingle.

Ipomoea rubra (Vahl) Millsp.
- Coleosporium Ipomoeae Burrill.
- Albugo Ipomoeae-panduranae (Farl.) Swingle.
- Meliola clavulata Wint.

Ipomoea sagittata Cav.
- Coleosporium Ipomoeae Burrill.

Ipomoea simulans Hanbury.
- Albugo Ipomoeae-panduranae (Farl.) Swingle.

Ipomoea speciosa P.

Ipomoea stans Cav.
- Coleosporium Ipomoeae Burrill.

Ipomoea Steudellii Millsp.
- Puccinia crassipes B. & C.

Ipomoea stolonifera (Cyrill) Poir.
- Coleosporium Ipomoeae Burrill.

Ipomoea tiliacea (W.) Choisy.
- Coleosporium Ipomoeae Burrill.
- Albugo Ipomoeae-panduranae (Farl.) Swingle.
- Meliola clavulata Wint.
- Meliola Ipomoeae Earle non Rehm.
- Allodus crassipes (B. & C.) Arth.
- Puccinia crassipes B. & C.

Ipomoea trichocarpa Ell.
  Coleosporium Ipomoeae Burrill.
  Albugo Ipomoeae-panduranae (Farl.) Swingle.
  ⎰ Allodus crassipes (B. & C.) Arth.
  ⎱ Puccinia crassipes B. & C.
Ipomoea trifida (H. B. K.) G. Don.
  Coleosporium Ipomoeae Burrill.
  ⎰ Allodus crassipes (B. & C.) Arth.
  ⎱ Puccinia crassipes B. & C.
Ipomoea triloba L.
  ⎧ Caeoma Ipomoeae (S.) Lk.
  ⎨ Coleosporium Ipomoeae Burrill.
  ⎩ Uredo Ipomoeae S.
  Albugo Ipomoeae-panduranae (Farl.) Swingle.
  ⎧ Allodus crassipes (B. & C.) Arth.
  ⎪ Puccinia crassipes B. & C.
  ⎨ Puccinia Ipomoeae-panduratae Holw.
  ⎩ Puccinia Ipomoeae-panduratae Syd.
  Puccinia opulenta Speg.
  Septoria Convolvuli Desm.
  Xyloma sphaerioides S. Syn. Car.
Ipomoea tyrianthina Lindl.
  Coleosporium Ipomoeae Burrill.
Ipomoea wolcottiana Rose.
  ⎰ Allodus insignis (Holw.) C. R. Orton.
  ⎱ Puccinia insignis Holw.
Ipomoea sp. indet.
  Aspergillus glaucus (L.) ex Lk.
  Metasphaeria Ipomoeae Ell. & Ev.
  Nectria perpusilla Sacc.
  Phyllosticta Ipomoeae Ell. & Kellerm.
  Physarella oblonga (B. & C.) Morg.
  Puccinia rubicunda Holw.
Exogonium arenarium Choisy.
  ⎰ Allodus opulenta (Speg.) C. R. Orton.
  ⎱ Puccinia opulenta Speg.
Exogonium repandum Choisy.
  Phyllosticta Ipomoeae Ell. & Kellerm.
Rivea speciosa Choisy.
  Coleosporium Ipomoeae Burrill.

POLEMONIACEAE

Phlox albomarginata M. E. Jones.
Phlox alyssifolia Greene.
  ⎰ Allodus Douglasii (Ell. & Ev.) C. R. Orton.
  ⎱ Puccinia Douglasii Ell. & Ev.
Phlox amoena Sims.
  Allodus Douglasii (Ell. & Ev.) C. R. Orton.
  Cercospora omphakodes Ell. & Holw.
  Erysiphe Cichoracearum DC. †
  Vermicularia phlogina Fairman.
Phlox caespitosa Nutt.
  Puccinia Giliae Hark.
  Sphaerella pachyasca Rostr.
Phlox canescens Torr. & Gr.
Phlox condensata (Gray) Nels.
  ⎰ Allodus Douglasii (Ell. & Ev.) C. R. Orton.
  ⎱ Puccinia Douglasii Ell. & Ev.

Phlox depressa (E. Nels.) Rydb.
  ⎰ Allodus Douglasii (Ell. & Ev.) C. R. Orton.
  ⎱ Puccinia Douglasii Ell. & Ev.
  Allodus Giliae C. R. Orton.
Phlox diapensioides Greene.
  ⎰ Allodus Douglasii (Ell. & Ev.) C. R. Orton.
  ⎱ Puccinia Richardsonii Syd.
Phlox divaricata L.
  ⎧ Aecidium Cerastii Wint.
  ⎨ Aecidium Phlogis Pk.
  ⎩ Aecidium wilcoxianum Thm.
  Allodus Giliae C. R. Orton.
  Puccinia arabicola Ell. & Ev.
  Puccinia plumbaria Pk.
  ⎰ Aecidium Polemonii Pk.
  ⎱ Nigredo Polemonii Arth. I.
  Cercospora omphakodes Ell. & Holw.
  ⎰ Erysiphe Cichoracearum DC.
  ⎱ Erysiphe Phlogis S.
  Peronospora phlogina Diet. & Holw.
  Phoma Cichorii Pass.
  ⎰ Septoria divaricata Ell. & Ev.
  ⎱ Septoria Phlogis Auct. Amer.
  Sphaerotheca Castagnei Lév.
  Sphaerotheca Humuli (DC.) Burrill, var.
    fuliginea (Schl.) Salmon.
  Vermicularia phlogina Fairman.
Phlox Douglasii Hook.
  ⎧ Allodus Douglasii (Ell. & Ev.) C. R. Orton.
  ⎪ Puccinia Douglasii Ell. & Ev.
  ⎨ Aecidium wilcoxianum Thm.
  ⎪ Puccinia plumbaria Pk.
  ⎩ Puccinia plumbaria Pk., var. phlogina Ell.
  Sphaerella pachyasca Rostr.
Phlox Drummondii Hook.
  Ascochyta phlogina Fairman.
  Ascochyta Phlogis Vogl.
  ⎰ Erysiphe Cichoracearum DC.
  ⎱ Erysiphe lamprocarpa Lév. p. p.
  Oidium Drummondii Thm.
  Ophiobolus sceliscophorus Fairman.
  Rhizoctonia Solani Kühn.
  Septoria Drummondii Ell. & Ev.
  Thielavia basicola (B. & Br.) Zopf.
Phlox floridana Benth.
  Cercospora omphakodes Ell. & Holw.
Phlox glabrata (E. Nels.) A. Brand.
  Allodus Douglasii (Ell. & Ev.) C. R. Orton.
Phlox gracilis Greene.
  Puccinia plumbaria Pk.
Phlox Hoodii Richards.
  Aecidium Phlogis Ell. & Ev.
  Allodus Douglasii (Ell. & Ev.) C. R. Orton.
Phlox longifolia Nutt.
  ⎧ Aecidium Phlogis Ell. & Ev.
  ⎪ Allodus Giliae C. R. Orton.
  ⎨ Puccinia fragilis Tracy & Gall.
  ⎪ Puccinia plumbaria Pk.
  ⎩ Puccinia plumbaria, var. phlogina N. A.F. *1044.*

Phlox maculata L.
  Nigredo Polemonii Arth. I.
  Uromyces Polemonii (Arth.) Barthol. I.
  Cercospora omphakodes Ell. & Holw.
Phlox multiflora A. Nels.
Phlox nana Nutt.
  Allodus Douglasii (Ell. & Ev.) C. R. Orton.
  Puccinia Douglasii (Ell. & Ev.) C. R. Orton.
  Allodus Giliae C. R. Orton.
Phlox paniculata L.
  Aecidium Polemonii Pk.
  Puccinia plumbaria Pk.
  Erysiphe Cichoracearum DC. †
  Erysiphe lamprocarpa Lév. p. p.
  Erysiphe Phlogis S.
  Leptosphaeria comatella (C. & E.) Sacc.
  Dothidea Phlogis S.
  Phyllachora Phlogis (S.) Sacc.
  Phyllactinia corylea (P.) ex Karst.
  Septoria divaricatae Ell. & Ev.
  Septoria Phlogis Auct. Amer.
  Sphaeria Dematium P.
  Vermicularia Dematium (P.) Fr.
Phlox pilosa L.
  Allodus Giliae C. R. Orton.
  Puccinia fragilis Tracy & Gall.
  Aecidium Polemonii Pk.
  Uromyces acuminatus Arth. I.
Phlox procumbens Lehm.
Phlox rigida Benth.
Phlox scleranthifolia Rydb.
  Allodus Douglasii (Ell. & Ev.) C. R. Orton.
  Puccinia Douglasii Ell. & Ev.
Phlox Richardsoni Hook.
  Puccinia Giliae Hark.
  Puccinia Douglasii Ell. & Ev.
  Puccinia Richardsoni Syd.
Phlox speciosa Pursh.
  Aecidium Phlogis Ell. & Ev.
  Allodus Giliae C. R. Orton.
  Puccinia fragilis Tracy & Gall.
  Puccinia plumbaria Pk.
  Puccinia Purpusii Henn.
Phlox Stansburyi (Torr.) Heller.
  Allodus Giliae C. R. Orton.
  Puccinia plumbaria Pk.
Phlox subulata L.
  Allodus Douglasii (Ell. & Ev.) C. R. Orton.
  Puccinia Douglasii Ell. & Ev.
  ?Puccinia Giliae Hark.
  Sclerotium Rolfsii Sacc.
Phlox undulata Ait.
  Sclerotium medullare S.
Phlox sp. indet.
  Cercospora phlogina Pk.
  Erysiphe communis (Wallr.) Schl.
  Erysiphe Martii Lév.
  Leptosphaeria Phlogis Oud.

  Pleospora ciliata Ell.
  Pyrenophora ciliata (Ell.) Sacc.
  Pleospora magnifica Pk.
  Sphaerotheca Humuli (DC.) Burrill. †
Gilia aristella Gray.
  Sphaerotheca Humuli (DC.) Burrill. †
Gilia atractyloides Steud.
  Dicaeoma Giliae (Hark.) O. Kuntze.
  Puccinia Giliae Hark.
Gilia Bigelovii Gray.
  Dicaeoma Ciliac (Hark.) O. Kuntze.
  Dicaeoma Sarcobati Arth.
  Puccinia subnitens Diet.
Gilia Bolanderi Gray.
  Puccinia giliicola Henn.
  Puccinia plumbaria Pk.
Gilia californica Benth.
  Puccinia Giliae Hark.
  Puccinia giliicola Henn.
Gilia capitata Dougl.
  Dicaeoma Giliae (Hark.) O. Kuntze.
  Puccinia Giliae Hark.
  Puccinia plumbaria Pk.
  Sphaerotheca Humuli (DC.) Burrill. †
Gilia ciliata Benth.
  Dicaeoma Giliae (Hark.) O. Kuntze.
  Puccinia Giliae Hark.
  Allodus Giliae C. R. Orton.
  Puccinia giliicola Henn.
  Puccinia plumbaria Pk.
Gilia divaricata Torr.
Gilia filifolia Nutt.
Gilia gilioides (Benth.) Greene.
  Dicaeoma Giliae (Hark.) O. Kuntze.
  Puccinia Giliae Hark.
Gilia gracilis Hook.
  Peronospora Giliae Ell. & Ev.
  Aecidium Giliae Pk.
  Allodus Giliae C. R. Orton.
  Puccinia plumbaria Pk.
  Puccinia Purpusii Henn.
  Puccinia wilcoxiana Thm.
  Sphaerotheca Castagnei Lév. p. p.
  Sphaerotheca Humuli (DC.) Burrill. †
Gilia grandiflora Gray.
  Dicaeoma Giliae (Hark.) O. Kuntze.
  Puccinia Giliae Hark.
Gilia heterophylla Dougl.
  Sphaerotheca Castagnei Lév. p. p.
  Sphaerotheca Humuli (DC.) Burrill. †
Gilia humilis (Greene) Piper.
  Allodus Giliae C. R. Orton.
  Puccinia plumbaria Pk.
  Puccinia wilcoxiana Thm.
Gilia inconspicua (Sm.) Dougl.
  Dicaeoma Sarcobati Arth. I.
  Puccinia subnitens Diet. I.

Gilia intertexta Steud.
  { Dicaeoma Giliae (Hark.) O. Kuntze.
  { Puccinia Giliae Hark.
Gilia leptomeria Gray.
  { Dicaeoma Sarcobati Arth. I.
  { Puccinia subnitens Diet. I.
Gilia linearis (Nutt.) Gray.
  Puccinia plumbaria Pk.
  { Sphaerotheca Castagnei Lév. p. p.
  { Sphaerotheca Humuli (DC.) Burrill. †
  Sphaerotheca Humuli (DC.) Burrill, var. fuliginea (Schl.) Salmon.
  { Aecidium Polemonii Pk.
  { Nigredo Polemonii Arth. I.
  { Uromyces acuminatus Arth. I.
  { Uromyces Polemonii (Arth.) Barthol. I.
Gilia liniflora Benth.
  Puccinia Giliae Hark.
Gilia longiflora Don.
  Dicaeoma Sarcobati Arth. I.
  Puccinia Giliae Hark.
Gilia micrantha Steud.
  { Allodus Giliae C. R. Orton.
  { Puccinia plumbaria Pk.
  Sphaerotheca Humuli (DC.) Burrill. †
Gilia Nuttallii Gray.
  { Aecidium Giliae Pk.
  { Allodus Giliae C. R. Orton.
  { Puccinia plumbaria Pk.
  { Mycosphaerella phlogina (Ell. & Ev.) Earle.
  { Sphaerella phlogina Ell. & Ev.
Gilia pinnatifida Nutt.
  { Dicaeoma Giliae (Hark.) O. Kuntze.
  { Puccinia Giliae Hark.
Gilia pungens Benth.
  { Allodus Douglasii (Ell. & Ev.) C. R. Orton.
  { Puccinia Douglasii Ell. & Ev.
  Puccinia Giliae Hark.
Gilia pungens Benth., var. **Hookeri** Gray.
  { Allodus yosemitana (Blasdale) Arth. & Orton.
  { Puccinia yosemitana Blasdale.
Gilia rubra (L.) Heller.
  Sphaerotheca Humuli (DC.) Burrill. †
Gilia spicata Nutt.
  Nigredo Polemonii Arth. I.
Gilia squarrosa Hook. & Arn.
  Diplodia Leptodactyli Earle.
  ?Puccinia Giliae Hark.
Gilia tinctoria Benth.
  Puccinia plumbaria Pk.
Gilia tricolor Benth.
  { Artotrogus debaryanus (Hesse) Atk.
  { Pythium debaryanum Hesse.
Gilia virgata Steud., var. **floribunda** Gray.
  Puccinia Giliae Hark.
Polemonium boreale Adams.
  Gloeosporium Roaldii Lind.
  Rhabdospora Drabae (Fckl.) Berl. & Vogl.

Polemonium confertum Gray.
  Pleospora coloradensis Ell. & Ev.
Polemonium humile Willd.
  Phyllachora? Polemonii Hark.
  Pleospora herbarum (Fr.) Rabh.
  Pyrenophora polyphragmoides Sacc. & Scalia.
Polemonium micranthum Benth.
  Sphaerotheca Humuli (DC.) Burrill. †
Polemonium intermedium (A. Brand.) Rydb.
Polemonium occidentale Greene.
  { Micropuccinia Polemonii (Diet. & Holw.) Arth. & Jackson.
  { Puccinia Polemonii Diet. & Holw.
Polemonium pulcherrimum Hook.
  { Micropuccinia gulosa (H. S. Jackson) Arth. & Jackson.
  { Puccinia gulosa H. S. Jackson.
Polemonium reptans L.
  { Aecidium Polemonii Pk.
  { Nigredo Polemonii Arth. I.
  { Uromyces acuminatus Arth. I.
  { Uromyces Polemonii Barthol. I.
  { Uromyces Spartinae Farl. I.
  { Micropuccinia Polemonii (Diet. & Holw.) Arth. & Jackson.
  { Puccinia Polemonii Diet. & Holw.
  Septoria Polemonii Thm.
  Septoria polemoniicola Ell. & Martin.
Polemonium van Bruntiae Brit.
  Leptostroma herbarum (Fr.) Sacc.
  Phoma Oudemansii Berl. & Vogl.
  Puccinia Polemonii Diet. & Holw.
  Mycosphaerella pachyasca (Rostr.) Vgr.
  Vermicularia phlogina Fairman.
Loeselia ciliata L.
Loeselia glandulosa G. Don.
Loeselia mexicana Brand.
  { Dicaeoma fumosum (Holw.) Arth.
  { Puccinia fumosa Holw.

HYDROPHYLLACEAE

Hydrophyllum albifrons Heller.
  { Aecidium Hydrophylli Pk.
  { Dicaeoma apocryptum (Ell. & Tracy) O. Kuntze. I.
  { Puccinia apocrypta Ell. & Tracy.
  { Puccinia montanensis Auct. Amer. p. p. 1.
Hydrophyllum appendiculatum Michx.
  { Aecidium Hydrophylli Pk.
  { Dicaeoma apocryptum (Ell. & Tracy) O. Kuntze. I.
  Erysiphe Cichoracearum DC. †
Hydrophyllum canadense L.
  Aecidium Hydrophylli Pk.
  { Erysiphe Cichoracearum DC. †
  { Erysiphe lamprocarpa Auct. Amer. p. p.
  Gloeosporium Hydrophylli Dearness & House.
  Septocylindrium Hydrophylli Daniels.

Hydrophyllum capitatum Dougl.
  Aecidium Hydrophylli Pk.
  Dicaeoma apocryptum (Ell. & Tracy) O.
    Kuntze. I.
  Puccinia montanensis I. Auct. Amer. p. p.
  Erysiphe Cichoracearum DC. †
  Micropuccinia Hydrophylli (Pk. & Clinton)
    Arth. & Jackson.
  Puccinia Hydrophylli Pk. & Clinton.
  Ramularia Hydrophylli Ell. & Ev.

Hydrophyllum Fendleri (Gray) Heller.
  Aecidium Hydrophylli Pk.
  Dicaeoma apocryptum (Ell. & Tracy) O.
    Kuntze. I.
  Puccinia apocrypta Ell. & Tracy. I.
  Puccinia montanensis I. Auct. Amer. p. p.
  Erysiphe Cichoracearum DC. †
  Micropuccinia Hydrophylli (Pk. & Clinton)
    Arth. & Jackson.

Hydrophyllum macrophyllum Nutt.
  Erysiphe Cichoracearum DC. †
  Peronospora Hydrophylli Waite.

Hydrophyllum occidentale Gray.
  Aecidium Hydrophylli Pk.
  Dicaeoma apocryptum (Ell. & Tracy) O.
    Kuntze. I.
  Puccinia Agropyri I. Auct. Amer. p. p.
  Puccinia montanensis I. Auct. Amer. p. p.
  Erysiphe Cichoracearum DC. †
  Erysiphe Polygoni DC. †
  Micropuccinia Hydrophylli (Pk. & Clinton)
    Arth. & Jackson.
  Puccinia Hydrophylli Pk. & Clinton.

Hydrophyllum tenuipes Heller.
  Aecidium Hydrophylli Pk.
  Dicaeoma apocryptum (Ell. & Tracy) O.
    Kuntze. I.
  Puccinia montanensis I. Auct. Amer. p. p.

Hydrophyllum virginianum L.
  Aecidium Hydrophylli Pk.
  Dicaeoma apocryptum (Ellis & Tracy) O.
    Kuntze.
  Puccinia apocrypta Ell. & Tracy. I.
  Cicinnobolus Cesatii DBy.
  Erysiphe Cichoracearum DC. †
  Erysiphe lamprocarpa Auct. Amer. p. p.
  Gloeosporium Hydrophylli Dearness & House.
  Peronospora Hydrophylli Waite.
  Micropuccinia Hydrophylli (Pk. & Clinton)
    Arth. & Jackson.
  Puccinia Hydrophylli Pk. & Clinton.
  Septoria Hydrophylli Ell. & Dearness.
  Sphaerotheca Castagnei Lév.
  Sphaerotheca Humuli (DC.) Burrill, var. fuli-
    ginea (Schl.) Salmon.

Hydrophyllum Watsoni (Gray) Rydb.
  Aecidium Hydrophylli Pk.
  Dicaeoma apocryptum (Ell. & Tracy) O.
    Kuntze. I.

  Micropuccinia Hydrophylli (Pk. & Clinton)
    Arth. & Jackson.
  Puccinia Hydrophylli Pk. & Clinton.

Nemophila aurita Lindl.

Nemophila parviflora Dougl.
  Erysiphe Cichoracearum DC. †
  Thielavia basicola (B. & Br.) Zopf.

Nemophila insignis Dougl. ex Benth.
  Thielavia basicola (B. & Br.) Zopf.

Nemophila microcalyx (Nutt.) Fisch. & Mey.
  Aecidium Hydrophylli Pk.

Ellisia chrysanthemifolia Benth.
  Aecidium Hydrophylli Pk.
  Dicaeoma apocryptum (Ell. & Tracy) O.
    Kuntze. I.

Ellisia Nyctelea L.
  Aecidium Hydrophylli Pk.
  Dicaeoma apocryptum (Ell. & Tracy) O.
    Kuntze. I.
  Puccinia apocrypta Ell. & Tracy. I.
  Erysiphe Cichoracearum DC. †
  Peronospora Hydrophylli Waite.
  Puccinia Hydrophylli Pk. & Clinton.

Phacelia alpina Rydb.
  Aecidium Phaceliae Pk.
  Dicaeoma apocryptum (Ell. & Tracy) O.
    Kuntze. I.

Phacelia circinata Jacq.
  Aecidium Phaceliae Pk.
  Dicaeoma apocryptum (Ell. & Tracy) O.
    Kuntze. I.
  Puccinia apocrypta Ell. & Tracy. I.
  Puccinia montanensis I. Auct. Amer. p. p.
  Ampelomyces quisqualis Ces.
  Erysiphe Cichoracearum DC. †
  Puccinia Phaceliae Syd. & Holw.
  Uredo contraria Arth.

Phacelia crenulata Torr.
  Dicaeoma Sarcobati Arth. I.
  Puccinia subnitens Diet. I.

Phacelia distans Benth.

Phacelia hispida Gray.

Phacelia leucophylla Torr.
  Aecidium Phaceliae Pk.
  Dicaeoma apocryptum (Ell. & Tracy) O.
    Kuntze. I.
  Puccinia apocrypta Ell. & Tracy I.
  Puccinia montanensis I. Auct. Amer. p. p.

Phacelia Menziesii Torr.
  Erysiphe Cichoracearum DC. †

Phacelia nemoralis Greene.
  Aecidium Phaceliae Pk.
  Puccinia montanensis I. Auct. Amer. p. p.

Phacelia ramosissima Dougl.
  Aecidium Phaceliae Pk.
  Dicaeoma apocryptum (Ell. & Tracy) O.
    Kuntze. I.
  Oidium erysiphoides Fr.

Phacelia sericea (Graham) Gray.
Dicaeoma apocryptum Ell. & Tracy. I.
Cylindrosporium Phaceliae Ell. & Ev.
⎰Micropuccinia Phaceliae (Syd. & Holw.) Arth.
⎱ & Jackson.
Puccinia Phaceliae Syd. & Holw.
Phacelia tanacetifolia Benth.
⎰Aecidium Phaceliae Pk.
⎱Dicaeoma apocryptum (Ell. & Tracy) O.
Kuntze. I.
Puccinia montanensis I. Auct. Amer. p. p.
Uredo contraria Arth.
Phacelia sp. indet.
⎰Camarosporium Phaceliae (Cke. & Hark.)
⎱ Tassi.
Dichomera Phaceliae Cke. & Hark.
Diaporthe Phaceliae Cke. & Hark.
Romanzoffia sitchensis Bong.
⎰Micropuccinia Romanzoffiae (H. S. Jackson)
⎱ Arth. & Jackson.
Puccinia Romanzoffiae H. S. Jackson.
Eriodictyon californicum Dcne.
Heterosporium californicum Ell. & Ev.
Heterosporium Eucalypti Ell. & Ev., var.
maculicola Ell. & Ev.
Eriodictyon glutinosum Benth.
Heterosporium californicum Ell. & Ev.
Heterosporium Eucalypti Ell. & Ev., var. mac-
ulicola Ell. & Ev.
Torula glutinosa Cke. & Hark.
Hydrolea ovata Nutt.
Cercospora Namae Dearness & House.

BORAGINACEAE

Cordia
(Varronia alba Jacq.).
Metasphaeria abortiva F. L. Stevens.
Cordia alliodora (R. & Pav.) Cham.
⎰Bullaria Cordiae (Arth.) Arth. & Mains.
⎱Puccinia Cordiae Arth.
Cordia.
(Varronia angustifolia West.)
Dimeriella Cordiae (Henn.) Theissen.
Cordia borinquensis Urb.
Meliola longipoda Gaill.
Cordia bullata Roem. & Schult.
Aecidium Cordiae Henn.
Cordia collococca L.
Diatractium Cordiae (F. L. Stevens) Syd.
⎰Hypospila cordiana Ell. & Kelsey.
⎱Trabutiella Cordiae F. L. Stevens.
Cordia corymbosa Willd.
Alveolaria Cordiae Lagerh.
Dimerium Stevensii P. Garman.
⎰Irene longipoda (Gaill.) Toro.
⎱Meliola longipoda Gaill.
Metasphaeria abortiva F. L. Stevens.

Cordia cylindristachya Roem. & Schult.
Aecidium brasiliense Diet.
Aecidium Cordiae Henn.
Alveolaria Cordiae Lagerh.
Cordia ferruginea Roem. & Schult.
Alveolaria Cordiae Lagerh.
Dimeriella Cordiae (Henn.) Theissen.
Leptodothiorella concinna Syd.
Melanops concinna Syd.
Phyllostictina concinna Syd.
Cordia Gerascanthus L.
Dimeriella Cordiae (Henn.) Theissen.
Marasmius stenophyllus Mont.
Puccinia Cordiae (Henn.) Arth.
Puccinia corticola Arth. & Rorer.
Cordia heterophylla Roem. & Schult.
Linochora tetrica Syd.
Cordia laevigata Lam.
Panus Wrightii B. & C.
Stereum duriusculum B. & Br.
Cordia macrophylla L.
Megalonectria pseudotrichia (S.) Seaver.
Cordia nitida Vahl.
⎰Irene longipoda (Gaill.) Toro.
⎱Meliola longipoda Gaill.
Phyllachora orbicularis Speg.
Cordia panicularis Rudge.
Favolus dermoporus B.
Favolus tessellatus Mont.
Hypocrella phyllogena (Mont.) Petch.
Cordia riparia H. B. K.
Alveolaria Cordiae Lagerh.
Cordia sulcata DC.
Dimeriella Cordiae (Henn.) Theissen.
Seynesia Cordiae Ryan.
Cordia sp. indet.
Fumago vagans Fr.
Helminthosporium Varroniae F. L. Stevens.
Meliola molleriana Wint.
Bourreria havanensis Miers.
Aecidium Bourreriae Holw.
Bourreria succulenta Jacq.
Phyllachora Bourreriae Stevens & Dalby.
Tournefortia bicolor Sw.
Tournefortia peruviana Poir.
Tournefortia tomentosa Mill.
Aecidum Tournefortiae Henn.
Tournefortia hirsutissima L.
Aecidium Tournefortiae Henn.
Helminthosporium glabroides F. L. Stevens.
Meliola longipoda Gaill.
Tournefortia laurifolia Vent.
Asterina vagans Speg.
Tournefortia microphylla Bert.
Aecidium Tournefortiae Henn.
⎰Aecidium Tournefortiae Mycologia **9**: 88.
⎱Klebahnia dolichospora (Diet. & Holw.) Arth.
Uromyces dolichosporus Diet. & Holw.

Tournefortia peruviana Poir.
Tournefortia scabra Lam.
Tournefortia velutina H.B.K.
{ Klebahnia dolichospora (Diet. & Holw.) Arth.
{ Uromyces dolichosporus Diet. & Holw.
Tournefortia volubilis L.
　Aecidium Tournefortiae Henn.
　Hypoxylon dussianum Pat.
　Meliola longipoda Gaill.
{ Klebahnia dolichospora (Diet. & Holw.) Arth.
{ Uromyces dolichosporus Diet. & Holw.
Heliotropium Curassavicum L.
{ Aecidium biforme Pk.
{ Aecidium Heliotropii Tracy & Gall.
{ Puccinia subnitens Diet. I.
　Cercospora Heliotropii Ell. & Ev.
Heliotropium indicum L.
　Aecidium guatemalense Kern & Kellerm.
　Himantia stellifera Johnston.
{ Micropuccinia Heliotropii (Kern & Kellerm.)
{ 　Arth. & Jackson.
{ Puccinia Heliotropii Kern & Kellerm.
Heliotropium peruvianum L.
　Cladosporium Heliotropii Erikss.
Heliotropium physocalycinum Donn. Sm.
　Puccinia gilva Arth. & Holw.
Heliotropium spathulatum Rydb.
Heliotropium xerophyllum Cockerell.
{ Dicaeoma Sarcobati Arth. I.
{ Puccinia subnitens Diet. I.
Pectocarya linearis DC.
{ Dicaeoma Sarcobati Arth. I.
{ Puccinia subnitens Diet. I.
　Synchytrium Myosotidis Kühn.
Cynoglossum officinale L.
　Peronospora Cynoglossi Burrill.
　Phoma Cynoglossi Dearness.
　Phyllosticta decidua Ell. & Kellerm.
　Ramularia Lappulae J. J. Davis.
Cynoglossum virginianum L.
　Peronospora Cynoglossi Burrill.
Cynoglossum sp. indet.
{ Diplodia microscopica Cke. & Hark.
{ Microdiplodia microscopica (Cke. & Hark.)
{ 　Tassi.
　Erysiphe Cichoracearum DC. †
Lappula caerulescens Rydb.
　Aecidium sp. no. 147 Garrett.
　Dicaeoma apocryptum (Ell. & Tracy) O.
　　Kuntze. I.
Lappula cupulata Rydb.
　Peronospora Echinospermi Swingle.
Lappula echinata Gilibert.
　Ophiobolus collapsus Ell. & Ev.
　Peronospora Echinospermi Swingle.
Lappula floribunda (Lehm.) Greene.
　Peronospora Echinospermi Swingle.
　Peronospora Myosotidis DBy.

{ Micropuccinia Mertensiae (Pk.) Arth. &
{ 　Jackson.
{ Puccinia Mertensiae Pk.
Lappula heterosperma Greene.
　Dicaeoma Sarcobati Arth. I.
Lappula Redowskii (Hornem.) Greene.
　Erysiphe Cichoracearum DC. †
　Oidium erysiphoides Fr.
{ Peronospora Cynoglossi Burrill, var. Echino-
{ 　spermi Swingle.
{ Peronospora Echinospermi Swingle.
　Peronospora Myosotidis DBy.
Lappula Redowskii (Hornem.) Greene, var. occi-
　　dentalis (Watson) Rydb.
{ Dicaeoma Sarcobati Arth. I.
{ Puccinia subnitens Diet. I.
　Peronospora Echinospermi Swingle.
Lappula virginiana (L.) Greene.
{ Erysiphe Cichoracearum DC. †
{ Erysiphe lamprocarpa Auct. Amer. p. p.
{ Ovularia asperifolii Sacc., var. Lappulae J. J.
{ 　Davis.
{ Ramularia Lappulae J. J. Davis.
　Peronospora Echinospermi Swingle.
　Phyllosticta decidua Ell. & Kellerm.
Krynitzkia ambigua Gray.
　Dicaeoma (?) Cryptanthes (Diet. & Holw.)
　　Arth.
Krynitzkia angustifolia Gray.
　Puccinia subnitens Diet. I.
　Synchytrium Myosotidis Kühn.
Krynitzkia barbigera Gray.
Krynitzkia crassisepala Gray.
{ Dicaeoma Sarcobati Arth. I.
{ Puccinia subnitens Diet. I.
Krynitzkia intermedia Gray.
　Synchytrium Myosotidis Kühn.
Krynitzkia microstachys Greene.
Krynitzkia oxycarya Gray.
{ Dicaeoma (?) Cryptanthes (Diet. & Holw.)
{ 　Arth.
{ Puccinia Cryptanthes Diet. & Holw.
Krynitzkia pterocarya Gray.
{ Dicaeoma Sarcobati Arth. I.
{ Puccinia subnitens Diet. I.
Krynitzkia torreyana Gray.
{ Dicaeoma (?) Cryptanthes (Diet. & Holw.)
{ 　Arth.
{ Puccinia Cryptanthes Diet. & Holw.
Amsinckia lycopsoides Lehm.
　Oidium erysiphoides Fr.
Amsinckia intermedia Fisch. & Mey.
Amsinckia Menziesii (Lehm.) Nels. & Macbr.
　Dicaeoma Sarcobati Arth. I.
　Synchytrium Amsinckiae McMurphy.
Amsinckia spectabilis Fisch. & Mey.
　Erisyphe Cichoracearum DC. †

Anchusa capensis Thunb.
Anchusa officinalis L.
Lycopsis arvensis L.
  Aecidium Asperifolii P.
  Dicaeoma Asperifolii (Wettst.) O. Kuntze. I.
  Puccinia Asperifolii Wettst. I.
  Puccinia dispersa Erikss. I.
  Puccinia Rubigo-vera Wint. I.
  Puccinia Rubigo-vera, var. Secalis Erikss. &
    Henn. I.
Lycopsis capensis Thunb.
  Dicaeoma Asperifolii (Wettst.) O. Kuntze. I.
Nonea rosea Lk.
  Puccinia dispersa Erikss. & Henn. I.
Myosotis laxa Lehm.
  Peronospora Myosotidis DBy.
Myosotis sylvatica Hoffm., var. **alpestris** Koch.
  Peronospora Myosotidis DBy.
Myosotis virginica (L.) BSP.
  Aecidium Myosotidis Burrill.
  Dicaeoma Eatoniae Arth. I.
  Dicaeoma Myosotidis Arth. & Fromme.
  Pleomeris Eatoniae (Arth.) Syd.
  Peronospora Myosotidis DBy.
Myosotis sp. indet.
  Sclerotinia sclerotiorum (Lib.) Schrt.
Mertensia arizonica Greene.
Mertensia Bakeri Greene.
  Micropuccinia Mertensiae (Pk.) Arth. & Jack-
    son.
  Puccinia Mertensiae Pk.
Mertensia caelestina Nels. & Cockerell.
  Mycosphaerella pachyasca Rostr.
  Pyrenophora chrysospora (Niessl) Sacc., var.
    polaris Karst.
Mertensia cynoglossoides Greene.
Mertensia foliosa A. Nels.
  Micropuccinia Mertensiae (Pk.) Arth. &
    Jackson.
  Puccinia Mertensiae Pk.
Mertensia laevigata Piper.
  Aecidium Mertensiae Arth.
  Dicaeoma apocryptum (Ell. & Tracy) O.
    Kuntze. I.
  Puccinia montanensis I. Auct. Amer. p. p.
Mertensia lanceolata DC.
  Erysiphe Cichoracearum DC. †
  Dicaeoma apocryptum (Ell. & Tracy) O.
    Kuntze. I.
Mertensia maritima (L.) S. F. Gray.
  Didymosphaeria Johansenii Dearness.
  Heterosporium Stenhammariae Rostr.
  Septoria Drygalskii Henn.
  Septoria Stenhammariae Rostr.
  Sphaerella pachyasca Rostr.

Mertensia oblongifolia G. Don.
Mertensia polyphylla Greene.
  Micropuccinia Mertensiae (Pk.) Arth. & Jack-
    son.
  Puccinia Mertensiae Pk.
Mertensia paniculata (Ait.) G. Don.
  Aecidium Mertensiae Arth.
  Dicaeoma apocryptum (Ell. & Tracy) O.
    Kuntze. I.
Mertensia pratensis Heller.
  Erysiphe Cichoracearum DC. †
Mertensia pulmonarioides Roth.
  Entyloma serotinum Schrt.
Mertensia sibirica G. Don.
  Aecidium Mertensiae Arth.
  Erysiphe Cichoracearum DC. †
  Erysiphe lamprocarpa Auct. Amer. p. p.
  Micropuccinia Mertensiae (Pk.) Arth. & Jack-
    son.
  Puccinia Mertensiae Pk.
Mertensia subcordata Greene.
  Dicaeoma apocryptum (Ell. & Tracy) O.
    Kuntze. I.
Mertensia virginica (L.) Lk.
  Entyloma leutomaculans Hume.
  Entyloma serotinum Schrt.
Mertensia sp. indet.
  Ampelomyces quisqualis Ces.
  Heptameria Mertensiae (Ell.) Cke.
  Leptosphaeria Mertensiae (Ell.) Sacc.
  Sphaeria Mertensiae Ell.
  Sphaerella pachyasca Rostr.
Lithospermum angustifolium Michx.
  Aecidium Onosmodii Arth.
  Aecidium Williamsii Ricker.
  Puccinia apocrypta Ell. & Tracy. I.
  Puccinia montanensis I. Auct. Amer. p. p.
Lithospermum arvense L.
  Erysiphe Cichoracearum DC. †
  Erysiphe horridula Lév. p. p.
  Erysiphe lamprocarpa Auct. Amer. p. p.
  Synchytrium Myosotidis Kühn.
Lithospermum canescens (Michx.) Lehm.
  Dicaeoma apocryptum (Ell. & Tracy) O.
    Kuntze. I.
  Puccinia apocrypta Ell. & Tracy. I.
  Niptera Lithospermi Ell. & Ev.
  Puccinia Lithospermi Ell. & Kellerm.
Lithospermum linearifolium Goldie.
  Aecidium Onosmodii Arth.
  Dicaeoma apocryptum (Ell. & Tracy) O.
    Kuntze. I.
  Puccinia apocrypta Ell. & Tracy. I.
Lithospermum multiflorum Torr.
  Pleospora herbarum (Fr.) Rabh.

Lithospermum officinale L.
- Mycosphaerella Lithospermi Ell. & Ev.
- Sphaerella Lithospermi Ell. & Ev. nom. nud.
- Sphaerella Lithospermi (Ell. & Ev.) Sacc. & Syd.

Lithospermum sp. indet.
- Pleosphaeria Lithospermi Clements.

Onosmodium carolinianum DC.
- Aecidium Onosmodii Arth.
- Puccinia Rubigo-vera I. Auct. Amer. p. p.
- Didymella onosmodina (Pk. & Clinton) Sacc.
- Sphaerella onosmodina (Pk. & Clinton) Pk.
- Sphaeria onosmodina Pk. & Clinton.

Onosmodium molle Michx.

Onosmodium occidentale Mackenzie.
- Aecidium Onosmodii Arth.
- Dicaeoma apocryptum (Ell. & Tracy) O. Kuntze. I.
- Puccinia apocrypta Ell. & Tracy. I.
- Puccinia montanensis I. Auct. Amer. p. p.

Onosmodium sp. indet.
- Ophiobolus acuminatus (Sow.) Duby.

Echium vulgare L.
- Cercospora Echii Wint.
- Ophiobolus cesatianus (Mont.) Sacc.

VERBENACEAE

Verbena angustifolia Michx.
- Aecidium verbenicola Ell. & Kellerm.
- Dicaeoma verbenicola Arth. I.
- Puccinia Vilfae Arth. & Holw. I.
- Erysiphe Cichoracearum DC. †
- Septoria Verbenae Rob.

Verbena bipinnatifida Nutt.
- Phyllosticta texensis Seaver.
- Phyllosticta verbenicola Tharp.

Verbena bracteata Cav.
- Erysiphe Cichoracearum DC. †

Verbena bracteosa Michx.
- Aecidium Verbenae Auct. Amer. non Speg.
- Aecidium verbenicola Ell. & Kellerm.
- Dicaeoma verbenicola Arth. I.
- Puccinia sydowiana Diet. I.
- Puccinia verbenicola Arth. I.
- Erysiphe Cichoracearum DC. †
- Septoria Verbenae Rob.

Verbena canadensis (L.) Brit.
- Dicaeoma verbenicola Arth. I.
- Erysiphe Cichoracearum DC. †
- Septoria Verbenae Rob.

Verbena caroliniana Michx.
- Cercospora septatissima Tracy & Earle.
- Cercospora truncatella Atk.
- Cercospora verbenicola Ell. & Ev.

Verbena ciliata Benth.
- Dicaeoma Sarcobati Arth. I.
- Puccinia subnitens Diet. I.

Verbena hastata L.
- Aecidium verbenicola Ell. & Kellerm.
- Dicaeoma verbenicola Arth. I.
- Puccinia sydowiana Diet. I.
- Puccinia verbenicola Arth. I.
- Puccinia Vilfae Arth. & Holw. I.
- Didymella Rehmii (J. Kze.) Sacc.
- Erysiphe Cichoracearum DC. †
- Phyllosticta verbenicola Martin.
- Septoria Verbenae Rob. 1847.
- Septoria Verbenae Gerard. 1873.

Verbena Macdougalii Heller.
- Erysiphe Cichoracearum DC. †
- Ophiobolus collapsus Sacc. & Ell.

Verbena officinalis L.
- Erysiphe Cichoracearum DC. †

Verbena prostrata R. Br.
- Pleospora herbarum (Fr.) Rabh.

Verbena stricta Vent.
- Aecidium Verbenae Auct. Amer. non Speg.
- Aecidium verbenicola Ell. & Kellerm.
- Dicaeoma verbenicola Arth. I.
- Puccinia sydowiana Diet. I.
- Puccinia verbenicola Arth. I.
- Puccinia Vilfae Arth. & Holw. I.
- Cercospora Verbenae-strictae Pk.
- Erysiphe Cichoracearum DC. †
- Erysiphe horridula Lév.
- Erysiphe lamprocarpa Auct. Amer. p. p.
- Phyllosticta verbenicola Martin.
- Septoria Verbenae Rob.

Verbena urticifolia L.
- Acrospermum compressum Tode ex Fr.
- Aecidium Verbenae Auct. Amer. non Speg.
- Aecidium verbenicola Ell. & Kellerm.
- Dicaeoma verbenicola Arth. I.
- Puccinia sydowiana Diet. I.
- Puccinia verbenicola Arth. I.
- Puccinia Vilfae Arth. & Holw. I.
- Erysibe Cichoracearum (DC.) Schrt.
- Erysiphe Cichoracerarum DC. †
- Erysiphe Galeopsidis Atk. 1897.
- Erysiphe lamprocarpa Auct. Amer. p. p.
- Erysiphe Verbenae S.
- Erysiphe Galeopsidis DC. † 1815.
- Oidium erysiphoides Fr.
- Septoria Verbenae Rob.
- Sphaerotheca Humuli (DC.) Burrill, var. fuliginea (Schl.) Salmon.

Verbena xutha Lehm.
- Cercospora papillosa Atk.
- Cercospora verbenicola Ell. & Ev.

Verbena sp. indet.
- Rhizoctonia Solani Kühn.
- Sphaerotheca Humuli (DC.) Burrill. †

Lantana aculeata L.
- Puccinia Lantanae Farl.

Lantana Camara L.
  Diatrypella Lantanae Earle.
  Meliola ambigua Pat. & Gaill.
  Perisporina Lantanae F. L. Stevens.
  ⎰Micropuccinia Lantanae (Farl.) Arth. & Jack-
  ⎱ son.
  Puccinia Lantanae Farl.
  ⎰Prospodium tuberculatum (Speg.) Arth.
  ⎱Puccinia tuberculata Speg.
  Septoria Lantanae P. Garman.

Lantana crocea Jacq.
  ⎧Micropuccinia Lantanae (Farl.) Arth. & Jack-
  ⎨ son.
  ⎩Puccinia Lantanae Farl.
  Prospodium tuberculatum (Speg.) Arth.

Lantana hispida H. B. K.
  Aecidium Verbenae Speg.
  Meliola ambigua Pat. & Gaill.
  ⎰Micropuccinia Lantanae (Farl.) Arth. & Jack-
  ⎱ son.
  Puccinia Lantanae Farl.
  Prospodium tuberculatum (Speg.) Arth.

Lantana horrida H. B. K.
  ⎰Prospodium tuberculatum (Speg.) Arth.
  ⎱Puccinia tuberculata Speg.

Lantana involucrata L.
  Darluca Filum (Biv.) Cast.
  Meliola ambigua Pat. & Gaill.
  Melomastia mastoidea (Fr.) Schrt.
  Nectria Lantanae Seaver.
  Phyllosticta Lantanae F. L. Stevens.
  Prospodium tuberculatum (Speg.) Arth.
  ⎧Micropuccinia Lantanae (Farl.) Arth. &
  ⎨ Jackson.
  ⎩Puccinia Lantanae Farl.

Lantana purpurea Benth. & Hook.

Lantana reticulata Raf.

Lantana stricta Sw.

Lantana trifolia L.
  ⎰Aecidium Verbenae Speg. non Auct. Amer.
  ⎱Aecidium verbenicola Speg. non E. & K.
  Meliola ambigua Pat. & Gaill.
  ⎰Micropuccinia Lantanae (Farl.) Arth. & Jack-
  ⎱ son.
  Puccinia Lantanae Farl.

Lantana sp. indet.
  Arthrobotryum caudatum Syd.
  Phyllosticta Lantanae Pass.

Lippia
  (Goniostachyum citrosum Small.)
  Micropuccinia Lantanae (Farl.) Arth. & Jack-
    son.

Lippia asperifolia Rich.

Lippia callicarpifolia H. B. K.
  ⎧Prospodium Lippiae (Speg.) Arth.
  ⎨Puccinia Lippiae Speg.
  ⎩Uredo Lippiae Speg.

Lippia dulcis Trevir.
  ⎧Micropuccinia Lantanae (Farl.) Arth. & Jack-
  ⎨ son.
  ⎩Puccinia Lantanae Farl.
  Prospodium Lippiae (Speg.) Arth.

Lippia lanceolata Michx.
  Cercospora Lippiae Ell. & Ev.

Lippia ligustrina Britton.
  Cylindrosporium Lippiae Heald & Wolf.

Lippia myriocephala Schl. & Cham.
  ⎰Bullaria elatipes (Arth. & Holw.) Arth. &
  ⎱ Mains.
  Puccinia elatipes Arth. & Holw.
  ⎧Prospodium Lippiae (Speg.) Arth.
  ⎨Puccinia Lippiae Speg.
  ⎩Uredo Lippiae Speg. 1898.
  ⎰Micropuccinia permagna (Arth. & Holw.)
  ⎱ Arth. & Jackson.
  Puccinia permagna Arth. & Holw.
  Puccinia senilis Arth.

Lippia nodiflora (L.) Michx.
  Cercospora Lippiae Ell. & Ev.
  Micropuccinia Lantanae (Farl.) Arth. & Jack-
    son.

Lippia Pringlei Briq.
  ⎧Nephlyctis conjuncta (Diet. & Holw.) Arth.
  ⎪Puccinia conjuncta Diet. & Holw.
  ⎨Prospodium Lippiae (Speg.) Arth.
  ⎪Puccinia Lippiae Speg.
  ⎪Uredo Lippiae Speg. 1898.
  ⎩Uredo Lippiae Diet. & Holw. 1901.

Lippia reticulata Hayek.
  Cladosporium herbarum (P.) ex Lk.
  Sphaerella Lippiae Fragoso & Ciferri.

Lippia stoechadifolia H. B. K.
  ⎰Micropuccinia Lantanae (Farl.) Arth. & Jack-
  ⎱ son.
  Puccinia Lantanae Farl.

Lippia strigosa Turcz.
  ⎰Prospodium Lippiae (Speg.) Arth.
  ⎱Puccinia Lippiae Speg.

Lippia umbellata Cav.
  Puccinia elatipes Arth. & Holw.
  ⎰Prospodium Lippiae (Speg.) Arth.
  ⎱Puccinia Lippiae Speg.

Lippia sp. indet.
  Meliola cookeana Speg.
  Meliola Lippiae Maubl.

Stachytarpheta cayennensis (L. C. Rich) Vahl.
  ⎧Aecidium Stachytarphetae Henn.
  ⎨Endophyllum Stachytarphetae Whetzel &
  ⎩ Olive.
  ⎰Irene glabroides (F. L Stevens) Toro.
  ⎱Meliola glabroides F. L. Stevens.
  ⎰Micropuccinia urbaniana (Henn.) Arth. &
  ⎱ Jackson.
  Puccinia urbaniana Henn.

Stachytarpheta jamaicensis Vahl.
  Cercospora Stachytarphetae Ell. & Ev.
  Puccinia Lantanae Farl.
  ⎰Micropuccinia urbaniana (Henn.) Arth. &
  ⎱ Jackson.
  Puccinia urbaniana Henn.
Stachytarpheta strigosa Vahl.
  ⎰Micropuccinia urbaniana (Henn.) Arth. &
  ⎱ Jackson.
  Puccinia urbaniana Henn.
Stachytarpheta sp. indet.
  Meliola cookeana Speg.
Priva lappulacea (L.) P.
  ⎰Micropuccinia Lantanae (Farl.) Arth. & Jack-
  ⎱ son.
  Puccinia Lantanae Farl.
  Uromyces Privae Syd.
Petraea volubilis L.
  Metasphaeria Petraeae Pat.
Citharexylum fruticosum L.
  Irene longipoda (Gaill.) Toro.
Citharexylum quadrangulare Jacq.
  ⎰Melanopus marasmioides Pat.
  ⎱Polyporus marasmioides (Pat.) Sacc. & D. Sacc.
Duranta repens L.
  Phyllachora fusicarpa Seaver.
  Sclerotium Rolfsii Sacc.
Callicarpa americana L.
  Atractilina Callicarpae Dearness & Barthol.
  ⎰Botryosphaeria Callicarpae Cke.
  ⎱Melogramma Callicarpae Cke.
  Cercospora Callicarpae Cke.
  Cercospora pulvinulata Sacc. & Wint.
  Coniothyrium Callicarpae Cke.
  Diatrype Callicarpae B. & Rav.
  ⎰Meliola amphitricha Rav. Fung. Am. *84*.
  ⎱Meliola cookeana Sacc. & Speg.
  Meliola inermis Kalchbr. & Cke.
Aegiphila martinicensis Jacq.
  ⎰Guignardia prominens Earle.
  ⎱Laestadia prominens (Earle) Sacc. & D. Sacc.
  Hobsonia Ackermanni Pat.
Petitia domingensis Jacq.
  Olivea Petitiae Arth.
  Septoria Petitiae P. Garman.
Cornutia grandifolia Schauer.
  ⎰Micropuccinia urbaniana (Henn.) Arth. &
  ⎱ Jackson.
  Puccinia urbaniana Henn.
Cornutia pyramidata L.
  ⎰Micropuccinia urbaniana (Henn.) Arth. &
  ⎱ Jackson.
  Puccinia urbaniana Henn.
Vitex Agnus-castus L.
  Cercospora Viticis Ell. & Ev.
  Pyrenochaete minor Ell. & Ev.
Vitex divaricata Sw.
  Laschia Dussii Pat.
  Phyllachora Taruma Speg.

  ⎰Plicatura guadalupensis (Pat.) Murrill.
  ⎱Xerotus guadalupensis Pat.
  ⎰Coriolus hirsutus (Wulf. ex Fr.) Quél.
  ⎱Polyporus hirsutus (Wulf.) ex Fr.
  ⎰Melanopus nephridius (B.) Pat.
  ⎱Polyporus nephridius B.
  ⎰Phellinus scruposus (Fr.) Pat.
  ⎱Polyporus scruposus Fr.
Vitex umbrosa Sw.
  Meliola campylopoda Syd.
Vitex sp. indet.
  Ophiobolus barbatus Pat. & Gaill.
  Uredo Viticis Juel.
Clerodendron sp. indet.
  Septoria phlyctaenoides B. & C.
Avicennia nitida Jacq.
  ⎰Irene sepulta (Pat.) Toro.
  ⎱Meliola sepulta Pat.

LABIATAE

Teucrium canadense L.
  Botrytis hypophylla Ell. & Kellerm.
  ⎰Caeoma Teucrii S.
  ⎱Cercospora racemosa Ell. & Martin.
  Cercospora Teucrii (S.) Ell. & Kellerm. 1884.
  Cercospora Teucrii (S.) Arth. & Bisby. 1918.
  Cercosporella racemosa (Ell. & Martin) Un-
    derw.
  Cercosporella Teucrii (S.) Underw.
  Erysiphe Cichoracearum DC. †
  ⎰Erysiphe Galeopsidis DC. †
  ⎱Erysiphe lamprocarpa Auct. Amer. p. p.
  Gymnosporium harknessioides Ell. & Holw.
  Phyllosticta decidua Ell. & Kellerm.
Teucrium canadense, var. littorale (Bicknell)
  Fern.
  Phacidium Teucrii Crouan.
Isanthus brachiatus (L.) BSP.
  Cercospora Isanthi Ell. & Kellerm.
Trichostema dichotomum L.
  Septoria Trichostematis Pk.
Scutellaria canescens Nutt.
  Cylindrosporium Scrophulariae Sacc. & Ell.
Scutellaria galericulata L.
  Erysiphe Cichoracearum DC. †
  Erysiphe Galeopsidis DC. †
  Phyllosticta decidua Ell. & Kellerm.
  Septoria Scutellariae Thm.
Scutellaria lateriflora L.
  ⎰Erysiphe Cichoracearum DC. †
  ⎱Erysiphe communis Auct. Amer. p. p.
  Erysiphe Galeopsidis DC. †
  Erysiphe Polygoni DC. †
  Phyllosticta decidua Ell. & Kellerm.
  Septoria Scutellariae Thm.
  Uncinula columbiana Selby.
  Uncinula Salicis (DC.) Wint. †

Scutellaria parvula Michx.
Cercospora Scutellariae Ell. & Ev.
Erysiphe Galeopsidis DC. †.

Scutellaria pilosa Michx.
Erysiphe Galeopsidis DC. †

Scutellaria tuberosa Benth.
Septoria Scutellariae Thm.

Scutellaria versicolor Nutt.
Cercospora Scutellariae Ell. & Ev.
Septoria Scutellariae Thm.

Scutellaria sp. indet.
{ Ophiobolus porphyrogonus (Tode ex Fr.) Sacc.
{ Sphaeria rubella P.
Phyllosticta Verbenae Sacc.

Lavandula sp. indet.
Pholiota praecox (P.) ex Fr.

Marrubium vulgare Fr.
Cercospora Marrubii Tharp.
Coniothyrium Marrubii Fairman.
Diplodia herbarum (Cda.) Lév.
Phoma lanuginis Fairman.
{ Pleospora Labiatarum (Cke. & Hark.) Sacc.
{ Sphaeria Labiatarum Cke. & Hark.
Stictis lanuginicincta Fairman.
Synchytrium Marrubii Tobler.

Agastache Foeniculum (Pursh) O. Kuntze.
Ascochyta Lophanthi, var. osmophila J. J.
    Davis.
Sphaerotheca Humuli (DC.) Burrill. †
{ Sphaerotheca Castagnei Auct. Amer. p. p.
{ Sphaerotheca Humuli (DC.) Burrill, var.
{   fuliginea (Schl.) Salmon.

Agastache nepetoides (L.) O. Kuntze.
Peronospora Lophanthi Farl.
Phoma Lophanthi Bubák.
{ Dothidea Hyssopi S.
{ Phyllachora Hyssopi (S.) Sacc.
{ Propolis Hyssopi (S.) Cke.
{ Stictis Hyssopi S.
Dasyspora Glechomatis Auct. Amer.
?Dicaeoma Menthae Wilson, Ind. Acad.
Micropuccinia Hyssopi (S.) Arth. & Jackson.
?Puccinia Bullaria S. non Lk.
Puccinia Glechomatis Auct. Amer.
Puccinia Hyssopi S.
Puccinia verrucosa Auct. Amer.
Septoria Lophanthi Wint.

Agastache scrophulariifolia (Willd.) O. Kuntze.
Ascochyta Lophanthi J. J. Davis.
Peronospora Lophanthi Farl.
{ Micropuccinia Hyssopi (S.) Arth. & Jackson.
{ Puccinia Hyssopi S.
{ Puccinia verrucosa Auct. Amer.
Ramularia Lophanthi Ell. & Ev.
Septoria Lophanthi Wint.
Sphaerotheca Humuli (DC.) Burrill. †
Sphaerotheca Humuli (DC.) Burrill, var. fuli-
    ginea (Schl.) Salmon.

Agastache urticifolia (Benth.) O. Kuntze.
Sphaerotheca Humuli (DC.) Burrill. †
Sphaerotheca Humuli (DC.) Burrill, var. fuli-
    ginea (Schl.) Salmon.

Agastache sp. indet.
{ Coniosporium harknessioides (Ell. & Holw.)
{   Sacc.
{ Species spuria sporae Piloboli.
{ Heptameria Lophanthi (B. & C.) Cke.
{ Leptosphaeria Lophanthi (B. & C.) Sacc.
{ Sphaeria Lophanthi B. & C.

Nepeta Cataria L.
Ascochyta Nepetae J. J. Davis.
Cercospora Nepetae Tehon.
{ Didymella Catariae (C. & E.) Sacc.
{ Physalospora Catariae (C. & E.) Ell.
{ Sphaeria Catariae C. & E.
{ Diplodia herbicola B. & C.
{ Diplodina herbicola (B. & C.) Sacc.
Phyllosticta decidua Ell. & Kellerm.
Pleospora vulgaris Niessl.
Puccinia Menthae P.
Septoria Nepetae Ell. & Ev.
Teichospora Nepetae Ell. & Ev.

Nepeta hederacea (L.) Trevisan.
Phyllosticta decidua Ell. & Kellerm.
Septoria alabamensis Atk.

Dracocephalum argunense Fisch.
Sclerotium Rolfsii Sacc.

Dracocephalum parviflorum Nutt.
{ Peronospora Hedeomae Kellerm. & Swingle.
{ Peronospora Lophanthi J. J. Davis.
{ Peronospora Lophanthi, var. Moldavicae
{   Dearness & Barthol.
Phyllosticta Dracocephali Dearness & Bisby.
Septoria Dracocephali Thm.

Prunella vulgaris L.
Diaporthe Desmazierii Niessl.
{ Ceuthocarpon Brunellae (Ell. & Ev.) Berl.
{ Hypospila Brunellae Ell. & Ev.
{ Linospora Brunellae Ell. & Ev.
Leptosphaeria Brunellae Ell. & Ev.
Phyllosticta Brunellae Ell. & Ev.
Ramularia Brunellae Ell. & Ev.
{ Rhabdospora Brunellae Ell. & Ev.
{ Septoria Brunellae Ell. & Holw.
Septoria trailiana Sacc.
Sphaerotheca Castagnei Lév.
Sphaerotheca Humuli (DC.) Burrill. †
Sphaerotheca Humuli (DC.) Burrill, var. fuli-
    ginea (Schl.) Salmon.

Prunella sp. indet.
Ophiobolus Rostrupii Ferdinandsen & Winge.

Physostegia parviflora Nutt.
Plasmopara cephalophora J. J. Davis.
{ Micropuccinia Physostegiae (Pk. & Clinton)
{   Arth. & Jackson.
{ Puccinia Physostegiae Pk. & Clinton.

Physostegia virginiana (L.) Benth.
  Leptosphaeria Physostegiae Fairman.
  { Dasyspora Physostegiae (Pk. & Clinton) H. S.
  { Jackson.
  { Dicaeoma Physostegiae (Pk. & Clinton) O.
  { Kuntze.
  { Micropuccinia Physostegiae (Pk. & Clinton)
  { Arth. & Jackson.
  { Puccinia Physostegiae Pk. & Clinton.
  Rhabdospora Physostegiae Pk. nom. nud.
  Septoria Physostegiae Ell. & Ev.
Leonotis nepetifolia (L.) R. Br.
  Cercospora Leonotidis Cke.
  Phoma Leonotidis Seaver.
  { Dicaeoma Leonotidis Arth.
  { Puccinia Leonotidis Arth.
  { Uredo Leonotidis Henn.
  { Puccinia leonotidicola Henn.
  { Uredo leonoticola Henn.
Galeopsis Tetrahit L.
  Erysiphe Galeopsidis DC. †
  Phyllosticta decidua Ell. & Kellerm.
  Septoria Galeopsidis Westd.
Lamium amplexicaule L.
  Peronospora Lamii A. Braun.
Lamium sp. indet.
  Oidium erysiphoides Fr.
Leonurus Cardiaca L.
  Ascochyta Leonuri Ell. & Dearness.
  Coniosporium culmigenum (B.) Sacc., var.
    minor Pk.
  Dinemasporium hispidulum (Schrad.) M. A.
    Curtis.
  Helotium fumosum Ell. & Ev.
  Phialea Urticae (P.) Sacc.
  Phyllosticta decidua Ell. & Kellerm.
Leonurus Marrubiastrum L.
  Septoria Lamii Pass.
Stachys affinis Bunge.
  Vermicularia Stachydis Tracy & Earle.
Stachys bullata Benth.
  Oidium erysiphoides Fr.
  Ovularia bullata Ell. & Ev.
  Septoria Stachydis Rob. in Desm.
Stachys ciliata Dougl.
  Erysiphe Cichoracearum DC. †
  Erysiphe Galeopsidis DC. †
  Ovularia Stachydis-ciliatae Pk.
Stachys cordata Riddell.
  Erysiphe Galeopsidis DC. †
Stachys costaricensis Briq.
  Polioma pallidissima (Speg.) Syd.
Stachys Drummondii Benth.
  Erysiphe Galeopsidis DC. †
Stachys germanica L.
  Septoria Stachydis Rob. in Desm.
Stachys lanata Jacq.
  Rhizoctonia Solani Kühn.

Stachys Lindenii Benth.
  { Micropuccinia pallidissima (Speg.) Arth. &
  { Jackson.
  { Puccinia pallidissima Speg.
Stachys palustris L.
  Cercospora Stachydis Ell. & Ev.
  Cylindrosporium Stachydis Ell.
  Erysiphe Cichoracearum DC. †
  Erysiphe Cichoracearum, var. Galeopsidis
    (DC.) Salmon.
  Erysiphe Galeopsidis DC. †
  Phyllosticta decidua Ell. & Kellerm.
  Phyllosticta palustris Ell. & Dearness.
  Septoria Stachydis Rob. in Desm.
Stachys scopulorum Greene.
  Erysiphe Galeopsidis DC. †
Stachys tenuifolia Willd.
  Erysiphe Galeopsidis DC. †
  Phyllosticta decidua Ell. & Kellerm.
  Septoria Stachydis Rob. in Desm.
Salvia alamosana Rose.
  { Dicaeoma gentile Arth.
  { Puccinia gentilis Arth.
Salvia albicans Fern.
  { Dicaeoma badium (Holw.) Arth.
  { Puccinia badia Holw.
Salvia albiflora Mart. & Gal.
  { Puccinia (?) degener Mains & Holw.
  { Uredo degener (Mains & Holw.) Arth.
Salvia amarissima Orteg.
  { Dicaeoma farinaceum (Long) Arth.
  { Puccinia farinacea Long.
  Puccinia mitrata Syd.
Salvia assurgens H. B. K.
  { Bullaria impedita (Mains & Holw.) Arth. &
  { Mains.
  { Puccinia impedita Mains & Holw.
Salvia azurea Lam.
  { Dicaeoma farinaceum (Long) Arth.
  { Puccinia farinacea Long.
  { Puccinia nigrescens Pk.
  { Puccinia Salviae-lanceolatae Bubák.
Salvia azurea Lam., var. grandiflora Benth.
  { Puccinia caulicola Tracy & Gall.
  { Puccinia nigrescens Pk.
  { Puccinia Salviae-lanceolatae Bubák.
  { Dicaeoma farinaceum (Long) Arth.
  { Puccinia farinacea Long.
  Puccinia Menthae P.
  Puccinia nigrescens Pk.
Salvia ballotiflora Benth.
  { Dicaeoma (?) ballotiflorae (Long) Arth.
  { Puccinia ballotiflora Long.
  { Allodus vertisepta (Tracy & Gall.) Arth.
  { Diorchidium Tracyi De Toni.
  { Puccinia vertisepta Tracy & Gall.
Salvia candicans Mart. & Gal.
  Aecidium subsimulans Arth. & Mains.

Salvia carnosa Dougl.
  Allodus mellifera (Diet. & Holw.) Arth.
Salvia chrysantha Mart. & Gal.
  Puccinia badia Holw.
  {Dicaeoma diutinum (Mains & Holw.) Arth.
  {Puccinia diutina Mains & Holw.
Salvia cinnabarina Mart. & Gal.
  {Micropuccinia delicatula (Arth.) Arth. & Jackson.
  {Puccinia delicatula (Arth.) Sacc. & Trott.
  {Dicaeoma infrequens (Holw.) Arth.
  {Puccinia infrequens Holw.
Salvia coccinea Juss.
  Puccinia farinacea Long.
  {Bullaria impedita (Mains & Holw.) Arth. & Mains.
  {Puccinia impedita Mains & Holw.
  {Dicaeoma salviicola (Diet. & Holw.) Arth.
  {Puccinia salviicola Diet. & Holw.
Salvia elegans Vahl.
  {Micropuccinia delicatula (Arth.) Arth. & Jackson.
  {Polioma delicatula Arth.
  {Puccinia delicatula (Arth.) Sacc. & Trott.
  {Dicaeoma farinaceum (Long) Arth.
  {Puccinia farinacea Long.
  {Polioma griseola (Lagerh.) Arth.
  {Puccinia griseola Lagerh.
Salvia farinacea Benth.
  Cercospora salviicola Tharp.
  {Dicaeoma farinaceum (Long) Arth.
  {Puccinia farinacea Long.
  Ramularia salviicola Tharp.
Salvia fluviatilis Fern.
  {Dicaeoma mitratum (Syd.) Arth.
  {Puccinia mitrata Syd.
Salvia fulgens Cav.
  Uredo biporula Arth.
Salvia glechomifolia H. B. K.
  Puccinia salviicola Diet. & Holw.
Salvia Holwayi Standley.
  {Micropuccinia delicatula (Arth.) Arth. & Jackson.
  {Puccinia delicatula (Arth.) Sacc. & Trott.
  {Dicaeoma farinaceum (Long) Arth.
  {Puccinia farinacea Long.
Salvia hyptoides Mart. & Gal.
  {Bullaria impedita (Mains & Holw.) Arth. & Mains.
  {Puccinia impedita Mains & Holw.
  Puccinia mitrata Syd.
Salvia involucrata Cav.
  {Dicaeoma filiolum (Mains & Holw.) Arth.
  {Puccinia filiola Mains & Holw.
Salvia lanceifolia Poir.
  Peronospora Lamii Braun.
  Peronospora Swinglei Ell. & Kellerm.

{Aecidium caulicola Kellerm.
{Dicaeoma caulicola (Tracy & Gall.) O. Kuntze.
{Puccinia caulicola Tracy & Gall.
  Puccinia nigrescens Pk.
Salvia lavanduloides H. B. K.
  Puccinia farinacea Long.
Salvia Lemmoni Gray.
  Aecidium subsimulans Arth. & Mains.
Salvia Lindenii Benth.
  {Dicaeoma farinaceum (Long) Arth.
  {Puccinia farinacea Long.
Salvia mellifera Benth.
  Puccinia mellifera Diet. & Holw.
Salvia mexicana L.
  {Dicaeoma mitratum (Syd.) Arth.
  {Puccinia mitrata Syd.
Salvia microphylla H. B. K.
  {Dicaeoma prosperum Arth.
  {Puccinia prospera Arth.
Salvia nepetoides H. B. K.
  {Dicaeoma farinaceum (Long) Arth.
  {Puccinia farinacea Long.
Salvia occidentalis Sw.
  {Bullaria impedita (Mains & Holw.) Arth. & Mains.
  {Puccinia impedita Mains & Holw.
  Puccinia Menthae P.
  Puccina salviicola Diet. & Holw.
Salvia officinalis L.
  Coniothyrium salviicola Ell. & Ev.
  Crucibulum vulgare Tul.
  Diaporthe salviicola (C. & E.) Sacc.
  Rhizoctonia Solani Kühn.
Salvia pinguifolia (Fern.) Woot. & Standl.
  Allodus vertisepta (Tracy & Gall.) Arth.
Salvia Pittieri (?) Briq.
  {Dicaeoma diutinum (Mains & Holw.) Arth.
  {Puccinia diutina Mains & Holw.
Salvia polystachya Orteg.
  {Dicaeoma mitratum (Syd.) Arth.
  {Puccinia mitrata Syd.
Salvia prunelloides H. B. K.
  Puccinia salviicola Diet. & Holw.
Salvia pulchella DC.
  {Micropuccinia delicatula (Arth.) Arth. & Jackson.
  {Puccinia delicatula (Arth.) Sacc. & Trott.
  Puccinia farinacea Long.
  {Dicaeoma filiolum (Mains & Holw.) Arth.
  {Puccinia filiola Mains & Holw.
Salvia purpurea Cav.
  {Micropuccinia nivea (Holw.) Arth. & Jackson.
  {Polioma nivea (Holw.) Arth.
  {Puccinia nivea Holw.
  Dicaeoma mitratum (Syd.) Arth.

Salvia rubiginosa Benth.
  {Bullaria impedita (Mains & Holw.) Arth. &
    Mains.
  {Puccinia impedita Mains & Holw.
Salvia scorodoniifolia Poir.
  {Dicaeoma diutinum (Mains & Holw.) Arth.
  {Puccinia diutina Mains & Holw.
Salvia Sessei Benth.
  {Allodus vertisepta (Tracy & Gall.) Arth.
  {Puccinia vertisepta Tracy & Gall.
Salvia sessiliflora Gray.
  {Dicaeoma mitratum (Syd.) Arth.
  {Puccinia mitrata Syd.
  Tuberculina costaricana Syd.
Salvia splendens Sellow.
  Rhizoctonia Solani Kühn.
Salvia tiliifolia Vahl.
  {Bullaria impedita (Mains & Holw.) Arth. &
    Mains.
  {Puccinia impedita Mains & Holw.
  {Dicaeoma mitratum (Syd.) Arth.
  {Puccinia mitrata Syd.
  Tuberculina costaricana Syd.
Salvia vitifolia Benth.
  Dicaeoma farinaceum (Long) Arth.
  Puccinia mitrata Syd.
Salvia sp. indet.
  Aecidium Salviae Hazsl.
  Aecidium zonatum Sacc.
  {Diaporthe salviicola (C. & E.) Sacc.
  {Sphaeria salviicola C. & E.
  Dothidea collecta (S.) Ell. & Ev.
  Ovularia ovata (Fckl.) Sacc.
  Peziza virginea Batsch ex Fr.
  Phyllosticta Bonanseae Sacc.
  {Polyporus Salviae B. & C.
  {Poria Salviae (B. & C.) Sacc.
  Volutella flexuosa C. & E.
Audibertia grandiflora Benth.
  {Allodus mellifera (Diet. & Holw.) Arth.
  {Puccinia mellifera Diet. & Holw.
Audibertia humilis Benth.
  Allodus mellifera (Diet. & Holw.) Arth.
  {Ophiobolus claviger Hark.
  {Rhaphidospora clavigera (Hark.) Cke.
Audibertia incana Benth.
  Allodus mellifera (Diet. & Holw.) Arth.
  Puccinia nigrescens Pk.
Audibertia nivea Benth.
  Allodus mellifera (Diet. & Holw.) Arth.
Audibertia Palmeri Gray.
  Camarosporium eriocryptum Fairman.
  {Allodus mellifera (Diet. & Holw.) Arth.
  {Puccinia mellifera Diet. & Holw.
Audibertia polystachya Benth.
  Allodus mellifera (Diet. & Holw.) Arth.
  Septoria rhabdocarpa Ell. & Barthol.

  {Mycosphaerella Audibertiae Rehm.
  {Sphaerella Audibertiae (Rehm) Sacc. & Trott.
  Thyridium lividum (P. ex Fr.) Sacc.
Audibertia stachyoides Benth.
  Didymella Ramonae Fairman.
  Microdiplodia Ramonae Fairman.
  Myriangium Catalinae Fairman.
  {Durella nigrocyanea (Phil. & Hark.) Sacc.
  {Patellaria nigrocyanea Phil. & Hark.
  Pleospora Labiatarum Cke. & Hark.
  {Allodus mellifera (Diet. & Holw.) Arth.
  {Puccinia mellifera Diet. & Holw.
  Puccinia nigrescens Pk.
Monarda bradburiana Beck.
  {Dicaeoma Menthae (P.) S. F. Gray.
  {Puccinia Menthae P.
Monarda citriodora Cerv.
  Phyllosticta decidua Ell. & Kellerm.
  Phyllosticta Monardae Ell. & Barthol.
  Puccinia Menthae P., var. americana Pk.
Monarda clinopodia L.
  {Dicaeoma Menthae (P.) S. F. Gray.
  {Puccinia Menthae P.
  Ramularia brevipes Ell. & Ev.
Monarda comata Rydb.
Monarda didyma L.
  {Dicaeoma Menthae (P.) S. F. Gray.
  {Puccinia Menthae P.
  {Puccinia Menthae P., var. americana Pk.
Monarda fistulosa L.
  Dicaeoma angustatum (Pk.) O. Kuntze. I.
  Darluca Filum (Biv.) Cast.
  {Aecidium Menthae DC.
  {Dicaeoma Menthae (P.) S. F. Gray.
  {Puccinia Menthae P.
  {Puccinia Menthae P., var. americana Pk.
  Phyllosticta decidua Ell. & Kellerm.
  Ramularia variata J. J. Davis.
  Synchytrium Holwayi Farl.
Monarda menthifolia Benth.
Monarda mollis L.
  {Dicaeoma Menthae (P.) S. F. Gray.
  {Puccinia Menthae P.
  {Puccinia Menthae P., var. americana Pk.
Monarda punctata L.
  Phyllosticta decidua Ell. & Kellerm.
  {Dicaeoma Menthae (P.) S. F. Gray.
  {Puccinia Menthae P.
  {Puccinia Menthae P., var. americana Pk.
Monarda Ramaleyi A. Nels.
Monarda stricta Woot.
  {Dicaeoma Menthae (P.) S. F. Gray.
  {Puccinia Menthae P.
  {Puccinia Menthae P., var. americana Pk.
Monarda sp. indet.
  Phialea Dearnessii Ell. & Ev.
  Sphaerella Monardae Ell. & Ev.
  {Pycnochytrium Holwayi (Farl.) Schrt.
  {Synchytrium Holwayi Farl.

Blephilia hirsuta (Pursh) Benth.
  ⎧ Dicaeoma Menthae (P.) S. F. Gray.
  ⎨ Puccinia Menthae P.
  ⎩ Puccinia Menthae P., americana Pk.
Sphacele calycina Benth.
    Hendersonia varians Cke. & Hark.
    Uredo sphacelicola Diet. & Holw.
Hedeoma Drummondii Benth.
    Dicaeoma Menthae (P.) S. F. Gray.
Hedeoma hispida Pursh.
    Peronospora Hedeomae Kellerm. & Swingle.
  ⎧ Puccinia Menthae P.
  ⎨ Puccinia Menthae P., var. americana Pk.
  ⎩ Rhabdospora hedeomina (Pk.) Sacc.
  ⎩ Septoria hedeomina Pk.
Hedeoma nana (Torr.) Greene.
    Dicaeoma Menthae (P.) S. F. Gray.
Hedeoma pulegioides (L.) P.
    Erysiphe Cichoracearum DC. †
  ⎧ Peronospora Hedeomae Kellerm. & Swingle.
  ⎨ Peronospora Hedeomatis Berl.
  ⎧ Dicaeoma Menthae (P.) S. F. Gray.
  ⎨ Puccinia Menthae P.
  ⎩ Puccinia Menthae P., var. americana Pk.
    Septoria Hedeomae Dearness & House.
  ⎧ Rhabdospora hedeomina (Pk.) Sacc.
  ⎩ Septoria hedeomina Pk.
Hedeoma thymoides Gray, var. **oblongifolia**
      Gray.
    Dicaeoma Menthae (P.) S. F. Gray.
Melissa officinalis L.
  ⎧ Puccinia Menthae P.
  ⎩ Puccinia Menthae P., var. americana Pk.
Micromeria Chamissonis (Benth.) Greene.
    Puccinia Menthae P.
  ⎧ Dicaeoma Micromeriae (Dudley & Thompson)
  ⎨   Arth.
  ⎩ Puccinia Micromeriae Dudley & Thompson.
Micromeria Douglasii Benth.
    Puccinia Menthae P.
Satureja vulgaris (L.) Fritsch.
    Darluca Filum (Biv.) Cast.
    Phacidium simulatum B. & C.
  ⎧ Phyllosticta Calaminthae Ell. & Ev.
  ⎨ Phyllosticta decidua Ell. & Kellerm.
  ⎧ Dicaeoma Menthae (P.) S. F. Gray.
  ⎨ Puccinia Menthae P.
  ⎩ Puccinia Menthae P., var. americana Pk.
  ⎩ Trichobasis Labiatarum Lév.
Monardella lanceolata Gray.
Monardella macrantha Gray.
Monardella
    (Madronella oblongifolia Rydb.)
Monardella odoratissima Benth.
  ⎧ Puccinia Menthae P.
  ⎨ Puccinia Menthae P., var. americana Pk.
  ⎧ Dicaeoma Monardellae (Dudley & Thompson)
  ⎨   Arth.
  ⎩ Puccinia Monardellae Dudley & Thompson.

Monardella parviflora Greene.
  ⎧ Dicaeoma Monardellae (Dudley & Thompson)
  ⎨   Arth.
  ⎩ Puccinia Monardellae Dudley & Thompson.
Monardella undulata Benth.
Monardella villosa Benth.
  ⎧ Dicaeoma Monardellae (Dudley & Thompson)
  ⎨   Arth.
  ⎧ Puccinia Menthae Fung. Columb. *188b*.
  ⎩ Puccinia Monardellae Dudley & Thompson.
Monardella viridis Jepson.
    Puccinia Menthae P.
  ⎧ Dicaeoma Monardellae (Dudley & Thompson)
  ⎨   Arth.
  ⎩ Puccinia Monardellae Dudley & Thompson.
Pycnanthemum albescens Torr. & Gr.
  ⎧ Dicaeoma Menthae (P.) S. F. Gray.
  ⎩ Puccinia Menthae P., var. americana Pk.
Pycnanthemum
      (Koellia americana).
    Puccinia Menthae P., var. americana Pk.
Pycnanthemum flexuosum (Walt.) BSP.
Pycnathemum incanum (L.) Michx.
Pycnanthemum muticum (Michx.) P.
Pycnanthemum pilosum Nutt.
Pycnanthemum verticillatum (Michx.) P.
  ⎧ Aecidium Menthae DC.
    Caeoma Labiatarum Lk.
    Dicaeoma Menthae (P.) S. F. Gray.
    Puccinia Menthae P.
    Puccinia Menthae P., var. americana Pk.
    Puccinia Pycnanthemi S.
    Trichobasis Labiatarum Lév.
    Trichobasis Labiatarum, var. Pycnanthemi
      Fung. Am. *490*.
  ⎩ Uredo Labiatarum DC.
Pycnanthemum virginianum (L.) Durand &
      Jackson.
  ⎧ Dicaeoma angustatum (Pk.) O. Kuntze. I.
  ⎨ Puccinia angustata Pk. I.
  ⎧ Dothidea Brachystemonis (S.) Fr.
  ⎨ Phyllachora Brachystemonis (S.) Sacc.
  ⎩ Sphaeria Brachystemonis S.
  ⎧ Dicaeoma Menthae (P.) S. F. Gray.
  ⎨ Puccinia Menthae P.
  ⎩ Puccinia Menthae P., var. americana Pk.
Pycnanthemum sp. indet.
    Cercosporella Pycnanthemi Atk.
    Darluca Filum (Biv.) Cast.
    Sporidesmium asteriscus B. & C.
Thymus Serpyllum L.
  ⎧ Micropuccinia Schneideri (Schrt.) Arth. &
  ⎨   Jackson.
  ⎩ Puccinia Schneideri Schrt.
    Sphaerella pachyasca Rostr.
Cunila leucantha Benth.
  ⎧ Dicaeoma fuscatum (Arth. & Holw.) Arth.
  ⎩ Puccinia fuscata Arth. & Holw.

Cunila origanoides (L.) Brit.
  Darluca Filum (Biv.) Cast.
  ⎰Dicaeoma Menthae (P.) S. F. Gray.
  ⎱Puccinia Menthae P.
  Puccinia Menthae P., var. americana Pk.
  Trichobasis Labiatarum Lév.
Cunila polyantha Benth.
  ⎰Dicaeoma fuscatum (Arth. & Holw.) Arth.
  ⎱Puccinia fuscata Arth. & Holw.
Lycopus americanus Muhl.
  ⎰Aecidium Lycopi Gerard.
  ⎰Dicaeoma angustatum (Pk.) O. Kuntze. I.
  ⎱Puccinia angusta Pk. I.
  Ascochyta Leonuri Ell. & Dearness.
  Septoria Lycopi Pass.
  Synchytrium cellulare, var. Lycopodis J. J.
    Davis.
Lycopus europaeus L.
  ⎰Aecidium Lycopi Gerard.
  ⎱Puccinia angustata Pk. I.
  Puccinia Menthae P.
Lycopus lucidus Turcz., var. americanus Gray.
  Puccinia angustata Pk. I.
  ?Puccinia Eriophori Thm. I.
Lycopus rubellus Moench.
  ⎰Dicaeoma angustatum (Pk.) O. Kuntze. I.
  ⎱Puccinia angustata Pk. I.
  Cercospora Lycopi Ell. & Ev.
  Phyllosticta decidua Ell. & Kellerm.
Lycopus uniflorus Michx.
  ⎰Dicaeoma angustatum (Pk.) O. Kuntze. I.
  ⎱Puccinia angustata Pk. I.
  Ascochyta Lophanthi, var. lycopina J. J.
    Davis.
  Phyllosticta decidua Ell. & Kellerm.
  Septoria Lycopi Pass.
  ⎰Synchytrium aureum J. J. Davis p. p.
  ⎰Synchytrium cellulare, var. Lycopodis J. J.
  ⎱ Davis.
Lycopus virginicus L.
  ⎰Aecidium Lycopi Gerard.
  ⎰Dicaeoma angustatum (Pk.) O. Kuntze. I.
  ⎱Puccinia angustata Pk. I.
  Ascochyta Lophanthi, var. lycopina J. J. Davis.
  ?Phyllosticta Lycopodis Ell. & Ev.
  ⎰Synchytrium aureum J. J. Davis p. p.
  ⎱Synchytrium cellulare J. J. Davis.
Mentha arvensis L.
  Dicaeoma angustatum (Pk.) O. Kuntze. I.
  ⎰Dicaeoma Menthae (P.) S. F. Gray.
  ⎱Puccinia menthae P.
  Ramularia variata J. J. Davis.
  Septoria menthicola Sacc. & Let.
Mentha arvensis L., var. canadensis (L.) Briq.
  ⎰Dicaeoma angustatum (Pk.) O. Kuntze. I.
  ⎱Puccinia angustata Pk. I.
  Cercospora menthicola Tehon & Daniels.

Erysiphe Galeopsidis DC. †
Erysiphe Polygoni DC. †
  ⎰Phyllosticta Calaminthae Ell. & Ev.
  ⎱Phyllosticta decidua Ell. & Kellerm.
  ⎰Dicaeoma Menthae (P.) S. F. Gray.
  ⎱Puccinia Menthae P.
  Puccinia Menthae P., var. americana Pk.
  Ramularia menthicola Sacc.
  Septoria menthicola Sacc. & Let.
  Sphaerotheca Humuli (DC.) Burrill. †
Mentha cardiaca Baker.
  ⎰Dicaeoma Menthae (P.) S. F. Gray.
  ⎱Puccinia Menthae P.
Mentha gentilis L.
  Dicaeoma Menthae (P.) S. F. Gray.
  Phyllosticta decidua Ell. & Kellerm.
Mentha glabrior (Hook.) Rydb.
Mentha lanceolata Gray.
Mentha longifolia (L.) Huds.
  ⎰Dicaeoma Menthae (P.) S. F. Gray.
  ⎱Puccinia Menthae P.
Mentha pectinata Nutt.
  Phyllosticta decidua Ell. & Kellerm.
Mentha piperita L.
  Leptosphaeria substerilis Pk.
  Phyllosticta decidua Ell. & Kellerm.
  ⎰Dicaeoma Menthae (P.) S. F. Gray.
  ⎰Puccinia Menthae P.
  ⎱Puccinia Menthae P., var. americana Pk.
Mentha spicata L.
  Phyllactinia corylea (P.) ex Karst.
  Phyllosticta decidua Ell. & Kellerm.
  ⎰Dicaeoma Menthae (P.) S. F. Gray.
  ⎱Puccinia Menthae P.
Collinsonia canadensis L.
  Helminthosporium interseminatum B. & Rav.
  Leptosphaeria acuta (M. & N.) Karst.
  Phyllosticta Collinsoniae Sacc. & Dearness.
  ⎰Gonatobotryum tenellum Pk.
  ⎱Spondylocladium tenellum Pk.
Collinsonia sp. indet.
  Excipula majuscula S.
  ⎰Dothidea elliptica S.
  ⎱Phyllachora elliptica (S.) Sacc.
Hyptis atrorubens Poit.
  ⎰Irene hyptidicola (F. L. Stevens) Toro.
  ⎱Meliola hyptidicola F. L. Stevens.
  ⎰Dicaeoma medellinense (Mayor) Arth.
  ⎱Puccinia medellinensis Mayor.
Hyptis capitata (L.) Jacq.
  Calloriopsis gelatinosa (Ell. & Martin) Syd.
  Dimerina eutricha (Sacc. & Berl.) Theissen.
  Ectosticta costaricana Syd.
  ⎰Irene hyptidicola (F. L. Stevens) Toro.
  ⎱Meliola hyptidicola F. L. Stevens.
  Pseudomeliola (?) collapsa Earle.

Hyptis capitata (*cont.*)
Dicaeoma Hyptidis (Tracy & Earle) Arth.
Eriosporangium Hyptidis (Tracy & Earle) Arth.
Puccinia Hyptidis Tracy & Earle.
Uredo Hyptidis Henn.
Stigme costaricana Syd.

Hyptis Emoryi Torr.
Micropuccinia distorta (Holw.) Arth. & Jackson.
Puccinia distorta Holw.

Hyptis lantanifolia Poit.
Arthrobotryum caudatum Syd.
Dimerina eutricha (Sacc. & Berl.) Theissen.
Irene hyptidicola (F. L. Stevens) Toro.
Meliola hyptidicola F. L. Stevens.
Dicaeoma insititium Arth.
Puccinia insititia Arth.

Hyptis lilacina Schiede & Deppe.
Dicaeoma fidele Arth.
Puccinia fidelis Arth.

Hyptis mutabilis (A. Rich) Briq.
Puccinia Hyptidis-murabilis Mayor.
Puccinia medellinensis Mayor..

Hyptis pectinata (L.) Poit.
Meliola hyptidicola F. L. Stevens.
Naemosphaera hyptidicola F. L. Stevens.
Micropuccinia distorta (Holw.) Arth. & Jackson.
Puccinia distorta Holw.
Dicaeoma fidele Arth.
Puccinia fidelis Arth.
Dicaeoma medellinense (Mayor) Arth.
Eriosporangium Hyptidis Arth. p. p.
Eriosporangium tucumanense Arth. p. p.
Puccinia Hyptidis Kern.
Puccinia medellinensis Mayor.
Argomyces parilis Arth.
Bullaria parilis (Arth.) Arth. & Mains.
Puccinia Hyptidis N. Am. Uredinales *641*.
Puccinia parilis Arth.

Hyptis polystachya H. B. K.
Dicaeoma Hyptidis-mutabilis (Mayor) Arth.
Puccinia Hyptidis-mutabilis Mayor.
Dicaeoma medellinense (Mayor) Arth.
Eriosporangium Hyptidis Arth. p. p.
Puccinia Hyptidis Kern.
Puccinia medellinensis Mayor.

Hyptis radiata Willd.
Asterina spurca B. & C.
Asterina spuria B. & C.
Dicaeoma Hyptidis (Tracy & Earle) Arth.
Eriosporangium Hyptidis (Tracy & Earle) Arth.
Gymnoconia Hyptidis (Tracy & Earle) Lagerh.
Uredo Hyptidis M. A. Curtis.

Hyptis Shaferi Britton.
Dicaeoma Hyptidis (Tracy & Earle) Arth.

Hyptis stellulata Benth.
Dicaeoma fidele Arth.
Eriosporangium fidelis Arth.
Puccinia fidelis Arth.
Bullaria parilis (Arth.) Arth. & Mains.
Puccinia parilis Arth.

Hyptis suaveolens Poit.
Puccinia Gilbertii Speg.?
Coleosporium brasiliense Diet.
Dicaeoma medellinense (Mayor) Arth.
Eriosporangium Hyptidis Arth. p. p.
Eriosporangium medellinense (Mayor) Diet.
Eriosporangium tucumanense Arth. p. p.
Puccinia Hyptidis Arth. p. p.
Puccinia medellinensis Mayor.

Hyptis urticoides H. B. K.
Dicaeoma fidele Arth.
Eriosporangium fidele Arth.
Puccinia fidelis Arth.

Hyptis verticillata Jacq.
Irene hyptidicola (F. L. Stevens) Toro.

Hyptis sp. indet.
Cercospora Ellisii Sacc. & Syd.
Cercospora Hyptidis Ell. & Ev.

Ocimum micranthum Willd.
Sphaerotheca Humuli (DC.) Burrill. †

Coleus sp. indet.
Pythium complectens Braun.
Rhizoctonia Solani Kühn.

SOLANACEAE

Nicandra physalodes (L.) P.
Sclerotium Nicandrae S.

Lycium Andersonii Gray.
Lycium californicum Nutt.
Lycium carolinianum Walt.
Lycium cedronense Greene.
Lycium Fremontii Gray.
Lycium gracilipes Gray.
Bullaria globosipes (Pk.) H. S. Jackson.
Puccinia globosipes Pk.

Lycium halimifolium Mill.
Cercospora Lycii Ell. & Halsted.
Cicinnobolus Cesatii DBy.
Erysiphe Polygoni DC. †
Phyllosticta Lycii Ell. & Kellerm.
Bullaria globosipes (Pk.) H. S. Jackson.
Uredo inquirenda Arth.
Uredo similis Ell.
Bullaria tumidipes (Pk.) Arth.
Puccinia Lycii Auct. Amer.
Puccinia tumidipes Pk.
Sphaerella Lycii Ell. & Ev.
Sphaeropsis Lycii Dearness & Barthol.
Sphaerotheca pannosa (Wallr.) Lév.

Lycium pallidum Miers.
Lycium parviflorum Gray.
  Aecidium Lycii Arth.
  Bullaria tumidipes (Pk.) Arth.
Lycium Torreyi Gray.
  { Bullaria globosipes (Pk.) H. S. Jackson.
   Puccinia globosipes Pk.
   Bullaria tumidipes (Pk.) Arth.
   Puccinia tumidipes Pk.
Acnistus aggregatus Miers.
  Puccinia Acnisti Arth.
Acnistus arborescens Schl.
  Aecidium tenerius Arth. & Holw.
  Calopeltis Acnisti Syd.
  Irene portoricensis Toro.
  Mycobonia flava Pat.
  Physarum connatum Pk.
  { Leptoporus molluscus (P. ex Fr.) Pat.
   Polyporus molluscus (P.) ex Fr.
   Allodus Acnisti (Arth.) Arth. & Orton.
   Puccinia Acnisti Arth.
Chamaesaracha Coronopus (Dunal) Gray.
  { Aecidium Cockerellii Arth.
   Dicaeoma Sarcobati Arth. I.
Chamaesaracha nana Gray.
  Aecidium Solani Mont.
  { Allodus Chamaesarachae (Syd.) Arth.
   Puccinia Chamaesarachae Syd.
   Puccinia Solani Auct. Amer. saltem p. p.
Physalis angulata L.
  Entyloma Physalidis (Kalchb. & Cke.) Wint.
Physalis comata Rydb.
  Aecidium Physalidis Burrill.
Physalis Francheti Masters.
  Entyloma australe Speg.
  Rhizoctonia Solani Kühn.
Physalis heterophylla Nees.
  Aecidium Physalidis Burrill. 1884.
  Aecidium Physalidis Pk. ex Stuart. 1902.
  Cercospora diffusa Ell. & Ev.
  Cercospora Physalidis Ell.
  { Entyloma australe Speg.
   Entyloma Physalidis (Kalchb. & Cke.) Farl.
   Micropuccinia Physalidis (Pk.) Arth. &
    Jackson.
   Puccinia Physalidis Pk.
Physalis lanceolata Michx.
  Aecidium Physalidis Burrill.
  Aecidium Solani Mont.
  Cercospora diffusa Ell. & Ev.
  Cercospora Physalidis Ell.
  Cercospora Physalidis Ell., var. concentrica
   C. & E.
  Entyloma Physalidis (Kalchb. & Cke.) Wint.
  { Micropuccinia Physalidis (Pk.) Arth. & Jack-
   son. 1922.
   Micropuccinia Physalidis (Pk.) Arth. & Holw.
   1926.
   Puccinia Physalidis Pk.

Physalis lanceolata Michx., var. **laevigata** Gray.
  Entyloma Physalidis (Kalchb. & Cke.) Wint.
Physalis lobata Torr.
  Cercospora Physalidis Ell.
  { Dicaeoma Sarcobati (Pk.) Arth. I.
   Puccinia subnitens Diet. I.
Physalis longifolia Nutt.
  Aecidium Physalidis Burrill.
  Cercospora Physalidis Ell.
  { Entyloma australe Speg.
   Entyloma Physalidis (Kalchb. & Cke.) Wint.
   Puccinia Physalidis Pk.
Physalis neomexicana Rydb.
Physalis philadelphica Lam.
  { Entyloma australe Speg.
   Entyloma Physalidis (Kalchb. & Cke.) Wint.
Physalis pruinosa L.
  Entyloma australe Speg.
  Meliola acervata Ell. & Ev.
Physalis pubescens L.
  Alternaria Solani (Ell. & Martin) Jones &
   Grout.
  Cercospora Physalidis Ell.
  { Entyloma australe Speg.
   Entyloma Physalidis (Kalchb. & Cke.) Wint.
  Leptosphaeria Physalidis Ell. & Ev.
  Puccinia Physalidis Pk.
Physalis subglabrata Mackenzie & Bush.
  Cercospora Physalidis Ell.
Physalis virginiana Mill.
  Aecidium Physalidis Burrill.
  Aecidium Solani Mont.
  Cercospora physalicola Ell. & Barthol.
  Cercospora Physalidis Ell.
  { Entyloma australe Speg.
   Entyloma Besseyi Farl.
   Entyloma Physalidis (Kalchb. & Cke.) Wint.
   Protomyces Physalidis Kalchb. & Cke.
   Micropuccinia Physalidis (Pk.) Arth. & Jack-
    son.
   Puccinia Physalidis Pk.
Physalis viscosa L.
  Aecidium Physalidis Burrill.
  Aecidium Solani Mont.
  { Entyloma Besseyi Farl.
   Entyloma Physalidis (Kalchb. & Cke.) Wint.
   Puccinia Physalidis Pk.
Saracha antillarum Krug & Urb.
  Micropuccinia Sarachae (Mayor) Arth. &
   Jackson.
Saracha jaltomata Schl.
  Cercosporina Sarachae Syd.
  { Micropuccinia Sarachae (Mayor) Arth. &
   Jackson.
   Puccinia Sarachae Mayor.
Capsicum annuum L.
  Acrostalagmus albus Preuss.
  Alternaria Solani (Ell. & Martin) Jones &
   Grout.

Capsicum annuum (*cont.*)
Botrytis cinerea P. †
Cercospora Capsici Heald & Wolf.
Cladosporium herbarum (P.) ex Lk.
Colletotrichum lagenarium (Pass.) Ell. &
   Halsted.
Colletotrichum nigrum Ell. & Halsted.
{Corticium vagum B. & C.
{Rhizoctonia Solani Kühn.
Fusarium annuum Leonian.
Fusarium radicicola Wr.
{Gloeosporium piperatum Ell. & Ev.
{Glomerella piperata (Stoneman) Spauld. & v.
   Schrenk.
{Gnomoniopsis piperata Stoneman.
{Gloeosporium fructigenum B.
{Gloeosporium versicolor B. & C.
{Glomerella rufomaculans Spaulding & v.
   Schrenk.
{Glomerella cingulata (Stoneman) Spaulding &
   v. Schrenk.
Macrosporium commune Rabh.
Macrosporium Solani Ell. & Martin.
Meliola capsicola F. L. Stevens.
Ozonium omnivorum Shear.
Pestalozzia Guepini Desm.
Phoma destructiva Plowr.
Phytophthora Capsici Leonian.
Phytophthora terrestris Sherbakoff.
Pythium debaryanum Hesse.
{Sclerotinia libertiana Fckl.
{Sclerotinia sclerotiorum (Lib.) Massee.
Sclerotium baticola Taubenhaus.
Sclerotium Rolfsii Sacc.

Capsicum baccatum L.
{Meliola capsicicola F. L. Stevens ex Sacc.
{ Syll.
{Meliola capsicola F. L. Stevens.

Capsicum frutescens L.
{Gloeosporium piperatum Ell. & Ev.
{Glomerella piperata (Stoneman) Spaulding &
   v. Schrenk.
Meliola capsicola F. L. Stevens.

Capsicum sp. indet.
Labrella Capsici Fr.
Ozonium omnivorum Shear.
Phoma destructiva Plowr.
Rhizoctonia pallida Matz.
Rhizopus nigricans Ehrenb. ex Fr.

Lycopersicum esculentum Mill.

PHYCOMYCETES

Aphanomyces euteiches Drechsler.
{Chrysophlyctis endobiotica Schilbersky.
{Synchytrium endobioticum (Schilbersky) Percival.
Mucor abundans Povah.
Mucor hiemalis Wehmer.

Olpidium Brassicae (Wor.) Dangeard.
Phytophthora infestans (Mont.) DBy.
Phytophthora mexicana Hotson & Hartge.
Phytophthora terrestris Sherbakoff.
Plectospira myriandra Drechsler.
Pythium debaryanum Hesse.
Rhizopus nigricans Ehrenb. ex Fr.

ASCOMYCETES

{Dialonectria Peponum (B. & C.) Cke.
{Nectria Peponum B. & C.
{Nectria perpusilla Rav. Fung. Car.
{Erysiphe communis Auct. Amer.
{Erysiphe Polygoni DC. †
{Glomerella cingulata (Stoneman) Spaulding &
   v. Schrenk.
{Glomerella rufomaculans Spaulding & v.
   Schrenk.
Nematospora Lycopersici Schneider.
Ophiobolus consimilis Ell. & Ev.
{Ophiobolus porphyrogonus (Tode) ex Sacc.
{Sphaeria rubella P. ex Fr.
Sclerotinia libertiana Fckl.
Mycosphaerella citrullina Grossenbacher.

BASIDIOMYCETES

{Corticium vagum B. & C.
{Corticium vagum, var. Solani Burt.
{Rhizoctonia Solani Kühn.
Puccinia pittieriana Henn.
Rhizoctonia potomacensis Wr.

SPHAEROPSIDALES

Ascochyta hortorum C. O. Sm.
{Ascochyta Lycopersici Brun.
{Didymella Lycopersici Klebahn.
{Diplodina destructiva (Plowr.) Petrak.
{Phoma destructiva Plowr.
{Phyllosticta Lycopersici Pk.
Phyllosticta hortorum Auct. Amer. non Speg.
Septoria Dulcamarae Desm.
Septoria Gladioli Pass.
Septoria hortensis Ell. & Ev.
Septoria Lycopersici (Speg.) Sacc.
Vermicularia varians Ducomet.

MELANCONIALES

{Colletotrichum gloeosporioides Penz.
{Gloeosporium fructigenum B.
{Gloeosporium versicolor B. & C.
{Glomerella rufomaculans Spaulding & v.
   Schrenk.
Colletotrichum lagenarium (Pass.) Ell. &
   Halsted.
{Colletotrichum lindemuthianum (Sacc. &
   Magn.) Br. & Cav.
{Gloeosporium lindemuthianum Sacc. & Magn.
{Colletotrichum Lycopersici Chester. 1891.
{Colletotrichum Lycopersici Ell. & Ev. 1893.
Colletotrichum nigrum Ell. & Halsted.

Lycopersicum esculentum (*cont.*)
{ Colletotrichum phomoides (Sacc.) Chester.
{ Gloeosporium phomoides Sacc.
Gloeosporium phyllachorides Ell. & Ev.

Hyphomycetes
Mucedinaceae
Aspergillus niger Van Tiegh.
Basisporum gallarum Molliard.
Botrytis cinerea P. †
Botrytis hortensis Ell. & Ev.
Monilia fructigena Auct. Amer.
Oospora lactis Fres.
Oospora lactis, var. parasitica F. J. Pritchard.
Sporotrichum solubile S.
Trichothecium subfulvum Ell. & Ev.
Verticillium albo-atrum Reinke & Berthold.
Verticillium Lycopersici Pritchard & Porte.

Dematiaceae
{ Alternaria fasciculata (C. & E.) Jones & Grout.
{ Macrosporium fasciculatum C. & E.
{ Macrosporium Tomato Cke.
{ Alternaria Solani (Ell. & Martin) Jones & Grout.
{ Alternaria Solani Sorauer p. p.
{ Macrosporium Cookei Sacc.
{ Macrosporium Solani Ell. & Martin. 1882.
{ Macrosporium Solani Cke. 1883.
Botryosporium pulchrum Cda.
Cercospora canescens Ell. & Martin.
Cercospora cruenta Sacc.
Cercospora diffusa Ell. & Ev.
Cercospora Physalidis Ell. & Barthol.
Cladosporium fulvum Cke.
Cladosporium herbarum (P.) ex Lk.
Cladosporium lycoperdinum Cke.?
Cladosporium scabies Cke.
Dendryphium cladosporioides Ell. & Ev.
Fumago vagans Fr.
Helminthosporium rhopaloides Fres.
Helminthosporium Tomato Ell. & Barthol.
Sirodesmium herbarum (Cke.) Sacc.
Stachybotrys atrogrisea Ell. & Ev.

Stilbaceae
Isaria clonostachoides Pritchard & Porte.

Tuberculariaceae
Dendrodochium Lycopersici March.
Fusarium acuminatum Ell. & Ev.
Fusarium citrinum Wr.
Fusarium erubescens B. & C.
Fusarium falcatum App. & Wr.
Fusarium ferruginosum Sherbakoff.
{ Fusarium Lycopersici Sacc.
{ Fusarium oxysporum Schl., var. Lycopersici Sacc.
Fusarium moniliforme Sheldon.
Fusarium orthoceras App. & Wr.

Fusarium oxysporum Schl.
Fusarium radicicola Wr.
Fusarium roseum Lk.
Fusarium sclerotium Wr.
Fusarium Solani Mart.

Miscellanea
Ozonium omnivorum Shear.
Sclerotium bataticola Taubenhaus.
Sclerotium Rolfsii Sacc.
Spermatophthora Gossypii Ashby & Nowell.
Spongospora subterranea (Wallr.) Lagerh.
Solanum acerifolium Humb. & Bonpl. ex Dun.
Asterina diplopoda Syd.
Solanum appendiculatum Humb. & Bonpl.
{ Nigredo Solani (Diet. & Holw.) Arth.
{ Uromyces Solani Diet. & Holw.
Solanum carolinense L.
Ascochyta hortorum (Speg.) C. O. Sm.
Ascochyta Lycopersici Brun.
Cercospora atromarginalis Atk.
Cercospora carolinensis Tharp.
Cladosporium fulvum Cke.
Erysiphe Cichoracearum DC. †
Macrosporium Solani Cke.
Phyllosticta Dulcamarae Sacc.
Phyllosticta hortorum Speg.
Phyllosticta Solani Ell. & Martin.
Rhizoctonia Solani Kühn.
Septoria Lycopersici Speg.
Thielavia basicola (B. & Br.) Zopf.
Verticillium Lycopersici Pritchard & Porte.
Solanum ciliatum Blume.
Solanum Commersoni Dun.
Phytophthora infestans (Mont.) DBy.
Spongospora subterranea (Wallr.) Lagerh.
Solanum diversifolium Schl.
{ Micropuccinia Solani (S.) Arth. & Jackson.
{ Micropuccinia solanita (Arth.) Arth. & Jackson
Dicaeoma tubulosum (Pat. & Gaill.) Arth. & Fromme.
Solanum Donnell-Smithii Coult.
{ Micropuccinia solanita (Arth.) Arth. & Jackson.
{ Puccinia solanita Arth.
Solanum Douglasii Dunal.
Septoria Dulcamarae Desm.
Solanum Dulcamara L.
{ Cercospora Dulcamarae (Pk.) Ell.
{ Ramularia Dulcamarae Pk.
{ Chrysophlyctis endobiotica Schilbersky.
{ Synchytrium endobioticum (Schilbersky) Percival.
Cladosporium elegans Penz.
Diplodia Dulcamarae Fckl.
Haplosporella Dulcamara Dearness & House.
Leptosphaeria Solani Ell. & Ev.
Phoma dulcamarina Sacc.
Phyllosticta decidua Ell. & Kellerm.

Solanum Dulcamara (*cont.*)
Phyllosticta Dulcamarae Sacc.
{Phyllosticta perforans Ell. & Ev.
{Phyllostictella perforans (Ell. & Ev.) Tassi.
Sphaerella Solani Ell. & Ev.
Vermicularia solanoica Fairman.

Solanum elaeagnifolium Cav.
Dicaeoma tubulosum (Pat. & Gaill.) Arth. &
Fromme.

Solanum Hartwegi Benth.
Aecidium tubulosum Pat. & Gaill.

Solanum jamaicense Mill.
Alternaria Solani (Ell. & Martin) Jones &
Grout.
Meliola Solani F. L. Stevens.

Solanum Melongena L.
Acrostalagmus albus Preuss.
Alternaria Solani (Ell. & Martin) Jones &
Grout.
Ascochyta Lycopersici Brun.
Ascochyta Solani-nigri Died.
Botrytis cinerea Auct.
{Botrytis fascicularis (Cda.) Sacc.
{Polyactis fascicularis Cda.
Botrytis vulgaris (Lk.) ex Fr.
Cladosporium (?) herbarum Lk.
Colletotrichum atramentarium (B. & Br.)
Taubenhaus.
Colletotrichum lagenarium (Pass.) Ell. &
Halsted.
Colletotrichum lindemuthianum (Sacc. &
Magn.) Br. & Cav.
Colletotrichum solanicola O'Gara.
{Corticium vagum B. & C., var. Solani Burt.
{Rhizoctonia Solani Kühn.
Diplodia natalensis Evans.
{Gloeosporium fructigenum B.
{Gloeosporium Melongenae Ell. & Halsted.
{Gloeosporium phomoides Sacc.
{Glomerella rufomaculans Spaulding & v.
{ Schrenk.
Macrosporium esculentum Ell. & Ev.
Macrosporium Solani Ell. & Martin.
Meliola Camelliae (Catt.) Sacc.
Mystrosporium polytrichum Cke.
Nectria Ipomoeae Halsted.
Ozonium omnivorum Shear.
Phlyctaena arcuata B.
{Ascochyta hortorum C. O. Sm.
{Phoma Solani Halsted.
{Phomopsis vexans (Sacc. & Syd.) Harter.
{Phyllosticta hortorum Auct. Amer. non Speg.
Phyllosticta Solani Ell. & Martin.
Phytophthora infestans (Mont.) DBy.
Phytophthora terrestris Sherbakoff.
Pythium aphanidermatum (Edson) Fitzpat-
rick.
Pythium debaryanum Hesse.

Rhizoctonia Melongena Matz.
{Sclerotinia libertiana Fckl.
{Sclerotinia sclerotiorum (Lib.) Massee.
Sclerotium Rolfsii Sacc.
Septoria Lycopersici (Speg.) Sacc.
Thielavia basicola (B. & Br.) Zopf.
Tuberculina solanicola Ell.
Verticillium albo-atrum Reinke & Berthold.

Solanum muricatum Ait.
Phytophthora terrestris Sherbakoff.

Solanum nigrum L.
Alternaria Solani Ell. & Martin.
Cercospora atromarginalis Atk.
Cercospora nigri Tharp.
?Cercospora rigospora Atk.
{Chrysophlyctis endobiotica Schilbersky.
{Synchytrium endobioticum (Schilbersky) Per-
{ cival.
Cladosporium fulvum Cke.
{Entyloma Besseyi Farl.
{Entyloma Physalidis (Kalchb. & Cke.) Wint.
Macrophoma subconica Ell. & Ev.

Solanum nudum H. B. K.
{Nigredo Solani (Diet. & Holw.) Arth.
{Uromyces Solani Diet. & Holw.

Solanum persicifolium Dunal.
Meliola glabroides F. L. Stevens.

Solanum pseudocapsicum L.
Alternaria Solani (Ell. & Martin) Jones &
Grout.

Solanum racemosum Jacq.
{Bullaria adducta (Arth.) Arth. & Mains.
{Puccinia adducta Arth.

Solanum rostratum Dunal.
Alternaria Solani (Ell. & Martin) Jones &
Grout.
Macrosporium Solani Ell. & Martin.
Phyllosticta Dulcamarae Sacc.

Solanum rugosum Dunal.
Asterina dilabens Syd.
Irene plebeia (Speg.) Theissen & Syd.
Macrosporium Solani Ell. & Martin.
Meliola Camelliae (Catt.) Sacc.
Meliola glabroides F. L. Stevens.
Mystrosporium polytrichum Cke.
Nectria Ipomoeae Halsted.
Phlyctaena arcuata B.
{Ascochyta hortorum C. O. Sm.
{Phoma Solani Halsted.
{Phomopsis vexans (Sacc. & Syd.) Harter.
{Phyllosticta hortorum Auct. Amer. non Speg.

Solanum salviifolium Lam.
Puccinia impressa Syd.

Solanum tequilense Gray.
{Dicaeoma tubulosum (Arth.) Arth. & Fromme.
{ I.
{Puccinia tubulosa Arth. I.

Solanum torvum Sw.

Aecidium Cestri Mont.

Aecidium Solani Mont.

⎰ Aecidium tubulosum Pat. & Gaill.
⎱ Dicaeoma tubulosum (Arth.) Arth. & Fromme.

⎰ Puccinia substriata I. Auct.
⎱ Puccinia tubulosa Arth. I.

Cercospora Solani-torvi Fragoso & Ciferri.

Cercospora trichophila F. L. Stevens.

Cladosporium fulvum Cke.

Erysiphe Cichoracearum DC. (?).

Irene Solani (F. L. Stevens) Toro.

Ramularia torvi Ell. & Ev.

Solanum triflorum Nutt.

Entyloma Physalidis (Kalchb. & Cke.) Wint.

Solanum triquetrum Cav.

⎰ Micropuccinia incondita (Arth.) Arth. & Jackson.
⎱ Puccinia incondita Arth.

Solanum tuberosum L.

Phycomycetes

⎰ Chrysophlyctis endobiotica Schilbersky.
⎱ Synchytrium endobioticum (Schilbersky) Percival.

Phytophthora Arecae (Colem.) Pethyb.

Phytophthora erythroseptica Pethyb.

⎰ Botrytis infestans Mont.
⎰ Peronospora infestans (Mont.) Casp.
⎱ Phytophthora infestans (Mont.) DBy.

Pythium debaryanum Hesse.

Pythium vexans DBy.

Rhizopus nigricans Ehrenb. ex Fr.

Ascomycetes

⎰ Dialonectria Brassicae (Ell. & Sacc.) Cke.
⎱ Nectria Brassicae Ell. & Sacc.

⎰ Hypocopra fimicola (Rob.) Sacc.
⎱ Sordaria fimicola (Rob.) Ces. & De Not.

⎰ Heptameria comatella C. & E.
⎰ Leptosphaeria comatella (C. & E.) Sacc.
⎱ Sphaeria comatella C. & E.

⎰ Leptosphaeria Doliolum (P. ex Fr.) De Not.
⎱ Sphaeria Doliolum P. ex Fr.

Melanospora ornata Zukal.

Nectria ditissima Tul.

Neocosmospora vasinfecta Erw. Sm.

Neocosmospora vasinfecta Erw. Sm., var. tracheiphila Erw. Sm.

⎰ Ophiobolus porphyrogonus (Tode ex Fr.) Sacc.
⎰ Raphidospora rubella (P. ex Fr.) Fckl.
⎱ Sphaeria rubella P. ex Fr.

Sclerotinia libertiana Fckl.

Sclerotinia sclerotiorum (Lib.) Massee.

Mycosphaerella Solani (Ell. & Ev.) Wr.

Basidiomycetes

Armillaria mellea (Vahl) ex Fr.

⎰ Micropuccinia pittieriana (Henn.) Arth. & Jackson.
⎱ Puccinia pittieriana Henn.

⎰ Corticium vagum B. & C.
⎰ Corticium vagum B. & C., var Solani Burt.
⎰ Hypochnus Solani Prill. & Delacr.
⎱ Rhizoctonia Solani Kühn.

Ozonium omnivorum Shear.

⎰ Rhizoctonia Crocorum (P.) ex Fr.
⎱ Rhizoctonia violacea Tul.

Sphaeropsidales

Ascochyta Lycopersici Brun.

Lasiodiplodia tubericola Ell. & Ev.

Phoma eupyrena Sacc.

⎰ Phoma nebulosa (P. ex Fr.) Mont.
⎱ Sphaeria nebulosa P. ex Fr.

⎰ Ascochyta hortorum C. O. Sm.
⎱ Phoma Solani Halsted.

Phyllosticta hortorum Auct. Amer. non Speg.

Phoma solanicola Prill. & Delacr.

Phoma tuberosa Melhus et al.

Phyllosticta Solani Ell. & Martin.

Plenodomus destruens Harter.

Vermicularia varians Duc.

Melanconiales

Colletotrichum maculans (Lk.) Dickson.

Colletotrichum tabificum (Hallier p. p.) Pethybr.

Gloeosporium fructigenum B., forma americanum Krueger.

⎰ Colletotrichum atramentarium (B. & Br.) Taubenhaus.
⎱ Colletotrichum solanicola O'Gara.

Phellomyces sclerotiophorus Frank.

Vermicularia atramentaria B. & Br.

Hyphomycetes
mucedinaceae

⎰ Actinomyces scabies (Thax.) Güssow.
⎰ Oospora scabies Thax.
⎱ Streptothrix scabies (Thax.) Cunningham.

Aspergillus niger van Tiegh.

Botrytis cinerea P. †

Clonostachys araucaria, var. rosea Preuss.

Oospora pustulans Owen & Wakefield.

Oospora rosea (Preuss) Sacc. & Vogl.

Papulospora coprophila (Zukal) Hotson.

Penicillium oxalicum Currie & Thom.

Ramularia didymum (Harting) Wr.

Ramularia macrospora Fres.

Ramularia magnusiana (Sacc.) Lindau.

Ramularia Solani Sherbakoff.

Rhopalomyces elegans Cda.

Spicaria nivea Harz.

Sporotrichum flavissimum Lk.

⎰ Verticillium albo-atrum E. Dale. 1912.
⎰ Periola tomentosa (Fr.) Reinke & Berth.
⎱ Verticillium albo-atrum Reinke & Berth. 1879.

Verticillium lateritium (B.) Cke.

Solanum tuberosum (*cont.*)

Verticillium Lycopersici Pritchard & Poole.
Verticillium Solani nom. nud.

DEMATIACEAE

Alternaria fasciculata (C. & E.) Jones & Grout.
Alternaria Solani Sorauer p. p.
Alternaria Tomato L. R. Jones.
Macrosporium chartarum Pk.
Macrosporium fasciculatum C. & E.
Macrosporium Maydis C. & E.
Macrosporium Tomato Cke.
Alternaria Solani (Ell. & Martin) Jones & Grout.
Alternaria Solani Sorauer p. p.
Macrosporium Solani Ell. & Martin. 1882.
Macrosporium Solani Cke. 1883.
Cercospora concors (Casp.) Sacc.
Cercospora solanicola Atk.
Cladosporium fulvum Cke.
Helminthosporium interseminatum B. & Rav.
Spondylocladium atrovirens Harz.
Torula convoluta Harz.
Torula herbarum Lk.

STILBACEAE

Stysanus Stemonitis Cda.
Stysanus tubericola Ell. & Dearness.

TUBERCULARIACEAE

Fusarium acuminatum Ell. & Ev. em. Wr.
Fusarium affine Fautr. & Lamb.
Hymenula affinis (Fautr. & Lamb.) Wr.
Fusarium anguioides Sherbakoff.
Fusarium anguioides Sherbakoff, var. caudatum Sherbakoff.
Fusarium angustum Sherbakoff.
Fusarium arcuosporum Sherbakoff.
Fusarium argillaceum (Fr.) Sacc.
Fusarium cuneiforme Sherbakoff.
Fusarium ventricosum App. & Wr.
Fusarium aridum Pratt.
Fusarium arthrosporioides Sherbakoff, var. asporotrichius Sherbakoff.
Fusarium asclerotium (Sherbakoff) Wr.
Fusarium oxysporum, var. asclerotium Sherbakoff.
Fusarium avenaceum (Fr.) Sacc.
Fusarium lucidum Sherbakoff.
Fusarium subulatum App. & Wr.
Fusarium avenaceum (Fr.) Sacc., var. brevius (Sherbakoff) Farl.
Fusarium subulatum App. & Wr., var. brevius Sherbakoff.
Fusarium biforme Sherbakoff.
Fusarium blasticola Rostr.
Fusarium sclerotioides, var. brevius Sherbakoff.
Fusarium bulbigenum Cke. & Massee.
Fusarium bullatum Sherbakoff.

Fusarium caudatum Wr., var. Solani Sherbakoff.
Fusarium clavatum Sherbakoff.
Fusarium coeruleum (Lib.) Sacc.
Fusarium conglutinans Wollenw.
Fusarium culmorum (W. G. Sm.) Sacc.
Fusarium culmorum (W. G. Sm.) Sacc., var. leteius Sherbakoff.
Fusarium dimerum Penz.
Fusarium dimerum Penz., var. Solani Sherbakoff.
Fusarium diplosporum C. & E.
Fusarium discolor, var. sulphureum App. & Wr.
Fusarium diversisporum Sherbakoff.
Fusarium effusum Sherbakoff.
Fusarium eumartii Carpenter.
Fusarium falcatum App. & Wollenw.
Fusarium vasinfectum, var. Pisi Schikorra non van Hall.
Fusarium ferruginosum Sherbakoff.
Fusarium Helianthi C. E. Lewis.
Fusarium herbarum (Cda.) Fr.
Fusarium hyperoxysporum Wr.
Fusarium lutulatum Sherbakoff.
Fusarium Lini Bolley.
Fusarium Martii App. & Wollenw.
Fusarium vasinfectum Auct. p. p.
Fusarium Martii App. & Wr., var. minus Sherbakoff.
Fusarium Martii App. & Wr., var. viride Sherbakoff.
Fusarium merismoides Cda.
Fusarium udum (B.) Wr., var. Solani Sherbakoff.
Fusarium metachroum App. & Wr.
Fusarium metachroum App. & Wr., var. minus Sherbakoff.
Fusarium moniliforme Sheldon.
Fusarium orthoceras App. & Wr.
Fusarium oxysporum Sm. & Swingle non Auct.
Fusarium orthoceras App. & Wr., var. longius (Sherbakoff) Wr.
Fusarium oxysporum, var. longius Sherbakoff.
Fusarium orthoceras App. & Wr., var. albidoviolaceum (Dasz.) Wr.
Fusarium oxysporum Schl., var. resupinatum Sherbakoff.
Fusarium falcatum, var. fuscum Sherbakoff.
Fusarium ossicola (B. & C.) Sacc.
Fusisporium ossicola B. & C.
Fusarium oxysporum Schl. em Wr.
Fusarium Poae (Pk.) C. E. Lewis.
Fusarium radicicola Wollenw..
Fusarium redolens Wr.
Fusarium redolens, var. Solani Sherbakoff.
Fusarium rhizochromatistes Sideris.
Fusarium bullatum, var. roseum Sherbakoff.
Fusarium roseobullatum (Sherbakoff) Wr.

Solanum tuberosum (*cont.*)
- Fusarium roseolum (H. O. Stephens) Sacc.
- Fusisporium roseolum H. O. Stephens.
- Fusarium rubiginosum App. & Wr.
- Fusarium discolor App. & Wr.
- Fusarium discolor, var. triseptatum Sherbakoff.
- Fusarium sambucinum Fckl.
- Fusarium sanguineum Sherbakoff non Fr.
- Fusarium sclerotioides Sherbakoff.
- Fusarium semitectum B. & Rav.
- Fusarium Solani (Mart. p. p.) App. & Wr.
- Fusarium Solani (Mart. p. p.) App. & Wr., var. cyanum Sherbakoff.
- Fusarium Solani (Mart. p. p.) App. & Wr. var. suffuscum Sherbakoff.
- Fusarium striatum Sherbakoff.
- Fusarium subpallidum Sherbakoff.
- Fusarium subpallidum Sherbakoff., var. roseum Sherbakoff.
- Fusarium sanguineum, var. pallidius Sherbakoff.
- Fusarium Succisae (Schrt.) Sacc.
- Fusarium discolor, var. sulphureum (Schl.) App.
- Fusarium sulphureum Schl.
- Fusarium trichothecioides Wr.
- Fusarium tuberivorum Wilcox & Link.
- Fusarium truncatum Sherbakoff.
- Fusarium udum (B.) Wr.
- Fusarium violaceum Fckl.
- Fusarium Willkommii Lindau.
- Fusarium lutulatum, var. zonatum Sherbakoff.
- Fusarium zonatum (Sherbakoff) Wr.

MISCELLANEA

- Cystospora batata Elliott.
- Sclerotium Rolfsii Sacc.
- Sorosporium scabies (B.) Fisch. Wald.
- Spongospora Solani Brunch.
- Spongospora subterranea (Wallr.) Lagerh.

Solanum umbellatum Mill.
- Cercospora brachyclada Syd.

Solanum umbelliferum Esch.
- Phoma Solani Cke. & Hark.
- Septoria solanicola Ell. & Ev.

Solanum verbascifolium L.
- Cercospora trichophila F. L. Stevens.
- Corticium vagum B. & C.

Solanum villosum Auct.
- Erysiphe Cichoracearum DC. †

Solanum Warszewiczii Hort.
- Spongospora subterranea (Wallr.) Lagerh.

Solanum Xanti Gray.
- Septoria solanicola Ell. & Ev.

Solanum Xanti Gray, var. **Wallacei** Gray.
- Metasphaeria anisometra (Cke. & Hark.) Sacc.
- Phlyctaena arcuata B.
- Phoma eupyrena Sacc.?

Solanum sp. indet.
- Aphanostigme Solani Syd.
- Appendiculella adelphica Syd.
- Asterina consobrina Syd.
- Asterina diplopoda Syd.
- Asterina portoricensis Ryan.
- Asterina solanicola B. & C.
- Asterina vagans Speg.
- Botrytis diffusa var. b. S. Syn. Car.
- Botrytis ramulosa Lk.
- Cercospora modesta Syd.
- Cercospora tosensis Henn.
- Chaetotrichum Solani Syd.
- Cicinnobella costaricensis Syd.
- Colletotrichum omnivora Halsted.
- Didymaria Solani Seaver.
- Dimerium costaricense Syd.
- Meliola solanicola Gaill.
- Mycosphaerella dubia Miles.
- Ophiobolus acuminatus (Sow.) Duby.
- Sphaeria rubicunda S.
- Sphaeria Solani P. ex Fr.
- Uredo domingensis B.

Cyphomandra betacea Sendt.
- Septoria Lycopersici Speg.

Datura cornucopia Hort.
- Thielavia basicola (B. & Br.) Zopf.

Datura fastuosa L.

Datura ferox L.
- Alternaria crassa (Sacc.) Rands.

Datura inermis Jacq.
- Alternaria crassa (Sacc.) Rands.
- Macrosporium Cookei Sacc.?

Datura laevis L. f.

Datura Leichhardtii F. Müll.
- Alternaria crassa (Sacc.) Rands.

Datura Metel L.
- Alternaria crassa (Sacc.) Rands.
- Thielavia basicola (B. & Br.) Zopf.

Datura meteloides DC.
- Dicaeoma Sarcobati Arth. I.
- Puccinia subnitens Diet. I.

Datura quercifolia H. B. K.
- Alternaria crassa (Sacc.) Rands.

Datura Stramonium L.
- Alternaria crassa (Sacc.) Rands.
- Cercospora Daturae Pk.
- Alternaria Solani (Ell. & Martin) Jones & Grout.
- Alternaria Solani Sorauer p. p.
- Macrosporium Cookei Sacc.
- Macrosporium Solani Ell. & Martin. 1882.
- Macrosporium Solani Cke. 1883.
- Diplodia atrocaerulea Ell. & Ev.
- Helminthosporium socium Ell. & Ev.
- Phlyctaena arcuata B.
- Phomopsis Daturae (Roll. & Fautr.) Sacc.
- Phyllosticta hortorum Auct. Amer.
- Thielavia basicola (B. & Br.) Zopf.

Datura suaveolens Humb. & Bonpl.
  Alternaria Solani (Ell. & Martin) Jones & Grout.
  Lachnocladium furcellatum Lév.
Datura Tatula L.
  { Agyrium rufum (P.) Fr.
   Tremella Stictis P.
  { Alternaria Solani (Ell. & Martin) Jones & Grout.
  { Macrosporium Cookei Sacc.
   Macrosporium Solani Ell. & Martin. 1882.
   Macrosporium Solani Cke. 1883.
  Ascochyta Lycopersici Brun.
  Septoria Lycopersici Speg.
  Sphaeria Daturae S.
  Thielavia basicola (B. & Br.) Zopf.
Cestrum aurantiacum Lindl.
  Chrysopsora Cestri (Diet. & Henn.) Arth.
  { Pucciniola Cestri (Lév.) Arth.
   Uromyces Cestri Lév.
Cestrum bahamense Brit.
  Dimerosporium guarapiense Speg.
Cestrum diurnum L.
  Asterina coriacella Speg.
  Pucciniola Cestri (Lév.) Arth.
  Sphaerostilbe cinnabarina Tul.
Cestrum lanatum Mart. & Gal.
  Asterina coriacella Speg.
  { Pucciniola maculans (Pat.) Arth.
   Uromyces maculans (Pat.) Arth.
Cestrum laurifolium L'Her.
  Androsaceus corrugatus Pat.
  Asterina coriacella Speg.
  Asterina solanicola B. & C.
  Helminthosporium glabroides F. L. Stevens.
  Meliola Gesneriae F. L. Stevens.
  { Pucciniola Cestri (Lév.) Arth.
   Uromyces Cestri Lév.
Cestrum macrophyllum Vent.
  Acrodesmis Cestri Syd.
  Allosoma Cestri Syd.
  Asterina coriacella Speg.
  Asterina diplocarpa Cke., var. cestricola Ryan.
  Asterina solanicola B. & C.
  Meliola Gesneriae F. L. Stevens.
  { Pucciniola Cestri (Lév.) Arth.
   Uromyces Cestri Lév.
  Pucciniola maculans (Pat.) Arth.
Cestrum megalophyllum Dun.
  { Chrysocyclus Cestri (Diet. & Henn.) Syd.
   Chrysopsora Cestri (Diet. & Henn.) Arth.
  Meliola dicranochaeta Syd.
Cestrum nitidum Mart. & Gal.
  Uromyces venustus Diet. & Holw.
Cestrum nocturnum L.
  { Uromyces maculans (Pat.) Arth.
   Uromyces Cestri, var. maculans Pat.

Cestrum pallidum Lam.
  { Aecidium Cestri Mont.
   Pucciniola Cestri (Lév.) Arth.
Cestrum sp. indet.
  Aulographum Cestri Ryan.
  Epicoccum neglectum Desm.
  Meliola Cestri Tehon.
  Scolecopeltis Cestri Toro.
  Stigmatea Cestri Pat.
Nicotiana alata Lk. & Otto.
Nicotiana angustifolia Ruiz. & Pav.
  Thielavia basicola (B. & Br.) Zopf.
Nicotiana Bigelovii Watson.
  Peronospora sordida B. & Br.
  Uredo Nicotianae Arth.
Nicotiana chinensis Fisch.
  Thielavia basicola (B. & Br.) Zopf.
Nicotiana glauca Graham.
  Botryosphaeria fuliginosa sec. Fairman.
  Fusarium oxysporum, var. Nicotianae J. Johnson.
  Glonium vestigiale Fairman.
  Metasphaeria anisometra (Cke. & Hark.) Sacc.
  { Peronospora Hyoscyami DBy.
   Peronospora Nicotianae G. W. Wilson an Speg.
  Phomopsis Nicotianae Fairman.
  Physalospora erratica (C. & E.) Sacc.
  Stereum ochraceoflavum S.
  Thielavia basicola (B. & Br.) Zopf.
Nicotiana glutinosa L.
Nicotiana Langsdorffii Schrank.
Nicotiana laterrima Mill.
Nicotiana longiflora Cav.
Nicotiana macrophylla Spreng.
  Thielavia basicola (B. & Br.) Zopf.
Nicotiana repanda Willd.
  Cercospora Nicotianae Ell. & Ev.
  Thielavia basicola (B. & Br.) Zopf.
Nicotiana rustica L.
  Fusarium oxysporum, var. Nicotianae J. Johnson.
Nicotiana Sanderae Sander.
Nicotiana silvestris Speg. & Comes.
  Thielavia basicola (B. & Br.) Zopf.
Nicotiana Tabacum L.
  Alternaria tenuis ? Nees ex Fr.
  Ascochyta Nicotianae Pass.
  Aspergillus candidus Lk.
  Aspergillus flavus Lk.
  Aspergillus terreus Thom.
  Botryosporium pulchrum Cda.
  Botrytis cinerea P. †
  Botrytis longibrachiata Oud.
  Cercospora Nicotianae Ell. & Ev.
  Cladosporium Tabaci Oud.
  Corticium vagum, var. Solani Burt.
  Erysiphe Cichoracearum DC. †
  Fusarium affine Faut. & Lam.

Nicotiana Tabacum (*cont.*)
  Fusarium oxysporum, var. Nicotianae J. Johnson.
  Fusarium tabacivorum Delacr.
  Macrosporium longipes Ell. & Ev.
  Macrosporium tabacinum Ell. & Ev.
  Olpidium Brassicae (Wor.) Dangeard.
  Penicillium brevicaule Sacc.
  Penicillium glaucum Lk.
  { Peronospora Hyoscyami DBy.
  { Peronospora Nicotianae Wilson an Speg.
  Phyllosticta hainaensis Fragoso & Ciferri.
  Phyllosticta nicotiana Ell. & Ev.
  Phyllosticta Tabaci Pass.
  Physarum nefroideum Rostf.
  Phytophthora Nicotianae (Speg.) van Breda de Haan.
  Phytophthora terrestris Sherbakoff.
  Plasmodiophora Tabaci P. M. Jones.
  Pythium debaryanum Hesse.
  Rhizoctonia Solani Kühn.
  Sclerotinia libertiana Fckl.
  Sclerotinia sclerotiorum (Lib.) Schrt.
  Sclerotium Rolfsii Sacc.
  Septoria Nicotianae Pat.
  Sphaerella Nicotianae Ell. & Ev.
  Sphaerulina hainensis Fragoso & Ciferri.
  Sterigmatocystis niger van Tiegh.
  Thielavia basicola (B. & Br.) Zopf.
  Toruloidea Nicotianae (Penz. & Sacc.) Sumstine.
  Trichothecium roseum Lk.
Nicotiana trigonophylla Dunal.
  { Aecidium biforme Pk.
  { Dicaeoma Sarcobati Arth. I.
  { Puccinia subnitens Diet. I.
Petunia hybrida Hort.
  Ascochyta Petuniae Speg.
  Corticium vagum B. & C.
  Macrosporium Sarcinula, var. parasiticum (Thm.).
  Thielavia basicola (B. & Br.) Zopf.
Petunia parviflora Juss.
  { Dicaeoma Sarcobati Arth. I.
  { Puccinia subnitens Diet. I.
Petunia sp. indet.
  Rhizoctonia Solani Kühn.
Schizanthus sp. indet.
  Colletotrichum Schizanthi Jen. & Stewart.
  Rhizoctonia Solani Kühn.
Browallia americana L.
  Entyloma Browalliae Syd.

SCROPHULARIACEAE

Verbascum Blattaria L.
  Phoma verbascicarpa Fairman.
  Rhabdospora pleosporoides Sacc.
  Septoria verbascicola B. & C.

Verbascum Lychnitis L.
  Phyllosticta verbascicola Ell. & Kellerm.
  Septoria verbascicola B. & C.
Verbascum Thapsus L.
  Cercospora verbascicola Ell. & Ev.
  Hysterographium praelongum (S.) Ell. & Ev.
  { Leptosphaeria comatella (C. & E.) Sacc.
  { Sphaeria comatella C. & E.
  Leptosphaeria Doliolum (P. ex Fr.) De Not.
  { Lophiostoma Thapsi (S.) Sacc.
  { Sphaeria Thapsi S.
  Mycorrhiza of Legumes F. R. Jones.
  Phacidium capsulare S.
  Phoma Thapsi Ell. & Ev.
  Phyllosticta Verbasci Sacc.
  Phyllosticta verbascicola Ell. & Kellerm.
  Pleospora vulgaris Niessl.
  Ramularia variabilis Fckl.
  { Hysterium Verbasci S.
  { Schizothyrium Verbasci (S.) Sacc.
  Septoria verbasicola B. & C.
  { Mycosphaerella verbascicola (S.) Fairman.
  { Phoma verbascicola (S.) Cke.
  { Sphaerella verbascicola (S.) Ell.
  { Sphaeria verbascicola S.
Verbascum sp. indet.
  { Dinemasporium decipiens (De Not.) Sacc.
  { Sphaeria nigrita S.
  { Lachnella fuscobarbata (S.) Sacc.
  { Peziza fuscobarbata S.
  Lophiostoma caulium (Fr.) De Not.
  Patellaria Verbasci S.
  Peziza nigrescens Cke.
Linaria amethystina Spreng.
  Puccinia Antirrhini Diet. & Holw.
Linaria canadensis (L.) Dumont.
  Aecidium sp. indet.
  Puccinia Andropogonis S. I.
  Colletotrichum Antirrhini F. C. Stewart.
  Peronospora Linariae Fckl.
  Thielavia basicola (B. & Br.) Zopf.
Linaria Cymbalaria (L.) Mill.
Linaria maroccana Hook.
  Rhizoctonia Solani Kühn.
  Thielavia basicola (B. & Br.) Zopf.
Linaria vulgaris Hill.
  Colletotrichum vermicularioides Halsted.
  Entyloma Linariae Schrt.
  { Heterosphaeria Linariae (Rabh.) Rehm.
  { Peziza corneola C. & P.
  Macrosporium fallax Bubák & Dearness.
  Phoma Linariae Dearness & House.
Antirrhinum assurgens Bianca.
  Puccinia Antirrhini Diet. & Holw.
Antirrhinum majus L.
  Colletotrichum Antirrhini F. C. Stewart.
  { Corticium vagum B. & C.
  { Rhizoctonia Solani Kühn.
  Phoma poolensis Taubenhaus.

Antirrhinum majus (*cont.*)
Phyllosticta Antirrhini Syd.
{ Dicaeoma Antirrhini (Diet. & Holw.) O.
{   Kuntze.
{ Puccinia Antirrhini Diet. & Holw.
Sclerotinia sclerotiorum (Lib.) Schrt.
Thielavia basicola (B. & C.) Zopf.
Verticillium albo-atrum Reinke & Berth.
Antirrhinum nuttallianum Benth.
Puccinia Antirrhini Diet. & Holw.
Antirrhinum Virga Gray.
Puccinia Antirrhini Diet. & Holw.
Antirrhinum sp. indet.
Septoria Antirrhini Desm.
Maurandia antirrhiniflora Willd.
Septoria Antirrhinorum Tharp.
Maurandia semperflorens Jacq.
Phyllosticta Maurandiae Dearness & House.
Collinsia bartsiifolia Benth.
Entyloma Collinsiae Hark.
Collinsia bicolor Benth.
Aecidium Collinsiae Ell. & Ev.
Collinsia grandiflora Dougl.
Entyloma Collinsiae Hark.
Collinsia parviflora Lindl.
Aecidium insulsum Arth.
{ Aecidium Collinsiae Ell. & Ev.
{ Puccinia Collinsiae Henn.
Collinsia Rattani Gray.
Aecidium Collinsiae Ell. & Ev.
Collinsia tenella (Pursh) Piper.
Entyloma Collinsiae Hark.
Collinsia verna Nutt.
Septoria Collinsiae H. W. Anderson.
Tonella collinsioides Nutt.
Aecidium Collinsiae Ell. & Ev.
Scrophularia californica Cham. & Schl.
Coniothyrium herbarum C. & E.
Coniothyrium Scrophulariae (Fckl.) Sacc.
Diaporthe immutabilis Cke. & Hark.
Leptosphaeria consessa (C. & E.) Sacc.
Peronospora sordida B. & Br.
Septonema toruloideum C. & E.
Septoria Scrophulariae Pk.
Trichaegum atrum Preuss.
Scrophularia leporella Bicknell.
Peronospora sordida B. & Br.
Septoria Scrophulariae Pk.
Scrophularia marilandica L.
Cylindrosporium Scrophulariae Sacc. & Ell.
{ Lophiosphaera Scrophulariae (Pk.) Cke.
{ Lophiostoma Scrophulariae Pk.
{ Lophiotrema Scrophulariae (Pk.) Sacc.
{ Peronospora sordida B. & Br.
{ Plasmopara sordida (B. & Br.) Kellerm.
Rhabdospora Kellermani Ell. & Martin.
{ Septoria Scrophulariae Westd. nom. nud. 1859.
{ Septoria Scrophulariae Pk. 1876.
Septoria verbascicola B. & C.
Sphaerella decidua Ell. & Kellerm.

Scrophularia sp. indet.
Laestadia Scrophularia Ell. & Ev.
Chelone glabra L.
{ Aecidium Chelonis Gerard.
{ Dicaeoma Andropogonis (S.) O. Kuntze. I.
{ Puccinia Andropogi S. I.
{ Puccinia Andropogonis S. I.
Erysiphe Cichoracearum DC. †
{ Erysiphe Chelones S.
{ Erysiphe communis Auct. Amer. p. p.
{ Erysiphe Galeopsidis DC. †
{ Erysiphe lamprocarpa Auct. Amer. p. p.
Erysiphe Polygoni DC. †
Microthyrium microscopicum Desm.
Periconia (?) albiceps Pk.
{ Phyllactinia corylea (P.) ex Karst.
{ Phyllactinia suffulta (Reb.) ex Sacc.
Septoria Wilsonii G. W. Clinton.
Chelone nemorosa Dougl.
{ Micropuccinia Chelonis (Diet. & Holw.) Arth.
{   & Jackson.
{ Puccinia Chelonis Diet. & Holw.
Pentstemon acuminatus Dougl.
Pentstemon albidus Nutt.
Pentstemon alpinus Torr.
Pentstemon ambiguus Torr.
Pentstemon angustifolius Nutt.
{ Aecidium Pentstemonis S.
{ Dicaeoma Andropogonis (S.) O. Kuntze. I.
{ Puccinia Andropogonis S. I.
Pentstemon antirrhinoides Benth.
Pentstemon attenuatus Dougl.
Allodus complicata Arth. & Orton.
Pentstemon australis Small.
{ Caeoma pentstemoniatum S.
{ Dicaeoma Andropogonis (S.) O. Kuntze. I.
{ Puccinia Andropogonis S. I.
Pentstemon barbatus Nutt., var. **Torreyi** Gray.
{ Aecidium Pentastemonis S.
{ Puccinia Andropogonis S. I.
Pentstemon breviflorus Lindl.
Tryblidium turgidulum Phil. & Hark.
Pentstemon azureus Benth.
Pentstemon Bridgesii Gray.
{ Micropuccinia Pentstemonis (Pk.) Arth. &
{   Jackson.
{ Puccinia Pentstemonis Pk.
Pentstemon caeruleus Nutt.
Aecidium Pentastemonis S.
Pentstemon campanulatus Willd.
Puccinia mexicana Diet. & Holw.
Pentstemon canescens Britton.
Dicaeoma Andropogonis (S.) O. Kuntze. I.
Pentstemon centranthifolius Benth.
Septoria Pentstemonis Ell. & Ev.
Pentstemon chionophilus Greene.
Allodus Palmeri (Diet. & Holw.) C. R. Orton.

Pentstemon Cobaea Nutt.
{Aecidium Pentastemonis S.
{Puccinia Andropogonis S. I.
Cercospora Pentstemonis Ell. & Kellerm.

Pentstemon confertus Dougl.
Aecidium Palmeri F. W. Anderson.
Erysiphe Cichoracearum DC. †
Leptosphaeria lethalis Ell. & Ev.
{Allodus complicata Arth. & Orton.
{Allodus Palmeri (Diet. & Holw.) C. R. Orton.
{Puccinia Palmeri Diet. & Holw.
Puccinia Pentstemonis Pk.

Pentstemon cordifolius Benth.
Acerbia bacillata (Cke.) Berl.

Pentstemon corymbosus Benth.
Septoria Pentstemonis Ell. & Ev.

Pentstemon Davidscnii Greene.
Allodus complicata Arth. & Orton.

Pentstemon deustus Dougl.
Pentstemon diffusus Dougl.
{Micropuccinia Pentstemonis (Pk.) Arth. &
{ Jackson.
{Puccinia Pentstemonis Pk.

Pentstemon ellipticus Coult. & Fish.
{Allodus complicata Arth. & Orton.
{Allodus Palmeri (Diet. & Holw.) C. R. Orton.

Pentstemon fruticosus (Pursh) Greene.
Dicaeoma Andropogonis (S.) O. Kuntze. I.
Puccinia Palmeri Diet. & Holw.

Pentstemon glaber Pursh.
{Aecidium Pentastemonis S.
{Dicaeoma Andropogonis (S.) O. Kuntze. I.
{Puccinia Andropogonis S. I.
Cercospora Pentstemonis Ell. & Kellerm.

Pentstemon gracilis Nutt.
{Aecidium Pentastemonis S.
{Caeoma pentstemoniatum S.
{Dicaeoma Andropogonis (S.) O. Kuntze. I.
{Puccinia Andropogonis S. I.
Septoria pentstemonicola Ell. & Ev.

Pentstemon grandiflorus Nutt.
{Aecidium Pentastemonis S.
{Dicaeoma Andropogonis (S.) O. Kuntze. I.
{Puccinia Andropogonis S. I.
Cercospora Pentstemonis Ell. & Kellerm.

Pentstemon Harbourii Gray.
{Allodus complicata Arth. & Orton.
{Allodus Palmeri (Diet. & Holw.) C. R. Orton.

Pentstemon hirsutus (L.) Willd.
{Aecidium Pentastemonis S.
{Caeoma pentstemoniatum S.
{Dicaeoma Andropogonis (S.) O. Kuntze. I.
{Puccinia Andropogonis S. I.
{Uredo Chelones Spreng.
Cercospora Pentstemonis Ell. & Ev.
Sclerotium Rolfsii Sacc.

Pentstemon humilis Nutt.
Pentstemon Jamesii Benth.
{Dicaeoma Andropogonis (S.) O. Kuntze. I.
{Puccinia Andropogonis S. I.

Pentstemon laevigatus Ait.
{Dicaeoma Andropogonis (S.) O. Kuntze. I.
{Puccinia Andropogonis S. I.
{Puccinia ellisiana Thm. I.
Septoria Pentstemonis Ell. & Ev.

Pentstemon laevigatus, var. **Digitalis** (Sweet) Gray.
{Aecidium Pentastemonis S.
{Dicaeoma Andropogonis (S.) O. Kuntze. I.
Cercospora Pentstemonis Ell. & Ev.
Cercosporella nivosa Ell. & Ev.
Septoria Pentstemonis Ell. & Ev.

Pentstemon linarioides Gray.
{Micropuccinia Pentstemonis (Pk.) Arth. &
{ Jackson.
{Puccinia Pentstemonis Pk.

Pentstemon Menziesii Hook.
{Dicaeoma Andropogoni (S.) O. Kuntze. I.
{Puccinia Andropogonis S. I.
Puccinia Palmeri Diet. & Holw.

Pentstemon murrayanus Hook.
Sclerotium Rolfsii Sacc.

Pentstemon Newberryi Gray.
Allodus complicata Arth. & Orton.

Pentstemon nitidus Dougl.
Dicaeoma Andropogonis (S.) O. Kuntze. I.

Pentstemon ovatus Dougl.
Cercosporella nivosa Ell. & Ev.

Pentstemon Palmeri Gray.
Cercospora Pentstemonis Ell. & Kellerm.
Puccinia Pentstemonis Pk.
Septoria Pentstemonis Ell. & Ev.

Pentstemon pinetorum Piper.
Pentstemon procerus Dougl.
{Allodus complicata Arth. & Orton.
{Puccinia complicata (Arth. & Orton) Hotson.
{Puccinia Palmeri Diet. & Holw.

Pentstemon Roezli Regel.
{Micropuccinia Pentstemonis (Pk.) Arth. &
{ Jackson.
{Puccinia Pentstemonis Pk.

Penstemon secundiflorus Benth.
Dicaeoma Andropogonis (S.) O. Kuntze. I.

Pentstemon spectabilis Thurb.
{Micropuccinia Pentstemonis (Pk.) Arth. &
{ Jackson.
{Puccinia chasmatis Ell. & Ev.
{Puccinia circinans Ell. & Ev.
{Puccinia Pentstemonis Pk.
{Puccinia Toumeyi Syd.
Septoria Pentstemonis Ell. & Ev.

Pentstemon tenuiflorus Pennell.
Pentstemon Torreyi Benth.
Pentstemon tubiflorus Nutt.
Pentstemon unilateralis Rydb.
⎰ Aecidium Pentastemonis S.
⎱ Dicaeoma Andropogonis (S.) O. Kuntze. I.
⎰ Puccinia Andropogonis S. I.
⎱ Puccinia ellisiana I. Auct. Amer. p. p.
Pentstemon venustus Dougl.
 Cercosporella nivosa Ell. & Ev.
⎰ Allodus complicata Arth. & Orton.
⎱ Puccinia complicata (Arth. & Orton) Hotson.
Pentstemon virens Pennell.
 Allodus complicata Arth. & Orton.
 Dicaeoma Andropogonis (S.) O. Kuntze. I.
Pentstemon virgatus Gray.
⎰ Aecidium Palmeri F. W. Anderson.
⎱ Dicaeoma Andropogonis (S.) O. Kuntze. I.
Pentstemon sp. indet.
 Calloria oleosa (Ell.) Sacc.
 Coniothyrium Pentstemonis Earle.
 Excipulina conglutinata (Ell. & Ev.) Sacc.
 Gloniella Pentstemonis Earle.
 Phyllosticta Paulowniae Sacc.
 Sphaerella fuscata Ell.
⎰ Mycosphaerella Pentstemonis Earle.
⎱ Sphaerella Pentstemonis (Earle) Sacc. & Syd.
Paulownia tomentosa (Thunb.) Steud.
 Ascochyta Paulowniae Sacc. & Brun.
 Phoma imperialis Sacc. & Roum.
Mimulus alatus [Solander in] Ait.
 Cercospora Mimuli Ell. & Ev.
⎰ Septoria Mimuli Ell. & Kellerm. 1883.
⎱ Septoria Mimuli Wint. 1885.
Mimulus cardinalis Dougl.
 Microdiplodia Mimuli Fairman.
Mimulus glutinosus Wendl.
⎰ Amphisphaeria dothideospora Cke. & Hark.
⎱ Melanomma dothideasporum (Cke. & Hark.) Cke.
 Diatrype prominens Cke. & Hark.
⎰ Endophlaea anisometra Cke. & Hark.
⎱ Metasphaeria anisometra (Cke. & Hark.) Sacc.
 Sphaeria anisometra Cke. & Hark.
 Septoria Mimuli Ell. & Kellerm.
 Stictis radiata (L.) ex P., var. pumila Cke. & Hark.
Mimulus luteus L.
 Erysiphe Cichoracearum DC. †
 Ramularia Mimuli Ell. & Kellerm.
Mimulus ringens L.
 Aecidium Pentastemonis S., var. Mimuli Wint.
 Ramularia Mimuli Ell. & Kellerm.
 Rhabdospora Kellermani Ell. & Martin.
⎰ Septoria Mimuli Ell. & Kellerm. 1883.
⎱ Septoria Mimuli Wint. 1885.
 Septoria purpureocincta Wint.

Gratiola pilosa Michx.
 Cercospora Gratiolae Ell. & Ev.
Gratiola ramosa Walt.
⎰ Septoria Ellisii Berl. & Vogl.
⎱ Septoria Gratiolae Sacc. & Speg. 1878.
 Septoria Gratiolae Ell. & Martin. 1885.
Gratiola virginiana L.
 Entyloma Linariae Schrt., var. Gratiolae J. J. Davis.
 Septoria Gratiolae Sacc. & Speg.
Bacopa sp. indet.
 Vermicularia rectispora Cke.
Veronica alpina L.
 Leptosphaeria striata Wint.
 Peronospora grisea Ung.
 Phoma Veronicae Roum.
 Puccinia Porteri Pk.
⎰ Leptopuccinia Veronicarum (DC.) Rostr.
⎱ Puccinia Veronicae Auct. Amer.
 Puccinia Veronicarum DC.
 Septoria Veronicae Rob.
Veronica alpina L., var. **unalaschcensis** C. & S.
 Peronospora grisea Ung.
⎰ Micropuccinia albulensis (Magn.) Arth. & Jackson.
⎱ Puccinia albulensis Magn.
Veronica americana S.
⎰ Entyloma Linariae Schrt., var. Veronicae Lagerh.
⎱ Entyloma Veronicae (Wint.) Lagerh.
 Peronospora grisea Ung.
Veronica anagallis-aquatica L.
 Peronospora aquatica Gäuman.
 Peronospora grisea Ung.
Veronica arvensis L.
 Peronospora grisea Ung.
 Septoria Veronicae Rob.
Veronica Cusickii Gray.
⎰ Micropuccinia albulensis (Magn.) Arth. & Jackson.
⎱ Puccinia albulensis Magn.
 Puccinia Porteri Pk.
⎰ Micropuccinia rhaetica (Ed. Fisch.) Arth. & Jackson.
⎱ Puccinia rhaetica Ed. Fisch.
Veronica fruticosa L.
 Septoria semilunaris Johans.
 Septoria Veronicae Rob.
Veronica officinalis L.
 Gloeosporium Veronicae Dearness & House.
Veronica peregrina L.
⎰ Entyloma Linariae Auct. Amer. p. p.
 Entyloma Linariae, var. Veronicae Wint.
 Entyloma Veronicae (Wint.) Lagerh.
 Ovularia Veronicae (Fckl.) Sacc.
⎱ Ramularia Veronicae Fckl.
 Peronospora grisea Ung.

Veronica saxatilis Scop.
  Peronospora grisea Ung.
  Pyrenophora comata (Niessl) Sacc.
  Septoria cercosperma Rostr.
Veronica scutellata L.
  Cercospora tortipes J. J. Davis.
  Puccinia albulensis Magn.
Veronica serpyllifolia L.
  Erysiphe Labiatarum S. Am. bor.
  Peronospora grisea Ung.
  Ramularia Veronicae Fckl.
  Rhizoctonia Solani Kühn.
Veronica virginica L.
  Cercospora Leptandrae J. J. Davis.
  Erysiphe Cichoracearum DC. †
  Phyllosticta decidua Ell. & Kellerm.
  { Micropuccinia Veronicarum (DC.) Arth. &
    Jackson.
  Puccinia Veronicae Auct. Amer.
  Puccinia Veronicae, forma fragilipes Wint.
  Puccinia Veronicae, forma persistens Wint.
  Puccinia Veronicarum DC.
  Puccinia Veronicarum DC., var. fragilipes
    Körn.
  Septoria Veronicae Rob.
  Sphaerotheca Humuli (DC.) Burrill. †
  { Sphaerotheca Castagnei Auct. Amer. p. p.
  { Sphaerotheca Humuli (DC.) Burrill, var. fuli-
    ginea (Schl.) Salmon.
Synthyris alpina Gray.
Synthyris dissecta Rydb.
  Micropuccinia acrophila (Pk.) Arth. & Jackson.
Synthyris pinnatifida Watson.
  { Micropuccinia acrophila (Pk.) Arth. & Jack-
    son.
  Puccinia acrophila Pk.
Synthyris reniformis (Dougl.) Benth.
  Micropuccinia Wulfeniae (Diet. & Holw.)
    Arth. & Jackson.
Synthyris ritteriana Eastw.
  { Micropuccinia acrophila (Pk.) Arth. & Jack-
    son.
  Puccinia acrophila Pk.
Synthyris rotundifolia Gray, var. **cordata** Gray.
  { Micropuccinia Wulfeniae (Diet. & Holw.)
    Arth. & Jackson.
  Puccinia Wulfeniae Diet. & Holw.
Synthyris rubra Benth.
  { Micropuccinia acrophila (Pk.) Arth. & Jack-
    son.
  Puccinia acrophila Pk.
  { Micropuccinia Wulfeniae (Diet. & Holw.)
    Arth. & Jackson.
  Puccinia Synthyridis Ell. & Ev.
  Puccinia Wulfeniae Diet. & Holw.
Synthyris wyomingensis (A. Nels.) Rydb.
  Micropuccinia Wulfeniae (Diet. & Holw.)
    Arth. & Jackson.

Digitalis purpurea L.
  Phyllosticta Digitalis Bellynck.
  Ramularia variabilis Fckl.
Seymeria macrophylla Nutt.
  { Aecidium Gerardiae Pk.
  { Dicaeoma Andropogonis (S.) O. Kuntze. I.
  Fusarium parasiticum Ell. & Kellerm.
  { Dasyspora Seymeriae (Burrill) Arth.
  { Micropuccinia Seymeriae (Burrill) Arth. &
    Jackson.
  Puccinia Seymeriae Burrill.
Seymeria virgata Benth.
  Puccinia Seymeriae Burrill.
Gerardia flava L.
  { Aecidium Gerardiae Pk.
  { Puccinia Andropogi S. I.
  { Dicaeoma Andropogonis (S.) O. Kuntze. I.
Gerardia grandiflora Benth.
  Cercospora Gerardiae Ell. & Dearness.
  { Sphaerotheca Castagnei Auct. Amer. p. p.
  { Sphaerotheca Humuli (DC.) Burrill, var. fuli-
    ginea (Schl.) Salmon.
Gerardia tenuifolia Vahl.
  { Micropuccinia Seymeriae (Burrill) Arth. &
    Jackson.
  Puccinia Gerardiae Syd.
  Puccinia Seymeriae Burrill.
  Sphaerotheca Humuli (DC.) Burrill. †
Gerardia virginica (L.) B. S. P.
  Aecidium Gerardiae Pk.
  Dicaeoma Andropogonis (S.) O. Kuntze. I.
  Cercospora clavata (Gerard) Cke.
  Cercospora Gerardiae Ell. & Dearness.
  Erysiphe Gerardiae S.
  { Leptosphaeria comatella (C. & E.) Sacc.
  { Sphaeria comatella C. & E.
  { Asterinula Dearnessii Ell. & Ev.
  { Leptothyrella Dearnessii (Ell. & Ev.) Sacc.
  Pleospora vulgaris Niessl.
  Sphaerotheca Humuli (DC.) Burrill, var. fuli-
    ginea (Schl.) Salmon.
  Vermicularia Gerardiae S.
Buchnera elongata Sw.
  Uredo cumula Arth.
Castilleja affinis Hook. & Arn.
  { Puccinia Castillejae Arth.
  { Uredo Castilleiae Diet. & Holw. 1893.
  { Uredo Castilleiae Tracy & Earle. 1895.
  { Uredo utahensis Syd.
Castilleja coccinea (L.) Spreng.
  { Aecidium micropunctum Ell. & Ev.
  { Aecidium Pentastemonis S.
  { Dicaeoma Andropogonis (S.) O. Kuntze. I.
Castilleja communis Benth.
  { Micropuccinia nesodes (Arth. & Holw.) Arth.
    & Jackson.
  Puccinia nesodes Arth. & Holw.

610 SCROPHULARIACEAE

Castilleja confusa Greene.
{ Cronartium coleosporioides Arth.
{ Cronartium Harknessii Meinecke.
Ophiobolus Castillejae Tracy & Earle.

Castilleja crispula Piper.
{ Cronartium coleosporioides Arth.
{ Cronartium Harknessii Meinecke.
{ Peridermium Harknessii J. P. Moore. III.

Castilleja Crista-galli Rydb.
{ Cronartium coleosporioides Arth.
{ Cronartium Harknessii Meinecke.
{ Peridermium Harknessii J. P. Moore. III.

Castilleja exilis A. Nels.
Puccinia Castillejae Arth.

Castilleja foliolosa Hook & Arn.
{ Aecidium micropunctum Ell. & Ev.
{ Dicaeoma Andropogonis (S.) O. Kuntze. I.
{ Cronartium coleosporioides Arth.
{ Uredo coleosporioides Diet. & Holw.
{ Puccinia Castillejae Arth.
{ Uredo Castillejae Diet. & Holw.

Castilleja integra Gray.
{ Dicaeoma Andropogonis (S.) O. Kuntze. I.
{ Puccinia Andropogonis S. I.
{ Cronartium coleosporioides Arth.
{ Cronartium Harknessii Meinecke.
{ Peridermium Harknessii J. P. Moore. III.
Macrosporium commune Rabh.

Castilleja integrifolia L.
Aecidium micropunctum Ell. & Ev.

Castilleja latifolia Hook. & Arn.
{ Cronartium coleosporioides Arth.
{ Cronartium Harknessii Meinecke.
{ Peridermium Harknessii J. P. Moore. III.

Castilleja linariifolia Benth.
{ Cronartium coleosporioides Arth.
{ Cronartium filamentosum Hedgc.
{ Cronartium Harknessii Meinecke.
{ Peridermium Harknessii J. P. Moore. III.
Sphaerotheca Humuli (DC.) Burrill, var. fuli-
ginea (Schl.) Salmon.

Castilleja linearis Rydb.
Castilleja Martini Abrams.
{ Cronartium coleosporioides Arth.
{ Cronartium stalactiforme Arth. & Kern.
{ Peridermium stalactiforme Arth. & Kern. III.

Castilleja miniata Dougl.
{ Cronartium coleosporioides Arth.
{ Cronartium filamentosum Hedgc.
{ Peridermium Harknessii J. P. Moore. III.
Leptosphaeria concinna Ell. & Ev.
Ramularia Castilleiae Ell. & Ev.
Sphaerella vagans Ell. & Ev.
Sphaerotheca Humuli (DC.) Burrill, var. fuli-
ginea (Schl.) Salmon.

Castilleja pallida (L.) Spreng.
Castilleja parviflora Bong.
{ Cronartium coleosporioides Arth.
{ Cronartium Harknessii Meinecke.
{ Peridermium Harknessii J. P. Moore. III.
Leptosphaeria Castilleiae Clements.

Castilleja sessiliflora Pursh.
{ Aecidium micropunctum Ell. & Ev.
{ Aecidium Pentastemonis S.
{ Dicaeoma Andropogonis (S.) O. Kuntze. I.

Castilleja stenantha Gray.
{ Puccinia Castillejae Arth.
{ Uredo Castillejae Diet. & Holw.

Castilleja sulphurea Rydb.
{ Dicaeoma Andropogonis (S.) O. Kuntze. I.
{ Puccinia Andropogonis S. I.
Cronartium coleosporioides Arth.

Castilleja sulphurescens Rydb.
{ Cronartium coleosporioides Arth.
{ Cronartium Harknessii Meinecke.
{ Peridermium Harknessii J. P. Moore. III.

Castilleja tenuiflora Benth.
{ Cronartium coleosporioides Arth.
{ Cronartium Harknessii Meinecke.
{ Peridermium Harknessii J. P. Moore. III.
{ Micropuccinia nesodes (Arth. & Holw.) Arth.
{   & Jackson.
{ Puccinia nesodes Arth. & Holw.

Castilleja Wightii Elmer.
Cronartium coleosporioides Arth.

Castilleja sp. indet.
Pyrenophora Castillejae Earle.

Cordylanthus filifolius Nutt.
Cordylanthus pilosus Gray.
{ Puccinia Adenostegiae Arth.
{ Puccinia Antirrhini Diet. & Holw.
{ Puccinia Cordylanthi Blasdale.

Cordylanthus rigidus (Benth.) Jepson.
{ Cronartium coleosporioides Arth.
{ Cronartium Harknessii Meinecke.
{ Peridermium Harknessii J. P. Moore. III.
Puccinia Adenostegiae Arth.

Cordylanthus tenuis Gray.
{ Cronartium coleosporioides Arth.
{ Cronartium Harknessii Meinecke.
{ Peridermium Harknessii J. P. Moore. III.

Orthocarpus luteus Nutt.
{ Cronartium coleosporioides Arth.
{ Cronartium filamentosum Hedgc.
{ Cronartium Harknessii Meinecke.
{ Peridermium Harknessii J. P. Moore. III.

Orthocarpus Tolmiei Hook. & Arn.
Ascochyta garrettiana Syd.

Orthocarpus sp. indet.
Melampyrum lineare Lam.
{ Dicaeoma Andropogonis (S.) O. Kuntze. I.
{ Puccinia Andropogonis S. I.
Ramularia Melampyri Ell. & Dearness.

Euphrasia officinalis L.
  Phoma herbarum Westd.
  Pleospora herbarum (Fr.) Rabh.

Bartsia alpina L.
  Asteroma Bartsiae Rostr.
  Botrytis cinerea P. †
  Helotium cyathoideum (Bull. ex P.) Karst.
  Helotium nigrescens (Cke.) Rehm.
  Mollisia atrata (P.) Karst.
  Phoma irregularis Rostr.
  Placosphaeria Bartsiae Massee.
  Sclerotium rufum Rostr.
  ⎧ Rhabdospora cercosperma (Rostr.) Sacc.
  ⎩ Septoria cercosperma Rostr.

Rhinanthus Crista-galli L.
  Botrytis cinerea P. †
  Ephelina Rhinanthi (Phil.) Sacc.
  Helotium cyathoideum (Bull. ex P.) Karst.
  Metasphaeria affinis (Karst.) Sacc.
  Mollisia atrata (P.) Karst.
  Phoma herbarum Westd.
  Pleospora herbarum (Fr.) Rabh.
  Septoria cercosperma Rostr.

Pedicularis arctica R. Br.
  Pyrenophora Cerastii (Oud.) J. Lind.
  Pyrenophora chrysospora (Niessl) Sacc.

Pedicularis bracteosa Benth.
  ⎧ Micropuccinia Clintonii (Pk.) Arth. & Jackson.
  ⎩ Puccinia Clintonii Pk.

Pedicularis canadensis L.
  Allodus rufescens (Diet. & Holw.) Arth.
  ⎧ Micropuccinia Clintonii (Pk.) Arth. & Jackson.
  ⎩ Puccinia Clintonii Pk.
  Septoria cylindrospora J. J. Davis.
  Sphaerotheca Castagnei Lév.
  Synchytrium aureum Schrt.

Pedicularis capitata Adams.
  Pleospora herbarum (Fr.) Rabh.
  Pyrenophora Cerastii (Oud.) J. Lind.
  Pyrenophora comata (Niessl) Sacc.

Pedicularis centranthera Gray.
  Allodus rufescens (Diet. & Holw.) Arth.

Pedicularis crenulata Benth.
  ⎧ Charonectria Pedicularis Tracy & Earle.
  ⎩ Nectriella Pedicularis (Tracy & Earle) Seaver.

Pedicularis densiflora Benth.
  Allodus rufescens (Diet. & Holw.) Arth.

Pedicularis euphrasioides Stephan.
  Helminthosporium nanum Nees.
  Phoma Sceptri Karst.
  Sphaerella trichophila Karst.

Pedicularis flammea L.
  Phoma Sceptri Karst.
  Pleospora vulgaris Niessl.
  Septoria cercosperma Rostr.
  Sphaerella pachyasca Rostr.
  Sphaerella trichophila Karst.

Pedicularis fluviatilis Heller.
  ⎧ Micropuccinia Clintonii (Pk.) Arth. & Jackson.
  ⎩ Puccinia Clintonii Pk.
  Phoma herbarum Westd.

Pedicularis Grayi A. Nels.
  ⎧ Cronartium coleosporioides Arth.
  ⎨ Cronartium Harknessii Meinecke.
  ⎩ Peridermium Harknessii J. P. Moore. III.
  Sphaerotheca Humuli (DC.) Burrill, var. fuliginea (Schl.) Salmon.

Pedicularis groenlandica Rctz.
  ⎧ Cronartium coleosporioides Arth.
  ⎪ Cronartium filamentosum (Pk.) Hedgc. & Long.
  ⎨ Cronartium Harknessii Meinecke.
  ⎩ Peridermium Harknessii J. P. Moore. III.
  ⎧ Micropuccinia Clintonii (Pk.) Arth. & Jack-
  ⎨   son.
  ⎩ Puccinia Clintonii Pk.
  Sphaerotheca Castagnei Lév.
  Sphaerotheca Humuli (DC.) Burrill, var. fuliginea (Schl.) Salmon.

Pedicularis hirsuta L.
  Gloeosporium Pedicularidis Rostr.
  Phoma herbarum Westd.
  Phoma irregularis Rostr.
  Phoma Sceptri Karst.
  Pleospora herbarum (Fr.) Rabh.
  Pleospora vulgaris Niessl.
  Pyrenophora comata (Niessl) Sacc.
  Septoria cercosperma Rostr.
  Sphaerella Pedicularis Karst.
  Sphaerella trichophila Karst.

Pedicularis lanata Michx.
  Gloeosporium Pedicularis-lanatae Henn.
  Pleospora herbarum (Fr.) Rabh.
  Pyrenophora comata (Niessl) Sacc.

Pedicularis lanceolata Michx.
  ⎧ Sphaerotheca Castagnei Auct. Amer. p. p.
  ⎩ Sphaerotheca Humuli (DC.) Burrill. †
  Sphaerotheca Humuli (DC.) Burrill, var. fuliginea (Schl.) Salmon.

Pedicularis Langsdorffii Fisch., var. **lanata** Gray.
  Phoma herbarum Westd.
  Schizoxylon berkeleyanum (Dur. & Lév.) Fckl.
  Sphaerella Pedicularis Karst.

Pedicularis lapponica L.
  Phoma herbarum Westd.
  Phoma irregularis Rostr.
  Phoma Sceptri Karst.
  Pyrenophora comata (Niessl) Sacc.
  Sphaerella pachyasca Rostr.

Pedicularis mexicana Zucc.
  Dicaeoma pediculariatum (Lk.) Arth. & Kern. I.
  Puccinia paludosa Plowr.

Pedicularis procera Gray.
  ⎧ Mycosphaerium lineatum Clements.
  ⎩ Sphaerella lineata (Clements) Sacc. & D. Sacc.

Pedicularis racemosa Dougl.
  Phoma coloradensis Earle.
  { Micropuccinia Clintonii (Pk.) Arth. & Jackson.
  { Puccinia Clintonii Pk.
  Sirocyphis nivea Clements.

Pedicularis semibarbata Gray.
  { Cronartium coleosporioides Arth.
  { Cronartium filamentosum Hedge.
  { Cronartium Harknessii Meinecke.
  { Peridermium Harknessii J. P. Moore. III.
  { Allodus rufescens (Diet. & Holw.) Arth.
  { Puccinia rufescens Diet. & Holw.

Pedicularis sudetica Willd.
  { Mycosphaerella Pedicularis (Karst.) Dearness.
  { Sphaerella Pedicularis Karst.

Pedicularis sudetica Willd., var. **lanata** Auct.
  Mycosphaerella pachyasca (Rostr.)Vestergren.
  Phoma complanata (Tode) Desm.
  Pyrenophora comata (Niessl) Sacc.

Pedicularis surrecta Benth.
  Cronartium coleosporioides Arth.

Pedicularis sp. indet.
  Cyathicula alpina Ell. & Ev.
  Gloeosporium Pedicularis Rostr.
  Ramularia obducens Thm.

Lamourouxia cordifolia Cham. & Schl.
Lamourouxia dependens Benth.
  { Cronartium coleosporioides Arth.
  { Cronartium Harknessii Meinecke.
  { Peridermium Harknessii J. P. Moore. III.

Lamourouxia Gutierrezii Oerst.
  { Micropuccinia nesodes (Arth. & Holw.) Arth.
  {   & Jackson.
  { Puccinia nesodes Arth. & Holw.

Lamourouxia rhinanthifolia H. B. K.
  { Cronartium coleosporioides Arth.
  { Cronartium Harknessii Meinecke.
  { Peridermium Harknessii J. P. Moore. III.

Lamourouxia viscosa H. B. K.
  { Micropuccinia nesodes (Arth. & Holw.) Arth.
  {   & Jackson.
  { Puccinia nesodes Arth. & Holw.

BIGNONIACEAE

Macrodiscus lactiflorus (Vahl) Bur.
  Meliola furcata Lév.

Pithecoctenium echinatum K. Schum.
  Prospodium Amphilophii (Diet. & Holw.)Arth.

Pithecoctenium hexagonum DC.
  Prospodium Amphilophii (Diet. & Holw.)
  Arth.
  Puccinia phlyctopus Syd.

Pithecoctenium muricatum Moc. ex DC.
  Prospodium Amphilophii (Diet. & Holw.)
  Arth.

{ Micropuccinia depallens (Arth. & Holw.)
{   Arth. & Jackson.
{ Puccinia depallens Arth. & Holw.

Distictis lactiflora (Vahl) Bur.
  Meliola furcata Lév.

Amphilophium molle Cham. & Schl.
  { Prospodium Amphilophii (Diet. & Holw.)
  {   Arth.
  { Puccinia Amphilophii Diet. & Holw.

Amphilophium sp. indet.
  Fumago vagans Fr.

Pyrostegia venusta Miers.
  Uredo Adenocalymnatis Henn.

Bignonia aequinoctialis L.
  { Puccinia Adenocalymnatis Arth. & Johnston.
  { Puccinia aequinoctialis Holw.

Bignonia capreolata L.
  { Asterella Bignoniae (Ell. & Ev.) Sacc.
  { Asterina Bignoniae Ell. & Ev.
  { Botrytis grisea (S.) Sacc.
  { Polyactis grisea S.
  Capnodium elongatum B. & Desm.
  Cercospora capreolata Ell. & Ev.
  Cladosporium Bignoniae S.
  Dimerosporium tropicale Speg.
  { Dothidea Bignoniae Fr.
  { Dothidea capreolatae S.
  { Dothidea ribesia Auct. Amer. p. p.
  { Haplosporella capreolata (S.) Ell. & Ev.
  { Meliola bidentata Cke.
  { Meliola furcata N. A. F. *2979* nec Lév.
  Oedemium atrum Lk.
  { Dematium crucigerae S.
  { Helminthosporium rigidum Fr.
  { Podosporium rigidum S.
  Sphaeria sulcata Fr.

Bignonia pentaphylla L.
  Agaricus crinitus Bert.
  Lentinus fuligineus B. & C.
  Pluteus alborubellus (Mont.) Pat.

Bignonia Unguis-cati L.
  Hypocrella disjuncta Seaver.
  Ravenelia versatilis (Pk.) Diet.

Bignonia sp. indet.
  Apiosporium elongatum B. & Desm.

Chilopsis saligna Don.
  Phyllosticta erysiphoides Sacc.

Catalpa bignonioides Walt.
  Capnodium axillatum Cke.
  Cercospora Catalpae Wint.
  Cladosporium herbarum (P.) ex Lk.
  { Clasterosporium capsularum (Thm.) Sacc.
  { Sporidesmium capsularum Thm.
  Epicoccum neglectum Desm.
  Gloeosporium Catalpae Ell. & Ev.
  Macrosporium Catalpae Ell. & Martin.
  Microsphaera Alni (DC.) Wint. †

Catalpa bignonioides (*cont.*)
  Microsphaera Alni (DC.) Wint.,† var. Vac-
    cinii (S.) Salmon.
  Microsphaera elevata Burrill.
  Phyllactinia corylea (P.) ex Karst.
  Phyllactinia guttata (Wallr. ex Fr.) Lév.
  Phyllactinia suffulta (Reb.) ex Sacc.
  Phyllosticta Bignoniae Westd.
  Depazea catalpicola S.
  Phyllosticta Catalpae Ell. & Martin.
  Phyllosticta catalpicola (S.) Ell. & Ev.
  Sphaerella catalpicola (S.) Cke.
  Sphaeria catalpicola S.
  Boletus distortus S.
  Polyporus distortus (S.) Fr.
Catalpa Bungei C. Meyer.
  Macrosporium Catalpae Ell. & Martin.
  Microsphaera Alni (DC.) Wint., var. Vaccinii
    (S.) Salmon.
  Phyllosticta Catalpae Ell. & Martin.
Catalpa cordifolia Jaume.
  Phyllactinia corylea (P.) ex Karst.
Catalpa Kaempferi Sieb. & Zucc.
  Macrosporium Catalpae Ell. & Martin.
Catalpa speciosa Warder.
  Capnodium axillatum Cke.
  Cercospora Catalpae Wint.
  Chaetophoma Catalpae Cke.
  Alternaria Catalpae (Ell. & Martin) J. B.
    Parker.
  Macrosporium Catalpae Ell. & Martin.
  Microsphaea Alni (DC.) Wint.†
  Microsphaera Alni (DC.) Wint., var. Vaccinii
    (S.) Salmon.
  Microsphaera elevata Burrill.
  Microsphaera Vaccinii C. & P.
  Phyllactinia guttata (Wallr. ex Fr.) Lév.
  Phyllosticta Catalpae Ell. & Martin.
  Polyporus Catalpae v. Schrenk.
  Coriolus versicolor (L. ex Fr.) Quél.
  Polyporus versicolor L. ex Fr.
  Polystictus versicolor (L.) ex Fr.
  Sirodesmium compositum (B. & Rav.) Sacc.
  Sporidesmium compositum B. & Rav.
  Thielavia basicola (B. & Br.) Zopf.
Catalpa syringifolia Bunge.
  Phyllactinia corylea (P.) ex Karst.
  Phyllactinia suffulta (Reb.) ex Sacc.
Catalpa sp. indet.

ASCOMYCETES

  Diaporthe Catalpae Ell. & Ev.
  Didymosphaeria Catalpae J. B. Parker.
  Dothidea Catalpae B. & C.
  Hypoxylon Catalpae (S.) Sacc.
  Sphaeria Catalpae S.
  Lophiostoma subrugosum (S.) Sacc.
  Sphaeria subrugosa S.
  Nummularia Clypeus (S.) Cke.

  Helotium leguminum (S.) Cke.
  Peziza leguminum S.
  Pezizella leguminum (S.) Sacc.
  Phyllachora cinerea Ell. & Ev.
  Sphaeria sphinctrina Fr.
  Valsa sphinctrina Fr.

BASIDIOMYCETES

  Collybia velutipes (W. Curtis) ex Fr.
  Ozonium omnivorum Shear.
  Polyporus adustus (Willd.) ex Fr.
  Schizophyllum commune Fr.
  Stereum albobadium (S.) Fr.
  Stereum versicolor (Sw.) ex Fr.
  Coriolellus sepium (B.) Murrill.
  Trametes sepium B.

FUNGI IMPERFECTI

  Helminthosporium crustuosum S.
  Macrophoma baculum (Gerard) Berl. & Vogl.
  Phoma baculum (Gerard) Sacc.
  Sphaeropsis baculum Gerard.
  Sphaeronema Catalpae S.
  Torula olivascens S.
  Vermicularia angustata S.
  Vermicularia petiolorum S.

MISCELLANEA

  Exidia saccharina Fr.
  Mucor truncorum Lk.
  Stemonitis Morgani Pk.

Tabebuia haemantha (Bert.) DC.
  Meliola bidentata Cke.
  Mycosphaerella Tabebuiae Miles.

Tabebuia pallida Miers.
  Aecidium simplicius Arth. & Johnston.
  Lentinus nigripes Fr.
  Lentinus vellereus B. & C.
  Meliola bidentata Cke.
  Meliola Tecomae F. L. Stevens.
  Ovulariopsis obclavata Wakefield.
  Prospodium appendiculatum (Wint.) Arth.
  Prospodium bahamense Arth.
  Prospodium plagiopus (Mont.) Arth.
  Trichothecium roseum Lk.

Tabebuia sp. indet.
  Prospodium suppressum Arth.

Tecoma bahamensis Northrop.
  Prospodium bahamense Arth.
  Puccinia bahamensis (Arth.) Sacc. & Trott.

Tecoma lepidota (H. B. K.) DC.
  Prospodium plagiopus (Mont.) Arth.
  Puccinia plagiopus Mont.

Tecoma mollis H. B. K.
  Prospodium appendiculatum (Wint.) Arth.
  Nephlyctis transformans (Ell. & Ev.) Arth.
  Puccinia exitiosa Syd. & Holw.
  Puccinia transformans Ell. & Ev.

Tecoma radicans (L.) Juss.
  Botryosphaeria van Vleckii (S.) Sacc.
  Melogramma van Vleckii (S.) B.
  Sphaeria van Vleckii S.
  Cercospora duplicata Ell. & Ev.
  Cercospora Langloisii Sacc.
  Cercospora pallida Ell. & Ev.
  Cercospora sordida Sacc.
  Cladosporium Bignoniae S.
  Coniothyrium olivaceum Bon., var. Tecomae
    Sacc.
  Didymosphaeria Tecomatis Cke.
  Diplodia minuta Ell. & Tracy.
  Microdiplodia minuta (Ell. & Tracy) Tassi.
  Diplodia Tecomae Cke.
  Diplodiella Tecomae (Cke.) Sacc.
  Erysiphe Cichoracearum DC. †
  Exidia glandulosa (Bull.) ex Fr.
  Haplosporella Bignoniae (S.) Starb.
  Pseudovalsa Bignoniae (S.) Cke.
  Haplosporella Tecomae (Dearness) Petrak &
    Syd.
  Sphaeropsis Tecomae Dearness.
  Helicoma larvale Morg.
  Helicomyces Clavus Morg.
  Hendersonia Fiedleri Westd.
  Hendersonia Peckii G. W. Clinton.
  Leptostroma hysterioides Fr.
  Microsphaera Alni (DC.) Wint.†
  Microsphaera semitosta Atk. non. B. & C.
  Pestalozzia brevi-aristata Tracy & Earle.
  Helotium leguminum (S.) Cke.
  Peziza leguminum S.
  Pezizella leguminum (S.) Sacc.
  Phomopsis majuscula Sacc.
  Phyllosticta Tecomae Sacc.
  Pseudovalsa Bignoniae (S.) Cke.
  Sphaeria Bignoniae S.
  Valsa Bignoniae (S.) M. A. Curtis.
  Valsaria Bignoniae S. in Herb. sec. Cke.
  Rabenhorstia sacculus (S.) Starb.
  Sphaeria sacculus S.
  Torselia sacculus (S.) Fr.
  Rhabdospora translucens Fairman.
  Sacidium Bignoniae S.
  Septoria Tecomae Ell. & Ev.
  Stictis Stigma C. & E.
  Sphaeria coronata Hoffm. ex Fr.
  Valsa coronata (Hoffm.) ex Fr.

Tecoma stans (L.) Juss.
  Cyphospilea polylopha Syd.
  Prospodium appendiculatum (Wint.) Arth.
  Puccinia appendiculata Wint.
  Puccinia medusaeoides Arth.
  Puccinia ornata Hark.
  Puccinia Tecomae Sacc. & Syd.
  Puccinia maligna Diet.

  Nephlyctis transformans (Ell. & Ev.) Arth.
  Puccinia transformans Ell. & Ev.
  Tryblidiella rufula Spreng.
Couralia rosea Donn. Sm.
  Plagiostigme Couraliae Syd.
  Prospodium Couraliae Syd.
Enallagma latifolia (Mill.) Small.
  Xylaria appendiculata Ferdinandsen & Winge.
Parmentiera alata Miers.
  Phyllactinia corylea (P.) ex Karst., var. rigida
    Salmon.
Crescentia cucurbitina L.
  Xylaria appendiculata Ferdinandsen & Winge.
Crescentia Cuiete L.
  Hysterium Calabash Seaver.
  Marasmius Crescentiae Murrill.
  Morenoella Calami Racib.
Schlegelia portoricensis (Urb.) Britton.
  Phyllachora nitens P. Garman.
Schlegelia sp. indet.
  Meliola glabroides, var. Schlegeliae F. L.
    Stevens.
Bignoniaceae gen. indet.
  Cerotelium minutum Arth.
  Puccinia Bignoniacearum Speg.

PEDALIACEAE

Sesamum indicum L.
  Diplodia herbarum Lév.
  Helminthosporium sesamum Sacc.
  Pistillaria micans (P.) ex Fr.
Sesamum orientale L.
  Cercospora Sesami Zimm.
  Metasphaeria Carveri Ell. & Ev.

MARTYNIACEAE

Martynia louisiana Mill.
  Cercospora beticola Sacc.

OROBANCHACEAE

Epifagus virginiana (L.) Bart.

GESNERIACEAE

Gesneria sp. indet.
  Asterina dilabens Syd.
  Asterinia punctiformis Lév.
  Clintoniella viridans (B. & C.) Sacc. & Syd.
  Hypocrea viridans B. & C.
  Hypocrea insignis B. & C.
Pentarhaphia albiflora Dcne.
  Meliola Gesneriae F. L. Stevens.
  Botrytis seriata Ell. & Ev.
  Nitschkia nervincola Rehm. nom. nud.
  Rostronitschkia nervincola Fitzpatrick.
Rhytidophyllum auriculatum Hook.
  Asterina dilabens Syd.

LENTIBULARIACEAE

Pinguicula vulgaris L.
   Sphaerella pachyasca Rostr.

ACANTHACEAE

Elytraria squamosa Lindau.
Elytraria tridentata Vahl.
   ⌈ Micropuccinia Elytrariae (Henn.) Arth. &
      Jackson.
   ⌊ Puccinia Elytrariae Henn.
Hygrophila brasiliensis (Spreng.) Lind.
   ⌈ Irene irregularis (F. L. Stevens) Toro.
   ⌊ Meliola irregularis F. L. Stevens.
Blechum Brownei (Sw.) Juss.
   ⌈ Dicaeoma Ruelliae (Lagerh.) O. Kuntze.
   | Puccinia Blechi Lagerh.
   | Puccinia Ruelliae Lagerh.
   ⌊ Uredo balaensis Syd.
Blechum sp. indet.
   ⌈ Comesella anomala (B. & C.) Speg.
   ⌊ Dothidea anomala B. & C.
Dyschoriste capitata (Oerst.) O. Kuntze.
Dyschoriste oblongifolia (Michx.) O. Kuntze.
   Aecidium tracyanum Syd.
Ruellia Bourgaei Hemsl.
   ⌈ Dicaeoma Ruelliae (Lagerh.) O. Kuntze.
   ⌊ Puccinia Ruelliae-Bourgaei Diet. & Holw.
Ruellia ciliosa Pursh.
   Cercospora consociata Wint.
   ⌈ Dicaeoma Ruelliae (Lagerh.) O. Kuntze.
   | Diorchidium lateripes (B. & Rav.) Magn.
   | Puccinia lateripes B. & Rav.
   ⌊ Puccinia Ruelliae Lagerh.
Ruellia drummondiana (Nees) Gray.
Ruellia Haenkei (Nees) Lindau.
Ruellia nudiflora (Engelm. & Gray) Urban.
Ruellia paniculata L.
Ruellia pedunculata Torr.
   ⌈ Dicaeoma Ruelliae (Lagerh.) O. Kuntze.
   | Puccinia Ruelliae Lagerh.
   ⌊ Puccinia Ruelliae-Bourgaei Diet. & Holw.
Ruellia strepens L.
   Darluca Filum (Biv.) Cast.
   ⌈ Aecidium lateripes Kellerm.
   | Dicaeoma lateripes (B. & Rav.) O. Kuntze.
   | Dicaeoma Ruelliae (Lagerh.) O. Kuntze.
   | Diorchidium lateripes (B. & Rav.) Magn.
   | Puccinia lateripes B. & Rav.
   | Puccinia Ruelliae Lagerh.
   ⌊ Puccinia Ruelliae-Bourgaei Diet. & Holw.
   Uromyces texensis B. & C.
   Vermicularia ovata S.
Ruellia tuberosa L.
   ⌈ Aecidium tracyanum Syd.
   | Dicaeoma Ruelliae (Lagerh.) O. Kuntze.
   | Puccinia lateripes B. & Rav.
   | Puccinia longiana Syd.
   ⌊ Puccinia Ruelliae Lagerh.

Ruellia sp. indet.
   ⌈ Dicaeoma(?) varium Arth.
? | Puccinia varia Arth.
   | Nigredo (?) Ruelliae (Holw.) Arth.
   ⌊ Uromyces Ruelliae Holw.
Aphelandra pectinata Willd.
   Uromyces Aphelandrae Syd.
Graptophyllum pictum Griff.
   Rosellinia bunodes (B. & Br.) Sacc.
Anisacanthus Thurberi Gray.
Anisacanthus virgularis Nees.
Anisacanthus Wrightii (Torr.) Gray.
   ⌈ Aecidium Anisacanthi Pk.
   | Dicaeoma Anisacanthi (Diet. & Holw.) Arth.
   ⌊ Puccinia Anisacanthi Diet. & Holw.
Pseuderanthemum cuspidatum (Nees) Radlk.
   Uromyces hariotianus Lagerh.
Tetramerium aureum Rose.
Tetramerium hispidum Nees.
   ⌈ Dicaeoma Tetramerii (Seym.) Arth.
   ⌊ Puccinia Tetramerii Seym.
Dicliptera sp. indet.
   Uromyces induratus Syd. & Holw.
   Uromyces tweediana (Speg.) Arth.
Anthacanthus spinosus Nees.
   Uromyces Anthacanthi H. S. Jackson.
Thyrsacanthus strictus Nees.
   Uromyces hariotianus Lagerh.
Jacobinia tinctoria Hemsl.
   Asterina costaricensis Syd.
Beloperone californica Benth.
   ⌈ Nigredo (?) Ruelliae (Holw.) Arth.
   | Uredo Beloperones Arth.
   ⌊ Uromyces Ruelliae Holw.
Justicia verticillaris L.
   Guignardia Justiciae F. L. Stevens.
Justicia sp. indet.
   ⌈ Dicaeoma Ruelliae (Lagerh.) O. Kuntze.
   ⌊ Puccinia Ruelliae Lagerh.
Dianthera americana L.
   ⌈ Bagnisiella Diantherae J. M. Lewis.
   | Dothideovalsa Diantherae (J. M. Lewis)
   ⌊   Theissen & Syd.
   Cercospora Diantherae Ell. & Kellerm.
Dianthera humilis Engelm. & Gray.
   Dimerosporium Langloisii Ell. & Martin.
Dianthera pectoralis (Jacq.) Gmel.
   Puccinia Ruelliae Lagerh.
Acanthaceae gen. indet.
   Puccinia varia (Diet.) Arth.

PHRYMACEAE

Phryma leptostachya L.
   ⌈ Aecidium Phrymae Halsted.
   | Dicaeoma Phrymae (Arth.) Arth. & Kern. I.
   | Puccinia Phrymae Arth. I.
   ⌊ Cercosporella exilis J. J. Davis.

Phryma leptostachya (*cont.*)
Gymnosporium harknessioides Ell. & Holw.
Coniosporium harknessioides (Ell. & Holw.)
  Sacc.
Species spuria sporae Piloboli.
Septoria Leptostachyae Ell. & Kellerm.

PLANTAGINACEAE

Plantago aristata Michx.
Aecidium Plantaginis Burrill.
Nigredo seditiosa (Kern) Arth. I.
Uromyces Aristidae Auct. I.
Uromyces seditiosus Kern.
Erysiphe Cichoracearum DC. †
Peronospora alta Fckl.
Peronospora Plantaginis Underw.
Rhizoctonia Solani Kühn.
Septoria inconspicua B. & C.

Plantago cordata Lam.
Ramularia Plantaginis Ell. & Martin.

Plantago decipiens Barneoud.
Erysiphe Cichoracearum DC. †
Pleospora clarkeiana Ell. & Ev.
Pleospora herbarum (Fr.) Rabh.
Puccinia pacifica Blasdale.
Septoria semilunaris Johans.
Septoria Vanhoeffenii Henn.
Sphaerella pachyasca Rostr.

Plantago elongata Pursh.
Rhabdospora continua (B. & C.) Sacc.

Plantago eriopoda Torr.
Aecidium Plantaginis Burrill.
Nigredo seditiosa (Kern) Arth. I.
Uromyces Aristidae Auct. I.
Uromyces seditiosus Kern. I.
Dicaeoma Sarcobati Arth. I.
Puccinia subnitens Diet. I.

Plantago heterophylla Nutt.
Nigredo seditiosa (Kern) Arth. I.

Plantago lanceolata L.
Aecidium Plantaginis Burrill.
Uromyces seditiosus Kern. I.
Cercospora Plantaginis Sacc.
Diaporthe adunca (Desm.) Niessl.
Peronospora alta Fckl.
Phoma polygramma (Fr.) Sacc., var. Plan-
  taginis Sacc.
Physarum cinereum (Batsch) P.
Rhabdospora continua (B. & C.) Sacc.
Ramularia lanceolata Dearness & House.
Ramularia Peckii Sacc. & Syd.
Ramularia plantaginea Sacc. & Berl.
Ramularia Plantaginis Ell. & Martin.
Septoria inconspicua B. & C.
Sphaerella plantaginicola (S.) Cke.
Sphaeria plantaginicola S.
Synchytrium plantagineum Sacc. & Speg.

Plantago major L.
Asterella Plantaginis (Ell.) Sacc.
Asterina Plantaginis Ell.
Cercospora Plantaginis Sacc.
Corticium vagum B. & C.
Erysiphe Cichoracearum DC. †
Erysiphe lamprocarpa Auct. Amer. p. p.
Peronospora alta Fckl.
Peronospora effusa (Grev.) Rabh.
Phyllactinia corylea (P.) ex Karst.
Phyllosticta plantaginella Sacc.
Physarum cinereum (Batsch) P.
Ramularia Plantaginis Ell. & Martin.
Ramularia Plantaginis Ell. & Martin, var.
  nigromaculans Pk.
Ramularia Tulasnei Sacc.?
Rhabdospora continua (B. & C.) Sacc.
Septoria continua B. & C.
Septoria Plantaginis Sacc.
Mycosphaerella plantaginicola (S.) Dearness.
Sphaeria plantaginicola S.
Sphaerotheca Humuli (DC.) Burrill, var.
  fuliginea (Schl.) Salmon.

Plantago minor Fr.
Ramularia Plantaginis Ell. & Martin.

Plantago Purshii R. & S.
Aecidium Plantaginis Burrill.
Nigredo seditiosa (Kern) Arth. I.
Uromyces Aristidae Auct. I.
Uromyces seditiosus Kern. I.

Plantago rhodosperma Dcne.
Nigredo seditiosa (Kern) Arth. I.

Plantago Rugelii Dcne.
Aecidium Plantaginis Burrill.
Nigredo seditiosa (Kern) Arth. I.
Uromyces Aristidae Auct. I.
Uromyces seditiosus Kern. I.
Asterina Plantaginis Ell.
Byssocystis textilis Riess.
Cercospora plantaginella Tehon.
Cercospora Plantaginis Sacc.
Erysiphe Cichoracearum DC. †
Peronospora alta Fckl.
Phyllachora Plantaginis Ell. & Ev.
Ramularia plantaginea Sacc. & Berl.
Ramularia Plantaginis Pk. 1886.
Ramularia Plantaginis Ell. & Martin. 1882.
Mycosphaerella Columbi Rehm.
Sphaerella Columbi (Rehm) Sacc. & Trott.

Plantago Tweedyi Gray.
Nigredo seditiosus (Kern) Arth. I.
Uromyces Aristidae Auct. I.
Uromyces seditiosus Kern. I.

Plantago virginica L.
Aecidium Plantaginis Burrill.
Nigredo seditiosus (Kern) Arth. I.
Uromyces seditiosus Kern. I.
Peronospora alta Fckl.

Plantago virginica (*cont.*)
Phyllosticta plantaginicola Tehon & Daniels.
Ramularia Peckii Sacc. & Syd.
Stigmatea Plantaginis Tehon & Daniels.

RUBIACEAE

Chimarrhis cymosa Jacq.
Arcyria digitata S.
Lentinus Lecomtei Fr.
Houstonia angustifolia Michx.
{ ?Aecidium cylindricum Ell. & Ev.
{ Aecidium houstoniatum S.
{ Uromyces houstoniatus J. L. Sheldon. I.
Aecidium oldenlandianum Ell. & Tracy.
{ Micropuccinia lateritia (B. & C.) Arth. & Jackson.
{ Puccinia Houstoniae Syd.
{ Puccinia lateritia B. & C.
Houstonia caerulea L.
{ Aecidium houstoniatum S.
{ Caeoma houstoniatum S.
{ Nigredo houstoniata J. L. Sheldon. I.
{ Uromyces houstoniatus J. L. Sheldon. I.
{ Uromyces Murrillii Ricker. I.
Aecidium oldenlandianum Ell. & Tracy.
Peronospora Seymourii Burrill.
Houstonia longifolia Gaertn.
{ Aecidium houstoniatum S.
{ Caeoma houstoniatum S.
{ Nigredo houstoniata J. L. Sheldon. I.
{ Uromyces houstoniatus J. L. Sheldon. I.
Houstonia minima Beck.
{ Aecidium houstoniatum S.
{ Nigredo houstoniata J. L. Sheldon. I.
{ ?Nigredo seditiosa (Kern) Arth. I.
Houstonia patens Ell.
{ Aecidium houstoniatum S.
{ Aecidium oldenlandianum Ala. Bull.
{ Aecidium oldenlandianum Ell. & Tracy.?
{ Nigredo seditiosa (Kern) Arth. I.
{ Peronospora calotheca DBy.
{ Peronospora Seymourii Underw. non Burrill.
Peronospora Seymourii Burrill.
Septoria Galiorum Ell.
Houstonia purpurea L.
{ Caeoma houstoniatum S.
{ Nigredo houstoniata J. L. Sheldon. I.
{ Aecidium oldenlandianum Ell. & Tracy.
{ Nigredo seditiosa (Kern) Arth. I.
Rondeletia affinis Hemsl.
Asterina advenula Syd.
Byssocallis aphanes Syd.
Rhynchostoma pusillum Syd.
Trichothyrium dubiosum (Bomm. & Rouss.) Theissen.
Rondeletia cordata Benth.
Uredo Rondeletiae Arth. & Holw.

Rondeletia stereocarpa Griseb.
Leptoporus anebus (B.) Pat.
Rondeletia sp. indet.
Echidnodella Rondeletiae Ryan.
Morenoella decalvans (Pat.) Theissen, var. Rondeletiae Ryan.
Xerotus guadalupensis Pat.
Cinchona sp. indet.
Cercospora Cinchonae Ell. & Ev.
Polystictus fimbriatus Fr.
Bouvardia laevis Mart. & Gall.
Bouvardia leiantha Benth.
Uromyces Bouvardiae Syd.
Bouvardia ternifolia (Cav.) Schl.
Aecidium Bouvardiae Diet. & Holw.
{ Allodus Bouvardiae (Griff.) C. R. Orton.
{ Allodus scaberistipes Arth. & Orton.
{ Puccinia Bouvardiae Griffiths.
{ Nigredo Bouvardiae (Syd.) Arth.
{ Uromyces Bouvardiae Syd.
Bouvardia versicolor Ker-Gawl.
{ Nigredo Bouvardiae (Syd.) Arth.
{ Uromyces Bouvardiae Syd.
Bouvardia sp. indet.
{ Micropuccinia lateritia (B. & C.) Arth. & J.
{ Puccinia lateritia B. & C.
Hillia parasitica Jacq.
Asterina dilabens Syd., var. Hilliae Ryan.
Exostemma caribaeum Roem. & Schult.
Meliola Psychotriae Earle.
Exostemma floribundum Roem. & Schult.
{ Coccomyces limitatus (B. & C.) Sacc.
{ Phacidium limitatum B. & C.
Cephalanthus occidentalis L.
{ Aecidium Cephalanthi Seymour.
{ Dicaeoma Cephalanthi H. S. Jackson.
{ Dicaeoma seymouriana Arth. I.
{ Puccinia Cephalanthi (H. S. Jackson) Arth. I. 1920.
{ Puccinia Cephalanthi (H. S. Jackson) Barthol. I. 1922.
{ Puccinia seymouriana Arth. I.
Ascochyta Cephalanthi Ell. & Ev.
Capnodium elongatum B. & Desm.
{ Cercospora Cephalanthi Ell. & Kellerm.
{ Ramularia Cephalanthi (E. & K.) Heald.
Cercospora perniciosa Heald & Wolf.
{ Coniothyrium Cephalanthi Ell. & Ev.
{ Phyllostictella Cephalanthi (Ell. & Ev.) Tassi.
{ Cryptovalsa Cephalanthi (S.) Berl.
{ Diatrype Cephalanthi (S.) B.
{ Diatrypella aspera Pk.
{ Diatrypella Cephalanthi (S.) Sacc.
{ Sphaeria Cephalanthi S.
Dendrophoma Cephalanthi Pk.
Discosia Artocreas (Tode) ex Fr.
Epicoccum maculatum Cke.
Lentodium squamulosum Morg.
Lophiostoma Cephalanthi Fairman.

Cephalanthus occidentalis (*cont.*)
  Lophiostoma prominens Pk.
  { Microsphaera Alni (DC.) Wint. †
  { Microsphaera semitosta B. & C.
  Pestalozzia funerea Desm.
  { Phyllactinia corylea (P.) ex Karst.
  { Phyllactinia guttata (Wallr. ex Fr.) Lév.
  { Phyllactinia suffulta (Reb.) ex Sacc.
  Phyllost icta Cephalanthi Tharp.
  Pyrenopeziza Cephalanthi Fairman.
  { Rhabdospora verruciformis (B. & C.) Sacc.
  { Septoria verruciformis B. & C.
  { Cenangium Cephalanthi (S.) Pk.
  { Godronia Cephalanthi (S.) Dearness & House.
  { Peziza Cephalanthi S.
  { Scleroderris Cephalanthi (S.) Farl.
  Septoria Cephalanthi Ell. & Kellerm.
  Sphaerella maculiformis (Fr.) Awd.
  Tympanis Cephalanthi Dearness & House.
  Uredo Cephalanthi Arth.
  Valsa ceratophora Tul.
Gonzalagunia spicata (Lam.) G. Maza.
  Arthrobotryum caudatum Syd.
  Isthmospora glabra F. L. Stevens.
  Meliola Psychotriae Earle.
  Wageria portoricensis Stevens & Dalbey.
Schradera capitata Vahl.
  Hymenochaete Cacao B. & C.
Coccocypselum hirsutum Bartl.
  { Micropuccinia lateritia (B. & C.) Arth. &
    Jackson.
  { Puccinia lateritia B. & C.
Coccocypselum repens Sw.
  Irene seminata (B. & C.) Seaver & Chardon.
  Meliola glabra B. & C., var. Psychotriae F. L.
    Stevens.
Sabicea aspera Aubl.
  Uredo sabiceicola Arth.
Randia mitis L.
  Aecidium abscedens Arth.
  Meliola amphitricha Fr.
  Meliola Psychotriae Earle.
  Monospermella portoricensis Speg.
  Phyllachora Randiae Rehm.
  Phyllachora Randiae Rehm., var. aculeatae
    Ferdinandsen & Winge.
  Podosporium pallidum Pat.
  Trabutia Randiae (Rehm) Theissen & Syd.
Randia spinosa (Jacq.) Karst.
  Aecidium pulverulentum Arth.
Randia Watsoni B. L. Robinson.
  Aecidium abscedens Arth.
  Aecidium pulverulentum Arth.
Gardenia florida L.
  Capnodium Citri B. & Desm.
  { Phyllosticta Gardeniae Cke.
  { Sphaerella Gardeniae Cke.
Gardenia jasminoides Ell.
  Fumago vagans Fr.

Gardenia sp. indet.
  Diplodia cacaoicola Henn.
Genipa americana L.
  Asterina Genipae Ryan.
  Meliola sterinoides Wint.
  Phyllachora Gnipae Stevens & Dalbey.
  { Cyclomyces tabacinus (Mont.) Pat.
  { Polyporus tabacinus Mont.
Alibertia sp. indet.
  Aecidium Alibertiae Arth.
Hamelia erecta Jacq.
  Uredo Hameliae Arth.
Hoffmannia tubiflora Griseb.
  Trogia cinerea Pat.
Guettarda ovalifolia Urban.
  Meliola Psychotriae Earle.
  Septoria Guettardae P. Garman.
  Stigmatea Guettardae Tehon.
Guettarda scabra Lam.
  Meliola Psychotriae Earle.
  Stigmatea Guettardae Tehon.
Antirrhoea lucida (Gaertn.) Benth. & Hook.
  Trametes coriacea (B. & Rav.) Pat.
Laugeria resinosa Vahl.
  Morenoella decalvans (Pat.) Theissen, var.
    Laugeriae Ryan.
Malanea macrophylla Bartl.
  Meliola Malaneae Stevens & Tehon.
Erithalis angustifolia DC.
  Asterella Erithalidis Ell. & Ev.
Erithalis fruticosa L.
  Meliola Psychotriae Earle.
Chiococca alba (L.) Hitchc.
  Belonidium leucorrhodinum (Mont.) Sacc.
  Helminthosporium glabroides F. L. Stevens.
  Isthmospora spinosa F. L. Stevens.
  Meliola Chiococcae F. L. Stevens.
  Meliola Psychotriae Earle.
  Triposporium stelligerum Speg.
Chione glabra DC.
  Hymenochaete formosa Lév.
  Orbilia? lancicula (Mont.) Pat.
Coffea arabica L.
  { Anthostomella Coffeae Delacr.
  { ?Hendersonia Coffeae Delacr.
  { Capnodium trichostomum Speg.
  { Microxyphiella trichostoma Speg.
  { Cercospora coffeicola B. & Cke.
  { Cercospora herrerana Farneti.
  { Cercosporina coffeicola (B. & Cke.) Speg.
  Clypeolum megalosporum Speg.
  Colletotrichum coffeanum Noack.
  { Corticium koleroga (Cke.) v. Höhnel.
  { Pellicularia koleroga Cke.
  Dimerosporium? coronatum Speg.
  Glomerella cincta (Stoneman) Spaulding & v.
    Schrenk.
  Glomerella cingulata (Stoneman) Spaulding &
    v. Schrenk.

Coffea arabica (*cont.*)
  Laestadia coffeicola Speg.
  Leptosphaeria coffeigena (B. & C.) Sacc.
  Metasphaeria bifoveolata Speg.
  Micropeltis coffeicola Henn.
  { Micropeltis longispora Earle.
  { Scolecopeltis longispora (Earle) Toro.
  Phthora vastatrix D'Herelle.
  { Phyllosticta coffeicola Speg. 1896.
  { Phyllosticta coffeicola Delacr. 1904.
  Rhabdospora coffeicola Delacr.
  Rosellinia bunodes (B. & Br.) Sacc.
  Rosellinia coffeicola Pat.
  Rostrella Coffeae Zimm.
  Saccardinula costaricensis Speg.
  { Omphalia flavida (Cke.) Maubl. & Rangel.
  { Pistillaria flavida (Cke.) Speg.
  { Stilbella flavida (Cke.) Henn.
  { Stilbum flavidum Cke.
Coffea excelsa Cheval.
  Stilbella flavida (Cke.) Henn.
Coffea Laurentii Wildem.
  Pellicularia koleroga Cke.
  Stilbella flavida (Cke.) Henn.
Coffea macrocarpa A. Rich.
Coffea Perrieri Drake.
Coffea robusta L. Linden.
  Stilbella flavida (Cke.) Henn.
Coffea stenophylla G. Don.
  Pellicularia koleroga Cke.
  Stilbella flavida (Cke.) Henn.
Coffea sp. indet.

ASCOMYCETES

Angelina nigrocinnabarina B. & C.
Asterina coffeicola Ell. & Ev.
Asterina pelliculosa B.
{ ?Brachysporium sp. indet.
{ Capnodium Coffeae Pat.
Leptosphaerella pusilla Speg.
Leptosphaeria coffaeicida Speg.
Leptosphaeria Tonduzi Speg.
Lisea Tonduzi Speg.
{ Melanopsamma coffeicola (B. & C.) Sacc.
{ Sphaeria coffeicola B. & C.
Meliola glabra B. & C.
Micropeltis Tonduzii Speg.
Nectria saccharina B. & C.
Phaeosaccardinula costaricensis (Speg.)
  Theissen.
{ Rosellinia inaequatilis (B. & C.) Sacc.
{ Sphaeria inaequatilis B. & C.
Rosellinia necatrix (Hartig) Berl.
Rosellinia Pepo Pat.
Rosellinia quercina Hartig.
Sphaerella coffeicola Cke.
Sphaerostilbe flavida Massee.
Sphaerostilbe Musarum Ashby.
Vizella Hieronymi Wint., var. coffeae Maubl.

BASIDIOMYCETES

Armillaria mellea (Vahl) ex Fr.
{ Auricularia polytricha (Mont.) Sacc.
{ Exidia polytricha Mont.
Collybia xuchilensis Murrill.
Corticium salmonicolor B. & Br.
Flammula aureobrunnea B. & C.
Hirneola coffeicolor B.
Hymenochaete noxia B.
Lentinus tener Klotzsch.
Lentinus velutinus Fr.
Lentinus villosus Klotzsch.
{ Hiatula fragilissimus Rav.
{ Leucocoprinus fragilissimus (Rav.) Pat.
Marasmius bermudensis B.
Nolanea cubensis Murrill.
Pleurotus lignatilis Fr.
Stereum coffearum B. & C.
Stereum fasciatum S.

POLYPORACEAE

Gloeoporus thelephoroides (Hook.) Bres.
Lenzites tenuis Lév.
Polyporus blanchetianus Mont.
Polyporus flavus Klotzsch.
{ Leptoporus nauseosus Pat.
{ Polyporus nauseosus (Pat.) Sacc. & D. Sacc.
Polyporus sanguineus (L.) ex Fr.
{ Leucoporus Tricholoma (Mont.) Pat.
{ Polyporus Tricholoma Mont.
Polystictus sobrius B. & C.
Trametes elegans Fr.

FUNGI IMPERFECTI

Cercospora Coffeae Zimm.
Cladosterigma fusisporum Pat.
Colletotrichum brachysporum Speg.
Colletotrichum coffaeophilum Speg.
Leptothyrium costaricense Speg.
Microcera coccophila Desm.
Phoma coffaeicida Speg.
Rhabdospora Coffeae Delacr.
Triposporium Gardneri B.

MISCELLANEA

Arcyria nutans Grev.
Chondrioderma floriforme Rostf.
Lycoperdon epixylon B. & Cke.
Pseudomicrocera Henningsii (Koord.) Petch.
Rhizomorpha sphaerocrystalligera Speg.
Saccharomyces apiculatus Loew.
Saccharomyces ellipsoideus Reess.
Tilmadoche mutabilis Rostf.
Siderodendron triflorum Vahl.
  Aecidium Ixorae Arth.
Ixora ferrea Benth.
  Aecidium Ixorae Arth.
  Asterina Ixorae Ryan.
  Asterinella Ixorae Ryan.
  Collybia cyanocephala Pat.

Psychotria berteriana DC.
  Arthrobotryum caudatum Syd.
  ⎧Irene seminata (B. & C.) Seaver & Chardon.
  ⎩Meliola glabra, var. Psychotriae F. L. Stevens.
Psychotria glabrata Sw.
  Crepidotus Psychotriae Pat.
Psychotria grandis Sw.
  Helminthosporium Melastomacearum F. L.
    Stevens.
  Meliola glabra B. & C.
  Meliola glabra, var. Psychotriae F. L. Stevens.
  Podosporium? penicillium Speg.
Psychotria patens Sw.
  ⎧Puccinia fallaciosa Arth.
  ⎩Uredo fallaciosa Arth.
Psychotria pubescens Sw.
  Arthrobotryum caudatum Syd.
  Asterina Psychotriae Ryan.
  ⎧Irene seminata (B. & C.) Seaver & Chardon.
  ⎩Meliola glabra var. Psychotriae F. L. Stevens.
  Meliola bayamonensis Tehon.
Psychotria rufescens Spreng.
  Pestalozzia maura Ell. & Ev.
Psychotria uliginosa Sw.
  Stilbella flavida (Cke.) Henn.
Psychotria sp. indet.
  Arthrobotryum melanoplaca B. & C.
  Asterina acanthopoda Speg.
  Dimerium piceum (B. & C.) Theissen.
  Marasmius candidus Fr.
  Meliola Malaneae Stevens & Tehon.
  Meliola Psychotriae Earle.
  ⎧Calothyrium Psychotriae Ryan.
  ⎩Microthyrium Psychotriae (Ryan) Toro.
Palicourea costaricensis Benth.
  Asterina erebia Syd.
Palicourea crocea (Sw.) Roem.
  Aschersonia cubensis B. & C.
  Grallomyces portoricensis F. L. Stevens.
  Hypoxylon annulatum L.
  Isaria Saussurei Cke.
  Meliola mayaguesiana F. L. Stevens.
  Puccinia fallaciosa Arth.
Palicourea domingensis (Jacq.) DC.
  Meliola mayaguesiana F. L. Stevens.
Palicourea riparia Benth.
  Meliola mayaguesiana F. L. Stevens.
  Puccinia fallaciosa Arth.
Palicourea sp. indet.
  Acrostalagmus albus Preuss.
  Arthrobotryum caudatum Syd.
  Asterina miconicola Ryan.
  ⎧Meliola glabra, var. Psychotriae F. L. Stevens.
  ⎩Meliola seminata B. & C.
  Rosellinia bunodes (B. & Br.) Sacc.
Cephaelis muscosa Sw.
  Xerotus lateritius B. & C.

Mitchella repens L.
  Leptostroma Mitchellae Fairman.
  Meliola Mitchellae Cke.
Faramea occidentalis Muell.
  Aecidium Farameae Arth.
Richardsonia pilosa H. B. K.
  Cercospora Richardsoniae Ell. & Ev.
  ⎧Corticium vagum B. & C.
  ⎩Rhizoctonia Solani Kühn.
  Phyllosticta Richardsoniae Ell. & Ev.
Ernodea angusta Small.
Ernodea littoralis Sw.
Crusea calocephala DC.
Diodia maritima Thonn.
  ⎧Micropuccinia lateritia (B. & C.) Arth. &
  ⎱ Jackson.
  ⎰Puccinia lateritia B. & C.
  ⎩Puccinia Spermacoces B. & C.
Diodia rigida Cham. & Schl.
  ⎧Micropuccinia lateritia (B. & C.) Arth. &
  ⎱ Jackson.
  ⎰Puccinia lateritia B. & C.
  ⎩Puccinia Spermacoces B. & C.
  Uromyces Spermacoces (S.) M. A. Curtis.
Diodia teres Walt.
  Cercospora Diodiae Cke.
  Cercospora Diodiae-virginianae Atk.
  Puccinia lateritia B. & C.
  ⎧Aecidium Diodiae Burrill.
  ⎪Caeoma Spermacoces Lk.
  ⎨Nigredo Spermacoces (S.) Arth.
  ⎪Puccinia Spermacoces S.
  ⎩Uromyces Spermacoces (S.) M. A. Curtis.
Diodia virginiana L.
  Cercospora Diodiae-virginianae Atk.
Hemidiodia ocimifolia (Willd.) Schum.
  Aecidium Borreriae Pat.
  ⎧Micropuccinia lateritia (B. & C.) Arth. &
  ⎪ Jackson.
  ⎨Puccinia Houstoniae Syd.
  ⎩Puccinia lateritia B. & C.
Borreria laevis (Lam.) Griseb.
Borreria ocymoides (Burm. f.) DC.
  Meliola Psychotriae Earle.
  Puccinia lateritia B. & C.
Borreria micrantha Torr. & Gr.
  Asterula Tracyi Pk.
  Cercospora Borreriae Ell. & Ev.
Borreria parviflora Meyer.
Borreria tenella (H. B. K.) Cham. & Schl.
Borreria terminalis Small.
  ⎧Micropuccinia lateritia (B. & C.) Arth. &
  ⎪ Jackson.
  ⎨Puccinia lateritia B. & C.
  ⎩Puccinia Spermacoces B. & C.
Borreria verticillata (L.) Meyer.
  Puccinia lateritia B. & C.
  Uredo Borreriae (Henn.) Kern & Whetzel.

Borreria sp. indet.
  Aecidium Borreriae Pat.
  Dimerosporium eutrichum Sacc. & Berl.

Spermacoce aspera Hemsl.
  Puccinia Spermacoces B. & C.

Spermacoce diodina Michx.
  Uromyces Spermacoces (S.) M. A. Curtis.

Spermacoce glabra Michx.
  Micropuccinia lateritia (B. & C.) Arth. & Jackson.
  Puccinia lateritia B. & C.
  Puccinia Spermacoces B. & C.
  Uromyces Spermacoces (S.) M. A. Curtis.

Spermacoce haenkeana Hemsl.
Spermacoce levis Lam.
  Micropuccinia lateritia (B. & C.) Arth. & Jackson.
  Puccinia lateritia B. & C.
  Puccinia Spermacoces B. & C.

Spermacoce parviflora Gray.
  Asterula Tracyi Pk.

Spermacoce podocephala DC.
Spermacoce Pringlei Watson.
Spermacoce riparia Cham. & Schl.
Spermacoce tenuior L.
  Micropuccinia lateritia (B. & C.) Arth. & Jackson.
  Puccinia lateritia B. & C.
  Puccinia Spermacoces B. & C.

Mitracarpus portoricensis Urb.
  Meliola Psychotriae Earle.
  Micropuccinia lateritia (B. & C.) Arth. & Jackson.
  Puccinia lateritia B. & C.

Asperula sp. indet.
  Thekopsora guttata (Schrt.) Syd.

Galium angustifolium Nutt.
  Metasphaeria anisometra (Cke. & Hark.) Sacc.
  Neosphaeropsis nebelina (Fairman) Petrak & Syd.
  Sphaeropsis nebelina Fairman.

Galium Aparine L.
  Cercospora Galii Ell. & Holw.
  Erysiphe Cichoracearum DC.†
  Leptostroma clandestinum S.
  Mazzantia Galii (Fr.) Mont.
  Oidium erysiphoides Fr.
  Peronospora calotheca DBy.
  Allodus ambigua (Lagerh.) Arth.
  Dicaeoma ambiguum Arth.
  Dicaeoma Galiorum Arth.
  Puccinia ambigua Lagerh.
  Puccinia difformis Kze.
  Puccinia Galii Auct. Amer. p. p.
  Puccinia Galiorum Auct. Amer. p. p

  Dicaeoma Galiorum Arth. p. p.
  Dicaeoma punctatum (Lk.) Arth.
  Puccinia chondrioderma Lindr.
  Puccinia Galiorum Arth. 1899 p. p.
  Puccinia punctata Lk.
  Vermicularia scandentium S.

Galium asperrimum Gray.
  Dicaeoma punctatum (Lk.) Arth.
  Puccinia punctata Lk.

Galium asprellum Michx.
  Cercospora Galii Ell. & Holw.
  Darluca Filum (Biv.) Cast.
  Peronospora calotheca DBy.
  Dicaeoma Galiorum Arth. p. p.
  Dicaeoma punctatum (Lk.) Arth.
  Puccinia Galii S.
  Puccinia Galiorum Auct. p. p.
  Puccinia punctata Lk.
  Septoria Aparines Ell. & Ev.

Galium Bloomeri Gray.
  Peronospora calotheca DBy.
  Micropuccinia rubefaciens (Johans.) Arth. & Jackson.
  Puccinia rubefaciens Johans.

Galium boreale L.
  Hymenula Galii Pk.
  Melasmia Galii Ell. & Ev.
  Microdiplodia galiicola Fairman.
  Peronospora borealis Gäuman.
  Peronospora calotheca DBy.
  Peziza nigritella Phil. & Hark.
  Phoma elliptica Pk.
  Physalospora Galii Rostr.
  Placosphaeria Galii Sacc.
  Placosphaeria punctiformis (Fckl.) Sacc.
  Puccinia punctata Lk.
  Micropuccinia rubefaciens (Johans.) Arth. & & Jackson.
  Puccinia Galiorum Auct. Amer. p. p.
  Puccinia rubefaciens Johans.
  Septoria cruciatae Rob. & Desm.
  Septoria psilostega Ell. & Martin.

Galium buxifolium Greene.
  Dicaeoma punctatum (Lk.) Arth. Proc. Ind.

Galium californicum Hook. & Arn.
  Dicaeoma punctatum (Lk.) Arth.
  Puccinia Galii S.
  Puccinia Valantiae Auct. Amer.
  Micropuccinia rubefaciens (Johans.) Arth. & Johnston.
  Puccinia rubefaciens Johans.

Galium circaezans Michx.
  Erysiphe Cichoracearum DC.†
  Phyllactinia corylea (P.) ex Karst.
  Septoria psilostega Ell. & Martin.

Galium Claytoni Michx.
  Phacidium brunneolum Pk.
  Pseudopeziza autumnalis (Fckl.) Sacc.

Galium concinnum Torr. & Gr.
Aecidium Galii Auct.
Dicaeoma Galiorum Arth. p. p.
Dicaeoma punctatum (Lk.) Arth.
Puccinia Galii S.
Puccinia punctata Lk.

Galium lanceolatum Torr.
Peronospora calotheca DBy.
Phyllactinia corylea (P.) ex Karst.

Galium linearifolium Turcz.
Puccinia rubefaciens Johans.

Galium mexicanum H. B. K.
Dicaeoma eximium (Arth. & Holw.) Arth.
Puccinia eximia Arth. & Holw.

Galium Nuttallii Gray.
Puccinia Galii S.
Puccinia Valantiae Auct. Amer.

Galium pilosum Ait.
Cercospora Galii Ell. & Holw.
Cercospora tenuis Pk.
Puccinia Galii S.
Dicaeoma punctatum (Lk.) Arth.
Septoria psilostega Ell. & Martin.

Galium purpureum L.
Puccinia Galii S.

Galium tinctorium L.
Cercospora Galii Ell. & Holw.
Melasmia? Galii Ell. & Ev.
Puccinia Galii S.
Dicaeoma punctatum (Lk.) Arth.
Puccinia punctata Lk.
Pseudopeziza repanda (Fr.) Karst.
Septoria psilostega Ell. & Martin.

Galium trifidum L.
Cercospora punctoidea Ell. & Holw.
Erysiphe Cichoracearum DC. †
Phacidium brunneolum Pk.
Phacidium repandum Fr.
Pseudopeziza repanda (Fr.) Karst.
Xyloma herbarum A. & S. ex Fr.
Dicaeoma punctatum (Lk.) Arth.
Puccinia Galii S.
Puccinia Galiorum Auct. Amer. p. p.
Septoria psilostega Ell. & Martin.

Galium triflorum Michx.
Cercospora Galii Ell. & Holw.
Erysiphe Cichoracearum DC. †
Dialonectria Galii (Plowr. & Hark.) Cke.
Nectria Galii Plowr. & Hark.
Peronospora calotheca DBy.
Dicaeoma Galiorum Auct. Amer. p. p.
Dicaeoma troglodytes (Lindr.) H. S. Jackson.
Puccinia Galii Auct. p. p.
Puccinia Galiorum Auct. p. p.
Puccinia punctata Auct. p. p.
Puccinia troglodytes Lindr.
Pucciniastrum Galii (Wint.) Ed. Fisch.

Galium uncinulatum DC.
Dicaeoma punctatum (Lk.) Arth.
Puccinia Galii S.
Puccinia punctata Lk.

Galium sp. indet.
Camarosporium Galiorum (Cke. & Hark.) Sacc.
Hendersonia Galiorum Cke. & Hark.
Dacryomyces epiphyllus S.
Erysiphe Cichoracearum DC. †
Erysiphe communis Auct. Amer. p. p.
Septoria Galii Ell.
Septoria Galiorum Ell.

Didymaea mexicana Hook.
Orbilia coleosporioides Sacc.

Rubiaceae gen. indet.
Cavaraella micraspis (B. & C.) Speg.
Rhytisma micraspis B. & C.
Meliola glabra B. & C.
Pestalozzia truncata Lév., var. septoriana Fairman.

CAPRIFOLIACEAE

Sambucus callicarpa Greene.
Diaporthe Callicarpae Pk.
Hypochnus Sambuci (P.) Sacc. Syll.
Septoria sambucina Pk.

Sambucus canadensis L.

ASCOMYCETES

Anthostoma pulviniceps Pk.
Cryptospora pulviniceps (Pk.) Sacc.
Valsa pulviniceps Pk.
Diaporthe calosphaerioides Ell. & Ev.
Diaporthe megalospora Ell. & Ev.
Diaporthe Sambuci Ell. & Ev.
Diatrype sambucivora (S.) Cke.
Sphaeria sambucivora S.
Dothidea Sambuci (P.) ex Fr.
Sphaeria Sambuci P.
Herpotrichia rhenana Fckl.
Hypoderma commune (Fr.) Duby.
Hysterium commune Fr.
Lophiostoma insidiosum (Desm.) Ces. & De Not.
Microsphaera Alni (DC.) Wint. †
Microsphaera Hedwigii Lév.
Microsphaera vanbruntiana Gerard.
Microsphaera Grossulariae (Wallr.) Lév.
Creonectria purpurea (L.) Seaver.
Nectria cinnabarina (Tode) ex Fr.
Nectria Sambuci Ell. & Ev.
Phomatospora Berkeleyi Sacc.
Phyllactinia corylea (P.) ex Karst.
Physalospora Cydoniae Arnaud.
Sphaerulina sambucina Pk.
Valsa ambiens (P.) ex Fr.
Valsella minima Niessl.
Zignoella Ebuli Malbr. & Brun.

Sambucus canadensis (*cont.*)

UREDINALES

{ Aecidium Sambuci S.
  Caeoma sambuciatum S.
  Dicaeoma Sambuci (S.) Arth. I.
  Puccinia atkinsoniana Diet. I.
  Puccinia bolleyana Sacc. I.
  Puccinia Caricis Auct. p. p. I.
  Puccinia Sambuci Arth. I.

BASIDIOMYCETES

Corticium incarnatum (P.) ex Fr.
Corticium scutellare B. & C.
{ Corticium Sambuci P. ex Fr.
  Hypochnus Sambuci (P. ex Fr.) Sacc. Syll.
  Peniophora Sambuci (P. ex Fr.) Burt.
Polyporus brumalis (P.) ex Fr.

SPHAEROPSIDALES

Ascochyta Sambuci Sacc.
Ascochyta wisconsina J. J. Davis.
Camarosporium dichomeroides Brun.
Cytospora sambucina Ell. & Barthol. 1897.
Cytospora sambucina Tehon & Daniels. 1927.
{ Dinemasporium hispidulum (Schrad. ex P.) M. A. Curtis.
  Peziza hispidula Schrad. ex P.
Dinemasporium Pezizula B.
Diplodia cacaoicola Henn.
Diplodia Sambuci Tehon & Daniels.
{ Dothiorella macrospora (B. & C.) Sacc.
  Sphaeropsis macrospora B. & C.
{ Haplosporella Sambuci (Pk.) Petrak.
  Haplosporella sambucina Ell. & Barthol.
  Sphaeropsis Sambuci Pk.
{ Hendersonia microspora B. & C.
  Stagonospora microspora (B. & C.) Sacc.
Hendersonia pubentis Cke.
{ Diplodia paupercula B. & Br.
  Microdiplodia paupercula (B. & Br.) Dearness.
Phyllosticta Sambuci Desm.
Phyllosticta sambucicola Kalchbr.
Septoria sambucina Pk.
{ Macroplodia sambucina Cke.
  Phoma sambucina Sacc.
  Sphaeropsis sambucina (Cke.) Sacc.
Vermicularia herbarum (P.) ex Fr.
Vermicularia sambucina Ell. & Dearness.

MELANCONIALES

Melanconium truncatum S.

HYPHOMYCETES

Cercospora catenospora Atk.
Cercospora depazeoides (Desm.) Sacc.
Cercospora lateritia Ell. & Halsted.
Cercospora sambucina Ell. & Kellerm.
{ Helminthosporium interseminatum B. & Rav.
  Heterosporium interseminatum (B. & Rav.) Atk.
  Heterosporium Sambuci Earle.

Ramularia sambucina Pk.
Tubercularia nigricans (Bull.) ex Lk.
Tubercularia Sambuci Cda.

Sambucus glauca Nutt.

Armillaria putrida (Scop.) ex Murrill.
Brachysporium pedunculatum Ell. & Ev.
{ Cercospora prolificans Ell. & Holw.
  Cercosporella prolificans (Ell. & Holw.) Sacc.
Corticium serum (P.) Bres.
Cytospora chrysosperma (P.) ex Fr.
Eutypella stellulata (Fr.) Sacc.
Exidia Zelleri Lloyd.
Fomes igniarius (L. ex Fr.) Gill.
Hendersonia diplodioides Ell. & Ev.
Hydnum ohiense B.
Hymenochaete rubiginosa (Schrad. ex Fr.) Lév.
Hypomyces rosellus (A. & S. ex Fr.) Tul.
Lecanidion atratum (Hedw. ex Fr.) Rabh.
Lophiosphaeria querceti (Sacc. & Speg.) Sacc.
Melanomma medium Sacc. & Speg.
Naematelia nucleata (S.) Fr.
Nectria cinnabarina (Tode) ex Fr.
Ophiobolus byssicola Hark.
Orbilia chrysocoma (Bull. ex Fr.) Sacc.
Peroneutypa heteracantha (Sacc.) Berl.
Phoma Asteriscus B.
Phoma sambucina Cke.
Poria rhodella (Fr.) Cke.
Ramularia glauca Ell. & Ev.
Rosellinia aquila (Fr.) De Not.
Rosellinia rhynchospora Hark.
Sebacina calcea (P.) Bres.
Trichoderma lignorum (Tode) ex Harz.

Sambucus melanocarpa Gray.

Aposphaeria alpigena Ell. & Ev.
Creonectria purpurea (L.) Seaver.
Exosporium Sambuci Tracy & Earle.
{ Haplosporella alpina Ell. & Ev.
  Lasmeniella alpina (Ell. & Ev.) Petrak & Syd.
Leptosphaeria sambucina Ell. & Ev.
Sporodesmium subcupulatum Ell. & Ev.
Tapesia coloradensis Ell. & Ev.

Sambucus mexicana Presl.

Trichothecium roseum Lk.

Sambucus microbotrys Rydb.

Ramularia sambucina Pk.

Sambucus racemosa L.

ASCOMYCETES

Diaporthe calosphaerioides Ell. & Ev.
Dothidea Sambuci (P.) ex Fr.
Lophiostoma congregatum Hark.
{ Massaria distincta (S.) Cke.
  Sphaeria distincta S.
Microsphaera Grossulariae (Wallr.) Lév.?
Nectria cinnabarina (Tode) ex Fr.
Rosellinia ambigua Sacc.

Sambucus racemosa (*cont.*)

Rosellinia ligniaria (Grev.) Nits.
Tripospora elegans Cda.

BASIDIOMYCETES

Exidia recisa (Ditm.) ex Fr.
Irpex tabacinus B. & C.
Dicaeoma Sambuci Arth. I.
Puccinia bolleyana Sacc. I.
Puccinia Sambuci Arth. I.

FUNGI IMPERFECTI

Ascochyta wisconsina J. J. Davis.
Cercospora lateritia Ell. & Halsted.
Cercospora Symphoricarpi Ell. & Ev.
Coniothyrium olivaceum Bon.
Dinemasporium Pezizula B.
Excipula strigosa Fr.
Hendersonia pubens Cke.
Hendersonia pubentis Cke.
Hendersonia Sambuci Pk.
Hendersonulina pubentis (Cke.) Tassi.
Ramularia sambucina Sacc.
Septoria sambucina Pk.
Sporidesmium tuberculiforme Ell. & Ev.
Tubercularia Sambuci Cda.
Tubercularia vulgaris Tode ex Fr.

Sambucus sp. indet.

PEZIZINEAE

Cenangium acutum (Schum.) ex Fr.
Peziza fusca P.

HYPOCREALES

Hypocrea gelatinosa (Tode) ex Fr.
Sphaeria gelatinosa Tode ex Fr.
Nectria ochraceopallida B. & Br.
Thyronectria sambucina Ell. & Ev.

SPHAERIALES

Botryosphaeria Ribis (Tode ex Fr.) Grossen-
bacher & Duggar.
Botryosphaeria Ribis (Tode ex Fr.) Grossen-
bacher & Duggar, var. chromogena Shear
et al.
?Ceratosphaeria microdoma Ell. & Ev.
Chaetomium comatum (Tode) ex Fr.
Sphaeria comata Tode ex Fr.
Diatrype verruciformis (Ehrh.) ex Fr.
Diatrypella affinis Cke.
Diatrypella informis Ell. & Ev.
Diatrypella subglobata Cke. & Gerard.
Diatrypella tocciiana, var. subeffusa Ell. &
Ev.
Diatrypella verruciformis (Ehrh. ex Fr.) Nits.
Sphaeria verruciformis Ehrh. ex Fr.
Didymosphaeria epidermidis (Fr.) Fckl.
Sphaeria epidermidis Fr.
Enchnoa floccosa (Fr.) Karst.
Sphaeria floccosa Fr.
Eriosphaeria alligata (Fr.) Sacc.

Gibberella pulicaris (Fr.) Sacc.
Sphaeria pulicaris Fr.
Lophidium diminuens (P. ex Fr.) Ces. & De
Not.
Sphaeria diminuens P. ex Fr.
Melanomma Sambuci Earle.
Delacourea Sambuci (Plowr.) Cke.
Pleospora Sambuci (Plowr.) Sacc.
Sphaeria Sambuci Plowr.
Pseudovalsa sambucina (Pk.) Sacc.
Valsa sambucina Pk.
Psilosphaeria myriocarpa (Fr.) Hark.
Sphaeria myriocarpa Fr.
Rosellinia ligniaria (Grev.) Nits.
Rosellinia ligniaria (Grev.) Nits., var. micro-
spora Ell. & Ev.
Sphaeria clandestina Fr.
Sphaeria paetula Fr.

VALSACEAE

Diaporthe calosphaerioides Ell. & Ev.
Diaporthe spiculosa (A. & S.) ex Nits.
Sphaeria spiculosa A. & S. ex Nits.
Eutypella stellulata (Fr.) Sacc.
Valsa stellulata Fr.
Fenestella vestita (Fr.) Sacc.
Thyridium Sambuci Earle.
Sphaeria abnormis Fr.
Valsa abnormis Fr.

THELEPHORACEAE

Corticium sulfureum Fr., var. ochroideum
Hark. & Moore.
Cyphella alboviolascens (A. & S.) Karst.
Stereum purpureum P. †

SPHAEROPSIDALES

Coniothyrium Sambuci Earle.
Coniothyrium sambucinum (Cke.) Tassi.
Cystotricha stenospora B. & C.
Cytospora chrysosperma (P.) Fr.
Dendrophoma Sambuci (B. & C.) Sacc.
Sphaeronema Sambuci B. & C.
Diplodia sambucina Sacc.
Haplosporella seriata Ell. & Ev.
Hendersonia diplodioides Ell. & Ev.
Otthia amica Sacc.
Hendersonia diplodioides Ell. & Ev., var.
divergens Pk.
Hendersonia Sambuci Pk.
Phoma exigua Desm.
Phoma surculi (Fr.) Cke.
Sphaeria surculi Fr.
Rhabdospora maculans (B. & C.) Sacc.
Septoria maculans B. & C.
Sphaeropsis mutica B. & Br.
?Sphaeropsis pennsylvanica B. & C.
Hendersonia caespitosa B. & C.
Stagonospora caespitosa (B. & C.) Sacc.
Vermicularia Dematium (P.) ex Fr.

Sambucus sp. indet. (*cont.*)

MELANCONIALES

Coryneum sambucinum Ell. & Ev.
Gloeosporium Sambuci Dearness & House.
Gloeosporium tineum Sacc.

HYPHOMYCETES

Cercosporella prolificans (Ell. & Holw.) Sacc.
Clasterosporium strepsiceras (Ces.) Sacc.
Fusisporium bacilligerum B. & Br.
Graphium squarrosum Ell. & Langlois.
Macrosporium Cheiranthi Fr.
Ramularia glauca Ell. & Ev.
Tubercularia miniata Earle.

Viburnum acerifolium L.
Cercospora varia Pk.
Dothiorella peckiana Sacc.
⎰Microsphaera Alni (DC.) Wint. †
⎱Microsphaera penicillata Lév.
Microsphaera Viburni (S.) Howe.
⎰Plasmopara Viburni Pk.
⎱Rhysotheca Viburni (Pk.) G. W. Wilson.

Viburnum alnifolium Marsh.
⎰Cenangium Viburni (S.) Fr.
⎱Peziza Viburni S.
Dothiorella peckiana Sacc.
Microsphaera Alni (DC.) Wint. †
⎰Dermatea minuta Pk.
⎱Pezicula minuta Pk.
Phyllosticta lantanoides Pk.
Phyllosticta tinea Sacc.
Phyllosticta tinea N. A. F. *3257* non Sacc.
⎰Rhabdospora lantanoides (Pk.) Jacz.
⎨Sphaerographium lantanoides Pk.
⎩Sphaeronema lantanoides Auct.

Viburnum cassinoides L.
Cercospora varia Pk.
Micropeltis Viburni Dearness & House.
Microsphaera Alni (DC.) Wint. †
Phyllosticta lantanoides Pk.
Sphaerographium hystricinum (Ell.) Sacc.
Sphaerographium hystricinum (Ell.) Sacc., var.
  Viburni Dearness & House.
Tympanis fasciculata S.
Tympanis turbinata (S.) Sacc.

Viburnum dentatum L.

ASCOMYCETES

Diaporthe Ailanthi Sacc., var. Viburni Dearness & House.
Hypoxylon notatum B. & C.
⎰Massaria Corni Sacc. p. p.
⎨Massaria gigaspora (Desm.) Ces. & De Not.
⎩Massaria inquinans (Tode) ex Fr.
⎰Massaria Corni Pk. in herb.
⎨Massaria gigaspora Pk. 31 Rept.
⎩Massaria plumigera Ell. & Ev., var. tetraspora
  Dearness & House.

⎰Microsphaera Alni (DC.) Wint. †
⎨Microsphaera sparsa Howe.
⎩Microsphaera Viburni (S.) Howe.
⎰Nectria punicea Fr.
⎱Sphaeria punicea (Fr.) Schm.
Nummularia subconcava Ell. & Ev.
Sphaeria inclinata S.
Tympanis fasciculata S.
Valsa ambiens (P.) ex Fr.
Valsa mesoleuca B. & C.
Valsa salicina (P.) ex Fr.

FUNGI IMPERFECTI

Cercospora varia Pk.
⎰Cytoplea subconcava (S.) Starb.
⎱Sphaeria subconcava S.
Dinemasporium hispidulum (Schrad. ex P.) M. A. Curtis.
Diplodia microspora B. & C.
Haplosporella pennsylvanica (B. & C.) Petrak & Syd.
⎰Dothidea Viburni-dentati S.
⎨Haplosporella Viburni-dentati (S.) Ell. & Ev.
⎩Haplosporella Viburni (Ell. & Dearness) Petrak.
Sphaeropsis Viburni-dentati Dearness & House.
Hendersonia Viburni Ell.
⎰Macrophoma hyalina (B. & C.) Berl. & Vogl.
⎨Phoma hyalina (B. & C.) Sacc.
⎩Sphaeropsis hyalina B. & C.
Phyllosticta tineola Sacc.
Sphaerographium hystricinum (Ell.) Sacc.

MISCELLANEA

⎰Corticium cinereum P. ex Fr.
⎱Peniophora cinerea (P. ex Fr.) Cke.
⎰Plasmopara Viburni Pk.
⎱Rhysotheca Viburni (Pk.) G. W. Wilson.

Viburnum Lantana L.
Eutypella ludibunda Sacc.
Rhysotheca Viburni (Pk.) G. W. Wilson.

Viburnum Lentago L.
Cercospora varia Pk.
Coleosporium Viburni Arth.
⎰Cryptosphaeria secreta (C. & E.) Sacc.
⎱Sphaeria secreta C. & E.
⎰Cryptosporella Lentaginis (Ell. & Ev.) Rehm.
⎱Valsa Lentaginis Ell. & Ev.
⎰Dasyscypha Lentaginis (S.) Sacc.
⎱Peziza Lentaginis S.
Hendersonia Viburni Ell.
⎰Massaria gigaspora (Desm.) Ces. & De Not.
⎱Massaria inquinans (Tode) ex Fr.
⎰Massaria plumigera Ell. & Ev.
⎨Massarina plumigera (Ell. & Ev.) Sacc. & Trott.

Viburnum Lentago (*cont.*)
Massaria Corni Pk. in herb.
Massaria gigaspora Pk. an Fckl.
Massaria plumigera Ell. & Ev., var. tetraspora Dearness & House.
Microsphaera Alni (DC.) Wint. †
Microsphaera Hedwigii Lév.
Microsphaera penicillata Lév.
Microsphaera sparsa Howe.
Microsphaera Viburni (S.) Howe.
Pestalozzia veneta Sacc.
Phyllosticta Lentaginis Sacc. & Syd.
Phyllosticta Viburni Ell. & Dearness.
Phyllostictella Lentaginis (Sacc. & Syd.) Tassi.
Phyllosticta punctata Ell. & Dearness.
Ramularia Viburni Ell. & Ev.
Sphaeropsis Viburni Ell. & Dearness.
Tympanis fasciculata S.
Valsa ceratophora Tul.
Viburnum nudum L.
Plasmopara Viburni Pk.
Rhysotheca Viburni (Pk.) G. W. Wilson.
Sphaerographium hystricinum (Ell.) Sacc.
Sphaeronema hystricinum Ell.
Viburnum Opulus L.
Botryosphaeria Viburni Cke.
Cercospora Opuli (Fckl.) v. Höhnel.
Cercospora varia Pk.
Hypoderma variegatum (B. & C.) Duby.
Hysterium variegatum B. & C.
Macrophoma Viburni Dearness & House.
Diplodia microspora B. & C.
Microdiplodia microspora (B. & C.) Tassi.
Phoma mixta B. & C.
Phyllosticta punctata Ell. & Dearness.
Pistillaria elegans B. & C.
Plasmopara Viburni Pk.
Rhysotheca Viburni (Pk.) G. W. Wilson.
Rhabdospora interrupta (B. & C.) Sacc.
Septoria interrupta B. & C.
Stictis glaucoma B. & C.
Stictis pupula Fr.
Viburnum Opulus L., var. **americanum** (Mill.) Ait.
Plasmopara Viburni Pk.
Rhysotheca Viburni (Pk.) G. W. Wilson.
Viburnum pauciflorum Raf.
Micropuccinia Linkii (Klotzsch) Arth. & Jackson.
Puccinia Linkii Klotzsch.
Puccinia Pringlei Pk.
Viburnum plicatum Thunb.
Cercospora tinea Sacc.
Viburnum prunifolium L.
Diatrype friabilis (P. ex Fr.) M. A. Curtis.
Diatrypella friabilis (P. ex Fr.) Ell. & Ev.
Sphaeria friabilis P. ex Fr.
Eutypa Viburni Herb. B.
Sphaeria Viburni S.

Hendersonia foliorum Fckl., var. Viburnum Sacc.
Massaria Corni Sacc. p. p.
Massaria gigaspora (Desm.) Ces. & De Not.
Massaria inquinans (Tode) ex Fr.
Erysiphe Viburni S.
Microsphaera Alni (DC.) Wint. †
Pestalozzia Jefferisii Ell.
Polyporus conchatus (P.) ex Fr.
Radulum molare Fr.
Trametes sepium B.
Tympanis fasciculata S.
Tympanis turbinata S.
Sphaeria flabelliformis S.
Xylaria flabelliformis (S.) Tul.
Viburnum pubescens (Ait.) Pursh.
Cercospora varia Pk.
Coleosporium Viburni Arth.
Microsphaera Alni (DC.) Wint. †
Phyllosticta tineola Sacc.
Rhysotheca Viburni (Pk.) G. W. Wilson.
Viburnum stellato-tomentosum (Oerst.) Hemsl.
Phyllachora leptasca Syd.
Viburnum Tinus L.
Hendersonia Tini Ell. & Langlois.
Leptosphaeria Tini Ell. & Ev.
Viburnum sp. indet.

ASCOMYCETES
Cenangium Ellisii Sacc.
Dermatea purpurea Ell.
Dermatea viburnicola Ell.
Dothidea collecta (S.) Ell. & Ev.
Hypoxylon subchlorinum Ell. & Calkins.
Lophiostoma scelestum C. & E.
Patellaria atrata (Hedw.) ex Fr.
Dothidea frigoris S.
Phyllachora frigoris (S.) Sacc.
Dothidea subcuticularis S.
Phyllachora subcuticularis (S.) Sacc.
Physalospora Malorum Shear et al.
Sphaeria deformata S.
Sphaeria elliptica S.
Teichospora obducens (Fr.) Fckl.
?Uncinula macrospora Pk.

BASIDIOMYCETES
Corticium Stevensii Burt.
Hypochnus ochroleucus Noack.
Hydnum ochraceum P. ex Fr.
Steccherinum ochraceum (P. ex Fr.) S. F. Gray.
Hydnum conchiforme Sacc.
Hydnum plumarium B. & C.
Hymenochaete agglutinans Ell.

FUNGI IMPERFECTI
Helminthosporium Beaumontii Sacc.
Helminthosporium Berkeleyi Cke.
Helminthosporium dubium B. & C.
Helminthosporium macrocarpum Grev.
Hendersonia foliorum Fckl.

Triosteum angustifolium L.
Aecidium Triostei Arth.
Triosteum aurantiacum Bicknell.
Cladosporium Triostei Pk.
Cylindrosporium Triostei Kellerm. & Swingle.
Metasphaeria aulica (C. & E.) Sacc.
Triosteum perfoliatum L.
Aecidium Triostei Arth.
Cladosporium Triostei Pk.
Cylindrosporium Triostei Kellerm. & Swingle.
Phyllactinia corylea (P.) ex Karst.
Symphoricarpos albus (L.) Blake.
Aecidium abundans Pk.
Dicaeoma abundans (H. S. Jackson) Arth. & Fromme. I.
Puccinia abundans H. S. Jackson. I.
Puccinia Crandallii Pammel & Hume. I.
Anthostoma (?) gigasporum (Cke. & Hark.) Berl. & Vogl.
Sphaeria gigaspora Cke. & Hark.
Anthostomella perfidiosa (De Not.) Sacc.
Ascochyta symphoricarpophila Fairman.
Cercospora Symphoricarpi Ell. & Ev.
Diplodia Symphoricarpi Sacc.
Diplodia thorniana Gerard.
Haplosporella Symphoricarpi Pk.
Helminthosporium leptosporium Sacc.
Microsphaera Alni Fung. Columb. *3149*.
Microsphaera diffusa C. & P.
Microsphaera Symphoricarpi Howe.
Phyllosticta Symphoricarpi Westd.
Podosphaera Oxyacanthae DC. †
Micropuccinia Symphoricarpi (Hark.) Arth. & Jackson.
Puccinia Symphoricarpi Hark.
Septogloeum symphoricarpophilum Fairman.
Septoria Symphoricarpi Ell. & Ev.
Thyridium cingulatum (Mont.) Sacc.
Symphoricarpos mollis Nutt.
Puccinia abundans H. S. Jackson. I.
Gloniopsis Mülleri (Duby) Sacc.
Microsphaera Symphoricarpi Howe.
Micropuccinia Symphoricarpi (Hark.) Arth. & & Jackson.
Puccinia Symphoricarpi Hark.
Symphoricarpos occidentalis Hook.
Aecidium abundans Pk.
Dicaeoma abundans (H. S. Jackson) Arth. & Fromme. I.
Puccinia abundans H. S. Jackson. I.
Puccinia Crandallii Pammel & Hume. I.
Anthostoma melanotes (B. & Br.) Sacc. var. Symphoricarpi Brenkle.
Bactrospora dryina (Ach.) Massee.
Blytridium Symphoricarpi Ell. & Ev.
Cercospora Symphoricarpi Ell. & Ev.
Corticium byssinum (Karst.) Burt.
Corticium incarnatum Fr.
Corticium laetum Karst.

Creonectria Coryli (Fckl.) Seaver.
Curreyella Symphoricarpi (Rehm) Petrak.
Diaporthe Ryckholstii (Westd.) Nits.
Diaporthe stereostoma Ell. & Ev.
Diatrype Stigma (Hoffm.) De Not.
Dibotryon Symphoricarpi (Rehm) Petrak.
Dothidotthia Symphoricarpi (Rehm) v. Höhnel.
Otthia Symphoricarpi Fung. Dak. *98*.
Pseudotthia Symphoricarpi (Ell. & Ev. p. p.[2]) Rehm, Syd. Fung. Exot. *391*.
Didymosphaeria albescens Niessl.
Didymosphaeria decolorans Rehm.
Dinemasporium hispidulum (Schrad. ex Fr.) M. A. Curtis).
Dothichiza Symphoricarpi Petrak.
Enteridium splendens Morg. ex P.
Eutypa lata (P. ex Fr.) Tul.
Exidia glandulosa Bull. ex Fr.
Fomes Ribis (Schum. ex Fr.) Cke.
Pyropolyporus Ribis (Schum. ex Fr.) Murrill.
Irpex lacteus Fr.
Lophiostoma caulium (Fr.) De Not.
Lophiostoma praemorsum (Lasch) Fckl.
Lophiostoma triseptatum Pk.
Marasmius rotula Fr.
Microsphaera diffusa C. & P.
Microsphaera Symphoricarpi Howe.
Mollisia caesia (Fckl.) Sacc.
Otthia Symphoricarpi Ell. & Ev.
Plowrightia Symphoricarpi Ell. & Ev.
Patellaria atrata (Hedw.) ex Fr.
Peniophora cinerea (P. ex Fr.) Cke.
Pezizella dakotensis Rehm.
Diatrype americana Rehm.
Phaeotrype Brencklei Sacc.
Phyllosticta Symphoricarpi Westd.
Pleurotus cyphelliformis B.
Polystictus hirsutus (Wulf.) ex Fr.
Otthia Symphoricarpi Ell. & Ev. N. Am. Pyr. p. p.[1]
Plowrightia Symphoricarpi Ell. & Ev. type.
Pseudotthia Symphoricarpi (Ell. & Ev. p. p.[1]) Rehm.
Valsaria Symphoricarpi (Ell. & Ev.) Theissen & Syd.
Rosellinia parasitica Ell. & Ev.
Rosellinia pulveracea (Ehrh. ex Fr.) Fckl.
Schizoxylon compositum Ell. & Ev.
Schizoxylon decipiens, var. Symphoricarpi Rehm.
Septoria Symphoricarpi Ell. & Ev.
Stictis fusca Ell. & Barthol.
Teichospora umbonata Ell. & Ev.
Thyronectria Xanthoxyli (Pk.) Ell. & Ev.
Torula brachiata Ell. & Barthol.
Valsa Symphoricarpi Rehm.
Volutella nectrioides Sacc.
Zignoella Morthieri (Fckl.) Sacc.

Symphoricarpos orbiculatus Moench.
  Aecidium abundans Pk.
  Dicaeoma abundans (H. S. Jackson) Arth. &
    Fromme. I.
  Blytridium Symphoricarpi Ell. & Ev.
  Cercospora Symphoricarpi Ell. & Ev.
  Corticium incarnatum (P.) ex Fr., var. consueta Bres.
  Cryptospora kansensis Ell. & Ev.
  Cryptovalsa pustulata Ell. & Ev.
  Microsphaera Alni (DC.) Wint. †
  Microsphaera diffusa C. & P.
  Microsphaera Symphoricarpi Howe.
  Stictis fusca Ell. & Barthol.

Symphoricarpos oreophilus Gray.
  Aecidium abundans Pk.
  Dicaeoma abundans (H. S. Jackson) Arth. &
    Fromme. I.
  Puccinia abundans H. S. Jackson. I.
  Didymella nigrescens Dearness & Fairman.
  Lophidiopsis nuculoides (Rehm) Berl.
  Lophidium incisum Ell. & Ev.
  Patellea oreophila Fairman.
  Phyllosticta Symphoricarpi Westd.

Symphoricarpos racemosus Michx., var. **pauciflorus** Robbins.
  Lasiobotrys Lonicerae Kze., var. subcircinata
    Ell. & Ev.

Symphoricarpos rotundifolius Gray.
  Aecidium abundans Pk.
  Dicaeoma abundans (H. S. Jackson) Arth. &
    Fromme. I.
  Microsphaera Symphoricarpi Howe.

Symphoricarpos vaccinioides Rydb.
  Aecidium abundans Pk.
  Dicaeoma abundans (H. S. Jackson) Arth. &
    Fromme. I.
  Puccinia abundans H. S. Jackson. I.
  Puccinia Crandallii Pammel & Hume. I.

Symphoricarpos sp. indet.
  Diaporthe Ryckholtii (Westd.) Nits.
  Didymaria Symphoricarpi Ell. & Ev.
  Gibberidea Symphoricarpi Tracy & Earle.
  Karschia impressa Ell. & Ev.
  Lachnella Symphoricarpi Ell. & Ev.
  Lasiobotrys Lonicerae Kze.
  Lasiobotrys Lonicerae Kze., var. Symphoricarpi Ell. & Ev.
  Lophiostoma macrostomoides De Not.
  Microthyrium microscopicum Desm.
  Nectria Coryli Fckl.
  Physarum melanospermum Sturgis.
  Lasiobotrys Symphoricarpi Syd.
  Rhizogene Symphoricarpi Syd.
  Septoria oedospora Clements.
  Solenopezia Symphoricarpi Ell. & Ev.
  Teichospora strigosa Ell. & Ev.

  Strickeria Symphoricarpi Tracy & Earle.
  Teichospora Symphoricarpi (Tracy & Earle)
    Sacc. & D. Sacc.
  Trichosphaeria Barbula (B. & Br.) Wint.

Linnaea borealis L., var. **americana** (Forbes) Rehder.
  Coleroa Dickiei (B. & Br.) Sacc.
  Venturia Dickiei (B. & Br.) Ces. & De Not.
  Dothidea Wittrockii Erikss.
  Phyllachora Wittrockii (Erikss.) Sacc.
  Septoria breviuscula Sacc.
  Sphaerella minor Karst.

Linnaea longiflora Howell.
  Phyllachora Wittrockii (Erikss.) Sacc.

Lonicera arborea Boiss.
  Lasiobotrys hispanica Theissen & Syd.

Lonicera caerulea L.
  Dicaeoma Periclymeni Arth. & Fromme. I.

Lonicera californica Torr. & Gray.
  Lasiobotrys affinis Hark.

Lonicera canadensis Marsh.
  Glomerularia Corni Pk.
  Glomerularia Lonicerae (Pk.) Dearness &
    House.
  Leptothyrium Periclymeni (Desm.) Sacc.
  Microsphaera Alni (DC.) Wint. †
  Phyllosticta Lonicerae Desm.
  Septoria sambucina Pk.
  Septoria xylostei Sacc. & Wint.

Lonicera Caprifolium L.
  Diplodia Lonicerae Fckl.
  Hormococcus nitidulus Sacc.
  Microsphaera Alni (DC.) Wint. †

Lonicera catalinensis Millsp.
  Hypoxylon Botrys Nits.

Lonicera ciliosa Poir.
  Microsphaera Alni (DC.) Wint. †

Lonicera conjugalis Kellogg.
  Gloeosporium Lonicerae Hark.
  Marssonia Lonicerae Hark.
  Marssonina Lonicerae (Hark.) Magn.

Lonicera dioica L.
  Microsphaera Alni (DC.) Wint. †
  Microsphaera Dubyi Auct. Amer.
  Microsphaera Lonicerae Auct. Amer.
  Microsphaera pulchra C. & E.

Lonicera flava Sims.
  Dicaeoma Periclymeni Arth. & Fromme. I.
  Puccinia Festucae Plowr. I.
  Cercospora antipus Ell. & Holw.
  Hendersonia Mariae G. W. Clinton.
  Hendersonia Peckii G. W. Clinton.
  Microsphaera Alni (DC.) Wint. †
  Microsphaera pulchra C. & P.
  Phoma Mariae G. W. Clinton.
  Sphaeropsis puncta C. & E.
  Sphaeropsis Wilsoni G. W. Clinton.

Lonicera glaucescens Rydb.
Cercospora antipus Ell. & Holw.
Microsphaera Alni (DC.) Wint.†
Lonicera hirsuta Eat.
Cercospora antipus Ell. & Holw.
Macroplodia Wilsonii (Pk.) O. Kuntze.
⎰Microsphaera Alni (DC.) Wint.†
⎱Microsphaera Dubyi Auct. Amer.
Septoria sambucina Pk.
Sphaeronema Lonicerae Pk.
Lonicera hispidula Dougl.
Guignardia Lonicerae Dearness & Barthol.
⎧Lasiobotrys affinis Hark.
⎨Lasiobotrys Lonicerae (Fr.) Kze.
⎪Peltosphaeria vitrispora (Cke. & Hark.) Berl.
⎩Pleospora vitrispora Cke. & Hark.
Phoma Xylostei Cke. & Hark.
Stictis annulata Cke. & Phil.
Lonicera involucrata (Richards.) Banks.
Anthostomella hypsophila Ell. & Ev.
Botrytis vulgaris (Lk.) ex Fr.
Diaporthe cryptica Nits.
Erysibe communis (Wallr.) Lk.
Eutypa lata (P. ex Fr.) Tul.
Fomes Ribis (Schum. ex Fr.) Cke.
⎧Gloniopsis Lonicerae (Phil. & Hark.) Berl. &
⎪ Vogl.
⎨Hysterium Lonicerae Phil. & Hark.
⎪Hysterographium Lonicerae (Phil. & Hark.)
⎩ Ell. & Ev.
Libertella Lonicerae Cke. & Hark.
Marssonia Lonicerae Hark.
⎧Endophloea anisometra (Cke. & Hark.) Cke.
⎨Metasphaeria anisometra (Cke. & Hark.) Sacc.
⎩Sphaeria anisometra Cke. & Hark.
Microsphaera Alni (DC.) Wint.†
Otthia Distegiae Tracy & Earle.
Stemphylium subradians Ell. & Ev.
Zignoella lonicerina Ell. & Ev.
Lonicera japonica Thunb.
Cryptovalsa prominens (Howe) Berl.
Diaporthe cryptica Nits.
Diatrypella ramularis Ell. & Ev.
Gloniopsis Lonicerae (Phil. & Hark.) Berl. &
 Vogl.
⎰Phoma cryptica (Nits.) Sacc.
⎱Phomopsis cryptica (Nits.) v. Höhnel.
Phoma Mariae G. W. Clinton.
⎰Cryptosporium Lonicerae C. & E.
⎱Rhabdospora Lonicerae (C. & E.) Sacc.
Sphaeropsis punctatum C. & E.
Lonicera oblongifolia (Goldie) Hook.
Anthostomella limitata Sacc.
⎧Glomerularia Corni Pk.
⎨Glomerularia Lonicerae (Pk.) Dearness &
⎩ House.
Leptothyrium Periclymeni (Desm.) Sacc.
Marssonia Lonicerae Hark.
Microsphaera Alni (DC.) Wint.†

Lonicera parviflora Lam.
Microsphaera Alni (DC.) Wint.†
Lonicera pilosa H. B. K.
⎧Micropuccinia Apocyni (Diet. & Holw.) Arth.
⎨ & Jackson.
⎩Puccinia Apocyni Diet. & Holw.
Lonicera sempervirens L.
⎧Conisphaeria Friesii (Nits.) Cke.
⎨Melomastia Friesii Nits.
⎩Sphaeria Lonicerae Sow.
⎧Cryptospora umbilicata (P. ex Fr.) Ell. & Ev.
⎨Sphaeria umbilicata P. ex Fr.
⎩Valsa umbilicata (P.) ex Fr.
⎧Dothidea collecta (S.) Ell. & Ev.
⎨Dothidea Lonicerae Cke.
⎩Dothidea tetraspora B. & Br.
⎰Microsphaera Alni (DC.) Wint.†
⎱Microsphaera penicillata Lév.
Lonicera Sullivantii Gray.
Aecidium Periclymeni Schum.
Cercospora antipus Ell. & Holw.
Microsphaera Alni (DC.) Wint.†
Sarcinula heterospora Sacc.
Lonicera tatarica L.
⎧Lophiostoma pseudomacrostomum Sacc.
⎪Lophiostoma sexnucleatum N. A. F. *1659*.
⎪Lophiostoma vagans H. Fabre.
⎨Microsphaera Alni (DC.) Wint.†
⎪Microsphaera diffusa Auct. Amer. p. p.
⎩Microsphaera Dubyi Auct. Amer.
Phoma Mariae G. W. Clinton.
Phyllosticta Hydrangeae Ell. & Ev.
Lonicera Xylosteum L.
Leptothyrium Periclymeni (Desm.) Sacc.
Lonicera sp. indet.

Ascomycetes

Creonectria Coryli (Fckl.) Seaver.
⎰Cryptovalsa pustulata Ell. & Ev.
⎱Diatrypella pustulata Ell. & Ev.
Dothidea ribesia (P.) ex Fr.
Hypocrea subcarnea Ell. & Ev.
Leptosphaeria dumetorum Niessl.
Lichenopsis sphaeroboloidea S.
Lophiostoma caulinum (Fr.) De Not.
⎧Endophlaea aulica (C. & E.) Cke.
⎨Leptosphaeria aulica (C. & E.) Ell.
⎪Metasphaeria aulica (C. & E.) Sacc.
⎩Sphaeria aulica C. & E.
Microsphaera Alni, var. Lonicerae (DC.) Sal-
 mon.
Mycosphaerella Clymenia (Sacc.) Fairman.
⎰Physalospora erratica (C. & E.) Sacc.
⎱Sphaeria erratica C. & E.
⎰Peziza atrata P.
⎱Pyrenopeziza atrata (P.) Fckl.
Sphaeria saepincola Fr.
Teichosporella lonicerina Fairman.

Lonicera sp. indet. (*cont.*)

FUNGI IMPERFECTI

Cercospora varia Pk.
{ Diplodia paupercula (B. & C.) B. & Br.
{ Diplodia quisquiliarum B. & C.
Leptothyrium Periclymeni (Desm.) Sacc., var. americanum Ell. & Ev.
{ Pestalozzia concentrica B. & Rav.
{ Pestalozzia rostrata Zabriskie.
Phoma Lonicerae Cke.
Phyllosticta vulgaris Desm.
{ Rhabdospora decipiens (B. & C.) Sacc.
{ Septoria decipiens B. & C.

Diervilla florida Sieb. & Zucc.
Diplodia Weigeliae Sacc.
{ Mycosphaerella Weigeliae (Sacc. & Trott.) Fairman.
{ Sphaerella Weigeliae Sacc. & Trott.

Diervilla Lonicera Mill.
Cercospora Diervillae Ell. & Ev.
{ Dothidea rimicola (S.) Pk.
{ Hysterium rimicola S.
{ Godronia turbinata (S.) Farl.
{ Tympanis turbinata (S.) Sacc.
Microdiplodia Diervillae Fairman.
Phyllosticta Diervillae J. J. Davis.
Radulum investiens S.
{ Ramularia Diervillae Pk.
{ Ramularia umbrina J. J. Davis.
Sclerotium deciduum J. J. Davis.
{ Septoria Diervillae Ell. & Ev. Mar. 1885.
{ Septoria Diervillae Pk. Oct. 1885.
{ Septoria diervillicola Ell. & Ev.
Sphaeropsis Diervillae Fairman.

Diervilla sp. indet.
Cercospora Weigeliae Ell. & Ev.
Microsphaera Alni (DC.) Wint., var. Lonicerae (DC.) Salmon.
Pestalozzia Syringae Oud.

Adoxa moschatellina L.
Aecidium albescens Grev.
{ Dicaeoma nolitangeris (Cda.) Arth. I.
{ Puccinia argentata Wint. I.
Phyllosticta Adoxae Clements.
{ Micropuccinia Adoxae (Hedw. f.) Arth. & Jackson.
{ Puccinia Adoxae Hedw. f.
Synchytrium anomalum Schrt.

VALERIANACEAE

Valerianella congesta Lindl.
Aecidium Valerianellae Biv.

Valerianella radiata (L.) Dufr.
Septoria Valerianellae L. E. Miles.

Valeriana capitata Pall.
{ Excipula conglutinata Ell. & Ev.
{ Excipulina conglutinata (Ell. & Ev.) Sacc.
Puccinia Valerianae Carest.

Valeriana edulis Nutt.
Aecidium Valerianearum Duby.
Coniothyrium infuscans Ell. & Ev.
Erysiphe Cichoracearum DC. †

Valeriana occidentalis Heller.
Aecidium valerianum Duby.
Puccinia commutata Syd.

Valeriana officinalis L.
Ramularia Valerianae Speg.

Valeriana sitchensis Bong.
Agyrium elongatum Ell. & Ev.
{ Allodus commutata (Syd.) Arth.
{ Puccinia commutata Syd.

Valeriana subincisa Benth.
Uredo reicheana Arth.
Uromyces Valerianae Fckl.

Valeriana sylvatica Banks.
Sphaerella vagans Ell. & Ev.

Valeriana uliginosa (Torr. & Gr.) Rydb.
Pleospora herbarum (Fr.) Rabh.
{ Allodus commutata (Syd.) Arth.
{ Puccinia commutata Syd.

DIPSACACEAE

Dipsacus sylvestris Mill.
Cercospora elongata Pk.
Peronospora Dipsaci Tul.
Phoma oleracea Sacc., var. Dipsaci Sacc.
{ Mycosphaerella asterinoides (Ell. & Ev.) Fairman.
{ Sphaerella asterinoides Ell. & Ev.

Scabiosa japonica Miq.
Sclerotinia sclerotiorum (Lib.) Massee.

CUCURBITACEAE

Fevillea cordifolia L.
{ Nigredo helleriana Arth.
{ Uromyces hellerianus Arth.

Melothria maderaspatana Cogn.
{ Plasmopara cubensis (B. & C.) J. E. Humphrey.
{ Pseudoperonospora cubensis (B. & C.) Rostowzew.

Melothria pendula L.
Puccinia Melothriae F. L. Stevens.

Melothria pervaga Griseb.
{ Nigredo helleriana Arth.
{ Uromyces hellerianus Arth.

Melothria scabra Naud.
Erysiphe Cichoracearum DC. †
{ Plasmopara cubensis (B. & C.) J. E. Humphrey.
{ Pseudoperonospora cubensis (B. & C.) Rostowzew.
{ Nigredo helleriana Arth.
{ Uromyces hellerianus Arth.

Anguria sp. indet.
  Uromyces poliotelis Syd.
Gurania levyana Cogn.
  Cercospora praelonga Syd.
Gurania sp. indet.
  ?Uromyces poliotelis Syd.
Momordica Balsamina L.
  Colletotrichum lagenarium (Pass.) Ell. & Halsted.
  {Peronoplasmopara cubensis (B. & C.) G. P. Clinton.
  Plasmopara cubensis (B. & C.) J. E. Humphrey.
  Ramularia Momordicae Heald & Wolf.
Momordica Charantia L.
  Colletotrichum lagenarium (Pass.) Ell. & Halsted.
  Pseudoperonospora cubensis (B. & C.) Rostowzew.
Luffa acutangula Roxb.
  Cercospora Cucurbitae Ell. & Ev.
  Macrophoma subconica Ell. & Ev.
  {Plasmopara cubensis (B. & C.) J. E. Humphrey.
  Pseudoperonospora cubensis (B. & C.) Rostowzew.
  Thielavia basicola (B. & Br.) Zopf.
Luffa aegyptiaca Mill.
  {Corticium koleroga (Cke.) v. Höhnel.
  Pellicularia koleroga Cke.
Luffa cylindrica Roem.
  Peronoplasmopara cubensis (B. & C.) G. P. Clinton.
Ecballium Elaterium A. Rich.
  Erysiphe Cichoracearum DC. †
Citrullus vulgaris Schrad.

PHYCOMYCETES

{Peronoplasmopara cubensis (B. & C.) G. P. Clinton.
Peronospora cubensis B. & C.
{Plasmopara cubensis (B. & C.) J. E. Humphrey.
Pseudoperonospora cubensis (B. & C.) Rostowzew.
Pythium aphanidermatum (Edson) Fitzpatrick.
Pythium artotrogus (Mont.) DBy.
Pythium debaryanum Hesse.
Rhizopus nigricans Ehrenb. ex Fr.

ASCOMYCETES

Erysiphe Cichoracearum DC. †
Neocosmospora vasinfecta Erw. Sm.
Neocosmospora vasinfecta Erw. Sm., var. nivea Erw. Sm.
Sclerotinia sclerotiorum (Lib.) Massee.
{Mycosphaerella citrullina (C. O. Sm.) Grossenbacher.
Sphaerella citrullina C. O. Sm.
Thielavia basicola (B. & Br.) Zopf.

BASIDIOMYCETES

{Corticium vagum B. & C.
Corticium vagum B. & C., var. Solani Burt.
Rhizoctonia Solani Kühn.

SPHAEROPSIDALES

{Ascochyta citrullina C. O. Sm.
Diplodina citrullina (C. O. Sm.) Grossenbacher.
Diplodia tubericola (Ell. & Ev.) Taubenhaus.
{Macrophoma Citrulli (B. & C.) Berl. & Vogl.
Phoma Citrulli B. & C.
{Macrophoma seminalis (B. & C.) Berl. & Vogl.
Phoma seminalis (B. & C.) Sacc.
Sphaeropsis seminalis B. & C.
Phoma cucurbitalis B. & C.
Phyllosticta citrullina Chester.
Phyllosticta Cucurbitacearum Sacc.
Septoria Citrulli Ell. & Ev.
Septoria Cucurbitacearum Sacc.

MELANCONIALES

{Colletotrichum lagenarium (Pass.) Ell. & Halsted.
Gloeosporium lagenarium (Pass.) Sacc. & Roum.
Gloeosporium lindemuthianum Auct. p. p.
Gloeosporium lagenarium (Pass.) Sacc. & Roum., var. foliicola Ell. & Ev.
Pestalozzia torulosa B. & C.

HYPHOMYCETES

Alternaria Brassicae (B.) Sacc., var. nigrescens Pegl.
Alternaria Citri Pierce, var. Cerasi C. A. Rudolph.
Cephalothecium roseum Cda.
Cercospora citrullina Cke.
Cercospora Cucurbitae Ell. & Ev.
Cercospora melonis Cke.
Cladosporium atrum Lk.
{Fusarium niveum Erw. Sm.
Fusarium vasinfectum Atk., var. niveum (Erw. Sm.) Stevens & Hall.
Fusarium sclerotium Wr.
Fusarium vasinfectum Atk.
Macrosporium commune Rabh.
Macrosporium cucumerinum Ell. & Ev.
Macrosporium Sarcinula B.
Macrosporium Sarcinula B. var. parasiticum (B.) Thm.
Myrothecium Verrucaria (A. & S. ex Fr.) Dittm.
Volutella Citrulli Stoneman.

MISCELLANEA

Sclerotium bataticola Taubenhaus.
Sclerotium Rolfsii Sacc.
Cucumis Anguria L.
  Colletotrichum lagenarium (Pass.) Ell. & Halsted.

Cucumis Anguria (*cont.*)
- Corticium koleroga (Cke.) v. Höhnel.
- Pellicularia koleroga Cke.
- Erysiphe Cichoracearum DC.†
- Peronoplasmopara cubensis (B. & C.) G. P. Clinton.
- Peronospora cubensis B. & C.
- Plasmopara cubensis (B. & C.) J. E. Humphrey.
- Pseudoperonospora cubensis (B. & C.) Rostowzew.

Cucumis colocynthis L.
- Colletotrichum lagenarium (Pass.) Ell. & Halsted.

Cucumis dipsaceus Ehrh.
- Erysiphe Cichoracearum DC.†
- Plasmopara cubensis (B. & C.) J. E. Humphrey.

Cucumis Melo L.

PHYCOMYCETES

- Mucor curtus B. & C.
- Peronoplasmopara cubensis (B. & C.) G. P. Clinton.
- Peronospora cubensis B. & C.
- Plasmopara cubensis (B. & C.) J. E. Humphrey.
- Pseudoperonospora cubensis (B. & C.) Rostowzew.

ASCOMYCETES

- Erysiphe Cichoracearum DC.†
- Erysiphe Polygoni DC. †
- Neocosmospora vasinfecta Erw. Sm.
- Sclerotinia libertiana Fckl.
- Mycosphaerella citrullina (C. O. Sm.) Grossenbacher.
- Sphaerella citrullina C. O. Sm.
- Thielavia basicola (B. & Br.) Zopf.

SPHAEROPSIDALES

- Diplodina citrullina (C. O. Sm.) Grossenbacher.
- Macrophoma Citrulli (B. & C.) Berl. & Vogl.
- Phyllosticta citrullina Chester.
- Phyllosticta Cucurbitacearum Sacc.
- Septoria Cucurbitacearum Sacc.

MELANCONIALES

- Colletotrichum lagenarium (Pass.) Ell. & Halsted.
- Gloeosporium lagenarium (Pass.) Sacc. & Roum.
- Colletotrichum lindemuthianum (Sacc. & Magn.) Briosi & Cavara.
- Colletotrichum oligochaetum Cav.

HYPHOMYCETES

- Alternaria Brassicae (B.?) Sacc.
- Alternaria Brassicae, var. nigrescens Pegl.
- Macrosporium cucumerinum Ell. & Ev.
- Cercospora citrullina Cke.

Cercospora Cucurbitae Ell. & Ev.
- Cladosporium cucumerinum Ell. & Arth.
- Scolecotrichum melophthorum Prill. & Delacr.
- Fumago vagans Fr.
- Fusarium vasinfectum Atk.
- Fusarium niveum Erw. Sm.
- Fusarium vasinfectum Atk., var. niveum (Erw. Sm.) Stevens & Hall.
- Macrosporium Solani Ell. & Martin.
- Oospora Cucumeris Pk.

MISCELLANEA

Rhizoctonia Solani Kühn.
Sclerotium Rolfsii Sacc.

Cucumis Melo L., var. **Dudaim** Naud.
- Plasmopara cubensis (B. & C.) J. E. Humphrey.
- Pseudoperonospora cubensis (B. & C.) Rostowzew.

Cucumis Melo L., var. **flexuosus** Naud.
- Thielavia basicola (B. & Br.) Zopf.

Cucumis sativus L.

PHYCOMYCETES

- Aphanomyces euteiches Drechsler.
- Choanephora Cucurbitarum (B. & Rav.) Thax.
- Peronoplasmopara cubensis (B. & C.) G. P. Clinton.
- Peronospora cubensis B. & C.
- Plasmopara cubensis (B. & C.) J. E. Humphrey.
- Pseudoperonospora cubensis (B. & C.) Rostowzew.
- Pythium aphanidermatum (Edson) Fitzpatrick.
- Pythium debaryanum Hesse.
- Rhizopus nigricans Ehrenb. ex Fr.

PYRENOMYCETINEAE

- Erysiphe Cichoracearum DC. †
- Oidium erysiphoides Fr., var. Cucurbitacearum J. E. Humphrey.
- Erysiphe Polygoni DC.†
- Mycosphaerella citrullina (C. O. Sm.) Grossenbacher.
- Neocosmospora vasinfecta (Atk.) Erw. Sm.
- Sclerotinia perplexa Lawrence.
- Sclerotinia libertiana Fckl.
- Sclerotinia sclerotiorum (Lib.) Schrt.
- Thielavia basicola (B. & Br.) Zopf.

SPHAEROPSIDALES

- Ascochyta Cucumis Fautr. & Roum.
- Ascochyta Cucumis-sativa Fautr.
- Phyllosticta Cucurbitacearum Sacc.

MELANCONIALES

- Colletotrichum lagenarium (Pass.) Ell. & Halsted.
- Gloeosporium lagenarium (Pass.) Sacc. & Roum.

Cucumis sativus (*cont.*)
Gloeosporium lagenarium (Pass.) Sacc. & Roum,. var. foliicola Ell. & Ev.

HYPHOMYCETES
Acrostalagmus albus Preuss.
Alternaria Brassicae (B.) Sacc., var. nigrescens Pegl.
Alternaria Cucurbitae Letendre & Roum.
Cercospora Armoraciae Sacc.
Cercospora Cucurbitae Ell. & Ev.
Cercospora Melonis Cke.
Cladosporium cucumerinum Ell. & Arth.
Epicoccum neglectum Desm.
Fusarium argillaceum (Fr.) Sacc.
Fusarium niveum Erw. Sm.
Fusarium orthoceras App. & Wr.
Fusarium radicicola Wr.
Fusarium reticulatum Mont.
Fusarium vasinfectum Atk.
Macrosporium commune Rabh.
Macrosporium cucumerinum Ell. & Ev.
Ramularia Armoraciae Fckl.
Stemphylium Cucurbitacearum Osner.

MISCELLANEA
Corticium vagum B. & C.
Physarum cinereum (Batsch) P.
Rhizoctonia Solani Kühn.
Sclerotium bataticola Taubenhaus.
Sclerotium Rolfsii Sacc.

Bryonopsis laciniosa Naud., var. **erythrocarpa** Naud.
Plasmopara cubensis (B. & C.) J. E. Humphrey.
Pseudoperonospora cubensis (B. & C.) Rostowzew.

Benincasa cerifera Savi.
Colletotrichum lagenarium (Pass.) Ell. & Halsted.

Lagenaria leucantha Rusby.
Cercospora Cucurbitae Ell. & Ev.
Colletotrichum lagenarium (Pass.) Ell. & Halsted.
Gloeosporium lagenarium (Pass.) Sacc. & Roum.
Diatrypella verruciformis (Ehrh. ex Fr.) Nits., var. spegazziniana Sacc.
Erysiphe Cichoracearum DC.†
Fusarium aurantiacum Cda.
Fusarium Lagenariae (S.) Sacc.
Fusisporium Lagenariae S.
Gloeosporium lagenarium (S.) Sacc. & Roum.
Laestadia Cucurbitacearum (Cke.) Sacc.
Sphaerella Cucurbitacearum Cke.
Sphaeria Cucurbitacearum Fr. p. p.
Macrosporium Lagenariae Thm.
Mucor Cucurbitarum B. & C.

Dialonectria Peponum (B. & C.) Cke.
Nectria Peponum B. & C.
Nectria perpusilla B. & C.
Nectriella Peponum (B. & C.) Seaver.
Phoma Cucurbitacearum M. A. Curtis.
Sphaeria Cucurbitacearum Fr. p. p.
Peronoplasmopara cubensis (B. & C.) G. P. Clinton.
Plasmopara cubensis (B. & C.) J. E. Humphrey.
Pseudoperonospora cubensis (B. & C.) Rostowzew.
Septoria vestita B. & C.
Torula Cucurbitarum S.
Vermicularia Cucurbitae Cke.
Verticillium stigmatellum B. & C.

Trichosanthes Anguina L.
Peronospora cubensis B. & C.

Trichosanthes colubrina Jacq.
Colletotrichum lagenarium (Pass.) Ell. & Halsted.
Plasmopara cubensis (B. & C.) J. E. Humphrey.
Pseudoperonospora cubensis (B. & C.) Rostowsew.

Cucurbita foetidissima H. B. K.
Cercospora Cucurbitae Ell. & Ev.
Erysiphe Cichoracearum DC.†
Macrosporium Sarcinula B.

Cucurbita maxima Duchesne.
Cercospora Cucurbitae Ell. & Ev.
Choanephora Curcubitarum (B. & Rav.) Thax.
Cladosporium cucumerinum Ell. & Arth.
Colletotrichum lagenarium Ell. & Halsted.
Corticium vagum B. & C.
Erysiphe Cichoracearum DC.†
Fusarium niveum Erw. Sm.
Macrosporium cucumerinum Ell. & Ev.
Monilia fumosa Sacc.?
Plasmopara cubensis (B. & C.) J. E. Humphrey.
Pseudoperonospora cubensis (B. & C.) Rostowzew.
Ozonium omnivorum Shear.
Septoria Cucurbitacearum Sacc.
Thielavia basicola (B. & Br.) Zopf.
Trichurus cylindricus Clements & Shear.

Cucurbita Melopepo L.
Gloeosporium lagenarium (Pass.) Sacc.
Plasmopara cubensis (B. & C.) J. E. Humphrey.
Vermicularia Wallrothii Sacc.

Cucurbita moschata Dcne.
Cercospora Cucurbitae Ell. & Ev.
Erysiphe Cichoracearum DC.†
Fusarium Cucurbitae Taubenhaus.
Macrosporium heteronemum (Desm.) Sacc., var. pantophaeum Sacc.

Cucurbita moschata (cont.)

Peronoplasmopara cubensis (B. & C.) G. P. Clinton.
Plasmopara cubensis (B. & C.) J. E. Humphrey.
Pseudoperonospora cubensis (B. & C.) Rostowzew.
Thielavia basicola (B. & Br.) Zopf.

Cucurbita ovifera L.

Plasmopara cubensis (B. & C.) J. E. Humphrey.
Pseudoperonospora cubensis (B. & C.) Rostowzew.

Curcurbita Pepo L.

Botrytis cinerea P. †
Cercospora citrullina Cke.
Cercospora Cucurbitae Ell. & Ev.
Choanephora Cucurbitarum (B. & Rav.) Thax.
Rhopalomyces Curcubitarum B. & Rav.
Cladosporium cucumerinum Ell. & Arth.
Colletotrichum lagenarium (Pass.) Ell. & Halsted.
Gloeosporium lagenarium (Pass.) Sacc. & Roum.
Colletotrichum? nigrum Ell. & Halsted.
Coniosporium Fairmani Sacc.
Corticium vagum B. & C.
Corticium vagum B. & C., var. Solani Burt.
Rhizoctonia Solani Kühn.
Diplodia Cucurbitaceae Ell. & Langlois.
Diplodia tubericola (Ell. and Ev.) Taubenhaus.
Epicoccum micropus Cda.
Erysiphe Cichoracearum DC. †
Fusarium aurantiacum Cda.
Fusarium Helianthi C. E. Lewis.
Fusarium niveum Erw. Sm.
Gloeosporium allantoideum Pk.
Macrosporium peponicola Rabh.
Mucor inaequalis Pk.
Phoma Lagenariae (Thm.) Sacc.
Phyllosticta orbicularis Ell. & Ev.
Peronoplasmopara cubensis (B. & C.) G. P. Clinton.
Peronospora cubensis B. & C.
Plasmopara cubensis (B. & C.) J. E. Humphrey.
Pseudoperonospora cubensis (B. & C.) Rostowzew.
Rhagadolobium Cucurbitacearum (Rehm) Theissen & Syd.
Septoria Cucurbitacearum Sacc.
Sphaeria Peponis S.
Spilocaea concentrica S.
Sporidesmium mucosum, var. pluriseptatum Karst. & Hariot.
Sporidesmium pluriseptatum (Karst. & Hariot) Pk.

Stemphylium Cucurbitacearum Osner.
Thielavia basicola (B. & Br.) Zopf.
Torula herbarum Lk.
Volutella cucurbitina Pk.

Cucurbita perennis Gray.

Cercospora Cucurbitae Ell. & Ev.

Cucurbita verrucosa L.

Verticillium verrucosum B. & C.

Cucurbita (Squash)

Aspergillus clavellus Pk.
Aspergillus niger van Tiegh.
Coniosporium Fairmani Sacc.
Epicoccum purpurascens Ehrenb. ex S.
Erysiphe Polygoni DC. †
Fusarium citrulli Taubenhaus.
Fusarium Cucurbitae Taubenhaus.
Fusarium lateritium Nees, var. aurantiacum Cda.
Fusarium poolensis Taubenhaus.
Fusarium reticulatum Mont.
Gloeosporium lagenarium (Pass.) Sacc. & Roum.
Gloeosporium orbiculare B.
Macrosporium Lagenariae Thm.
Macrosporium Sarcinula B.
Mucor inaequalis Pk.
Mycosphaerella citrulina (C. O. Sm.) Grossenbacher.
Peronospora cubensis B. & C.
Plasmopara cubensis (B. & C.) J. E. Humphrey.
Peziza Cucurbitae Gerard.
Pezizella Cucurbitae (Gerard) Sacc.
Phoma Cucurbitacearum (Fr.) M. A. Curtis.
Phoma cucurbitalis B. & C.
Phyllosticta citrullina Chester.
Phyllosticta Cucurbitacearum Sacc.
Rhopalomyces Cucurbitarum B. & Rav.
Rhopalomyces elegans Cda.
Sclerotinia libertiana Fckl.

Cucurbita sp. indet.

Alternaria Brassicae (B.) Sacc., var. nigrescens Pegl.
Botrytis cinerea P. †
Cercospora cucurbitacea Ell. & Gall.
Coniothyrium arthurianum Sacc. & Berl.
?Epicoccum neglectum Desm.
Erysiphe Cichoracearum DC. †
Fusarium oxysporum Schl., var. aurantiacum Cda.
Fusarium vasinfectum Atk., var. niveum Erw. Sm.
Macrosporium sarcinula B.
Mucor clavatus Lk.
Mucor minimus Lk.
Rhizopus nigricans Ehrenb. ex Fr.
Sclerotium Rolfsii Sacc.

Cucurbita sp. indet. (*cont.*)
  Septomyxa persicina (Fres.) Sacc., var. nigricans Pk.
  Septoria vestita B. & C.
  Sphaeria mucosa P.
  Sporidesmium pluriseptatum (Karst. & Hariot) Pk.
  Torula herbarum Lk.
  { Fusarium ciliatum Lk.
  { Volutella ciliata (Lk.) Fr.

Cayaponia americana Cogn.
  Dimerium Cayaponiae P. Garman.
  Phaeodimeriella guarapiensis (Speg.) Theissen.
  { Nigredo helleriana Arth.
  { Uromyces hellerianus Arth.

Cayaponia attenuata Cogn.
Cayaponia racemosa (Sw.) Cogn.
  { Nigredo helleriana Arth.
  { Uromyces hellerianus Arth.

Cayaponia racemosa (Sw.) Cogn.
  Leptothyrium glomeratum Pat.

Cayaponia sp. indet.
  Cercospora cucurbiticola Henn.
  Diplosporium album Bon., var. fungicola F. L. Stevens.
  Parodiella Cayaponiae P. Garman.

Coccinia indica Wight & Arn.
  { Plasmopara cubensis (B. & C.) J. E. Humphrey.
  { Pseudoperonospora cubensis (B. & C.) Rostowzew.

Megarrhiza californica Torr.
  { Didymella cookeana Berl. & Vogl.
  { Didymella Megarrhizae Cke. & Hark.
  { Sphaeria Megarrhizae Cke. & Hark.
  Gibberella pulicaris (Fr.) Sacc.
  Hymenula Megarrhizae Cke. & Hark.
  Stictis Megarrhizae Phil. & Hark.
  Vermicularia rectispora Cke.

Megarrhiza fabacea Naud.
  Phoma Megarrhizae Fairman.
  Septoria Megarrhizae Ell. & Ev.

Megarrhiza Marah Watson.
  Septoria Echinocystis Ell. & Ev.

Megarrhiza oregana Torr.
  Phleospora Megarrhizae Ell. & Ev.
  Phyllosticta orbicularis Ell. & Ev.
  Septoria Megarrhizae Ell. & Ev.
  Vermicularia rectispora Cke.

Echinocystis lobata Torr. & Gr.
  Cercospora Echinocystis Ell. & Martin.
  Didymella superflua (Fckl.) Sacc.
  Didymium squamulosum, var. claviforme Sturgis.
  Erysiphe Cichoracearum DC.†
  { Peronospora australis Speg.
  { Plasmopara australis (Speg.) Swingle.
  { Rhysotheca australis (Speg.) G. W. Wilson.

{ Plasmopara cubensis (B. & C.) J. E. Humphrey.
{ Pseudoperonospora cubensis (B. & C.) Rostowzew.
  Pythium debaryanum Hesse.
  Septoria Brencklei Sacc.
  Septoria Sicyi Pk.
  Stachybotryella destructiva Sacc. & Dearness.

Sechium edule Sw.
  Cercospora Cucurbitae Ell. & Ev.
  Cercospora Sechiae Stevenson.
  Colletotrichum lagenarium (Pass.) Ell. & Halsted.
  Helminthosporium sechicola Stevenson.
  Nectria Brassicae Ell. & Sacc.
  Phyllosticta Sechii E. Young.
  { Peronoplasmopara cubensis (B. & C.) G. P. Clinton.
  { Plasmopara cubensis (B. & C.) J. E. Humphrey.

Sicyos angulatus L.
  Cercospora Echinocystis Ell. & Martin.
  Erysiphe Cichoracearum DC.†
  { Peronospora australis Speg.
  { Peronospora sicyicola Trelease.
  { Plasmopara australis (Speg.) Swingle.
  Phyllosticta sicyna Sacc.
  { Peronospora australis Speg.
  { Peronospora sicyicola Trelease.
  { Plasmopara australis (Speg.) Swingle.
  { Rhysotheca australis (Speg.) G. W. Wilson.
  { Plasmopara cubensis (B. & C.) J. E. Humphrey.
  { Pseudoperonospora cubensis (B. & C.) Rostowzew.
  Septoria Sicyi Pk.
  Sphaerella sicyicola Ell. & Ev.

Cyclanthera explodens Naud.
  Erysiphe Cichoracearum DC.†

Cucurbitaceae (Melon).
  Alternaria Brassicae (B.) Sacc.
  Alternaria Brassicae, var. alternans Auct.
  { Alternaria Brassicae (B.) Sacc., var. nigrescens Pegl.
  { Alternaria nigrescens (Pegl.) Coons.
  Alternaria Cucurbitae Letendre & Roum.
  Cercospora Cucurbitae Ell. & Ev.
  Cladosporium cucumerinum Ell. & Arth.
  Colletotrichum lagenarium (Pass.) Ell. & Halsted.

Cucurbitaceae gen. indet.
  Acrospermum compressum Tode ex Fr.
  { Asterina Wrightii B. & C.
  { Calothyrium Wrightii (B. & C.) Theissen.
  Chondromyces crocatus B. & C.
  Meliola Cucurbitacearum F. L. Stevens.
  Septoria Cucurbitacearum Sacc.
  Sporocybe byssoides (P.) Fr.

CAMPANULACEAE

Campanula americana L.
Aecidium Campanulastri G. W. Wilson.
Coleosporium Campanulae Lév.
Septoria Campanulae (Lév.) Sacc.
Sphaerella Campanulae Ell. & Kellerm.

Campanula aparinoides Pursh.
Cercoseptoria minuta J. J. Davis.
Coleosporium Campanulae Lév.

Campanula carpatica Jacq.
Sclerotium Rolfsii Sacc.

Campanula divaricata Michx.
Coleosporium Campanulae Lév.

Campanula glomerata L.
Phyllosticta alliariifoliae Allescher.

Campanula linifolia Scop.
Ramularia macrospora Fres.

Campanula media L.
Campanula nobilis Lindl.
Sclerotium Rolfsii Sacc.

Campanula persica A. DC.
Rhizoctonia Solani Kühn.

Campanula persicifolia L.
Coleosporium Campanulae Lév.
Sclerotium Rolfsii Sacc.

Campanula rapunculoides L.
{ Coleosporium Campanulae Lév.
{ Peridermium Pini Auct. Amer. p. p.
{ Peridermium Rostrupi Ed. Fisch.

Campanula rotundifolia L.
Botrytis cinerea P. †
Cladosporium herbarum (P.) ex Lk.
Coleosporium Campanulae Lév.
Leptosphaeria Doliolum (P. ex Fr.) De Not.
Mollisia atrata (P.) Karst.
Phoma groenlandica Allescher.
Pleospora herbarum (Fr.) Rabh.
{ Micropuccinia Campanulae (Carm.) Arth. &
{   Jackson.
{ Puccinia Campanulae Carm.
Pyrenophora comata (Niessl) Sacc.
Sphaerella pachyasca Rostr.

Campanula rotundifolia L., var. **arctica** Lange.
Rhabdospora cercosperma (Rostr.) Sacc.

Campanula Scouleri Hook.
{ Micropuccinia Campanulae (Carm.) Arth. &
{   Jackson.
{ Puccinia Campanulae Carm.

Campanula uniflora L.
Coniothyrium olivaceum Bon.
Pleospora herbarum (Fr.) Rabh.
Micropuccinia nova-zembliae (Jørsted) Arth.
Pyrenophora chrysospora (Niessl) Sacc.
{ Rhabdospora cercosperma (Rostr.) Sacc.
{ Septoria cercosperma Rostr.
Rhabdospora Drabae (Fckl.) Berl. & Vogl.

{ Mycosphaerella pachyasca (Rostr.) Vestergren.
{ Sphaerella pachyasca Rostr.
Mycosphaerella tassiana (De Not.) Johans.

Campanula sp. indet.
Corticium vagum B. & C.
Ophiobolus acuminatus (Sow. ex Fr.) Duby.
Ramularia macrospora Fres.
Ramularia macrospora Fres., var. major
    Lindr.
Sclerotinia sclerotiorum (Lib.) Massee.

Specularia biflora (R. & P.) Fisch. & Mey.
Specularia leptocarpa Gray.
Septoria Speculariae B. & C.

Specularia perfoliata (L.) A. DC.
Coleosporium Campanulae Lév.
{ Septoria Speculariae B. & C. 1874.
{ Septoria Speculariae Sacc. 1884.
{ Septoria specularina Sacc.
? { Uredo Campanulae P.
  { Caeoma (Uredo) Campanularum Lk.

Platycodon grandiflorum A. DC.
Rhizoctonia Solani Kühn.

Sphenoclea zeylanica Gaertn.
Cercosporidium Helleri Earle.

Nemacladus ramosissimus Nutt.
{ Dicaeoma Sarcobati Arth. I.
{ Puccinia subnitens Diet. I.

Clermontia persicifolia Gaudich.
Asterina sphaerelloides Ell. & Ev. nec Speg.

LOBELIACEAE

Lobelia amoena Michx.
Cercospora effusa (B. & C.) Ell. & Ev.
Cercospora Lobeliae Kellerm. & Swingle.

Lobelia assurgens L., var. **portoricensis** Urb.
Colletotrichum Lobeliae F. L. Stevens.

Lobelia cardinalis L.
{ Caeoma Lobeliae-cardinalis S.
{ Cercospora effusa (B. & C.) Ell. & Ev.
Septoria Lobeliae Pk.

Lobelia cliffortiana L.
Entyloma Lobeliae Farl.

Lobelia Erinus L.
Rhizoctonia Solani Kühn.

Lobelia inflata L.
Cercospora effusa (B. & C.) Ell. & Ev.
Cercospora Lobeliae Kellerm. & Swingle.
Entyloma Lobeliae Farl.
Septoria Lobeliae Pk.
Septoria Lobeliae Pk., var. Lobeliae-inflatae
    Sacc.

Lobelia Kalmii L.
Micropuccinia Lobeliae (Gerard) Arth. &
    Jackson.

Lobelia laxiflora HBK.
Septoria ramonensis Syd.

Lobelia puberula Michx.
Cercospora ferruginea Fckl.
Cladosporium effusum B. & C.
Micropuccinia Lobeliae (Gerard) Arth. & Jackson.
Puccinia Lobeliae Gerard.
Puccinia microsperma B. & C.
Lobelia siphilitica L.
Cercospora effusa (B. & C.) Ell.
Cladosporium effusum B. & C.
Cladosporium pelliculosum B. & C.
Cercospora Lobeliae Kellerm. & Swingle.
Dasyspora Lobeliae (Gerard) Arth.
Dicaeoma Lobeliae (Gerard) Arth.
Micropuccinia Lobeliae (Gerard) Arth. & Jackson.
Puccinia Lobeliae Gerard.
Puccinia microsperma B. & C.
Phyllosticta Bridgesii Speg.
Septoria Lobeliae Pk.
Septoria Lobeliae-syphiliticae Henn.
Lobelia spicata Lam.
Puccinia microsperma B. & C.
Septoria Lobeliae Pk.
Lobelia sp. indet.
Phoma devastatrix B. & Br.?
Bullaria vacua (Diet. & Holw.) Arth. & Mains.
Puccinia vacua Diet. & Holw.
Sphaeropsis Huffeli B. & C.

GOODENIACEAE

Scaevola chamissoniana Gaudich.
Phyllosticta Scaevolae Ell. & Ev.
Cerbera Thevetia L.
Diplodia aegyptiaca Tassi.
Diplodia aegyptiaca Tassi, forma incrustans Tassi.
Cerbera venenifera Steud.
Laestadia Cerberae Tassi.

COMPOSITAE

Sparganophorus Vaillantii Crantz.
Puccinia Xanthii S.
Uredo Sparganophori Henn.
Vernonia Alamani DC.
Bullaria semiinsculpta (Arth.) Arth. & Mains.
Puccinia semiinsculpta Arth.
Vernonia albicaulis Vahl.
Argomyces Vernoniae Arth.
Bullaria arthuriana (H. S. Jackson) Arth. & Mains.
Puccinia arthuriana H. S. Jackson.
Argomyces insulanus Arth.
Bullaria insulana (Arth.) Arth. & Mains.
Puccinia insulana (Arth.) H. S. Jackson.
Vernonia altissima Nutt.
Cercospora Vernoniae Ell. & Kellerm.
Coleosporium carneum H. S. Jackson. III.
Coleosporium Vernoniae B. & C.

Erysiphe Cichoracearum DC. †
Bullaria Vernoniae (S.) Arth.
Puccinia Vernoniae S.
Septoria oculata Ell. & Kellerm.
Vernonia angustifolia Michx.
Cercospora Vernoniae Ell. & Kellerm.
Coleosporium carneum H. S. Jackson. III.
Coleosporium Vernoniae B. & C.
Vernonia arborescens (L.) Sw.
Bullaria insulana (Arth.) Arth. & Mains.
Puccinia insulana (Arth.) II. S. Jackson.
Vernonia arbuscula Less.
Vernonia bahamensis Griseb.
Bullaria arthuriana (H. S. Jackson) Arth. & Mains.
Puccinia arthuriana H. S. Jackson.
Vernonia Baldwinii Torr.
Cercospora oculata Ell. & Kellerm.
Cercospora Vernoniae Ell. & Kellerm.
Coleosporium carneum H. S. Jackson.
Coleosporium Sonchi-arvensis Auct. Amer. p. p.
Coleosporium Vernoniae B. & C.
Erysiphe Cichoracearum DC. †
Peronospora Halstedii Farl.
Plasmopara Halstedii (Farl.) Berl. & DeToni.
Rhysotheca Halstedii (Farl.) G. W. Wilson.
Bullaria Vernoniae (S.) Arth.
?Puccinia flosculosorum Auct. Amer. p. p.
Puccinia Hieracii Syd. Ured. 273.
Puccinia Vernoniae S.
Puccinia Vernoniae S., var. foliicola Ell. & Ev.
Sphaerella decidua Ell. & Kellerm.
Vernonia Blodgetii Small.
Coleosporium carneum H. S. Jackson.
Coleosporium Vernoniae B. & C.
Vernonia borinquensis Urb.
Puccinia arthuriana H. S. Jackson.
Vernonia bullata Benth.
Argomyces Vernoniae Arth.
Bullaria Vernoniae (S.) Arth.
Spilodochium Vernoniae Syd.
Vernonia canescens H. B. K.
Argomyces Vernoniae Arth.
Bullaria arthuriana (H. S. Jackson) Arth. & Mains.
Puccinia arthuriana H. S. Jackson.
Vernonia corymbosa S.
Argomyces Vernoniae Arth.
Bullaria Vernoniae (S.) Arth.
Vernonia crinita Raf.
Coleosporium carneum H. S. Jackson.
Coleosporium Vernoniae B. & C.
Bullaria Vernoniae (S.) Arth.
Puccinia Vernoniae S.
Vernonia deppeana Less.
Dietelia Vernoniae Arth.
Endophyllum Vernoniae Arth.
Puccinia discreta Jackson & Holw.

Vernonia deppeana (*cont.*)
{ Klebahnia pressa (Arth. & Holw.) Arth.
{ Uromyces pressus Arth. & Holw.
Vernonia dictyophlebia Gleason.
{ Bullaria semiinsculpta (Arth.) Arth. & Mains.
{ Puccinia semiinsculpta Arth.
Vernonia divaricata Sw.
{ Dicaeoma Becki (Mayor) Arth. & Jackson.
{ Puccinia Becki Mayor.
  Puccinia insulana (Arth.) H. S. Jackson.
Vernonia Ervendbergii Gray.
{ Bullaria Vernoniae (S.) Arth.
{ Puccinia Vernoniae S.
Vernonia fasciculata Michx.
  Cercospora Vernoniae Ell. & Kellern.
{ Coleosporium Sonchi Auct. Amer. p. p.
{ Coleosporium Sonchi-arvensis Auct. Amer. p.p.
{ Coleosporium Vernoniae B. & C.
  Stichopsora Vernoniae (B. & C.) Diet.
{ Erysiphe Cichoracearum DC. †
{ Erysiphe lamprocarpa Auct. Amer. p. p.
{ Bullaria Vernoniae (S.) Arth.
  Dicaeoma Vernoniae (S.) O. Kuntze.
  Puccinia flosculosorum Auct. Amer. p. p.
  ?Puccinia Heliopsidis Auct. Amer. p. p.
  Puccinia Tanaceti, var. Vernoniae Burrill.
  Puccinia Vernoniae S.
  Puccinia Vernoniae S., var. caulicola Ell. & Ev.
  Puccinia Vernoniae S., var. longipes Diet.
Vernonia flaccidifolia Small.
{ Coleosporium carneum H. S. Jackson.
{ Coleosporium Vernoniae B. & C.
Vernonia gigantea (Walt.) Brit.
{ Coleosporium carneum H. S. Jackson.
{ Coleosporium Vernoniae B. & C.
  Erysiphe Cichoracearum DC. †
{ Bullaria Vernoniae (S.) Arth.
{ Puccinia Tanaceti Auct. Amer. p. p.
{ Puccinia Vernoniae S.
Vernonia glauca (L.) Willd.
{ Coleosporium carneum H. S. Jackson.
{ Coleosporium Vernoniae B. & C.
Vernonia guadalupensis Heller.
Vernonia illinoensis Gleason.
{ Coleosporium carneum H. S. Jackson.
{ Coleosporium Vernoniae B. & C.
{ Bullaria Vernoniae (S.) Arth.
{ Puccinia Vernoniae S.
Vernonia insularis Gleason.
Vernonia interior Small.
{ Coleosporium carneum H. S. Jackson.
{ Coleosporium Vernoniae B. & C.
Vernonia karwinskiana DC.
{ Bullaria semiinsculpta (Arth.) Arth. & Mains.
{ Puccinia semiinsculpta Arth.
Vernonia leiocarpa DC.
{ Dicaeoma nothum (Jackson & Holw.) Arth. &
{   Jackson.
{ Puccinia notha Jackson & Holw.

{ Dicaeoma ratum (Jackson & Holw.) Arth. &
{   Jackson.
{ Puccinia rata Jackson & Holw.
Vernonia longifolia P.
{ Argomyces insulanus Arth.
{ Bullaria insulana (Arth.) Arth. & Mains.
{ Puccinia insulana (Arth.) H. S. Jackson.
{ Bullaria fuscella (Arth. & Johnston) Arth. &
{   Mains.
{ Puccinia fuscella Arth. & Johnston.
  Puccinia Vernoniae N. Am. Uredinales *772.*
Vernonia marginata (Torr.) Raf.
{ Bullaria Vernoniae (S.) Arth.
{ Puccinia Vernoniae S., var. brevipes Diet.
Vernonia menthifolia Less.
{ Bullaria fuscella (Arth. & Johnston) Arth. &
{   Mains.
{ Puccinia fuscella Arth. & Johnston.
Vernonia missurica Raf.
{ Coleosporium carneum H. S. Jackson.
{ Coleosporium Vernoniae B. & C.
{ Bullaria Vernoniae (S.) Arth.
{ Puccinia Vernoniae S.
Vernonia noveboracensis Willd.
  Aecidium Compositarum Auct. Amer. p. p.
  Ascochyta Treleasei Berl. & Vogl.
  Cercospora noveboracensis Ell. & Ev.
  Cercospora oculata Ell. & Kellerm.
  Cercospora Vernoniae Ell. & Kellerm.
  Caeoma Solidaginis Auct. Amer. p. p.
  Coleosporium carneum H. S. Jackson. III.
  Coleosporium Compositarum Auct. Amer. p. p.
{ Coleosporium Sonchi Auct. Amer. p. p.
{ Coleosporium Sonchi-arvensis Auct. Amer. p.p.
{ Coleosporium Sonchi-arvensis, var. Vernoniae
{   Burrill.
  Coleosporium Vernoniae B. & C.
  Stichopsora Vernoniae (B. & C.) Diet.
  Uredo Solidaginis Auct. Amer. p. p.
{ Didymosphaerella tenebrosa (B. & Br.) Cke.
{ Didymosphaeria tenebrosa (B. & Br.) Sacc.
{ Sphaeria tenebrosa B. & Br.
  Erysiphe Cichoracearum DC. †
  Ophiobolus fulgidus (C. & P.) Sacc.
  Ophiobolus porphyrogonus (Tode ex Fr.) Sacc.
{ Peronospora Halstedii Farl.
{ Rhysotheca Halstedii (Farl.) G. W. Wilson.
  Phlyctaena vagabunda Desm.
{ Bullaria Vernoniae Arth.
  Dicaeoma longipes (Lagerh.) O. Kuntze.
  Puccinia bullata S.
  Puccinia flosculosorum Auct. Amer. p. p.
{ Puccinia Heliopsidis Auct. Amer. p. p.
{ Puccinia longipes Lagerh.
  Puccinia Tanaceti Auct. Amer. p. p.
  Puccinia Tanaceti var. Vernoniae Burrill.
  Puccinia Vernoniae S.
  Puccinia Vernoniae S., var. brevipes Diet.
  Puccinia Vernoniae S., var. longipes Diet.

Vernonia noveboracensis (*cont.*)
⎰Sphaerotheca Castagnei Auct. Amer. p. p.
⎱Sphaerotheca Humuli (DC.) Burrill, var. fuliginea (Schl.) Salmon.
Vernonia oligantha Greene.
Vernonia ovalifolia Torr. & Gr.
⎰Coleosporium carneum H. S. Jackson.
⎱Coleosporium Vernoniae B. & C.
Vernonia patens H. B. K.
Argomycetella pura Syd.
⎧Bullaria inaequata (Jackson & Holw.) Arth. &
⎨ Mains.
⎪Puccinia inaequata Jackson & Holw.
⎪Micropuccinia rotundata (Diet.) Arth. & Jackson.
⎪Puccinia rotundata Diet.
⎩Puccinia rugosa Speg.
Vernonia phyllostachys Gleason.
Puccinia arthuriana H. S. Jackson.
Vernonia piloselloides (Rich.) Gomez.
Coleosporium Vernoniae B. & C.
Vernonia pluvialis Gleason.
⎧Dicaeoma fraternum (H. S. Jackson) Arth. &
⎨ Jackson.
⎩Puccinia fraterna H. S. Jackson.
Vernonia pulchella Small.
⎧Coleosporium carneum H. S. Jackson.
⎪Coleosporium Vernoniae B. & C.
⎨Bullaria Vernoniae Arth.
⎩Bullaria Vernoniae (S.) Arth.
Vernonia racemosa Delponte.
Bullaria insulana (Arth.) Arth. & Mains.
Vernonia schiedeana Less.
⎧Dicaeoma erraticum (Jackson & Holw.) Arth.
⎪ & Jackson.
⎨Dietelia Vernoniae Arth.
⎪Endophyllum Vernoniae Arth.
⎩Puccinia erratica Jackson & Holw.
Vernonia sericea Rich.
⎧Argomyces Vernoniae Arth.
⎪Bullaria arthuriana (H. S. Jackson) Arth. &
⎨ Mains.
⎩Puccinia arthuriana H. S. Jackson.
Vernonia serratuloides H. B. K.
Bullaria semiinsculpta (Arth.) Arth. & Mains.
Vernonia Shannoni Coult.
⎧Dicaeoma nothum (Jackson. & Holw.) Arth. &
⎨ Jackson.
⎩Puccinia notha Jackson & Holw.
Veronia sprengeliana Sch.-Bip.
⎰Bullaria furcella (Arth. & Johnston) Arth. &
⎱ Mains.
Vernonia stellaris Llave & Lex.
⎧Micropuccinia discreta (Jackson & Holw.)
⎨ Arth. & Jackson.
⎩Puccinia discreta Jackson & Holw.

Vernonia texana Small.
Vernonia tomentosa Ell.
⎰Coleosporium carneum H. S. Jackson.
⎱Coleosporium Vernoniae B. & C.
Vernonia triflosculosa H. B. K.
Phylloporthe Vernoniae Syd.
⎧Bullaria idonea (Jackson & Holw.) Arth. &
⎨ Mains.
⎩Puccinia idonea Jackson & Holw.
⎧Bullaria praealta (Jackson & Holw.) Arth. &
⎪ Mains.
⎨Puccinia praealta Jackson & Holw.
⎩Puccinia tonduziana Speg.
Vernonia umbellifera Gleason.
Puccinia semiinsculpta Arth.
Vernonia uniflora Sch. Bip.
⎰Bullaria (?) egregia (Arth.) Arth. & Mains.
⎱Puccinia egregia Arth.
Vernonia sp. indet.
Aecidium Vernoniae Henn.
Cercospora consimilis Syd.
⎧?Coleosporium Elephantopodis Hedgc. & Long
⎪ p. p.
⎨Coleosporium Vernoniae B. & C.
⎩Puccinia Beckii Mayor.
Oliganthes condensatus (Less.) Sch. Bip.
Puccinia seaveriana Arth.
Elephantopus angustifolius Sw.
Coleosporium Elephantopodis Thm.
Elephantopus carolinianus Willd.
Cercospora Elephantopodis Ell. & Ev.
⎧Caeoma Elephantopodis (S.) Lk.
⎪Coleosporium Elephantopodis Thm.
⎨Coleosporium Sonchi Auct. Amer. p. p.
⎪Coleosporium Sonchi-arvensis Auct. Amer.
⎪ p. p.
⎩Uredo Elephantopodis S.
Elephantopus hypomalachus Blake.
Coleosporium Elephantopodis Thm.
Elephantopus mollis H. B. K.
⎰Coleosporium Elephantopodis Thm.
⎱Coleosporium Sonchi Auct. Amer. p. p.
Stilbella flavida (Cke.) Henn.
Elephantopus nudatus Gray.
Cercospora Elephantopodis Ell. & Ev.
⎧Coleosporium Elephantopodis (S.) Thm.
⎪Coleosporium Sonchi-arvensis Auct. Amer. p.p.
⎨Coleosporium Sonchi-arvensis Auct. Amer.
⎩ p. p.
Elephantopus spicatus Juss.
⎰Irene cyclopoda (F. L. Stevens) Toro.
⎱Meliola cyclopoda F. L. Stevens.
⎧Micropuccinia paupercula (Arth.) Arth. &
⎪ Jackson.
⎨Puccinia Elephantopodis-spicati Pat.
⎩Puccinia paupercula Arth.

Elephantopus tomentosus L.
  Cercospora Elephantopodis Ell. & Ev.
  ⎧ Caeoma Elephantopodis Lk.
  ⎪ Coleosporium Elephantopodis Thm.
  ⎨ Coleosporium Sonchi-arvensis Auct. Amer. p.p.
  ⎩ Uredo Elephantopodis S.
Piqueria trinervia Cav.
  Rhizoctonia Solani Kühn.
Alomia microcarpa (Benth.) B. L. Robinson.
  Cystopus brasiliensis Speg.
Ageratum conyzoides L.
  Fumago vagans Fr.
  ⎧ Bullaria (?) Conoclinii (Seym.) Arth. & Mains.
  ⎨ Puccinia Conoclinii Seym.
  ⎩ Puccinia rosea Arth.
  Rhizoctonia Solani Kühn.
  Uredo Agerati Mayor.
Ageratum corymbosum Zucc.
Ageratum maritimum H. B. K.
  ⎧ Bullaria Conoclinii (Seym.) Arth. & Mains.
  ⎨ Puccinia Conoclinii Seym.
Ageratum rugosum Coult.
Ageratum strictum Hemsl.
  ⎧ Bullaria (?) Conoclinii (Seym.) Arth. & Mains.
  ⎨ Puccinia Conoclinii Seym.
Stevia clinopodioides Greenm.
Stevia lucida Lag.
Stevia monardifolia H. B. K.
Stevia reglensis Benth.
  Coleosporium Steviae Arth.
Stevia rhombifolia H. B. K.
  Coleosporium Steviae Arth.
  ⎧ Puccinia Conoclinii Seym.
  ⎨ Puccinia rosea Arth.
  Nigredo Aegopogonis (Diet. & Holw.) Arth. I.
Stevia salicifolia Cav.
Stevia subpubescens Lag.
Stevia trachelioides (DC.) Hook.
Stevia viscida H. B. K.
  Coleosporium Steviae Arth.
Stevia sp. indet.
  Aecidium steviicola Arth.
  Erysiphe Cichoracearum DC. †
  ⎧ Coleosporium Reichei Diet.
  ⎨ Synomyces Reichei (Diet.) Arth.
Eupatorium album L.
  Cercospora ageratoides Ell. & Ev.
  Cercospora Eupatorii Pk.
Eupatorium altissimum L.
  Caeoma (Aecidium) tenue S.
Eupatorium aschenbornianum Schauer.
  ⎧ Baeodromus Eupatorii (Lagerh.) Arth.
  ⎨ Pucciniosira Eupatorii Lagerh.
Eupatorium atriplicifolium Hort. & Lam.
  ⎧ Bullaria (?) redempta (H. S. Jackson) Arth. &
  ⎨   Mains.
  ⎩ Puccinia redempta H. S. Jackson.
Eupatorium betonicum Hemsl.
  Bullaria (?) Conoclinii (Seym.) Arth. & Mains.

Eupatorium brevipes DC.
  ⎧ Bullaria (?) inanipes (Diet. & Holw.) Arth. &
  ⎨   Mains.
  ⎩ Puccinia inanipes Diet. & Holw.
Eupatorium coelestinum L.
  ⎧ Bullaria (?) Conoclinii (Seym.) Arth. & Mains.
  ⎪ Dicaeoma Conoclinii (Seym.) O. Kuntze.
  ⎨ Puccinia Centaureae B.
  ⎩ Puccinia Conoclinii Seym.
Eupatorium collinum DC.
  Coleosporium Eupatorii Arth.
  ⎧ Bullaria (?) Conoclinii (Seym.) Arth. & Mains.
  ⎨ Puccinia Conoclinii Seym.
Eupatorium coronopifolium Willd.
  ⎧ Heptameria mesoedema (B. & C.) Sacc.
  ⎨ Leptosphaeria mesoedema (B. & C.) Ell. & Ev.
  ⎩ Sphaeria mesoedema B. & C.
  ⎧ Dothidea Eupatorii B & C.
  ⎨ Phyllachora Eupatorii (B. & C.) Sacc.
  ⎧ Rosellinia umbrinella (B. & C.) Sacc.
  ⎨ Sphaeria umbrinella B. & C.
Eupatorium daleoides (DC.) Hemsl.
  Cionothrix praelonga (Wint.) Arth.
  Uredo suspecta Jackson & Holw.
Eupatorium deltoideum Jacq.
  Nigredo Aegopogonis (Diet. & Holw.) Arth. I.
  ⎧ Bullaria (?) Conoclinii (Seym.) Arth. & Mains.
  ⎨ Puccinia rosea Arth.
Eupatorium dolicholepis Urb.
  ⎧ Appendiculella Compositarum (Earle) Toro,
  ⎪   var. portoricensis (F. L. Stevens) Seaver &
  ⎨   Chardon.
  ⎪ Meliola Compositarum Earle, var. portoricen-
  ⎩   sis F. L Stevens.
Eupatorium Espinosarum Gray.
  ⎧ Bullaria (?) Espinosarum (Diet. & Holw.)
  ⎨   Arth. & Mains.
  ⎩ Puccinia Espinosarum Diet. & Holw.
Eupatorium fistulosum B. L. Robinson.
  Peziza virginea Batsch ex Fr.
Eupatorium geranifolium Urb.
  Bullaria (?) Conoclinii (Seym.) Arth. & Mains.
Eupatorium glabratum H. B. K.
  Nigredo Aegopogonis (Diet. & Holw.) Arth. I.
  Puccinia rosea Arth.
Eupatorium glandulosum H. B. K.
  ⎧ Bullaria (?) Conoclinii (Seym.) Arth. & Mains.
  ⎨ Puccinia Conoclinii Seym.
  Sphaerotheca Humuli (DC.) Burrill. †
Eupatorium Gonzalezii B. L. Robinson.
  ⎧ Bullaria (?) Conoclinii (Seym.) Arth. & Mains.
  ⎨ Puccinia rosea Arth.
Eupatorium Greggii Gray.
  ⎧ Bullaria concinna (Arth.) Arth. & Mains.
  ⎨ Puccinia concinna Arth.
Eupatorium hirsutum DC.
  ⎧ Bullaria (?) inanipes (Diet. & Holw.) Arth. &
  ⎨   Mains.
  ⎩ Puccinia inanipes Diet. & Holw.

Eupatorium holwayanum B. L. Robinson.
{ Bullaria (?) Conoclinii (Seym.) Arth. & Mains.
  Puccinia rosea Arth.

Eupatorium hylonomum B. L. Robinson.
Aschersonia basicystis B. & C., forma pulvinata Syd.

Eupatorium hymenolepis B. L. Robinson.

Eupatorium incarnatum Walt.
{ Bullaria (?) Conoclinii (Seym.) Arth. & Mains.
  Puccinia Conoclinii Seym.

Eupatorium inulifolium H. B. K.
Puccinia Eupatorii-columbiani Mayor.

Eupatorium iresinoides H. B. K.
Puccinia Eupatorii Diet.

Eupatorium macrophyllum L.
Coleosporium Eupatorii Arth.
?Puccinia sepulta B. & C.

Eupatorium mairetianum DC.
Aecidium roseum Diet. & Holw.
Puccinia Aegopogonis Arth. & Holw.
{ Bullaria (?) basiporula (Jackson & Holw.)
    Arth. & Mains.
  Puccinia basiporula Jackson & Holw.

Eupatorium Mendezii DC.
{ Bullaria (?) Conoclinii (Seym.) Arth. & Mains.
  Puccinia Conoclinii Seym.
  Puccinia rosea Arth.

Eupatorium microstemum Cass.
Erysiphe Cichoracearum DC. †

Eupatorium morifolium Mill.
Cionothrix praelonga (Wint.) Arth.

Eupatorium neianum DC.
{ Bullaria (?) Conoclinii (Seym.) Arth. & Mains.
  Puccinia Conoclinii Seym.

Eupatorium nubigenum Benth.
Septoria albomaculans Syd.

Eupatorium occidentale Hook.
Pleospora utahensis Ell. & Ev.

Eupatorium odoratum L.
Acrostalagmus albus Preuss.
Calonectria melioloides Speg.
Cionothrix praelonga (Wint.) Arth.
Helminthosporium glabroides F. L. Stevens.
{ Appendiculella Compositarum (Earle) Toro.
  Meliola Compositarum Earle.
Phyllosticta eupatoriicola Kabát & Bubák.

Eupatorium oerstedianum Benth.
Appendiculella Compositarum (Earle) Toro.
Cercospora costaricensis Syd.
Cicinnobella costaricensis Syd.
Coleosporium Eupatorii Arth.
Dimerium costaricense Syd.
Irene escharoides Syd.
Paranectria meliolicola F. L. Stevens.
Trichothyrium dubiosum (Bomm. & Rouss.)
  Theissen.

Eupatorium pansamalense B. L. Robinson.
{ Micropuccinia tolimensis (Mayor) Arth. &
    Jackson.
  Puccinia tolimensis Mayor.

Eupatorium pazcuarense H. B. K.
{ Baeodromus Eupatorii Arth.
  Dietelia Eupatorii Arth.

Eupatorium perfoliatum L.
Aecidium Compositarum Auct. Amer. p. p.
{ Aecidium Compositarum, var. Eupatorii (S.)
    B.
  Dicaeoma Eleocharidis (Arth.) O. Kuntze. I.
  Puccinia Eleocharidis Arth. I.
Caeoma (Aecidium) tenue S.
Cercospora Eupatorii Pk.
Cercospora perfoliata Ell. & Ev.
Erysiphe Cichoracearum DC. †
Erysiphe Cichoracearum DC., var. Eupatorii
  Salmon.
Mycorrhiza of Legumes F. R. Jones.
Periconia pycnospora Fres.
Phyllosticta decidua Ell. & Kellerm.

Eupatorium phoenicolepis B. L. Robinson, var.
  guatemalensis B. L. Robinson.
{ Bullaria (?) hodgsoniana (Kern) Arth. &
    Mains.
  Puccinia hodgsoniana Kern.

Eupatorium polyodon Urb.
{ Bullaria (?) Conoclinii (Seym.) Arth. & Mains.
  Puccinia rosea Arth.

Eupatorium pomaderrifolium Benth.
Septoria albomaculans Syd.

Eupatorium populifolium H. B. K.
{ Cionothrix praelonga (Wint.) Arth.
  Cronartium praelongum Wint.

Eupatorium porphyranthemum Gray.
Bullaria (?) Conoclinii (Seym.) Arth. & Mains.

Eupatorium portoricense Urb.
{ Appendiculella Compositarum (Earle) Toro,
    var. portoricensis (F. L. Stevens) Seaver &
    Chardon.
  Meliola Compositarum Earle, var. portori-
    censis F. L. Stevens.
Calonectria melioloides Speg.
Dimerium piceum (B. & C.) Theissen.
Helminthosporium glabroides F. L. Stevens.
Meliola Compositarum Earle.
{ Perisporina Meliolae (F. L. Stevens) Speg.
  Perisporium Meliolae F. L. Stevens.
Phaeodothopsis Eupatorii F. L. Stevens.
Puccinia Conoclinii Seym.

Eupatorium purpureum L.
{ ?Aecidium Compositarum Auct. Amer. p. p.
  Aecidium Compositarum, var. Eupatorii (S.) B.
  Caeoma (Aecidium) Compositarum Lk., var.
    Eupatoriae S.
  Dicaeoma Eleocharidis (Arth.) O. Kuntze. I.
  Puccinia Eleocharidis Arth. I.

Eupatorium purpureum (*cont.*)

{ Anthostoma mortuosum (Ell.) Sacc.
{ Sphaeria mortuosa Ell.

Ascochyta Compositarum J. J. Davis.
Cercospora perfoliata Ell. & Ev.
Diaporthe linearis (Nees ex Fr.) Nits.

{ Erysiphe Cichoracearum DC. †
{ Erysiphe horridula Lév.
{ Erysiphe lamprocarpa Auct. Amer. p. p.

{ Hypoderma commune (Fr.) Duby.
{ Hysterium commune Fr.

Leptosphaeria agnita (Desm.) Ces. & De Not.

{ Leptostroma vulgare Fr.
{ Leptothyrium vulgare (Fr.) Sacc.

Oidium erysiphoides Fr.

{ Peronospora Halstedii Farl.
{ Plasmopora Halstedii (Farl.) Berl. & De Toni.
{ Rhysotheca Halstedii (Farl.) G. W. Wilson.

Phyllosticta eupatorina Thm.
?Puccinia tenuis Burrill.
Ramularia dispar J. J. Davis.

{ Dasyscypha Eupatorii (S.) Massee.
{ Peziza Eupatorii S.
{ Trichopeziza Eupatorii (S.) Sacc.

Eupatorium purpureum L., var. **maculatum** (L.)
Darl.

{ Dasyscypha longipila (Pk.) Sacc.
{ Peziza longipila Pk.

Dendrophoma variabilis Dearness & House.

{ Rhytisma confluens S.
{ Xyloma confluens S.

Eupatorium pycnocephaloides B. L. Robinson.
Eupatorium pycnocephalum Less.

{ Bullaria (?) Conoclinii (Seym.) Arth. & Mains.
{ Puccinia Conoclinii Seym.
{ Puccinia rosea Arth.

Eupatorium rafaelense Coult.

{ Bullaria (?) basiporula (Jackson & Holw.)
{ Arth. & Mains.
{ Puccinia basiporula Jackson & Holw.
{ Puccinia Conoclinii Kellerm.

Eupatorium rotundifolium L.

{ Aecidium Compositarum, var. Eupatorii (S.) B.
{ Dicaeoma Eleocharidis (Arth.) O. Kuntze. I.
{ Puccinia Eleocharidis Arth. I.

Cercospora ageratoides Ell. & Ev.
Cercospora Eupatorii Pk.

Eupatorium Schaffneri Sch.-Bip.

{ Bullaria (?) Conoclinii (Seym.) Arth. & Mains.
{ Puccinia Conoclinii Seym.

Eupatorium Schultzii Schnittsp.

{ Bullaria (?) hodgsoniana (Kern) Arth. &
{ Mains.
{ Puccinia hodgsoniana Kern.

Tuberculina costaricana Syd.

Eupatorium serotinum Michx.

{ Aecidium Compositarum, var. Eupatorii (S.)
{ B.
{ Dicaeoma Eleocharidis (Arth.) O. Kuntze. I.
{ Puccinia Eleocharidis Arth. I.

Septoria Eupatorii Rob.

Eupatorium sessilifolium L.

Patinella vagans Ell. & Ev.

Eupatorium Sinclairi Benth.

Eudarluca australis Speg.

{ Bullaria (?) Conoclinii (Seym.) Arth. & Mains.
{ Puccinia Conoclinii Seym.

Eupatorium Smithii B. L. Robinson.
Eupatorium solidaginifolium Gray.
Eupatorium sordidum Less.
Eupatorium spiriifolium Sch.-Bip.

{ Bullaria (?) Espinosarum (Diet. & Holw.)
{ Arth. & Mains.
{ Puccinia Espinosarum Diet. & Holw.

Eupatorium tomentellum Schrad.

Pucciniosira Brickelliae Diet. & Holw.

Eupatorium tubiflorum Benth.

{ Aecidium roseum Diet. & Holw.
{ Puccinia rosea I, Auct. Amer. non Arth.
{ Uromyces Aegopogonis Diet. & Holw. I.

{ Bullaria (?) solidipes (Jackson & Holw.) Arth.
{ & Mains.
{ Puccinia inanipes Kern non Diet. & Holw.
{ Puccinia solidipes Jackson & Holw.

Eupatorium urticifolium Reichard.

{ Aecidium Compositarum, var. Eupatorii Fung.
{ Columb. *498*.
{ Aecidium tenue S.
{ Allodus tenuis (Burrill) Arth.
{ Caeoma tenue S.
{ Dicaeoma tenue (Burrill) O. Kuntze.
{ Puccinia tenuis Burrill.

Puccinia Eleocharidis Arth. I.
Ascochyta Compositarum J. J. Davis.
Cercospora ageratoides Ell. & Ev.
Cercospora Eupatorii Pk.
Entyloma Compositarum Farl.

{ Erysiphe Cichoracearum DC. †
{ ?Erysiphe communis Auct. Amer. p. p.

Erysiphe Galeopsidis DC. †
Erysiphe Martii Lév.
Helicia buccina Dearness & House.
Hymenula olivacea Pk.

{ Hypocrea phyllogena Mont.
{ Hypocrella phyllogena (Mont.) Speg.

{ Peronospora Halstedii Farl.
{ Plasmopara Halstedii (Farl.) Berl. & De Toni.
{ Rhysotheca Halstedii (Farl.) G. W. Wilson.

{ Micropuccinia tolimensis (Mayor) Arth. &
{ Jackson.
{ Puccinia tolimensis Mayor.

Ramularia dispar J. J. Davis.
Sclerotium Rolfsii Sacc.
Septoria Eupatorii Rob.

Eupatorium urticifolium (*cont.*)
  〔Peziza Solenia Pk.
  〔Solenopezia Solenia (Pk.) Sacc.
Eupatorium verbenifolium Michx.
  〔Aecidium Compositarum Auct. Amer. p. p.
  〔Aecidium Compositarum, var. Eupatorii (S.)
  〔 B.
  〔Dicaeoma Eleocharidis (Arth.) O. Kuntze. I.
  〔Puccinia Eleocharidis Arth. I.
  Cercospora ageratoides Atk.
Eupatorium villosum Sw.
  〔Bullaria (?) Conoclinii (Seym.) Arth. & Mains.
  〔Puccinia Conoclinii Seym.
Eupatorium sp. indet.
  Actinothyrium caulincola S.
  Aecidium ampliatum Jackson & Holw.
  Belonium bicolor Ell. & Ev.
  Erysiphe Polygoni DC. †
  Heptameria mesoedema (B. & C.) Sacc.
  Peziza atrata P.
  Phacidium caulincola S.
  〔Bullaria (?) inermis (Jackson & Holw.) Arth. &
  〔 Mains.
  〔Puccinia inermis Jackson & Holw.
  Sporidesmium irregulare Cke.
  Subiculicola ambigua Speg.
Mikania congesta DC.
  Puccinia Spegazzinii De Toni.
Mikania cordifolia (L. f.) Willd.
  Aecidium expansum Diet.
  〔Cronartium portoricense (Whetzel & Olive)
  〔 Sacc. & Trott.
  〔Endophylloides portoricensis Whetzel & Olive.
  〔Appendiculella Compositarum (Earle) Toro.
  〔Meliola Compositarum Earle.
  〔Micropuccinia Spegazzinii (De-Toni) Arth. &
  〔 Jackson.
  〔Puccinia australis Speg.
  〔Puccinia Spegazzinii De Toni.
Mikania hirsutissima DC.
  Chrysella Mikaniae Syd.
Mikania houstoniana (L.) B. L. Robinson.
  Aecidium Mikaniae Henn.
Mikania fragilis Urb.
Mikania odoratissima Urb.
Mikania stevensiana Brit.
  〔Cronartium portoricense (Whetzel & Olive)
  〔 Sacc. & Trott.
  〔Endophylloides portoricensis Whetzel & Olive.
Mikania micrantha H. B. K.
  Endophylloides portoricensis Whetzel & Olive.
  Puccinia Spegazzinii De Toni.
Mikania scandens (L.) Willd.
  Cercospora Mikaniae Ell. & Ev.
  Endophylloides portoricensis Whetzel & Olive.
  Erysiphe Cichoracearum DC. †
  Fusarium Mikaniae B. & C.

  〔Dicaeoma Spegazzinii (De Toni) O. Kuntze.
  〔Micropuccinia Spegazzinii (De Toni) Arth. &
  〔 Jackson.
  〔Puccinia Spegazzinii De Toni.
Mikania sp. indet.
  Aecidium Compositarum Mart.?
  Cercospora mikaniola F. L. Stevens.
  Cladosporium Mikaniae F. L. Stevens.
  Septoria Mikaniae Wint.
Trilisa odoratissima Cass.
  Phoma minutissima Cke.
Carphochaete Grahami Gray.
  Aecidium Carphochaetes Syd.
Brickellia adenocarpa B. L. Robinson.
  Puccinia subdecora Syd. & Holw.
  Pucciniosira Brickelliae Diet. & Holw.
Brickellia californica (T. & G.) Gray.
  Cercospora Coleosanthi Ell. & Ev.
  Coleosporium aridum H. S. Jackson.
Brickellia Cavanillesii (Cass.) Gray.
  Pucciniosira Brickelliae Diet. & Holw.
Brickellia Coulteri Gray.
  〔Bullaria Kuhniae (S.) Kern.
  〔Puccinia Kuhniae S.
  〔Puccinia Brickelliae Pk.
Brickellia grandiflora (Hook.) Nutt.
  Aecidium arcularium Arth.
  Aecidium Compositarum Auct.
  Clathrospora permunda (Cke.) Berl.
  〔Bullaria subdecora (Syd. & Holw.) Arth. &
  〔 Mains.
  〔Puccinia subdecora Syd. & Holw.
Brickellia hebecarpa Gray.
  Aecidium guadalajarae Syd.
  Pucciniosira Brickelliae Diet. & Holw.
Brickellia reniformis Gray.
  Leptosphaeria Coleosanthi Fairman.
Brickellia secundiflora Gray.
Brickellia tomentella Gray.
  Pucciniosira Brickelliae Diet. & Holw.
Brickellia veronicifolia (H.B.K.) Gray.
  〔Micropuccinia praemorsa (Diet. & Holw.)
  〔 Arth. & Jackson.
  〔Puccinia praemorsa Diet. & Holw.
Brickellia sp. indet.
  〔Bullaria decora (Diet. & Holw.) Arth. & Mains.
  〔Puccinia decora Diet. & Holw.
  〔Puccinia Pinguis Diet. & Holw.
Barroetia subuligera (Schauer) Gray.
  〔Bullaria Kuhniae (S.) Kern.
  〔Puccinia Barroetiae Syd.
  〔Puccinia Kuhniae S.
Kuhnia rosmarinifolia Vent.
  Pleospora Compositarum Earle.
  〔Bullaria Kuhniae (S.) Kern.
  〔Puccinia Kuhniae S.

Kuhnia eupatorioides L.
Kuhnia Hitchcockii A. Nels.
Kuhnia leptophylla Scheele.
Kuhnia reticulata Nels.
   Bullaria Kuhniae (S.) Kern. 1913.
   Bullaria Kuhniae (S.) H. S. Jackson. 1917.
   Dicaeoma Kuhniae (S.) O. Kuntze.
   Puccinia Kuhniae S.
   ?Uredo flosculosorum Auct. Amer. p. p.
Liatris cylindracea Michx.
   Aecidium Liatridis Ell. & Anderson.
   Puccinia Koeleriae I. J. J. Davis.
   Puccinia Liatridis Bethel.
Liatris Chapmanii Torr. & Gr.
Liatris
       (Laciniaria Earlei Greene).
Liatris elegans (Walt.) Willd.
Liatris elegantula K. Sch.
Liatris
       (Laciniaria elongata Greene.)
Liatris gracilis Pursh.
   Coleosporium Laciniariae Arth.
Liatris graminifolia Pursh.
   Clasterosporium Laciniariae Arth.
   Coleosporium Laciniariae Arth.
   Coleosporium Sonchi-arvensis Auct. Amer. p. p.
Liatris laxa (Small) K. Sch.
Liatris Nashii (Small) Weatherby ined.
Liatris pauciflora Pursh.
Liatris pilosa Ait.
   Coleosporium Laciniariae Arth.
Liatris punctata Hook.
   Aecidium Compositarum, var. Liatridis Weber.
   Aecidium Liatridis Ell. & Anderson.
   Dicaeoma Liatridis (Bethel) Arth. & Fromme. I.
   Puccinia Liatridis Bethel. I.
   Pleospora herbarum (P.) ex Rabh.
Liatris scariosa Willd.
   Aecidium Compositarum, var. Liatridis Weber.
   Aecidium Liatridis Ell. & Anderson.
   Dicaeoma Liatridis (Bethel) Arth. & Fromme. I.
   Coleosporium Laciniariae Arth.
   Helminthosporium macrocarpum Grev.
   Leptosphaeria trimeroides Rehm.
   Septoria Liatridis Ell. & Davis.
Liatris serotina (Greene) K. Sch.
   Coleosporium Laciniariae Arth.
Liatris spicata (L.) Willd.
   Aecidium Liatridis Ell. & Anderson.
   Dicaeoma Liatridis (Bethel) Arth. & Fromme. I.
   Puccinia Liatridis Bethel. I.
   Phyllosticta Liatridis J. J. Davis.
   Septoria Liatridis Ell. & Davis.

Liatris squarrosa Willd.
   Aecidium Compositarum, var. Liatridis Weber.
   Aecidium Liatridis Ell. & Anderson.
   Puccinia Liatridis Bethel. I.
Liatris tenuifolia Nutt.
   Coleosporium Laciniariae Arth.
Carphephorus tomentosus Torr. & Gr.
   Fusisporium aurantiacum Lk.
Gymnosperma corymbosum DC.
   Micropuccinia Grindeliae (Pk.) Arth. & Jackson.
Grindelia aphanactis Rydb.
   Micropuccinia Grindeliae (Pk.) Arth. & Jackson.
   Puccinia Grindeliae Pk.
   Erysiphe Cichoracearum DC. †?
Grindelia cuneifolia Nutt.
Grindelia erecta A. Nels.
Grindelia fastigiata Greene.
Grindelia inornata Greene.
Grindelia perennis A. Nels.
   Micropuccinia Grindeliae (Pk.) Arth. & Jackson.
   Puccinia Grindeliae Pk.
Grindelia oregana Gray.
   Coleosporium Solidaginis Thm.
Grindelia robusta Nutt.
   Nigredo Junci (Desm.) Arth. I.
   Micropuccinia Grindeliae (Pk.) Arth. & Jackson.
   Puccinia Grindeliae Pk.
   Sorosporium californicum Hark.
   Thecaphora californica (Hark.) G. P. Clinton.
Grindelia squarrosa (Pursh) Dunal.
   Aecidium Bigeloviae Pk.
   Aecidium Grindeliae Griffiths non Syd.
   Dicaeoma Stipae (Arth.) O. Kuntze. I.
   Puccinia Stipae Arth. I.
   Aecidium Grindeliae Syd.
   Dicaeoma Asterum (Kern) Arth. & Kern. I.
   Puccinia Asterum Kern. I.
   Puccinia extensicola Plowr. I.
   Ampelomyces quisqualis Ces.
   Cercospora Grindeliae Ell. & Ev.
   Cicinnobolus major Dearness & Barthol.
   Coleosporium Solidaginis Thm.
   Erysiphe Cichoracearum DC. †
   Leptosphaeria nigricans (Desm.) Ces. & De Not., var. inculta Sacc.
   Phoma leptospora Sacc.
   Micropuccinia Grindeliae (Pk.) Arth. & Jackson.
   Puccinia Grindeliae Pk.
   Puccinia tuberculans Ell. & Ev.
   Puccinia variolans Hark.
   Ramularia Grindeliae Ell. & Kellerm.
   Septoria Grindeliae Ell. & Barthol.

Grindelia squarrosa (*cont.*)
⎰Sorosporium cuneatum Scofield.
⎱Thecaphora cuneata (Scofield) G. P. Clinton.
Grindelia subalpina Greene.
Grindelia texana Scheele.
⎰Micropuccinia Grindeliae (Pk.) Arth. & Jackson.
⎨Puccinia Grindeliae Pk.
⎱Puccinia Tracyi Sacc. & Syd.
Gutierrezia californica (DC.) Torr. & Gray.
Gutierrezia diversifolia Greene.
Gutierrezia filifolia Greene.
Gutierrezia glomerella Greene.
Gutierrezia juncea Greene.
Gutierrezia longifolia Greene.
⎰Micropuccinia Grindeliae (Pk.) Arth. & Jackson.
⎱Puccinia Gutierreziae Ell. & Ev.
Gutierrezia Sarothrae (Pursh) Britton & Rusby.
⎰Aecidium Bigeloviae Pk.
⎨Aecidium Chrysopsidis Ell. & Anderson.
⎨Dicaeoma Stipae (Arth.) O. Kuntze. I.
⎱Puccinia Stipae Arth. I.
Coleosporium Solidaginis Thm.
⎰Diplodina coloradensis Ell. & Ev.
⎱Diplodinula coloradensis (Ell. & Ev.) Tassi.
Erysiphe Cichoracearum DC. †
Erysiphe Polygoni DC. †
⎰Micropuccinia Grindeliae (Pk.) Arth. & Jackson.
⎨Puccinia Bigeloviae Ell. & Ev.
⎨Puccinia Grindeliae Pk.
⎱Puccinia Gutierreziae Ell. & Ev.
Gutierrezia tenuis Greene.
Puccinia Gutierreziae Ell. & Ev.
Gutierrezia texana (DC.) Torr. & Gr.
⎰Aecidium Chrysopsidis Ell. & Anderson.
⎱Puccinia Stipae Arth. I.
Coleosporium Solidaginis Thm.
Gutierrezia sp. indet.
?Camerosporium rosellinioides Ell. & Ev.
Rhabdospora Gutierreziae Earle.
?Stemphylium subradians Ell. & Ev., var.
Xanthisma texanum DC.
Septoria Xanthismatis Dearness & House.
Heterotheca grandiflora Nutt.
Oidium erysiphoides Fr.
Heterotheca subaxillaris (Lam.) Britt. & Rusby.
Dicaeoma Asterum (Kern) Arth. & Kern.
Coleosporium Solidaginis Thm.
Corticium vagum B. & C.
Entyloma Compositarum Farl.
Rhizoctonia Solani Kühn.
Chrysopsis Bakeri Greene.
Chrysopsis Berlandieri Greene.
⎰Micropuccinia Grindeliae (Pk.) Arth. & Jackson.
⎱Puccinia Grindeliae Pk.

Chrysopsis caudata Rydb.
Coleosporium Solidaginis Thm.
Chrysopsis fastigiata Greene.
Micropuccinia Grindeliae (Pk.) Arth. & Jackson.
Chrysopsis graminifolia (Michx.) Nutt.
Cercospora macroguttata Atk.
Chrysopsis hirsutissima Greene.
Coleosporium Solidaginis Thm.
Chrysopsis hispida DC.
Pleospora herbarum (Fr.) Rabh.
Chrysopsis horrida Rydb.
⎰Coleosporium Solidaginis Thm.
⎱Puccinia Grindeliae Pk.
Chrysopsis imbricata A. Nels.
Micropuccinia Grindeliae (Pk.) Arth. & Jackson.
Chrysopsis mariana (L.) Nutt.
⎰Coleosporium Solidaginis Thm.
⎱Puccinia marianae Syd.
Chrysopsis resinolens A. Nels.
Micropuccinia Grindeliae (Pk.) Arth. & Jackson.
Chrysopsis scabrella Torr. & Gr.
Coleosporium Solidaginis Thm.
Chrysopsis villosa Nutt.
⎰Aecidium Bigeloviae Pk.
⎨Aecidium Chrysopsidis Ell. & Anderson.
⎱Puccinia Stipae Arth. I.
Coleosporium Solidaginis Thm.
Erysiphe Cichoracearum DC. †
⎰Micropuccinia Grindeliae (Pk.) Arth. & Jackson.
⎨Puccinia Grindeliae Pk.
⎱Puccinia hyalomitra Diet. & Holw.
Solidago altissima L.
⎰Dicaeoma Asterum (Kern) Arth. & Kern. I.
⎨Puccinia Asterum Kern. I.
⎱Puccinia Caricis-Solidaginis Arth. I.
Cercosporella Dearnessii Bubák & Sacc.
⎰Caeoma Solidaginis S.
⎱Coleosporium Solidaginis Thm.
Colletotrichum solitarium Ell. & Barthol.
Erysiphe Cichoracearum DC. †
⎰Puccinia minutula Pk.
⎱Puccinia Virgaureae (DC.) Lib.
Ramularia Virgaureae Thm.
Sclerotium mendax Sacc.
Sphaeria Solidaginis S.
Solidago altissima L., var. **procera** (Ait.) Fern.
Cicinnobolus Cesatii DBy.
Solidago amplexicaulis Torr. & Gr.
Coleosporium Solidaginis Thm.
Solidago arguta Ait.
⎰Aecidium Asterum S.
⎱Puccinia extensicola Plowr. I.
Cicinnobolus Cesatii DBy.

Solidago arguta (*cont.*)
　Coleosporium Solidaginis Thm.
　Coleosporium Sonchi-arvensis Auct. Amer.
　　p. p.
　Stichopsora Solidaginis (Thm.) Diet.
　Septoria intermedia Ell. & Ev.
　Septoria solidaginicola Pk.
Solidago aspera Ait.
　Coleosporium Solidaginis Thm.
Solidago austrina (Torr. & Gr.) Small.
　Coleosporium Solidaginis Thm.
Solidago bicolor L.
　Aecidium Compositarum Auct. Amer. p. p.
　Puccinia Caricis-Solidaginis Arth. I.
　Uromyces perigynius Halsted. I.
　Coleosporium Solidaginis Thm.
Solidago Boottii Hook.
Solidago brachyphylla Chapm.
　Coleosporium Solidaginis Thm.
Solidago caesia L.
　Aecidium Solidaginis S.
　Dicaeoma Asterum (Kern) Arth. & Kern. I.
　Dicaeoma Caricis-Solidaginis Arth. I.
　Dicaeoma extensicola (Plowr.) O. Kuntze. I.
　Puccinia Asterum Kern. I.
　Puccinia Caricis-Solidaginis Arth. I.
　Uromyces Solidagini-Caricis Arth. I.
　Coleosporium Solidaginis Thm.
　Coleosporium Sonchi-arvensis Auct. Amer. p.p.
　Rhytisma Solidaginis S. Spec. Dub.
　Septoria solidaginicola Pk.
Solidago californica Nutt.
　Coleosporium Solidaginis Thm.
　Micropuccinia Grindeliae (Pk.) Arth. & Jack-
　　son.
　Puccinia Solidaginis Pk.
　Septoria fumosa Pk.
Solidago canadensis L.
　Aecidium Asterum S.
　?Aecidium Compositarum, var. Solidaginis
　　Wint.
　Aecidium Solidaginis S.
　Dicaeoma Asterum (Kern) Arth. & Kern. I.
　Dicaeoma Caricis-Solidaginis Arth. I.
　Dicaeoma extensicola (Plowr.) O. Kuntze. I.
　Puccinia Asterum Kern. I.
　Puccinia Caricis-Solidaginis Arth. I.
　Puccinia Dulichii Syd. I.
　Puccinia extensicola Plowr. I.
　Puccinia vulpinoidis Diet. & Holw. I.
　Aecidium Solidaginis West Am. Fung. *362*.
　Uromyces perigynius Halsted. I.
　Uromyces Solidaginis-Caricis Arth. I.
　Ascochyta Solidaginum (S.) Starb.
　Dothidea Solidaginis (S.) Fr.
　Sphaeria Solidaginum S.
　Cercosporella cana (Pass.) Sacc.
　Cercosporella Dearnessii Bubák & Sacc.
　Cercosporella nivea Ell. & Barthol.

Coleosporium Solidaginis Thm.
Coleosporium Sonchi Auct. Amer. p. p.
Coleosporium Sonchi-arvensis Auct. Amer. p.p.
Stichopsora Solidaginis (Thm.) Diet.
Erysiphe Cichoracearum DC. †
Erysiphe lamprocarpa Auct. Amer. p. p.
Helotium herbarum (P.) Fr.
Mollisia erigeronata Cke.
Oidium erysiphoides Fr.
Ascospora pseudhimantia Rehm.
Discosphaerina pseudhimantia (Rehm) Petrak.
Dothidea Haydeni B. & C.
Ophiodothis Haydeni (B. & C.) Sacc.
Phyllachora Haydeni Dearness.
Placosphaeria Haydeni (B. & C.) Petrak.
Rhopographus Haydeni (B. & C.) Cke.
Phyllachora Solidaginum Sacc.
Peronospora Halstedii Farl.
Plasmopara Halstedii (Farl.) Berl. & De Toni.
Rhysotheca Halstedii (Farl.) G. W. Wilson.
Phoma herbarum Westd.
Ramularia Virgaureae Thm.
Cryptosporium Solidaginis C. & E.
Rhabdospora Solidaginis (C. & E.) Sacc.
Rhabdospora subgrisea Pk.
Rhinotrichum herbicola Ell. & Dearness.
Rhytisma Solidaginis S. Spec. Dub.
Sclerotium deciduum J. J. Davis.
Septoria canadensis Ell. & Davis.
Septoria Davisii Sacc.
Septoria fumosa Pk.
Septoria solidaginicola Pk.
Septoria Solidaginum Thm.
Sphaerella solidaginea Ell. & Kellerm.
Puccinia Solidaginis West Am. Fung. *361*.
Teleutospora Solidaginis (Niessl) Arth. &
　Bisby.
Uromyces Solidaginis Niessl.
Solidago caurina Piper.
Solidago celtidifolia Small.
Solidago Chandonnettii Steele.
Solidago Chapmani Gray.
　Coleosporium Solidaginis Thm.
Solidago concinna A. Nels.
　Aecidium Bigeloviae Pk.
　Dicaeoma Stipae (Arth.) O. Kuntze. I.
　Coleosporium Solidaginis Thm.
Solidago confinis Gray.
　Coleosporium Solidaginis Thm.
　Macrophoma sphaeropsispora (Ell. & Ev.)
　　Tassi.
　Phyllosticta sphaeropsispora Ell. & Ev.
Solidago Curtisii Torr. & Gr.
　Coleosporium Solidaginis Thm.
Solidago Cutleri Fern.
　Septoria brevis Pk.
Solidago decumbens Greene.
　Coleosporium Solidaginis Thm.
　Puccinia Solidaginis Pk.

Solidago Drummondii Torr. & Gr.
Solidago Elliottii Torr. & Gr.
  Coleosporium Solidaginis Thm.
Solidago elongata Nutt.
  { Dicaeoma Asterum (Kern) Arth. & Kern. I.
  { Puccinia Asterum Kern. I.
  Coleosporium Solidaginis Thm.
  Teleutospora Solidaginis (Niessl) Arth. &
    Bisby.
Solidago erecta Pursh.
  Dicaeoma Asterum (Kern) Arth. & Kern. I.
  Coleosporium Solidaginis Thm.
Solidago fistulosa Mill.
  Coleosporium Solidaginis Thm.
Solidago gilvocanescens (Rydb.) Smyth.
  Coleosporium Solidaginis Thm.
Solidago glaberrima Martens.
  { Dicaeoma Asterum (Kern) Arth. & Kern. I.
  { Puccinia Asterum Kern. I.
  { Puccinia extensicola Plowr. I.
  { Puccinia vulpinoidis Diet. & Holw. I.
  { Aecidium Bigeloviae Pk.
  { Dicaeoma Stipae (Arth.) O. Kuntze. I.
  { Puccinia Stipae Arth. I.
  Coleosporium Solidaginis Thm.
Solidago glomerata Michx.
Solidago hispida Muhl.
  Coleosporium Solidaginis Thm.
Solidago humilis Pursh vel Porter.
  Beloniella brevipila (Rob. & Desm.) Rehm.
Solidago juncea Ait.
  Dicaeoma Asterum (Kern) Arth. & Kern. I.
  { Coleosporium Solidaginis Thm.
  { Coleosporium Sonchi Auct. Amer. p. p.
  Erysiphe Cichoracearum DC. †
  { Laestadia biennis Dearness.
  { Paramazzantia biennis (Dearness) Petrak.
  Mollisia subatrata Cke.
  Pyrenopeziza Artemisiae (Lasch) Rehm, var.
    Solidaginis Rehm.
  Sclerotium deciduum J. J. Davis.
  Sphaerotheca Castagnei Lév.
Solidago juncea Ait, var. **scabrella** (Torr. & Gr.)
  Gray.
  Cercosporella nivea Ell. & Barthol.
Solidago lancifolia Chapm.
  Coleosporium Solidaginis Thm.
Solidago latifolia L.
  { Aecidium Asterum S.
  { Aecidium Compositarum, var. Solidaginis Ell.
  { Aecidium Solidaginis S.
  { Caeoma asteratum Lk.
  { Dicaeoma Asterum (Kern) Arth. & Kern. I.
  { Dicaeoma Caricis-Solidaginis Arth. I.
  { Dicaeoma extensicola (Plowr.) O. Kuntze. I.
  { Puccinia Asterum Kern. I.
  { Puccinia Caricis-Solidaginis Arth. I.
  { Uredo Asterum Spreng. p. p.

  Uromyces Solidaginis-Caricis Arth. I.
  Aecidium Verbesinae S.
  Cercospora reticulata (Pk.) Ell. & Ev.
  Cercospora stomatica Ell. & Davis.
  Cicinnobolus Cesatii DBy.
  { Coleosporium Solidaginis Thm.
  { Coleosporium Sonchi-arvensis Auct. Amer. p.p.
  Erysiphe Cichoracearum DC. †
  Ramularia tenuis J. J. Davis.
  Ramularia Virgaureae Thm.
  Rhytisma Solidaginis S. Spec. Dub.
  Septoria angularis Dearness & Barthol.
  Septoria atropurpurea Pk.
  { Septoria dolichospora Ell. & Ev.
  { Septoria Francisci Sacc.

Solidago lindheimeriana Scheele.
  Ramularia Virgaureae Thm.

Solidago macrophylla Pursh.
  Dicaeoma Asterum (Kern) Arth. & Kern. I.
  Coleosporium Solidaginis Thm.
  Diaporthe aorista Ell. & Ev.

Solidago missouriensis Nutt.
  { Aecidium Compositarum Auct. Amer. p. p.
  { Aecidium Solidaginis S.
  { Puccinia Asterum Kern. I.
  { Puccinia Caricis-Solidaginis Arth. I.
  { Puccinia extensicola Plowr. I.
  { Aecidium Bigelowiae Pk.
  { Puccinia Stipae Arth. I.
  { Coleosporium Solidaginis Thm.
  { Coleosporium Sonchi-arvensis Auct. Amer. p.p.
  { Stichopsora Solidaginis (Thm.) Diet.
  Cyathicula coronata (Bull. ex Fr.) De Not.
  Diaporthe lineariformis Petrak.
  Diaporthe linearis (Nees) Nits.
  Erysiphe Cichoracearum DC. †
  Phyllosticta gallicola Ell. & Ev.
  { Micropuccina Grindeliae (Pk.) Arth. & Jack-
  {   son.
  { Puccinia Grindeliae Pk.
  Sydowiella dakotensis Petrak.
  { Sorosporium cuneatum Schofield.
  { Sorosporium Solidaginis Ell. & Ev.
  { Thecaphora cuneata (Schofield) G. P. Clinton.

Solidago mollis Bartl.
  { Aecidium Bigeloviae Pk.
  { Aecidium recedens Arth.
  { Aecidium solidaginicola Ell. & Ev.
  { Dicaeoma Stipae (Arth.) O. Kuntze. I.
  { Puccinia Stipae Arth. I.
  { Aecidium Solidaginis S.
  { Dicaeoma Asterum (Kern) Arth. & Kern. I.
  { Puccinia Asterum Kern. I.
  { Puccinia extensicola Plowr. I.
  { Puccinia vulpinoidis Diet. & Holw. I.
  Cercosporella nivea Ell. & Barthol.
  Coleosporium Solidaginis Thm.

Solidago mollis (*cont.*)
Erysiphe Cichoracearum DC. †
{ Botryodiplodia gallicola (Sacc.) Petrak.
{ Macrophoma gallicola Sacc.
{ Traversoa gallicola (Sacc.) Petrak.
{ Puccinia Solidaginis Auct. Amer. p. p.
{ Puccinia Solidaginis-mollis Diet.
{ Micropuccinia Grindeliae (Pk.) Arth. & Jackson.
{ Puccinia irregularis Ell. & Tracy.
{ Puccinia Solidaginis Pk.
{ Puccinia Tracyi Sacc. & Syd.

Solidago multiradiata Ait.
Coleosporium Solidaginis Thm.

Solidago nana Nutt.
Erysiphe Cichoracearum DC. †
Micropuccinia Grindeliae (Pk.) Arth. & Jackson.

Solidago neglecta Torr. & Gr.
Dicaeoma Asterum (Kern) Arth. & Kern. I.
Coleosporium Solidaginis Thm.

Solidago nemoralis Ait.
Dicaeoma Asterum (Kern) Arth. & Kern. I.
Puccinia Stipae Arth. I.
Coleosporium Solidaginis Thm.
Colletotrichum solitarium Ell. & Barthol.
{ Micropuccinia Grindeliae (Pk.) Arth. & Jackson.
{ Puccinia Solidaginis Pk.
Ramularia Virgaureae Thm.

Solidago occidentalis Nutt.
Dicaeoma Asterum (Kern) Arth. & Kern. I.
Didymaria spissa Hark.
Erysiphe Cichoracearum DC. †

Solidago odora Ait.
Coleosporium Solidaginis Thm.
Septoria Solidaginis Cke.

Solidago ohioensis Riddell.
Phyllosticta similispora Ell. & Davis.

Solidago oreophila Rydb.
{ Coleosporium Solidaginis Thm.
{ Stichopsora Solidaginis (Thm.) Diet.
{ Micropuccinia Grindeliae (Pk.) Arth. & Jackson.
{ Puccinia Solidaginis Pk.

Solidago Parryi Pursh.
Dicaeoma Asterum (Kern) Arth. & Kern. I.

Solidago patula Muhl.
{ Dicaeoma Caricis-Solidaginis Arth. I.
{ Dicaeoma extensicola (Plowr.) O. Kuntze. I.
{ Puccinia Caricis-Solidaginis Arth. I.
{ Puccinia extensicola Plowr. I.
{ Coleosporium Solidaginis Thm.
{ Coleosporium Sonchi-arvensis Auct. Amer. p.p.
Septoria dolichospora Ell. & Ev.
Septoria solidaginicola Pk.

Solidago pauciflosculosa Michx.
Solidago petiolaris Ait.
Solidago pinensis Coult. & Small.
Solidago pinetorum Small.
{ Coleosporium Solidaginis Thm.
{ Coleosporium Sonchi Auct. Amer. p. p.
{ Coleosporium Sonchi-arvensis Auct. Amer. p.p.
Solidago Pitcheri Nutt.
Puccinia extensicola Plowr. I.
Puccinia Stipae Arth. I.
Coleosporium Solidaginis Thm.
Phoma herbarum Westd., var. Solidaginis Sacc.
Solidago polyphylla Rydb.
Dicaeoma Asterum (Kern) Arth. & Kern. I.
Uromyces Solidaginis Niessl.
Solidago puberula Nutt.
{ Coleosporium Solidaginis Thm.
{ Coleosporium Sonchi Auct. Amer. p. p.
Darluca Filum (Biv.) Cast.
Puccinia Solidaginis Pk.
{ Micropuccinia Virgaureae (DC.) Arth. & Jackson.
{ Puccinia Virgaureae (DC.) Lib.
Solidago pulcherrima A. Nels.
{ Micropuccinia Grindeliae (Pk.) Arth. & Jackson.
{ Puccinia Solidaginis Pk.
Teleutospora Solidaginis (Niessl) Arth. & Bisby.
Solidago pulverulenta Nutt.
Coleosporium Solidaginis Thm.
Solidago pumila Torr. & Gr.
{ Micropuccinia Grindeliae (Pk.) Arth. & Jackson.
{ Puccinia Solidaginis Pk.
Solidago Purshii Porter.
Coleosporium Solidaginis (S.) Thm.
Solidago radula Nutt.
{ Cercospora nivea Ell. & Barthol.
{ Cercosporella nivea Ell. & Barthol.
Coleosporium Solidaginis Thm.
Colletotrichum solitarium Ell. & Barthol.
Solidago Riddellii Frank.
Aecidium Compositarum Auct. Amer. p. p.
Coleosporium Solidaginis Thm.
{ Peronospora Halstedii Farl.
{ Plasmopara Halstedii (Farl.) Berl. & De Toni.
{ Rhysotheca Halstedii (Farl.) G. W. Wilson.
Solidago rigida L.
{ Aecidium Asterum S.
{ Aecidium Compositarum Auct. Amer. p.p.
{ Aecidium Solidaginis S.
{ Dicaeoma Asterum (Kern) Arth. & Kern. I.
{ Puccinia Asterum Kern. I.
{ Puccinia Caricis-Solidaginis Arth. I.
{ Aecidium Bigeloviae Pk.
{ Dicaeoma Stipae (Arth.) O. Kuntze. I.
{ Puccinia Stipae Arth. I.

Solidago rigida (*cont.*)
  Coleosporium Solidaginis Thm.
  Erysiphe Cichoracearum DC. †
  Ovularia occulta Sacc.
  { Leptothyrium tumidulum Sacc.
  { Phyllosticta similispora Ell. & Davis.
  { Peronospora entospora (Roze & Cornu) B. &
  {   Br.
  { Plasmopara entospora (Roze & Cornu) Schrt.
  Ramularia minax J. J. Davis.
  { Stachylidium roseum S.
  { Sporotrichum Schweinitzii Sacc.

Solidago rugosa Mill.
  { Aecidium Asterum S.
  { Aecidium Compositarum, var. Solidaginis Ell.
  { Dicaeoma Asterum (Kern) Arth. & Kern. I.
  { Dicaeoma erigeronatum Arth. I.
  { Puccinia Asterum Kern. I.
  { Puccinia Caricis-Solidaginis Arth. I.
  { Puccinia extensicola Plowr. I.
  { Puccinia Peckii Auct. Amer. p. p.
  { Puccinia vulpinoidis Diet. & Holw. I.
  { Nigredo perigynia (Halsted) Arth. I.
  { Uromyces perigynius Halsted. I.
  { Cercospora reticulata (Pk.) Ell. & Ev.
  { Cercosporella reticulata Pk.
  { Caeoma Solidaginis S.
  { Coleosporium Solidaginis Thm.
  { Coleosporium Sonchi Auct. Amer. p. p.
  { Coleosporium Sonchi-arvensis Auct. Amer. p.p.
  { Micropuccinia Virgaureae (DC.) Arth. & Jack-
  {   son.
  { Puccinia minutula Pk.
  { Puccinia Virgaureae (DC.) Lib.
  Ramularia serotina Ell. & Ev.
  Rhytisma Solidaginis S. Spec. Dub.

Solidago rupestris Raf.
  Coleosporium Solidaginis Thm.

Solidago sempervirens L.
  { Dicaeoma Asterum (Kern) Arth. & Kern. I.
  { Puccinia Asterum Kern. I.
  { Puccinia Caricis-Solidaginis Arth. I.
  { Caeoma Solidaginis S.
  { Coleosporium Solidaginis Thm.
  { Coleosporium Sonchi-arvensis Auct. Amer. p.p.
  Puccinia Virgaureae (DC.) Lib.
  Rhabdospora subgrisea Pk.
  Rhytisma bifrons S. Spec. Dub.

Solidago serotina Ait.
  { Aecidium Bigeloviae Pk.
  { Dicaeoma Stipae (Arth.)O. Kuntze. I.
  { Aecidium Asterum S.
  { Aecidium Compositarum Auct. Amer. p. p.
  { Aecidium Solidaginis S.
  { Dicaeoma Asterum (Kern) Arth. & Kern. I.
  { Dicaeoma extensicola (Plowr.) O. Kuntze. I.
  { Puccinia Caricis-Solidaginis Arth. I.
  { Puccinia extensicola Plowr. I.

  { Uromyces perigynius Halsted. I.
  { Uromyces Solidagini-Caricis Arth. I.
  { Cercospora reticulata (Pk.) Ell. & Ev.
  { Cercosporella reticulata Pk.
  Cercospora stomatica Ell. & Davis.
  Cladosporium astericola J. J. Davis.
  { Caeoma Solidaginis S.
  { Coleosporium Solidaginis Thm.
  { Coleosporium Sonchi Auct. Amer. p. p.
  { Coleosporium Sonchi-arvensis Auct. Amer. p.p.
  { Stichopsora Solidaginis (Thm.) Diet.
  { Uredo Solidaginis S.
  Erysiphe Cichoracearum DC. †
  Ramularia serotina Ell. & Ev.
  Ramularia Virgaureae Thm.
  { Septoria canadensis Ell. & Davis.
  { Septoria Davisii Sacc.
  { Septoria intermedia Ell. & Ev.
  { Septoria solidaginicola Pk.
  Septoria Virgaureae Desm.
  { Teleutospora Solidaginis (Niessl) Arth. &
  {   Bisby.
  { Uromyces Solidaginis Niessl.

Solidago serotina Ait., var. **gigantea** (Ait.) Gray.
  Basidiophora entospora Roze & Cornu.
  Coleosporium Solidaginis Thm.

Solidago speciosa Nutt.
  { Dicaeoma Asterum (Kern) Arth. & Kern. I.
  { Puccinia Caricis-Solidaginis Arth. I.
  Coleosporium Solidaginis Thm.
  Colletotrichum solitarium Ell. & Barthol.
  { Micropuccinia Grindeliae (Pk.) Arth. & Jack-
  {   son.
  { Puccinia irregularis Ell. & Tracy.
  { Puccinia Solidaginis Pk.
  { Puccinia Tracyi Sacc. & Syd.
  Ramularia Virgaureae Thm.

Solidago squarrosa Muhl.
Solidago stricta Ait.
Solidago tolmieana Gray.
Solidago tortifolia Ell.
  Coleosporium Solidaginis Thm.

Solidago trinervata Greene.
  { Micropuccinia Grindeliae (Pk.) Arth. & Jack-
  {   son.
  { Puccinia Solidaginis Pk.

Solidago uliginosa Nutt.
  { Dicaeoma Asterum (Kern) Arth. & Kern. I.
  { Puccinia Caricis-Solidaginis Arth. I.
  Cercosporella nivea Ell. & Barthol.
  Coleosporium Solidaginis Thm.

Solidago ulmifolia Muhl.
  { Aecidium Asterum S.
  { Aecidium Solidaginis S.
  { Dicaeoma Asterum (Kern) Arth. & Kern. I.
  { Dicaeoma extensicola (Plowr.) Arth. & Kern. I.
  { Puccinia Caricis-Solidaginis Arth. I.
  { Puccinia extensicola Plowr. I.

Solidago ulmifolia (*cont.*)
- Coleosporium Solidaginis Thm.
- Coleosporium Sonchi-arvensis Auct. Amer. p.p.
- Stichopsora Solidaginis (Thm.) Diet.
- Micropuccinia Virgaureae (DC.) Arth. & Jackson.
- Puccinia Virgaureae (DC.) Lib.
- Ramularia serotina Ell. & Ev.
- Ramularia Virgaureae J. J. Davis non Thm.

Solidago uniligulata (DC.) Porter.
- Cercosporella nivea Ell. & Barthol.
- Coleosporium Solidaginis Thm.

Solidago Virgaurea L.
- Cercosporella Virgaureae (Thm.) Lindau.
- Coleosporium Solidaginis Thm.
- Puccinia Solidaginis (Niessl) Maire.
- Uromyces Solidaginis Niessl.

Solidago sp. indet.

PEZIZINEAE

Lachnum niveum (Hedw. ex Fr.) Karst., var. Fairmani Rehm.
- Mollisia atrata (P.) Karst.
- Peziza atrata P.
- Pyrenopeziza atrata (P.) Fckl.
- Mollisia atrata (P.) Karst., var. megalospora Ell. & Ev.
- Mollisia atrocinerea (Cke.) Phil.
- Peziza atrocinerea Cke.
- Peziza subatra C. & P.
- Pyrenopeziza subatra (C. & P.) Sacc.

PHACIDIINEAE

Hypoderma nitidum De Not.

HYSTERIINEAE

Rhytisma punctatum (P.) ex Fr.

PYRENOMYCETINEAE

Diaporthe mucronulata Sacc.
- Diaporthe orthoceras (Fr.) Nits.
- Sphaeria orthoceras Fr.
- Endophlaea aulica C. & E.
- Leptosphaeria aulica (C. & E.) Ell.
- Metasphaeria aulica (C. & E.) Sacc.
- Sphaeria aulica C. & E.
Leptosphaeria Doliolum (P. ex Fr.) De Not.
Leptosphaeria ogilviensis (B. & Br.) Ces. & De Not.
Leptosphaeria perplexa Sacc. & Fairman.
Leptoshpaeria subconica (C. & P.) Sacc.
- Bertiella brenckleana Rehm.
- Dothidea Heliopsidis S.?
- Montagnella Heliopsidis (S.) Sacc.
- Rosenscheldia Heliopsidis (S.) Theissen & Syd.
- Dothidea Solidaginis (S.) Fr.
- ?Phyllachora Solidaginis (S.) Sacc.
- Sphaeria Solidaginis S. (in litt.).
- Physalospora erratica (C. & E.) Sacc.
- Sphaeria erratica C. & E.

- Rhabdospora linearis Ell. & Ev.:
- Sphaeria linearis S. Am. Bor. 1452.
- Ophiobolus Solidaginis Sacc.
- Raphidospora Solidaginis (Sacc.) Cke.
- Xylaria filiformis (A. & S.) Fr., var. caulincola Rehm.

FUNGI IMPERFECTI

Cercospora fulvescens Sacc.
Dinemasporium strigosum (Fr.) Sacc.
Helminthosporium naviculatum Dearness & House.
Leptostroma vulgare Fr.
Phlyctaena arcuata B.
Phoma Solidaginis Cke., var. longiscula Sacc. sec. House.
Phoma Solidaginis Cke., var. longispora Sacc.
Phyllosticta similispora Ell. & Davis.
Phyllosticta solidaginicola Tehon & Daniels.
Septoria Gallarum Ell. & Ev.

MISCELLANEA

Cyphella villosa (Fr.) Karst.
Hymenula vulgaris Fr.
Hypochnus rubiginosus Bres.
- Puccinia Asteris Duby.
- Puccinia Virgaurea Fung. Columb. *1385.*

Euthamia graminifolia (L.) Nutt.
- Aecidium Asterum S.
- Aecidium Compositarum Auct. Amer. p. p.
- Aecidium Solidaginis S.
- Dicaeoma Asterum (Kern) Arth. & Kern. I.
- Puccinia Asterum Kern. I.
- Puccinia Caricis-Asteris Arth. I.
- Puccinia Caricis-Solidaginis Arth. I.
- Puccinia extensicola Plowr. I.
- Cercosporella ontariensis Sacc.
- Coleosporium delicatulum Hedgc. & Long.
- Coleosporium Solidaginis Carl. Ured. Amer. *44.*
- Coleosporium Solidaginis Fung. Columb. *2509.*
- Rhytisma Solidaginis S. Spec. Dub.
- Uromyces perigynius Halsted. I.

Euthamia gymnospermoides Greene.
- Coleosporium delicatulum Hedgc. & Long.

Euthamia leptocephala (Torr. & Gr.) Greene.
- Coleosporium delicatulum Hedgc. & Long.
- Coleosporium Solidaginis Auct. Amer. p. p.
- Rhytisma Solidaginis S. Spec. Dub.

Euthamia minor (Michx.) Greene.
- Coleosporium delicatulum Hedgc. & Long.

Euthamia tenuifolia (Pursh) Greene.
- Dicaeoma Asterum (Kern) Arth. & Kern. I.
- Puccinia Caricis-Solidaginis Arth. I.
- Coleosporium delicatulum Hedgc. & Long.
- Coleosporium Solidaginis Crypt. Farl. Herb. *215b.*
- Darluca Filum (Biv.) Cast.

Brachychaeta sphacelata (Raf.) Britt.
- Dicaeoma Asterum (S.) Arth. & Kern. I.

Aplopappus Bloomeri Gray.
  Lamproderma robustum Ell. & Ev.
  Micropuccinia Grindeliae (Pk.) Arth. & Jackson.

Aplopappus ciliatus (Nutt.) DC.
  Micropuccinia Grindeliae (Pk.) Arth. & Jackson.

Aplopappus croceus Gray.
  Phoma inulina Sacc.

Aplopappus ericoides Hook. & Arn.
  Tremella moriformis B.

Aplopappus gracilis Gray.
  Micropuccinia Grindeliae (Pk.) Arth. & Jackson.

Aplopappus integrifolius T. C. Porter.
  Pleospora herbarum (Fr.) Rabh.

Aplopappus lanceolatus Torr. & Gr.
  Coleosporium Solidaginis Thm.
  Erysiphe Cichoracearum DC. †
  Micropuccinia Grindeliae (Pk.) Arth. & Jackson.

Aplopappus laricifolius Gray.
  { Micropuccinia Grindeliae (Pk.) Arth. & Jackson.
  { Puccinia Grindeliae Pk.

Aplopappus megacephalus Hitchc.
  Micropuccinia marianae (Syd.) Arth. & Jackson.

Aplopappus Nuttallii Torr. & Gr.
  { Micropuccinia Grindeliae (Pk.) Arth. & Jackson.
  { Puccinia Grindeliae Pk.
  { Puccinia tuberculans Ell. & Ev.
  Dicaeoma Stipae (Arth.) O. Kuntze. I.

Aplopappus Parryi Gray.
  { Aecidium Compositarum Auct. p. p.
  { Dicaeoma Asterum (S.) Arth. & Kern. I.

Aplopappus rubiginosus Torr. & Gr.
  { Micropuccinia Grindeliae (Pk.) Arth. & Jackson.
  { Puccinia Grindeliae Pk.
  { Puccinia variolans Hark.

Aplopappus spinulosus (Pursh) DC.
Aplopappus squarrosus Hook. & Arn.
  { Micropuccinia Grindeliae (Pk.) Arth. & Jackson.
  { Puccinia Aplopappi Syd.
  { Puccinia Grindeliae Pk.
  { Puccinia tuberculans Ell. & Ev.
  { Puccinia variolans Hark.

Aplopappus venetus (H. B. K.) Blake.
  { Micropuccinia Grindeliae (Pk.) Arth. & Jackson.
  { Puccinia Grindeliae Pk.
  { Puccinia tuberculans Ell. & Ev.

  { Thecaphora piluliformis B. & C.
  { Poecilosporium Davidsohnii (Diet. & Holw.) Sacc. & Syd.
  { Poikilosporium Davidsohnii (Diet. & Holw) Diet.
  { Tolyposporium Davidsonii Diet. & Holw.

Sideranthus australis (Greene) Rydb.
  Micropuccinia Grindeliae (Pk.) Arth. & Jackson.

Stenotus acaulis Nutt.
  Micropuccinia Grindeliae (Pk.) Arth. & Jackson.

Stenotus latifolius A. Nels.
  Micropuccinia Grindeliae (Pk.) Arth. & Jackson.

Bigelovia sp. indet. (Compare Aplopappus Isocoma Chrysothamnus.)
  { Agyriella Betheli Ell. & Ev.
  { Agyriopsis Betheli (Ell. & Ev.) Sacc. & Syd.
  Aposphaeria condensata Ell. & Ev.
  Camarosporium rosellinioides Ell. & Ev.
  Clasterosporium pulvinatum Ell. & Ev.
  Cylindrocolla Bigeloviae Ell. & Ev.
  { Dothidea Bigeloviae Ell. & Ev.
  { Dothidea montaniensis Ell. & Ev.
  Macrosporium puccinioides Ell. & Anderson.
  Phleospora Bigeloviae Ell.
  Rosellinia pulveracea Fckl.
  { Sorosporium Bigeloviae Griffiths.
  { Thecaphora piluliformis B. & C.
  Stemphylium subradians Ell. & Ev., var.
  Trematosphaeria Chrysothamni Earle.

Isocoma coronopifolia (Gray) Greene.
  Thecaphora piluliformis B. & C.

Isocoma Wrightii (Gray) Rydb.
  Phoma Estrelti Fairman.
  Pleospora Bardanae Niessl.
  { Micropuccinia Grindeliae (Pk.) Arth. & Jackson.
  { Puccinia Gutierreziae Ell. & Ev.
  { Puccinia tuberculans Ell. & Ev.

Chrysothamnus Bigelovii (Gray) Greene.
  Micropuccinia Grindeliae (Pk.) Arth. & Jackson.

Chrysothamnus elegans Greene.
  Micropuccinia Grindeliae (Pk.) Arth. & Jackson.

Chrysothamnus glaucus A. Nels.
  { Micropuccinia Grindeliae (Pk.) Arth. & Jackson.
  { Puccinia Bigeloviae Ell. & Ev.
  { Puccinia Grindeliae Pk.

Chrysothamnus linifolius Greene.
  Erysiphe Cichoracearum DC. †
  Micropuccinia Grindeliae (Pk.) Arth. & Jackson.

Chrysothamnus marianus Rydb.
{ Micropuccinia Grindeliae (Pk.) Arth. & Jackson.
Puccinia tuberculans Ell. & Ev.
Chrysothamnus nauseosus (Pall.) Britt.
{ Aecidium Bigeloviae Pk.
Dicaeoma Stipae (Arth.) O. Kuntze. I.
Puccinia Stipae Arth. I.
Cucurbitaria umbilicata Ell.
Epochnium isthmophorum Sacc.
Erysiphe Cichoracearum DC. †
Erysiphe Cichoracearum DC. †, var. sepulta (Ell. & Ev.) Salmon.
{ Erysiphe Polygoni DC. †, var. sepulta (Ell. & Ev.) Salmon.
Erysiphe sepulta Ell. & Ev.
Gibberidia arthrophyma Fairman.
Lophiostoma brenckleanum Sacc.
Macrosporium puccinioides Ell. & F. W. Anderson.
Melanomma occidentale (Ell.) Sacc.
{ Montagnella tumefaciens (Ell. & Hark) Berl. & Vogl.
Sphaeria tumefaciens Ell. & Hark.
Syncarpella tumefaciens (Ell. & Hark.) Theissen & Syd.
Montagnella tumefaciens (Ell. & Hark.) Berl. & Vogl., var. reducta Ell. & Ev.
{ Micropuccinia Grindeliae (Pk.) Arth. & Jackson.
Puccinia Bigeloviae Ell. & Ev.
Puccinia Grindeliae Pk.
Puccinia tuberculans Ell. & Ev.
Rhizoctonia Solani Kühn.
Rosellinia Bigeloviae Ell. & Ev.
Rosellinia ovalis (Ell.) Sacc.
{ Steganosporium utahense Sacc.
Thyrostroma utahense (Sacc.) Petrak.
Stemphylium laxum Ell. & Ev.
Tapesia tumefaciens Ell. & Ev.
Chrysothamnus plattensis Greene.
Micropuccinia Grindeliae (Pk.) Arth. & Jackson.
Chrysothamnus pulcherrimus A. Nels.
{ Dicaeoma Stipae (Arth.) O. Kuntze. I.
Puccinia Stipae Arth. I.
{ Micropuccinia Grindeliae (Pk.) Arth. & Jackson.
Puccinia tuberculans Ell. & Ev.
Chrysothamnus tortifolius Gray.
Puccinia Gutierreziae Ell. & Ev.
Chrysothamnus Vaseyi (Gray) Greene.
Erysiphe Cichoracearum DC. †
Chrysothamnus viscidiflorus (Hook.) Nutt.
{ Aecidium Bigeloviae Pk.
Dicaeoma Stipae (Arth.) O. Kuntze. I.
Dendryphium sphaerioides Ell. & Ev.
Ersiyphe Cichoracearum DC. †

{ Micropuccinia Grindeliae (Pk.) Arth. & Jackson.
Puccinia tuberculans Ell. & Ev.
Glycyderas sp. indet.
Cercospora Glyceridasis Fragoso & Ciferri.
Keerlia mexicana Gray.
Aecidium Keerliae Arth.
Psilactis asteroides Gray.
Coleosporium Solidaginis Thm.
Micropuccinia Asteris (Duby) Arth. & Jackson.
Boltonia asteroides (L.) L'Her.
{ Aecidium Boltoniae Arth.
Dicaeoma Asterum (Kern) Arth. & Kern. ī.
Entyloma Compositarum Farl.
Erysiphe Cichoracearum DC. †
Septoria Erigerontis B. & C., var. Boltoniae Webber.
Boltonia diffusa Ell.
Guignardia Boltoniae Dearness & Barthol.
Macrophoma Boltoniae Dearness.
Phoma Boltoniae Dearness.
Uromyces Boltoniae H. S. Jackson.
Townsendia grandiflora Nutt.
Dicaeoma Stipae (Arth.) O. Kuntze. I.
Callistephus chinensis Nees.
   (See also Aster sp. indet.)
Ascochyta Asteris (Bres.) Gloyer.
Botrytis cinerea P. †
{ Coleosporium Solidaginis Thm.
Coleosporium Sonchi Auct. Amer. p. p.
Coleosporium Sonchi-arvensis Auct. Amer. p.p.
Corticium vagum B. & C.
Erysiphe Cichoracearum DC. †
Fusarium conglutinans Wr.
Fusarium conglutinans Wr., var. Callistephi Beach.
Fusarium incarnatum Wollenw.
Fusarium oxysporum Schl.
Macrosporium caudatum C. & E.
Macrosporium florigenum Ell. & Dearness.
Phomopsis Callistephi Tehon & Daniels.
Phytophthora omnivora DBy.
Rhizoctonia Solani Kühn.
Sclerotinia sclerotiorum (Lib.) Schrt.
Septoria Callistephi Gloyer.
Aster acuminatus Michx.
Dicaeoma Asterum (Kern) Arth. & Kern. I.
{ Coleosporium Asterum (Diet.) Syd.
Coleosporium Solidaginis Thm.
{ Micropuccinia Asteris (Duby) Arth. & Jackson.
Puccinia Asteris Duby.
Puccinia Asteris Duby, var. purpurascens C. & P.
Puccinia purpurascens C. & P.

Aster adscendens Lindl.
⎰ Aecidium Asterum S.
⎱ Dicaeoma Asterum (Kern) Arth. & Kern. I.
Puccinia Asterum Kern. I.
Puccinia Caricis-Asteris Arth. I.
⎰ Coleosporium Asterum (Diet.) Syd.
⎱ Coleosporium Solidaginis Thm.
Entyloma Compositarum Farl.
Erysiphe Cichoracearum DC.†
⎰ Micropuccinia Asteris (Duby) Arth. & Jackson.
Puccinia Asteris Duby.
Puccinia magnoecia Ell. & Ev.
Puccinia Solidaginis N. Am. Ured. *1472*.

Aster amethystinus Nutt.
Dicaeoma Stipae (Arth.) O. Kuntze. I.

Aster amplissimus Greene.
Coleosporium Solidaginis Thm.

Aster Andersoni Gray.
Dicaeoma Asterum (Kern) Arth. & Kern. I.

Aster arenarioides D. C. Eaton.
Puccinia Asteris Duby.

Aster armeriifolius Greene.
Dicaeoma Asterum (Kern) Arth. & Kern. I.

Aster azureus Lindl.
⎰ Coleosporium Solidaginis Thm.
⎱ Coleosporium Sonchi-arvensis Auct. Amer. p.p.
Erysiphe Cichoracearum DC.†
⎰ Micropuccinia Asteris (Duby) Arth. & Jackson.
Puccinia Asteris Duby.
Ramularia Asteris (Phil. & Plowr.) Bubák.
Septoria solidaginicola Pk.

Aster Bigelovii Gray.
Leptosphaeria ogilviensis (B. & Br.) Ces. & De Not.

Aster canescens Pursh.
Puccinia Asterum Kern. I.
Erysiphe Cichoracearum DC.†
?Micropuccinia Grindeliae (Pk.) Arth. & Jackson.

Aster canescens Pursh, var. **viscosus** Gray.
⎰ Coleosporium Asterum (Diet.) Syd.
⎱ Coleosporium Solidaginis Thm.

Aster Chamissonis Gray.
Dicaeoma Asterum (Kern) Arth. & Kern. I.
Coleosporium Solidaginis Thm.
⎰ Micropuccinia Asteris (Duby) Arth. & Jackson.
Puccinia Asteris Duby.

Aster ciliomarginatus Rydb.
⎰ Dicaeoma Asterum (Kern) Arth. & Kern. I.
⎱ Puccinia Caricis-Asteris Arth. I.

Aster commutatus (Torr. & Gr.) Gray.
Coleosporium Solidaginis Thm.
⎰ Erysiphe Cichoracearum DC.†
⎱ Erysiphe communis Auct. Amer. p. p.

⎰ Montagnella Heliopsidis (S.) Sacc.
⎱ Rosenscheldia Heliopsidis (S.) Theissen & Syd.
Puccinia Asteris Duby.

Aster concinnus Willd.
⎰ Coleosporium Asterum (Diet.) Syd.
⎱ Coleosporium Solidaginis Thm.

Aster conspicuus Lindl.
Dicaeoma Asterum (Kern) Arth. & Kern. I.
⎰ Coleosporium Solidaginis Thm.
⎱ Coleosporium Sonchi-arvensis Auct. Amer. p.p.
Erysiphe Cichoracearum DC.†
⎰ Micropuccinia Asteris (Duby) Arth. & Jackson.
Puccinia Asteris Duby.

Aster cordifolius L.
⎰ Aecidium Asterum S.
Caeoma asteratum Lk.
Dicaeoma Asterum (Kern) Arth. & Kern. I.
Dicaeoma Caricis-Asteris Arth. I.
Dicaeoma extensicola (Plowr.) O. Kuntze. I.
Puccinia Asterum Kern. I.
Puccinia Caricis-Asteris Arth. I.
Puccinia extensicola Plowr. I.
⎰ Coleosporium Solidaginis Thm.
Coleosporium Sonchi Auct. Amer. p. p.
Coleosporium Sonchi-arvensis Auct. Amer. p.p.
Uredo Solidaginis S.
⎰ Erysiphe Asterum S.
Erysiphe Cichoracearum DC.†
Erysiphe lamprocarpa Auct. Amer. p. p.
Eutypella herbicola Ell. & Ev.
⎰ Dicaeoma Asteris (Duby) O. Kuntze.
Micropuccinia Asteris (Duby) Arth. & Jackson.
Puccinia Asteris Duby.
Ramularia macrospora Fr., var. Senecionis Sacc.
Rhytisma Solidaginis S. sp. dub.
Septoria astericola Ell. & Ev.
Septoria atropurpurea Pk.

Aster crassulus Rydb.
Coleosporium Solidaginis Thm.
Micropuccinia Asteris (Duby) Arth. & Jackson.

Aster Cusickii Gray.
Coleosporium Solidaginis Thm.
⎰ Micropuccinia Asteris (Duby) Arth. & Jackson.
Puccinia Asteris Duby.

Aster divaricatus L.
⎰ Aecidium Asterum S.
⎱ Puccinia Asterum Kern. I.
⎰ Coleosporium Solidaginis Thm.
⎱ Coleosporium Sonchi-arvensi Auct. Amer. p.p.
Erysiphe Cichoracearum DC.†
Puccinia Asteris Duby.
Septoria atropurpurea Pk.

Aster Douglasii Lindl.
　Coleosporium Solidaginis Thm.
Aster Drummondii Lindl.
　⎰Dicaeoma Asterum (Kern) Arth. & Kern. I.
　⎰Dicaeoma Caricis-Asteris Arth. I.
　⎱Dicaeoma extensicola (Plowr.) O. Kuntze. I.
　⎰Puccinia Asterum Kern. I.
　⎱Puccinia Caricis-Asteris Arth. I.
　Ascochyta Compositarum J. J. Davis.
　Basidiophora entospora Roze & Cornu.
　⎰Coleosporium Solidaginis Thm.
　⎱Coleosporium Sonchi-arvensis Auct. Amer. p.p.
　Erysiphe Cichoracearum DC. †
　⎰Micropuccinia Asteris (Duby) Arth. & Jack-
　⎱　son.
　Puccinia Asteris Duby.
　Puccinia Gerardii Pk.
　Septoria angularis Tharp.
　Septoria astericola Ell. & Ev.
　Septoria asterina Tharp.
　Septoria atropurpurea Pk.
Aster dumosus L.
　⎰Coleosporium Solidaginis Thm.
　⎱Coleosporium Sonchi-arvensis Auct. Amer. p.p.
　⎰Ophiodothis Haydeni (B. & C.) Sacc.
　⎱Phyllachora Haydeni Dearness.
Aster ericoides L.
　⎰Aecidium Bigeloviae Pk.
　⎱Puccinia Stipae Arth. I.
　Uromyces perigynius Halsted. I.
　⎰Coleosporium Asterum (Diet.) Syd.
　⎰Coleosporium Solidaginis Thm.
　⎰Coleosporium Sonchi Auct. Amer. p. p.
　⎱Coleosporium Sonchi-arvensis Auct. Amer. p.p.
　Erysiphe Cichoracearum DC. †
　⎰Dothidea Haydeni B. & C.
　⎰Ophiodothis Haydeni (B. & C.) Sacc.
　⎱Rhopographus Haydeni (B. & C.) Cke.
　⎰Micropuccinia Asteris (Duby) Arth. & Jack-
　⎱　son.
　Puccinia Asteris Duby.
Aster exiguus (Fernald) Rydb.
　⎰Aecidium Asterum S.
　⎰Dicaeoma Asterum (Kern) Arth. & Kern. I.
　⎰Puccinia Asterum Kern. I.
　⎱Puccinia Caricis-Asteris Arth. I.
　⎰Aecidium Bigeloviae Pk.
　⎰Dicaeoma Stipae (Arth.) O. Kuntze. I.
　⎱Puccinia Stipae Arth. I.
Aster foliaceus Lindl.
　⎰Aecidium Asterum S.
　⎱Dicaeoma Asterum (Kern) Arth. & Kern. I.
　Coleosporium Solidaginis Thm.
　Puccinia Asteris Duby.
Aster foliaceus Lindl., var. **apricus** Gray.
　⎰Dicaeoma Asterum (Kern) Arth. & Kern. I.
　⎱Puccinia Caricis-Asteris Arth. I.

Aster foliaceus Lindl., var. **Burkei** Gray.
　⎰Micropuccinia Asteris (Duby) Arth. & Jack-
　⎰　son.
　⎱Puccinia Asteris S.
Aster foliaceus Lindl., var. **Canbyi** Vasey.
　⎰Aecidium Asterum S.
　⎰Dicaeoma Asterum (Kern) Arth. & Kern. I.
　⎰Puccinia Asterum Kern. I.
　⎰Puccinia Caricis-Asteris Arth. I.
　⎰Puccinia extensicola Plowr.
　⎰Micropuccinia Asteris (Duby) Arth. & Jack-
　⎰　son.
　⎱Puccinia Asteris Duby.
Aster foliaceus Lindl., var. **Eatoni** Gray.
　⎰Coleosporium Solidaginis Thm.
　⎱Coleosporium Sonchi-arvensis Auct. Amer.p.p.
　Erysiphe Cichoracearum DC. †
　⎰Micropuccinia Asteris (Duby) Arth. & Jack-
　⎰　son.
　⎱Puccinia Asteris Duby.
Aster foliaceus Lindl., var. **frondeus** Gray.
　Dicaeoma Asterum (S.) Arth. & Kern. I.
　Coleosporium Solidaginis Thm.
Aster Fremontii Gray.
　⎰Dicaeoma Asterum (Kern) Arth. & Kern. I.
　⎱Puccinia Caricis-Asteris Arth. I.
　⎰Coleosporium Asterum (Diet.) Syd.
　⎱Coleosporium Solidaginis Thm.
　Erysiphe Cichoracearum DC. †
　Micropuccinia Asteris (Duby) Arth. & Jack-
　　son.
Aster frondosus (Nutt.) Torr. & Gr.
　Puccinia Asterum Kern. I.
　⎰Coleosporium Asterum (Diet.) Syd.
　⎱Coleosporium Solidaginis Thm.
　⎰Micropuccinia Asteris (Duby) Arth. & Jack-
　⎰　son.
　⎱Puccinia Asteris Duby.
Aster glabriusculus Torr. & Gr.
　Micropuccinia Grindeliae (Pk.) Arth. & Jack-
　　son.
Aster glaucus Torr. & Gr.
　⎰Micropuccinia Asteris (Duby) Arth. & Jack-
　⎰　son.
　⎱Puccinia Asteris Duby.
　Micropuccinia Grindeliae (Pk.) Arth. & Jack-
　　son.
Aster gracilis Nutt.
　Micropuccinia Asteris (Duby) Arth. & Jack-
　　son.
Aster Hallii Gray.
Aster hesperius Gray.
　Coleosporium Solidaginis Thm.
Aster infirmus Michx.
　Fusicladium virginiense Ell. & Ev. nom. nud.
Aster junceus Ait.
　⎰Coleosporium Asterum (Diet.) Syd.
　⎱Coleosporium Solidaginis Thm.
　Erysiphe Cichoracearum DC. †

Aster junciformis Rydb.
  Micropuccinia Asteris (Duby) Arth. & Jackson
Aster kentuckiensis Brit.
  Coleosporium Solidaginis Thm.
  { Micropuccinia Asteris (Duby) Arth. & Jackson.
  { Puccinia Asteris Duby.
Aster laetivirens Greene.
  Dicaeoma Asterum (Kern) Arth. & Kern. I.
Aster laevis L.
  { Aecidium Asterum S.
  { ?Aecidium Compositarum Auct. Amer. p. p.
  { Dicaeoma Asterum (Kern) Arth. & Kern.
  { Dicaeoma erigeronatum Arth. I.
  { Puccinia extensicola Plowr. I.
  { Coleosporium Solidaginis Thm.
  { Coleosporium Sonchi Auct. Amer. p. p.
  { Erysiphe Cichoracearum DC. †
  { Erysiphe lamprocarpa Auct. Amer. p. p.
  { Micropuccinia Asteris (Duby) Arth. & Jackson.
  { Puccinia Asteris Duby.
  Septoria atropurpurea Pk.
Aster laevis L., var. **Geyeri** Gray.
  { Coleosporium Asterum (Diet.) Syd.
  { Coleosporium Solidaginis Thm.
  { Peridermium montanum Arth. & Kern. III.
  Micropuccinia Asteris (Duby) Arth. & Jackson.
Aster lateriflorus (L.) Brit.
  Asteromella astericola J. J. Davis.
  Basidiophora entospora Roze & Cornu.
  { Coleosporium Asterum (Diet.) Syd.
  { Coleosporium Solidaginis Thm.
  { Coleosporium Sonchi Auct. Amer. p. p.
  { Coleosporium Sonchi-arvensis Auct. Amer. p.p.
  Diaporthe aorista Ell. & Ev.
  Erysiphe Cichoracearum DC. †
  Ophiodothis Haydeni (B. & C.) Sacc.
  { Dicaeoma Asteris (Duby) O. Kuntze.
  { Micropuccinia Asteris (Duby) Arth. & Jackson.
  { Puccinia Asteris Duby.
  { Ramularia macrospora Fres., var. Asteris Sacc. 10 April 1886.
  { Ramularia Asteris (Phil. & Plowr.) Bubák. 15 Dec. 1906.
  { Ramularia Asteris (Sacc.) Barthol. 30 Nov. 1911.
  Septoria atropurpurea Pk.
  Septoria solidaginicola Pk.
  Synchytrium nigrescens J. J. Davis.
Aster ledophyllus Gray.
  { Aecidium Asterum S.
  { Dicaeoma Asterum (Kern) Arth. & Kern. I.
  { Puccinia Asterum Kern. I.
  { Puccinia Caricis-Asteris Arth. I.

Aster lindleyanus Torr. & Gr.
?{ Aecidium Asterum S.
 { Aecidium Compositarum Auct. Amer. p. p.
  Coleosporium Solidaginis Thm.
  Erysiphe Cichoracearum DC. †
Aster longifolius Lam.
  { Dicaeoma Asterum (Kern) Arth. & Kern. I.
  { Puccinia Caricis-Asteris Arth. I.
  { Puccinia extensicola Plowr. I.
  Clypeoporthella Brencklei Petrak.
  Coleosporium Solidaginis Thm.
  Erysiphe Cichoracearum DC. †
  Leptosphaeria Erigerontis Berl.
  Puccinia Asteris Duby.
Aster lowrieanus Porter.
  { Coleosporium Asterum (Diet.) Syd.
  { Coleosporium Solidaginis Thm.
  Micropuccinia Asteris (Duby) Arth. & Jackson.
Aster lucayanus Brit.
  Micropuccinia Asteris (Duby) Arth. & Jackson.
Aster macrophyllus L.
  { Dicaeoma Asterum (Kern) Arth. & Kern. I.
  { Puccinia Asterum Kern. I.
  { Puccinia Caricis-Asteris Arth. I.
  Nigredo Junci (Desm.) Arth. I.
  Nigredo Silphii Arth. I.
  { Coleosporium Solidaginis Thm.
  { Coleosporium Sonchi Auct. Amer. p.p.
  { Coleosporium Sonchi-arvensis Auct. Amer. p.p.
  Entyloma Compositarum Farl.
  Erysiphe Cichoracearum DC. †
  { Micropuccinia Asteris (Duby) Arth. & Jackson.
  { Puccinia Asteris Duby.
  { Puccinia Asteris Duby, var. purpurascens C. & P.
  { Puccinia Gerardii Pk.
  { Puccinia purpurascens C. & P.
  Septoria atropurpurea Pk.
  Vermicularia herbarum Westd.
Aster meritus A. Nels.
  Coleosporium Solidaginis Thm.
Aster multiflorus Ait.
  { Aecidium Asterum S.
  { Aecidium Compositarum Auct. Amer. p. p.
  { Dicaeoma Asterum (Kern) Arth. & Kern. I.
  { Puccinia Caricis-Asteris Arth. I.
  { Puccinia extensicola Plowr. I.
  { Aecidium Bigeloviae Pk.
  { Dicaeoma Stipae (Arth.) O. Kuntze. I.
  { Puccinia Stipae Arth. I.
  Camarosporium astericola Ell. & Barthol.
  Camarosporium asterinum Petrak.
  Coleosporium Solidaginis Thm.
  Coniothecium mollerianum Thm.
  Coniothecium mollerianum Thm., var. astericola Sacc.

Aster multiflorus (*cont*)
  Erysiphe Cichoracearum DC. †
  Laestadia Scabiosa Lambotte & Fautr.
  Leptosphaeria astericola Ell. & Ev.
  Lophiostoma caulinum (Fr.).
  Lophiostoma insidiosum (Desm.) Ces. & De Not.
  {Bertiella brenckleana Rehm.
  {Dothidea Heliopsidis S.
  {Euryachora Heliopsidis (S.) Cke.
  {Montagnella Heliopsidis (S.) Sacc.
  {Phaeoderris Heliopsidis (S.) v. Höhnel.
  {Rosenscheldia Heliopsidis (S.) Theissen & Syd.
  {Clypeoporthella Brencklei Petrak.
  {Phomopsis Brencklei Petrak.
  Pleospora vulgaris Niessl., var. astericola Rehm.
  {Micropuccinia Asteris (Duby) Arth. & Jackson.
  {Puccinia Asteris Duby.
Aster nebraskensis Brit.
  {Dicaeoma Asterum (Kern) Arth. & Kern. I.
  {Puccinia asterum Kern. I.
  {Puccinia Caricis-Asteris Arth. I.
  {Coleosporium Solidaginis Thm.
  {Stichopsora Solidaginis Diet.
  Erysiphe Cichoracearum DC. †
  Erysiphe Polygoni DC. †
  {Micropuccinia Asteris (Duby) Arth. & Jackson.
  {Puccinia Asteris Duby.
Aster nemoralis Ait.
  Dicaeoma Asterum (Kern) Arth. & Kern. I.
Aster novae-angliae L.
  {Dicaeoma Asterum (Kern) Arth. & Kern. I.
  {Puccinia extensicola Plowr. I.
  Aecidium Bigeloviae Pk.
  Puccinia Stipae Arth. I.
  Basidiophora entospora Roze & Cornu.
  {Peronospora entospora (Roze & Cornu) B. & Br.
  {Peronospora simplex Pk.
  {Plasmopara entospora (Roze & Cornu) Schrt.
  {Coleosporium Solidaginis Thm.
  {Coleosporium Sonchi-arvensis Auct. Amer. p.p.
  Erysiphe Cichoracearum DC. †
  Phoma herbarum Westd.
  {Micropuccinia Asteris (Duby) Arth. & Jackson.
  {Puccinia Asteris Duby.
  {Ramularia macrospora Fres., var. Asteris Sacc. 10 April 1886.
  {Ramularia macrospora Fres., var. Senecionis Trel. Nov. 1894.
  {Ramularia Asteris (Phil. & Plowr.) Bubák. 15 Dec. 1906.
  {Ramularia Asteris (Sacc.) Barthol. 30 Nov. 1911.
  Septoria atropurpurea Pk.

Aster novi-belgii L.
  Coleosporium Solidaginis Thm.
  Entyloma Compositarum Farl.
  {Micropuccinia Asteris (Duby) Arth. & Jackson.
  {Puccinia Asteris Duby.
Aster oblongifolius Nutt.
  {Basidiophora entospora Roze & Cornu.
  {Plasmopara entospora (Roze & Cornu) Schrt.
  {Coleosporium Asterum (Diet.) Syd.
  {Coleosporium Solidaginis Thm.
  Erysiphe Cichoracearum DC. †
  Phyllachora asterigena Ell. & Ev.
  {Micropuccinia Asteris (Duby) Arth. & Jackson.
  {Puccinia Asteris Duby.
Aster occidentalis Nutt.
  {Dicaeoma Asterum (Kern) Arth. & Kern. I.
  {Puccinia Asterum Kern. I.
  Coleosporium Solidaginis Thm.
Aster paniculatus Lam.
  {Aecidium Asterum S.
  {Aecidium Compositarum Auct. Amer. p. p.
  {Caeoma asteratum Lk.
  {Dicaeoma Asterum (Kern) Arth. & Kern. I.
  {Dicaeoma Caricis-Asteris Arth. I.
  {Dicaeoma extensicola (Plowr.) O. Kuntze. I.
  {Puccinia Asterum Kern. I.
  {Puccinia Caricis-Asteris Arth. I.
  {Puccinia extensicola Plowr. I.
  Uromyces perigynius Halsted. I.
  Asteromella Asteris Pk.
  {Coleosporium Asterum (Diet.) Syd.
  {Coleosporium Solidaginis Thm.
  {Coleosporium Sonchi Auct. Amer. p. p.
  {Coleosporium Sonchi-arvensis Auct. Amer. p.p.
  {Stichopsora Solidaginis (Thm.) Diet.
  Entyloma Compositarum Farl.
  Erysiphe Cichoracearum DC. †
  {Ascospora pseudhimantia Rehm. nom. nud.
  {Discosphaerina pseudhimantia (Rehm) Petrak.
  {Ophiodothis Haydeni (B. & C.) Sacc.
  {Phyllachora Haydeni Dearness.
  {Dicaeoma Asteris (Duby) O. Kuntze.
  {Micropuccinia Asteris (Duby) Arth. & Jackson.
  {Puccinia Asteris Duby.
  {Puccinia Gerardii Pk.
  Ramularia Asteris (Phil. & Plowr.) Bubák.
  Rhytisma Asteris S.
  Sclerotium deciduum J. J. Davis.
  Septoria atropurpurea Pk.
Aster Parryi Gray.
  Micropuccinia Grindeliae (Pk.) Arth. & Jackson.
Aster patens Ait.
  {Coleosporium Solidaginis Thm.
  {Coleosporium Sonchi-arvensis Auct. Amer. p.p.

Aster pauciflorus Nutt.
Coleosporium Solidaginis Thm.
{ Micropuccinia Asteris (Duby) Arth. & Jackson.
{ Puccinia Asteris Duby.
Aster Porteri Gray.
Dicaeoma Stipae (Arth.) O. Kuntze. I.
Coleosporium Solidaginis Thm.
Aster prenanthoides Muhl.
Dicaeoma Asterum (Kern) Arth. & Kern. I.
{ Coleosporium Solidaginis Thm.
{ Coleosporium Sonchi-arvensis Auct. Amer. p.p.
Erysiphe Cichoracearum DC. †
{ Micropuccinia Asteris (Duby) Arth. & Jackson.
{ Puccinia Asteris Duby.
Aster proximus Greene.
Diplodina coloradensis Ell. & Ev.
Aster ptarmicoides Torr. & Gr.
Phoma iowana Sacc.
Aster pulchellus D. C. Eaton.
Puccinia magnoecia Ell. & Ev.
Aster puniceus L.
{ Dicaeoma Asterum (Kern) Arth. & Kern. I.
{ Puccinia Asterum Kern. I.
{ Puccinia extensicola Plowr. I.
Uromyces perigynius Halsted. I.
{ Basidiophora entospora Roze & Cornu.
{ Plasmopara entospora (Roze & Cornu) Schrt.
Cercosporella cana Sacc.
Cercosporella cana Sacc., var. gracilis J. J. Davis.
{ Coleosporium Compositarum Auct. Amer. p.p.
{ Coleosporium Solidaginis Thm.
{ Coleosporium Sonchi-arvensis Auct. Amer. p.p.
Entyloma Compositarum Farl.
Erysiphe Cichoracearum DC. †
Oidium Asteris-punicei Pk.
{ Orbilia assimilis (C. & P.) Sacc.
{ Peziza assimilis C. & P.
Phoma iowana Sacc.
{ Micropuccinia Asteris (Duby) Arth. & Jackson.
{ Puccinia Asteris Duby.
Ramularia filaris Fres.
Septoria astericola Ell. & Ev.
Septoria atropurpurea Pk.
Septoria solidaginicola Pk.
Aster radulinus Gray.
{ Coleosporium Solidaginis Thm.
{ Stichopsora Asterum Diet.
Aster sagittifolius Wedemeyer.
{ Aecidium Asterum S.
Aecidium Compositarum, var. Asteris Wint.
Dicaeoma Asterum (Kern) Arth. & Kern. I.
Dicaeoma Caricis-Asteris Arth. I.
Dicaeoma extensicola (Plowr.) O. Kuntze. I.
Puccinia Asterum Kern. I.
{ Puccinia Caricis-Asteris Arth. I.

{ Basidiophora entospora Roze & Cornu.
{ Plasmopara entospora (Roze & Cornu) Schrt.
Coleosporium Solidaginis Thm.
{ Coleosporium Sonchi Auct. Amer. p. p.
{ Coleosporium Sonchi-arvensis Auct. Amer. p.p.
Erysiphe Cichoracearum DC. †
{ Dasyspora Asteris (Duby) Arth.
Leptopuccinia Asteris Syd.
Micropuccinia Asteris (Duby) Arth. & Jackson.
{ Puccinia Asteris Duby.
Ramularia Asteris (Phil. & Plowr.) Bubák.
Septoria astericola Ell. & Ev.
Septoria atropurpurea Pk.
{ Septoria fumosa Pk.
{ Septoria solidaginicola Pk.
Aster salicifolius Ait.
{ Aecidium Asterum S.
Dicaeoma Asterum (Kern) Arth. & Kern. I.
Dicaeoma extensicola (Plowr.) O. Kuntze. I.
{ Puccinia Caricis-Asteris Arth. I.
{ Coleosporium Solidaginis Thm.
{ Coleosporium Sonchi-arvensis Auct. Amer. p.p.
Erysiphe Cichoracearum DC. †
{ Micropuccinia Asteris (Duby) Arth. & Jackson.
{ Puccinia Asteris Duby.
Septoria atropurpurea Pk.
Aster sericeus Vent.
Aecidium Compositarum Auct. Amer. p. p.
Aster Shortii Lindl.
Puccinia extensicola Plowr. I.
Cicinnobolus Cesatii DBy.
{ Coleosporium Solidaginis Thm.
{ Coleosporium Sonchi-arvensis Auct. Amer. p.p.
Erysiphe Cichoracearum DC. †
Puccinia Asteris Duby.
Septoria astericola Ell. & Ev.
Septoria solidaginicola Pk.
Aster spathulatus Lindl.
{ Aecidium Asterum S.
{ Puccinia Caricis-Asteris Arth. I.
Aster spectabilis Ait.
{ Coleosporium Asterum (Diet.) Syd.
{ Coleosporium Solidaginis Thm.
Aster spinosus Benth.
{ Nigredo compacta (Pk.) Arth.
{ Uromyces compactus Pk.
Aster tanacetifolius H. B. K.
Micropuccinia Grindeliae (Pk.) Arth. & Jackson.
Aster tardiflorus L.
{ Coleosporium Asterum (Diet.) Syd.
{ Coleosporium Solidaginis Thm.
Aster Tradescanti L.
{ Dicaeoma Asterum (Kern) Arth. & Kern. I.
{ Puccinia Caricis-Asteris Arth. I.
Basidiophora entospora Roze & Cornu.

Aster Tradescanti (*cont.*)
{ Coleosporium Solidaginis Thm.
{ Coleosporium Sonchi-arvensis Auct. Amer. p.p.
　Darluca Filum (Biv.) Cast.
　Erysibe Cichoracearum (DC.) Schrt. †
{ Bertiella brenckleana Rehm.
| Montagnella Heliopsidis (S.) Sacc.
| Phaeodothis Heliopsidis (S.) v. Höhnel.
| Rosenscheldia Heliopsidis (S.) Theissen & Syd.
{ Micropuccinia Asteris (Duby) Arth. & Jackson.
{ Puccinia Asteris Duby.
　Ramularia Asteris (Phil. & Plowr.) Bubák.
{ Rhytisma astericola Sacc.
| Rhytisma Asteris S.
| Xyloma Asteris S.
{ Fungus dubius
　Septoria atropurpurea Pk.
Aster Tweedyi Rydb.
　Dicaeoma Asterum (Kern) Arth. & Kern. I.
　Uromyces perigynius Halsted. I.
　Coleosporium Solidaginis Thm.
　Ramularia filaris Fres., var. astericola Sacc.
Aster umbellatus Mill.
　Dicaeoma Asterum (Kern) Arth. & Kern. I.
　Cladosporium astericola J. J. Davis.
{ Coleosporium Solidaginis Thm.
{ Coleosporium Sonchi-arvensis Auct. Amer. p.p.
{ Erysiphe Cichoracearum DC. †
{ Erysiphe lamprocarpa Auct. Amer. p.p.
　Phyllosticta astericola Ell. & Ev.
　Septoria solidaginicola Pk.
Aster undulatus L.
　Coleosporium Solidaginis Thm.
{ Erysiphe Cichoracearum DC. †
{ Erysiphe lamprocarpa Auct. Amer. p. p.
{ Micropuccinia Asteris (Duby) Arth. & Jackson.
{ Puccinia Asteris Duby.
Aster vallicola Greene.
　Erysiphe Cichoracearum DC. †
　Placosphaeria decipiens Dearness & Fairman.
Aster vimineus Lam.
　Cercospora viminei Tehon.
　Coleosporium Solidaginis Thm.
{ Micropuccinia Asteris (Duby) Arth. & Jackson.
{ Puccinia Asteris Duby.
　Septoria atropurpurea Pk.
Aster vimineus Lam., var. **foliolosus** (Ait.) Gray.
{ Erysiphe Cichoracearum DC. †
{ Erysiphe lamprocarpa Auct. Amer. p. p.
Aster
　(Macjaeranthera viscosula Rydb.)
　Coleosporium Solidaginis Thm.
Aster Wootonii Greene.
{ Micropuccinia Asteris (Duby) Arth. & Jackson.
{ Puccinia Asteris Duby.

Aster Xylorrhiza Torr. & Gr.
　Puccinia Xylorrhizae Arth.
Aster yosemitanus Greene.
　Dicaeoma Asterum (Kern) Arth. & Kern. I.
{ Micropuccinia Asteris (Duby) Arth. & Jackson.
{ Puccinia Asteris Duby.
Aster sp. indet. (Callistephus?)
　Alternaria fasciculata (C. & E.) Jones & Grout.
　Cercospora asterata Atk.
　Diaporthe mucronulata Sacc.
{ Diaporthe orthoceras (Fr.) Nits.
{ Sphaeria orthoceras Fr.
　Fusarium conglutinans Wr.
　Fusarium conglutinans Wr., var. Callistephi Beach.
{ Hypoderma expallens (S.) Cke.
{ Hysterium expallens S.
{ Leptosphaeria comatella (C. & E.) Sacc.
{ Sphaeria comatella C. & E.
　Leptosphaeria Doliolum (P. ex Fr.) De Not.
{ Leptosphaeria ogilviensis (B. & Br.) Sacc.
{ Sphaeria ogilviensis B. & Br.
　Lophiostoma vagabundum Sacc., var. Asteris Ell. & Ev.
　Macrophoma astericola (Atk.) Tassi.
{ Mollisia astericola (C. & E.) Sacc.
{ Peziza astericola C. & E.
　Mycorrhiza of Legumes F. R. Jones.
{ Ophiobolus anguillides (Cke.) Sacc.
{ Raphidospora anguillida Cke.
{ Sphaeria anguillida Cke.
　Phoma astericola Atk.
{ Phoma macularis B. & C.
{ Phoma maculifera Sacc.
　Pleospora Compositarum Earle.
　Ramularia Virgaureae Thm.
　Rhizoctonia Solani Kühn.
　Sclerotinia libertiana Fckl.
　Septoria Callistephi Gloyer. ?
{ Hypocenia herbarum Cke. & Hark.
{ Stagonospora herbarum (Cke. & Hark.) Sacc.
　Thelephora sebacea P.
Erigeron annuus (L.) P.
{ Aecidium Compositarum, var. Erigerontis Wint.
| Aecidium erigeronatum S.
| Caeoma erigeronatum S.
| Dicaeoma Asterum (Kern) Arth. & Kern. I.
| Dicaeoma Caricis-Erigerontis Arth. I.
| Puccinia Asterum Kern. I.
| Puccinia Caricis-Erigerontis Arth. I.
{ Puccinia extensicola Plowr. I.
　Basidiophora entospora Roze & Cornu.
　Cercospora griseella Pk.
{ Cercospora cana (Pass.) Sacc.
{ Cercosporella cana (Pass.) Sacc.
　Erysiphe Cichoracearum DC. †

Erigeron annuus (*cont.*)
{ Fusarium phyllogenum (C. & P.) Sacc.
{ Fusisporium phyllogenum C. & P.
Leptothyrium Dearnessii Kabát & Bubák.
Leptothyrium punctiforme B. & C.
Mollisia atrata (P.) Karst.
Ophiobolus tenellus (Awd.) Sacc.
{ Plasmopara Halstedii (Farl.) Berl. & De Toni.
{ Rhysotheca Halstedii (Farl.) G. W. Wilson.
Ramularia macrospora Fres.
{ Septoria Erigerontis Pk.
{ Septoria erigerontea Sacc.
Sphaerotheca Humuli (DC.) Burrill, var. fuliginea (Schl.) Salmon.

Erigeron armeriifolius Turcz.
Micropuccinia Grindeliae (Pk.) Arth. & Jackson.
Erysiphe Cichoracearum DC. †

Erigeron bonariensis L.
{ Dimeriella erigeronicola F. L. Stevens.
{ Pseudoperisporium erigeronicola (F. L. Stevens) Toro.
{ Micropuccinia Asteris (Duby) Arth. & Jackson.
{ Puccinia doloris Speg.

Erigeron caespitosus Nutt.
{ Micropuccinia Grindeliae (Pk.) Arth. & Jackson.
{ Puccinia Erigerontis Ell. & Ev.

Erigeron canadensis L.
{ Aecidium erigeronatum S.
{ Caeoma erigeronatum S.
{ Dicaeoma Asterum (Kern) Arth. & Kern. I.
{ Puccinia Asterum Kern. I.
Puccinia Caricis Auct. p. p. I.
Puccinia Caricis-Erigerontis Arth. I.
Puccinia extensicola Plowr. I.
{ Basidiophora entospora Roze & Cornu.
{ Peronospora entospora (Roze & Cornu) B. & Br.
{ Peronospora Basidiophora Schrt.
Peronospora simplex Pk.
{ Plasmopara entospora (Roze & Cornu) Schrt.
Cercospora griseella Pk.
{ Cercospora cana (Pass.) Sacc.
{ Cercosporella cana (Pass.) Sacc.
{ Fusidium canum Pass.
{ Ramularia cana (Pass.) Halsted.
Diaporthe apiculosa Ell.
{ Diaporthe Arctii (Lasch), var. Artemisiae Rehm.
{ Diaporthe incrustans N. A. F. *1194.*
Dimeriella erigeronicola F. L. Stevens.
Erysiphe Cichoracearum DC. †
{ Helotium nigrescens (Cke.) Rehm.
{ Peziza nigrescens Cke.
Lasiostemma melioloides (B. & C.) Theissen & Syd.

{ Leptosphaeria agnita (Desm.) Ces. & De Not., var. Erigerontis Berl.
Leptosphaeria Erigerontis Berl.
{ Leptosphaeria ogilviensis (B. & Br.) Ces. & De Not.
{ Sphaeria ogilviensis B. & Br.
Leptosphaeria planiuscula (Riess) Ces. & De Not.
{ Metasphaeria bucera (C. & E.) Sacc.
{ Sphaeria bucera C. & E.
{ Metasphaeria leiostega (Ell.) Sacc.
{ Sphaeria leiostega Ell.
{ Mollisia erigeronata (Cke.) Sacc.
{ Peziza erigeronata Cke.
{ Septoria Erigeronis Pk.
{ Septoria erigerontea Sacc.
Septoria Erigerontis, var. effusa J. J. Davis.
Sphaerotheca Castagnei Auct. Amer. p. p.
Sphaerotheca Humuli (DC.) Burrill. †
Sphaerotheca Humuli (DC.) Burrill, var. fuliginea (Schl.) Salmon.

Erigeron compositus Pursh.
Pleospora herbarum (Fr.) Rabh.
Pleospora platyspora Sacc.
Pleospora vulgaris Niessl.
Pyrenophora chrysospora (Niessl) Sacc.
{ Mycosphaerella eriophila (Niessl) Dearness.
{ Sphaerella eriophila Niessl.

Erigeron corymbosus Nutt.
Erysiphe Cichoracearum DC. †

Erigeron Coulteri Porter & Coulter.
Entyloma Compositarum Farl.

Erigeron Deamii B. L. Robinson.
{ Micropuccinia Asteris (Duby) Arth. & Jackson.
{ Puccinia Doloris Speg.

Erigeron divaricatus Michx.
Erysiphe Cichoracearum DC. †

Erigeron Eatoni Gray.
{ Micropuccinia Grindeliae (Pk.) Arth. & Jackson.
{ Puccinia Erigerontis Ell. & Ev.

Erigeron elatus Greene.
Entyloma Compositarum Farl.

Erigeron eriocephalus Regel & Schmalh.
Phoma complanata (Tode ex Fr.) Desm.
Pyrenophora chrysospora (Niessl) Sacc.
Sclerotium durum P. ex Fr.
Sphaerella confinis Karst.

Erigeron filiformis (Hook.) Nutt.
{ Micropuccinia Grindeliae (Pk.) Arth. & Jackson.
{ Puccinia Grindeliae Pk.

Erigeron flagellaris Gray.
{ Aecidium Bigeloviae Pk.
{ Dicaeoma Stipae (Arth.) O. Kuntze. I.
{ Puccinia Stipae Arth. I.
Aecidium incurvum Tracy & Earle.
Pleospora herbarum (Fr.) Rabh.

Erigeron glabellus Nutt.
Erysiphe Cichoracearum DC.†
Sclerotium Rolfsii Sacc.

Erigeron grandiflorus Hook.
Gloeosporium Roaldii Lind.
Rhabdospora Drabae (Fckl.) Berl. & Vogl.

Erigeron inornatus Gray.
Coleosporium Solidaginis Thm.

Erigeron macranthus Nutt.
{ Dicaeoma Asterum (Kern) Arth. & Kern. I.
{ Puccinia Asterum Kern. I.
Erysiphe Cichoracearum DC.†
{ Micropuccinia Grindeliae (Pk.) Arth. & Jackson.
{ Puccinia confluens Syd.
{ Puccinia Erigerontis Ell. & Ev.

Erigeron melanocephalus A. Nels.
Sphaerotheca Humuli (DC.) Burrill, var. fuliginea (Schl.) Salmon.

Erigeron microlonchus Greene.
{ Micropuccinia Grindeliae (Pk.) Arth. & Jackson.
{ Puccinia Erigerontis Ell. & Ev.

Erigeron philadelphicus L.
{ Aecidium Compositarum Auct. Amer. p. p.
{ Aecidium erigeronatum S.
{ Dicaeoma Asterum (Kern) Arth. & Kern. I.
{ Puccinia Asterum Kern. I.
{ Puccinia Caricis-Erigerontis Arth.
Basidiophora entospora Roze & Cornu.
Cercosporella cana (Pass.) Sacc.
Entyloma Compositarum Farl.
Erysiphe communis Auct. Amer. p. p.
?Plasmopara Halstedii (Farl.) Berl. & De Toni.
Pleospora herbarum (Fr.) Rabh.
{ Septoria Erigeronis Pk. Jan. 1872.
{ Septoria Erigerontis B. & C. Sept. 1874.
Sphaerotheca Humuli (DC.) Burrill.†

Erigeron peregrinus (Pursh) Greene.
Coleosporium Solidaginis Thm.

Erigeron pulchellus Michx.
{ Aecidium Compositarum Auct. Amer. p. p.
{ Aecidium Compositarum, var. Erigerontis Wint.
{ Aecidium erigeronatum S.
{ Caeoma erigeronatum S.
{ Dicaeoma Asterum (Kern) Arth. & Kern. I.
{ Puccinia Caricis-Erigerontis Arth. I.
Septoria Erigeronis Pk.

Erigeron pumilus Nutt.
{ Dicaeoma Stipae (Arth.) O. Kuntze. I.
{ Puccinia Stipae Arth. I.

Erigeron quercifolius Lam.
{ Aecidium Compositarum, var. Erigerontis Wint.
{ Puccinia Caricis-Erigerontis Arth. I.

Erigeron ramosus (Walt.) B. S. P.
{ Aecidium Compositarum, var. Erigerontis Wint.
{ Aecidium erigeronatum S.
{ Caeoma erigeronatum S.
{ Dicaeoma Asterum (Kern) Arth. & Kern. I.
{ Dicaeoma Caricis-Erigerontis Arth. I.
{ Dicaeoma extensicola (Plowr.) O. Kuntze. I.
{ Puccinia Asterum Kern. I.
{ Puccinia Caricis-Erigerontis Arth. I.
{ Puccinia extensicola Plowr. I.
Basidiophora entospora Roze & Cornu.
Cercosporella cana (Pass.) Sacc.
Erysiphe Cichoracearum DC.†
Leptothyrium Dearnessii Bubák
Leptothyrium punctiforme B. & C.
Puccinia Asteris?
{ Septoria Erigeronis Pk.
{ Septoria erigerontea Sacc.
{ Septoria Erigerontis B. & C.
{ Septoria "Erigerontis Pk." Auct.
Septoria fusariospora Ell. & Ev.

Erigeron salsuginosus Gray.
Entyloma Compositarum Farl.
{ Clathrospora permunda (Cke.) Berl.
{ Pleospora permunda (Cke.) Sacc.
Micropuccinia Grindeliae (Pk.) Arth. & Jackson.
{ Puccinia confluens Syd.
{ Puccinia Erigerontis Ell. & Ev.
Sphaerella subcongregata Ell. & Ev.

Erigeron spathulatus Vahl.
Dimeriella erigeronicola F. L. Stevens.

Erigeron speciosus DC.
{ Dicaeoma Asterum (Kern) Arth. & Kern. I.
{ Puccinia Asterum Kern. I.

Erigeron subtrinervis Rydb.
Erysiphe Cichoracearum DC. †

Erigeron tomentosus L.
Cercospora ferruginea Fckl.

Erigeron uniflorus L.
Laestadia circumtegens Rostr.
Torula abbreviata Cda.

Erigeron sp. indet.
Asterina nigerrima Ell.
Chaetomium olivaceum C. & E.
Cicinnobolus Cesatii DBy.
Exilispora plurisepta Tehon & Daniels.
Macrosporium atrichum C. & E.
Ophiobolus acuminatus (Sow. ex Fr.) Duby.
{ Ophiobolus anguillides (Cke.) Sacc.
{ Sphaeria anguillida Cke.
{ Dothidea Haydeni B. & C.
{ Ophiodothis Haydeni (B. & C.) Sacc.
{ Phyllachora Haydeni Dearness.
{ Rhopographus Haydeni (B. & C.) Cke.
{ Peziza exigua Cke.
{ Pezizella exigua (Cke.) Sacc.

Erigeron sp. indet. (*cont.*)
  Rhabdospora pachyspora Ell. & Ev.
  {Peziza carneorubra Ell.
  {Trichopeziza carneorubra (Ell.)Sacc.
Sericocarpus asteroides (L.) B. S. P.
  Coleosporium Solidaginis Thm.
Pleurophyllum speciosum Hook.
  Stemphylium insidens Cke. & Massee.
Diplostephium rupestre Wedd.
  Rhynchostoma biolleyana Bomm. & Rouss.
Baccharis caerulescens DC.
  {Caeoma punctatostriatum Diet. & Neger.
  {Dicaeoma Baccharidis (Diet. & Holw.) Arth. &
  { Jackson.
  {Eriosporangium punctatostriatum Arth.
  {Puccinia Baccharidis Diet. & Holw.
Baccharis consanguinea DC.
  {Coleosporium Baccharidis Cke. & Hark.
  {Dicaeoma evadens (Hark.) Arth. & Jackson.
  {Eriosporangium evadens (Hark.) Arth.
  {Puccinia evadens Hark.
Baccharis Douglasii DC.
  Cercospora Baccharidis Ell. & Ev.
  Cercosporella Baccharidis Ell. & Ev.
Baccharis elegans H. B. K.
  {Bullaria Baccharidis-multiflorae (Diet. &
  { Holw.) Arth. & Mains.
  {Puccinia Baccharidis-multiflorae Diet. &
  { Holw.
Baccharis Emoryi Gray.
  Dicaeoma Baccharidis (Diet. & Holw.) Arth.
   & Jackson.
  Dicaeoma evadens (Hark.) Arth. & Jackson.
Baccharis glomeruliflora P.
  Dimerosporium vestitum Earle.
  {Dicaeoma pistoricum (Arth.) Arth. & Jackson.
  {Eriosporangium pistoricum Arth.
  {Puccinia pistorica Arth.
Baccharis glutinosa P.
  {Caeoma punctatostriatum Diet.
  {Dicaeoma Baccharidis (Diet. & Holw.) Arth.
  { & Jackson.
  {Eriosporangium punctatostriatum Arth.
  {Puccinia Baccharidis Diet. & Holw.
  ?Puccinia evadens Hark.
Baccharis halimifolia L.
  Diaporthe Baccharidis (Cke.)Sacc.
  Diatrype Baccharidis Earle.
  {Asterina melioloides B. & C.
  {Dimerosporium Baccharidis (B. & Rav.) Sacc.
  {Dimerosporium melioloides (B. & C.) Martin.
  {Meliola Baccharidis B. & Rav.
  {Dothidea Baccharidis Cke.
  {Systremma Baccharidis (Cke.) Theissen &
  { Syd.
  {Eriosporangium pistoricum Arth.
  Fomes applanatus (P. ex Wallr.) Gill.
  Fomes conchatus (P. ex Fr.) Karst.

Hysterium Prostii Duby.
Hysterographium Mori (S.) Rehm.
Irpex Tulipiferae S.
Leptosphaeria dumetorum Niessl.
{Creonectria purpurea (L.) Seaver.
{Nectria cinnabarina (Tode) ex Fr.
Panus torulosus Fr.
Phoma Baccharidis Brun.
Phyllosticta Baccharidis Dearness & House.
Placosphaeria Baccharidis Dearness & House.
Pleurotus approximans Pk.
Dicaeoma evadens (Hark.) Arth. & Jackson.
Rosellinia protuberans Karst.
Schizophyllum commune Fr.
{Haplosporella baccharidicola (Dearness) Pe-
{ trak & Syd.
{Sphaeropsis baccharidicola Dearness.
Baccharis hirtella DC.
  {Dicaeoma Baccharidis-hirtellae (Diet. &
  { Holw.) Arth. & Jackson.
  {Eriosporangium Baccharidis-hirtellae (Diet. &
  { Holw.) Arth.
  {Puccinia Baccharidis-hirtellae Diet. & Holw.
  {Aecidium fragile Holw.
  {Dicaeoma oaxacanum (Diet. & Holw.) Arth. &
  { Jackson.
  {Eriosporangium oaxacanum (Diet. & Holw.)
  { Arth.
  {Puccinia oaxacana Diet. & Holw.
Baccharis laurifolia Lees.
  {Allodus Ancizari (Mayor) Arth. & Orton.
  {Puccinia Ancizari Mayor.
Baccharis multiflora H. B. K.
  {Argomyces Baccharidis-multiflorae (Diet. &
  { Holw.) Arth.
  {Bullaria Baccharidis-multiflorae (Diet. &
  { Holw.) Arth. & Mains.
  {Puccinia Baccharidis-multiflorae Diet. & Holw.
Baccharis oaxacana Greenm.
  {Dicaeoma egressum (Arth.) Arth. & Jackson.
  {Eriosporangium egregium Arth.
  {Puccinia egregia Arth. 1911 not 1905.
  {Puccinia egressa Arth.
Baccharis oblongifolia P.
  {Polyporus Baccharidis Pat.
  {Pyropolyporus Baccharidis (Pat.) Murrill.
Baccharis pilularis DC.
  Capnodium salicinum (A. & S.) Mont.?
  {Heptameria bicuspidata (Berl. & Vogl.) Cke.
  {Leptosphaeria bicuspidata (Cke. & Hark.)
  { Berl. & Vogl.
  {Sphaeria bicuspidata Cke. & Hark.
  Sphaeria (Melanomma) seminis Cke. & Hark.
  {Coleosporium Baccharidis Cke. & Hark.
  {Dicaeoma evadens (Hark.) Arth. & Jackson.
  {Eriosporangium evadens (Hark.) Arth.
  {Puccinia evadens Hark.

Baccharis pteronioides DC.
  Dicaeoma evadens (Hark.) Arth. & Jackson.
  Eriosporangium evadens (Hark.) Arth.
  Puccinia evadens Hark.
Baccharis rhexioides H. B. K.
  Dicaeoma exornatum (Arth.) Arth. & Jackson.
  Eriosporangium exornatum Arth.
  Puccinia exornata Arth.
Baccharis salicina Torr. & Gr.
  Dicaeoma evadens (Hark.) Arth. & Jackson.
  Eriosporangium evadens (Hark.) Arth.
Baccharis sarothroides Gray.
  Dicaeoma evadens (Hark.) Arth. & Jackson.
  Eriosporangium evadens (Hark.) Arth.
  Puccinia evadens Hark.
Baccharis serrifolia DC.
  Bullaria Baccharidis-multiflorae (Diet. &
    Holw.) Arth. & Mains.
  Puccinia Baccharidis-multiflorae Diet. & Holw.
Baccharis sordescens DC.
  Dicaeoma sphenicum (Arth.) Arth. & Jackson.
  Eriosporangium sphenicum Arth.
  Puccinia sphenica Arth.
Baccharis thesioides H. B. K.
  Dicaeoma evadens (Hark.) Arth. & Jackson.
  Dicaeoma exornatum (Arth.) Arth. & Jackson.
  Eriosporangium exornatum Arth.
  Puccinia exornata Arth.
Baccharis viminea DC.
  Lecidiopsis californica Rehm.
  Metasphaeria anisometra (Cke. & Hark.) Sacc.
  Dicaeoma Baccharidis (Diet. & Holw.) Arth. &
    Jackson.
  Eriosporangium punctatostriatum Arth.
  Puccinia Baccharidis Diet. & Holw.
  Coleosporium Baccharidis Cke. & Hark.
  Puccinia evadens Hark.
Baccharis Wrightii Gray.
  Pleospora vulgatissima Speg.
Baccharis sp. indet.
  Botryosphaeria Ribis (Tode ex Fr.) Grossen-
    bacher & Duggar.
  Botryosphaeria Ribis (Tode ex Fr.) Grossen-
    bacher & Duggar, var. chromogena Shear
    et al.
  Corticium incarnatum Fr.
  Diaporthe Baccharidis (Cke.) Sacc.
  Sphaeria Baccharidis Cke.
  Diatrype Baccharidis Earle.
  Dothidea Baccharidis Cke.
  Dothidea tetraspora B. & Br.
  Dothidella berkeleyana (Cke.) Berl. & Vogl.
  Phyllachora berkeleyana Cke.
  Peniophora violaceolivida (Sommerf.) Bres.
  Physalospora arthuriana Sacc.
  Stereum tabacinum (Sow.) ex Fr.
Archibaccharis torquis Blake.
  Eriosporangium oaxacanum (Diet. & Holw.)
    Arth.

Pluchea borealis Gray.
  Puccinia notabilis Tracy & Earle.
  Puccinia splendens Vize.
  Puccinia xylariiformis Henn.
Pluchea camphorata (L.) DC.
  Didymosphaeria brunneola Niessl.
  Dicaeoma Plucheae (Syd.) Arth. & Jackson.
  Uredo Plucheae Syd.
Pluchea odorata Cass.
Pluchea purpurascens (Sw.) DC.
  Dicaeoma Plucheae (Arth.) Arth. & Jackson.
  Puccinia Plucheae Arth.
  Uredo biocellata Arth.
  Uredo Plucheae Syd.
Antennaria alpina Gaertn.
  Pyrenophora chrysospora (Niessl) Sacc.
  Rhabdospora cercosperma (Rostr.) Sacc.
  Septoria cercosperma Rostr.
  Sphaerella Compositarum Awd.
  Sphaerella confinis Karst.
Antennaria Brainerdii Fernald.
Antennaria canadensis Greene.
Antennaria neglecta Greene.
Antennaria neodioica Greene.
  Septoria mollisia Dearness & House.
Antennaria Parlinii Fernald.
  Phyllosticta Antennariae Ell. & Ev.
Antennaria plantaginifolia (L.) Richards.
  Albugo Tragopogonis (P.) ex S. F. Gray.
  Cystopus Tragopogonis (P. ex S. F. Gray)
    Schrt.
  Globulina Antennariae Hasselbring.
  Mollisia lanaria Fairman.
  Ophiobolus Gnaphalii (Sacc. & Br.) Fairman.
  Ophiobolus Gnaphalii (Sacc. & Br.) Fairman,
    var. lanaria Fairman.
  Phialea phaeoconia Fairman.
  Phyllosticta Antennariae Ell. & Ev.
  Septoria lanaria Fairman.
  ?Septoria mollisia Dearness & House.
Antennaria sp. indet.
  Venturia fimbriata Dearness & House.
Anaphalis margaritacea (L.) Benth. & Hook.
  Allodus gnaphaliata Arth.
  Puccinia investita S.
  Septoria margaritaceae Pk.
  Septoria mollisia Dearness & House.
Anaphalis margaritacea (L.) Benth. & Hook.,
  var. occidentalis Greene.
Anaphalis subalpina (Gray) Rydb.
  Teleutospora amoena (Syd.) Arth. & Bisby.
  Uromyces amoenus Syd.
  Uromyces Gnaphalii Fung. Columb. *1795.*
Gnaphalium chilense Spreng.
  Allodus gnaphaliata Arth.
  Puccinia investita S.

Gnaphalium decurrens Ives.
  Cercospora gnaphaliacea Cke.
  {Patellaria gnaphaliana C. & E.
  {Patinella gnaphaliana (C. & E.) Sacc.
  Aecidium gnaphaliatum S.
  Allodus gnaphaliata Arth.
  Puccinia gnaphaliata (Arth.) Arth. & Bisby.
  Puccinia investita S.
Gnaphalium leptophyllum DC.
Gnaphalium leucocephalum Gray.
  {Aecidium gnaphaliatum S.
  {Allodus gnaphaliata Arth.
  {Caeoma gnaphaliatum S.
  {Puccinia investita S.
Gnaphalium norvegicum Gunner.
  Botrytis cinerea P. †
  Septoria cercosperma Rostr.
Gnaphalium oxyphyllum DC.
  {Allodus gnaphaliata Arth.
  {Puccinia investita S.
Gnaphalium polycephalum Michx.
  Cercospora gnaphaleacea Cke.
  {Aecidium gnaphaliatum S.
  {Allodus gnaphaliata Arth.
  {Caeoma gnaphaliatum S.
  {Puccinia investita S.
Gnaphalium purpureum L.
  Cercospora gnaphaliacea Cke.?
  {Peronospora Halstedii Farl.
  {Plasmopara Halstedii (Farl.) Berl. & De Toni.
  {Physotheca Halstedii (Farl.) G. W. Wilson.
  Puccinia Gnaphalii Henn.
  {Aecidium gnaphaliatum S.
  {Caeoma gnaphaliatum S.
  {Puccinia investita S.
Gnaphalium ramosissimum Nutt.
  Allodus gnaphaliata Arth.
Gnaphalium rhodoxanthum Sch. Bip.
  Puccinia Gnaphalii Henn.
Gnaphalium semiamplexicaule DC.
  {Allodus gnaphaliata Arth.
  {Puccinia investita S.
Gnaphalium spathulatum Lam.
  Puccinia Gnaphalii Henn.
Gnaphalium uliginosum L.
  Macrosporium commune Rabh.
Gnaphalium sp. indet.
  Cercospora Gnaphalii Hark.
  Cylindrosporium gnaphalicola Atk.
  Entyloma Compositarum Farl.
  Leptosphaeria Galiorum Sacc., var. gnaphaliana Fairman.
  {Mycosphaerella Bakeri Rehm.
  {Sphaerella Bakeri (Rehm) Sacc. & Trott.
  Phoma erysiphoides Ell. & Ev.
Inula Helenium L.
  {Anthostomella rostrospora (Gerard) Sacc.
  {Sphaeria rostrospora Gerard.
  Erysiphe Cichoracearum DC. †

Adenocaulon bicolor Hook.
  Coleosporium Adenocaulonis H. S. Jackson.
  Septoria Adenocauli Ell. & Ev.
  Septoria Adenocaulonis Dearness.
Nocca decipiens (Hemsl.) O. Kuntze.
Nocca rigida Cav.
  Puccinia Noccae Arth.
Tetranthus hirsutus Spreng.
  {Micropuccinia Melampodii (Diet. & Holw.) Arth. & Jackson.
  {Puccinia Tetranthi Syd.
Elvira biflora (L.) Cass.
  Cercosporella Elvirae Syd.
Desmanthodium fruticosum Greenm.
Desmanthodium ovatum Benth.
  {Allodus Desmanthodii (Diet. & Holw.) Arth.
  {Puccinia Desmanthodii Diet. & Holw.
Milleria quinqueflora L.
  {Cincinnobella asperula Syd.
  {Phaeodimeriella asperula Syd.
  Sarcinella Milleriae Syd.
Clibadium arboreum Don. Sm.
  Phyllocelis Clibadii Syd.
Clibadium arboreum Donn. Sm.
Clibadium Donnell-Smithii Coult.
  {Aecidium Clibadii Syd.
  {Aecidium decoloratum S.
  {Endophyllum decoloratum Whetzel & Olive.
  {Endophyllum pumilio Syd.
  {Endophyllum Wedeliae Whetzel & Olive.
Clibadium erosum (Sw.) DC.
  {Aecidium Clibadii Syd.
  {Aecidium decoloratum S.
  {Endophyllum decoloratum Whetzel & Olive.
  {Endophyllum Wedeliae Whetzel & Olive.
  {Crinipellis calosporus Pat.
  {Marasmius calosporus (Pat.) Sacc.
Clibadium surinamense L.
  {Endophyllum decoloratum Whetzel & Olive.
  {Endophyllum Wedeliae Whetzel & Olive.
Polymnia canadensis L.
  {Aecidium Compositarum Auct. Amer. p. p.
  {Dicaeoma Asterum (Arth.) Arth. & Kern. I.
  Phialea Scutula (P.) Gill.
  Septoria Polymniae Ell. & Ev.
Polymnia maculata Cav.
  {Coleosporium Polymniae Syd.
  {Coleosporium Terebinthinaceae Arth.
  {Nigredo Polymniae (Diet. & Holw.) Arth.
  {Uromyces Polymniae Diet. & Holw.
Polymnia Uvedalia L.
  Coleosporium Terebinthinaceae Arth.
  Helotium herbarum (P.) Fr.
  Leptosphaeria Doliolum (P. ex Fr.) De Not.
  Periconia pycnospora Fres.
  Pleurotus cyphelliformis B.
  Septoria Polymniae Ell. & Ev.

Baltimora erecta L.
{ Nigredo cucullata (Syd.) Arth.
{ Uromyces cucullatus Syd.
Guardiola mexicana Humb. & Bonpl.
  Puccinia Guardiolae Diet. & Holw.
Guardiola platyphylla Gray.
  Thecaphora mexicana Ell. & Ev.
Melampodium divaricatum (Rich.) DC.
{ Micropuccinia Melampodii (Diet. & Holw.) Arth.
{ Puccinia Melampodii Diet. & Holw.
Acanthospermum xanthioides DC.
  Phyllosticta Acanthospermi Ell. & Ev.
Silphium asperrimum Hook.
{ Coleosporium Sonchi-arvensis Auct. Amer.p.p.
{ Coleosporium Terebinthinaceae Arth.
  Micropuccinia Silphii (S.) Arth. & Jackson.
Silphium Asteriscus L.
  Coleosporium Terebinthinaceae Arth.
{ Micropuccinia Silphii (S.) Arth. & Jackson.
{ Puccinia Silphii S.
Silphium compositum Michx.
  Cercospora Silphii Ell. & Ev.
  Coleosporium Terebinthinaceae Arth.
  Micropuccinia Silphii (S.) Arth. & Jackson.
Silphium dentatum Ell.
Silphium glabrum Eggert.
Silphium gracile Gray.
  Coleosporium Terebinthinaceae Arth.
Silphium integrifolium Michx.
{ Aecidium Compositarum Auct. Amer. p. p.
{ Aecidium Compositarum, var. Silphii Bron.
{ Uromyces Junci-tenuis Syd. I.
{ Uromyces Silphii Arth. I.
  Ascochyta Treleasei Berl. & Vogl.
  Cercospora Silphii Ell. & Ev.
{ Coleosporium Sonchi Auct. Amer. p. p.
{ Coleosporium Sonchi-arvensis Auct. Amer. p.p.
{ Coleosporium Terebinthinaceae Arth.
  Entyloma Compositarum Farl.
  Metasphaeria Silphii Ell. & Ev.
{ Peronospora Halstedii Farl.
{ Plasmopara Halstedii (Farl.) Berl. & De Toni.
{ Rhysotheca Halstedii (Farl.) G. W. Wilson.
{ Dasyspora Silphii (S.) Arth.
{ Dicaeoma Silphii (S.) O. Kuntze.
{ Micropuccinia Silphii (S.) Arth. & Jackson.
{ Puccinia Silphii S.
  Septoria alba Ell. & Barthol.
  Septoria Silphii Ell. & Ev.
Silphium laciniatum L.
{ Aecidium Compositarum Auct. Amer. p. p.
{ Aecidium Compositarum, var. Silphii Burrill.
{ Aecidium Silphii (Burrill) Syd.
{ Nigredo Silphii Arth. I.
{ Uromyces Silphii Arth. I.
  Cercospora Silphii Ell. & Ev., var. laciniata
    Tehon & Daniels.

{ Coleosporium Sonchi-arvensis Auct. Amer.p.p.
  Coleosporium Terebinthinaceae Arth.
  Peronospora Halstedii Farl.
  Rhysotheca Halstedii (Farl.) G. W. Wilson.
  Micropuccinia Silphii (S.) Arth. & Jackson.
  Puccinia Silphii S.
Silphium perfoliatum L.
{ ?Aecidium Compositarum Auct. p. p.
  Aecidium Silphii (Burrill) Syd.
{ Nigredo Silphii Arth. I.
  Uromyces Junci-tenuis Syd. I.
  Uromyces Silphii Arth. I.
  Cladosporium herbarum (P.) ex Lk.
  Coleosporium Terebinthinaceae Arth.
  Colletotrichum Silphii J. J. Davis.
  Erysiphe Cichoracearum DC. †
{ Peronospora Halstedii Farl.
{ Plasmopara Halstedii (Farl.) Berl. & De Toni.
{ Rhysotheca Halstedii (Farl.) G. W. Wilson.
{ Micropuccinia Silphii (S.) Arth. & Jackson.
{ Puccinia Silphii S.
  Septoria Silphii Ell. & Ev.
  Sphaeria Silphii S.
Silphium scaberrimum Ell.
{ Coleosporium Sonchi Auct. Amer. p. p.
{ Coleosporium Terebinthinaceae Arth.
Silphium terebinthinaceum Jacq.
{ Aecidium Compositarum Auct. Amer. p. p.
{ Uromyces Junci-tenuis Syd. I.
{ Uromyces Silphii Arth. I.
  Chaetophoma maculans Wint.
{ Caeoma Terebinthinaceae S.
{ Coleosporium Sonchi-arvensis Auct. Amer.
    p. p.
{ Coleosporium Terebinthinaceae Arth.
{ Uredo Terebinthinaceae S.
  Erysiphe Cichoracearum DC. †
{ Peronospora Halstedii Farl.
{ Plasmopara Halstedii (Farl.) Berl. & De Toni.
{ Rhysotheca Halstedii (Farl.) G. W. Wilson.
  Puccinia Silphii S.
  Sclerotium deciduum J. J. Davis.
Silphium trifoliatum L.
  Coleosporium Terebinthinaceae Arth.
  Peronospora Halstedii Farl.
  Plasmopara Halstedii (Farl.) Berl. & De Toni.
{ Dicaeoma Silphii (S.) O. Kuntze.
{ Micropuccinia Silphii (S.) Arth. & Jackson.
{ Puccinia Silphii S.
Silphium trifoliatum L., var. **latifolium** Gray.
  Ellisiella mutica Wint.
Silphium sp. indet.
{ ?Erysiphe depressa Lk.
{ ?Erysiphe Linkii Lév.
{ Dothidea Silphii S.
{ Phyllachora Silphii (S.) Sacc.
{ Leptostroma Silphii (S.) Cke.
{ Rhytisma Silphii S.

Silphium sp. indet. (*cont.*)
Septoria gallarum Ell. & Ev.
Vermicularia Silphii S.
Chrysogonum virginianum L.
{Aecidium Compositarum Auct. p. p.
{Dicaeoma Asterum (Kern) Arth. & Kern. I.
Engelmannia pinnatifida Torr. & Gr.
Synchytrium Taraxaci DBy. & Wor.??
Parthenium argentatum Gray.
Puccinia Parthenii Arth.
Parthenium Hysterophorus L.
Micropuccinia Melampodii (Diet. & Holw.)
Arth.
Puccinia Xanthii S., var. Ambrosiae B. & Rav.?
{Puccinia Parthenii Arth. p. p. II.
{Uredo Parthenii Speg.?
Parthenium incanum H. B. K.
Puccinia Parthenii Arth.
Parthenium integrifolium L.
{Albugo Tragopogonis (P.) ex S. F. Gray.
{Cystopus cubicus (Strauss) ex Lév.
{Cystopus Tragopogonis (P. ex S. F. Gray)
{ Schrt.
{Caeoma Terebinthinaceae S.
{Coleosporium Terebinthinaceae Arth.
{Coleosporium Sonchi-arvensis E. F., *B 22.*
{Uredo Terebinthinaceae S.
Parthenium repens Eggert.
Albugo Tragopogonis (P.) ex S. F. Gray.
Parthenice mollis Gray.
Puccinia Parthenices H. S. Jackson.
Iva ambrosiifolia Gray.
Albugo Tragopogonis (P.) ex S. F. Gray.
Iva axillaris Pursh.
{Aecidium intermixtum Pk.
{Allodus intermixta (Pk.) Arth.
{Puccinia intermixta Pk.
Iva ciliata Willd.
{Albugo Tragopogonis (P.) ex S. F. Gray.
{Cystopus Tragopogonis (P. ex S. F. Gray)
{ Schrt.
Septoria xanthiifolia Ell. & Kellerm.
Iva frutescens L.
Aecidium Ivae H. S. Jackson.
{Asteroma infuscans Ell. & Ev.
{Asteroma ivicola Ell. & Ev.
{Dothidea collecta (S.) Ell. & Ev.
{Dothidea tetraspora B. & Br.
Erysiphe Cichoracearum DC. †
Phyllosticta ivicola Ell. & Ev.
Iva xanthifolia Nutt.
Basidiophora entospora Roze & Cornu.
{Albugo Tragopogonis J. J. Davis.
{Basidiophora Kellermanii (Ell. & Halsted)
{ G. W. Wilson.
{Peronospora Kellermanii Ell. & Halsted.
{Plasmopara Kellermanii (Ell. & Halsted)
{ Swingle.

Basidiophora Kellermanii (Ell. & Halsted) G.
W. Wilson, var. paupercula Pk.
Dasyscypha Ivae Rehm.
Diplodia ivicola Ell. & Ev.
Erysiphe Cichoracearum DC. †
Heterosporium tuberculans Ell. & Ev.
Metasphaeria ambrosiicola Atk., var. Ivae
Rehm.
Ophiobolus anguillides (Cke.) Sacc.
Ophiobolus claviger Hark.
Phialea cyathoides (Bull. ex P.) Gill.
Phyllosticta ivicola Ell. & Ev.
{Physalospora arthuriana Sacc.
{Laestadia arthuriana Cke.
{Plasmopara Halstedii (Farl.) Berl. & De Toni.
{Rhysotheca Halstedii (Farl.) G. W. Wilson.
Puccinia Helianthi S.
{Dicaeoma (?) Xanthiifoliae (Ell. & Ev.) O.
{ Kuntze.
{Puccinia Compositarum N. A. F. *2252a* nec
{ Schl.
{Puccinia Tanaceti E. F., *B 21.*
{Puccinia xanthiifolia Ell. & Ev.
Pyrenopeziza Absinthii (Lasch) Rehm.
Septoria ivicola Ell. & Ev.
Septoria xanthiifolia Ell. & Kellerm.
Xylaria filiformis (A. & S.) ex Fr., var. caulin-
cola Rehm.
Hymenoclea monogyra Torr. & Gr.
Hymenoclea Salsola Torr. & Gr.
{Dicaeoma splendens (Vize) O. Kuntze.
{Puccinia notabilis Tracy & Earle.
{Puccinia splendens Vize.
Ambrosia aptera DC.
Septoria ambrosiicola Speg.
Ambrosia artemisiifolia L.
{Aecidium Compositarum Mart.?
{Puccinia canaliculata (S.) Lagerh. I.
{Albugo Tragopogonis (P.) ex S. F. Gray.
{Cystopus cubicus (Strauss) ex Lév.
{Cystopus Tragopogonis (P. ex S. F. Gray)
{ Schrt.
Entyloma Compositarum Farl.
{Entyloma Compositarum Auct. Amer. p. p.
{Entyloma polysporum (Pk.) Farl.
{Erysiphe Ambrosiae S.
{Erysiphe Cichoracearum DC. †
{Erysiphe communis Auct. Amer. p. p.
Lentomita longirostrata Atk.
Lophiostoma niessleanum Sacc.
Metasphaeria ambrosiicola Atk.
Metasphaeria leiostega (Ell.) Sacc.
Monochytrium stevensianum Griggs.
Oidium Ambrosiae Thm.
Ophiobolus anguillides (Cke.) Sacc.
Ophiobolus fulgidus (C. & P.) Sacc.
{Ophiobolus Glomus (B. & C.) Sacc.
{Raphidospora Glomus (B. & C.) Cke.
{Sphaeria Glomus B. & C.

Ambrosia artemisiifolia 0*cont.***)**

Dothidea Ambrosiae B. & C.
Laestadia arthuriana (Sacc.) Cke.
Phyllachora Ambrosiae (B. & C.) Sacc.
Physalospora Ambrosiae Ell. & Ev.
Physalospora arthuriana Sacc.
Sphaeria arthuriana Sacc.

Peronospora Halstedii Farl.
Plasmopara Halstedii (Farl.) Berl. & De Toni.
Rhysotheca Halstedii (Farl.) G. W. Wilson.

Protomyces andinus Lagerh.
Protomyces gravidus J. J. Davis. p.p.

Micropuccinia Xanthii (S.) Arth. & Jackson.
Puccinia Xanthii S.
Puccinia Xanthii S., var. Ambrosiae B. & Rav.
Pyrenopeziza atrata (P.) Fckl.
Rhodochytrium Spilanthidis Lagerh.

Ambrosia bidendata Michx.

Erysiphe Cichoracearum DC.†

Ambrosia media Rydb.

Micropuccinia Xanthii (S.) Arth. & Jackson.

Ambrosia psilostachya DC.

Aecidium Cardui Fung. Dak. *26.*
Aecidium Compositarum Fung. Dak. *26.*
Nigredo Junci (Desm.) Arth. I.
Uromyces Junci (Desm.) Tul. I.

Albugo Tragopogonis (P.) ex S. F. Gray.
Cystopus Tragopogonis (P. ex S. F. Gray) Schrt.

Entyloma Compositarum Farl.
Erysiphe Cichoracearum DC.†
Leptosphaeria consessa (C. & E.) Sacc.
Metasphaeria ambrosiicola Atk.
Ophiobolus anguillides (Cke.) Sacc.
Ozonium auricomum Lk.

Peronospora Halstedii Farl.
Plasmopara Halstedii (Farl.) Berl. & De Toni.
Rhysotheca Halstedii (Farl.) G. W. Wilson.

Phyllachora Ambrosiae (B. & C.) Sacc.
Physalospora arthuriana Sacc.

Micropuccinia Xanthii (S.) Arth. & Jackson.
Puccinia Xanthii S.
Puccinia Xanthii S., var. Ambrosiae B. & Rav.

Rhizoctonia Solani Kühn.

Ambrosia trifida L.

PHYCOMYCETES

Albugo Tragopogonis (P.) ex S. F. Gray.
Cystopus Tragopogonis (P. ex S. F. Gray) Schrt.

Peronospora Halstedii Farl.
Plasmopara Halstedii (Farl.) Berl. & De Toni.
Rhysotheca Halstedii (Farl.) G. W. Wilson.

Rhodochytrium Spilanthidis Lagerh.

HEMIASCI

Protomyces andinus Lagerh.
Protomyces gravidus J. J. Davis p.p.
?Protomyces macrosporus Pk. 35 Rept.

PEZIZINEAE

Mollisia atrata (P.) Fckl.
Peziza atrata P.
Pyrenopeziza atrata (P.) Fckl.
Pyrenopeziza Artemisiae (Lasch) Sacc., var. Solidaginis Rehm.

PYRENOMYCETINEAE

Diaporthe Arctii (Lasch) Nits.
Diatrypella herbacea Ell. & Ev.
Didymella prominens Ell. & Ev.

Erysiphe Ambrosiae S.
Erysiphe Cichoracearum DC.†
Erysiphe lamprocarpa Auct. Amer. p. p.

Hyponectria dakotensis Seaver.
Leptosphaeria consessa (C. & E.) Sacc.
Leptosphaeria subconica (C. & P.) Sacc.
Metasphaeria ambrosiicola Atk., var. praetans Rehm.

Ophiobolus anguillides (Cke.) Sacc.
Sphaeria fulgida Auct. Amer. p. p.

Ophiobolus fulgidus (C. & P.) Sacc.
Sphaeria fulgida C. & P.

Ophiobolus Solidaginis (Fr.) Sacc.

Phyllachora Ambrosiae (B. & C.) Sacc.
Physalospora Ambrosiae Ell. & Ev.

USTILAGINALES

Entyloma Compositarum Farl.

Entyloma polysporum (Pk.) Farl.
Protomyces polysporus Pk.

UREDINALES

Aecidium Compositarum Auct. Amer. p. p.
Aecidium Compositarum, var. Ambrosiae Burrill.
Aecidium Compositarum, var. Xanthii Ell.
Dicaeoma canaliculatum (S.) O. Kuntze. I.
Puccinia canaliculata (S.) Lagerh. I.
Puccinia Cyperi Arth. I.

Dicaeoma Xanthii (S.) O. Kuntze.
Micropuccinia Xanthii (S.) Arth. & Jackson.
Puccinia Xanthii S.
Puccinia Xanthi S., var. Ambrosiae B. & Rav.

SPHAEROPSIDALES

Cicinnobolus Cesatii DBy.
Phlyctaena arcuata B.
Phyllosticta Ambrosiae J. J. Davis.
Septoria bacilligera Wint.
Vermicularia Dematium (P.) ex Fr.

Ambrosia trifida (*cont.*)

HYPHOMYCETES

Botrytis tephroidea Sacc. & Ell.
Cercospora Arcti-Ambrosiae Halsted.
Cercospora ferruginea Fckl.
Cercospora racemosa Ell. & Martin.
Cercospora racemosa Ell. & Martin, var. Ambrosiae Seymour & Earle.
Hormiscium Ambrosiae Pk.

Ambrosia trifida L., var. **integrifolia** (Muhl.) Torr. & Gr.

Entyloma Compositarum Farl.
Erysiphe Cichoracearum DC. †

Ambrosia sp. indet.

{ Didymella? nigrella (Fr.) Sacc.
{ Sphaeria nigrella Fr.
Leptosphaeria rubicunda Rehm.
Leptostroma vulgare Fr.
Nectria sanguinea Fr.
{ Phoma Anethi (P. ex Fr.) Sacc.
{ Sphaeria Anethi P. ex Fr.
Sclerotium Rolfsii Sacc.

Franseria acanthicarpa (Hook.) Coville.

{ Albugo Tragopogonis (P.) ex S. F. Gray.
{ Cystopus Tragopogonis (P. ex S. F. Gray) Schrt.
Cercospora ferruginea Fckl.
Phoma herbarum Westd.

Franseria ambrosioides Cav.

Erysiphe Cichoracearum DC. †
{ Puccinia Franseriae Syd.
{ Puccinia Tanaceti West Am. Fung. *257.*
{ Dicaeoma splendens (Vize) O. Kuntze.
{ Puccinia splendens Vize.

Franseria Chamissonis Less.

Cercospora ferruginea Fckl.

Franseria deltoides Torr.

{ Dicaeoma splendens (Vize) O. Kuntze.
{ Puccinia splendens Vize.

Franseria discolor Nutt.

Albugo Tragopogonis (P.) ex S. F. Gray.

Franseria dumosa Gray.

Puccinia Franseriae Syd.
{ Dicaeoma splendens (Vize) O. Kuntze.
{ Puccinia splendens Vize.

Franseria hookeriana Nutt.

Cercospora racemosa Ell. & Martin.

Franseria tenuifolia Harv. & Gray.

Albugo Tragopogonis (P.) ex S. F. Gray.

Xanthium acerosum Greene.

Micropuccinia Xanthii (S.) Arth. & Jackson.

Xanthium canadense Mill.

Botrytis vulgaris (Lk.) Fr.
Cercospora xanthicola Heald & Wolf.
Colletotrichum Xanthii Halsted.
{ Erysiphe Cichoracearum DC. †
{ Erysiphe spadicea B. & C.

{ Asteroma Xanthii (DC.) M. A. Curtis.
{ Dothidea Xanthii DC.
Phyllachora Xanthii (DC.) Sacc.
{ Plasmopara Halstedii (Farl.) Berl. & De Toni.
{ Rhysotheca Halstedii (Farl.) G. W. Wilson.
Dasyspora Xanthii (S.) Arth.
{ Dicaeoma Xanthii (S.) O. Kuntze.
{ Micropuccinia Xanthii (S.) Arth. & Jackson.
{ Puccinia Xanthii S.
Rhabdospora Xanthii Pk.
Septoria Xanthii Desm.
Sphaerella xanthicola Cke. & Hark.

Xanthium cenchroides Millsp. & Sherff.

Micropuccinia Xanthii (S.) Arth. & Jackson.

Xanthium chinense Mill.

{ Micropuccinia Xanthii (S.) Arth. & Jackson.
{ Puccinia Xanthii S.
Sphaerotheca Humuli (DC.) Burrill. †

Xanthium commune Brit.

Puccinia Xanthii S.

Xanthium echinatum Murr.

Xanthium inflexum Mackenzie & Bush.

{ Micropuccinia Xanthii (S.) Arth. & Jackson.
{ Puccinia Xanthii S.

Xanthium orientale L.

{ Dicaeoma canaliculatum (S.) O. Kuntze. I.
{ Puccinia canaliculata (S.) Lagerh. I.
{ Micropuccinia Xanthii (S.) Arth. & Jackson.
{ Puccinia Xanthii S.

Xanthium oviforme Wallr.

Xanthium pennsylvanicum Wallr.

Xanthium speciosum Kern.

Xanthium spinosum L.

{ Dasypora Xanthii (S.) Arth.
{ Micropuccinia Xanthii (S.) Arth. & Jackson.
{ Puccinia Xanthii S.

Xanthium strumarium L.

Aecidium Compositarum Auct. Amer. p. p.
Aecidium Compositarum, var. Xanthii N. A. F. *1018b.*
Aecidium Compositarum, var. Xanthii Burrill.
{ Dicaeoma canaliculatum (S.) O. Kuntze. I.
{ Puccinia canaliculata (S.) Lagerh. I.
Puccinia Cyperi Auct. p. p. I.
Erysibe Cichoracearum (DC.) Schrt. †
{ Erysiphe horridula Lév.
{ Erysiphe lamprocarpa Auct. Amer. p. p.
{ Erysiphe Montagnei Lév.
{ Oidium erysiphoides Fr.
Ozonium omnivorum Shear.
?Puccinia Helianthi S.
Puccinia Xanthii S.
Vermicularia Dematium (P.) Fr.
Verticillium albo-atrum Reinke & Berthold.

Xanthium varians Greene.

Puccinia Xanthii S.

Zinnia elegans Jacq.

Cercospora atricincta Heald & Wolf.

Zinnia elegans (*cont.*)
Cercospora Zinniae Ell. & Martin.
Erysiphe Cichoracearum DC. †
Zinnia multiflora L.
Cercospora Zinniae Ell. & Martin.
Sphaeria Zinniae S.
Zinnia tenuiflora Jacq.
⎧ Micropuccinia Melampodii (Diet. & Holw.)
⎨ Arth.
⎪ Puccinia Melampodii Diet. & Holw.
⎩ Puccinia Zinniae Syd.
?Puccinia Xanthii S.
Zinnia sp. indet.
Cercospora atricincta Heald & Wolf.
Cryptosporium aurantiacum Lk.
Heliopsis helianthoides (L.) Sweet.
Aecidium Compositarum, var. Heliopsidis
  Wint.
Nigredo Junci (Desm.) Arth. I.
⎧ Dothidea Heliopsidis S.
⎪ Euryachora Heliopsidis (S.) Cke.
⎪ Montagnella Heliopsidis (S.) Sacc.
⎨ Phaeoderris Heliopsidis (S.) v. Höhnel.
⎪ Rosenscheldia Heliopsidis (S.) Theissen & Syd.
⎩ Sphaeria Heliopsidis S.
⎧ Allodus batesiana Arth.
⎪ Puccinia batesiana Arth.
⎪ Dicaeoma Helianthi-mollis Arth.
⎨ Dicaeoma Heliopsidis (S.) O. Kuntze.
⎩ Puccinia Heliopsidis S.
Septoria Helianthi Ell. & Kellerm.
Septoria Heliopsidis Ell. & Dearness.
Heliopsis helianthoides Sweet, var. **pitcheriana**
  L. H. Bailey.
Phyllosticta pitcheriana Fairman.
Heliopsis? hirsuta Auct.
Montagnella Heliopsidis (S.) Sacc.
Heliopsis scabra Dunal.
Erysiphe Cichoracearum DC. †
Erysiphe taurica Lév.
Leptosphaeria Doliolum (P. ex Fr.) De Not.
Phoma oleracea Sacc.
⎧ Allodus batesiana Arth.
⎪ Puccinia batesiana Arth.
⎪ Dicaeoma Heliopsidis (S.) O. Kuntze.
⎨ Puccinia Helianthi S.
⎩ Puccinia Heliopsidis S.
Septoria Silphii Ell. & Ev.
Montanoa dumicola Klatt.
Montanoa hibiscifolia Benth.
Montanoa Pittieri Rob. & Greenm.
⎧ Klebahnia Montanoae (Arth. & Holw.) Arth.
⎩ Uromyces Montanoae Arth. & Holw.
Montanoa sp. indet.
⎧ Aecidium Montanoae Diet. & Holw.
⎩ Pucciniosira Brickeliae Diet. & Holw.
Axiniphyllum tomentosum Benth.
Puccinia Axiniphylli Arth.

Brauneria angustifolia (DC.) Heller.
Aecidium Compositarum Auct. Amer. p. p.
Rudbeckia fulgida Ait.
⎧ Basidiophora entospora Roze & Cornu.
⎨ Peronospora entospora (Roze & Cornu) B. &
⎩ Br.
Uromyces Rudbeckiae Arth. & Holw.
Rudbeckia hirta L.
Aecidium Batesii Arth.
Aecidium Compositarum Auct. Amer. p. p.
Cercospora tabacina Ell. & Ev.
Entyloma polysporum (Pk.) Farl.
Erysiphe Cichoracearum DC. †
Plasmopara Halstedii (Farl.) Berl. & De Toni.
Septoria Rudbeckiae Ell. & Halsted.
Septoria Rudbeckiae Ell. & Halsted, var. oak-
  landica Sacc.
Rudbeckia laciniata L.
⎧ ?Aecidium Compositarum Auct. Amer. p. p.
⎨ Nigredo perigynia (Halsted) Arth. I.
⎩ Uromyces perigynius Halsted I.
Cercospora Rudbeckiae Pk.
Cercospora tabacina Ell. & Ev.
Colletotrichum Rudbeckiae Pk.
Entyloma Compositarum Farl.
Erysiphe Cichoracearum DC. †
Phoma Rudbeckiae Fairman.
Phyllosticta Rudbeckiae Ell. & Ev.
⎧ Peronospora Halstedii Farl.
⎨ Plasmopara Halstedii (Farl.) Berl. & De Toni.
⎩ Rhysotheca Halstedii (Farl.) G. W. Wilson.
Ramularia Rudbeckiae Pk.
Septoria Rudbeckiae Ell. & Halsted.
Synchytrium aureum Schrt.
Tubercularia persicina (Ditm. ex Fr.) Sacc.
⎧ Caeomurus Rudbeckiae (Arth. & Holw.) O.
⎪ Kuntze.
⎪ Teleutospora Rudbeckiae (Arth. & Holw.)
⎨ Arth. & Bisby.
⎪ Telospora Rudbeckiae (Arth. & Holw.) Arth.
⎪ Uromyces Rudbeckiae Arth. & Holw.
⎩ Uromyces Solidaginis Auct. Amer. p. p.
Vermicularia Dematium (P.) ex Fr.
Rudbeckia maxima Nutt.
⎧ Micropuccinia Rudbeckiae (Barthol.) Arth. &
⎨ Jackson.
⎩ Puccinia Rudbeckiae Barthol.
Rudbeckia occidentalis Nutt.
Erysiphe Cichoracearum DC. †
Ramularia Rudbeckiae Pk.
Rudbeckia triloba L.
Aecidium Compositarum Auct. Amer. p. p.
Cercospora tabacina Ell. & Ev.
Cicinnobolus Cesatii DBy.
⎧ Peronospora Halstedii Farl.
⎩ Rhysotheca Halstedii (Farl.) G. W. Wilson.
Septoria Rudbeckiae Ell. & Halsted.
Lepachys columnaris (Sims) Torr. & Gr.
Aecidium Compositarum Auct. Amer. p. p.

Lepachys columnaris (*cont.*)
  {Nigredo perigynia (Halsted) Arth. I.
  {Puccinellia perigynia (Halsted) Syd. I.
  Cercospora Ratibidae Ell. & Barthol.
  Leptosphaeria dumetorum Niessl.
  Physalospora Lepachydis Ell. & Ev.
  Septoria Lepachydis Ell. & Ev.
  Septoria Rudbeckiae Ell. & Halsted.
Lepachys pinnata (Vent.) Torr. & Gr.
  Cercospora Ratibidae Ell. & Barthol.
  Entyloma Compositarum Farl.
  Rhysotheca Halstedii (Farl.) G. W. Wilson.
  Septoria infuscata Wint.
Wulffia stenoglossa DC.
  Uromyces Wulffiae-stenoglossae Diet.
Gymnolomia Ghiesbreghtii Hemsl.
  ?Puccinia Viguierae Pk.
Gymnolomia microcephala Less.
  {Dicaeoma (?) Gymnolomiae (Arth.) Arth. &
  { Jackson.
  {Puccinia Gymnolomiae Arth. non Diet. &
  { Holw.
Gymnolomia multiflora Nutt.
  {Dicaeoma aemulans (Syd.) Arth. & Jackson.
  {Puccinia aemulans Syd.
  {Puccinia Gymnolomiae Diet. & Holw. non
  { Arth.
  Puccinia Lygodesmiae Pk.
Gymnolomia patens Gray, var. **brachypoda** Robinson & Greenm.
  {Dicaeoma? Gymnolomiae (Arth.) Arth. &
  { Jackson.
  {Puccinia Gymnolomiae Arth. non Diet. &
  { Holw.
Gymnolomia subflexuosa Benth. & Hook.
  Puccinia Gymnolomiae Arth.
  {Micropuccinia semota (Jackson & Holw.)
  { Arth.
  {Puccinia semota Jackson & Holw.
  ?Puccinia Viguierae Pk.
Gymnolomia sp. indet.
  ?Puccinia Helianthi S.
Agiabampoa congesta Rose.
  Dicaeoma Caleae (Arth.) Arth. & Jackson.
Iostephane heterophylla Benth.
  Puccinia Jostephanes Diet. & Holw.
Zaluzania asperrima Sch. Bip.
  Puccinia Zaluzaniae Arth.
Balsamorrhiza deltoidea Nutt.
  Pleospora Balsamorrhizae Tracy & Earle.
  {Bullaria Balsamorrhizae (Pk.) Arth. & Mains.
  {Puccinia Balsamorrhizae Pk.
Balsamorrhiza hirsuta Nutt.
Balsamorrhiza Hookeri Nutt.
Balsamorrhiza macrophylla Nutt.
  {Bullaria Balsamorhizae (Pk.) Arth. & Mains.
  {Puccinia Balsamorrhizae Pk.
Balsamorrhiza sagittata (Pursh) Nutt.
  Erysiphe Cichoracearum DC. †

  {Bullaria Balsamorrhizae (Pk.) Arth. & Mains.
  {Puccinia Balsamorrhizae Pk.
  {Puccinia flosculosorum Auct. Amer. p. p.
  {Puccinia Hieracii Auct. Amer. p. p.
  {Trichobasis Balsamorrhizae Pk.
  {Uredo Balsamorrhizae De Toni.
Balsamorrhiza sp. indet.
  {Mycosphaerella Balsamorrhizae Earle.
  {Sphaerella Balsamorrhizae (Earle) Sacc. &
  { Trott.
Borrichia argentea DC.
  {Sorosporium Borrichiae Ell. & Ev.
  {Sterigmatocystis sp. indet. sec. G. P. Clinton.
Borrichia arborescens (L.) DC.
Borrichia frutescens (L.) DC.
  Aecidium Borrichiae Syd.
  {Bullaria triannulata (B. & C.) Arth. & Mains.
  {Puccinia mirifica Diet. & Holw.
  {Puccinia triannulata (B. & C.) H. S. Jackson.
  {Uromyces triannulatus B. & C.
Wedelia buphthalmoides Griseb.
  Fumago vagans Fr.
Wedelia hispida H. B. K.
  Aecidium Wedeliae-hispidae Diet.
Wedelia Jacquini Rich.
Wedelia lanceolata DC.
  Uredo vicina Arth.
Wedelia reticulata DC.
  Chaetothyrium variabilis Toro.
  Uromyces piauhyensis Henn.
Wedelia trilobata (L.) Hitchc.
  Didymium nigripes (L.) Fr.
  {Aecidium Wedeliae Earle.
  {Endophyllum decoloratum Whetzel & Olive.
  {Endophyllum Wedeliae Whetzel & Olive.
Wyethia amplexicaulis Nutt.
  Didymaria conferta Syd.
  Bullaria Balsamorrhizae (Pk.) Arth. & Mains.
  Puccinia Wyethiae Ell. & Ev.
  Sphaerotheca Humuli (DC.) Burrill, var.
    fuliginea (Schl.) Salmon.
Wyethia angustifolia Nutt.
Wyethia arizonica Gray.
  {Bullaria Balsamorrhizae (Pk.) Arth. & Mains.
  {Puccinia Wyethiae Hark.
  {Trichobasis Wyethiae Pk.
  {Uredo Wyethiae De Toni.
Wyethia glabra Gray.
  {Marssonia Wyethiae Ell. & Ev.
  {Marssonina Wyethiae (Ell. & Ev.) Magn.
Wyethia mollis Gray.
  Puccinia Wyethiae Hark.
  Septoria Wyethiae Hark.
Tithonia diversifolia (Hemsl.) Gray.
Tithonia rotundifolia (Mill.) Blake.
Tithonia scaberrima Benth.
Tithonia tubiformis (Jacq.) Cass.
  Puccinia Tithoniae Diet & Holw.

Viguiera annua (M. E. Jones) Elake.
Viguiera buddleiformis Benth. & Hook.
  { Dicaeoma abruptum (Diet. & Holw.) Arth. &
    Jackson.
  { Puccinia abrupta Diet. & Holw.
Viguiera deltoidea Gray, var. **Parishii** Vasey &
  Rose.
  Puccinia turgidipes H. S. Jackson.
Viguiera excelsa Benth. & Hook.
  { Dicaeoma abruptum (Diet. & Holw.) Arth. &
    Jackson.
  { Puccinia abrupta Diet. & Holw.
  Puccinia Viguierae Pk.
Viguiera eriophora Greenm.
  Puccinia nanomitra Syd.
Viguiera helianthoides H. B. K.
  ?Coleosporium Helianthi Arth.
  Coleosporium Viguierae Diet. & Holw.
  Puccinia abrupta Diet. & Holw.
  ?Puccinia Iostephanes Diet. & Holw.
  Puccinia nanomitra Syd.
  Puccinia Viguierae Pk.
Viguiera Palmeri Gray.
  Puccinia abrupta Diet. & Holw.
  Puccinia subglobosa Diet. & Holw.
Viguiera Pringlei Robinson & Greenm.
  Puccinia punctoides Syd.
Viguiera silvatica Klatt.
  Entyloma Compositarum Farl.
  { Dicaeoma abruptum (Diet. & Holw.) Arth. &
    Jackson.
  { Puccinia abrupta Diet & Holw.
Viguiera tenuis Gray.
  { Dicaeoma abruptum (Diet. & Holw.) Arth. &
    Jackson.
  { Puccinia abrupta Diet. & Holw.
Helianthus angustifolius L.
  Aecidium Helianthi-mollis S.
  Dicaeoma Helianthi-mollis Arth.
  Puccinia Helianthi S.
  { Puccinia Helianthi-mollis (Arth.) H. S. Jack-
    son. 6 June 1918.
  { Puccinia Helianthi-mollis (Arth.) Arth. &
    Bisby. 16 July 1918.
  Puccinia Heliopsidis S.
  Puccinia Tanaceti Auct. Amer. p. p.
  { Montagnella Heliopsidis (S.) Sacc.
  { Rosenscheldia Heliopsidis (S.) Theissen & Syd.
Helianthus annuus L.
  Nigredo Junci (Desm.) Arth. I.
  Alternaria tenuis Nees ex Fr.
  Armillaria mellea (Vahl) ex Fr.
  Cercospora pachypus Ell. & Kellerm.
  Cladosporium Aphidis Thm.
  Coniothyrium Helianthi Ell. & Barthol.
  { Albugo Tragopogonis (P.) ex S. F. Gray.
  { Cystopus Tragopogonis (P. ex S. F. Gray)
    Schrt.

{ Entyloma Compositarum Auct. Amer. p. p.
{ Entyloma polysporum (Pk.) Farl.
{ Erysiphe Cichoracearum DC. †
{ Erysiphe lamprocarpa Auct. Amer. p. p.
Leptosphaeria consessa (C. & E.) Sacc.
Macrosporium inquinans C. & E.
Mollisia lilacina Clements.
Ophiobolus fulgidus (C. & P.) Sacc.
Ophiobolus porphyrogonus (Tode ex Fr.) Sacc.
Ozonium omnivorum Shear.
Phlyctaena arcuata B.
{ Dothidea effusa S.
{ Phyllachora effusa (S.) Sacc.
{ Peronospora Halstedii Farl.
{ Plasmopara Halstedii (Farl.) Berl. & De Toni.
{ Rhysotheca Halstedii (Farl.) G. W. Wilson.
Polyactis simplex (P.) Lk.
{ Aecidium Compositarum Auct. Amer. p. p.
{ Aecidium Compositarum, var. Helianthi Bur-
  rill.
Dicaeoma Helianthi (S.) O. Kuntze.
Dicaeoma Helianthi-mollis Arth.
Puccinia Helianthi S.
{ Puccinia Helianthi-mollis (Arth.) H. S. Jack-
  son.
Puccinia Helianthorum S.
Puccinia Tanaceti Auct. Amer. p. p.
Uredo Helianthi M. A. Curtis.
Pyrenopeziza fuscorubra Rehm.
Pythium debaryanum Hesse.
{ Rhabdospora helianthicola (Cke. & Hark.)
  Sacc.
{ Septoria helianthicola Cke. & Hark.
Rhizoctonia Solani Kühn.
{ Sclerotinia libertiana Fckl.
{ Sclerotinia sclerotiorum (Lib.) Schrt.
Septoria Helianthi Ell. & Kellerm.
?Trichopeziza subochracea (C. & P.) Sacc.
Vermicularia subeffigurata S., var. Helianthi S.

Helianthus argophyllus Torr. & Gr.
  Septoria Helianthi Ell. & Kellerm.

Helianthus atrorubens L.
  { Dicaeoma Helianthi-mollis Arth.
  { Puccinia Helianthi S.

Helianthus australis Small.
  Coleosporium Helianthi Arth.
  { Dicaeoma Helianthi-mollis Arth.
  { Puccinia Helianthi S.

Helianthus californicus DC.
  { Dicaeoma Helianthi-mollis Arth.
  { Puccinia Helianthi S.
  { Puccinia Tanaceti Auct. Amer. p. p.
  Septoria Helianthi Ell. & Kellerm.

Helianthus californicus DC., var. **utahensis**
  Gray.
  Erysiphe Cichoracearum DC. †

Helianthus ciliaris DC.
Dicaeoma massale (Arth.) Arth. & Jackson.
Puccinia Helianthi Auct. p. p.
Puccinia massalis Arth.
Helianthus debilis Nutt.
Dicaeoma Helianthi-mollis Arth.
Puccinia Helianthi S.
Helianthus debilis Nutt., var. **cucumerifolius**
(Torr. & Gr.) Gray.
Septoria Helianthi Ell. & Kellerm.
Helianthus decapetalus L.
Nigredo Junci (Desm.) Arth. I.
Coleosporium Helianthi Arth.
Peridermium Helianthi (Arth.) Hedgc. &
Hunt. III.
Cylindrocolla flagellaris Ell. & Ev.
Cylindrocolla lactea Sacc. & Ell. p. p.
Erysiphe Cichoracearum DC. †
Leptosphaeria Doliolum (P. ex Fr.) De Not.
Leptostromella hysterioides (Fr.) Sacc.
Aecidium Compositarum, var. Helianthi Bur-
rill.
Dicaeoma Helianthi-mollis Arth.
Puccinia Helianthi S.
Puccinia Helianthi-mollis (Arth.)H. S. Jackson.
Puccinia Tanaceti Auct. Amer. p. p.
Septoria Helianthi Ell. & Kellerm.
Helianthus decapetalus L., var. **multiflorus**(?)
(L.) Gray.
Dothidea Heliopsidis (S.) Fr.
Montagnella Heliopsidis (S.) Sacc.
Helianthus divaricatus L.
Nigredo Junci (Desm.) Arth. I.
Coleosporium Helianthi Arth.
Peridermium Helianthi (Arth.) Hedgc. &
Hunt. III.
Erysiphe Cichoracearum DC. †
Metasphaeria Maximiliani Ell. & Ev., var.
divaricata Ell. & Ev.
Dothidea Heliopsidis (S.) Fr.
Montagnella Heliopsidis (S.) Sacc.
Plasmopara Halstedii (Farl.) Berl. & De Toni.
Rhysotheca Halstedii (Farl.) G. W. Wilson.
Aecidium Compositarum, var. Helianthi Bur-
rill.
Caeoma tracheliifoliatum S.
Dicaeoma Helianthi (S.) O. Kuntze.
Dicaeoma Helianthi-mollis Arth.
Puccinia Helianthi S.
Puccinia Tanaceti Auct. Amer. p. p.
Septoria Helianthi Ell. & Kellerm.
Septoria paupera Ell.
Helianthus doronicoides Lam.
Cercospora Helianthi Ell. & Ev.
Coleosporium Helianthi Arth.
Coleosporium Sonchi Auct. Amer. p. p.
Coleosporium Sonchi-arvensis Auct. Amer.p.p.
Erysiphe Cichoracearum DC. †
Erysiphe lamprocarpa Auct. Amer. p. p.

Peronospora Halstedii Farl.
Plasmopara Halstedii (Farl.) Berl. & De Toni.
Rhysotheca Halstedii (Farl.) G. W. Wilson.
Aecidium Compositarum Auct. Amer. p. p.
Aecidium Compositarum, var. Helianthi Bur-
rill.
Caeoma (Aecidium) helianthatum S.
Dicaeoma Helianthi-mollis Arth.
Puccinia Helianthi S.
Puccinia Tanaceti Auct. Amer. p. p.
Septoria Helianthi Ell. & Kellerm.
Helianthus Eggertii Small.
Coleosporium Helianthi Arth.
Helianthus exilis Gray.
Ramularia Helianthi Ell. & Ev.
Helianthus fascicularis Greene.
Physalospora aurantia Ell & Ev.
Dicaeoma Helianthi-mollis Arth.
Puccinia Helianthi-mollis (Arth.) H. S. Jack-
son.
Helianthus giganteus L.
Caeoma Helianthi S.
Coleosporium Helianthi Arth.
Peridermium Helianthi (Arth.) Hedgc. &
Hunt. III.
Diaporthe orthoceras (Fr.) Nits.
Erysiphe Cichoracearum DC. †
Gloniopsis Lathami Fairman.
Leptosphaeria Helianthi Ell. & Ev.
Caeoma (Aecidium) helianthatum S.
Dicaeoma Helianthi (S.) O. Kuntze.
Dicaeoma Helianthi-mollis Arth.
Puccinia Helianthi S.
Puccinia Tanaceti Auct. Amer. p. p.
Helianthus glaucus Small.
Coleosporium Helianthi Arth.
Helianthus gracilentus Gray.
Phyllachora effusa (S.) Sacc.
Helianthus grosseserratus Martens.
Coleosporium Helianthi Arth.
Erysiphe Cichoracearum DC. †
Peronospora Halstedii Farl.
Plasmopara Halstedii (Farl.) Berl. & De Toni.
Rhysotheca Halstedii (Farl.) G. W. Wilson.
Aecidium Compositarum, var. Helianthi Bur-
rill.
Dicaeoma Helianthi (S.) O. Kuntze.
Dicaeoma Helianthi-mollis Arth.
Puccinia Helianthi S.
Puccinia Tanaceti Auct. Amer. p. p.
Septoria Helianthi Ell. & Kellerm.
Helianthus heterophyllus Nutt.
Dicaeoma Helianthi-mollis Arth.
Dicaeoma Viguierae (Pk.) O. Kuntze.
Puccinia Helianthi S.
Puccinia Helianthi-mollis (Arth.) H. S. Jack-
son.
Puccinia Helianthorum S.

Helianthus hirsutus Raf.
Cercospora Helianthi C. & E.
Coleosporium Helianthi Arth.
{ Dicaeoma Helanthi-mollis Arth.
{ Puccinia Helianthi S.
Rhysotheca Halstedii (Farl.) G. W. Wilson.
Septoria Helianthi Ell. & Kellerm.
Helianthus hirsutus Raf., var. **trachyphyllus**
Torr. & Gr.
Montagnella Heliopsidis (S.) Sacc.
Helianthus Kellermani Brit.
{ Dicaeoma Helianthi-mollis Arth.
{ Puccinia Helianthi S.
Helianthus laciniatus Gray.
Dicaeoma Helianthi-mollis Arth.
Pyrenopeziza compressula Rehm.
Helianthus laetiflorus P.
Erysiphe Cichoracearum DC. †
{ Dicaeoma Helianthi-mollis Arth.
{ Puccinia Helianthi S.
{ Puccinia Tanaceti Auct. Amer. p. p.
Helianthus lenticularis Dougl.
Cercospora pachypus Ell. & Kellerm.
{ Dicaeoma Helianthi-mollis Arth.
{ Puccinia Helianthi S.
Helianthus longifolius Pursh.
Erysiphe Cichoracearum DC. †
Plasmopara Halstedii (Farl.) Berl. & De Toni.
Helianthus Maximiliani Schrad.
Nigredo Junci (Desm.) Arth. I.
Cercospora Helianthi Ell. & Ev.
Erysiphe Cichoracearum DC. †
Leptosphaeria doliolum (P. ex Fr.) Ell. & Ev.
Leptosphaeria Helianthi Ell. & Ev.
Metasphaeria Maximiliani Ell. & Ev.
Ophiobolus Helianthi Ell. & Ev.
Phyllachora Ambrosiae (B. & C.) Sacc.
Rhysotheca Halstedii (Farl.) G. W. Wilson.
Pleospora diaportheoides Ell. & Ev.
{ Dicaeoma Helianthi-mollis Arth.
{ Puccinia Helianthi S.
{ Puccinia Helianthorum S.
{ Puccinia Tanaceti Auct. Amer. p. p.
Schizoxylon berkeleyanum (Dur. & Lév.) Fckl.
Helianthus microcephalus Torr. & Gr.
Coleosporium Helianthi Arth.
{ Dicaeoma Helianthi-mollis Arth.
{ Puccinia Helianthi S.
Helianthus mollis Lam.
Erysiphe Cichoracearum DC. †
{ Aecidium Helianthi-mollis S.
{ Caeoma helianthatum S.
{ Dicaeoma Helianthi (S.) O. Kuntze.
{ Dicaeoma Helianthi-mollis Arth.
{ Puccinia Helianthi S.
{ Puccinia Helianthi-mollis (Arth.) H. S. Jack-
{ son.
{ Puccinia Tanaceti Auct. Amer. p. p.
Septoria Inulae Sacc. & Speg.

Helianthus multiflorus L.?
Erysiphe Cichoracearum DC. †
Puccinia Helianthi S.
Helianthus nitidus Lunell.
{ Dicaeoma Helianthi-mollis Arth.
{ Puccinia Helianthi S.
Helianthus Nuttallii Torr. & Gr.
Nigredo Junci (Desm.) Arth. I.
Erysiphe Cichoracearum DC. †
Rhysotheca Halstedii (Farl.) G. W. Wilson.
{ Aecidium Compositarum, var. Helianthi Bur-
{ rill.
{ Dicaeoma Helianthi-mollis Arth.
{ Puccinia Helianthi S.
Helianthus occidentalis Riddell.
Nigredo Junci (Desm.) Arth. I.
Cercospora Helianthi Ell. & Ev.
Coleosporium Helianthi Arth.
{ Peronospora Halstedii Farl.
{ Plasmopara Halstedii (Farl.) Berl. & De Toni.
{ Rhysotheca Halstedii (Farl.) G. W. Wilson.
{ Aecidium Compositarum, var. Helianthi Bur-
{ rill.
{ Dicaeoma Helianthi-mollis Arth.
{ Puccinia Helianthi S.
{ Puccinia Tanaceti Auct. Amer. p. p.
Helianthus orgyalis DC.
Erysiphe Cichoracearum DC. †
{ Aecidium Compositarum, var. Helianthi Bur-
{ rill.
{ Dicaeoma Helianthi-mollis Arth.
{ Puccinia Helianthi S.
Helianthus Parishii Gray.
Nigredo Junci (Desm.) Arth. I.
Erysiphe Cichoracearum DC. †
{ Dicaeoma Helianthi-mollis Arth.
{ Puccinia Helianthi S.
Helianthus parviflorus Bernh. ?
Erysiphe Cichoracearum DC. †
Puccinia Helianthi S.
Helianthus peploides (L.) Fr.
Septoria Ammodeniae Dearness.
Sphaerella Stellarinearum (Rabh.) Karst.
Helianthus petiolaris Nutt.
Nigredo Junci (Desm.) Arth. I.
Cercospora pachypus Ell. & Kellerm.
Erysiphe Cichoracearum DC. †
{ Dicaeoma Helianthi-mollis Arth.
{ Puccinia Helianthi S.
{ Puccinia Tanaceti Auct. Amer. p. p.
Septoria Helianthi Ell. & Kellerm.
Helianthus Radula Torr. & Gr.
Coleosporium Helianthi Arth.
Helianthus Rydbergi Brit.
{ Dicaeoma Helianthi-mollis Arth.
{ Puccinia Helianthi S.
Helianthus saxicola Small.
Coleosporium Helianthi Arth.

Helianthus scaberrimus Ell.
{ Nigredo Junci (Desm.) Arth. I.
{ Uromyces Junci (Desm.) Tul. I.
Cercospora Helianthi Ell. & Ev.
Coleosporium Helianthi Arth.
Erysiphe Cichoracearum DC. †
{ Plasmopara Halstedii (Farl.) Berl. & De Toni.
{ Rhysotheca Halstedii (Farl.) G. W. Wilson.
{ Aecidium Compositarum, var. Helianthi Bur-
{   rill.
{ Aecidium helianthatum S.
{ Caeoma helianthatum S.
{ Dicaeoma Helianthi-mollis Arth.
{ Puccinia Helianthi S.
{ Puccinia Helianthorum S.
{ Puccinia Tanaceti Auct. Amer. p. p.
Septoria Helianthi Ell. & Kellerm.
Vermicularia Helianthi Ell. & Kellerm.

Helianthus strumosus L.
Nigredo Junci (Desm.) Arth. I.
Ascochyta Compositarum J. J. Davis.
Ascochyta Compositarum J. J. Davis, var.
  parva J. J. Davis.
Cercospora Helianthi Ell. & Ev.
Coleosporium Helianthi Arth.
{ Erysiphe Cichoracearum DC. †
{ Erysiphe lamprocarpa Auct. Amer. p. p.
{ Dothidea Heliopsidis (S.) Fr.
{ Euryachora Heliopsidis (S.) Cke.
{ Montagnella Heliopsidis (S.) Sacc.
{ Sphaeria Heliopsidis S.
{ Peronospora Halstedii Farl.
{ Plasmopara Halstedii (Farl.) Berl. & DeToni.
{ Rhysotheca Halstedii (Farl.) G. W. Wilson.
{ Aecidium Compositarum Auct. Amer. p. p.
{ Dicaeoma Helianthi (S.) O. Kuntze.
{ Dicaeoma Helianthi-mollis Arth.
{ Puccinia Helianthi S.
{ Puccinia Tanaceti Auct. Amer. p. p.
Ramularia Cynarae Sacc.

Helianthus subrhomboideus Rydb.
Leptosphaeria consessa (C. & E.) Sacc.
Plasmopara Halstedii (Farl.) Berl. & De Toni.
{ Dicaeoma Helianthi-mollis Arth.
{ Puccinia Helianthi S.

Helianthus subtomentosus Bourg.
Rhysotheca Halstedii (Farl.) G. W. Wilson.

Helianthus subtuberosus Bourg.
{ Nigredo Junci (Desm.) Arth. I.
{ Uromyces Junci (Desm.) Tul. I.

Helianthus tomentosus Michx.
Coleosporium Helianthi Arth.
{ Dicaeoma Helianthi-mollis Arth.
{ Puccinia Helianthi S.

Helianthus tracheliifolius Willd.
{ Plasmopara Halstedii (Farl.) Berl. & De Toni.
{ Rhysotheca Halstedii (Farl.) G. W. Wilson.

{ Aecidium trachelifoliatum S.
{ Caeoma trachelifoliatum S.
Dicaeoma Helianthi (S.) O. Kuntze.
Dicaeoma Helianthi-mollis Arth.
{ Puccinia Helianthi S.
{ Puccinia Helianthi-mollis (Arth.) H. S. Jack-
{   son.

Helianthus tuberosus L.
Nigredo Junci (Desm.) Arth. I.
Cercospora Helianthi Ell. & Ev.
{ Coleosporium Helianthi Arth.
{ Coleosporium Sonchi Auct. Amer. p. p.
{ Coleosporium Sonchi-arvensis Auct. Amer. p.p.
{ Peridermium Helianthi Hedgc. & Hunt. III.
Erysiphe Cichoracearum DC. †
{ Heptameria consessa (C. & E.) Cke.
{ Leptosphaeria consessa (C. & E.) Sacc.
{ Sphaeria consessa C. & E.
Oidium erysiphoides Fr.
Ozonium omnivorum Shear.
{ Peronospora Halstedii Farl.
{ Plasmopara Halstedii (Farl.) Berl. & De Toni.
{ Rhysotheca Halstedii (Farl.) G. W. Wilson.
{ Aecidium Compositarum Auct. Amer. p. p.
{ Aecidium Compositarum, var. Helianthi Bur-
{   rill.
{ Dicaeoma Helianthi (S.) O. Kuntze.
{ Dicaeoma Helianthi-mollis Arth.
{ Puccinia Helianthi S.
{ Puccinia Helianthi-mollis (Arth.) H. S.
{   Jackson.
{ Puccinia Helianthorum S.
{ Puccinia Tanaceti Auct. Amer. p. p.
{ Trichobasis Helianthi Rav. Fung. Am.
Ramularia Cynarae Sacc.
{ Sclerotinia libertiana Fckl.
{ Sclerotinia sclerotiorum (Lib.) Schrt.
Sclerotinia perplexa Lawrence.
Sclerotium Rolfsii Sacc.
Septoria Helianthi Ell. & Kellerm.
Sphaerophoma Brencklei Petrak.

Helianthus sp. indet.
Cladosporium apiculatum B. & C.
Colletotrichum Helianthi J. J. Davis.
Cyphella pezizoides Zopf.
Cyphella villosa (Fr.) Karst.
Dinemasporium strigosum (Fr.) Sacc., var.
  leptosporum Sacc.
Fusarium Helianthi C. E. Lewis.
Fusarium hymenula Pound & Clements.
Fusarium salmonicolor B. & C.
Fusarium tenuissimum (Pk.) Sacc.
Helotium parile Karst., var. languidum Karst.
Leptosphaeria dumetorum Niessl.
Leptosphaeria subconica (B. & C.) Sacc.
Leptothyrium vulgare (Fr.) Sacc.
Macrosporium commune Rabh.
Phoma herbarum Westd., var. helianthella
  Sacc.

Helianthus sp. indet. (*cont.*)
  Phyllosticta Helianthi Ell. & Ev.
  Pleospora Richtophensis Ell. & Ev.
  Pyrenopeziza dermatoides Rehm.
  Sclerotinia minor Jagger.
  { Sirodesmium Fumago (Cke.) Sacc.
  { Sporidesmium Fumago Cke.
  Vermicularia subglabra Cke. & Hark.
Eleutheranthera ruderalis (Sw.) Sch. Bip.
  { Dicaeoma cubense O. Kuntze.
  { Micropuccinia Melampodii (Diet. & Holw.)
     Arth.
  { Puccinia Eleutherantherae Diet.
  { Puccinia Melampodii Diet. & Holw.
  { Puccinia solida B. & C. non S.
  { Puccinia Synedrellae Henn.
Perymenium Berlandieri DC.
Perymenium discolor Schrad.
Perymenium macrocephalum Greenm.
Perymenium Mendezii DC.
Perymenium Purpusii Brandegee.
Perymenium strigillosum (Robinson & Greenm.)
  Greenm.
Perymenium verbesinoides DC.
  { Nigredo cucullata (Syd.) Arth.
  { Uromyces cucullatus Syd.
Melanthera angustifolia A. Rich.
Melanthera aspera (Jacq.) Steud.
  { Nigredo columbiana (Mayor) Arth.
  { Uromyces columbianus Mayor.
Melanthera canescens (O. Kuntze) Schultz.
  Sphaerotheca Humuli (DC.) Burrill. †
  { Nigredo columbiana (Mayor) Arth.
  { Uromyces columbianus Mayor.
Melanthera deltoidea Michx.
  Puccinia obtecta Pk. I.
  { Nigredo columbiana (Mayor) Arth.
  { Uromyces columbianus Mayor.
Melanthera hastata Michx.
  { Nigredo Martinii (Farl.) Arth.
  { Uromyces Martinii Farl.
  { Uromyces Melantherae Cke.
Melanthera hastata Michx., var. **cubensis**
  Schultz.
  Uromyces columbianus Mayor.
Melanthera nivea (L.) Small.
  Puccinia Melantherae Henn.
  { Nigredo columbiana (Mayor) Arth.
  { Nigredo Martinii (Farl.) Arth.
Melanthera parvifolia Small.
  Nigredo Martinii (Farl.) Arth.
Spilanthes oleracea Jacq.
  Micropuccinia Melampodii (Diet. & Holw.)
    Arth. & Jackson.
  Puccinia Spilanthis Henn.
Salmea scandens (L.) DC.
  { Nigredo Salmeae (Arth. & Holw.) Arth.
  { Uromyces Salmeae Arth. & Holw.

Notoptera brevipes (Robinson) Blake.
  { Allodus cornuta (Jackson & Holw.) Arth. &
  {   Orton.
  { Puccinia cornuta Jackson & Holw.
Notoptera hirsuta (Sw.) Urban.
  { Micropuccinia Notopterae (Arth.) Arth. &
  {   Jackson.
  { Puccinia Notopterae Arth.
Encelia adenophora Greenm.
  { Bullaria Enceliae (Diet. & Holw.) Arth.
  { Puccinia Enceliae Diet. & Holw.
Encelia californica Nutt.
  Cyphella villosa (P. ex Fr.) Karst.
  Stereum heterosporum Burt.
Encelia grandiflora Benth.
Encelia
  (Simsia Holwayi Blake).
Encelia mexicana Mart.
Encelia polycephala Hemsl.
Encelia sericea Hemsl.
Encelia viscida Gray.
  { Bullaria Enceliae (Diet. & Holw.) Arth.
  { Puccinia Enceliae Diet. & Holw.
Helianthella californica Gray.
  { Puccinia Helianthellae Arth.
  { Trichobasis Helianthellae Pk.
  { Uredo Helianthellae (Pk.) De Toni.
Helianthella Douglasii Torr. & Gr.
  Erysiphe Cichoracearum DC. †
Helianthella nevadensis Greene.
  Puccinia Helianthellae Arth.
Helianthella Parryi Gray.
  Erysiphe Cichoracearum DC. †
Helianthella quinquenervis Gray.
  Cercosporella Helianthellae Ell. & Ev.
  { ?Aecidium Helianthellae Arth.
  { Puccinia Helianthellae Arth.
Helianthella uniflora (Nutt.) Torr. & Gr.
  Puccinia Helianthellae Arth.
Hymenostephium cordatum (Hook. & Arn.)
  Blake.
Hymenostephium microcephalum (Less.)
  Blake.
  Puccinia Gymnolomiae Arth.
Actinomeris alternifolia (L.) DC.
  Cercospora anomala Ell. & Halsted.
  { Erysiphe Cichoracearum DC. †
  { Erysiphe lamprocarpa Auct. Amer. p. p.
Actinomeris sp. indet.
  Diaporthe orthoceras (Fr.) Nits.
Otopappus alternifolius B. L. Robinson.
  Puccinia Otopappi Syd.
Otopappus epaleaceus Hemsl., var. **Pringlei**
  Greenm.
  Puccinia globulifera Arth.
Otopappus verbesinoides Benth.
  Aecidium poasense Syd.
  Puccinia brachytela Syd.

Zexmenia aurea Benth. & Hook.
  Dicaeoma Zexmeniae (Diet. & Holw.) Arth.
  Puccinia opaca Diet. & Holw.
  Puccinia Zexmeniae Diet. & Holw.
  Nigredo cucullata (Syd.) Arth.
  Uromyces cucullatus Syd.
Zexmenia ceanothifolia Sch. Bip.
  Dicaeoma Zexmeniae (Diet. & Holw.) Arth.
  Puccinia opaca Diet. & Holw.
Zexmenia costaricensis Benth.
  Dicaeoma Zexmeniae (Diet. & Holw.) Arth.
  Puccinia opaca Diet. & Holw.
  Puccinia proba Jackson & Holw.
Zexmenia crocea Gray.
  Dicaeoma Zexmeniae (Diet. & Holw.) Arth.
Zexmenia elegans Sch. Bip.
  Bullaria proba (Jackson & Holw.) Arth. &
    Mains.
  Puccinia proba Jackson & Holw.
  Dicaeoma Zexmeniae (Diet. & Holw.) Arth.
  Puccinia opaca Diet. & Holw.
  Puccinia Zexmeniae Diet. & Holw.
Zexmenia fasciculata Hemsl.
  Dicaeoma Zexmeniae (Diet. & Holw.) Arth.
Zexmenia frutescens (Mill.) Blake.
  Bullaria proba (Jackson & Holw.) Arth. &
    Mains.
  Puccinia proba Jackson & Holw.
  Dicaeoma Zexmeniae (Diet. & Holw.) Arth.
  Puccinia Zexmeniae Diet. & Holw.
Zexmenia frutescens (Mill.) Blake, var. **villosa**
  (Polak.) Blake.
  Micropuccinia absicca (Jackson & Holw.)
    Arth. & Jackson.
  Puccinia absicca Jackson & Holw.
Zexmenia helianthoides Gray.
  Coleosporium Verbesinae Diet. & Holw.
  Coleosporium Viguierae Diet. & Holw.
  Dicaeoma Zexmeniae (Diet. & Holw.) Arth.
Zexmenia hispida (H. B. K.) Gray.
  Dicaeoma Zexmeniae (Diet. & Holw.) Arth.
  Puccinia Zexmeniae Diet. & Holw.
Zexmenia leucactis Blake.
Zexmenia longipes Benth.
  Dicaeoma inauditum (Jackson & Holw.) Arth.
    & Jackson.
  Puccinia inaudita Jackson & Holw.
Zexmenia podocephala Gray
  Dicaeoma abruptum (Diet. & Holw.) Arth. &
    Jackson.
  Dicaeoma Zexmeniae (Diet. & Holw.) Arth.
  Puccinia opaca Diet. & Holw.
  Puccinia Zexmeniae Diet. & Holw.
Zexmenia Salvinii Hemsl.
  Bullaria proba (Jackson & Holw.) Arth. &
    Mains.
  Puccinia proba Jackson & Holw.

Zexmenia scandens Hemsl.
  Dicaeoma inauditum (Jackson & Holw.) Arth.
  Nigredo cucullata (Syd.) Arth.
  Uromyces cucullatus Syd.
Oyedaea acuminata (Benth.) Hook.
  Dicaeoma Oyedaeae (Mayor) Arth. & Jackson.
  Puccinia Oyedaeae Mayor.
Oyedaea verbesinoides DC.
  Eriosporangium Oyedaeae (Mayor) Syd.
  Phyllocelis Oyedaeae Syd.
Verbesina apleura Blake.
  Coleosporium Verbesinae Diet. & Holw.
  Coleosporium Viguierae Diet. & Holw.
Verbesina densifolia Blake.
  Puccinia ferox Diet. & Holw.
Verbesina dissita Gray.
  Dicaeoma abruptum (Diet. & Holw.) Arth. &
    Jackson.
Verbesina diversifolia DC.
  Dicaeoma cognatum (Syd.) Arth. & Jackson.
  Micropuccinia ferox (Diet. & Holw.) Arth. &
    Jackson.
  Puccinia ferox Diet. & Holw.
Verbesina encelioides (Cav.) Benth. & Hook.
  Erysiphe Cichoracearum DC. †
  Dicaeoma abruptum (Diet. & Holw.) Arth. &
    Jackson.
  Puccinia Ximenesiae Long.
  Dicaeoma cognatum (Syd.) Arth. & Jackson.
  Micropuccinia Melampodii (Diet. & Holw.)
    Arth. & Jackson.
  Puccinia diaziana Arth.
  Rhysotheca Halstedii (Farl.) G. W. Wilson.
Verbesina encelioides (Cav.) Benth. & Hook.,
    var. **exauriculata** Robinson & Greenm.
  Coleosporium Viguierae Diet. & Holw.
  Erysiphe Cichoracearum DC.? †
  Rhysotheca Halstedii (Farl.) G. W. Wilson.
Verbesina Fraseri Hemsl.
  Dicaeoma cognatum (Syd.) Arth. & Jackson.
  Puccinia cognata Syd.
Verbesina gigantea Jacq.
Verbesina guatemalensis Robinson & Greenm.
  Coleosporium Helianthi Auct. Amer. p. p.
  Coleosporium Verbesinae Diet. & Holw.
  Coleosporium Viguierae Diet. & Holw.
Verbesina helianthoides Michx.
  Erysiphe Cichoracearum DC. †
Verbesina Holwayi B. L. Robinson.
  Coleosporium Verbesinae Diet. & Holw.
  Coleosporium Viguierae Diet. & Holw.
  Dicaeoma cognatum (Syd.) Arth. & Jackson.
  Puccinia cognata Syd.
Verbesina laciniata Nutt.
  Coleosporium Helianthi Auct. Amer. p. p.
  Coleosporium Verbesinae Diet. & Holw.
  Coleosporium Viguierae Diet. & Holw.

Verbesina longipes Hemsl.
Dicaeoma abruptum (Diet. & Holw.) Arth. & Jackson.

Verbesina montanoifolia Robinson & Greenm.
{ Coleosporium Helianthi Auct. Amer. p. p.
{ Coleosporium Verbesinae Diet. & Holw.
{ Coleosporium Viguierae Diet. & Holw.
Dicaeoma abruptum (Diet. & Holw.) Arth. & Jackson.
{ Dicaeoma invelatum (H. S. Jackson) Arth. & Jackson.
{ Puccinia cognata N. Am. Uredinales *426*.
{ Puccinia invelata H. S. Jackson.
Puccinia Viguierae Pk.

Verbesina myriocephala Sch. Bip.
{ Cicinnobella costaricensis Syd.
{ Dimerium costaricense Syd.
{ Coleosporium Verbesinae Diet. & Holw.
{ Coleosporium Viguierae Diet. & Holw.
Phaeoschiffnerula Compositarum Theissen.
Phyllachora baphispora Syd.
{ Micropuccinia ferox (Diet. & Holw.) Arth. & Jackson.
{ Puccinia ferox Diet. & Holw.

Verbesina nicaraguensis Benth.
{ Coleosporium Verbesinae Diet. & Holw.
{ Coleosporium Viguierae Diet. & Holw.

Verbesina occidentalis (L.) Walt.
Erysiphe Cichoracearum DC.†
{ Aecidium Asterum Auct. Amer. p. p.
{ Aecidium Verbesinae S.
{ Dicaeoma Verbesinae (S.) O. Kuntze.
{ Puccinia Actinomeridis Magn.
{ Puccinia Verbesinae S.

Verbesina pallens Benth.
{ Dicaeoma irregulare (Diet.) Arth.
{ Puccinia irregularis Diet.

Verbesina perymenioides Sch. Bip.
{ Coleosporium Verbesinae Diet. & Holw.
{ Coleosporium Viguierae Diet. & Holw.
{ Dicaeoma abruptum (Diet. & Holw.) Arth. & Jackson.
{ Puccinia abrupta Diet. & Holw.
{ Puccinia affinis Syd.

Verbesina pinnatifida Cav.
{ Coleosporium Helianthi N. Am. Uredinales *4*.
{ Coleosporium Verbesinae Diet. & Holw.
{ Coleosporium Viguierae Diet. & Holw.
{ Dicaeoma cognatum (Syd.) Arth. & Jackson.
{ Puccinia cognata Syd.

Verbesina Rothrockii Robinson & Greenm.
Dicaeoma abruptum (Diet. & Holw.) Arth. & Jackson.

Verbesina scabriuscula Blake.
{ Coleosporium Verbesinae Diet. & Holw.
{ Coleosporium Viguierae Diet. & Holw.

Verbesina sphaerocephala Gray.
Coleosporium anceps Diet. & Holw.
{ Dicaeoma cognatum (Syd.) Arth. & Jackson.
{ Puccinia cognata Syd.

Verbesina sublobata Benth.
{ Coleosporium Verbesinae Diet. & Holw.
{ Coleosporium Viguierae Diet. & Holw.
{ Dicaeoma cognatum (Syd.) Arth. & Jackson.
{ Puccinia cognata Syd.

Verbesina tetraptera Gray.
{ Dicaeoma cognatum (Syd.) Arth. & Jackson.
{ Puccinia cognata Syd.

Verbesina texana Buckl.
Cercospora fulvella Heald & Wolf.
Coleosporium Viguierae Diet. & Holw.
Phyllosticta Verbesinae Heald & Wolf.
{ Dicaeoma cognatum (Syd.) Arth. & Jackson.
{ Puccinia cognata Syd.

Verbesina trilobata Robinson & Greenm.
{ Dicaeoma abruptum (Diet. & Holw.) Arth. & Jackson.
{ Puccinia abrupta Diet. & Holw.
{ Puccinia affinis Syd.
{ ?Puccinia Viguierae Auct. p. p.
{ Puccinia Ximenesiae Long.

Verbesina turbacensis H. B. K.
{ Coleosporium Helianthi Auct. Amer. p. p.
{ Coleosporium Verbesinae Diet. & Holw.
{ Coleosporium Viguierae Diet. & Holw.
{ Dicaeoma cognatum (Syd.) Arth. & Jackson.
{ Puccinia cognata Syd.

Verbesina virgata Cav.
{ Coleosporium Helianthi Auct. Amer. p. p.
{ Coleosporium Verbesinae Diet. & Holw.
{ Coleosporium Viguierae Diet. & Holw.
{ Dicaeoma abruptum (Diet. & Holw.) Arth. & Jackson.
{ ?Puccinia Viguierae Auct. p. p.

Verbesina virginica L.
{ Coleosporium Helianthi Auct. Amer. p. p.
{ Coleosporium Verbesinae Diet. & Holw.
{ Dicaeoma cognatum (Syd.) Arth. & Jackson.
{ Puccinia affinis N. Am. Ured. *323*.
{ Puccinia cognata Syd.
{ Puccinia similis Long.
Stachybotryella repens Ell. & Barthol.

Verbesina sp. indet.
Puccinia vaga H. S. Jackson.

Garcilassa rivularis Poepp. & Endl.
Uredo Garcilassae Henn.

Synedrella nodiflora (L.) Gaertn.
{ Micropuccinia Melampodii (Diet. & Holw.) Arth. & Jackson.
{ Puccinia Melampodii Diet. & Holw.
{ Puccinia Synedrellae Henn.
Stilbella flavida (Cke.) Henn.

Coreopsis delphinifolia Lam.
Coleosporium inconspicuum Hedgc. & Long.

Coreopsis Galeottii Hemsl.
  Puccinia Electrae Diet. & Holw.

Coreopsis lanceolata L.
  Coleosporium inconspicuum Hedgc. & Long.
  Rhizoctonia Solani Kühn.

Coreopsis major Walt.
  ⎰Coleosporium Helianthi N. Am. Uredinales
  ⎱ *2109.*
  ⎱Coleosporium inconspicuum Hedgc. & Long.

Coreopsis mexicana (DC.) Hemsl.

Coreopsis mutica DC.
  ⎰Puccinia Coreopsidis Jackson & Holw.
  ⎱Puccinia Jackson-Holwayi Trotter.
  Puccinia Electrae Diet. & Holw.

Coreopsis palmata Nutt.
  Septoria Coreopsidis J. J. Davis.

Coreopsis tinctoria Nutt.
  Erysiphe Cichoracearum DC. †

Coreopsis tripteris L.
  Coleosporium inconspicuum Hedgc. & Long.
  Sphaerotheca Humuli (DC.) Burrill, var. fuli-
    ginea (Schl.) Salmon.

Coreopsis verticillata L.
  Coleosporium inconspicuum Hedgc. & Long.

Dahlia rosea Cav.
  Aecidium Dahliae Syd.

Dahlia variabilis (Willd.) Desf.
  Aecidium Dahliae Syd.
  Alternaria fasciculata (C. & E.) Jones & Grout.
  Botryosporium pulchrum Cda.
  Botrytis cinerea P. †
  Coleosporium Dahliae Arth.
  ⎰Erysiphe Cichoracearum DC. †
  ⎱?Erysiphe communis Auct. p. p.
  Leptosphaeria dumetorum Niessl.
  Macrosporium cercosporioides Ell. & Ev.

Dahlia sp. indet.
  Choanephora americana Moll.
  Corticium vagum B. & C.
  Erysiphe Polygoni DC. †
  Macrosporium erumpens Cke.
  Mystrosporium polytrichum Cke.
  Phoma Dahliae B.
  Pythium debaryanum Hesse.
  ⎰Sclerotinia libertiana Fckl.
  ⎱Sclerotinia sclerotiorum (Lib.) Schrt.
  Sclerotium Rolfsii Sacc.
  ⎰Mycosphaerella Dahliae (C. & E.) Coons.
  ⎱Sphaerella Dahliae C. & E.
  Vermicularia compacta C. & E.
  Verticillium albo-atrum Reinke & Berthold.

Bidens aristosa (Michx.) Brit.
  Sphaerotheca Castagnei Lév.

Bidens bipinnata L.
  ?Puccinia Hieracii Mart.
  Septoria Bidentis Sacc.
  Sphaerotheca Castagnei Lév.
  Uromyces Bidentis Lagerh.

Bidens cernua L.
  Cercospora megalopotamica Speg.
  Cercospora umbrata Ell. & Holw.
  ⎰Peronospora Halstedii Farl.
  ⎱Plasmopara Halstedii (Farl.) Berl. & De Toni.
  ⎱Rhysotheca Halstedii (Farl.) G. W. Wilson.
  ⎰Protomyces andinus Lagerh.
  ⎱Protomyces gravidus J. J. Davis.
  Sphaerotheca Humuli (DC.) Burrill. †
  ⎰Sphaerotheca Castagnei Auct. Amer. p. p.
  ⎱Sphaerotheca Humuli (DC.) Burrill, var. fuli-
    ginea (Schl.) Salmon.
  Sphaerotheca pannosa (Wallr.) Lév.

Bidens comosa (Gray) Wiegand.
  Rhysotheca Halstedii (Farl.) G. W. Wilson.

Bidens connata Muhl.
  ⎰Dicaeoma obtectum (Pk.) O. Kuntze. I.
  ⎱Puccinia obtecta Pk. I.
  Cercospora megalopotamica Speg.
  Cercospora umbrata Ell. & Holw.
  Erysiphe fuscata B. & C.
  ⎰Peronospora Halstedii Farl.
  ⎱Plasmopara Halstedii (Farl.) Berl. & De Toni.
  ⎱Rhysotheca Halstedii (Farl.) G. W. Wilson.
  ⎰Protomyces andinus Lagerh.
  ⎱Protomyces gravidus J. J. Davis.
  Ramularia concomitans Ell. & Holw.
  Sphaerotheca Castagnei Lév.
  Sphaerotheca Humuli (DC.) Burrill. †
  Sphaerotheca Humuli (DC.) Burrill, var. fuli-
    ginea (Schl.) Salmon.

Bidens coronata (L.) Fisch.
  Sphaerotheca Castagnei Lév.
  Sphaerotheca Humuli (DC.) Burrill, var.
    fuliginea (Schl.) Salmon.

Bidens cyanapiifolia H. B. K.
  Rhysotheca Halstedii (Farl.) G. W. Wilson.
  ⎰Klebahnia Bidentis (Diet. & Holw.) Arth.
  ⎱Uromyces bidenticola Arth.

Bidens discoidea (Torr. & Gr.) Brit.
  Peronospora Halstedii Farl.

Bidens expansa Greene.
  ⎰Klebahnia Bidentis (Diet. & Holw.) Arth.
  ⎱Uromyces Bidentis Fung. Columb. *4887.*

Bidens frondosa L.
  ⎰?Aecidium Compositarum J. J. Davis 1903.
  ⎱Aecidium Compositarum, var. Bidentis Burrill.
  ⎱Dicaeoma obtectum (Pk.) O. Kuntze. I.
  ⎱Puccinia obtecta Pk. I.
  Cercospora umbrata Ell. & Holw.
  Entyloma Compositarum Farl.
  Entyloma guaraniticum Speg.
  ⎰Peronospora Halstedii Farl.
  ⎱Plasmopara Halstedii (Farl.) Berl. & De Toni.
  ⎱Rhysotheca Halstedii (Farl.) G. W. Wilson.
  Phyllosticta decidua Ell. & Kellerm.

Bidens frondosa (*cont.*)
Protomyces andinus Lagerh.
Protomyces gravidus J. J. Davis p. p.
Ramularia concomitans Ell. & Holw.
Septocylindrium concomitans (Ell. & Holw.)
  Halsted.
Septoria Bidentis Sacc.
Sphaerotheca Castagnei Auct. p. p.
Sphaerotheca Humuli (DC.) Burrill.†
Erysiphe fuscata B. & C.
Sphaerotheca Castagnei Fung. Eur. *3657*.
Sphaerotheca fuscata (B. & C.) Ell. & Ev.
Sphaerotheca Humuli (DC.) Burrill, var. fuli-
  ginea (Schl.) Salmon.

Bidens glaucescens Greene.
Dicaeoma obtectum (Pk.) O. Kuntze. I.
Puccinia obtecta Pk. I.

Bidens heterophylla Ort.

Bidens Holwayi Sherff & Blake.
Klebahnia Bidentis (Diet. & Holw.) Arth.
Uromyces bidenticola Arth.

Bidens involucrata (Nutt.) Brit.
Sphaerotheca Humuli (DC.) Burrill. †

Bidens laevis (L.) B. S. P.
Cercospora umbrata Ell. & Holw.
Entyloma Compositarum Farl.
Peronospora Halstedii Farl.
Plasmopara Halstedii (Farl.) Berl. & De Toni.
Rhysotheca Halstedii (Farl.) G. W. Wilson.
Sphaerotheca Castagnei Lév.
Sphaerotheca Humuli (DC.) Burrill.
Sphaerotheca Humuli (DC.) Burrill, var. fuli-
  ginea (Schl.) Salmon.

Bidens leucantha (L.) Willd.
Entyloma guaraniticum Speg.
Sphaerotheca Humuli (DC.) Burrill (?).
Thecaphora pustulata G. P. Clinton.
Klebahnia Bidentis (Diet. & Holw.) Arth.
Uredo bidenticola Henn.
Uromyces bidenticola Arth.
Teleutospora Bidentis (Lagerh.) Arth. &
  Bisby.
Uromyces Bidentis Lagerh.
Uromyces densus Arth.

Bidens Nashii Small.
Cercospora bidentis Tharp.

Bidens pilosa L.
Thecaphora pustulata G. P. Clinton.
Klebahnia Bidentis (Diet. & Holw.) Arth.
Puccinia Bidentis Diet. & Holw.
Uromyces bidenticola Arth.
Teleutospora Bidentis (Lagerh.) Arth. &
  Bisby.
Uromyces Bidentis Lagerh.
Uromyces densus Arth.

Bidens reptans G. Don.
Sphaerotheca Humuli (DC.) Burrill (?).

Bidens squarrosa HBK.
Appendiculella Compositarum (Earle) Toro.
Klebahnia Bidentis (Diet. & Holw.) Arth.
Uromyces bidenticola Arth.
Teleutospora Bidentis (Lagerh.) Arth. &
  Bisby.
Uromyces densus Arth.

Bidens tenuisecta Gray.
Entyloma Compositarum Farl.

Bidens trichosperma (Michx.) Brit.
Plasmopara Halstedii (Farl.) Berl. & De Toni.
Dicaeoma obtectum (Pk.) O. Kuntze. I.
Puccinia obtecta Pk. I.
Sphaerotheca Castagnei Lév.
Sphaerotheca Humuli (DC.) Burrill, var. fuli-
  ginea (Schl.) Salmon.

Bidens vulgata Greene.
Mycorrhiza of Legumes F. R. Jones.
Plasmopara Halstedii (Farl.) Berl. & De Toni.
Ramularia concomitans Ell. & Holw.
Septocylindrium concomitans (Ell. & Holw.)
  Halsted.
Sphaerotheca Castagnei Lév.
Sphaerotheca Humuli (DC.) Burrill, var. fuli-
  ginea (Schl.) Salmon.

Bidens sp. indet.
Leptosphaeria Ogilviensis (B. & Br.) Ces. &
  De Not.
Sphaeria Ogilviensis B. & Br.
Ophiobolus acuminatus (Sow. ex Fr.) Duby.
Sphaeria acuminata Sow. ex Fr.
Ophiobolus anguillides (Cke.) Sacc.
Raphidospora anguillida Cke.
Sphaeria anguillida Cke.
Peziza fuscorubra Rehm.
Peziza heterocarpa Ell.
Saccardia quercina S.
Sporocybe byssoides (P.) ex Fr.

Cosmos bipinnatus Cav.
Erysiphe Cichoracearum DC. †
Phomopsis Stewartii Pk.

Cosmos caudatus H. B. K.
Erysiphe Cichoracearum DC. †
Klebahnia Bidentis (Diet. & Holw.) Arth.
Uromyces bidenticola Arth.

Cosmos sulphureus Cav.
Entyloma Holwayi Syd.
Entyloma polysporum Auct. Amer. p. p.

Cosmos sp. indet.
Sphaerotheca Humuli (DC.) Burrill.

Calea axillaris DC.
Dicaeoma Caleae (Arth.) Arth. & Jackson.
Puccinia Caleae Arth.

Calea hypoleuca Robinson & Greenm.
Dicaeoma Caleae (Arth.) Arth. & Jackson.
Puccinia Caleae Arth.
Puccinia Viguierae Pk.

Calea insignis Blake.
{ Micropuccinia ordinata (Jackson & Holw.)
    Arth. & Jackson.
{ Puccinia ordinata Jackson & Holw.
Calea urticifolia (Mill.) DC.
{ Dicaeoma Caleae (Arth.) Arth. & Jackson.
{ Puccinia Caleae Arth.
Calea zacatechichi Schl.
{ Dicaeoma Caleae (Arth.) Arth. & Jackson.
{ Puccinia Caleae Arth.
  Puccinia Viguierae Pk.
Tridax procumbens L.
{ Micropuccinia Melampodii (Diet. & Holw.)
    Arth. & Jackson.
{ Puccinia Synedrellae Henn.
{ Puccinia Tridacis Arth.
Galinsoga parviflora Cav.
  Erysiphe Cichoracearum DC. †
Madia anomala Greene.
Madia capitata Nutt.
Madia citriodora Greene.
Madia corymbosa Lindl.
Madia dissitiflora (Nutt.) Torr. & Gr.
Madia exigua (Sm.) Greene.
Madia Nuttallii Gray.
Madia racemosa (Nutt.) Torr. & Gr.
Madia ramosa Piper.
{ Coleosporium Madiae Cke.
{ Stichopsora Madiae (Cke.) Syd.
Madia elegans Don.
  Coleosporium Madiae Cke.
{ Puccinia Madiae Syd.
{ Puccinia nuda Ell. & Ev.
Madia glomerata Hook.
  Coleosporium Madiae Cke.
  Entyloma Compositarum Farl.
  Erysiphe Cichoracearum DC. †
  Puccinia Madiae Syd.
Madia sativa Molina.
{ Coleosporium Madiae Cke.
{ Stichopsora Madiae (Cke.) Syd.
{ Peronospora Halstedii Farl.
{ Rhysotheca Halstedii (Farl.) G. W. Wilson.
  Puccinia nuda Ell. & Ev.
Hemizonia citrina Greene.
Hemizonia Clevelandi Greene.
{ Puccinia Hemizoniae Ell. & Tracy.
{ Puccinia Lagophyllae Diet. & Holw.
{ Puccinia nuda Ell. & Ev.
Hemizonia congesta DC.
Hemizonia corymbosa Torr. & Gr.
Hemizonia Durandi Gray.
  Coleosporium Madiae Cke.
Hemizonia luzulifolia DC.
{ Puccinia Hemizoniae Ell. & Tracy.
{ Puccinia nuda Ell. & Ev.
Hemizonia pungens Torr. & Gr.
  Coleosporium Madiae Cke.

Hemizonia truncata Gray.
{ Puccinia Hemizoniae Ell. & Tracy.
{ Puccinia nuda Ell. & Ev.
Lagophylla congesta Greene.
Lagophylla ramosissima Nutt.
{ Puccinia Hemizoniae Ell. & Tracy.
{ Puccinia Lagophyllae Diet. & Holw.
{ Puccinia nuda Ell. & Ev.
Riddellia Cooperi Gray
  Micropuccinia Grindeliae (Pk.) Arth. & Jackson.
  Gymnoconia Riddelliae Griffiths.
Riddellia tagetina Torr. & Gr.
  Micropuccinia Grindeliae (Pk.) Arth. & Jackson.
Perityle californica Benth., var. **nuda** Gray.
  Cystopus cubicus (Strauss) Lév.
Pericome caudata Gray.
  Leptosphaeria ogilviensis (B. & Br.) Ces. & De Not.
Flaveria angustifolia Gray.
{ Micropuccinia Flaveriae (H. S. Jackson) Arth.
    & Jackson.
{ Puccinia Flaveriae H. S. Jackson.
Hymenopappus arenosus A. Heller.
  Dicaeoma Stipae (Arth.) O. Kuntze. I.
Hymenopappus carolinensis (Lam.) Porter.
{ Micropuccinia Grindeliae (Pk.) Arth. & Jackson.
{ Puccinia Grindeliae Pk.
Eriophyllum integrifolium (Hook.) Greene.
  Puccinia Eriophylli H. S. Jackson.
Eriophyllum lanatum (Pursh) Forbes.
Eriophyllum leucophyllum (DC.) Rydb.
Eriophyllum Nevinii Gray.
  Puccinia Eriophylli H. S. Jackson.
Eriophyllum staechadifolium Lag.
{ Aecidium Bahiae B. & C.
{ Nigredo Junci (Desm.) Arth. I.
  Heptameria mesoedema (B. & C.) Sacc.
  Puccinia Eriophylli H. S. Jackson.
Eriophyllum trifidum (Nutt.) Rydb.
{ Puccinia Eriophylli H. S. Jackson.
{ Uredo abdita H. S. Jackson.
Actinea acaulis (Nutt.) Spreng.
  Pleospora herbarum (Fr.) Rabh.
{ Micropuccinia Grindeliae (Pk.) Arth. & Jackson.
{ Puccinia Actinellae (Webber) Syd.
{ Puccinia Grindeliae Pk.
{ Puccinia Tanaceti, var. Actinellae Webber.
{ Puccinia variolans Hark.
Actinea acaulis (Nutt.) Spreng., var. **arizonica** (Greene) Blake.
  Dicaeoma Stipae (Arth.) O. Kuntze. I.
Actinea argentea (Gray) O. Kuntze.
  Micropuccinia Grindeliae (Pk.) Arth. & Jackson.

Actinea
 (Actinella fastigiata A. Nels.)
Actinea leptoclada (Gray) O. Kuntze.
 {Micropuccinia Grindeliae (Pk.) Arth. & Jackson.
 Puccinia Actinellae (Webber) Syd.
 Puccinia cornigera Ell. & Ev.
 Puccinia Tanaceti, var. Actinellae Webber.
Actinea Osterhoutii A. Nels.
 Puccinia Stipae Arth. I.
Actinea scaposa (DC.) O. Kuntze.
 {Puccinia Actinellae (Webber) Syd.
 Puccinia Tanaceti, var. Actinellae Webber.
Actinea simplex A. Nels.
Actinea torreyana (Nutt) Macb.
 {Micropuccinia Grindeliae (Pk.) Arth. & Jackson.
 Puccinia Actinellae (Webber) Syd.
 Puccinia cornigera Ell. & Ev.
Actinea sp. indet.
 Pyrenophora Tetraneuris Earle.
Helenium autumnale L.
 {Aecidium Compositarum E. F. Suppl. *B 28*.
 Aecidium Compositarum Fung. Columb. *3801*.
 Dicaeoma Asterum (Kern) Arth. & Kern. I.
 Entyloma Compositarum Farl.
 Entyloma polysporum (Pk.) Farl.
 Erysiphe Cichoracearum DC. †
 Puccinia Helenii S.
 Septoria Helenii Ell. & Ev.
 Septoria nubilosa Ell. & Ev.
Helenium Hoopesii Gray.
 Aecidium Compositarum Auct. Amer. p. p.
 Aecidium conspicuum Arth.
 Aecidium Prenanthis P.
 Cladosporium herbarum (P.) ex Lk.
 Septoria Helenii Ell. & Ev.
Helenium macranthum Rydb.
 Dicaeoma Asterum (Kern) Arth. & Kern. I.
Helenium microcephalum DC.
 Cercospora Helenii Tharp.
Helenium montanum Nutt.
 Erysiphe Cichoracearum DC. †
Helenium tenuifolium Nutt.
 Erysiphe Cichoracearum DC. †
 Metasphaeria sanguinea Ell. & Ev.
Gaillardia aristata Pursh.
 {Bullaria Gaillardiae Arth. & Mains.
 Uredo Gaillardiae Diet. & Holw.
 Erysiphe Cichoracearum DC. †
 {Sphaerotheca Castagnei Auct. Amer. p. p.
 Sphaerotheca Humuli (DC.) Burrill, var. fuliginea (Schl.) Salmon.
Gaillardia pulchella Foug.
 Entyloma Compositarum Farl.
 Entyloma polysporum (Pk.) Farl.
 Septoria Gaillardiae Ell. & Ev.

Tagetes erecta L.
Tagetes filifolia Lag.
Tagetes lucida Cav.
Tagetes micrantha Cav.
Tagetes microglossa Benth.
Tagetes multifida DC.
 Puccinia tageticola Diet. & Holw.
Tagetes patula L.
 Cercospora tageticola Ell. & Ev.
 Puccinia tageticola Diet. & Holw.
Tagetes sp. indet.
 Botrytis cinerea Auct.
 Botrytis vulgaris (Lk.) ex Fr.
 {Phoma herbarum Westd., var. tageticola (S.) Starb.
 Sphaeria tageticola S.
Dyssodia papposa (Vent.) Hitchc.
 Erysiphe Cichoracearum DC. †
Porophyllum holwayanum Greenm.
 Puccinia jaliscana Arth.
Porophyllum macrocephalum DC.
 Puccinia Porophylli Henn.
Anthemis Cotula L.
 Oidium erysiphoides Fr.
Achillea lanulosa Nutt.
 {Micropuccinia Millefolii (Fckl.) Arth. & Jackson.
 Puccinia Millefolii Fckl.
Achillea Millefolium L.
 {Camarosporium Compositarum (Cke. & Hark.) Sacc.
 Dichomera Compositarum Cke. & Hark.
 Erysiphe Cichoracearum DC. †
 Leptosphaeria ogilviensis (B. & Br.) Ces. & De Not.
 Leptostroma herbarum (Fr.) Lk.
 Oidium erysiphoides Fr.
 Phoma erysiphoides Ell. & Ev.
 Pleospora megalotheca Tracy & Earle.
 {Micropuccinia Millefolii (Fckl.) Arth. & Jackson.
 Puccinia Millefolii Fckl.
 Rhizoctonia Solani Kühn.
Achillea Ptarmica L.
 Hypoderma ptarmicola Fairman.
Achillea sp. indet.
 Diaporthe orthoceras (Fr.) Nits.
 Lophiostoma caulicum (Fr.) Ces. & De Not.
Matricaria inodora L.
 Phoma herbarum Westd.
Matricaria inodora L., var. **grandiflora** (Hook.) Ostenf.
 Rhabdospora cercosperma (Rostr.) Sacc.
Matricaria suaveolens (Pursh) Buchenau.
 {Albugo Tragopogonis (P.) ex S. F. Gray.
 Cystopus cubicus (Strauss) ex Lév.
 Erysiphe Cichoracearum DC. †
 Sphaerotheca Humuli (DC.) Burrill, var. fuliginea (Schl.) Salmon.

Pyrethrum sp. indet.
  Rhizoctonia Solani Kühn.
Chrysanthemum hybridum Hort.
  Septoria Leucanthemi Sacc. & Speg.
Chrysanthemum integrifolium Richards.
  Mycosphaerella pachyasca (Rostr.) Vester-
    gren.
  Pyrenophora chrysospora (Niessl) Sacc.
  Rhabdospora cercosperma (Rostr.) Sacc.
Chrysanthemum Leucanthemum L.
  Phoma herbarum Westd.
  Septoria Chrysanthemi Allescher. 1891.
  Septoria Chrysanthemi Halsted. 1893.
  Septoria Halstedii Ell. & Ev.
  Septoria herbarum B. & C.
  Septoria macrosporia Dearness.
Chrysanthemum maximum Ramond.
  Sclerotinia sclerotiorum (Lib.) Massee.
Chrysanthemum morifolium Ramat.
  Ascochyta Chrysanthemi Cav.
  Ascochyta Chrysanthemi F. L. Stevens.
  Cylindrosporium Chrysanthemi Ell. & Dear-
    ness.
  ⎰Erysiphe Cichoracearum DC. †
  ⎱Oidium Chrysanthemi Rabh.
  Fumago vagans Fr.
  Phyllosticta Chrysanthemi Ell. & Dearness.
  ⎧Bullaria (?) Chrysanthemi (Roze) Arth.
  ⎪Dicaeoma Chrysanthemi (Roze) Arth.
  ⎨Puccinia Chrysanthemi Roze.
  ⎪?Puccinia Hieracii Auct. Amer. p. p.
  ⎩Puccinia Tanaceti Auct. Amer. p. p.
  Rhizoctonia Solani Kühn.
Chrysanthemum sp. indet.
  Botrytis cinerea P. †
  Botrytis vulgaris (Lk.) ex Fr.
  Cercospora Chrysanthemi Heald & Wolf.
  Corticium vagum B. & C.
  Ozonium omnivorum Shear.
  Pilobolus crystallinus (Wigg.) Tode. †
  Sclerotium Rolfsii Sacc.
  Septoria cercosporoides Trail.
  ⎧Septoria chrysanthemella Sacc.
  ⎪Septoria Chrysanthemi Cav. 1892.
  ⎨Septoria Chrysanthemi Ell. & Dearness. 24
  ⎩ Feb. 1892.
  Septoria Leucanthemi Sacc. & Speg.
  Septoria Rostrupii Sacc. & Syd.
  Verticillium albo-atrum Reinke & Berthold.
Sphaeromeria capitata Nutt.
Sphaeromeria diversifolia (D. C. Eaton) Rydb.
  ⎰Bullaria Absinthii (DC.) Arth. & Mains.
  ⎱Puccinia Absinthii DC.
Tanacetum vulgare L.
  ⎰Leptosphaeria comatella (C. & E.) Sacc.
  ⎱Sphaeria comatella C. & E.
  Pistillaria coccinea (Cda.) Fr.
  Ramularia Tanaceti Lind.

Tanacetum sp. indet.
  Lophiostoma insidiosum (Desm.) Ces. & De
    Not.
Artemisia Abrotanum L.
  Diplodia Abrotani Fckl.
  ⎧Dothidea Artemisiae (S.) B.
  ⎪Dothidella Artemisiae (S.) Ell. & Ev.
  ⎨Nummularia Artemisiae (S.) Sacc.
  ⎪Sphaeria Artemisiae S.
  ⎩Systremma Artemisiae (S.) Theissen & Syd.
Artemisia Absinthium L.
  ⎰Cercospora Absinthii (Pk.) Sacc.
  ⎱Helminthosporium Absinthii Pk.
  Nidularia fascicularis S.
Artemisia albula Wooton.
  ⎧Micropuccinia Millefolii (Fckl.) Arth. &
  ⎨ Jackson.
  ⎩Puccinia conferta Diet. & Holw.
Artemisia arbuscula Nutt.
  Bullaria Absinthii (DC.) Arth. & Mains.
Artemisia argophylla Rydb.
  Dicaeoma Dracunculi Arth. & Kern. I.
Artemisia aromatica A. Nels.
  ⎧Aecidium Dracunculi Thm.
  ⎪Dicaeoma Dracunculi Arth. & Kern. I.
  ⎨Puccinia universalis Arth. I.
  ⎪Bullaria Absinthii (DC.) Arth. & Mains.
  ⎩Puccinia Absinthii DC.
Artemisia bidentata Auct.
  ⎰Puccinia Absinthii DC.
  ⎱Puccinia Tanaceti Syd. Ured. *836.*
Artemisia biennis Willd.
  ⎧Dicaeoma Dracunculi Arth. & Kern. I.
  ⎪Puccinia universalis Arth. I.
  ⎪Albugo Tragopogonis (P.) ex S. F. Gray.
  ⎨Cystopus cubicus (Strauss) ex Lév.
  ⎪Cystopus Tragopogonis (P. ex S. F. Gray)
  ⎩ Schrt.
  Didymella effusa (Niessl) Sacc.
  Erysiphe Cichoracearum DC. †
  Ophiobolus claviger Hark.
  Ophiobolus instabilis Ell. & Ev.
  Peronospora leptosperma DBy.
  Synchytrium aureum Schrt.
Artemisia Bigelowii Gray.
  ⎰Bullaria Absinthii (DC.) Arth. & Mains.
  ⎱Puccinia Absinthii DC.
Artemisia borealis Pall.
  Camarosporium vetustum Ell. & Ev.
  Erysiphe Cichoracearum DC. †
  Pleospora bromeitiana Henn.
  ⎰Pleospora herbarum (Fr.) Rabh.
  ⎱Sphaeria herbarum Fr.
  Pleospora vulgaris Niessl.
  ⎰Rhabdospora cercosperma (Rostr.) Sacc.
  ⎱Septoria cercosperma Rostr.

Artemisia Brittonii Rydb.
  Dicaeoma Dracunculi Arth. & Kern. I.
  Bullaria Absinthii (DC.) Arth. & Mains.
Artemisia californica Less.
  Didymosphaeria Catalinae Ell. & Ev.
  { Montagnella tumefaciens (Ell. & Hark.) Berl.
      & Vogl.
  { Sphaeria tumefaciens Ell. & Hark.
  { Syncarpella tumefaciens (Ell. & Hark.)
      Theissen & Syd.
  { Plowrightia tuberculiformis (Ell.) Sacc.
  { Sphaeria tuberculiformis Ell.
  { Bullaria Absinthii (DC.) Arth. & Mains.
  { Puccinia Artemisiarum Schm. & Kze.
  { Puccinia Absinthii DC.
  { Puccinia Tanaceti Auct. Amer. p. p.
  { Micropuccinia Millefolii (Fckl.) Arth. & Jack-
      son.
  { Puccinia conferta Diet. & Holw.
  { Puccinia recondita Diet. & Holw.
Artemisia camporum Rydb.
  { Dicaeoma Dracunculi Arth. & Kern. I.
  { Puccinia universalis Arth.
  Bullaria Absinthii (DC.) Arth. & Mains.
Artemisia cana Pursh.
  { Dicaeoma Dracunculi Arth. & Kern. I.
  { Puccinia universalis Arth. I.
  Clasterosporium dothideoides Ell. & Ev.
  Leptosphaeria Artemisiae (Fckl.) Awd.
  { Melanomma occidentale (Ell.) Sacc., var.
      tetonense Ell. & Ev.
  { Melanomma tetonense Ell. & Ev.
  { Bullaria Absinthii (DC.) Arth. & Mains.
  { Puccinia Absinthii DC.
  { Puccinia Artemisiae Auct.
  { Puccinia Tanaceti Fung. Dak. *418*.
  { Puccinia Tanaceti West Am. Fung. *354b*.
  Puccinia conferta Diet. & Holw.
Artemisia canadensis Michx.
  { Albugo Tragopogonis (P.) ex S. F. Gray.
  { Cystopus Tragopogonis (P. ex S. F. Gray)
      Schrt.
  Dicaeoma Dracunculi Arth. & Kern. I.
  Erysiphe Cichoracearum DC. †
  Puccinia Tanaceti Auct. Amer. p. p.
  Teichospora solitaria (Ell.) Ell. & Ev.
Artemisia caudata Michx.
  { Dicaeoma Dracunculi Arth. & Kern. I.
  { Puccinia universalis Arth. I.
  Leptosphaeria Artemisiae (Fckl.) Awd.
  Ramularia Artemisiae J. J. Davis.
Artemisia coloradensis Osterhout.
  { Bullaria Absinthii (DC.) Arth. & Mains.
  { Puccinia Absinthii DC.
Artemisia discolor Dougl.
  Aecidium Compositarum Auct. Amer. p. p.
  Erysiphe Cichoracearum DC. †

Artemisia diversifolia Rydb.
Artemisia douglasiana Bess.
  { Bullaria Absinthii (DC.) Arth. & Mains.
  { Puccinia Absinthii DC.
Artemisia dracunculoides Pursh.
  { Aecidium Compositarum Auct. Amer. p. p.
  { ?Aecidium Compositarum, var. Artemisiae Ell.
      & Ev.
  { Dicaeoma Dracunculi Arth. & Kern. I.
  { Puccinia Tanaceti I. Fung. Columb. *1664*.
  { Puccinia universalis Arth. I.
  { Erysiphe Cichoracearum DC. †
  { Erysiphe Linkii Lév.
  { Bullaria Absinthii (DC.) Arth. & Mains.
  { Puccinia Absinthii DC.
  { Rhabdospora Artemisiae Ell. & Ev.
  { Rhabdospora Ellisii Sacc. & Syd.
Artemisia elatior (Torr. & Gr.) Rydb.
  Erysiphe Cichoracearum DC. †
  { Bullaria Absinthii (DC.) Arth. & Mains.
  { Puccinia Absinthii DC.
Artemisia filifolia Torr.
  Dicaeoma Dracunculi Arth. & Kern. I.
  ?Puccinia Tanaceti Auct. Amer. p. p.
Artemisia Forwoodii Watson.
  { Dicaeoma Dracunculi Arth. & Kern. I.
  { Puccinia universalis Arth.
Artemisia franserioides Greene.
  { ?Aecidium Compositarum, var. Ambrosiae
      Auct. Amer. p. p.
  { Dicaeoma Dracunculi Arth. & Kern. I.
  { Puccinia universalis Arth. I.
Artemisia frigida Willd.
  { Dicaeoma Dracunculi Arth. & Kern. I.
  { Puccinia universalis Arth. I.
  { Camarosporium Compositarum (Cke. &
      Hark.) Sacc.
  { Dichomera Compositarum Cke. & Hark.
  Eutypella herbicola Ell. & Ev.
  Leptosphaeria tetonensis (Ell. & Ev.) Rehm.
  Lophiostoma quadrinucleatum Karst.
  { Bullaria Absinthii (DC.) Arth. & Mains.
  { Puccinia Absinthii DC.
  { Puccinia Tanaceti Fung. Dak. *318*.
  { Micropuccinia Millefolii (Fckl.) Arth. & Jack-
      son.
  { Puccinia conferta Diet. & Holw.
  { Puccinia Tanaceti West Am. Fung. *354a*.
Artemisia glauca Pall.
  Dicaeoma Dracunculi Arth. & Kern. I.
Artemisia glomerata Auct. p. p.
  Sphaerella eriophila Niessl.
Artemisia gnaphalodes Nutt.
  { Dicaeoma Dracunculi Arth. & Kern. I.
  { Puccinia universalis Arth. I.
  Cylindrosporium Artemisiae Dearness &
    Barthol.

Artemisia gnaphalodes (*cont.*)
Erysiphe Cichoracearum DC. †
⎰ Bullaria Absinthii (DC.) Arth. & Mains.
⎱ Puccinia Absinthii DC.
⎰ Micropuccinia Millefolii (Fckl.) Arth. & Jack-
⎱ son.
Puccinia conferta Diet. & Holw.

Artemisia heterophylla Nutt.
Dicaeoma Dracunculi Arth. & Kern. I.
Gloeosporium heterophyllum Ell. & Ev.
Phomopsis oblita Sacc.
⎰ Bullaria Absinthii (DC.) Arth. & Mains.
⎱ Puccinia Absinthii DC.
⎰ Micropuccinia Millefolii (Fckl.) Arth. & Jack-
⎱ son.
Puccinia conferta Diet. & Holw.
Puccinia recondita Diet. & Holw.
Sphaerella eriophila Niessl.

Artemisia hyperborea Rydb.
Mycosphaerella pachyasca (Rostr.) Vestergren.

Artemisia kansana Brit.
⎰ Dicaeoma Dracunculi Arth. & Kern. I.
⎱ Puccinia universalis Arth. I.
Bullaria Absinthii (DC.) Arth. & Mains.

Artemisia longifolia Nutt.
⎰ Dicaeoma Dracunculi Arth. & Kern. I.
⎱ Puccinia universalis Arth. I.
⎰ Bullaria Absinthii (DC.) Arth. & Mains.
⎨ Puccinia Absinthii DC.
⎩ Puccinia Tanaceti Auct. Amer. p. p.

Artemisia ludoviciana Nutt.
⎰ Acanthostigma occidentalis (Ell. & Ev.) Sacc.
⎨ Chaetomella (?) perforata Ell. & Ev.
⎩ Venturia occidentalis Ell. & Ev.
⎰ Acanthostigma occidentalis (Ell. & Ev.) Sacc.,
⎨ var. minor (Ell. & Ev.) Sacc.
⎩ Venturia occidentalis Ell. & Ev., var. minor
Ell. & Ev.
⎰ ?Aecidium Compositarum Auct. Amer. p. p.
⎱ Puccinia universalis Arth. I.
Cercospora Absinthii (Pk.) Sacc.
⎰ Erysiphe Cichoracearum DC. †
⎱ Erysiphe Linkii Lév.
Leptosphaeria Artemisiae (Fckl.) Awd.
Peronospora leptosperma DBy.
⎰ Peronospora Halstedii Farl.
⎨ Plasmopara Halstedii (Farl.) Berl. & De Toni.
⎩ Rhysotheca Halstedii (Farl.) G. W. Wilson.
⎰ Bullaria Absinthii (DC.) Arth. & Mains.
⎨ Puccinia Absinthii DC.
⎪ Puccinia Artemisiarum Schm. & Kze.
⎩ Puccinia Tanaceti Auct. Amer. p. p.
⎰ Micropuccinia Millefolii (Fckl.) Arth. &
⎱ Jackson.
Puccinia conferta Diet. & Holw.
Septoria Artemisiae Pass.

Artemisia mexicana Willd.
⎰ Bullaria Absinthii (DC.) Arth. & Mains.
⎨ Puccinia Absinthii DC.
⎪ Micropuccinia Millefolii (Fckl.) Arth. & Jack-
⎪ son.
⎩ Puccinia conferta Diet. & Holw.

Artemisia nova A. Nels.

Artemisia pabularis Rydb.

Artemisia Parishii Gray.
⎰ Bullaria Absinthii (DC.) Arth. & Mains.
⎨ Puccinia Absinthii DC.
⎩ Puccinia Artemisiae Auct.

Artemisia purshiana Bess.
⎰ Dicaeoma Dracunculi Arth. & Kern. I.
⎱ Puccinia universalis Arth. I.
Erysiphe Cichoracearum DC. †
Bullaria Absinthii (DC.) Arth. & Mains.
⎰ Micropuccinia Millefolii (Fckl.) Arth. & Jack-
⎨ son.
⎩ Puccinia conferta Diet. & Holw.

Artemisia pycnocephala DC.
Diplodia herbarum (Cda.) Lév.
Gibberella Saubinetii (Mont.) Sacc.
⎰ Bullaria Absinthii (DC.) Arth. & Mains.
⎱ Puccinia Artemisiarum Schm. & Kze.

Artemisia redolens Gray.
⎰ Bullaria Absinthii (DC.) Arth. & Mains.
⎱ Puccinia Absinthii DC.

Artemisia richardsoniana Besser.
Pleospora vulgaris Niessl.

Artemisia rigida (Nutt.) Gray.
⎰ Bullaria Absinthii (DC.) Arth. & Mains.
⎨ Puccinia Absinthii DC.
⎩ Puccinia Tanaceti West. Am. Fung. *354.*

Artemisia scopulorum Gray.
⎰ Macrophoma Raui (Pk.) Berl. & Vogl.
⎨ Phoma Raui (Pk.) Sacc.
⎪ Phyllosticta Raui (Pk.) Dearness & House.
⎩ Sphaeropsis Raui Pk.
Pleospora permunda (Cke.) Sacc.

Artemisia scouleriana (Besser) Rydb.
Ophiobolus claviger Hark.

Artemisia serrata Nutt.
Cylindrosporium Artemisiae Dearness & Bar-
thol.
⎰ Erysiphe Cichoracearum DC. †
⎱ Erysiphe Linkii Lév.
Peronospora leptosperma DBy.
⎰ Bullaria Absinthii (DC.) Arth. & Mains.
⎱ Puccinia Absinthii DC.

Artemisia silvicola Osterhaut.
⎰ Dicaeoma Dracunculi Arth. & Kern. I.
⎨ Puccinia universalis Arth. I.
⎪ Bullaria Absinthii (DC.) Arth. & Mains.
⎩ Puccinia Absinthii DC.

Artemisia spinescens D. C. Eaton.
Bullaria Absinthii (DC.) Arth. & Mains.

Artemisia Suksdorfii Piper.
  Cercospora Absinthii (Pk.) Sacc.
  Cylindrosporium Artemisiae Dearness & Bar-
    thol.
  Erysiphe Cichoracearum DC. †
  { Bullaria Absinthii (DC.) Arth. & Mains.
  { Puccinia Absinthii DC.
  { Micropuccinia Millefolii (Fckl.) Arth. & Jack-
  {   son.
  { Puccinia conferta Diet. & Holw.
  { Puccinia Millefolii Fckl.
Artemisia tridentata Nutt.
  Cucurbitaria minima Ell. & Ev.
  Gibberidea Artemisiae Earle.
  Leptosphaeria lasioderma Ell. & Ev.
  Melanomma nitidum Ell. & Ev.
  { Bullaria Absinthii (DC.) Arth. & Mains.
  { Puccinia Absinthii DC.
  { Puccinia Artemisiae Auct.
  { Puccinia similis Ell. & Ev.
  { Puccinia Tanaceti Auct. Amer. p. p.
  Rhizoctonia Solani Kühn.
  Sporidesmium macrosporoides Ell. & Gall.
  Trematosphaeria calvispora Ell. & Ev.
  Uromyces oblongisporus Ell. & Ev.
  Zignoella ostiolata Dearness & Barthol.
Artemisia tripartita Rydb.
  Dicaeoma Dracunculi Arth. & Kern. I.
  Bullaria Absinthii (DC.) Arth. & Mains.
Artemisia viscidula Osterhout.
  Bullaria Absinthii (DC.) Arth. & Mains.
Artemisia vulgaris L.
  { Diaporthe orthoceras (Fr.) Nits.
  { Sphaeria orthoceras Fr.
  Erysiphe Cichoracearum DC. †
  Gloeosporium phyllachoroides Ell. & Ev.
  { Haplosporella opaca (C. & E.) Sacc.
  { Sphaeropsis opaca C. & E.
  Oidium erysiphoides Fr.
  Phoma herbarum Westd.
  { Bullaria Absinthii (DC.) Arth. & Mains.
  { Puccinia Absinthii DC.
  { Puccinia Tanaceti Auct. Amer. p. p.
  Septoria fusca Pk.
Artemisia Wrightii Gray.
  Bullaria Absinthii (DC.) Arth. & Mains.
Artemisia sp. indet.
  Alternaria hispidula Ell.
  Camarosporium astericola Ell. & Barthol., var.
    latispora Dearness.
  Coniothecium applanatum Sacc.
  Cucurbitaria umbilicata Ell.
  Cyphella villosa P. ex Karst.
  Epochnium isthmophorum Sacc.
  Fusarium roseum Lk.
  Macrosporium puccinioides Ell. & Anderson.
  { Cucurbitaria occidentalis Ell.
  { Melanomma occidentalis (Ell.) Sacc.

  { Melanomma sulcatum (Ell.) Berl. & Vogl.
  { Sphaeria sulcata Ell.
  { Stuartella sulcata (Ell.) Sacc.
  Platystomum desertorum Tracy & Earle.
  Poria Medulla-panis (P. ex Fr.) Cke.
  { Peziza Artemisiae Lasch.
  { Pyrenopeziza Artemisiae (Lasch) Sacc.
  { Rosellinia ovalis (Ell.) Sacc.
  { Sphaeria ovalis Ell.
  { Sirodesmium herbarum (Cke.) Sacc.
  { Sporidesmium herbarum Cke.
  Sphaeria aculeata S., var. artemisiicola S.
  Stictis decipiens (Karst.) Cke.
  { Cucurbitaria solitaria Ell.
  { Teichospora solitaria (Ell.) Ell. & Ev.
  Teichospora variabilis Ell. & Ev.
  Tubercularia herbarum Fr.
Liabum discolor Benth. & Hook.
Liabum hypochlorum Blake.
  Coleosporium paraphysatum Diet. & Holw.
Liabum sublobatum B. L. Robinson.
  Coleosporium paraphysatum Diet. & Holw.
Liabum sp. indet.
  { Aecidium Liabi Mayor. 1913.
  { Aecidium Liabi Arth. 1920.
  { Aecidium liabicola Trott.
Schistocarpha platyphylla Greenm.
  { Micropuccinia Schistocarphae (Jackson &
  {   Holw.) Arth. & Jackson.
  { Puccinia Schistocarphae Jackson & Holw.
Calea insignis Blake.
Calea integrifolia Hemsl.
  Puccinia ordinata Jackson & Holw.
Neurolaena lobata (L.) Br.
  { Micropuccinia Emiliae (Henn.) Arth. & Jack-
  {   son.
  { Puccinia Emiliae Henn.
  { Puccinia Synedrellae Auct.
Tussilago Farfara L.
  Didymium squamulosum Fr.
  { Dicaeoma epiphyllum (Wettst.) O. Kuntze. I.
  { Puccinia Poarum Nielsen. I.
  { Ramularia brunnea Pk.
  { Sphaerella Tussilaginis Rehm.
Tussilago sp. indet.
  Capnodium elongatum B. & Desm.
Petasites corymbosus (R. Br.) Rydb.
Petasites frigidus (L.) Fr.
  { Aecidium Tussilaginis P.
  { Dicaeoma epiphyllum (Wettst.) O. Kuntze. I.
  { Micropuccinia conglomerata (Schm. & Kze.)
  {   Arth. & Jackson.
  { Puccinia Petasitis Vestergren.
Petasites palmatus (Ait.) Gray.
  Phyllosticta Petasitidis Ell. & Ev.
  { Micropuccinia conglomerata (Schm. & Kze.)
  {   Arth. & Jackson.
  { Puccinia Nardosmiae Ell. & Ev.

Petasites palmatus (*cont.*)
Ramularia variegata Ell. & Holw.
Stagonospora Petasitidis Ell. & Ev.
Synchytrium aureum Schrt.
Erechtites hieracifolia (L.) Raf.
Cercospora Erechtitis Atk.
{ Erysiphe communis Auct. Amer. p. p.
{ Erysiphe Polygoni DC. †
{ Peronospora Halstedii Farl.
{ Plasmopara Halstedii (Farl.) Berl. & De Toni.
{ Rhysotheca Halstedii (Farl.) G. W. Wilson.
Septoria Erechtitis Ell. & Ev.
Sphaerotheca Humuli (DC.) Burrill. †
{ Sphaerotheca Castagnei Auct. Amer. p. p.
{ Sphaerotheca Humuli (DC.) Burrill, var.
{   fuliginea (Schl.) Salmon.
Arnica alpina (L.) Olin.
Mycosphaerella pachyasca (Rostr.) Vester-
gren.
Pleospora herbarum (Fr.) Rabh.
Puccinia arnicalis Pk.
Arnica cana Greene.
Nigredo Junci (Desm.) Arth. I.
Coleosporium arnicale Arth.
Arnica celsa A. Nels.
Nigredo Junci (Desm.) Arth. I.
Arnica Chamissonis Less.
{ Entyloma arnicalis Ell. & Ev.
{ Ramularia? arnicalis Ell. & Ev.
Arnica cordifolia Hook.
{ Nigredo Junci (Desm.) Arth. I.
{ Uromyces Junci (Desm.) Tul. I.
{ Entyloma arnicale Ell. & Ev.
{ Ramularia arnicalis Ell. & Ev.
Phyllosticta Arnicae Fckl.
Puccinia arnicalis Pk.
{ Sphaerotheca Castagnei Auct. Amer. p. p.
{ Sphaerotheca Humuli (DC.) Burrill, var.
{   fuliginea (Schl.) Salmon.
Arnica diversifolia Greene.
Arnica fulgens Pursh.
Puccinia arnicalis Pk.
Arnica latifolia Bong.
Entyloma arnicalis Ell. & Ev.
Puccinia arnicalis Pk.
Sphaerotheca Humuli (DC.) Burrill, var. fuli-
ginea (Schl.) Salmon.
Arnica mollis Hook.
Nigredo Junci (Desm.) Arth. I.
Arnica paniculata A. Nels.
Arnica pedunculata Rydb.
Arnica rhizomata A. Nels.
Puccinia arnicalis Pk.
Arnica stricta A. Nels.
{ Nigredo Junci (Desm.) Arth. I.
{ Uromyces Junci (Desm.) Tul. I.
Arnica subplumosa Greene.
Puccinia arnicalis Pk.
Ramularia arnicalis Ell. & Ev.

Arnica sp. indet.
Ovularia hughesiana Sacc.
Phyllosticta Arnicae Fckl.
Cacalia amplifolia DC.
Cacalia ampullacea Greenm.
{ Dicaeoma senecionicola (Arth.) Arth. & Jack-
{   son.
{ Puccinia senecionicola Arth.
Cacalia atriplicifolia L.
Aecidium Compositarum Auct. Amer. p. p.
Aecidium Mesadeniae Arth.
Septoria Cacaliae Ell. & Kellerm.
Septoria Nabali B. & C.
Cacalia calotricha Blake.
Cacalia obtusiloba Robinson & Greenm.
Cacalia Pringlei Watson.
{ Dicaeoma senecionicola Arth.
{ Puccinia senecionicola Arth.
Cacalia reniformis Muhl.
Aecidium Compositarum Auct. Amer. p. p.
Aecidium Mesadeniae Arth.
Septoria Cacaliae Ell. & Kellerm.
Septoria Nabali B. & C.
Sphaerotheca Castagnei Lév.
Cacalia sagittata Vahl.
{ Micropuccinia Emiliae (Henn.) Arth. & Jack-
{   son.
{ Puccinia Emiliae Henn.
Cacalia sinuata Cerv.
{ Dicaeoma senecionicola Arth.
{ Puccinia senecionicola Arth.
Cacalia sonchifolia L.
{ Micropuccinia Emiliae (Henn.) Arth. & Jack-
{   son.
{ Puccinia Emiliae Henn.
{ Puccinia Synedrella Auct.
Cacalia tuberosa Nutt.
Septoria Cacaliae Ell. & Kellerm.
Sphaerotheca Castagnei Lév.
Sphaerotheca Humuli (DC.) Burrill, var.
fuliginea (Schl.) Salmon.
Cacalia sp. indet.
Uromyces senecionicola Arth.
Tetradymia canescens DC.
Tetradymia comosa Gray.
Tetradymia glabrata Gray.
Tetradymia Nuttallii Torr. & Gr.
Tetradymia spinosa Hook. & Arn.
{ Micropuccinia Grindeliae (Pk.) Arth. & Jack-
{   son.
{ Puccinia Grindeliae Pk.
{ Puccinia variolans Hark.
Tetradymia sp. indet.
Amphisphaeria asperata Ell. & Ev.
Senecio amplectens Gray.
Pleospora vulgaris Niessl.
Senecio angulifolius DC.
{ Dicaeoma senecionicola Arth.
{ Puccinia senecionicola Arth.

Senecio aronicoides DC.
  Coleosporium occidentale Arth.
  Gloeosporium Senecionis Ell. & Ev.
  { Micropuccinia expansa (Lk.) Arth. & Jackson.
  { Puccinia expansa Lk.
Senecio atriapiculatus Rydb.
  { Allodus subcircinata (Ell. & Ev.) Arth.
  { Puccinia subcircinata Ell. & Ev.
Senecio aureus L.
  Aecidium Compositarum Auct. Amer. p. p.
  Aecidium Jacobeae Grev.
  Aecidium Senecionis Desm.
  { Dicaeoma Eriophori (Thm.) O. Kuntze. I.
  { Puccinia Eriophori Thm. I.
  Cercospora Senecionis Ell. & Ev.
  { Albugo Tragopogonis (P.) ex S. F. Gray.
  { Cystopus Tragopogonis (P. ex S. F. Gray.)
  {   Schrt.
  Entyloma Compositarum Farl.
  Erysiphe Cichoracearum DC. †
  Puccinia conglomerata Kze. & Schm.
  { Micropuccinia recedens (Syd.) Arth. &
  {   Jackson.
  { Puccinia recedens Syd.
  Septoria Senecionis-aurei J. J. Davis.
Senecio Balsamitae Muhl.
  Entyloma Compositarum Farl.
  { Micropuccinia recedens (Syd.) Arth. & Jack-
  {   son.
  { Puccinia recedens Syd.
Senecio blitoides Greene.
  Allophylaria Senecionis Clements.
Senecio canus Hook.
  Coleosporium occidentale Arth.
Senecio cinerarioides H. B. K.
  Baeodromus Holwayi Arth.
Senecio
    (Emilia flammea Cass.).
  Puccinia Emiliae Henn.
Senecio columbianus Greene.
  Allodus subcircinata (Ell. & Ev.) Arth.
Senecio compactus Rydb.
  Puccinia Stipae Arth. I.
Senecio crassulus Gray.
  { Allodus subcircinata (Ell. & Ev.) Arth.
  { Puccinia subcircinata Ell. & Ev.
Senecio crocatus Rydb.
  { Micropuccinia recedens (Syd.) Arth. & Jack-
  {   son.
  { Dasyspora recedens Arth.
Senecio cruentus DC.
  Erysiphe Cichoracearum DC. †
Senecio cymbalarioides Nutt.
  Albugo Tragopogonis (P.) ex S. F. Gray.
Senecio densus Greene.
  Dicaeoma Stipae (Arth.) O. Kuntze. I.
Senecio dimorphophyllus Greene.
  Micropuccinia expansa (Lk.) Arth. & Jackson.

Senecio dispar A. Nels.
  Phyllosticta Garrettii Syd.
  { Micropuccinia expansa (Lk.) Arth. & Jackson.
  { Puccinia expansa Lk.
  { Puccinia recedens Fung. Utah. *102.*
  { Puccinia subcircinata Ell. & Ev.
Senecio Douglasii DC.
  Baeodromus californicus Arth.
Senecio ductaris Piper.
  { Dicaeoma Eriophori (Thm.) O. Kuntze. I.
  { Puccinia Eriophori Thm. I.
Senecio Fendleri Gray.
  Coleosporium occidentale Arth.
Senecio Fremontii Torr. & Gr.
  Sphaerotheca Humuli (DC.) Burrill. †
Senecio Harfordii Greenm.
  { Micropuccinia recedens (Syd.) Arth. & Jack-
  {   son.
  { Puccinia recedens Syd.
Senecio hartianus Heller.
  Albugo Tragopogonis (P.) ex S. F. Gray.
Senecio hydrophiloides Rydb.
  Coleosporium occidentale Arth.
Senecio hydrophilus Nutt.
  Allodus subcircinata (Ell. & Ev.) Arth.
Senecio integerrimus Nutt.
  { Aecidium Bigeloviae Pk.
  { Dicaeoma Stipae (Arth.) O. Kuntze. I.
  { Allodus subcircinata (Ell. & Ev.) Arth.
  { Puccinia subcircinata Ell. & Ev.
Senecio lugens Richards.
  { Aecidium Bigeloviae Pk.
  { Puccinia Stipae Arth I.
  Aecidium sclerothecioides Ell. & Ev.
  { Albugo Tragopogonis (P.) ex S. F. Gray.
  { Cystopus cubicus (Strauss) ex Lév.
  { Allodus subcircinata (Ell. & Ev.) Arth.
  { Puccinia expansa Syd. p. p.
  { Puccinia Senecionis Syd. Ured. *782.*
  { Puccinia subcircinata Ell. & Ev.
  Sphaerotheca Humuli (DC.) Burrill, var. fuli-
    ginea (Schl.) Salmon.
Senecio MacDougalii Heller.
  Albugo Tragopogonis (P.) ex S. F. Gray.
Senecio Muhlenbergii Sch. Bip.
  Sphaerotheca Humuli (DC.) Burrill, var. fuli-
    ginea (Schl.) Salmon.
Senecio oblanceolatus Rydb.
  Dicaeoma Stipae (Arth.) O. Kuntze. I.
  Albugo Tragopogonis (P.) ex S. F. Gray.
  Puccinia senecionicola Arth.
Senecio obovatus Muhl.
  Entyloma Compositarum Farl.
Senecio peninsularis Vasey & Rose.
  Albugo Tragopogonis (P.) ex S. F. Gray.
Senecio perplexus A. Nels.
  Dicaeoma Stipae (Arth.) O. Kuntze. I.
  { Allodus subcircinata (Ell. & Ev.) Arth.
  { Puccinia subcircinata Ell. & Ev.

Senecio petasioides Greenm.
Senecio petasites DC.
  { Dicaeoma senecionicola Arth.
  { Puccinia senecionicola Arth.
Senecio praecox DC.
  . Aecidium praecipuum Arth.
Senecio pseudaureus Rydb.
  Micropuccinia recedens (Syd.) Arth. & Jackson.
Senecio pudicus Greene.
  Dicaeoma Stipae (Arth.) O. Kuntze. I.
Senecio rawsonianus Greene.
  Asteroma Senecionis Ell. & Ev.
Senecio Riddellii Torr. & Gr.
  Dicaeoma Stipae (Arth.) O. Kuntze. I.
Senecio Robbinsii Oakes.
  Dicaeoma Eriophori (Thm.) O. Kuntze. I.
Senecio roldana DC.
  { Nigredo senecionicola Arth.
  { Uromyces senecionicola Arth.
Senecio
  (Emilia sagittata DC.).
  Puccinia Emiliae Henn.
Senecio salicinus Rydb.
  Dicaeoma Stipae (Arth.) O. Kuntze. I.
Senecio salignus DC.
  Aecidium herrerianum Arth.
  Aecidium hualtatinum Speg.
Senecio scopulina Greene.
  Leptosphaeria dumetorum Niessl.
  Rhabdospora dumetorum Fairman.
Senecio Serra Hook.
  Coleosporium occidentale Arth.
  { Albugo Tragopogonis (P.) ex S. F. Gray.
  { Cystopus Tragopogonis (P. ex S. F. Gray) Schrt.
  Sphaerotheca Humuli (DC.) Burrill, var. fuliginea (Schl.) Salmon.
Senecio sinuatus H. B. K.
  { Dicaeoma senecionicola Arth.
  { Puccinia senecionicola Arth.
Senecio
  (Emilia sonchifolia L.)
  Puccinia Emiliae Henn.
Senecio spartioides Torr. & Gr.
  { Aecidium Bigeloviae Pk.
  { Dicaeoma Stipae (Arth.) O. Kuntze. I.
  { Puccinia Stipae Arth. I.
  Phoma herbarum Westd.
Senecio taraxacoides (Gray) Greene.
  Allodus subcircinata (Ell. & Ev.) Arth.
Senecio triangularis Hook.
  Dicaeoma Eriophori (Thm.) O. Kuntze.
  Coleosporium occidentale Arth.
  Coniosporium microsporum Ell. & Ev.
  Puccinia conglomerata Schm. & Kze.
  { Allodus subcircinata (Ell. & Ev.) Arth.
  { Puccinia subcircinata Ell. & Ev.

{ Sphaerotheca Castagnei Auct. Amer.
{ Sphaerotheca Humuli (DC.) Burrill, var. fuliginea (Schl.) Salmon.
Senecio uintahensis (A. Nels.) Greenm.
  Coleosporium occidentale Arth.
Senecio vulgaris L.
  Bremia Lactucae Regel.
  { Coleosporium Senecionis (Schum.) Fr.
  { Peridermium oblongisporum Fckl. III.
Senecio Warszewiczii A. Braun & Bouché.
  { Dicaeoma senecionicola Arth.
  { Puccinia senecionicola Arth.
Senecio sp. indet.
  Diplodina coloradensis Ell. & Ev.
  Pleospora Senecionis Earle.
  Ramularia Senecionis (B. & Br.) Sacc.
  Rhizoctonia Solani Kühn.
  Septoria Senecionis Westd.
Calendula officinalis L.
  Corticium vagum B. & C.
  { Micropuccinia Emiliae (Henn.) Arth. & Jackson.
  { Puccinia Emiliae Henn.
  ?Puccinia recedens Auct. Amer. p. p.
Calendula Pongei Hort.
  { Corticium vagum B. & C.
  { Rhizoctonia Solani Kühn.
Dimorphotheca cuneata (Thunb.) DC.
  { Micropuccinia Emiliae (Henn.) Arth. & Jackson.
  { Puccinia recedens N. Am. Uredinales *1863*.
Arctium Lappa L.
  Ascochyta Lappae Kabát & Bubák.
  Cercospora Arcti-Ambrosiae Halsted.
  Diaporthe Arctii (Lasch) Nits.
  Erysiphe Cichoracearum DC. †
  Helotium fumosum Ell. & Ev.
  Lachnea aurantia (Clements) Sacc. & Syd.
  Leptosphaeria Doliolum (P. ex Fr.) De Not.
  { Leptosphaeria eriophora (Cke.) Sacc.
  { Pocosphaeria eriophora (Cke.) Berl.
  { Sphaeria eriophora Cke.
  Ophiobolus acuminatus (Sow. ex Fr.) Duby.
  Phialea Urticae (P.) Sacc.
  Phyllosticta Lappae Sacc.
  Pseudohelotium canadense Ell.
  { Bullaria Bardanae (Cda.) Arth.
  { Puccinia Bardanae Cda.
  Septoria Lapparum Sacc.
  Sphaeropsis Lappae Ell. & Ev.
  Vermicularia Arctii S.
  Verticillium lateritium B.
Arctium minus Bernh.
  Diaporthe Arctii (Lasch) Nits.
  Gloeosporium Lappae Dearness & House.
  Phlyctaena arcuata Б.
  Phomopsis Arctii (Lasch) Trav.
  Phyllosticta decidua Ell. & Kellerm.

Arctium minus (*cont.*)
, Phyllosticta Lappae Sacc.
{ Bullaria Bardanae (Cda.) Arth.
{ Puccinia Bardanae Cda.
Lappa sp. indet.
  Oidium erysiphoides Fr.
Saussurea angustifolia DC.
  Pleospora vulgaris Niessl.
Cirsium acaulescens (Gray) K. Schumann.
{ Bullaria Cirsii (Lasch) Arth.
{ Puccinia Cirsii Lasch.
Cirsium altissimum (L.) Spreng.
{ Acanthostigma occidentale (Ell. & Ev.) Sacc.
{ Venturia occidentalis Ell. & Ev.
  Cercospora kansensis Syd.
  Albugo Tragopogonis (P.) ex S. F. Gray.
{ Erysiphe Cichoracearum DC. †
{ Erysiphe lamprocarpa Auct. Amer. p. p.
{ Ophiobolus acuminatus (Sow. ex Fr.) Duby.
{ Raphidospora acuminata (Sow. ex Fr.) Rabh.
{ Sphaeria acuminata Sow. ex Fr.
{ Bullaria Cirsii (Lasch) Arth.
{ Puccinia Cirsii Lasch.
{ Puccinia Compositarum Auct. Amer. p. p.
  Septoria Cirsii Niessl.
  Septoria Commonsii Ell. & Ev.
  Stagonospora Cirsii J. J. Davis.
Cirsium americanum (Gray) B. L. Robinson.
  Microstroma americanorum Pammel.
  Puccinia Cirsii Lasch.
Cirsium arizonicum (Gray) Petrak.
{ Bullaria Cirsii (Lasch) Arth.
{ Puccinia Cirsii Lasch.
Cirsium arvense (L.) Scop.
{ Albugo Tragopogonis (P.) ex S. F. Gray.
{ Cystopus cubicus (Strauss) ex Lév.
{ Cystopus spinulosus DBy.
{ Cystopus Tragopogonis (P. ex S. F. Gray)
{   Schrt.
  Erysiphe Cichoracearum DC. †
{ Hainesia Lythri (Desm.) v. Höhnel.
{ Sclerotiopsis concava (Desm.) Shear &
{   Dodge.
  Phyllosticta Cirsii Desm.
{ Bullaria suaveolens (Rostr.) Arth.
{ Puccinia Cirsii Auct. Amer. p. p.
{ Puccinia Compositarum Auct. Amer. p. p.
{ Puccinia Hieracii Auct. Amer. p. p.
{ Puccinia obtegens Tul.
{ Puccinia suaveolens Rostr.
{ Trichobasis suaveolens (P.) Lév.
  Pyrenochaeta erysiphoides Sacc.
  Sclerotinia sclerotiorum (Lib.) Massee.
  Septoria Cirsii Niessl.
Cirsium Breweri (Gray) Jepson.
{ Bullaria Cirsii (Lasch) Arth.
{ Puccinia californica Diet.
{ Puccinia Cirsii Lasch.
{ Puccinia inclusa Syd.

Pyrenochaete erysiphoides Sacc.
Sclerotinia libertiana Fckl.
Septoria Cirsii Niessl.
Cirsium californicum Gray.
Cirsium canescens Nutt.
{ Bullaria Cirsii (Lasch) Arth.
{ Puccinia flosculosorum Auct. Amer. p. p.
Cirsium Centaureae (Rydb.) K. Schumann.
{ Bullaria Cirsii (Lasch) Arth.
{ Puccinia Cirsii Lasch.
  Thecaphora Trailii Cke.
Cirsium coloradense (Rydb.) Cockerell.
{ Bullaria Cirsii (Lasch) Arth.
{ Puccinia Cirsii Lasch.
Cirsium discolor (Muhl.) Spreng.
{ Acanthostigma occidentalis (Ell. & Ev.) Sacc.
{ Chaetomella (?) perforata Ell. & Ev.
{ Venturia occidentalis Ell. & Ev.
  Erysiphe Cichoracearum DC. †
{ Bullaria Cirsii (Lasch) Arth.
{ Puccinia Cirsii Lasch.
{ Puccinia Compositarum Auct. Amer. p. p.
{ Puccinia flosculosorum E. F. *306*.
  Septoria Cirsii Niessl.
  Septoria Commonsii Ell. & Ev.
Cirsium Drummondii Torr. & Gr.
{ Bullaria Cirsii (Lasch) Arth.
{ Puccinia Cirsii Lasch.
Cirsium Eatoni (Gray) B. L. Robinson.
{ Bullaria Cirsii (Lasch) Arth.
{ Puccinia Carduorum Fung. Utah *69*.
  Thecaphora Trailii Cke.
Cirsium edule Nutt.
{ Bullaria Cirsii (Lasch) Arth.
{ Puccinia Cirsii Lasch.
Cirsium Flodmannii (Rydb.) Arth.
{ Nigredo Junci (Desm.) Arth. I.
{ Uromyces Junci (Desm.) Tul. I.
  Erysiphe Cichoracearum DC. †
  Ophiobolus acuminatus (Sow. ex Fr.) Duby.
  Ophiobolus Cirsii (Karst.) Sacc., var. furcatus
    Rehm.
{ Bullaria Cirsii (Lasch) Arth.
{ Puccinia Cirsii Lasch.
Cirsium foliosum (Hook.) DC.
  Nigredo Junci (Desm.) Arth. I.
  Bullaria Cirsii (Lasch) Arth.
Cirsium griseum (Rydb.) K. Schumann.
{ Bullaria Cirsii (Lasch) Arth.
{ Puccinia Cirsii Lasch.
Cirsium hookerianum Nutt.
{ Aecidium Cardui Arth.
{ Nigredo Junci (Desm.) Arth. I.
{ Bullaria Cirsii (Lasch) Arth.
{ Puccinia Cirsii Lasch.
Cirsium horridulum Michx.
  Albugo Tragopogonis (P.) ex S. F. Gray.
Cirsium inornatum Wooton & Standley
  Bullaria Cirsii (Lasch) Arth.

Cirsium iowense (Pammel) Fern.
  Erysiphe Cichoracearum DC. †
Cirsium lanceolatum (L.) Hill.
  { Albugo Tragopogonis (P.) ex S. F. Gray.
  { Cystopus cubicus (Strauss) ex Lév.
  Ophiobolus acuminatus (Sow. ex Fr.) Duby.
  Erysiphe Cichoracearum DC. †
  Phyllactinia corylea (P.) ex Karst.
  { Bullaria Cirsii (Lasch) Arth.
  { Puccinia Cirsii Lasch.
? { Puccinia obtegens Tul.
  { Puccinia suaveolens Rostr.
  Aecidium Cirsii-lanceolati Kellerm.
  Dicaeoma Cnici (Mart.) Arth.
  Dicaeoma flosculosorum Auct. Amer. p. p.
  Jackya Cnici (Mart.) Arth.
  Puccinia Cirsii Fung. Columb. *3168.*
  Puccinia Cirsii-lanceolati Schrt.
  { Puccinia Cnici Mart.
  { ?Puccinia Compositarum Auct. Amer. p. p.
  { Puccinia flosculosorum E. F. *307a, b.*
  { ?Puccinia Hieracii Auct. Amer. p. p.
  { ?Puccinia variabilis Auct. Amer. p. p.
  { ?Uredo Cichoracearum Auct. Amer. p. p.
  { Uredo flosculosorum Auct. Amer. p. p.
Cirsium lomatolepis (Hemsl.) Petrak.
Cirsium megacephalum (Gray) Cockerell.
  { Bullaria Cirsii (Lasch) Arth.
  { Puccinia Cirsii Lasch.
Cirsium muticum Michx.
  { Albugo Tragopogonis (P.) ex S. F. Gray.
  { Cystopus spinulosus DBy.
  { Cystopus Tragopogonis (P. ex S. F. Gray)
  {   Schrt.
  Erysiphe Cichoracearum DC. †
  { Heptameria mesoedema (B. & C.) Sacc.
  { Leptosphaeria mesoedema (B. & C.) Ell. & Ev.
  { Sphaeria mesoedema B. & C.
  { Bullaria Cirsii (Lasch.) Arth.
  { Puccinia Cirsii Lasch.
  Septoria Cirsii Niessl.
  Septoria Commonsii Ell. & Ev.
Cirsium Nelsonii (Pammel) Rydb.
Cirsium neomexicanum Gray.
  { Bullaria Cirsii (Lasch) Arth.
  { Puccinia Cirsii Lasch.
Cirsium occidentale (Nutt.) Jepson.
  Pleospora herbarum (Fr.) Rabh.
  { Bullaria Cirsii (Lasch) Arth.
  { Puccinia Cirsii Lasch.
  { Puccinia flosculosorum Auct. Amer. p. p.
Cirsium ochrocentrum Gray.
  { Bullaria Cirsii (Lasch) Arth.
  { Puccinia Cirsii Lasch.
  { Schizonella subtrifida Ell. & Ev.
  { Thecaphora Trailii Cke.
Cirsium odoratum (Muhl.) Britton.
  Septoria Cirsii Niessl.

Cirsium oreophilum Rydb.
Cirsium orizabensis Klatt.
Cirsium pallidum Wooton & Standley.
Cirsium palousense Piper.
Cirsium Parryi (Gray) Petrak.
Cirsium perennans (Greene) Wooton & Standley.
Cirsium perplexans Rydb.
Cirsium plattense (Rydb.) Cockerell.
Cirsium pulchellum (Greene) Wooton & Standley.
Cirsium quercetorum (Gray) Jepson.
  { Bullaria Cirsii (Lasch) Arth.
  { Puccinia Cirsii Lasch.
Cirsium remotifolium (Hook.) DC.
  Cercospora Cirsii Ell. & Ev.
  { Bullaria Cirsii (Lasch) Arth.
  { Puccinia Cirsii Lasch.
Cirsium scopulorum (Greene) Cockerell.
Cirsium spathulifolium Rydb.
Cirsium Tracyi Rydb.
  Bullaria Cirsii (Lasch) Arth.
Cirsium undulatum (Nutt.) Spreng.
  { Aecidium Cardui Arth.
  { Puccinia Cirsii Auct. p. p. I.
  { Nigredo Junci (Desm.) Arth. I.
  { Uromyces Junci (Desm.) Tul. I.
  Cercospora ditissima Ell. & Ev.
  Cercospora obesa Ell. & Ev.
  Albugo Tragopogonis (P.) ex S. F. Gray.
  Erysiphe Cichoracearum DC. †
  Phyllosticta Cirsii Desm.
  { Bullaria Cirsii (Lasch) Arth.
  { Puccinia Cirsii Lasch.
  { Puccinia flosculosorum Auct. Amer. p. p.
  { Puccinia Hieracii Auct. Amer. p. p.
  { Puccinia Hieracii N. Dak. Fungi *51.*
  { Puccinia inclusa Syd.
  { ?Puccinia suaveolens Wint.
  { ?Puccinia Tanaceti DC.
Cirsium vernale (Osterhout) Cockerell.
Cirsium virginianum (L.) Michx.
Cirsium Wrightii Gray.
  { Bullaria Cirsii (Lasch) Arth.
  { Puccinia Cirsii Lasch.
Cirsium sp. indet.
  { Clathrospora permunda (Cke.) Berl.
  { Pleospora baccata Ell.
  { Leptosphaeria modesta (Desm.) Karst.
  { Sphaeria modesta Desm.
  Macrosporium commune Rabh.
  { Pyrenophora pellita (Fr.) Sacc.
  { Sphaeria pellita Fr.
  Rhizoctonia Solani Kühn.
  Synchytrium Taraxaci DBy. & Wor.
Cynara Scolymus L.
  Botrytis cinerea P. †
  Cercospora obscura Heald & Wolf.
  Corticium vagum B. & C.
  Erysiphe Cichoracearum DC. †

Cynara Scolymus (*cont.*)
  Ozonium omnivorum Shear.
  Sclerotium Rolfsii Sacc.
Onopordum Acanthium L.
  Ophiobolus acuminatus (Sow. ex Fr.) Duby.
  Puccinia Onopordi Syd.
  Rhabdospora pleosporoides Sacc.
Centaurea americana Nutt.
  { Bullaria irrequisita (H. S. Jackson) Arth. &
  { Mains.
  { Puccinia Centaureae Fung. Columb. *1642*, N.
  { Am. Ured. *1338*.
  { Puccinia Centaureae Mart.
  { Puccinia irrequisita H. S. Jackson.
Centaurea Cyanus L.
  { Bullaria Cyani (Pass.) Arth.
  { ?Puccinia Centaureae Auct. Amer. p. p.
  { Puccinia Cyani Pass.
  { Puccinia suaveolens, var. Cyani Pk. p. p.
  Septoria centaureicola Brun., var. brevispora
  Pk.
Centaurea gymnocarpa Moris & De Not.
  Rhizoctonia Solani Kühn.
Centaurea sp. indet.
  { Plasmopara Halstedii (Farl.) Berl. & De Toni.
  { Rhysotheca Halstedii (Farl.) G. W. Wilson.
Carthamus tinctorius L.
  { Bullaria Carthami (Cda.) Arth. & Mains.
  { Puccinia Carthami Cda.
  Sclerotinia sclerotiorum (Lib.) Massee.
Anastraphia bahamensis Urb.
  Uredo Wilsoni Arth.
Anastraphia northrupiana Greenm.
  Platystomum phyllogenum Fairman.
Perezia sp. indet.
  Aecidium Pereziae Arth.
Trixis frutescens P. Br.
  { Puccinia Trixitis Arth.
  { Uredo Trixitis Kern & Kellerm.
Cichorium Endivia L.
  Corticium vagum B. & C.
  { Bullaria Hieracii (Mart.) Arth.
  { Puccinia Endiviae Pass.
  Pythium debaryanum Hesse.
  Rhizoctonia Solani Kühn.
  Sclerotinia sclerotiorum (Lib.) Massee.
Cichorium Intybus L.
  Cercospora Cichorii J. J. Davis.
  { Bullaria Hieracii (Mart.) Arth.
  { Puccinia Cichorii Bellynck.
  { Puccinia Hieracii Mart.
  Ramularia Cichorii Dearness & House.
  Sclerotinia perplexa Lawrence.
Lapsana communis L.
  { Dicaeoma Lapsanae (Fckl.) O. Kuntze.
  { Puccinia Lapsanae Fckl.
  Ramularia Lapsanae (Desm.) Sacc.

Microseris aphantocarpha Gr., var. **tenella** Gr.
  { Sphaerotheca Castagnei Auct. Amer. p. p.
  { Sphaerotheca Humuli (DC.) Burrill, var.
  { fuliginea (Schl.) Salmon.
Microseris Lindleyi DC.
Microseris
  (Ptilocalais macrolepis Rydb.)
Microseris major Gray.
Microseris nutans Gray.
Microseris
  (Ptilocalais tenuifolia Osterhout.)
  { Bullaria Hieracii (Mart.) Arth.
  { Puccinia Hieracii Mart.
  { Puccinia rugosa Billings.
  { Puccinia Troximontis Pk.
Nothocalais sp. indet.
  Puccinia Stipae Arth. I.
Krigia amplexicaulis Nutt.
  { ?Aecidium Compositarum Auct. Amer. p. p.
  { Puccinia patruelis Arth. I.
  Bremia Lactucae Regel.
  Puccinia flosculosorum Auct. Amer. p. p.
  Bullaria Hieracii (Mart.) Arth.
  Puccinia Krigiae Syd.
  { Micropuccinia maculosa (S.) Arth. & Jack-
  { son.
  { Puccinia maculosa S.
  Septoria Krigiae Dearness & House.
  Sphaerella Krigiae Ell. & Ev.
Krigia Dandelion (L.) Nutt.
  { Aecidium Compositarum Auct. p. p.
  { Aecidium Dandelionis S.
  { ?Caeoma Compositarum, var. Prenanthis S.
  { Uredo Compositarum Spreng. p. p.
  Bremia Lactucae Regel.
  Phoma Krigiae Tassi.
  Dicaeoma atropunctum (Pk. &⸍Clinton) O.
  Kuntze. I.
  Puccinia maculosa S. non Strauss.
Krigia virginica (L.) Willd.
  { Aecidium Compositarum Auct. Amer. p. p.
  { Dicaeoma hieraciatum (H. S. Jackson) Arth.
  { & Kern. I.
  Bullaria Hieracii (Mart.) Arth.
  { Puccinia Asteris Auct. p. p.
  { Puccinia maculosa S.
Hypochaeris glabra L.
Hypochaeris radicata L.
  { Bullaria Hieracii (Mart.) Arth.
  { Puccinia Hieracii Mart.
  { Puccinia Hypochaeridis Oud.
Leontodon autumnalis L.
  { Bullaria Hieracii (Mart.) Arth.
  { Puccinia Hieracii Mart.
  { Puccinia Leontodontis Jacky.
  Septoria cercosperma Rostr.
Leontodon lyratus Ledeb.
  Bullaria Hieracii (Mart.) Arth.

Stephanomeria
  (Ptiloria carduacea ex Blasdale.)
  Puccinia Stephanomeriae Syd.
Stephanomeria cichoriacea Gray.
  Puccinia Harknessii Vize.
  ⌠ Dicaeoma (?) Stephanomeriae (Syd.) Arth.
  ⌡ Puccinia Stephanomeriae Syd.
Stephanomeria exigua Nutt.
  Dicaeoma (?) Harknessii (Vize) O. Kuntze.
Stephanomeria lactucina Gray.
  Puccinia Stephanomeriae Syd.
Stephanomeria minor Nutt.
Stephanomeria myrioclada D. C. Eaton.
Stephanomeria
  (Ptiloria neomexicana Greene).
Stephanomeria paniculata Nutt.
  ⌠ Dicaeoma (?) Harknessii (Vize) O. Kuntze.
  ⎨ Puccinia cladophila Pk.
  ⌡ Puccinia Harknessii Vize.
Stephanomeria pauciflora (**Torr.**) A. Nels.
  Discula runcinata Ell. & Ev.
  ⌠ Dicaeoma (?) Harknessii (Vize) O. Kuntze.
  ⎨ Puccinia cladophila Pk.
  ⌡ Puccinia Harknessii Vize.
Stephanomeria
  (Ptiloria pleurocarpa Greene.)
  ⌠ Dicaeoma (?) Stephanomeriae (Syd.) Arth.
  ⌡ Puccinia Stephanomeriae Syd.
Stephanomeria
  (Ptiloria ramosa Rydb.)
  Puccinia Harknessii Vize.
Stephanomeria runcinata Nutt.
  Discula runcinata Ell. & Ev.
  Puccinia cladophila Pk.
  Puccinia Stephanomeriae Syd.
Stephanomeria virgata Benth.
  Cercospora clavicarpa Ell. & Ev.
  Pleospora herbarum (Fr.) Rabh.
Rafinesquia californica Nutt.
  Cercospora Rafinesquiae Hark.
  Mycosphaerella Nemoseridis Fairman.
  Pleospora herbarum (Fr.) Rabh.
Tragopogon porrifolius L.
  Cercospora Tragopogonis Ell. & Ev.
  Corticium vagum B. & C.
  ⌠ Albugo Tragopogonis (P.) ex S. F. Gray.
  ⎪ Cystopus cubicus (Strauss) ex Lév.
  ⎨ Cystopus Tragopogonis (P. ex S. F. Gray)
  ⌡   Schrt.
  Erysiphe Cichoracearum DC. †
  Ozonium omnivorum Shear.
  ⌠ Puccinia Tragopogi Cda.
  ⌡ Puccinia Tragopogonis Fckl.
  Sclerotinia intermedia Ramsey.
  Sclerotinia libertiana Fckl.
  Vermicularia subeffigurata S.
Tragopogon pratensis L.
  Albugo Tragopogonis (P.) ex S. F. Gray.
  Erysiphe Cichoracearum DC. †

Pinaropappus roseus Less.
  ⌠ Bullaria (?) Pinaropappi (Syd.) Arth. & Mains.
  ⌡ Puccinia Pinaropappi Syd.
Malacothrix arachnoidea McGregor.
Malacothrix saxatilis (Nutt.) Torr. & Gr.
  ⌠ Dicaeoma (?) Harknessii (Vize) O. Kuntze.
  ⌡ Dicaeoma Nemoseridis Fairman.
Malacothrix tenuifolia Torr. & Gr.
  Puccinia Hieracii Mart.
  Puccinia Stephanomeriae Syd.
Malacothrix sp. indet.
  Synchytrium innominatum Farl.
Chondrilla juncea L.
  Metasphaeria trichostoma (Pass.) Sacc.
  ⌠ Bullaria chondrillina (Bubák & Syd.) Arth. &
  ⎨   Mains.
  ⌡ Puccinia chondrillina Bubák & Syd.
  Sphaeria defodiens Ell.
Taraxacum arctogena Dahlst.
  Mycosphaerella Taraxaci (Karst.) J. Lind.
Taraxacum ceratophorum DC.
  Sphaerella Compositarum Awd.
Taraxacum dumetorum Greene.
  Bullaria Hieracii (Mart.) Arth.
  Sphaerotheca Humuli (DC.) Burrill. †
Taraxacum erythrospermum Andrz.
  ⌠ Bullaria Hieracii (Mart.) Arth.
  ⎨ Bullaria Taraxaci (Reb.) Arth.
  ⌡ Puccinia Taraxaci (Reb.) Plowr.
  Ramularia Taraxaci Karst.
Taraxacum eurylepium Dahlst.
  Mycosphaerella pachyasca (Rostr.) Vester-
    gren.
Taraxacum hyparcticum Dahlst.
  Cladosporium herbarum (P.) ex Lk.
  Phoma Cichoracearum Sacc.
  Pleospora herbarum (Fr.) Rabh.
  Pleospora infectoria Fckl.
  ⌠ Mycosphaerella Taraxaci (Karst.) J. Lind.
  ⌡ Sphaerella Taraxaci Karst.
  Sphaerotheca fuliginea (Fr.) J. Lind.
Taraxacum hyperboreum Dahlst.
  Mycosphaerella pachyasca (Rostr.) Vester-
    gren.
Taraxacum officinale Weber.
  Cicinnobolus Cesatii DBy.
  Mycorrhiza of Legumes F. R. Jones.
  ⌠ Bullaria Hieracii (Mart.) Arth.
  ⎪ Bullaria Taraxaci (Reb.) Arth.
  ⎪ Dicaeoma flosculosorum Arth. p. p.
  ⎪ Dicaeoma Taraxaci (Plowr.) O. Kuntze.
  ⎪ Puccinia Cirsii Auct. Amer. p. p.
  ⎪ Puccinia Compositarum Auct. Amer. p. p.
  ⎨ Puccinia flosculosorum Auct. Amer. p. p.
  ⎪ Puccinia Hieracii Mart.
  ⎪ Puccinia Taraxaci Plowr.
  ⎪ Trichobasis Compositarum Auct. Amer. p. p.
  ⎪ Uredo Cichoracearum Auct. Amer. p. p.
  ⌡ Uredo flosculosorum Auct. Amer. p. p.

Taraxacum officinale (*cont.*)
  ⎰Erysiphe Cichoracearum DC. †
  ⎱Erysiphe Montagnei Lév.
  Physarum cinereum (Batsch) P.
  ⎰Aecidium Taraxaci Grev.
  ⎱Dicaeoma variabile (Grev.) O. Kuntze.
  ⎱Puccinia variabilis Grev.
  Ramularia lineola Pk.
  Ramularia Taraxaci Karst.
  Rhabdospora Taraxaci-officinalis Atk.
  Sphaerella Compositarum Awd.
  ⎰Mycosphaerella Taraxaci (Karst.) Dearness.
  ⎱Sphaerella Taraxaci Karst.
  Sphaerotheca Humuli (DC.) Burrill. †
  ⎰Erysiphe Cichoracearum Auct. p. p.
  ⎪Sphaerotheca Castagnei Auct. Amer. p. p.
  ⎨Sphaerotheca Humuli (DC.) Burrill, var.
  ⎪ fuliginea (Schl.) Salmon.
  ⎩Sphaerotheca pannosa Auct. Amer. p. p.
  Vermicularia Dematium (P.) ex Fr., var.
    minor Sacc.

Taraxacum phymatocarpum Vahl.
  Puccinia variabilis Grev.

Taraxacum sp. indet.
  Oidium Fragariae Harz.?
  Septoria cercosperma Rostr.
  Synchytrium Taraxaci DBy. & Wor.

Sonchus arvensis L.
  Marssonia Sonchi Dearness & Bisby.
  ⎰Sclerotinia libertiana Fckl.
  ⎱Sclerotinia sclerotiorum (Lib.) Massee.
  Septoria lactucicola Ell. & Martin.
  Septoria sonchifolia Cke.

Sonchus asper (L.) Hill.
  Alternaria Sonchi J. J. Davis.
  ⎰Bremia Lactucae Regel.
  ⎱Peronospora gangliformis (B.) DBy.
  ⎰Coleosporium Sonchi Schrt.
  ⎱Coleosporium Sonchi-arvensis Auct. Amer. p.p.
  Septoria Lactucae Pass.
  Septoria lactucicola Ell. & Martin.
  Septoria sonchifolia Cke.

Sonchus oleraceus L.
  Bremia Lactucae Regel.
  Septoria sonchifolia Cke.
  Septoria sonchina Thm.
  Sphaerotheca Humuli (DC.) Burrill. †
  ⎰Sphaerotheca Castagnei Auct. Amer.
  ⎨Sphaerotheca Humuli (DC.) Burrill, var. fuli-
  ⎩ ginea (Schl.) Salmon.

Sonchus sp. indet.
  Sphaeria Lactucarum S.

Lactuca canadensis L.
  Alternaria Sonchi J. J. Davis.
  Asteroma Lactucae J. J. Davis.
  ⎰Bremia Lactucae Regel.
  ⎱Peronospora gangliformis (B.) DBy.

?Aecidium Compositarum Auct. Amer. p. p.
Aecidium Compositarum, var. Lactucae Bur-
  rill.
⎰Dicaeoma hieraciatum (H. S. Jackson) Arth.
⎪ & Kern. I.
⎨Dicaeoma patruelis (Arth.) H. S. Jackson. I.
⎪Puccinia hieraciata H. S. Jackson. I.
⎩Puccinia patruelis Arth. I.
⎰Calosphaeria herbicola Ell. & Ev.
⎱Jattaea herbicola (Ell. & Ev.) Berl.
Botryosporium pulchrum Cda.
Diaporthe orthoceras (Fr.) Nits., var. Lactucae
  Ell. & Ev.
Diaporthe placoides Ell. & Ev.
⎰Didymella subexserta (C. & E.) Sacc.
⎱Sphaeria subexserta C. & E.
Entyloma Compositarum Farl.
Erysiphe Cichoracearum DC. †
Macrosporium inquinans C. & E.
Phyllosticta decidua Ell. & Kellerm.
Phyllosticta Lactucae Atk.
Pleospora lactucicola Ell. & Ev.
⎰Aecidium hemisphaericum Pk.
⎱Dicaeoma hemisphaericum Arth. I.
Septoria Lactucae Pass.
Septoria lactucicola Ell. & Martin.
Sphaerella Lactucae Ell. & Kellerm.
Sphaerella praecox Pass.
Vermicularia venturioides C. & E.

Lactuca floridana (L.) Gaertn.
  ⎰Aecidium Compositarum, var. Lactucae Bur-
  ⎪ rill.
  ⎨Dicaeoma hieraciatum (H. S. Jackson) Arth.
  ⎩ & Kern. I.
  Didymella subexserta (C. & E.) Sacc.
  Puccinia Prenanthis (P.) Fckl.?
  Septoria lactucicola Ell. & Martin.
  ⎰Sphaerotheca Castagnei Auct. Amer. p. p.
  ⎨Sphaerotheca Humuli (DC.) Burrill, var. fuli-
  ⎩ ginea (Schl.) Salmon.

Lactuca graminifolia Michx.
  Dicaeoma hieraciatum (H. S. Jackson) Arth.
    & Kern. I.

Lactuca hirsuta Muhl.
  Dicaeoma hieraciatum (H. S. Jackson) Arth.
    & Kern. I.
  Bremia Lactucae Regel.
  Pyrenopeziza Artemisiae (Lasch) Sacc.
  Septoria lactucicola Ell. & Martin.

Lactuca integrata (Grev. & Godr.) A. Nels.
  ⎰Puccinia Opizii Arth. I.
  ⎱Puccinia patruelis Arth. I.
  Bremia Lactucae Regel.
  Erysiphe Cichoracearum DC. †

Lactuca integrifolia Bigel.
  Bremia Lactucae Regel.
  Septoria lactucicola Ell. & Martin.

Lactuca intybacea Jacq.
Dicaeoma (?) proximellum Arth.
Puccinia Arthurella Trott.
Puccinia proximella Arth.
Uredo proximella Arth.

Lactuca ludoviciana (Nutt.) Riddell.
Aecidium Compositarum, var. Lactucae Burrill.
Dicaeoma hieraciatum (H. S. Jackson) Arth. & Kern. I.
Puccinia patruelis Arth. I.
Bremia Lactucae Regel.
Peronospora gangliformis (B.) DBy.
Cylindrosporium lactucicola Ell. & Ev.
Gloeosporium? myriosporum Ell. & Ev.
Puccinia hemisphaerica Ell. & Ev.
Septoria ludoviciana Ell. & Ev.
Septoria unicolor Wint.

Lactuca pulchella (Pursh) DC.
Aecidium Compositarum, var. Lactucae Burrill.
Aecidium Prenanthis N. A. F. *3054*.
Dicaeoma hieraciatum (H. S. Jackson) Arth. & Kern. I.
Puccinia hieraciata H. S. Jackson. I.
Puccinia Opizii Arth. I.
Puccinia Prenanthis West Am. Fung. *372a*.
Aecidium hemisphaericum Pk.
Puccinia Chondrillae Auct. Amer.
Puccinia hemisphaerica Ell. & Ev. 1894.
Puccinia hemisphaerica Lindr. 1901.
Puccinia Prenanthis Fung. Columb. *1654*.
Puccinia Prenanthis West Am. Fung. *372*.
Bremia Lactucae Regel.
Peronospora gangliformis (B.) DBy.
Erysiphe Cichoracearum DC. †
Ovularia Carletoni Ell. & Kellerm.
Rhabdospora Lactucarum (S.) Starb.
Sphaeria Lactucarum S.
Septoria Lactucae Pass.
Tuberculina vinosa Sacc.?

Lactuca sagittifolia Ell.
Dicaeoma hieraciatum (H. S. Jackson) Arth. I.
Puccinia patruelis Arth. I.
Bremia Lactucae Regel.

Lactuca sativa L.
Dicaeoma hieraciatum (H. S. Jackson) Arth. & Kern. I.
Dicaeoma patruelis H. S. Jackson. I.
Puccinia hieraciata H. S. Jackson. I.
Puccinia Opizii Arth. I.
Alternaria Sonchi J. J. Davis.
Botrytis cinerea P. †
Botrytis vulgaris (Lk.) ex Fr.
Bremia Lactucae Regel.
Peronospora gangliformis (B.) DBy.
Cercospora Apii Fres. ?

Cercospora Lactucae Stevenson. 1918.
Cercospora Lactucae Welles. 1923.
Cercospora longispora Cugini ex Trav. 1903 non Pk. 1885.
Cercospora longissima Sacc. 1906 non C. & E. 1888.
Corticium vagum B. & C.
Corticium vagum B. & C., var. Solani Burt.
Rhizoctonia Solani Kühn.
Erysiphe Cichoracearum DC. †
Macrosporium cladosporioides Desm.
Didymaria perforans (Ell. & Ev.) Dandeno.
Marssonia perforans Ell. & Ev.
Marssonina panattoniana (Berl.) Magn.
Ozonium omnivorum Shear.
Peziza vesiculosa Bull. ex Fr.
Physarum cinereum (Batsch) P.
Pythium debaryanum Hesse.
Sclerotinia fuckeliana (DBy.) Fckl.
Sclerotinia libertiana Fckl.
Sclerotinia sclerotiorum (Lib.) Massee.
Sclerotinia minor Jagger.
Sclerotium Rolfsii Sacc.
Septoria consimilis Ell. & Martin.
Septoria Lactucae Pk. June 1879.
Septoria Lactucae Pass. Oct. 1879.
Septoria lactucicola Ell. & Martin.

Lactuca scariola L.
Bremia Lactucae Regel.
Leptothyrium Lactucae Dearness & Barthol.
Marssonia panattoniana Magn.
Phyllactinia corylea (P.) ex Karst.
Rhizoctonia Solani Kühn.
Sclerotinia libertiana Fckl.
Septoria consimilis Ell & Martin.
Septoria Lactucae Pass.
Septoria lactucicola Ell. & Martin.
Septoria unicolor Wint.

Lactuca spicata (Lam.) Hitchc.
Aecidium Compositarum, var. Lactucae Burrill.
Dicaeoma hieraciatum (H. S. Jackson) Arth. & Kern. I.
Puccinia Opizii Arth. I.
Puccinia patruelis Arth. I.
Bremia Lactucae Regel.
Peronospora gangliformis (B.) DBy.
Erysiphe Cichoracearum DC. †
Ozonium omnivorum Shear.
Phyllosticta Mulgedii J. J. Davis.
Septoria Lactucae Pass.
Sphaerotheca Castagnei Auct. Amer. p. p.
Sphaerotheca Humuli (DC.) Burrill, var. fuliginea (Schl.) Salmon.

Lactuca villosa Jacq.
Puccinia patruelis Arth. I.
Septoria unicolor Wint.

Lactuca virosa L.
  Dicaeoma hieraciatum (H. S. Jackson) Arth. &
    Kern. I.
  Dicaeoma patruelis (Arth.) H. S. Jackson. I.
  Puccinia Opizii Arth. I.
  Erysiphe Cichoracearum DC.†
  Haplosporella lactucicola (Kellerm.) Petrak &
    Syd.
  Naemosphaera lactucicola Kellerm.
  Septoria Lactucae Pass.
  Septoria lactucicola Ell. & Martin.

Lactuca sp. indet.
  Cercospora longissima Trav.
  Dactylium roseum (Lk.) B.
  Diplodia herbarum (Cda.) Lév.
  Diplodia herbarum (Cda.) Lév., var. Lactucae
    C. & E.
  Dothidea crustosa C. & E.
  Leptosphaeria agnita (Desm.) De Not.
  Macrosporium atrichum C. & E.
  Macrosporium caudatum C. & E.
  Macrosporium cladosporioides Desm.
  ?Montagnella Heliopsidis (S.) Sacc.
  Myrothecium Verrucaria (A. & S. ex Fr.)
    Ditm.
  Ophiobolus porphyrogonus (Tode ex Fr.) Sacc.
  Pleospora herbarum (Fr.) Rabh.
  Sphaeria herbarum Fr.
  Guignardia depressa (Pk.) Dearness & House.
  Laestadia depressa (Pk.) Berl. & Vogl.
  Mycosphaerella depressa (Pk.) House.
  Sphaerella depressa Pk.
  Sphaerella Lactucae Ell. & Kellerm.

Apargidium boreale Torr. & Gr.
  Dicaeoma hieraciatum (H. S. Jackson) Arth.
    & Kern. I.

Lygodesmia juncea Don.
  Aecidium Bigeloviae Pk.
  Dicaeoma Stipae (Arth.) O. Kuntze. I.
  Aecidium Compositarum, var. Lygodesmiae
    Webber.
  Aecidium Lygodesmiae (Webber) Shear.
  Puccinia hieraciata H. S. Jackson. I.
  Ampelomyces quisqualis Ces.
  Capnodium Lygodesmiae Ell. & Ev.
  Limacinia Lygodesmiae (Ell. & Ev.) Sacc.
  Darluca Filum (Biv.) Cast.
  Erysiphe Cichoracearum DC.†
  Micropuccinia Grindeliae (Pk.) Arth. & Jack-
    son.
  Puccinia Grindeliae Pk.
  Puccinia Lygodesmiae Ell. & Ev.
  Puccinia variolans, var. caulicola Ell. & Ev.
  Puccinia Harknessii Vize.
  Tubercularia persicina Ditm.
  Tuberculina persicina (Ditm.) Sacc.
  Uromyces Eriogoni Fung. Columb. *650.*

Lygodesmia spinosa Nutt.
Lygodesmia texana (Torr. & Gr.) Greene.
  Dicaeoma (?) Harknessii (Vize) O. Kuntze.
  Puccinia Harknessii Vize.

Agoseris agrestris Osterhout.
  Bullaria Hieracii (Mart.) Arth.

Agoseris aspera Rydb.
  Dicaeoma hieraciatum (H. S. Jackson) Arth. &
    Kern. I.

Agoseris aurantiaca (Hook.) Greene.
  Dicaeoma hieraciatum (H. S. Jackson) Arth.
    & Kern. I.
  Ovularia compacta Ell. & Ev.
  Bullaria Hieracii (Mart.) Arth.
  Puccinia Compositarum Auct. Amer. p. p.
  Puccinia Hieracii Mart.
  Puccinia rugosa Billings.
  Micropuccinia Suksdorfii (Ell. & Ev.) Arth. &
    Jackson.

Agoseris barbellulata Greene.
  Bullaria Hieracii (Mart.) Arth.
  Puccinia Troximontis Pk.

Agoseris cuspidata (Pursh) Steud.
  Bullaria Hieracii (Mart.) Arth.
  Puccinia flosculosorum Auct. Amer. p. p.
  Puccinia Hieracii Mart.
  Puccinia Troximontis Pk.
  Micropuccinia Suksdorfii (Ell. & Ev.) Arth. &
    Jackson.

Agoseris elata (Nutt.) Greene.
  Bullaria Hieracii (Mart.) Arth.
  Micropuccinia Suksdorfii (Ell. & Ev.) Arth. &
    Jackson.
  Puccinia Suksdorfii Ell. & Ev.

Agoseris glauca (Pursh) Steud.
  ?Aecidium Compositarum Auct. Amer. p. p.
  Dicaeoma hieraciatum (H. S. Jackson) Arth.
    & Kern. I.
  Puccinia hieraciata H. S. Jackson. I. 6 June
    1918.
  Puccinia hieraciata Arth. & Bisby. I. 16 July
    1918.
  Puccinia patruelis Arth. I.
  Micropuccinia columbiensis (Ell. & Ev.) Arth.
    & Jackson.
  Puccinia columbiensis Ell. & Ev.
  Bullaria Hieracii (Mart.) Arth.
  Puccinia flosculosorum Auct. Amer. p. p.
  Puccinia Hieracii Mart.
  Puccinia Taraxaci Plowr.
  Puccinia Troximontis Pk.
  Micropuccinia Suksdorfii (Ell. & Ev.) Arth. &
    Jackson.
  Puccinia Suksdorfii Ell. & Ev.
  Sphaerotheca Castagnei Auct. Amer. p. p.
  Sphaerotheca Humuli (DC.) Burrill, var. fuli-
    ginea (Schl.) Salmon.

Agoseris gracilens (Gray) Greene.
  ?Aecidium Compositarum Auct. Amer. p. p.
  Aecidium Compositarum, var. Lactucae Bur-
    rill.
  Dicaeoma hieraciatum (H. S. Jackson) Arth.
    & Kern. I.
  Bullaria Hieracii (Mart.) Arth.
  Puccinia Hieracii Mart.
  Puccinia Troximontis Pk.
Agoseris graminifolia Greene.
  Bullaria Hieracii (Mart.) Arth.
  Puccinia Troximontis Pk.
Agoseris grandiflora (Nutt.) Greene.
  Bullaria Hieracii (Mart.) Arth.
  Puccinia Hieracii Mart.
  Puccinia Troximontis Pk.
  Micropuccinia Suksdorfii (Ell. & Ev.) Arth. &
    Jackson.
  Ramularia Agoseridis Ell. & Ev.
  Synchytrium innominatum Farl.
Agoseris heterophylla Greene.
Agoseris hirsuta Greene.
  Bullaria Hieracii (Mart.) Arth.
  Puccinia Troximontis Pk.
Agoseris laciniata (Nutt.) Greene.
  Dicaeoma Stipae (Arth.) O. Kuntze. I.
  Bullaria Hieracii (Mart.) Arth.
  Puccinia Hieracii Mart.
  Puccinia rugosa Billings.
Agoseris Leontodon Rydb.
  Puccinia Troximontis Pk.
Agoseris leptocarpa Osterhout.
  Dicaeoma Stipae (Arth.) O. Kuntze. I.
  Bullaria Hieracii (Mart.) Arth.
  Micropuccinia Suksdorfii (Ell. & Ev.) Arth. &
    Jackson.
  Puccinia Suksdorfii Ell. & Ev.
Agoseris montana Osterhout.
  Dicaeoma hieraciatum (H. S. Jackson) Arth. &
    Kern. I.
  Bullaria Hieracii (Mart.) Arth.
Agoseris
  (Troximon Nuttallii Gray).
  Sphaerotheca Humuli (DC.) Burrill. †
Agoseris parviflora (Nutt.) Greene.
  Dicaeoma hieraciatum (H. S. Jackson) Arth. &
    Kern. I.
  Puccinia hieraciata H. S. Jackson. I.
  Sphaerotheca Humuli (DC.) Burrill, var.
    fuliginea (Schl.) Salmon.
Agoseris plebeia Greene.
  Bullaria Hieracii (Mart.) Arth.
  Puccinia Troximontis Pk.
  Ramularia Agoseridis Ell. & Ev.
Agoseris purpurea (Gray) Greene.
Agoseris turbinata Rydb.
Agoseris villosa A. Nels.
  Bullaria Hieracii (Mart.) Arth.
  Puccinia Troximontis Pk.

Agoseris sp. indet.
  Bremia Lactucae Regel.
  Mycosphaerella pachyasca (Rostr.) Vester-
    gren.
  Ramularia Crepidis Ell. & Ev.
Pyrrhopappus carolinianus (Walt.) DC.
Pyrrhopappus multicaulis DC.
Pyrrhopappus scaposus DC.
  Bullaria Hieracii (Mart.) Arth.
  Puccinia Hieracii Mart.
  Puccinia Pyrrhopappi Syd.
Crepis acuminata Nutt.
  Aecidium Bigeloviae Pk.
  Aecidium crepidicola Ell. & Gall.
  Dicaeoma Stipae (Arth.) O. Kuntze. I.
  Erysiphe Cichoracearum DC. †.
  Phyllosticta eximia Bubák.
  Puccinia Crepidis-montanae (Syd.) Magn.
  Bullaria Hieracii (Mart.) Arth.
  Puccinia Crepidis-acuminatae Syd.
  Puccinia Hieracii Mart.
Crepis angustata Rydb.
  Bullaria Hieracii (Mart.) Arth.
Crepis barbigera L.
  Dicaeoma Crepidis-montanae (Syd.) Arth.
  Puccinia Crepidis-acuminatae Fung. Columb.
    4459.
  Puccinia Crepidis-montanae Magn.
Crepis glauca (Nutt.) Torr. & Gr.
  Aecidium Bigeloviae Pk.
  Aecidium crepidicola Ell. & Gall.
  Dicaeoma Stipae (Arth.) O. Kuntze. I.
  Dicaeoma hieraciatum (H. S. Jackson) Arth.
    & Kern. I.
  Puccinia hieraciata H. S. Jackson. I.
  Puccinia Crepidis-montanae Magn.
  Bullaria Hieracii (Mart.) Arth.
  Puccinia Crepidis-acuminatae Syd.
Crepis gracilis (D. C. Eaton) Rydb.
  Puccinia Crepidis-montanae Magn.
  Bullaria Hieracii (Mart.) Arth.
  Puccinia Crepidis-acuminatae Syd.
  Puccinia Hieracii Mart.
  Ramularia Crepidis Ell. & Ev.
Crepis intermedia Gray.
  Dicaeoma hieraciatum (H. S. Jackson) Arth. &
    Kern. I.
  Puccinia hieraciata H. S. Jackson. I.
  Bullaria Hieracii (Mart.) Arth.
  Puccinia crepidicola Syd.
  Puccinia Crepidis-acuminatae Syd.
  Puccinia Hieracii Mart.
Crepis occidentalis Nutt.
  Bullaria Hieracii (Mart.) Arth.
  Puccinia crepidicola Fung. Columb. *1959.*
  Puccinia Crepidis-acuminatae Syd.
  Puccinia Hieracii Mart.

Crepis riparia A. Nels.
  Dicaeoma hieraciatum (H. S. Jackson) Arth.
    & Kern. I.
Crepis rostrata Coville.
  { Puccinia Crepidis-acuminatae Syd.
  { Puccinia Hieracii Mart.
Crepis runcinata (James) Torr. & Gr.
  Aecidium crepidicolum Fung. Columb. *3101*,
    Ured. *702*.
  Dicaeoma hieraciatum (H. S. Jackson) Arth.
    & Kern. I.
  { Bullaria Hieracii (Mart.) Arth.
  { Dicaeoma Troximontis (Pk.) O. Kuntze.
  { Sphaerotheca Castagnei Auct. Amer. p. p.
  { Sphaerotheca Humuli (DC.) Burrill, var. fuli-
  {   ginea (Schl.) Salmon.
Crepis scopulorum Coville.
Crepis subacaulis (Kellogg) Coville.
  Bullaria Hieracii (Mart.) Arth.
Crepis sp. indet.
  Synchytrium Taraxaci DBy. & Wor.
Prenanthes alata Hook. f. & Thoms.
  Puccinia Prenanthis Fckl.
Prenanthes alba L.
  { Dicaeoma hieraciatum (H. S. Jackson) Arth. &
  {   Kern. I.
  { Puccinia hieraciata H. S. Jackson. I.
  { Puccinia orbicula Pk. p. p. non Pk. & Clinton.
  {   I.
  { Puccinia patruelis Arth. I.
  { Bremia Lactucae Regel.
  { Peronospora gangliformis (B.) DBy.
  Cercospora brunnea Pk.
  Cercospora Prenanthis Ell. & Kellerm.
  Cercospora tabacina Ell. & Ev.
  Erysiphe Cichoracearum DC. †
  { Aecidium Compositarum Auct. Amer. p. p.
  { Aecidium Compositarum, var. Prenanthis
  {   Auct. Amer.
  { ?Aecidium orbicula Pk. ex Kauffm.
  { Dicaeoma orbicula (Pk. & Clinton) O. Kuntze.
  { Dicaeoma Prenanthis Ind. Acad.
  { ?Puccinia Chondrillae Auct. Amer. p. p.
  { Puccinia Compositarum N. A. F. *263*.
  { ?Puccinia Hieracii Auct. p. p.
  { Puccinia orbicula Pk. & Clinton.
  { Puccinia Prenanthis Auct. Amer. p. p.
  { ?Puccinia variabilis Grev.
  { Septoria Nabali B. & C.
  { Septoria Prenanthis Ell. & Ev.
  { Sphaerotheca Castagnei Auct. Amer. p. p.
  { Sphaerotheca Humuli (DC,) Burrill, var. fuli-
  {   ginea (Schl.)Salmon.
  Synchytrium aureum Schrt.
Prenanthes altissima L.
  { Bremia Lactucae Regel.
  { Peronospora gangliformis (B.) DBy.
  Cercospora brunnea Pk.
  Cladosporium effusum B. & C.

{ ?Puccinia Hieracii Auct. p. p.
{ Puccinia orbicula Pk.
{ Septoria Nabali B. & C.
{ Septoria Prenanthis Ell. & Ev.
  Sphaerotheca Humuli (DC.) Burrill. †
  Sphaerotheca Castagnei Auct. Amer. p. p.
  { Sphaerotheca Humuli (DC.) Burrill, var. fuli-
  {   ginea (Schl.) Salmon.
Prenanthes aspera Michx.
  Cercospora Prenanthis Ell. & Kellerm.
Prenanthes Boottii (DC.) Gray.
  { Dicaeoma orbicula (Pk. & Clinton) O. Kuntze.
  { Puccinia orbicula Pk. & Clinton.
Prenanthes crepidinea Michx.
  { Dicaeoma hieraciatum (H. S. Jackson) Arth.
  {   & Kern. I.
  { Puccinia patruelis Arth. I.
  Cercospora Prenanthis Ell. & Kellerm.
  Laestadia Prenanthis Ell. & Ev.
Prenanthes hastata (Less.) A. Heller.
  { Dicaeoma insperatum (H. S. Jackson) Arth.
  { Puccinia insperata H. S. Jackson.
Prenanthes racemosa Michx.
  { Micropuccinia columbiensis (Ell. & Ev.)
  {   Arth. & Jackson.
  { Puccinia Nabali Arth.
  Puccinia Opizii Auct. I.
  { Dicaeoma orbicula (Pk. & Clinton) O. Kuntze.
  { Puccinia orbicula Pk. & Clinton.
  { Puccinia Prenanthis-racemosae Syd.
  Septoria Nabali B. & C.
Prenanthes serpentaria Pursh.
  Septoria Nabali B. & C.
Prenanthes trifoliolata (Cass.) Fern.
  Puccinia atropuncta Pk., var. Chrospermae
    Orton & Weiss. I.
  { Puccinia orbicula Pk. & Clinton. I.
  { Puccinia Prenanthis-racemosae Syd.
Prenanthes sp. indet.
  Diaporthe prenanthicola Atk.
  { Phlyctaena simulans (B. & C.) Sacc.
  { Septoria simulans B. & C.
  Septoria lactucicola Ell. & Martin.
Hieracium albertinum Parr.
  Aecidium columbiense Ell. & Ev.
Hieracium albiflorum Hook.
  Aecidium columbiense Ell. & Ev.
  { Aecidium hieraciatum S.
  { Dicaeoma hieraciatum (H. S. Jackson) Arth. &
  {   Kern. I.
  Erysiphe Cichoracearum DC. †
  Oidium erysiphoides Fr.
  Micropuccinia Fraseri (Arth.) Arth. & Jackson.
  { Bullaria Hieracii (Mart.) Arth.
  { Puccinia Hieracii Mart.
  { Puccinia sejuncta Syd.
Hieracium alpinum L.
  { Rhabdospora cercosperma (Rostr.) Sacc.
  { Septoria cercosperma Rostr.

Hieracium aurantiacum L.
Phyllosticta decidua Ell. & Kellerm.
Hieracium canadense Michx.
[?Aecidium Compositarum Auct. Amer. p. p.
Aecidium hieraciatum S.
Dicaeoma hieraciatum (H. S. Jackson) Arth. &
Kern. I.
Puccinia patruelis Arth. I.
Erysiphe Cichoracearum DC.†
Phoma Hieracii Rostr.
[Bullaria Hieracii (Mart.) Arth.
Puccinia flosculosorum Auct. Amer. p. p.
Puccinia Hieracii Mart.
Ramularia macrospora Fres.
Septoria cercosperma Rostr.
Hieracium cinereum Howell.
[Micropuccinia columbiensis (Ell. & Ev.) Arth.
Puccinia bicolor Ell. & Ev.
Bullaria Hieracii (Mart.) Arth.
Puccinia Hieracii Mart.
Hieracium columbianum Rydb.
Dicaeoma hieraciatum (H. S. Jackson) Arth. &
Kern. I.
[Bullaria Hieracii (Mart.) Arth.
Puccinia Hieracii Mart.
Hieracium cynoglossoides Arvet.
Aecidium hieraciatum S.
Hieracium dovrense Fr.
Leptosphaeria agnita (Desm.) De Not.
Hieracium Fendleri Sch. Bip.
[Bullaria Hieracii (Mart.) Arth.
Puccinia Hieracii Mart.
Hieracium gracile Hook.
[Aecidium hieraciatum S.
Dicaeoma hieraciatum (H. S. Jackson) Arth.
& Kern. I.
Bullaria Hieracii (Mart.) Arth.
Puccinia Hieracii Mart.
Hieracium griseum Rydb.
Hieracium Gronovii L.
Hieracium horridum Fr.
[Bullaria Hieracii (Mart.) Arth.
Puccinia Hieracii Mart.
Hieracium maculatum Auct.
[Aecidium hieraciatum S.
Caeoma hieraciatum S.
Hieracium nigrescens Auct.
Puccinia Hieracii Mart.
Hieracium scabrum Michx.
[Aecidium hieraciatum S.
Dicaeoma hieraciatum (H. S. Jackson) Arth. &
Kern. I.
Puccinia hieraciata H. S. Jackson. I.
Puccinia patruelis Arth. I.

Puccinia bicolor Ell. & Ev.
[Micropuccinia Fraseri (Arth.) Arth. & Jackson.
Puccinia Fraseri Arth.
Bullaria Hieracii (Mart.) Arth.
Puccinia Hieracii Mart.
Hieracium paniculatum L.
[Aecidium hieraciatum S.
Caeoma hieraciatum S.
Dicaeoma hieraciatum (H. S. Jackson) Arth.
& Kern. I.
Puccinia hicraciata H. S. Jackson. I. 6 June
1918.
Puccinia hieraciata Arth. & Bisby. I. 16 July
1918.
Septoria hieracicola Dearness & House.
Hieracium scabriusculum S.
Bullaria Hieracii (Mart.) Arth.
Hieracium Scouleri Hook.
Aecidium columbiense Ell. & Ev.
[Micropuccinia columbiensis (Ell. & Ev.) Arth.
& Jackson.
Puccinia bicolor Ell. & Ev.
Puccinia columbiensis Ell. & Ev.
Bullaria Hieracii (Mart.) Arth.
Puccinia Hieracii Mart.
Hieracium umbellatum L.
[Bullaria Hieracii (Mart.) Arth.
Puccinia Hieracii Mart.
?Puccinia universalis Arth. I.
Hieracium venosum L.
Cercospora Hieracii Ell. & Ev.
Micropuccinia Fraseri (Arth.) Arth. & Jackson.
Hieracium vulgatum Fr.
Aecidium hieraciatum S.
Leptosphaeria agnita (Desm.) De Not.
Puccinia Hieracii Mart.
Hieracium sp. indet.
Coleosporium Sonchi-arvensis Auct. Amer. p.p.
Naevia diaphana Rehm.
Puccinia Crepidis Schrt.?
Septoria Helenii Ell. & Ev.
Sphaerella Compositarum Awd.
Sphaerotheca Castagnei Lév.?
Compositae gen. indet.
[Albugo pulverulenta (B. & C.) O. Kuntze.
Cystopus pulverulentus B. & C.
Leptosphaeria planiuscula (Riess) Ces. & De
Not.
Leptosphaeria pyrenopezizoides Sacc. & Speg.
Pleospora permunda (Cke.) Sacc.
?Polyactis quadrifida Lk.
Thecaphora piluliformis B. & C.
Uromyces compactus Pk.

ANIMALIA

NEMATHELMINTHES

Aorurus sp. indet.
  Enterobryus elegans Leidy.
Ascaris infecta Leidy.
  Arthromitus cristatus Leidy.
  Cladophytum comatum Leidy.
  Enterobryus elegans Leidy.
Ascaris sp. indet.
  Achlya prolifera Nees.
Streptostomum agile Leidy.
  Arthromitus cristatus Leidy.
  Cladophytum comatum Leidy.
  Enterobryus elegans Leidy.
Thelastomum attenuatum Leidy.
  Arthromitus cristatus Leidy.
  Cladophytum comatum Leidy.

PLATYHELMINTHES

Taenia Solium Rud.
  Mucor Taeniae Fairman.

ARTHROPODA

CRUSTACEA

Crawfish
  Saprolegnia ferax Auct.

MYRIAPODA

Julus pusillus Say.
  Enterobryus spiralis Leidy.
Polydesmus granulatus Say.
  Eccrina moniliformis Leidy.
Polydesmus virginiensis (Drury).
  Arthromitus cristatus Leidy.
  Cladophytum comatum Leidy.
  Eccrina longa Leidy.
Polydesmus sp. indet.
  Sporotrichum globuliferum Speg.
Spirobolus marginatus (Say.).
  { Arthromitus cristatus Leidy.
  { Arthromitus nitidus Leidy.
  Cladophytum comatum Leidy.
  Enterobryus elegans Leidy.

HEXAPODA

Insects:
  Species of
  Aschersonia
  Entomophthora
  Hypocrella
  Myriangium
  Septobasidium
    whenever reported on plant hosts are under-
    stood to be primarily on insect hosts.

THYSANOPTERA

Heliothrips rubrocincta Giard.
  Sporotrichum globuliferum Speg.
Thrips sp. indet.
  Cladosporium sp. indet.
  Empusa sphaerosperma (Fres.) Thax.
  Sporotrichum globuliferum Speg.

NEUROPTERA

Phryganeidae gen. indet.
  { Empusa rhizospora (Cke.) Thax.
  { Entomophthora rhizospora Cke.
Psocus sp. indet.
  Entomophthora Chromaphidis Burger &
  Swain.

TERMITIDAE

Eutermes morio Latr., var. **St. Lucia.**
  Coreomycetopsis Oedipus Thax.
  Laboulbeniopsis termitarius Thax.
  Termitaria coronata Thax.
Reticulitermes flavipes Kollar.
Reticulitermes virginicus Banks.
  Termitaria Snyderi Thax.

ORTHOPTERA

ACRIDIIDAE

Dissoteira carolina L.
  Entomophthora Grylli Fres.
Melanoplus atlantis Riley.
Melanoplus bivittatus Say.
Melanoplus differentialis Thomas.
Melanoplus femur-rubrum De Geer.
  { Empusa Grylli (Fres.) Nowak.
  { Entomophthora Calopteni Bessey.
  { Entomophthora Grylli Fres.

Melanoplus spretus Uhl.
  Sporotrichum globuliferum Speg.
Tomonotus sp. indet.
Trimerotropis maritima Harv.
  Empusa Grylli (Fres.) Nowak.
Acridiidae gen. sp. indet.
  Isaria arbuscula Hariot.
  Mucor ramosus Fres.

BLATTIDAE

Blabera spp. indet.
  Herpomyces Paranensis Thax.
  Herpomyces tricuspidatus Thax.
Ectobia germanica Scudd.
  Herpomyces Ectobiae Thax.
Epilampra sp. indet.
  Herpomyces tricuspidatus Thax.
Ischnoptera sp. indet.
  Herpomyces arietinus Thax.
Nyctobora latipennis Brunn.
  Herpomyces Nyctoborae Thax.
Periplaneta americana Sauss.
Periplaneta australasiae Sauss.
  Herpomyces Periplanetae Thax.
Platyzosteria ingens Scudd.
  Herpomyces Platyzosteriae Thax.
Stylopyga orientalis (L.) Scudd.
  Herpomyces Periplanetae Thax.
Temnopteryx sp. indet.
  Herpomyces arietinus Thax.
Blattidae gen. indet.
  Amphoromorpha blattina Thax.
  Metarrhizium Anisopliae (Metsch.) Sorok.

FORFICULIDAE

Anisolabis annulipes Luc.
  Dimeromyces Anisolabis Thax.
Labia minor Burm.
  Dimeromyces Labiae Thax.
  Dimeromyces minutissimus Thax.
Labia sp. indet.
  Dimeromyces appressus Thax.
Sphingolabis taeniata Dohrn.
  Dimeromyces Forficulae Thax.
Forficulidae gen. indet.
  {Metarrhizium Anisopliae (Metsch.) Sorok.
  {Oospora destructor (Metsch.) Delacr.

GRYLLIDAE

Gryllotalpa sp. indet.
  Cordyceps Gryllotalpae M. A. Curtis nom. nud.
Gryllidae gen. indet.
  Cordyceps albida B. & C. Herb.
  Sphaeria entomorrhiza Dicks. ex Fr.

LOCUSTIDAE

Ceuthophilus sp. indet.
  Empusa Grylli (Fres.) Nowak.
Hadenoecus subterraneus Scudd.
  {Isaria densa (Lk.) Giard.
  {Sporotrichum densum Lk.
Orthoptera fam. indet.
  Entomopthora Aulicae Reich.

MALLOPHAGA

Docophorus californiensis Kellogg.
Docophorus colymbinus Denny.
Docophorus Montereyi Kellogg.
  Trenomyces circinans Thax.
Docophorus sp. indet.
Goniocotes sp. indet.
  Trenomyces histophtorus Chat. & Picard.
Laemobothrium atrum Nitzsch.
  Trenomyces Laemobothrii Thax.
Lipeurus celer Kellogg.
  Trenomyces Lipeuri Thax.
Lipeurus longipilus Kellogg.
  Trenomyces gibbus Thax.
Lipeurus sp. indet.
  Trenomyces circinans Thax.
Menopon mesoleucum Nitzsch.
Menopon numerosum Kellogg.
Menopon tridens Nitzsch.
Nirmus maritimus Kellogg & Chapm.
Nirmus punctatus Nitzsch.
  Trenomyces histophtorus Chat. & Picard.

HEMIPTERA
ALEYRODIDAE

Aleurodicus minimus Quaint.
  Aegerita Webberi Fawcett.
  Aschersonia Aleyrodis Webber.
  Aschersonia flavocitrina Henn.
Aleyrodes citri Riley & Howard.
  Aegerita Webberi Fawcett.
  Aschersonia Aleyrodis Webber.
  {Aschersonia flavocitrina Fla.
  {Aschersonia goldiana Sacc. & Ell.
  Aschersonia tahitensis Mont.
  Aschersonia Webberi Fawcett.
  Capnodium Citri B. & Desm.
  Fusarium Aleyrodis Petch.
  {Hypocrella disjuncta Seaver.
  {Hypocrella phyllogena (Mont.) Speg.
  Meliola Camelliae (Catt.) Sacc.
  Sphaerostilbe coccophila Tul.
  Verticillium heterocladum Penz.
Aleyrodes Howardi Quaint.
  Aegerita Webberi Fawcett.
  Aschersonia Aleyrodis Webber.

Aleyrodes nubifera Berger.
  Aegerita Webberi Fawcett.
  Aschersonia Aleyrodis Webber.
  Aschersonia flavocitrina Henn.
  Sphaerostilbe coccophila Tul.
  Verticillium heterocladum Penz.
Aleyrodes psidii Auct.
  Aschersonia Aleyrodis Webber.
Aleyrodes variabilis Quaint.
  Spicaria Aleyrodis Johnston.
Aleyrodes (black fly).
  Aschersonia Aleyrodis Webber.
Aleyrodes sp. indet.
  { Aschersonia basicystis B. & C.
  { Hypocrella phyllogena (Mont.) Petch.
  Aschersonia columnifera Petch.
  Microcera fujikuroi Miyabe & Sawada.
Bemisia inconspicua Quaint.
  Aschersonia Aleyrodis Webber.
Dialeurodes citrifolii Morg.
  Aegerita Webberi Fawcett.
  Aschersonia Aleyrodis Webber.
  { Aschersonia flavocitrina **Fla.**
  { Aschersonia goldiana Sacc. & Ell.
  Verticillium heterocladum Penz.
Paraleyrodes perseae Quaint.
  Sphaerostilbe coccophila Tul.

ANTHOCORIDAE

Lasiochilus pallidus Reut.
  Stigmatomyces Lasiochili Thax.

APHIDIDAE

Aphis gossypii Glover.
  Cephalosporium Lecanii Zimm.
  Meliola Camelliae (Catt.) Sacc.
Aphis helianthi Monell.
  Cladosporium Aphidis Thm.
Aphis mali Fabr.
  Empusa Aphidis Hoffm.
  Empusa Fresenii Nowak.
Aphis pseudobrassicae Davis.
  Empusa Aphidis Hoffm.
Aphis sp. indet.
  Acrostalagmus albus Preuss.
  Aphanomyces laevis DBy.
  Blastocladia strangulata Barrett.
  Empusa lageniformis Thax.
  { Empusa occidentalis Thax.
  { Entomophthora occidentalis Thax.
  Empusa planchoniana (Cornu?) Thax.
  Empusa sphaerosperma (Fres.) Thax.
Chromaphis juglandicola (Karst.).
  Entomophthora Chromaphidis Burger &
    Swain.
Myzus persicae Sulzer.
Phorodon humuli Schrank.
  Empusa Aphidis Hoffm.

Schizoneura imbricator (Fitch).
  Scorias spongiosa (S.) Fr.
Sipha flava Forbes.
Sipha graminis Ktl.
  Acrostalagmus albus Preuss.
Tamalia pubescens Auct.
  Aschersonia cubensis B. & C.

ARADIDAE

Mezira emarginata Say.
Mezira lobata Say.
  Synnematium Jonesii Speare.

CERCOPIDAE

Tomaspis postica Walker.
  { Metarrhizium Anisopliae (Metsch.) Sorok.
  { Oospora destructor (Metsch.) Delacr.
  { Penicillium Anisopliae (Metsch.) Vuillemin.
  { Septocylindrium suspectum Massee.
Tomaspis saccharina Auct.
Tomaspis varia Auct.
  Metarrhizium Anisopliae (Metsch.) Sorok.

CICADELLIDAE

Diedrocephalus mollipes Say.
  Empusa Jassi (Cohn) Wint.?
Tettigonia similis Walk.
  Empusa Muscae Cohn.
Typhlocyba mali LeBaron.
  Empusa sphaerosperma (Fres.) Thax.
Typhlocyba sp. indet.
  Empusa apiculata Thax.
Cicadellidae gen. indet.
  Metarrhizium Anisopliae (Metsch.) Sorok.
    var. minor Johnston.
  Sporotrichum globuliferum Speg.

CICADIDAE

Cicada septendecim L.
  Massospora cicadina Pk.
Cicada tredecim Riley.
  { Beauveria globulifera (Speg.) Picard.
  { Sporotrichum globuliferum Speg.
Cicada sp. indet.
  Cordyceps Cicadae (Miq.) Massee.
  { Clavaria sobolifera Hill ex B.
  { Cordyceps sobolifera (Hill ex B.) Sacc.
  { Sphaeria sobolifera (Hill.) ex B.
  Vermicularia cicadina Ell. & Kellerm.

COCCIDAE
Asterolecaniinae

Asterolecanium pustulans Ckll.
  Sphaerostilbe coccophila Tul.

Coccinae

Coccus mangiferae Green.
  { Aschersonia cubensis B. & C.
  { Hypocrella epiphylla (Massee) Sacc.

Coccus mangiferae (*cont.*)
- Aschersonia turbinata B.
- Hypocrella oxyspora Massee.
- Hypocrella turbinata Petch.
- Cephalosporium Lecanii Zimm.
- Sphaerostilbe coccophila Tul.

Coccus viridis Green.
- Cephalosporium Lecanii Zimm.
- Sphaerostilbe coccophila Tul.

Coccus sp. indet.
- ?Nectria aglaeothele B. & C.
- Verticillium heterocladum Penz.

DIASPIDINAE

Aspidiotus ancylus Putnam.
- Hyalopus Yvonis Dop.
- Myriangium Duriaei Mont. & B.
- Sphaerostilbe coccophila Tul.

Aspidiotus destructor Sign.
- Cephalosporium Lecanii Zimm.

Aspidiotus ficus Comst.
- Sphaerostilbe coccophila Tul.

Aspidiotus Forbesii Johnson.
- Hyalopus Yvonis Dop.
- Sphaerostilbe coccophila Tul.

Aspidiotus hederae Vallot.

Aspidiotus nerii Bouché.

Aspidiotus obscurus Comst.
- Sphaerostilbe coccophila Tul.

Aspidiotus perniciosus Comst.
- Fusarium pallens Nees ex Fr.
- Microcera coccophila Desm.
- Volutella pallens (Nees) ex Fr.
- Hyalopus Yvonis Dop.
- Myriangium Duriaei Mont. & B.
- Sphaerostilbe aurantiicola B. & Br.
- Sphaerostilbe coccophila Tul.

Chionaspis biclavis Comst.
- Myriangium Duriaei Mont. & B.
- Sphaerostilbe coccophila Tul.

Chionaspis citri Comst.
- Myriangium Duriaei Mont. & B.
- Septobasidium Spongia (B. & C.) Pat.
- Sphaerostilbe coccophila Tul.
- Tubercularia coccicola Stevenson.

Chrysomphalus aonidum L.
- Microcera aurantiicola Petch.
- Microcera fujikuroi Miyabe & Sawada.
- Pseudomicrocera Henningsii (Koord.) Petch.
- Sphaerostilbe coccophila Berger.

Chrysomphalus aurantii Mask.
- Microcera fujikuroi Miyabe & Sawada.
- Sphaerostilbe coccophila Tul.

Chrysomphalus obscurus Comst.
- Sphaerostilbe coccophila Tul.

Chrysomphalus tenebricosus Comst.
- Microcera fujikuroi Miyabe & Sawada.
- Sphaerostilbe coccophila Tul.

Diaspis pentagona Targ.
- Myriangium Duriaei Mont. & B.

Diaspis sp. indet.
- Sphaerostilbe coccophila Tul.
- Verticillium heterocladum Penz.

Ischnaspis filiformis Dougl.
- ?Microcera coccophila Desm.
- Microcera coccophila Fawcett.
- Microcera fujikuroi Miyabe & Sawada.
- ?Nectria diploa B. & C.
- Pseudomicrocera Henningsii (Koord.) Petch.
- Sphaerostilbe coccophila Berger.

Lepidosaphes Becki Newman.
- Aschersonia cubensis B. & C.
- Hypocrella epiphylla (Masee) Sacc.
- Aschersonia turbinata B.
- Hypocrella turbinata Petch.
- Atichia dominicana Cotton.
- Cephalosporium Lecanii Zimm.
- Fusarium Aleyrodis Petch.
- Microcera aurantiicola Petch.
- Myriangium Duriaei Mont. & B.
- Microcera coccophila Fawcett.
- Microcera fujikuroi Miyabe & Sawada.
- ?Nectria diploa B. & C.
- Pseudomicrocera Henningsii (Koord.) Petch.
- Sphaerostilbe coccophila Berger.
- Dialonectria coccicola Ell. & Ev.
- Nectria coccicola Ell. & Ev.
- Ophionectria coccicola (Ell. & Ev.) Berl. & Vogl.
- Podonectria coccicola (Ell. & Ev.) Petch.
- ?Scleroderris gigaspora Massee.
- Scoleconectria coccicola (Ell. & Ev.) Seaver.
- Tetracrium coccicola v. Hoehnel.
- Septobasidium pedicellatum Pat.
- Septobasidium Spongia (B. & C.) Pat.
- Sphaerostilbe aurantiicola B. & Br.
- Sphaerostilbe coccophila Tul.
- Tubercularia coccicola Stevenson & Rose.
- Verticillium heterocladum Penz.

Lepidosaphes Gloveri Pack.
- Myriangium Duriaei Mont. & B.
- Ophionectria coccicola (Ell. & Ev.) Berl. & Vogl.
- Scoleconectria coccicola (Ell. & Ev.) Seaver.
- Sphaerostilbe coccophila Tul.
- Verticillium heterocladum Penz.

Mytilaspis citricola Comst.
- Myriangium Duriaei Mont. & B.
- Ophionectria coccicola (Ell. & Ev.) Berl. & Vogl.
- Scleroderris gigaspora Massee.
- Scoleconectria coccicola (Ell. & Ev.), Seaver.
- Sphaerostilbe coccophila Tul.
- Verticillium heterocladum Penz.

Parlatoria Pergandei Comst.
  Myriangium Duriaei Mont. & B.
  Ophionectria coccicola (Ell. & Ev.) Berl. &
    Vogl.
  Sphaerostilbe coccophila Tul.
  Verticillium heterocladum Penz.
Selenaspidus articulatus Morg.
  ⎰Microcera coccophila Fawcett.
  ⎮Microcera fujikuroi Miyabe & Sawada.
  ⎨?Nectria diploa B. & C.
  ⎮Pseudomicrocera Henningsii (Koord.) Petch.
  ⎱Sphaerostilbe coccophila Berger.

Eriococcinae

Phenococcus sp. indet.
  Empusa Fresenii Nowak.
Pseudococcus calceolariae Mask.
  Aspergillus flavus Lk.
Pseudococcus citri Risso.
  Entomophthora fumosa Speare.
  Sphaerostilbe coccophila Tul.
Pseudococcus nipae Mask.
  Cephalosporium Lecanii Zimm.
  Empusa Fresenii Nowak.
Pseudococcus sacchari Ckll.
  Aspergillus flavus Lk.
Eriococcinae gen. indet.
  ⎰Aschersonia cubensis B. & C.
  ⎱Hypocrella epiphylla (Massee) Sacc.
  ⎰Aschersonia turbinata B.
  ⎱Hypocrella turbinata Petch.

Lecaniinae

Ceroplastes floridensis Comst.
  ⎰Aschersonia cubensis B. & C.
  ⎱Hypocrella epiphylla (Massee) Sacc.
  ⎰Aschersonia turbinata B.
  ⎱Hypocrella turbinata Petch.
  Cephalosporium Lecanii Zimm.
  Meliola Camelliae (Catt.) Sacc.
Eucalymnatus tessellatus Sign.
  ⎰Aschersonia cubensis B. & C.
  ⎱Hypocrella epiphylla (Massee) Sacc.
Lecanium corni Bouché.
  Cordyceps clavulata (S.) Ell. & Ev.
Lecanium hesperidum L.
  Cephalosporium Lecanii Zimm.
  Hypocrella epiphylla (Massee) Sacc.
  Meliola Camelliae (Catt.) Sacc.
  Verticillium heterocladum Speg.
Lecanium longulum Dougl.
  Isaria lecanifera Petit.
Lecanium quercifex Fitch.
  ⎰Cordyceps clavulata (S.) Ell. & Ev.
  ⎨Cordyceps pistillariiformis B. & Br.
  ⎱Torrubia clavulata S.
Lecanium sp. indet.
  Aschersonia tahitensis Mont.
  Sporotrichum globuliferum Speg.
  Sporotrichum Lecanii Pk.

Pulvinaria pyriformis Ckll.
  ⎰Aschersonia cubensis B. & C.
  ⎱Hypocrella epiphylla (Massee) Sacc.
  Cephalosporium Lecanii Zimm.
Saissetia hemisphaerica Targ.
  ⎰Aschersonia cubensis B. & C.
  ⎱Hypocrella epiphylla (Massee) Sacc.
  Cephalosporium Lecanii Zimm.
  Torrubiella Lecanii Johnston.
Saissetia nigra Auct.
Saissetia oleae Bern.
  Cephalosporium Lecanii Zimm.
  Meliola Camelliae (Catt.) Sacc.
  Sphaerostilbe coccophila Tul.
Toumeyella liriodendri Gmel.
  ⎰Aschersonia cubensis B. & C.
  ⎱Hypocrella epiphylla (Massee) Sacc.

Monophlebiinae

Icerya Purchasi Mask.
  Meliola Camelliae (Catt.) Sacc.
Icerya rosae Riley & Howard.
  Aspergillus flavus Lk.?
Coccidae gen. indet.
  Aegerita Webberi Fawcett.
  Cordyceps pistillaris B. & Br.
  ⎰Corticium caulium B. & C.
  ⎱Hypocrella caulia (B. & C.) Pat.
  Hypocrella cretacea v. Höhnel.
  ⎰Aschersonia Aleyrodis Webber.
  ⎮Hypocrella libera Syd.
  ⎱Hypocrella nectrioides Thax.
  Hypocrella Tamoneae Earle.
  Microcera Tonduzii Pat.
  Myriangium Curtisii B. & Mont.
  Nectria Tuberculariae Petch.
  Saprolegnia ferax Auct.
  Scleroderris gigaspora Massee.
  Septobasidium canescens Burt.
  Septobasidium pseudopedicellatum Burt.
  Sphaerostilbe flammea (B. & Rav.) Tul.
  Thelephora lichenicola B. & Br.

CORIXIDAE

Corixa Kennicottii Uhl.
  Coreomyces Corisae Thax.
Corixa spp. indet.
  Coreomyces Corisae Thax.
  Coreomyces curvatus Thax.

FULGORIDAE

Bothriocera sp. indet.
  Isaria Saussurii Cke.
Peregrinus maidis Ashm.
  Hirsutella floccosa Speare.
Fulgoridae gen. indet.
  Hirsutella citriformis Speare.

LYGAEIDAE

Blissus leucopterus Say.
  { Empusa Aphidis (Hoffm.) Thax.
  { Entomophthora Aphidis Hoffm.
  { Beauveria globulifera (Speg.) Pic.
  { Sporotrichum globuliferum Speg.
Microtoma carbonaria Uhl.
  Sporotrichum globuliferum Speg.

NABIDAE

Coriscus ferus L.
Nabis fusca Stein.
  Sporotrichum globuliferum Speg.

PENTATOMIDAE

Nezara viridula L.
  Isaria Pattersonii Massee.

PYRRHOCORIDAE

Dysdercus sp. indet.
  Isaria Pattersonii Massee.

TINGITIDAE

Corythucha gossypii Fab.
  Sporotrichum globuliferum Speg.
Corythaica monacha Stål.
  Acrostalagmus albus Preuss.
Siphanta acuta Auct.
  Hirsutella citriformis Speare.
Hemiptera fam. indet.
  Aspergillus [parasiticus Speare?]
  Empusa Fresenii Nowak.

COLEOPTERA
ANTHICIDAE

Anthicus californicus Laf.
  Dioicomyces Anthici Thax.
Anthicus floralis L.
  Dioicomyces Anthici Thax.
  Dioicomyces onchophorus Thax.
  Dioicomyces spinigerus Thax.

CANTHARIDAE

Chauliognathus pennsylvanicus De G.
  { Empusa Lampyridarum Thax.
  { Entomophthora Lampyridarum Thax.

CARABIDAE

Acupalpus carus Lec.
  Rhachomyces lasiophorus Thax.
Agonoderus pallipes Fab.
  Laboulbenia polyphaga Thax.
Anchomenus albipes Fabr.
Anchomenus viduus Pz.
  Laboulbenia anceps Pyr.

Anchonoderus binotatus Reiche.
Anchonoderus subaeneus Reiche.
  Laboulbenia Anchonoderi Thax.
Anillus fortis Horn.
  Dimeromyces Anilli Thax.
Anisodactylus baltimorensis Say.
  Laboulbenia compressa Thax.
  Laboulbenia elongata Thax.
  Laboulbenia macrotheca Thax.
Anisodactylus Harrisi Lec.
Anisodactylus interpunctatus Kirby.
  Laboulbenia filifera Thax.
Anisodactylus nigerrimus Dej.
  Laboulbenia filifera Thax.
  Laboulbenia lepida Thax.
  Laboulbenia Pterostichi Thax.
Anomoglossus pusillus Say.
  Laboulbenia variabilis Thax.
Anophthalmus angustatus Lec.
Anophthalmus Menetriesii Motsch.
Anophthalmus Motschulskyi Schm.
  Laboulbenia subterranea Thax.
Anophthalmus pusio Horn.
  Laboulbenia subterranea Thax.
  Rhachomyces speluncalis Thax.
Anophthalmus Tellkampfi Er.
  Laboulbenia subterranea Thax.
Anophthalmus sp. indet.
  Sporotrichum densum Lk.
  Sporotrichum flavissimum Lk.
Apenes pallidipes Chaud.
  Laboulbenia Catoscopi Thax.
Ardistomis educta Bates.
Ardistomis viridis Say.
  Dimeromyces nanomasculus Thax.
Aspidoglossa subangulata Chaud.
  Laboulbenia Aspidoglossae Thax.
Aspidoglossa sp. indet.
  Laboulbenia variabilis Thax.
Atranus pubescens Dej.
  { Acanthomyces lasiophorus Thax.
  { Rhachomyces lasiophorus Thax.
  Eucantharomyces Atrani Thax.
Badister maculatus Lec.
  Laboulbenia polyphaga Thax.
Badister micans Lec.
  Rhachomyces lasiophorus Thax.
Bembidium bimaculatum Kirby.
  Laboulbenia curtipes Thax.
  Laboulbenia parvula Thax.
Bembidium complanulum Mann.
  Laboulbenia cornuta Thax.
Bembidium fasciolatum Duft.
  Laboulbenia vulgaris Peyr.
Bembidium laevigatum Say.
  Laboulbenia vulgaris Peyr., var. suboncogona
    Speg.

Bembidium littorale Oliv.
Bembidium lunatum Duft.
Bembidium mexicanum Dej.
Bembidium obsoletum Dej.
Bembidium punctulatum Duft.
  Laboulbenia vulgaris Peyr.
Bembidium varium Oliv.
  Laboulbenia luxurians Peyr.
Bembidium sp. indet.
  Laboulbenia compacta Thax.
  Laboulbenia confusa Thax.
  Laboulbenia inflata Thax.
  Laboulbenia pedicellata Thax.
  Laboulbenia perpendicularis Thax.
  Laboulbenia truncata Thax.
Brachinus elongatus Dej.
Brachinus fumans Fab.
Brachinus geniculatus Dej.
Brachinus kansanus Lec.
  Laboulbenia Brachini Thax.
Brachinus lateralis Dej.
  { Laboulbenia oaxacana Thax. nov. comb.
  { Laboulbenia texana Thax., var. oaxacana
      Thax.
  { Laboulbenia pendula Thax. nov. comb.
  { Laboulbenia texana, var. pendula Thax.
  { Laboulbenia rostellata Thax. nov. comb.
  { Laboulbenia texana, var. rostellata Thax.
Brachinus mexicanus Dej.
Brachinus rhytiderus Chd.
  Laboulbenia Brachini Thax.
Brachinus sp. indet.
  Laboulbenia texana Thax.
  { Laboulbenia retusa Thax. nov. comb.
  { Laboulbenia texana, var. retusa Thax.
  { Laboulbenia texana, var. tibialis Thax.
  { Laboulbenia tibialis Thax. nov. comb.
Bradycellus circumdatus Bates.
  Laboulbenia polyphaga Thax.
Bradycellus rupestris Say.
  Laboulbenia inflata Thax.
  Laboulbenia polyphaga Thax.
Callida onypterigioides Auct.
Callida pallidipennis Chaud.
  Laboulbenia minima Thax.
Callida quadrispora Bates.
  Laboulbenia Catoscopi Thax.
Callida scintillans Bates.
  Laboulbenia chiriquensis Thax.
Calophaena sp. indet.
  Laboulbenia triordinata Thax.
Carabus sp. indet.
  Cordyceps entomorrhiza Auct.
Casnonia pennsylvanica L.
  Laboulbenia Casnoniae Thax.
Casnonia subdistincta Chaud.
  Eucantharomyces Casnoniae Thax.
  Laboulbenia flaccida Thax.

Catoscopus guatemalensis Bates.
  Laboulbenia Catoscopi Thax.
Chlaenius aestivus Say.
Chlaenius chlorochrous Chaud.
Chlaenius cumatilis Lec.
Chlaenius cursor Chev.
Chlaenius floridanus Horn.
Chlaenius Gundlachi Chaud.
Chlaenius leucoscelis Chaud.
Chlaenius pennsylvanicus Say.
Chlaenius prasinus Dej.
Chlaenius ruficauda Chaud.
Chlaenius sericeus Forst.
Chlaenius solitarius Say.
Chlaenius sparsus Lec.
Chlaenius texanus Horn.
Chlaenius tricolor Dej.
Chlaenius viridicollis Reiche.
  Laboulbenia variabilis Thax.
Clivina cordata Putz.
  Laboulbenia Schizogenii Thax.
Clivina dentifemorata Putz.
Clivina dentipes Dej.
  Laboulbenia Clivinae Thax.
Clivina dilutipennis Putz.
Clivina fasciata Putz.
  Laboulbenia pallescens Thax.
  Laboulbenia pallida Thax.
Colpodes agilis Chaud.
  Laboulbenia erecta Thax.
  Rhachomyces velatus Thax.
Colpodes atratus Chaud.
  Laboulbenia Catoscopi Thax.
  Laboulbenia flagellata Peyr.
Colpodes chiriquinus Bates.
  Laboulbenia Colpodis Thax.
Colpodes caeruleomarginatus Chaud.
Colpodes cyanonotus Chaud.
Colpodes duplex Bates.
  { Laboulbenia elongata Thax.
  { Laboulbenia flagellata Peyr.
Colpodes evanescens Bates.
  Acanthomyces longissimus Thax.
  Laboulbenia erecta Thax.
Colpodes grata Bates.
Colpodes incultus Bates.
  { Laboulbenia elongata Thax.
  { Laboulbenia flagellata Peyr.
Colpodes melanocremis Chaud.
  Laboulbenia flagellata Peyr.
Colpodes petilus But.
Colpodes purpuripennis Chaud.
Colpodes sphodroides Chaud.
Colpodes tenuicornis Chaud.
  { Laboulbenia elongata Thax.
  { Laboulbenia flagellata Peyr.
Coptodera arcuata Chev.
  Laboulbenia Catoscopi Thax.

Coptodera Championi Bates.
  Laboulbenia Coptoderae Thax.
  Laboulbenia flagellata Peyr.
Cordistes sp. indet.
  Laboulbenia triordinata Thax.
Cymindis sp. indet.
  Laboulbenia Catoscopi Thax.
Diaphorus tenuicornis Chaud.
  Eucantharomyces Diaphori Thax.
Ega Sallei Chev.
  Laboulbenia Egae Thax.
Euproctus quadrinus Bates.
  Eucantharomyces Euprocti Thax.
Euproctus sp. indet.
  Laboulbenia Catoscopi Thax.
Galerita aequinoctialis Chaud.
  Laboulbenia decipiens Thax.
  Laboulbenia mexicana Thax.
Galerita americana L.
  Laboulbenia mexicana Thax.
Galerita atripes Lec.
Galerita californica Mann.
Galerita Forreri Bates.
Galerita Janus Fab.
  Laboulbenia Galeritae Thax.
Galerita Lecontei Dej.
  Laboulbenia media Thax.
  Laboulbenia melanotheca Thax.
  Laboulbenia mexicana Thax.
Galerita mexicana Chaud.
  Laboulbenia Galeritae Thax.
  Laboulbenia melanotheca Thax.
  Laboulbenia mexicana Thax.
Galerita nigra Chev.
  Laboulbenia decipiens Thax.
  Laboulbenia mexicana Thax.
Galerita pallidicornis Reiche.
  Laboulbenia mexicana Thax.
Galerita ruficollis Dej.
  Laboulbenia melanotheca Thax.
  Laboulbenia mexicana Thax.
Galerita striata Klg.
  Laboulbenia decipiens Thax.
  Laboulbenia mexicana Thax.
Galerita tenebriosa Klg.
  Laboulbenia Galeritae Thax.
Galerita sp. indet.
  Laboulbenia pygmaea Thax.
Gynandropus mexicanus Putz.
  Rhachomyces velatus Thax.
Harpalus erythropus Dej.
  Laboulbenia filifera Thax.
Harpalus pennsylvanicus DeGeer.
  Laboulbenia arcuata Thax.
  Laboulbenia conferta Thax.
  Laboulbenia elegans Thax.
  Laboulbenia Harpali Thax.

Harpalus pleuriticus Kirby.
  Laboulbenia filifera Thax.
  Laboulbenia polyphaga Thax.
Harpalus viridiaeneus Beauv.
  Laboulbenia macrotheca Thax.
  Laboulbenia uncinata Thax.
Ina costulata Chaud.
  Laboulbenia Catoscopi Thax.
Loxandrus unistigma Bates.
  Laboulbenia Loxandri Thax.
  Laboulbenia polyphaga Thax.
Morio georgiae Pal.
  Laboulbenia barbata Thax.
  Laboulbenia Morionis Thax.
Morio monilicornis Latr.
  Laboulbenia barbata Thax.
  Laboulbenia Morionis Thax.
Moriosomus sylvestris Motsch.
  Laboulbenia Morionis Thax.
Nebria brunnea Duft.
Nebria gregaria Fisch.
  Laboulbenia Nebriae Peyr.
Nebria pallipes Say.
  Laboulbenia Nebriae Peyr.
  Laboulbenia variabilis Thax.
Nebria Sahlbergi Fisch.
Nebria villae Dej.
  Laboulbenia Nebriae Peyr.
Nitobia cupreola Bates.
  Laboulbenia polyphaga Thax.
Nitobia disposita Bates.
  Laboulbenia dentifera Thax.
Nitobia luroides Bates.
  Laboulbenia flagellata Peyr.
Olisthopus parmatus Say.
  Laboulbenia polyphaga Thax.
Onypterigia pusilla Chaud.
  Laboulbenia flagellata Peyr.
Pachyteles mexicanus Chaud.
  Laboulbenia Pachytelis Thax.
Pachyteles porrectus Chaud.
  Laboulbenia punctulata Thax.
Pachyteles seriatoporus Chaud.
  Laboulbenia Pachytelis Thax.
Pachyteles testaceus Horn.
  Laboulbenia tortuosa Thax.
Pachyteles sp. indet.
  Dimeromyces eximius Thax.
  Dimorphomyces obliqueseptatus Thax.
  Dimorphomyces ramosus Thax.
Panagaeus crucigerus Say.
Panagaeus fasciatus Say.
  Laboulbenia Panagaei Thax.
Patrobus longicornis Say.
  Laboulbenia brachiata Thax.
  Laboulbenia variabilis Thax.
Patrobus tenuis Lec.
  Laboulbenia brachiata Thax.

Pelmatellus nitescens Bates.
Laboulbenia microscopica Thax.
Laboulbenia polyphaga Thax.
Pelmatellus obtusus Bates.
Laboulbenia parvula Thax.
Pelmatellus vexator Bates.
Laboulbenia polyphaga Thax.
Perigona sp. indet.
Dimeromyces caribbeus Thax.
Pheropsophus aequinoctialis L.
Pheropsophus biplagiatus Chaud.
Laboulbenia Pheropsophi Thax.
Phloeotheratus quadricollis Chaud.
Laboulbenia polyphaga Thax.
Phytalus insularis Smyth.
Metarrhizium Anisopliae (Metsch.) Sorok.
Pinacodera atrata Chev.
Laboulbenia Catoscopi Thax.
Platynus aeruginosus Dej.
Laboulbenia parvula Thax.
Platynus affinis Kirby.
Laboulbenia contorta Thax.
Platynus bicolor Lec.
Laboulbenia elongata Thax.
Laboulbenia flagellata Peyr.
Platynus cincticollis Say.
Laboulbenia elongata Thax.
Laboulbenia flagellata Peyr.
Laboulbenia fumosa Thax.
Peyritschiella curvata Thax.
Peyritschiella minima Thax.
Platynus dissectus Lac.
Laboulbenia elongata Thax.
Laboulbenia flagellata Peyr.
Platynus extensicollis Say.
Laboulbenia anceps Peyr.
Laboulbenia contorta Thax.
Laboulbenia elongata Thax.
Laboulbenia flagellata Peyr.
Laboulbenia gibberosa Thax.
Laboulbenia parvula Thax.
Laboulbenia paupercula Thax.
Laboulbenia recta Thax.
Laboulbenia scelophila Thax.
Laboulbenia variabilis Thax.
Platynus floridanus Lec.
Laboulbenia elongata Thax.
Laboulbenia flagellata Peyr.
Platynus melanarius Dej.
Laboulbenia elongata Thax.
Laboulbenia flagellata Peyr.
Laboulbenia paupercula Thax.
Platynus ovipennis Mann.
Platynus picticornis Newm.
Platynus pusillus Lec.
Laboulbenia elongata Thax.
Laboulbenia flagellata Peyr.

Platynus ruficornis Lec.
Laboulbenia elongata Thax.
Laboulbenia flagellata Peyr.
Laboulbenia paupercula Thax.
Platynus sinuatus Dej.
Laboulbenia elongata Thax.
Platynus striatopunctatus Dej.
Laboulbenia parvula Thax.
Poecilus mexicanus Chaud.
Laboulbenia variabilis Thax.
Pterostichus adoxus Say.
Laboulbenia Pterostichi Thax.
Laboulbenia variabilis Thax.
Pterostichus caudicollis Say.
Pterostichus corvinus Dej.
Laboulbenia variabilis Thax.
Pterostichus erythropus Dej.
Peyritschiella geminata Thax.
Pterostichus lacunosus Dej.
Laboulbenia Pterostichi Thax.
Pterostichus luctuosus Dej.
Laboulbenia terminalis Thax.
Laboulbenia variabilis Thax.
Peyritschiella geminata Thax.
Pterostichus mancus Lec.
Laboulbenia Pterostichi Thax.
Pterostichus patruelis Dej.
Laboulbenia rigida Thax.
Peyritschiella geminata Thax.
Pterostichus relictus Newm.
Laboulbenia Pterostichi Thax.
Pterostichus Sayi Brullé.
Laboulbenia variabilis Thax.
Schizogenius ferrugineus Putz.
Schizogenius lineolatus Say.
Laboulbenia Schizogenii Thax.
Stenolophus fuliginosus Dej.
Laboulbenia Anaplogenii Thax.
Laboulbenia polyphaga Thax.
Stenolophus limbalis Lec.
Laboulbenia polyphaga Thax.
Stenolophus ochropezus Say.
Laboulbenia umbonata Thax.
Tachys incurvus Say.
Laboulbenia Tachyis Thax.
Thalpius rufulus Lec.
Rhachomyces Thalpii Thax.
Trechus chalybeus Mann.
Laboulbenia vulgaris Peyr.
Trechus sp. indet.
Laboulbenia subterranea Thax.
Zuphium mexicanum Chaud.
Rhachomyces Zuphii Thax.

Carabidae gen. indet.
Cordyceps stylophora B. & Br.
Dimeromyces pinnatus Thax.

CERAMBYCIDAE

Parandra brunnea Fab.
Sporotrichum globuliferum Speg.

CHRYSOMELIDAE

Aphthona Deyrollei Baly.
Dimeromyces Longitarsi Thax.
Asphaera nobilitata Fab.
Asphaera transversofasciata Jac.
Laboulbenia Homophoetae (Speg.) Thax.
Chaetocnema minuta Melsh.
⎰Ceraiomyces Chaetocnemae Thax.
⎱Laboulbenia Chaetocnemae Thax. nov. comb.
⎰Ceraiomyces dislocatus Thax.
⎱Laboulbenia dislocata Thax. nov. comb.
Chaetocnema nana Jac.
⎰Ceraiomyces minisculus Thax.
⎱Laboulbenia miniscula Thax. nov. comb.
Colaspis sp. indet.
Hirsutella entomophila Pat.
Diabrotica Fairmairei Baly.
Laboulbenia Diabroticae Thax.
Diabrotica vittata Fab.
⎰Beauveria globulifera (Speg.) Picard.
⎱Sporotrichum globuliferum Speg.
Diabrotica sp. indet.
Hirsutella entomophila Pat.
Disonycha austriaca Schf.
Laboulbenia arietina Thax.
Laboulbenia Disonychae (Speg.) Thax.
Disonycha figurata Jac.
Laboulbenia Dysonichae (Speg.) Thax.
Disonycha pennsylvanica Ill.
Sporotrichum globuliferum Speg.
Disonycha reticollis Jac.
Laboulbenia arietina Thax.
Laboulbenia Homophoetae (Speg.) Thax.
Disonycha triangularis Say.
Sporotrichum globuliferum Speg.
Epitrix convexa Jac.
⎰Ceraiomyces Chaetocnemae Thax.
⎱Laboulbenia Chaetocnemae Thax. nov. comb.
⎰Ceraiomyces Epitricis Thax.
⎱Laboulbenia Epitricis Thax. nov. comb.
⎰Ceraiomyces obesus Thax.
⎱Laboulbenia obesa Thax. nov. comb.
⎰Ceraiomyces trinidadensis Thax.
⎱Laboulbenia trinidadensis Thax. nov. comb.
Epitrix lucidula Har.
⎰Ceraiomyces Chaetocnemae Thax.
⎱Laboulbenia Chaetocnemae Thax. nov. comb.
Galerucella luteola Mull.
Sporotrichum entomophilum Pk.
Haltica amethystina Oliv.
Laboulbenia fuliginosa Thax.
Haltica bimarginata Say.
⎰Sporotrichum larvatum Pk.
⎱Sporotrichum larvicola Pk.

Haltica jamaicensis Fab.
Laboulbenia fuliginosa Thax.
Laboulbenia idiostoma Thax.
Haltica plebeja Oliv.
Laboulbenia fuliginosa Thax.
Haltica scutellata Oliv.
Laboulbenia cristatella Thax.
Haltica sp. indet.
Laboulbenia funebris Thax.
Hermaeophaga insularis Jac.
Dimeromyces Hermaeophagae Thax.
Homophoeta aequinoctialis L.
Dimeromyces Homophoetae Thax.
Laboulbenia Homophoetae (Speg.) Thax.
Lactica scutellaris Oliv.
Laboulbenia Homophoetae (Speg.) Thax.
Lema Albini Lac.
Laboulbenia Bruchii (Speg.) Thax.
Lema gracilis Jac.
Laboulbenia Bruchii (Speg.) Thax.
Laboulbenia rhinoceralis Thax.
Lema dimidiaticornis de Borre.
Lema Sallei Jac.
Laboulbenia Bruchii (Speg.) Thax.
Longitarsus subcinctus Har.
Longitarsus testaceus Melsh.
Dimeromyces Longitarsi Thax.
Oedionychus sublineatus Jac.
Laboulbenia armata Thax.
Laboulbenia Homophoetae (Speg.) Thax.
Paria canella Fab.
Sporotrichum globuliferum Speg.
Psylliodes sp. indet.
Laboulbenia Homophoetae (Speg.) Thax.
Systena basalis Jacq.
Laboulbenia Homophoetae (Speg.) Thax.
Systena Deyrollei Boh.
Laboulbenia Halticae Thax.

COCCINELLIDAE

Chilocorus bivulnerus Muls.
⎰Hesperomyces virescens Thax.
⎱Stigmatomyces virescens Thax.
Coccinella novemnotata Hbst.
Hippodamia convergens Guér.
Sporotrichum globuliferum Speg.
Coccinellidae gen. indet.
Stigmatomyces coccinelloides Thax.

CRYPTOPHAGIDAE

Atomaria ephippiata Zimm.
Acompsomyces Atomariae Thax.
Atomaria sp. indet.
Acompsomyces pauperculus Thax.
Tomarus atomarius Sharp.
Dimeromyces aberrans Thax.
Tomarus bellus Gronv.
Dimeromyces Tomari Thax.

CURCULIONIDAE

Anthonomus fulvus Lec.
Conotrachelus erinaceus Lec.
  Sporotrichum globuliferum Speg.
Cryptorhynchus sp. indet.
  Cordyceps peltata Wakefield.
Hyperus variabilis Hbst.
  Metarrhizium Anisopliae (Metsch.) Sorok.
  Sporotrichum globuliferum Speg.
Metamasius hemipterus Auct.
  Metarrhizium Anisopliae (Metsch.) Sorok.
Phytonomus punctatus Fab.
  Empusa sphaerosperma (Fres.) Thax.
  Entomophthora Phytonomi Arth.
  Entomophthora sphaerosperma Fres.
Sitones sp. indet.
  Sporotrichum globuliferum Speg.
Sphenophorus sp. indet.
  Cordyceps sp. indet.
Curculionidae gen. indet. (Clover weevil).
  Empusa sphaerosperma (Fres.) Thax.

DYTISCIDAE

Bidessus granarius Aubé.
  Chitonomyces bidessarius Thax.
  Heimatomyces bidessarius Thax.
Desmopachria convexa Aubé.
  Chitonomyces aurantiacus Thax.
  Chitonomyces borealis Thax.
Hydroporus modestus Aubé.
  Chitonomyces Hydropori Thax.
Hydroporus sp. indet.
  Heimatomyces affinis Thax.
Laccophilus maculosus Germ.
  Chitonomyces affinis Thax.
  Heimatomyces affinis Thax.
  Chitonomyces appendiculatus Thax.
  Heimatomyces appendiculatus Thax.
  Chitonomyces distortus Thax.
  Heimatomyces distortus Thax.
  Chitonomyces hyalinus Thax.
  Heimatomyces hyalinus Thax.
  Chitonomyces lichanophorus Thax.
  Heimatomyces lichanophorus Thax.
  Chitonomyces marginatus Thax.
  Heimatomyces marginatus Thax.
  Chitonomyces paradoxus (Peyr.) Thax.
  Heimatomyces paradoxus Peyr.
  Chitonomyces rhynchostoma Thax.
  Heimatomyces rhynchostoma Thax.
  Chitonomyces simplex Thax.
  Heimatomyces simplex Thax.
  Chitonomyces spinigerus Thax.
  Heimatomyces spinigerus Thax.

Chitonomyces uncigerus Thax.
Heimatomyces uncigerus Thax.
Chitonomyces uncinatus Thax.
Heimatomyces uncinatus Thax.
Laccophilus optatus Sharp.
  Chitonomyces bicolor Thax.
  Chitonomyces cerviculatus Thax.
  Chitonomyces manubriolatus Thax.
  Chitonomyces Oedipus Thax.
  Chitonomyces psittacopsis Thax.
Laccophilus proximus Say.
  Chitonomyces affinis Thax.
  Chitonomyces dentiferus Thax.
  Chitonomyces psittacopsis Thax.
Laccophilus sp. indet.
  Chitonomyces aripensis Thax.
  Chitonomyces corniculatus Thax.
  Chitonomyces gracilipes Thax.
  Chitonomyces Grenadae Thax.
  Chitonomyces helicophorus Thax.
  Chitonomyces introversus Thax.
  Chitonomyces longirostratus Thax.
  Chitonomyces orientalis Thax.
  Chitonomyces prolongatus Thax.
  Chitonomyces seticola Thax.
  Chitonomyces striatus Thax.
  Chitonomyces elongatus Thax. non Speg.
  Chitonomyces Thaxteri Speg.
  Chitonomyces uncinulatus Thax.

ELATERIDAE

Agriotes mancus Say.
  Isaria Anisopliae (Metsch.), var. americana Pettit.
  Metarrhizium Anisopliae (Metsch.) Sorok.
  Metarrhizium Anisopliae (Metsch.) Sorok., var. americana (Pettit) Johnston.
Monocrepidius sp. indet.
  Sporotrichum globuliferum Speg.
Elateridae gen. indet.
  Cordyceps acicularis B. & Rav.
  Sorosporella uvella Speare.
  Stigmatomyces Anoplischii Thax.

EROTYLIDAE

Heterophyllus sp. indet.
  Dimeromyces Heterophylli Thax.
  Dimeromyces proximus Thax.

GYRINIDAE

Dineutes longimanus Oliv.
  Laboulbenia cubensis Thax.
Gyretes acutangulus Sharp.
  Laboulbenia drepanalis Thax.
  Laboulbenia fallax Thax.
  Laboulbenia Guerinii Robin.

Gyretes Boreandri Chev.
Gyretes compressus Lec.
Gyretes guatemalensis Reg.
Gyretes immarginatus Auct.
Gyretes leionanthus Duby.
Gyretes minor Reg.
Gyretes proximus Sharp.
Gyretes sericeus Lab.
Gyretes sinuatus Lec.
   Laboulbenia Guerinii Robin.
Gyrinus affinis Aubé.
Gyrinus analis Say.
Gyrinus confinis Lec.
Gyrinus consobrinus Lec.
Gyrinus fraternus Coup.
Gyrinus plicifer Lec.
Gyrinus ventralis Kirby.
   Laboulbenia Gyrinidarum Thax.
Gyrinus sp. indet.
   Laboulbenia chaetophora Thax.

HALIPLIDAE

Cnemidotus muticus Lec.
{ Heimatomyces Halipli Thax.
{ Hydraeomyces Halipli Thax.
Cnemidotus 12-punctatus Say.
   Chitonomyces Bullardi Thax.
   Chitonomyces floridanus Thax.
Cnemidotus sp. indet.
   Chitonomyces occultus Thax.
   Hydraeomyces Cnemidoti Thax.
Haliplus ruficollis DeG.
{ Heimatomyces Halipli Thax.
{ Hydraeomyces Halipli Thax.

HELODIDAE

Ptilodactyla serricollis (Say).
   Empusa apiculata Thax., var. major Thax.

HETEROCERIDAE

Heterocerus sp. indet.
   Laboulbenia Heteroceratis Thax.

HYDROPHILIDAE

Berosus striatus Say.
{ Autoicomyces contortus Thax.
{ Ceratomyces contortus Thax.
{ Autoicomyces furcatus Thax.
{ Ceratomyces furcatus Thax.
{ Autoicomyces humilis Thax.
{ Ceratomyces humilis Thax.
{ Autoicomyces ornithocephalus Thax.
{ Ceratomyces ornithocephalus Thax.
Berosus sp. indet.
{ Autoicomyces acuminatus Thax.
{ Ceratomyces acuminatus Thax.
Hydrobius sp. indet.
{ Ceratomyces elephantinus Thax.
{ Rhynchophoromyces elephantinus Thax.

Hydrocharis obtusus Say.
   Limnaiomyces Hydrocharis Thax.
Hydrocombus fimbriatus Melsh.
{ Ceratomyces rostratus Thax.
{ Rhynchophoromyces rostratus Thax. nov.
{   comb.
   Zodiomyces vorticellarius Thax.
Hydrocombus lacustris Lec.
   Zodiomyces vorticellarius Thax.
Philhydrus cinctus Say.
Philhydrus nebulosus Say.
   Ceratomyces rostratus Thax.
Phoenonotum estriatum Say.
{ Ceratomyces reflexus Thax.
{ Hydrophilomyces reflexus Thax.
{ Ceratomyces rhynchophorus Thax.
{ Hydrophilomyces rhynchophorus Thax.
Pleurohomus obscurus Sharp.
   Ceratomyces filiformis Thax.
   Ceratomyces mirabilis Thax.
Tropisternus apicipalpis Cast.
   Ceratomyces spinigerus Thax.
Tropisternus chalybeus Cast.
   Ceratomyces mexicanus Thax.
Tropisternus dorsalis Brullé.
   Ceratomyces californicus Thax.
   Ceratomyces minisculus Thax.
Tropisternus glaber Herbst.
   Ceratomyces californicus Thax.
   Ceratomyces camptosporus Thax.
   Ceratomyces confusus Thax.
   Ceratomyces filiformis Thax.
   Ceratomyces floridanus Thax.
   Ceratomyces mirabilis Thax.
Tropisternus lateralis Fab.
Tropisternus limbatus Lec.
   Ceratomyces camptosporus Thax.
   Ceratomyces minisculus Thax.
Tropisternus nimbatus Say.
   Ceratomyces cladophorus Thax.
   Ceratomyces confusus Thax.
   Ceratomyces filiformis Thax.
   Ceratomyces minisculus Thax.
   Ceratomyces mirabilis Thax.
Tropisternus nitidus Sharp.
   Ceratomyces mexicanus Thax.
Tropisternus striolatus Lec.
   Ceratomyces ansatus Thax.
   Ceratomyces camptosporus Thax.
   Ceratomyces minisculus Thax.
Tropisternus sp. indet.
   Limnaiomyces Tropisterni Thax.

LAMPYRIDAE

Lampyridae gen. indet.
   Empusa sphaerosperma (Fres.) Thax.

LATHRIDIIDAE

Corticaria sp. indet.
  Acompsomyces brunneolus Thax.
  Acompsomyces Corticariae Thax.

MELOIDAE

Epicauta vittata Fab.
  Sporotrichum globuliferum Speg.

OMOPHRONIDAE

Omophron americanum Dej.
Omophron nimbatum F.
  Laboulbenia variabilis Thax.

PASSALIDAE

Neleides antillarum Arrow.
  Rickia apiculifera Thax.
Passalus cornutus Fab.
  Achlya prolifera Nees.
  Arthromitus cristatus Leidy.
  {Cladophytum comatum Leidy.
  {Cladophytum ramosissimum Leidy.
  Corynocladus radiatus Leidy.
  Cryptodesma tenuis Leidy.
  Enterobryus attenuatus Leidy.
  Rickia Cornuti Thax.
  Rickia passalina Thax.
Passalus tlascala Perch.
  Rickia apiculifera Thax.
Passalus spp. indet.
  Enterobryus compressus Thax.
Passalidae gen. indet.
  Rickia bifida Thax.
  Rickia dominicensis Thax.

PHALACRIDAE

Eustilbus apicalis Melsh.
  Dimeromyces unguipes Thax.
Olibrus sp. indet.
  Sporotrichum globuliferum Speg.

PTILIIDAE

Trichopteryx Haldemani Lec.
  Ecteinomyces trichopterophilus Thax.

PYROCHROIDAE

Dendroides canadensis Lec.
  Cordyceps stylophora B. & Br.

SCARABAEIDAE

Aphodius sp. indet.
  Metarrhizium Anisopliae (Metsch.) Sorok.
Ataenius stercorator Fab.
  Sporotrichum globuliferum Speg.
Canthon sp. indet.
  Metarrhizium Anisopliae (Metsch.) Sorok.

Dynastinae gen. indet.
  Metarrhizium Anisopliae (Metsch.) Sorok.
  Metarrhizium Anisopliae (Metsch.) Sorok.,
    var. major Johnston.
Dyscinetus barbatus Fab.
  Metarrhizium Anisopliae (Metsch.) Sorok.
Lachnosterna fusca Froelich.
  {Botrytis bassiana var. tenella Sacc.
  {Botrytis tenella Sacc.
  {Cordyceps Melolonthae (Tul.) Sacc.
  {Torrubia Melolonthae Tul.
  {Cordyceps Ravenelii B. & C.
  {Torrubia elongata Riley.
  {Torrubia Ravenelii B. & C.
  Isaria densa (Lk.) Giard.
Lachnosterna guanicana (Smyth).
  Metarrhizium Anisopliae (Metsch.) Sorok.
Lachnosterna hirticula Knoch.
Lachnosterna inversa Horn.
  Sporotrichum globuliferum Speg.
Lachnosterna quercina Knoch.
  {Cordyceps militaris (L.) ex Lk.
  {Torrubia militaris (L. ex Lk.) Tul.
Lachnosterna sp. indet.
  Cordyceps herculea (S.) Ell. & Ev.
  {Beauveria vexans (Pettit) Petch.
  {Isaria vexans Pettit.
Ligyrus tumulosus Auct.
Strataegus titanus Fab.
  Metarrhizium Anisopliae (Metsch.) Sorok.
Scarabaeidae sp. indet.
  Cordyceps Miguelii (Tul.) Sacc.

SCOLYTIDAE

Dendroctonus frontalis Zimm.
  Cylindrocolla Dendroctoni Pk.
Xyleborus sp. indet.
  Melanconium Sacchari Massee.

SCYDMAENIDAE

Scydmaenus bicolor Auct.
  Rickia Scydmaeni Thax.

STAPHYLINIDAE

Actobius nanus Horn.
  Diplomyces actobianus Thax.
  Teratomyces Actobii Thax.
  Teratomyces brevicaulis Thax.
Acylophorus flavicollis Sachs.
Acylophorus flavipes Lec.
Acylophorus pronus Er.
  Teratomyces mirificus Thax.
Aleochara repetita Sharp.
  {Kleidiomyces furcillatus Thax.
  {Monoicomyces furcillatus Thax.
Aleochara? sp. indet.
  Dimorphomyces grenadinus Thax.

Apocellus sp. indet.
  Dimorphomyces furcatus Thax.
Astenus sp. indet.
  Camptomyces guatemalensis Thax.
Atheta sp. indet.
  Dimorphomyces verticalis Thax.
Belonuchus formosus Grav.
  Dichomyces exilis Thax.
Bledius armatus Er.
  Cantharomyces occidentalis Thax.
Bledius assimilis Csy.
  Cantharomyces Bledii Thax.
Bledius basalis Lec.
  ⎰Amorphomyces floridanus Thax.
  ⎱Dioicomyces floridanus Thax.
  Laboulbenia Bledii Thax.
Bledius emarginatus Say.
  Dimorphomyces Bledii Thax.
  Haplomyces virginianus Thax.
Bledius jacobinus Lec.
  Laboulbenia Bledii Thax.
Bledius ornatus Lec.
  Haplomyces californicus Thax.
Bledius rubiginosus Er.
  Haplomyces texanus Thax.
Cafius canescens Mäkl.
Cafius seminitens Horn.
  Laboulbenia Cafii Thax.
Calodera sp. indet.
  Monoicomyces nigrescens Thax.
Conosoma pubescens Payk.
  ⎰Rhachomyces anomalus Thax.
  ⎱Smeringomyces anomalus Thax.
  Stichomyces Conosomae Thax.
Cryptobium bicolor Grav.
  Corethromyces Cryptobii Thax.
Cryptobium Flohri Sharp.
  Corethromyces brazilianus Thax.
Cryptobium pallipes Grav.
  Corethromyces Cryptobii Thax.
Cryptobium similipenne Say.
Cryptobium venustum Sharp.
  Corethromyces brazilianus Thax.
Cryptobium sp. indet.
  Corethromyces purpurascens Thax.
Echidnoglossa americana Fauvel.
  Monoicomyces Echidnoglossae Thax.
Erchomus rutilis Er.
  Ecteinomyces Coropori Thax.
Erchomus sp. indet.
  Dimorphomyces brevirostris Thax.
Falagria dissecta Er.
  Amorphomyces Falagriae Thax.
  Dimorphomyces denticulatus Thax.
  Dimorphomyces muticus Thax.
Gyrophaena sp. indet.
  Dimeromyces Roreri Thax.
Homalota sordida Marsh.
  Dichomyces Homalotae Thax.

Homalota sp. indet.
  Acallomyces Homalotae Thax.
  Monoicomyces Homalotae Thax.
  Monoicomyces similis Thax.
Lathrobium angulare Lec.
  Rhadinomyces pallidus Thax.
Lathrobium collare Er.
Lathrobium jacobinum Lec.
  Corethromyces jacobinum Thax.
Lathrobium longiusculum Grav.
  ⎰Acanthomyces Lathrobii Thax.
  ⎱Rhachomyces Lathrobii Thax.
Lathrobium nitidulum Lec.
  ⎰Corethromyces cristatus Thax.
  ⎱Rhadinomyces cristatus Thax.
  ⎰Corethromyces Lathrobii Thax.
  ⎱Sphaleromyces Lathrobii Thax.
  Corethromyces setigerus Thax.
Lathrobium punctulatum Lec.
  Ceratomyces terrestris Thax.
  ⎰Corethromyces Lathrobii Thax.
  ⎱Sphaleromyces Lathrobii Thax.
  ⎰Corethromyces pallidus Thax.
  ⎱Rhadinomyces pallidus Thax.
  Rhadinomyces pallidus Thax., var. a.
Lathrobium pustulatum Lec.
  ⎰Corethromyces cristatus Thax.
  ⎱Rhadinomyces cristatus Thax.
  ⎰Corethromyces pallidus Thax.
  ⎱Rhadinomyces pallidus Thax.
Lathrobium tenue Lec.
  Corethromyces setigerus Thax.
Lispinus tenellus Er.
  ⎰Diaphoromyces Lispini Thax.
  ⎱Rickia Lispini Thax.
Myrmedonia flavicornis Fauv.
  Dimorphomyces Myrmedoniae Thax.
Oxypoda sp. indet.
  Monoicomyces Oxypodae Thax.
Oxytelus sp. indet.
  Eumonoicomyces californicus Thax.
  Peyritschiella protea Thax.
Paederus erythroderus Er.
Paederus littorarius Grav.
Paederus obliteralis Lec.
  Laboulbenia cristata Thax.
Philonthus acciderus Sharp.
Philonthus aequalis Horn.
  Laboulbenia Philonthi Thax.
Philonthus aeneus Rossi.
  Dichomyces dubius Thax.
Philonthus atriceps Sharp.
  Dichomyces mexicanus Thax.
Philonthus californicus Mann.
  Laboulbenia Philonthi Thax.
Philonthus centralis Sharp.
  Dichomyces furciferus Thax.
Philonthus cunctans Horn.
  Laboulbenia Philonthi Thax.

Philonthus debilis Grav.
  Dichomyces furciferus Thax.
  ⎰Dichomyces inaequalis Thax.
  ⎱Peyritschiella nigrescens Thax.
  Laboulbenia Philonthi Thax.
Philonthus discoideus Grav.
  Dichomyces furciferus Thax.
Philonthus flavolimbatus Er.
  Dichomyces vulgatus Thax.
Philonthus furvus Nordm.
Philonthus incertus Solsk.
  Laboulbenia Philonthi Thax.
Philonthus longicornis Steph.
  Dichomyces vulgatus Thax.
Philonthus micans Grav.
  Laboulbenia Philonthi Thax.
Philonthus oxysporus Sharp.
  Dichomyces exilis Thax.
Philonthus parvimanus Sharp.
  Dichomyces vulgatus Thax.
Philonthus sordidus Grav.
  Dichomyces princeps Thax.
Philonthus umbratilis Grav.
  Dichomyces biformis Thax.
Philonthus ventralis Grav.
  Dichomyces hybridus Thax.
Philonthus xanthomerus Kraatz.
  Dichomyces exilis Thax.
Piestus minutus Er.
Piestus pygmaeus Cast.
  Diaphoromyces Zirophori Thax.
Pinophilus densus Lec.
  ⎰Corethromyces occidentalis Thax.
  ⎱Sphaleromyces occidentalis Thax.
Pinophilus latipes Er.
  Chaetomyces Pinophili Thax.
Quediomarcus puniceipennis Solsk.
  Dichomyces princeps Thax.
Quedionuchus impunctus Sharp.
  ⎰Corethromyces Quedionuchi Thax.
  ⎱Sphaleromyces Quedionuchi Thax.
Quedius basiventris Sharp.
  ⎰Corethromyces atropurpureus Thax.
  ⎱Sphaleromyces atropurpureus Thax.
Quedius ferox Lec.
  Teratomyces quedianus Thax.
Quedius flavicaudus Sharp.
  ⎰Corethromyces chiriquensis Thax.
  ⎱Sphaleromyces chiriquensis Thax.
Quedius graciliventris Sharp.
  ⎰Corethromyces atropurpureus Thax.
  ⎱Sphaleromyces atropurpureus Thax.
Quedius occultus Auct.
Quedius peregrinus Grav.
  ⎰Symplectromyces vulgaris Thax.
  ⎱Teratomyces vulgaris Thax.

Quedius vernilis Lec.
Quedius vernix Lec.
  Laboulbenia Quedii Thax.
Stilicus angularis Lec.
  Corethromyces longicaulis Thax.
  Corethromyces Stilici Thax.
  ⎰Corethromyces stilicola Thax.
  ⎱Stichomyces stilicola Thax.
Sunius longiusculus Mann.
  Camptomyces melanopus Thax.
  ⎰Cantharomyces verticillatus Thax.
  ⎱Compsomyces verticillatus Thax.
Sunius prolixus Er.
  Camptomyces melanopus Thax.
  Moschomyces insignis Thax.
Tachyusa sp. indet.
  Monoicomyces nigrescens Thax.
Trogophloeus sp. indet.
  Cantharomyces pusillus Thax.
  Monoicomyces Homalotae Thax.
Xantholinus obsidianus Melsh.
  Chantransiopsis Xantholini Thax.
  Dichomyces infectus Thax.
Xanthopygus Solskyi Sharp.
  Peyritschiella Xanthopygi Thax.
Zirophorus sp. indet.
  ⎰Diaphoromyces Zirophori Thax.
  ⎱Rickia Zirophori Thax.

TENEBRIONIDAE

Centronopus calcarata Fab.
  Isaria gigantea Mont.
Nictobates? sp. indet.
  ⎰Cordyceps acicularis B. & Rav.
  ⎱Cordyceps carolinensis B. & Rav.
Platydema sp. indet.
  Dimeromyces anomalus Thax.

Lamellicorn beetles
  Cordyceps sobolifera B.

Coleoptera fam. indet.

Coleoptera (cane beetle)
  Metarrhizium Anisopliae (Metsch.) Sorok.
Coleoptera (borer) fam. indet.
  Cordyceps stylophora B. & Br.
Coleoptera (larvae) fam. indet.
  Cordyceps herculea (S.) Sacc.
  Cordyceps palustris B. & Br.
  Cordyceps Ravenelii B. & C.
  Cordyceps sobolifera B. & Br.
Coleoptera fam. indet.
  Cordyceps Pittieri Bomm. & Rouss.
  Cylindrocolla Dendroctoni Pk.
  Sporotrichum densum Lk.
  Sporotrichum flavissimum Lk.

DIPTERA

ANTHOMYIDAE

Anthomyia sp. indet.
  Empusa Muscae (Fr.) Cohn.
Leucomelina sp. indet.
Limnophora sp. indet.
  ⎰Stigmatomyces Limnophorae Thax.
  ⎱Stigmatomyces Sarcophagae Thax.

BORBORIDAE

Limosina ferruginea St.
  Stigmatomyces grenadinus Thax.
Limosina fontinalis Fallen.
  Stigmatomyces Limosinae Thax.
Limosina sp. indet.
  Stigmatomyces crassicollis Thax.
  Stigmatomyces longicollis Thax.
Borboridae gen. indet.
  Stigmatomyces pentandrus Thax.

CHIRONOMIDAE

Chironomus (gnats) sp. indet.
  ⎰Empusa conica (Nowak.) Thax.
  ⎱Entomophthora conica Nowak.
  Empusa Culicis A. Br.
  ⎰Empusa montana Thax.
  ⎱Entomophthora montana Thax.

CULICIDAE

Culicidae gen. indet.
  Empusa Culicis A. Br.
  ⎰Empusa sphaerosperma (Fres.) Thax.
  ⎱Entomophthora sphaerosperma Fres.
  Saprolegnia monoica Pringsh.

DROSOPHILIDAE

Drosophila melanogaster Meigen.
Drosophila repleta Wollaston.
  Empusa Muscae (Fr.) Cohn?
Drosophila nigricornis Loew.
  ⎧Appendicularia entomophila Pk.
  ⎨Appendiculina entomophila (Pk.) Berl.
  ⎩Stigmatomyces entomophilus (Pk.) Thax.
Drosophila sp. indet.
  Cordyceps dipterigena B. & Br.
  Muiaria curvata Thax.
  Sporotrichum globuliferum Speg.
Leucophenga sp. indet.
  Stigmatomyces Leucophengae Thax.
Scaptomyza graminum Fallen.
  Stigmatomyces Scaptomyzae Thax.
Sigaloëssa sp. indet.
  Stigmatomyces Sigaloëssae Thax.

EMPIDIDAE

Clinocera binotata Loew.
  Stigmatomyces Clinocerae Thax.
Drapetis sp. indet.
  Stigmatomyces Drapetis Thax.

EPHYDRIDAE

Atissa sp. indet.
  Stigmatomyces micrandus Thax. var. Atissae
    Thax.
Discocerina sp. indet.
  Stigmatomyces caribbeus Thax.
  Stigmatomyces chilensis Thax.
  Stigmatomyces Discocerinae Thax.
Hydrellia sp. indet.
  Stigmatomyces Hydrelliae Thax.
Hydrina sp. indet.
  Stigmatomyces spiralis Thax.
Ilythea spilota Curtis.
  Stigmatomyces Ilytheae Thax.
Ilythea sp. indet.
  Ilytheomyces anomalus Thax.
  Ilytheomyces calycinus Thax.
  Ilytheomyces elegans Thax.
  Ilytheomyces lingulatus Thax.
  Ilytheomyces major Thax.
  Ilytheomyces manubriolatus Thax.
  Ilytheomyces minisculus Thax.
  Ilytheomyces obtusus Thax.
  Ilytheomyces panamensis Thax.
Notiphila sp. indet.
  Stigmatomyces Notiphilae Thax.
Ochthera exsculpta Loew.
  Stigmatomyces dubius Thax.
Ochthera mantis DG.
  Stigmatomyces gracilis Thax.
Ochthera sp. indet.
  Stigmatomyces Ochtherae Thax.
Ochtheroidea glaphropus Loew.
  Stigmatomyces compressus Thax.
Ochtheroidea sp. indet.
  Stigmatomyces ambiguus Thax.
  Stigmatomyces Ochtheroideae Thax.
Paralimna ciliata Cress.
  Stigmatomyces curvirostris Thax.
  Stigmatomyces jamaicensis Thax.
  Stigmatomyces Paralimnae Thax.
Paralimna decipiens Loew.
  Stigmatomyces rostratus Thax.
Parydra humilis Will.
  Stigmatomyces lingulatus Thax.
Parydra imitans Loew.
  Stigmatomyces borealis Thax.
Parydra pinguis Walk.
  Stigmatomyces pinguis Thax.
  Stigmatomyces protrudens Thax.
Parydra quadrituberculata Loew.
  Stigmatomyces Parydrae Thax.

Psilopa sp. indet.
    Stigmatomyces brevicollis Thax.
    Stigmatomyces compressus Thax.
    Stigmatomyces indentatus Thax.
    Stigmatomyces Psilopae Thax.
Scatella stagnalis Fallen.
    Stigmatomyces purpureus Thax.

MUSCIDAE

Calliphora vomitoria L.
    ⌠Empusa americana Thax.
    ⌡Entomophthora americana Thax.
    Empusa Muscae (Fr.) Cohn.
Chrysomyia macellaria Fab.
    Cordyceps dipterigena B. & Br.
Lucilia Caesar L.
    ⌠Empusa americana Thax.
    ⌡Entomophthora americana Thax..
    Empusa Muscae (Fr.) Cohn.
Musca domestica L.
    ⌠Empusa americana Thax.
    ⌡Entomophthora americana Thax.
    Empusa Grylli (Fres.) Nowak.
    ⌠Empusa Muscae (Fr.) Cohn.
    ⌡Entomophthora Muscae (Fr.) Fres.
Muscidae gen. indet.
    Achlya americana J. E. Humphrey.
    Achlya apiculata DBy.
    Achlya oblongata DBy., var. globosa J. E.
      Humphrey.
    Empusa Grylli (Fres.) Nowak.
    Empusa sphaerosperma (Fres.) Thax.
    Saprolegnia diclina J. E. Humphrey.
    Saprolegnia monoica Pringsh.

MYCETOPHILIDAE

Sciara sp. indet.
    Empusa Sciarae Olive.
Mycetophilidae gen. indet.
    Empusa dipterigena Thax.
    Empusa sphaerosperma (Fres.) Thax.

NYCTERIBIIDAE

Nycteribiidae gen. indet.
    Stigmatomyces Nycteribiidarum Thax.

OSCINIDAE

Elachiptera longula Loew.
    Stigmatomyces Elachipterae Thax.
Hippelates sp. indet.
    Laboulbenia anguifera Thax.
    Laboulbenia crispata Thax.
    Stigmatomyces constrictus Thax.
Oscinis sp. indet.
    Empusa Muscae (Fr.) Cohn.
    Stigmatomyces constrictus Thax.
Siphonella sp. indet.
    Stigmatomyces constrictus Thax.

SAPROMYZIDAE

Sapromyza longipennis Fab.
    ⌠Empusa echinospora (Cke.) Thax.
    ⌡Entomophthora echinospora Cke.
Sapromyza muscaria Auct.
    Laboulbenia muscariae Thax.
Sapromyza triseriata Coq.
    Laboulbenia Sapromyzae Thax.
Sapromyza sp. indet.
    Stigmatomyces inflatus Thax.

SARCOPHAGIDAE

Onesia sp. indet.
    Stigmatomyces Limnophorae Thax.

STREBLIDAE

Strebla vespertilionis Fab.
    Nycteromyces streblidinus Thax.
    Stigmatomyces Streblae Thax.

SYRPHIDAE

Syrphus sp. indet.
    Empusa Muscae (Fr.) Cohn.

TACHINIDAE

Tachina sp. indet.
    Empusa Muscae (Fr.) Cohn.

TIPULIDAE

Pachyrrhina sp. indet.
    Empusa Pachyrrinae Arth.
Tipula sp. indet.
    Cladosporium Aphidis Thm.
    Empusa caroliniana Thax.
    Empusa conglomerata (Sorok.) Thax.?
    ⌠Empusa dipterigena Thax.
    ⌡Entomophthora dipterigena Thax.
    ⌠Empusa sepulchralis Thax.
    ⌡Entomophthora sepulchralis Thax.
Tipulidae? gen. indet.
    Achlya hypogyna Coker & Pemberton.
    ⌠Empusa gracilis Thax.
    ⌡Entomophthora gracilis Thax.
    Empusa Grylli (Fres.) Nowak.
    Empusa papillata Thax.
    Empusa sphaerosperma (Fres.) Thax.
    ⌠Empusa variablis Thax.
    ⌡Entomophthora variabilis Thax.

TRYPETIDAE

Aciura sp. indet.
    Stigmatomyces Aciurae Thax.
Ensina sp. indet.
    Stigmatomyces Aciurae Thax.
    Stigmatomyces Ensinae Thax.
    Stigmatomyces verruculosus Thax.

Diptera fam. indet.

Achlya americana J. E. Humphrey.
Achlya klebsiana Pieters.
Achyla oblongata, var. globosa J. E. Humphrey.
Achlya prolifera Nees ex DBy.
Achlya racemosa Hildb.
Cordyceps dipterigena B. & Br.?
Cordyceps flavella B. & C.
Empusa apiculata Thax.
Empusa Muscae (Fr.) Cohn.
Leptomitus lacteus (Roth.) Agardh.
Saprolegnia ferax Auct.
Saprolegnia kaufmanniana Pieters.
Saprolegnia monoica Pringsh.
Saprolegnia monoica Prings., var. vexans Pieters.
Saprolegnia Thuretii DBy.
Thraustotheca clavata (DBy.) J. E. Humphrey.

LEPIDOPTERA
ARCTIIDAE

Ecpantheria eridanus Cramer.
Estigmene acraea Drury.
Entomophthora Aulicae (Reich.) Wint.
Euchaetes Egle Drury.
Entomophthora Aulicae Reich.
Hyphantria cunea Drury.
Empusa apiculata Thax.
Empusa Grylli (Fres.) Nowak.
Empusa Grylli, var. Aulicae (Reich.) Thax.
Hyphantria textor Harris.
{ Empusa Grylli, var. Aulicae (Reich.) Thax.
{ Entomphthora Aulicae (Reich.) Wint.
Pyrrharctia isabella S. & A.
Cordyceps militaris (L.) ex Lk.
Entomophthora Aulicae (Reich.) Wint.
Isaria farinosa (Dicks.) ex Fr.
Spilosoma virginica Fab.
{ Empusa Aulicae Reich.
{ Empusa Grylli, var. Aulicae (Reich.) Thax.
{ Entomophthora Aulicae (Reich.) Wint.

BOMBYCIDAE

Bombyx mori L.
{ Beauveria bassiana (Bals.) Vuill.
{ Botrytis bassiana Bals.

GEOMETRIDAE

Eupythecia sp. indet.
Empusa geometralis Thax.
Petrophora sp. indet.
Empusa apiculata Thax.
{ Empusa geometralis Thax.
{ Entomophthora geometralis Thax.
Thera sp. indet.
Empusa geometralis Thax.

LASIOCAMPIDAE

Malacosoma americana Fab.
Aspergillus flavescens Eidam.
Entomophthora Aulicae (Reich.) Wint.

LIPARIDAE

Dasychira groenlandica Homeyer.
Cladosporium Aphidis Thm.
Isaria densa (Lk.) Giard.
Euproctis chrysorrhoea L.
Entomophthora Aulicae Reich.
Euproctis sp. indet.
Penicillium brevicaule Sacc.
Orgyia nova Fitch.
{ Empusa Grylli, var. Aulicae (Reich.) Thax.
{ Entomophthora Aulicae (Reich.) Wint.
Porthetria dispar L.
Entomophthora sp. indet.

NOCTUIDAE

Agrotis fennica Tausch.
{ Empusa virescens Thax.
{ Entomophthora virescens Thax.
Agrotis ypsilon Rott.
Sorosporella uvella (Krass.) Gd.
Agrotis sp. indet.
Empusa Grylli., var. Aulicae (Reich.) Thax.
Amphipyra pyramidoides Guen.
Entomophthora Aulicae (Reich.) Wint.
Anticarsia gemmatilis Hübner.
Botrytis Rileyi Farl.
Spicaria prasina (Maubl.) Saw.
Catocala sp. indet.
Entomophthora Aulicae (Reich.) Wint.
Copipanolis vernalis Morr.
Sporotrichum globuliferum Speg.
Deltoidinae gen. indet.
Empusa apiculata Thax.
Euoxa tessellata Harris.
Sorosporella uvella (Krass.) Gd.
Feltia jaculifera Guen.
Feltia subgothica Harv.
Sorosporella uvella (Krass.) Gd.
Hyblaea sp. indet.
Aspergillus glaucus Lk.
Laphygma frugiperda S. & A.
Botrytis Rileyi Farl.
{ Empusa sphaerosperma (Fres.) Thax.
{ Entomophthora sphaerosperma Fres.
Leucania unipuncta Haworth.
Empusa virescens Thax.
Lithophane sp. indet.
Mamestra sp. indet.
{ Empusa Aulicae Reich.
{ Empusa Grylli, var. Aulicae (Reich.) Thax.
{ Entomophthora Aulicae (Reich.) Wint.

Noctua nigra L.
    Sorosporella uvella (Krass.) Gd.
Plathypena scabra Fab.
Plusia brassicae Riley.
    Botrytis Rileyi Farl.

NOTODONTIDAE
Oedemasia concinna S. & A.
    Isaria vexans Pettit.

NYMPHALIDAE
Argynnis sp. indet.
    Botrytis tenella Sacc.
Grapta interrogationis Fab.
    Sporotrichum globuliferum Speg.
Melitaea phaeton Drury.
    Isaria vexans Pettit.
Vanessa sp. indet.
    Entomophthora Aulicae (Reich.) Wint.

PIERIDAE
Colias philodice Godt.
    Empusa sphaerosperma (Fres.) Thax.
Pieris rapae L.
    { Empusa sphaerosperma (Fres.) Thax.
    { Entomophthora sphaerosperma Fres.
    Isaria vexans Pettit.
    Sporotrichum globuliferum Speg.
Pieris sp. indet.
    (Cabbage butterfly.)
    Entomophthora radicans Bref.

PYRALIDAE
Diatraea saccharalis Fab.
    { Cordyceps Barberi Giard.
    { Isaria Barberi Giard.
    Metarrhizium Anisopliae (Metsch.) Sorok.

SATURNIIDAE
Samia cecropia L.
    Metarrhizium Anisopliae (Metsch.) Sorok.

SPHINGIDAE
Anceryx fasciata Butler.
    Isaria Sphingum S.
Cocytius antaeus Drury.
    Ophionectria Cockerellii Ell. & Ev.
Philampelus vitis L.
    Ophionectria Cockerellii Ell. & Ev.
Phlegethontius carolina L.
Phlegethontius Celeus Hübner.
    Empusa Grylli (Fres.) Nowak.
    { Empusa Grylli, var. Aulicae (Reich.) Thax.
    { Entomophthora Aulicae Reich.
    Sporotrichum globuliferum Speg.
Protoparce sp. indet.
    Sporotrichum globuliferum Speg.

Smerinthus modestus Harris.
    Entomophthora Aulicae (Reich.) Wint.
Sphinx sp. indet.
    Cordyceps Sphingum (Tul.) B. & C.
    Isaria Sphingum S.
    Sporotrichum globuliferum Speg.
Sphingidae gen. indet.
    Cordyceps Cockerellii (Ell. & Ev.) Ell.
    { Cordyceps Sphingum (Tul.) B. & C.
    { Isaria Sphingum S.
    { Torrubia Sphingum Tul.

SYNTOMIDAE
Ctenucha virginica Charpentier.
    Entomophthora Grylli Fres.

TORTRICIDAE
Tortrix sp. indet.
    Empusa apiculata Thax.
Lepidoptera fam. indet.
    Aspergillus flavus Lk.
    Cordyceps isarioides M. A. Curtis.
    Cordyceps militaris (L.) ex Lk.
    { Isaria farinosa Fr.
    { Stilbum ramosum Pk.
    Isaria nigripes S.
Lepidoptera (larvae) fam. indet.
    Chaetomium sphaerale Chivers.
    Cordyceps flavella B. & C.
    Isaria Dussii Pat.

HYMENOPTERA
ANDRENIDAE
Halictus? sp. indet.
    Empusa sphaerosperma (Fres.) Thax.

APIDAE
Apis mellifica L. (larva).
    Aspergillus flavus Lk.

FORMICIDAE
Camponotus abdominalis Fab.
    Cordyceps sp. indet.
Camponotus herculeanus L.
    Cordyceps unilateralis (Tul.) Sacc.
    Desmidiospora myrmecophila Thax.
Camponotus sp. indet.
    Cordyceps Lloydii Fawcett.
    Sporotrichum minimum Speg.
Formica pallidefulva Latrielle.
Formica subpolita Mayr.
Formica subpolita Mayr, var. **neogagates** Emery.
    Laboulbenia Formicarum Thax.
Formica sp. indet.
    Cordyceps Sherringii Massee.
    Desmidiospora myrmecophila Thax.

Lasius americanus (Emery).
Lasius neoniger Emery.
  Laboulbenia Formicarum Thax.
Formicidae gen. indet.
  Cordyceps myrmecophila Ces.
  Isaria vexans Pettit.
  Saprolegnia ferax Auct.
  Sporotrichum globuliferum Speg.

ICHNEUMONIDAE

Ichneumonidae gen. indet.
  Empusa sphaerosperma (Fres.) Thax.

SCOLIIDAE

Tiphia inornata Say.
  Metarrhizium Anisopliae (Metsch.) Sorok.

TENTHREDINIDAE

Tenthredinidae gen. indet.
  Empusa Tenthredinis (Fres.) Thax.

VESPIDAE

Eumenes sp. indet. (Mason Wasp larva).
  Cordyceps Langloisii Ell. & Ev.
Polistes americana Fab.
  { Cordyceps sphaeocephala (Klotzsch) B.
  { Polistophthora Antillarum Lebert.
  Isaria Saussurei Cke.
Polistes annularis L.
  { Hirsutella Saussurei (Cke.) Speare.
  { Isaria Saussurei Cke.
Polistes sp. indet.
  ?Cordyceps Sphingum S.
Vespa sp. indet.
  { Cordyceps sphecocephala (Klotzsch) B.
  { Cordyceps sphaecophila B.
  Sphaeria entomorhiza Dicks. ex Fr.
  Sporotrichum globuliferum Speg.
Hymenoptera fam. indet.
  { Botrytis bassiana Bals., var. tenella Sacc.
  { Botrytis tenella Sacc.

Hexapoda fam. indet.

Aphanomyces scaber DBy.
Aphanomyces stellatus DBy.
Cordyceps caloceroides B. & C.
{ Cordyceps ophioglossoides (Ehrenb. ex Fr.) Lk.
{ Torrubia ophioglossoides (Ehrenb. ex Fr.) Tul.
Cordyceps Puiggarii (Speg.) Bomm. & Rouss.
{ Cordyceps superficialis (Pk.) Sacc.
{ Torrubia superficialis Pk.
Empusa Fresenii Nowak.
Gibellula capillaris Morg.
Isaria crassa S.
Isaria densa (Lk.) Giard.
Isaria Dussii Pat.
Isaria furcata S.
Isaria tenuipes Pk.

ARACHNIDA

ARANEIDA

ATTIDAE

Attidae gen. indet.
  Gibellula arachnophila (P. ex Ditm.) Vuillemin.

THERAPHOSIDAE

Mygale cubana Walk.
  { Cordyceps gigantea Massee.
  { Cordyceps Montagnei B. & C.
  { Isaria gigantea Mont.

ACARINA

PARASITIDAE

Celaenopsis sp. indet.
  Rickia Celaenopsis Thax.
  Rickia depauperata Thax.
  Rickia excavata Thax.
  Rickia parvula Thax.
Discopoma sp. indet.
  Rickia arachnoidea Thax.
  Rickia elliptica Thax.
Euzercon sp. indet.
  Rickia arachnoidea Thax.
  Rickia dichotoma Thax.
  Rickia euzerconalis Thax.
  Rickia furcata Thax.
  Rickia parvula Thax.
Hypoaspis sp. indet.
  Rickia Hypoaspidis Thax.
Iphiopsis sp. indet.
  Rickia anomala Thax.
Macrocheles sp. indet.
  Dimeromyces Parasiti Thax.
Megisthanus sp. indet.
  Rickia Megisthani Thax.
  Rickia trinitatis Thax.
Parasitus sp. indet.
  Dimeromyces Parasiti Thax.
  Rickia Parasiti Thax.
Trachyuropoda sp. indet.
  Rickia arachnoidea Thax.
  Rickia Megisthani, var. Trachyuropodae Thax.
Uropoda sp. indet.
  Dimeromyces subuliferus Thax.
Parasitidae gen. indet.
  Rickia discreta Thax.

Acarina fam. indet.

Moniliopsis rigida Petch.
Rickia anomala Thax.
Rickia arimensis Thax.
Rickia discreta Thax.
Rickia haytiensis Thax.
Rickia inclinata Thax.
Rickia minuta Paoli.

Araneida fam. indet.

Gibellula arachnophila (P. ex Ditm.) Vuille-
min.
Isaria arachnophila P. ex Ditm.
Isaria aranearum S.
Isaria phalangiophila Lk.

Arachnida fam. indet.

Botrytis tenella Sacc.

**Galls and other Hypertrophies Caused by Mites
or Insects**

Amphibolips ilicifoliae Boss.
Phoma glandicola Desm.
Phoma nervisequa (Cke) Sacc.
Cynips sp. indet.
Cryptoderis gallae Trotter.
Sclerotium gallarum S.
Sphaeria tumorum S.
Diplodia gallae (B. & C.) Cke. ex Oud.
Diplodinula gallae (Ell. & Ev.) Tassi.
Sphaeropsis gallae (S.) Archer.
Hexapoda fam. indet.
Coryne urnalis (Nyl.) Sacc.
Dothiorella gallae (S.) Ell. & Ev.
Phyllosticta gloeosporioides Trotter.
Septonema toruloideum C. & E.
Sphaerella gallae Ell. & Ev.
Staurochaete membranacea Cke.
Phytoptus sp. indet.
Microsphaera erineophila Pk.
Sphaerotheca phytoptophila Kellerm. & Sw.

VERTEBRATA

Cod.
Sclerotium ossicola Rostr.
Oidium pulvinatum Farl. nec B. & C.
Torula Muriae (Kickx) Vestrgren.
Torula pulvinata Farl.
Salmon.
Saprolegnia ferax Auct.
Trout eggs
Achlya racemosa Hildb.

Sea-horse.
(Hippocampus heptagona).
Devoea infundibilis Lockwood.
Fishes, not named.
Saprolegnia ferax Auct.
Saprolegnia mixta DBy.?
Saprolegnia parasitica Coker.
Salamander.
(Menobranchus lanceolatus)
Saprolegnia sp. indet.
Turtles and Frogs.
Achlya polyandra Hildb.
Achlya racemosa Hildb.
Canary bird.
Aspergillus aviarius Pk.
Common fowl (skin).
Achorion Schoenleinii Remak.
Birds (feathers).
Fusarium gallinaceum Cke. & Hark.
Cow (bones).
Fusarium ossicola (B. & C.) Sacc.
Fusisporium ossicola B. & C.
Verticillium osteophilum Ell. & Ev.
Horse (skin).
Fusarium equinum Novgaard.
Horse (hoofs).
Onygena equina (Willd.) P.
Mouse.
Oospora?
Sporendonema myophilum Sacc.
Torula sp. indet. Leidy.
Whale (bone).
Pleurotus Coldwelli McKay.
Vertebrates (bones).
Gymnascella aurantiaca Pk.
Isaria flavissima Lk.
Mucor griseo-cyanus Hagem.
Mucor hiemalis Wehmer.
Rhopalomyces elegans Cda.
Rhopalomyces strangulatus Thax.
Sporotrichum flavissimum Lk.
Man.
Allescheria Boydii Shear.
Phialophora verrucosa Medlar.
Also many species recorded in medical works,
qv.

INDEX

INDEX